SCOTT®

1999
Standard Postage
Stamp Catalogue

ONE HUNDRED AND FIFTY-FIFTH EDITION IN SIX VOLUMES

VOLUME 1

UNITED STATES
and Affiliated Territories

UNITED NATIONS

COUNTRIES OF THE WORLD

A-B

VICE PRESIDENT/PUBLISHER	Stuart J. Morrissey
EDITOR	James E. Kloetzel
ASSOCIATE EDITOR	William W. Cummings
VALUING EDITOR	Martin J. Frankevicz
NEW ISSUES EDITOR	David C. Akin
COMPUTER CONTROL COORDINATOR	Denise Oder
VALUING ANALYST	Jose R. Capote
EDITORIAL ASSISTANTS	Judith E. Bertrand, Beth Brown
ART/PRODUCTION DIRECTOR	Janine C. S. Apple
PRODUCTION COORDINATOR	Nancy S. Martin
MARKETING/SALES DIRECTOR	William Fay
ADVERTISING	Sabrina D. Morton
CIRCULATION/PRODUCT PROMOTION MANAGER	Tim Wagner

Released April 1998
Includes New Stamp Listings through the March, 1998 *Scott Stamp Monthly* Catalogue Update

Value Priced Stockbooks

Stockbooks are a classic and convenient storage alternative for many collectors.

These German-made stockbooks feature heavyweight archival quality paper with 9 pockets on each page. The 8½" x 11⅝" pages are bound inside a handsome leatherette grain cover and include glassine interleaving between the pages for added protection. The Value Priced Stockbooks are available in two page styles, the white page stockbooks feature glassine pockets while the black page variety includes clear acetate pockets

Value Priced Stockbooks are available from your favorite dealer or direct from Scott Publishing Co. P.O. Box 828 Sidney OH 45365-0828

White Page Stockbooks Glassine Pockets

Item	Color	Pages	Retail
SW16BL	Blue	16 pages	$5.95
SW16GR	Green	16 pages	$5.95
SW16RD	Red	16 pages	$5.95

Black Page Stockbooks Acetate Pockets

Item	Color	Pages	Retail
ST16GR	Red	16 pages	$9.95
ST16GR	Green	16 pages	$9.95
ST16BL	Blue	16 pages	$9.95
ST16BK	Black	16 pages	$9.95
ST32RD	Red	32 pages	$14.95
ST32GR	Green	32 pages	$14.95
ST32BL	Blue	32 pages	$14.95
ST32BK	Black	32 pages	$14.95
ST64RD	Red	64 pages	$27.95
ST64GR	Green	64 pages	$27.95
ST64BL	Blue	64 pages	$27.95
ST64BK	Black	64 pages	$27.95

SCOTT

To order call 1-800-572-6885

Table of Contents

See Volumes 2 through 6 for Countries of the World, C-Z

Scott Publishing Mission Statement

The Scott Publishing Team exists to serve the recreational,
educational and commercial hobby needs of stamp collectors and dealers.

We strive to set the industry standard for philatelic information and products by developing and
providing goods that help collectors identify, value, organize and present their collections.

Quality customer service is, and will continue to be, our highest priority.
We aspire toward achieving total customer satisfaction.

Scott Publishing Co.

SCOTT

911 VANDEMARK ROAD, SIDNEY, OHIO 45365 937-498-0802

Dear Catalogue User,

Robust stamp buying activity continues with new levels of support arising from many quarters. Since the previous edition of this volume there has been increased competition at auctions, an ever-diminishing supply of good material coming to market and the emergence of a whole new world of philatelic commerce on the Internet.

More than 6,000 values have changed in Volume 1 of the *1999 Scott Standard Postage Stamp Catalogue.* Value changes appear across the board with many revisions in U.S., Austria and Australia. This volume contains listings for the United States and affiliated territories, United Nations, and countries of the world A-B.

Values for unused stamps without gum have been added to the listings of some turn-of-the-century stamps in the United States postage section. The new values pertain mostly to stamps that have original gum counterparts with values greater than $1000. Not only should these new listings prove helpful to collectors and dealers in valuing their stamps, but it will also allow them to expertize these items less expensively. In the past collectors have had to pay expertizing services the same fees for stamps with no gum as stamps with original gum due to a lack of valuing in the catalogue for stamps without gum.

As faithful readers of this letter page know, I have the curious habit of asking myself questions. Here goes:

What's happening with U.S. values?

Scott 1 and 2, the 1847 5¢ and 10¢ first issue, remain at $5,000 unused, $600 used and $26,000 unused, $1,400 used, respectively, though the scarce Scott 1b in orange brown skips to $6,250 unused, from $6,000. Several 1857-61 perforated stamps show significant gains. Scott 28, the 5¢ red brown type I, moves to $2,750 unused and $425 used, from $2,500 unused and $400 used. A more significant increase is seen in Scott 30A, the 5¢ brown type II stamp. It leaps to $1,500 unused and $260 used, from $1,150 unused and $240 used.

The 1867 grilled issues continue to advance, as do unused examples of the 1869 Pictorials. Out of reach of most collectors, but indicative of what is happening to the values of rare classics in the marketplace, all of the unused 1869 inverted center issues, Scott 119b, 120b and 121b, jump more than 20% in value.

Scott 240-245, the 50¢-$5 1893 Columbians, jump 5%-10% both unused and used. The 1911 3¢ deep violet type I "Orangeburg" coil, Scott 389, is valued unused for the first time. An unused hinged single is valued at $37,500, and a never-hinged single, now known to exist and expertized as such, is valued at $50,000. More down to earth, the moderately priced used coils from the same time period move ahead slightly. For example, Scott 390 and 391, the 1910 1¢ and 2¢ coils perf 8 1/2 horizontally, advance used to $5 and $10, from $4.25 and $9, respectively.

Postal stationery continues to advance as more than 600 new value changes appear in Volume 1 in addition to the significant new and higher values that were carried over from the *U.S. Specialized.*

Important activity in the marketplace for Confederate States postmasters' provisionals and regular issues during the past year has resulted in a number of value changes in Volume 1 that did not appear in last year's *U.S. Specialized.* Scattered changes also are seen in the U.S. Possessions and in United Nations.

The list of philatelic societies in the introduction has been expanded to include topical societies and on-line addresses for societies that are on the Internet. The illustrated identifier in the back of the book has also been expanded to include more stamps and more explanatory notes.

What's up with ducks?

Additionally, values for unused stamps with no gum have been installed in the Federal Duck Stamp section of the catalogue. These stamps, often removed from unsigned licenses, are widely used for framed sets and are also collected by the budget-conscious collector. Federal duck stamps are now valued in both mint never hinged and unused without gum condition, and the first 12 stamps in the series are also valued with hinged original gum.

Another innovation in the U.S. section is the inclusion for the first time of values for sets of never-hinged stamps where previously totals were included only for hinged sets. These listings include all commemorative sets from 1901 to 1934, beginning with the 1901 Pan-Americans, Scott 294-299, and ending with the 1934 National Parks, Scott 740-749. Also included are definitive sets beginning with the 1922-25 issue, Scott 551-573, and continuing through the 1931 rotary press issue, Scott 692-701.

Are values for foreign stamps on the rise too?

Many foreign country stamps show value increases. For example, there are a large number of changes in the Albania section this year, all up and dramatically so.

Scott 129-134, the 1920 eagle stamps with black post horn overprint, increase to $49.50 unused, $39 used from the 1998 level of $17 unused, $13 used. The 1928 Kingdom of Albania overprints, Scott 227-237, jump to $24 unused and $18 used, from $18 unused and $12 used. The 1945 Liberation Army overprints, Scott 354-360, jump to $30 unused and used, from $20 unused and used.

Afars and Issas records numerous sharp increases. The 1972 Shells set, Scott 358-361, leaps to $14 never hinged from $3.74, and the 1975-76 Butterflies, Scott 392-399, shoot to $29 never hinged from $16.

In Australia, some of the lower values from the 1913 Wide Crown and Wide A watermarked Kangaroos inch up slightly. Scott 3, the 2p gray, pushes up to $22.50 unused from $20. The 1935 George V 25th anniversary set, Scott 152-154, charges to $41 hinged from $37. A few of the better modern commemoratives sag. In the postage dues, Scott J27a, the perf. 11 Crown and Single-lined A watermarked 4p, leaps to $900 unused and $400 used, from $300 unused and $110 used.

Slightly more than 200 changes are found in Austria. The 1936 Dollfuss 10s, Scott 380, nudges upward slightly to $675 unused from $650.

What are the editorial changes collectors should look out for?

The second type of the 1947 Belgium air post semi-postals have been upgraded to major status as Scott CB4A-CB12A. They were previously minors, Scott CB4a-CB12a.

A printing variety of Australia's 1970 Sturt's Desert Rose 2¢ with bolder lettering and value has been added as Scott 439Ai.

Renumberings affect Australia's 1996-97 Flora and Fauna definitives and Benin's 1996 Lions International commemoratives.

Are you still having your share of collecting fun?

If you've peaked in your specialty, have only the expensive stamps to buy in France, or if the mania surrounding gum condition is getting you down, maybe you need a new area to collect. Perhaps you're the type that just likes to dream. If so I would highly recommend the Scott Product Guide. There is no other wishbook like it in the hobby. The Product Guide is chockfull of collecting ideas and it is absolutely free. Just call 1-800-572-6885.

Stuart Morrissey

Stuart Morrissey/ Publisher

Acknowledgments

Our appreciation and gratitude go to the following individuals who have assisted us in preparing information included in the 1999 Scott Catalogues. Some helpers prefer anonymity. These individuals have generously shared their stamp knowledge with others through the medium of the Scott Catalogue.

Those who follow provided information that is in addition to the hundreds of dealer price lists and advertisements and scores of auction catalogues and realizations which were used in producing the catalogue values. It is from those noted here that we have been able to obtain information on items not normally seen in published lists and advertisements. Support from these people goes beyond data leading to catalogue values, for they also are key to editorial changes.

A.R. Allison (Orange Free State Study Circle)
B. J. Ammel (The Nile Post)
Mike Armus
Robert Ausubel
Jack Hagop Barsoumian (International Stamp Co.)
Jules K. Beck
John Birkinbine II
John R. Boker, Jr.
Victor Bove
Jeff Brasor (Honduras Collectors Club, Associated Collectors of El Salvador)
George W. Brett
Roger S. Brody
Lawrence A. Bustillo
Nathan Carlin
Richard A. Champagne
Charlie Chesloe (Tribuna Stamp Co.)
Henry Chlanda
Laurie Conrad
Frank D. Correl
Andrew Cronin (Canadian Society of Russian Philately)
William T. Crowe
Bob Dumaine (Sam Houston Duck Company)
William S. Dunn
Leon Finik (Loral Stamps)
Henry Fisher
Geoffrey Flack
Joseph E. Foley (Eire Philatelic Association)
Marvin Frey
Huguette Gagnon (Ethiopian Philatelic Society)
Bob Genisol (Sultan Stamp Center)
Richard B. Graham
Gary Griffith
Harry Hagendorf
Calvet M. Hahn
Rudolf Hamar (Estonian Philatelic Society)
John B. Head
Robert R. Hegland
Dale S. Hendricks (Dale Enterprises, Inc.)
Clifford O. Herrick (Fidelity Trading Company)
Lee H. Hill, Jr.
Dr. Eugene H. Holmok (Tatra Stamps, Reg'd.)
Jack R. Hughes (Fellowship of Samoa Specialists)
Wilson Hulme (U.S. Philatelic Classics Society)
Eric Jackson
Peter C. Jeannopoulos
Clyde Jennings
Stanford M. Katz
Lewis Kaufman
Dr. James W. Kerr
Charles Kezbers
Ken Lawrence
Pedro Llach (Filatelia Llach S.L.)

David MacDonnell
F. Brian Marshall (Sarawak Specialists' Society)
Marilyn R. Mattke
Dr. Hector R. Mena (Society of Costa Rica Collectors)
Robert Meyersburg
Jack E. Molesworth (Jack E. Molesworth, Inc.)
William E. Mooz
Gary M. Morris (Pacific-Midwest Co.)
Peter Mosiondz, Jr.
Bruce M. Moyer
Richard H. Muller (Richard's Stamps)
Victor Ostolaza
John E. Pearson (Pittwater Philatelic Service)
Otto Peetoom (Ormskirk Stamps)
Donald J. Peterson
Stanley Piller (Stanley M. Piller & Associates)
Siddique Mahmudur Rahman (Bangladesh Institute of Philatelic Studies)
Jon W. Rose
Frans H. A. Rummens (American Society for Netherlands Philately)
Richard H. Salz
Theodosios Sampson (Superior Stamp & Coin)
Jacques C. Schiff, Jr. (Jacques C. Schiff, Jr., Inc.)
Bernard Seckler (Fine Arts Philatelists)
F. Burton Sellers
Jeff Siddiqui (Pakistan Study Circle)
Richard Simchak
Sergio & Liane Sismondo (The Classic Collector)
Dr. Russell V. Skavaril (St. Helena, Ascension & Tristan da Cunha Philatelic Society)
Dr. Hubert C. Skinner
Jay Smith
Ekrem Spahich (Croatian Philatelic Society)
Richard Stambaugh
Scott R. Trepel (Siegel Auction Galleries, Inc.)
Ming W. Tsang (Hong Kong Stamp Society)
Jerome S. Wagshal
Richard A. Washburn
Giana Wayman
Raymond H. Weill
Dr. Gary B. Weiss
Hans A. Westphal
Robert F. Yacano (K-Line Philippines)
Val Zabijaka

A special acknowledgment to Liane and Sergio Sismondo of The Classic Collector for their extraordinary assistance and knowledge sharing that has aided in the preparation of this year's Standard and Classic Specialized Catalogues.

Addresses, Telephone Numbers, Web Sites, E-Mail Addresses of General & Specialized Philatelic Societies

Collectors can contact the following groups for information about the philately of the areas within the scope of these societies, or inquire about membership in these groups. Aside from the general societies, we limit this list to groups that specialize in particular fields of philately, particular areas covered by the Scott Standard Postage Stamp Catalogue, and topical groups. Many more specialized philatelic societies exist than those listed below. These addresses were compiled in January 1998, and are, to the best of our knowledge, correct and current. Groups should inform the editors of address changes whenever they occur. The editors also want to hear from other such specialized groups not listed.

General "Umbrella" Societies

American Philatelic Society
PO Box 8000
State College PA 16803
Ph: (814) 237-3803
http://www.west.net/~stamps1/aps.html
E-mail: relamb@stamps.org

American Stamp Dealers' Association
Joseph Savarese
3 School St.
Glen Cove NY 11542
Ph: (516) 759-7000
http://www.amerstampdlrs.com
E-mail: asda@inx.net

International Society of Worldwide Stamp Collectors
Carol Cervenka
2502 Second St.
Caddo Mills TX 75135-9704
Ph: (903) 527-3957
http://www.frontiernet/~stamptmf/iswsc.html
E-mail: iswsc@webwide.net

Junior Philatelists of America
Ellie Chapman
PO Box 850
Boalsburg PA 16827-0850
http://www.jpastamps.org
E-mail: jpaellie@aol.com

Royal Philatelic Society
41 Devonshire Place
London, United Kingdom W1N 1PE

Royal Philatelic Society of Canada
PO Box 929, Station Q
Toronto, ON, Canada M4T 2P1
http://www.interlog.com/~rspc
E-mail: rpsc@interlog.com

Groups focusing on fields or aspects found in world-wide philately (some may cover U.S. area only)

American Air Mail Society
Stephen Reinhard
PO Box 110
Mineola NY 11501
http://ourworld.compuserve.com/homepages/aams/
E-mail: sr1501@aol.com

American First Day Cover Society
Douglas Kelsey
PO Box 65960
Tucson AZ 85728-5960
E-mail: afdcs@aol.com

American Revenue Association
Bruce Miller
Suite 332, 701 South First Ave.
Arcadia CA 91006

American Topical Association
Douglas Kelsey
PO Box 65749
Tucson AZ 85728
Ph: (520) 321-9292
E-mail: ataoffice@aol.com

Errors, Freaks and Oddities Collectors Club
Jim McDevitt
138 Lakemont Dr. East
Kingsland GA 31548
Ph: (912) 729-1573
E-mail: cwouscg@aol.com

National Duck Stamp Collectors Society
Anthony J. Monico
PO Box 43
Harleysville PA 19438-0043

No Value Identified Club
Albert Sauvanet
Le Clos Royal B, Boulevard des Pas Enchantes
St. Sebastien-sur Loire, France 44230
E-mail: alain.vailly@irin.univ_nantes.fr

The Perfins Club
Kurt Ottenheimer
462 West Walnut St.
Long Beach NY 11561

Post Mark Collectors Club
Larry Boing
2351 Grandview Road
Crest Hill IL 60435-1951

Postal History Society
Kalman V. Illyefalvi
8207 Daren Court
Pikesville MD 21208-2211
Ph: (410) 653-0665

Precancel Stamp Society
1750 Skippack Pk. #1603
Center Square PA 19422
Ph: (610) 279-6014

United Postal Stationery Society
Joann Thomas
PO Box 48
Redlands CA 92373
http://www.uh.edu/~lib19/upss.htm

Groups focusing on U.S. area philately as covered in the Standard Catalogue

Bureau Issues Association
David G. Lee
PO Box 2641
Reston VA 20195-0641

Canal Zone Study Group
Richard H. Salz
60 27th Ave.
San Francisco CA 94121

Carriers and Locals Society
Steven M. Roth
PO Box 57160
Washington DC 20036
Ph: (202) 293-6813
E-mail: smroth@wizard.net

Confederate Stamp Alliance
Richard L. Calhoun
PO Box 581
Mt. Prospect IL 60056-0581

Hawaiian Philatelic Society
Kay H. Hoke
PO Box 10115
Honolulu HI 96816-0115
Ph: (808) 521-5721
http://www.stampshows.com/hps.html

Plate Number Coil Collectors Club
Gene C. Trinks
3603 Bellows Court
Troy MI 48083
http://www.geocities.com/Heartland/Hills/6283
E-mail: gctrinks@tir.com

United Nations Philatelists
Alex Bereson
18 Portola Drive
San Francisco CA 94131-1518
E-mail: bereson@ix.netcom.com

U.S. Philatelic Classics Society
Mark D. Rogers
PO Box 80708
Austin TX 78708-0708
http://www.scruz.net/~eho/uspcs
E-mail: mdr3@swbell.net

U.S. Possessions Philatelic Society
David S. Durbin
1608 S. 22nd St.
Blue Springs MO 64015

Groups focusing on philately of foreign countries or regions

American Society of Polar Philatelists (Antarctic areas)
Richard Julian
1153 Fairview Dr.
York PA 17403
E-mail: rajulian@netrax.net

American Belgian Philatelic Society
Kenneth L. Costilow
621 Virginius Dr.
Virginia Beach VA 23452-4417
Ph: (757) 463-6081
E-mail: ken_costilow@prodigy.com

Bermuda Collectors Society
Thomas J. McMahon
364 Nash Road
North Salem NY 10560

Brazil Philatelic Association
Kurt Ottenheimer
462 West Walnut St.
Long Beach NY 11561

British Caribbean Philatelic Study Group
Gale J. Raymond
Bali-Hai, PO Box 228
Sugar Land TX 77478-0228

British North America Philatelic Society (Canada & Provinces)
Jerome C. Jarnick
108 Duncan Drive
Troy MI 48098
Ph: (248) 689-1966
http://www.compusmart.ab.ca/stalbert/bnaps.htm
E-mail: jarnick@compuserve.com

Burma Philatelic Study Circle
A. Meech
7208 91st Ave.
Edmonton, AB, Canada T6B 0R8
E-mail: alan.meech@ualberta.ca

China Stamp Society
Paul H. Gault
120 West 18th Ave.
Columbus OH 43210
http://www.azstarnet.com/~gersten/China.Stamp.Society.html
E-mail: gault.1@osu.edu

Colombia/Panama Philatelic Study Group
PO Box 2245
El Cajon CA 92021
E-mail: jimacross@juno.com

Society of Costa Rica Collectors
Dr. Hector R. Mena
PO Box 14831
Baton Rouge LA 70808
http://www.intersurf.com/~hrmena
E-mail: hrmena@intersurf.com

Croatian Philatelic Society (Croatia & other Balkan areas)
Ekrem Spahich
502 Romero, PO Box 696
Fritch TX 79036-0696
Ph: (806) 857-0129
http://www.hrnet.org/cps
E-mail: ou812@arn.net

Society for Czechoslovak Philately
Robert T. Cossaboom
PO Box 25332
Scott AFB IL 62225-0332
http://www.erols.com/sibpost
E-mail: klfck1@aol.com

Estonian Philatelic Society
Rudolf Hamar
1912 Nugget Drive
Felton CA 95018

Ethiopian Philatelic Society
Huguette Gagnon
PO Box 8110-45
Blaine WA 98231-8110
Ph: (604) 584-1701

Falkland Islands Philatelic Study Group
Carl J. Faulkner
Williams Inn, On-the-Green
Williamstown MA 01267-2620

France & Colonies Philatelic
  Society
Walter Parshall
103 Spruce St.
Bloomfield NJ 07003-3514

Germany Philatelic Society
PO Box 779
Arnold MD 21012-4779

Great Britain Collectors Club
Frank J. Koch
PO Box 309
Batavia OH 45103-0309
http://www.netxpress.com/users/
winphins/gbcc/gbcc_hp.html
E-mail: koch.fj@pg.com

Hellenic Philatelic Society of
  America (Greece and related
  areas)
Dr. Nicholas Asimakopulos
541 Cedar Hill Ave.
Wyckoff NJ 07481
Ph: (201) 447-6262

International Society of Guatemala
  Collectors
Mrs. Mae Vignola
105 22nd Ave.
San Francisco CA 94121

Haiti Philatelic Society
Ubaldo Del Toro
5709 Marble Archway
Alexandria VA 22310

Honduras Collectors Club
Jeff Brasor
PO Box 173
Coconut Creek FL 33097

Hong Kong Stamp Society
Dr. An-Min Chung
120 Deerfield Rd.
Broomall PA 19008
Ph: (215) 576-6850

Hungary Philatelic Society
Thomas Phillips
PO Box 1162
Fairfield CT 06432-1162

India Study Circle
John Warren
PO Box 70775
Washington DC 20024
Ph: (202) 260-9464
E-mail: warren.john@epamail.epa.gov

Society of Indochina Philatelists
Paul Blake
1466 Hamilton Way
San Jose CA 95125

Iran Philatelic Study Circle
David J. Armacost
PO Box 33381
Phoenix AZ 85067

Eire Philatelic Association (Ireland)
Michael J. Conway
19 Pine Needle Drive
Shelton CT 06484
http://ourworld.compuserve.com/
homepages/aranman/epa.htm
E-mail: brennan704@aol.com

Society of Israel Philatelists
Paul S. Aufrichtig
300 East 42nd St.
New York NY 10017

International Society for Japanese
  Philately
Kenneth Kamholz
PO Box 1283
Haddonfield NJ 08033
http://www.west.net/~lmevans/
isjp.html
E-mail: kamholz@mosquito.com

Korea Stamp Society
William M. Collyer
PO Box 4158
Saticoy CA 93007-0158

Latin American Philatelic Society
Piet Steen
197 Pembina Ave.
Hinton, AB, Canada T7V 2B2

Cuyahoga Latvian Philatelist Club
Arturs Rubenis
1460 West Clifton Blvd.
Lakewood OH 44107-3309

Latvian Philatelic Society
J. Ronis
7 Lowes Ave.
Brampton, ON, Canada L6X 1R8

Liberian Philatelic Society
William Thomas Lockard
PO Box 267
Wellston OH 45692
Ph: (614) 384-2020

Liechtenstudy USA (Liechtenstein)
Ralph Schneider
PO Box 23049
Belleville IL 62223
Ph: (618) 277-8543
http://www.rschneiderstamps.com/
info.html
E-mail: rschneider@aol.com

Lithuanian Philatelic Society
Fred Baumgartner
446 S. 6th Ave.
La Grange IL 60525
Ph: (708) 354-5909

Lithuanian Philatelic Society of
  New York
Vincent M. Alones
217 McKee St.
Floral Park NY 11001-1314

Mexico-Elmhurst Philatelic Society
  International
Juan Jose Cabuto-Vidrio
PO Box 435360
San Ysidro CA 92143-5360

Nepal & Tibet Philatelic Study Group
Roger D. Skinner
1020 Covington Road
Los Altos CA 94022-5003
Ph: (415) 968-4163

American Society of Netherlands
  Philately
Jan Enthoven
W6428 Riverview Drive
Onalaska WI 54650
Ph: (608) 781-8612
http://www.cs.cornell.edu/Info/
People/aswin/NL/neth

Society of Australasian Specialists /
  Oceania
Henry Bateman
PO Box 4862
Monroe LA 71211
Ph: (800) 571-0293
E-mail: ck100@iamerica.net

Orange Free State Study Circle
J. R. Stroud
28 Oxford St.
Burnham-on-sea, Somerset,
United Kingdom TA8 1LQ

Pakistan Study Circle
Jeff Siddiqui
PO Box 7002
Lynnwood WA 98046
E-mail: jeffsiddiqui@msn.com

Papuan Philatelic Society
Steven Zirinsky
PO Box 49, Ansonia Station
New York NY 10023
Ph: (212) 665-0765
E-mail: szirinsky@compuserve.com

International Philippine Philatelic
  Society
Robert F. Yacano
PO Box 94
Eden NY 14057
Ph: (716) 992-9665

Pitcairn Islands Study Group
Nelson A. L. Weller
2940 Wesleyan Lane
Winston-Salem NC 27106
Ph: (910) 724-6398
E-mail: nalweller@juno.com

Plebiscite-Memel-Saar Study Group
Clay Wallace
100 Lark Court
Alamo CA 94507

Polonus Philatelic Society (Poland)
PO Box 458
Berwyn IL 60402

International Society for
  Portuguese Philately
Clyde Homen
1491 Bonnieview
Hollister CA 95023-5117
E-mail: cjh@hollinet.com

Rhodesian Study Circle
William R. Wallace
PO Box 16381
San Francisco CA 94116

Romanian Chapter of Croatian
  Philatelic Society
Dan Demetriade
PO Box 09700
Detroit MI 48209

Canadian Society of Russian
  Philately
Andrew Cronin
PO Box 5722, Station A
Toronto, ON, Canada M5W 1P2
Ph: (905) 764-8968

Rossica Society of Russian Philately
George G. Werbizky
409 Jones Rd.
Vestal NY 13850

Ryukyu Philatelic Specialist Society
Carmine J. DiVincenzo
PO Box 381
Clayton CA 94517-0381

St. Helena, Ascension & Tristan Da
  Cunha Philatelic Society
Dr. Russell V. Skavaril
222 East Torrance Road
Columbus OH 43214-3834
Ph: (614) 262-3046
http://ourworld.compuserve.com/
homepages/st_helena_ascen_tdc

St. Pierre & Miquelon Study Group
David Salovey
PO Box 464
New York NY 10014-0464

Associated Collectors of El Salvador
Jeff Brasor
PO Box 173
Coconut Creek FL 33097

Fellowship of Samoa Specialists
Jack R. Hughes
1541 Wellington St.
Oakland CA 94602-1751

Sarawak Specialists' Society
Art Bunce
PO Box 2516
Escondido CA 92033

Arabian Philatelic Association
  (Saudi Arabia)
ARAMCO, Box 1929
Dhahran, Saudi Arabia 31311

Scandinavian Collectors Club
Donald B. Brent
PO Box 13196
El Cajon CA 92020
http://www.nb.net/~downs/scc/
scc.htm
E-mail: dbrent47@sprynet.com

Slovakia Stamp Society
Jack Benchik
PO Box 555
Notre Dame IN 46556

Philatelic Society for Greater
  Southern Africa
William C. Brooks VI
PO Box 2698
San Bernardino CA 92406-2698

Spanish Philatelic Society
Robert H. Penn
3021 Valley View Dr.
Bangor PA 18013
Ph: (610) 588-5627

American Helvetia Philatelic
  Society (Switzerland,
  Liechtenstein)
Richard T. Hall
PO Box 666
Manhattan Beach CA 90267-0666
E-mail: rtavish@pacbell.net

Tannu Tuva Collectors Society
Ken Simon
513 Sixth Ave. So.
Lake Worth FL 33460-4507
Ph: (561) 588-5954
http://www.blarg.net/~brad/ttcs.htm
E-mail: p003115b@pb.seflin.org

Society for Thai Philately
H. R. Blakeney
PO Box 25644
Oklahoma City OK 73125

Tonga/Tin Can Mail Study Circle
Tom Jackson
121 Mullingar Ct., #1A
Schaumburg IL 60193
http://members.aol.com/tongajan/
ttcmsc.html
E-mail: tjackso3@ix.netcom.com

Turkish and Ottoman Philatelic
   Society
Gary F. Paiste
4249 Berritt St.
Fairfax VA 22030

Ukrainian Philatelic & Numismatic
   Society
Bohdan O. Pauk
PO Box 11184
Chicago IL 60611-0184
Ph: (773) 276-0355

Yugoslavia Study Group
Michael Lenard
1514 North 3rd Ave.
Wausau WI 54401

Topical Groups

American Indian Philatelic Society
Charles Eson
128 Western Ave. Altamont NY 12009

Americana Unit
Dennis Dengel
17 Peckham Rd.
Poughkeepsie NY 12603-2018
http://www.philately.com/society_
news/americana_unit.htm
E-mail: 70363.3621@compuserve.com

Astronomy Study Unit
George Young
PO Box 632
Tewksbury MA 01876-0632
Ph: (978) 851-8283
http://www.fandm.edu/departments/
astronomy/miscell/astunit.html
E-mail: george-young@msn.com

Bicycle Stamp Club
Norman Batho
358 Iverson Place
East Windsor NJ 08520
Ph: (609) 448-9547
E-mail: normbatho@worldnet.att.net

Canadiana Study Unit
John Peebles
PO Box 3262, Station "A"
London, ON, Canada N6A 4K3
E-mail: john.peebles@odyssey.on.ca

Captain Cook Study Unit
Brian P. Sandford
173 Minuteman Dr.
Concord MA 01742-1923
http://freespace.virgin.net/chris.jones/
index.htm
E-mail: borehami@wcg.co.uk

Casey Jones Railroad Unit
Oliver Atchison
PO Box 31631
San Francisco CA 94131-0631
Ph: (415) 648-8057
E-mail: casey_jones@gowebway.com

Cats on Stamps Study Unit
Mary Ann Brown
3006 Wade Rd.
Durham NC 27705

Chess on Stamps Study Unit
Anne Kasonic
7624 County Road #153
Interlaken NY 14847
http://www.iglobal.net/home/reott/
stamps1.htm#cossu
E-mail: akasonic@epix.net

Christopher Columbus Philatelic
   Society
Donald R. Ager
PO Box 71
Hillsboro NH 03244
Ph: (603) 464-5379
E-mail: don_ager@conknet.com

Dogs on Stamps Study Unit
Morris Raskin
202A Newport Rd.
Cranbury NJ 08512
Ph: (609) 655-7411
E-mail: mraskin@worldnet.att.net

Earth's Physical Features Study
   Group
Fred Klein
515 Magdalena Ave.
Los Altos CA 94024
http://www.philately.com/society_
news/earths_physical.htm

Embroidery, Stitchery, Textile Unit
Helen N. Cushman
1001 Genter St., Apt. 9H
La Jolla CA 92037
Ph: (619) 459-1194

Europa Study Unit
Hank Klos
PO Box 611
Bensenville IL 60106
E-mail: hank@bensenville.lib.il.us

Fine & Performing Arts
Ruth Richards
10393 Derby Dr.
Laurel MD 20723
E-mail: bersec@aol.com

Gay & Lesbian History Stamp Club
Joe Petronie
PO Box 515981
Dallas TX 75251-5981

Gems, Minerals & Jewelry Study
   Group
George Young
PO Box 632
Tewksbury MA 01876-0632
Ph: (978) 851-8283
http://www.rockhounds.com/
rockshop/gmjsuapp.txt
E-mail: george-young@msn.com

Graphics Philately Association
Dulcie Apgar
PO Box 1513
Thousand Oaks CA 91358

Lighthouse Stamp Society
Dalene Thomas
8612 West Warren Lane
Lakewood CO 80227-2352
Ph: (303) 986-6620
http://www.nyx.net/~dathomas
E-mail: dathomas@nyx.net

Mask Study Unit
Carolyn Weber
PO Box 2542
Oxnard CA 93034
http://www.philately.com/society_
news/masks.htm

Mathematical Study Unit
Estelle Buccino
5615 Glenwood Rd.
Bethesda MD 20817
Ph: (301) 718-8898

Medical Subjects Unit
Dr. Frederick C. Skvara
PO Box 6228
Bridgewater NJ 08807

Mesoamerican Archeology Study
   Unit
Chris Moser
PO Box 1442, Riverside CA 92502

Napoleonic Age Philatelists
Ken Berry
7513 Clayton Dr.
Oklahoma City OK 73132-5636
Ph: (405) 721-0044

Petroleum Philatelic Society
   International
Feitze Papa
922 Meander Dr.
Walnut Creek CA 94598-4239

Philatelic Music Circle
Cathleen Osborne
PO Box 1781
Sequim WA 98382

Rainbow Study Unit
Shirley Sutton
PO Box 37
Lone Pine, AB, Canada T0G 1M0
Ph: (304) 584-2268
E-mail: george-young@msn.com

Rotary on Stamps Unit
Donald Fiery
PO Box 333, Hanover PA 17331
Ph: (717) 632-8921

Scouts on Stamps Society
   International
Carl Schauer
PO Box 526
Belen NM 87002
Ph: (505) 864-0098

Ships on Stamps Unit
Robert Stuckert
2750 Highway 21 East
Paint Lick KY 40461
Ph: (606) 925-4901

Sports Philatelists International
Margaret Jones
5310 Lindenwood Ave.
St. Louis MO 63109-1758
http://www.concentric.net/~laimins/
spi.html

Stamps on Stamps/Centenary Unit
William Critzer
13385 Country Way
Los Altos Hills CA 94022
Ph: (650) 941-1567
E-mail: willcrit@aol.com

Windmill Study Unit
Walter J. Hollien
PO Box 346
Long Valley NJ 07853-0346

Wine on Stamps Study Unit
James Crum
5132 Sepulveda
San Bernardino CA 92404-1134
Ph: (909) 886-3186

Women on Stamps Study Unit
Phebe Quattrucci
259 Middle Road
Falmouth ME 04105

Expertizing Services

The following organizations will, for a fee, provide expert opinions about stamps submitted to them. Collectors should contact these organizations to find out about their fees and requirements before submitting philatelic material to them. The listing of these groups here is not intended as an endorsement by Scott Publishing Co.

American Philatelic Expertizing
   Service
PO Box 8000
State College PA 16803

Philatelic Foundation
501 Fifth Ave., Rm. 1901
New York NY 10017

Professional Stamp Experts
1 Datran Center, Suite 1149
9100 South Dadeland Blvd.
Miami FL 33156

Confederate Stamp Alliance
   Authentication Service
10833 Greencrest Dr.
Baton Rouge LA 70811

Ukrainian Philatelic & Numismatic
   Society Expertizing Service
30552 Dell Lane
Warren MI 48092-1862

Information on Catalogue Values, Grade and Condition

Catalogue Value

The Scott Catalogue value is a retail value; that is, an amount you could expect to pay for a stamp in the grade of Very Fine with no faults. Any exceptions to the grade valued will be noted in the text. The general introduction on the following pages and the individual section introductions further explain the type of material that is valued. The value listed for any given stamp is a reference that reflects recent actual dealer selling prices for that item.

Dealer retail price lists, public auction results, published prices in advertising and individual solicitation of retail prices from dealers, collectors and specialty organizations have been used in establishing the values found in this catalogue. Scott Publishing Co. values stamps, but Scott is not a company engaged in the business of buying and selling stamps as a dealer.

Use this catalogue as a guide for buying and selling. The actual price you pay for a stamp may be higher or lower than the catalogue value because of many different factors, including the amount of personal service a dealer offers, or increased or decreased interest in the country or topic represented by a stamp or set. An item may occasionally be offered at a lower price as a "loss leader," or as part of a special sale. You also may obtain an item inexpensively at public auction because of little interest at that time or as part of a large lot.

Stamps that are of a lesser grade than Very Fine, or those with condition problems, generally trade at lower prices than those given in this catalogue. Stamps of exceptional quality in both grade and condition often command higher prices than those listed.

Values for pre-1900 unused issues are for stamps with approximately half or more of their original gum. Stamps with most or all of their original gum may be expected to sell for more, and stamps with less than half of their original gum may be expected to sell for somewhat less than the values listed. On rarer stamps, it may be expected that the original gum will be somewhat more disturbed than it will be on more common issues. Post-1900 unused issues are assumed to have full original gum. From breakpoints in most countries' listings, stamps are valued as never hinged, due to the wide availability of stamps in that condition. These notations are prominently placed in the listings and in the country information preceding the listings. Some countries also feature listings with dual values for hinged and never-hinged stamps.

Grade

A stamp's grade and condition are crucial to its value. The accompanying illustrations show examples of Very Fine stamps from different time periods, along with examples of stamps in Fine to Very Fine and Extremely Fine grades as points of reference.

FINE stamps (illustrations not shown) have designs that are noticeably off center on two sides. Imperforate stamps may have small margins, and earlier issues may show the design touching one edge of the stamp design. For perforated stamps, perfs may barely clear the design on one side, and very early issues normally will have the perforations slightly cutting into the design. Used stamps may have heavier than usual cancellations.

FINE-VERY FINE stamps may be somewhat off center on one side, or slightly off center on two sides. Imperforate stamps will have two margins of at least normal size, and the design will not touch any edge. For perforated stamps, the perfs are well clear of the design, but are still noticeably off center. *However, early issues of a country may be printed in such a way that the design naturally is very close to the edges. In these cases, the perforations may cut into the design very slightly.* Used stamps will not have a cancellation that detracts from the design.

VERY FINE stamps may be slightly off center on one side, but the design will be well clear of the edge. The stamp will present a nice, balanced appearance. Imperforate stamps will have three normal-sized margins. *However, early issues of many countries may be printed in such a way that the perforations may touch the design on one or more sides. Where this is the case, a boxed note will be found defining the centering and margins of the stamps being valued.* Used

stamps will have light or otherwise neat cancellations. This is the grade used to establish Scott Catalogue values.

EXTREMELY FINE stamps are close to being perfectly centered. Imperforate stamps will have even margins that are larger than normal. Even the earliest perforated issues will have perforations clear of the design on all sides.

Condition

Grade addresses only centering and (for used stamps) cancellation. *Condition* refers to factors other than grade that affect a stamp's desirability.

Factors that can increase the value of a stamp include exceptionally wide margins, particularly fresh color, the presence of selvage, and plate or die varieties. Unusual cancels on used stamps (particularly those of the 19th century) can greatly enhance their value as well.

Factors other than faults that decrease the value of a stamp include loss of original gum, regumming, a hinge remnant or foreign object adhering to the gum, natural inclusions, straight edges, and markings or notations applied by collectors or dealers.

Faults include missing pieces, tears, pin or other holes, surface scuffs, thin spots, creases, toning, short or pulled perforations, clipped perforations, oxidation or other forms of color changelings, soiling, stains, and such man-made changes as reperforations or the chemical removal or lightening of a cancellation.

Scott Publishing Co. recognizes that there is no formally enforced grading scheme for postage stamps, and that the final price you pay or obtain for a stamp will be determined by individual agreement at the time of transaction.

On the following two pages are illustrations of various stamps from countries appearing in this volume. These stamps are arranged by country, and they represent early or important issues that are often found in widely different grades in the marketplace. The editors believe the illustrations will prove useful in showing the margin size and centering that will be seen on the various issues.

In addition to the matters of margin size and centering, collectors are reminded that the very fine stamps valued in the Scott catalogues also will possess fresh color and intact perforations, and they will be free from defects.

Most examples shown are computer – manipulated images made from single digitized master illustrations.

Fine-Very Fine ➡️

SCOTT
CATALOGUES
VALUE
STAMPS IN
THIS GRADE

Very Fine ➡️

Extremely Fine ➡️

Fine-Very Fine ➡️

SCOTT
CATALOGUES
VALUE
STAMPS IN
THIS GRADE

Very Fine ➡️

Extremely Fine ➡️

Fine-Very Fine →

SCOTT
CATALOGUES
VALUE
STAMPS IN
THIS GRADE

Very Fine →

Extremely Fine →

Fine-Very Fine →

SCOTT
CATALOGUES
VALUE
STAMPS IN
THIS GRADE

Very Fine →

Extremely Fine →

For purposes of helping to determine the gum condition and value of an unused stamp, Scott Publishing Co. presents the following chart which details different gum conditions and indicates how the conditions correlate with the Scott values for unused stamps. Used together, the Illustrated Grading Chart on the previous pages and this Illustrated Gum Chart should allow catalogue users to better understand the grade and gum condition of stamps valued in the Scott catalogues.

Gum Categories:	MINT N.H.	ORIGINAL GUM (O.G.)				NO GUM
	Mint Never Hinged *Free from any disturbance*	**Lightly Hinged** *Faint impression of a removed hinge over a small area*	**Hinge Mark or Remnant** *Prominent hinged spot with part or all of the hinge remaining*	**Large part o.g.** *Approximately half or more of the gum intact*	**Small part o.g.** *Approximately less than half of the gum intact*	**No gum** *Only if issued with gum*
Commonly Used Symbol:	★★	★	★	★	★	(★)
Pre-1900 Issues (Pre-1890 for U.S.)	*Very fine pre-1900 stamps in these categories trade at a premium over Scott value*			Scott Value for "Unused"		Scott "No Gum" listings for selected unused classic stamps
From 1900 to break-points for listings of never-hinged stamps	Scott "Never Hinged" listings for selected unused stamps	Scott Value for "Unused" (Actual value will be affected by the degree of hinging of the full o.g.)				
From breakpoints noted for many countries	Scott Value for "Unused"					

Never Hinged (NH; ★★): A never-hinged stamp will have full original gum that will have no hinge mark or disturbance. The presence of an expertizer's mark does not disqualify a stamp from this designation.

Original Gum (OG; ★): Pre-1900 stamps should have approximately half or more of their original gum. On rarer stamps, it may be expected that the original gum will be somewhat more disturbed that it will be on more common issues. Post-1900 stamps should have full original gum. Original gum will show some disturbance caused by a previous hinge(s) which may be present or entirely removed. The actual value of a post-1900 stamp will be affected by the degree of hinging of the full original gum.

Disturbed Original Gum: Gum showing noticeable effects of humidity, climate or hinging over more than half of the gum. The significance of gum disturbance in valuing a stamp in any of the Original Gum categories depends on the degree of disturbance, the rarity and normal gum condition of the issue and other variables affecting quality.

Regummed (RG; (★)): A regummed stamp is a stamp without gum that has had some type of gum privately applied at a time after it was issued. This normally is done to deceive collectors and/or dealers into thinking that the stamp has original gum and therefore has a higher value. A regummed stamp is considered the same as a stamp with none of its original gum for purposes of grading.

National Albums

SCOTT NATIONAL SERIES

The National series offers a panoramic view of our country's heritage through postage stamps. It is the most complete and comprehensive U.S. album series you can buy. There are spaces for every major U.S. stamp listed in the Scott Catalogue, including Special Printings, Newspaper stamps and much more.

* Pages printed on one side.
* All spaces identified by Scott numbers.
* All major variety of stamps or either illustrated or described.
* Chemically neutral paper protects stamps.

Item			Retail
100NTL1	1845-1934	97 pgs	**$29.95**
100NTL2	1935-1976	108 pgs	**$29.95**
100NTL3	1977-1993	110 pgs	**$29.95**
100NTL4	1994-1997	81 pgs	**$25.95**

Supplemented in March. Back supplements available.

Computer Vended Postage
103CVP0	1989-1994	11 pgs	**$3.95**

National Blank Pages (Border B)
ACC120	20 per pack		**$6.95**

National Quad Blank Pages (Border B)
ACC121	20 per pack		**$6.95**

National Album Package

Get everything you need to house and value your collection in one convenient and affordable package. There's never been a better or more economical way to get the album pages, accessories and catalogues you need to build a better collection for one low price.

The National Album Package Include

1	National Pages Part 1 1845 - 1934 97 pgs.
1	National Pages Part 2 1935 - 1976 108 pgs.
1	National Pages Part 3 1977 - 1993 110 pgs.
1	National Pages Part 4 1994 - 1997 81 pgs.
4	Large three-ring binders
4	Large Slipcases
4	Black Protector Fly Sheets
4	National Album Labels
1	ScottMount Assortment (Item 966B)
1	Current U.S. Specialized Catalogue

SET PRICE $249.00

Scott albums are available from your favorite stamp dealer or direct from:

Scott Publishing Co.
P.O. Box 828
Sidney OH 45365-0828

1-800-572-6885

Catalogue Listing Policy

It is the intent of Scott Publishing Co. to list all postage stamps of the world in the *Scott Standard Postage Stamp Catalogue*. The only strict criteria for listing is that stamps be decreed legal for postage by the issuing country. Whether the primary intent of issuing a given stamp or set was for sale to postal patrons or to stamp collectors is not part of our listing criteria. Scott's role is to provide basic comprehensive postage stamp information. It is up to each stamp collector to choose which items to include in a collection.

It is Scott's objective to seek reasons why a stamp should be listed, rather than why it should not. Nevertheless, there are certain types of items that will not be listed. These include the following:

1. Unissued items that are not officially distributed or released by the issuing postal authority. Even if such a stamp is "accidentally" distributed to the philatelic or even postal market, it remains unissued. If such items are officially issued at a later date by the country, they will be listed. Unissued items consist of those that have been printed and then held from sale for reasons such as change in government, errors found on stamps or something deemed objectionable about a stamp subject or design.

2. Stamps "issued" by non-existent postal entities or fantasy countries, such as Nagaland, Occusi-Ambeno, Staffa, Sedang, Torres Straits and others.

3. Semi-official or unofficial items not required for postage. Examples include items issued by private agencies for their own express services. When such items are required for delivery, or are valid as prepayment of postage, they are listed.

4. Local stamps issued for local use only. Postage stamps issued by governments specifically for "domestic" use, such as Haiti Scott 219-228, or the United States non-denominated stamps, are not considered to be locals, since they are valid for postage throughout the country of origin.

5. Items not valid for postal use. For example, a few countries have issued souvenir sheets that are not valid for postage. This area also includes a number of worldwide charity labels (some denominated) that do not pay postage.

6. Intentional varieties, such as imperforate stamps that look like their perforated counterparts and are issued in very small quantities. These are often controlled issues intended for speculation.

7. Items distributed by the issuing government only to a limited group, such as a stamp club, philatelic exhibition or a single stamp dealer, and later brought to market at inflated prices. These items normally will be included in a footnote.

The fact that a stamp has been used successfully as postage, even on international mail, is not in itself sufficient proof that it was legitimately issued. Numerous examples of so-called stamps from non-existent countries are known to have been used to post letters that have successfully passed through the international mail system.

There are certain items that are subject to interpretation. When a stamp falls outside our specifications, it may be listed along with a cautionary footnote.

A number of factors are considered in our approach to analyzing how a stamp is listed. The following list of factors is presented to share with you, the catalogue user, the complexity of the listing process.

Additional printings — "Additional printings" of a previously issued stamp may range from an item that is totally different to cases where it is impossible to differentiate from the original. At least a minor number (a small-letter suffix) is assigned if there is a distinct change in stamp shade, noticeably redrawn design, or a significantly different perforation measurement. A major number (numeral or numeral and capital-letter combination) is assigned if the editors feel the "additional printing" is sufficiently different from the original that it constitutes a different issue.

Commemoratives — Where practical, commemoratives with the same theme are placed in a set. For example, the U.S. Civil War Centenniel set of 1961-65 and the Constitution Bicentennial series of 1989-90 appear as sets. Countries such as Japan and Korea issue such material on a regular basis, with an announced, or at least predictable, number of stamps known in advance. Occasionally, however, stamp sets that were released over a period of years have been separated. Appropriately placed footnotes will guide you to each set's continuation.

Definitive sets — Blocks of numbers generally have been reserved for definitive sets, based on previous experience with any given country. If a few more stamps were issued in a set than originally expected, they often have been inserted into the original set with a capital-letter suffix, such as U.S. Scott 1059A. If it appears that many more stamps than the originally allotted block will be released before the set is completed, a new block of numbers will be reserved, with the original one being closed off. In some cases, such as the British Machin Head series or the U.S. Transportation and Great Americans series, several blocks of numbers exist. Appropriately placed footnotes will guide you to each set's continuation.

New country — Membership in the Universal Postal Union is not a consideration for listing status or order of placement within the catalogue. The index will tell you in what volume or page number the listings begin.

"No release date" items — The amount of information available for any given stamp issue varies greatly from country to country and even from time to time. Extremely comprehensive information about new stamps is available from some countries well before the stamps are released. By contrast some countries do not provide information about stamps or release dates. Most countries, however, fall between these extremes. A country may provide denominations or subjects of stamps from upcoming issues that are not issued as planned. Sometimes, philatelic agencies, those private firms hired to represent countries, add these later-issued items to sets well after the formal release date. This time period can range from weeks to years. If these items were officially released by the country, they will be added to the appropriate spot in the set. In many cases, the specific release date of a stamp or set of stamps may never be known.

Overprints — The color of an overprint is always noted if it is other than black. Where more than one color of ink has been used on overprints of a single set, the color used is noted. Early overprint and surcharge illustrations were altered to prevent their use by forgers.

Se-tenants — Connected stamps of differing features (se-tenants) will be listed in the format most commonly collected. This includes pairs, blocks or larger multiples. Se-tenant units are not always symmetrical. An example is Australia Scott 508, which is a block of seven stamps. If the stamps are primarily collected as a unit, the major number may be assigned to the multiple, with minors going to each component stamp. In cases where continuous-design or other unit se-tenants will receive significant postal use, each stamp is given a major Scott number listing. This includes issues from the United States, Canada, Germany and Great Britain, for example.

Understanding the Listings

On the opposite page is an enlarged "typical" listing from this catalogue. Below are detailed explanations of each of the highlighted parts of the listing.

1 **Scott number** — Scott catalogue numbers are used to identify specific items when buying, selling or trading stamps. Each listed postage stamp from every country has a unique Scott catalogue number. Therefore, Germany Scott 99, for example, can only refer to a single stamp. Although the Scott catalogue usually lists stamps in chronological order by date of issue, there are exceptions. When a country has issued a set of stamps over a period of time, those stamps within the set are kept together without regard to date of issue. This follows the normal collecting approach of keeping stamps in their natural sets.

When a country issues a set of stamps over a period of time, a group of consecutive catalogue numbers is reserved for the stamps in that set, as issued. If that group of numbers proves to be too few, capital-letter suffixes, such as "A" or "B," may be added to existing numbers to create enough catalogue numbers to cover all items in the set. A capital-letter suffix indicates a major Scott catalogue number listing. Scott uses a suffix letter only once. Therefore, a catalogue number listing with a capital-letter prefix will not also be found with the same letter (lower case) used as a minor-letter listing. If there is a Scott 16A in a set, for example, there will not also be a Scott 16a.

Suffix letters are not cumulative. A minor variety of Scott 16A would be Scott 16b, not Scott 16Ab. Any exceptions, such as Great Britain Scott 358cp, are clearly indicated.

There are times when a reserved block of Scott catalogue numbers is too large for a set, leaving some numbers unused. Such gaps in the numbering sequence also occur when the catalogue editors move an item's listing elsewhere or have removed it entirely from the catalogue. Scott does not attempt to account for every possible number, but rather attempts to assure that each stamp is assigned its own number.

Scott numbers designating regular postage normally are only numerals. Scott numbers for other types of stamps, such as air post, semipostal, postal tax, postage due, occupation and others have a prefix consisting of one or more capital letters or a combination of numerals and capital letters.

2 **Illustration number** — Illustration or design-type numbers are used to identify each catalogue illustration. For most sets, the lowest face-value stamp is shown. It then serves as an example of the basic design approach for other stamps not illustrated. Where more than one stamp use the same illustration number, but have differences in design, the design paragraph or the description line clearly indicates the design on each stamp not illustrated. Where there are both vertical and horizontal designs in a set, a single illustration may be used, with the exceptions noted in the design paragraph or description line.

When an illustration is followed by a lower-case letter in parentheses, such as "A2(b)," the trailing letter indicates which overprint or surcharge illustration applies.

Illustrations normally are 75 percent of the original size of the stamp. An effort has been made to note all illustrations not illustrated at that percentage. Virtually all souvenir sheet illustrations are reduced even more. Overprints and surcharges are shown at 100 percent of their original size, unless otherwise noted. In some cases, the illustration will be placed above the set, between listings or omitted completely. Overprint and surcharge illustrations are not placed in this catalogue for purposes of expertizing stamps.

3 **Paper color** — The color of a stamp's paper is noted in italic type when the paper used is not white.

4 **Listing styles** — There are two principal types of catalogue listings: major and minor.

Major listings are in a larger type style than minor listings. The catalogue number is a numeral that can be found with or without a capital-letter suffix, and with or without a prefix.

Minor listings are in a smaller type style and have a small-letter suffix or (if the listing immediately follows that of the major number) may show only the letter. These listings identify a variety of the major item. Examples include perforation, color, watermark or printing method differences, multiples (some souvenir sheets, booklet panes and se-tenant combinations), and singles of multiples.

Examples of major number listings include 16, 28A, B97, C13A, 10N5, and 10N6A. Examples of minor numbers are 16a and C13b.

5 **Basic information about a stamp or set** — Introducing each stamp issue is a small section (usually a line listing) of basic information about a stamp or set. This section normally includes the date of issue, method of printing, perforation, watermark and, sometimes, some additional information of note. *Printing method, perforation and watermark apply to the following sets until a change is noted.* Stamps created by overprinting or surcharging previous issues are assumed to have the same perforation, watermark and printing method as the original. Dates of issue are as precise as Scott is able to confirm and often reflect the dates on first-day covers, rather than the actual date of release.

6 **Denomination** — This normally refers to the face value of the stamp; that is, the cost of the unused stamp at the post office at the time of issue. When a denomination is shown in parentheses, it does not appear on the stamp. This includes the non-denominated stamps of the United States, Brazil and Great Britain, for example.

7 **Color or other description** — This area provides information to solidify identification of a stamp. In many recent cases, a description of the stamp design appears in this space, rather than a listing of colors.

8 **Year of issue** — In stamp sets that have been released in a period that spans more than a year, the number shown in parentheses is the year that stamp first appeared. Stamps without a date appeared during the first year of the issue. Dates are not always given for minor varieties.

9 **Value unused and Value used** — The Scott catalogue values are based on stamps that are in a grade of Very Fine unless stated otherwise. Unused values refer to items that have not seen postal, revenue or any other duty for which they were intended. Pre-1900 unused stamps that were issued with gum must have at least most of their original gum. Later issues are assumed to have full original gum. From breakpoints specified in most countries' listings, stamps are valued as never hinged. Stamps issued without gum are noted. Modern issues with PVA or other synthetic adhesives may appear ungummed. Self-adhesive stamps are valued as appearing undisturbed on their original backing paper. For a more detailed explanation of these values, please see the "Catalogue Value," "Condition" and "Understanding Valuing Notations" elsewhere in this introduction.

In some cases, where used stamps are more valuable than unused stamps, the value is for an example with a contemporaneous cancel, rather than a modern cancel or a smudge or other unclear marking. For those stamps that were released for postal and fiscal purposes, the used value represents a postally used stamp. Stamps with revenue cancels generally sell for less.

10 **Changes in basic set information** — Bold type is used to show any changes in the basic data given for a set of stamps. This includes perforation differences from one stamp to the next or a different paper, printing method or watermark.

11 **Total value of a set** — The total value of sets of three or more stamps issued after 1900 are shown. The set line also notes the range of Scott numbers and total number of stamps included in the grouping. *Set value* is the term used to indicate the value of a stamp set when its combined total is less than the sum of the individual stamps. This happens when some of the stamps in a set have the minimum catalogue value.

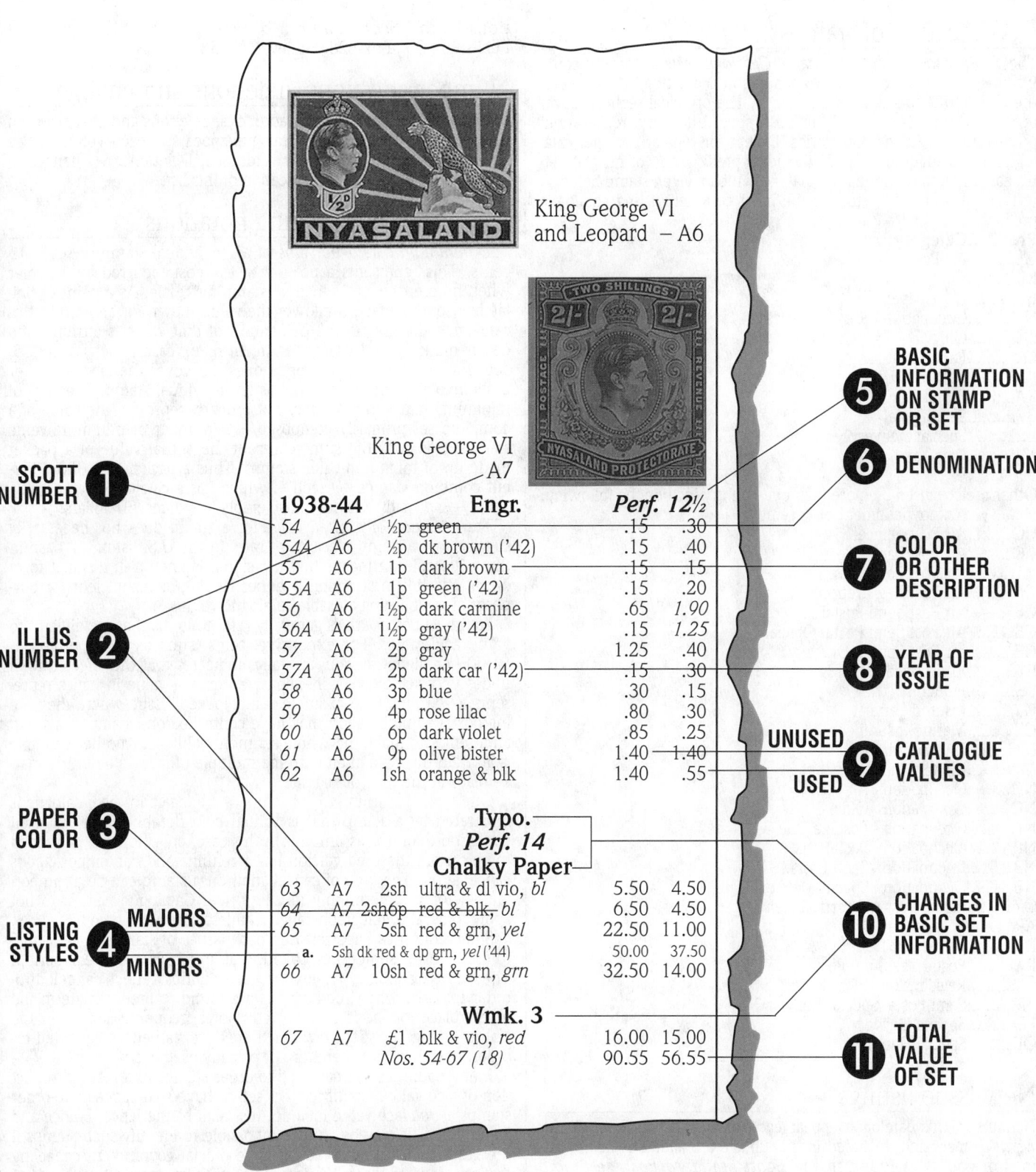

King George VI
and Leopard – A6

King George VI
A7

SCOTT NUMBER ❶

ILLUS. NUMBER ❷

PAPER COLOR ❸

LISTING STYLES ❹ MAJORS / MINORS

5 BASIC INFORMATION ON STAMP OR SET

6 DENOMINATION

7 COLOR OR OTHER DESCRIPTION

8 YEAR OF ISSUE

9 CATALOGUE VALUES (UNUSED / USED)

10 CHANGES IN BASIC SET INFORMATION

11 TOTAL VALUE OF SET

				Unused	Used
1938-44		**Engr.**		***Perf. 12½***	
54	A6	½p	green	.15	.30
54A	A6	½p	dk brown ('42)	.15	.40
55	A6	1p	dark brown	.15	.15
55A	A6	1p	green ('42)	.15	.20
56	A6	1½p	dark carmine	.65	*1.90*
56A	A6	1½p	gray ('42)	.15	*1.25*
57	A6	2p	gray	1.25	.40
57A	A6	2p	dark car ('42)	.15	.30
58	A6	3p	blue	.30	.15
59	A6	4p	rose lilac	.80	.30
60	A6	6p	dark violet	.85	.25
61	A6	9p	olive bister	1.40	1.40
62	A6	1sh	orange & blk	1.40	.55

Typo.
Perf. 14
Chalky Paper

63	A7	2sh	ultra & dl vio, *bl*	5.50	4.50
64	A7	2sh6p	red & blk, *bl*	6.50	4.50
65	A7	5sh	red & grn, *yel*	22.50	11.00
	a.	5sh	dk red & dp grn, *yel* ('44)	50.00	37.50
66	A7	10sh	red & grn, *grn*	32.50	14.00

Wmk. 3

67	A7	£1	blk & vio, *red*	16.00	15.00
		Nos. 54-67 (18)		90.55	56.55

Special Notices

Classification of stamps

The *Scott Standard Postage Stamp Catalogue* lists stamps by country of issue. The next level of organization is a listing by section on the basis of the function of the stamps. The principal sections cover regular postage, semi-postal, air post, special delivery, registration, postage due and other categories. Except for regular postage, catalogue numbers for all sections include a prefix letter (or number-letter combination) denoting the class to which a given stamp belongs.

The following is a listing of the most commonly used catalogue prefixes.

Prefix....Category
C ....Air Post
M...........Military
P.............Newspaper
N ....Occupation - Regular Issues
O ....Official
Q...........Parcel Post
J.............Postage Due
RA ....Postal Tax
B............Semi-Postal
E............Special Delivery
MR ....War Tax

Other prefixes used by more than one country include the following:
H ....Acknowledgment of Receipt
CO.........Air Post Official
CQ.........Air Post Parcel Post
RAC.......Air Post Postal Tax
CF..........Air Post Registration
CB.........Air Post Semi-Postal
CBO.......Air Post Semi-Postal Official
CE ....Air Post Special Delivery
EY..........Authorized Delivery
S ....Franchise
G ....Insured Letter
GY ....Marine Insurance
MC ....Military Air Post
MQ........Military Parcel Post
NC.........Occupation - Air Post
NO.........Occupation - Official
NJ ....Occupation - Postage Due
NRA.......Occupation - Postal Tax
NB ....Occupation - Semi-Postal
NE ....Occupation - Special Delivery
QY ....Parcel Post Authorized Delivery
AR ....Postal-fiscal
RAJ ....Postal Tax Due
RAB ....Postal Tax Semi-Postal
F.............Registration
EB..........Semi-Postal Special Delivery
EO ....Special Delivery Official
QE ....Special Handling

New issue listings

Updates to this catalogue appear each month in the *Scott Stamp Monthly* magazine. Included in this update are additions to the listings of countries found in the *Scott Standard Postage Stamp Catalogue* and the *Specialized Catalogue of United States Stamps*, as well as corrections and updates to current editions of this catalogue.

From time to time there will be changes in the final listings of stamps from the *Scott Stamp Monthly* to the next edition of the catalogue. This occurs as more information about certain stamps or sets becomes available.

The catalogue update section of the *Scott Stamp Monthly* is the most timely presentation of this material available. Annual subscriptions to the *Scott Stamp Monthly* are available from Scott Publishing Co., Box 828, Sidney, OH 45365-0828.

Number additions, deletions and changes

A listing of catalogue number additions, deletions and changes from the previous edition of the catalogue appears in each volume. See Volume 1 Catalogue Number Additions, Deletions, & Changes in the table of contents for the location of this list.

Understanding valuing notations

The *minimum catalogue value* of an individual stamp or set is 15 cents. This represents a portion of the cost incurred by a dealer when he prepares an individual stamp for resale. As a point of philatelic-economic fact, the lower the value shown for an item in this catalogue, the greater the percentage of that value is attributed to dealer mark up and profit margin. In many cases, such as the 15-cent minimum value, that price does not cover the labor or other costs involved with stocking it as an individual stamp. The sum of minimum values in a set does not properly represent the value of a complete set primarily composed of a number of minimum-value stamps, nor does the sum represent the actual value of a packet made up of minimum-value stamps. Thus a packet of 1,000 different common stamps — each of which has a catalogue value of 15 cents — normally sells for considerably less than 150 dollars!

The *absence of a retail value* for a stamp does not necessarily suggest that a stamp is scarce or rare. In the U.S. listings, a dash in the value column means that the stamp is known in a stated form or variety, but information is either lacking or insufficient for purposes of establishing a usable catalogue value.

Stamp values in *italics* generally refer to items that are difficult to value accurately. For expensive items, such as those priced at $1,000 or higher, a value in italics indicates that the affected item trades very seldom. For inexpensive items, a value in italics represents a warning. One example is a "blocked" issue where the issuing postal administration may have controlled one stamp in a set in an attempt to make the whole set more valuable. Another example is an item that sold at an extreme multiple of face value in the marketplace at the time of its issue.

One type of warning to collectors that appears in the catalogue is illustrated by a stamp that is valued considerably higher in used condition than it is as unused. In this case, collectors are cautioned to be certain the used version has a genuine and contemporaneous cancellation. The type of cancellation on a stamp can be an important factor in determining its sale price. Catalogue values do not apply to fiscal or telegraph cancels, unless otherwise noted.

Some countries have released back issues of stamps in canceled-to-order form, sometimes covering as much as a 10-year period. The Scott Catalogue values for used stamps reflect canceled-to-order material when such stamps are found to predominate in the marketplace for the issue involved. Notes frequently appear in the stamp listings to specify which items are valued as canceled-to-order, or if there is a premium for postally used examples.

Many countries sell canceled-to-order stamps at a marked reduction of face value. Countries that sell or have sold canceled-to-order stamps at *full* face value include Australia, Netherlands, France and Switzerland. It may be almost impossible to identify such stamps if the gum has been removed, because official government canceling devices are used. Postally used copies of these items on cover, however, are usually worth more than the canceled-to-order stamps with original gum.

Abbreviations

Scott Publishing Co. uses a consistent set of abbreviations throughout this catalogue to conserve space, while still providing necessary information.

COLOR ABBREVIATIONS

amb	amber	crim	crimson	ol	olive
anil	aniline	cr	cream	olvn	olivine
ap	apple	dk	dark	org	orange
aqua	aquamarine	dl	dull	pck	peacock
az	azure	dp	deep	pnksh	pinkish
bis	bister	db	drab	Prus	Prussian
bl	blue	emer	emerald	pur	purple
bld	blood	gldn	golden	redsh	reddish
blk	black	grysh	grayish	res	reseda
bril	brilliant	grn	green	ros	rosine
brn	brown	grnsh	greenish	ryl	royal
brnsh	brownish	hel	heliotrope	sal	salmon
brnz	bronze	hn	henna	saph	sapphire
brt	bright	ind	indigo	scar	scarlet
brnt	burnt	int	intense	sep	sepia
car	carmine	lav	lavender	sien	sienna
cer	cerise	lem	lemon	sil	silver
chlky	chalky	lil	lilac	sl	slate
cham	chamois	lt	light	stl	steel
chnt	chestnut	mag	magenta	turq	turquoise
choc	chocolate	man	manila	ultra	ultramarine
chr	chrome	mar	maroon	Ven	Venetian
cit	citron	mv	mauve	ver	vermilion
cl	claret	multi	multicolored	vio	violet
cob	cobalt	mlky	milky	yel	yellow
cop	copper	myr	myrtle	yelsh	yellowish

When no color is given for an overprint or surcharge, black is the color used. Abbreviations for colors used for overprints and surcharges include: "(B)" or "(Blk)," black; "(Bl)," blue; "(R)," red; and "(G)," green.

Additional abbreviations in this catalogue are shown below:

Adm.	Administration
AFL	American Federation of Labor
Anniv.	Anniversary
APS	American Philatelic Society
Assoc.	Association
ASSR.	Autonomous Soviet Socialist Republic
b.	Born
BEP	Bureau of Engraving and Printing
Bicent.	Bicentennial
Bklt.	Booklet
Brit.	British
btwn.	Between
Bur.	Bureau
c. or ca.	Circa
Cat.	Catalogue
Cent.	Centennial, century, centenary
CIO	Congress of Industrial Organizations
Conf.	Conference
Cong.	Congress
Cpl.	Corporal
CTO	Canceled to order
d.	Died
Dbl.	Double
EKU	Earliest known use
Engr.	Engraved
Exhib.	Exhibition
Expo.	Exposition
Fed.	Federation
GB	Great Britain
Gen.	General
GPO	General post office
Horiz.	Horizontal
Imperf.	Imperforate
Impt.	Imprint

Intl.	International
Invtd.	Inverted
L.	Left
Lieut., lt.	Lieutenant
Litho.	Lithographed
LL	Lower left
LR	Lower right
mm.	Millimeter
Ms.	Manuscript
Natl.	National
No.	Number
NY	New York
NYC	New York City
Ovpt.	Overprint
Ovptd.	Overprinted
P.	Plate number
Perf.	Perforated, perforation
Phil.	Philatelic
Photo.	Photogravure
PO	Post office
Pr.	Pair
P.R.	Puerto Rico
Prec.	Precancel, precanceled
Pres.	President
PTT	Post, Telephone and Telegraph
Rio	Rio de Janeiro
Sgt.	Sergeant
Soc.	Society
Souv.	Souvenir
SSR	Soviet Socialist Republic, see ASSR
St.	Saint, street
Surch.	Surcharge
Typo.	Typographed
UL	Upper left
Unwmkd.	Unwatermarked
UPU	Universal Postal Union
UR	Upper Right
US	United States
USPOD	United States Post Office Department
USSR	Union of Soviet Socialist Republics
Vert.	Vertical
VP	Vice president
Wmk.	Watermark
Wmkd.	Watermarked
WWI	World War I
WWII	World War II

Examination

Scott Publishing Co. will not comment upon the genuineness, grade or condition of stamps, because of the time and responsibility involved. Rather, there are several expertizing groups that undertake this work for both collectors and dealers. Neither will Scott Publishing Co. appraise or identify philatelic material. The company cannot take responsibility for unsolicited stamps or covers sent by individuals.

How to order from your dealer

When ordering stamps from a dealer, it is not necessary to write the full description of a stamp as listed in this catalogue. All you need is the name of the country, the Scott catalogue number and whether the desired item is unused or used. For example, "Japan Scott 422 unused" is sufficient to identify the unused stamp of Japan listed as "422 A206 5y brown."

Basic Stamp Information

A stamp collector's knowledge of the combined elements that make a given stamp issue unique determines his or her ability to identify stamps. These elements include paper, watermark, method of separation, printing, design and gum. On the following pages each of these important areas is briefly described.

Paper

Paper is an organic material composed of a compacted weave of cellulose fibers and generally formed into sheets. Paper used to print stamps may be manufactured in sheets, or it may have been part of a large roll (called a web) before being cut to size. The fibers most often used to create paper on which stamps are printed include bark, wood, straw and certain grasses. In many cases, linen or cotton rags have been added for greater strength and durability. Grinding, bleaching, cooking and rinsing these raw fibers reduces them to a slushy pulp, referred to by paper makers as "stuff." Sizing and, sometimes, coloring matter is added to the pulp to make different types of finished paper.

After the stuff is prepared, it is poured onto sieve-like frames that allow the water to run off, while retaining the matted pulp. As fibers fall onto the screen and are held by gravity, they form a natural weave that will later hold the paper together. If the screen has metal bits that are formed into letters or images attached, it leaves slightly thinned areas on the paper. These are called watermarks.

When the stuff is almost dry, it is passed under pressure through smooth or engraved rollers - dandy rolls - or placed between cloth in a press to be flattened and dried.

Stamp paper falls broadly into two types: wove and laid. The nature of the surface of the frame onto which the pulp is first deposited causes the differences in appearance between the two. If the surface is smooth and even, the paper will be of fairly uniform texture throughout. This is known as *wove paper*. Early papermaking machines poured the pulp onto a continuously circulating web of felt, but modern machines feed the pulp onto a cloth-like screen made of closely interwoven fine wires. This paper, when held to a light, will show little dots or points very close together. The proper name for this is "wire wove," but the type is still considered wove. Any U.S. or British stamp printed after 1880 will serve as an example of wire wove paper.

Closely spaced parallel wires, with cross wires at wider intervals, make up the frames used for what is known as *laid paper*. A greater thickness of the pulp will settle between the wires. The paper, when held to a light, will show alternate light and dark lines. The spacing and the thickness of the lines may vary, but on any one sheet of paper they are all alike. See Russia Scott 31-38 for examples of laid paper.

Batonne, from the French word meaning "a staff," is a term used if the lines in the paper are spaced quite far apart, like the printed ruling on a writing tablet. Batonne paper may be either wove or laid. If laid, fine laid lines can be seen between the batons. The laid lines, which are a form of watermark, may be geometrical figures such as squares, diamonds, rectangles or wavy lines.

Quadrille is the term used when the lines in the paper form little squares. *Oblong quadrille* is the term used when rectangles, rather than squares, are formed. See Mexico-Guadalajara Scott 35-37 for examples of oblong quadrille paper.

Paper also is classified as thick or thin, hard or soft, and by color if dye is added during manufacture. Such colors may include yellowish, greenish, bluish and reddish.

Brief explanations of other types of paper used for printing stamps, as well as examples, follow.

Pelure — Pelure paper is a very thin, hard and often brittle paper that is sometimes bluish or grayish in appearance. See Serbia Scott 169-170.

Native — This is a term applied to handmade papers used to produce some of the early stamps of the Indian states. Stamps printed on native paper may be expected to display various natural inclusions that are normal and do not negatively affect value. Japanese paper, originally made of mulberry fibers and rice flour, is part of this group. See Japan Scott 1-18.

Manila — This type of paper is often used to make stamped envelopes and wrappers. It is a coarse-textured stock, usually smooth on one side and rough on the other. A variety of colors of manila paper exist, but the most common range is yellowish-brown.

Silk — Introduced by the British in 1847 as a safeguard against counterfeiting, silk paper contains bits of colored silk thread scattered throughout. The density of these fibers varies greatly and can include as few as one fiber per stamp or hundreds. U.S. revenue Scott R152 is a good example of an easy-to-identify silk paper stamp.

Silk-thread paper has uninterrupted threads of colored silk arranged so that one or more threads run through the stamp or postal stationery. See Great Britain Scott 5-6 and Switzerland Scott 14-19.

Granite — Filled with minute cloth or colored paper fibers of various colors and lengths, granite paper should not be confused with either type of silk paper. Austria Scott 172-175 and a number of Swiss stamps are examples of granite paper.

Chalky — A chalk-like substance coats the surface of chalky paper to discourage the cleaning and reuse of canceled stamps, as well as to provide a smoother, more acceptable printing surface. Because the designs of stamps printed on chalky paper are imprinted on what is often a water-soluble coating, any attempt to remove a cancellation will destroy the stamp. *Do not soak these stamps in any fluid.* To remove a stamp printed on chalky paper from an envelope, wet the paper from underneath the stamp until the gum dissolves enough to release the stamp from the paper. See St. Kitts-Nevis Scott 89-90 for examples of stamps printed on this type of chalky paper.

India — Another name for this paper, originally introduced from China about 1750, is "China Paper." It is a thin, opaque paper often used for plate and die proofs by many countries.

Double — In philately, the term double paper has two distinct meanings. The first is a two-ply paper, usually a combination of a thick and a thin sheet, joined during manufacture. This type was used experimentally as a means to discourage the reuse of stamps.

The design is printed on the thin paper. Any attempt to remove a cancellation would destroy the design. U.S. Scott 158 and other Banknote-era stamps exist on this form of double paper.

The second type of double paper occurs on a rotary press, when the end of one paper roll, or web, is affixed to the next roll to save time feeding the paper through the press. Stamp designs are printed over the joined paper and, if overlooked by inspectors, may get into post office stocks.

Goldbeater's Skin — This type of paper was used for the 1866 issue of Prussia, and was a tough, translucent paper. The design was printed in reverse on the back of the stamp, and the gum applied over the printing. It is impossible to remove stamps printed on this type of paper from the paper to which they are affixed without destroying the design.

Ribbed — Ribbed paper has an uneven, corrugated surface made by passing the paper through ridged rollers. This type exists on some copies of U.S. Scott 156-165.

Various other substances, or substrates, have been used for stamp manufacture, including wood, aluminum, copper, silver and gold foil, plastic, and silk and cotton fabrics.

Wove   Laid   Granite

Quadrille   Oblong Quadrille   Batonne

Watermarks

Watermarks are an integral part of some papers. They are formed in the process of paper manufacture. Watermarks consist of small designs, formed of wire or cut from metal and soldered to the surface of the mold or, sometimes, on the dandy roll. The designs may be in the form of crowns, stars, anchors, letters or other characters or symbols. These pieces of metal - known in the paper-making industry as "bits" - impress a design into the paper. The design sometimes may be seen by holding the stamp to the light. Some are more easily seen with a watermark detector. This important tool is a small black tray into which a stamp is placed face down and dampened with a fast-evaporating watermark detection fluid that brings up the watermark image in the form of dark lines against a lighter background. These dark lines are the thinner areas of the paper known as the watermark. Some watermarks are extremely difficult to locate, due to either a faint impression, watermark location or the color of the stamp. There also are electric watermark detectors that come with plastic filter disks of various colors. The disks neutralize the color of the stamp, permitting the watermark to be seen more easily.

Multiple watermarks of Crown Agents and Burma

Watermarks of Uruguay, Vatican City and Jamaica

WARNING: Some inks used in the photogravure process dissolve in watermark fluids (Please see the section on Soluble Printing Inks). Also, see "chalky paper."

Watermarks may be found normal, reversed, inverted, reversed and inverted, sideways or diagonal, as seen from the back of the stamp.

The relationship of watermark to stamp design depends on the position of the printing plates or how paper is fed through the press. On machine-made paper, watermarks normally are read from right to left. The design is repeated closely throughout the sheet in a "multiple-watermark design." In a "sheet watermark," the design appears only once on the sheet, but extends over many stamps. Individual stamps may carry only a small fraction or none of the watermark.

"Marginal watermarks" occur in the margins of sheets or panes of stamps. They occur on the outside border of paper (ostensibly outside the area where stamps are to be printed). A large row of letters may spell the name of the country or the manufacturer of the paper, or a border of lines may appear. Careless press feeding may cause parts of these letters and/or lines to show on stamps of the outer row of a pane.

Soluble Printing Inks

WARNING: Most stamp colors are permanent; that is, they are not seriously affected by short-term exposure to light or water. Many colors, especially of modern inks, fade from excessive exposure to light. There are stamps printed with inks that dissolve easily in water or in fluids used to detect watermarks. Use of these inks was intentional to prevent the removal of cancellations. Water affects all aniline inks, those on so-called safety paper and some photogravure printings - all such inks are known as *fugitive colors. Removal from paper of such stamps requires care and alternatives to traditional soaking.*

Separation

"Separation" is the general term used to describe methods used to separate stamps. The three standard forms currently in use are perforating, rouletting and die-cutting. These methods are done during the stamp production process, after printing. Sometimes these methods are done on-press or sometimes as a separate step. The earliest issues, such as the 1840 Penny Black of Great Britain (Scott 1), did not have any means provided for separation. It was expected the stamps would be cut apart with scissors or folded and torn. These are examples of imperforate stamps. Many stamps were first issued in imperforate formats and were later issued with perforations. Therefore, care must be observed in buying single imperforate stamps to be certain they were issued imperforate and are not perforated copies that have been altered by having the perforations trimmed away. Stamps issued imperforate usually are valued as singles. However, imperforate varieties of normally perforated stamps should be collected in pairs or larger pieces as indisputable evidence of their imperforate character.

PERFORATION

The chief style of separation of stamps, and the one that is in almost universal use today, is perforating. By this process, paper between the stamps is cut away in a line of holes, usually round, leaving little bridges of paper between the stamps to hold them together. Some types of perforation, such as hyphen-hole perfs, can be confused with roulettes, but a close visual inspection reveals that paper has been removed. The little perforation bridges, which project from the stamp when it is torn from the pane, are called the teeth of the perforation.

As the size of the perforation is sometimes the only way to differentiate between two otherwise identical stamps, it is necessary to be able to accurately measure and describe them. This is done with a perforation gauge, usually a ruler-like device that has dots or graduated lines to show how many perforations may be counted in the space of two centimeters. Two centimeters is the space universally adopted in which to measure perforations.

Perforation gauge

perce en arc   perce en lignes

perce en points   oblique roulette

perce en scie   perce serpentin

To measure a stamp, run it along the gauge until the dots on it fit exactly into the perforations of the stamp. If you are using a graduated-line perforation gauge, simply slide the stamp along the surface until the lines on the gauge perfectly project from the center of the bridges or holes. The number to the side of the line of dots or lines that fit the stamp's perforation is the measurement. For example, an "11" means that 11 perforations fit between two centimeters. The description of the stamp therefore is "perf. 11." If the gauge of the perforations on the top and bottom of a stamp differs from that on the sides, the result is what is known as *compound perforations*. In measuring compound perforations, the gauge at top and bottom is always given first, then the sides. Thus, a stamp that measures 11 at top and bottom and 10 1/2 at the sides is "perf. 11 x 10 1/2." See U.S. Scott 632-642 for examples of compound perforations.

Stamps also are known with perforations different on three or all four sides. Descriptions of such items are clockwise, beginning with the top of the stamp.

A perforation with small holes and teeth close together is a "fine perforation." One with large holes and teeth far apart is a "coarse perforation." Holes that are jagged, rather than clean-cut, are "rough perforations." *Blind perforations* are the slight impressions left by the perforating pins if they fail to puncture the paper. Multiples of stamps showing blind perforations may command a slight premium over normally perforated stamps.

The term *syncopated perfs* describes intentional irregularities in the perforations. The earliest form was used by the Netherlands from 1925-33, where holes were omitted to create distinctive patterns. Beginning in 1992, Great Britain has used an oval perforation to help prevent counterfeiting. Several other countries have started using the oval perfs.

A new type of perforation, still primarily used for postal stationery, is known as microperfs. Microperfs are tiny perforations (in some cases hundreds of holes per two centimeters) that allows items to be intentionally separated very easily, while not accidentally breaking apart as easily as standard perforations. These are not currently measured or differentiated by size, as are standard perforations.

ROULETTING

In rouletting, the stamp paper is cut partly or wholly through, with no paper removed. In perforating, some paper is removed. Rouletting derives its name from the French roulette, a spur-like wheel. As the wheel is rolled over the paper, each point makes a small cut. The number of cuts made in a two-centimeter space determines the gauge of the roulette, just as the number of perforations in two centimeters determines the gauge of the perforation.

The shape and arrangement of the teeth on the wheels varies. Various roulette types generally carry French names:

Perce en lignes - rouletted in lines. The paper receives short, straight cuts in lines. This is the most common type of rouletting. See Mexico Scott 500.

Perce en points - pin-rouletted. This differs from a small perforation because no paper is removed, although round, equidistant holes are pricked through the paper. See Mexico Scott 242-256.

Perce en arc and *perce en scie* - pierced in an arc or saw-toothed designs, forming half circles or small triangles. See Hanover (German States) Scott 25-29.

Perce en serpentin - serpentine roulettes. The cuts form a serpentine or wavy line. See Brunswick (German States) Scott 13-18.

Once again, no paper is removed by these processes, leaving the stamps easily separated, but closely attached.

DIE-CUTTING

The third major form of stamp separation is die-cutting. This is a method where a die in the pattern of separation is created that later cuts the stamp paper in a stroke motion. Although some standard stamps bear die-cut perforations, this process is primarily used for self-adhesive postage stamps. Die-cutting can appear in straight lines, such as U.S. Scott 2522, shapes, such as U.S. Scott 1551, or imitating the appearance of perforations, such as New Zealand Scott 935A and 935B.

Printing Processes

ENGRAVING (Intaglio, Line-engraving, Etching)

Master die - The initial operation in the process of line engraving is making the master die. The die is a small, flat block of softened steel upon which the stamp design is recess engraved in reverse.

Master die

Photographic reduction of the original art is made to the appropriate size. It then serves as a tracing guide for the initial outline of the design. The engraver lightly traces the design on the steel with his graver, then slowly works the design until it is completed. At various points during the engraving process, the engraver hand-inks the die and makes an impression to check his progress. These are known as progressive die proofs. After completion of the engraving, the die is hardened to withstand the stress and pressures of later transfer operations.

Transfer roll

Transfer roll — Next is production of the transfer roll that, as the name implies, is the medium used to transfer the subject from the master die to the printing plate. A blank roll of soft steel, mounted on a mandrel, is placed under the bearers of the transfer press to allow it to roll freely on its axis. The hardened die is placed on the bed of the press and the face of the transfer roll is applied to the die, under pressure. The bed or the roll is then rocked back and forth under increasing pressure, until the soft steel of the roll is forced into every engraved line of the die. The resulting impression on the roll is known as a "relief" or a "relief transfer." The engraved image is now positive in appearance and stands out from the steel. After the required number of reliefs are "rocked in," the soft steel transfer roll is hardened.

Different flaws may occur during the relief process. A defective relief may occur during the rocking in process because of a minute piece of foreign material lodging on the die, or some other cause. Imperfections in the steel of the transfer roll may result in a breaking away of parts of the design. This is known as a relief break, which will show up on finished stamps as small, unprinted areas. If a damaged relief remains in use, it will transfer a repeating defect to the plate. Deliberate alterations of reliefs sometimes occur. "Altered reliefs" designate these changed conditions.

Plate — The final step in pre-printing production is the making of the printing plate. A flat piece of soft steel replaces the die on the bed of the transfer press. One of the reliefs on the transfer roll is positioned over this soft steel. Position, or layout, dots determine the correct position on the plate. The dots have been lightly marked

on the plate in advance. After the correct position of the relief is determined, the design is rocked in by following the same method used in making the transfer roll. The difference is that this time the image is being transferred from the transfer roll, rather than to it. Once the design is entered on the plate, it appears in reverse and is recessed. There are as many transfers entered on the plate as there are subjects printed on the sheet of stamps. It is during this process that double and shifted transfers occur, as well as re-entries. These are the result of improperly entered images that have not been properly burnished out prior to rocking in a new image.

Modern siderography processes, such as those used by the U.S. Bureau of Engraving and Printing, involve an automated form of rocking designs in on preformed cylindrical printing sleeves. The same process also allows for easier removal and re-entry of worn images right on the sleeve.

Transferring the design to the plate

Following the entering of the required transfers on the plate, the position dots, layout dots and lines, scratches and other markings generally are burnished out. Added at this time by the siderographer are any required *guide lines, plate numbers* or other *marginal markings.* The plate is then hand-inked and a proof impression is taken. This is known as a plate proof. If the impression is approved, the plate is machined for fitting onto the press, is hardened and sent to the plate vault ready for use.

On press, the plate is inked and the surface is automatically wiped clean, leaving ink only in the recessed lines. Paper is then forced under pressure into the engraved recessed lines, thereby receiving the ink. Thus, the ink lines on engraved stamps are slightly raised, and slight depressions (debossing) occur on the back of the stamp. Prior to the advent of modern high-speed presses and more advanced ink formulations, paper had to be dampened before receiving the ink. This sometimes led to uneven shrinkage by the time the stamps were perforated, resulting in improperly perforated stamps, or misperfs. Newer presses use drier paper, thus both *wet* and *dry printings* exist on some stamps.

Rotary Press — Until 1914, only flat plates were used to print engraved stamps. Rotary press printing was introduced in 1914, and slowly spread. Some countries still use flat-plate printing.

After approval of the plate proof, older *rotary press plates* require additional machining. They are curved to fit the press cylinder. "Gripper slots" are cut into the back of each plate to receive the "grippers," which hold the plate securely on the press. The plate is then hardened. Stamps printed from these bent rotary press plates are longer or wider than the same stamps printed from flat-plate presses. The stretching of the plate during the curving process is what causes this distortion.

Re-entry — To execute a re-entry on a flat plate, the transfer roll is re-applied to the plate, often at some time after its first use on the press. Worn-out designs can be resharpened by carefully burnishing out the original image and re-entering it from the transfer roll. If the original impression has not been sufficiently removed and the transfer roll is not precisely in line with the remaining impression, the resulting double transfer will make the re-entry obvious. If the registration is true, a re-entry may be difficult or impossible to distinguish. Sometimes a stamp printed from a successful re-entry is identified by having a much sharper and clearer impression than its neighbors. With the advent of rotary presses, post-press re-entries were not possible. After a plate was curved for the rotary press, it was impossible to make a re-entry. This is because the plate had already been bent once (with the design distorted).

However, with the introduction of the previously mentioned modern-style siderography machines, entries are made to the pre-formed cylindrical printing sleeve. Such sleeves are dechromed and softened. This allows individual images to be burnished out and re-entered on the curved sleeve. The sleeve is then rechromed, resulting in longer press life.

Double Transfer — This is a description of the condition of a transfer on a plate that shows evidence of a duplication of all, or a portion of the design. It usually is the result of the changing of the registration between the transfer roll and the plate during the rocking in of the original entry. Double transfers also occur when only a portion of the design has been rocked in and improper positioning is noted. If the worker elected not to burnish out the partial or completed design, a strong double transfer will occur for part or all of the design.

It sometimes is necessary to remove the original transfer from a plate and repeat the process a second time. If the finished re-worked image shows traces of the original impression, attributable to incomplete burnishing, the result is a partial double transfer.

With the modern automatic machines mentioned previously, double transfers are all but impossible to create. Those partially doubled images on stamps printed from such sleeves are more than likely re-entries, rather than true double transfers.

Re-engraved — Alterations to a stamp design are sometimes necessary after some stamps have been printed. In some cases, either the original die or the actual printing plate may have its "temper" drawn (softened), and the design will be re-cut. The resulting impressions from such a re-engraved die or plate may differ slightly from the original issue, and are known as "re-engraved." If the alteration was made to the master die, all future printings will be consistently different from the original. If alterations were made to the printing plate, each altered stamp on the plate will be slightly different from each other, allowing specialists to reconstruct a complete printing plate.

Dropped Transfers — If an impression from the transfer roll has not been properly placed, a dropped transfer may occur. The final stamp image will appear obviously out of line with its neighbors.

Short Transfer — Sometimes a transfer roll is not rocked its entire length when entering a transfer onto a plate. As a result, the finished transfer on the plate fails to show the complete design, and the finished stamp will have an incomplete design printed. This is known as a "short transfer." U.S. Scott No. 8 is a good example of a short transfer.

TYPOGRAPHY (Letterpress, Surface Printing, Flexography, Dry Offset, High Etch)

Although the word "Typography" is obsolete as a term describing a printing method, it was the accepted term throughout the first century of postage stamps. Therefore, appropriate Scott listings in this catalogue refer to typographed stamps. The current term for this form of printing, however, is "letterpress."

As it relates to the production of postage stamps, letterpress printing is the reverse of engraving. Rather than having recessed areas trap the ink and deposit it on paper, only the raised areas of the design are inked. This is comparable to the type of printing seen by inking and using an ordinary rubber stamp. Letterpress includes all printing where the design is above the surface area, whether it is wood, metal or, in some instances, hardened rubber or polymer plastic.

For most letterpress-printed stamps, the engraved master is made in much the same manner as for engraved stamps. In this instance, however, an additional step is needed. The design is transferred to another surface before being transferred to the transfer roll. In this way, the transfer roll has a recessed stamp design, rather than one done in relief. This makes the printing areas on the final plate raised, or relief areas.

For less-detailed stamps of the 19th century, the area on the die not used as a printing surface was cut away, leaving the surface area raised. The original die was then reproduced by stereotyping or electrotyping. The resulting electrotypes were assembled in the required number and format of the desired sheet of stamps. The plate used in printing the stamps was an electroplate of these assembled electrotypes.

Once the final letterpress plates are created, ink is applied to the raised surface and the pressure of the press transfers the ink impression to the paper. In contrast to engraving, the fine lines of letterpress are impressed on the surface of the stamp, leaving a debossed surface. When viewed from the back (as on a typewritten page), the corresponding line work on the stamp will be raised slightly (embossed) above the surface.

PHOTOGRAVURE (Gravure, Rotogravure, Heliogravure)

In this process, the basic principles of photography are applied to a chemically sensitized metal plate, rather than photographic paper. The design is transferred photographically to the plate through a halftone, or dot-matrix screen, breaking the reproduction into tiny dots. The plate is treated chemically and the dots form depressions, called cells, of varying depths and diameters, depending on the degrees of shade in the design. Then, like engraving, ink is applied to the plate and the surface is wiped clean. This leaves ink in the tiny cells that is lifted out and deposited on the paper when it is pressed against the plate.

Gravure is most often used for multicolored stamps, generally using the three primary colors (red, yellow and blue) and black. By varying the dot matrix pattern and density of these colors, virtually any color can be reproduced. A typical full-color gravure stamp will be created from four printing cylinders (one for each color). The original multicolored image will have been photographically separated into its component colors.

For examples of the first photogravure stamps printed (1914), see Bavaria Scott 94-114.

LITHOGRAPHY (Offset Lithography, Stone Lithography, Dilitho, Planography, Collotype)

The principle that oil and water do not mix is the basis for lithography. The stamp design is drawn by hand or transferred from engraving to the surface of a lithographic stone or metal plate in a greasy (oily) substance. This oily substance holds the ink, which will later be transferred to the paper. The stone (or plate) is wet with an acid fluid, causing it to repel the printing ink in all areas not covered by the greasy substance.

Transfer paper is used to transfer the design from the original stone or plate. A series of duplicate transfers are grouped and, in turn, transferred to the final printing plate.

Photolithography — The application of photographic processes to lithography. This process allows greater flexibility of design, related to use of halftone screens combined with line work. Unlike photogravure or engraving, this process can allow large, solid areas to be printed.

Offset — A refinement of the lithographic process. A rubber-covered blanket cylinder takes the impression from the inked lithographic plate. From the "blanket" the impression is *offset* or transferred to the paper. Greater flexibility and speed are the principal reasons offset printing has largely displaced lithography. The term "lithography" covers both processes, and results are almost identical.

EMBOSSED (Relief) Printing

Embossing, not considered one of the four main printing types, is a method in which the design first is sunk into the metal of the die. Printing is done against a yielding platen, such as leather or linoleum. The platen is forced into the depression of the die, thus forming the design on the paper in relief. This process is often used for metallic inks.

Embossing may be done without color (see Sardinia Scott 4-6); with color printed around the embossed area (see Great Britain Scott 5 and most U.S. envelopes); and with color in exact registration with the embossed subject (see Canada Scott 656-657).

COMBINATION PRINTINGS

Sometimes two or even three printing methods are combined in producing stamps. In these cases, such as Austria Scott 933, the stamp's dual printing technique can be determined by studying the individual characteristics of each printing type (intaglio and offset). A few stamps, such as Singapore Scott 684-684A, combine as many as three of the four major printing types (offset, intaglio and letterpress). When this is done it often indicates the incorporation of security devices against counterfeiting.

INK COLORS

Inks or colored papers used in stamp printing often are of mineral origin, although there are numerous examples of organic-based pigments. As a general rule, organic-based pigments are far more subject to varieties and change than those of mineral-based origin.

The appearance of any given color on a stamp may be affected by many aspects, including printing variations, light, color of paper, aging and chemical alterations.

Numerous printing variations may be observed. Heavier pressure or inking will cause a more intense color, while slight interruptions in the ink feed or lighter impressions will cause a lighter appearance. Stamps printed in the same color by water-based and solvent-based inks can differ significantly in appearance. This affects several stamps in the U.S. Prominent Americans series. Hand-mixed ink formulas (primarily from the 19th century) produced under different conditions (humidity and temperature) account for notable color variations in early printings of the same stamp (see U.S. Scott 248-250, 279B, for example). Different sources of pigment can also result in significant differences in color.

Light exposure and aging are closely related in the way they affect stamp color. Both eventually break down the ink and fade colors, so that a carefully kept stamp may differ significantly in color from an identical copy that has been exposed to light. If stamps are exposed to light either intentionally or accidentally, their colors can be faded or completely changed in some cases.

Papers of different quality and consistency used for the same stamp printing may affect color appearance. Most pelure papers, for example, show a richer color when compared with wove or laid papers. See Russia Scott 181a, for an example of this effect.

The very nature of the printing processes can cause a variety of differences in shades or hues of the same stamp. Some of these shades are scarcer than others, and are of particular interest to the advanced collector.

Luminescence

All forms of tagged stamps fall under the general category of luminescence. Within this broad category is fluorescence, dealing with forms of tagging visible under longwave ultraviolet light, and phosphorescence, which deals with tagging visible only under shortwave light. Phosphorescence leaves an afterglow and fluorescence does not. These treated stamps show up in a range of different colors when exposed to UV light. The differing wavelengths of the light activates the tagging material, making it glow in various colors that usually serve different mail processing purposes.

Intentional tagging is a post-World War II phenomenon, brought about by the increased literacy rate and rapidly growing mail volume. It was one of several answers to the problem of the need for more automated mail processes. Early tagged stamps served the purpose of triggering machines to separate different types of mail. A natural outgrowth was to also use the signal to trigger machines that faced all envelopes the same way and canceled them.

Tagged stamps come many different ways and in different forms. Some tagged stamps have luminescent shapes or images imprinted on them as a form of security device. Others have blocks (United States), stripes, frames (South Africa and Canada), overall coatings (United States), bars (Great Britain and Canada) and many other types. Some types of tagging are even mixed in with the pigmented printing ink (Australia Scott 366, Netherlands Scott 478 and U.S. Scott 1359 and 2443). Each form of tagging has a different purpose, some to give different machines different types of signals, and others as adaptive forms of technological growth.

The means of applying taggant to stamps differs as much as the intended purposes for the stamps. The most common form of tagging is a coating applied to the surface of the printed stamp. Since the taggant ink is frequently invisible except under UV light, it does not interfere with the appearance of the stamp. Another common application is the use of phosphored papers. In this case the paper itself either has a coating of taggant applied before the stamp is printed or has taggant applied during the papermaking process, incorporating it into the fibers. This is currently in use in the United States. A similar form is the application of a fluorescent coating either to the finished paper or during the papermaking process. This type of tagging has been extensively used by Australia and Germany.

Many countries now use tagging in various forms to either expedite mail handling or to serve as a printing security device against counterfeiting. Following the introduction of tagged stamps for public use in 1959 by Great Britain, other countries have steadily joined the parade. Among those are Germany (1961); Canada and Denmark (1962); United States, Australia, France and Switzerland (1963); Belgium and Japan (1966); Sweden and Norway (1967); Italy (1968); and Russia (1969). Since then, many other countries have begun using forms of tagging, including Brazil, China, Czechoslovakia, Hong Kong, Guatemala, Indonesia, Israel, Lithuania, Luxembourg, Netherlands, Penrhyn Islands, Portugal, St. Vincent, Singapore, South Africa, Spain and Sweden to name a few.

In some cases, including United States, Canada, Great Britain and Switzerland, stamps were released both with and without tagging. Many of these were released during each country's experimental period. Tagged and untagged versions are listed for the aforementioned countries and are noted in some other countries' listings. For at least a few stamps, the experimentally tagged version is worth far more than its untagged counterpart, such as the 1963 experimental tagged version of France Scott 1024.

In some cases, luminescent varieties of stamps were inadvertently created. Several Russian stamps, for example, sport highly fluorescent ink that was not intended as a form of tagging. Older stamps, such as early U.S. postage dues, can be positively identified by the use of UV light, since the organic ink used has become slightly fluorescent over time. Other stamps, such as Austria Scott

70a-82a (varnish bars) and Obock Scott 46-64 (printed quadrille lines), have become fluorescent over time.

Various fluorescent substances have been added to paper to make it appear brighter. These optical brightners, as they are known, greatly affect the appearance of the stamp under UV light. The brightest of these is known as Hi-Brite paper. These paper varieties are beyond the scope of the Scott Catalogue.

Shortwave UV light also is used extensively in expertizing, since each form of paper has its own fluorescent characteristics that are impossible to perfectly match. It is therefore a simple matter to detect filled thins, added perforation teeth and other alterations that involve the addition of paper. UV light also is used to examine stamps that have had cancels chemically removed and for other purposes as well.

Gum

The Illustrated Gum Chart in the first part of this introduction shows and defines various types of gum condition. Because gum condition has an important impact on the value of unused stamps, we recommend studying this chart and the accompanying text carefully.

The gum on the back of a stamp may be shiny, dull, smooth, rough, dark, white, colored or tinted. Most stamp gumming adhesives use gum arabic or dextrine as a base. Certain polymers such as polyvinyl alcohol (PVA) have been used extensively since World War II.

The *Scott Standard Postage Stamp Catalogue* does not list items by types of gum. The *Scott Specialized Catalogue of United States Stamps* does differentiate among some types of gum for certain issues.

Reprints of stamps may have gum differing from the original issues. In addition, some countries have used different gum formulas for different seasons. These adhesives have different properties that may become more apparent over time.

Many stamps have been issued without gum, and the catalogue will note this fact. See United States Scott PR33-PR56. Sometimes, gum may have been removed to preserve the stamp. Germany Scott B68, for example, has a highly acidic gum that eventually destroys the stamps. This item is valued in the catalogue with gum removed.

Reprints and Reissues

These are impressions of stamps (usually obsolete) made from the original plates or stones. If they are valid for postage and reproduce obsolete issues (such as U.S. Scott 102-111), the stamps are *reissues*. If they are from current issues, they are designated as *second, third, etc., printing*. If designated for a particular purpose, they are called *special printings*.

When special printings are not valid for postage, but are made from original dies and plates by authorized persons, they are *official reprints*. *Private reprints* are made from the original plates and dies by private hands. An example of a private reprint is that of the 1871-1932 reprints made from the original die of the 1845 New Haven, Conn., postmaster's provisional. *Official reproductions* or imitations are made from new dies and plates by government authorization. Scott will list those reissues that are valid for postage if they differ significantly from the original printing.

The U.S. government made special printings of its first postage stamps in 1875. Produced were official imitations of the first two stamps (listed as Scott 3-4), reprints of the demonetized pre-1861 issues (Scott 40-47) and reissues of the 1861 stamps, the 1869 stamps and the then-current 1875 denominations. Even though the official imitations and the reprints were not valid for postage, Scott lists all of these U.S. special printings.

Most reprints or reissues differ slightly from the original stamp in some characteristic, such as gum, paper, perforation, color or watermark. Sometimes the details are followed so meticulously that only a student of that specific stamp is able to distinguish the reprint or reissue from the original.

Remainders and Canceled to Order

Some countries sell their stock of old stamps when a new issue replaces them. To avoid postal use, the *remainders* usually are canceled with a punch hole, a heavy line or bar, or a more-or-less regular-looking cancellation. The most famous merchant of remainders was Nicholas F. Seebeck. In the 1880s and 1890s, he arranged printing contracts between the Hamilton Bank Note Co., of which he was a director, and several Central and South American countries. The contracts provided that the plates and all remainders of the yearly issues became the property of Hamilton. Seebeck saw to it that ample stock remained. The "Seebecks," both remainders and reprints, were standard packet fillers for decades.

Some countries also issue stamps *canceled-to-order (CTO)*, either in sheets with original gum or stuck onto pieces of paper or envelopes and canceled. Such CTO items generally are worth less than postally used stamps. In cases where the CTO material is far more prevalent in the marketplace than postally used examples, the catalogue value relates to the CTO examples, with postally used examples noted as premium items. Most CTOs can be detected by the presence of gum. However, as the CTO practice goes back at least to 1885, the gum inevitably has been soaked off some stamps so they could pass as postally used. The normally applied postmarks usually differ slightly from standard postmarks, and specialists are able to tell the difference. When applied individually to envelopes by philatelically minded persons, CTO material is known as *favor canceled* and generally sells at large discounts.

Cinderellas and Facsimiles

Cinderella is a catch-all term used by stamp collectors to describe phantoms, fantasies, bogus items, municipal issues, exhibition seals, local revenues, transportation stamps, labels, poster stamps and many other types of items. Some cinderella collectors include in their collections local postage issues, telegraph stamps, essays and proofs, forgeries and counterfeits.

A *fantasy* is an adhesive created for a nonexistent stamp-issuing authority. Fantasy items range from imaginary countries (Occusi-Ambeno, Kingdom of Sedang, Principality of Trinidad or Torres Straits), to non-existent locals (Winans City Post), or nonexistent transportation lines (McRobish & Co.'s Acapulco-San Francisco Line).

On the other hand, if the entity exists and could have issued stamps (but did not) or was known to have issued other stamps, the items are considered *bogus* stamps. These would include the Mormon postage stamps of Utah, S. Allan Taylor's Guatemala and Paraguay inventions, the propaganda issues for the South Moluccas and the adhesives of the Page & Keyes local post of Boston.

Phantoms is another term for both fantasy and bogus issues.

Facsimiles are copies or imitations made to represent original stamps, but which do not pretend to be originals. A catalogue illustration is such a facsimile. Illustrations from the Moens catalogue of the last century were occasionally colored and passed off as stamps. Since the beginning of stamp collecting, facsimiles have been made for collectors as space fillers or for reference. They often carry the word "facsimile," "falsch" (German), "sanko" or "mozo" (Japanese), or "faux" (French) overprinted on the face or stamped on the back. Unfortunately, over the years a number of these items have had fake cancels applied over the facsimile notation and have been passed off as genuine.

Forgeries and Counterfeits

Forgeries and counterfeits have been with philately virtually from the beginning of stamp production. Over time, the terminology for the two has been used interchangeably. Although both forgeries and counterfeits are reproductions of stamps, the purposes behind their creation differ considerably.

Among specialists there is an increasing movement to more specifically define such items. Although there is no universally accepted terminology, we feel the following definitions most closely mirror the items and their purposes as they are currently defined.

Forgeries (also often referred to as *Counterfeits*) are reproductions of genuine stamps that have been created to defraud collectors. Such spurious items first appeared on the market around 1860, and most old-time collections contain one or more. Many are crude and easily spotted, but some can deceive experts.

An important supplier of these early philatelic forgeries was the Hamburg printer Gebruder Spiro. Many others with reputations in this craft included S. Allan Taylor, George Hussey, James Chute, George Forune, Benjamin & Sarpy, Julius Goldner, E. Oneglia and L.H. Mercier. Among the noted 20th-century forgers were Francois Fournier, Jean Sperati and the prolific Raoul DeThuin.

Forgeries may be complete replications, or they may be genuine stamps altered to resemble a scarcer (and more valuable) type. Most forgeries, particularly those of rare stamps, are worth only a small fraction of the value of a genuine example, but a few types, created by some of the most notable forgers, such as Sperati, can be worth as much or more than the genuine. Fraudulently produced copies are known of most classic rarities and many medium-priced stamps.

In addition to rare stamps, large numbers of common 19th- and early 20th-century stamps were forged to supply stamps to the early packet trade. Many can still be easily found. Few new philatelic forgeries have appeared in recent decades. Successful imitation of well-engraved work is virtually impossible. It has proven far easier to produce a fake by altering a genuine stamp than to duplicate a stamp completely.

Counterfeit (also often referred to as *Postal Counterfeit* or *Postal Forgery*) is the term generally applied to reproductions of stamps that have been created to defraud the government of revenue. Such items usually are created at the time a stamp is current and, in some cases, are hard to detect. Because most counterfeits are seized when the perpetrator is captured, postal counterfeits, particularly used on cover, are usually worth much more than a genuine example to specialists. The first postal counterfeit was of Spain's 4-cuarto carmine of 1854 (the real one is Scott 25). Apparently, the counterfeiters were not satisfied with their first version, which is now very scarce, and they soon created an engraved counterfeit, which is common. Postal counterfeits quickly followed in Austria, Naples, Sardinia and the Roman States. They have since been created in many other countries as well, including the United States.

An infamous counterfeit to defraud the government is the 1-shilling Great Britain "Stock Exchange" forgery of 1872, used on telegraph forms at the exchange that year. The stamp escaped detection until a stamp dealer noticed it in 1898.

Fakes

Fakes are genuine stamps altered in some way to make them more desirable. One student of this part of stamp collecting has estimated that by the 1950s more than 30,000 varieties of fakes were known. That number has grown greatly since then. The widespread existence of fakes makes it important for stamp collectors to study their philatelic holdings and use relevant literature. Likewise, collectors should buy from reputable dealers who guarantee their stamps and make full and prompt refunds should a purchased item be declared faked or altered by some mutually agreed-upon authority. Because fakes always have some genuine characteristics, it is not always possible to obtain unanimous agreement among experts regarding specific items. These students may change their opinions as philatelic knowledge increases. More than 80 percent of all fakes on the philatelic market today are regummed, reperforated (or perforated for the first time), or bear forged overprints, surcharges or cancellations.

Stamps can be chemically treated to alter or eliminate colors. For example, a pale rose stamp can be re-colored to resemble a blue shade of high market value. In other cases, treated stamps can be made to resemble missing color varieties. Designs may be changed by painting, or a stroke or a dot added or bleached out to turn an ordinary variety into a seemingly scarcer stamp. Part of a stamp can be bleached and reprinted in a different version, achieving an inverted center or frame. Margins can be added or repairs done so deceptively that the stamps move from the "repaired" into the "fake" category.

Fakers have not left the backs of the stamps untouched either. They may create false watermarks, add fake grills or press out genuine grills. A thin India paper proof may be glued onto a thicker backing to create the appearance an issued stamp, or a proof printed on cardboard may be shaved down and perforated to resemble a stamp. Silk threads are impressed into paper and stamps have been split so that a rare paper variety is added to an otherwise inexpensive stamp. The most common treatment to the back of a stamp, however, is regumming.

Some in the business of faking stamps have openly advertised fool-proof application of "original gum" to stamps that lack it, although most publications now ban such ads from their pages. It is believed that very few early stamps have survived without being hinged. The large number of never-hinged examples of such earlier material offered for sale thus suggests the widespread extent of regumming activity. Regumming also may be used to hide repairs or thin spots. Dipping the stamp into watermark fluid, or examining it under longwave ultraviolet light often will reveal these flaws.

Fakers also tamper with separations. Ingenious ways to add margins are known. Perforated wide-margin stamps may be falsely represented as imperforate when trimmed. Reperforating is commonly done to create scarce coil or perforation varieties, and to eliminate the naturally occurring straight-edge stamps found in sheet margin positions of many earlier issues. Custom has made straight-edged stamps less desirable. Fakers have obliged by perforating straight-edged stamps so that many are now uncommon, if not rare.

Another fertile field for the faker is that of overprints, surcharges and cancellations. The forging of rare surcharges or overprints began in the 1880s or 1890s. These forgeries are sometimes difficult to detect, but experts have identified almost all. Occasionally, overprints or cancellations are removed to create non-overprinted stamps or seemingly unused items. This is most commonly done by removing a manuscript cancel to make a stamp resemble an unused example. "SPECIMEN" overprints may be removed by scraping and repainting to create non-overprinted varieties. Fakers use inexpensive revenues or pen-canceled stamps to generate unused stamps for further faking by adding other markings. The quartz lamp or UV lamp and a high-powered magnifying glass help to easily detect removed cancellations.

The bigger problem, however, is the addition of overprints, surcharges or cancellations - many with such precision that they are very difficult to ascertain. Plating of the stamps or the overprint can be an important method of detection.

Fake postmarks may range from many spurious fancy cancellations to a host of markings applied to transatlantic covers, to adding normally appearing postmarks to definitives of some countries with stamps that are valued far higher used than unused. With the increased popularity of cover collecting, and the widespread interest in postal history, a fertile new field for fakers has come about. Some have tried to create entire covers. Others specialize in adding stamps, tied by fake cancellations, to genuine stampless covers, or replacing less expensive or damaged stamps with more valuable ones. Detailed study of postal rates in effect at the time a cover in question was mailed, including the analysis of each handstamp used during the period, ink analysis and similar techniques, usually will unmask the fraud.

Restoration and Repairs

Scott Publishing Co. bases its catalogue values on stamps that are free of defects and otherwise meet the standards set forth earlier in this introduction. Most stamp collectors desire to have the finest copy of an item possible. Even within given grading categories there are variances. This leads to a controversial practice that is not defined in any universal manner: stamp *restoration*.

There are broad differences of opinion about what is permissible when it comes to restoration. Carefully applying a soft eraser to a stamp or cover to remove light soiling is one form of restoration, as is washing a stamp in mild soap and water to clean it. These are fairly accepted forms of restoration. More severe forms of restoration include pressing out creases or removing stains caused by tape. To what degree each of these is acceptable is dependent upon the individual situation. Further along the spectrum is the freshening of a stamp's color by removing oxide build-up or the effects of wax paper left next to stamps shipped to the tropics.

At some point in this spectrum the concept of *repair* replaces that of restoration. Repairs include filling thin spots, mending tears by reweaving or adding a missing perforation tooth. Regumming stamps may have been acceptable as a restoration or repair technique many decades ago, but today it is considered a form of fakery.

Restored stamps may or may not sell at a discount, and it is possible that the value of individual restored items may be enhanced over that of their pre-restoration state. Specific situations dictate the resultant value of such an item. Repaired stamps sell at substantial discounts from the value of sound stamps.

Terminology

Booklets — Many countries have issued stamps in small booklets for the convenience of users. This idea continues to become increasingly popular in many countries. Booklets have been issued in many sizes and forms, often with advertising on the covers, the panes of stamps or on the interleaving.

The panes used in booklets may be printed from special plates or made from regular sheets. All panes from booklets issued by the United States and many from those of other countries contain stamps that are straight edged on the sides, but perforated between. Others are distinguished by orientation of watermark or other identifying features. Any stamp-like unit in the pane, either printed or blank, that is not a postage stamp, is considered to be a *label* in the catalogue listings.

Scott lists and values booklet panes only. Complete booklets are listed and valued in only a few cases, such as Grenada Scott 1055 and some forms of British prestige booklets. Individual booklet panes are listed only when they are not fashioned from existing sheet stamps and, therefore, are identifiable from their sheet stamp counterparts.

Panes usually do not have a used value assigned to them because there is little market activity for used booklet panes, even though many exist used and there is some demand for them.

Cancellations — The marks or obliterations put on stamps by postal authorities to show that they have performed service and to prevent their reuse are known as cancellations. If the marking is made with a pen, it is considered a "pen cancel." When the location of the post office appears in the marking, it is a "town cancellation." A "postmark" is technically any postal marking, but in practice the term generally is applied to a town cancellation with a date. When calling attention to a cause or celebration, the marking is known as a "slogan cancellation." Many other types and styles of cancellations exist, such as duplex, numerals, targets, fancy and others. See also "precancels," below.

Coil Stamps — These are stamps that are issued in rolls for use in dispensers, affixing and vending machines. Those coils of the United States, Canada, Sweden and some other countries are perforated horizontally or vertically only, with the outer edges imperforate. Coil stamps of some countries, such as Great Britain and Germany, are perforated on all four sides and may in some cases be distinguished from their sheet stamp counterparts by watermarks, counting numbers on the reverse or other means.

Covers — Entire envelopes, with or without adhesive postage stamps, that have passed through the mail and bear postal or other markings of philatelic interest are known as covers. Before the introduction of envelopes in about 1840, people folded letters and wrote the address on the outside. Some people covered their letters with an extra sheet of paper on the outside for the address, producing the term "cover." Used airletter sheets, stamped envelopes and other items of postal stationery also are considered covers.

Errors — Stamps that have some major, consistent, unintentional deviation from the normal are considered errors. Errors include, but are not limited to, missing or wrong colors, wrong paper, wrong watermarks, inverted centers or frames on multicolor printing, inverted or missing surcharges or overprints, double impressions, missing perforations and others. Factually wrong or misspelled information, if it appears on all examples of a stamp, are not considered errors in the true sense of the word. They are errors of design. Inconsistent or randomly appearing items, such as misperfs or color shifts, are classified as freaks.

Overprints and Surcharges — Overprinting involves applying wording or design elements over an already existing stamp. Overprints can be used to alter the place of use (such as "Canal Zone" on U.S. stamps), to adapt them for a special purpose ("Porto" on Denmark's 1913-20 regular issues for use as postage due stamps, Scott J1-J7) or to commemorate a special occasion (United States Scott 647-648).

A *surcharge* is a form of overprint that changes or restates the face value of a stamp or piece of postal stationery.

Surcharges and overprints may be handstamped, typeset or, occasionally, lithographed or engraved. A few hand-written overprints and surcharges are known.

Precancels — Stamps that are canceled before they are placed in the mail are known as precancels. Precanceling usually is done to expedite the handling of large mailings and generally allow the affected mail pieces to skip certain phases of mail handling.

In the United States, precancellations generally identified the point of origin; that is, the city and state. This information appeared across the face of the stamp, usually centered between parallel lines. More recently, bureau precancels retained the parallel lines, but the city and state designations were dropped. Recent coils have a service inscription that is present on the original printing plate. These show the mail service paid for by the stamp. Since these stamps are not intended to receive further cancellations when used as intended, they are considered precancels. Such items often do not have parallel lines as part of the precancellation.

In France, the abbreviation *Affranchts* in a semicircle together with the word *Postes* is the general form of precancel in use. Belgian precancellations usually appear in a box in which the name of the city appears. Netherlands precancels have the name of the city enclosed between concentric circles, sometimes called a "lifesaver." Precancellations of other countries usually follow these patterns, but may be any arrangement of bars, boxes and city names.

Precancels are listed in the Scott catalogues only if the precancel changes the denomination (Belgium Scott 477-478); if the precanceled stamp is different from the non-precanceled version (such as untagged U.S. precancels); or if the stamp exists only precanceled (France Scott 1096-1099, U.S. Scott 2265).

Proofs and Essays — Proofs are impressions taken from an approved die, plate or stone in which the design and color are the same as the stamp issued to the public. Trial color proofs are impressions taken from approved dies, plates or stones in colors that vary from the final version. An essay is the impression of a design that differs in some way from the issued stamp. "Progressive die proofs" generally are considered to be essays.

Provisionals — These are stamps that are issued on short notice and intended for temporary use pending the arrival of regular issues. They usually are issued to meet such contingencies as changes in government or currency, shortage of necessary postage values or military occupation.

During the 1840s, postmasters in certain American cities issued stamps that were valid only at specific post offices. In 1861, postmas-ters of the Confederate States also issued stamps with limited validity. Both of these examples are known as "postmaster's provisionals."

Se-tenant — This term refers to an unsevered pair, strip or block of stamps that differ in design, denomination or overprint.

Unless the se-tenant item has a continuous design (see U.S. Scott 1451a, 1694a) the stamps do not have to be in the same order as shown in the catalogue (see U.S. Scott 2158a).

Specimens — The Universal Postal Union required member nations to send samples of all stamps they released into service to the International Bureau in Switzerland. Member nations of the UPU received these specimens as samples of what stamps were valid for postage. Many are overprinted, handstamped or initial-perforated "Specimen," "Canceled" or "Muestra." Some are marked with bars across the denominations (China-Taiwan), punched holes (Czechoslovakia) or back inscriptions (Mongolia).

Stamps distributed to government officials or for publicity purposes, and stamps submitted by private security printers for official approval, also may receive such defacements.

The previously described defacement markings prevent postal use, and all such items generally are known as "specimens."

Tete Beche — This term describes a pair of stamps in which one is upside down in relation to the other. Some of these are the result of intentional sheet arrangements, such as Morocco Scott B10-B11. Others occurred when one or more electrotypes accidentally were placed upside down on the plate, such as Colombia Scott 57a. Separation of the tete-beche stamps, of course, destroys the tete beche variety.

Currency Conversion

Country	Dollar	Pound	S Franc	Guilder	Yen	Lira	HK Dollar	D-Mark	Fr Franc	Cdn Dollar	Aust Dollar
Australia	1.5244	2.5549	1.0653	0.7652	0.0118	0.0009	0.1967	0.8623	0.2575	1.0683	....
Canada	1.427	2.3917	0.9972	0.7163	0.0111	0.0008	0.1841	0.8072	0.241	....	.09361
France	5.9207	9.9231	4.1375	2.9721	0.046	0.0034	0.764	3.3492	....	4.1491	3.884
Germany	1.7678	2.9628	1.2354	0.8874	0.0137	0.001	0.2281	....	0.2986	1.2388	1.1597
Hong Kong	7.7497	12.988	5.4156	3.8902	0.0602	0.0045	....	4.3838	1.3089	5.4308	5.0838
Italy	1735.4	2908.53	1212.72	871.14	13.487	....	223.93	981.67	293.11	1216.12	1138.42
Japan	128.675	215.66	89.92	64.593	....	0.0741	16.604	72.788	21.733	90.172	84.41
Netherlands	1.9921	3.3388	1.3921	....	0.0155	0.0011	0.2571	1.1269	0.3365	1.396	1.3068
Switzerland	1.431	2.3984	....	0.7183	0.0111	0.0008	0.1847	0.8095	0.2417	1.0028	0.9387
U.K.	0.5957	....	0.417	0.2995	0.0046	0.0003	0.0770	0.3375	0.1008	0.4181	0.3914
U.S.	....	1.676	0.6988	0.502	0.0078	0.0006	0.129	0.5657	0.1689	0.7008	0.656

Country	Currency	U.S. $ Equiv.
Afghanistan	afghani	.0002
Aitutaki	New Zealand dollar	.5840
Albania	lek	.0068
Algeria	dinar	.0173
Andorra (French)	franc	.1689
Andorra (Spanish)	peseta	.0067
Angola	kwanza	.00001
Anguilla	East Caribbean dollar	.3703
Antigua	East Caribbean dollar	.3703
Argentina	peso	1.00
Aruba	guilder	.5586
Ascension	British pound	1.676
Australia	dollar	.656
Australian Antarctic Territory	dollar	.656
Austria	schilling	.0804
Azerbaijan	manat	.00025
Bahamas	dollar	1.00
Bahrain	dinar	2.65
Bangladesh	taka	.022
Barbados	dollar	.4972
Barbuda	East Caribbean dollar	.3703
Belgium	franc	.0274
Belize	dollar	.5000
Benin	Community of French Africa (CFA) franc	.00169
Bermuda	dollar	1.00
Bhutan	ngultrum	.0255
Bolivia	boliviano	.1873
Botswana	pula	.2632
Brazil	real	.8973
British Antarctic Territory	British pound	1.676
British Indian Ocean Territory	British pound	1.676
Brunei	dollar	.60
Bulgaria	lev	.0006
Burkina Faso	CFA franc	.00169
Burma	kyat	.1565
Burundi	franc	.0025
United Nations-New York	U.S. dollar	1.00
United Nations-Geneva	Swiss franc	.6988
United Nations-Vienna	Austria shilling	.0804
United States	dollar	1.00

Source: **Wall Street Journal** Dec. 22 1997. Figures reflect values as of Dec. 19, 1997.

Colonies, Former Colonies, Offices, Territories Controlled by Parent States

Belgium
Belgian Congo
Ruanda-Urundi

Denmark
Danish West Indies
Faroe Islands
Greenland
Iceland

Finland
Aland Islands

France

COLONIES PAST AND PRESENT, CONTROLLED TERRITORIES
Afars & Issas, Territory of
Alaouites
Alexandretta
Algeria
Alsace & Lorraine
Anjouan
Annam & Tonkin
Benin
Cambodia (Khmer)
Cameroun
Castellorizo
Chad
Cilicia
Cochin China
Comoro Islands
Dahomey
Diego Suarez
Djibouti (Somali Coast)
Fezzan
French Congo
French Equatorial Africa
French Guiana
French Guinea
French India
French Morocco
French Polynesia (Oceania)
French Southern & Antarctic Territories
French Sudan
French West Africa
Gabon
Germany
Ghadames
Grand Comoro
Guadeloupe
Indo-China
Inini
Ivory Coast
Laos
Latakia
Lebanon
Madagascar
Martinique
Mauritania
Mayotte
Memel
Middle Congo
Moheli
New Caledonia
New Hebrides
Niger Territory
Nossi-Be
Obock
Reunion
Rouad, Ile
Ste.-Marie de Madagascar
St. Pierre & Miquelon
Senegal
Senegambia & Niger
Somali Coast
Syria
Tahiti
Togo
Tunisia
Ubangi-Shari
Upper Senegal & Niger
Upper Volta
Viet Nam
Wallis & Futuna Islands

POST OFFICES IN FOREIGN COUNTRIES
China
Crete
Egypt
Turkish Empire
Zanzibar

Germany

EARLY STATES
Baden
Bavaria
Bergedorf
Bremen
Brunswick
Hamburg
Hanover
Lubeck
Mecklenburg-Schwerin
Mecklenburg-Strelitz
Oldenburg
Prussia
Saxony
Schleswig-Holstein
Wurttemberg

FORMER COLONIES
Cameroun (Kamerun)
Caroline Islands
German East Africa
German New Guinea
German South-West Africa
Kiauchau
Mariana Islands
Marshall Islands
Samoa
Togo

Italy

EARLY STATES
Modena
Parma
Romagna
Roman States
Sardinia
Tuscany
Two Sicilies
    Naples
    Neapolitan Provinces
    Sicily

FORMER COLONIES, CONTROLLED TERRITORIES, OCCUPATION AREAS
Aegean Islands
    Calimno (Calino)
    Caso
    Cos (Coo)
    Karki (Carchi)
    Leros (Lero)
    Lipso
    Nisiros (Nisiro)
    Patmos (Patmo)
    Piscopi
    Rodi (Rhodes)
    Scarpanto
    Simi
    Stampalia
Castellorizo
Corfu
Cyrenaica
Eritrea
Ethiopia (Abyssinia)
Fiume
Ionian Islands
    Cephalonia
    Ithaca
    Paxos
Italian East Africa
Libya
Oltre Giuba
Saseno
Somalia (Italian Somaliland)
Tripolitania

POST OFFICES IN FOREIGN COUNTRIES
"ESTERO"*
Austria
China
    Peking
    Tientsin
Crete
Tripoli
Turkish Empire
    Constantinople
    Durazzo
    Janina
Jerusalem
Salonika
Scutari
Smyrna
Valona
*Stamps overprinted "ESTERO" were used in various parts of the world.

Netherlands
Aruba
Netherlands Antilles (Curacao)
Netherlands Indies
Netherlands New Guinea
Surinam (Dutch Guiana)

Portugal

COLONIES PAST AND PRESENT, CONTROLLED TERRITORIES
Angola
Angra
Azores
Cape Verde
Funchal
Horta
Inhambane
Kionga
Lourenco Marques
Macao
Madeira
Mozambique
Mozambique Co.
Nyassa
Ponta Delgada
Portuguese Africa
Portuguese Congo
Portuguese Guinea
Portuguese India
Quelimane
St. Thomas & Prince Islands
Tete
Timor
Zambezia

Russia

ALLIED TERRITORIES AND REPUBLICS, OCCUPATION AREAS
Armenia
Aunus (Olonets)
Azerbaijan
Batum
Estonia
Far Eastern Republic
Georgia
Karelia
Latvia
Lithuania
North Ingermanland
Ostland
Russian Turkestan
Siberia
South Russia
Tannu Tuva
Transcaucasian Fed. Republics
Ukraine
Wenden (Livonia)
Western Ukraine

Spain

COLONIES PAST AND PRESENT, CONTROLLED TERRITORIES
Aguera, La
Cape Juby
Cuba
Elobey, Annobon & Corisco
Fernando Po
Ifni
Mariana Islands
Philippines
Puerto Rico
Rio de Oro
Rio Muni
Spanish Guinea
Spanish Morocco
Spanish Sahara
Spanish West Africa

POST OFFICES IN FOREIGN COUNTRIES
Morocco
Tangier
Tetuan

British Commonwealth of Nations

Dominions, Colonies, Territories, Offices and Independent Members

Comprising stamps of the British Commonwealth and associated nations.

A strict observance of technicalities would bar some or all of the stamps listed under Burma, Ireland, Kuwait, Nepal, New Republic, Orange Free State, Samoa, South Africa, South-West Africa, Stellaland, Sudan, Swaziland, the two Transvaal Republics and others but these are included for the convenience of collectors.

1. Great Britain

Great Britain: Including England, Scotland, Wales and Northern Ireland.

2. The Dominions, Present and Past

AUSTRALIA

The Commonwealth of Australia was proclaimed on January 1, 1901. It consists of six former colonies as follows:

New South Wales	Victoria
Queensland	Tasmania
South Australia	Western Australia

Territories belonging to, or administered by Australia: Australian Antarctic Territory, Christmas Island, Cocos (Keeling) Islands, Nauru, New Guinea, Norfolk Island, Papua New Guinea.

CANADA

The Dominion of Canada was created by the British North America Act in 1867. The following provinces were former separate colonies and issued postage stamps:

British Columbia and Vancouver Island	Newfoundland
New Brunswick	Nova Scotia
	Prince Edward Island

FIJI

The colony of Fiji became an independent nation with dominion status on Oct. 10, 1970.

GHANA

This state came into existence Mar. 6, 1957, with dominion status. It consists of the former colony of the Gold Coast and the Trusteeship Territory of Togoland. Ghana became a republic July 1, 1960.

INDIA

The Republic of India was inaugurated on January 26, 1950. It succeeded the Dominion of India which was proclaimed August 15, 1947, when the former Empire of India was divided into Pakistan and the Union of India. The Republic is composed of about 40 predominantly Hindu states of three classes: governor's provinces, chief commissioner's provinces and princely states. India also has various territories, such as the Andaman and Nicobar Islands.

The old Empire of India was a federation of British India and the native states. The more important princely states were autonomous. Of the more than 700 Indian states, these 43 are familiar names to philatelists because of their postage stamps.

CONVENTION STATES

Chamba	Jhind
Faridkot	Nabha
Gwalior	Patiala

NATIVE FEUDATORY STATES

Alwar	Jammu
Bahawalpur	Jammu and Kashmir
Bamra	Jasdan
Barwani	Jhalawar
Bhopal	Jhind (1875-76)
Bhor	Kashmir
Bijawar	Kishangarh
Bundi	Las Bela
Bussahir	Morvi
Charkhari	Nandgaon
Cochin	Nowanuggur
Dhar	Orchha
Duttia	Poonch
Faridkot (1879-85)	Rajpeepla
Hyderabad	Sirmur
Idar	Soruth
Indore	Travancore
Jaipur	Wadhwan

NEW ZEALAND

Became a dominion on September 26, 1907. The following islands and territories are, or have been, administered by New Zealand:

Aitutaki	Ross Dependency
Cook Islands (Rarotonga)	Samoa (Western Samoa)
Niue	Tokelau Islands
Penrhyn	

PAKISTAN

The Republic of Pakistan was proclaimed March 23, 1956. It succeeded the Dominion which was proclaimed August 15, 1947. It is made up of all or part of several Moslem provinces and various districts of the former Empire of India, including Bahawalpur and Las Bela. Pakistan withdrew from the Commonwealth in 1972.

SOUTH AFRICA

Under the terms of the South African Act (1909) the self-governing colonies of Cape of Good Hope, Natal, Orange River Colony and Transvaal united on May 31, 1910, to form the Union of South Africa. It became an independent republic May 3, 1961.

Under the terms of the Treaty of Versailles, South-West Africa, formerly German South-West Africa, was mandated to the Union of South Africa.

SRI LANKA (CEYLON)

The Dominion of Ceylon was proclaimed February 4, 1948. The island had been a Crown Colony from 1802 until then. On May 22, 1972, Ceylon became the Republic of Sri Lanka.

3. Colonies, Past and Present; Controlled Territory and Independent Members of the Commonwealth

Aden	Bechuanaland
Aitutaki	Bechuanaland Prot.
Antigua	Belize
Ascension	Bermuda
Bahamas	Botswana
Bahrain	British Antarctic Territory
Bangladesh	British Central Africa
Barbados	British Columbia and
Barbuda	Vancouver Island
Basutoland	British East Africa
Batum	British Guiana

British Honduras
British Indian Ocean Territory
British New Guinea
British Solomon Islands
British Somaliland
Brunei
Burma
Bushire
Cameroons
Cape of Good Hope
Cayman Islands
Christmas Island
Cocos (Keeling) Islands
Cook Islands
Crete,
   British Administration
Cyprus
Dominica
East Africa & Uganda
   Protectorates
Egypt
Falkland Islands
Fiji
Gambia
German East Africa
Gibraltar
Gilbert Islands
Gilbert & Ellice Islands
Gold Coast
Grenada
Griqualand West
Guernsey
Guyana
Heligoland
Hong Kong
Indian Native States
   (see India)
Ionian Islands
Jamaica
Jersey

Kenya
Kenya, Uganda & Tanzania
Kuwait
Labuan
Lagos
Leeward Islands
Lesotho
Madagascar
Malawi
Malaya
   Federated Malay States
   Johore
   Kedah
   Kelantan
   Malacca
   Negri Sembilan
   Pahang
   Penang
   Perak
   Perlis
   Selangor
   Singapore
   Sungei Ujong
   Trengganu
Malaysia
Maldive Islands
Malta
Man, Isle of
Mauritius
Mesopotamia
Montserrat
Muscat
Namibia
Natal
Nauru
Nevis
New Britain
New Brunswick
Newfoundland
New Guinea

New Hebrides
New Republic
New South Wales
Niger Coast Protectorate
Nigeria
Niue
Norfolk Island
North Borneo
Northern Nigeria
Northern Rhodesia
North West Pacific Islands
Nova Scotia
Nyasaland Protectorate
Oman
Orange River Colony
Palestine
Papua New Guinea
Penrhyn Island
Pitcairn Islands
Prince Edward Island
Queensland
Rhodesia
Rhodesia & Nyasaland
Ross Dependency
Sabah
St. Christopher
St. Helena
St. Kitts
St. Kitts-Nevis-Anguilla
St. Lucia
St. Vincent
Samoa
Sarawak
Seychelles
Sierra Leone
Solomon Islands
Somaliland Protectorate
South Arabia
South Australia
South Georgia

Southern Nigeria
Southern Rhodesia
South-West Africa
Stellaland
Straits Settlements
Sudan
Swaziland
Tanganyika
Tanzania
Tasmania
Tobago
Togo
Tokelau Islands
Tonga
Transvaal
Trinidad
Trinidad and Tobago
Tristan da Cunha
Trucial States
Turks and Caicos
Turks Islands
Tuvalu
Uganda
United Arab Emirates
Victoria
Virgin Islands
Western Australia
Zambia
Zanzibar
Zululand

POST OFFICES IN FOREIGN COUNTRIES
Africa
   East Africa Forces
   Middle East Forces
Bangkok
China
Morocco
Turkish Empire

Common Design Types

Pictured in this section are issues where one illustration has been used for a number of countries in the Catalogue. Not included in this section are overprinted stamps or those issues which are illustrated in each country.

EUROPA

Europa Issue, 1956

The design symbolizing the cooperation among the six countries comprising the Coal and Steel Community is illustrated in each country.

Belgium	496-497
France	805-806
Germany	748-749
Italy	715-716
Luxembourg	318-320
Netherlands	368-369

Europa Issue, 1958

"E" and Dove
CD1

European Postal Union at the service of European integration.

1958, Sept. 13

Belgium	527-528
France	889-890
Germany	790-791
Italy	750-751
Luxembourg	341-343
Netherlands	375-376
Saar	317-318

Europa Issue, 1959

6-Link Endless Chain – CD2

1959, Sept. 19

Belgium	536-537
France	929-930
Germany	805-806
Italy	791-792
Luxembourg	354-355
Netherlands	379-380

Europa Issue, 1960

19-Spoke Wheel – CD3

First anniverary of the establishment of C.E.P.T. (Conference Europeenne des Administrations des Postes et des Telecommunications.)
The spokes symbolize the 19 founding members of the Conference.

1960, Sept.

Belgium	553-554
Denmark	379
Finland	376-377
France	970-971
Germany	818-820
Great Britain	377-378

Greece	688
Iceland	327-328
Ireland	175-176
Italy	809-810
Luxembourg	374-375
Netherlands	385-386
Norway	387
Portugal	866-867
Spain	941-942
Sweden	562-563
Switzerland	400-401
Turkey	1493-1494

Europa Issue, 1961

19 Doves Flying as One – CD4

The 19 doves represent the 19 members of the Conference of European Postal and Telecommunications Administrations C.E.P.T.

1961-62

Belgium	572-573
Cyprus	201-203
France	1005-1006
Germany	844-845
Great Britain	383-384
Greece	718-719
Iceland	340-341
Italy	845-846
Luxembourg	382-383
Netherlands	387-388
Spain	1010-1011
Switzerland	410-411
Turkey	1518-1520

Europa Issue 1962

Young Tree with 19 Leaves CD5

The 19 leaves represent the 19 original members of C.E.P.T.

1962-63

Belgium	582-583
Cyprus	219-221
France	1045-1046
Germany	852-853
Greece	739-740
Iceland	348-349
Ireland	184-185
Italy	860-861
Luxembourg	386-387
Netherlands	394-395
Norway	414-415
Switzerland	416-417
Turkey	1553-1555

Europa Issue, 1963

Stylized Links, Symbolizing Unity – CD6

1963, Sept.

Belgium	598-599
Cyprus	229-231
Finland	419
France	1074-1075
Germany	867-868
Greece	768-769
Iceland	357-358
Ireland	188-189
Italy	880-881
Luxembourg	403-404
Netherlands	416-417
Norway	441-442
Switzerland	429
Turkey	1602-1603

Europa Issue, 1964

Symbolic Daisy – CD7

5th anniversary of the establishment of C.E.P.T. The 22 petals of the flower symbolize the 22 members of the Conference.

1964, Sept.

Austria	738
Belgium	614-615
Cyprus	244-246
France	1109-1110
Germany	897-898
Greece	801-802
Iceland	367-368
Ireland	196-197
Italy	894-895
Luxembourg	411-412
Monaco	590-591
Netherlands	428-429
Norway	458
Portugal	931-933
Spain	1262-1263
Switzerland	438-439
Turkey	1628-1629

Europa Issue, 1965

Leaves and "Fruit" CD8

1965

Belgium	636-637
Cyprus	262-264
Finland	437
France	1131-1132
Germany	934-935
Greece	833-834
Iceland	375-376
Ireland	204-205
Italy	915-916
Luxembourg	432-433
Monaco	616-617
Netherlands	438-439
Norway	475-476
Portugal	958-960
Switzerland	469
Turkey	1665-1666

Europa Issue, 1966

Symbolic Sailboat – CD9

1966, Sept.

Andorra, French	172
Belgium	675-676
Cyprus	275-277
France	1163-1164
Germany	963-964
Greece	862-863
Iceland	384-385
Ireland	216-217
Italy	942-943
Liechtenstein	415
Luxembourg	440-441
Monaco	639-640
Netherlands	441-442
Norway	496-497
Portugal	980-982
Switzerland	477-478
Turkey	1718-1719

Europa Issue, 1967

Cogwheels CD10

1967

Andorra, French	174-175
Belgium	688-689
Cyprus	297-299
France	1178-1179
Greece	891-892
Germany	969-970
Iceland	389-390
Ireland	232-233
Italy	951-952
Liechtenstein	420
Luxembourg	449-450
Monaco	669-670
Netherlands	444-447
Norway	504-505
Portugal	994-996
Spain	1465-1466
Switzerland	482
Turkey	B120-B121

Europa Issue, 1968

Golden Key with C.E.P.T. Emblem CD11

1968

Andorra, French	182-183
Belgium	705-706
Cyprus	314-316
France	1209-1210
Germany	983-984
Greece	916-917
Iceland	395-396
Ireland	242-243
Italy	979-980
Liechtenstein	442
Luxembourg	466-467
Monaco	689-691
Netherlands	452-453
Portugal	1019-1021
San Marino	687
Spain	1526
Turkey	1775-1776

Europa Issue, 1969

"EUROPA" and "CEPT" – CD12

Tenth anniversary of C.E.P.T.

1969

Andorra, French	188-189
Austria	837
Belgium	718-719
Cyprus	326-328
Denmark	458
Finland	483
France	1245-1246
Germany	996-997
Great Britain	585
Greece	947-948
Iceland	406-407
Ireland	270-271
Italy	1000-1001
Liechtenstein	453
Luxembourg	474-475
Monaco	722-724
Netherlands	475-476
Norway	533-534
Portugal	1038-1040
San Marino	701-702
Spain	1567

Sweden 814-816
Switzerland 500-501
Turkey 1799-1800
Vatican 470-472
Yugoslavia 1003-1004

Europa Issue, 1970

Interwoven
Threads
CD13

1970
Andorra, French 196-197
Belgium 741-742
Cyprus 340-342
France 1271-1272
Germany 1018-1019
Greece 985, 987
Iceland 420-421
Ireland 279-281
Italy 1013-1014
Liechtenstein 470
Luxembourg 489-490
Monaco 768-770
Netherlands 483-484
Portugal 1060-1062
San Marino 729-730
Spain 1607
Switzerland 515-516
Turkey 1848-1849
Yugoslavia 1024-1025

Europa Issue, 1971

"Fraternity, Cooperation,
Common Effort" – CD14

1971
Andorra, French 205-206
Belgium 803-804
Cyprus 365-367
Finland 504
France 1304
Germany 1064-1065
Greece 1029-1030
Iceland 429-430
Ireland 305-306
Italy 1038-1039
Liechtenstein 485
Luxembourg 500-501
Malta 425-427
Monaco 797-799
Netherlands 488-489
Portugal 1094-1096
San Marino 749-750
Spain 1675-1676
Switzerland 531-532
Turkey 1876-1877
Yugoslavia 1052-1053

Europa Issue, 1972

Sparkles,
Symbolic of
Communications
CD15

1972
Andorra, French 210-211
Andorra, Spanish 62
Belgium 825-826
Cyprus 380-382
Finland 512-513
France 1341
Germany 1089-1090
Greece 1049-1050
Iceland 439-440
Ireland 316-317
Italy 1065-1066
Liechtenstein 504

Luxembourg 512-513
Malta 450-453
Monaco 831-832
Netherlands 494-495
Portugal 1141-1143
San Marino 771-772
Spain 1718
Switzerland 544-545
Turkey 1907-1908
Yugoslavia 1100-1101

Europa Issue, 1973

Post Horn
and Arrows
CD16

1973
Andorra, French 319-320
Andorra, Spanish 76
Belgium 839-840
Cyprus 396-398
Finland 526
France 1367
Germany 1114-1115
Greece 1090-1092
Iceland 447-448
Ireland 329-330
Italy 1108-1109
Liechtenstein 528-529
Luxembourg 523-524
Malta 469-471
Monaco 866-867
Netherlands 504-505
Norway 604-605
Portugal 1170-1172
San Marino 802-803
Spain 1753
Switzerland 580-581
Turkey 1935-1936
Yugoslavia 1138-1139

PORTUGAL & COLONIES
Vasco da Gama Issue

Fleet Departing
CD20

Fleet Arriving
at Calicut
CD21

Embarking
at Rastello
CD22

Muse of   San Gabriel, da Gama
History – CD23   and Camoens – CD24

Archangel Gabriel,   Flagship
the Patron Saint   San Gabriel
CD25   CD26

Vasco da
Gama
CD27

Fourth centenary of Vasco da Gama's discovery of the route to India.

1898
Azores 93-100
Macao 67-74
Madeira 37-44
Portugal 147-154
Port. Africa 1-8
Port. india 189-196
Timor 45-52

Pombal Issue
POSTAL TAX

Marquis   Planning
de   Reconstruction
Pombal   of Lisbon, 1755
CD28   CD29

Pombal
Monument,
Lisbon
CD30

Sebastiao Jose de Carvalho e Mello,
Marquis de Pombal (1699-1782), statesman,
rebuilt Lisbon after earthquake of 1755. Tax
was for the erection of Pombal monument.
Obligatory on all mail on certain days
throughout the year.
Postal Tax Dues are inscribed "Multa."

1925
Angola RA1-RA3, RAJ1-RAJ3
Azores RA9-RA11, RAJ2-RAJ4
Cape Verde RA1-RA3, RAJ1-RAJ3
Macao RA1-RA3, RAJ1-RAJ3
Madeira RA1-RA3, RAJ1-RAJ3
Mozambique RA1-RA3, RAJ1-RAJ3
Nyassa RA1-RA3, RAJ1-RAJ3
Portugal RA11-RA13, RAJ2-RAJ4
Port. Guinea RA1-RA3, RAJ1-RAJ3
Port. India RA1-RA3, RAJ1-RAJ3
St. Thomas & Prince
  Islands RA1-RA3, RAJ1-RAJ3
Timor RA1-RA3, RAJ1-RAJ3

Vasco   Mousinho de
da Gama   Albuquerque
CD34   CD35

Dam   Prince Henry the
CD36   Navigator – CD37

Affonso de   Plane over
Albuquerque   Globe
CD38   CD39

1938-39
Angola 274-291
Cape Verde 234-251
Macao 289-305
Mozambique 270-287
Port. Guinea 233-250
Port. India 439-453
St. Thomas & Prince
  Islands 302-319, 323-340
Timor 223-239

1938-39
Angola C1-C9
Cape Verde C1-C9
Macao C7-C15
Mozambique C1-C9
Port. Guinea C1-C9
Port. India C1-C8
St. Thomas & Prince Islands C1-C18
Timor C1-C9

Lady of Fatima Issue

Our Lady of
the Rosary,
Fatima,
Portugal
CD40

1948-49
Angola 315-318
Cape Verde 266
Macao 336
Mozambique 325-328
Port. Guinea 271
Port. India 480
St. Thomas & Prince Islands 351
Timor 254

A souvenir sheet of 9 stamps was issued in
1951 to mark the extension of the 1950
Holy Year. The sheet contains: Angola No.
316, Cape Verde No. 266, Macao No. 336,
Mozambique No. 325, Portuguese Guinea
No. 271, Portugese India Nos. 480, 485, St.
Thomas & Prince Islands No. 351, Timor No.
254.

The sheet also contains a portrait of Pope Pius XII and is inscribed "Encerramento do Ano Santo, Fatima 1951." It was sold for 11 escudos.

Holy Year Issue

Church Bells and Dove
CD41

Angel Holding Candelabra
CD42

Holy Year, 1950.
1950-51
Angola..331-332
Cape Verde..................................268-269
Macao...339-340
Mozambique.................................330-331
Port. Guinea.................................273-274
Port. India 490-491, 496-503
St. Thomas & Prince Islands 353-354
Timor..258-259

A souvenir sheet of 8 stamps was issued in 1951 to mark the extension of the Holy Year. The sheet contains: Angola No. 331, Cape Verde No. 269, Macao No. 340, Mozambique No. 331, Portuguese Guinea No. 275, Portuguese India No. 490, St. Thomas & Prince Islands No. 354, Timor No. 258, some with colors changed. The sheet contains doves and is inscribed "Encerramento do Ano Santo, Fatima 1951." It was sold for 17 escudos.

Holy Year Conclusion Issue

Our Lady of Fatima
CD43

Conclusion of Holy Year. Sheets contain alternate vertical rows of stamps and labels bearing quotation from Pope Pius XII, different for each colony.
1951
Angola...357
Cape Verde..270
Macao...352
Mozambique.......................................356
Port. Guinea.......................................275
Port. India...506
St. Thomas & Prince Islands..................355
Timor..270

Medical Congress Issue

CD44

First National Congress of Tropical Medicine, Lisbon, 1952.
Each stamp has a different design.
1952
Angola...358
Cape Verde..287
Macao...364
Mozambique.......................................359
Port. Guinea.......................................276
Port. India...516
St. Thomas & Prince Islands..................356
Timor..271

POSTAGE DUE STAMPS

   CD45

1952
Angola...J37-J42
Cape Verde...................................J31-J36
Macao..J53-J58
Mozambique..................................J51-J56
Port. Guinea..................................J40-J45
Port. India....................................J47-J52
St. Thomas & Prince Islands.............J52-J57
Timor...J31-J36

Sao Paulo Issue

Father Manuel de Nobrega and View of Sao Paulo
CD46

Founding of Sao Paulo, Brazil, 400th anniv.
1954
Angola...385
Cape Verde..297
Macao...382
Mozambique.......................................395
Port. Guinea.......................................291
Port. India...530
St. Thomas & Prince Islands..................369
Timor..279

Tropical Medicine Congress Issue

CD47

Sixth International Congress for Tropical Medicine and Malaria, Lisbon, Sept. 1958.
Each stamp shows a different plant.
1958
Angola...409
Cape Verde..303
Macao...392
Mozambique.......................................404
Port. Guinea.......................................295
Port. India...569
St. Thomas & Prince Islands 371
Timor..289

Sports Issue

CD48

Each stamp shows a different sport.
1962
Angola...433-438
Cape Verde...................................320-325
Macao..394-399
Mozambique..................................424-429
Port. Guinea.................................299-304
St. Thomas & Prince Islands 374-379
Timor...313-318

Anti-Malaria Issue

Anopheles Funestus and Malaria Eradication Symbol
CD49

World Health Organization drive to eradicate malaria.
1962
Angola...439
Cape Verde..326
Macao...400
Mozambique.......................................430
Port. Guinea.......................................305
St. Thomas & Prince Islands..................380
Timor..319

Airline Anniversary Issue

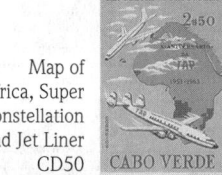

Map of Africa, Super Constellation and Jet Liner
CD50

Tenth anniversary of Transportes Aereos Portugueses (TAP).
1963
Angola...490
Cape Verde..327
Mozambique.......................................434
Port. Guinea.......................................318
St. Thomas & Prince Islands 381

National Overseas Bank Issue

Antonio Teixeira de Sousa
CD51

Centenary of the National Overseas Bank of Portugal.
1964, May 16
Angola...509
Cape Verde..328
Port. Guinea.......................................319
St. Thomas & Prince Islands 382
Timor..320

ITU Issue

ITU Emblem and the archangel Gabriel
CD52

International Communications Union, Cent.
1965, May 17
Angola...511
Cape Verde..329
Macao...402
Mozambique.......................................464
Port. Guinea.......................................320
St. Thomas & Prince Islands..................383
Timor..321

National Revolution Issue

CD53

40th anniv. of the National Revolution. Different buildings on each stamp.
1966, May 28
Angola...525
Cape Verde..338
Macao...403
Mozambique.......................................465
Port. Guinea.......................................329
St. Thomas & Prince Islands..................392
Timor..322

Navy Club Issue

CD54

Centenary of Portugal's Navy Club. Each stamp has a different design.
1967, Jan. 31
Angola...527-528
Cape Verde...................................339-340
Macao..412-413
Mozambique..................................478-479
Port. Guinea.................................330-331
St. Thomas & Prince Islands 393-394
Timor...323-324

Admiral Coutinho Issue

   CD55

Centenary of the birth of Admiral Carlos Viegas Gago Coutinho (1869-1959), explorer and aviation pioneer.
Each stamp has a different design.
1969, Feb. 17
Angola...547
Cape Verde..355
Macao...417
Mozambique.......................................484
Port. Guinea.......................................335
St. Thomas & Prince Islands 397
Timor..335

Administration Reform Issue

Luiz Augusto Rebello da Silva – CD56

Centenary of the administration reforms of the overseas territories.
1969, Sept. 25
Angola...549
Cape Verde..357
Macao...419
Mozambique.......................................491
Port. Guinea.......................................337
St. Thomas & Prince Islands 399
Timor..338

Marshal Carmona Issue

CD57

Birth centenary of Marshal Antonio Oscar Carmona de Fragoso (1869-1951), President of Portugal.

Each stamp has a different design.

1970, Nov. 15
Angola..563
Cape Verde..................................359
Macao..422
Mozambique................................493
Port. Guinea................................340
St. Thomas & Prince Islands........403
Timor..341

Olympic Games Issue

CD59

20th Olympic Games, Munich, Aug. 26-Sept. 11.

Each stamp shows a different sport.

1972, June 20
Angola..569
Cape Verde..................................361
Macao..426
Mozambique................................504
Port. Guinea................................342
St. Thomas & Prince Islands........408
Timor..343

Lisbon-Rio de Janeiro Flight Issue

CD60

50th anniversary of the Lisbon to Rio de Janeiro flight by Arturo de Sacadura and Coutinho, March 30-June 5, 1922.

Each stamp shows a different stage of the flight.

1972, Sept. 20
Angola..570
Cape Verde..................................362
Macao..427
Mozambique................................505
Port. Guinea................................343
St. Thomas & Prince Islands........409
Timor..344

WMO Centenary Issue

WMO Emblem – CD61

Centenary of international meterological cooperation.

1973, Dec. 15
Angola..571
Cape Verde..................................363
Macao..429
Mozambique................................509
Port. Guinea................................344
St. Thomas & Prince Islands........410
Timor..345

FRENCH COMMUNITY
Upper Volta can be found under Burkina Faso in Vol. 1

Colonial Exposition Issue

People of French Empire CD70

Women's Heads CD71

France Showing Way to Civilization CD72

"Colonial Commerce" CD73

International Colonial Exposition, Paris.

1931
Cameroun....................................213-216
Chad..60-63
Dahomey.....................................97-100
Fr. Guiana..................................152-155
Fr. Guinea..................................116-119
Fr. India.....................................100-103
Fr. Polynesia................................76-79
Fr. Sudan...................................102-105
Gabon..120-123
Guadeloupe................................138-141
Indo-China.................................140-142
Ivory Coast..................................92-95
Madagascar...............................169-172
Martinique.................................129-132
Mauritania...................................65-68
Middle Congo..............................61-64
New Caledonia...........................176-179
Niger..73-76
Reunion.....................................122-125
St. Pierre & Miquelon.................132-135
Senegal.....................................138-141
Somali Coast.............................135-138
Togo...254-257
Ubangi-Shari................................82-85
Upper Volta..................................66-69
Wallis & Futuna Isls. 85-88

Paris International Exposition Issue
Colonial Arts Exposition Issue

"Colonial Resources"
CD74   CD77

Overseas Commerce – CD75

Exposition Building and Women CD76

"France and the Empire" CD78

Cultural Treasures of the Colonies CD79

Souvenir sheets contain one imperf. stamp.

1937
Cameroun...................................217-222A
Dahomey...................................101-107
Fr. Equatorial Africa.................27-32, 73
Fr. Guiana..................................162-168
Fr. Guinea..................................120-126
Fr. India.....................................104-110
Fr. Polynesia.............................117-123
Fr. Sudan...................................106-112
Guadeloupe................................148-154
Indo-China.................................193-199
Inini..41
Ivory Coast................................152-158
Kwangchowan................................132
Madagascar...............................191-197
Martinique.................................179-185
Mauritania...................................69-75
New Caledonia...........................208-214
Niger..72-83
Reunion.....................................167-173
St. Pierre & Miquelon.................165-171
Senegal.....................................172-178
Somali Coast.............................139-145
Togo...258-264
Wallis & Futuna Isls. 89

Curie Issue

Pierre and Marie Curie CD80

40th anniversary of the discovery of radium. The surtax was for the benefit of the Intl. Union for the Control of Cancer.

1938
Cameroun...B1
Cuba..B1-B2
Dahomey...B2
France..B76
Fr. Equatorial Africa..........................B1
Fr. Guiana..B3
Fr. Guinea..B2
Fr. India...B6
Fr. Polynesia......................................B5
Fr. Sudan...B1
Guadeloupe..B3
Indo-China..B14
Ivory Coast..B2
Madagascar..B2
Martinique..B2
Mauritania..B3
New Caledonia....................................B4
Niger..B1
Reunion..B4
St. Pierre & Miquelon..........................B3
Senegal...B3
Somali Coast.......................................B2
Togo...B1

Caillie Issue

Rene Caille and Map of Northwestern Africa - CD81

Death centenary of Rene Caillie (1799-1838), French explorer.

All three denominations exist with colony name omitted.

1939
Dahomey....................................108-110
Fr. Guinea..................................161-163
Fr. Sudan...................................113-115
Ivory Coast................................160-162
Mauritania.................................109-111
Niger..84-86
Senegal.....................................188-190
Togo...265-267

New York World's Fair Issue

Natives and New York Skyline CD82

1939
Cameroun...................................223-224
Dahomey...................................111-112
Fr. Equatorial Africa....................78-79
Fr. Guiana..................................169-170
Fr. Guinea..................................164-165
Fr. India.....................................111-112
Fr. Polynesia.............................124-125
Fr. Sudan...................................116-117
Guadeloupe................................155-156
Indo-China.................................203-204
Inini...42-43
Ivory Coast................................163-164
Kwangchowan...........................121-122
Madagascar...............................209-210
Martinique.................................186-187
Mauritania.................................112-113
New Caledonia...........................215-216
Niger..87-88
Reunion.....................................174-175
St. Pierre & Miquelon.................205-206
Senegal.....................................191-192
Somali Coast.............................179-180
Togo...268-269
Wallis & Futuna Isls. 90-91

French Revolution Issue

Storming of the Bastille – CD83

French Revolution, 150th anniv. The surtax was for the defense of the colonies.

1939
Cameroun......................................B2-B6
Dahomey.......................................B3-B7
Fr. Equatorial Africa..............B4-B8, CB1
Fr. Guiana..............................B4-B8, CB1
Fr. Guinea.....................................B3-B7
Fr. India......................................B7-B11
Fr. Polynesia......................B6-B10, CB1
Fr. Sudan......................................B2-B6
Guadeloupe....................................B4-B8
Indo-China........................B15-B19, CB1
Inini..B1-B5
Ivory Coast...................................B3-B7
Kwangchowan...............................B1-B5
Madagascar......................B3-B7, CB1
Martinique.....................................B3-B7
Mauritania.....................................B4-B8
New Caledonia...................B5-B9, CB1
Niger...B2-B6
Reunion............................B5-B9, CB1
St. Pierre & Miquelon.....................B4-B8
Senegal...........................B4-B8, CB1
Somali Coast..................................B3-B7
Togo...B2-B6
Wallis & Futuna Isls. B1-B5

Plane over Coastal Area CD85

All five denominations exist with colony name omitted.

1940

Dahomey	C1-C5
Fr. Guinea	C1-C5
Fr. Sudan	C1-C5
Ivory Coast	C1-C5
Mauritania	C1-C5
Niger	C1-C5
Senegal	C12-C16
Togo	C1-C5

Colonial Infantryman CD86

1941

Cameroun	B13B
Dahomey	B13
Fr. Equatorial Africa	B8B
Fr. Guiana	B10
Fr. Guinea	B13
Fr. India	B13
Fr. Polynesia	B12
Fr. Sudan	B12
Guadeloupe	B10
Indo-China	B19B
Inini	B7
Ivory Coast	B13
Kwangchowan	B7
Madagascar	B9
Martinique	B9
Mauritania	B14
New Caledonia	B11
Niger	B12
Reunion	B11
St. Pierre & Miquelon	B8B
Senegal	B14
Somali Coast	B9
Togo	B10B
Wallis & Futuna Isls.	B7

Cross of Lorraine & Four-motor Plane CD87

1941-5

Cameroun	C1-C7
Fr. Equatorial Africa	C17-C23
Fr. Guiana	C9-C10
Fr. India	C1-C6
Fr. Polynesia	C3-C9
Fr. West Africa	C1-C3
Guadeloupe	C1-C2
Madagascar	C37-C43
Martinique	C1-C2
New Caledonia	C7-C13
Reunion	C18-C24
St. Pierre & Miquelon	C1-C7
Somali Coast	C1-C7

Transport Plane CD88

Caravan and Plane CD89

1942

Dahomey	C6-C13
Fr. Guinea	C6-C13
Fr. Sudan	C6-C13
Ivory Coast	C6-C13
Mauritania	C6-C13
Niger	C6-C13
Senegal	C17-C25
Togo	C6-C13

Red Cross Issue

Marianne CD90

The surtax was for the French Red Cross and national relief.

1944

Cameroun	B28
Fr. Equatorial Africa	B38
Fr. Guiana	B12
Fr. India	B14
Fr. Polynesia	B13
Fr. West Africa	B1
Guadeloupe	B12
Madagascar	B15
Martinique	B11
New Caledonia	B13
Reunion	B15
St. Pierre & Miquelon	B13
Somali Coast	B13
Wallis & Futuna Isls.	B9

Eboue Issue

CD91

Felix Eboue, first French colonial administrator to proclaim resistance to Germany after French surrender in World War II.

1945

Cameroun	296-297
Fr. Equatorial Africa	156-157
Fr. Guiana	171-172
Fr. India	210-211
Fr. Polynesia	150-151
Fr. West Africa	15-16
Guadeloupe	187-188
Madagascar	259-260
Martinique	196-197
New Caledonia	274-275
Reunion	238-239
St. Pierre & Miquelon	322-323
Somali Coast	238-239

Victory Issue

Victory – CD92

European victory of the Allied Nations in World War II.

1946, May 8

Cameroun	C8
Fr. Equatorial Africa	C24
Fr. Guiana	C11
Fr. India	C7
Fr. Polynesia	C10
Fr. West Africa	C4
Guadeloupe	C3
Indo-China	C19
Madagascar	C44
Martinique	C9
New Caledonia	C14
Reunion	C25
St. Pierre & Miquelon	C8
Somali Coast	C8
Wallis & Futuna Isls.	C1

Chad to Rhine Issue

Leclerc's Departure from Chad – CD93

Battle at Cufra Oasis – CD94

Tanks in Action, Mareth – CD95

Normandy Invasion – CD96

Entering Paris – CD97

Liberation of Strasbourg – CD98

"Chad to the Rhine" march, 1942-44, by Gen. Jacques Leclerc's column, later French 2nd Armored Division.

1946, June 6

Cameroun	C9-C14
Fr. Equatorial Africa	C25-C30
Fr. Guiana	C12-C17
Fr. India	C8-C13
Fr. Polynesia	C11-C16
Fr. West Africa	C5-C10
Guadeloupe	C4-C9
Indo-China	C20-C25
Madagascar	C45-C50
Martinique	C4-C9
New Caledonia	C15-C20
Reunion	C26-C31
St. Pierre & Miquelon	C9-C14
Somali Coast	C9-C14
Wallis & Futuna Isls.	C2-C7

UPU Issue

French Colonials, Globe and Plane CD99

Universal Postal Union, 75th anniv.

1949, July 4

Cameroun	C29
Fr. Equatorial Africa	C34
Fr. India	C17
Fr. Polynesia	C20
Fr. West Africa	C15
Indo-China	C26
Madagascar	C55
New Caledonia	C24
St. Pierre & Miquelon	C18
Somali Coast	C18
Togo	C18
Wallis & Futuna Isls.	C10

Tropical Medicine Issue

Doctor Treating Infant CD100

The surtax was for charitable work.

1950

Cameroun	B29
Fr. Equatorial Africa	B39
Fr. India	B15
Fr. Polynesia	B14
Fr. West Africa	B3
Madagascar	B17
New Caledonia	B14
St. Pierre & Miquelon	B14
Somali Coast	B14
Togo	B11

Military Medal Issue

Medal, Early Marine and Colonial Soldier CD101

Centenary of the creation of the French Military Medal.

1952

Cameroun	332
Comoro Isls.	39
Fr. Equatorial Africa	186
Fr. India	233
Fr. Polynesia	179
Fr. West Africa	57
Madagascar	286
New Caledonia	295
St. Pierre & Miquelon	345
Somali Coast	267
Togo	327
Wallis & Futuna Isls.	149

Liberation Issue

Allied Landing, Victory Sign and Cross of Lorraine – CD102

Lberation of France, 10th anniv.
1954, June 6
Cameroun..C32
Comoro Isls..C4
Fr. Equatorial Africa...........................C38
Fr. India..C18
Fr. Polynesia...C22
Fr. West Africa..C17
Madagascar...C57
New Caledonia...C25
St. Pierre & Miquelon........................C19
Somali Coast..C19
Togo...C19
Wallis & Futuna Isls...........................C11

FIDES Issue

Plowmen
CD103

Efforts of FIDES, the Economic and Social Development Fund for Overseas Possessions (Fonds d' Investissement pour le Developpement Economique et Social).

Each stamp has a different design.
1956
Cameroun...326-329
Comoro Isls..43
Fr. Polynesia...181
Madagascar.................................292-295
New Caledonia...303
Somali Coast..268
Togo...331

Flower Issue

CD104

Each stamp shows a different flower.
1958-9
Cameroun..333
Comoro Isls..45
Fr. Equatorial Africa.................200-201
Fr. Polynesia...192
Fr. So. & Antarctic Terr.........................11
Fr. West Africa..................................79-83
Madagascar.................................301-302
New Caledonia............................304-305
St. Pierre & Miquelon........................357
Somali Coast..270
Togo..348-349
Wallis & Futuna Isls.............................152

Human Rights Issue

Sun, Dove and U.N. Emblem – CD105

10th anniversary of the signing of the Universal Declaration of Human Rights.
1958
Comoro Isls..44
Fr. Equatorial Africa...........................202
Fr. Polynesia...191
Fr. West Africa..85
Madagascar...300
New Caledonia...306
St. Pierre & Miquelon........................356
Somali Coast..274
Wallis & Futuna Isls.............................153

C.C.T.A. Issue

CD106

Commission for Technical Cooperation in Africa south of the Sahara, 10th anniv.
1960
Cameroun..335
Cent. African Rep...3
Chad..66
Congo, P.R...90
Dahomey..138
Gabon..150
Ivory Coast...180
Madagascar...317
Mali...9
Mauritania..117
Niger..104
Upper Volta...89

Air Afrique Issue, 1961

Modern and Ancient Africa,
Map and Planes – CD107

Founding of Air Afrique (African Airlines).
1961-62
Cameroun..C37
Cent. African Rep..................................C5
Chad..C7
Congo, P.R...C5
Dahomey...C17
Gabon...C5
Ivory Coast...C18
Mauritania...C17
Niger..C22
Senegal..C31
Upper Volta..C4

Anti-Malaria Issue

CD108

World Health Organization drive to eradicate malaria.
1962, Apr. 7
Cameroun...B36
Cent. African Rep.....................................B1
Chad..B1
Comoro Isls..B1
Congo, P.R..B3
Dahomey..B15
Gabon...B4
Ivory Coast...B15
Madagascar...B19
Mali..B1
Mauritania..B16
Niger..B14
Senegal..B16
Somali Coast..B15
Upper Volta...B1

Abidjan Games Issue

CD109

Abidjan Games, Ivory Coast, Dec. 24-31, 1961. Each stamp shows a different sport.
1962
Chad...83-84
Cent. African Rep..........................19-20
Congo, P.R..................................103-104
Gabon................................163-164, C6
Niger..109-111
Upper Volta................................103-105

African and Malagasy Union Issue

Flag of
Union
CD110

First anniversary of the Union.
1962, Sept. 8
Cameroun..373
Cent. African Rep......................................21
Chad..85
Congo, P.R..105
Dahomey..155
Gabon..165
Ivory Coast...198
Madagascar...332
Mauritania..170
Niger..112
Senegal..211
Upper Volta...106

Telstar Issue

Telstar and Globe Showing Andover and Pleumeur-Bodou – CD111

First television connection of the United States and Europe through the Telstar satellite, July 11-12, 1962.
1962-63
Andorra, French 154
Comoro Isls...C7
Fr. Polynesia...C29
Fr. So. & Antarctic Terr.....................C5
New Caledonia.......................................C33
Somali Coast..C31
St. Pierre & Miquelon C26
Wallis & Futuna Isls........................C17

Freedom From Hunger Issue

World Map
and Wheat
Emblem
CD112

U.N. Food and Agriculture Organization's "Freedom from Hunger" campaign.
1963, Mar. 21
Cameroun...B37-B38
Cent. African Rep.....................................B2
Chad..B2
Congo, P.R..B4
Dahomey..B16
Gabon...B5
Ivory Coast...B16
Madagascar...B21
Mauritania..B17
Niger..B15
Senegal..B17
Upper Volta...B2

Red Cross Centenary Issue

CD113

Centenary of the International Red Cross.
1963, Sept. 2
Comoro Isls..55
Fr. Polynesia...205
New Caledonia...328
St. Pierre & Miquelon........................367
Somali Coast..297
Wallis & Futuna Isls.............................165

African Postal Union Issue

UAMPT
Emblem,
Radio Masts,
Plane and
Mail
CD114

Establishment of the African and Malagasy Posts and Telecommunications Union.
1963, Sept. 8
Cameroun..C47
Cent. African Rep................................C10
Chad..C9
Congo, P.R...C13
Dahomey...C19
Gabon...C13
Ivory Coast...C25
Madagascar..C75
Mauritania...C22
Niger..C27
Rwanda..36
Senegal..C32
Upper Volta..C9

Air Afrique Issue, 1963

Symbols of Flight – CD115

First anniversary of Air Afrique and inauguration of DC-8 service.
1963, Nov. 19
Cameroun..C48
Chad..C10
Congo, P.R...C14
Gabon...C18
Ivory Coast...C26
Mauritania...C26
Niger..C35
Senegal..C33

Europafrica Issue

Europe and
Africa
Linked
CD116

Signing of an economic agreement between the European Economic Community and the African and Malagasy Union, Yaounde, Cameroun, July 20, 1963.

1963-64
Cameroun	402
Chad	C11
Cent. African Rep.	C12
Congo, P.R.	C16
Gabon	C19
Ivory Coast	217
Niger	C43
Upper Volta	C11

Human Rights Issue

Scales of Justice and Globe CD117

15th anniversary of the Universal Declaration of Human Rights.

1963, Dec. 10
Comoro Isls.	58
Fr. Polynesia	206
New Caledonia	329
St. Pierre & Miquelon	368
Somali Coast	300
Wallis & Futuna Isls.	166

PHILATEC Issue

Stamp Album, Champs Elysees Palace and Horses of Marly – CD118

Intl. Philatelic and Postal Techniques Exhibition, Paris, June 5-21, 1964.

1963-64
Comoro Isls.	60
France	1078
Fr. Polynesia	207
New Caledonia	341
St. Pierre & Miquelon	369
Somali Coast	301
Wallis & Futuna Isls.	167

Cooperation Issue

CD119

Cooperation between France and the French-speaking countries of Africa and Madagascar.

1964
Cameroun	409-410
Cent. African Rep.	39
Chad	103
Congo, P.R.	121
Dahomey	193
France	1111
Gabon	175
Ivory Coast	221
Madagascar	360
Mauritania	181
Niger	143
Senegal	236
Togo	495

ITU Issue

Telegraph, Syncom Satellite and ITU Emblem CD120

Intl. Telecommunication Union, Cent.

1965, May 17
Comoro Isls.	C14
Fr. Polynesia	C33
Fr. So. & Antarctic Terr.	C8
New Caledonia	C40
New Hebrides	124-125
St. Pierre & Miquelon	C29
Somali Coast	C36
Wallis & Futuna Isls.	C20

French Satellite A-1 Issue

Diamant Rocket and Launching Installation – CD121

Launching of France's first satellite, Nov. 26, 1965.

1965-66
Comoro Isls.	C15-C16
France	1137-1138
Fr. Polynesia	C40-C41
Fr. So. & Antarctic Terr.	C9-C10
New Caledonia	C44-C45
St. Pierre & Miquelon	C30-C31
Somali Coast	C39-C40
Wallis & Futuna Isls.	C22-C23

French Satellite D-1 Issue

D-1 Satellite in Orbit – CD122

Launching of the D-1 satellite at Hammaguir, Algeria, Feb. 17, 1966.

1966
Comoro Isls.	C17
France	1148
Fr. Polynesia	C42
Fr. So. & Antarctic Terr.	C11
New Caledonia	C46
St. Pierre & Miquelon	C32
Somali Coast	C49
Wallis & Futuna Isls.	C24

Air Afrique Issue, 1966

Planes and Air Afrique Emblem – CD123

Introduction of DC-8F planes by Air Afrique.

1966
Cameroun	C79
Cent. African Rep.	C35

Chad	C26
Congo, P.R.	C42
Dahomey	C42
Gabon	C47
Ivory Coast	C32
Mauritania	C57
Niger	C63
Senegal	C47
Togo	C54
Upper Volta	C31

African Postal Union, 1967

Telecommunications Symbols and Map of Africa – CD124

Fifth anniversary of the establishment of the African and Malagasy Union of Posts and Telecommunications, UAMPT.

1967
Cameroun	C90
Cent. African Rep.	C46
Chad	C37
Congo, P.R.	C57
Dahomey	C61
Gabon	C58
Ivory Coast	C34
Madagascar	C85
Mauritania	C65
Niger	C75
Rwanda	C1-C3
Senegal	C60
Togo	C81
Upper Volta	C50

Monetary Union Issue

Gold Token of the Ashantis, 17-18th Centuries – CD125

West African Monetary Union, 5th anniv.

1967, Nov. 4
Dahomey	244
Ivory Coast	259
Mauritania	238
Niger	204
Senegal	294
Togo	623
Upper Volta	181

WHO Anniversary Issue

Sun, Flowers and WHO Emblem CD126

World Health Organization, 20th anniv.

1968, May 4
Afars & Issas	317
Comoro Isls.	73
Fr. Polynesia	241-242
Fr. So. & Antarctic Terr.	31
New Caledonia	367
St. Pierre & Miquelon	377
Wallis & Futuna Isls.	169

Human Rights Year Issue

Human Rights Flame CD127

1968, Aug. 10
Afars & Issas	322-323
Comoro Isls.	76
Fr. Polynesia	243-244
Fr. So. & Antarctic Terr.	32
New Caledonia	369
St. Pierre & Miquelon	382
Wallis & Futuna Isls.	170

2nd PHILEXAFRIQUE Issue

CD128

Opening of PHILEXAFRIQUE, Abidjan, Feb. 14. Each stamp shows a local scene and stamp.

1969, Feb. 14
Cameroun	C118
Cent. African Rep.	C65
Chad	C48
Congo, P.R.	C77
Dahomey	C94
Gabon	C82
Ivory Coast	C38-C40
Madagascar	C92
Mali	C65
Mauritania	C80
Niger	C104
Senegal	C68
Togo	C104
Upper Volta	C62

Concorde Issue

Concorde in Flight CD129

First flight of the prototpye Concorde super-sonic plane at Toulouse, Mar. 1, 1969.

1969
Afars & Issas	C56
Comoro Isls.	C29
France	C42
Fr. Polynesia	C50
Fr. So. & Antarctic Terr.	C18
New Caledonia	C63
St. Pierre & Miquelon	C40
Wallis & Futuna Isls.	C30

Development Bank Issue

Bank Emblem CD130

African Development Bank, fifth anniv.

1969
Cameroun	499
Chad	217

Congo, P.R.	181-182
Ivory Coast	281
Mali	127-128
Mauritania	267
Niger	220
Senegal	317-318
Upper Volta	201

ILO Issue

ILO Headquarters, Geneva,
and Emblem – CD131

Intl. Labor Organization, 50th anniv.

1969-70
Afars & Issas	337
Comoro Isls.	83
Fr. Polynesia	251-252
Fr. So. & Antarctic Terr.	35
New Caledonia	379
St. Pierre & Miquelon	396
Wallis & Futuna Isls.	172

ASECNA Issue

Map of Africa, Plane and Airport – CD132

10th anniversary of the Agency for the Security of Aerial Navigation in Africa and Madagascar (ASECNA, Agence pour la Securité de la Navigation Aerienne en Afrique et a Madagascar).

1969-70
Cameroun	500
Cent. African Rep.	119
Chad	222
Congo, P.R.	197
Dahomey	269
Gabon	260
Ivory Coast	287
Mali	130
Niger	221
Senegal	321
Upper Volta	204

U.P.U. Headquarters Issue

CD133

New Universal Postal Union headquarters, Bern, Switzerland.

1970
Afars & Issas	342
Algeria	443
Cameroun	503-504
Cent. African Rep.	125
Chad	225
Comoro Isls.	84
Congo, P.R.	216
Fr. Polynesia	261-262
Fr. So. & Antarctic Terr.	36
Gabon	258
Ivory Coast	295
Madagascar	444
Mali	134-135
Mauritania	283
New Caledonia	382
Niger	231-232
St. Pierre & Miquelon	397-398
Senegal	328-329
Tunisia	535
Wallis & Futuna Isls.	173

De Gaulle Issue

CD134

First anniversay of the death of Charles de Gaulle, (1890-1970), President of France.

1971-72
Afars & Issas	356-357
Comoro Isls.	104-105
France	1322-1325
Fr. Polynesia	270-271
Fr. So. & Antarctic Terr.	52-53
New Caledonia	393-394
Reunion	377, 380
St. Pierre & Miquelon	417-418
Wallis & Futuna Isls.	177-178

African Postal Union Issue, 1971

UAMPT Building,
Brazzaville, Congo – CD135

10th anniversary of the establishment of the African and Malagasy Posts and Telecommunications Union, UAMPT.

Each stamp has a different native design.

1971, Nov. 13
Cameroun	C177
Cent. African Rep.	C89
Chad	C94
Congo, P.R.	C136
Dahomey	C146
Gabon	C120
Ivory Coast	C47
Mauritania	C113
Niger	C164
Rwanda	C8
Senegal	C105
Togo	C166
Upper Volta	C97

West African Monetary Union Issue

African Couple, City, Village and Commemorative Coin – CD136

West African Monetary Union, 10th anniv.

1972, Nov. 2
Dahomey	300
Ivory Coast	331
Mauritania	299
Niger	258
Senegal	374
Togo	825
Upper Volta	280

African Postal Union Issue, 1973

Telecommunications Symbols and
Map of Africa – CD137

11th anniversary of the African and Malagasy Posts and Telecommunications Union (UAMPT).

1973, Sept. 12
Cameroun	574
Cent. African Rep.	194
Chad	294
Congo, P.R.	289
Dahomey	311
Gabon	320
Ivory Coast	361
Madagascar	500
Mauritania	304
Niger	287
Rwanda	540
Senegal	393
Togo	849
Upper Volta	297

Philexafrique II — Essen Issue

CD138

CD139

Designs: Indigenous fauna, local and German stamps.

Types CD138-CD139 printed horizontally and vertically se-tenant in sheets of 10 (2x5). Label between horizontal pairs alternately commemoratives Philexafrique II, Libreville, Gabon, June 1978, and 2nd International Stamp Fair, Essen, Germany, Nov. 1-5.

1978-1979
Benin	C285-C286
Central Africa	C200-C201
Chad	C238-C239
Congo Republic	C245-C246
Djibouti	C121-C122
Gabon	C215-C216
Ivory Coast	C64-C65
Mali	C356-C357
Mauritania	C185-C186
Niger	C291-C292
Rwanda	C12-C13
Senegal	C146-C147
Togo	C363-C364
Upper Volta	C253-C254

BRITISH COMMONWEALTH OF NATIONS

The listings follow established trade practices when these issues are offered as units by dealers. The Peace issue, for example, includes only one stamp from the Indian state of Hyderabad. The U.P.U. issue includes the Egypt set. Pairs are included for those varieties issues with bilingual designs se-tenant.

Silver Jubilee Issue

Windsor Castle and King George V
CD301

Reign of King George V, 25th anniv.

1935
Antigua	77-80
Ascension	33-36
Bahamas	92-95
Barbados	186-189
Basutoland	11-14
Bechuanaland Protectorate	117-120
Bermuda	100-103
British Guiana	223-226
British Honduras	108-111
Cayman Islands	81-84
Ceylon	260-263
Cyprus	136-139
Dominica	90-93
Falkland Islands	77-80
Fiji	110-113
Gambia	125-128
Gibraltar	100-103
Gilbert & Ellice Islands	33-36
Gold Coast	108-111
Grenada	124-127
Hong Kong	147-150
Jamaica	109-112
Kenya, Uganda, Tanganyika	42-45
Leeward Islands	96-99
Malta	184-187
Mauritius	204-207
Montserrat	85-88
Newfoundland	226-229
Nigeria	34-37
Northern Rhodesia	18-21
Nyasaland Protectorate	47-50
St. Helena	111-114
St. Kitts-Nevis	72-75
St. Lucia	91-94
St. Vincent	134-137
Seychelles	118-121
Sierra Leone	166-169
Solomon Islands	60-63
Somaliland Protectorate	77-80
Straits Settlements	213-216
Swaziland	20-23
Trinidad & Tobago	43-46
Turks & Caicos Islands	71-74
Virgin Islands	69-72

The following have different designs but are included in the omnibus set:
Great Britain	226-229
Offices in Morocco	67-70, 226-229, 422-425, 508-510
Australia	152-154
Canada	211-216
Cook Islands	98-100
India	142-148
Nauru	31-34
New Guinea	46-47
New Zealand	199-201
Niue	67-69
Papua	114-117
Samoa	163-165
South Africa	68-71
Southern Rhodesia	33-36
South-West Africa	121-124

249 stamps, Never Hinged $975.

Coronation Issue

Queen Elizabeth and King George VI
CD302

1937
Aden	13-15
Antigua	81-83
Ascension	37-39
Bahamas	97-99
Barbados	190-192
Basutoland	15-17
Bechuanaland Protectorate	121-123

Peace Issue

King George VI and
Parliament Buildings, London – CD303

Return to peace at the close of World War II.

1945-46

Silver Wedding Issue

King George VI and Queen Elizabeth
CD304   CD305

1948-49

U.P.U. Issue

Mercury and Symbols of
Communications – CD306

Plane, Ship and Hemispheres – CD307

Mercury Scattering Letters over Globe
CD308

U.P.U. Monument, Bern – CD309
Universal Postal Union, 75th anniversary.

1949

University Issue

Arms of   Alice, Princess
University College   of Athlone
CD310   CD311

1948 opening of University College of the West Indies at Jamaica.

1951

Trinidad & Tobago 70-71
Virgin Islands..............................96-97
28 stamps

Coronation Issue

Queen
Elizabeth II
CD312

1953
Aden 47
 Kathiri State of Seiyun.....................28
 Qu'aiti State of Shihr and Mukalla........28
Antigua 106
Ascension 61
Bahamas 157
Barbados 234
Basutoland 45
Bechuanaland Protectorate...............153
Bermuda 142
British Guiana..................................252
British Honduras..............................143
Cayman Islands...............................150
Cyprus 167
Dominica...141
Falkland Islands...............................121
Falkland Islands Dependencies........1L18
Fiji 145
Gambia 152
Gibraltar 131
Gilbert & Ellice Islands 60
Gold Coast 160
Grenada 170
Hong Kong 184
Jamaica 153
Kenya, Uganda, Tanganyika 101
Leeward Islands...............................132
Malaya
 Johore 155
 Kedah 82
 Kelantan 71
 Malacca 27
 Negri Sembilan 63
 Pahang 71
 Penang 27
 Perak 126
 Perlis 28
 Selangor 101
 Trengganu 74
Malta 241
Mauritius..250
Montserrat 127
New Hebrides 77
Nigeria 260
North Borneo 260
Northern Rhodesia 60
Nyasaland Protectorate 96
Pitcairn 19
St. Helena 139
St. Kitts-Nevis 119
St. Lucia 156
St. Vincent 185
Sarawak 196
Seychelles 172
Sierra Leone 194
Singapore 27
Solomon Islands 88
Somaliland Protectorate 127
Swaziland 54
Trinidad & Tobago 84
Tristan da Cunha 13
Turks & Caicos Islands 118
Virgin Islands 114

The following have different designs but
are included in the omnibus set:
Great Britain.............................313-316
 Offices in Morocco................579-582
Australia 259-261
Bahrain..92-95
Canada 330
Ceylon 317
Cook Islands 145-146
Kuwait 113-116
New Zealand 280-284
Niue 104-105
Oman 52-55
Samoa 214-215
South Africa 192
Southern Rhodesia 80
South-West Africa 244-248
Tokelau Islands 4
 106 stamps, Never Hinged $70.

Royal Visit 1953

Separate designs for each country for the
visit of Queen Elizabeth II and the Duke of
Edinburgh.
1953
Aden 62
Australia 267-269
Bermuda 163
Ceylon 318
Fiji 146
Gibraltar 146
Jamaica 154
Kenya, Uganda, Tanganyika 102
Malta 242
New Zealand 286-287
 13 stamps

West Indies Federation

Map of the Caribbean – CD313
Federation of the West Indies, April 22,
1958.
1958
Antigua 122-124
Barbados 248-250
Dominica...................................161-163
Grenada 184-186
Jamaica 175-177
Montserrat 143-145
St. Kitts-Nevis 136-138
St. Lucia 170-172
St. Vincent 198-200
Trinidad & Tobago 86-88
 30 stamps, Never Hinged $6.

Freedom from Hunger Issue

Protein
Food
CD314

U.N. Food and Agricultural Organization's
"Freedom from Hunger" campaign.
1963
Aden 65
Antigua 133
Ascension 89
Bahamas 180
Basutoland 83
Bechuanaland Protectorate...............194
Bermuda 192
British Guiana..................................271
British Honduras..............................179
Brunei 100
Cayman Islands...............................168
Dominica...181
Falkland Islands...............................146
Fiji 198
Gambia 172
Gibraltar 161
Gilbert & Ellice Islands 76
Grenada 190
Hong Kong 218
Malta 291
Mauritius..270
Montserrat 150
New Hebrides 93
North Borneo 296
Pitcairn 35
St. Helena 173
St. Lucia 179
St. Vincent 201
Sarawak 212
Seychelles 213
Solomon Islands 109
Swaziland 108
Tonga 127
Tristan da Cunha 68
Turks & Caicos Islands 138
Virgin Islands 140
Zanzibar 280
 37 stamps

Red Cross Centenary Issue

Red Cross and Elizabeth II – CD315
1963
Antigua 134-135
Ascension 90-91
Bahamas 183-184
Basutoland 84-85
Bechuanaland Protectorate.........195-196
Bermuda 193-194
British Guiana............................272-273
British Honduras........................180-181
Cayman Islands.........................169-170
Dominica...................................182-183
Falkland Islands.........................147-148
Fiji 203-204
Gambia 173-174
Gibraltar 162-163
Gilbert & Ellice Islands 77-78
Grenada 191-192
Hong Kong 219-220
Jamaica 203-204
Malta 292-293
Mauritius....................................271-272
Montserrat 151-152
New Hebrides 94-95
Pitcairn Islands 36-37
St. Helena 174-175
St. Kitts-Nevis 143-144
St. Lucia 180-181
St. Vincent 202-203
Seychelles 214-215
Solomon Islands 110-111
South Arabia 1-2
Swaziland 109-110
Tonga 134-135
Tristan da Cunha 69-70
Turks & Caicos Islands 139-140
Virgin Islands 141-142
 70 stamps

Shakespeare Issue

Shakespeare Memorial Theatre,
Stratford-on-Avon – CD316
400th anniversary of the birth of William
Shakespeare.
1964
Antigua 151
Bahamas 201
Bechuanaland Protectorate...............197
Cayman Islands...............................171
Dominica...184
Falkland Islands...............................149
Gambia 192
Gibraltar 164
Montserrat 153
St. Lucia 196
Turks & Caicos Islands 141
Virgin Islands 143
 12 stamps

ITU ISSUE

ITU
Emblem
CD317

Intl. Telecommunication Union, cent.
1965
Antigua 153-154
Ascension 92-93
Bahamas 219-220
Barbados 265-266
Basutoland 101-102
Bechuanaland Protectorate.........202-203
Bermuda 196-197
British Guiana............................293-294

Churchill Memorial Issue

British Honduras........................187-188
Brunei 116-117
Cayman Islands.........................172-173
Dominica...................................185-186
Falkland Islands.........................154-155
Fiji 211-212
Gibraltar 167-168
Gilbert & Ellice Islands 87-88
Grenada 205-206
Hong Kong 221-222
Mauritius....................................291-292
Montserrat 157-158
New Hebrides 108-109
Pitcairn Islands 52-53
St. Helena 180-181
St. Kitts-Nevis 163-164
St. Lucia 197-198
St. Vincent 224-225
Seychelles 218-219
Solomon Islands 126-127
Swaziland 115-116
Tristan da Cunha 85-86
Turks & Caicos Islands 142-143
Virgin Islands 159-160
 64 stamps, Never Hinged $50.

Intl. Cooperation Year Issue

ICY Emblem – CD318
1965
Antigua 155-156
Ascension 94-95
Bahamas 222-223
Basutoland 103-104
Bechuanaland Protectorate.........204-205
Bermuda 199-200
British Guiana............................295-296
British Honduras........................189-190
Brunei 118-119
Cayman Islands.........................174-175
Dominica...................................187-188
Falkland Islands.........................156-157
Fiji 213-214
Gibraltar 169-170
Gilbert & Ellice Islands 104-105
Grenada 207-208
Hong Kong 223-224
Mauritius....................................293-294
Montserrat 176-177
New Hebrides 110-111
Pitcairn Islands 54-55
St. Helena 182-183
St. Kitts-Nevis 165-166
St. Lucia 199-200
Seychelles 220-221
Solomon Islands 143-144
South Arabia 17-18
Swaziland 117-118
Tristan da Cunha 87-88
Turks & Caicos Islands 144-145
Virgin Islands 161-162
 62 stamps

Churchill Memorial Issue

Winston Churchill and St. Paul's,
London, During Air Attack – CD319
1966
Antigua 157-160
Ascension 96-99
Bahamas 224-227
Barbados 281-284
Basutoland 105-108
Bechuanaland Protectorate.........206-209
Bermuda 201-204
British Antarctic Territory 16-19
British Honduras........................191-194
Brunei 120-123
Cayman Islands.........................176-179
Dominica...................................189-192
Falkland Islands.........................158-161

Fiji 215-218
Gibraltar 171-174
Gilbert & Ellice Islands 106-109
Grenada 209-212
Hong Kong 225-228
Mauritius 295-298
Montserrat 178-181
New Hebrides 112-115
Pitcairn Islands 56-59
St. Helena 184-187
St. Kitts-Nevis 167-170
St. Lucia 201-204
St. Vincent 241-244
Seychelles 222-225
Solomon Islands 145-148
South Arabia 19-22
Swaziland 119-122
Tristan da Cunha 89-92
Turks & Caicos Islands 146-149
Virgin Islands 163-166
132 stamps

Royal Visit Issue, 1966

Queen Elizabeth II and Prince Philip CD320

Caribbean visit, Feb. 4 - Mar. 6, 1966.

1966
Antigua 161-162
Bahamas 228-229
Barbados 285-286
British Guiana................299-300
Cayman Islands 180-181
Dominica 193-194
Grenada 213-214
Montserrat 182-183
St. Kitts-Nevis 171-172
St. Lucia 205-206
St. Vincent 245-246
Turks & Caicos Islands 150-151
Virgin Islands................167-168
26 stamps

World Cup Soccer Issue

Soccer Player and Jules Rimet Cup CD321

World Cup Soccer Championship, Wembley, England, July 11-30.

1966
Antigua 163-164
Ascension 100-101
Bahamas 245-246
Bermuda 205-206
Brunei 124-125
Cayman Islands 182-183
Dominica 195-196
Fiji 219-220
Gibraltar 175-176
Gilbert & Ellice Islands 125-126
Grenada 230-231
New Hebrides 116-117
Pitcairn Islands 60-61
St. Helena 188-189
St. Kitts-Nevis 173-174
St. Lucia 207-208
Seychelles 226-227
Solomon Islands 167-168
South Arabia...................23-24
Tristan da Cunha 93-94
40 stamps

WHO Headquarters Issue

World Health Organization Headquarters, Geneva – CD322

1966
Antigua 165-166
Ascension 102-103
Bahamas 247-248
Brunei 126-127
Cayman Islands 184-185
Dominica 197-198
Fiji 224-225
Gibraltar 180-181
Gilbert & Ellice Islands 127-128
Grenada 232-233
Hong Kong 229-230
Montserrat 184-185
New Hebrides 118-119
Pitcairn Islands 62-63
St. Helena 190-191
St. Kitts-Nevis 177-178
St. Lucia 209-210
St. Vincent 247-248
Seychelles 228-229
Solomon Islands 169-170
South Arabia 25-26
Tristan da Cunha 99-100
44 stamps

UNESCO Anniversary Issue

"Education" – CD323

"Science" (Wheat ears & flask enclosing globe). "Culture" (lyre & columns).
20th anniversary of the UNESCO.

1966-67
Antigua 183-185
Ascension 108-110
Bahamas 249-251
Barbados 287-289
Bermuda 207-209
Brunei 128-130
Cayman Islands 186-188
Dominica 199-201
Gibraltar 183-185
Gilbert & Ellice Islands 129-131
Grenada 234-236
Hong Kong 231-233
Mauritius 299-301
Montserrat 186-188
New Hebrides 120-122
Pitcairn Islands 64-66
St. Helena 192-194
St. Kitts-Nevis 179-181
St. Lucia 211-213
St. Vincent 249-251
Seychelles 230-232
Solomon Islands 171-173
South Arabia 27-29
Swaziland 123-125
Tristan da Cunha 101-103
Turks & Caicos Islands 155-157
Virgin Islands 176-178
81 stamps

Silver Wedding Issue, 1972

Queen Elizabeth II and Prince Philip CD324

Designs: borders differ for each country.

1972
Anguilla 161-162
Antigua 295-296
Ascension 164-165
Bahamas 344-345
Bermuda 296-297
British Antarctic Territory 43-44
British Honduras............306-307
British Indian Ocean Territory............48-49
Brunei 186-187
Cayman Islands 304-305
Dominica 352-353
Falkland Islands 223-224

Fiji 328-329
Gibraltar 292-293
Gilbert & Ellice Islands 206-207
Grenada 466-467
Hong Kong 271-272
Montserrat 286-287
New Hebrides 169-170
Pitcairn Islands 127-128
St. Helena 271-272
St. Kitts-Nevis 257-258
St. Lucia 328-329
St.Vincent 344-345
Seychelles 309-310
Solomon Islands 248-249
South Georgia 35-36
Tristan da Cunha 178-179
Turks & Caicos Islands 257-258
Virgin Islands 241-242
60 stamps

Princess Anne's Wedding Issue

Princess Anne and Mark Phillips CD325

Wedding of Princess Anne and Mark Phillips, Nov. 14, 1973.

1973
Anguilla 179-180
Ascension 177-178
Belize 325-326
Bermuda 302-303
British Antarctic Territory 60-61
Cayman Islands 320-321
Falkland Islands 225-226
Gibraltar 305-306
Gilbert & Ellice Islands 216-217
Hong Kong 289-290
Montserrat 300-301
Pitcairn Island 135-136
St. Helena 277-278
St. Kitts-Nevis 274-275
St. Lucia 349-350
St. Vincent 358-359
St. Vincent Grenadines 1-2
Seychelles 311-312
Solomon Islands 259-260
South Georgia 37-38
Tristan da Cunha 189-190
Turks & Caicos Islands 286-287
Virgin Islands 260-261
44 stamps

Elizabeth II Coronation Anniversary Issue

CD326   CD327

CD328

Designs: Royal and local beasts in heraldic form and simulated stonework. Portrait of Elizabeth II by Peter Grugeon.

25th anniversary of coronation of Queen Elizabeth II.

1978
Ascension 229
Barbados 474
Belize 397
British Antarctic Territory 71
Cayman Islands 404
Christmas Island 87
Falkland Islands 275
Fiji 384
Gambia 380
Gilbert Islands 312
Mauritius 464
New Hebrides 258
St. Helena 317
St. Kitts-Nevis 354
Samoa 472
Solomon Islands 368
South Georgia 51
Swaziland 302
Tristan da Cunha 238
Virgin Islands 337
20 sheets

Queen Mother Elizabeth's 80th Birthday

CD330

Designs: Photographs of Queen Mother Elizabeth. Falkland Islands issued in sheets of 50; others in sheets of 9.

1980
Ascension 261
Bermuda 401
Cayman Islands 443
Falkland Islands 305
Gambia 412
Gibraltar 393
Hong Kong 364
Pitcairn Islands 193
St. Helena 341
Samoa 532
Solomon Islands 426
Tristan da Cunha 277
12 stamps

Royal Wedding Issue, 1981

Prince Charles and Lady Diana CD331

Wedding of Charles, Prince of Wales, and Lady Diana Spencer, St. Paul's Cathedral, London, July 29, 1981.

1981
Antigua 623-625
Ascension 294-296
Barbados 547-549
Barbuda 497-499
Bermuda 412-414
Brunei 268-270
Cayman Islands 471-473
Dominica 701-703
Falkland Islands 324-326
Falkland Islands Dep. 1L59-1L61
Fiji 442-444
Gambia 426-428
Ghana 759-761
Grenada 1051-1053
Grenada Grenadines 440-443
Hong Kong 373-375
Jamaica 500-503
Lesotho 335-337
Maldive Islands 906-908
Mauritius 520-522
Norfolk Island 280-282
Pitcairn Islands 206-208
St. Helena 353-355
St. Lucia 543-546
Samoa 558-560
Sierra Leone 509-517
Solomon Islands 450-452
Swaziland 382-384

Tristan da Cunha 294-296
Turks & Caicos Islands 486-488
Caicos Island 8-10
Uganda 314-316
Vanuatu 308-310
Virgin Islands 406-408

Princess Diana

CD332   CD333

Designs: Photographs and portrait of Princess Diana, wedding or honeymoon photographs, royal residences, arms of issuing country. Portrait photograph by Clive Friend. Souvenir sheet margins show family tree, various people related to the princess. 21st birthday of Princess Diana of Wales, July 1.

1982
Antigua 663-666
Ascension 313-316
Bahamas 510-513
Barbados 585-588
Barbuda 544-546
British Antarctic Territory 92-95
Cayman Islands 486-489
Dominica 773-776
Falkland Islands 348-351
Falkland Islands Dep. 1L72-1L75
Fiji 470-473
Gambia 447-450
Grenada 1101A-1105
Grenada Grenadines 485-491
Lesotho 372-375
Maldive Islands 952-955
Mauritius 548-551
Pitcairn Islands 213-216
St. Helena 372-375
St. Lucia 591-594
Sierra Leone 531-534
Solomon Islands 471-474
Swaziland 406-409
Tristan da Cunha 310-313
Turks and Caicos Islands 530A-534
Virgin Islands 430-433

250th anniv. of first edition of Lloyd's List (shipping news publication) and of Lloyd's marine insurance.

CD335

Designs: First page of early edition of the list; historical ships, modern transportation or harbor scenes.

1984
Ascension 351-354
Bahamas 555-558
Barbados 627-630
Cayes of Belize 10-13
Cayman Islands 522-525
Falkland Islands 404-407
Fiji 509-512
Gambia 519-522
Mauritius 587-590
Nauru 280-283
St. Helena 412-415
Samoa 624-627
Seychelles 538-541
Solomon Islands 521-524
Vanuatu 368-371
Virgin Islands 466-469

Queen Mother 85th Birthday

CD336

Designs: Photographs tracing the life of the Queen Mother, Elizabeth. The high value in each set pictures the same photograph taken of the Queen Mother holding the infant Prince Henry.

1985
Ascension 372-376
Bahamas 580-584
Barbados 660-664
Bermuda 469-473
Falkland Islands 420-424
Falkland Islands Dep. 1L92-1L96
Fiji 531-535
Hong Kong 447-450
Jamaica 599-603
Mauritius 604-608
Norfolk Island 364-368
Pitcairn Islands 253-257
St. Helena 428-432
Samoa 649-653
Seychelles 567-571
Solomon Islands 543-547
Swaziland 476-480
Tristan da Cunha 372-376
Vanuatu 392-396
Zil Elwannyen Sesel 101-105

Queen Elizabeth II, 60th Birthday

CD337

1986, April 21
Ascension 389-393
Bahamas 592-596
Barbados 675-679
Bermuda 499-503
Cayman Islands 555-559
Falkland Islands 441-445
Fiji 544-548
Hong Kong 465-469
Jamaica 620-624
Kiribati 470-474
Mauritius 629-633
Papua New Guinea 640-644
Pitcairn Islands 270-274
St. Helena 451-455
Samoa 670-674
Seychelles 592-596
Solomon Islands 562-566
South Georgia 101-105
Swaziland 490-494
Tristan da Cunha 388-392
Vanuatu 414-418
Zambia 343-347
Zil Elwannyen Sesel 114-118

Royal Wedding

Marriage of Prince Andrew and Sarah Ferguson
CD338

1986, July 23
Ascension 399-400
Bahamas 602-603
Barbados 687-688
Cayman Islands 560-561
Jamaica 629-630
Pitcairn Islands 275-276
St. Helena 460-461
St. Kitts 181-182
Seychelles 602-603

Solomon Islands 567-568
Tristan da Cunha 397-398
Zambia 348-349
Zil Elwannyen Sesel 119-120

Queen Elizabeth II, 60th Birthday

Queen Elizabeth II Inspecting Guard, 1946
CD339

Designs: Photographs tracing the life of Queen Elizabeth II.

1986
Anguilla 674-677
Antigua 925-928
Barbuda 783-786
Dominica 950-953
Gambia 611-614
Grenada 1371-1374
Grenada Grenadines 749-752
Lesotho 531-534
Maldive Islands 1172-1175
Sierra Leone 760-763
Uganda 495-498

Royal Wedding Issue, 1986

CD340

Designs: Photographs of Prince Andrew and Sarah Ferguson during courtship, engagement and marriage.

1986
Antigua 939-942
Barbuda 809-812
Dominica 970-973
Gambia 635-638
Grenada 1385-1388
Grenada Grenadines 758-761
Lesotho 545-548
Maldive Islands 1181-1184
Sierra Leone 769-772
Uganda 510-513

Lloyds of London, 300th Anniv.

CD341

Designs: 17th century aspects of Lloyds, representations of each country's individual connections with Lloyds and publicized disasters insured by the organization.

1986
Ascension 454-457
Bahamas 655-658
Barbados 731-734
Bermuda 541-544
Falkland Islands 481-484
Liberia 1101-1104
Malawi 534-537
Nevis 571-574
St. Helena 501-504
St. Lucia 923-926
Seychelles 649-652
Solomon Islands 627-630
South Georgia 131-134
Trinidad & Tobago 484-487

Tristan da Cunha 439-442
Vanuatu 485-488
Zil Elwannyen Sesel 146-149

Moon Landing, 20th Anniv.

CD342

Designs: Equipment, crew photographs, spacecraft, official emblems and report profiles created for the Apollo Missions. Two stamps in each set are square in format rather than like the stamp shown; see individual country listings for more information.

1989
Ascension Is...................................468-472
Bahamas 674-678
Belize 916-920
Kiribati 517-521
Liberia 1125-1129
Nevis 586-590
St. Kitts 248-252
Samoa 760-764
Seychelles 676-680
Solomon Islands 643-647
Vanuatu 507-511
Zil Elwannyen Sesel 154-158

Queen Mother, 90th Birthday

CD343   CD344

Designs: Portraits of Queen Elizabeth, the Queen Mother. See individual country listings for more information.

1990
Ascension Is...................................491-492
Bahamas 698-699
Barbados 782-783
British Antarctic Territory 170-171
British Indian Ocean Territory 106-107
Cayman Islands 622-623
Falkland Islands 524-525
Kenya 527-528
Kiribati 555-556
Liberia 1145-1146
Pitcairn Islands 336-337
St. Helena 532-533
St. Lucia 969-970
Seychelles 710-711
Solomon Islands 671-672
South Georgia 143-144
Swaziland 565-566
Tristan da Cunha 480-481
Zil Elwannyen Sesel 171-172

Queen Elizabeth II, 65th Birthday, and Prince Philip, 70th Birthday

CD345   CD346

Designs: Portraits of Queen Elizabeth II and Prince Philip differ for each country. Printed in sheets of 10 + 5 labels (3 different) between. Stamps alternate, producing 5 different triptychs.

1991

Ascension Is........................505-506
Bahamas............................730-731
Belize................................969-970
Bermuda.............................617-618
Kiribati..............................571-572
Mauritius...........................733-734
Pitcairn Islands..................348-349
St. Helena..........................554-555
St. Kitts............................318-319
Samoa................................790-791
Seychelles..........................723-724
Solomon Islands..................688-689
South Georgia.....................149-150
Swaziland...........................586-587
Vanuatu..............................540-541
Zil Elwannyen Sesel...........177-178

Royal Family Birthday, Anniversary

CD347

Queen Elizabeth II, 65th birthday, Charles and Diana, 10th wedding anniversary: Various photographs of Queen Elizabeth II, Prince Philip, Prince Charles, Princess Diana and their sons William and Henry.

1991

Antigua 1446-1455
Barbuda...........................1229-1238
Dominica..........................1328-1337
Gambia............................1080-1089
Grenada...........................2006-2015
Grenada Grenadines 1331-1340
Guyana.............................2440-2451
Lesotho...............................871-875
Maldive Islands..............1533-1542
Nevis.................................666-675
St. Vincent.......................1485-1494
St. Vincent Grenadines 769-778
Sierra Leone....................1387-1396
Turks & Caicos Islands 913-922
Uganda.............................918-927

Queen Elizabeth II's Accession to the Throne 40th Anniversary

CD348

CD349

Various photographs of Queen Elizabeth II with local Scenes.

1992 - CD348

Antigua 1513-1518
Barbuda...........................1306-1309
Dominica..........................1414-1419
Gambia............................1172-1177
Grenada...........................2047-2052
Grenada Grenadines 1368-1373
Lesotho...............................881-885
Maldive Islands..............1637-1642
Nevis.................................702-707
St. Vincent.......................1582-1587
St. Vincent Grenadines 829-834
Sierra Leone....................1482-1487

Turks and Caicos Islands................978-987
Uganda.............................990-995
Virgin Islands....................742-746

1992 - CD349

Ascension Islands.............531-535
Bahamas............................744-748
Bermuda.............................623-627
British Indian Ocean Territory.......119-123
Cayman Islands..................648-652
Falkland Islands................549-553
Gibraltar............................605-609
Hong Kong.........................619-623
Kenya................................563-567
Kiribati..............................582-586
Pitcairn Islands..................362-366
St. Helena..........................570-574
St. Kitts............................332-336
Samoa................................805-809
Seychelles..........................734-738
Soloman Islands.................708-712
South Georgia.....................157-161
Tristan da Cunha................508-512
Vanuatu..............................555-559
Zambia...............................561-565
Zil Elwannyen Sesel...........183-187

Royal Air Force, 75th Anniversary

CD350

1993

Ascension 557-561
Bahamas............................771-775
Barbados...........................842-846
Belize.............................1003-1008
Bermuda.............................648-651
British Indian Ocean Territory.........136-140
Falkland Is........................573-577
Fiji...................................687-691
Montserrat 830-834
St. Kitts............................351-355

End of World War II, 50th Anniv.

CD351

CD352

1995

Ascension 613-617
Bahamas............................824-828
Barbados...........................891-895
Belize.............................1047-1050
British Indian Ocean Territory 163-167
Cayman Islands 704-708
Falkland Islands 634-638
Fiji...................................720-724
Kiribati..............................662-668
Liberia 1175-1179
Mauritius...........................803-805
St. Helena..........................646-654

St. Kitts 389-393
St. Lucia 1018-1022
Samoa................................890-894
Solomon Islands 799-803
South Georgia & S. Sandwich Is. 198-200
Tristan da Cunha 562-566

UN, 50th Anniv.

CD353

1995

Bahamas 839-842
Barbados 901-904
Belize 1055-1058
Jamaica 847-851
Liberia 1187-1190
Mauritius 813-816
Pitcairn Islands 436-439
St. Kitts 398-401
St. Lucia 1023-1026
Samoa 900-903
Tristan da Cunha 568-571
Virgin Islands 807-810

Queen Elizabeth, 70th Birthday

CD354

1996

Ascension 632-635
British Antarctic Territory 240-243
British Indian Ocean Territory 176-180
Falkland Islands 653-657
Pitcairn Islands 446-449
St. Helena 672-676
Samoa 912-916
Tokelau 223-227
Tristan da Cunha 576-579
Virgin Islands 824-828

UNITED STATES

yù-,nī-təd 'stāts

GOVT. — Republic
AREA — 3,615,211 sq. mi.
POP. — 226,545,805 (1980)
CAPITAL — Washington, DC

In addition to the 50 States and the District of Columbia, the Republic includes Guam, the Commonwealth of Puerto Rico, the Virgin Islands, American Samoa, Wake, Midway, and a number of small islands in the Pacific Ocean, all of which use stamps of the United States.

100 Cents = 1 Dollar

Catalogue values for unused stamps in this country are for Never Hinged items, beginning with Scott 772 in the regular postage section, Scott C19 in the air post section, Scott E17 in the special delivery section, Scott FA1 in the certified mail section, Scott O127 in officials section, Scott J88 in the postage due section, Scott R733 in the revenues section, Scott RW1 in the hunting permit stamps section.

Watermarks

Wmk. 190- "USPS" in Single-lined Capitals

Wmk. 191- Double-lined "USPS" in Capitals

Wmk. 190PI - PIPS, used in the Philippines
Wmk. 191PI - PIPS, used in the Philippines
Wmk. 191C - US-C, used for Cuba
Wmk. 191R - USIR

PROVISIONAL ISSUES BY POSTMASTERS

Values for Envelopes are for entires.
Alexandria, Va.

A1

Type I - 40 asterisks in circle.
Type II - 39 asterisks in circle.

1846	Typeset		*Imperf.*
1X1	A1	5c black, *buff*, Type I	
a.		5c black, *buff*, Type II	75,000.
1X2	A1	5c black, *blue*, Type I, on cover	—

All known copies of Nos. 1X1-1X2 are cut to shape.

Annapolis, Md.

ENVELOPE

E1

1846
2XU1 E1 5c carmine red 210,000.

Handstamped impressions of the circular design with "2" in blue or red exist on envelopes and letter sheets. Values: blue $2,500, red $3,500.
A letter sheet exists with circular design and "5" handstamped in red. Values: blue $3,500, red $5,000.
A similar circular design in blue was used as a postmark.

Baltimore, Md.

Signature of Postmaster — A1

1845	Engr.		*Imperf.*
3X1	A1	5c black	5,000.
3X2	A1	10c black, on cover	50,000.
3X3	A1	5c black, *bluish*	65,000. 5,000.
3X4	A1	10c black, *bluish*	60,000.

Nos. 3X1-3X4 were printed from a plate of 12 (2x6) containing nine 5c and three 10c.

ENVELOPES

E1

The color given is that of the "PAID 5" and oval. "James M. Buchanan" is handstamped in black, blue or red. The paper is manila, buff, white, salmon or grayish.

1845	Handstamped	
	Various Papers	
3XU1	E1 5c blue	6,000.
3XU2	E1 5c red	10,000.
3XU3	E1 10c blue	17,500.
3XU4	E1 10c red	20,000.

On the formerly listed "5+5" envelopes, the second "5" in oval is believed not to be part of the basic prepaid marking.

Boscawen, N. H.

PAID 5 CENTS A1

1846(?)	Typeset	*Imperf.*
4X1 A1 5c dull blue, *yellowish*, on cover		175,000.

Brattleboro, Vt.

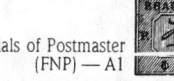

Initials of Postmaster (FNP) — A1

Plate of 10 (5x2).

1846	Engr.	*Imperf.*
5X1 A1 5c black, *buff*		8,500.

Lockport, N. Y.

A1

Handstamped, "5" in Black Ms

1846
6X1 A1 5c red, *buff*, on cover 150,000.

Millbury, Mass.

George Washington — A1

Printed from a Woodcut

1846		*Imperf.*
7X1 A1 5c blue, *bluish*		130,000. 20,000.

New Haven, Conn.

ENVELOPES

E1

1845	Handstamped
Signed in Blue, Black, Magenta or Red	
8XU1 E1 5c red (Bl or M)	75,000.
8XU2 E1 5c red, *light bluish* (Bk)	100,000.
8XU3 E1 5c dull blue, *buff* (Bl)	100,000.
8XU4 E1 5c dull blue (Bl)	100,000.

Values of Nos. 8XU1-8XU4 are a guide to value. They are based on auction realizations and retail sales and take condition into consideration. All New Haven envelopes are of almost equal rarity. An entire of No. 8XU2 is the finest example known. The other envelopes are valued according to condition as much as rarity.

Reprints were made at various times between 1871 and 1932. They differ in shade and paper from the originals.

New York, N. Y.

George Washington — A1

Plate of 40 (5x8). Nos. 9X1-9X3 and varieties unused are valued without gum. Examples with original gum are extremely scarce and will command higher prices.

1845	Engr.		*Imperf.*
	Bluish Wove Paper		
9X1	A1 5c blk, signed ACM, connected	1,300.	500.
a.	Signed ACM, AC connected	1,600.	600.
b.	Signed A.C.M.	3,750.	700.
c.	Signed MMJr		9,000.
d.	Signed RHM	13,000.	3,250.
e.	Without signature	3,250.	750.

These stamps were usually initialed "ACM" in magenta ink, as a control, before being sold or passed through the mails.
A plate of 9 (3x3) was made from which proofs were printed in black on white and deep blue papers; also in blue, green, brown and red on white bond paper.

1847	Engr.		*Imperf.*
	Blue Wove Paper		
9X2	A1 5c blk, signed ACM, connected	6,500.	3,250.
a.	Signed RHM	11,000.	6,500.
d.	Without signature		

On the listing example of No. 9X2a the "R" is illegible and does not match those of the other "RHM" signatures.

1847	Engr.		*Imperf.*
	Gray Wove Paper		
9X3	A1 5c blk, signed ACM, connected	5,250.	1,900.
a.	Signed RHM		6,000.
b.	Without signature		6,500.

Providence, R.I.

A1 A2

1846	Engr.		*Imperf.*
10X1	A1 5c gray black	425.	1,750.
10X2	A2 10c gray black	1,300.	15,000.
a.	Se-tenant with 5c	2,350.	

Plate of 12 (3x4) contains 11-5c and 1-10c.
Reprints were made in 1898. Each stamp bears one of the following letters on the back: B. O. G. E. R. T. D. U. R. B. I. N. Value of 5c, $50; 10c, $125; sheet, $725.
Reprint singles or sheets without back print sell for more.

St. Louis, Mo.

Missouri Coat of Arms
A1   A2   A3

Unused are valued without gum.

1845-46	Engr.		*Imperf.*
	Greenish Wove Paper		
11X1	A1 5c black	5,000.	2,750.
11X2	A2 10c black	4,500.	2,500.
11X3	A3 20c black		20,000.

Three varieties of 5c, 3 of 10c, 2 of 20c.

1846			
	Gray Lilac Paper		
11X4	A1 5c black	—	4,250.
11X5	A2 10c black	4,500.	2,200.
11X6	A3 20c black		13,500.

One variety of 5c, 3 of 10c, 2 of 20c.

1847			
	Pelure Paper		
11X7	A1 5c black *bluish*	—	6,250.
11X8	A2 10c black, *bluish*		6,250.
a.	Impression of 5c on back		

Three varieties of 5c, 3 of 10c.
Used values are for pencanceled copies.

Tuscumbia, Ala.

ENVELOPE

E1

1861 Handstamped
12XU1 E1 3c dull red, *buff* 16,000.

See Confederate States Nos. 84XU1-84XU6.

GENERAL ISSUES
All Issues from 1847 to 1894 are Unwatermarked.

Benjamin Franklin
A1

George Washington
A2

1847, July 1		**Engr.**			***Imperf.***
1	A1	5c red brown, *bluish*		5,000.	600.
		No gum		2,750.	
a.		5c dark brown, *bluish*		5,000.	625.
		No gum		2,900.	
b.		5c orange brown, *bluish*		6,250.	700.
		No gum		3,500.	
c.		5c red orange, *bluish*		12,500.	5,000.
		No gum		8,000.	
d.		Double impression			
		Pen cancel			300.

The only known double impression shows part of the design doubled.

2	A2	10c black, *bluish*		26,000.	1,400.
		No gum		16,500.	
a.		Diagonal half used as 5c on cover			13,000.
b.		Vertical half used as 5c on cover			35,000.
c.		Horizontal half used as 5c on cover			—
		Pen cancel			625.

REPRODUCTIONS

Actually, official imitations made from new plates by order of the Post Office Department.

A3

A4

1875				***Imperf.***
Bluish Paper Without Gum				
3	A3	5c red brown		800.
4	A4	10c black		1,000.

Reproductions. The letters R. W. H. & E. at the bottom of each stamp are less distinct on the reproductions than on the originals.

5c. On the originals the left side of the white shirt frill touches the oval on a level with the top of the "F" of "Five." On the reproductions it touches the oval about on a level with the top of the figure "5."

10c. On the reproductions, line of coat at left points to right tip of "X" and line of coat at right points to center of "S" of CENTS. On the originals, line of coat points to "T" of TEN and between "T" and "S" of CENTS. On the reproductions the eyes have a sleepy look, the line of the mouth is straighter, and in the curl of hair near the left cheek is a strong black dot, while the originals have only a faint one.

VALUES FOR VERY FINE STAMPS

Stamps are valued in the grade of very fine unless otherwise indicated.

Values for unused stamps with no gum are for examples with certificates of authenticity or examples sold with the buyer having the right of certification. Beware of unused, no gum stamps that are offered "as is." Expertization by competent authorities is recommended.

Franklin — A5

ONE CENT

Type I. Has complete curved lines outside the labels with "U.S. Postage" and "One Cent." The scrolls below the lower label are turned under, forming little balls. The ornaments at top are substantially complete.

Values for type I are for stamps showing the marked characteristics plainly. Copies of type I showing the balls indistinctly sell for much lower prices.

Type Ib. Same as I but balls below the bottom label are not so clear. The plumelike scrolls at bottom are not complete.

A6

Type Ia. Same as I at bottom but top ornaments and outer line at top are partly cut away.

Type Ic. Same as Ia, but bottom right plume and ball ornament incomplete. Bottom left plume complete or nearly complete.

A7

Type II. The little balls of the bottom scrolls and the bottoms of the lower plume ornaments are missing. The side ornaments are complete.

A8

Type III. The top and bottom curved lines outside the labels are broken in the middle. The side ornaments are complete.

Type IIIa. Similar to type III with the outer line broken at top or bottom but not both.

A9

Type IV. Similar to type II, but with the curved lines outside the labels recut at top or bottom or both.

Washington — A10

THREE CENTS
Type I. There is an outer frame line on all four sides.

Thomas Jefferson — A11

FIVE CENTS
Type I. There are projections on all four sides.

Washington — A12

TEN CENTS
Type I. The "shells" at the lower corners are practically complete. The outer line below the label is very nearly complete. The outer lines are broken above the middle of the top label and the "X" in each upper corner.

A13

Type II. The design is complete at the top. The outer line at the bottom is broken in the middle. The shells are partly cut away.

A14

Type III. The outer lines are broken above the top label and the "X" numerals. The outer line at the bottom and the shells are partly cut away, similar to Type II.

A15

Washington — A10

Type IV. The outer lines have been recut at top or bottom or both.

Types I, II, III and IV have complete ornaments at the sides of the stamps and three pearls at each outer edge of the bottom panel.

Washington — A16

In Nos. 5-17, the 1c, 3c, and 12c have very small margins between the stamps. The 5c and 10c have moderate size margins. The values of these stamps take the margin size into consideration.

Values for No. 5A, 6b and 19b are for the less distinct positions. Best examples sell for more.

Values for No. 16 are for outer line recut at top. Other recuts sell for more.

1851-57					***Imperf.***
5	A5	1c blue, I		175,000.	30,000.

Values for No. 5 are for copies with margins touching or slightly cutting into the design. Value unused is for an example with no gum.

5A	A5	1c blue, Ib		11,500.	4,500.
		No gum		6,500.	
6	A6	1c blue, Ia ('57)		30,000.	8,000.
		No gum		20,000.	
b.		Type Ic		6,000.	1,300.
		No gum		4,000.	
7	A7	1c blue, II		950.	150.
		No gum		500.	
8	A8	1c blue, III		9,000.	2,250.
		No gum		5,750.	

Values for type III are for at least a 2mm break in each outer line. Examples of type III with wide breaks in outer lines command higher prices; those with small breaks sell for less.

8A	A8	1c blue, IIIa		4,000.	900.
		No gum		2,250.	

Stamps of type IIIa with bottom line broken command higher prices than those with top line broken. See note after No. 8 on width of break of outer lines.

9	A9	1c blue, IV ('52)		650.	125.
		No gum		400.	
a.		Printed on both sides, reverse inverted			—
10	A10	3c org brown, I		2,500.	85.
		No gum		1,500.	
a.		Printed on both sides			—
11	A10	3c dull red, I		225.	10.
		No gum		100.	
c.		Vertical half used as 1c on cover			5,000.
d.		Diagonal half used as 1c on cover			5,000.
e.		Double impression			5,000.
12	A11	5c red brown, I ('56)		15,000.	1,100.
		No gum		9,500.	
13	A12	10c green, I ('55)		13,000.	775.
		No gum		7,750.	
14	A13	10c green, II ('55)		3,000.	225.
		No gum		1,750.	
15	A14	10c green, III ('55)		3,000.	225.
		No gum		1,750.	
16	A15	10c green, IV ('55)		18,000.	1,500.
		No gum		12,500.	
17	A16	12c black		4,000.	325.
		No gum		2,500.	
a.		Diagonal half used as 6c on cover			2,500.
b.		Vertical half used as 6c on cover			8,500.
c.		Printed on both sides			10,000.

Same Designs as 1851-56 Issues

Franklin — A20

ONE CENT

Type V. Similar to type III of 1851-57 but with side ornaments partly cut away.

Washington — A21

THREE CENTS
Type II. The outer frame line has been removed at top and bottom. The side frame lines were recut so as to be continuous from the top to the bottom of the plate. Stamps from the top or bottom rows show the ends of the side frame lines and may be mistaken for type IIa.
Type IIa. The side frame lines extend only to the top and bottom of the stamp design.

Jefferson — A22

FIVE CENTS
Type II. The projections at top and bottom are partly cut away.

Washington
(Two typical
examples) — A23

TEN CENTS
Type V. The side ornaments are slightly cut away. Usually only one pearl remains at each end of the lower label but some copies show two or three pearls at the right side. At the bottom the outer line is complete and the shells nearly so. The outer lines at top are complete except over the right "X."

Washington
A17

Franklin
A18

Washington — A19

TWELVE CENTS
Plate I. Outer frame lines complete.
Plate III. Outer frame lines noticeably uneven or broken, sometimes partly missing.

Nos. 18-39 have small or very small margins. The values take into account the margin size.

1857-61			Perf. 15½	
18	A5	1c blue, type I ('61)	1,300.	475.
		No gum	850.	
19	A6	1c blue, type Ia	15,000.	4,000.
		No gum	10,000.	
	b.	Type Ic	2,500.	1,000.
		No gum	1,750.	
20	A7	1c blue, type II	850.	225.
		No gum	525.	
21	A8	1c blue, type III	8,500.	1,600.
		No gum	4,750.	

22	A8	1c blue, type IIIa	1,500.	400.
		No gum	950.	
	b.	Horiz. pair, imperf. btwn.		5,000.

One pair of No. 22b has been reported. Beware of pairs with blind perforations.

23	A9	1c blue, type IV	5,000.	525.
		No gum	3,100.	
24	A20	1c blue, type V	175.	40.
		No gum	90.	
	b.	Laid paper	—	
25	A10	3c rose, type I	1,800.	70.
		No gum	1,100.	
	b.	Vert. pair, imperf. horiz.		10,000.
26	A21	3c dull red, type II	75.	5.
		No gum	30.	
	a.	3c dull red, type IIa	200.	45.
		No gum	110.	
	b.	Horiz. pair, imperf. vert., type	4,000.	—
	c.	Vert. pair, imperf. horiz., type II		—
	d.	Horizontal pair, imperf. between, type II		—
	e.	Dbl. impression, type II	2,500.	
	f.	Horiz. strip of 3, imperf. vert., type IIa, on cover		8,250.
27	A11	5c brick red, type I ('58)	14,000.	950.
		No gum	8,000.	
28	A11	5c red brown, type I	2,750.	425.
		No gum	1,600.	
	b.	5c bright red brown	3,000.	600.
		No gum	1,800.	
28A	A11	5c Indian red, type I ('58)	19,000.	2,500.
		No gum	13,000.	
29	A11	5c brown, type I ('59)	1,750.	300.
		No gum	1,000.	
30	A22	5c org brown, type II ('61)	1,100.	1,100.
		No gum	675.	
30A	A22	5c brown, type II ('60)	1,500.	260.
		No gum	900.	
	b.	Printed on both sides	4,000.	4,250.
31	A12	10c green, type I	12,000.	700.
		No gum	7,500.	
32	A13	10c green, type II	3,750.	275.
		No gum	2,500.	
33	A14	10c green, type III	3,750.	275.
		No gum	2,500.	
34	A15	10c green, type IV	25,000.	2,000.
		No gum	16,000.	
35	A23	10c green, type V ('59)	275.	65.
		No gum	150.	
36	A16	12c black, plate I	1,100.	180.
		No gum	700.	
	a.	Diagonal half used as 6c on cover (I)		17,500.
	b.	12c black, plate III ('59)	675.	160.
		No gum	400.	
	c.	Horizontal pair, imperf. between (I)		12,500.
37	A17	24c gray lilac ('60)	1,200.	300.
	a.	24c gray	1,200.	300.
		No gum	650.	
38	A18	30c orange ('60)	1,500.	400.
		No gum	850.	
39	A19	90c blue ('60)	2,400.	5,500.
		No gum	1,450.	
		Pen cancel		1,250.

See Die and Plate proofs in the Scott United States Specialized Catalogue for imperfs. of the 12c, 24c, 30c, 90c.
Genuine cancellations on the 90c are rare.

REPRINTS OF 1857-60 ISSUE
White Paper
Without Gum

1875			Perf. 12
40	A5	1c bright blue	525.
41	A10	3c scarlet	2,200.
42	A22	5c orange brown	950.
43	A12	10c blue green	1,900.
44	A16	12c greenish blk	2,250.
45	A17	24c black violet	2,250.
46	A18	30c yellow orange	2,250.
47	A19	90c deep blue	3,500.
		Nos. 40-47 (8)	15,825.

Nos. 41-46 are valued in the grade of fine. Nos. 40-47 exist imperf., value, set $25,000.

Essays - Trial Color Proofs
The paper of former Nos. 55-62 (Nos. 63E11e, 65-E15h, 67-E9e, 69-E6e, 72-E7h, Essay section, Nos. 70eTC, 71bTC, Trial Color Proof section, Scott U.S. Specialized) is thin and semitransparent. That of the postage issues is thicker and more opaque, except Nos. 62B, 70c and 70d.

Franklin — A24

1c - There is a dash under the tip of the ornament at right of the numeral in upper left corner. There is no dash on the essay.

Washington — A25

3c - Ornaments at corners are large and end in a small ball. The ornaments are smaller and there is no ball on the essay.

Jefferson — A26

5c - Leaflets appear at each corner. These do not appear on the essay.

Washington — A27

A27a

A27

10c - On A27 a heavy curved line appears below the stars and an outer line above them which does not appear on A27a.

Washington — A28

12c - Ovals and scrolls appear at each corners. These do not appear on the essay.

Washington
A29

Franklin
A30

Washington — A31

90c. Two pairs of parallel lines form an angle above the ribbon with "U. S. Postage"; between these lines is a row of dashes, and there is a point of color to the apex of the lower pair. These do not appear on the essay.

1861   *Perf. 12*

62B	A27a	10c dark green	*5,500.*	675.
		No gum	*3,500.*	

1861-62   *Perf. 12*

63	A24	1c blue	240.00	25.00
		No gum	115.00	
a.		1c ultramarine	600.00	225.00
		No gum	350.00	
b.		1c dark blue	450.00	55.00
		No gum	260.00	
c.		Laid paper	—	—
d.		Vert. pair, imperf. horiz.	—	—
e.		Printed on both sides	—	2,500.
64	A25	3c pink	5,750.	650.00
		No gum	3,500.	
a.		3c pigeon blood pink	14,000.	3,100.
		No gum	8,500.	
b.		3c rose pink	450.00	110.00
		No gum	225.00	
65	A25	3c rose	125.00	2.50
		No gum	55.00	
b.		Laid paper	—	—
d.		Vert. pair, imperf. horiz.	3,500.	750.00
e.		Printed on both sides	2,000.	1,600.
f.		Double impression		6,000.

The 3c lake can be found under No. 66 in the Trial Color Proofs section of the Scott U.S. Specialized Catalogue. The imperf 3c lake under No. 66P in the same section. The imperf 3c rose can be found in the Die and Plate Proofs section of the Specialized.

67	A26	5c buff	13,000.	650.00
a.		5c brown yellow	13,000.	650.00
		No gum	8,250.	
b.		5c olive yellow	—	750.00

Values for Nos. 67, 67a, 67b reflect the normal small margins.

68	A27	10c yellow green	475.00	47.50
		No gum	240.00	
a.		10c dark green	500.00	50.00
		No gum	250.00	
b.		Vert. pair, imperf. horiz.		3,500.
69	A28	12c black	850.00	85.00
		No gum	525.00	
70	A29	24c red lilac ('62)	1,250.	125.00
		No gum	750.00	
a.		24c brown lilac	1,200.	115.00
		No gum	725.00	
b.		24c steel blue	6,500.	450.00
		No gum	4,250.	
c.		24c violet, thin paper	9,000.	850.00
		No gum	5,500.	
d.		24c pale gray violet, thin paper	2,250.	500.00
		No gum	1,400.	
71	A30	30c orange	975.00	120.00
		No gum	600.00	
a.		Printed on both sides		—

Values for No. 71 are for copies with small margins, especially at sides. Large margined examples sell for much more.

72	A31	90c blue	2,100.	350.00
a.		90c pale blue	2,100.	350.00
		No gum	1,300.	
b.		90c dark blue	2,300.	400.00
		No gum	1,425.	

Nos. 70c, 70d are on a thinner, harder and more transparent paper than Nos. 70, 70a, 70b, or the later Nos. 78, 78a, 78b and 78c.

Designs as 1861 Issue

Andrew
Jackson
A32

Abraham
Lincoln
A33

1861-66   *Perf. 12*

73	A32	2c black ('63)	300.00	45.00
		No gum	140.00	
a.		Vert. or diag. half used as 1c as part of 3c rate on cover		1,250.
b.		Diagonal half used alone as 1c on cover		3,000.
c.		Horiz. half used as 1c as part of 3c rate on cover		—
d.		Laid paper		—
e.		Printed on both sides		5,000.

The 3c scarlet can be found under No. 74 in the Scott U.S. Specialized Catalogue Trial Color Proofs section.

75	A26	5c red brown ('62)	3,500.	400.00
		No gum	2,000.	
76	A26	5c brown ('63)	800.00	95.00
		No gum	450.00	
a.		5c black brown	900.00	110.00
		No gum	500.00	
b.		Laid paper		—
77	A33	15c black ('66)	1,100.	120.00
		No gum	600.00	
78	A29	24c lilac ('63)	650.00	80.00
a.		24c grayish lilac	650.00	80.00
		No gum	650.00	
b.		24c gray	650.00	80.00
		No gum	400.00	
c.		24c blackish violet	21,000.	1,750.
		No gum	15,000.	
d.		Printed on both sides		3,500.

Values for Nos. 75, 76, 76a reflect the normal small margins.

Grill

Same as 1861-66 Issues
Embossed with grills of various sizes

Grill with Points Up

Grills A and C were made by a roller covered with ridges shaped like an inverted V. Pressing the ridges into the stamp paper forced the paper into the pyramidal pits between the ridges, causing irregular breaks in the paper.

Grill B was made by a roller with raised bosses.

A. Grill covering the entire stamp

1867   *Perf. 12*

79	A25	3c rose	3,750.	800.
		No gum	2,250.	
b.		Printed on both sides		—
80	A26	5c brown		—
a.		5c dark brown		50,000.
81	A30	30c orange		—

An essay which is often mistaken for No. 79 (#79-E15) shows the points of the grill as small squares faintly impressed in the paper, but not cutting through it. On No. 79 the grill breaks through the paper. Copies free from defects are rare.

Six copies of Nos. 80, 80a, and eight copies of No. 81 are known. All are more or less faulty and/or off-center. Values range from $15,000 to $50,000 depending on condition and appearance.

Nos. 79, 79b, are valued for fine · very fine centering but with minor perforation faults.

The imperf. of the 3c rose can be found in the Scott U.S. Specialized Catalogue Die and Plate Proofs section.

B. Grill about 18x15mm (22 by 18 points)

82	A25	3c rose		100,000.

The four known copies of No. 82 are fine.

C. Grill about 13x16mm (16 to 17 by 18 to 21 points)

83	A25	3c rose	4,000.	750.
		No gum	2,250.	

The grilled area on each of four C grills in the sheet may total about 18x15mm when a normal C grill adjoins a fainter grill extending to the right or left edge of the stamp. This is caused by a partial erasure on the grill roller when it was changed to produce C grills instead of the all-over A grill.

The imperf. can be found in the Scott U.S. Specialized Catalogue Die and Plate Proofs section.

Grill with Points Down

The grills were produced by rollers with the surface covered by pyramidal bosses. On the Z grill the tips of the pyramids are very short horizontal ridges. On the D, E and F grills the ridges are vertical.

D. Grill about 12x14mm (15 by 17 to 18 points)

84	A32	2c black	*12,000.*	2,000.
		No gum	*7,750.*	

No. 84 is valued in the grade of fine.

85	A25	3c rose	4,250.	750.
		No gum	2,500.	

Z. Grill about 11x14mm (13 to 14 by 17 to 18 points)

85A	A24	1c blue		—
85B	A32	2c black	4,750.	750.
		No gum	3,000.	
85C	A25	3c rose	7,750.	2,000.
		No gum	4,500.	
85D	A27	10c green		45,000.
85E	A28	12c black	6,750.	950.
		No gum	4,250.	
85F	A33	15c black		100,000.

Two copies of No. 85A are known. One is contained in the New York Public Library collection. Five copies of No. 85D and two copies of No. 85F are known.

E. Grill about 11x13mm (14 by 15 to 17 points)

86	A24	1c blue	1,900.	400.
		No gum	1,100.	
a.		1c dull blue	1,750.	375.
		No gum	1,000.	
87	A32	2c black	800.	100.
		No gum	475.	
a.		Half used as 1c on cover, diagonal or vert.		2,000.
88	A25	3c rose	575.	15.
		No gum	350.	
a.		3c lake red	625.	19.
		No gum	375.	
89	A27	10c green	2,750.	275.
		No gum	1,650.	
90	A28	12c black	3,000.	300.
		No gum	1,800.	
91	A33	15c black	6,000.	575.
		No gum	3,500.	

F. Grill about 9x13mm (11 to 12 by 15 to 17 points)

92	A24	1c blue	800.	150.00
a.		1c pale blue	800.	150.00
		No gum	475.	
93	A32	2c black	300.	35.00
		No gum	160.	
a.		Vert. or diag. half used as 1c as part of 3c rate on cover		1,250.
c.		Horiz. or diagonal half used alone as 1c on cover		2,500.
94	A25	3c red	260.	4.25
a.		3c rose	260.	4.25
		No gum	130.	
c.		Vert. pair, imperf. horiz.	1,000.	
d.		Printed on both sides	1,000.	

The imperf. 3c can be found in the Scott U.S. Specialized Catalogue Die and Plate Proofs section.

95	A26	5c brown	2,250.	550.
		No gum	1,300.	
a.		5c black brown	2,500.	600.
		No gum	1,500.	

Values for Nos. 95, 95a reflect the normal small margins.

96	A27	10c yellow green	1,750.	175.
a.		10c dark green	1,750.	175.
		No gum	1,100.	
97	A28	12c black	2,100.	200.
		No gum	1,300.	
98	A33	15c black	2,200.	275.
		No gum	1,400.	

99	A29	24c gray lilac	3,500.	625.
		No gum	2,100.	
100	A30	30c orange	4,000.	600.
		No gum	2,500.	

Values for No. 100 are for copies with small margins, especially at sides. Large-margined examples sell for much more.

101	A31	90c blue	6,500.	1,100.

Some authorities believe that more than one size of grill probably existed on one of the grill rolls.

Re-issue of 1861-66 Issues
Without Grill
Hard White Paper
White Crackly Gum

1875   *Perf. 12*

102	A24	1c blue	*650.*	950.
		No gum	*425.*	
103	A32	2c black	*2,500.*	4,500.
		No gum	*1,750.*	
104	A25	3c brown red	*2,750.*	4,750.
		No gum	*1,950.*	
105	A26	5c brown	*2,100.*	2,500.
		No gum	*1,400.*	
106	A27	10c green	*2,250.*	4,250.
		No gum	*1,500.*	
107	A28	12c black	*3,000.*	5,000.
		No gum	*2,100.*	
108	A33	15c black	*3,000.*	5,250.
		No gum	*2,100.*	
109	A29	24c deep violet	*3,750.*	6,750.
		No gum	*2,750.*	
110	A30	30c brownish org	*4,000.*	7,000.
		No gum	*2,800.*	
111	A31	90c blue	*5,250.*	22,500.
		No gum	*3,750.*	

These stamps can be distinguished from the 1861-66 issues by the shades and the paper which is hard and very white instead of yellowish. The gum is white and crackly.

Franklin
A34

Post Horse and
Rider
A35

Locomotive
A36

Washington
A37

Shield and
Eagle
A38

S. S. Adriatic
A39

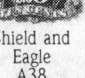

Landing of
Columbus — A40

FIFTEEN CENTS
Type I. Picture unframed.

A40a

Type II. Picture framed.
Type III. Same as type I but without fringe of brown shading lines around central vignette.

"The Declaration of Independence"
A41

Shield, Eagle and Flags
A42

Lincoln — A43

G. Grill measuring 9½x9mm
(12 by 11 to 11½ points)

1869			Perf. 12	
112	A34	1c buff	525.00	125.00
		No gum	300.00	
b.		Without grill	3,500.	
113	A35	2c brown	450.00	45.00
		No gum	250.00	
b.		Without grill	975.00	
c.		Half used as 1c on cover, diagonal, vert. or horiz.		3,000.
d.		Printed on both sides		9,000.
114	A36	3c ultramarine	275.00	15.00
		No gum	140.00	
b.		Without grill	750.00	
b.		Vertical one third used as 1c on cover		—
c.		Vertical two thirds used as 2c on cover		4,000.
d.		Double impression		3,500.
e.		Printed on both sides		
115	A37	6c ultramarine	1,750.	160.00
		No gum	850.00	
b.		Vertical half used as 3c on cover		—

No. 115 is the most difficult value in this issue to find well centered. Such examples sell for much more.

116	A38	10c yellow	1,500.	120.
		No gum	850.	
117	A39	12c green	1,500.	130.
		No gum	850.	
118	A40	15c brn & blue, Type I	5,500.	550.
		No gum	3,750.	
a.		Without grill	6,500.	
119	A40a	15c brn & blue, Type II	2,250.	225.
		No gum	1,250.	
b.		Center inverted	275,000.	17,500.
c.		Center dbl. one invtd.		—
120	A41	24c green & vio	4,750.	650.
		No gum	2,750.	
a.		Without grill	7,000.	
b.		Center inverted	275,000.	20,000.
121	A42	30c ultra & car	5,250.	500.
		No gum	3,250.	
a.		Without grill	6,500.	
b.		Flags inverted	210,000.	57,500.
122	A43	90c car & black	7,250.	2,000.
		No gum	4,250.	
a.		Without grill	11,000.	

Values of varieties of Nos. 112-122 without grill are for copies with original gum.

Most copies of Nos. 119b, 120b are faulty. Values are for fine centered copies with only minimal faults.

Re-issues of the 1869 Issue
Without Grill
Hard White Paper
White Crackly Gum

1875			Perf. 12	
123	A34	1c buff	425.	290.
		No gum	275.	
124	A35	2c brown	525.	400.
		No gum	350.	
125	A36	3c blue	4,250.	12,500.
		No gum	3,250.	

Used value for No. 125 is for an attractive copy with minimal faults.

126	A37	6c blue	1,100.	1,250.
		No gum	750.	
127	A38	10c yellow	1,750.	1,400.
		No gum	1,250.	
128	A39	12c green	1,900.	2,250.
		No gum	1,400.	
129	A40	15c brown & blue, type III	1,600.	900.
		No gum	1,100.	
a.		Imperf. horiz., single	2,500.	—

Type III is same as type I but without fringe of brown shading lines around central vignette.

130	A41	24c green & violet	1,600.	1,050.
		No gum	1,100.	
131	A42	30c ultra & carmine	2,100.	2,000.
		No gum	1,750.	
132	A43	90c carmine & black	4,750.	4,500.
		No gum	3,500.	

1880
Soft Porous Paper

133	A34	1c buff	250.	170.
		No gum	125.	
a.		1c brown orange	210.	150.

No. 133 was issued with gum, No. 133a without gum.

Printed by the National Bank Note Company

Franklin — A44

A44

Jackson — A45

A45

Washington — A46

A46

Lincoln — A47

A47

Edwin M. Stanton — A48

A48

Jefferson — A49

A49

Henry Clay — A50

A50

Daniel Webster — A51

A51

Gen. Winfield Scott
A52

Alexander Hamilton
A53

Commodore O. H. Perry — A54

Two varieties of grill are known on this issue.

H. Grill about 10x12mm
(11 to 13 by 14 to 16 points)
On all values, 1c to 90c
I. Grill about 8½x10mm
(10 to 11 by 10 to 13 points)
On 1, 2, 3, 6, 7 and 15c

On the 1870-71 stamps the grill impressions are usually faint or incomplete. This is especially true of the H grill, which often shows only a few points.

Values for 1c - 7c are for stamps showing well-defined grills.

White Wove Paper

1870-71			Perf. 12	
134	A44	1c ultramarine	1,300.	90.00
		No gum	700.00	
135	A45	2c red brown	800.00	52.50
		No gum	400.00	
a.		Diagonal half used as 1c on cover		—
136	A46	3c green	550.00	15.00
		No gum	275.00	

The imperf. 3c can be found in the Scott U.S. Specialized Catalogue Die and Plate Proofs section.

137	A47	6c carmine	3,000.	425.
		No gum	1,600.	
138	A48	7c vermilion ('71)	2,100.	375.
		No gum	1,175.	
139	A49	10c brown	3,250.	600.
		No gum	1,750.	
140	A50	12c dull violet	18,000.	2,750.
		No gum	10,000.	
141	A51	15c orange	4,000.	950.
		No gum	2,400.	
142	A52	24c purple		8,000.
143	A53	30c black	8,500.	1,400.
		No gum	5,500.	
144	A54	90c carmine	9,500.	1,200.
		No gum	6,000.	

Without Grill
White Wove Paper

1870-71			Perf. 12	
145	A44	1c ultramarine	325.00	12.00
		No gum	160.00	
146	A45	2c red brown	240.00	7.50
		No gum	120.00	
a.		Half used as 1c on cover, diagonal or vert.		—
c.		Double impression		—
147	A46	3c green	240.00	1.10
		No gum	120.00	
a.		Printed on both sides		1,750.
b.		Double impression		1,250.

The imperf. 3c can be found in the Scott U.S. Specialized Catalogue Die and Plate Proofs section.

148	A47	6c carmine	500.00	20.00
		No gum	260.00	
a.		Vert. half used as 3c on cover		—
b.		Double impression		1,500.
149	A48	7c vermilion ('71)	575.00	80.00
		No gum	350.00	
150	A49	10c brown	500.00	17.50
		No gum	290.00	
151	A50	12c dull violet	1,200.	110.00
		No gum	675.00	
152	A51	15c bright orange	1,200.	110.00
		No gum	675.00	
a.		Double impression		—
153	A52	24c purple	1,200.	120.00
		No gum	675.00	
154	A53	30c black	2,500.	145.00
		No gum	1,450.	
155	A54	90c carmine	2,500.	240.00
		No gum	1,450.	

Printed by the Continental Bank Note Co.

Designs of the 1870-71 Issue with secret marks on the values from 1c to 15c as described and illustrated below.

Franklin — A44a

1c. In pearl at left of numeral "1" is a small crescent.

Jackson — A45a

2c. Under the scroll at the left of "U. S." there is a small diagonal line. This mark seldom shows clearly. The stamp, No. 157, can be distinguished by its color.

Washington — A46a

3c. The under part of the upper tail of the left ribbon is heavily shaded.

Lincoln — A47a

6c. The first four vertical lines of the shading in the lower part of the left ribbon have been strengthened.

Stanton — A48a

7c. Two small semi-circles are drawn around the ends of the lines that outline the ball in the lower right hand corner.

Jefferson — A49a

10c. There is a small semi-circle in the scroll at the right end of the upper label.

Clay — A50a

12c. The balls of the figure "2" are crescent shaped.

Webster — A51a

15c. In the lower part of the triangle in the upper left corner two lines have been made heavier forming a "V." This mark can be found on some of the Continental and American (1879) printings, but not all stamps show it.

Secret marks were added to the dies of the 24c, 30c and 90c but new plates were not made from them. The various printings of these stamps can be distinguished only by the shades and paper.

White Wove Paper, thin to thick
Without Grill*

1873			Perf. 12	
156	A44a	1c ultramarine	180.00	2.50
		No gum	95.00	
	e.	With grill	1,750.	
	f.	Imperf., pair		550.00
157	A45a	2c brown	325.00	15.00
		No gum	175.00	
	c.	With grill	1,500.	700.00
	d.	Double impression		
	e.	Vertical half used as 1c on cover		—
158	A46a	3c green	110.00	.30
		No gum	45.00	
	e.	With grill	225.00	
	h.	Horiz. pair, imperf. vert.		
	i.	Horiz. pair, imperf. btwn.		1,300.
	j.	Double impression		1,250.
	k.	Printed on both sides		

The imperf. 3c, with and without grill, can be found in the Scott U.S. Specialized Catalogue Die and Plate Proofs section.

159	A47a	6c dull pink	375.00	15.00
		No gum	200.00	
	b.	With grill	1,400.	
160	A48a	7c orange ver	800.00	75.00
		No gum	450.00	
	a.	With grill	2,000.	
161	A49a	10c brown	525.00	16.00
		No gum	290.00	
	c.	With grill	2,500.	
	d.	Horiz. pair, imperf. btwn.		2,500.
162	A50a	12c black violet	1,350.	85.00
		No gum	725.00	
	a.	With grill	4,000.	
163	A51a	15c yellow orange	1,350.	85.00
		No gum	750.00	
	a.	With grill	4,000.	
164	A52	24c purple	1,500.	—
165	A53	30c gray black	1,500.	80.00
		No gum	800.00	
	c.	With grill	4,000.	
166	A54	90c rose carmine	2,250.	230.00
		No gum	1,400.	

The Philatelic Foundation has certified as genuine a 24c on vertically ribbed paper. Specialists believe that only Continental used ribbed paper.

* All values except 24c, 90c exist with experimental (J) grill, about 7x9½mm.

Special Printing of the 1873 Issue
Hard, White Wove Paper
Without Gum

1875			Perf. 12
167	A44a	1c ultramarine	8,500.
168	A45a	2c dark brown	3,900.
169	A46a	3c blue green	10,500.
170	A47a	6c dull rose	9,250.
171	A48a	7c redsh vermilion	2,200.
172	A49a	10c pale brown	9,000.
173	A50a	12c dark violet	3,250.
174	A51a	15c bright orange	9,000.
175	A52	24c dull purple	2,000.
176	A53	30c greenish black	6,500.
177	A54	90c violet carmine	8,250.

Although perforated, these stamps were usually cut apart with scissors. As a result, the perforations are often much mutilated and the design is frequently damaged.

These can be distinguished from the 1873 issue by the shades, also by the paper, which is very white instead of yellowish.

These and the subsequent issues listed under this heading are special printings of stamps then in current use which, together with the reprints and reissues, were made for sale to collectors. They were available for postage.

Zachary Taylor — A55

Yellowish Wove Paper

1875, June 21			Perf. 12	
178	A45a	2c vermilion	300.00	7.50
		No gum	160.00	
	b.	Half used as 1c on cover		—
	c.	With grill	400.00	
179	A55	5c blue	400.00	14.00
		No gum	200.00	
	c.	With grill	750.00	

The imperf. 2c can be found in the Scott U.S. Specialized Catalogue Die and Plate Proofs section.

Almost all of the stamps of the Continental Bank Note Co. printing including the Department stamps and some of the Newspaper stamps may be found upon a paper that shows more or less of the characteristics of a ribbed paper.

Special Printing of the 1875 Issue
Hard, White Wove Paper
Without Gum

1875			
180	A45a	2c carmine ver	24,000.
181	A55	5c bright blue	36,500.

> **VALUES FOR VERY FINE STAMPS**
> Stamps are valued in the grade of very fine unless otherwise indicated.
> Values for unused stamps with no gum are for examples with certificates of authenticity or examples sold with the buyer having the right of certification. Beware of unused, no gum stamps that are offered "as is." Expertization by competent authorities is recommended.

Printed by the American Bank Note Company
Same as 1870-75 Issues
Soft Porous Paper
Varying from Thin to Thick

1879			Perf. 12	
182	A44a	1c dark ultra	225.00	2.00
		No gum	120.00	
183	A45a	2c vermilion	110.00	2.00
		No gum	55.00	
	a.	Double impression		500.00
184	A46a	3c green	85.00	.25
		No gum	35.00	
	b.	Double impression		

The imperf. 3c can be found in the Scott U.S. Specialized Catalogue Die and Plate Proofs section.

185	A55	5c blue	425.00	12.00
		No gum	190.00	
186	A47a	6c pink	750.00	17.50
		No gum	400.00	
187	A49	10c brown (without secret mark)	1,450.	22.50
		No gum	800.00	
188	A49a	10c brown (with secret mark)	1,100.	22.50
		No gum	575.00	
189	A51a	15c red orange	300.00	21.00
		No gum	150.00	
190	A53	30c full black	850.00	50.00
		No gum	500.00	
191	A54	90c carmine	1,750.	220.00
		No gum	1,000.	

The ABN Co. used many Continental plates to print the postage, Departmental and Newspaper stamps. Therefore, stamps bearing the Continental imprint were not always its product.

The ABN Co. also used the National 90c plate and possibly the 30c plate.

Early printings of No. 188 were from Continental plates 302 and 303 which contained the normal secret mark of 1873. After those plates were re-entered by the ABN Co. in 1880, pairs or multiple pieces contained combinations of normal, hairline or missing marks. The pairs or other multiples usually found contain at least one hairline mark which tended to disappear as the plate wore.

ABN Co. plates 377 and 378 were made in 1881 from the National transfer roll of 1870. No. 187 from those plates has no secret mark.

Perf 12 Trial Color Proofs on gummed stamp paper exist, as does a 15c without the blue "SAMPLE" overprint.

The ABN Co. used many Continental plates to print the postage, Departmental and Newspaper stamps. Therefore, stamps bearing the Continental imprint were not always its product. The imperf. 90c can be found in the Scott U.S. Specialized Catalogue Die and Plate Proofs section.

Special Printing of the 1879 Issue
Soft Porous Paper
Without Gum

1880			Perf. 12
192	A44a	1c dark ultra	11,000.
193	A45a	2c black brown	6,500.
194	A46a	3c blue green	16,250.
195	A47a	6c dull rose	12,500.
196	A48a	7c scar vermilion	2,450.
197	A49a	10c deep brown	11,000.
198	A50a	12c black purple	4,000.
199	A51a	15c orange	12,500.
200	A52	24c dark violet	4,000.
201	A53	30c grnsh black	9,000.
202	A54	90c dull carmine	10,000.
203	A45a	2c scar vermilion	20,000.
204	A55	5c deep blue	35,000.

No. 197 was printed from Continental plate 302 (or 303) after plate was re-entered, therefore stamp may show normal, hairline or missing secret mark.

James A. Garfield — A56

1882, Apr. 10			Perf. 12	
205	A56	5c yellow brown	190.00	6.00
		No gum	85.00	

Special Printing
Soft Porous Paper
Without Gum

1882			
205C	A56	5c gray brown	20,000.

Designs of 1873 Re-engraved

Franklin — A44b

1c. The vertical lines in the upper part of the stamp have been so deepened that the background often appears to be solid. Lines of shading have been added to the upper arabesques.

Washington — A46b

3c. The shading at the sides of the central oval appears only about one-half the previous width. A short horizontal dash has been cut about 1mm below the "TS" of "CENTS."

Lincoln — A47b

6c. On the original stamps four vertical lines can be counted from the edge of the panel to the outside of the stamp. On the re-engraved stamps there are but three lines in the same place.

Jefferson — A49b

10c. On the original stamps there are five vertical lines between the left side of the oval and the edge of the shield. There are only four lines on the re-engraved stamps. In the lower part of the latter,

also, the horizontal lines of the background have been strengthened.

1881-82			Perf. 12	
206	A44b	1c gray blue	55.00	.60
		No gum	25.00	
207	A46b	3c blue green	60.00	.30
		No gum	27.50	
	c.	Double impression		
208	A47b	6c rose ('82)	400.00	60.00
		No gum	225.00	
	a.	6c deep brown red	350.00	85.00
		No gum	190.00	
209	A49b	10c brown ('82)	120.00	3.50
		No gum	55.00	
	b.	10c black brown	275.00	22.50
		No gum	140.00	
	c.	Double impression		
		Nos. 206-209 (4)	635.00	64.40

Specimen stamps without overprint exist in a brown shade that differs from No. 209 and in green. The unoverprinted brown specimen is cheaper than No. 209.

Washington   Jackson
A57   A58

1883, Oct. 1			Perf. 12	
210	A57	2c red brown	45.00	.25
		No gum	20.00	
211	A58	4c blue green	200.00	10.00
		No gum	90.00	

Imperfs. can be found in the Scott U.S. Specialized Catalogue Die and Plate Proofs section.
Special Printings of 1883 follow.

Special Printing
Soft Porous Paper

1883-85			
211B	A57	2c pale red brown	650. —
		No gum	350.
	c.	Horiz. pair, imperf. btwn.	2,250.
211D	A58	4c deep blue green	17,000.

No. 211D is without gum.

Franklin — A59

1887			Perf. 12	
212	A59	1c ultramarine	90.00	1.00
		No gum	35.00	
213	A57	2c green	35.00	.30
		No gum	12.50	
	b.	Printed on both sides		
214	A46b	3c vermilion	65.00	45.00
		No gum	30.00	
		Nos. 212-214 (3)	190.00	46.30

Imperf. 1c, 2c can be found in the Scott U.S. Specialized Catalogue Die and Plate Proofs section.

1888			Perf. 12	
215	A58	4c carmine	200.00	15.00
		No gum	90.00	
216	A56	5c indigo	200.00	8.50
		No gum	85.00	
217	A53	30c orange brown	425.00	90.00
		No gum	220.00	
218	A54	90c purple	1,100.	190.00
		No gum	650.00	
		Nos. 215-218 (4)	1,925.	303.50

Imperfs. can be found in the Scott U.S. Specialized Catalogue Die and Plate Proofs section.

> **Set Values**
> A 15-cent minimum now applies to individual stamps and sets. Where the 15-cent minimum per stamp would increase the value of a set beyond retail, there is a "Set Value" notation giving the retail value of the set.

IMPORTANT INFORMATION REGARDING VALUES FOR NEVER-HINGED STAMPS

Collectors should be aware that the values given for never-hinged stamps from No. 219 on are for stamps in the grade of very fine. The never-hinged premium as a percentage of value will be larger for stamps in extremely fine or superb grades, and the premium will be smaller for fine-very fine, fine or poor examples. This is particularly true of the issues of the late-19th and early-20th centuries. For example, in the grade of very fine, an unused stamp from this time period may be valued at $100 hinged and $150 never hinged. The never-hinged premium is thus 50%. But in a grade of extremely fine, this same stamp will not only sell for more hinged, but the never-hinged premium will increase, perhaps to 75%-100% or more over the higher extremely fine value. In a grade of superb, a hinged copy will sell for much more than a very fine copy, and additionally the never-hinged premium will be much larger, perhaps as large as 100%-200%. On the other hand, the same stamp in a grade of fine or fine-very fine not only will sell for less than a very fine stamp in hinged condition, but additionally the never-hinged premium will be smaller than the never-hinged premium on a very fine stamp, perhaps as small as 15%-30%.

Please note that the above statements and percentages are NOT a formula for arriving at the values of stamps in hinged or never-hinged condition in the grades of fine, fine to very fine, extremely fine or superb. The percentages given apply only to the size of the premium for never-hinged condition that might be added to the stamp value for hinged condition. The marketplace will determine what this value will be for grades other than very fine. Further, the percentages given are only generalized estimates. Some stamps or grades may have percentages for never-hinged condition that are higher or lower than the ranges given.

Franklin — A60   Washington — A61

Jackson — A62   Lincoln — A63

Ulysses S.   Garfield — A65
Grant — A64

William T.   Daniel
Sherman — A66   Webster — A67

Henry Clay — A68   Jefferson — A69

Perry — A70

1890-93				Perf. 12	
219	A60	1c dull blue	25.00	.25
		Never hinged	40.00	
219D	A61	2c lake	190.00	.60
		Never hinged	260.00	
220	A61	2c carmine	20.00	.25
a.		Cap on left "2"	65.00	2.00
		Never hinged	105.00	
c.		Cap on both "2's"	190.00	15.00
		Never hinged	300.00	
221	A62	3c purple	65.00	6.00
		Never hinged	105.00	
222	A63	4c dark brown	67.50	2.25
		Never hinged	115.00	
223	A64	5c chocolate	65.00	2.25
		Never hinged	105.00	
224	A65	6c brown red	67.50	18.00
		Never hinged	105.00	
225	A66	8c lilac ('93)	52.50	11.00
		Never hinged	85.00	
226	A67	10c green	140.00	2.75
		Never hinged	215.00	
227	A68	15c indigo	180.00	18.00
		Never hinged	275.00	
228	A69	30c black	300.00	25.00
		Never hinged	475.00	
229	A70	90c orange	450.00	115.00
		Never hinged	700.00	
	Nos. 219-229 (12)		1,622.	201.35

The "cap on right 2" variety is due to imperfect inking, not a plate defect.
Imperfs. can be found in the Scott U.S. Specialized Catalogue Die and Plate Proofs section.

Columbian Exposition Issue

Columbus in Sight of Land — A71

Landing of Columbus — A72

Flagship of Columbus — A73

Fleet of Columbus — A74

Columbus Soliciting Aid from Isabella — A75

Columbus Welcomed at Barcelona — A76

Columbus Restored to Favor — A77

Columbus Presenting Natives — A78

Columbus Announcing his Discovery — A79

Columbus at La Rábida — A80

Recall of Columbus — A81

Isabella Pledging her Jewels — A82

Columbus in Chains — A83

Columbus Describing his Third Voyage — A84

Isabella and Columbus — A85

Columbus — A86

1893				Perf. 12	
230	A71	1c deep blue	25.00	.40
		Never hinged	40.00	
231	A72	2c brown violet	22.50	.20
		Never hinged	35.00	
232	A73	3c green	62.50	15.00
		Never hinged	95.00	
233	A74	4c ultra	87.50	7.50
		Never hinged	130.00	
a.		4c blue (error)	16,000.	5,500.
		Never hinged	22,500.	
234	A75	5c chocolate	95.00	8.00
		Never hinged	140.00	
235	A76	6c purple	90.00	22.50
		Never hinged	135.00	
a.		6c red violet	90.00	22.50
		Never hinged	135.00	
236	A77	8c magenta	80.00	11.00
		Never hinged	120.00	
237	A78	10c black brown	135.00	8.00
		Never hinged	210.00	
238	A79	15c dark green	240.00	65.00
		Never hinged	375.00	
239	A80	30c orange brown	300.00	85.00
		Never hinged	450.00	
240	A81	50c slate blue	600.00	160.00
		Never hinged	875.00	
241	A82	$1 salmon	1,500.	650.00
		Never hinged	2,400.	
		No gum	725.00	
242	A83	$2 brown red	1,550.	600.00
		Never hinged	2,450.	
		No gum	750.00	
243	A84	$3 yellow green	2,400.	975.00
		Never hinged	4,000.	
		No gum	1,150.	
a.		$3 olive green	2,400.	975.00
		Never hinged	4,000.	
		No gum	1,150.	
244	A85	$4 crimson lake	3,250.	1,350.
		Never hinged	5,000.	
		No gum	1,500.	
a.		$4 rose carmine	3,250.	1,350.
		Never hinged	5,000.	
		No gum	1,500.	
245	A86	$5 black	3,750.	1,600.
		Never hinged	5,750.	
		No gum	1,750.	

World's Columbian Expo., Chicago, May 1-Oct. 30, 1893.

Nos. 230-245 are known imperf., but were not regularly issued. (See Scott U. S. Specialized Catalogue Die and Plate Proofs for the 2c.)

Never-Hinged Stamps
See note after No. 218 regarding premiums for never-hinged stamps.

Bureau Issues

Starting in 1894, the Bureau of Engraving and Printing at Washington has produced most U.S. postage stamps. Until 1965 Bureau-printed stamps were engraved except Nos. 525-536, which are offset. The combination of lithography and engraving (see No. 1253) was first used in 1964, and photogravure (see No. 1426) in 1971.

Franklin   Washington
A87   A88

Jackson   Lincoln
A89   A90

Grant   Garfield
A91   A92

Sherman   Webster
A93   A94

Clay   Jefferson
A95   A96

Perry   James
A97   Madison
A98

John Marshall — A99

TWO CENTS

Type I   Type II

Type I. The horizontal lines of the ground work run across the triangle and are of the same thickness within it as without.

Type II. The horizontal lines cross the triangle but are thinner within it than without.

Type III

Type III. The horizontal lines do not cross the double frame lines of the triangle. The lines within the triangle are thin, as in type II.

ONE DOLLAR

Type I

Type I. The circles enclosing "$1" are broken where they meet the curved line below "One Dollar." The 15 left vert. rows of impressions from plate 76 are Type I, the balance Type II.

Type II

Type II. The circles are complete.

1894	Unwmk.		Perf. 12	
246	A87	1c ultramarine	27.50	4.00
		Never hinged	42.50	
247	A87	1c blue	60.00	2.00
		Never hinged	90.00	
248	A88	2c pink, Type I	25.00	3.00
		Never hinged	37.50	
249	A88	2c carmine lake, Type I	125.00	2.25
		Never hinged	190.00	
250	A88	2c car, Type I	27.50	.50
		Never hinged	40.00	
a.		Vert. pair, imperf. horiz.	1,500.	
b.		Horiz. pair, imperf. btwn.	1,500.	
251	A88	2c car, Type II	200.00	3.50
		Never hinged	300.00	
252	A88	2c car, Type III	110.00	3.75
		Never hinged	170.00	
a.		Horiz. pair, imperf. vert.	1,350.	
b.		Horiz. pair, imperf. btwn.	1,500.	
253	A89	3c purple	95.00	8.00
		Never hinged	140.00	
254	A90	4c dark brown	120.00	3.75
		Never hinged	180.00	
255	A91	5c chocolate	85.00	4.75
		Never hinged	130.00	
c.		Vert. pair, imperf. horiz.	1,350.	
256	A92	6c dull brown	135.00	21.00
		Never hinged	210.00	
a.		Vert. pair, imperf. horiz.	850.00	
257	A93	8c vio brn ('95)	130.00	14.00
		Never hinged	200.00	
258	A94	10c dark green	200.00	10.00
		Never hinged	300.00	
259	A95	15c dark blue	260.00	45.00
		Never hinged	390.00	
260	A96	50c orange	375.00	95.00
		Never hinged	550.00	
261	A97	$1 black, Type I	800.00	250.00
		Never hinged	1,250.	
		No gum	325.	
261A	A97	$1 black, Type II	1,900.	550.00
		Never hinged	3,000.	
		No gum	750.	
262	A98	$2 bright blue	2,600.	825.00
		Never hinged	4,250.	
		No gum	1,050.	
263	A99	$5 dark green	4,000.	1,750.
		Never hinged	6,000.	
		No gum	1,900.	

For imperfs. and the 2c pink, vert. pair, imperf. horiz., see Scott U. S. Specialized Catalogue Die and Plate Proofs.

Same as 1894 Issue

1895	Wmk. 191		Perf. 12	
264	A87	1c blue	5.50	.25
		Never hinged	9.00	
265	A88	2c car, Type I	27.50	.80
		Never hinged	42.50	
266	A88	2c car, Type II	27.50	3.00
		Never hinged	42.50	
267	A88	2c car, Type III	4.50	.25
		Never hinged	6.75	

The three left vertical rows from plate 170 are Type II, the balance being Type III.

268	A89	3c purple	35.00	1.10
		Never hinged	52.50	
269	A90	4c dark brown	37.50	1.60
		Never hinged	55.00	
270	A91	5c chocolate	35.00	1.90
		Never hinged	52.50	
271	A92	6c dull brown	75.00	4.25
		Never hinged	115.00	
a.		Wmkd. USIR	2,250.	400.00
272	A93	8c violet brown	55.00	1.25
		Never hinged	85.00	
a.		Wmkd. USIR	1,750.	110.00
273	A94	10c dark green	75.00	1.50
		Never hinged	115.00	
274	A95	15c dark blue	190.00	9.00
		Never hinged	280.00	

275	A96	50c orange	260.00	20.00
		Never hinged	390.00	
a.		50c red orange	290.00	24.00
		Never hinged	450.00	
276	A97	$1 blk, Type I	600.00	65.00
		Never hinged	900.00	
		No gum	175.00	
276A	A97	$1 blk, Type II	1,200.	140.00
		Never hinged	1,850.	
		No gum	400.00	
277	A98	$2 bright blue	975.00	300.00
		Never hinged	1,500.	
		No gum	350.00	
a.		$2 dark blue	975.00	300.00
		Never hinged	1,500.	
		No gum	350.00	
278	A99	$5 dark green	2,250.	425.00
		Never hinged	3,500.	
		No gum	850.	

For imperfs. and the 1c horiz. pair, imperf. vert., see Scott U. S. Specialized Catalogue Die and Plate Proofs.
For "I.R." overprints see Nos. R155-R158.

TEN CENTS

Type I

Type I. Tips of foliate ornaments do not impinge on white curved line below "TEN CENTS."

Type II

Type II. Tips of ornaments break curved line below "E" of "TEN" and "T" of "CENTS."

1898	Wmk. 191		Perf. 12	
279	A87	1c deep green	9.00	.25
		Never hinged	13.50	
279B	A88	2c red, Type III	9.00	.25
		Never hinged	13.50	
c.		2c rose carmine, Type III	225.00	65.00
		Never hinged	300.00	
d.		2c orange red, Type III	10.00	.30
		Never hinged	15.00	
e.		Booklet pane of 6	400.00	350.00
		Never hinged	600.00	
f.		2c deep red, Type III	13.50	1.00
		Never hinged	21.00	
280	A90	4c rose brown	30.00	.90
		Never hinged	45.00	
a.		4c lilac brown	30.00	.90
		Never hinged	45.00	
b.		4c orange brown	30.00	.90
		Never hinged	45.00	
281	A91	5c dark blue	35.00	.75
		Never hinged	52.50	
282	A92	6c lake	45.00	2.50
		Never hinged	67.50	
a.		6c purple lake	55.00	3.50
		Never hinged	82.50	
282C	A94	10c brown, Type I	180.00	2.50
		Never hinged	275.00	
283	A94	10c org brown, Type II	110.00	2.00
		Never hinged	165.00	
284	A95	15c olive green	150.00	7.50
		Never hinged	225.00	
		Nos. 279-284 (8)	568.00	16.65

For "I.R." overprints see Nos. R153-R154.

VALUES FOR VERY FINE STAMPS
Please note: Stamps are valued in the grade of Very Fine unless otherwise indicated.

Trans-Mississippi Exposition Issue

Marquette on the Mississippi — A100

Farming in the West — A101

Indian Hunting Buffalo — A102

Frémont on the Rocky Mountains A103

Troops Guarding Wagon Train — A104

Hardships of Emigration A105

Western Mining Prospector A106

Western Cattle in Storm — A107

Mississippi River Bridge — A108

1898, June 17	Wmk. 191		Perf. 12	
285	A100	1c dk yel green	27.50	6.00
		Never hinged	42.50	
286	A101	2c copper red	25.00	1.50
		Never hinged	37.50	
287	A102	4c orange	140.00	21.00
		Never hinged	210.00	
288	A103	5c dull blue	130.00	19.00
		Never hinged	200.00	
289	A104	8c violet brown	175.00	37.50
		Never hinged	260.00	
a.		Vert. pair, imperf. horiz.	17,500.	
290	A105	10c gray violet	170.00	22.50
		Never hinged	250.00	
291	A106	50c sage green	550.00	170.00
		Never hinged	900.00	
292	A107	$1 black	1,250.	500.00
		Never hinged	1,900.	
		No gum	600.	
293	A108	$2 orange brown	2,100.	850.00
		Never hinged	3,250.	
		No gum	1,000.	
		Nos. 285-293 (9)	4,567.	1,627.

Trans-Mississippi Exposition, Omaha, Neb., June 1 to Nov. 1, 1898.
For "I.R." overprints see #R158A-R158B.

Never-Hinged Stamps
See note after No. 218 regarding premiums for never-hinged stamps.

Pan-American Exposition Issue

Fast Lake Navigation — A109

"Empire State" Express — A110

Electric Automobile A111

Bridge at Niagara Falls A112

Canal Locks at Sault Ste. Marie — A113

Fast Ocean Navigation — A114

1901, May 1	Wmk. 191		Perf. 12	
294	A109	1c green & black	19.00	3.00
		Never hinged	29.00	
a.		Center inverted	10,000.	6,500.
		Never hinged	15,000.	
295	A110	2c car & black	18.00	1.00
		Never hinged	27.50	
a.		Center inverted	37,500.	16,000.
296	A111	4c dp red brn & black	85.00	15.00
		Never hinged	130.00	
a.		Center inverted	17,000.	
297	A112	5c ultra & black	100.00	14.00
		Never hinged	150.00	
298	A113	8c brn vio & black	125.00	50.00
		Never hinged	190.00	
299	A114	10c yel brn & black	175.00	25.00
		Never hinged	260.00	
		Nos. 294-299 (6)	522.00	108.00
		Nos. 294-299, never hinged	786.50	

Buffalo, NY, May 1-Nov. 1, 1901.
No. 296a was a special printing.
Almost all unused copies of Nos. 295a and 296a have partial or disturbed gum. Values are for examples with full original gum that is slightly disturbed.

Franklin A115

Washington A116

Jackson A117

Grant A118

Lincoln A119

Garfield A120

Martha Washington A121

Webster A122

Benjamin Harrison A123

Clay A124

Jefferson A125

David G. Farragut A126

Madison A127

Marshall A128

1902-03	Wmk. 191		Perf. 12	
300	A115	1c blue grn ('03)	9.00	.20
		Never hinged	13.50	
b.		Booklet pane of 6	550.00	
		Never hinged	775.00	
301	A116	2c carmine ('03)	12.50	.20
		Never hinged	19.00	
c.		Booklet pane of 6	450.00	—
302	A117	3c brt violet ('03)	50.00	2.75
		Never hinged	75.00	

303	A118	4c brown ('03)	55.00	1.25
		Never hinged	82.50	
304	A119	5c blue ('03)	55.00	1.50
		Never hinged	82.50	
305	A120	6c claret ('03)·	65.00	2.50
		Never hinged	97.50	
306	A121	8c violet black	40.00	2.00
		Never hinged	60.00	
307	A122	10c pale red brn ('03)	60.00	1.40
		Never hinged	90.00	
308	A123	13c purple black	45.00	7.50
		Never hinged	67.50	
309	A124	15c olive green ('03)	150.00	4.75
		Never hinged	225.00	
310	A125	50c orange ('03)	400.00	22.50
		Never hinged	600.00	
311	A126	$1 black ('03)	700.00	55.00
		Never hinged	1,050.	
		No gum	160.00	
312	A127	$2 dark blue ('03)	1,100.	170.00
		Never hinged	1,650.	
		No gum	275.	
313	A128	$5 dark green ('03)	2,750.	650.00
		Never hinged	4,100.	
		No gum	825.	
		Nos. 300-313 (14)	5,491.	921.55

For listings of designs A127 and A128 with Perf. 10, see Nos. 479 and 480.

1906-08   Imperf.

314	A115	1c blue green	21.00	15.00
		Never hinged	32.50	
314A	A118	4c brown ('08)	25,000.	20,000.
315	A119	5c blue ('08)	325.00	425.00
		Never hinged	475.00	

No. 314A was issued imperforate but all copies were privately perforated with large oblong perforations at the sides (Schermack type III).

Beware of copies of No. 303 with trimmed perforations and fake private perfs added.

Used copies of Nos. 314 & 315 must have contemporaneous cancels.

Coil Stamps

Imperforate stamps are known fraudulently perforated to resemble coil stamps and part perforate varieties.

1908   Perf. 12 Horizontally

316	A115	1c blue green, pair	90,000.	—
317	A119	5c blue, pair	10,000.	—

Perf. 12 Vertically

318	A115	1c blue green, pair	6,500.	—

Coil stamps for use in vending and affixing machines are perforated on two sides only, either horizontally or vertically. They were first issued in 1908, using perf. 12. This was changed to 8½ in 1910, and to 10 in 1914.

Imperforate sheets of certain denominations were sold to the vending machine companies which applied a variety of private perforations and separations.

Several values of the 1902 and later issues are found on an apparently coarse ribbed paper. This is caused by worn blankets on the printing press and is not a true paper variety.

Washington — A129

Type I	Type II

Type I. Leaf next to left "2" penetrates the border.
Type II. Strong line forming border left of leaf.

1903, Nov. 12   Wmk. 191   Perf. 12

319	A129	2c carmine (I)	4.75	.15
		Never hinged	7.25	
a.		2c lake (I)	—	
b.		2c carmine rose (I)	6.50	.35
		Never hinged	10.50	
c.		2c scarlet (I)	4.75	.25
		Never hinged	7.25	
d.		Vert. pair, imperf. horiz.	3,000.	
e.		Vert. pair, imperf. btwn.	950.00	
f.		2c lake (II)	6.25	.15
		Never hinged	9.75	
g.		Booklet pane of 6, car (I)	110.00	150.00
		Never hinged	160.00	
h.		As "g" (II)	225.00	
		Never hinged	350.00	
i.		2c carmine (II)	22.50	50.00
		Never hinged	35.00	
j.		2c carmine rose (II)	17.50	.75
		Never hinged	27.50	
k.		2c scarlet (II)	14.00	.45
		Never hinged	21.00	

m.		As "g," lake (I)	—	
n.		As "g," car rose (I)	150.00	160.00
		Never hinged	215.00	
p.		As "g," scarlet (I)	140.00	150.00
		Never hinged	200.00	
q.		As "g," lake (II)	175.00	250.00
		Never hinged	250.00	

1906, Oct. 2   Imperf.

320	A129	2c carmine (I)	20.00	12.00
		Never hinged	30.00	
a.		2c lake (II)	50.00	40.00
		Never hinged	70.00	
b.		2c scarlet (I)	19.00	12.50
		Never hinged	27.50	
c.		2c carmine rose (I)	60.00	40.00
		Never hinged	85.00	
d.		2c carmine (II)	—	

Coil Stamps

1908   Perf. 12 Horizontally

321	A129	2c car, pair (I)	100,000.	110,000.

Five authenticated unused pairs are known. The used value is for a single on cover, of which 2 authenticated examples are known, both used from Indianapolis in 1908. Numerous counterfeits exist.

Perf. 12 Vertically

322	A129	2c carmine, pair	7,500.	5,000.

Louisiana Purchase Exposition Issue

Robert R. Livingston A130

Thomas Jefferson A131

James Monroe — A132

William McKinley A133

Map of Louisiana Purchase — A134

1904, Apr. 30   Wmk. 191   Perf. 12

323	A130	1c green	30.00	3.75
		Never hinged	45.00	
324	A131	2c carmine	27.50	1.50
		Never hinged	41.00	
a.		Vert. pair, imperf. horiz.	6,750.	
325	A132	3c violet	90.00	30.00
		Never hinged	135.00	
326	A133	5c dark blue	95.00	20.00
		Never hinged	142.50	
327	A134	10c red brown	180.00	27.50
		Never hinged	270.00	
		Nos. 323-327 (5)	422.50	82.75
		Nos. 323-327, never hinged	633.50	

Louisiana Purchase Expo., St. Louis, Mo., Apr. 30 to Dec. 1, 1904.

Jamestown Exposition Issue

Captain John Smith A135

Founding of Jamestown A136

Pocahontas — A137

1907   Wmk. 191   Perf. 12

328	A135	1c green	27.50	4.00
		Never hinged	40.00	

329	A136	2c carmine	32.50	3.50
		Never hinged	50.00	
330	A137	5c blue	130.00	27.50
		Never hinged	200.00	
		Nos. 328-330 (3)	190.00	35.00
		Nos. 328-330, never hinged	290.00	

Jamestown Expo., Hampton Roads, Va., Apr. 26 to Dec. 1.

Franklin A138

Washington A139

Washington — A140

There are several types of some of the 2c and 3c stamps of this and succeeding issues. These types are described under the dates when they first appeared.

Illustrations of Types I-VII of the 2c (A140) and Types I-IV of the 3c (A140) are reproduced by permission of H. L. Lindquist.

TYPE I

THREE CENTS

Type I. The top line of the toga rope is weak and the rope shading lines are thin. The fifth line from the left is missing.

The line between the lips is thin.

Used on both flat plate and rotary press printings.

1908-09   Wmk. 191   Perf. 12

331	A138	1c green	6.50	.15
		Never hinged	9.75	
a.		Booklet pane of 6	150.00	125.00
		Never hinged	210.00	
332	A139	2c carmine	6.00	.15
		Never hinged	9.00	
a.		Booklet pane of 6	130.00	125.00
		Never hinged	190.00	
333	A140	3c deep violet, Type I	30.00	2.50
		Never hinged	45.00	
334	A140	4c orange brown	37.50	1.00
		Never hinged	57.50	
335	A140	5c blue	47.50	2.00
		Never hinged	72.50	
336	A140	6c red orange	60.00	5.00
		Never hinged	90.00	
337	A140	8c olive green	45.00	2.50
		Never hinged	67.50	
338	A140	10c yellow ('09)	65.00	1.40
		Never hinged	100.00	
339	A140	13c blue green ('09)	37.50	19.00
		Never hinged	57.50	
340	A140	15c pale ultra ('09)	62.50	5.50
		Never hinged	95.00	
341	A140	50c violet ('09)	300.00	17.50
		Never hinged	475.00	
342	A140	$1 vio brown ('09)	475.00	70.00
		Never hinged	725.00	
		Nos. 331-342 (12)	1,172.	126.70

For listings of China Clay papers see the Scott U.S. Specialized Catalogue.

For listing of other perforated stamps of designs A138, A139 and A140 see

#357-366	Bluish Paper	
#374-382, 405-407	Single line wmk.	Perf. 12
#424-430	Single line wmk.	Perf. 10
#461	Single line wmk.	Perf. 11
#462-469	Unwmkd.	Perf. 10
#498-507	Unwmkd.	Perf. 11
#519	Double line wmk.	Perf. 11
#525-530, 536	Offset printing	
#538-546	Rotary press printing	

Imperf

343	A138	1c green	6.50	4.50
		Never hinged	10.00	
344	A139	2c carmine	8.00	3.00
		Never hinged	12.00	
345	A140	3c dp violet, Type I	15.00	20.00
		Never hinged	21.00	
346	A140	4c org brown ('09)	25.00	22.50
		Never hinged	37.50	
347	A140	5c blue ('09)	45.00	32.50
		Never hinged	65.00	
		Nos. 343-347 (5)	99.50	82.50

For listings of other imperforate stamps of designs A138, A139 and A140 see

#383 & 384, 408 & 409, 459	Single line wmk.
#481-485	Unwmkd.
#531-535	Offset printing

Coil Stamps

1908-10   Perf. 12 Horizontally

348	A138	1c green	27.50	14.00
		Never hinged	40.00	
349	A139	2c carmine ('09)	50.00	8.00
		Never hinged	72.50	
350	A140	4c orange brown ('10)	120.00	85.00
		Never hinged	180.00	
351	A140	5c blue ('09)	130.00	110.00
		Never hinged	200.00	
		Nos. 348-351 (4)	327.50	217.00

1909   Perf. 12 Vertically

352	A138	1c green	60.00	32.50
		Never hinged	87.50	
353	A139	2c carmine	60.00	9.00
		Never hinged	87.50	
354	A140	4c orange brown	150.00	65.00
		Never hinged	225.00	
355	A140	5c blue	160.00	85.00
		Never hinged	240.00	
356	A140	10c yellow	2,150.	1,000.
		Never hinged	2,750.	

Beware of stamps offered as No. 356 which may be examples of No. 338 with perforations trimmed at top and/or bottom..

For listings of other coil stamps of designs A138, A139 and A140 see

#385-396, 410-413, 441-458	Single line wmk.
#486-496	Unwmkd.

Bluish Paper

This was made with 35 per cent rag stock instead of all wood pulp. The grayish blue color goes through the paper showing clearly on the back as well as on the face.

1909   Perf. 12

357	A138	1c green	95.00	95.00
		Never hinged	140.00	
358	A139	2c carmine	90.00	80.00
		Never hinged	130.00	
359	A140	3c dp violet, Type I	1,800.	2,000.
360	A140	4c orange brown	17,500.	
		Never hinged	23,000.	
361	A140	5c blue	4,500.	5,000.
		Never hinged	6,000.	
362	A140	6c red orange	1,350.	1,500.
		Never hinged	1,850.	
363	A140	8c olive green	18,500.	
		Never hinged	24,000.	
364	A140	10c yellow	1,600.	1,750.
		Never hinged	2,150.	
365	A140	13c blue green	2,800.	1,900.
		Never hinged	3,750.	
366	A140	15c pale ultra	1,350.	1,500.
		Never hinged	1,850.	

Nos. 360, 363 not regularly issued.

Lincoln Centenary of Birth Issue

Lincoln — A141

1909, Feb. 12   Wmk. 191   Perf. 12

367	A141	2c carmine	5.50	1.75
		Never hinged	8.00	

Imperf

368	A141	2c carmine	22.50	20.00
		Never hinged	35.00	

Bluish Paper

1909   Perf. 12

369	A141	2c carmine	225.00	240.00
		Never hinged	310.00	

Alaska-Yukon-Pacific Exposition Issue

William H. Seward — A142

1909, June 1 — Wmk. 191 — Perf. 12

370 A142 2c carmine — 9.00 / 2.00
  Never hinged — 13.00

1909 — Imperf.

371 A142 2c carmine — 30.00 / 22.50

Seattle, Wash., June 1 to Oct. 16.

Hudson-Fulton Celebration Issue

"Half Moon" and Steamship A143

1909, Sept. 25 — Wmk. 191 — Perf. 12

372 A143 2c carmine — 13.00 / 4.50
  Never hinged — 18.00

Imperf

373 A143 2c carmine — 35.00 / 25.00
  Never hinged — 47.50

Tercentenary of the discovery of the Hudson River and Centenary of Robert Fulton's steamship.

Designs of 1908-09 Issue

1910-11 — Wmk. 190 — Perf. 12

374 A138 1c green — 6.50 / .20
  Never hinged — 9.50
 a. Booklet pane of 6 — 140.00 / 100.00
  Never hinged — 200.00
375 A139 2c carmine — 6.50 / .20
  Never hinged — 9.50
 a. Booklet pane of 6 — 95.00 / 85.00
  Never hinged — 135.00
376 A140 3c dp vio, Type I ('11) — 17.50 / 1.40
  Never hinged — 25.00
377 A140 4c brown ('11) — 27.50 / .50
  Never hinged — 42.50
378 A140 5c blue ('11) — 27.50 / .50
  Never hinged — 42.50
379 A140 6c red orange ('11) — 32.50 / .70
  Never hinged — 50.00
380 A140 8c olive green ('11) — 110.00 / 12.50
  Never hinged — 165.00
381 A140 10c yellow ('11) — 100.00 / 3.75
  Never hinged — 145.00
382 A140 15c pale ultra ('11) — 260.00 / 15.00
  Never hinged — 390.00
  Nos. 374-382 (9) — 588.00 / 34.75

1910 — Imperf.

383 A138 1c green — 2.60 / 2.00
  Never hinged — 3.90
384 A139 2c carmine — 4.25 / 2.50
  Never hinged — 6.50

Coil Stamps

1910 — Perf. 12 Horizontally

385 A138 1c green — 25.00 / 13.00
  Never hinged — 37.50
386 A139 2c carmine — 45.00 / 17.50
  Never hinged — 67.50

1910-11 — Perf. 12 Vertically

387 A138 1c green — 100.00 / 42.50
  Never hinged — 150.00
388 A139 2c carmine — 750.00 / 300.00
  Never hinged — 1,050.
389 A140 3c dp vio, Type I ('11) — 37,500. / 10,000.
  Never hinged — 50,000.

Stamps sold as No. 388 frequently are privately perforated examples of No. 384, or examples of No. 375, with top and/or bottom perfs trimmed.
Stamps offered as No. 389 sometimes are examples of No. 376 with top and/or bottom perfs trimmed.
Expertization by competent authorities is recommended.

1910 — Perf. 8½ Horizontally

390 A138 1c green — 4.25 / 5.00
  Never hinged — 6.25
391 A139 2c carmine — 30.00 / 10.00
  Never hinged — 45.00

1910-13 — Perf. 8½ Vertically

392 A138 1c green — 20.00 / 19.00
  Never hinged — 30.00
393 A139 2c carmine — 35.00 / 7.75
  Never hinged — 52.50
394 A140 3c dp vio, Type I ('11) — 45.00 / 47.50
  Never hinged — 67.50
395 A140 4c brown ('12) — 45.00 / 42.50
  Never hinged — 67.50
396 A140 5c blue ('13) — 45.00 / 42.50
  Never hinged — 67.50
  Nos. 392-396 (5) — 190.00 / 159.25

Panama-Pacific Exposition Issue

Vasco Nunez de Balboa — A144

Pedro Miguel Locks, Panama Canal — A145

Golden Gate — A146

Discovery of San Francisco Bay — A147

1913 — Wmk. 190 — Perf. 12

397 A144 1c green — 17.50 / 1.50
  Never hinged — 26.00
398 A145 2c carmine — 20.00 / .50
  Never hinged — 30.00
399 A146 5c blue — 77.50 / 9.50
  Never hinged — 120.00
400 A147 10c orange yellow — 125.00 / 20.00
  Never hinged — 190.00
400A A147 10c orange — 210.00 / 16.00
  Never hinged — 325.00
  Nos. 397-400A (5) — 450.00 / 47.50
  Nos. 397-400A, never hinged — 691.00

1914-15 — Perf. 10

401 A144 1c green — 25.00 / 5.50
  Never hinged — 37.00
402 A145 2c carmine ('15) — 75.00 / 1.50
  Never hinged — 115.00
403 A146 5c blue ('15) — 175.00 / 15.00
  Never hinged — 260.00
404 A147 10c orange ('15) — 950.00 / 62.50
  Never hinged — 1,400.
  Nos. 401-404 (4) — 1,225. / 84.50
  Nos. 401-404, never hinged — 1,812.

San Francisco, Cal., Feb. 20 to Dec. 4.

TYPE I

TWO CENTS

Type I. There is one shading line in the first curve of the ribbon above the left "2" and one in the second curve of the ribbon above the right "2."
The button of the toga has a faint outline.
The top line of the toga rope, from the button to the front of the throat, is also very faint.
The shading lines at the face terminate in front of the ear with little or no joining, to form a lock of hair.
Used on both flat and rotary press printings.

1912-14 — Wmk. 190 — Perf. 12

405 A140 1c green — 5.25 / .15
  Never hinged — 7.75
 a. Vert. pair, imperf. horiz. — 650.00 / —
 b. Booklet pane of 6 — 60.00 / 35.00
  Never hinged — 90.00
406 A140 2c carmine, Type I — 5.00 / .15
  Never hinged — 7.50
 a. Booklet pane of 6 — 60.00 / 60.00
  Never hinged — 90.00
 b. Double impression
407 A140 7c black ('14) — 80.00 / 11.00
  Never hinged — 120.00
  Nos. 405-407 (3) — 90.25 / 11.30

1912 — Imperf.

408 A140 1c green — 1.15 / .55
  Never hinged — 1.70
409 A140 2c carmine, Type I — 1.40 / .60
  Never hinged — 2.00

Coil Stamps

1912 — Perf. 8½ Horizontally

410 A140 1c green — 6.00 / 4.00
  Never hinged — 9.00
411 A140 2c carmine, Type I — 9.00 / 3.75
  Never hinged — 13.50

Perf. 8½ Vertically

412 A140 1c green — 22.50 / 5.50
  Never hinged — 32.50

413 A140 2c carmine, Type I — 37.50 / 1.10
  Never hinged — 55.00
  Nos. 410-413 (4) — 75.00 / 14.35

Franklin — A148

1912-14 — Wmk. 190 — Perf. 12

414 A148 8c pale olive green — 45.00 / 1.25
  Never hinged — 67.50
415 A148 9c salmon red ('14) — 55.00 / 12.50
  Never hinged — 82.50
416 A148 10c orange yellow — 45.00 / .40
  Never hinged — 67.50
417 A148 12c claret brown ('14) — 50.00 / 4.25
  Never hinged — 75.00
418 A148 15c gray — 85.00 / 3.50
  Never hinged — 130.00
419 A148 20c ultra ('14) — 200.00 / 15.00
  Never hinged — 300.00
420 A148 30c orange red ('14) — 125.00 / 15.00
  Never hinged — 190.00
421 A148 50c violet ('14) — 425.00 / 17.50
  Never hinged — 650.00
  Nos. 414-421 (8) — 1,030. / 69.40

No. 421 almost always has an offset of the frame lines on the back under the gum. No. 422 does not have this offset.

1912, Feb. 12 — Wmk. 191 — Perf. 12

422 A148 50c violet — 250.00 / 15.00
  Never hinged — 375.00
423 A148 $1 violet brown — 500.00 / 60.00
  Never hinged — 750.00

Other stamps of type A148:

#431-440	Single line wmk.	Perf. 10
#460	Double line wmk.	Perf. 10
#470-478	Unwmkd.	Perf. 10
#508-518	Unwmkd.	Perf. 11

1914-15 — Wmk. 190 — Perf. 10

424 A140 1c green — 2.20 / .20
  Never hinged — 3.25
 a. Perf. 12x10 — 850.00 / 750.00
 b. Perf. 10x12 — 375.00
 c. Vert. pair, imperf. horiz. — 425.00 / 250.00
 d. Booklet pane of 6 — 4.75 / 2.00
  Never hinged — 7.25
 e. As "d," imperf. — 1,500.

Most copies of No. 424b are precanceled Dayton, Ohio, to which the value applies.
All known examples of No. 424e are without gum.

425 A140 2c rose red, Type I — 2.10 / .20
  Never hinged — 3.00
 c. Perf. 10x12
 d. Perf. 12x10 — 800.00
 e. Booklet pane of 6 — 15.00 / 10.00
  Never hinged — 22.50
426 A140 3c deep vio, Type I — 13.50 / 1.25
  Never hinged — 20.00
427 A140 4c brown — 32.50 / .50
  Never hinged — 50.00
428 A140 5c blue — 30.00 / .50
  Never hinged — 45.00
 a. Perf. 12x10 — 2,250.
429 A140 6c red orange — 45.00 / 1.40
  Never hinged — 67.50
430 A140 7c black — 80.00 / 4.00
  Never hinged — 120.00
431 A148 8c pale olive green — 32.50 / 1.50
  Never hinged — 50.00
432 A148 9c salmon red — 47.50 / 7.50
  Never hinged — 72.50
433 A148 10c orange yellow — 45.00 / .40
  Never hinged — 67.50
434 A148 11c dark green ('15) — 21.00 / 7.50
  Never hinged — 32.50
435 A148 12c claret brown — 24.00 / 4.00
  Never hinged — 36.00
 a. 12c copper red — 27.50 / 4.00
  Never hinged — 41.00
437 A148 15c gray — 120.00 / 7.25
  Never hinged — 180.00
438 A148 20c ultra — 200.00 / 4.00
  Never hinged — 300.00
439 A148 30c orange red — 250.00 / 16.00
  Never hinged — 375.00
440 A148 50c violet ('15) — 550.00 / 16.00
  Never hinged — 825.00
  Nos. 424-440 (16) — 1,495. / 72.20

Coil Stamps

1914 — Perf. 10 Horizontally

441 A140 1c green — 1.00 / 1.00
  Never hinged — 1.45
442 A140 2c carmine, Type I — 8.00 / 6.00
  Never hinged — 11.50

1914 — Perf. 10 Vertically

443 A140 1c green — 22.50 / 5.00
  Never hinged — 32.50
444 A140 2c carmine, Type I — 30.00 / 1.50
  Never hinged — 42.50

445 A140 3c violet, Type I — 220.00 / 125.00
  Never hinged — 325.00
446 A140 4c brown — 120.00 / 42.50
  Never hinged — 175.00
447 A140 5c blue — 42.50 / 27.50
  Never hinged — 62.50
  Nos. 443-447 (5) — 435.00 / 201.50

TYPE II

TWO CENTS

Type II. Shading lines in ribbons as on type I.
The toga button, rope, and shading lines are heavy.
The shading lines of the face at the lock of hair end in a strong vertical curved line.
Used on rotary press printings only.

TYPE III

TWO CENTS

Type III. Two lines of shading in the curves of the ribbons.
Other characteristics similar to type II.
Used on rotary press printings only.

Fraudulently altered copies of Type III (Nos. 455, 488, 492 and 540) have had one line of shading scraped off to make them resemble Type II (Nos. 454, 487, 491 and 539).

ROTARY PRESS STAMPS

The Rotary Press stamps are printed from plates that are curved to fit around a cylinder. This curvature produces stamps that are slightly larger, either horizontally or vertically, than those printed from flat plates. Stamps from flat plates measure about 18½-19mm wide by 22mm high. When the impressions are placed sideways on the curved plates the stamps are 19½-20mm wide; when they are placed vertically the stamps are 23mm high.

Coil Stamps

Rotary Press Printing

1915-16 — Perf. 10 Horizontally

448 A140 1c green — 6.00 / 3.25
  Never hinged — 8.75
449 A140 2c red, Type I — 2,250. / 400.00
  Never hinged — 3,100.
450 A140 2c car, Type III ('16) — 9.50 / 3.00
  Never hinged — 14.00

1914-16 — Perf. 10 Vertically

452 A140 1c green — 9.50 / 2.00
  Never hinged — 14.00
453 A140 2c carmine rose, Type I — 110.00 / 4.25
  Never hinged — 160.00
454 A140 2c red, Type II — 87.50 / 10.00
  Never hinged — 130.00
455 A140 2c carmine, Type III — 9.00 / 1.00
  Never hinged — 13.00
456 A140 3c violet, Type I ('16) — 230.00 / 85.00
  Never hinged — 325.00
457 A140 4c brown ('16) — 25.00 / 17.50
  Never hinged — 35.00

458	A140	5c blue ('16)		30.00	17.50
		Never hinged		42.50	
		Nos. 452-458 (7)		501.00	137.25

1914, June 30   *Imperf.*

459	A140	2c car, Type I		250.00	900.00
		Never hinged		350.00	

No. 459 is a horizontal coil.
The used value is for a copy with a contemporaneous cancel.

Flat Plate Printings
1915, Feb. 8   **Wmk. 191**   *Perf. 10*

460	A148	$1 violet black		800.00	80.00
		Never hinged		1,200.	

1915, June 17   **Wmk. 190**   *Perf. 11*

461	A140	2c pale carmine red, Type I		110.00	220.00
		Never hinged		150.00	

Fraudulently perforated copies of No. 409 are offered as No. 461.

Unwatermarked
From 1916 onward all postage stamps except Nos. 519 and 832b are on unwatermarked paper.

1916-17   **Unwmk.**   *Perf. 10*

462	A140	1c green		6.25	.35
		Never hinged		9.50	
a.		Booklet pane of 6		9.00	1.60
		Never hinged		12.50	
463	A140	2c carmine, Type I		4.00	.25
		Never hinged		6.00	
a.		Booklet pane of 6		90.00	40.00
		Never hinged		135.00	
464	A140	3c violet, Type I		72.50	12.50
		Never hinged		110.00	
465	A140	4c orange brown		42.50	1.70
		Never hinged		65.00	
466	A140	5c blue		72.50	1.70
		Never hinged		110.00	
467	A140	5c car (error in plate of 2c, '17)		550.00	675.00
		Never hinged		800.00	
468	A140	6c red orange		90.00	7.00
		Never hinged		135.00	
469	A140	7c black		115.00	11.00
		Never hinged		175.00	
470	A148	8c olive green		55.00	5.50
		Never hinged		82.50	
471	A148	9c salmon red		55.00	14.00
		Never hinged		82.50	
472	A148	10c orange yel		100.00	1.25
		Never hinged		150.00	
473	A148	11c dark green		35.00	16.00
		Never hinged		52.50	
474	A148	12c claret brown		47.50	5.00
		Never hinged		72.50	
475	A148	15c gray		180.00	10.50
		Never hinged		270.00	
476	A148	20c lt ultra		240.00	12.00
		Never hinged		360.00	
476A	A148	30c orange red		4,500.	—
		Never hinged		5,500.	
477	A148	50c lt violet ('17)		1,000.	60.00
		Never hinged		1,500.	
478	A148	$1 violet black		750.00	16.00
		Never hinged		1,125.	
		Nos. 462-466,468-476,477-478 (16)		2,865.	174.75

No. 476A is valued in the grade of fine.

Types of 1903 Issue
1917, Mar. 22   *Perf. 10*

479	A127	$2 dark blue		325.00	40.00
		Never hinged		500.00	
480	A128	$5 light green		250.00	42.50
		Never hinged		375.00	

TYPE Ia

TWO CENTS

Type Ia. Design characteristics similar to type I except that all lines of design are stronger. The toga button, toga rope and rope shading lines are heavy. The latter characteristics are those of type II, which, however, occur only on impressions from rotary plates.
Used only on flat plates 10208 and 10209.

TYPE II

THREE CENTS

Type II. The top line of the toga rope is strong and the rope shading lines are heavy and complete. The line between the lips is heavy.
Used on both flat plate and rotary press printings.

1916-17   *Imperf.*

481	A140	1c green		1.00	.55
		Never hinged		1.50	
482	A140	2c carmine, Type I		1.50	1.25
		Never hinged		2.25	
482A	A140	2c dp rose, Type Ia		10,000.	

No. 482A was issued imperforate but all copies were privately perforated with large oblong perforations at the sides (Schermack type III). No. 500 exists with imperforate top sheet margin. Copies have been altered by trimming perforations. Some also have faked Schermack perfs.

483	A140	3c violet, Type I ('17)		14.00	7.50
		Never hinged		21.00	
484	A140	3c violet, Type II		11.00	5.00
		Never hinged		16.50	
485	A140	5c car (error in plate of 2c) ('17)		12,000.	

No. 485 is valued never hinged.

Coil Stamps
Rotary Press Printing
1916-19   *Perf. 10 Horizontally*

486	A140	1c green ('18)		.90	.25
		Never hinged		1.40	
487	A140	2c car, Type II		14.00	3.00
		Never hinged		22.50	
488	A140	2c car, Type III ('19)		2.50	1.75
		Never hinged		3.75	
489	A140	3c violet, Type I ('17)		5.00	1.50
		Never hinged		7.50	
		Nos. 486-489 (4)		22.40	6.50

1916-22   *Perf. 10 Vertically*

490	A140	1c green		.55	.25
		Never hinged		.80	
491	A140	2c car, Type II		2,000.	525.00
		Never hinged		2,600.	
492	A140	2c car, Type III		9.00	.25
		Never hinged		13.50	
493	A140	3c vio, Type I ('17)		16.00	3.00
		Never hinged		25.00	
494	A140	3c vio, Type II ('18)		10.00	1.00
		Never hinged		15.00	
495	A140	4c org brown ('17)		10.00	4.00
		Never hinged		15.00	
496	A140	5c blue ('19)		3.50	1.00
		Never hinged		5.25	
497	A148	10c orange yel ('22)		20.00	10.50
		Never hinged		30.00	
		Nos. 490,492-497 (7)		69.05	20.00

See note above #448 regarding #487, 491.

Blind Perfs.
Listings of imperforate-between varieties are for examples which show no trace of "blind perfs.," traces of impressions from the perforating pins which do not cut into the paper.

Types of 1912-14 Issue
1917-19   **Flat Plate Printings**   *Perf. 11*

498	A140	1c green		.40	.25
		Never hinged		.60	
a.		Vert. pair. imperf. horiz.		175.00	
b.		Horiz. pair. imperf. btwn.		100.00	
c.		Vert. pair. imperf. btwn.		450.00	—
d.		Double impression		175.00	
e.		Booklet pane of 6		2.50	.50
		Never hinged		4.00	
f.		Booklet pane of 30		1,000.	
		Never hinged		1,300.	
499	A140	2c rose, Type I		.40	.25
		Never hinged		.60	
a.		Vert. pair. imperf. horiz.		150.00	
b.		Horiz. pair. imperf. btwn.		275.00	150.00
c.		Vert. pair. imperf. btwn.		500.00	225.00
e.		Booklet pane of 6		4.00	.65
		Never hinged		5.50	
f.		Booklet pane of 30		27,500.	
		Never hinged		33,000.	
g.		Double impression		160.00	—
500	A140	2c deep rose, Type Ia		240.00	180.00
		Never hinged		360.00	

501	A140	3c lt violet, Type I		11.00	.25
		Never hinged		16.50	
b.		Booklet pane of 6		70.00	20.00
		Never hinged		100.00	
c.		Vert. pair. imperf. horiz.		300.00	
d.		Double impression		200.00	
502	A140	3c dk violet, Type II		14.00	.40
		Never hinged		22.50	
b.		Booklet pane of 6		60.00	22.50
		Never hinged		85.00	
c.		Vert. pair. imperf. horiz.		250.00	125.00
d.		Double impression		200.00	
503	A140	4c brown		10.00	.25
		Never hinged		15.00	
b.		Double impression			
504	A140	5c blue		9.00	.25
		Never hinged		13.50	
a.		Horiz. pair, imperf. btwn.		2,500.	—
505	A140	5c rose (error in plate of 2c)		400.00	500.00
		Never hinged		550.00	
506	A140	6c red orange		12.50	.25
		Never hinged		19.00	
507	A140	7c black		27.50	1.10
		Never hinged		42.50	
508	A148	8c olive bister		12.00	.50
		Never hinged		18.00	
b.		Vert. pair. imperf. btwn.		—	
509	A148	9c salmon red		14.00	1.75
		Never hinged		21.00	
510	A148	10c orange yellow		17.00	.15
		Never hinged		26.00	
511	A148	11c lt green		9.00	2.50
		Never hinged		13.50	
512	A148	12c claret brown		9.00	.35
		Never hinged		13.50	
		12c brown carmine		9.50	.40
		Never hinged		14.00	
513	A148	13c apple green ('19)		11.00	6.00
		Never hinged		16.50	
514	A148	15c gray		37.50	1.00
		Never hinged		57.50	
515	A148	20c light ultra		47.50	.25
		Never hinged		72.50	
b.		Vert. pair. imperf. btwn.		325.00	
c.		Double impression		1,250.	

Beware of pairs with blind perforations inside the design of the top stamp that are offered as No. 515b.

516	A148	30c orange red		37.50	1.00
		Never hinged		57.50	
b.		Double impression		—	
517	A148	50c red violet		70.00	.50
		Never hinged		110.00	
b.		Vert. pair. imperf. btwn. & at bottom		1,750.	1,000.
518	A148	$1 violet brown		55.00	1.50
		Never hinged		85.00	
b.		$1 deep brown		1,400.	825.00
		Never hinged		2,100.	
		Nos. 498-504,506-518 (20)		644.30	198.50

No. 518b is valued in the grade of fine to very fine.

Type of 1908-09 Issue
1917, Oct. 10   **Wmk. 191**   *Perf. 11*

519	A139	2c carmine		350.00	550.00

Fraudulently perforated copies of No. 344 are offered as No. 519.
The used value is for a stamp with a contemporaneous cancel.

Franklin — A149

1918, Aug. 19   **Unwmk.**   *Perf. 11*

523	A149	$2 orange red & blk		675.00	230.00
		Never hinged		1,000.	
524	A149	$5 dp grn & black		240.00	35.00
		Never hinged		360.00	

See No. 547 for $2 carmine & black.

Types of 1912-14 Issue

TYPE IV

TWO CENTS

Type IV. Top line of toga rope is broken. Shading lines in toga button are so arranged that the curving of the first and last form a "D (reversed) ID." Line of color in left "2" is very thin and usually broken.
Used on offset printings only.

TYPE V

TWO CENTS

Type V. Top line of toga is complete.
Five vertical shading lines in toga button.
Line of color in left "2" is very thin and usually broken.
Shading dots on the nose and lip are as indicated on the diagram.
Used on offset printings only.

TYPE Va

TWO CENTS

Type Va. Characteristics same as type V, except in shading dots of nose. Third row from bottom has 4 dots instead of 6. Overall height of type Va is 1/3mm less than type V.
Used on offset printings only.

TYPE VI

TWO CENTS

Type VI. General characteristics same as type V, except that line of color in left "2" is very heavy.
Used on offset printings only.

TYPE VII

TWO CENTS

Type VII. Line of color in left "2" is invariably continuous, clearly defined, and heavier than in type V or Va, but not as heavy as in type VI.

Additional vertical row of dots has been added to the upper lip.

Numerous additional dots have been added to hair on top of head.

Used on offset printings only.

TYPE III

THREE CENTS

Type III. The top line of the toga rope is strong but the fifth shading line is missing as in type I.

Center shading line of the toga button consists of two dashes with a central dot.

The "P" and "O" of "POSTAGE" are separated by a line of color.

The frame line at the bottom of the vignette is complete.

Used on offset printings only.

TYPE IV

THREE CENTS

Type IV. Shading lines of toga rope are complete. Second and fourth shading lines in toga button are broken in the middle and the third line is continuous with a dot in the center.

"P" and "O" of "POSTAGE" are joined.

Frame line at bottom of vignette is broken.

Used on offset printings only.

1918-20		**Offset Printing**	**Perf. 11**	
525	A140	1c gray green	2.50	.50
		Never hinged	3.75	
a.		1c dark green	2.75	.95
		Never hinged	4.00	
c.		Horiz. pair, imperf. btwn.	100.00	
d.		Double impression	27.50	25.00
526	A140	2c car, Type IV ('20)	27.50	3.50
		Never hinged	42.50	
527	A140	2c car, Type V ('20)	20.00	1.00
		Never hinged	30.00	
a.		Double impression	60.00	10.00
b.		Vert. pair, imperf. horiz.	600.00	
c.		Horiz. pair, imperf. vert.	1,000.	—
528	A140	2c car, Type Va ('20)	9.00	.25
		Never hinged	13.50	
c.		Double impression	27.50	
g.		Vert. pair, imperf. btwn.	1,000.	
528A	A140	2c car, Type VI ('20)	52.50	1.50
		Never hinged	77.50	
d.		Double impression	160.00	—
f.		Vert. pair, imperf. horiz.	1,000.	
h.		Vert. pair, imperf. btwn.	1,000.	
528B	A140	2c car, Type VII ('20)	21.00	.35
		Never hinged	31.00	
e.		Double impression	70.00	
529	A140	3c vio, Type III	3.25	.25
		Never hinged	5.00	
a.		Double impression	32.50	—
b.		Printed on both sides	450.00	
530	A140	3c pur, Type IV	1.60	.20
		Never hinged	2.25	
a.		Double impression	20.00	6.00
b.		Printed on both sides	250.00	
		Nos. 525-530 (8)	137.35	7.55

1918-20			**Imperf.**	
531	A140	1c green ('19)	9.00	8.00
		Never hinged	13.50	
532	A140	2c car rose, Type IV ('20)	40.00	27.50
		Never hinged	60.00	
533	A140	2c car, Type V ('20)	200.00	80.00
		Never hinged	300.00	

534	A140	2c car, Type Va ('20)	11.00	6.50
		Never hinged	16.50	
534A	A140	2c car, Type VI ('20)	40.00	22.50
		Never hinged	60.00	
534B	A140	2c car, Type VII ('20)	1,400.	800.00
		Never hinged	1,850.	
535	A140	3c vio, Type IV	9.00	5.00
		Never hinged	13.50	
a.		Double impression	100.00	—
		Nos. 531-534A,535 (6)	309.00	149.50

1919, Aug. 15			**Perf. 12½**	
536	A140	1c gray green	17.50	20.00
		Never hinged	27.50	
a.		Horiz. pair, imperf. vert.	500.00	

Victory Issue

"Victory" and Flags of the Allies — A150

Flat Plate Printing

1919, Mar. 3		**Engr.**	**Perf. 11**	
537	A150	3c violet	10.00	3.25
		Never hinged	15.00	
a.		3c deep red violet	450.00	150.00
		Never hinged	650.00	
b.		3c light reddish violet	10.00	3.00
		Never hinged	15.00	
c.		3c red violet	40.00	12.00
		Never hinged	60.00	

Victory of Allies in World War I.
No. 537a is valued in the grade of fine.

Rotary Press Printings

1919   **Perf. 11x10**
Size: 19½ to 20mm wide by 22 to 22¼mm high

538	A140	1c green	11.00	8.50
		Never hinged	16.50	
a.		Vert. pair, imperf. horiz.	50.00	100.00
		Never hinged	75.00	
539	A140	2c carmine rose, Type II	3,000.	3,750.
		Never hinged	4,250.	
540	A140	2c carmine rose, Type III	12.00	8.50
		Never hinged	18.00	
a.		Vert. pair, imperf. horiz.	50.00	100.00
		Never hinged	75.00	
b.		Horiz. pair, imperf. vert.	750.00	
541	A140	3c vio, Type II	37.50	30.00
		Never hinged	57.50	

The part perforate varieties of Nos. 538a and 540a were issued in sheets and may be had in blocks; similar part perforate varieties, Nos. 490 and 492, are from coils and are found only in strips. See note over No. 448 regarding No. 539.

No. 539 is valued in the grade of fine.

Size: 19x22½-22¾mm

1920, May 26			**Perf. 10x11**	
542	A140	1c green	13.50	1.10
		Never hinged	20.00	

Size: 19x22½mm

1921			**Perf. 10**	
543	A140	1c green	.50	.25
		Never hinged	.75	
a.		Horiz. pair, imperf. btwn.	1,100.	

Size: 19x22½mm

1922			**Perf. 11**	
544	A140	1c green	13,500.	3,000.
		Never hinged	17,000.	

No. 544 is valued in the grade of fine.

Size: 19½-20x22mm

1921			**Perf. 11**	
545	A140	1c green	150.00	160.00
		Never hinged	225.00	
546	A140	2c car rose, Type III	95.00	150.00
		Never hinged	150.00	

Flat Plate Printing

1920, Nov. 1			**Perf. 11**	
547	A149	$2 carmine & black	200.00	40.00
		Never hinged	300.00	

Pilgrim Tercentenary Issue

"Mayflower" — A151   Landing of the Pilgrims A152

Signing of the Compact — A153

1920, Dec. 21			**Perf. 11**	
548	A151	1c green	4.50	2.25
		Never hinged	6.75	
549	A152	2c carmine rose	6.50	1.60
		Never hinged	10.00	
550	A153	5c deep blue	42.50	12.50
		Never hinged	65.00	
		Nos. 548-550 (3)	53.50	16.35

Tercentenary of the landing of the Pilgrims at Plymouth, Mass.

Nathan Hale A154

Harding A156

Lincoln A158

Theodore Roosevelt A160

McKinley A162

Jefferson A164

Rutherford B. Hayes A166

American Indian A168

Franklin A155

Washington A157

Martha Washington A159

Garfield A161

Grant A163

Monroe A165

Grover Cleveland A167

Statue of Liberty A169

Golden Gate — A170

Buffalo A172

Niagara Falls — A171

Arlington Amphitheater A173

Lincoln Memorial A174

US Capitol A175

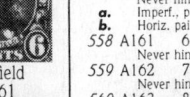

Head of Freedom Statue, Capitol Dome — A176

1922-25			**Perf. 11**	
551	A154	½c olive brn ('25)	.15	.15
		Never hinged	.25	
552	A155	1c dp green ('23)	1.40	.15
		Never hinged	2.50	
a.		Booket pane of 6	6.50	.80
		Never hinged	9.50	
553	A156	1½c yel brn ('25)	2.60	.15
		Never hinged	3.90	
554	A157	2c carmine ('23)	1.40	.15
		Never hinged	2.20	
a.		Horiz. pair, imperf. vert.	200.00	
b.		Vert. pair, imperf. horiz.	500.00	
c.		Booklet pane of 6	7.00	1.50
		Never hinged	10.50	
555	A158	3c violet ('23)	19.00	1.00
		Never hinged	28.50	
556	A159	4c yel brn ('23)	20.00	.25
		Never hinged	30.00	
a.		Vert. pair, imperf. horiz.		
557	A160	5c dark blue	20.00	.20
		Never hinged	30.00	
a.		Imperf., pair	1,500.	
b.		Horiz. pair, imperf. vert.		
558	A161	6c red orange	37.50	.85
		Never hinged	55.00	
559	A162	7c black ('23)	9.00	.55
		Never hinged	13.50	
560	A163	8c olive grn ('23)	50.00	.60
		Never hinged	75.00	
561	A164	9c rose ('23)	13.50	1.10
		Never hinged	22.00	
562	A165	10c orange ('23)	19.00	.15
		Never hinged	28.50	
a.		Vert. pair, imperf. horiz.	1,250.	
b.		Imperf., pair	1,250.	
563	A166	11c light blue	1.40	.40
		Never hinged	2.30	
d.		Imperf., pair		—
564	A167	12c brn vio ('23)	6.25	.15
		Never hinged	9.50	
a.		Horiz. pair, imperf. vert.	1,000.	
565	A168	14c blue ('23)	4.25	.75
		Never hinged	6.50	
566	A169	15c gray	25.00	.15
		Never hinged	37.50	
567	A170	20c car rose ('23)	22.50	.15
		Never hinged	35.00	
a.		Horiz. pair, imperf. vert.	1,500.	
568	A171	25c yellow green	19.00	.45
		Never hinged	29.00	
b.		Vert. pair, imperf. horiz.	850.00	
569	A172	30c olive brn ('23)	35.00	.35
		Never hinged	52.50	
570	A173	50c lilac	57.50	.15
		Never hinged	87.50	
571	A174	$1 vio black ('23)	47.50	.45
		Never hinged	72.50	
572	A175	$2 dp blue ('23)	100.00	9.00
		Never hinged	150.00	
573	A176	$5 car & bl ('23)	175.00	15.00
		Never hinged	260.00	
		Nos. 551-573 (23)	686.95	32.30
		Nos. 551-573, never hinged	1,034.	

For listings of other perforated stamps of designs A154 to A176 see

#578-579	Perf. 11x10
#581-591	Perf. 10
#594-595	Perf. 11
#632-642, 653, 692-696	Perf. 11x10½
#697-701	Perf. 10½x11

This series includes Nos. 622-623 (perf. 11).

1923-25			**Imperf.**	
575	A155	1c green	7.50	5.00
		Never hinged	11.50	
576	A156	1½c yel brn ('25)	1.60	1.50
		Never hinged	2.40	

577 A157 2c carmine 1.75 1.25
Never hinged 2.60
Nos. 575-577 (3) 10.85 7.75
Nos. 575-577, never hinged 16.50

The 1½c A156 rotary press imperforate is listed as No. 631.

Rotary Press Printings
Perf. 11x10

578 A155 1c green 95.00 *140.00*
Never hinged 140.00
579 A157 2c carmine 85.00 *125.00*
Never hinged 125.00

Nos. 578-579 were made from coil waste of Nos. 597, 599 and measure approximately 19¾x22¼mm.

1923-26 **Perf. 10**

581 A155 1c green 9.50 .65
Never hinged 14.50
582 A156 1½c brown ('25) 4.50 .60
Never hinged 6.75
583 A157 2c carmine ('24) 2.50 .25
Never hinged 3.75
a. Booklet pane of 6 85.00 27.50
Never hinged 125.00
584 A158 3c violet ('25) 26.50 2.25
Never hinged 40.00
585 A159 4c yel brn ('25) 16.00 .45
Never hinged 24.00
586 A160 5c blue ('25) 16.00 .25
Never hinged 24.00
a. Horiz. pair, imperf. btwn. —
587 A161 6c red org ('25) 7.50 .35
Never hinged 11.50
588 A162 7c black ('26) 10.50 5.50
Never hinged 16.00
589 A163 8c ol grn ('26) 25.00 3.50
Never hinged 37.50
590 A164 9c rose ('26) 5.00 2.25
Never hinged 7.50
591 A165 10c orange ('25) 60.00 .25
Never hinged 90.00
Nos. 581-591 (11) 183.00 16.30
Nos. 581-591, never hinged 275.50

Perf. 11

594 A155 1c green 16,000. 5,000.
595 A157 2c carmine 275. 300.
Never hinged 425.

Nos. 594-595 were made from coil waste of Nos. 597 and 599, and measure approximately 19¾x22¼mm.
No. 594 unused is valued without gum; perforations may touch one side.

Perf. 11

596 A155 1c green 45,000.
Precancelled 40,000.

No. 596 was made from rotary press sheet waste and measures approximately 19¼x22½mm. A majority of the copies carry the Bureau precancel "Kansas City, Mo." No. 596 is valued in the grade of fine.

ROTARY PRESS DOUBLE PAPER
The web of paper used on rotary presses must be continuous, therefore any break in the paper must be lapped and pasted, causing the "double paper" varieties. These are no longer listed since they may occur on any rotary press stamp.

Type I

Type II

Type I   Type II

Type I. No heavy hair lines at top center of head. Outline of left acanthus scroll generally faint at top and toward base at left side.
Type II. The heavy hair lines at top center of head; two being outstanding in the white area. Outline of left acanthus scroll very strong and clearly defined at top (under left edge of lettered panel) and at lower curve (above and to left of numeral oval). Type II is found only on Nos. 599A and 634A.

Coil Stamps
Rotary Press Printing

1923-29 **Perf. 10 Vertically**

597 A155 1c green .35 .15
Never hinged .50
598 A156 1½c brown ('25) 1.00 .15
Never hinged 1.50
599 A157 2c car, Type I ('23) .40 .15
Never hinged .60
599A A157 2c car, Type II ('29) 125.00 11.00
Never hinged 190.00
600 A158 3c violet ('24) 7.00 .15
Never hinged 10.50
601 A159 4c yellow brown 4.25 .35
Never hinged 6.50
602 A160 5c dk bl ('24) 1.75 .15
Never hinged 2.60
603 A165 10c orange ('24) 4.00 .15
Never hinged 6.00

Perf. 10 Horizontally

604 A155 1c green ('24) .35 .15
Never hinged .50
605 A156 1½c yel brn ('25) .35 .15
Never hinged .50
606 A157 2c carmine .35 .20
Never hinged .50
Nos. 597-599,600-606 (10) 19.80
Nos. 597-599, 600-606, never hinged 29.70
Set value 1.20

Harding Memorial Issue

Warren G. Harding — A177

Flat Plate Printing
(19¼x22¼mm)

1923, Sept. 1 **Perf. 11**

610 A177 2c black .65 .15
Never hinged 1.00
a. Horiz. pair, imperf. vert. 1,750.

1923, Nov. 15 **Imperf.**

611 A177 2c black 7.00 4.00
Never hinged 10.50

Rotary Press Printing
(19¼x22½mm)

1923, Sept. 12 **Perf. 10**

612 A177 2c black 16.00 1.75
Never hinged 24.00

1923 **Perf. 11**

613 A177 2c black 17,500.

Tribute to President Warren G. Harding, who died August 2, 1923.
Nos. 610a, 613 valued in the grade of fine.

Huguenot-Walloon Tercentenary Issue

"New Netherland" A178

Landing at Fort Orange — A179

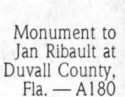

Monument to Jan Ribault at Duvall County, Fla. — A180

Flat Plate Printings

1924, May 1 **Perf. 11**

614 A178 1c dark green 3.00 3.25
Never hinged 4.25
615 A179 2c carmine rose 6.00 2.10
Never hinged 8.50

---

616 A180 5c dark blue 27.50 12.50
Never hinged 40.00
Nos. 614-616 (3) 36.50 17.85
Nos. 614-616, never hinged 52.75

Tercentenary of the settling of the Walloons and in honor of the Huguenots.

Lexington-Concord Issue

Washington at Cambridge A181

"Birth of Liberty," by Henry Sandham A182

The Minute Man, by Daniel Chester French A183

1925, Apr. 4 **Perf. 11**

617 A181 1c deep green 2.80 2.40
Never hinged 4.00
618 A182 2c carmine rose 5.50 3.90
Never hinged 7.75
619 A183 5c dark blue 25.00 12.50
Never hinged 35.00
Nos. 617-619 (3) 33.30 18.80
Nos. 617-619, never hinged 46.75

150th anniv. of the Battle of Lexington-Concord.

Norse-American Issue

Sloop "Restauration" A184

Viking Ship A185

1925, May 18 **Perf. 11**

620 A184 2c carmine & black 4.00 3.00
Never hinged 5.75
621 A185 5c dk blue & black 16.00 10.50
Never hinged 25.00

100th anniv. of the arrival in NY on Oct. 9, 1825, of the sloop "Restauration" with the first group of immigrants from Norway to the US.

Benjamin Harrison A186

Woodrow Wilson A187

1925-26 **Perf. 11**

622 A186 13c green ('26) 14.50 .45
Never hinged 21.00
623 A187 17c black 16.00 .25
Never hinged 24.00

Sesquicentennial Exposition Issue

Liberty Bell — A188

1926, May 10 **Perf. 11**

627 A188 2c carmine rose 3.25 .50
Never hinged 4.50

150th anniv. of the Declaration of Independence, Philadelphia, June 1-Dec. 1.

Statue of John Ericsson A189

Alexander Hamilton's Battery A190

Ericsson Memorial Issue

1926, May 29 **Perf. 11**

628 A189 5c gray lilac 6.50 3.25
Never hinged 9.50

John Ericsson, builder of the "Monitor."

Battle of White Plains Issue

1926, Oct. 18 **Perf. 11**

629 A190 2c carmine rose 2.25 1.70
Never hinged 3.25
a. Vertical pair, imperf. btwn. —

Battle of White Plains, NY, 150th anniv.

International Philatelic Exhibition
Souvenir Sheet

A190a

1926, Oct. 18 **Perf. 11**

630 A190a 2c carmine rose, sheet of 25 450.00 450.00
Never hinged 575.00

Intl. Phil. Exhib. in NYC, Oct. 16-23. Size: 158-160¼x136-146½mm.
Condition Valued:
Centering: Overall centering will average very fine, but individual stamps may be better or worse.
Perforations: No folds along rows of perforations.
Gum: There may be some light gum bends but no gum creases.
Hinging: There may be hinge marks in the selvage and on up to two or three stamps, but no heavy hingling or hinge remnants (except in the ungummed portion of the wide selvage).
Margins: Top panes should have about ½ inch bottom margin and 1 inch top margin. Bottom panes should have about ½ inch top margin and just under ¾ inch bottom margin. Both will have one wide side (usually 1½ inches plus) and one narrow (½ inch) side margin. The wide margin corner will have a small diagonal notch on top panes.

Types of 1922-26
Rotary Press Printings

1926, Aug. 27 **Imperf.**

631 A156 1½c yellow brown 2.00 1.70
Never hinged 2.75

1926-34 **Perf. 11x10½**

632 A155 1c green ('27) .15 .15
Never hinged .15
a. Booklet pane of 6 5.50 1.25
Never hinged 7.00
b. Vert. pair, imperf. btwn. 600.00 125.00
Never hinged 850.00
633 A156 1½c yel brown ('27) 2.00 .15
Never hinged 2.60
634 A157 2c car, Type I .15 .15
Never hinged .15
b. 2c carmine lake —
c. Horiz. pair, imperf. btwn. 2,000.
d. Booklet pane of 6 1.75 .75
Never hinged 2.50
634A A157 2c car, Type II ('28) 350.00 13.50
Never hinged 475.00
635 A158 3c violet ('27) .45 .15
Never hinged .55
a. 3c bright violet ('34) .25 .15
Never hinged .30
636 A159 4c yel brown ('27) 2.25 .15
Never hinged 3.00
637 A160 5c dk blue ('27) 2.25 .15
Never hinged 3.00

638	A161	6c red orange ('27)	2.25	.15
		Never hinged	3.00	
639	A162	7c black ('27)	2.25	.15
		Never hinged	3.00	
a.		Vert. pair, imperf. btwn.	275.00	85.00
640	A163	8c ol grn ('27)	2.25	.15
		Never hinged	3.00	
641	A164	9c rose ('27)	2.25	.15
		Never hinged	3.00	
642	A165	10c orange ('27)	3.75	.15
		Never hinged	5.00	
		Nos. 632-634,635-642 (11)	20.00	
		Nos. 632-634, 635-642, never hinged	26.45	
		Set value		.60

The 1½c, 2c, 4c, 5c, 6c, 8c imperf. (dry print) are printer's waste.
For ½c, 11c-50c see Nos. 653, 692-701.

Vermont Sesquicentennial Issue

Green Mountain Boy — A191

Flat Plate Printing

1927, Aug. 3			**Perf. 11**	
643	A191	2c carmine rose	1.40	.80
		Never hinged	2.00	

Battle of Bennington, Vt., and independence of the State of Vermont, 150th anniv.

Surrender of Gen. John Burgoyne A192

Washington at Prayer A193

Burgoyne Campaign Issue

1927, Aug. 3			**Perf. 11**	
644	A192	2c carmine rose	3.50	2.10
		Never hinged	5.00	

Battles of Bennington, Oriskany, Fort Stanwix and Saratoga.

Valley Forge Issue

1928, May 26			**Perf. 11**	
645	A193	2c carmine rose	1.05	.40
		Never hinged	1.40	

150th anniv. of Washington's encampment at Valley Forge, Pa.

Battle of Monmouth Issue

No. 634 Overprinted **MOLLY PITCHER**

Rotary Press Printing

1928, Oct. 20			**Perf. 11x10½**	
646	A157	2c carmine	1.10	1.10
		Never hinged	1.45	
a.		"Pitcher" only		

The normal space between a vertical pair of the overprints is 18mm, but pairs are known with the space measuring 28mm.
150th anniv. of the Battle of Monmouth, NJ, and as a memorial to "Molly Pitcher" (Mary Ludwig Hays), the heroine of the battle.

Hawaii Sesquicentennial Issue

Nos. 634 and 637 Overprinted **HAWAII 1778 - 1928**

Rotary Press Printing

1928, Aug. 13			**Perf. 11x10½**	
647	A157	2c carmine	5.00	4.50
		Never hinged	6.75	
648	A160	5c dark blue	14.50	13.50
		Never hinged		

150th anniv. of the discovery of the Hawaiian Islands by Captain Cook.
These stamps were on sale at post offices in the Hawaiian Islands and at the Postal Agency in Washington, DC They were not on sale at post offices in the Continental US, though they were valid for postage there.
Normally the overprints were placed 18mm apart vertically, but pairs exist with a space of 28mm between the overprints.

Aeronautics Conference Issue

Wright Airplane A194

Globe and Airplane A195

Flat Plate Printing

1928, Dec. 12			**Perf. 11**	
649	A194	2c carmine rose	1.25	.80
		Never hinged	1.75	
650	A195	5c blue	5.25	3.25
		Never hinged	7.00	

Intl. Civil Aeronautics Conf. at Washington, DC, Dec. 12-14, 1928, and of the 25th anniv. of the 1st airplane flight by the Wright brothers, Dec. 17, 1903.

George Rogers Clark Issue

Surrender of Fort Sackville A196

1929, Feb. 25			**Perf. 11**	
651	A196	2c carmine & black	.65	.50
		Never hinged	.90	

150th anniv. of the surrender of Fort Sackville, the present site of Vincennes, Ind., to George Rogers Clark.

Type of 1925

Rotary Press Printing

1929, May 25			**Perf. 11x10½**	
653	A154	½c olive brown	.15	.15
		Never hinged	.20	

Edison's First Lamp A197

Maj. Gen. John Sullivan A198

Electric Light Jubilee Issue

1929	**Flat Plate Printing**		**Perf. 11**	
654	A197	2c carmine rose	.70	.70
		Never hinged	1.00	

Rotary Press Printing Perf. 11x10½

655	A197	2c carmine rose	.65	.15
		Never hinged	.90	

Coil Stamp (Rotary Press) Perf. 10 Vertically

656	A197	2c carmine rose	14.00	1.75
		Never hinged	20.00	
		Nos. 654-656 (3)	15.35	2.60

50th anniv. of invention of the incandescent lamp by Thomas Alva Edison, Oct. 21, 1879. Issued: No. 654, June 5; Nos. 655-656, June 11.

Sullivan Expedition Issue

Flat Plate Printing

1929, June 17			**Perf. 11**	
657	A198	2c carmine rose	.70	.60
		Never hinged	1.00	

150th anniv. of the Sullivan Expedition in NY State during the Revolutionary War.

Nos. 632-634, 635-642 Overprinted **Kans.**

Rotary Press Printing

1929			**Perf. 11x10½**	
658	A155	1c green	2.50	2.00
		Never hinged	3.50	
a.		Vert. pair, one without ovpt.	325.00	
659	A156	1½c brown	4.00	2.90
		Never hinged	5.50	
a.		Vert. pair, one without ovpt.	350.00	
660	A157	2c carmine	4.50	1.10
		Never hinged	6.25	

661	A158	3c violet	22.50	15.00
		Never hinged	31.00	
a.		Vert. pair, one without ovpt.	425.00	
662	A159	4c yellow brown	22.50	9.00
		Never hinged	31.00	
663	A160	5c deep blue	14.00	9.75
		Never hinged	20.00	
664	A161	6c red orange	32.50	18.00
		Never hinged	45.00	
665	A162	7c black	30.00	27.50
		Never hinged	42.50	
a.		Vert. pair, one without ovpt.	425.00	
666	A163	8c olive green	110.00	75.00
		Never hinged	150.00	
667	A164	9c light rose	16.00	11.25
		Never hinged	22.50	
668	A165	10c orange yel	25.00	12.00
		Never hinged	34.00	
		Nos. 658-668 (11)	283.50	183.50
		Nos. 658-668, never hinged	391.25	

See note following No. 679.

Overprinted **Nebr.**

669	A155	1c green	4.00	2.25
		Never hinged	5.75	
a.		Vert. pair, one without ovpt.	300.00	
b.		No period after "Nebr." (19338, 19339 L.R. 26, 36)	50.00	
670	A156	1½c brown	3.75	2.50
		Never hinged	5.25	
671	A157	2c carmine	3.75	1.30
		Never hinged	5.25	
672	A158	3c violet	15.00	12.00
		Never hinged	21.00	
a.		Vert. pair, one without ovpt.	425.00	
673	A159	4c yellow brown	22.50	15.00
		Never hinged	32.50	
674	A160	5c deep blue	20.00	15.00
		Never hinged	27.50	
675	A161	6c red orange	47.50	24.00
		Never hinged	65.00	
676	A162	7c black	27.50	18.00
		Never hinged	37.50	
677	A163	8c olive green	37.50	25.00
		Never hinged	52.50	
678	A164	9c light rose	42.50	27.50
		Never hinged	60.00	
a.		Vert. pair, one without ovpt.	650.00	
679	A165	10c orange yel	135.00	22.50
		Never hinged	190.00	
		Nos. 669-679 (11)	359.00	165.05
		Nos. 669-679, never hinged	502.25	

Nos. 658-660, 669-673, 677 and 678 are known with the overprints on vertical pairs spaced 32mm apart instead of the normal 22mm.
Important: Nos. 658-679 with original gum have either one horizontal gum breaker ridge per stamp or portions of two at the extreme top and bottom of the stamps, 21mm apart. Multiple complete gum breaker ridges indicate a fake overprint. Absence of the gum breaker ridges indicates either regumming or regumming and a fake overprint.

Gen. Anthony Wayne Memorial — A199

Lock No. 5, Monongahela River — A200

Battle of Fallen Timbers Issue

Flat Plate Printing

1929, Sept. 14			**Perf. 11**	
680	A199	2c carmine rose	.80	.80
		Never hinged	1.10	

General Anthony Wayne memorial and the 135th anniv. of the Battle of Fallen Timbers, Ohio.

Ohio River Canalization Issue

1929, Oct. 19			**Perf. 11**	
681	A200	2c carmine rose	.70	.65
		Never hinged	.90	

Completion of the Ohio River Canalization Project between Cairo, Ill. and Pittsburgh.

Massachusetts Bay Colony Issue

Mass. Bay Colony Seal — A201

1930, Apr. 8			**Perf. 11**	
682	A201	2c carmine rose	.60	.50
		Never hinged	.80	

300th anniv. of the founding of the Massachusetts Bay Colony.

Carolina-Charleston Issue

Gov. Joseph West and Chief Shadoo, a Kiowa — A202

1930, Apr. 10			**Perf. 11**	
683	A202	2c carmine rose	1.20	1.20
		Never hinged	1.60	

260th anniv. of the founding of the Province of Carolina, and the 250th anniv. of the City of Charleston, SC.

Warren G. Harding — A203

William H. Taft — A204

Type of 1922-26 Issue

Rotary Press Printing

1930			**Perf. 11x10½**	
684	A203	1½c brown	.35	.15
		Never hinged	.45	
685	A204	4c brown	.90	.15
		Never hinged	1.25	
		Set value		.15

Coil Stamps Perf. 10 Vertically

686	A203	1½c brown	1.80	.15
		Never hinged	2.50	
687	A204	4c brown	3.25	.45
		Never hinged	4.50	
		Set value		.50

Braddock's Field Issue

Statue of Col. George Washington — A205

Flat Plate Printing

1930, July 9			**Perf. 11**	
688	A205	2c carmine rose	1.00	.85
		Never hinged	1.30	

175th anniv. of the Battle of Braddock's Field, otherwise the Battle of Monongahela.

General von Steuben — A206

General Casimir Pulaski — A207

Von Steuben Issue

1930, Sept. 17			**Perf. 11**	
689	A206	2c carmine rose	.55	.55
		Never hinged	.70	
a.		Imperf., pair	2,500.	
		Never hinged	3,250.	

Gen. Baron Friedrich Wilhelm von Steuben (1730-1794), German soldier who served with distinction in American Revolution.

Pulaski Issue

1931, Jan. 16			**Perf. 11**	
690	A207	2c carmine rose	.30	.15
		Never hinged	.40	

150th anniv. (in 1929) of the death of Gen. Count Casimir Pulaski (1748-1779), Polish patriot and hero of American Revolution.

Types of 1922-26

Rotary Press Printing

1931			**Perf. 11x10½**	
692	A166	11c light blue	2.60	.15
		Never hinged	3.70	
693	A167	12c brown violet	5.50	.15
		Never hinged	7.75	
694	A186	13c yellow green	2.00	.15
		Never hinged	2.80	
695	A168	14c dark blue	3.75	.25
		Never hinged	5.25	
696	A169	15c gray	8.00	.15
		Never hinged	11.25	

Perf. 10½x11

697	A187	17c black	4.50	.15
		Never hinged	6.25	

698 A170	20c carmine rose	8.75	.15
	Never hinged	12.50	
699 A171	25c blue green	9.00	.15
	Never hinged	12.50	
700 A172	30c brown	17.50	.15
	Never hinged	25.00	
701 A173	50c lilac	40.00	.15
	Never hinged	55.00	
	Nos. 692-701 (10)	101.60	
	Nos. 692-701, never hinged	142.00	
	Set value		1.00

"The Greatest Mother" A208

Count de Rochambeau, Washington, Count de Grasse A209

Red Cross Issue
Flat Plate Printing
1931, May 21   *Perf. 11*

702 A208	2c black & red	.25	.15
	Never hinged	.30	
a.	Red cross omitted	40,000.	

50th anniv. of the founding of the American Red Cross Society.

Yorktown Issue
1931, Oct. 19   *Perf. 11*

703 A209	2c carmine rose & black	.40	.25
	Never hinged	.50	
a.	2c lake & black	4.50	.65
	Never hinged	6.25	
b.	2c dark lake & black	375.00	
	Never hinged	525.00	
c.	Horiz. pair, imperf. vert.	5,000.	
	Never hinged	5,000.	

Surrender of Yorktown, sesquicentennial.

Washington Bicentennial Issue
Various Portraits of George Washington

A210   A211

A212   A213

A214   A215

A216   A217

A218   A219

A220   A221

Rotary Press Printings
1932, Jan. 1   *Perf. 11x10½*

704 A210	½c olive brown	.15	.15
	Never hinged	.15	
705 A211	1c green	.15	.15
	Never hinged	.15	

706 A212	1½c brown	.45	.15
	Never hinged	.60	
707 A213	2c carmine rose	.15	.15
	Never hinged	.15	
708 A214	3c deep violet	.60	.15
	Never hinged	.80	
709 A215	4c light brown	.30	.15
	Never hinged	.40	
710 A216	5c blue	1.80	.15
	Never hinged	2.40	
711 A217	6c red orange	3.50	.15
	Never hinged	4.60	
712 A218	7c black	.30	.15
	Never hinged	.40	
713 A219	8c olive bister	3.00	.50
	Never hinged	4.00	
714 A220	9c pale red	2.60	.15
	Never hinged	3.50	
715 A221	10c orange yellow	11.00	.15
	Never hinged	14.50	
	Nos. 704-715 (12)	24.00	
	Nos. 704-715, never hinged	31.65	
	Set value		1.40

200th anniv. of the birth of Washington.

Skier — A222

Boy and Girl Planting Tree — A223

Olympic Winter Games Issue
Flat Plate Printing
1932, Jan. 25   *Perf. 11*

716 A222	2c carmine rose	.40	.20
	Never hinged	.50	

Olympic Winter Games, Lake Placid, NY, Feb. 4-13.

Arbor Day Issue
Rotary Press Printing
1932, Apr. 22   *Perf. 11x10½*

717 A223	2c carmine rose	.15	.15
	Never hinged	.20	

60th anniv. of the 1st observance of Arbor Day in Nebr., April, 1872, and the birth centenary of Julius Sterling Morton, who conceived the plan and the name "Arbor Day," while a member of the Nebr. State Board of Agriculture.

10th Olympic Games Issue

Runner at Starting Mark A224

Myron's Discobolus A225

1932, June 15   *Perf. 11x10½*

718 A224	3c violet	1.40	.15
	Never hinged	1.75	
719 A225	5c blue	2.20	.20
	Never hinged	2.75	

Los Angeles, Cal., July 30-Aug. 14.

Washington — A226

1932, June 16   *Perf. 11x10½*

720 A226	3c deep violet	.15	.15
	Never hinged	.20	
b.	Booklet pane of 6	32.50	5.00
	Never hinged	42.50	
c.	Vert. pair, imperf. btwn.	300.00	250.00

Coil Stamps
Rotary Press Printing
1932, June 24   *Perf. 10 Vertically*

721 A226	3c deep violet	2.75	.15
	Never hinged	3.50	

1932, Oct. 12   *Perf. 10 Horizontally*

722 A226	3c deep violet	1.50	.35

Garfield Type of 1922-26 Issue
1932, Aug. 18   *Perf. 10 Vertically*

723 A161	6c deep orange	11.00	.30
	Never hinged	14.50	

William Penn A227

Daniel Webster A228

William Penn Issue
Flat Plate Printing
1932, Oct. 24   *Perf. 11*

724 A227	3c violet	.25	.15
	Never hinged	.35	
a.	Vert. pair, imperf. horiz.	.35	

250th anniv. of the arrival in America of William Penn (1644-1718), English Quaker and founder of Pennsylvania.

Daniel Webster Issue
1932, Oct. 24   *Perf. 11*

725 A228	3c violet	.30	.25
	Never hinged	.40	

Daniel Webster (1782-1852), statesman.

Georgia Bicentennial Issue

Gen. James Edward Oglethorpe — A229

1933, Feb. 12   *Perf. 11*

726 A229	3c violet	.25	.20
	Never hinged	.35	

200th anniv. of the founding of the Colony of Georgia and James Edward Oglethorpe, who landed from England, Feb. 12th, 1733, and personally supervised the establishing of the colony.

Peace of 1783 Issue

Washington's Headquarters, Newburgh, NY — A230

Rotary Press Printing
1933, Apr. 19   *Perf. 10½x11*

727 A230	3c violet	.15	.15
	Never hinged	.20	

150th anniv. of the Proclamation of Peace between the US and Great Britain at the end of the Revolutionary War.
See No. 752.

Century of Progress Issue

Restoration of Fort Dearborn A231

Federal Building at Chicago, 1933 A232

1933, May 25   *Perf. 10½x11*

728 A231	1c yellow green	.15	.15
	Never hinged	.20	
729 A232	3c violet	.15	.15
	Never hinged	.20	
	Set value	.20	.15

"Century of Progress" Intl. Phil. Exhib., Chicago, 1933 and 100th anniv. of the incorporation of Chicago as a city.

American Philatelic Society Issue
Souvenir Sheets
Without Gum
Flat Plate Printing
1933, Aug. 25   *Imperf.*

730	Sheet of 25	27.50	27.50
a.	A231 1c deep yellow green	.75	.45
731	Sheet of 25	25.00	25.00
a.	A232 3c deep violet	.65	.45

Sheet measures 134x120mm.
See Nos. 766-767.

National Recovery Act Issue

Group of Workers — A233

Rotary Press Printing
1933, Aug. 15   *Perf. 10½x11*

732 A233	3c violet	.15	.15
	Never hinged	.20	

Issued to direct attention to and arouse support of the Nation for the NRA.

Byrd Antarctic Issue

World Map on van der Grinten's Projection — A234

Flat Plate Printing
1933, Oct. 9   *Perf. 11*

733 A234	3c dark blue	.50	.50
	Never hinged	.60	

Second Antarctic expedition of Rear Admiral Richard E. Byrd.
In addition to the 3 cents postage, letters sent by the ships of the expedition to be canceled in Little America were subject to a service charge of 50 cents each.
See Nos. 735, 753.

Kosciuszko Issue

Statue of Gen. Tadeusz Kosciuszko — A235

1933, Oct. 13   *Perf. 11*

734 A235	5c blue	.55	.25
	Never hinged	.65	
a.	Horiz. pair, imperf. vert.	2,000.	
	Never hinged	2,500.	

Gen. Tadeusz Kosciuszko (1746-1807), Polish soldier and statesman who served in American Revolution. 150th anniv. of grant of American citizenship.

National Stamp Exhibition Issue
Souvenir Sheet
Without Gum
1934, Feb. 10   *Imperf.*

735	Sheet of 6	13.00	10.00
a.	A234 3c dark blue	2.10	1.65

Sheet measures 87x93mm. See #768.

Maryland Tercentenary Issue

"The Ark" and "The Dove" — A236

1934, Mar. 23   *Perf. 11*

736 A236	3c carmine rose	.15	.15
	Never hinged	.20	

300th anniv. of the founding of Maryland.

Mothers of America Issue

Adaptation of Whistler's Portrait of his Mother A237

Rotary Press Printing
1934, May 2   *Perf. 11x10½*

737 A237	3c deep violet	.15	.15
	Never hinged	.20	

Flat Plate Printing
Perf. 11

738 A237	3c deep violet	.15	.15
	Never hinged	.20	
	Set value	.20	.15

Mother's Day. See No. 754.

Wisconsin Tercentenary Issue

Nicolet's Landing
A238

1934, July 7 *Perf. 11*
739 A238 3c deep violet .15 .15
  Never hinged .15
a. Vert. pair, imperf. horiz. 250.00
  Never hinged 325.00
b. Horiz. pair, imperf. vert. 325.00
  Never hinged 400.00

Tercentenary of the arrival of French explorer Jean Nicolet at Green Bay, Wis.
See No. 755.

National Parks Issue

El Capitan, Yosemite (California) A239
Old Faithful, Yellowstone (Wyoming) A243

Grand Canyon (Arizona) A240

Mt. Rainier and Mirror Lake (Washington) A241

Mesa Verde (Colorado) A242

Crater Lake (Oregon) A244

Great Head, Acadia Park (Maine) A245

Great White Throne, Zion Park (Utah) A246
Great Smoky Mts. (North Carolina) A248

Mt. Rockwell (Mt. Sinopah) and Two Medicine Lake, Glacier Natl. Park (Montana) A247

1934 **Flat Plate Printing** *Perf. 11*
740 A239 1c green .15 .15
  Never hinged .15
a. Vert. pair, imperf. horiz., with gum 450.00
  Never hinged 550.00
741 A240 2c red .15 .15
  Never hinged .15
a. Vert. pair, imperf. horiz., with gum 450.00
  Never hinged 525.00
b. Horiz. pair, imperf. vert., with gum 300.00
  Never hinged 375.00
742 A241 3c deep violet .15 .15
  Never hinged .15
a. Vert. pair, imperf. horiz., with gum 350.00
  Never hinged 435.00
743 A242 4c brown .40 .40
  Never hinged .50
a. Vert. pair, imperf. horiz., with gum 500.00
  Never hinged 625.00
744 A243 5c blue .75 .65
  Never hinged .95
a. Horiz. pair, imperf. vert., with gum 400.00
  Never hinged 500.00
745 A244 6c dark blue 1.20 .85
  Never hinged 1.60
746 A245 7c black .65 .75
  Never hinged .85
a. Horiz. pair, imperf. vert., with gum 550.00
  Never hinged 685.00
747 A246 8c sage green 1.70 1.50
  Never hinged 2.20
748 A247 9c red orange 1.60 .65
  Never hinged 2.10
749 A248 10c gray black 3.25 1.25
  Never hinged 4.25
  Nos. 740-749 (10) 10.00 6.50
  Nos. 740-749, never hinged 12.90

National Parks Year.
See Nos. 750-751, 756-765, 769-770, 797.

American Philatelic Society Issue
Souvenir Sheet

1934, Aug. 28 *Imperf.*
750 Sheet of 6 30.00 27.50
  Never hinged 37.50
a. A241 3c deep violet 3.50 3.25
  Never hinged 4.50

Sheet measures approximately 98x93mm. See #770.

Trans-Mississippi Philatelic Exposition Issue
Souvenir Sheet

1934, Oct. 10 *Imperf.*
751 Sheet of 6 12.50 12.50
  Never hinged 16.00
a. A239 1c green 1.40 1.60
  Never hinged 1.85

Sheet measures approximately 92x99mm. See #769.

Special Printing (Nos. 752-771)

"Issued for a limited time in full sheets as printed, and in blocks thereof, to meet the requirements of collectors and others who may be interested."—From Postal Bulletin, No. 16614.

Issuance of the following 20 stamps in complete sheets resulted from the protest of collectors and others at the practice of presenting, to certain government officials, complete sheets of unsevered panes, imperforate (except Nos. 752 and 753) and generally ungummed.

Without Gum.

Note. In 1940 the P.O. Department offered to and did gum full sheets of Nos. 754 to 771 sent in by owners.

Type of Peace Issue
Issued in sheets of 400
Rotary Press Printing
1935, Mar. 15 *Perf. 10½x11*
752 A230 3c violet .15 .15

Type of Byrd Issue
Issued in sheets of 200
Flat Plate Printing
Perf. 11
753 A234 3c dark blue .50 .45

No. 753 is similar to No. 733. Positive identification is by pairs or blocks showing a guide line between stamps. These lines are found only on No. 753.

Type of Mothers of America Issue
Issued in sheets of 200
Imperf
754 A237 3c deep violet .55 .55

Type of Wisconsin Issue
Issued in sheets of 200
Imperf
755 A238 3c deep violet .55 .55

Types of National Parks Issue
Issued in sheets of 200
Imperf
756 A239 1c green .20 .20
757 A240 2c red .25 .25
758 A241 3c deep violet .50 .45
759 A242 4c brown .95 .95
760 A243 5c blue 1.50 1.30
761 A244 6c dark blue 2.40 2.10
762 A245 7c black 1.50 1.40
763 A246 8c sage green 1.60 1.50
764 A247 9c red orange 1.90 1.65
765 A248 10c gray black 3.75 3.25
  Nos. 756-765 (10) 14.55 13.05

Souvenir Sheets
Type of Century of Progress Issue
Issued in sheets of 9 panes of 25 stamps each

Note: Single items from these sheets are identical with other varieties, 766 & 730, 766a & 730a, 767 & 731, 767a & 731a, 768 & 735, 768a & 735a, 769 & 756, 770 & 758. Positive identification is by blocks or pairs showing wide gutters between stamps. These wide gutters occur only on Nos. 766 to 770 and measure, horizontally, 13mm on Nos. 766-767; 16mm on No. 768, and 23mm on Nos. 769-770.

Imperf
766 Pane of 25 25.00 25.00
a. A231 1c yellow green .70 .40
767 Pane of 25 23.50 23.50
a. A232 3c violet .60 .40

National Exhibition Issue
Type of Byrd Issue
Issued in sheets of 25 panes of 6 stamps each
Imperf
768 Pane of 6 20.00 15.00
a. A234 3c dark blue 2.80 2.40

Types of National Parks Issue
Issued in sheets of 20 panes of 6 stamps each
Imperf
769 Pane of 6 12.50 11.00
a. A239 1c green 1.85 1.80
770 Pane of 6 30.00 24.00
a. A241 3c deep violet 3.25 3.10

Type of Air Post Special Delivery
Issued in sheets of 200
Imperf
771 APSD1 16c dark blue 2.25 2.25

> Catalogue values for unused stamps in this section, from this point to the end of the section, are for Never Hinged items.

Connecticut Tercentenary Issue

Charter Oak — A249

Rotary Press Printing
1935, Apr. 26 *Perf. 11x10½*
772 A249 3c violet .15 .15
300th anniv. of the settlement of Conn.
See No. 778a.

California-Pacific Exposition Issue

View of San Diego Exposition A250

1935, May 29 *Perf. 11x10½*
773 A250 3c purple .15 .15
California-Pacific Expo., San Diego.
See No. 778b.

Boulder Dam Issue

Boulder Dam — A251

Flat Plate Printing
1935, Sept. 30 *Perf. 11*
774 A251 3c purple .15 .15
Dedication of Boulder Dam.

Michigan Centenary Issue

Michigan State Seal — A252

Rotary Press Printing
1935, Nov. 1 *Perf. 11x10½*
775 A252 3c purple .15 .15
Advance celebration of Michigan statehood centenary. Michigan was admitted to Union Jan. 26, 1837.
See No. 778c.

Texas Centennial Issue

Sam Houston, Stephen F. Austin and the Alamo — A253

1936, Mar. 2 *Perf. 11x10½*
776 A253 3c purple .15 .15
Centennial of Texas independence.
See No. 778d.

Rhode Island Tercentenary Issue

Statue of Roger Williams — A254

1936, May 4 *Perf. 10½x11*
777 A254 3c purple .15 .15
Settlement of Rhode Island, 1636.

Third International Philatelic Exhibition Issue
Souvenir Sheet

A254a

Flat Plate Printing
1936, May 9 *Imperf.*
778 A254a Sheet of 4 1.75 1.75
a. A249 3c violet .40 .30
b. A250 3c violet .40 .30
c. A252 3c violet .40 .30
d. A253 3c violet .40 .30

Sheet measures 98x66mm.

Arkansas Centennial Issue

Arkansas Post, Old and New State Houses A255

Rotary Press Printing

1936, June 15   *Perf. 11x10½*
782 A255 3c purple   .15 .15
Centennial of Arkansas statehood.

Map of Oregon Territory A256

Susan B. Anthony A257

Oregon Territory Issue

1936, July 14   *Perf. 11x10½*
783 A256 3c purple   .15 .15
Centenary of Oregon Territory opening.

Susan B. Anthony Issue

1936, Aug. 26   *Perf. 11x10½*
784 A257 3c dark violet   .15 .15
Susan Brownell Anthony (1820-1906), woman suffrage advocate, honored on 16th anniv. of ratification of 19th Amendment granting American women the right to vote.

Army Issue

George Washington, Nathanael Greene and Mount Vernon — A258

Andrew Jackson, Winfield Scott and the Hermitage A259

Generals Sherman, Grant and Sheridan A260

Generals Robert E. Lee, "Stonewall" Jackson and Stratford Hall — A261

US Military Academy, West Point — A262

1936-37   *Perf. 11x10½*
785 A258 1c green   .15 .15
786 A259 2c carmine ('37)   .15 .15
787 A260 3c purple ('37)   .20 .15
788 A261 4c gray ('37)   .30 .15
789 A262 5c ultra ('37)   .60 .15
   Nos. 785-789 (5)   1.40
   Set value   .45
Issued in honor of the United States Army.

Navy Issue

John Paul Jones and John Barry — A263

Stephen Decatur and Thomas MacDonough A264

Admirals David G. Farragut and David D. Porter — A265

Admirals William T. Sampson, George Dewey and Winfield S. Schley — A266

Seal of US Naval Academy and Naval Cadets — A267

1936-37   *Perf. 11x10½*
790 A263 1c green   .15 .15
791 A264 2c carmine ('37)   .15 .15
792 A265 3c purple ('37)   .15 .15
793 A266 4c gray ('37)   .30 .15
794 A267 5c ultra ('37)   .60 .15
   Nos. 790-794 (5)   1.35
   Set value   .45
Issued in honor of the United States Navy.

Northwest Ordinance Sesquicentennial Issue

Manasseh Cutler, Rufus Putnam and Map of Northwest Territory A268

1937, July 13   *Perf. 11x10½*
795 A268 3c red violet   .15 .15
150th anniv. of the adoption of the Ordinance of 1787 and the creation of the Northwest Territory.

Virginia Dare Issue

Virginia Dare and Parents — A269

Flat Plate Printing

1937, Aug. 18   *Perf. 11*
796 A269 5c gray blue   .20 .20
350th anniv. of the birth of Virginia Dare and the settlement at Roanoke Island. Virginia was the first child born in America of English parents (Aug. 18, 1587).

Society of Philatelic Americans
Souvenir Sheet

A269a

1937, Aug. 26   *Imperf.*
797 A269a 10c blue green   .60 .40
Sheet measures 67x78mm.

Constitution Sesquicentennial Issue

Signing of the Constitution A270

Rotary Press Printing

1937, Sept. 17   *Perf. 11x10½*
798 A270 3c bright red violet   .15 .15
Sesquicentennial of the Signing of the Constitution, Sept. 17, 1787.

Territorial Issues
Hawaii

Statue of Kamehameha I, Honolulu — A271

1937, Oct. 18   *Perf. 10½x11*
799 A271 3c violet   .15 .15

Alaska

Landscape with Mt. McKinley A272

1937, Nov. 12   *Perf. 11x10½*
800 A272 3c violet   .15 .15

Puerto Rico

La Fortaleza, San Juan — A273

1937, Nov. 25   *Perf. 11x10½*
801 A273 3c bright violet   .15 .15

Virgin Islands

Charlotte Amalie — A274

1937, Dec. 15   *Perf. 11x10½*
802 A274 3c light violet   .15 .15

Presidential Issue

Benjamin Franklin A275

Martha Washington A277

Thomas Jefferson A279

George Washington A276

John Adams A278

James Madison A280

White House A281

John Q. Adams A283

Martin Van Buren A285

John Tyler A287

Zachary Taylor A289

Franklin Pierce A291

Abraham Lincoln A293

Ulysses S. Grant A295

James A. Garfield A297

James Monroe A282

Andrew Jackson A284

William H. Harrison A286

James K. Polk A288

Millard Fillmore A290

James Buchanan A292

Andrew Johnson A294

Rutherford B. Hayes A296

Chester A. Arthur A298

Grover
Cleveland
A299

Benjamin
Harrison
A300

William
McKinley
A301

Theodore
Roosevelt
A302

William
Howard Taft
A303

Woodrow
Wilson
A304

Warren G.
Harding
A305

Calvin
Coolidge
A306

1938-54   Perf. 11x10½

803	A275	½c deep orange	.15	.15
804	A276	1c green	.15	.15
b.		Booklet pane of 6	2.00	.75
805	A277	1½c bister brown	.15	.15
b.		Horiz. pair, imperf. btwn.	175.00	30.00
806	A278	2c rose carmine	.15	.15
b.		Booklet pane of 6	4.75	.75
807	A279	3c deep violet	.15	.15
a.		Booklet pane of 6	8.50	1.00
b.		Horiz. pair, imperf. btwn.	900.00	—
c.		Imperf., pair	2,500.	
808	A280	4c red violet	.75	.15
809	A281	4½c dark gray	.15	.15
810	A282	5c bright blue	.20	.15
811	A283	6c red orange	.20	.15
812	A284	7c sepia	.25	.15
813	A285	8c olive green	.30	.15
814	A286	9c rose pink	.30	.15
815	A287	10c brown red	.25	.15
816	A288	11c ultra	.65	.15
817	A289	12c bright violet	.90	.15
818	A290	13c blue green	1.25	.15
819	A291	14c blue	.90	.15
820	A292	15c blue gray	.40	.15
821	A293	16c black	.90	.25
822	A294	17c rose red	.85	.15
823	A295	18c brown car	1.75	.15
824	A296	19c bright violet	1.25	.35
825	A297	20c brt blue green	.70	.15
826	A298	21c dull blue	1.25	.15
827	A299	22c vermilion	1.00	.40
828	A300	24c gray black	3.50	.20
829	A301	25c deep red lilac	.60	.15
830	A302	30c deep ultra	4.25	.15
831	A303	50c lt red violet	6.00	.15

Flat Plate Printing
Perf. 11

832	A304	$1 pur & black	7.00	.15
a.		Vert. pair, imperf. horiz.	1,500.	
b.		Wmkd. USIR ('51)	275.00	70.00
c.		$1 red violet & black ('54)	6.00	.15
d.		As "c." vert. pair, imperf. horiz.	1,250.	
e.		Vert. pair, imperf. btwn.	2,750.	
f.		As "c." vert. pair, imperf. btwn.	7,000.	
833	A305	$2 yel grn & blk	22.50	3.75
834	A306	$5 car & black	105.00	3.00
a.		$5 red brown & black	3,500.	1,500.
		Hinged	2,750.	
		Nos. 803-834 (32)	163.80	
		Set value		9.50

No. 832c is printed on thick white paper with smooth, colorless gum.

No. 834 can be chemically altered to resemble No. 834a. No. 834a should be purchased only with competent expert certification.

See Nos. 839-851.

Constitution Ratification Issue

Old Court
House,
Williamsburg,
Va. — A307

Rotary Press Printing

1938, June 21   *Perf. 11x10½*
835 A307 3c deep violet   .25   .15

150th anniv. of the ratification of the US Constitution.

Landing of the
Swedes and
Finns — A308

Statue Symbolizing
Colonization of the
West — A309

Swedish-Finnish Tercentenary Issue
Flat Plate Printing

1938, June 27   *Perf. 11*
836 A308 3c red violet   .15   .15

Tercentenary of the founding of the Swedish and Finnish settlement at Wilmington, Del.

Northwest Territory Issue
Rotary Press Printing

1938, July 15   *Perf. 11x10½*
837 A309 3c bright violet   .15   .15

Sesquicentennial of the settlement of the Northwest Territory.

Iowa Territory Centennial Issue

Old Capitol,
Iowa
City — A310

1938, Aug. 24   *Perf. 11x10½*
838 A310 3c violet   .15   .15

Centenary of Iowa Territory.

Presidential Types of 1938
Coil Stamps
Rotary Press Printing

1939   *Perf. 10 Vertically*

839	A276	1c green	.30	.15
840	A277	1½c bister brown	.30	.15
841	A278	2c rose carmine	.40	.15
842	A279	3c deep violet	.50	.15
843	A280	4c red violet	8.00	.40
844	A281	4½c dark gray	.70	.40
845	A282	5c bright blue	5.00	.35
846	A283	6c red orange	1.10	.20
847	A287	10c brown red	11.00	.50

Perf. 10 Horizontally

848	A276	1c green	.85	.15
849	A277	1½c bister brown	1.25	.30
850	A278	2c rose carmine	2.50	.40
851	A279	3c deep violet	2.25	.35
		Nos. 839-851 (13)	34.15	3.65

"Tower of the
Sun"
A311

Trylon and
Perisphere
A312

Golden Gate International Exposition Issue
Rotary Press Printing

1939, Feb. 18   *Perf. 10½x11*
852 A311 3c bright purple   .15   .15

Golden Gate Intl. Expo., San Francisco.

New York World's Fair Issue

1939, Apr. 1   *Perf. 10½x11*
853 A312 3c deep purple   .15   .15

Washington Inauguration Issue

George Washington
Taking Oath of
Office — A313

Flat Plate Printing

1939, Apr. 30   *Perf. 11*
854 A313 3c bright red violet   .40   .15

Sesquicentennial of the inauguration of George Washington as 1st president.

Baseball Centennial Issue

Sand-lot Baseball
Game — A314

Rotary Press Printing

1939, June 12   *Perf. 11x10½*
855 A314 3c violet   1.75   .15

Centennial of baseball.

Panama Canal Issue

Theodore
Roosevelt, Gen.
George W.
Goethals and
Gaillard
Cut — A315

Flat Plate Printing

1939, Aug. 15   *Perf. 11*
856 A315 3c deep red violet   .25   .15

25th anniv. of the Panama Canal opening.

Printing Tercentenary Issue

Stephen Daye
Press — A316

Rotary Press Printing

1939, Sept. 25   *Perf. 10½x11*
857 A316 3c violet   .15   .15

300th anniv. of printing in Colonial America.

50th Anniversary of Statehood Issue.

Map of North
and South
Dakota,
Montana and
Washington
A317

1939, Nov. 2   *Perf. 11x10½*
858 A317 3c rose violet   .15   .15

50th anniv. of admission to Statehood of North Dakota, South Dakota, Montana and Washington.

Famous Americans Issues
Authors

Washington
Irving
A318

James
Fenimore
Cooper
A319

Ralph Waldo
Emerson
A320

Louisa May
Alcott
A321

Samuel L. Clemens (Mark
Twain) — A322

1940   *Perf. 10½x11*

859	A318	1c bright blue green	.15	.15
860	A319	2c rose carmine	.15	.15
861	A320	3c bright red violet	.15	.15
862	A321	5c ultra	.30	.20
863	A322	10c dark brown	1.65	1.20
		Nos. 859-863 (5)	2.40	1.85

Poets

Henry W.
Longfellow
A323

John Greenleaf
Whittier
A324

James Russell
Lowell
A325

Walt Whitman
A326

James Whitcomb
Riley — A327

1940   *Perf. 10½x11*

864	A323	1c bright blue green	.15	.15
865	A324	2c rose carmine	.15	.15
866	A325	3c bright red violet	.15	.15
867	A326	5c ultra	.35	.15
868	A327	10c dark brown	1.75	1.25
		Nos. 864-868 (5)	2.55	1.85

Educators

Horace Mann
A328

Mark Hopkins
A329

Charles W.
Eliot
A330

Frances E.
Willard
A331

Booker T.
Washington — A332

1940   *Perf. 10½x11*

869	A328	1c bright blue green	.15	.15
870	A329	2c rose carmine	.15	.15
871	A330	3c bright red violet	.15	.15

872 A331 5c ultra .40 .20
873 A332 10c dark brown 1.25 1.10
 Nos. 869-873 (5) 2.10 1.75

Scientists

John James
Audubon
A333

Augustus Saint-
Gaudens
A345

Daniel Chester
French
A346

Dr. Crawford
W. Long
A334

Luther Burbank
A335

Dr. Walter
Reed
A336

Frederic
Remington — A347

1940 *Perf. 10½x11*
884 A343 1c bright blue green .15 .15
885 A344 2c rose carmine .15 .15
886 A345 3c bright red violet .15 .15
887 A346 5c ultra .50 .20
888 A347 10c dark brown 1.75 1.25
 Nos. 884-888 (5) 2.70 1.90

Inventors

Jane Addams — A337

1940 *Perf. 10½x11*
874 A333 1c bright blue green .15 .15
875 A334 2c rose carmine .15 .15
876 A335 3c bright red violet .15 .15
877 A336 5c ultra .25 .15
878 A337 10c dark brown 1.10 .85
 Nos. 874-878 (5) 1.80 1.45

Composers

Eli Whitney
A348

Samuel F. B.
Morse
A349

Cyrus Hall
McCormick
A350

Elias Howe
A351

Stephen Collins
Foster — A338

John Philip
Sousa — A339

Victor Herbert
A340

Edward
MacDowell
A341

Alexander Graham
Bell — A352

1940 *Perf. 10½x11*
889 A348 1c brt blue green .15 .15
890 A349 2c rose carmine .15 .15
891 A350 3c bright red violet .25 .15
892 A351 5c ultra 1.10 .30
893 A352 10c dark brown 11.00 2.00
 Nos. 889-893 (5) 12.65 2.75
 Nos. 859-893 (35) 28.80 13.40

Pony Express Issue

Pony Express
Rider — A353

1940, Apr. 3 *Perf. 11x10½*
894 A353 3c henna brown .25 .15
 80th anniv. of the Pony Express.

Pan American Union Issue

Ethelbert Nevin — A342

1940 *Perf. 10½x11*
879 A338 1c bright blue green .15 .15
880 A339 2c rose carmine .15 .15
881 A340 3c bright red violet .15 .15
882 A341 5c ultra .40 .20
883 A342 10c dark brown 3.75 1.20
 Nos. 879-883 (5) 4.60 1.85

Artists

Gilbert Charles
Stuart
A343

James A.
McNeill
Whistler
A344

The Three Graces from
Botticelli's
"Spring" — A354

1940, Apr. 14 *Perf. 10½x11*
895 A354 3c light violet .20 .15
 Pan American Union founding, 50th anniv.

Idaho Statehood Issue

Idaho Capitol,
Boise — A355

1940, July 3 *Perf. 11x10½*
896 A355 3c bright violet .15 .15
 Idaho statehood, 50th anniv.

Wyoming Statehood Issue

Wyoming State
Seal — A356

1940, July 10 *Perf. 10½x11*
897 A356 3c brown violet .15 .15
 Wyoming statehood, 50th anniv.

Coronado Expedition Issue

"Coronado and
His Captains"
Painted by
Gerald Cassidy
A357

1940, Sept. 7 *Perf. 11x10½*
898 A357 3c violet .15 .15
 400th anniv. of the Coronado Expedition.

National Defense Issue

Statue of
Liberty — A358

90-millimeter Anti-
aircraft
Gun — A359

Torch of
Enlightenment — A360

1940, Oct. 16 *Perf. 11x10½*
899 A358 1c bright blue green .15 .15
 a. Vert. pair, imperf. btwn. 650.00 —
 b. Horiz. pair, imperf. btwn. 40.00 —
900 A359 2c rose carmine .15 .15
 a. Horiz. pair, imperf. btwn. 40.00 —
901 A360 3c bright violet .15 .15
 a. Horiz. pair, imperf. btwn. 30.00 —
 Set value .20 .15

Thirteenth Amendment Issue

"Emancipation," Statue of
Lincoln and Slave, by
Thomas Ball — A361

1940, Oct. 20 *Perf. 10½x11*
902 A361 3c deep violet .20 .15
 75th anniv. of the 13th Amendment to the
Constitution.

Vermont Statehood Issue

Vermont Capitol,
Montpelier
A362

1941, Mar. 4 *Perf. 11x10½*
903 A362 3c light violet .15 .15
 Vermont statehood, 150th anniv.

Kentucky Statehood Issue

Daniel Boone
and Three
Frontiersmen,
from Mural by
Gilbert
White — A363

1942, June 1 *Perf. 11x10½*
904 A363 3c violet .15 .15
 Kentucky statehood, 150th anniv.

American
Eagle
A364

Lincoln, Sun Yat-sen and
Map
A365

Win the War Issue

1942, July 4 *Perf. 11x10½*
905 A364 3c violet .15 .15
 b. 3c purple

Chinese Resistance Issue

1942, July 7 *Perf. 11x10½*
906 A365 5c bright blue .30 .20

 Five years' resistance of the Chinese people to
Japanese aggression.

Allegory of
Victory
A366

Liberty Holding Torch of
Freedom and
Enlightenment
A367

Allied Nations Issue

1943, Jan. 14 *Perf. 11x10½*
907 A366 2c rose carmine .15 .15

Four Freedoms Issue

1943, Feb. 12 *Perf. 11x10½*
908 A367 1c bright blue green .15 .15

Overrun Countries Issue

Flag of
Poland — A368

Frames Engraved, Centers Offset
Letterpress
Rotary Press Printing
1943-44 Unwmk. *Perf. 12*
909 A368 5c Poland .20 .15
910 A368 5c Czechoslovakia .20 .15
911 A368 5c Norway .15 .15
912 A368 5c Luxembourg .15 .15
913 A368 5c Netherlands .15 .15
914 A368 5c Belgium .15 .15
915 A368 5c France .15 .15
916 A368 5c Greece .35 .25
917 A368 5c Yugoslavia .25 .15
918 A368 5c Albania .20 .15
919 A368 5c Austria .20 .15
920 A368 5c Denmark .20 .15
921 A368 5c Korea ('44) .15 .15
 Nos. 909-921 (13) 2.50
 Set value 1.50

Transcontinental Railroad Issue

"Golden Spike
Ceremony"
Painting by John
McQuarrie
A369

Engraved; Rotary Press Printing
1944, May 10   *Perf. 11x10½*
922 A369 3c violet   .20   .15
75th anniv. of the completion of the first transcontinental railroad.

Steamship Issue

"Savannah"
A370

1944, May 22   *Perf. 11x10½*
923 A370 3c violet   .15   .15
125th anniv. of the first steamship to cross the Atlantic Ocean.

Telegraph Issue

Telegraph Wires and the First Transmitted
Words "What Hath God Wrought"
A371

1944, May 24   *Perf. 11x10½*
924 A371 3c bright red violet   .15   .15
100th anniv. of the 1st message transmitted by telegraph.

Philippines Issue

View of
Corregidor
A372

1944, Sept. 27   *Perf. 11x10½*
925 A372 3c deep violet   .15   .15
Final resistance of the US and Philippine defenders on Corregidor.

Motion Pictures, 50th Anniv.

Motion Picture
Showing for the
Armed Forces in
South
Pacific — A373

1944, Oct. 31   *Perf. 11x10½*
926 A373 3c deep violet   .15   .15

Florida Statehood Centenary

Old Florida Seal,
St. Augustine
Gates and State
Capitol — A374

1945, Mar. 3   *Perf. 11x10½*
927 A374 3c bright red violet   .15   .15

United Nations Conference Issue

A375

1945, Apr. 25   *Perf. 11x10½*
928 A375 5c ultramarine   .15   .15
United Nations conference, San Francisco.

Iwo Jima (Marines) Issue

Marines Raising the Flag
on Mt. Suribachi, Iwo
Jima — A376

1945, July 11   *Perf. 10½x11*
929 A376 3c yellow green   .15   .15
Achievements of the US Marines in WWII.

Franklin D. Roosevelt Issue

Roosevelt and
Hyde Park
Home — A377

Roosevelt and
"Little White
House," Warm
Springs, Georgia
A378

Roosevelt and
White
House — A379

Roosevelt, Globe
and Four
Freedoms
A380

1945-46   *Perf. 11x10½*
930 A377 1c blue green   .15   .15
931 A378 2c carmine rose   .15   .15
932 A379 3c purple   .15   .15
933 A380 5c bright blue ('46)   .15   .15
     Set value   .25   .20
Franklin Delano Roosevelt (1882-1945).

Army Issue

US Troops
Passing Arch of
Triumph,
Paris — A381

1945, Sept. 28   *Perf. 11x10½*
934 A381 3c olive   .15   .15
Achievements of the US Army in WWII.

Navy Issue

US
Sailors — A382

1945, Oct. 27   *Perf. 11x10½*
935 A382 3c blue   .15   .15
Achievements of the US Navy in WWII.

Coast Guard Issue

Coast Guard
Landing Craft
and Supply
Ship — A383

1945, Nov. 10   *Perf. 11x10½*
936 A383 3c bright blue green   .15   .15
Achievements of the US Coast Guard in WWII.

Alfred E.
Smith
A384

US and Texas State Flags
A385

Alfred E. Smith Issue

1945, Nov. 26   *Perf. 11x10½*
937 A384 3c purple   .15   .15
Smith (1873-1944), governor of NY.

Texas Statehood Centenary

1945, Dec. 29   *Perf. 11x10½*
938 A385 3c dark blue   .15   .15

Liberty Ship Unloading
Cargo
A386

Honorable
Discharge
Emblem
A387

Merchant Marine Issue

1946, Feb. 26   *Perf. 11x10½*
939 A386 3c blue green   .15   .15
Achievements of the US Merchant Marine in WWII.

Veterans of World War II Issue

1946, May 9   *Perf. 11x10½*
940 A387 3c dark violet   .15   .15
Issued to honor all veterans of WWII.

Tennessee Statehood, 150th Anniv.

Andrew Jackson,
John Sevier and
Tennessee
Capitol — A388

1946, June 1   *Perf. 11x10½*
941 A388 3c dark violet   .15   .15

Iowa Statehood Centenary

Iowa State Flag
and
Map — A389

1946, Aug. 3   *Perf. 11x10½*
942 A389 3c deep blue   .15   .15

Smithsonian Institution Issue

Smithsonian
Institution
A390

1946, Aug. 10   *Perf. 11x10½*
943 A390 3c violet brown   .15   .15
Centenary of the establishment of the Smithsonian Institution, Washington, DC.

Kearny Expedition Issue

"Capture of
Santa Fe" by
Kenneth M.
Chapman
A391

1946, Oct. 16   *Perf. 11x10½*
944 A391 3c brown violet   .15   .15
Centenary of the entry of General Stephen Watts Kearny into Santa Fe.

Thomas Alva Edison Issue

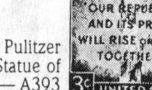

Thomas A. Edison, Birth
Centenary — A392

1947, Feb. 11   *Perf. 10½x11*
945 A392 3c bright red violet   .15   .15

Joseph Pulitzer Birth Centenary

Joseph Pulitzer
and Statue of
Liberty — A393

1947, Apr. 10   *Perf. 11x10½*
946 A393 3c purple   .15   .15

US Postage Stamp Centenary

Washington and
Franklin, Early
and Modern
Mail-carrying
Vehicles
A394

1947, May 17   *Perf. 11x10½*
947 A394 3c deep blue   .15   .15

Centenary International Philatelic Exhibition (CIPEX)
Souvenir Sheet

A395

Flat Plate Printing
1947, May 19   *Imperf.*
948 A395 Sheet of 2   .55   .45
     a.   A1 5c blue   .20   .20
     b.   A2 10c brown orange   .25   .25
     Sheet size varies: 96-98x66-68mm

Doctors Issue

"The Doctor,"
by Sir Luke
Fildes — A396

Rotary Press Printing
1947, June 9   *Perf. 11x10½*
949 A396 3c brown violet   .15   .15
Issued to honor the physicians of America.

Utah Settlement Centenary

Pioneers
Entering the
Valley of Great
Salt
Lake — A397

1947, July 24   *Perf. 11x10½*
950 A397 3c dark violet   .15   .15

US Frigate Constitution Issue

Naval Architect's
Drawing of
Frigate
Constitution
A398

1947, Oct. 21   *Perf. 11x10½*
951 A398 3c blue green   .15   .15
150th anniv. of the launching of the US Frigate Constitution ("Old Ironsides").

Everglades National Park Issue

Great White Heron and
Map of Florida — A399

1947, Dec. 5   *Perf. 10¹/₂x11*
952 A399 3c bright green   .15 .15
Dedication of Everglades Natl. Park, Florida,
Dec. 6, 1947.

Dr. George Washington Carver Issue

Dr. George Washington
Carver — A400

1948, Jan. 5   *Perf. 10¹/₂x11*
953 A400 3c bright red violet   .15 .15
5th anniv. of the death of Dr. George Washington Carver, scientist.

California Gold Centennial Issue

Sutter's Mill,
Coloma,
California
A401

1948, Jan. 24   *Perf. 11x10¹/₂*
954 A401 3c dark violet   .15 .15
Discovery of gold in California, centenary.

Mississippi Territory, 150th Anniv.

Map, Seal and
Gov. Winthrop
Sargent — A402

1948, Apr. 7   *Perf. 11x10¹/₂*
955 A402 3c brown violet   .15 .15

Four Chaplains Issue

Four Chaplains
and Sinking S.
S. Dorchester
A403

1948, May 28   *Perf. 11x10¹/₂*
956 A403 3c gray black   .15 .15
Honoring George L. Fox, Clark V. Poling, John P.
Washington and Alexander D. Goode, the four
chaplains who sacrificed their lives in the sinking of
the SS Dorchester, Feb. 3, 1943.

Wisconsin Statehood Centenary

Map on Scroll
and State
Capitol
A404

1948, May 29   *Perf. 11x10¹/₂*
957 A404 3c dark violet   .15 .15

Swedish Pioneer Issue

Swedish Pioneer
with Covered
Wagon Moving
Westward
A405

1948, June 4   *Perf. 11x10¹/₂*
958 A405 5c deep blue   .15 .15
Centenary of the coming of the Swedish pioneers
to the Middle West.

Progress of Women Issue

Elizabeth
Stanton, Carrie
C. Catt and
Lucretia
Mott — A406

1948, July 19   *Perf. 11x10¹/₂*
959 A406 3c dark violet   .15 .15
Century of progress of American women.

William Allen White Issue

William Allen White,
Editor and
Author — A407

1948, July 31   *Perf. 10¹/₂x11*
960 A407 3c bright red violet   .15 .15

US-Canada Friendship Centenary

Niagara Railway
Suspension
Bridge — A408

1948, Aug. 2   *Perf. 11x10¹/₂*
961 A408 3c blue   .15 .15

Francis Scott Key Issue

Key and
American Flags
of 1814 and
1948 — A409

1948, Aug. 9   *Perf. 11x10¹/₂*
962 A409 3c rose pink   .15 .15
Francis Scott Key (1779-1843), Maryland lawyer
and author of "The Star-Spangled Banner" (1813).

Salute to Youth Issue

Girl and Boy
Carrying
Books — A410

1948, Aug. 11   *Perf. 11x10¹/₂*
963 A410 3c deep blue   .15 .15
Youth of America and "Youth Month," Sept.
1948.

Oregon Territory Issue

John
McLoughlin,
Jason Lee and
Wagon on
Oregon
Trail — A411

1948, Aug. 14   *Perf. 11x10¹/₂*
964 A411 3c brown red   .15 .15
Centenary of the establishment of Ore. Terr.

Chief Justice
Harlan Fiske
Stone — A412

Observatory, Palomar
Mt., Cal. — A413

Harlan Fiske Stone Issue

1948, Aug. 25   *Perf. 10¹/₂x11*
965 A412 3c bright red violet   .15 .15

Palomar Mountain Observatory Issue

1948, Aug. 30   *Perf. 10¹/₂x11*
966 A413 3c blue   .15 .15
  a. Vert. pair, imperf btwn.   550.00

Clara Barton, 1821-1912

Founder of the
American Red
Cross
(1882) — A414

1948, Sept. 7   *Perf. 11x10¹/₂*
967 A414 3c rose pink   .15 .15

Poultry Industry Issue

Light Brahma
Rooster — A415

1948, Sept. 9   *Perf. 11x10¹/₂*
968 A415 3c sepia   .15 .15
Centenary of the establishment of the American
poultry industry.

Gold Star Mothers Issue

Star and Palm
Frond — A416

1948, Sept. 21   *Perf. 10¹/₂x11*
969 A416 3c orange yellow   .15 .15
Honoring mothers of deceased members of the
US armed forces.

Fort Kearny Issue

Fort Kearny and
Pioneer
Group — A417

1948, Sept. 22   *Perf. 11x10¹/₂*
970 A417 3c violet   .15 .15
Cent. of the establishment of Fort Kearny, Nebr.

Volunteer Firemen Issue

Peter Stuyvesant;
Early and
Modern Fire
Engines
A418

1948, Oct. 4   *Perf. 11x10¹/₂*
971 A418 3c bright rose carmine   .15 .15
300th anniv. of the organization of the 1st volunteer firemen in America by Peter Stuyvesant (1592-
1672), Dutch colonial gov. of New Netherland.

Indian Centennial Issue

Map of
Indian
Territory and
Seals of Five
Tribes
A419

1948, Oct. 15   *Perf. 11x10¹/₂*
972 A419 3c dark brown   .15 .15
Cent. of the arrival in Indian Territory, later
Okla., of the Five Civilized Indian Tribes.

Rough Riders Issue

Statue of Capt.
William O.
(Bucky) O'Neill
A420

1948, Oct. 27   *Perf. 11x10¹/₂*
973 A420 3c violet brown   .15 .15
50th anniv. of the organization of the Rough
Riders of the Spanish-American War.

Low and Girl Scout
Emblem — A421

Will
Rogers — A422

Juliette Low Issue

1948, Oct. 29   *Perf. 11x10¹/₂*
974 A421 3c blue green   .15 .15
Juliette Gordon Low (1860-1927), organizer of
the Girl Scouts of America.

Will Rogers Issue

1948, Nov. 4   *Perf. 10¹/₂x11*
975 A422 3c bright red violet   .15 .15
Will Rogers, 1879-1935, humorist and political
commentator.

Fort Bliss and
Rocket
A423

Moina Michael and
Poppy Plant
A424

Fort Bliss Centennial Issue

1948, Nov. 5   *Perf. 10¹/₂x11*
976 A423 3c henna brown   .15 .15
Centenary of Fort Bliss, Texas.

Moina Michael Issue

1948, Nov. 9   *Perf. 11x10¹/₂*
977 A424 3c rose pink   .15 .15
Michael (1870-1944), educator who originated
(1918) Flanders Field Poppy Day idea as memorial
to war dead.

Gettysburg Address Issue

Lincoln and
Quotation from
Gettysburg
Address
A425

1948, Nov. 19   *Perf. 11x10¹/₂*
978 A425 3c bright blue   .15 .15
85th anniv. of Abraham Lincoln's address at Gettysburg, Pa.

Torch and American
Turners' Emblem
A426

Joel Chandler
Harris
A427

American Turners Issue

1948, Nov. 20   *Perf. 10¹/₂x11*
979 A426 3c carmine   .15 .15
Centenary of the formation of the American
Turners Society.

Joel Chandler Harris Issue

1948, Dec. 9   *Perf. 10¹/₂x11*
980 A427 3c bright red violet   .15 .15
Harris (1848-1908), editor and author.

---

*Footnotes near stamp listings often
refer to other stamps of the same
design.*

Minnesota Territory Issue

Pioneer and Red River Oxcart — A428

1949, Mar. 3   *Perf. 11x10½*
981 A428 3c blue green   .15   .15
   Cent. of the establishment of Minn. Terr.

Washington and Lee University Issue

George Washington, Robert E. Lee and University Building A429

1949, Apr. 12   *Perf. 11x10½*
982 A429 3c ultramarine   .15   .15
   200th anniv. of the founding of Washington and Lee Univ.

Puerto Rico Election Issue

Puerto Rican Farmer Holding Cogwheel and Ballot Box — A430

1949, Apr. 27   *Perf. 11x10½*
983 A430 3c green   .15   .15
   1st gubernatorial election in the Territory of P.R., Nov. 2, 1948.

Annapolis Tercentenary Issue

Stoddert's 1718 Map of Regions about Annapolis, Redrawn A431

1949, May 23   *Perf. 11x10½*
984 A431 3c aquamarine   .15   .15
   300th anniv. of the founding of Annapolis, Md.

Union Soldier and GAR Veteran of 1949 — A432   Edgar Allan Poe — A433

GAR Issue
1949, Aug. 29   *Perf. 11x10½*
985 A432 3c bright rose carmine   .15   .15
   Final encampment of the Grand Army of the Republic, Indianapolis, Aug. 28 to Sept. 1.

Edgar Allan Poe Issue
1949, Oct. 7   *Perf. 10½x11*
986 A433 3c bright red violet   .15   .15
   Poe (1809-1849), writer and poet.

Coin, Symbolizing Fields of Banking Service A434   Samuel Gompers A435

Bankers Issue
1950, Jan. 3   *Perf. 11x10½*
987 A434 3c yellow green   .15   .15
   75th anniv. of the formation of the American Bankers Assoc.

Samuel Gompers Issue
1950, Jan. 27   *Perf. 10½x11*
988 A435 3c bright red violet   .15   .15
   Gompers (1850-1924), labor leader.

National Capital Sesquicentennial Issue

Statue of Freedom on Capitol Dome A436   Executive Mansion A437

Supreme Court Building — A438

United States Capitol — A439

1950   *Perf. 10½x11, 11x10½*
989 A436 3c bright blue   .15   .15
990 A437 3c deep green   .15   .15
991 A438 3c light violet   .15   .15
992 A439 3c bright red violet   .15   .15
         Set value   .30   .20
   150th anniv. of the establishment of the National Capital, Washington, DC.
   Issued: Apr. 20, June 12, Aug. 2 and Nov. 22.

Railroad Engineers Issue

"Casey" Jones and Locomotives of 1900 and 1950 A440

1950, Apr. 29   *Perf. 11x10½*
993 A440 3c violet brown   .15   .15

Kansas City, Missouri, Issue

Kansas City Skyline, 1950 and Westport Landing, 1850 — A441

1950, June 3   *Perf. 11x10½*
994 A441 3c violet   .15   .15
   Cent. of the incorporation of Kansas City, Mo.

Boy Scouts Issue

Three Boys, Statue of Liberty and Scout Badge — A442

1950, June 30   *Perf. 11x10½*
995 A442 3c sepia   .15   .15
   Honoring the BSA on the occasion of the 2nd Natl. Jamboree, held at Valley Forge, Pa.

Indiana Territory Issue

Gov. William Henry Harrison and First Indiana Capitol, Vincennes A443

1950, July 4   *Perf. 11x10½*
996 A443 3c bright blue   .15   .15
   150th anniv. of the establishment of Ind. Terr.

California Statehood Centenary

Gold Miner, Pioneers and S.S. *Oregon* A444

1950, Sept. 9   *Perf. 11x10½*
997 A444 3c yellow orange   .15   .15

United Confederate Veterans Final Reunion Issue

Confederate Soldier and United Confederate Veteran — A445

1951, May 30   *Perf. 11x10½*
998 A445 3c gray   .15   .15
   Final reunion of the United Confederate Veterans, Norfolk, Va, May 30, 1951.

Nevada Settlement Centennial

Carson Valley, c. 1851 A446

1951, July 14   *Perf. 11x10½*
999 A446 3c light olive green   .15   .15

Landing of Cadillac Issue

Detroit Skyline and Cadillac Landing A447

1951, July 24   *Perf. 11x10½*
1000 A447 3c blue   .15   .15
   250th anniv. of the landing of Antoine de la Mothe Cadillac at Detroit.

Colorado Statehood Issue

Colorado Capitol and Mount of the Holy Cross — A448

1951, Aug. 1   *Perf. 11x10½*
1001 A448 3c blue violet   .15   .15
   Colorado statehood, 75th anniv. Design includes columbine and statue, "The Bronco Buster," by A. Phimister Proctor.

American Chemical Society Issue

A. C. S. Emblem and Symbols of Chemistry A449

1951, Sept. 4   *Perf. 11x10½*
1002 A449 3c violet brown   .15   .15
   American Chemical Soc., 75th anniv.

Battle of Brooklyn Issue

Gen. George Washington Evacuating Army — A450

1951, Dec. 10   *Perf. 11x10½*
1003 A450 3c violet   .15   .15
   175th anniv. of the Battle of Brooklyn. Design includes Fulton Ferry House.

Betsy Ross Issue

Betsy Ross Showing Flag to Gen. George Washington, Robert Morris and George Ross — A451

1952, Jan. 2   *Perf. 11x10½*
1004 A451 3c carmine rose   .15   .15
   200th anniv. of the birth of Betsy Ross, maker of the 1st American flag.

4-H Club Issue

Farm, Club Emblem, Boy and Girl — A452

1952, Jan. 15   *Perf. 11x10½*
1005 A452 3c blue green   .15   .15

B. & O. Railroad Issue

Charter and Three Stages of Rail Transportation A453

1952, Feb. 28   *Perf. 11x10½*
1006 A453 3c bright blue   .15   .15
   125th anniv. of the granting of a charter to the Baltimore and Ohio Railroad Company by the Maryland Legislature.

A. A. A., 50th Anniv.

School Girls and Safety Patrolman, Automobiles of 1902 and 1952 — A454

1952, Mar. 4   *Perf. 11x10½*
1007 A454 3c deep blue   .15   .15

Torch of Liberty and Globe A455   Spillway, Grand Coulee Dam A456

NATO Issue
1952, Apr. 4   *Perf. 11x10½*
1008 A455 3c deep violet   .15   .15
   3rd anniv. of the signing of the North Atlantic Treaty.

Grand Coulee Dam Issue
1952, May 15   *Perf. 11x10½*
1009 A456 3c blue green   .15   .15
   50 years of Federal cooperation in developing the resources of rivers and streams in the West.

Lafayette Issue

Marquis de Lafayette, Flags, Cannon and Landing Party — A457

1952, June 13   *Perf. 11x10½*
1010 A457 3c bright blue   .15   .15
   175th anniv. of the arrival of Lafayette in America.

Mt. Rushmore Memorial Issue

Sculptured Heads on Mt. Rushmore — A458

1952, Aug. 11   *Perf. 10½x11*
1011 A458 3c blue green   .15   .15
25th anniv. of the dedication of the Mt. Rushmore Natl. Memorial.

Engineering Centennial Issue

George Washington Bridge and Covered Bridge of 1850's — A459

1952, Sept. 6   *Perf. 11x10½*
1012 A459 3c violet blue   .15   .15
Centenary of the founding of the American Soc. of Civil Engineers.

Service Women Issue

Women of the Marine Corps, Army, Navy and Air Force — A460

1952, Sept. 11   *Perf. 11x10½*
1013 A460 3c deep blue   .15   .15
Honoring the women in the US Armed Services.

Gutenberg Bible Issue

Gutenberg Showing Proof to the Elector of Mainz — A461

1952, Sept. 30   *Perf. 11x10½*
1014 A461 3c violet   .15   .15
500th anniv. of the printing of the 1st book, the Holy Bible, from movable type, by Johann Gutenberg.

Newspaper Boys Issue

Newspaper Boy, Torch and Group of Homes — A462

1952, Oct. 4   *Perf. 11x10½*
1015 A462 3c violet   .15   .15

Red Cross Issue

Globe, Sun and Cross — A463

    Perf. 11x10½
1952, Nov. 21   Cross Typo.
1016 A463 3c deep blue & carmine   .15   .15

National Guard Issue

National Guardsman and Amphibious Landing A464

1953, Feb. 23   *Perf. 11x10½*
1017 A464 3c bright blue   .15   .15

Ohio Statehood Sesquicentennial

Map and Ohio State Seal — A465

1953, Mar. 2   *Perf. 11x10½*
1018 A465 3c chocolate   .15   .15

Washington Territory Issue

Medallion, Pioneers and Washington Scene — A466

1953, Mar. 2   *Perf. 11x10½*
1019 A466 3c green   .15   .15
Centenary of the organization of Washington Territory.

Louisiana Purchase, 150th Anniv.

Monroe, Livingston and Barbé-Marbois A467

1953, Apr. 30   *Perf. 11x10½*
1020 A467 3c violet brown   .15   .15

Opening of Japan Centennial Issue

Commodore Perry and 1st Anchorage off Tokyo Bay — A468

1953, July 14   *Perf. 11x10½*
1021 A468 5c green   .15   .15
Cent. of Commodore Matthew Calbraith Perry's negotiations with Japan, which opened her doors to foreign trade.

American Bar Association, 75th Anniv.

Section of Frieze, Supreme Court Room — A469

1953, Aug. 24   *Perf. 11x10½*
1022 A469 3c rose violet   .15   .15

Sagamore Hill Issue

Home of Theodore Roosevelt A470

1953, Sept. 14   *Perf. 11x10½*
1023 A470 3c yellow green   .15   .15
Opening of Sagamore Hill, Theodore Roosevelt's home, as a national shrine.

Future Farmers Issue

Agricultural Scene and Future Farmer — A471

1953, Oct. 13   *Perf. 11x10½*
1024 A471 3c deep blue   .15   .15
25th anniv. of the organization of Future Farmers of America.

Trucking Industry Issue

Truck, Farm and Distant City — A472

1953, Oct. 27   *Perf. 11x10½*
1025 A472 3c violet   .15   .15
Trucking Industry in the US, 50th anniv.

General Patton Issue

Gen. George S. Patton, Jr., and Tank in Action — A473

1953, Nov. 11   *Perf. 11x10½*
1026 A473 3c blue violet   .15   .15
Honoring Patton and the armored forces of the US army.

New York City, 300th Anniv.

Dutch Ship in New Amsterdam Harbor — A474

1953, Nov. 20   *Perf. 11x10½*
1027 A474 3c bright red violet   .15   .15

Gadsden Purchase Issue

Map and Pioneer Group — A475

1953, Dec. 30   *Perf. 11x10½*
1028 A475 3c copper brown   .15   .15
Centenary of James Gadsden's purchase of territory from Mexico, to adjust US-Mexico boundary.

Columbia University, 200th Anniv.

Low Memorial Library — A476

1954, Jan. 4   *Perf. 11x10½*
1029 A476 3c blue   .15   .15

Wet and Dry Printings

In 1953 the Bureau of Engraving and Printing began experiments in printing on "dry" paper (moisture content 5-10 per cent). In previous "wet" printings the paper had a moisture content of 13-35 per cent.

The new process required a thicker, stiffer paper, special types of inks and greater pressure to force the paper into the recessed plates. The "dry" printings show whiter paper, a higher sheen on the surface, feel thicker and stiffer, and the designs stand out more clearly than on the "wet" printings.

Nos. 832c and 1041 (flat plate) were the first "dry" printings to be issued of flat-plate, regular-issue stamps. No. 1063 was the first rotary-press stamp to be produced entirely by "dry" printing.

All postage stamps have been printed by the "dry" process since the late 1950's.

See the Scott Specialized Catalogue of United States Stamps for listings of the wet and dry printings and for No. 1033 on Silkote paper.

Liberty Issue

Franklin A477   Washington A478

Palace of the Governors, Santa Fe — A478a   Mount Vernon — A479

Thomas Jefferson A480   Bunker Hill Monument, Mass. Flag, 1776 A481

Statue of Liberty A482   Abraham Lincoln A483

The Hermitage A484   James Monroe A485

Theodore Roosevelt A486   Woodrow Wilson A487

Statue of Liberty
A488   A489

John J. Pershing A489a   The Alamo A490

Independence Hall — A491

Statue of
Liberty
A491a

Benjamin
Harrison
A492

John Jay
A493

Monticello
A494

Paul Revere
A495

Robert E. Lee
A496

John Marshall
A497

Susan B.
Anthony
A498

Patrick Henry
A499

Alexander
Hamilton
A500

Perf. 11x10¹/₂, 10¹/₂x11

1954-68   **Rotary Press Printing**

1030	A477	¹/₂c red orange ('55)	.15	.15
1031	A478	1c dark green	.15	.15
1031A	A478a	1¹/₄c turq ('60)	.15	.15
1032	A479	1¹/₂c brown carmine ('56)	.15	.15
1033	A480	2c car rose	.15	.15
1034	A481	2¹/₂c gray blue ('59)	.15	.15
1035	A482	3c deep violet	.15	.15
a.		Booklet pane of 6	4.00	.90
b.		Tagged ('66)	.25	.25
c.		Imperf., pair	2,250.	
d.		Horiz. pair, imperf. btwn.		
g.		As "a." vert. imperf. btwn.	5,000.	

No. 1057a measures about 19¹/₂x22mm; No. 1035c, about 18³/₄x22¹/₂mm.

1036	A483	4c red violet	.15	.15
a.		Booklet pane of 6 ('58)	2.75	.80
b.		Tagged ('63)	.50	.40
d.		As "a." imperf. horiz.		
1037	A484	4¹/₂c blue green ('59)	.15	.15
1038	A485	5c deep blue	.15	.15
1039	A486	6c car ('55)	.25	.15
1040	A487	7c rose carmine ('56)	.20	.15

Flat Plate Printing
Perf. 11
Size: 22.7mm high

1041	A488	8c dk vio blue & carmine	.25	.15
a.		Double impression of carmine	650.00	

Rotary Press Printing
Size: 22.9mm high

1041B	A488	8c dk vio blue & carmine	.25	.15

Giori Press Printing
Redrawn Design

1042	A489	8c dk vio bl & car rose ('58)	.20	.15

Rotary Press Printing
Perf. 11x10¹/₂, 10¹/₂x11

1042A	A489a	8c brown ('61)	.20	.15
1043	A490	9c rose lilac ('56)	.25	.15
1044	A491	10c rose lake ('56)	.25	.15
b.		Tagged ('66)	2.00	1.00

Giori Press Printing
Perf. 11

1044A	A491a	11c car & dk vio blue ('61)	.30	.15
c.		Tagged ('67)	2.00	1.60

Rotary Press Printing
Perf. 11x10¹/₂, 10¹/₂x11

1045	A492	12c red ('59)	.35	.15
a.		Tagged ('68)	.35	.15
1046	A493	15c rose lake ('58)	.60	.15
a.		Tagged ('66)	1.10	.35
1047	A494	20c ultra ('56)	.40	.15
1048	A495	25c green ('58)	1.10	.15
1049	A496	30c black ('55)	.70	.15
1050	A497	40c brown red ('55)	1.50	.15
1051	A498	50c brt purple ('55)	1.50	.15
1052	A499	$1 purple ('55)	5.00	.15

Flat Plate Printing
Perf. 11

1053	A500	$5 black ('56)	80.00	6.75
		Nos. 1030-1053 (28)	94.85	
		Set value		8.00

Luminescence

During 1963 quantities of certain issues (Nos. C64a, 1213b, 1213c and 1229a) were overprinted with phosphorescent coating, "tagged," for use in testing automated facing and canceling machines. Listings for tagged varieties of stamps previously issued without tagging start with Nos. 1035b and C59a.

The entire printings of Nos. 1238, 1278, 1280-1281, 1283B, 1286-1288, 1298-1305, 1323-1340, 1342-1362, 1364, and C69-C75 and all following listings, unless otherwise noted, were tagged.

Stamps tagged with zinc orthosilicate glow yellow green. Airmail stamps with calcium silicate overprint glow orange red. Both tagging overprints are activated only by shortwave ultraviolet light.

Coil Stamps
Perf. 10 Vert., Horiz. (1¹/₄c, 4¹/₂c)
1954-73

1054	A478	1c dark green	.20	.15
b.		Imperf., pair	2,500.	
1054A	A478a	1¹/₄c turq ('60)	.15	.15
1055	A480	2c rose car	.15	.15
b.		Tagged ('68)	.15	.15
c.		Imperf., pair (Bureau precanceled)	550.00	
		As "c." imperf. pair	550.00	
1056	A481	2¹/₂c gray blue ('59)	.25	.25
1057	A482	3c dp violet	.15	.15
a.		Imperf., pair	1,750.	
b.		Tagged ('66)	1.00	.50

No. 1057a measures about 19¹/₂x22mm; No. 1035c, about 18³/₄x22¹/₂mm.

1058	A483	4c red vio ('58)	.15	.15
a.		Imperf., pair	110.00	70.00
1059	A484	4¹/₂c blue grn ('59)	1.50	1.20
1059A	A495	25c grn ('65)	.50	.30
b.		Tagged ('73)	.65	.20
c.		Imperf., pair	50.00	
		Nos. 1054-1059A (8)	3.05	
		Set value		2.15

Value for No. 1059c is for fine centering.

Nebraska Territory Issue

Mitchell Pass, Scotts Bluff and "The Sower," by Lee Lawrie — A507

1954, May 7   **Perf. 11x10¹/₂**
1060 A507 3c violet   .15 .15

Centenary of the establishment of the Nebraska Territory.

Kansas Territory Issue

Wheat Field and Pioneer Wagon Train — A508

1954, May 31   **Perf. 11x10¹/₂**
1061 A508 3c brown orange   .15 .15

Centenary of the establishment of the Kansas Territory.

George Eastman Issue

George Eastman (1854-1932), Inventor and Philanthropist — A509

1954, July 12   **Perf. 10¹/₂x11**
1062 A509 3c violet brown   .15 .15

Lewis and Clark Expedition Sesquicentennial

Landing of Lewis and Clark — A510

1954, July 28   **Perf. 11x10¹/₂**
1063 A510 3c violet brown   .15 .15

Pennsylvania Acad. of the Fine Arts

Charles Willson Peale in his Museum, Self-portrait — A511

1955, Jan. 15   **Perf. 10¹/₂x11**
1064 A511 3c violet brown   .15 .15

150th anniv. of the founding of the Pa. Acad. of the Fine Arts, Philadelphia.

Land Grant Colleges Issue

Open Book and Symbols of Subjects Taught — A512

1955, Feb. 12   **Perf. 11x10¹/₂**
1065 A512 3c green   .15 .15

Cent. of the founding of Mich. State College and Penn. State Univ., 1st of the land-grant institutions.

Rotary International, 50th Anniv.

Torch, Globe and Rotary Emblem A513

1955, Feb. 23   **Perf. 11x10¹/₂**
1066 A513 8c deep blue   .20 .15

Armed Forces Reserve Issue

Marine, Coast Guard, Army, Navy, and Air Force Personnel A514

1955, May 21   **Perf. 11x10¹/₂**
1067 A514 3c purple   .15 .15

New Hampshire Issue

Great Stone Face — A515

1955, June 21   **Perf. 10¹/₂x11**
1068 A515 3c green   .15 .15

Honor NH on the occasion of the sesquicentennial of the discovery of the "Old Man of the Mountains."

Soo Locks Opening, Centenary

Map of Great Lakes and Two Steamers A516

1955, June 28   **Perf. 11x10¹/₂**
1069 A516 3c blue   .15 .15

Atoms for Peace Policy

Atomic Energy Encircling the Hemispheres A517

1955, July 28   **Perf. 11x10¹/₂**
1070 A517 3c deep blue   .15 .15

Fort Ticonderoga Bicentenary

Map of the Fort, Ethan Allen and Artillery A518

1955, Sept. 18   **Perf. 11x10¹/₂**
1071 A518 3c light brown   .15 .15

Andrew W. Mellon Issue

Andrew W. Mellon — A519

1955, Dec. 20   **Perf. 10¹/₂x11**
1072 A519 3c rose carmine   .15 .15

Mellon, US Sec. of the Treasury (1921-32), financier and art collector.

Benjamin Franklin Issue

"Franklin Taking Electricity from the Sky," by Benjamin West — A520

1956, Jan. 17   **Perf. 10¹/₂x11**
1073 A520 3c bright carmine   .15 .15

250th anniv. of the birth of Franklin.

Booker T. Washington Issue

Log Cabin — A521

1956, Apr. 5   **Perf. 11x10¹/₂**
1074 A521 3c deep blue   .15 .15

Washington (1856-1915), black educator.

Fifth Intl. Phil. Exhib. Issues
Souvenir Sheet

A522

Flat Plate Printing
1956, Apr. 28 *Imperf.*
1075 A522 Sheet of 2   2.25 2.00
  a. A482 3c deep violet   .90 .80
  b. A488 8c dk vio bl & carmine   1.25 1.00

No. 1075 measures 108x73mm; Nos. 1075a and 1075b measure 24x28mm.

New York Coliseum and Columbus Monument A523

Rotary Press Printing
1956, Apr. 30 *Perf. 11x10½*
1076 A523 3c deep violet   .15 .15

FIPEX, New York City, Apr. 28-May 6.

Wildlife Conservation Issue

Wild Turkey A524

Pronghorn Antelope A525

King Salmon — A526

1956 *Perf. 11x10½*
1077 A524 3c rose lake   .15 .15
1078 A525 3c brown   .15 .15
1079 A526 3c blue green   .15 .15
  Set value   .20 .15

Emphasizing the importance of Wildlife conservation in America.
Issued May 5, June 22 and Nov. 9.
See Nos. 1098, 1392.

Pure Food and Drug Laws, 50th Anniv.

Harvey W. Wiley — A527

1956, June 27 *Perf. 10½x11*
1080 A527 3c dark blue green   .15 .15

Wheatland Issue

President Buchanan's Home, "Wheatland," Lancaster, PA — A528

1956, Aug. 5 *Perf. 11x10½*
1081 A528 3c black brown   .15 .15

Labor Day Issue

Mosaic, AFL-CIO Headquarters — A529

1956, Sept. 3 *Perf. 10½x11*
1082 A529 3c deep blue   .15 .15

Nassau Hall Issue

Nassau Hall, Princeton, NJ — A530

1956, Sept. 22 *Perf. 11x10½*
1083 A530 3c black, orange   .15 .15
200th anniv. of Nassau Hall, Princeton University.

Devils Tower Issue

Devils Tower — A531

1956, Sept. 24 *Perf. 10½x11*
1084 A531 3c violet   .15 .15
50th anniv. of the Federal law providing for protection of American natural antiquities. Devils Tower Natl. Monument, Wyoming, is an outstanding example.

Children's Issue

Children of the World A532

1956, Dec. 15 *Perf. 11x10½*
1085 A532 3c dark blue   .15 .15
Promoting friendship among the world's children.

Alexander Hamilton Issue

Alexander Hamilton (1757-1804) and Federal Hall — A533

1957, Jan. 11 *Perf. 11x10½*
1086 A533 3c rose red   .15 .15

Polio Issue

Allegory — A534

1957, Jan. 15 *Perf. 10½x11*
1087 A534 3c red lilac   .15 .15
Honoring "those who helped fight polio," and 20th anniv. of the Natl. Foundation for Infantile Paralysis and the March of Dimes.

Coast and Geodetic Survey Issue

Flag of Coast and Geodetic Survey and Ships at Sea — A535

1957, Feb. 11 *Perf. 11x10½*
1088 A535 3c dark blue   .15 .15
150th anniv. of the establishment of the Coast and Geodetic Survey.

Architects Issue

Corinthian Capital and Mushroom Type Head and Shaft — A536

1957, Feb. 23 *Perf. 11x10½*
1089 A536 3c red lilac   .15 .15
Centenary of the American Institute of Architects.

Steel Industry Centenary

American Eagle and Pouring Ladle — A537

1957, May 22 *Perf. 10½x11*
1090 A537 3c bright ultra   .15 .15

International Naval Review Issue

Aircraft Carrier and Jamestown Festival Emblem A538

1957, June 10 *Perf. 11x10½*
1091 A538 3c blue green   .15 .15
Intl. Naval Review and Jamestown Festival.

Oklahoma Statehood, 50th Anniv.

Map of Oklahoma, Arrow and Atom Diagram A539

1957, June 14 *Perf. 11x10½*
1092 A539 3c dark blue   .15 .15

School Teachers Issue

Teacher and Pupils — A540

1957, July 1 *Perf. 11x10½*
1093 A540 3c rose lake   .15 .15
Honoring the school teachers of America.

Flag Issue

"Old Glory" (48 Stars) — A541

Giori Press Printing
1957, July 4 *Perf. 11*
1094 A541 4c dk blue & dp carmine   .15 .15

Shipbuilding Issue

"Virginia of Sagadahock" and Seal of Maine — A542

Rotary Press Printing
1957, Aug. 15 *Perf. 10½x11*
1095 A542 3c deep violet   .15 .15
350th anniv. of shipbuilding in America.

Champion of Liberty Issue

Ramon Magsaysay, (1907-1957), Philippines President — A543

Giori Press Printing
1957, Aug. 31 *Perf. 11*
1096 A543 8c carmine, ultra & ocher   .20 .15
For other Champion of Liberty issues, see Nos. 1110-1111, 1117-1118, 1125-1126, 1136-1137, 1147-1148, 1159-1160, 1165-1166, 1168-1169, 1174-1175.

Marquis de Lafayette A544   Whooping Cranes A545

Lafayette Bicentenary Issue
Rotary Press Printing
1957, Sept. 6 *Perf. 10½x11*
1097 A544 3c rose lake   .15 .15
Bicentenary of the birth of Lafayette.

Wildlife Conservation Issue
Giori Press Printing
1957, Nov. 22 *Perf. 11*
1098 A545 3c blue, ocher & green   .15 .15
Emphasizing the importance of Wildlife Conservation in America.

Bible, Hat and Quill Pen — A546   "Bountiful Earth" — A547

Religious Freedom Issue
Rotary Press Printing
1957, Dec. 27 *Perf. 10½x11*
1099 A546 3c black   .15 .15
Flushing Remonstrance, 300th anniv.

Gardening-Horticulture Issue
1958, Mar. 15
1100 A547 3c green   .15 .15
Garden clubs of America and cent. of the birth of Liberty Hyde Bailey, horticulturist.

Brussels Fair Issue

US Pavilion at Brussels A551

Rotary Press Printing
1958, Apr. 17 *Perf. 11x10½*
1104 A551 3c deep claret   .15 .15
Opening of the Universal and Intl. Exhib., Brussels, Apr. 17.

James Monroe Issue

James Monroe, by Gilbert
Stuart — A552

1958, Apr. 28   **Perf. 11x10½**
1105 A552 3c purple   .15 .15
Monroe (1758-1831), 5th pres. of the US.

Minnesota Statehood Centenary

Minnesota Lakes
and
Pines — A553

1958, May 11   Rotary Press Printing
1106 A553 3c green   .15 .15

Geophysical Year (IGY, 1957-58)

Solar Disc and
Hands from
Michelangelo's
"Creation of
Adam" — A554

Giori Press Printing
1958, May 31   **Perf. 11**
1107 A554 3c black & red orange   .15 .15

Gunston Hall Issue

Gunston Hall,
Virginia
A555

Rotary Press Printing
1958, June 12   **Perf. 11x10½**
1108 A555 3c light green   .15 .15
Bicent. of Gunston Hall and honoring George
Mason, author of the Constitution of Va. and the
Va. Bill of Rights.

Mackinac
Bridge
A556

Simon Bolivar
A557

Mackinac Bridge Issue

1958, June 25   **Perf. 10½x11**
1109 A556 3c bright greenish blue   .15 .15
Dedication of Mackinac Bridge, Mich.

Champion of Liberty Issue
Rotary Press Printing
1958, July 24   **Perf. 10½x11**
1110 A557 4c olive bister   .15 .15
Giori Press Printing
Perf. 11
1111 A557 8c carmine, ultra & ocher   .20 .15
Set value   .30 .15
Simon Bolivar, So. American freedom fighter.

Atlantic Cable Centennial Issue

Neptune, Globe
and Mermaid
A558

Rotary Press Printing
1958, Aug. 15   **Perf. 11x10½**
1112 A558 4c reddish purple   .15 .15
Centenary of the Atlantic Cable, linking the Eastern and Western hemispheres.

Lincoln Sesquicentennial Issue

Lincoln, by
George Healy
A559

Lincoln, by
Gutzon
Borglum
A560

Abraham Lincoln
and Stephen A.
Douglas
Debating
A561

Lincoln, by
Daniel Chester
French — A562

1958-59   Perf. 10½x11, 11x10½
1113 A559 1c green ('59)   .15 .15
1114 A560 3c purple ('59)   .15 .15
1115 A561 4c sepia   .15 .15
1116 A562 4c dark blue ('59)   .15 .15
Set value   .30 .20
No. 1114 also for the founding of Cooper Union
cent., NYC. No. 1115 also for the Lincoln-Douglas
debates, cent.
Issue dates: Nos. 1113, 1114, 1116, Feb. 12,
Feb. 27 and May 30. No. 1115, Aug. 27.

Lajos Kossuth,
(1802-1892)
A563

Early Press and Hand
Holding Quill
A564

Champion of Liberty Issue
Rotary Press Printing
1958, Sept. 19   **Perf. 10½x11**
1117 A563 4c green   .15 .15
Giori Press Printing
Perf. 11
1118 A563 8c carmine, ultra & ocher   .20 .15
Set value   .30 .15
Kossuth, Hungarian freedom fighter.

Freedom of Press Issue
Rotary Press Printing
1958, Sept. 22   **Perf. 10½x11**
1119 A564 4c black   .15 .15
Honoring journalism and freedom of the press in
connection with the 50th anniv. of the 1st School
of Journalism at the Univ. of Mo.

Overland Mail Centenary

Mail Coach and
Map of
Southwest
US — A565

1958, Oct. 10   **Perf. 11x10½**
1120 A565 4c crimson rose   .15 .15

Noah Webster
A566

Forest Scene
A567

Noah Webster Issue

1958, Oct. 16   **Perf. 10½x11**
1121 A566 4c dark carmine rose   .15 .15
Webster (1758-1843), lexicographer.

Forest Conservation Issue
Giori Press Printing
1958, Oct. 27   **Perf. 11**
1122 A567 4c green, yel & brown   .15 .15
Publicizing forest conservation and the protection of natural resources and honoring Theodore
Roosevelt, a leading forest conservationist, on the
cent. of his birth.

Fort Duquesne Issue

Occupation of
Fort Duquesne
A568

Rotary Press Printing
1958, Nov. 25   **Perf. 11x10½**
1123 A568 4c blue   .15 .15
Bicentennial of Fort Duquesne (Fort Pitt).

Oregon Statehood Centenary

Covered Wagon
and Mt.
Hood — A569

1959, Feb. 14   **Perf. 11x10½**
1124 A569 4c blue green   .15 .15

José de San
Martin — A570

NATO
Emblem — A571

Champion of Liberty Issue
Rotary Press Printing
1959, Feb. 25   **Perf. 10½x11**
1125 A570 4c blue   .15 .15
a.   Horiz. pair, imperf. btwn.   1,500.
Giori Press Printing
Perf. 11
1126 A570 8c car, ultra & ocher   .20 .15
Set value   .30 .15
San Martin, South American soldier and
statesman.

NATO Issue
Rotary Press Printing
1959, Apr. 1   **Perf. 10½x11**
1127 A571 4c blue   .15 .15
North Atlantic Treaty Organ., 10th anniv.

Arctic Explorations Issue

North Pole, Dog
Sled and
"Nautilus"
A572

1959, Apr. 6   **Perf. 11x10½**
1128 A572 4c brt greenish blue   .15 .15
Conquest of the Arctic by land by Rear Admiral
Robert Edwin Peary in 1909 and by sea by the
submarine "Nautilus" in 1958.

World Peace Through World Trade Issue

Globe and
Laurel — A573

1959, Apr. 20   **Perf. 11x10½**
1129 A573 8c rose lake   .20 .15
Issued in conjunction with the 17th Cong. of the
Intl. Chamber of Commerce, Washington, DC, Apr.
19-25.

Silver Centennial Issue

Henry
Comstock at
Mount
Davidson
Site — A574

1959, June 8   **Perf. 11x10½**
1130 A574 4c black   .15 .15
Cent. of the discovery of silver at the Comstock
Lode, Nev.

St. Lawrence Seaway Issue

Great Lakes,
Maple Leaf and
Eagle Emblems
A575

Giori Press Printing
1959, June 26   **Perf. 11**
1131 A575 4c red & dark blue   .15 .15
Opening of the St. Lawrence Seaway, June 26,
1959. See Canada No. 387.

49-Star Flag Issue

US Flag,
1959 — A576

1959, July 4   **Perf. 11**
1132 A576 4c ocher, dk blue & dp   .15 .15
car

Soil Conservation Issue

Modern
Farm — A577

1959, Aug. 26
1133 A577 4c blue, green & ocher   .15 .15
Tribute to farmers and ranchers who use soil and
water conservation measures.

Petroleum Industry Issue

Oil Derrick — A578

Rotary Press Printing
1959, Aug. 27   **Perf. 10½x11**
1134 A578 4c brown   .15 .15
Cent. of the completion of the nation's 1st oil
well at Titusville, Pa.

Dental Health Issue

Children A579

1959, Sept. 14 *Perf. 11x10½*
1135 A579 4c green .15 .15

Publicizing dental health and cent. of the American Dental Assoc.

Ernst Reuter A580

Dr. Ephraim McDowell A581

Champion of Liberty Issue
Rotary Press Printing
1959, Sept. 29 *Perf. 10½x11*
1136 A580 4c gray .15 .15

Giori Press Printing
Perf. 11
1137 A580 8c carmine, ultra & ocher .20 .15
a.   Ocher omitted —
b.   Ultramarine omitted —
c.   Ocher & ultramarine omitted —
d.   All colors omitted —
   Set value .30 .15

Ernst Reuter, mayor of Berlin 1948-53.

Dr. Ephraim McDowell Issue
Rotary Press Printing
1959, Dec. 3 *Perf. 10½x11*
1138 A581 4c rose lake .15 .15
a.   Vert. pair, imperf. btwn. 450.00
b.   Vert. pair, imperf. horiz. 350.00

Honoring McDowell on the 150th anniv. of the 1st successful ovarian operation performed in the US.

American Credo Issue

Quotation from Washington's Farewell Address, 1796 — A582

Benjamin Franklin Quotation A583

Thomas Jefferson Quotation A584

Francis Scott Key Quotation A585

Abraham Lincoln Quotation A586

Patrick Henry Quotation A587

Giori Press Printing
Perf. 11
1139 A582 4c dk violet blue & car .15 .15
1140 A583 4c olive bister & green .15 .15
1141 A584 4c gray & vermilion .15 .15
1142 A585 4c carmine & dark blue .15 .15

1143 A586 4c magenta & green .15 .15
1144 A587 4c green & brown ('61) .15 .15
   Set value .60 .30

Re-emphasizing the ideals upon which America was founded and honoring those great Americans who wrote or uttered the credos. Issue dates: Jan. 20, Mar. 31, May 18, Sept. 14, Nov. 19, and Jan. 11.

Boy Scout Jubilee Issue

Boy Scout Giving Scout Sign — A588

Giori Press Printing
1960, Feb. 8 *Perf. 11*
1145 A588 4c red, dk blue & dk bis .15 .15
   50th anniv. of the BSA.

Olympic Rings and Snowflake A589

Thomas G. Masaryk A590

Olympic Winter Games Issue
Rotary Press Printing
1960, Feb. 18 *Perf. 10½x11*
1146 A589 4c dull blue .15 .15

Opening of the 8th Olympic Winter Games, Squaw Valley, Feb. 18-29.

Champion of Liberty Issue
Rotary Press Printing
1960, Mar. 7 *Perf. 10½x11*
1147 A590 4c blue .15 .15
a.   Vert. pair, imperf. btwn. 3,250.

Giori Press Printing
Perf. 11
1148 A590 8c carmine, ultra & ocher .20 .15
a.   Horiz. pair, imperf. btwn. —
   Set value .30 .15

Masaryk, founder and pres. of Czechoslovakia (1918-35), on the 110th anniv. of his birth.

World Refugee Year Issue

Refugee Family Walking Toward New Life — A591

Rotary Press Printing
1960, Apr. 7 *Perf. 11x10½*
1149 A591 4c gray black .15 .15
   WRY, July 1, 1959-June 30, 1960.

Water Conservation Issue

Water, from Watershed to Consumer A592

Giori Press Printing
1960, Apr. 18 *Perf. 11*
1150 A592 4c dk blue, brn org & green .15 .15
a.   Brown orange omitted —

Stressing the importance of water conservation, and 7th Watershed Cong., Washington, DC.

SEATO Issue

SEATO Emblem — A593

Rotary Press Printing
1960, May 31 *Perf. 10½x11*
1151 A593 4c blue .15 .15
a.   Vert. pair, imperf. btwn. 175.00

South-East Asia Treaty Org. and the SEATO Conf., Washington, DC, May 31-June 3.

American Woman Issue

Mother and Daughter A594

1960, June 2 *Perf. 11x10½*
1152 A594 4c deep violet .15 .15

A tribute to American women and their accomplishments in civic affairs, education, arts and industry.

50-Star Flag Issue

US Flag, 1960 — A595

Giori Press Printing
1960, July 4 *Perf. 11*
1153 A595 4c dark blue & red .15 .15

Pony Express Centennial Issue

Pony Express Rider — A596

Rotary Press Printing
1960, July 19 *Perf. 11x10½*
1154 A596 4c sepia .15 .15

Man in Wheelchair Operating Drill Press — A597

5th World Forestry Congress Seal — A598

Employ the Handicapped Issue
1960, Aug. 28 *Perf. 10½x11*
1155 A597 4c dark blue .15 .15

Promoting employment of the physically handicapped and publicizing the 8th World Cong. of the Intl. Soc. for the Welfare of Cripples, NYC.

World Forestry Congress Issue
1960, Aug. 29
1156 A598 4c green .15 .15

5th World Forestry Cong., Seattle, Wash., Aug. 29-Sept. 10.

Mexican Independence Issue

Independence Bell — A599

Giori Press Printing
1960, Sept. 16 *Perf. 11*
1157 A599 4c green & rose red .15 .15

150th anniv. of Mexican independence. See Mexico No. 910.

US-Japan Treaty Issue

Washington Monument and Cherry Blossoms — A600

1960, Sept. 28 *Perf. 11*
1158 A600 4c blue & pink .15 .15

Cent. of the US-Japan Treaty of Amity and Commerce.

Ignacy Jan Paderewski A601

Robert A. Taft A602

Champion of Liberty Issue
Rotary Press Printing
1960, Oct. 8 *Perf. 10½x11*
1159 A601 4c blue .15 .15

Giori Press Printing
Perf. 11
1160 A601 8c carmine, ultra & ocher .20 .15
   Set value .30 .15

Paderewski (1866-1941), Polish statesman and musician.

Senator Taft Memorial Issue
Rotary Press Printing
1960, Oct. 10 *Perf. 10½x11*
1161 A602 4c dull violet .15 .15

Senator Taft (1889-1953), of Ohio.

Wheels of Freedom Issue

Globe and Steering Wheel with Tractor, Car and Truck — A603

1960, Oct. 15 *Perf. 11x10½*
1162 A603 4c dark blue .15 .15

Honoring the automotive industry and in connection with the National Automobile Show, Detroit, Oct. 15-23.

Boys' Clubs of America Issue

Profile of a Boy — A604

Giori Press Printing
1960, Oct. 18   *Perf. 11*
1163 A604 4c indigo, slate & rose
       red   .15 .15
Cent. of the Boys' Clubs of America movement.

Automated Post Office Issue

Architect's Sketch
of New Post
Office,
Providence,
RI — A605

1960, Oct. 20   *Perf. 11*
1164 A605 4c dk blue & carmine   .15 .15
Opening of the 1st automated PO in the US.

Baron Gustaf
Emil
Mannerheim
A606

Camp Fire
Girls Emblem
A607

Champion of Liberty Issue
Rotary Press Printing
1960, Oct. 26   *Perf. 10½x11*
1165 A606 4c blue   .15 .15
Giori Press Printing
Perf. 11
1166 A606 8c car, ultra & ocher   .20 .15
       Set value   .30 .15
Mannerheim (1867-1951), marshal and pres. of
Finland.

Camp Fire Girls Issue
Giori Press Printing
1960, Nov. 1   *Perf. 11*
1167 A607 4c dk blue & brt red   .15 .15
50th anniv. of the Camp Fire Girls' movement
and with their Golden Jubilee Convention
celebration.

Giuseppe
Garibaldi (1807-
1882)
A608

Walter F. George
(1878-1957)
A609

Champion of Liberty Issue
Rotary Press Printing
1960, Nov. 2   *Perf. 10½x11*
1168 A608 4c green   .15 .15
Giori Press Printing
Perf. 11
1169 A608 8c carmine, ultra & ocher .20 .15
       Set value   .30 .15
Garibaldi, Italian patriot and freedom fighter.

Senator George Memorial Issue
Rotary Press Printing
1960, Nov. 5   *Perf. 10½x11*
1170 A609 4c dull violet   .15 .15
Senator Walter F. George of Georgia.

Andrew
Carnegie
A610

John Foster
Dulles
A611

Andrew Carnegie Issue
1960, Nov. 25
1171 A610 4c deep claret   .15 .15
Carnegie (1835-1919), industrialist and
philanthropist.

John Foster Dulles Memorial Issue
1960, Dec. 6   *Perf. 10½x11*
1172 A611 4c dull violet   .15 .15
John Foster Dulles (1888-1959), Sec. of State
(1953-1959).

Echo I -- Communications for Peace Issue

Radio Waves
Connecting
Echo I and
Earth — A612

1960, Dec. 15   *Perf. 11x10½*
1173 A612 4c deep violet   .15 .15
World's 1st communications satellite, Echo I,
placed in orbit by NASA, Aug. 12, 1960.

Champion of Liberty Issue

Mahatma
Gandhi — A613

Rotary Press Printing
1961, Jan. 26   *Perf. 10½x11*
1174 A613 4c red orange   .15 .15
Giori Press Printing
Perf. 11
1175 A613 8c carmine, ultra & ocher .20 .15
       Set value   .30 .15
Mohandas K. Gandhi, leader in India's struggle
for independence.

Range Conservation Issue

The Trail Boss
and Modern
Range — A614

Giori Press Printing
1961, Feb. 2   *Perf. 11*
1176 A614 4c blue, slate & brown
       orange   .15 .15
Importance of range conservation and meeting of
the American Soc. of Range Management, Washington, DC. "The Trail Boss" from a drawing by
Charles M. Russell is the Society's emblem.

Horace Greeley Issue

Horace Greeley (1811-
1872), Publisher and
Editor — A615

Rotary Press Printing
1961, Feb. 3   *Perf. 10½x11*
1177 A615 4c dull violet   .15 .15

Civil War Centennial Issue

Sea Coast Gun
of 1861 — A616

Rifleman at
Shiloh,
1862 — A617

Blue and Gray
at Gettysburg,
1863 — A618

Battle of the Wilderness,
1864 — A619

Appomattox,
1865 — A620

1961-65   *Perf. 11x10½*
1178 A616 4c light green   .15 .15
1179 A617 4c blk, *peach blossom*   .15 .15
Giori Press Printing
Perf. 11
1180 A618 5c gray & blue   .15 .15
1181 A619 5c dark red & black   .15 .15
1182 A620 5c Prus blue & black   .30 .15
   a.   Horiz. pair, imperf. vert.   4,500.
       Set value   .70 .25
Cent. of the firing on Fort Sumter, No. 1178;
cent. of the Battle of Shiloh, No. 1179; cent. of
the Battle of Gettysburg, No. 1180; cent. of the Battle
of the Wilderness, No. 1181; cent. of the surrender
of Gen. Robert E. Lee to Lt. Gen. Ulysses S. Grant
at Appomattox Court House, No. 1182.
Issue dates of Nos. 1178-1182: Apr. 12; Apr. 7,
1962; July 1, 1963; May 5, 1964; Apr. 9, 1965.

Kansas Statehood Centenary

Sunflower,
Pioneer Couple
and Stockade
A621

Giori Press Printing
1961, May 10   *Perf. 11*
1183 A621 4c brn, dk red & grn, *yellow*   .15 .15

Senator George W. Norris Issue

Norris and
Norris Dam,
Tenn. — A622

Rotary Press Printing
1961, July 11   *Perf. 11x10½*
1184 A622 4c blue green   .15 .15
Norris (1861-1944) of Nebraska.

Naval Aviation, 50th Anniv.

Navy's First
Plane (Curtiss
A-1 of 1911)
and Naval Air
Wings — A623

1961, Aug. 20
1185 A623 4c blue   .15 .15

Scales of Justice, Factory,
Worker and Family
A624

Remington's
"Smoke Signal"
A625

Workmen's Compensation Issue
1961, Sept. 4   *Perf. 10½x11*
1186 A624 4c ultra, *grayish*   .15 .15
50th anniv. of the 1st successful Workmen's
Compensation Law, enacted by the Wis. legislature.

Frederic Remington Issue
Giori Press Printing
1961, Oct. 4   *Perf. 11*
1187 A625 4c multicolored   .15 .15
Frederic Remington (1861-1909), artist of the
West. The design is from an oil painting, Amon
Carter Museum of Western Art, Fort Worth, Texas.

Sun Yat-sen
A626

Basketball
A627

Republic of China, 50th Anniv.
Rotary Press Printing
1961, Oct. 10   *Perf. 10½x11*
1188 A626 4c blue   .15 .15

Naismith-Basketball Issue
1961, Nov. 6   *Perf. 10½x11*
1189 A627 4c brown   .15 .15
Honoring basketball and James A. Naismith
(1861-1939), who invented the game in 1891.

Nursing Issue

Student Nurse Lighting
Candle — A628

Giori Press Printing
1961, Dec. 28   *Perf. 11*
1190 A628 4c blue, green, org & blk   .15 .15

New Mexico Statehood, 50th Anniv.

Shiprock
A629

1962, Jan. 6   *Perf. 11*
1191 A629 4c lt blue, maroon & bis   .15 .15

Arizona Statehood, 50th Anniv.

Giant Saguaro
Cactus — A630

1962 Feb. 14   *Perf. 11*
1192 A630 4c car, vio blue & green .15 .15

Project Mercury Issue

"Friendship 7"
Capsule and
Globe — A631

1962, Feb. 20   *Perf. 11*
1193 A631 4c dark blue & yellow   .15 .15
First orbital flight of a US astronaut, Lt. Col. John
H. Glenn, Jr., Feb. 20, 1962. Imperfs. are printers
waste.

Malaria Eradication Issue

Great Seal of US and WHO Symbol — A632

1962, Mar. 30   *Perf. 11*
1194 A632 4c blue & bister   .15 .15

WHO drive to eradicate malaria.

Charles Evans Hughes A633   Space Needle and Monorail A634

Charles Evans Hughes Issue
Rotary Press Printing

1962, Apr. 11   *Perf. 10½x11*
1195 A633 4c black, *buff*   .15 .15

Hughes (1862-1948), Gov. of NY, Chief Justice of the US.

Seattle World's Fair Issue
Giori Press Printing

1962, Apr. 25   *Perf. 11*
1196 A634 4c red & dark blue   .15 .15

"Century 21" Intl. Expo., Seattle, Wash., Apr. 21-Oct. 21.

Louisiana Statehood Sesquicentennial

Riverboat on the Mississippi A635

1962, Apr. 30   *Perf. 11*
1197 A635 4c blue, dk sl grn & red   .15 .15

Homestead Act Centenary

Sod Hut and Settlers — A636

Rotary Press Printing

1962, May 20   *Perf. 11x10½*
1198 A636 4c slate   .15 .15

Girl Scout of America, 50th Anniv.

Senior Girl Scout and Flag — A637

1962, July 24   *Perf. 11x10½*
1199 A637 4c rose red   .15 .15

Senator Brien McMahon Issue

Brien McMahon and Atomic Diagram A638

1962, July 28   *Perf. 11x10½*
1200 A638 4c violet   .15 .15

Honoring Sen. McMahon, Conn., for his role in opening the way to peaceful uses of atomic energy.

Apprenticeship Issue

Machinist Handing Micrometer to Apprentice A639

1962, Aug. 31   *Perf. 11x10½*
1201 A639 4c black, *yellow bister*   .15 .15

Natl. Apprenticeship Program and 25th anniv. of the Natl. Apprenticeship Act.

Sam Rayburn Issue

Sam Rayburn and Capitol — A640

Giori Press Printing

1962, Sept. 16   *Perf. 11*
1202 A640 4c dk blue & red brown   .15 .15

Sam Rayburn (1882-1961), Speaker of the House of Representatives.

Dag Hammarskjold Issue

UN Headquarters and Dag Hammarskjold A641

Giori Press Printing

1962, Oct. 23   *Perf. 11*
1203 A641 4c black, brown & yellow   .15 .15

Hammarskjold, Sec. Gen. of the UN, 1953-61.

Hammarskjold Special Printing

1962, Nov. 16
1204 A641 4c blk, brn & yel (yel inverted)   .15 .15

No. 1204 was issued following discovery of No. 1203 with yellow background inverted.

Wreath and Candles A642   Map of US and Lamp A643

Christmas Issue
Giori Press Printing

1962, Nov. 1   *Perf. 11*
1205 A642 4c green & red   .15 .15

Higher Education Issue

1962, Nov. 14   *Perf. 11*
1206 A643 4c blue green & black   .15 .15

Higher education's role in American cultural and industrial development in connection with the centenary celebrations of the signing of the law creating land-grant colleges and universities.

Winslow Homer Issue

"Breezing Up" — A644

1962, Dec. 15   *Perf. 11*
1207 A644 4c multicolored   .15 .15
   a. Horiz. pair, imperf. btwn. & at right   6,750.

Winslow Homer (1836-1910), painter (showing his oil which hangs in the Natl. Gallery, Washington, DC).

Flag Issue

Flag over White House — A645

1963-66   *Perf. 11*
1208 A645 5c blue & red   .15 .15
   a. Tagged ('66)   .20 .15
   b. Horiz. pair, imperf. btwn.   1,500.

Issue dates: #1208, Jan. 9. #1208a, Aug. 25. Beware of pairs with faint blind perforations between offered as No. 1208b.

Regular Issue

Andrew Jackson A646   George Washington A650

Rotary Press Printing

1962-66   *Perf. 11x10½*
1209 A646 1c green ('63)   .15 .15
   a. Tagged ('66)   .15 .15
1213 A650 5c dark blue gray   .15 .15
   a. Booklet pane 5 + label   3.00 1.75
   b. Tagged ('63)   .50 .20
   c. As "a," tagged ('63)   1.75 1.50
     Set value   .15

See Luminescence note after No. 1053. Three different messages are found on the label in No. 1213a, and two messages on that of No. 1213c.
Unused catalogue numbers (1210-1212, 1214-1224, 1226-1228) were left vacant for additional denominations in this regular series which were not produced.

Coil Stamps; Rotary Press

1962-66   *Perf. 10 Vertically*
1225 A646 1c green ('63)   .15 .15
   a. Tagged ('66)   .15 .15
1229 A650 5c dark blue gray   1.25 .15
   a. Tagged ('63)   1.25 .15
   b. Imperf., pair   400.00
     Set value   .15

Carolina Charter Issue

First Page of Carolina Charter — A662

Giori Press Printing

1963, Apr. 6   *Perf. 11*
1230 A662 5c dk carmine & brown   .15 .15

Carolina Charter, 1663, granting to 8 Englishmen lands, extending coast-to-coast roughly along the present border of Va. to the north and Fla. to the south. Original charter on display at Raleigh.

Food for Peace-Freedom from Hunger

Wheat — A663

1963, June 4   *Perf. 11*
1231 A663 5c green, buff & red   .15 .15

American "Food for Peace" program and FAO "Freedom from Hunger" campaign.

West Virginia Statehood Centenary

Map of West Virginia and State Capitol — A664

1963, June 20
1232 A664 5c green, red & blk   .15 .15

Emancipation Proclamation Issue

Severed Chain — A665

1963, Aug. 16   *Perf. 11*
1233 A665 5c dk blue, black & red   .15 .15

Cent. of Lincoln's Emancipation Proclamation, freeing about 3,000,000 slaves in 10 southern states.

Alliance for Progress Issue

Alliance Emblem A666

1963, Aug. 17
1234 A666 5c ultra & green   .15 .15

2nd anniv. of the Alliance for Progress, which aims to stimulate economic growth and raise living standards in Latin America.

Cordell Hull Issue

Cordell Hull (1871-1955), Sec. of State (1933-44) — A667

Rotary Press Printing

1963, Oct. 5   *Perf. 10½x11*
1235 A667 5c blue green   .15 .15

Eleanor Roosevelt Issue

Mrs. Franklin D. Roosevelt (1884-1962) A668

1963, Oct. 11   *Perf. 11x10½*
1236 A668 5c bright purple   .15 .15

Science Issue

"The Universe" A669

Giori Press Printing

1963, Oct. 14   *Perf. 11*
1237 A669 5c Prus blue & black   .15 .15

Honoring the sciences and cent. of the Natl. Academy of Science.

Free City Mail Delivery Centenary

Letter Carrier, 1863 — A670

1963, Oct. 26   **Tagged**   *Perf. 11*
1238 A670 5c gray, dark blue & red   .15 .15

International Red Cross Centenary

Cuban Refugees on S.S. *Morning Light* and Red Cross Flag — A671

1963, Oct. 29   *Perf. 11*
1239 A671 5c bluish black & red   .15   .15

Christmas Issue

National Christmas Tree and White House — A672

1963, Nov. 1   *Perf. 11*
1240 A672 5c dk blue, bluish black
              & red   .15   .15
  a.   Tagged   .65   .40
    See Luminescence note after No. 1053.

"Columbia Jays" A673

Sam Houston A674

John James Audubon Issue

1963, Dec. 7   *Perf. 11*
1241 A673 5c dark blue & multi   .15   .15
    John James Audubon (1785-1851), ornithologist and artist. The birds pictured are actually Collie's magpie jays.

Sam Houston Issue
Rotary Press Printing

1964, Jan. 10   *Perf. 10¹/₂x11*
1242 A674 5c black   .15   .15
    Sam Houston (1793-1863), soldier, pres. of Texas, US senator.

Charles M. Russell Issue

"Jerked Down" — A675

Giori Press Printing

1964, Mar. 19   *Perf. 11*
1243 A675 5c indigo, red brn & olive .15 .15
    Russell (1864-1926), painter. The design is from a painting, Thomas Gilcrease Inst. of American History and Art, Tulsa, Okla.

New York World's Fair (1964-65)

Mall with Unisphere and "Rocket Thrower," by Donald De Lue — A676

Rotary Press Printing

1964, Apr. 22   *Perf. 11x10¹/₂*
1244 A676 5c blue green   .15   .15

John Muir Issue

John Muir (1838-1914), naturalist and conservationist and Redwood Forest — A677

Giori Press Printing

1964, Apr. 29   *Perf. 11*
1245 A677 5c brn, grn, yel grn & ol .15 .15

Kennedy Memorial Issue

Pres. John F. Kennedy (1917-63) and Eternal Flame — A678

Rotary Press Printing

1964, May 29   *Perf. 11x10¹/₂*
1246 A678 5c blue gray   .15   .15

New Jersey Tercentenary Issue

Philip Carteret Landing at Elizabethtown, and Map of New Jersey — A679

1964, June 15   *Perf. 10¹/₂x11*
1247 A679 5c bright ultra   .15   .15
    300th anniv. of English colonization of NJ. The design is from a mural by Howard Pyle in the Essex County Courthouse, Newark.

Nevada Statehood Centenary

Virginia City and Map of Nevada — A680

Giori Press Printing

1964, July 22   *Perf. 11*
1248 A680 5c red, yellow & blue   .15   .15

Flag A681

William Shakespeare A682

Register and Vote Issue
Giori Press Printing

1964, Aug. 1   *Perf. 11*
1249 A681 5c dark blue & red   .15   .15
    Campaign to draw more voters to the polls.

Shakespeare Issue
Rotary Press Printing

1964, Aug. 14   *Perf. 10¹/₂x11*
1250 A682 5c black brown, *tan*   .15   .15
    400th anniv. of the birth of Shakespeare (1564-1616).

Doctors Mayo Issue

Drs. William and Charles Mayo — A683

1964, Sept. 11   *Perf. 10¹/₂x11*
1251 A683 5c green   .15   .15
    William (1861-1939) and his brother, Charles (1865-1939), surgeons who founded the Mayo Foundation for Medical Education and Research in affiliation with the Univ. of Minn. at Rochester. From a sculpture by James Earle Fraser.

American Music Issue

Lute, Horn, Laurel, Oak and Music Score — A684

Giori Press Printing

1964, Oct. 15   *Perf. 11*
Gray Paper with Blue Threads
1252 A684 5c red, black & blue   .15   .15
  a.   Blue omitted   1,000.
    50th anniv. of the founding of ASCAP (American Soc. of Composers, Authors and Publishers). Beware of copies offered as No. 1252a which have traces of blue.

Homemakers Issue

Farm Scene Sampler — A685

Lithographed, Engraved (Giori)

1964, Oct. 26   *Perf. 11*
1253 A685 5c multicolored   .15   .15
    Honoring American women as homemakers and 50th anniv. of the passage of the Smith-Lever Act. By providing economic experts under an extension service of the US Dept. of Agriculture, this legislation helped to improve homelife.

Christmas Issue

Holly A686   Mistletoe A687

Poinsettia A688   Sprig of Conifer A689

Giori Press Printing

1964, Nov. 9   *Perf. 11*
1254 A686 5c green, car & black   .25   .15
  a.   Tagged   .60   .50
1255 A687 5c car, green & black   .25   .15
  a.   Tagged   .60   .50
1256 A688 5c car, green & black   .25   .15
  a.   Tagged   .60   .50
1257 A689 5c black, green & car   .25   .15
  a.   Tagged   .60   .75
  b.   Block of 4, #1254-1257   1.10 1.00
  c.   Block of 4, #1254a-1257a 2.50 2.00
         Set value   .20
    Tagged stamps issued Nov. 10.

Verrazano-Narrows Bridge Issue

Verrazano-Narrows Bridge and Map of NY Bay — A690

Rotary Press Printing

1964, Nov. 21   *Perf. 10¹/₂x11*
1258 A690 5c blue green   .15   .15
    Opening of the Verrazano-Narrows Bridge connecting Staten Island and Brooklyn, NY.

Fine Arts Issue

Abstract Design by Stuart Davis — A691

Giori Press Printing

1964, Dec. 2   *Perf. 11*
1259 A691 5c ultra, blk & dull red .15 .15

Amateur Radio Issue

Radio Waves and Dial — A692

Rotary Press Printing

1964, Dec. 15   *Perf. 10¹/₂x11*
1260 A692 5c red lilac   .15   .15
    Honoring radio amateurs on the 50th anniv. of the American Radio Relay League.

Battle of New Orleans Issue

General Andrew Jackson and Sesquicentennial Medal — A693

Giori Press Printing

1965, Jan. 8   *Perf. 11*
1261 A693 5c dp car, violet blue &
              gray   .15   .15
    Battle of New Orleans, Chalmette Plantation, Jan. 8-18, 1815, which established 150 years of peace and friendship between the US and Great Britain.

Discus Thrower A694

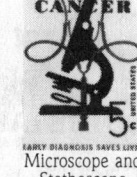

Microscope and Stethoscope A695

Physical Fitness-Sokol Issue

1965, Feb. 15   *Perf. 11*
1262 A694 5c maroon & black   .15   .15
    Importance of physical fitness and cent. of the founding of the Sokol (athletic) org. in America.

Crusade Against Cancer Issue

1965, Apr. 1   *Perf. 11*
1263 A695 5c blk, pur & red org   .15   .15
    "Crusade Against Cancer" and stressing the importance of early diagnosis.

Churchill Memorial Issue

Winston Churchill — A696

Rotary Press Printing

1965, May 13   *Perf. 10¹/₂x11*
1264 A696 5c black   .15   .15
    Sir Winston Spencer Churchill (1874-1965), British statesman and WWII leader.

Magna Carta Issue

Procession of Barons and King John's Crown — A697

Giori Press Printing

1965, June 15   *Perf. 11*
1265 A697 5c blk, yel ocher & red lilac   .15 .15

750th anniv. of the Magna Carta, the basis of English and American common law.

International Cooperation Year Issue

ICY Emblem A698

1965, June 26   *Perf. 11*
1266 A698 5c dull blue & black   .15 .15

ICY, 1965, and 20th anniv. of the UN.

A699   Dante — A700

Salvation Army Issue

1965, July 2   *Perf. 11*
1267 A699 5c red, black & dark blue   .15 .15

Cent. of the founding of the Salvation Army in London by William Booth.

Dante Alighieri Issue
Rotary Press Printing

1965, July 17   *Perf. 10½x11*
1268 A700 5c maroon, *tan*   .15 .15

Dante Alighieri (1265-1321), Italian poet. Design after a 16th cent. painting.

Herbert Hoover Issue

Pres. Herbert Clark Hoover (1874-1964) — A701

1965, Aug. 10   *Perf. 10½x11*
1269 A701 5c rose red   .15 .15

Robert Fulton Issue

Robert Fulton and Clermont A702

Giori Press Printing

1965, Aug. 19   *Perf. 11*
1270 A702 5c black & blue   .15 .15

Fulton (1765-1815), inventor of the 1st commercial steamship.

Settlement of Florida Issue

Spanish Explorer, Royal Flag of Spain and Ships — A703

1965, Aug. 28   Giori Press Printing
1271 A703 5c red, yel & blk   .15 .15
   a.   Yellow omitted   425.00

400th anniv. of the settlement of Fla., and the 1st permanent European settlement in the continental US, St. Augustine, Fla. See Spain #1312.

Traffic Safety Issue

Traffic Signal A704

1965, Sept. 3   *Perf. 11*
1272 A704 5c emerald, black & red   .15 .15

Traffic safety and the prevention of traffic accidents.

John Singleton Copley Issue

Elizabeth Clarke Copley — A705

1965, Sept. 17
1273 A705 5c black, brown & olive   .15 .15

Copley (1738-1815), painter. The portrait of the artist's daughter is from the oil painting "The Copley Family," which hangs in the Natl. Gallery of Art, Washington, DC.

International Telecommunication Union Centenary

Gall Projection World Map and Radio Sine Wave — A706

1965, Oct. 6   *Perf. 11*
1274 A706 11c black, car & bister   .35 .20

Adlai E. Stevenson A707   Angel with Trumpet, 1840 Weather Vane A708

Adlai E. Stevenson Issue

1965, Oct. 23   Litho., Engr. (Giori)
1275 A707 5c pale blue, blk, car & vio blue   .15 .15

Stevenson (1900-65), gov. of Ill., US ambassador to the UN.

Christmas Issue
Giori Press Printing

1965, Nov. 2   *Perf. 11*
1276 A708 5c car, dk ol grn & bis   .15 .15
   a.   Tagged   .75 .25

Prominent Americans Issue

Thomas Jefferson A710   Albert Gallatin A711

Frank Lloyd Wright and Guggenheim Museum, New York A712

Francis Parkman A713

Lincoln A714   Washington A715

Washington (Redrawn) A715a   Franklin D. Roosevelt A716

Albert Einstein A717   Andrew Jackson A718

Henry Ford, 1909 Model T A718a   John F. Kennedy A719

Oliver Wendell Holmes A720   George Catlett Marshall A721

Frederick Douglass A722   John Dewey A723

Thomas Paine — A724   Lucy Stone — A725

Eugene O'Neill A726   John Bassett Moore A727

Perf. 11x10½, 10½x11

1965-78   Rotary Press Printing
1278 A710 1c green, tagged   .15 .15
   a.   Booklet pane of 8   1.00 .50
   b.   Bklt. pane of 4 + 2 labels   .80 .30
   c.   Untagged (Bureau precanceled)   .15

1279 A711 1¼c lt green   .15 .15
1280 A712 2c dk blue gray, tagged   .15 .15
   a.   Booklet pane of 5 + label   1.25 .60
   b.   Untagged (Bureau precanceled)   .15
   c.   Booklet pane of 6   1.00 .50
1281 A713 3c vio, tagged   .15 .15
   a.   Untagged (Bureau precanceled)   .15
1282 A714 4c black   .15 .15
   a.   Tagged   .15 .15
1283 A715 5c blue   .15 .15
   a.   Tagged   .15 .15
1283B A715a 5c blue, tagged   .15 .15
   d.   Untagged (Bureau precanceled)   .15
1284 A716 6c gray brown   .15 .15
   a.   Tagged   .15 .15
   b.   Booklet pane of 8   1.50 .75
   c.   Booklet pane of 5 + label   1.50 .75
1285 A717 8c violet   .20 .15
   a.   Tagged   .20 .15
1286 A718 10c lilac, tagged   .20 .15
   a.   Untagged (Bureau precanceled)   .20
1286A A718a 12c black, tagged   .25 .15
   c.   Untagged (Bureau precanceled)   .25
1287 A719 13c brn, tagged   .30 .15
   a.   Untagged (Bureau precanceled)   .35
1288 A720 15c rose claret, tagged   .30 .15
   a.   Untagged (Bureau precanceled)   .30
   d.   Type II   .55 .15

Type II: necktie does not touch coat at bottom.

Perf. 10

1288B A720 15c dk rose cl (from bklt. pane)   .30 .15
   c.   Booklet pane of 8   2.50 1.75
   e.   As "c," vert. imperf. btwn.   —

Perf. 11x10½, 10½x11

1289 A721 20c deep olive   .45 .15
   a.   Tagged   .40 .15
1290 A722 25c rose lake   .55 .15
   a.   Tagged   .45 .15
   b.   25c maroon   —
1291 A723 30c red lilac   .60 .15
   a.   Tagged   .50 .15
1292 A724 40c blue black   .85 .15
   a.   Tagged   .65 .15
1293 A725 50c rose magenta   1.00 .15
   a.   Tagged   .85 .15
1294 A726 $1 dull purple   2.25 .15
   a.   Tagged   1.65 .15
1295 A727 $5 gray black   10.00 2.25
   a.   Tagged   8.00 2.00
    Nos. 1278-1295 (21)   18.45
    Set value   3.00

On No. 1283B the highlights and shadows have been softened.

No. 1288B issued in booklets only. All stamps have one or two straight edges.

Issue dates (without tagging)—1965: 4c, Nov. 19.
1966: 5c, Feb. 22; 6c, Jan. 29; 8c, Mar. 14; $5, Dec. 3.
1967: 1¼c, Jan. 30; 20c, Oct. 24; 25c, Feb. 14; $1, Oct. 16.
1968: 30c, Oct. 21; 40c, Jan. 29; 50c, Aug. 13.
Dates for tagged: 1965: 4c, Dec. 1.
1966: 2c, June 8; 5c, Feb. 23; 6c, Dec. 29; 8c, July 6.
1967: 3c, Sept. 16; No. 1283B, Nov. 17; No. 1284b, Dec. 28; 10c, Mar. 15; 13c, May 29.
1968: 1c & No. 1284c, Jan. 12; No. 1280a, Jan. 8; 12c, July 30; 15c, Mar. 8.
1973: 20c, 25c, 30c, 40c, 50c, $1, $5, Apr. 3.
1978: No. 1288B, June 14.

Franklin D. Roosevelt — A727a

Coil Stamps
Rotary Press Printing

1966-81   Tagged   *Perf. 10 Horiz.*
1297 A713 3c violet   .15 .15
   a.   Imperf., pair   30.00
   b.   Untagged (Bureau precanceled)   .15
   c.   As "b," imperf. pair   6.00
1298 A716 6c gray brn   .15 .15
   a.   Imperf., pair   2,000.

Perf. 10 Vertically

1299 A710 1c green   .15 .15
   a.   Untagged (Bureau precanceled)   .15
   b.   Imperf., pair   30.00 —
1303 A714 4c black   .15 .15
   a.   Untagged (Bureau precanceled)   .15
   b.   Imperf., pair   900.00
1304 A715 5c blue   .15 .15
   a.   Untagged (Bureau precanceled)   .15
   b.   Imperf., pair   175.00
   e.   As "a," imperf. pair   450.00

No. 1304b is valued in the grade of fine.

1304C A715a 5c blue   .15 .15
   d.   Imperf., pair   1,000.
1305 A727a 6c gray brn   .15 .15
   a.   Imperf., pair   75.00
   b.   Untagged (Bureau precanceled)   .20
1305E A720 15c rose claret   .25 .15
   f.   Untagged (Bureau precanceled)   .30
   g.   Imperf., pair   30.00
   h.   Pair, imperf. between   225.00

i.	Type II		.35	.15
j.	Imperf., pair, type II		90.00	
1305C	A726	$1 dull pur	1.75	.20
d.	Imperf., pair		2,250.	
	Nos. 1297-1305C (9)		3.05	
	Set value			.60

Issued dates: 1c, Jan. 12, 1968. 3c, Nov. 4, 1975. 4c, May 28, 1966. No. 1304, Sept. 8, 1966. 6c, No. 1298, Dec. 28, 1967; No. 1305, Feb. 28, 1968. $1, Jan. 12, 1973. 15c, June 14, 1978.

See Nos. 1393-1395, 1397-1402 for more Prominent Americans.

Migratory Bird Treaty Issue

Migratory Birds over Canada-US Border — A728

Giori Press Printing
1966, Mar. 16   *Perf. 11*
1306 A728 5c blk, crim & dk blue   .15   .15

50th anniv. of the Migratory Bird Treaty between the US and Canada.

Humane Treatment of Animals Issue

Mongrel
A729

Lithographed, Engraved (Giori)
1966, Apr. 9   *Perf. 11*
1307 A729 5c org brown & black   .15   .15

Humane treatment of all animals and cent. of the ASPCA.

Indiana Statehood Sesquicentennial

Sesquicentennial Seal; Map of Indiana with 19 Stars and Old Capitol at Corydon — A730

1966, Apr. 16   **Giori Press Printing**
1308 A730 5c yel, ocher & vio blue   .15   .15

American Circus Issue

Clown — A731

1966, May 2   *Perf. 11*
1309 A731 5c multicolored   .15   .15

Honoring the American circus on the cent. of the birth of John Ringling.

Sixth Intl. Phil. Exhib. Issues

Stamped Cover — A732

SIXTH INTERNATIONAL PHILATELIC EXHIBITION WASHINGTON D.C. 1966

A733

Lithographed, Engraved (Giori)
1966, May   *Perf. 11*
1310 A732 5c multicolored   .15   .15

Souvenir Sheet
Imperf
1311 A733 5c multicolored   .15   .15
Set value   .25   .20

SIPEX, Washington, DC, May 21-30.
No. 1311 measures 108x74mm.
Issue dates: #1310, 21st. #1311, 23rd.

"Freedom" Checking "Tyranny" A734

Polish Eagle and Cross A735

Bill of Rights, 175th Anniv.
Giori Press Printing
1966, July 1   *Perf. 11*
1312 A734 5c carmine, dk & lt blue   .15   .15

Polish Millennium Issue
Rotary Press Printing
1966, July 30   *Perf. 10½x11*
1313 A735 5c red   .15   .15

1000th anniv. of the adoption of Christianity in Poland.

Tagging Extended
During 1966 experimental use of tagged stamps was extended to the Cincinnati Postal Region covering offices in Indiana, Kentucky and Ohio. To supply these offices about 12 percent of the following nine issues (Nos. 1314-1322) were tagged.

National Park Service Issue

National Park Service Emblem — A736

Lithographed, Engraved (Giori)
1966, Aug. 25   *Perf. 11*
1314 A736 5c yel, black & green   .15   .15
a.   Tagged   .30   .25

50th anniv. of the Natl. Park Service of the Interior Dept. The design "Parkscape U.S.A." identifies Natl. Park Service facilities. No. 1314a was issued Aug. 26.

Marine Corps Reserve Issue

Combat Marine, 1966; Frogman; WW II Flier; WW I "Devil Dog" and Marine, 1775 — A737

Lithographed, Engraved (Giori)
1966, Aug. 29   *Perf. 11*
1315 A737 5c black, bister, red & ultra   .15   .15
a.   Tagged   .30   .20
b.   Black & bister (engr.) omitted   16,000.

50th anniv. of the founding of the US Marine Corps Reserve.

General Federation of Women's Clubs

Women of 1890 and 1966 — A738

Giori Press Printing
1966, Sept. 12   *Perf. 11*
1316 A738 5c black, pink & blue   .15   .15
a.   Tagged   .30   .20

75 years of service by the Gen. Fed. of Women's Clubs. No. 1316a was issued Sept. 13.

American Folklore Issue

Johnny Appleseed — A739

1966, Sept. 24   *Perf. 11*
1317 A739 5c green, red & black   .15   .15
a.   Tagged   .30   .20

Johnny Appleseed, (John Chapman, 1774-1845), who wandered over 100,000 square miles planting apple trees, and who gave away and sold seedlings to Midwest pioneers. No. 1317a issued Sept. 26.

Beautification of America Issue

Jefferson Memorial, Tidal Basin and Cherry Blossoms — A740

1966, Oct. 5   *Perf. 11*
1318 A740 5c emerald, pink & black   .15   .15
a.   Tagged   .30   .20

Pres. Johnson's "Plant for a more beautiful America" campaign.

Central US Map With Great River Road — A741

Statue of Liberty and "Old Glory" — A742

Great River Road Issue
Lithographed, Engraved (Giori)
1966, Oct. 21   *Perf. 11*
1319 A741 5c ver, yellow, blue & green   .15   .15
a.   Tagged   .30   .20

5,600-mile Great River Road connecting New Orleans with Kenora, Ontario, following the Mississippi most of the way. No. 1319a issued Oct. 22.

Savings Bond-Servicemen Issue
1966, Oct. 26
1320 A742 5c red, dk & lt blue, black   .15   .15
a.   Tagged   .30   .20
b.   Red, dark blue & black omitted   5,000.
c.   Dark blue (engr.) omitted   8,000.

25th anniv. of US Savings Bonds, and to honor American servicemen. No. 1320a issued Oct. 27.

Christmas Issue

Madonna and Child, by Hans Memling — A743

Lithographed, Engraved (Giori)
1966, Nov. 1   *Perf. 11*
1321 A743 5c multicolored   .15   .15
a.   Tagged   .30   .20

The design is from "Madonna and Child with Angels," by the Flemish artist Hans Memling (c. 1430-1494), National Gallery of Art, Washington, DC. No. 1321a was issued Nov. 2. See No. 1336.

Mary Cassatt Issue

"The Boating Party" — A744

Giori Press Printing
1966, Nov. 17   *Perf. 11*
1322 A744 5c multicolored   .15   .15
a.   Tagged   .30   .25

Cassatt (1844-1926), painter. The original painting is in the Natl. Gallery of Art, Washington, DC.

National Grange Issue

Grange Poster, 1870 — A745

1967, Apr. 17   **Tagged**   *Perf. 11*
1323 A745 5c multicolored   .15   .15

Cent. of the founding of the National Grange, American farmers' organization.

Phosphor Tagging
From No. 1323 onward, all postage issues are tagged, unless otherwise noted.

Tagging Omitted
Inadvertent omissions of tagging occurred on Nos. 1238, 1278, 1281, 1298 and 1305. In addition most tagged issues from 1967 on exist with tagging unintentionally omitted.

Canada Centenary Issue

Canadian Landscape A746

Giori Press Printing
1967, May 25   *Perf. 11*
1324 A746 5c multicolored   .15   .15

Cent. of Canada's emergence as a nation.

Erie Canal Issue

Stern of Early Canal Boat — A747

Lithographed, Engraved (Giori)
1967, July 4   *Perf. 11*
1325 A747 5c multicolored   .15   .15

150th anniv. of the Erie Canal ground-breaking ceremony. The canal links Lake Erie and NYC.

"Peace"—Lions Issue

Peace Dove — A748

Giori Press Printing
1967, July 5   *Perf. 11*
Gray Paper with Blue Threads
1326 A748 5c blue, red & black   .15   .15

Publicizing the Search for Peace. This was the theme of an essay contest for young men and women sponsored by Lions Intl. on its 50th anniv.

Henry David Thoreau Issue

THOREAU

Henry David Thoreau (1817-1862), Writer — A749

1967, July 12
1327 A749 5c red, black & green .15 .15

Nebraska Statehood Centenary

Hereford Steer and Corn — A750

Lithographed, Engraved (Giori)
1967, July 29 *Perf. 11*
1328 A750 5c dk red brn, lem & yel .15 .15

Voice of America Issue

Radio Transmission Tower and Waves — A751

1967, Aug. 1 Giori Press Printing
1329 A751 5c red, blue, black & car .15 .15
25th anniv. of the radio branch of the US Information Agency (USIA).

American Folklore Issue

Davy Crockett (1786-1836) and Scrub Pines — A752

Lithographed, Engraved (Giori)
1967, Aug. 17 *Perf. 11*
1330 A752 5c green, black & yellow .15 .15
a. Vert. pair. imperf. btwn. 6,000.
b. Green (engr.) omitted —
c. Black & green (engr.) omitted —
d. Yellow & green (litho.) omitted —
Crockett, frontiersman and congressman, died in defense of the Alamo.
A foldover on one pane created one each of Nos. 1330b-1330d. Part of the colors appear on the back of the selvage or stamps.

Space Accomplishments Issue

Space-Walking Astronaut — A753

Gemini 4 Capsule and Earth A754

Lithographed, Engraved (Giori)
1967, Sept. 29 *Perf. 11*
1331 A753 5c multicolored .55 .15
a. Pair, #1331-1332 1.30 1.20
1332 A754 5c multicolored .55 .15
US accomplishments in space.

View of Model City — A755

Finnish Coat of Arms — A756

Urban Planning Issue
Lithographed, Engraved (Giori)
1967, Oct. 2 *Perf. 11*
1333 A755 5c dk & lt blue, black .15 .15
Importance of Urban Planning and the Intl. Conf. of the American Inst. of Planners, Washington, DC, Oct. 1-6.

Finnish Independence, 50th Anniv.
Engraved (Giori)
1967, Oct. 6 *Perf. 11*
1334 A756 5c blue .15 .15

Thomas Eakins Issue

"The Biglin Brothers Racing" (Sculling on Schuylkill River, Philadelphia) A757

1967, Nov. 2 Photo. *Perf. 12*
1335 A757 5c gold & multi .15 .15
Eakins (1844-1916), painter and sculptor. The painting is in the Natl. Gallery of Art, Washington, DC.

Christmas Issue

Madonna and Child, by Hans Memling — A758

Lithographed, Engraved (Giori)
1967, Nov. 6 *Perf. 11*
1336 A758 5c multicolored .15 .15
See note after No. 1321.

Magnolia — A759

Flag and White House — A760

Mississippi Statehood, 150th Anniv.
Giori Press Printing
1967, Dec. 11 *Perf. 11*
1337 A759 5c brt grnsh blue, green & red brown .15 .15

Flag Issue
Giori Press Printing
1968-71 *Perf. 11*
Size: 19x22mm
1338 A760 6c dk blue, red & green .15 .15
k. Vert. pair, imperf. btwn. 550.00
Vert. pairs have been offered as imperf. horiz. Some have had the gum washed off to remove blind perfs.

Coil Stamp
Multicolor Huck Press
Perf. 10 Vert.
Size: 18¼x21mm
1338A A760 6c dk blue, red & green ('69) .15 .15
b. Imperf., pair 500.00

Multicolor Huck Press
Perf. 11x10½
Size: 18¼x21mm
1338D A760 6c dk blue, red & green ('70) .15
e. Horiz. pair, imperf. btwn. 175.00
1338F A760 8c multi ('71) .15 .15
i. Vert. pair, imperf. 50.00
j. Horiz. pair, imperf. btwn. 60.00
p. Slate green omitted 450.00
Issued: #1338, Jan. 24, 1968; #1338A, May 30, 1969; #1338D, Aug. 7, 1970; 8c, May 10, 1971.

Coil Stamp
1971, May 10 *Perf. 10 Vert.*
Size: 18¼x21mm
1338G A760 8c multi ('71) .20 .15
h. Imperf., pair 55.00
Set value, #1338-1338G .25

Farm House and Fields of Ripening Grain A761

Map of North and South America A762

Illinois Statehood, 150th Anniv.
Lithographed, Engraved (Giori)
1968, Feb. 12 *Perf. 11*
1339 A761 6c multicolored .15 .15

HemisFair '68 Issue
1968, Mar. 30 *Perf. 11*
1340 A762 6c blue, rose red & white .15 .15
a. White omitted 1,500.
HemisFair '68 exhib. at San Antonio, Tex., Apr. 6-Oct. 6, for the 250th anniv. of San Antonio.

Airlift Issue

Eagle Holding Pennant A763

Lithographed, Engraved (Giori)
1968, Apr. 4 Untagged *Perf. 11*
1341 A763 $1 sep, dk blue, ocher & brn red 2.25 1.25
Issued to pay for airlift of parcels from and to US ports to servicemen overseas and in Alaska, Hawaii and P.R. Valid for all regular postage.
On Apr. 26, 1969, the POD ruled that henceforth No. 1341 "may be used toward paying the postage or fees for special services on airmail articles."

"Youth"—Elks Issue

Girls and Boys — A764

Lithographed, Engraved (Giori)
1968, May 1 *Perf. 11*
1342 A764 6c ultra & orange red .15 .15
Support Our Youth program, and honoring the Benevolent and Protective Order of Elks, which extended its youth service program in observance of its centennial year.

Policeman and Small Boy — A765

Eagle Weather Vane — A766

Law and Order Issue
Giori Press Printing
1968, May 17 *Perf. 11*
1343 A765 6c chlky blue, blk & red .15 .15
The police as protector and friend and respect for law and order.

Register and Vote Issue
Lithographed, Engraved (Giori)
1968, June 27 *Perf. 11*
1344 A766 6c blk, yel & org .15 .15
Campaign to draw more voters to the polls. The weather vane is from an old house in the Russian Hill section of San Francisco.

Historic Flag Series

Ft. Moultrie, 1776 — A767

Ft. McHenry, 1795-1818 — A768

Washington's Cruisers, 1775 — A769

Bennington, 1777 — A770

Rhode Island, 1775 — A771

First Stars and Stripes, 1777 — A772

Bunker Hill, 1775 A773

Grand Union, 1776 — A774

Philadelphia Light Horse, 1775 A775

First Navy Jack, 1775 — A776

Engraved (Giori) (#1345-1348, 1350):
Engr. & Litho. (#1349, 1351-1354)
1968, July 4 *Perf. 11*
1345 A767 6c dark blue .40 .25
1346 A768 6c dk blue & red .30 .25
1347 A769 6c dk blue & ol green .25 .25
1348 A770 6c dk blue & red .25 .25
1349 A771 6c dk blue, yel & red .25 .25
1350 A772 6c dk blue & red .25 .25
1351 A773 6c dk bl, ol grn & red .25 .25
1352 A774 6c dk blue & red .25 .25

SUPPORT OUR YOUTH

1353 A775 6c dk blue, yel & red   .25 .25
1354 A776 6c dk blue, red & yel   .25 .25
   a. Strip of 10, Nos. 1345-1354 2.75 3.25

Flags carried by American colonists and by citizens of the new United States. The flag sequence on the upper panes is as listed. On the lower panes the sequence is reversed with the Navy Jack in the 1st row and the Fort Moultrie flag in the 10th.

Walt Disney Issue

Disney and Children of the World — A777

1968, Sept. 11   Photo.   Perf. 12
1355 A777 6c multicolored   .15 .15
   a. Ocher (Walt Disney, 6c. etc.)
      omitted   850. —
   b. Vert. pair. imperf. horiz.   750.
   c. Imperf., pair   675.
   d. Black omitted   2,000.
   e. Horiz. pair, imperf. btwn.   4,750.
   f. Blue omitted   2,250.

Disney (1901-1966), cartoonist, film producer, creator of Mickey Mouse.

Father Marquette Issue

Father Marquette and Louis Jolliet Exploring the Mississippi A778

Giori Press Printing
1968, Sept. 20   Perf. 11
1356 A778 6c black, apple green &
     org brn   .15 .15

Father Jacques Marquette (1637-1675). French Jesuit missionary, who with Louis Jolliet explored the Mississippi and its tributaries.

American Folklore Issue
Daniel Boone (1734-1820)

Pennsylvania Rifle, Powder Horn, Tomahawk Pipe and Knife — A779

Lithographed, Engraved (Giori)
1968, Sept. 26   Perf. 11
1357 A779 6c yel, dp yel, mar & blk .15 .15

Daniel Boone, frontiersman and trapper.

Arkansas River Navigation Issue

Ship's Wheel, Power Transmission Tower and Barge — A780

1968, Oct. 1   Perf. 11
1358 A780 6c brt bl, dk bl & blk   .15 .15

Opening of the Arkansas River to commercial navigation.

Leif Erikson Issue

Leif Erikson, by Stirling Calder — A781

1968, Oct. 9   Litho., Engr.   Perf. 11
1359 A781 6c lt gray brn & blk brn   .15 .15

Erikson, 11th cent. Norse explorer, was the 1st European to set foot on the American continent, at a place he called Vinland. The statue by an American sculptor is in Reykjavik, Iceland.
   The light gray brown ink carries the tagging element.

Cherokee Strip Issue

Homesteaders Racing to Cherokee Strip — A782

Rotary Press Printing
1968, Oct. 15   Perf. 11x10½
1360 A782 6c brown   .15 .15

75th anniv. of the opening of the Cherokee Strip to settlers, Sept. 16, 1893.

John Trumbull Issue

Detail from "The Battle of Bunker's Hill" — A783

Lithographed, Engraved
1968, Oct. 18   Perf. 11
1361 A783 6c multicolored   .15 .15

Trumbull (1756-1843), painter. The stamp shows Lt. Thomas Grosvenor and his attendant, Peter Salem. The painting is at Yale Univ., New Haven, CT.

Waterfowl Conservation Issue

Wood Ducks — A784

Lithographed, Engraved (Giori)
1968, Oct. 24   Perf. 11
1362 A784 6c black & multi   .15 .15
   a. Vert. pair. imperf. btwn.   550.
   b. Red & dark blue omitted   1,200.

Gabriel, from van Eyck's Annunciation A785

Chief Joseph, by Cyrenius Hall A786

Christmas Issue
Engraved (Multicolor Huck)
1968, Nov. 1   Tagged   Perf. 11
1363 A785 6c multicolored   .15 .15
   a. Untagged   .15 .15
   b. Imperf., pair, tagged   250.00
   c. Light yellow omitted   85.00
   d. Imperf., pair, untagged   325.00

"The Annunciation" by the 15th cent. Flemish artist Jan van Eyck is in the Natl. Gallery of Art, Washington, DC. No. 1363a was issued Nov. 2.

Luminescence
No. 1364 and all following postage stamps are tagged, unless otherwise noted.

American Indian Issue
Lithographed, Engraved (Giori)
1968, Nov. 4   Perf. 11
1364 A786 6c black & multi   .15 .15

Honoring American Indians and the opening of the Natl. Portrait Gallery, Oct. 5, 1968. Chief Joseph (Indian name Thunder Traveling over the Mountains) a leader of the Nez Percé tribe, was born c. 1840 in eastern Oregon and died at the Colesville Reservation in Washington in 1904.

Beautification of America Issue

Capitol, Azaleas and Tulips A787

Washington Monument, Potomac River and Daffodils A788

Poppies and Lupines along Highway A789

Blooming Crabapples along Street A790

Lithographed, Engraved (Giori)
1969, Jan. 16   Perf. 11
1365 A787 6c multicolored   .35 .15
1366 A788 6c multicolored   .35 .15
1367 A789 6c multicolored   .35 .15
1368 A790 6c multicolored   .35 .15
   a. Block of 4, #1365-1368 1.50 1.75
     Set value   .50

Natural Beauty Campaign for more beautiful cities, parks, highways and streets.

Eagle from Great Seal of US A791

July Fourth, by Grandma Moses A792

American Legion, 50th Anniv.
Lithographed, Engraved (Giori)
1969, Mar. 15   Perf. 11
1369 A791 6c red, blue & black   .15 .15

American Folklore Issue
Grandma Moses
Lithographed, Engraved (Giori)
1969, May 1   Perf. 11
1370 A792 6c multicolored   .15 .15
   a. Horiz. pair, imperf. btwn.   250.00
   b. Black and Prus blue omitted   900.00

Grandma Moses (Anna Mary Robertson Moses, 1860-1961), primitive painter of American life. Beware of pairs with blind perfs. being offered as No. 1370a. No. 1370b often comes with mottled or disturbed gum. Such stamps sell for about two-thirds as much as copies with perfect gum.

Apollo 8 Issue

Moon Surface and Earth — A793

Giori Press Printing
1969, May 5   Perf. 11
1371 A793 6c black, blue & ocher   .15 .15

Apollo 8 mission, which put the 1st men into orbit around the moon, Dec. 21-27, 1968. Imperfs. exist from printer's waste.

William Christopher Handy Issue

W. C. Handy (1873-1958), Jazz Musician and Composer A794

Lithographed, Engraved (Giori)
1969, May 17   Perf. 11
1372 A794 6c multicolored   .15 .15

California Settlement, 200th Anniv.

Carmel Mission Belfry — A795

1969, July 16   Perf. 11
1373 A795 6c multicolored   .15 .15

John Wesley Powell Issue

Powell Exploring Colorado River — A796

1969, Aug. 1   Perf. 11
1374 A796 6c multicolored   .15 .15

Powell (1834-1902), geologist and explorer of the Green and Colorado Rivers, 1869-1875.

Alabama Statehood, 150th Anniv.

Camellia and Yellow-shafted Flicker — A797

1969, Aug. 2   Perf. 11
1375 A797 6c multicolored   .15 .15

Botanical Congress Issue

Douglas Fir (Northwest) A798

Lady's-slipper (Northeast) A799

Ocotillo (Southwest) A800

Franklinia (Southeast) A801

Lithographed, Engraved (Giori)
1969, Aug. 23   Perf. 11
1376 A798 6c multicolored   .45 .15
1377 A799 6c multicolored   .45 .15
1378 A800 6c multicolored   .45 .15
1379 A801 6c multicolored   .45 .15
   a. Block of 4, #1376-1379 2.00 2.25

11th Intl. Botanical Cong., Seattle, Wash., Aug. 24-Sept. 2.

Dartmouth College Case Issue

6c Daniel Webster and Dartmouth Hall — A802

Rotary Press Printing
1969, Sept. 22   *Perf. 10½x11*
1380 A802 6c green   .15 .15

Sesquicentennial of the Dartmouth College case, argued by Daniel Webster before the Supreme Court, which reasserted the sanctity of contracts.

Professional Baseball Centenary

Batter — A803

Lithographed, Engraved (Giori)
1969, Sept. 24   *Perf. 11*
1381 A803 6c yel, red, black & green   .65 .15
   a.   Black (1869-1969, United States, 6c, Professional Baseball) omitted   1,100.

Intercollegiate Football Centenary

Football Player and Coach — A804

1969, Sept. 26   *Perf. 11*
1382 A804 6c red & green   .15 .15

Dwight D. Eisenhower Issue

Dwight D. Eisenhower — A805

Giori Press Printing
1969, Oct. 14   *Perf. 11*
1383 A805 6c blue, black & red   .15 .15

Gen. Eisenhower, 34th Pres. (1890-1969).

Christmas Issue

Winter Sunday in Norway, Maine A806

Engraved (Multicolor Huck)
1969, Nov. 3   *Perf. 11x10½*
1384 A806 6c dk green & multi   .15 .15
    Precanceled   .50 .15
   b.   Imperf., pair   1,100.
   c.   Light green omitted   25.00
   d.   Lt grn, red & yel omitted   1,000. —
   e.   Yellow omitted   —
   g.   Red & yellow omitted   —

The precancel value applies to the experimental precancel printed in four cities with the names between lines 4½mm apart: in black or green "ATLANTA, GA" and in green only "BALTIMORE, MD," "MEMPHIS, TN" and "NEW HAVEN, CT." They were sold freely to the public and could be used on any class of mail at all post offices during the experimental program and thereafter.

Most examples of No. 1384c show orange where the offset green was. Value is for this variety. Copies without orange sell for a premium.

Cured Child A807

"Old Models" A808

Hope for Crippled Issue
Lithographed, Engraved (Giori)
1969, Nov. 20   *Perf. 11*
1385 A807 6c multicolored   .15 .15

Issued to encourage the rehabilitation of crippled children and adults, and to honor the Natl. Soc. for Crippled Children and Adults (Easter Seal Soc.) on its 50th anniv.

William M. Harnett Issue
1969, Dec. 3   *Perf. 11*
1386 A808 6c multicolored   .15 .15

Harnett (1848-1892), painter. The painting is in the Museum of Fine Arts, Boston.

Natural History Issue

American Bald Eagle — A809

African Elephant Herd — A810

Tlingit Chief in Haida Ceremonial Canoe — A811

Brontosaurus, Stegosaurus and Allosaurus from Jurassic Period — A812

Lithographed, Engraved (Giori)
1970, May 6   *Perf. 11*
1387 A809 6c multicolored   .15 .15
1388 A810 6c multicolored   .15 .15
1389 A811 6c multicolored   .15 .15
1390 A812 6c multicolored   .15 .15
   a.   Block of 4. #1387-1390   .50 .60

1969-1970 celebration of the cent. of the American Museum of Natural History in NYC. The design of No. 1390 is a detail from a mural by Rudolph Zallinger in Yale's Peabody Museum.

Maine Statehood Issue

Lighthouse at Two Lights, Maine — A813

Lithographed, Engraved (Giori)
1970, July 9   *Perf. 11*
1391 A813 6c black & multi   .15 .15

Sesquicentennial of Maine statehood. The painting by Edward Hopper (1882-1967) hangs in the Metropolitan Museum of Art, NYC.

Wildlife Conservation Issue

American Buffalo 6c A814

Rotary Press Printing
1970, July 20   *Perf. 10½x11*
1392 A814 6c black, *light brown*   .15 .15

Regular Issue
Dwight David Eisenhower

A815
Dot between "R" and "U"

A815a
No dot between "R" and "U"

Benjamin Franklin A816

USPS Emblem A817

Fiorello H. LaGuardia A817a

Ernest Taylor Pyle A818

Dr. Elizabeth Blackwell A818a

Amadeo P. Giannini A818b

Rotary (6c, 7c, 14c, 16c, 21c, #1395); Giori (#1394); Photo. (#1396)
Perf. 11x10½, 10½x11; 11 (#1394)
1970-74
1393 A815   6c dark blue gray   .15 .15
   a.   Booklet pane of 8   1.50 .65
   b.   Booklet pane of 5 + label   1.50 .65
   c.   Untagged (Bureau precanceled)   .15
1393D A816   7c brt blue ('72)   .15 .15
   e.   Untagged (Bureau precanceled)   .15
1394 A815a   8c blk, red & bl gray ('71)   .15 .15
1395 A815   8c dp claret ('71)   .20 .15
   a.   Booklet pane of 8   1.80 1.25
   b.   Booklet pane of 6   1.25 .90
   c.   Booklet pane of 4 + 2 labels ('72)   1.65 .80
   d.   Booklet pane of 7 + label ('72)   1.90 1.00
1396 A817   8c multi ('71)   .15 .15
1397 A817a   14c gray brn ('72)   .25 .15
   a.   Untagged (Bureau precanceled)   .25
1398 A818   16c brown ('71)   .30 .15
   a.   Untagged (Bureau precanceled)   .35
1399 A818a   18c violet ('74)   .35 .15
1400 A818b   21c green ('73)   .40 .15
   Nos. 1393-1400 (9)   2.10
   Set value   .50

No. 1395 was issued in booklets only. All stamps have one or two straight edges.
Issue dates: 6c, Aug. 6, 1970; 7c, Oct. 20, 1972; Nos. 1394-1395, May 10, 1971; No. 1396, July 1, 1971; 14c, Apr. 24, 1972; 16c, May 7, 1971; 18c, Jan. 23, 1974; 21c, June 27, 1973.

Coil Stamps
1970-71   Rotary Press   *Perf. 10 Vert.*
1401 A815 6c dark blue gray   .15 .15
   a.   Untagged (Bureau precanceled)   .15
   b.   Imperf., pair   2,000.

1402 A815 8c deep claret   .15 .15
   a.   Imperf., pair   45.00
   b.   Untagged (Bureau precanceled)   .15
   c.   Pair, imperf. btwn.   6,250.
    Set value   .15

Issue dates: 6c, Aug. 6; 8c, May 10, 1971.

Edgar Lee Masters Issue

Edgar Lee Masters (1869-1950), Poet — A819

Lithographed, Engraved (Giori)
1970, Aug. 22   *Perf. 11*
1405 A819 6c black & olive bister   .15 .15

Woman Suffrage Issue

Suffragettes, 1920, and Woman Voter, 1970 — A820

Giori Press Printing
1970, Aug. 26   *Perf. 11*
1406 A820 6c blue   .15 .15

50th anniv. of the 19th Amendment, which gave women the vote.

South Carolina Issue

Symbols of South Carolina A821

Lithographed, Engraved (Giori)
1970, Sept. 12   *Perf. 11*
1407 A821 6c bister, black & red   .15 .15

300th anniv. of the founding of Charles Town (Charleston), the 1st permanent settlement of SC. Against a background of pine wood the line drawings of the design represent the economic and historic development of SC: the spire of St. Phillip's Church, Capitol, state flag, a ship, 17th cent. man and woman, a Fort Sumter cannon, barrels, cotton, tobacco and yellow jessamine.

Stone Mountain Memorial Issue

Robert E. Lee, Jefferson Davis and "Stonewall" Jackson — A822

Giori Press Printing
1970, Sept. 19   *Perf. 11*
1408 A822 6c gray   .15 .15

Dedication of the Stone Mountain Confederate Memorial, GA, May 9, 1970.

Fort Snelling Issue

Fort Snelling, Keelboat and Tepees — A823

Lithographed, Engraved (Giori)
1970, Oct. 17   *Perf. 11*
1409 A823 6c yellow & multi   .15 .15

150th anniv. of Fort Snelling, MN, which was an important outpost for the opening of the Northwest.

Anti-Pollution Issue

Globe and Wheat — A824

Globe and
City — A825

Globe and
Bluegill — A826

Globe and
Seagull — A827

1970, Oct. 28   Photo.   Perf. 11x10½

1410	A824 6c multicolored	.20	.15
1411	A825 6c multicolored	.20	.15
1412	A826 6c multicolored	.20	.15
1413	A827 6c multicolored	.20	.15
a.	Block of 4, #1410-1413	1.00	1.25
	Set value		.40

Issued to focus attention on the mounting problems of pollution.

Christmas Issue

Nativity, by
Lorenzo Lotto
(1480-1556)
A828

Tin and Cast-iron
Locomotive
A829

Toy Horse on
Wheels — A830

Mechanical
Tricycle
A831

Doll Carriage
A832

1970, Nov. 5   Photo.   Perf. 10½x11

1414	A828 6c multicolored	.15	.15
a.	Precanceled	.15	.15
b.	Black omitted	650.00	
c.	As "a." blue omitted	1,500.	
	Perf. 11x10½		
1415	A829 6c multicolored	.30	.15
a.	Precanceled	.75	.15
b.	Black omitted	2,500.	
1416	A830 6c multicolored	.30	.15
a.	Precanceled	.75	.15
b.	Black omitted	2,500.	
c.	Imperf. pair (#1416, 1418)		4,000.
1417	A831 6c multicolored	.30	.15
a.	Precanceled	.75	.15
b.	Black omitted	2,500.	
1418	A832 6c multicolored	.30	.15
a.	Precanceled	.75	.15
b.	Block of 4, #1415-1418	1.25	1.50
c.	As "b." precanceled	3.25	3.25
d.	Black omitted	2,500.	
	Nos. 1414-1418 (5)	1.35	
	Set value		.45

Nos. 1415-1418 are antique Christmas toys. The precanceled stamps, Nos. 1414a-1418a, were furnished to 68 cities. The plates include two straight (No. 1414a) or two wavy (Nos. 1415a-1418a) black lines that make up the precancellation. Unused values are for copies with gum and used values are for copies with an additional cancellation or without gum.

United Nations, 25th Anniv.

"UN" and UN
Emblem
A833

Lithographed, Engraved (Giori)
1970, Nov. 20   Perf. 11
1419 A833 6c black, ver & ultra   .15   .15

Landing of the Pilgrims Issue

Mayflower and
Pilgrims — A834

Lithographed, Engraved (Giori)
1970, Nov. 21   Perf. 11

1420	A834 6c black, org, yel, brn, mag & blue	.15	.15
a.	Orange & yellow omitted	1,000.	

Mayflower landing, 350th anniv.

Disabled Veterans and Servicemen Issue

A835   A836

Lithographed, Engraved (Giori)
1970, Nov. 24   Perf. 11

1421	A835 6c multicolored	.15	.15
a.	Pair, #1421-1422	.25	.30
	Engr.		
1422	A836 6c dk blue, black & red	.15	.15
	Set value	.25	.15

50th anniv. of the Disabled Veterans of America Organization (No. 1421); honoring the contribution of servicemen, particularly those who were prisoners of war or missing in action (No. 1422).

Ewe and Lamb
A837

Douglas
MacArthur
A838

American Wool Industry Issue
Lithographed, Engraved (Giori)
1971, Jan. 19   Perf. 11

1423	A837 6c multicolored	.15	.15
a.	Teal blue ("United States") omitted	—	

450th anniv. of the introduction of sheep to the No. American continent and the beginning of the American wool industry.

Gen. Douglas MacArthur Issue
1971, Jan. 26   Giori Press Printing
1424 A838 6c black, red & dk blue   .15   .15

MacArthur (1880-1964), Chief of Staff, Supreme Commander for the Allied Powers in the Pacific Area during WW II and Supreme Commander in Japan after the war.

Blood Donor Issue

"Giving Blood
Saves
Lives" — A839

1971, Mar. 12   Perf. 11
1425 A839 6c lt blue, scar & indigo   .15   .15

Salute to blood donors and spur to participation in the blood donor program.

Missouri Sesquicentennial Issue

"Independence
and the Opening
of the West,"
Detail, by
Thomas Hart
Benton — A840

1971, May 8   Photo.   Perf. 11x10½
1426 A840 8c multicolored   .15   .15

The stamp design shows a Pawnee facing a hunter-trapper and a group of settlers.

Wildlife Conservation Issue

Trout
A841

Alligator — A842

Polar
Bear
and
Cubs
A843

California Condor — A844

Lithographed, Engraved (Giori)
1971, June 12   Perf. 11

1427	A841 8c multicolored	.15	.15
a.	Red omitted	700.00	
1428	A842 8c multicolored	.15	.15
1429	A843 8c multicolored	.15	.15
1430	A844 8c multicolored	.15	.15
a.	Block of 4, #1427-1430	.80	.90
b.	As "a." lt grn & dk grn omitted from #1427-1428	3,500.	
c.	As "a." red omitted from #1427, 1429-1430	9,000.	
	Set value		.40

Antarctic Treaty Issue

Map of
Antarctica
A845

1971, June 23   Giori Press Printing
1431 A845 8c red & dark blue   .15   .15

10th anniv. of the Antarctic Treaty pledging peaceful uses of and scientific cooperation in Antarctica.

American Revolution Bicentennial

Bicentennial Commission
Emblem — A846

Lithographed, Engraved (Giori)
1971, July 4   Perf. 11

1432	A846 8c red, blue, gray & black	.20	.15
a.	Gray & black omitted	750.00	
b.	Gray ("U.S. Postage 8c") omitted	1,250.	

John Sloan Issue

The Wake of
the
Ferry — A847

1971, Aug. 2   Perf. 11
1433 A847 8c multicolored   .15   .15

Sloan (1871-1951), painter.

Space Achievement Decade Issue

Earth, Sun,
Landing Craft
on Moon
A848

Lunar Rover
and
Astronauts
A849

Lithographed, Engraved (Giori)
1971, Aug. 2   Perf. 11

1434	A848 8c blk, bl, yel & red	.15	.15
a.	Pair, #1434-1435	.40	.45
b.	As "a." blue & red (litho.) omitted	1,500.	
1435	A849 8c blk, bl, yel & red	.15	.15
	Set value		.20

A decade of space achievements. Apollo 15 moon exploration mission July 26-Aug. 7.

Emily
Elizabeth
Dickinson
A850

Sentry Box,
Morro Castle,
San Juan
A851

Emily Dickinson Issue
Lithographed, Engraved (Giori)
1971, Aug. 28   Perf. 11

1436	A850 8c multi, greenish	.15	.15
a.	Black & olive (engr.) omitted	950.	
b.	Pale rose omitted	7,500.	
c.	Red omitted	—	

Dickinson (1830-1886), poet.

San Juan, PR, 450th Anniv.
1971, Sept. 12
1437 A851 8c multicolored   .15   .15

Young Woman Drug Addict — A852

Hands Reaching for CARE — A853

Prevent Drug Abuse Issue

1971, Oct. 5 Photo. *Perf. 10½x11*
1438 A852 8c bl, dp bl & blk   .15 .15
Drug Abuse Prevention Week, Oct. 3-9.

CARE Issue

1971, Oct. 27
1439 A853 8c multicolored   .15 .15
  a.   Black omitted   4,750.

25th anniv. of CARE, a US-Canadian Cooperative for American Relief Everywhere.

Historic Preservation Issue

HISTORIC PRESERVATION
Decatur House, Washington, DC — A854

HISTORIC PRESERVATION
Whaling Ship Charles W. Morgan, Mystic, Conn. — A855

HISTORIC PRESERVATION
Cable Car, San Francisco — A856

HISTORIC PRESERVATION
San Xavier del Bac Mission, Tucson, Ariz. — A857

Lithographed, Engraved (Giori)

1971, Oct. 29 Buff Paper *Perf. 11*
1440 A854 8c blk brn & ocher   .15 .15
1441 A855 8c blk brn & ocher   .15 .15
1442 A856 8c blk brn & ocher   .15 .15
1443 A857 8c blk brn & ocher   .15 .15
  a.   Block of 4, #1440-1443   .75 .85
  b.   As "a," black brown omitted   2,750.
  c.   As "a," ocher omitted   —
        Set value   .50

Christmas Issue

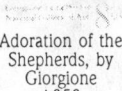

Adoration of the Shepherds, by Giorgione
A858

Partridge in a Pear Tree, by Jamie Wyeth
A859

1971, Nov. 10 Photo. *Perf. 10½x11*
1444 A858 8c gold & multi   .15 .15
  a.   Gold omitted   600.00
1445 A859 8c multicolored   .15 .15
        Set value   .15

Sidney Lanier (1842-1881)
A860

Peace Corps Poster, by David Battle
A861

Sidney Lanier Issue
Giori Press Printing

1972, Feb. 3   *Perf. 11*
1446 A860 8c black, brown & lt blue   .15 .15
Lanier, poet, musician, lawyer, educator.

Peace Corps Issue

1972, Feb. 11 Photo. *Perf. 10½x11*
1447 A861 8c dk blue, light blue & red   .15 .15

National Parks Centennial Issue

Hulk of Ship A862

Cape Hatteras Lighthouse A863

Laughing Gulls on Driftwood A864

Laughing Gulls and Dune A865

Wolf Trap Farm, Vienna, Va. — A866

Old Faithful, Yellowstone — A867

Mt. McKinley, Alaska — A868

Lithographed, Engraved (Giori)

1972   *Perf. 11*
1448 A862 2c black & multi   .15 .15
1449 A863 2c black & multi   .15 .15
1450 A864 2c black & multi   .15 .15
1451 A865 2c black & multi   .15 .15
  a.   Block of 4, #1448-1451   .25 .25
  b.   As "a," black (litho.) omitted   2,750.
1452 A866 6c black & multi   .15 .15
1453 A867 8c blk, blue, brn & multi   .15 .15
1454 A868 15c black & multi   .30 .20
        Set value   .80 .50

Cent. of Yellowstone Natl. Park, the 1st Natl. Park, and of the Natl. Park System. The four 2c stamps were issued for Cape Hatteras, NC, Natl. Seashore.
Issued: 2c, 4/5; 6c, 6/26; 8c, 3/1; 15c, 7/28.
See No. C84.

Family Planning Issue

Family — A869

1972, Mar. 18
1455 A869 8c black & multi   .15 .15
  a.   Yellow omitted   1,650.
  b.   Dark brown & olive omitted   —
  c.   Dark brown omitted   9,500

American Bicentennial
Colonial American Craftsmen

Glassmaker A870

Silversmith A871

Wigmaker A872

Hatter — A873

1972, July 4 Engr. *Perf. 11x10½*
Dull Yellow Paper
1456 A870 8c deep brown   .15 .15
1457 A871 8c deep brown   .15 .15
1458 A872 8c deep brown   .15 .15
1459 A873 8c deep brown   .15 .15
  a.   Block of 4, #1456-1459   .65 .75
        Set value   .35

Olympic Games Issue

Bicycling and Olympic Rings — A874

Bobsledding A875

Running A876

1972, Aug. 17 Photo. *Perf. 11x10½*
1460 A874 6c multicolored   .15 .15
1461 A875 8c multicolored   .15 .15
1462 A876 15c multicolored   .30 .20
        Nos. 1460-1462 (3)   .60
        Set value   .30

11th Winter Olympic Games, Sapporo, Japan, Feb. 3-13, and 20th Summer Olympic Games, Munich, Germany, Aug. 26-Sept. 11.
See No. C85.

Parent Teacher Association, 75th Anniv.

Blackboard A877

1972, Sept. 15 Photo. *Perf. 11x10½*
1463 A877 8c yellow & black   .15 .15

Wildlife Conservation Issue

Fur Seals A878

Cardinal — A879

Brown Pelican A880

Bighorn Sheep A881

Lithographed, Engraved

1972, Sept. 20   *Perf. 11*
1464 A878 8c multicolored   .15 .15
1465 A879 8c multicolored   .15 .15
1466 A880 8c multicolored   .15 .15
1467 A881 8c multicolored   .15 .15
  a.   Block of 4, #1464-1467   .65 .75
  b.   As "a," brown omitted   4,000.
  c.   As "a," green & blue omitted   4,750.
  d.   As "a," red & brown omitted   4,500.
        Set value   .35

Mail Order Issue

Rural Post Office Store — A882

1972, Sept. 27 Photo. *Perf. 11x10½*
1468 A882 8c multicolored   .15 .15

Cent. of mail order business, originated by Aaron Montgomery Ward, Chicago.

Osteopathic Medicine Issue

Man's Quest for Health — A883

1972, Oct. 9 Photo. *Perf. 10½x11*
1469 A883 8c yel, org & dk brn   .15 .15

75th anniv. of the American Osteopathic Assoc., founded by Dr. Andrew T. Still.

American Folklore Issue

Tom Sawyer, by Norman Rockwell — A884

Lithographed, Engraved (Giori)
1972, Oct. 13   *Perf. 11*
1470	A884	8c black & multi	.15	.15
a.		Horiz. pair, imperf. btwn.	4,500.	
b.		Red & black (engr.) omitted	2,250.	
c.		Yellow & tan (litho.) omitted	2,400.	

Tom Sawyer, hero of "The Adventures of Tom Sawyer," by Mark Twain.

Angel from "Mary, Queen of Heaven" A885

Santa Claus A886

1972, Nov. 9   **Photo.**   *Perf. 10½x11*
1471	A885	8c multicolored	.15	.15
a.		Pink omitted	200.	
b.		Black omitted	4,000.	
1472	A886	8c multicolored	.15	.15
		Set value		.15

Design of No. 1471 shows detail from a painting by the Master of the St. Lucy Legend.

Pharmacy Issue

Mortar and Pestle, Bowl of Hygeia, 19th Century Medicine Bottles A887

Lithographed, Engraved (Giori)
1972, Nov. 10   *Perf. 11*
1473	A887	8c black & multi	.15	.15
a.		Blue & orange omitted	1,000.	
b.		Blue omitted	2,250.	
c.		Orange omitted	2,250.	

Honoring American druggists, and 120th anniv. of the American Pharmaceutical Assoc.

Stamp Collecting Issue

US No. 1 Under Magnifying Glass A888

1972, Nov. 17   *Perf. 11*
1474	A888	8c dark blue green, black & brown	.15	.15
a.		Black (litho.) omitted	1,000.	

Love Issue

"Love," by Robert Indiana A889

1973, Jan. 26   **Photo.**   *Perf. 11x10½*
1475	A889	8c red, emer & vio blue	.15	.15

American Bicentennial
Communications in Colonial Times

Printer and Patriots Examining Pamphlet A890

Posting a Broadside A891

Postrider A892

Drummer A893

1973   **Giori Press Printing**   *Perf. 11*
1476	A890	8c ultra, grnsh blk & red	.15	.15
1477	A891	8c black, ver & ultra	.15	.15

Lithographed, Engraved (Giori)
1478	A892	8c multicolored	.15	.15
1479	A893	8c multicolored	.15	.15
		Nos. 1476-1479 (4)	.60	
		Set value		.30

Issue dates: No. 1476, Feb. 16; No. 1477, Apr. 13; No. 1478, June 22; No. 1479, Sept. 28.

Boston Tea Party

British Merchantman A894

British Three-master A895

Boats and Ship's Hull — A896

Boat and Dock — A897

Lithographed, Engraved (Giori)
1973, July 4   *Perf. 11*
1480	A894	8c black & multi	.15	.15
1481	A895	8c black & multi	.15	.15
1482	A896	8c black & multi	.15	.15
1483	A897	8c black & multi	.15	.15
a.		Block of 4, #1480-1483	.65	.75
b.		As "a," black (engr.) omitted	1,500.	
c.		As "a," black (litho.) omitted	1,500.	

American Arts Issue

Gershwin, Sportin' Life, Porgy and Bess — A898

Robinson Jeffers, Man and Children of Carmel with Burro A899

Henry Ossawa Tanner, Palette and Rainbow A900

Willa Cather, Pioneer Family and Covered Wagon A901

1973   **Photo.**   *Perf. 11*
1484	A898	8c dp green & multi	.15	.15
a.		Vert. pair, imperf. horiz.	250.00	
1485	A899	8c Prus blue & multi	.15	.15
a.		Vert. pair, imperf. horiz.	250.00	
1486	A900	8c yel brown & multi	.15	.15
1487	A901	8c dp brown & multi	.15	.15
a.		Vert. pair, imperf. horiz.	275.00	
		Nos. 1484-1487 (4)	.60	
		Set value		.20

Honoring: No. 1484, George Gershwin (1898-1937), composer. No. 1485, Robinson Jeffers (1887-1962), poet. No. 1486, Henry Ossawa Tanner (1859-1937), black painter (portrait by Thomas Eakins). No. 1487, Willa Sibert Cather (1873-1947), novelist.

Issue dates: No. 1484, Feb. 28; No. 1485, Aug. 13; No. 1486, Sept. 10; No. 1487, Sept. 20.

Copernicus Issue

Nicolaus Copernicus (1473-1543), Polish Astronomer — A902

Lithographed, Engraved (Giori)
1973, Apr. 23   *Perf. 11*
1488	A902	8c black & orange	.15	.15
a.		Orange omitted	1,000.	
b.		Black (engraved) omitted	1,500.	

The orange color can be chemically removed.

Postal Service Employees' Issue

Stamp Counter — A903

Mail Collection — A904

Letter Facing on Conveyor Belt — A905

Parcel Post Sorting — A906

Mail Canceling — A907

Manual Letter Routing — A908

Electronic Letter Routing — A909

Loading Mail on Truck — A910

Mailman — A911

Rural Mail Delivery — A912

1973, Apr. 30   **Photo.**   *Perf. 10½x11*
1489	A903	8c multicolored	.15	.15
1490	A904	8c multicolored	.15	.15
1491	A905	8c multicolored	.15	.15
1492	A906	8c multicolored	.15	.15
1493	A907	8c multicolored	.15	.15
1494	A908	8c multicolored	.15	.15
1495	A909	8c multicolored	.15	.15
1496	A910	8c multicolored	.15	.15
1497	A911	8c multicolored	.15	.15
1498	A912	8c multicolored	.15	.15
a.		Strip of 10, Nos. 1489-1498	1.50	1.75

A tribute to USPS employees. Emerald inscription on back, printed beneath gum in water-soluble ink, includes the USPS emblem, "People Serving You" and a statement, differing for each of the 10 stamps, about some aspect of postal service.

Each stamp in top or bottom row has a tab with blue inscription enumerating various jobs in postal service.

Harry S Truman Issue

Harry S Truman, 33rd President (1884-1972) A913

Giori Press Printing
1973, May 8   *Perf. 11*
1499	A913	8c car rose, black & blue	.15	.15

Electronics Progress Issue

Marconi's Spark Coil and Gap — A914

Transistors and Printed Circuit Board A915

Microphone, Speaker, Vacuum Tube, TV Camera Tube — A916

Lithographed, Engraved (Giori)
1973, July 10   *Perf. 11*
1500 A914 6c lilac & multi   .15 .15
1501 A915 8c tan & multi   .15 .15
  a. Black (inscriptions & "U.S. 8c")
          omitted   800.
  b. Tan (background) & lilac omitted 1,500.
1502 A916 15c gray green & multi   .30 .15
  a. Black (inscriptions & "U.S. 15c")
          omitted   1,500.
        Nos. 1500-1502 (3)   .60
          Set value   .30

No. 1501b hinged is ½ unhinged value.
See No. C86.

Lyndon B. Johnson Issue

Lyndon B. Johnson (1908-1973), 36th President — A917

1973, Aug. 27   Photo.   *Perf. 11*
1503 A917 8c black & multi   .15 .15
  a. Horiz. pair, imperf. vert.   350.00

Rural America Issue

Angus and Longhorn Cattle A918

Chautauqua Tent and Buggies A919

Wheat Fields and Train — A920

Lithographed, Engraved (Giori)
1973-74   *Perf. 11*
1504 A918 8c multicolored   .15 .15
  a. Green & red brown omitted   1,000.
  b. Vert. pair, imperf. between
1505 A919 10c multicolored   .20 .15
  a. Black (litho.) omitted
1506 A920 10c multicolored   .20 .15
  a. Black & blue (engr.) omitted   900.
        Nos. 1504-1506 (3)   .55
          Set value   .15

Cent. of introduction of Aberdeen Angus cattle to US (No. 1504); of Chautauqua Institution (No. 1505); of introduction of hard winter wheat into Kansas by Mennonite immigrants (No. 1506).
Issue dates: No. 1504, Oct. 5, 1973. No. 1505, Aug. 6, 1974. No. 1506, Aug. 16, 1974.

Christmas Issue

Small Cowper Madonna, by Raphael A921 | Christmas Tree in Needlepoint A922

1973, Nov. 7   Photo.   *Perf. 10½x11*
1507 A921 8c tan & multi   .15 .15
1508 A922 8c green & multi   .15 .15
  a. Vert. pair, imperf. btwn.   350.00
          Set value   .15

50-Star and 13-Star Flags — A923 | Jefferson Memorial and Signature — A924

Mail Transport — A925 | Liberty Bell — A926

Multicolor Huck Press
1973-74   Tagged   *Perf. 11x10½*
1509 A923 10c red & blue   .20 .15
  a. Horiz. pair, imperf. btwn.   60.
  b. Blue omitted   175.
  c. Vert. pair, imperf.   1,150.
  d. Horiz. pair, imperf. vert.
Rotary Press Printing
1510 A924 10c blue   .20 .15
  a. Untagged (Bureau precan-
          celed)   .20
  b. Booklet pane of 5 + label   1.65 .55
  c. Booklet pane of 8   1.65 .70
  d. Booklet pane of 6 ('74)   5.25 1.00
  e. Vert. pair, imperf. horiz.   525.00
  f. Vert. pair, imperf. btwn.
1511 A925 10c multi, photo   .20 .15
  a. Yellow omitted   65.00

The yellow can be chemically removed.

Coil Stamps
Perf. 10 Vert.
Rotary Press Printing
1518 A926 6.3c brick red   .15 .15
  a. Untagged (Bureau precan-
          celed)   .15
  b. Imperf., pair   225.00
  c. As "a," imperf. pair   110.00
Multicolor Huck Press
1519 A923 10c red & blue   .20 .15
  a. Imperf., pair   37.50
Rotary Press Printing
1520 A924 10c blue   .25 .15
  a. Untagged (Bureau precan-
          celed)   .25
  b. Imperf., pair   42.50
Issued: #1509, 1519, 12/8/73; #1510, 1520, 12/14/73; #1511, 1/4/74; #1518, 10/1/74.

Veterans of Foreign Wars Issue

V.F.W. Emblem A928

Giori Press Printing
1974, Mar. 11   *Perf. 11*
1525 A928 10c red & dark blue   .20 .15
75th anniv. of Veterans of Spanish American and other Foreign Wars.

Robert Frost Issue

Robert Frost (1874-1963), Poet — A929

Rotary Press Printing
1974, Mar. 26   *Perf. 10½x11*
1526 A929 10c black   .20 .15

EXPO '74 Issue

"Cosmic Jumper" A930

1974, Apr. 18   Photo.   *Perf. 11*
1527 A930 10c multicolored   .20 .15
EXPO '74, Spokane, Wash., May 4-Nov. 4. Theme, "Preserve the Environment."

Horse Racing Issue

Horses Rounding Turn — A931

1974, May 4   Photo.   *Perf. 11x10½*
1528 A931 10c yellow & multi   .20 .15
  a. Blue ("Horse Racing") omitted   1,000.
  b. Red ("U.S. postage 10 cents")
          omitted
Beware of stamps offered as No. 1528b that have traces of red.

Skylab Issue

Skylab — A932

Lithographed, Engraved (Giori)
1974, May 14   *Perf. 11*
1529 A932 10c multicolored   .20 .15
  a. Vert. pair, imperf. btwn.
1st anniv. of the launching of Skylab and to honor all who participated in the Skylab projects.

Centenary of UPU Issue

Michelangelo, from "School of Athens," by Raphael — A933 | "Five Feminine Virtues," by Hokusai — A934

Old Time Letter Rack, by Peto — A935 | Mlle. La Vergne, by Jean Liotard — A936

Lady Writing Letter, by Gerard Terborch — A937 | Inkwell and Quill, by Jean Chardin — A938

Mrs. John Douglas, by Thomas Gainsborough A939 | Don Antonio Noreiga, by Francisco de Goya A940

1974, June 6   Photo.   *Perf. 11*
1530 A933 10c multicolored   .20 .15
1531 A934 10c multicolored   .20 .15
1532 A935 10c multicolored   .20 .15
1533 A936 10c multicolored   .20 .15
1534 A937 10c multicolored   .20 .15
1535 A938 10c multicolored   .20 .15
1536 A939 10c multicolored   .20 .15
1537 A940 10c multicolored   .20 .15
  a. Block or strip of 8, #1530-1537 1.60 1.60
  b. As "a" (block), imperf. vert.   7,500.

Mineral Heritage Issue

Petrified Wood A941

Tourmaline — A942

Amethyst A943

Rhodochrosite — A944

Lithographed, Engraved (Giori)
1974, June 13   *Perf. 11*

1538	A941	10c lt blue & multi	.20	.15
a.		Light blue & yellow omitted	—	
1539	A942	10c lt blue & multi	.20	.15
a.		Light blue omitted	—	
b.		Black & purple omitted	—	
1540	A943	10c lt blue & multi	.20	.15
a.		Light blue & yellow omitted	—	
1541	A944	10c lt blue & multi	.20	.15
a.		Block or strip of 4, #1538-1541	.80	.90
b.		As "a." lt bl & yel omitted	2,000.	
c.		Light blue omitted	—	
d.		Black & red omitted	—	
		Set value		.40

Kentucky Settlement Issue

Fort Harrod — A945

Lithographed, Engraved (Giori)
1974, June 15   *Perf. 11*

1542	A945	10c green & multi	.20	.15
a.		Dull black (litho.) omitted	900.	
b.		Green (engr. & litho.), black (engr. & litho.), blue omitted	3,750.	
c.		Green (engr.) omitted	—	
d.		Grn (engr.), blk (litho.) omitted	—	

American Bicentennial
First Continental Congress

Carpenters' Hall — A946

A947

DERIVING THEIR JUST POWERS FROM THE CONSENT OF THE GOVERNED — A948

Bicentennial Era A948

Independence Hall — A949

Giori Press Printing
1974, July 4   *Perf. 11*

1543	A946	10c dark blue & red	.20	.15
1544	A947	10c gray, dk blue & red	.20	.15
1545	A948	10c gray, dk blue & red	.20	.15
1546	A949	10c red & dark blue	.20	.15
a.		Block of 4, #1543-1546	.80	.90
		Set value		.40

Energy Conservation Issue

Molecules and Drops of Gasoline and Oil — A950

Lithographed, Engraved (Giori)
1974, Sept. 23   *Perf. 11*

1547	A950	10c multicolored	.20	.15
a.		Blue & orange omitted	900.	
b.		Orange & green omitted	750.	
c.		Green omitted	900.	

To publicize the importance of conserving all forms of energy.

American Folklore Issue
Legend of Sleepy Hollow

Headless Horseman Pursuing Ichabod Crane A951

Lithographed, Engraved (Giori)
1974, Oct. 10   *Perf. 11*

1548	A951	10c dk blue, black, org & yel	.20	.15

Legend of Sleepy Hollow, by Washington Irving.

Retarded Children Issue

Retarded Child — A952   Retarded Children Can Be Helped

Giori Press Printing
1974, Oct. 12   *Perf. 11*

1549	A952	10c brn red & dk brn	.20	.15

Natl. Assoc. of Retarded Citizens.

Christmas Issue

Angel, from Perussis Altarpiece, 1480 — A953

"The Road-Winter," by Currier and Ives — A954

Dove Weather Vane, Mount Vernon A955

1974   **Photo.**   *Perf. 10½x11*

1550	A953	10c multicolored	.20	.15

Perf. 11x10½

1551	A954	10c multicolored	.20	.15
a.		Buff omitted	35.00	

No. 1551a is difficult to identify. Competent expertization is necessary.

Imperf., Paper Backing Rouletted
Self-adhesive
Inscribed "Precanceled"
Untagged

1552	A955	10c multicolored	.20	.15
		Set value		.20

Issued: #1550-1551, Oct. 23; #1552, Nov. 15.

Unused value of No. 1552 is for copy on rouletted paper backing as issued. Used value is for copy on piece, with or without postmark. Most copies are becoming discolored, probably from the adhesive. Unused and used values are for discolored copies.

Die cutting includes crossed slashes through dove, applied to prevent removal and re-use of stamp. The stamp will separate into layers if soaked.

American Arts Issue

Benjamin West, Self-portrait A956

Paul Laurence Dunbar A957

D. W. Griffith and Projector A958

1975   **Photo.**   *Perf. 10½x11*

1553	A956	10c multicolored	.20	.15

Perf. 11

1554	A957	10c multicolored	.20	.15
a.		Imperf., pair	1,300.	

Litho., Engr. (Giori)

1555	A958	10c multicolored	.20	.15
a.		Brown (engr.) omitted	750.	
		Nos. 1553-1555 (3)	.60	
		Set value		.15

Honoring: West (1738-1820), painter (#1553). Dunbar (1872-1906), poet (#1554). David Lewelyn Wark Griffith (1875-1948), motion picture producer (#1555).

Issued: #1553, Feb. 10; #1554, May 1; #1555, May 27.

Space Issue

PIONEER ★ JUPITER — Pioneer 10 Passing Jupiter A959

MARINER 10   VENUS/MERCURY — Mariner 10, Venus and Mercury A960

Lithographed, Engraved (Giori)
1975   *Perf. 11*

1556	A959	10c lt yel, dk yel, red, blue, & 2 dk blues	.20	.15
a.		Red & dk yel omitted	1,500.	
b.		Dk blues (engr.) omitted	950.	

Imperfs. exist from printer's waste.

1557	A960	10c blk, red, ultra & bis	.20	.15
a.		Red omitted	700.	
b.		Ultra & bister omitted	2,000.	
		Set value		.15

US unmanned accomplishments in space. Pioneer 10 passed within 81,000 miles of Jupiter, Dec. 3, 1973. Mariner 10 explored Venus and Mercury in 1974, and Mercury again in Mar. 1975.

Issue dates: #1556, Feb. 28; #1557, Apr. 4.

Collective Bargaining Issue

"Labor and Management" A961

1975, Mar. 13   **Photo.**   *Perf. 11*

1558	A961	10c multicolored	.20	.15

Collective Bargaining Law, enacted 1935 with Wagner Act. Imperfs. are printers waste.

American Bicentennial
Contributors to the Cause

Sybil Ludington A962

Salem Poor — A963

Haym Salomon A964

Peter Francisco A965

1975, Mar. 25   **Photo.**   *Perf. 11x10½*

1559	A962	8c multicolored	.15	.15
a.		Back inscription omitted	275.00	
1560	A963	10c multicolored	.20	.15
a.		Back inscription omitted	225.00	
1561	A964	10c multicolored	.20	.15
a.		Back inscription omitted	250.00	
b.		Red omitted	250.00	
1562	A965	18c multicolored	.35	.20
		Nos. 1559-1562 (4)	.90	
		Set value		.45

Ludington, age 16, rallied militia Apr. 26, 1777. Poor, black freeman, fought in Battle of Bunker Hill. Salomon, Jewish immigrant, raised money to finance Revolutionary War. Francisco, Portuguese-French immigrant, joined Continental Army at 15.

Emerald inscription on back, printed beneath gum in water-soluble ink, gives thumbnail sketch of portrayed contributor.

Lexington-Concord Battle, 200th Anniv.

"Birth of Liberty," by Henry Sandham A966

1975, Apr. 19   **Photo.**   *Perf. 11*

1563	A966	10c multicolored	.20	.15
a.		Vert. pair, imperf. horiz.	425.00	

Battle of Bunker Hill, 200th Anniv.

Battle of Bunker Hill, by John Trumbull — A967

1975, June 17   *Perf. 11*

1564	A967	10c multicolored	.20	.15

Military Uniforms

Soldier with Flintlock Musket, Uniform Button — A968

Sailor with Grappling Hook, First Navy Jack, 1775 — A969

Marine with Musket, Full-rigged Ship — A970

Militiaman with Musket, Powder Horn — A971

1975, July 4   *Perf. 11*
1565	A968	10c multicolored	.20	.15
1566	A969	10c multicolored	.20	.15
1567	A970	10c multicolored	.20	.15
1568	A971	10c multicolored	.20	.15
a.		Block of 4, #1565-1568	.85	.90

Set value' .35

Bicentenary of US Military Services.

Apollo Soyuz Space Issue

Apollo and Soyuz After Docking and Earth — A972

Spacecraft Before Docking, Earth and Project Emblem — A973

1975, July 15   Photo.   *Perf. 11*
1569	A972	10c multicolored	.20	.15
a.		Pair, #1569-1570	.45	.40
b.		As "a," vert. pair, imperf. horiz.	2,000.	
1570	A973	10c multicolored	.20	.15

Set value .20

Apollo Soyuz space test project (Russo-American cooperation); launching, July 15; link-up, July 17. See Russia Nos. 4339-4340.

International Women's Year Issue

Worldwide Equality for Women A974

1975, Aug. 26   Photo.   *Perf. 11x10½*
1571	A974	10c blue, org & dk blue	.20	.15

Postal Service Bicentennial Issue

Stagecoach and Trailer Truck A975

Old and New Locomotives A976

Early Mail Plane and Jet — A977

Satellite for Transmission of Mailgrams A978

1975, Sept. 3   Photo.   *Perf. 11x10½*
1572	A975	10c multicolored	.20	.15
1573	A976	10c multicolored	.20	.15
1574	A977	10c multicolored	.20	.15
1575	A978	10c multicolored	.20	.15
a.		Block of 4, #1572-1575	.85	.90
b.		As "a," red ("10c") omitted	9,500.	

Set value .35

World Peace Through Law Issue

Law Book, Olive Branch and Globe A979

Giori Press Printing
1975, Sept. 29   *Perf. 11*
1576	A979	10c green, Prus blue & rose brown	.20	.15
a.		Horiz. pair, imperf. vert.	—	

A prelude to 7th World Conf. of the World Peace Through Law Center at Washington, DC, Oct. 12-17.

Banking and Commerce Issue

Engine Turning, Indian Head Penny and Morgan Silver Dollar A980

Seated Liberty Quarter, $20 Gold (Double Eagle), Engine Turning A981

Lithographed, Engraved (Giori)
1975, Oct. 6   *Perf. 11*
1577	A980	10c multicolored	.20	.15
a.		Pair. #1577-1578	.40	.40
b.		As "a," brown & blue (litho.) omitted	2,250.	
c.		As "a," brown, blue & yellow (litho.) omitted	2,750.	
1578	A981	10c multicolored	.20	.15

Set value .20

Banking and commerce in the US and for the Centennial Convention of the American Bankers Association.

Christmas Issue

Madonna, by Domenico Ghirlandaio A982

Christmas Card, by Louis Prang, 1878 A983

1975, Oct. 14   Photo.   *Perf. 11*
1579	A982	(10c) multicolored	.20	.15
a.		Imperf., pair	110.00	
1580	A983	(10c) multicolored	.20	.15
a.		Imperf., pair	120.00	
b.		Perf. 10½x11	.60	.15

Set value .15

Americana Issue

Inkwell and Quill — A984

Speaker's Stand — A985

Early Ballot Box — A987

Books, Bookmark, Eyeglasses — A988

Dome of Capitol — A994

Contemplation of Justice — A995

Early American Printing Press — A996

Torch — A997

Liberty Bell — A998

Eagle and Shield — A999

Fort McHenry Flag — A1001

Head, Statue of Liberty — A1002

Old North Church, Boston — A1003

Fort Nisqually — A1004

Sandy Hook Lighthouse, NJ — A1005

Morris Township School No. 2, Devils Lake, ND — A1006

Iron "Betty" Lamp, 17th-18th Cent. — A1007

Rush Lamp and Candle Holder — A1008

Kerosene Table Lamp — A1009

Railroad Conductor's Lantern, c. 1850 — A1010

1975-81   Engr.   *Perf. 11x10½*
1581	A984	1c dk blue, grnsh	.15	.15
a.		Untagged (Bureau precanceled)		.15
1582	A985	2c red brown, grnsh	.15	.15
a.		Untagged (Bureau precanceled)		.15
b.		Cream paper ('81)	.15	
1584	A987	3c olive, grnsh	.15	.15
a.		Untagged (Bureau precanceled)		.15
1585	A988	4c rose mag, cr	.15	.15
a.		Untagged (Bureau precanceled)		1.25

Size: 17½x20½mm
1590	A994	9c slate green	.50	.20
a.		Perf. 10	20.00	12.50

Size: 18½x22½mm
1591	A994	9c slate green, gray	.20	.15
a.		Untagged (Bureau precanceled)		.20
1592	A995	10c violet, gray	.20	.15
a.		Untagged (Bureau precanceled)		.25
1593	A996	11c orange, gray	.20	.15
1594	A997	12c red brown, beige	.25	.15
1595	A998	13c brown	.25	.15
a.		Booklet pane of 6	2.00	.75
b.		Booklet pane of 7 + label	1.75	.75
c.		Booklet pane of 8	2.00	1.00
d.		Booklet pane of 5 + label ('76)	1.50	.75
e.		Vert. pair, imperf btwn.	—	

Photo.
Perf. 11
1596	A999	13c multicolored	.25	.15
a.		Imperf., pair	50.00	—
b.		Yellow omitted	225.00	

Engr.
1597	A1001	15c gray, dk blue & red	.30	.15
a.		Vert. pair, imperf.	20.00	
b.		Gray omitted	700.00	
c.		Vert. strip of 3, imperf. btwn. & at top or bottom	—	

Perf. 11x10½
1598	A1001	15c gray, dk blue & red	.35	.15
a.		Booklet pane of 8	3.50	.80
1599	A1002	16c blue	.35	.15
1603	A1003	24c red, blue	.45	.15
1604	A1004	28c brown, blue	.55	.15
1605	A1005	29c blue, blue	.55	.15
1606	A1006	30c green, blue	.55	.15

Engr. & Litho.
Perf. 11
1608	A1007	50c tan, black & org	.85	.15
a.		Black omitted	300.00	
b.		Vert. pair, imperf. horiz.	1,750.	

Beware of copies offered as No. 1608b that have blind perfs.

1610	A1008	$1 tan, brn, org & yel	1.75	.20
a.		Brown (engraved) omitted	300.	
b.		Tan, orange & yel omitted	350.	
c.		Brown inverted	16,000.	
1611	A1009	$2 tan, dk grn, org & yel	3.25	.75
1612	A1010	$5 tan, red brn, yel & org	7.75	1.75
		Nos. 1581-1612 (22)	19.15	

Set value 3.40

Nos. 1590, 1590a, 1595, 1598 issued in booklets only. All stamps have one or two straight edges. Years of issue: #1591, 1595-1596, 11c, 24c, 1975. #1590, 1c-4c, 10c, 1977. #1597-1598, 16c, 28c, 29c, $2, 1978. 30c-$1, $5, 1979. 12c, 1981.

Guitar A1011

Saxhorns A1012

Drum
A1013

Piano
A1014

Coil Stamps
Engr.
Perf. 10 Vertically

1613	A1011	3.1c brown, *yel*	.15	.15
a.		Untagged (Bureau precanceled)		.50
b.		Imperf., pair	1,400.	
1614	A1012	7.7c brown, *brt yel*	.20	.15
a.		Untagged (Bureau precanceled)		.35
b.		As "a," imperf., pair	1,400.	
1615	A1013	7.9c carmine, *yel*	.20	.15
a.		Untagged (Bureau precanceled)		.20
b.		Imperf., pair	600.00	
1615C	A1014	8.4c dk blue, *yel*	.20	.15
d.		Untagged (Bureau precanceled)		.30
e.		As "d," pair, imperf. btwn.		70.00
f.		As "d," imperf., pair		15.00
1616	A994	9c sl green, *gray*	.20	.15
a.		Imperf., pair	175.00	
b.		Untagged (Bureau precanceled)		.35
c.		As "b," imperf., pair	700.00	
1617	A995	10c violet, *gray*	.20	.15
a.		Untagged (Bureau precanceled)		.25
b.		Imperf., pair	70.00	
1618	A998	13c brown	.25	.15
a.		Untagged (Bureau precanceled)		.45
b.		Imperf., pair	25.00	
g.		Pair, ir. imperf. between	—	
h.		As "a," imperf., pair	—	
1618C	A1001	15c gray, dk blue & red	.40	.15
d.		Imperf., pair	25.00	
e.		Pair, imperf. between	150.00	
f.		Gray omitted	40.00	
1619	A1002	16c blue	.35	.15
a.		Huck press printing	.50	.15
		Nos. 1613-1619 (9)	2.15	
		Set value		.55

The 15c was printed on two different presses. Huck press printings have white background without bluish tinge, are a fraction of a millimeter smaller and have block instead of overall tagging. Cottrell press printings show a joint line.
Years of issue: 9c, 13c, 1975. 7.7c, 7.9c, 1976. 10c, 1977. 8.4c, 15c, 16c, 1978. 3.1c, 1979.
See Nos. 1811, 1813, 1816.

13-Star Flag, Independence Hall
A1015

Flag over Capitol
A1016

Multicolor Huck Press
1975-77   *Perf. 11x10½*

1622	A1015	13c dark blue & red	.25	.15
a.		Horiz. pair, imperf. btwn.	55.	
b.		Vert. pair, imperf.	1,100.	
c.		Perf. 11 ('81)	.65	.15
d.		As "c," vert. pair, imperf.	150.	
e.		Horiz. pair, imperf. vert.	—	

No. 1622 has overall tagging and nearly vertical multiple gum ridges. No. 1622c has block tagging and flat gum.

1623	A1016	13c blue & red ('77)	.25	.15
a.		Booklet pane of 8 (1 #1590 and 7 #1623)	2.25	1.10
b.		Perf. 10	1.00	1.00
c.		Booklet pane of 8 (1 #1590a + 7 #1623b)	30.00	—
d.		Se-tenant pair, #1590 & 1623	.75	.75
e.		Se-tenant pair, #1590a & 1623b	22.50	20.00

Coil Stamp
Perf. 10 Vertically

1625	A1015	13c dark blue & red	.25	.15
a.		Imperf., pair	25.00	
		Set value		.15

Nos. 1623 and 1623b issued in booklets only. All stamps have one or two straight edges.

American Bicentennial — Spirit of '76

Drummer Boy
A1019

Old Drummer
A1020

Fifer — A1021

Designed after painting "The Spirit of '76," by Archibald M. Willard.

1976, Jan. 1   Photo.   *Perf. 11*

1629	A1019	13c multicolored	.20	.15
1630	A1020	13c multicolored	.20	.15
1631	A1021	13c multicolored	.20	.15
a.		Strip of 3, #1629-1631	.60	.65
b.		As "a," imperf.	1,300.	
c.		Vert. pair, imperf.	800.	
		Set value		.25

Interphil Issue

"Interphil 76"
A1022

Lithographed, Engraved (Giori)
1976, Jan. 17   *Perf. 11*

1632	A1022	13c dk blue, red & ultra	.20	.15

Interphil 76 Intl. Phil. Exhib., Philadelphia, Pa., May 29-June 6.

State Flags
A1023-A1072

1976, Feb. 23   Photo.   *Perf. 11*

1633	A1023	13c Delaware	.25	.20
1634	A1024	13c Pennsylvania	.25	.20
1635	A1025	13c New Jersey	.25	.20
1636	A1026	13c Georgia	.25	.20
1637	A1027	13c Connecticut	.25	.20
1638	A1028	13c Massachusetts	.25	.20
1639	A1029	13c Maryland	.25	.20
1640	A1030	13c South Carolina	.25	.20
1641	A1031	13c New Hampshire	.25	.20
1642	A1032	13c Virginia	.25	.20
1643	A1033	13c New York	.25	.20
1644	A1034	13c North Carolina	.25	.20
1645	A1035	13c Rhode Island	.25	.20
1646	A1036	13c Vermont	.25	.20
1647	A1037	13c Kentucky	.25	.20
1648	A1038	13c Tennessee	.25	.20
1649	A1039	13c Ohio	.25	.20
1650	A1040	13c Louisiana	.25	.20
1651	A1041	13c Indiana	.25	.20
1652	A1042	13c Mississippi	.25	.20
1653	A1043	13c Illinois	.25	.20
1654	A1044	13c Alabama	.25	.20
1655	A1045	13c Maine	.25	.20
1656	A1046	13c Missouri	.25	.20
1657	A1047	13c Arkansas	.25	.20
1658	A1048	13c Michigan	.25	.20
1659	A1049	13c Florida	.25	.20
1660	A1050	13c Texas	.25	.20
1661	A1051	13c Iowa	.25	.20
1662	A1052	13c Wisconsin	.25	.20
1663	A1053	13c California	.25	.20
1664	A1054	13c Minnesota	.25	.20
1665	A1055	13c Oregon	.25	.20
1666	A1056	13c Kansas	.25	.20
1667	A1057	13c West Virginia	.25	.20
1668	A1058	13c Nevada	.25	.20
1669	A1059	13c Nebraska	.25	.20
1670	A1060	13c Colorado	.25	.20
1671	A1061	13c North Dakota	.25	.20
1672	A1062	13c South Dakota	.25	.20
1673	A1063	13c Montana	.25	.20
1674	A1064	13c Washington	.25	.20
1675	A1065	13c Idaho	.25	.20
1676	A1066	13c Wyoming	.25	.20
1677	A1067	13c Utah	.25	.20
1678	A1068	13c Oklahoma	.25	.20
1679	A1069	13c New Mexico	.25	.20
1680	A1070	13c Arizona	.25	.20
1681	A1071	13c Alaska	.25	.20
1682	A1072	13c Hawaii	.25	.20
a.		Pane of 50	13.00	—

Telephone Centenary Issue

Alexander Graham Bell **13c**

Bell's Telephone Patent Application
A1073

Telephone Centennial **USA**

Engraved (Giori)
1976, Mar. 10   *Perf. 11*

1683	A1073	13c blk, pur & red, *tan*	.25	.15

1st telephone call by Alexander Graham Bell, Mar. 10, 1876.

Commercial Aviation Issue

Ford-Pullman Monoplane and Laird Swallow Biplane
A1074

1976, Mar. 19   Photo.   *Perf. 11*

1684	A1074	13c blue & multi	.25	.15

50th anniv. of 1st contract airmail flights: Dearborn, MI to Cleveland, OH, Feb. 15, 1926; and Pasco, WA to Elko, NV, Apr. 6, 1926.

Chemistry Issue

Various Flasks, Separatory Funnel, Computer Tape — A1075

1976, Apr. 6   Photo.   *Perf. 11*

1685	A1075	13c multicolored	.25	.15

Honoring American chemists, cent. of the American Chemical Society.

Surrender of Cornwallis at Yorktown, by John Trumbull
A1076

The Surrender of Lord Cornwallis at Yorktown
From a Painting by John Trumbull

Declaration of Independence, by John Trumbull
A1077

The Declaration of Independence, 4 July 1776 at Philadelphia
From a Painting by John Trumbull

Washington Crossing the Delaware
From a Painting by Emanuel Leutze/Eastman Johnson

Washington Crossing the Delaware, by Emanuel Leutze/Eastman Johnson
A1078

Washington Reviewing His Ragged Army at Valley Forge
From a Painting by William T. Trego

Washington Reviewing Army at Valley Forge, by William T. Trego
A1079

Designs, from Left to Right, No. 1686: a, Two British officers. b, Gen. Benjamin Lincoln. c, George Washington. d, John Trumbull, Col. Cobb, von Steuben, Lafayette, Thomas Nelson. Alexander Hamilton, John Laurens, Walter Stewart, all vert.

No. 1687: a, John Adams, Roger Sherman, Robert R. Livingston. b, Jefferson, Franklin. c, Thomas Nelson, Jr., Francis Lewis, John Witherspoon, Samuel Huntington. d, John Hancock, Charles Thomson. e, George Read, John Dickinson, Edward Rutledge (a, d, vert., b, c, e, horiz.).

No. 1688: a, Boatsman. b, Washington. c, Flag bearer. d, Men in boat. e, Men on shore (a, d, horiz., b, c, e, vert.).

No. 1689: a, Two officers. b, Washington. c, Officer, black horse. d, Officer, white horse. e, Three soldiers (a, c, e, horiz., b, d, vert.).

1976, May 29   Litho.   *Perf. 11*

1686	A1076	Sheet of 5	3.25	
a.-e.		13c multi. any single	.45	.40
f.		USA 13c omitted on "b," "c" & "d," imperf., untagged	—	2,250.
g.		USA 13c omitted on "a" & "e"	450.	—
h.		Imperf., untagged	—	2,250.
i.		USA 13c omitted on "b," "c" & "d"	450.	—
j.		USA 13c double on "b"	—	
k.		USA 13c omitted on "c" & "d"	800.	
l.		USA 13c omitted on "e"	500.	
m.		USA 13c omitted, imperf., untagged	—	
n.		As "g," imperf., untagged	—	
1687	A1077	Sheet of 5	4.25	
a.-e.		18c multi, any single	.55	.55
f.		Design & marginal inscriptions omitted	3,000.	
g.		USA 18c omitted on "a" & "c"	800.	
h.		USA 18c omitted on "b," "d" & "e"	500.	
i.		USA 18c omitted on "d"	550.	500.
j.		Black omitted in design	2,000.	
k.		USA 18c omitted, imperf., untagged	3,000.	
m.		USA 18c omitted on "b" & "e"	500.	
n.		USA 18c omitted on "b"	—	
p.		Imperf., tagged	—	
q.		USA 18c omitted on "c"	—	
1688	A1078	Sheet of 5	5.25	—
a.-e.		24c multi, any single	.70	.70
f.		USA 24c omitted, imperf., untagged	3,500.	
g.		USA 24c omitted on "d" & "e"	450.	450.

h.		Design & marginal inscriptions omitted	3,250.	
i.		USA 24c omitted on "a," "b" & "c"	500.	—
j.		Imperf., untagged	3,000.	
k.		USA 24c of "d" & "e" inverted	—	
1689	A1079	Sheet of 5	6.25	—
a.-e.		31c multi, any single	.85	.85
f.		USA 31c omitted, imperf., untagged	2,750.	
g.		USA 31c omitted on "a" & "c"	450.	
h.		USA 31c omitted on "b," "d" & "e"	450.	
i.		USA 31c omitted on "e"	500.	
j.		Black omitted in design	2,000.	
k.		Imperf., untagged	—	2,250.
l.		USA 31c omitted on "b" & "d"	—	
m.		USA 31c omitted on "a" "c" & "e"	—	
n.		As "m," imperf., untagged	—	
p.		As "h," imperf., untagged	—	2,500.
q.		As "g," imperf., untagged	2,750.	
r.		USA 31c omitted on "d" & "e"	—	
		Nos. 1686-1689 (4)	19.00	

Nos. 1688-1689 exist with inverted perforations.
Issued in connection with Interphil 76 Intl. Phil. Exhib., Philadelphia, Pa., May 29-June 6. Size of sheets: 203x152mm; stamps: 25x39½mm, 39½x25mm.

Benjamin Franklin Issue

Franklin and Map of North America, 1776 — A1080

Lithographed, Engraved (Giori)
1976, June 1   *Perf. 11*

1690	A1080	13c ultra & multi	.25	.15
a.		Light blue omitted	300.00	

American Bicentennial; Franklin (1706-1790), deputy postmaster general for the colonies (1753-1774) and statesman.
See Canada No. 691.

American Bicentennial Issue

Declaration of Independence, by John Trumbull

A1081   A1082   A1083   A1084

1976, July 4 Photo. Perf. 11

1691	A1081	13c multicolored	.25	.15
1692	A1082	13c multicolored	.25	.15
1693	A1083	13c multicolored	.25	.15
1694	A1084	13c multicolored	.25	.15
a.		Strip of 4, #1691-1694	1.10	1.10
		Set value		.35

Olympic Games Issue

Diving
A1085

Skiing
A1086

Running
A1087

Skating
A1088

1976, July 16 Photo. Perf. 11

1695	A1085	13c multicolored	.25	.15
1696	A1086	13c multicolored	.25	.15
1697	A1087	13c multicolored	.25	.15
1698	A1088	13c multicolored	.25	.15
a.		Block of 4, #1695-1698	1.10	1.10
b.		As "a," imperf.	750.00	
		Set value		.35

12th Winter Olympic Games, Innsbruck, Austria, Feb. 4-15, and 21st Summer Olympic Games, Montreal, Canada, July 17-Aug. 1.

Clara Maass Issue

Clara Maass, Newark German Hospital Pin — A1089

1976, Aug. 18 Photo. Perf. 11

1699	A1089	13c multicolored	.25	.15
a.		Horiz. pair, imperf. vert.	475.00	

Clara Maass (1876-1901), volunteer in fight against yellow fever, birth centenary.

Adolph S. Ochs Issue

Adolph S. Ochs (1858-1935), Publisher of the NY Times, 1896-1935
A1090

Giori Press Printing

1976, Sept. 18 Perf. 11

1700	A1090	13c black & gray	.25	.15

Christmas Issue

Nativity, by John Singleton Copley
A1091

"Winter Pastime," by Nathaniel Currier
A1092

1976, Oct. 27 Photo. Perf. 11

1701	A1091	13c multicolored	.25	.15
a.		Imperf., pair	100.00	
1702	A1092	13c multicolored	.25	.15
a.		Imperf., pair	100.00	
1703	A1092	13c multicolored	.25	.15
a.		Imperf., pair	110.00	
b.		Vert. pair, imperf. btwn.	—	
d.		Red omitted	—	
e.		Yellow omitted	—	
		Nos. 1701-1703 (3)		.75
		Set value		.15

No. 1702 has overall tagging. Lettering at base is black and usually ½mm below design. As a rule, no "snowflaking" in sky or pond. Pane of 50 has margins on 4 sides with slogans.

No. 1703 has block tagging the size of printed area. Lettering at base is gray black and usually ¾mm below design. "Snowflaking" generally in sky and pond. Pane has margin only at right or left, and no slogans. Copies are known with various amounts of red or yellow missing. Nos. 1703d and 1703e have the color totally omitted. Expertization is recommended.

American Bicentennial Issue
Washington at Princeton

Washington, Nassau Hall, Hessians, 13-Star Flag, by Charles Willson Peale — A1093

1977, Jan. 3 Photo. Perf. 11

1704	A1093	13c multicolored	.25	.15
a.		Horiz. pair, imperf. vert.	550.00	

Washington's victory at Princeton over Lord Cornwallis, bicentennial.

Sound Recording Issue

Tin Foil Phonograph
A1094

Lithographed, Engraved (Giori)
1977, Mar. 23 Perf. 11

1705	A1094	13c black & multi	.25	.15

Centenary of invention of the phonograph by Thomas Alva Edison, and development of sophisticated recording industry.

American Folk Art Issue
Pueblo Pottery

Pueblo Art USA 13c
Zia Pot — A1095

Pueblo Art USA 13c
San Ildefonso Pot — A1096

Pueblo Art USA 13c
Hopi Pot — A1097

Pueblo Art USA 13c
Acoma Pot — A1098

1977, Apr. 13 Photo. Perf. 11

1706	A1095	13c multicolored	.25	.15
1707	A1096	13c multicolored	.25	.15
1708	A1097	13c multicolored	.25	.15
1709	A1098	13c multicolored	.25	.15
a.		Block or strip of 4	1.00	1.00
b.		As "a," imperf. vert.	2,500.	
		Set value		.35

Pueblo art, 1880-1920, from museums in NM, AZ and CO.

Lindbergh Flight Issue

Spirit of St. Louis
A1099

1977, May 20 Photo. Perf. 11

1710	A1099	13c multicolored	.25	.15
a.		Imperf., pair	1,250.	

Charles A. Lindbergh's solo transatlantic flight from NY to Paris, 50th anniv.

Colorado Statehood Issue

Columbine and Rocky Mountains — A1100

1977, May 21 Photo. Perf. 11

1711	A1100	13c multicolored	.25	.15
a.		Horiz. pair, imperf. btwn.	600.00	
b.		Horiz. pair, imperf. vert.	900.00	

Colorado became a state in 1876.

Butterfly Issue

Swallowtail
A1101

Checkerspot
A1102

Dogface
A1103

Orange Tip — A1104

1977, June 6 Photo. Perf. 11

1712	A1101	13c tan & multi	.25	.15
1713	A1102	13c tan & multi	.25	.15
1714	A1103	13c tan & multi	.25	.15
1715	A1104	13c tan & multi	.25	.15
a.		Block of 4, #1712-1715	1.00	1.00
b.		As "a," imperf. horiz.	15,000.	
		Set value		.35

American Bicentennial Issues
Lafayette

Marquis de Lafayette — A1105

1977, June 13 Engr. Perf. 11

1716	A1105	13c blue, black & red	.25	.15

200th anniv. of Lafayette's landing on the coast of SC, north of Charleston.

Skilled Hands for Independence

Seamstress
A1106

Blacksmith
A1107

Wheelwright
A1108

Leatherworker
A1109

1977, July 4 Photo. Perf. 11

1717	A1106	13c multicolored	.25	.15
1718	A1107	13c multicolored	.25	.15
1719	A1108	13c multicolored	.25	.15
1720	A1109	13c multicolored	.25	.15
a.		Block of 4, #1717-1720	1.00	1.00
		Set value		.35

Peace Bridge Issue

Peace Bridge and Dove — A1110

1977, Aug. 4 Engr. Perf. 11x10½

1721	A1110	13c blue	.25	.15

50th anniv. of the Peace Bridge, connecting Buffalo, NY with Fort Erie, Ontario.

American Bicentennial Issue
Battle of Oriskany

Herkimer at Oriskany, by Frederick Yohn
A1111

1977, Aug. 6 Photo. Perf. 11

1722	A1111	13c multicolored	.25	.15

200th anniv. of Battle of Oriskany, American Militia led by Brig. Gen. Nicholas Herkimer (1728-1777).

Energy Issue
Energy Conservation
A1112

Energy Development
A1113

1977, Oct. 20 Photo. Perf. 11

1723	A1112	13c multicolored	.25	.15
a.		Pair, #1723-1724	.50	.50
1724	A1113	13c multicolored	.25	.15
		Set value		.20

Conservation and development of nation's energy resources.

Alta California Issue

Farm Houses
A1114

First Civil Settlement-Alta California-1777

Litho. & Engraved (Giori)

1977, Sept. 9   *Perf. 11*
1725 A1114 13c black & multi   .25 .15

El Pueblo de San José de Guadalupe, 1st civil settlement in Alta California, 200th anniv.

American Bicentennial Issue
Articles of Confederation

Members of Continental Congress in Conference
A1115

Engraved (Giori)

1977, Sept. 30   *Perf. 11*
1726 A1115 13c red & brn, *cream*   .25 .15

200th anniv. of drafting the Articles of Confederation, York Town, Pa.

Talking Picture, 50th Anniv. Issue

Movie Projector and Phonograph
A1116

Litho. & Engraved (Giori)

1977, Oct. 6   *Perf. 11*
1727 A1116 13c multicolored   .25 .15

American Bicentennial Issue
Surrender at Saratoga

Surrender of Burgoyne, by John Trumbull
A1117

1977, Oct. 7   Photo.   *Perf. 11*
1728 A1117 13c multicolored   .25 .15

200th anniv. of Gen. John Burgoyne's surrender at Saratoga.

Christmas Issue

Washington at Valley Forge
A1118

Rural Mailbox
A1119

1977, Oct. 21   Photo.   *Perf. 11*
1729 A1118 13c multicolored   .25 .15
   a. Imperf., pair   75.00
1730 A1119 13c multicolored   .25 .15
   a. Imperf., pair   300.00
       Set value   .15

Carl Sandburg Issue

Carl Sandburg, by William A. Smith, 1952 — A1120

Engraved (Giori)

1978, Jan. 6   *Perf. 11*
1731 A1120 13c black & brown   .25 .15
   a. Brown omitted

Sandburg (1878-1967), poet, biographer and collector of American folk songs.

Captain Cook Issue

Capt. Cook, by Nathaniel Dance, 1776
A1121

"Resolution" and "Discovery," by John Webber
A1122

Giori Press Printing

1978, Jan. 20   *Perf. 11*
1732 A1121 13c dark blue   .25 .15
   a. Pair, #1732-1733   .50 .50
   b. As "a," imperf. between   4,500.
1733 A1122 13c green   .25 .15
   a. Vert. pair, imperf. horiz.   —
       Set value   .20

Capt. James Cook, 200th anniv. of his arrival in Hawaii, at Waimea, Kauai, Jan. 20, 1778, and of his anchorage in Cook Inlet, near Anchorage, Alaska, June 1, 1778. Nos. 1732-1733 issued in panes of 50, containing 25 each of Nos. 1732-1733 including 5 No. 1732a. Design of No. 1733 is after etching "A View of Karakekooa in Owyhee."

Indian Head Penny, 1877
A1123

Eagle
A1124

USA Roses — A1126

Engraved (Giori)

1978, Jan. 11   *Perf. 11*
1734 A1123 13c brown & blue green, *bister*   .25 .15
   a. Horiz. pair, imperf. vert.   300.00

1978, May 22   Photo.   *Perf. 11*
1735 A1124 (15c) orange   .25 .15
   a. Imperf., pair   110.00
   b. Vert. pair, imperf. horiz.   750.00

Engr.   *Perf. 11x10½*
1736 A1124 (15c) orange   .25 .15
   a. Booklet pane of 8   2.25 .90

See No. 1743

1978, July 11   Engr.   *Perf. 10*
1737 A1126 15c multicolored   .25 .15
   a. Booklet pane of 8   2.25 .90
   b. As "a," imperf.   —
      Set value, #1734-1737   .25

Nos. 1736, 1737 issued in booklets only. All stamps have 1 or 2 straight edges.

Robertson Windmill, Williamsburg
A1127

Old Windmill, Portsmouth
A1128

Cape Cod Windmill, Eastham — A1129

Dutch Mill, Batavia — A1130

Southwestern Windmill — A1131

1980, Feb. 7   Engr.   Perf. 11
Booklet Stamps

1738 A1127 15c sepia, *yellow*   .30 .15
1739 A1128 15c sepia, *yellow*   .30 .15
1740 A1129 15c sepia, *yellow*   .30 .15
1741 A1130 15c sepia, *yellow*   .30 .15
1742 A1131 15c sepia, *yellow*   .30 .15
  a. Bklt. pane, 2 each #1738-1742   3.50 3.00
  b. Strip of 5, #1738-1742   1.50 1.40
      Set value   .25

Coil Stamp

1978, May 22   Engr.   *Perf. 10 Vert.*
1743 A1124 (15c) orange   .25 .15
   a. Imperf., pair   100.00

No. 1743a is valued in the grade of fine.

Black Heritage Issue

Harriet Tubman (1820-1913), Cart Carrying Slaves — A1133

1978, Feb. 1   Photo.   *Perf. 10½x11*
1744 A1133 13c multicolored   .25 .15

Tubman, born a slave, helped more than 300 slaves escape to freedom.

American Folk Art Issue
American Quilts, Basket Design

A1134   A1135

A1136   A1137

1978, Mar. 8   Photo.   *Perf. 11*
1745 A1134 13c multicolored   .25 .15
1746 A1135 13c multicolored   .25 .15
1747 A1136 13c multicolored   .25 .15
1748 A1137 13c multicolored   .25 .15
   a. Block of 4, #1745-1748   1.00 1.00
       Set value   .35

American Dance Issue

Ballet
A1138

Theater
A1139

Folk Dance
A1140

Modern Dance
A1141

1978, Apr. 26   Photo.   *Perf. 11*
1749 A1138 13c multicolored   .25 .15
1750 A1139 13c multicolored   .25 .15
1751 A1140 13c multicolored   .25 .15
1752 A1141 13c multicolored   .25 .15
   a. Block of 4, #1749-1752   1.00 1.00
       Set value   .35

American Bicentennial Issue
French Alliance

Louis XVI and Franklin, Porcelain Sculpture by C. G. Sauvage — A1142

Giori Press Printing

1978, May 4   *Perf. 11*
1753 A1142 13c blue, black & red   .25 .15

Bicent. of French Alliance, signed in Paris, Feb. 6, 1778, and ratified by Continental Cong., May 4.

Early Cancer Detection Issue

Dr. George Papanicolaou (1883-1962), his Signature and Microscope — A1143

1978, May 18   Engr.   *Perf. 10½x11*
1754 A1143 13c brown   .25 .15

Papanicolaou, developer of Pap Test, early cancer detection in women.

Performing Arts Issues

Jimmie Rodgers and Locomotive
A1144

George M. Cohan, "Yankee Doodle Dandy" and Stars
A1145

1978   Photo.   *Perf. 11*
1755 A1144 13c multicolored   .25 .15
1756 A1145 15c multicolored   .25 .15
       Set value   .15

Rodgers (1897-1933), the "Singing Brakeman, Father of Country Music," and Cohan (1878-1942), actor and playwright.

Issue dates: #1755, May 24; #1756, July 3.

CAPEX Issue

Wildlife from Canadian-US Border — A1146

Litho. & Engr. (Giori)

1978, June 10		Perf. 11	
1757 A1146	Block of 8	2.10	2.10
a.	13c Cardinal	.25	.15
b.	13c Mallard	.25	.15
c.	13c Canada goose	.25	.15
d.	13c Blue jay	.25	.15
e.	13c Moose	.25	.15
f.	13c Chipmunk	.25	.15
g.	13c Red fox	.25	.15
h.	13c Raccoon	.25	.15
i.	Yellow, green, red, brown, blue, black (litho.) omitted	5,000.	

CAPEX, Canadian Intl. Phil. Exhib., Toronto, Ont., June 9-18.

Photography Issue

Photographic Equipment A1147

1978, June 26	Photo.	Perf. 11	
1758 A1147	15c multicolored	.30	.15

Viking Missions to Mars Issue

Viking 1 Lander Scooping Up Soil on Mars A1148

1978, July 20		Litho. & Engr.	
1759 A1148	15c multicolored	.30	.15

2nd anniv. of landing of Viking 1 on Mars.

American Owls Issue

Great Gray Owl A1149   Saw-whet Owl A1150

Barred Owl A1151   Great Horned Owl A1152

1978, Aug. 26	Engr.	Perf. 11	
1760 A1149	15c multicolored	.30	.15
1761 A1150	15c multicolored	.30	.15
1762 A1151	15c multicolored	.30	.15
1763 A1152	15c multicolored	.30	.15
a.	Block of 4, #1760-1763	1.25	1.25
	Set value		.35

American Trees Issue

Giant Sequoia A1153

White Pine A1154

White Oak — A1155

Gray Birch A1156

1978, Oct. 9	Photo.	Perf. 11	
1764 A1153	15c multicolored	.30	.15
1765 A1154	15c multicolored	.30	.15
1766 A1155	15c multicolored	.30	.15
1767 A1156	15c multicolored	.30	.15
a.	Block of 4, #1764-1767	1.25	1.25
b.	As "a," imperf. horiz.	12,500.	
	Set value		.35

Christmas Issue

Madonna and Child with Cherubim, by Andrea della Robbia — A1157   Child on Hobbyhorse and Christmas Trees — A1158

1978, Oct. 18	Photo.	Perf. 11	
1768 A1157	15c blue & multi	.30	.15
a.	Imperf., pair	90.00	
1769 A1158	15c red & multi	.30	.15
a.	Imperf., pair	100.00	
b.	Vert. pair, imperf. horiz.	2,250.	
	Set value		.15

Value for #1768a is for an uncreased pair.

Robert F. Kennedy Issue

Robert F. Kennedy (1925-68), US Attorney General — A1159

1979, Jan. 12	Engr.	Perf. 11	
1770 A1159	15c blue	.30	.15

Black Heritage Issue

Dr. Martin Luther King, Jr. (1929-68), and Civil Rights Marchers — A1160

1979, Jan. 13	Photo.	Perf. 11	
1771 A1160	15c multicolored	.30	.15
a.	Imperf., pair		

Civil rights leader.

Year of the Child Issue

Children A1161   International Year of the Child

1979, Feb. 15	Engr.	Perf. 11	
1772 A1161	15c orange red	.30	.15

International Year of the Child.

John Steinbeck A1162   Albert Einstein A1163

John Steinbeck Issue

1979, Feb. 27	Engr.	Perf. 10½x11	
1773 A1162	15c dark blue	.30	.15

John Ernst Steinbeck (1902-68), novelist.

Albert Einstein Issue

1979, Mar. 4	Engr.	Perf. 10½x11	
1774 A1163	15c chocolate	.30	.15

Einstein (1879-1955), theoretical physicist.

American Folk Art Issue
Pennsylvania Toleware

Coffeepot A1164   Tea Caddy A1165

Sugar Bowl A1166   Coffeepot A1167

1979, Apr. 19	Photo.	Perf. 11	
1775 A1164	15c multicolored	.30	.15
1776 A1165	15c multicolored	.30	.15
1777 A1166	15c multicolored	.30	.15
1778 A1167	15c multicolored	.30	.15
a.	Block of 4, #1775-1778	1.25	1.25
b.	As "a," imperf. horiz.	4,250.	
	Set value		.35

American Architecture Issue

Virginia Rotunda, by Thomas Jefferson A1168   Baltimore Cathedral, by Benjamin Latrobe A1169

Boston State House, by Charles Bulfinch A1170   Philadelphia Exchange, by William Strickland A1171

1979, June 4	Engr.	Perf. 11	
1779 A1168	15c black & brick red	.30	.15
1780 A1169	15c black & brick red	.30	.15
1781 A1170	15c black & brick red	.30	.15
1782 A1171	15c black & brick red	.30	.15
a.	Block of 4, #1779-1782	1.25	1.25
	Set value		.35

Endangered Flora Issue

Persistent Trillium A1172   Hawaiian Wild Broadbean A1173

Contra Costa Wallflower A1174   Antioch Dunes Evening Primrose A1175

1979, June 7	Photo.	Perf. 11	
1783 A1172	15c multicolored	.30	.15
1784 A1173	15c multicolored	.30	.15
1785 A1174	15c multicolored	.30	.15
1786 A1175	15c multicolored	.30	.15
a.	Block of 4, #1783-1786	1.25	1.25
b.	As "a," imperf.	600.00	
	Set value		.35

Seeing Eye Dogs Issue

Seeing for Me   German Shepherd Leading Man — A1176

1979, June 15			
1787 A1176	15c multicolored	.30	.15
a.	Imperf., pair	400.00	

Special Olympics Issue

Special Olympics

USA 15c

Child Holding Winner's Medal — A1177

Skill-Sharing Joy

1979, Aug. 9   *Perf. 11*
1788 A1177 15c multicolored   .30   .15
Special Olympics for special children, Brockport, NY, Aug. 8-13.

John Paul Jones Issue

I have not yet begun to fight

John Paul Jones
US Bicentennial 15c

John Paul Jones, by Charles Willson Peale — A1178

1979, Sept. 23   Photo.   *Perf. 11x12*
1789 A1178 15c multicolored   .30   .15
   a.   Perf. 11   .30   .15
   b.   Perf. 12   2,250. 1,000.
   c.   Vert. pair, imperf. horiz.   200.
   d.   As "a," vert. pair, imperf horiz.   150.
John Paul Jones (1747-1792), Naval Commander, American Revolution.
Imperfs., perf. or imperf. gutter pairs and blocks exist from printer's waste.

Olympic Games Issue

Javelin A1179

Running A1180

Swimming A1181

Rowing A1182

Equestrian A1183

1979   Photo.   *Perf. 11*
1790 A1179 10c multicolored   .20   .20
1791 A1180 15c multicolored   .30   .15
1792 A1181 15c multicolored   .30   .15
1793 A1182 15c multicolored   .30   .15
1794 A1183 15c multicolored   .30   .15
   a.   Block of 4, #1791-1794   1.25 1.25
   b.   As "a," imperf.   1,600.
   Nos. 1790-1794 (5)   1.40
    Set value   .55
22nd Summer Olympic Games, Moscow, July 19-Aug. 3, 1980.
Issue dates: 10c, Sept. 5; 15c, Sept. 28.

Winter Olympic Games Issue

Speed Skating A1184

Downhill Skiing A1185

Ski Jump A1186

Ice Hockey A1187

1980, Feb. 1   Photo.   *Perf. 11x10½*
1795 A1184 15c multicolored   .35   .15
   a.   Perf. 11   1.05   —
1796 A1185 15c multicolored   .35   .15
   a.   Perf. 11   1.05   —
1797 A1186 15c multicolored   .35   .15
   a.   Perf. 11   1.05   —
1798 A1187 15c multicolored   .35   .15
   a.   Perf. 11   1.05   —
   b.   Block of 4, #1795-1798   1.50 1.40
   c.   Block of 4, #1795a-1798a   4.25   —
    Set value   .35
13th Winter Olympic Games, Lake Placid, NY, Feb. 12-24.

Christmas Issue

Gerard David National Gallery
Christmas USA 15c

Virgin and Child, by Gerard David — A1188

Santa Claus, Christmas Tree Ornament — A1189

1979, Oct. 18   Photo.   *Perf. 11*
1799 A1188 15c multicolored   .30   .15
   a.   Imperf., pair   100.
   b.   Vert. pair, imperf. horiz.   700.
   c.   Vert. pair, imperf. btwn.   2,250.
1800 A1189 15c multicolored   .30   .15
   a.   Green & yellow omitted   750.
   b.   Green, yellow & tan omitted   800.
    Set value   .15
Nos. 1800a, 1800b always have the remaining colors misaligned.
No. 1800b is valued in the grade of fine.

Performing Arts Issue

WILL ROGERS

Performing Arts USA 15c

Will Rogers (1879-1935), Actor and Humorist — A1190

1979, Nov. 4   Photo.   *Perf. 11*
1801 A1190 15c multicolored   .30   .15
   a.   Imperf., pair   225.00

Viet Nam Veterans Issue

Ribbon for Viet Nam Service Medal A1191

1979, Nov. 11   Photo.   *Perf. 11*
1802 A1191 15c multicolored   .30   .15
A tribute to veterans of the Viet Nam War.

Performing Arts Issue

W.C. FIELDS

Performing Arts USA 15c

W.C. Fields (1880-1946), actor and comedian — A1192

1980, Jan. 29   Photo.   *Perf. 11*
1803 A1192 15c multicolored   .30   .15
   a.   Imperf., pair   —

Black Heritage

Benjamin Banneker
Black Heritage USA 15c

Benjamin Banneker (1731-1806), Astronomer and Mathematician, Transverse — A1193

1980, Feb. 15   Photo.   *Perf. 11*
1804 A1193 15c multicolored   .30   .15
   a.   Horiz. pair, imperf. vert.   800.00
Imperf. printer's waste has been fraudulently perforated to simulate No. 1804a. Legitimate examples of No. 1804a do not have colors misregistered.

Letter Writing

Letters Preserve Memories
USA 15c

Letters Preserve Memories A1194

P.S. Write Soon
USA 15c

P.S. Write Soon A1195

Letters Lift Spirits
USA 15c

Letters Lift Spirits A1196

Letters Shape Opinions
USA 15c

Letters Shape Opinions A1197

1980, Feb. 25
1805 A1194 15c multicolored   .30   .15
1806 A1195 15c purple & multi   .30   .15
1807 A1196 15c multicolored   .30   .15
1808 A1195 15c green & multi   .30   .15
1809 A1197 15c multicolored   .30   .15
1810 A1195 15c red & multi   .30   .15
   a.   Vert. strip of 6 #1805-1810   1.85 2.00
   Nos. 1805-1810 (6)   1.80
    Set value   .50
Natl. Letter Writing Week, Feb. 24-Mar. 1.

Americana Type

THE MUSIC OF AMERICA IS FREEDOM'S SYMPHONY
USA 3.5c

Weaver Violins — A1199

Coil Stamps

1980-81   Engr.   *Perf. 10 Vert.*
1811 A984 1c dk blue, *grnsh*   .15   .15
   a.   Imperf., pair   160.00
1813 A1199 3.5c purple, *yel*   .15   .15
   a.   Untagged (Bureau precanceled, lines only)   .15
   b.   Imperf., pair   225.00

1816 A997   12c brown red, *beige* ('81)   .25   .15
   a.   Untagged (Bureau precanceled)   .25
   b.   Imperf., pair   200.00
    Set value   .35   .15

US POSTAGE

A1207

1981, Mar. 15   Photo.   *Perf. 11x10½*
1818 A1207 (18c) violet   .35   .15
   Engr.   *Perf. 10*
Booklet Stamp
1819 A1207 (18c) violet   .40   .15
   a.   Booklet pane of 8   3.50 1.75
Coil Stamp
   Perf. 10 Vert.
1820 A1207 (18c) violet   .40   .15
   a.   Imperf., pair   125.00
   Nos. 1818-1820 (3)   1.15
    Set value   .15

Frances Perkins

Frances Perkins
USA 15c

Frances Perkins (1882-1965), Sec. of Labor, 1933-45 (1st Woman Cabinet Member) — A1208

1980, Apr. 10   *Perf. 10½x11*
1821 A1208 15c Prus blue   .30   .15

Dolley Madison

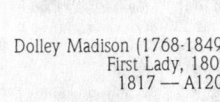

Dolley Madison USA 15c

Dolley Madison (1768-1849), First Lady, 1809-1817 — A1209

1980, May 20   *Perf. 11*
1822 A1209 15c red brown & sepia   .30   .15

Emily Bissell

Emily Bissell
USA 15c

Emily Bissell (1861-1948), Social Worker; Introduced Christmas seals in US — A1210

1980, May 31
1823 A1210 15c black & red   .30   .15
   a.   Vert. pair, imperf. horiz.   400.00

Helen Keller

USA 15c

Helen Keller and Anne Sullivan — A1211

HELEN KELLER
ANNE SULLIVAN

Litho. & Engr.
1980, June 27   *Perf. 11*
1824 A1211 15c multicolored   .30   .15
Keller (1880-1968), blind and deaf writer and lecturer taught by Sullivan (1867-1936).

Veterans
Admin-istration
Emblem
A1212

Gen. Bernardo
de Galvez
A1213

Veterans Administration
1980, July 21   Photo.
1825 A1212 15c car & vio bl   .30   .15
   a.   Horiz. pair, imperf. vert.   500.00

General Bernardo de Galvez
1980, July 23   Engr.   Perf. 11
1826 A1213 15c multicolored   .30   .15
   a.   Red, brn & bl (engr.) omitted   800.00
   b.   Red. brn. bl (engr.), bl & yel
       (litho.) omitted   1,400.

Galvez (1746-1786), helped defeat British in Battle of Mobile, 1780.

Coral Reefs
Brain Coral,
Beaugregory Fish
A1214

Elkhorn Coral,
Porkfish
A1215

Chalice Coral,
Moorish Idol Fish
A1216

Finger Coral,
Sabertooth Blenny
Fish
A1217

1980, Aug. 26   Photo.   Perf. 11
1827 A1214 15c multicolored   .30   .15
1828 A1215 15c multicolored   .30   .15
1829 A1216 15c multicolored   .30   .15
1830 A1217 15c multicolored   .30   .15
   a.   Block of 4. #1827-1830   1.25   1.10
   b.   As "a." imperf.   1,250.
   c.   As "a." vert. imperf. btwn.   —
   d.   As "a." imperf. vert.   3,000.
       Set value   .35

American Bald
Eagle
A1218

Edith Wharton
A1219

Organized Labor
1980, Sept. 1   Perf. 11
1831 A1218 15c multicolored   .30   .15
   a.   Imperf., pair   375.00

Edith Wharton
1980, Sept. 5   Engr.   Perf. 10½x11
1832 A1219 15c purple   .30   .15

Edith Wharton (1862-1937), writer.

American Education

"Homage to the Square:
Glow," by Josef
Albers — A1220

1980, Sept. 12   Photo.   Perf. 11
1833 A1220 15c multicolored   .30   .15
   a.   Horiz. pair, imperf. btwn.   250.00

American Folk Art
Pacific Northwest Indian Masks

Heiltsuk, Bella
Bella Tribe
A1221

Chilkat Tlingit
Tribe
A1222

Tlingit Tribe
A1223

Bella Coola Tribe
A1224

1980, Sept. 25
1834 A1221 15c multicolored   .30   .15
1835 A1222 15c multicolored   .30   .15
1836 A1223 15c multicolored   .30   .15
1837 A1224 15c multicolored   .30   .15
   a.   Block of 4. #1834-1837   1.25   1.25
       Set value   .35

American Architecture

Smithsonian
Institution,
by James
Renwick
A1225   Architecture USA 15c

Trinity
Church,
Boston, by
Henry
Hobson
Richardson
A1226

Pennsylvania
Academy of
Fine Arts, by
Frank
Furness
A1227   Architecture USA 15c

Lyndhurst,
Tarrytown,
NY, by
Alexander
Jackson Davis
A1228

1980, Oct. 9   Engr.   Perf. 11
1838 A1225 15c black & brick red   .30   .15
1839 A1226 15c black & brick red   .30   .15
1840 A1227 15c black & brick red   .30   .15
1841 A1228 15c black & brick red   .30   .15
   a.   Block of 4 #1838-1841   1.25   1.25
       Set value   .35

Christmas

Christmas USA 15c
Madonna and
Child
A1229

Season's Greetings
Wreath, Toys on
Windowsill
A1230

1980, Oct. 31   Photo.   Perf. 11
1842 A1229 15c multicolored   .30   .15
   a.   Imperf., pair   80.00
1843 A1230 15c multicolored   .30   .15
   a.   Imperf., pair   80.00
   b.   Buff omitted   25.00
   c.   Vert. pair, imperf. horiz.   —
       Set value   .15

No. 1843b is difficult to identify and should have a competent certificate.

Great Americans

Dorothea Dix
USA 1c
A1231

Igor Stravinsky
USA 2c
A1232

Henry Clay
USA 3c
A1233

Carl Schurz
4c USA
A1234

Pearl Buck
USA 5c
A1235

Walter Lippmann
6 USA
A1236

Abraham Baldwin
USA 7
A1237

Henry Knox
USA 8
A1238

Sylvanus Thayer
USA 9
A1239

Richard Russell
USA 10c
A1240

Alden Partridge
USA 11
A1241

USA 13c
Crazy Horse
A1242

Sinclair Lewis
USA 14
A1243

Rachel Carson
USA 17c
A1244

George Mason
USA 18c
A1245

USA 19c
Sequoyah
A1246

Ralph Bunche
USA 20c
A1247

Thomas H. Gallaudet
USA 20c
A1248

Harry S Truman
USA 20c
A1249

John J. Audubon
USA 22c
A1250

Frank C. Laubach
USA 30c
A1251

Charles R Drew MD
USA 35c
A1252

Robert Millikan
37c USA
A1253

Grenville Clark
USA 39c
A1254

Lillian M. Gilbreth
USA 40c
A1255

Chester W. Nimitz
USA 50c
A1256

*Perf. 11x10½, 11 (1, 6-11, 14, #1862,
22, 30, 39, 40, 50c)*
1980-85   Engr.
1844 A1231   1c black   .15   .15
   a.   Imperf. pair   425.
   b.   Vert. pair, imperf. btwn. and at
       bottom   3,000.
   d.   Vert. pair, imperf. horiz.   —
1845 A1232   2c brown black   .15   .15
1846 A1233   3c olive green   .15   .15
1847 A1234   4c violet   .15   .15
1848 A1235   5c henna brown   .15   .15
1849 A1236   6c orange ver   .15   .15
   a.   Vert. pair, imperf. btwn. and at
       bottom   2,500.
1850 A1237   7c brt carmine   .15   .15
1851 A1238   8c olive black   .15   .15
1852 A1239   9c dark green   .20   .15
1853 A1240   10c Prus blue   .20   .15
   a.   Vert. pair, imperf. btwn. & at
       bottom   1,100.
   b.   Horiz. pair, imperf. btwn.   2,250.

Completely imperforate tagged or untagged stamps are from printer's waste.

1854 A1241   11c dark blue   .20   .15
1855 A1242   13c lt maroon   .25   .15
1856 A1243   14c slate green   .25   .15
   a.   Vert. pair, imperf. horiz.   150.
   b.   Horiz. pair, imperf. btwn.   10.00
   c.   Vert. pair, imperf. btwn.   1,600.
   d.   All color omitted   —

No. 1856d comes from a parially printed pane and should be collected as a vertical strip of 10, one stamp normal, one stamp transitional and 8 stamps with color omitted.

1857 A1244   17c green   .35   .15
1858 A1245   18c dark blue   .35   .15
1859 A1246   19c brown   .35   .15
1860 A1247   20c claret   .40   .15
1861 A1248   20c green   .40   .15
1862 A1249   20c black   .40   .15
1863 A1250   22c dk chalky blue   .40   .15
   a.   Vert. pair, imperf. btwn.   2,500.
   b.   Vert. pair, imperf. btwn.   —
   c.   Horiz. pair, imperf. btwn.   2,500.
1864 A1251   30c olive gray   .55   .15
1865 A1252   35c gray   .65   .15
1866 A1253   37c blue   .70   .15
1867 A1254   39c rose lilac   .70   .15
   a.   Vert. pair, imperf. horiz.   600.
   b.   Vert. pair, imperf. btwn.   2,000.
1868 A1255   40c dark green   .70   .15
1869 A1256   50c rose lilac   .95   .15
     Nos. 1844-1869 (26)   9.20
       Set value   1.50

Years of issue: 19c, 1980. 17c, 18c, 35c, 1981. No. 1860, 2c, 13c, 37c, 1982. No. 1861, 1c, 3c-5c, 1983. No. 1862, 10c, 30c, 40c, 1984. 6c-9c, 11c, 14c, 22c, 39c, 50c, 1985.

Everett Dirksen

Everett Dirksen (1896-1969), Senate Minority Leader, 1960-69 — A1261

1981, Jan. 4   *Perf. 11*
1874 A1261 15c gray   .30   .15
   a.   All color omitted

No. 1874a comes from a parially printed pane and may be collected as either a vertical strip of 3 or 5 (1 or 3 stamps normal, one stamp transitional and one stamp with color omitted) or as a pair with one partially printed stamp.

Black Heritage

Whitney Moore Young (1921-1971), Civil Rights Leader — A1262

1981, Jan. 30   Photo.   *Perf. 11*
1875 A1262 15c multicolored   .30   .15

Flowers

A1263   A1264

Rose USA 18c   Camellia USA 18c

Dahlia USA 18c   Lily USA 18c

A1265   A1266

1981, Apr. 23   *Perf. 11*
1876 A1263 18c multicolored   .35   .15
1877 A1264 18c multicolored   .35   .15
1878 A1265 18c multicolored   .35   .15
1879 A1266 18c multicolored   .35   .15
   a.   Block of 4, #1876-1879   1.40   1.25
     Set value   .35

A1267-A1276

1981, May 14   Engr.   *Perf. 11*
Booklet Stamps
1880 A1267 18c Bighorn   .55   .15
1881 A1268 18c Puma   .55   .15
1882 A1269 18c Harbor seal   .55   .15
1883 A1270 18c Bison   .55   .15
1884 A1271 18c Brown bear   .55   .15
1885 A1272 18c Polar bear   .55   .15
1886 A1273 18c Elk (wapiti)   .55   .15
1887 A1274 18c Moose   .55   .15
1888 A1275 18c White-tailed deer   .55   .15
1889 A1276 18c Pronghorn   .55   .15
   a.   Bklt. pane of 10, #1880-1889   8.00   7.00
     Nos. 1880-1889 (10)   5.50
     Set value   .90
     See No. 1949.

A1277   A1278

A1279   A1280

Multicolor Huck Press
1981, Apr. 24   *Perf. 11*
1890 A1277 18c multicolored   .35   .15
   a.   Imperf., pair   125.00
   b.   Vert. pair, imperf. horiz.   1,100.

Coil Stamp
Perf. 10 Vert.
1891 A1278 18c multicolored   .35   .15
   a.   Imperf., pair   20.00
   b.   Pair, imperf. btwn.   —

Beware of pairs offered as imperf. between that have faint blind perfs.

Booklet Stamps
Perf. 11
1892 A1279 6c multicolored   .50   .15
1893 A1280 18c multicolored   .30   .15
   a.   Booklet pane, 2 #1892, 6 #1893   3.00   2.25
   b.   As "a," vert. imperf. btwn.   75.00
   c.   Pair, #1892, 1893   .90   1.00
     Set value, #1890-1893   .25

Bureau Precanceled Coils
Starting with No. 1895e, Bureau precanceled coil stamps are valued unused as well as used. The coils issued with dull finish gum may be difficult to distinguish. When used normally these stamps do not receive any postal markings so that used stamps with an additional post-cancellation of any kind are worth considerably less than the values shown here.

A1281

1981, Dec. 17   *Perf. 11*
1894 A1281 20c blk, dk blue & red   .40   .15
   a.   Vert. pair, imperf.   40.00
   b.   Vert. pair, imperf. horiz.   650.00
   c.   Dark blue omitted   90.00
   d.   Black omitted   325.00

Coil Stamp
Perf. 10 Vertical
1895 A1281 20c blk, dk blue & red   .35   .15
   a.   Imperf., pair   8.50
   b.   Black omitted   65.00
   c.   Dark blue omitted   1,500.
   d.   Pair, imperf. btwn.   1,250.
   e.   Untagged (Bureau precanceled)   .50   .50

Booklet Stamp
Perf. 11x10½
1896 A1281 20c blk, dk blue & red   .35   .15
   a.   Booklet pane of 6   2.50   2.00
   b.   Booklet pane of 10   4.25   3.25
     Set value, #1894-1896   .15

Transportation Coils

Omnibus 1880s USA 3c   Locomotive 1870s USA 2c

A1282   A1283

Handcar 1880s USA 3c   Stagecoach 1890s USA 4c

A1284   A1285

Motorcycle 1913 USA 5c   Sleigh 1880s USA 5.2c Auth. Nonprofit Org.

A1286   A1287

Bicycle 1870s USA 5.9c Auth. Nonprofit Org.   Baby Buggy 1880s USA 7.4c

A1288   A1289

Mail Wagon 1880s USA 9.3c   Hansom Cab 1890s USA 10.9c

A1290   A1291

RR Caboose 1890s USA 11c Bulk Rate   Electric Auto 1917 USA 17c

A1292   A1293

Surrey 1890s USA 18c   Fire Pumper 1860s USA 20c

A1294   A1295

1981-84   Engr.   *Perf. 10 Vert.*
1897 A1282 1c violet   .15   .15
   b.   Imperf., pair   700.00
1897A A1283 2c black   .15   .15
   e.   Imperf., pair   55.00

For similar designs to the 1c and 2c, see Nos. 2225-2226.

1898 A1284 3c dk green   .15   .15
1898A A1285 4c redsh brown   .15   .15
   b.   Untagged (Bureau precanceled)   .15   .15
   c.   As "b," imperf., pair   700.00
   d.   No. 1898A, imperf., pair   925.00   —
1899 A1286 5c gray green   .15   .15
   a.   Imperf., pair   2,750.
1900 A1287 5.2c carmine   .15   .15
   a.   Untagged (Bureau precanceled)   .15   .15
1901 A1288 5.9c blue   .20   .15
   a.   Untagged (Bureau precanceled, lines only)   .20   .20
   b.   As "a," imperf., pair   200.00
1902 A1289 7.4c brown   .20   .15
   a.   Untagged (Bureau precanceled)   .20   .20
1903 A1290 9.3c car rose   .30   .20
   a.   Untagged (Bureau precanceled, lines only)   .25   .25
   b.   As "a," imperf., pair   125.00
1904 A1291 10.9c purple   .25   .15
   a.   Untagged (Bureau precanceled, lines only)   .25   .25
   b.   As "a," imperf., pair   150.00
1905 A1292 11c red   .25   .15
   a.   Untagged   .25   .15
1906 A1293 17c ultra   .35   .15
   a.   Untagged (Bureau precanceled, Presorted First Class)   .35   .35
   b.   Imperf., pair   165.00
   c.   As "a," imperf., pair   650.00
1907 A1294 18c dark brown   .35   .15
   a.   Imperf., pair   150.00

1908 A1295 20c vermilion   .35   .15
   a.   Imperf., pair   110.00
     Nos. 1897-1908 (14)   3.15
     Set value   .75

Years of issue: 9.3c, 17c-20c, 1981. 2c, 4c, 5.9c, 10.9c, 1982. 1c, 3c, 5c, 5.2c, 1983. 7.4, 11c, 1984.
See Nos. 2123-2136, 2225-2231, 2252-2266, 2451-2468.

A1296

Perf. 10 Vert. on 1 or 2 Sides
1983, Aug. 12   Photo.
1909 A1296 $9.35 multi   21.00   14.00
   a.   Booklet pane of 3   65.00   —

The Gift of Self USA 18c   SAVINGS AND LOANS USA 18c
American Red Cross 1881-1981
A1297   A1298

American Red Cross Centennial
1981, May 1   *Perf. 10½x11*
1910 A1297 18c multicolored   .35   .15

Savings & Loan Sesquicentennial
1981, May 8   *Perf. 11*
1911 A1298 18c multicolored   .35   .15

Space Achievement

A1299   A1300

Exploring the Moon USA 18c   Benefiting Mankind USA 18c
Probing the Planets USA 18c   Benefiting Mankind

A1303   A1304

A1301   A1302

Benefiting Mankind USA 18c   Understanding the Sun USA 18c
Benefiting Mankind USA 18c   Comprehending the Universe USA 18c

A1305   A1306

1981, May 21   *Perf. 11*
1912 A1299 18c multicolored   .35   .15
1913 A1300 18c multicolored   .35   .15
1914 A1301 18c multicolored   .35   .15
1915 A1302 18c multicolored   .35   .15
1916 A1303 18c multicolored   .35   .15

1917	A1304	18c multicolored	.35	.15
1918	A1305	18c multicolored	.35	.15
1919	A1306	18c multicolored	.35	.15
a.		Block of 8, #1912-1919	3.00	3.00
b.		As "a," imperf.	9,000.	
		Nos. 1912-1919 (8)	2.80	
		Set value		.80

Professional Management

Joseph Wharton
A1307

1981, June 18

1920	A1307	18c blue & black	.35	.15

Preservation of Wildlife Habitats

A1308   A1309

Save Wetland Habitats   Save Grassland Habitats

A1310   A1311

Save Mountain Habitats   Save Woodland Habitats

1981, June 26

1921	A1308	18c multicolored	.35	.15
1922	A1309	18c multicolored	.35	.15
1923	A1310	18c multicolored	.35	.15
1924	A1311	18c multicolored	.35	.15
a.		Block of 4, #1921-1924	1.50	1.25
		Set value		.35

International Year of the Disabled

Man Looking through Microscope
A1312

Disabled doesn't mean Unable

1981, June 29   Photo.   Perf. 11

1925	A1312	18c multicolored	.35	.15
a.		Vert. pair, imperf. horiz.	2,750.	

Edna St. Vincent Millay, 1892-1950

A1313

Litho. & Engr.

1981, July 10   Perf. 11

1926	A1313	18c multicolored	.35	.15
a.		Black (engr., inscriptions) omitted	425.00	—

Alcoholism

Alcoholism You can beat it.
USA 18c   A1314

1981, Aug. 19   Engr.   Perf. 11

1927	A1314	18c blue & black	.40	.15
a.		Imperf., pair	450.	
b.		Vert. pair, imperf. horiz.	1,750.	

American Architecture

New York University Library by Sanford White
A1315   Architecture USA 18c

Biltmore House by Richard Morris Hunt
A1316

Architecture USA 18c

Palace of the Arts by Bernard Maybeck
A1317   Architecture USA 18c

National Farmer's Bank by Louis Sullivan
A1318

Architecture USA 18c

1981, Aug. 28   Engr.   Perf. 11

1928	A1315	18c black & red	.40	.15
1929	A1316	18c black & red	.40	.15
1930	A1317	18c black & red	.40	.15
1931	A1318	18c black & red	.40	.15
a.		Block of 4, #1928-1931	1.65	1.50
		Set value		.35

Athletes

Bobby Jones

Mildred Didrikson Zaharias
A1319

Robert Tyre Jones
A1320

1981, Sept. 22   Engr.   Perf. 10½x11

1932	A1319	18c purple	.35	.15
1933	A1320	18c green	.35	.15
		Set value		.15

Frederic Remington, 1861-1909

FREDERIC REMINGTON American Sculptor

Coming Through the Rye — A1321

18c USA

1981, Oct. 9   Perf. 11

1934	A1321	18c gray, green & brown	.35	.15
a.		Vert. pair, imperf. btwn.	275.00	
b.		Brown omitted	550.00	

James Hoban, 1762?-1831

USA 18c
James Hoban White House Architect

Irish-American Architect of White House
A1322

1981, Oct. 13   Photo.   Perf. 11

1935	A1322	18c multicolored	.35	.15
1936	A1322	20c multicolored	.35	.15
		Set value		.20

See Ireland No. 504.

American Bicentennial

Battle of Yorktown
A1323   18c USA

18c USA

Battle of Virginia Capes
A1324

1981, Oct. 16   Litho. & Engr.   Perf. 11

1937	A1323	18c multicolored	.35	.15
1938	A1324	18c multicolored	.35	.15
a.		Pair, #1937-1938	.90	.75
b.		As "a," black (engr., inscriptions) omitted	450.00	
		Set value		.15

Christmas

Christmas USA 1981

Season's Greetings USA 1981

Madonna and Child, Botticelli
A1325

Felt Bear on Sled
A1326

1981, Oct. 28   Photo.   Perf. 11

1939	A1325	(20c) multicolored	.40	.15
a.		Imperf., pair	125.	
b.		Vert. pair, imperf. horiz.	1,650.	
1940	A1326	(20c) multicolored	.40	.15
a.		Imperf., pair	350.	
b.		Vert. pair, imperf. horiz.		
		Set value		.15

John Hanson, 1721-1783

First President of Continental Congress — A1327

John Hanson
Continental Congress
USA 20c

1981, Nov. 5   Photo.   Perf. 11

1941	A1327	20c multicolored	.40	.15

Desert Plants

USA 20c   USA 20c

Barrel Cactus — A1328   Saguaro — A1331

USA 20c Agave   A1329

Agave deserti

Opuntia basilaris

Beavertail Cactus — A1330   USA 20c

1981, Dec. 11   Litho. & Engr.

1942	A1328	20c multicolored	.35	.15
1943	A1329	20c multicolored	.35	.15
1944	A1330	20c multicolored	.35	.15

1945	A1331	20c multicolored	.35	.15
a.		Block of 4, #1942-1945	1.50	1.25
b.		As "a," deep brown omitted	7,500.	
c.		No. 1945 imperf., vert. pair	5,250.	
		Set value		.25

Domestic Mail

C   US POSTAGE   USA 20c

A1332   A1333   A1334

1981, Oct. 11   Photo.   Perf. 11x10½

1946	A1332	(20c) brown	.40	.15

Coil Stamp

Perf. 10 Vert.

1947	A1332	(20c) brown	.60	.15
a.		Imperf., pair	2,000.	

Booklet Stamp

Perf. 11x10½

1948	A1333	(20c) brown	.40	.15
a.		Booklet pane of 10	4.50	3.00
		Set value		.15

1982, Jan. 8   Engr.   Perf. 11

1949	A1334	20c dk blue (from bklt. pane)	.50	.15
a.		Booklet pane of 10	5.00	3.50
b.		As "a," vert. imperf. btwn.	110.00	
c.		Type II	.50	.15
d.		As "c," booklet pane of 10	10.00	—

No. 1949 is 18¾mm wide and has overall tagging. No. 1949c is 18½mm wide and has block tagging.
See No. 1880.

Franklin Delano Roosevelt

1882 1982   USA 20c

A1335   Franklin D. Roosevelt

1982, Jan. 30   Engr.   Perf. 11

1950	A1335	20c blue	.40	.15

LOVE   USA 20c   A1336

1982, Feb. 1   Photo.   Perf. 11x10½

1951	A1336	20c multicolored	.65	.15
a.		Perf. 11	.40	.15
b.		Imperf., pair	350.00	
c.		Blue omitted	225.00	

No. 1951c is valued in the grade of fine.

George Washington

1732-1982   USA 20c
A1337

Alabama USA 20c

A1338-A1387
Yellowhammer &
Camellia

1982, Feb. 22   Photo.   Perf. 11

1952	A1337	20c multicolored	.40	.15

State Birds & Flowers

1982, Apr. 14   Photo.   Perf. 10½x11

1953	A1338	20c Alabama	.50	.25
1954	A1339	20c Alaska	.50	.25
1955	A1340	20c Arizona	.50	.25
1956	A1341	20c Arkansas	.50	.25
1957	A1342	20c California	.50	.25
1958	A1343	20c Colorado	.50	.25
1959	A1344	20c Connecticut	.50	.25
1960	A1345	20c Delaware	.50	.25
1961	A1346	20c Florida	.50	.25
1962	A1347	20c Georgia	.50	.25
1963	A1348	20c Hawaii	.50	.25
1964	A1349	20c Idaho	.50	.25
1965	A1350	20c Illinois	.50	.25
1966	A1351	20c Indiana	.50	.25
1967	A1352	20c Iowa	.50	.25
1968	A1353	20c Kansas	.50	.25
1969	A1354	20c Kentucky	.50	.25
1970	A1355	20c Louisiana	.50	.25

1971	A1356	20c Maine	.50 .25
1972	A1357	20c Maryland	.50 .25
1973	A1358	20c Massachusetts	.50 .25
1974	A1359	20c Michigan	.50 .25
1975	A1360	20c Minnesota	.50 .25
1976	A1361	20c Mississippi	.50 .25
1977	A1362	20c Missouri	.50 .25
1978	A1363	20c Montana	.50 .25
1979	A1364	20c Nebraska	.50 .25
1980	A1365	20c Nevada	.50 .25
1981	A1366	20c New Hampshire	.50 .25
1982	A1367	20c New Jersey	.50 .25
1983	A1368	20c New Mexico	.50 .25
1984	A1369	20c New York	.50 .25
1985	A1370	20c North Carolina	.50 .25
1986	A1371	20c North Dakota	.50 .25
1987	A1372	20c Ohio	.50 .25
1988	A1373	20c Oklahoma	.50 .25
1989	A1374	20c Oregon	.50 .25
1990	A1375	20c Pennsylvania	.50 .25
1991	A1376	20c Rhode Island	.50 .25
1992	A1377	20c South Carolina	.50 .25
1993	A1378	20c South Dakota	.50 .25
1994	A1379	20c Tennessee	.50 .25
1995	A1380	20c Texas	.50 .25
1996	A1381	20c Utah	.50 .25
1997	A1382	20c Vermont	.50 .25
1998	A1383	20c Virginia	.50 .25
1999	A1384	20c Washington	.50 .25
2000	A1385	20c West Virginia	.50 .25
2001	A1386	20c Wisconsin	.50 .25
2002	A1387	20c Wyoming	.50 .25

a. #1953a-2002a, any single, perf. 11 .55 .30
b. Pane of 50, perf. 10½x11 25.00 —
c. Pane of 50, perf. 11 27.50 —
d. Pane of 50, imperf. 27,500.

US-Netherlands

200th Anniv. of Diplomatic Recognition by the Netherlands
A1388

1982, Apr. 20 Photo. Perf. 11
2003 A1388 20c ver, brt blue & gray black .40 .15
a. Imperf., pair 325.00

See Netherlands Nos. 640-641.

Library of Congress

A1389

1982, Apr. 21 Engr. Perf. 11
2004 A1389 20c red & black .40 .15

Consumer Education

A1390

Coil Stamp

1982, Apr. 27 Engr. Perf. 10 Vert.
2005 A1390 20c sky blue .55 .15
a. Imperf., pair 100.00

Knoxville World's Fair

Solar energy Knoxville World's Fair A1391

A1392 Synthetic fuels Knoxville World's Fair

Breeder reactor Knoxville World's Fair A1393

A1394 Fossil fuels Knoxville World's Fair

1982, Apr. 29 Photo. Perf. 11
2006 A1391 20c multicolored .40 .15
2007 A1392 20c multicolored .40 .15
2008 A1393 20c multicolored .40 .15
2009 A1394 20c multicolored .40 .15
a. Block of 4, #2006-2009 1.65 1.50
Set value .35

American Author, 1832-1899

Horatio Alger

Frontispiece from "Ragged Dick" — A1395

1982, Apr. 30 Engr. Perf. 11
2010 A1395 20c red & black, tan .40 .15
a. Red & Black omitted

The Philatelic Foundation has issued a certificate for a pane of 50 with red and black colors omitted. Recognition of this error is by the paper and by a tiny residue of red ink from the tagging roller. The engraved plates did not strike the paper.

Aging Together

A1396

1982, May 21 Perf. 11
2011 A1396 20c brown .40 .15

Performing Arts USA 20c
A1397

Dr. Mary Walker
Medal of Honor
USA 20c
A1398

Performing Arts
Design: Actors John, Ethel & Lionel Barrymore.

1982, June 8 Photo. Perf. 11
2012 A1397 20c multicolored .40 .15

Dr. Mary E. Walker, 1832-1919
1982, June 10 Photo. Perf. 11
2013 A1398 20c multicolored .40 .15

International Peace Garden

International Peace Garden
A1399

1982, June 30 Photo. Perf. 11
2014 A1399 20c multicolored .40 .15
a. Black & green (engr.) omitted 275.00

A1400 America's ABC Libraries XYZ USA 20c Legacies To Mankind

A1401 Jackie Robinson

America's Libraries
1982, July 13 Engr. Perf. 11
2015 A1400 20c red & black .40 .15
a. Vert. pair, imperf. horiz. 325.00

Jackie Robinson, 1919-1972
1982, Aug. 2 Photo. Perf. 10½x11
2016 A1401 20c multicolored 1.10 .15

Touro Synagogue

A1402

Photogravure, Engraved
1982, Aug. 22 Perf. 11
2017 A1402 20c multicolored .40 .15
a. Imperf., pair 2,500.

Wolf Trap Farm Park

Wolf Trap Farm Park A1403

1982, Sept. 1 Photo. Perf. 11
2018 A1403 20c multicolored .40 .15

American Architecture

Fallingwater, Mill Run, Pa., by Frank Lloyd Wright A1404

Illinois Institute of Technology by Ludwig Mies van der Rohe A1405

Gropius House, Lincoln, Mass., by Walter Gropius A1406

Dulles Airport, by Eero Saarinen A1407

1982, Sept. 30 Engr. Perf. 11
2019 A1404 20c black & brown .40 .15
2020 A1405 20c black & brown .40 .15
2021 A1406 20c black & brown .40 .15
2022 A1407 20c black & brown .40 .15
a. Block of 4, #2019-2022 1.75 1.60
Set value .35

St. Francis of Assisi, 1182-1226

A1408 FRANCIS OF ASSISI 1182-1982 USA 20c

1982, Oct. 7 Photo. Perf. 11
2023 A1408 20c multicolored .40 .15

Ponce de Leon, 1527-1591

Ponce de León USA 20c
A1409

1982, Oct. 12 Photo. Perf. 11
2024 A1409 20c multicolored .40 .15
a. Imperf., pair 600.00
b. Vert. pair, Imperf. btwn. and at top —

Christmas

A1410 USA 13c

A1411 Christmas USA 20c

A1412 Season's Greetings USA 20c

Season's Greetings USA 20c A1413

A1414 Season's Greetings USA 20c

Season's Greetings USA 20c A1415

1982, Nov. 3 Photo. Perf. 11
2025 A1410 13c multicolored .25 .15
a. Imperf., pair 650.00

1982, Oct. 28
2026 A1411 20c multicolored .40 .15
a. Imperf., pair 150.00
b. Horiz. pair, imperf. vert. —
c. Vert. pair, imperf. horiz. —
2027 A1412 20c multicolored .45 .15
2028 A1413 20c multicolored .45 .15
2029 A1414 20c multicolored .45 .15
2030 A1415 20c multicolored .45 .15
a. Block of 4, #2027-2030 2.00 1.50
b. As "a," imperf. 3,000.
c. As "a," imperf. horiz. 3,250.
Nos. 2025-2030 (6) 2.45
Set value .30

Science & Industry

Science & Industry USA 20c
A1416

Litho. & Engr.
1983, Jan. 19 Perf. 11
2031 A1416 20c multicolored .40 .15
a. Black (engr.) omitted 1,400.

Balloons

A1417   A1420

A1418

A1419

1983, Mar. 31   **Photo.**   *Perf. 11*
2032 A1417 20c multicolored .40 .15
2033 A1418 20c multicolored .40 .15
2034 A1419 20c multicolored .40 .15
2035 A1420 20c multicolored .40 .15
  a.   Block of 4, #2032-2035 1.65 1.50
  b.   As "a," imperf. —
       Set value .35

US-Sweden

A1421

1983, Mar. 24   **Engr.**   *Perf. 11*
2036 A1421 20c multicolored .40 .15
     See Sweden No. 1453.

Civilian Conservation Corps

A1422

1983, Apr. 5   **Photo.**   *Perf. 11*
2037 A1422 20c multicolored .40 .15
  a.   Imperf., pair 2,500.

Joseph Priestley, 1733-1804

A1423

1983, Apr. 13   **Photo.**   *Perf. 11*
2038 A1423 20c multicolored .40 .15

Voluntarism

A1424

1983, Apr. 20   **Engr.**   *Perf. 11*
2039 A1424 20c red & black .40 .15
  a.   Imperf., pair 800.00

US-Germany

Concord,
1683
A1425

1983, Apr. 29   *Perf. 11*
2040 A1425 20c brown .40 .15
     See Germany No. 1397.

Brooklyn Bridge

A1426

1983, May 17   **Engr.**   *Perf. 11*
2041 A1426 20c blue .40 .15

T.V.A.

A1427

Photo. & Engr.
1983, May 18   *Perf. 11*
2042 A1427 20c multicolored .40 .15

Physical Fitness

A1428

1983, May 14   **Photo.**   *Perf. 11*
2043 A1428 20c multicolored .40 .15

Scott Joplin, 1868-1917

A1429

1983, June 9   **Photo.**
2044 A1429 20c multicolored .40 .15
  a.   Imperf., pair 550.00

Medal of Honor

A1430

1983, June 7   **Litho. & Engr.**   *Perf. 11*
2045 A1430 20c multicolored .40 .15
  a.   Red omitted 325.00

A1431   A1432

George Herman Ruth, 1895-1948

1983, July 6   **Engr.**   *Perf. 10½x11*
2046 A1431 20c blue 1.10 .15

Nathaniel Hawthorne, 1804-1864

1983, July 8   **Photo.**   *Perf. 11*
2047 A1432 20c multicolored .40 .15

1984 Summer Olympics

Discus
A1433

High Jump
A1434

Archery
A1435

Boxing
A1436

1983, July 28   **Photo.**   *Perf. 11*
2048 A1433 13c multicolored .35 .15
2049 A1434 13c multicolored .35 .15
2050 A1435 13c multicolored .35 .15
2051 A1436 13c multicolored .35 .15
  a.   Block of 4, #2048-2051 1.50 1.25
       Set value .20

Signing of Treaty of Paris

John Adams,
Franklin, John
Jay, David
Hartley
A1437

1983, Sept. 2   **Photo.**   *Perf. 11*
2052 A1437 20c multicolored .40 .15

Civil Service

A1438

1983, Sept. 9   **Photo. & Engr.**
2053 A1438 20c buff, blue & red .40 .15

Metropolitan Opera

A1439

1983, Sept. 14   **Litho. & Engr.**
2054 A1439 20c yellow & maroon .40 .15

American Inventors

A1440   A1441

A1442

A1443

1983, Sept. 21   **Litho. & Engr**
2055 A1440 20c multicolored .40 .15
2056 A1441 20c multicolored .40 .15
2057 A1442 20c multicolored .40 .15
2058 A1443 20c multicolored .40 .15
  a.   Block of 4, #2055-2058 1.60 1.25
  b.   As "a," black omitted 450.00
       Set value .35

Streetcars

A1444

A1445

A1446

A1447

1983, Oct. 8   **Photo. & Engr.**
2059 A1444 20c multicolored .40 .15
2060 A1445 20c multicolored .40 .15
2061 A1446 20c multicolored .40 .15
2062 A1447 20c multicolored .40 .15
  a.   Block of 4, #2059-2062 1.70 1.40
  b.   As "a," black omitted 475.00
  c.   As "a," black omitted on
       #2059, 2061 —
       Set value .35

Christmas

A1448

A1449

1983, Oct. 28   **Photo.**   *Perf. 11*
2063 A1448 20c multicolored .40 .15
2064 A1449 20c multicolored .40 .15
  a.   Imperf., pair 175.00
       Set value .15

Martin Luther — A1450

Caribou and Alaska Pipeline — A1451

Martin Luther, 1483-1546
1983, Nov. 11   Photo.   Perf. 11
2065 A1450 20c multicolored   .40 .15

25th Anniv. of Alaska Statehood
1984, Jan. 3   Photo.   Perf. 11
2066 A1451 20c multicolored   .40 .15

Winter Olympic Games
Ice Dancing A1452   Downhill Skiing A1453

Cross-country Skiing A1454   Hockey A1455

1984, Jan. 6   Perf. 10½x11
2067 A1452 20c multicolored   .45 .15
2068 A1453 20c multicolored   .45 .15
2069 A1454 20c multicolored   .45 .15
2070 A1455 20c multicolored   .45 .15
  a. Block of 4, #2067-2070   1.85 1.50
    Set value   .35

14th Winter Olympic Games, Sarajevo, Yugoslavia, Feb. 8-19.

A1456   A1457

Federal Deposit Insurance Corp., 50th Anniv.
1984, Jan. 12   Perf. 11
2071 A1456 20c multicolored   .40 .15

Love
1984, Jan. 31   Photo. & Engr.
2072 A1457 20c multicolored   .40 .15
  a. Horiz. pair, imperf. vert.   175.00

Carter G. Woodson (1875-1950), Writer — A1458   A1459

Black Heritage Issue
1984, Feb. 1   Photo.
2073 A1458 20c multicolored   .40 .15
  a. Horiz. pair, imperf. vert.   1,750.

Soil and Water Conservation
1984, Feb. 6
2074 A1459 20c multicolored   .40 .15

50th Anniv. of Credit Union Act

Dollar Sign, Coin — A1460

1984, Feb. 10   Photo.   Perf. 11
2075 A1460 20c multicolored   .40 .15

Orchids
A1461   A1462

A1463   A1464

1984, Mar. 5
2076 A1461 20c Wild pink   .45 .15
2077 A1462 20c Yellow lady's-slipper   .45 .15
2078 A1463 20c Spreading pogonia   .45 .15
2079 A1464 20c Pacific calypso   .45 .15
  a. Block of 4, #2076-2079   1.85 1.50
    Set value   .35

25th Anniv. of Hawaii Statehood

Eastern Polynesian Canoe, Golden Plover, Mauna Loa Volcano A1465

1984, Mar. 12   Photo.   Perf. 11
2080 A1465 20c multicolored   .40 .15

National Archives

Abraham Lincoln, George Washington — A1466

1984, Apr. 16   Photo.   Perf. 11
2081 A1466 20c multicolored   .40 .15

1984 Los Angeles Olympics
Diving A1467   Long Jump A1468

Wrestling A1469   Kayak A1470

1984, May 4   Perf. 11
2082 A1467 20c multicolored   .50 .15
2083 A1468 20c multicolored   .50 .15
2084 A1469 20c multicolored   .50 .15
2085 A1470 20c multicolored   .50 .15
  a. Block of 4, #2082-2085   2.25 1.90
    Set value   .35

New Orleans World Exposition

River Wildlife A1471

1984, May 11   Perf. 11
2086 A1471 20c multicolored   .40 .15

Health Research

Lab Equipment A1472

1984, May 17   Perf. 11
2087 A1472 20c multicolored   .40 .15

Actor Douglas Fairbanks (1883-1939) — A1473   Jim Thorpe A1474

1984, May 23   Photo. & Engr.
2088 A1473 20c multicolored   .40 .15
  b. Horiz. pair, imperf btwn.

Jim Thorpe, 1888-1953
1984, May 24   Engr.   Perf. 11
2089 A1474 20c dark brown   .40 .15

Performing Arts

Tenor John McCormack (1884-1945) — A1475

1984, June 6   Photo.   Perf. 11
2090 A1475 20c multicolored   .40 .15
  See Ireland No. 594.

25th Anniv. of St. Lawrence Seaway

Aerial View of Seaway, Freighters A1476

1984, June 26   Photo.   Perf. 11
2091 A1476 20c multicolored   .40 .15

50th Anniv. of Waterfowl Preservation Act

"Mallards Dropping In," by Jay N. Darling A1477

1984, July 2   Engr.   Perf. 11
2092 A1477 20c blue   .50 .15
  a. Horiz. pair, imperf. vert.   425.00
  See No. RW1.

A1478   Author — A1479

Roanoke Voyages
1984, July 13   Photo.   Perf. 11
2093 A1478 20c multicolored   .40 .15

Herman Melville (1819-1891)
1984, Aug. 1   Engr.   Perf. 11
2094 A1479 20c sage green   .40 .15

Horace Moses (1862-1947)

Junior Achievement Founder — A1480

1984, Aug. 6   Engr.
2095 A1480 20c orange & dk brown   .45 .15

Smokey
Bear — A1481

Roberto Clemente
USA 20c
Clemente,
Puerto Rican
Flag — A1482

1984, Aug. 13   Litho. & Engr.
2096 A1481 20c multicolored   .40   .15
  a. Horiz. pair, imperf. btwn.   300.
  b. Vert. pair, imperf. btwn.   300.
  c. Block of 4, imperf. btwn, vert.
    and horiz.   5,500.
  d. Horiz. pair, imperf. vert.   1,750.

Roberto Clemente (1934-1972)
1984, Aug. 17   Photo.   Perf. 11
2097 A1482 20c multicolored   1.40   .15
  a. Horiz. pair, imperf. vert.   1,800.

Dogs

USA 20c
Beagle,
Boston
Terrier
A1483

USA 20c
Chesapeake
Bay
Retriever,
Cocker
Spaniel
A1484

USA 20c
Alaskan
Malamute,
Collie
A1485

USA 20c
Black & Tan
Coonhound,
American
Foxhound
A1486

1984, Sept. 7   Photo.   Perf. 11
2098 A1483 20c multicolored   .40   .15
2099 A1484 20c multicolored   .40   .15
2100 A1485 20c multicolored   .40   .15
2101 A1486 20c multicolored   .40   .15
  a. Block of 4, #2098-2101   1.75   1.75
    Set value   .35

Crime Prevention

McGruff, The Crime
Dog — A1487

1984, Sept. 26   Photo.   Perf. 11
2102 A1487 20c multicolored   .40   .15

Hispanic Americans

A1488   A Proud Heritage USA 20c

1984, Oct. 31   Photo.   Perf. 11
2103 A1488 20c multicolored   .40   .15
  a. Vert. pair, imperf. horiz.   1,750.

Family Unity

A1489

1984, Oct. 1   Photo. & Engr.
2104 A1489 20c multicolored   .40   .15
  a. Horiz. pair, imperf. vert.   550.00
  c. Vert. pair, imperf. btwn. and at
    bottom   —

Eleanor Roosevelt

A1490

1984, Oct. 11   Engr.   Perf. 11
2105 A1490 20c deep blue   .40   .15

Nation of Readers

A Nation of
Readers
USA 20c
Lincoln, Son
Tad — A1491

1984, Oct. 16   Engr.   Perf. 11
2106 A1491 20c brown & maroon   .40   .15

Christmas

Madonna and
Child by Fra
Filippo
Lippi — A1492

Season's Greetings
Santa
Claus — A1493

1984, Oct. 30   Photo.   Perf. 11
2107 A1492 20c multicolored   .40   .15
2108 A1493 20c multicolored   .40   .15
  a. Horiz. pair, imperf. vert.   950.00
    Set value   .15

No. 2108a is valued in the grade of fine.

Vietnam Veterans Memorial

Vietnam Veterans Memorial USA 20c
Memorial Wall — A1494

1984, Nov. 10   Engr.   Perf. 10½
2109 A1494 20c multicolored   .40   .15

Performing Arts

JEROME KERN
Composer Jerome Kern
(1885-1945) — A1495   Performing Arts USA

1985, Jan. 23   Photo.   Perf. 11
2110 A1495 22c multicolored   .40   .15

A1496   A1497

1985, Feb. 1   Photo.   Perf. 11
2111 A1496 (22c) green   .55   .15
  a. Vert. pair, imperf.   50.
  b. Vert. pair, imperf. horiz.   1,350.

Coil Stamp
Perf. 10 Vert.
2112 A1496 (22c) green   .60   .15
  a. Imperf., pair   50.00

Booklet Stamp
Perf. 11
2113 A1497 (22c) green   .80   .15
  a. Booklet pane of 10   8.50   3.00
  b. As "a," imperf. btwn. horiz.   —
    Set value   .15

A1498

Flag over
Capitol
Dome
A1499

USA 22
Of the People
By the People
For the People

1985, Mar. 29   Engr.   Perf. 11
2114 A1498 22c blue, red & black   .40   .15

Coil Stamp
Perf. 10 Vert.
2115 A1498 22c blue, red & black   .40   .15
  a. Imperf., pair   12.50
  b. Inscribed "T" at bottom ('87)   .50   .15
  c. Black field of stars   —

Booklet Stamp
Perf. 10 Horiz. on 1 or 2 Sides
2116 A1499 22c blue, red & black   .50   .15
  a. Booklet pane of 5   2.50   1.25
    Set value   .15

Seashells

USA 22   USA 22
Frilled   Reticulated
Dogwinkle   Helmet
A1500   A1501

USA 22
New England Neptune
A1502

USA 22
Calico Scallop
A1503

USA 22
Lightning Whelk
Lightning Whelk — A1504

1985, Apr. 4   Engr.   Perf. 10
2117 A1500 22c black & brown   .40   .15
2118 A1501 22c multicolored   .40   .15
2119 A1502 22c black & brown   .40   .15
2120 A1503 22c black & violet   .40   .15
2121 A1504 22c multicolored   .40   .15
  a. Booklet pane of 10, 2 ea
    #2117-2121   4.00   2.50
  b. As "a," violet omitted   850.00
  c. As "a," vert. imperf. btwn.   600.00
  d. As "a," imperf.   —
  e. Strip of 5, #2117-2121   2.00   —
    Set value   .25

Issued in booklets only.

Eagle
and Half
Moon
A1505
USA $10.75

Type I. Washed out, dull appearance most evident in the black of the body of the eagle, and the red in the background between the eagle's shoulder and the moon. "$10.75" appears splotchy or grainy (P# 11111).

Type II. Brighter, more intense colors most evident in the black on the eagle's body, and red in the background. "$10.75" appears smoother, brighter, and less grainy (P# 22222).

Perf. 10 Vert. on 1 or 2 Sides
1985, Apr. 29   Photo.   Untagged
2122 A1505 $10.75 multi, type I   17.00 7.00
  a. Booklet pane of 3   52.50   —
  b. Type II   17.00   —
  c. As "b," booklet pane of 3   52.50   —

Issued in booklets only.

Transportation Coils

School Bus 1920s
3.4 USA
A1506

Buckboard 1880s
USA 4.9
A1507

Star Route Truck
5.5 USA 1910s
A1508

Tricycle 1880s
6 USA
A1509

Tractor 1920s
7.1 USA
A1510

Ambulance 1860s
8.3 USA
A1511

Tow Truck 1920s
8.5 USA
A1512

Oil Wagon 1890s
10.1 USA
A1513

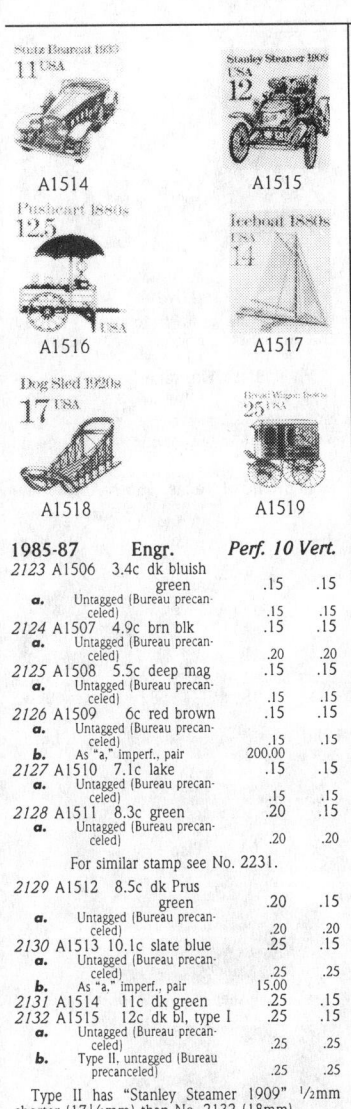

A1514   A1515

A1516   A1517

A1518   A1519

1985-87   **Engr.**   *Perf. 10 Vert.*
2123	A1506	3.4c dk bluish green	.15 .15
a.		Untagged (Bureau precanceled)	.15 .15
2124	A1507	4.9c brn blk	.15 .15
a.		Untagged (Bureau precanceled)	.20 .20
2125	A1508	5.5c deep mag	.15 .15
a.		Untagged (Bureau precanceled)	.15 .15
2126	A1509	6c red brown	.15 .15
a.		Untagged (Bureau precanceled)	.15 .15
b.		As "a," imperf., pair	200.00
2127	A1510	7.1c lake	.15 .15
a.		Untagged (Bureau precanceled)	.15 .15
2128	A1511	8.3c green	.20 .15
a.		Untagged (Bureau precanceled)	.20 .20

For similar stamp see No. 2231.

2129	A1512	8.5c dk Prus green	.20 .15
a.		Untagged (Bureau precanceled)	.20 .20
2130	A1513	10.1c slate blue	.25 .15
a.		Untagged (Bureau precanceled)	.25 .25
b.		As "a," imperf., pair	15.00
2131	A1514	11c dk green	.25 .15
2132	A1515	12c dk bl, type I	.25 .15
a.		Untagged (Bureau precanceled)	.25 .25
b.		Type II, untagged (Bureau precanceled)	.25 .25

Type II has "Stanley Steamer 1909" ½mm shorter (17½mm) than No. 2132 (18mm).

2133	A1516	12.5c olive green	.25 .15
a.		Untagged (Bureau precanceled)	.25 .25
b.		As "a," imperf., pair	50.00
2134	A1517	14c sky bl, type I	.30 .15
a.		Imperf., pair	100.00
b.		Type II	.30

Type II design is ¼mm narrower (17¼mm) than No. 2134 (17½mm) and has block tagging. No. 2134 has overall tagging.

2135	A1518	17c sky blue	.30 .15
a.		Imperf., pair	550.00
2136	A1519	25c org brown	.45 .15
a.		Imperf., pair	10.00
		Pair, imperf. between	
		Nos. 2123-2136 (14)	3.20
		Set value	.80

Years of issue: 3.4c, 4.9c, 6c, 8.3c, 10.1c-14c, 1985. 5.5c, 17c, 25c, 1986. 7.1c, 8.5c, 1987.
See Nos. 1897-1908, 2225-2231, 2252-2266, 2451-2468.

Black Heritage Issue

Mary McLeod Bethune (1875-1955), Educator — A1520

1985, Mar. 5   **Photo.**   *Perf. 11*
2137 A1520 22c multicolored   .40 .15

Duck Decoys

Broadbill A1521   Broadbill Decoy

Mallard Decoy   Mallard A1522

Canvasback Decoy   Canvasback A1523

Redhead Decoy   Redhead A1524

1985, Mar. 22   **Photo.**   *Perf. 11*
2138	A1521	22c multicolored	.60 .15
2139	A1522	22c multicolored	.60 .15
2140	A1523	22c multicolored	.60 .15
2141	A1524	22c multicolored	.60 .15
a.		Block of 4, #2138-2141	3.75 2.25
		Set value	.35

Winter Special Olympics

Ice Skater, Emblem, Skier A1525

1985, Mar. 25   **Photo.**   *Perf. 11*
2142	A1525	22c multicolored	.40 .15
a.		Vert. pair, imperf. horiz.	650.00

Love

A1526

1985, Apr. 17   **Photo.**
2143	A1526	22c multicolored	.40 .15
a.		Imperf., pair	1,750.

Rural Electrification Administration

Electrified Farm A1527

1985, May 11   **Photo. & Engr.**
2144	A1527	22c multicolored	.45 .15
a.		Vert. pair, imperf. btwn.	

AMERIPEX '86

US No. 134 — A1528

1985, May 25   **Litho. & Engr.**
2145	A1528	22c multicolored	.40 .15
a.		Red, black and blue omitted	200.
b.		Red & black omitted	1,250.
c.		Red omitted	

US First Lady

Abigail Adams (1744-1818) — A1529

1985, June 14   **Litho.**   *Perf. 11*
2146	A1529	22c multicolored	.40 .15
a.		Imperf., pair	275.00

Architect, Sculptor

F. A. Bartholdi, Statue of Liberty Sculptor
Frederic Auguste Bartholdi (1834-1904), Statue of Liberty A1530

1985, July 18   **Litho. & Engr.**
2147	A1530	22c multicolored	.40 .15
a.		Black (engr.) omitted	

Examples exist with most, but not all, of the engraved black omitted. Expertization of No. 2147a is recommended.

George Washington, Washington Monument A1532   Envelopes A1533

COIL STAMPS

1985   **Photo.**   *Perf. 10 Vert.*
2149	A1532	18c multicolored	.35 .15
a.		Untagged (Bureau precanceled)	.35 .35
b.		Imperf., pair	950.00
c.		As "a," imperf., pair	800.00
2150	A1533	21.1c multicolored	.40 .15
a.		Untagged (Bureau precanceled)	.40 .40
		Set value	.20

Issue dates: 18c, Nov. 6. 21.1c, Oct. 22. Precancellations on Nos. 2149a ("PRESORTED FIRST CLASS"), 2150a ("ZIP+4") do not have lines.

Korean War Veterans

American Troops Marching A1535

1985, July 26   **Engr.**   *Perf. 11*
2152 A1535 22c gray grn & rose red   .40 .15

Social Security Act, 50th Anniv.

Men, Women, Children, Corinthian Columns A1536

1985, Aug. 14   **Photo.**   *Perf. 11*
2153 A1536 22c deep blue & lt blue   .40 .15

World War I Veterans

The Battle of Marne, France, by Harvey Dunn A1537

1985, Aug. 26   **Engr.**   *Perf. 11*
2154 A1537 22c gray grn & rose red   .40 .15

Horses

Quarter horse   Quarter Horse A1538

Morgan A1539   Morgan

Saddlebred   Saddlebred A1540

Appaloosa A1541   Appaloosa

1985, Sept. 25   **Photo.**   *Perf. 11*
2155	A1538	22c multicolored	.90 .15
2156	A1539	22c multicolored	.90 .15
2157	A1540	22c multicolored	.90 .15
2158	A1541	22c multicolored	.90 .15
a.		Block of 4, #2155-2158	5.50 4.50
		Set value	.35

Public Education in America

Quill Pen, Apple, Spectacles, Penmanship Quiz — A1542

1985, Oct. 1   **Photo.**   *Perf. 11*
2159 A1542 22c multicolored   .45 .15

International Youth Year

YMCA Youth Camping, Cent. A1543   YMCA Youth Camping

Boy Scouts   Boy Scouts, 75th Anniv. A1544

Big Brothers/Big Sisters Fed., 40th Anniv. A1545   Big Brothers / Big Sisters

Camp Fire, Inc., 75th Anniv. A1546

1985, Oct. 7   **Photo.**   *Perf. 11*
2160	A1543	22c multicolored	.60 .15
2161	A1544	22c multicolored	.60 .15
2162	A1545	22c multicolored	.60 .15

2163 A1546 22c multicolored   .60   .15
   a.   Block of 4, #2160-2163   2.75 2.25
     Set value   .35

Help End Hunger

Youths and the
Elderly
Suffering from
Malnutrition
— A1547   Help End Hunger USA 22

1985, Oct. 15   **Photo.**
2164 A1547 22c multicolored   .45   .15

Christmas

Genoa Madonna,
Enameled Terra-Cotta by
Luca Della Robbia (1400-
1482) — A1548

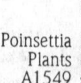

Poinsettia
Plants
A1549   Season's Greetings USA 22

1985, Oct. 30   **Photo.**
2165 A1548 22c multicolored   .40   .15
   a.   Imperf., pair   100.00
2166 A1549 22c multicolored   .40   .15
   a.   Imperf., pair   130.00
     Set value   .15

Arkansas Statehood, 150th Anniv.

Old State
House, Little
Rock
A1550

1986, Jan. 3   **Photo.**   *Perf. 11*
2167 A1550 22c multicolored   .40   .15
   a.   Vert. pair, imperf. horiz.

Great Americans

A1551   A1552

A1553   A1554

A1555   A1556

A1557   A1558

A1559   A1560

A1561   A1562

A1563   A1564

A1565   A1566

A1567   A1568

A1569   A1570

A1571   A1572

A1573   A1574

A1575   A1576

A1577   A1578

**Perf. 11, 11½x11 (#2185), 11.1x11
(#2179)**

1986-94   **Engr.**
2168 A1551   1c brnsh ver   .15   .15
2169 A1552   2c bright blue   .15   .15
   a.   Untagged   .15   .15
2170 A1553   3c bright blue   .15   .15
2171 A1554   4c blue violet   .15   .15
   a.   Untagged   .15   .15
2172 A1555   5c dk ol grn   .15   .15
2173 A1556   5c carmine   .15   .15
   a.   Untagged   .15   .15
2175 A1557 10c lake   .20   .15
   d.   carmine, phosphored paper (em-
       bedded taggant)   .20   .15
2176 A1558 14c crimson   .25   .15
2177 A1559 15c claret   .30   .15
2178 A1560 17c dull bl grn   .30   .15
2179 A1561 20c red brown   .40   .15
2180 A1562 21c blue vio   .40   .15
2181 A1563 23c purple   .45   .15
2182 A1564 25c blue   .45   .15
   a.   Booklet pane of 10 ('88) 4.75 3.75
2183 A1565 28c myrtle grn   .50   .15
2184 A1566 29c blue   .50   .15

2185 A1567 29c indigo   .50   .15
2186 A1568 35c black   .65   .15
2187 A1569 40c dark blue   .70   .15
2188 A1570 45c bright blue   .85   .15
2189 A1571 52c purple   1.00   .15
2190 A1572 56c scarlet   1.00   .15
2191 A1573 65c dark blue   1.20   .20
2192 A1574 75c dp magenta   1.30   .20
2193 A1575 $1 dk Prus grn   2.25   .50
2194 A1576 $1 deep blue   1.80   .50
2195 A1577 $2 brt violet   3.25   .50
2196 A1578 $5 copper red   7.50 1.00
   Nos. 2168-2196 (28)   26.65
     Set value   3.75

Booklet Stamp
Perf. 10 on 2 or 3 sides
2197 A1564 25c blue ('88)   .45   .15
   a.   Booklet pane of 6   3.00 2.25

Issued: #2182, 1/11/86; #2172, 2/27/86; $2,
3/19/86; 17c, 6/18/86; 1c, 6/30/86; 4c,
7/14/86; 56c, 9/3/86; 3c, 9/15/86; #2193,
9/23/86; 14c, 2/12/87; 2c, 2/28/87; 10c,
8/15/87; $5, 8/25/87; #2183a, 2197, 5/3/88;
15c, 6/6/88; 45c, 6/17/88; 21c, 10/21/88; 23c,
11/4/88; 65c, 11/5/88; #2194, 6/7/89; 28c,
9/14/89; #2173, 2/18/90; 40c, 9/6/90; 35c,
4/3/91; 52c, 6/3/91; 75c, 2/16/92; #2184,
3/9/92; #2185, 4/13/93; 20c, 10/24/94.

Stamp Collecting

Handstamped
Cover, No. 213,
Philatelic
Memorabilia
A1581

Boy Examining
Stamp Collection
A1582

No. 836 Under
Magnifying Glass,
Sweden Nos. 268,
271 — A1583

1986 Presidents
Miniature
Sheet — A1584

Perf. 10 Vert. on 1 or 2 Sides
1986, Jan. 23   **Litho. & Engr.**
Booklet Stamps
2198 A1581 22c multicolored   .45   .15
2199 A1582 22c multicolored   .45   .15
2200 A1583 22c multicolored   .45   .15
2201 A1584 22c multicolored   .45   .15
   a.   Bklt. pane of 4, #2198-2201 2.00 1.75
   b.   As "a," black omitted on #2198,
       2201   55.00
   c.   As "a," blue (litho.) omitted on
       #2198-2200   2,500.
   d.   As "a," buff (litho.) omitted —
     Set value   .20

See Sweden Nos. 1585-1588.

A1585   A1586

Love

1986, Jan. 30   **Photo.**   *Perf. 11*
2202 A1585 22c Puppy   .40   .15

Black Heritage Issue

1986, Feb. 4   **Photo.**   *Perf. 11*
2203 A1586 22c multicolored   .40   .15
  Sojourner Truth (c. 1797-1883), abolitionist.

Republic of Texas, 150th Anniv.

Texas State Flag and Silver
Spur — A1587   Republic of Texas

1986, Mar. 2   **Photo.**
2204 A1587 22c dk bl, dk red &
          grysh blk   .40   .15
   a.   Horiz. pair, imperf. vert. 1,250.
   b.   Dark red omitted   2,750.
   c.   Dark blue omitted   7,000.

Fish

Muskellunge — A1588

Atlantic Cod
A1589

Largemouth
Bass
A1590

Bluefin Tuna
A1591

Catfish
A1592

Perf. 10 Horiz. on 1 or 2 Sides
1986, Mar. 21   **Photo.**
2205 A1588 22c multicolored   .50   .15
2206 A1589 22c multicolored   .50   .15
2207 A1590 22c multicolored   .50   .15
2208 A1591 22c multicolored   .50   .15
2209 A1592 22c multicolored   .50   .15
   a.   Bklt. pane of 5, #2205-2209 5.00 2.75
     Set value   .25

Issued in booklets only.

Public Hospitals

A1593

1986, Apr. 11   Photo.   *Perf. 11*
2210 A1593 22c multicolored   .40   .15
  a. Vert. pair, imperf. horiz.   300.
  b. Horiz. pair, imperf. vert.   1,350.

Performing Arts

Edward Kennedy "Duke"
Ellington (1899-1974),
Jazz Composer — A1594

1986, Apr. 29   Photo.   *Perf. 11*
2211 A1594 22c multicolored   .40   .15
  a. Vert. pair, imperf. horiz.   1,000.   —

Miniature Sheets

35 Presidents — A1599

No. 2216: a, Washington. b, John Adams. c, Jefferson. d, Madison. e, Monroe. f, John Quincy Adams. g, Jackson. h, Van Buren. i, Harrison.
No. 2217: a, Tyler. b, Polk. c, Taylor. d, Fillmore. e, Pierce. f, Buchanan. g, Lincoln. h, Andrew Johnson. i, Grant.
No. 2218: a, Hayes. b, Garfield. c, Arthur. d, Cleveland. e, Harrison. f, McKinley. g, Theodore Roosevelt. h, Taft. i, Wilson.
No. 2219: a, Harding. b, Coolidge. c, Hoover. d, Franklin Delano Roosevelt. e, White House. f, Truman. g, Eisenhower. h, Kennedy. i, Lyndon B. Johnson.

1986, May 22   Litho. & Engr.
2216   Sheet of 9   3.75   —
  a.-i. A1599 22c any single   .40   .25
  j. Blue omitted   3,500.
  k. Black inscription omitted   2,000.
  l. Imperf.   10,500.
2217   Sheet of 9   3.75   —
  a.-i. A1599 22c any single   .40   .25
  j. Black inscription omitted   3,750.
2218   Sheet of 9   3.75   —
  a.-i. A1599 22c any single   .40   .25
  j. Brown omitted
  k. Black inscription omitted   3,000.
2219   Sheet of 9   3.75   —
  a.-i. A1599 22c any single   .40   .25
  j. Blackish blue (engr.) inscription omitted on a.-b., d.-e., g.-h.
  Nos. 2216-2219 (4)   15.00

Issued at AMERIPEX '86 Intl. Phil. Exhib., Chicago, IL, May 22-June 1.

Arctic Explorers

Elisha Kent
Kane
A1600

Adolphus
W. Greely
A1601

Vilhjalmur
Stefansson
A1602

Robert E.
Peary and
Matthew
Alexander
Henson
A1603

1986, May 28   Photo.   *Perf. 11*
2220 A1600 22c multicolored   .65   .15
2221 A1601 22c multicolored   .65   .15
2222 A1602 22c multicolored   .65   .15
2223 A1603 22c multicolored   .65   .15
  a. Block of 4, #2220-2223   2.75   2.25
  b. As "a." black (engr.) omitted 9,500.
  c. As "a." #2220 & 2221 black
     (engr.) omitted   —
     Set value   .35

Statue of Liberty,
Cent. — A1604

1986, July 4   Engr.   *Perf. 11*
2224 A1604 22c scarlet & dark blue   .40   .15
See France No. 2014.

Transportation Coils
Types of 1982-85 and

A1604a   A1604b

1986-87   Engr.   *Perf. 10 Vert.*
2225 A1604a 1c violet   .15   .15
  a. Untagged   .15   .15
  b. Imperf., pair   2,500.
2226 A1604b 2c black ('87)   .15   .15
  a. Untagged   .15   .15
2228 A1285   4c reddish brown   .15   .15
  b. Imperf., pair   300.00
2231 A1511   8.3c grn (Bureau
     precancel)   .20   .20
     Set value   .35   .30

Issue dates: 1c, Nov. 26. 2c, Mar. 6. Earliest known usage of 4c, Aug. 15, 1986. 8.3c, Aug. 29. On No. 2228 "Stagecoach 1890s" is 17¹/₂mm long, on No. 1898A 19¹/₂mm long. On No. 2231 "Ambulance 1860s" is 18mm long, on No. 2128 18¹/₂mm long.
No. 2226 inscribed "2 USA;" No. 1897A inscribed "USA 2c."

Navajo Art

A1605   A1606

A1607   A1608

Blankets in the Museum of the American Indian and Lowe Art Museum.

1986, Sept. 4   Litho. & Engr.   *Perf. 11*
2235 A1605 22c multicolored   .45   .15
2236 A1606 22c multicolored   .45   .15
2237 A1607 22c multicolored   .45   .15
2238 A1608 22c multicolored   .45   .15
  a. Block of 4, #2235-2238   2.25   2.00
  b. As "a." blk (engr.) omitted   450.00
     Set value   .35

Literary Arts

T. S. Eliot (1888-1965),
Poet — A1609

1986, Sept. 26   Engr.   *Perf. 11*
2239 A1609 22c copper red   .40   .15

Woodcarved Figurines

Highlander   Ship Figurehead
Figure   A1611
A1610

Nautical Figure   Cigar Store
A1612   Figure
                     A1613

1986, Oct. 1   Photo.   *Perf. 11*
2240 A1610 22c multicolored   .40   .15
2241 A1611 22c multicolored   .40   .15
2242 A1612 22c multicolored   .40   .15
2243 A1613 22c multicolored   .40   .15
  a. Block of 4, #2240-2243   1.75   1.75
  b. As "a." imperf. vert.   1,500.
     Set value   .35

Christmas

Madonna, by   Village Scene
Perugino (c. 1450-   A1615
1523)
A1614

1986, Oct. 24   *Perf. 11*
2244 A1614 22c multicolored   .40   .15
  a. Imperf.. pair
2245 A1615 22c multicolored   .40   .15
     Set value   .15

Michigan Statehood Sesquicent.

White Pine — A1616

1987, Jan. 26   Photo.   *Perf. 11*
2246 A1616 22c multicolored   .40   .15

Pan American Games, Indianapolis,
August 7-25

Runner in Full
Stride
A1617

1987, Jan. 29   *Perf. 11*
2247 A1617 22c multicolored   .40   .15
  a. Silver omitted   1,500.
No. 2247a is valued in the grade of fine.

A1618   A1619

Love

1987, Jan. 30   Photo.   *Perf. 11¹/₂x11*
2248 A1618 22c multicolored   .40   .15

Black Heritage

1987, Feb. 20   Photo.   *Perf. 11*
2249 A1619 22c multicolored   .40   .15
Jean Baptiste Pointe du Sable (c. 1750-1818), pioneer trader, founder of Chicago

A1620   A1621

Performing Arts
Enrico Caruso (1873-1921), Opera Tenor

Photo. & Engr.

1987, Feb. 27   *Perf. 11*
2250 A1620 22c multicolored   .40   .15
  a. Black (engr.) omitted   5,000.

Girl Scouts, 75th Anniv.
Litho. & Engr.

1987, Mar. 12   *Perf. 11*
2251 A1621 22c 14 Achievement
     Badges   .40   .15
  a. All litho. colors omitted   2,500.

All known examples of No. 2251a have been expertized, and certificate must accompany purchase.

Transportation Coils

Conestoga Wagon   Milk Wagon 1900s
1800s   5 USA
3 USA
A1622   A1623

Elevator 1900s   Carreta 1770s
5.3c   7.6c USA
Nonprofit   Nonprofit
A1624   A1625

Wheel Chair 1920s   Canal Boat 1880s
8.4c USA   10c USA
Nonprofit
A1626   A1627

Patrol Wagon 1880s
USA 13 Presorted First-Class
A1628

Coal Car 1870s
13.2 USA Bulk Rate
A1629

Tugboat 1900s
USA 15
A1630

Popcorn Wagon
16.7 USA 1902 Bulk Rate
A1631

Racing Car 1911
USA 17.5
A1632

Cable Car 1880s
USA 20
A1633

Fire Engine 1900s
20.5 USA ZIP+4 Presort
A1634

Railroad Mail Car 1920s
21 USA Presorted First-Class
A1635

Tandem Bicycle 1890s
24.1 USA
A1636 ZIP+4

1987-88   Engr.   Perf. 10 Vert.

2252	A1622	3c claret	.15	.15
a.		Untagged	.15	.15
2253	A1623	5c black	.15	.15
2254	A1624	5.3c blk (Bureau precancel in scarlet)	.15	.15
2255	A1625	7.6c brn (Bureau precancel in scarlet)	.15	.15
2256	A1626	8.4c dp clar (Bureau precancel in red)	.15	.15
a.		Imperf., pair	750.00	
2257	A1627	10c sky blue	.20	.15
2258	A1628	13c blk (Bureau precancel in red)	.25	.25
2259	A1629	13.2c slate grn (Bureau precancel in red)	.25	.25
a.		Imperf., pair	100.00	
2260	A1630	15c violet	.25	.15
c.		Imperf., pair	800.00	
2261	A1631	16.7c rose (Bureau precancel in black)	.30	.30
a.		Imperf., pair	225.00	

All known copies of No. 2261a are miscut top to bottom.

2262	A1632	17.5c dark violet	.30	.30
a.		Untagged (Bureau precancel)	.30	.15
b.		Imperf., pair	2,000.	
2263	A1633	20c blue vio	.35	.15
a.		Imperf., pair	75.00	
2264	A1634	20.5c rose (Bureau precancel in red)	.40	.40
2265	A1635	21c olive grn (Bureau precancel in red)	.40	.40
a.		Imperf., pair	65.00	
2266	A1636	24.1c deep ultra (Bureau precancel)	.45	.45
		Nos. 2252-2266 (15)	3.90	
		Set value		2.75

The 5.3c, 7.6c, 8.4c, 13c, 13.2c, 16.7c, 20.5c, 21c and 24.1c are only available precanceled and are untagged.
Years of issue: 5c, 10c, 17.5c, 1987; others, 1988.
See Nos. 1897-1908, 2123-2136, 2225-2231, 2451-2468.

Special Occasions

Congratulations! USA 22
A1637

Get Well!
A1638

USA 22
Thank You!
A1639

Love You, Dad! USA 22
A1640

Best Wishes! USA 22
A1641

Happy Birthday! USA 22
A1642

Love You Mother! USA 22 A1643

Keep In Touch! USA 22
A1644

Perf. 10 on 1, 2, or 3 sides

1987, Apr. 20   Photo.

Booklet Stamps

2267	A1637	22c multicolored	.55	.15
2268	A1638	22c multicolored	.55	.15
2269	A1639	22c multicolored	.55	.15
2270	A1640	22c multicolored	.55	.15
2271	A1641	22c multicolored	.55	.15
2272	A1642	22c multicolored	.55	.15
2273	A1643	22c multicolored	.55	.15
2274	A1644	22c multicolored	.55	.15
a.		Bklt. pane of 10, #2268-2271, 2273-2274, 2 each #2267, 2272	8.00	5.00
		Nos. 2267-2274 (8)	4.40	
		Set value		.80

United Way Centenary

Uniting Communities USA 22 Six Profiles A1645

Litho. & Engr.

1987, Apr. 28   Perf. 11

2275	A1645	22c multicolored	.40	.15

22 USA
A1646

E Domestic USA
A1647

USA 25
A1648

Yosemite USA 25
A1649

25 USA
Pheasant
A1649a

25 USA
Grosbeak
A1649b

25 USA
Owl
A1649c

25 USA
Honeybee
A1649d

Photo., Engr. (No. 2280), Litho. & Engr. (No. 2281)

1987-88   Perf. 11

2276	A1646	22c multicolored	.40	.15
a.		Booklet pane of 20	8.50	
b.		As "a." vert. pair, imperf. btwn.		
2277	A1647	(25c) multi ('88)	.45	.15
2278	A1648	(25c) multi ('88)	.40	.15
		Nos. 2276-2278 (3)	1.25	
		Set value		.15

Coil Stamps
Perf. 10 Vertical

2279	A1647	(25c) multi ('88)	.45	.15
a.		Imperf., pair	90.00	
2280	A1649	25c Green trees ('88)	.45	.15
a.		Imperf., pair	27.50	
b.		Black trees	100.00	—
d.		Pair, imperf. btwn.	800.00	
2281	A1649d	25c multi ('88)	.45	.15
a.		Imperf., pair	40.00	
b.		Black (engr.) omitted	65.00	
c.		Black (litho.) omitted	550.00	
d.		Pair, imperf. between	1,000.	
e.		Yellow (litho.) omitted	1,250.	
		Nos. 2279-2281 (3)	1.35	
		Set value		.15

Beware of copies with traces of the litho. black that are offered as No. 2281c. Vertical pairs or blocks of No. 2281 and imperfs. with the engr. black missing are from printer's waste.

Booklet Stamps
Perf. 10 on 2 or 3 Sides, 11 on 2 or 3 sides (#2283)

2282	A1647	(25c) multi ('88)	.50	.15
a.		Booklet pane of 10	6.50	3.50

Vert. pairs, imperf between, are printer's waste. Other "varieties" probably exist.

2283	A1649a	25c multi ('88)	.50	.15
a.		Booklet pane of 10	6.00	3.50
b.		25c multi, red removed from sky	6.00	.15
c.		As "b." booklet pane of 10	70.00	—
d.		As "a," horiz. pair, imperf. between	2,250.	

Imperfs. are printer's waste.

2284	A1649b	25c multi ('88)	.45	.15
2285	A1649c	25c multi ('88)	.45	.15
b.		Bklt. pane of 10, 5 each Nos. 2284-2285	4.50	
d.		Pair, Nos. 2284-2285	1.00	—
2285A	A1648	25c multi ('88)	.45	.15
c.		Booklet pane of 6	2.75	
		Nos. 2282-2285A (5)	2.35	
		Set value		.30

Issue dates: No. 2276, May 9; Nos. 2277, 2279, 2282, Mar. 22; No. 2278, May 6; No. 2280, May 20; No. 2281, Sept. 2; No. 2283, Apr. 29; Nos. 2284-2285, May 28. No. 2285A, July 5.

22 USA
Barn Swallow
North American Wildlife — A1650-A1699

1987, June 13   Photo.   Perf. 11

2286	A1650	22c Barn swallow	.85	.15
2287	A1651	22c Monarch butterfly	.85	.15
2288	A1652	22c Bighorn sheep	.85	.15
2289	A1653	22c Broad-tailed hummingbird	.85	.15
2290	A1654	22c Cottontail	.85	.15
2291	A1655	22c Osprey	.85	.15
2292	A1656	22c Mountain lion	.85	.15
2293	A1657	22c Luna moth	.85	.15
2294	A1658	22c Mule deer	.85	.15
2295	A1659	22c Gray squirrel	.85	.15
2296	A1660	22c Armadillo	.85	.15
2297	A1661	22c Eastern chipmunk	.85	.15
2298	A1662	22c Moose	.85	.15
2299	A1663	22c Black bear	.85	.15
2300	A1664	22c Tiger swallowtail	.85	.15
2301	A1665	22c Bobwhite	.85	.15
2302	A1666	22c Ringtail	.85	.15
2303	A1667	22c Red-winged blackbird	.85	.15
2304	A1668	22c American lobster	.85	.15
2305	A1669	22c Black-tailed jack rabbit	.85	.15
2306	A1670	22c Scarlet tanager	.85	.15
2307	A1671	22c Woodchuck	.85	.15
2308	A1672	22c Roseate spoonbill	.85	.15
2309	A1673	22c Bald eagle	.85	.15
2310	A1674	22c Alaskan brown bear	.85	.15
2311	A1675	22c Iiwi	.85	.15
2312	A1676	22c Badger	.85	.15
2313	A1677	22c Pronghorn	.85	.15
2314	A1678	22c River otter	.85	.15
2315	A1679	22c Ladybug	.85	.15
2316	A1680	22c Beaver	.85	.15
2317	A1681	22c White-tailed deer	.85	.15
2318	A1682	22c Blue jay	.85	.15
2319	A1683	22c Pika	.85	.15
2320	A1684	22c Bison	.85	.15
2321	A1685	22c Snowy egret	.85	.15
2322	A1686	22c Gray wolf	.85	.15
2323	A1687	22c Mountain goat	.85	.15
2324	A1688	22c Deer mouse	.85	.15
2325	A1689	22c Black-tailed prairie dog	.85	.15
2326	A1690	22c Box turtle	.85	.15
2327	A1691	22c Wolverine	.85	.15
2328	A1692	22c American elk	.85	.15
2329	A1693	22c California sea lion	.85	.15
2330	A1694	22c Mockingbird	.85	.15
2331	A1695	22c Raccoon	.85	.15
2332	A1696	22c Bobcat	.85	.15
2333	A1697	22c Black-footed ferret	.85	.15
2334	A1698	22c Canada goose	.85	.15
2335	A1699	22c Red fox	.85	.15
a.		Pane of 50, #2286-2335	47.50	
b.		2286b-2335b, any single, red omitted		

Ratification of the Constitution

Dec 7, 1787 USA
Delaware 22
A1700

Dec 12, 1787
Pennsylvania 22 USA
A1701

Dec 18, 1787 USA
New Jersey 22
A1702

22 USA
January 2, 1788
Georgia
A1703

January 9, 1788 USA
Connecticut
A1704

22 USA
Feb 6, 1788
Massachusetts
A1705

April 28, 1788 USA
Maryland 22
A1706

25 USA
May 23, 1788
South Carolina
A1707

25 USA
June 21, 1788
New Hampshire
A1708

June 25, 1788 USA
Virginia 25
A1709

July 26, 1788 USA
New York 25
A1710

November 21, 1789
North Carolina 25
A1711

May 29, 1790
Rhode Island 25
A1712

Litho. & Engr., Photo. (#2337, 2343-2344, 2347)

			Perf. 11	
2336	A1700 22c multi		.40	.15
2337	A1701 22c multi		.40	.15
2338	A1702 22c multi		.40	.15
a.	Black (engr.) omitted		6,000.	
2339	A1703 22c multi ('88)		.40	.15
2340	A1704 22c multi ('88)		.40	.15
2341	A1705 22c dk blue & dk red ('88)		.40	.15
2342	A1706 22c multi ('88)		.40	.15
2343	A1707 25c multi ('88)		.45	.15
a.	Strip of 3, vert. imperf. btwn.		—	
2344	A1708 25c multi ('88)		.45	.15
2345	A1709 25c multi ('88)		.45	.15
2346	A1710 25c multi ('88)		.45	.15
2347	A1711 25c multi ('89)		.45	.15
2348	A1712 25c multi ('90)		.45	.15
	Nos. 2336-2348 (13)		5.50	
	Set value			.65

Issue dates: No. 2336, July 4. No. 2337, Aug. 26. No. 2238, Sept. 11. No. 2339, Jan. 6. No. 2340, Jan. 9. No. 2341, Feb. 6. No. 2342, Feb. 15. No. 2343, May 23; No. 2344, June 21; No. 2345, June 25. No. 2346, July 26. No. 2347, Aug. 22; No. 2348, May 29.

US-Morocco Diplomatic Relations Bicentennial

Friendship with Morocco 1787-1987

Arabesque, Dar Batha Palace, Fez — A1713

Litho. & Engr.
		Perf. 11	
1987, July 18			
2349	A1713 22c scar & blk	.40	.15
a.	Black (engr.) omitted	350.00	

See Morocco No. 642.

Literary Arts

William Cuthbert Faulkner (1897-1962), Novelist — A1714

Engr.
		Perf. 11	
1987, Aug. 3			
2350	A1714 22c bright green	.40	.15

Imperfs. are from printer's waste.

Folk Art Issue

A1715 Lacemaking USA 22

Lacemaking USA 22 A1716

A1717 Lacemaking USA 22

Lacemaking USA 22 A1718

Litho. & Engr.
		Perf. 11	
1987, Aug. 14			
2351	A1715 22c ultra & white	.45	.15
2352	A1716 22c ultra & white	.45	.15
2353	A1717 22c ultra & white	.45	.15
2354	A1718 22c ultra & white	.45	.15
a.	Block of 4, #2351-2354	1.90	1.90
b.	As "a," white omitted	1,000.	
	Set value		.35

Drafting of the Constitution Bicentennial

A1719 The Bicentennial of the Constitution of the United States of America 1787-1987 USA 22

A1720 We the people of the United States, in order to form a more perfect Union... Preamble, U.S.Constitution USA 22

A1721 Establish justice, insure domestic tranquility, provide for the common defense, promote the general welfare... Preamble, U.S.Constitution USA 22

A1722 And secure the blessings of liberty to ourselves and our posterity... Preamble, U.S.Constitution USA 22

A1723 Do ordain and establish this Constitution for the United States of America. Preamble, U.S.Constitution USA 22

Perf. 10 Horiz. on 1 or 2 Sides
		Photo.	
1987, Aug. 28			
Booklet Stamps			
2355	A1719 22c multicolored	.50	.15
a.	Grayish grn (background) omitted		
2356	A1720 22c multicolored	.50	.15
a.	Grayish grn (background) omitted		
2357	A1721 22c multicolored	.50	.15
a.	Grayish grn (background) omitted		
2358	A1722 22c multicolored	.50	.15
a.	Grayish grn (background) omitted		
2359	A1723 22c multicolored	.50	.15
a.	Bklt. pane of 5, #2355-2359	3.00	2.50
b.	Grayish grn (background) omitted		
	Set value		.50

A1724   A1725

Signing of the Constitution
Litho. & Engr.
		Perf. 11	
1987, Sept. 17			
2360	A1724 22c multicolored	.40	.15

Certified Public Accounting
		Litho. & Engr.	
1987, Sept. 21			
2361	A1725 22c multicolored	1.90	.15
a.	Black (engr.) omitted	900.00	

Locomotives

Stourbridge Lion, 1829 A1726

Best Friend of Charleston, 1830 A1727

John Bull, 1831 A1728

Brother Jonathan, 1832 A1729

Gowan & Marx, 1839 A1730

Perf. 10 Horiz. on 1 or 2 Sides
1987, Oct. 1			
Booklet Stamps			
2362	A1726 22c multicolored	.55	.15
2363	A1727 22c multicolored	.55	.15
2364	A1728 22c multicolored	.55	.15
2365	A1729 22c multicolored	.55	.15
a.	Red omitted		
2366	A1730 22c multicolored	.55	.15
a.	Bklt. pane of 5, #2362-2366	2.75	2.50
b.	As "a," blk omitted on #2366	—	
c.	As No. 2366, blue omitted (single)		
	Set value		.50

Christmas

Moroni Madonna A1731

Christmas Ornaments A1732

		Photo.	Perf. 11
1987, Oct. 23			
2367	A1731 22c multicolored	.40	.15
2368	A1732 22c multicolored	.40	.15
	Set value		.15

1988 Winter Olympics, Calgary

Skiing — A1733

		Photo.	Perf. 11
1988, Jan. 10			
2369	A1733 22c multicolored	.40	.15

Australia Bicentennial

Caricature of Australian Koala and American Bald Eagle — A1734

		Photo.	Perf. 11
1988, Jan. 10			
2370	A1734 22c multicolored	.40	.15

See Australia No. 1052.

Black Heritage

James Weldon Johnson, 1871-1938, Author, Lyricist — A1735

		Photo.	Perf. 11
1988, Feb. 2			
2371	A1735 22c multicolored	.40	.15

Siamese, Exotic Shorthair A1736

Abyssinian, Himalayan A1737

Maine Coon, Burmese A1738

American Shorthair, Persian A1739

			Perf. 11
1988, Feb. 5			
2372	A1736 22c multicolored	.45	.15
2373	A1737 22c multicolored	.45	.15
2374	A1738 22c multicolored	.45	.15
2375	A1739 22c multicolored	.45	.15
a.	Block of 4, #2372-2375	1.90	1.90
	Set value		.35

American Sports Issues

A1740

A1741

1988, Mar. 9   Litho. & Engr.
2376 A1740 22c multicolored   .40   .15

Knute Kenneth Rockne (1888-1931), Notre Dame football coach.

1988, June 13   Photo.   Perf. 11
2377 A1741 25c multicolored   .45   .15

Francis Ouimet (1893-1967), 1st amateur golfer to win the US Open Championship.

Love Issue

Rose — A1742

A1743

1988   Photo.   Perf. 11
2378 A1742 25c multicolored   .45   .15
   a.   Imperf., pair
2379 A1743 45c multicolored   .65   .20
     Set value   .25

Issue dates: 25c, July 4; 45c, Aug. 8.

1988 Summer Olympics, Seoul

Gymnastic Rings
A1744

1988, Aug. 19   Photo.   Perf. 11
2380 A1744 25c multicolored   .45   .15

Classic Automobiles

1928 Locomobile — A1745

1929 Pierce-Arrow A1746

1929 Pierce-Arrow

1931 Cord A1747

1931 Cord

1932 Packard A1748

1932 Packard

1935 Duesenberg — A1749

Perf. 10 Horiz. on 1 or 2 Sides
1988, Aug. 25   Litho. & Engr.
Booklet Stamps
2381 A1745 25c multicolored   .50   .15
2382 A1746 25c multicolored   .50   .15
2383 A1747 25c multicolored   .50   .15
2384 A1748 25c multicolored   .50   .15
2385 A1749 25c multicolored   .50   .15
   a.   Bklt. pane of 5, #2381-2385   5.50   2.25
    Nos. 2381-2385 (5)   2.50
    Set value   .50

Antarctic Explorers

Nathaniel Palmer (1799-1877) A1750

Lt. Charles Wilkes (1798-1877) A1751

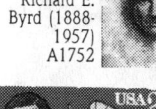

Richard E. Byrd (1888-1957) A1752

Lincoln Ellsworth (1880-1951) A1753

1988, Sept. 14   Photo.   Perf. 11
2386 A1750 25c multicolored   .65   .15
2387 A1751 25c multicolored   .65   .15
2388 A1752 25c multicolored   .65   .15
2389 A1753 25c multicolored   .65   .15
   a.   Block of 4, #2386-2389   2.75   2.00
   b.   Black (engr.) omitted   1,500.
   c.   As "a," imperf. horiz.   3,000.
    Set value   .35

Folk Art Issue
Carousel Animals

Deer — A1754

Horse — A1755

Camel — A1756

Goat — A1757

1988, Oct. 1   Litho. & Engr.   Perf. 11
2390 A1754 25c multicolored   .65   .15
2391 A1755 25c multicolored   .65   .15
2392 A1756 25c multicolored   .65   .15
2393 A1757 25c multicolored   .65   .15
   a.   Block of 4, #2390-2393   3.00   2.00
    Set value   .35

Express Mail Rate

Eagle in Flight — A1758

1988, Oct. 4   Litho. & Engr.   Perf. 11
2394 A1758 $8.75 multi   13.50   8.00

Special Occasions

Happy Birthday — A1759

Best Wishes — A1760

Thinking of You — A1761

Love You — A1762

Perf. 11 on 2 or 3 sides
1988, Oct. 22   Photo.
Booklet Stamps
2395 A1759 25c multicolored   .50   .15
2396 A1760 25c multicolored   .50   .15
   a.   Bklt. pane of 6, 3 #2395 + 3
      #2396 with gutter btwn.   3.75   —
2397 A1761 25c multicolored   .50   .15
2398 A1762 25c multicolored   .50   .15
   a.   Bklt. pane of 6, 3 #2397 + 3
      #2398 with gutter btwn.   3.75   3.25
   b.   As "a," imperf. horiz.
    Nos. 2395-2398 (4)   2.00
     Set value   .40

Madonna and Child, by Botticelli
A1763

Greetings

One-horse Open Sleigh and Village Scene
A1764

Litho. & Engr., Photo. (No. 2400)
1988, Oct. 20   Perf. 11½
2399 A1763 25c multicolored   .45   .15
   a.   Gold omitted   30.00
2400 A1764 25c multicolored   .45   .15
     Set value   .15

Montana Statehood Centennial

C.M. Russell and Friends, by Charles M. Russell (1865-1926)
A1765

1989, Jan. 15   Litho. & Engr.   Perf. 11
2401 A1765 25c multicolored   .45   .15

Black Heritage Issues

Asa Philip Randolph (1889-1979), Labor and Civil Rights Leader — A1766

1989, Feb. 3   Photo.   Perf. 11
2402 A1766 25c multicolored   .45   .15

North Dakota Statehood Centennial

A1767

1989, Feb. 21   Perf. 11
2403 A1767 25c multicolored   .45   .15

Washington Statehood Centennial

A1768

1989, Feb. 22   Perf. 11
2404 A1768 25c multicolored   .45   .15

Steamboats

Experiment, 1788-1790 — A1769

Phoenix, 1809 — A1770

New Orleans, 1812 — A1771

Washington, 1816 — A1772

Walk in the Water, 1818 — A1773

Perf. 10 Horiz. on 1 or 2 sides

1989, Mar. 3   Litho. & Engr.
Booklet Stamps

2405	A1769	25c multicolored	.45 .15
2406	A1770	25c multicolored	.45 .15
2407	A1771	25c multicolored	.45 .15
2408	A1772	25c multicolored	.45 .15
2409	A1773	25c multicolored	.45 .15
a.		Bklt. pane of 5, #2405-2409	2.25 1.75
		Set value	.50

A1774   A1775

World Stamp Expo '89
Nov. 17-Dec. 3, Washington, DC

1989, Mar. 16   Litho. & Engr.   *Perf. 11*

2410	A1774	25c No. 122	.45 .15

Performing Arts
Arturo Toscanini (1867-1975), Italian Conductor

1989, Mar. 25   Photo.   *Perf. 11*

2411	A1775	25c multicolored	.45 .15

Constitution Bicentennial

House of
Representatives
A1776   Senate
A1777

Executive
Branch — A1778   Supreme
Court — A1779

1989-90   Litho. & Engr.   *Perf. 11*

2412	A1776	25c multicolored	.45 .15
2413	A1777	25c multicolored	.45 .15
2414	A1778	25c multicolored	.45 .15
2415	A1779	25c multicolored	.45 .15
		Nos. 2412-2415 (4)	1.80
		Set value	.20

Issue dates: #2412, Apr. 4; #2413, Apr. 6; #2414, Apr. 16. #2415, Feb. 2, 1990.

South Dakota State Centenary

State Flower,
Pioneer
Woman and
Sod House on
Grasslands
A1780

1989, May 3   Photo.   *Perf. 11*

2416	A1780	25c multicolored	.45 .15

American Sports

Henry Louis "Lou"
Gehrig (1903-1941),
Baseball Player for the
New York
Yankees — A1781

1989, June 10   Photo.   *Perf. 11*

2417	A1781	25c multicolored	.50 .15

Literary Arts

Ernest Hemingway
(1899-1961), Nobel
Prize-winner for
Literature,
1954 — A1782

1989, July 17   Photo.   *Perf. 11*

2418	A1782	25c multicolored	.45 .15

Moon Landing, 20th Anniv.

Raising the Flag
on Lunar
Surface, July 20,
1969 — A1783

Perf. 11x11½

1989, July 20   Litho. & Engr.

2419	A1783	$2.40 multicolored	4.00 2.00
a.		Black (engr.) omitted	3,000.
b.		Imperf.. pair	1,000.
c.		Black (litho.) omitted	4,750.

Natl. Assoc. of Letter Carriers, Cent.

Letter
Carriers
A1784

1989, Aug. 30   Photo.   *Perf. 11*

2420	A1784	25c multicolored	.45 .15

Constitution Bicentennial

Bill of Rights — A1785

Litho. & Engr.

1989, Sept. 25   *Perf. 11*

2421	A1785	25c multicolored	.45 .15
a.		Black (engr.) omitted	375.00

Prehistoric Animals

Tyrannosaurus
Rex — A1786

USA 25 Pteranodon
A1787

Stegosaurus
A1788

Brontosaurus
A1789

1989, Oct. 1   Litho. & Engr.   *Perf. 11*

2422	A1786	25c multicolored	.65 .15
2423	A1787	25c multicolored	.65 .15
2424	A1788	25c multicolored	.65 .15
2425	A1789	25c multicolored	.65 .15
a.		Block of 4, #2422-2425	3.00 2.00
b.		As "a," black (engr.) omitted	1,250.
		Set value	.35

The correct name for "Brontosaurus" is "Apatosaurus."

No. 2425b is valued in the grade of fine.

Pre-Columbian America Issue

Southwest Carved
Figure, A. D. 1150-
1350 — A1790

Emblem of the Postal Union of the Americas and Spain (UPAE) and Southwestern Wood-carved Ritual Figure, Mogollon Culture, Mimbres Period, a Forerunner of the Hopi Indian Kachina Doll, A.D. 1150-1350.

1989, Oct. 12   Photo.   *Perf. 11*

2426	A1790	25c multicolored	.45 .15

Discovery of America, 500th anniv. (in 1992). See No. C121.

Christmas

Madonna and
Child, by Caracci
A1791   Sleigh Full of Presents
A1792

Litho. & Engr.

1989, Oct. 19   *Perf. 11½*

2427	A1791	25c multicolored	.45 .15
a.		Booklet pane of 10	4.75 —
b.		Red (litho.) omitted	900.00
c.		As "a," imperf.	

Photo.
Perf. 11

2428	A1792	25c multicolored	.45 .15
a.		Vert. pair, imperf. horiz.	2,000.

Booklet Stamp
Perf. 11½ on 2 or 3 sides

2429	A1792	25c multicolored	.45 .15
a.		Booklet pane of 10	4.75
b.		As "a," horiz. imperf. btwn.	—
c.		As "a," red omitted	—
		Set value	.15

Marked differences exist between Nos. 2428 and 2429: The runners on the sleigh in No. 2429 are twice as thick as those in No. 2428; in No. 2429 the package to the rear of the sleigh has an identically colored bow, whereas the same package in No. 2428 has a bow of different color; and the

---

board running underneath the sleigh on No. 2429 is pink, whereas it is the same color as the sleigh on No. 2428.

Eagle and
Shield — A1793

1989, Nov. 10   Photo.   *Die Cut*
Self-Adhesive

2431	A1793	25c multicolored	.50 .20
a.		Booklet pane of 18	11.00
b.		Vert. pair, no die cutting between	850.00
c.		Pair, no die cutting	

Issued unfolded in panes of 18; peelable paper backing is booklet cover. Sold for $5.

Also available in strips of 18 with stamps spaced for use in affixing machines to service first day covers. Sold for $5.

Sold in 15 test cities and through the philatelic agency only.

Souvenir Sheet

World Stamp Expo, Washington, DC, Nov. 17-Dec. 3 — A1794

1989, Nov. 17   Litho. & Engr.   *Imperf.*

2433	A1794	Sheet of 4	12.00 9.00
a.		90c like No. 122	2.00 1.75
b.		90c like No. 132TC (blue frame, brown center)	2.00 1.75
c.		90c like No. 132TC (green frame, blue center)	2.00 1.75
d.		90c like No. 132TC (scarlet frame, blue center)	2.00 1.75

Traditional Mail Delivery

Stagecoach, c.
1850 — A1795   Paddlewheel
Steamer — A1796

Biplane
A1797   Depot-hack Type
Automobile
A1798

Litho. & Engr.

1989, Nov. 19   *Perf. 11*

2434	A1795	25c multicolored	.45 .15
2435	A1796	25c multicolored	.45 .15
2436	A1797	25c multicolored	.45 .15
2437	A1798	25c multicolored	.45 .15
a.		Block of 4, #2434-2437	2.00 2.00
b.		As "a," dark blue (engr.) omitted	1,250.
		Set value	.35

1989, Nov. 28   *Imperf.*

2438		Sheet of 4	4.00 1.75
a.		A1795 25c multicolored	.65 .25
b.		A1796 25c multicolored	.65 .25
c.		A1797 25c multicolored	.65 .25
d.		A1798 25c multicolored	.65 .25
e.		Dark blue & gray (engr.) omitted	—

20th Universal Postal Union Congress.

Idaho State Centenary

Mountain Bluebird, Sawtooth Mountains — A1799

1990, Jan. 6   **Photo.**   *Perf. 11*
2439 A1799 25c multicolored   .45 .15

Love Issue

A1800

1990, Jan. 18   **Photo.**   *Perf. 12½x13*
2440 A1800 25c brt bl, dk pink & emer grn   .45 .15
   a.   Imperf., pair   850.00

Booklet Stamp
Perf. 11½ on 2 or 3 sides
2441 A1800 25c ultra, brt pink & dk grn   .45 .15
   a.   Booklet pane of 10   4.75 —
   b.   As "a," bright pink omitted   2,250.
   c.   As "b," single stamp   275.
    Set value   .15

No. 2441c may be obtained from booklet panes containing both normal and color-omitted stamps.

Black Heritage

Ida B. Wells (1862-1931), Journalist — A1801

1990, Feb. 1   **Photo.**   *Perf. 11*
2442 A1801 25c multicolored   .45 .15

Beach Umbrella — A1802

1990, Feb. 3   **Photo.**   *Perf. 11*
Booklet Stamp
2443 A1802 15c multicolored   .30 .15
   a.   Booklet pane of 10   3.00 2.00
   b.   As "a," blue omitted   2,000.

Wyoming State Centenary

High Mountain Meadows, by Conrad Schwiering A1803

1990, Feb. 23   **Litho. & Engr.**   *Perf. 11*
2444 A1803 25c multicolored   .45 .15
   a.   Black (engr.) omitted   2,500.

Classic Films

The Wizard of Oz — A1804   *Gone With the Wind* — A1805

Beau Geste A1806   *Stagecoach* A1807

1990, Mar. 23   **Photo.**   *Perf. 11*
2445 A1804 25c multicolored   1.00 .15
2446 A1805 25c multicolored   1.00 .15
2447 A1806 25c multicolored   1.00 .15
2448 A1807 25c multicolored   1.00 .15
   a.   Block of 4, #2445-2448   4.50 3.50
    Set value   .35

Literary Arts Series

Marianne Craig Moore (1887-1972), Poet — A1808

1990, Apr. 18   **Photo.**   *Perf. 11*
2449 A1808 25c multicolored   .45 .15

TRANSPORTATION ISSUE

A1810

Circus Wagon 1900s A1811

A1811a

Canoe 1800s A1812

A1816

Cog Railway 1870s A1822

A1823

A1825

A1827 Seaplane 1914

Engr., Photo. (#2452B, 2452D, 2454, 2458)
1990-95   **Coil Stamps**   *Perf. 9.8 Vert.*
Untagged: #2452B, 2452D, 2453, 2454, & 10c
2451 A1810   4c claret   .15 .15
   a.   Imperf., pair   700.00
   b.   Untagged   .15 .15
2452 A1811   5c carmine   .15 .15
   a.   Untagged   .15 .15
   b.   Imperf., pair   1,000.
2452B A1811   5c carmine   .15 .15
2452D A1811a   5c carmine   .15 .15
   e.   Imperf., pair   —
2453 A1812   5c brn (Bureau precancel in gray)   .15 .15
   a.   Imperf., pair   425.00
2454 A1812   5c red (Bureau precancel in gray)   .15 .15

2457 A1816   10c grn (Bureau precancel in gray)   .20 .20
   a.   Imperf., pair   425.00
2458 A1816   10c grn (Bureau precancel in black)   .20 .20
2463 A1822   20c green   .40 .15
   a.   Imperf., pair   150.00
2464 A1823   23c dark blue   .45 .15
   a.   Imperf., pair   200.00
2466 A1825   32c blue   .60 .15
2468 A1827 $1 blue & scar   1.75 .50
   a.   Imperf., pair   —
   Nos. 2451-2468 (12)   4.50
    Set value   1.35

Issued: $1, 4/20; #2452, 8/31; 4c, 1/25/91; #2453, 2457, 5/25/91; #2454, 10/22/91; 23c, 4/12/91; #2452B, 12/8/92; #2458, 5/25/94; #2452D, 3/20/95; 32c, 6/2/95; #2463, 6/9/95

This is an expanding set. Numbers will change if necessary.

Some pairs of No. 2468 appear to be imperf but have some blind perfs on the gum. Beware of copies with the gum removed.

Lighthouses

Admiralty Head, WA — A1829   Cape Hatteras, NC — A1830

West Quoddy Head, ME — A1831   American Shoals, FL — A1832

Sandy Hook, NJ — A1833

Perf. 10 Vert. on 1 or 2 Sides
1990, Apr. 26   **Litho. & Engr.**
Booklet Stamps
2470 A1829 25c multicolored   .45 .15
2471 A1830 25c multicolored   .45 .15
2472 A1831 25c multicolored   .45 .15
2473 A1832 25c multicolored   .45 .15
2474 A1833 25c multicolored   .45 .15
   a.   Bklt. pane of 5. #2470-2474   2.50 2.00
   b.   As "a," white (USA 25) omitted   75.00
    Set value   .40

Flag

A1834

1990, May 18   **Photo.**   *Die Cut*
Self-adhesive
2475 A1834 25c dk red & dk bl   .50 .25
   a.   Pane of 12   6.00

Sold only in panes of 12; peelable plastic backing inscribed in light ultramarine. Available for a test period of six months at 22 First National Bank automatic teller machines in Seattle.

Flora and Fauna Series

American Kestrel
A1840   A1841

Eastern Bluebird — A1842   Fawn — A1843

Cardinal A1844   Pumpkinseed Sunfish A1845

Bobcat A1846

Perf. 11, 11.2 (#2477)
1990-95   **Litho.**   **Untagged**
2476 A1840 1c multicolored   .15 .15
2477 A1841 1c multicolored   .15 .15
2478 A1842 3c multicolored   .15 .15
Photo.
Perf. 11½x11
2479 A1843 19c multicolored   .35 .15
   b.   Red omitted   850.00

On No. 2479b other colors are shifted.

2480 A1844 30c multicolored   .50 .15
Litho. & Engr.
Perf. 11
2481 A1845 45c multicolored   .80 .15
   a.   Black (engr.) omitted   650.00
2482 A1846 $2 multicolored   3.00 1.25
   a.   Black (engr.) omitted   375.00
   Nos. 2476-2482 (7)   5.10
    Set value   1.65

Issued: $2, 6/1/90; 19c, 3/11/91; 3c, 30c, #2476, 6/22/91; 45c, 12/2/92; #2477, 5/10/95. See No. 3044. Compare design A1842 with A2336.

Blue Jay — A1847   Wood Duck — A1848

African Violets — A1849   Peach — A1850

Pear — A1851   Red Squirrel — A1852

Rose — A1853   Pine Cone — A1854

Booklet Stamps

1991-95			*Perf. 10.9x9.8*	
2483	A1847	20c multicolored	.40	.15
a.		Booklet pane of 10	4.00	

Perf. 10 on 2 or 3 Sides

2484	A1848	29c black & multi	.50	.15
a.		Booklet pane of 10	5.50	—
b.		As "a," horiz. imperf. between		—

Perf. 11 on 2 or 3 Sides

2485	A1848	29c red & multi	.50	.15
a.		Booklet pane of 10	5.50	4.00
b.		Vert. pair, imperf. between		—

Perf. 10x11 on 2 or 3 Sides

2486	A1849	29c multicolored	.50	.15
a.		Booklet pane of 10	5.50	4.00
2487	A1850	32c multicolored	.60	.15
2488	A1851	32c multicolored	.60	.15
a.		Booklet pane, 5 each #2487-2488	6.00	—
b.		Pair, #2487-2488	1.25	.30

Issued: #2484-2485, 4/12/91; #2486,
10/8/93; 20c, 6/15/95; 32c 7/8/95.

Booklet Stamps

1993		**Photo.**	*Die Cut*	
		Self-Adhesive		
2489	A1852	29c multicolored	.50	.15
a.		Booklet pane of 18	10.00	
2490	A1853	29c red, green & black	.50	.15
a.		Booklet pane of 18	10.00	
2491	A1854	29c multicolored	.50	.15
a.		Booklet pane of 18	11.00	
b.		Horiz. pair, no die cutting between		—

Issued: #2489, June 25; #2490, Aug. 19; #2491, Nov. 5.

Serpentine Die Cut

2492	A1853	32c pink, green & black	.60	.15
a.		Booklet pane of 20+label	12.00	
b.		Booklet pane of 15+label ('96)	8.75	
c.		Horiz. pair, no die cutting between		—
d.		As "a," 2 stamps and parts of 7 others printed on backing liner		—
e.		Booklet pane of 14		—
f.		Booklet pane of 16		—
2493	A1850	32c multicolored	.60	.15
2494	A1851	32c multicolored	.60	.15
a.		Booklet pane, 10 each #2493-2494+label	12.00	

Coil Stamps

Serpentine Die Cut Vert.

2495	A1850	32c multicolored	.60	.15
2495A	A1851	32c multicolored	.60	.15

See Nos. 3048-3049, 3053-3054.

Olympians

Jesse Owens, 1936
A1855

Ray Ewry, 1900-08
A1856

Hazel Wightman, 1924
A1857

Eddie Eagan, 1920, 1932
A1858

Helene Madison, 1932
A1859

1990, July 6		**Photo.**	*Perf. 11*	
2496	A1855	25c multicolored	.60	.15
2497	A1856	25c multicolored	.60	.15
2498	A1857	25c multicolored	.60	.15
2499	A1858	25c multicolored	.60	.15
2500	A1859	25c multicolored	.60	.15
a.		Strip of 5, #2496-2500	3.25	2.50
		Set value		.40

Indian Headdresses

Assiniboin
A1860

Cheyenne
A1861

Comanche
A1862

Flathead
A1863

Shoshone
A1864

Perf. 11 on 2 or 3 sides

1990, Aug. 17			**Litho. & Engr.**	
		Booklet Stamps		
2501	A1860	25c multicolored	.55	.15
2502	A1861	25c multicolored	.55	.15
2503	A1862	25c multicolored	.55	.15
2504	A1863	25c multicolored	.55	.15
2505	A1864	25c multicolored	.55	.15
a.		Bklt. pane, 2 each #2501-2505	5.75	
b.		As "a," black (engr.) omitted		—
c.		Strip of 5, #2501-2505	2.25	—
d.		As "a," horiz. imperf. btwn.		
		Set value		.40

Micronesia, Marshall Islands

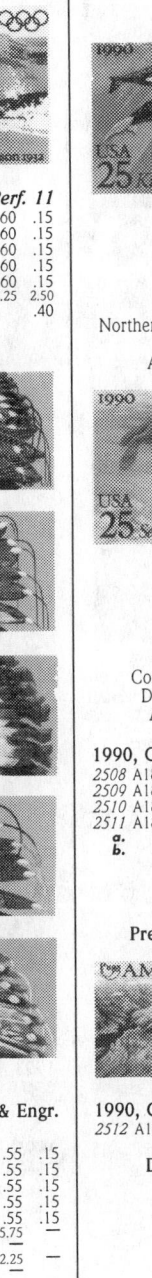

Canoe and Flag of the Federated States of Micronesia
A1865

Stick Chart, Canoe and Flag of the Republic of the Marshall Islands
A1866

1990, Sept. 28			*Perf. 11*	
2506	A1865	25c multicolored	.45	.15
2507	A1866	25c multicolored	.45	.15
a.		Pair, #2506-2507	.90	.60
b.		As "a," black (engr.) omitted	4,000.	
		Set value		.15

See Micronesia Nos. 124-126 and Marshall Islands No. 381.

Sea Creatures

Killer Whales
A1867

Northern Sea Lions
A1868

Sea Otter
A1869

Common Dolphin
A1870

1990, Oct. 3		**Litho. & Engr.**	*Perf. 11*	
2508	A1867	25c multicolored	.45	.15
2509	A1868	25c multicolored	.45	.15
2510	A1869	25c multicolored	.45	.15
2511	A1870	25c multicolored	.45	.15
a.		Block of 4, #2508-2511	1.90	1.75
b.		As "a," blk (engr.) omitted	1,250.	
		Set value		.35

See Russia Nos. 5933-5936.

Pre-Columbian America Issue

Grand Canyon
A1871

1990, Oct. 12		**Photo.**	*Perf. 11*	
2512	A1871	25c multicolored	.45	.15

Dwight David Eisenhower

A1872

1990, Oct. 13		**Photo.**	*Perf. 11*	
2513	A1872	25c multicolored	.45	.15
a.		Imperf., pair	2,000.	

Christmas

Madonna and Child by Antonello da Messina — A1873

Christmas Tree — A1874

		Litho. & Engr.		
1990, Oct. 18			*Perf. 11½*	
2514	A1873	25c multicolored	.45	.15
a.		Booklet pane of 10	5.00	

Photo.

			Perf. 11	
2515	A1874	25c multicolored	.45	.15
a.		Vert. pair, imperf horiz.	1,100.	

Perf. 11½x11 on 2 or 3 Sides

2516	A1874	25c multicolored	.45	.15
a.		Booklet pane of 10	5.00	
		Nos. 2514-2516 (3)	1.35	
		Set value		.15

Marked differences exist between Nos. 2515 and 2516. The background red on No. 2515 is even while that on No. 2516 is splotchy. The bands across the tree and "GREETINGS" are blue green on No. 2515 and yellow green on No. 2516.

A1875

A1876

A1877

1991, Jan. 22		**Photo.**	*Perf. 13*	
2517	A1875	(29c) yel, blk, red & yel grn	.50	.15
a.		Imperf., pair	750.00	
b.		Horiz. pair, imperf. vert.	1,250.	

Coil Stamp

Perf. 10 Vert.

2518	A1875	(29c) yel, blk, dull red & dk yel grn	.50	.15
a.		Imperf., pair	40.00	

Booklet Stamps

Perf. 11 on 2 or 3 Sides

2519	A1875	(29c) yel, blk, dull red & dk grn	.50	.15
a.		Booklet pane of 10	6.50	4.50
2520	A1875	(29c) pale yel, blk, red & brt grn	.50	.15
a.		Booklet pane of 10	7.00	4.50
b.		As "a," imperf horiz.		

No. 2519 has bullseye perforations that measure approximately 11.2. No. 2520 has less pronounced black lines in the leaf, which is a much brighter green than on No. 2519.

Litho.

			Perf. 11	
2521	A1876	(4c) bister & car	.15	.15
a.		Vert. pair, imperf. horiz.	125.00	

Photo.

Imperf., Die Cut
Self-Adhesive

2522	A1877	(29c) blk, dk blue & red	.50	.25
a.		Pane of 12	7.00	

No. 2522 sold only in panes of 12; peelable plastic backing inscribed in light ultramarine. Available during a test period at 22 First National Bank automatic teller machines in Seattle.

Flag Over Mt. Rushmore
A1878

Flower
A1879

1991, Mar. 29		**Engr.**	*Perf. 10 Vert.*	
		Coil Stamps		
2523	A1878	29c bl, red & claret	.50	.15
b.		Imperf., pair	20.00	
c.		Blue, red & brown	5.00	—

Photo.

2523A	A1878	29c blue, red & brown	.50	.15

On No. 2523A, USA and 29 are not outlined in white and appear farther from edge of design. Issue dates: #2523, Mar. 29. #2523A, July 4.

1991-92		**Photo.**	*Perf. 11*	
2524	A1879	29c dull yel, blk, red & pale yel grn	.50	.15
a.		Perf. 13x12½	.60	.15

Coil Stamps

Roulette 10 Vert.

2525	A1879	29c pale yel, blk, red & yel grn	.50	.15

Perf. 10 Vert.

2526 A1879 29c pale yel, blk, red & yel grn .50 .15

Perf. 11 on 2 or 3 Sides
Booklet Stamp

2527 A1879 29c pale yel, blk, red & brt grn .50 .15
a. Booklet pane of 10 5.50 3.50
b. As "a," vert. imperf between 1,500.
c. As "a," imperf horiz. 2,750.

Flower on No. 2524 has grainy appearance, inscriptions look rougher.
Issue dates: #2524, 2527, Apr. 5. #2525, Aug. 16. #2526, Mar. 3, 1992.

Flag, Olympic Rings — A1880

Perf. 11 on 2 or 3 Sides
1991, Apr. 21   Photo.
Booklet Stamp

2528 A1880 29c multicolored .50 .15
a. Booklet pane of 10 5.25 3.50
b. As "a," horiz. imperf. between —

Fishing Boat — A1881   Balloon — A1882

1991-94   Photo.   Perf. 9.8 Vert.
Coil Stamps

2529 A1881 19c multicolored .35 .15
a. Type II ('93) .35 .15
b. As "a." untagged ('93) 1.00 .40
2529C A1881 19c multicolored .50 .15

Design of Type II stamps is created by a finer dot pattern. The vertical sides of "1" are smooth on Type II and jagged on Type I stamps.

No. 2529C has one loop of rope tying boat to piling, numerals and USA are taller and thinner.
Issued: No. 2529, 8/8/91; No. 2529C, 6/25/94.

Perf. 10 on 2 or 3 Sides
1991, May 17   Photo.
Booklet Stamp

2530 A1882 19c multicolored .35 .15
a. Booklet pane of 10 3.50 2.75

Flags on Parade — A1883   Liberty Torch — A1884

1991, May 30   Photo.   Perf. 11
2531 A1883 29c multicolored .50 .15

1991, June 25   Photo.   Die Cut
Self-Adhesive

2531A A1884 29c blk, gold & grn .55 .25
b. Pane of 18 10.50
c. Pair, imperf —

Sold only in panes of 18; peelable paper backing inscribed in light blue.

Switzerland, 700th Anniv.

A1887

1991, Feb. 22   Photo.   Perf. 11
2532 A1887 50c multicolored 1.00 .25
a. Vert. pair, imperf horiz. 1,500.

Imperfs exist from printers' waste.
See Switzerland No. 888.

A1888   A1889

Vermont Statehood Bicentennial
1991, Mar. 1   Perf. 11
2533 A1888 29c multicolored .50 .15

Savings Bonds, 50th Anniv.
1991, Apr. 30   Photo.   Perf. 11
2534 A1889 29c multicolored .50 .15

Love

A1890   A1891

1991, May 9   Photo.   Perf. 12½x13
2535 A1890 29c multicolored .50 .15
a. Perf. 11 .60 .15
b. Imperf., pair —

Perf. 11 on 2 or 3 Sides
Booklet Stamp

2536 A1890 29c multicolored .50 .15
a. Booklet pane of 10 5.25 3.50

"29" is closer to edge of design on No. 2536 than on No. 2535.

Perf. 11

2537 A1891 52c multicolored .90 .20

Literary Arts Series

William Saroyan A1892

1991, May 22   Photo.   Perf. 11
2538 A1892 29c multicolored .50 .15

See Russia No. 6002.

Eagle, Olympic Rings — A1893

1991, Sept. 29   Photo.   Perf. 11
2539 A1893 $1 gold & multi 1.75 .50

A1894

A1895

A1896

1991   Litho. & Engr.   Perf. 11
Untagged (#2541-2542)

2540 A1894 $2.90 Priority 5.00 2.50
a. Vert. pair, imperf horiz. —
2541 A1895 $9.95 Domestic express 15.00 7.50
2542 A1896 $14 Intl. express 22.50 10.00
Nos. 2540-2542 (3) 42.50 20.00

Issued: $2.90, 7/7; $9.95, 6/16; $14, 8/31.

Priority Mail Rate

Futuristic Space Shuttle A1897

Space Shuttle Challenger A1898

Perf. 11x10½
1993, June 3   Litho. & Engr.
2543 A1897 $2.90 multicolored 5.00 2.25

Litho. & Engr.
1995, June 22   Perf. 11.2
2544 A1898 $3 multicolored 5.25 2.25

No. 2544 comes with either "1995" or "1996" below design at lower corner. Values the same.

Express Mail Rate

Space Shuttle Endeavour A1898a

1995, Aug. 4   Litho. & Engr.   Perf. 11
2544A A1898a $10.75 multi 17.50 7.50

Fishing Flies

Royal Wulff A1899

Jock Scott A1900

Apte Tarpon Fly — A1901

Lefty's Deceiver A1902

Muddler Minnow A1903

Perf. 11 Horiz. on 1 or 2 Sides
1991, May 31   Photo.
Booklet Stamps

2545 A1899 29c multicolored .55 .15
a. Black omitted —
2546 A1900 29c multicolored .55 .15
a. Black omitted —
2547 A1901 29c multicolored .55 .15
2548 A1902 29c multicolored .55 .15
2549 A1903 29c multicolored .55 .15
a. Bklt. pane of 5. #2545-2549 3.00 2.50
Set value .50

Horiz. pairs, imperf. vert., exist from printers' waste.

A1904   A1905

Performing Arts
Cole Porter (1891-1964), Composer
1991, June 8   Photo.   Perf. 11
2550 A1904 29c multicolored .50 .15
a. Vert. pair, imperf. horiz. 650.00

Operations Desert Shield & Desert Storm
1991, July 2   Photo.   Perf. 11
2551 A1905 29c Southwest Asia service medal .50 .15
a. Vert. pair, imperf horiz. 2,500.

Perf. 11 Vert. on 1 or 2 Sides
Booklet Stamp

2552 A1905 29c multicolored .50 .15
a. Booklet pane of 5 2.75 2.25

No. 2552 is 20½mm wide stamp. Inscriptions are shorter than on No. 2551.

Summer Olympics

Pole Vault A1907

Discus A1908

Women's Sprints A1909

Javelin
A1910

Women's Hurdles
A1911

1991, July 12   Photo.   *Perf. 11*
2553 A1907 29c multicolored   .50   .15
2554 A1908 29c multicolored   .50   .15
2555 A1909 29c multicolored   .50   .15
2556 A1910 29c multicolored   .50   .15
2557 A1911 29c multicolored   .50   .15
  a.   Strip of #2553-2557   2.75   2.25
        Set value   .50

Numismatics

1858 Flying Eagle Cent,
1907 Standing Liberty
Double Eagle, Series
1875 $1 Note, Series
1902 $10 National
Currency
Note — A1912

Litho. & Engr.
1991, Aug. 13   *Perf. 11*
2558 A1912 29c multicolored   .50   .15

World War II

A1913

Designs and events of 1941: a, Military vehicles (Burma Road, 717-mile lifeline to China). b, Recruits (America's 1st peacetime draft). c, Shipments for allies (US supports allies with Lend-Lease Act). d, Roosevelt, Churchill (Atlantic Charter sets war aims of allies). e, Tank (America becomes the "arsenal of democracy"). f, Sinking of Destroyer Reuben James, Oct. 31. g, Gas mask, helmet (Civil defense mobilizes Americans at home). h, Liberty Ship, sea gull (1st Liberty ship delivered Dec. 30). i, Sinking ships (Japanese bomb Pearl Harbor, Dec. 7). j, Congress in session (US declares war on Japan, Dec. 8). Central label is the size of 15 stamps and shows world map, extent of Axis control.
Illustration reduced.

1991, Sept. 3   Litho. & Engr.   *Perf. 11*
2559 A1913   Block of 10   5.25   4.50
a.-j.   29c any single   .50   .30
k.   Black (engr.) omitted   10,000.

Basketball, 100th Anniversary

Basketball, Hoop, Players' Arms — A1914

1991, Aug. 28   Photo.   *Perf. 11*
2560 A1914 29c multicolored   .55   .15

District of Columbia Bicentennial

Capitol Building from Pennsylvania Avenue, Circa 1903
A1915

1991, Sept. 7   Litho. & Engr.   *Perf. 11*
2561 A1915 29c multicolored   .50   .15
  a.   Black (engr.) omitted   175.00

Comedians

Stan Laurel and Oliver Hardy
A1916

Edgar Bergen and Charlie McCarthy
A1917

Jack Benny
A1918

Fanny Brice
A1919

Bud Abbott and Lou Costello
A1920

Perf. 11 on 2 or 3 Sides
1991, Aug. 29   Litho. & Engr.
Booklet Stamps
2562 A1916 29c multicolored   .50   .15
2563 A1917 29c multicolored   .50   .15
2564 A1918 29c multicolored   .50   .15
2565 A1919 29c multicolored   .50   .15
2566 A1920 29c multicolored   .50   .15
  a.   Bklt. pane, 2 each #2562-2566   5.50   —
  b.   As "a." scarlet & bright violet (engr.) omitted   900.00
  c.   Strip of 5, #2562-2566   2.50   —
        Set value   .50

Black Heritage

Jan E. Matzeliger

Jan E. Matzeliger (1852-1889), Inventor — A1921

1991, Sept. 15   Photo.   *Perf. 11*
2567 A1921 29c multicolored   .50   .15
  a.   Horiz. pair, imperf. vert.   1,750.
  b.   Vert. pair, imperf. horiz.   1,750.
  c.   Imperf. pair   2,750.

Space Exploration

Mercury, Mariner 10
A1922

Venus, Mariner 2
A1923

Earth, Landsat
A1924

Moon, Lunar Orbiter
A1925

Mars, Viking Orbiter
A1926

Jupiter, Pioneer 11
A1927

Saturn, Voyager 2
A1928

Uranus, Voyager 2
A1929

Neptune, Voyager 2
A1930

Pluto
A1931

Perf. 11 on 2 or 3 Sides
1991, Oct. 1   Photo.
Booklet Stamps
2568 A1922 29c multicolored   .50   .15
2569 A1923 29c multicolored   .50   .15
2570 A1924 29c multicolored   .50   .15
2571 A1925 29c multicolored   .50   .15
2572 A1926 29c multicolored   .50   .15
2573 A1927 29c multicolored   .50   .15
2574 A1928 29c multicolored   .50   .15
2575 A1929 29c multicolored   .50   .15
2576 A1930 29c multicolored   .50   .15
2577 A1931 29c multicolored   .50   .15
  a.   Bklt. pane of 10. #2568-2577   5.50   —
        Set value   .80

Christmas

Madonna and Child by Antoniazzo Romano
A1933

Santa Claus in Chimney
A1934

Santa Checking List — A1935

Santa with Present — A1936

Santa at Fireplace — A1937

Santa and Sleigh — A1938

1991, Oct. 17   Litho. & Engr.   *Perf. 11*
2578 A1933 (29c) multicolored   .50   .15
  a.   Booklet pane of 10   5.80   —
  b.   As "a." single, red & black (engr.) omitted   3,250.

Photo.
2579 A1934 (29c) multicolored   .50   .15
  a.   Horiz. pair, imperf. vert.   450.00
  b.   Vert. pair, imperf. horiz.   625.00

Booklet Stamps
Size: 25x18 1/2mm
Perf. 11 on 2 or 3 Sides
2580 A1934 (29c) Type I   1.75   .15
2581 A1934 (29c) Type II   1.75   .15
  a.   Pair, #2580, 2581   3.50   .25
  b.   Bklt. pane, 2 each #2580, 2581   7.50   —
2582 A1935 (29c) multicolored   .50   .15
  a.   Booklet pane of 4   2.00   —
2583 A1936 (29c) multicolored   .50   .15
  a.   Booklet pane of 4   2.00   —
2584 A1937 (29c) multicolored   .50   .15
  a.   Booklet pane of 4   2.00   —
2585 A1938 (29c) multicolored   .50   .15
  a.   Booklet pane of 4   2.00   —
        Nos. 2578-2585 (8)   6.50   .40

The extreme left brick in top row of chimney is missing from Type II, No. 2581.

James K. Polk (1795-1849)

A1939

1995, Nov. 2   Engr.   *Perf. 11.2*
2587 A1939 32c red brown   .60   .15

Surrender of Gen. John Burgoyne

A1942

1994, May 5   Engr.   *Perf. 11.5*
2590 A1942 $1 blue   1.90   .50

Washington and Jackson

A1944

1994, Aug. 19   Engr.   *Perf. 11.5*
2592 A1944 $5 slate green   8.00   2.50

Pledge of Allegiance — A1946

Eagle and Shield — A1947

A1950

Statue of Liberty — A1951

Perf. 10 on 2 or 3 sides

1992-93   Photo.

Booklet Stamps

2593	A1946	29c black & multi	.50	.15
a.		Booklet pane of 10	5.25	4.25
b.		Perf. 11x10 on 2 or 3 sides	.50	.15
c.		As "b," booklet pane of 10	5.50	4.25

Perf. 11x10 on 2 or 3 Sides

2594	A1946	29c red & multi	.50	.15
a.		Booklet pane of 10	5.25	4.25
b.		Imperf., pair	900.00	

Denomination is red on #2594 and black on #2593.

Issue dates: #2593, Sept. 8. #2594, 1993.

1992-94   **Litho. & Engr.**   *Die Cut*

Self-Adhesive

2595	A1947	29c brown & multi	.50	.25
a.		Pane of 17 + label	13.00	
b.		Pair, no die cutting	500.00	
c.		Brown (engr.) omitted	500.00	

Photo.

2596	A1947	29c green & multi	.50	.25
a.		Pane of 17 + label	12.00	
2597	A1947	29c red & multi	.50	.25
a.		Pane of 17 + label	10.00	
2598	A1950	29c red, cream & blue	.50	.15
a.		Booklet pane of 18	10.00	
2599	A1951	29c multicolored	.50	.15
a.		Booklet pane of 18	10.00	

Plate No. and inscription reads down on No. 2595a and up on Nos. 2596a-2597a. Design is sharper and more finely detailed on Nos. 2595, 2597.

Issued unfolded in panes of 17 + label; peelable paper backing is booklet cover. Sold for $5.

Issue dates: No. 2598, Feb. 4, 1994; No. 2599, June 24, 1994; others. Sept. 25, 1992.

See Nos. 3122, 3122E.

Bulk Rate USA   USA Bulk Rate
A1956   A1957

Presorted First-Class   USA 23
USA 23   Presorted
A1959   A1960

Flag Over White
House — A1961

Perf. 10 Vert.

1991-93   Photo.   Untagged

Coil Stamps

2602	A1956	(10c) multicolored	.20	.15
a.		Imperf., pair	—	
2603	A1957	(10c) orange yel & multi	.20	.20
a.		Imperf., pair	30.00	
b.		Tagged	2.00	
2604	A1957	(10c) gold & multi	.20	.20
2605	A1959	23c multi (Bureau precancel in blue)	.40	.40
2606	A1960	23c multi (Bureau Precanceled)	.40	.40
2607	A1960	23c multi (Bureau Precanceled)	.40	.40
c.		Imperf., pair	125.00	
2608	A1960	23c vio blue, red & blk (Bureau Precanceled)	.40	.40
a.		Imperf., pair	—	

"23" is 7mm long on No. 2607. "First Class" is 8½mm long on No. 2608.

Engr.

2609	A1961	29c blue & red	.50	.15
a.		Imperf., pair	20.00	
b.		Pair, imperf between	100.00	
		Nos. 2602-2609 (8)	2.70	2.30

Issue dates: #2602, Dec. 13. #2603-2604, May 29, 1993. #2605, Sept. 27. #2606, July 21, 1992. #2607, Oct. 9, 1992. #2608, May 14, 1993. 29c, Apr. 23, 1992.

See No. 2907.

Winter Olympics

Hockey
A1963

Figure Skating
A1964

Speed Skating
A1965

Skiing
A1966

Bobsledding
A1967

1992, Jan. 11   Photo.   *Perf. 11*

2611	A1963	29c multicolored	.50	.15
2612	A1964	29c multicolored	.50	.15
2613	A1965	29c multicolored	.50	.15
2614	A1966	29c multicolored	.50	.15
2615	A1967	29c multicolored	.50	.15
a.		Strip of 5, #2611-2615	2.75	2.25
		Set value		.40

A1968

W.E.B. Du Bois
A1969

World Columbian Stamp Expo

1992, Jan. 24   Litho. & Engr.

2616	A1968	29c Detail from #129	.50	.15

Black Heritage

1992, Jan. 31   Litho. & Engr.   *Perf. 11*

2617	A1969	29c multicolored	.50	.15

W.E.B. Du Bois (1868-1963), writer and civil rights leader.

Love

A1970

1992, Feb. 6   Photo.   *Perf. 11*

2618	A1970	29c multicolored	.50	.15
a.		Horiz. pair, imperf vert.	900.00	

Olympic Baseball

A1971

1992, Apr. 3   Photo.   *Perf. 11*

2619	A1971	29c multicolored	.50	.15

Voyages of Columbus

Seeking Queen Isabella's Support
A1972

Crossing the Atlantic
A1973

Approaching Land
A1974

Coming Ashore
A1975

1992, Apr. 24   Litho. & Engr.   *Perf. 11*

2620	A1972	29c multicolored	.50	.15
2621	A1973	29c multicolored	.50	.15
2622	A1974	29c multicolored	.50	.15
2623	A1975	29c multicolored	.50	.15
a.		Block of 4, #2620-2623	2.00	1.90
		Set value		.35

See Italy Nos. 1877-1880.

Voyages of Columbus
Souvenir Sheets

A1976

A1977

A1978

A1979

A1980

A1981

Illustrations reduced.

Margins on Nos. 2624-2628 are lithographed. Nos. 2624a-2628c, 2629 are similar in design to Nos. 230-245 but are dated 1492-1992.

Litho. & Engr.

1992, May 22   *Perf. 10½*

2624	A1976	Sheet of 3	1.75	—
a.		A71 1c deep blue	.15	.15
b.		A74 4c ultramarine	.15	.15
c.		A82 $1 salmon	1.65	1.00
2625	A1977	Sheet of 3	6.75	—
a.		A72 2c brown violet	.15	.15
b.		A73 3c green	.15	.15
c.		A85 $4 crimson lake	6.50	4.00
d.		As No. 2625, imperf		
2626	A1978	Sheet of 3	1.40	—
a.		A75 5c chocolate	.15	.15
b.		A80 30c orange brown	.50	.30
c.		A81 50c slate blue	.80	.50
2627	A1979	Sheet of 3	5.25	—
a.		A76 6c purple	.15	.15
b.		A77 8c magenta	.15	.15
c.		A84 $3 yellow green	4.75	3.00
d.		As No. 2627, imperf		
2628	A1980	Sheet of 3	3.75	—
a.		A78 10c black brown	.15	.15
b.		A79 15c dark green	.25	.15
c.		A83 $2 brown red	3.25	2.00
2629	A1981	$5 Sheet of 1 Type A86	8.50	—
a.		Imperf		
		Nos. 2624-2629 (6)	27.40	

See Italy Nos. 1883-1888, Portugal Nos. 1918-1923 and Spain Nos. 2677-2682.

New York Stock Exchange Bicentennial

A1982

1992, May 17 Litho. & Engr. *Perf. 11*
2630 A1982 29c green, red & black   .50 .15

Space Accomplishments

Cosmonaut, US Space Shuttle — A1983

Astronaut, Russian Space Station — A1984

Sputnik, Vostok, Apollo Command & Lunar Modules A1985

Soyuz, Mercury and Gemini Spacecraft A1986

1992, May 29 Photo. *Perf. 11*
2631 A1983 29c multicolored   .50 .15
2632 A1984 29c multicolored   .50 .15
2633 A1985 29c multicolored   .50 .15
2634 A1986 29c multicolored   .50 .15
  a. Block of 4, #2631-2634   2.00 1.75
    Set value   .35

See Russia Nos. 6080-6083.

Alaska Highway, 50th Anniversary

A1987

1992, May 30 Litho. & Engr. *Perf. 11*
2635 A1987 29c multicolored   .50 .15
  a. Black (engr.) omitted   750.00

Most known examples of No. 2635a have poor to fine centering. It is valued in the grade of fine.

Kentucky Statehood Bicentennial

A1988

1992, June 1 Photo. *Perf. 11*
2636 A1988 29c multicolored   .50 .15

Summer Olympics

Soccer A1989

Gymnastics A1990

Volleyball A1991

Boxing A1992

Swimming A1993

1992, June 11 Photo. *Perf. 11*
2637 A1989 29c multicolored   .50 .15
2638 A1990 29c multicolored   .50 .15
2639 A1991 29c multicolored   .50 .15
2640 A1992 29c multicolored   .50 .15
2641 A1993 29c multicolored   .50 .15
  a. Strip of 5, #2637-2641   2.50 2.25
    Set value   .40

Hummingbirds

Ruby-throated A1994

Broad-billed A1995

Costa's A1996

Rufous A1997

Calliope — A1998

Perf. 11 Vert. on 1 or 2 sides
1992, June 15   Photo.
Booklet Stamps
2642 A1994 29c multicolored   .50 .15
2643 A1995 29c multicolored   .50 .15
2644 A1996 29c multicolored   .50 .15
2645 A1997 29c multicolored   .50 .15
2646 A1998 29c multicolored   .50 .15
  a. Bklt. pane of 5, #2642-2646   2.75 2.25
    Set value   .40

Wildflowers

A1999-A2048

1992, July 24   Litho.   *Perf. 11*
2647 A1999 29c Indian paintbrush   .50 .15
2648 A2000 29c Fragrant water lily   .50 .15
2649 A2001 29c Meadow beauty   .50 .15
2650 A2002 29c Jack-in-the-pulpit   .50 .15
2651 A2003 29c California poppy   .50 .15
2652 A2004 29c Large-flowered trillium   .50 .15
2653 A2005 29c Tickseed   .50 .15
2654 A2006 29c Shooting star   .50 .15
2655 A2007 29c Stream violet   .50 .15
2656 A2008 29c Bluets   .50 .15
2657 A2009 29c Herb Robert   .50 .15
2658 A2010 29c Marsh marigold   .50 .15
2659 A2011 29c Sweet white violet   .50 .15
2660 A2012 29c Claret cup cactus   .50 .15
2661 A2013 29c White mountain avens   .50 .15
2662 A2014 29c Sessile bellwort   .50 .15
2663 A2015 29c Blue flag   .50 .15
2664 A2016 29c Harlequin lupine   .50 .15
2665 A2017 29c Twinflower   .50 .15
2666 A2018 29c Common sunflower   .50 .15
2667 A2019 29c Sego lily   .50 .15
2668 A2020 29c Virginia bluebells   .50 .15
2669 A2021 29c Ohi'a lehua   .50 .15
2670 A2022 29c Rosebud orchid   .50 .15
2671 A2023 29c Showy evening primrose   .50 .15
2672 A2024 29c Fringed gentian   .50 .15
2673 A2025 29c Yellow lady's slipper   .50 .15
2674 A2026 29c Passionflower   .50 .15
2675 A2027 29c Bunchberry   .50 .15
2676 A2028 29c Pasqueflower   .50 .15
2677 A2029 29c Round-lobed hepatica   .50 .15
2678 A2030 29c Wild columbine   .50 .15
2679 A2031 29c Fireweed   .50 .15
2680 A2032 29c Indian pond lily   .50 .15
2681 A2033 29c Turk's cap lily   .50 .15
2682 A2034 29c Dutchman's breeches   .50 .15
2683 A2035 29c Trumpet honeysuckle   .50 .15
2684 A2036 29c Jacob's ladder   .50 .15
2685 A2037 29c Plains prickly pear   .50 .15
2686 A2038 29c Moss campion   .50 .15
2687 A2039 29c Bearberry   .50 .15
2688 A2040 29c Mexican hat   .50 .15
2689 A2041 29c Harebell   .50 .15
2690 A2042 29c Desert five spot   .50 .15
2691 A2043 29c Smooth Solomon's seal   .50 .15
2692 A2044 29c Red maids   .50 .15
2693 A2045 29c Yellow skunk cabbage   .50 .15
2694 A2046 29c Rue anemone   .50 .15
2695 A2047 29c Standing cypress   .50 .15
2696 A2048 29c Wild flax   .50 .15
  a. Pane of 50, #2647-2696   25.00 —

World War II

1942: Into the Battle
A2049

Designs and events of 1942: a, B-25's take off to raid Tokyo, Apr. 18. b, Ration coupons (food and other commodities rationed). c, Divebomber and deck crewman (US wins Battle of the Coral Sea, May). d, Prisoners of war (Corregidor falls to Japanese, May 6). e, Dutch Harbor buildings on fire (Japan invades Aleutian Islands, June). f, Headphones, coded message (Allies decipher secret enemy codes). g, Yorktown lost, US wins at Midway. h, Woman with drill (millions of women join war effort). i, Marines land on Guadalcanal, Aug. 7. j, Tank in desert (Allies land in North Africa, Nov.). Central label is the size of 15 stamps and shows world map, extent of axis control.
Illustration reduced.

Litho. & Engr.
1992, Aug. 17   *Perf. 11*
2697 A2049 Block of 10   5.25 4.50
  a.-j.   29c any single   .50 .30
  k.   Red (litho.) omitted   10,000.

Dorothy Parker — A2050

A2051

Literary Arts Series
1992, Aug. 22   Photo.   *Perf. 11*
2698 A2050 29c multicolored   .50 .15

1992, Aug. 31   Photo.   *Perf. 11*
2699 A2051 29c multicolored   .50 .15
Dr. Theodore von Karman (1881-1963), rocket scientist.

Minerals

Azurite — A2052

Copper — A2053

Variscite — A2054

Wulfenite — A2055

Litho. & Engr.
1992, Sept. 17   *Perf. 11*
2700 A2052 29c multicolored   .50 .15
2701 A2053 29c multicolored   .50 .15
2702 A2054 29c multicolored   .50 .15
2703 A2055 29c multicolored   .50 .15
  a. Block or strip of 4, #2700-2703   2.00 1.75
  b. As "a," silver (litho.) omitted   8,500.
  c. As "a," red (litho.) omitted
    Set value   .35

Juan Rodriguez Cabrillo

Cabrillo (d. 1543), Ship, Map of San Diego Bay Area — A2056

Litho. & Engr.
1992, Sept. 28   *Perf. 11*
2704 A2056 29c multicolored   .50 .15

Wild Animals

Giraffe A2057

Giant Panda A2058

Flamingo
A2059

King Penguins
A2060

White Bengal
Tiger
A2061

Perf. 11 Horiz. on 1 or 2 sides
1992, Oct. 1   Photo.
Booklet Stamps

2705	A2057	29c multicolored	.50	.15
2706	A2058	29c multicolored	.50	.15
2707	A2059	29c multicolored	.50	.15
2708	A2060	29c multicolored	.50	.15
2709	A2061	29c multicolored	.50	.15
a.		Booklet pane of 5, #2705-2709	2.50	2.00
b.		As "a," imperforate	2,750.	
		Set value		.40

Christmas

Madonna and Child, by
Giovanni Bellini — A2062

A2063   A2064

A2065   A2066

1992   Litho. & Engr.   *Perf. 11.2*

2710	A2062	29c multicolored	.50	.15
a.		Booklet pane of 10	5.25	—

Litho.
Perf. 11½x11

2711	A2063	29c multicolored	.50	.15
2712	A2064	29c multicolored	.50	.15
2713	A2065	29c multicolored	.50	.15
2714	A2066	29c multicolored	.50	.15
a.		Block of 4, #2711-2714	2.00	1.10
		Set value		.40

Booklet Stamps
Photo.
Perf. 11 on 2 or 3 Sides

2715	A2063	29c multicolored	.50	.15
2716	A2064	29c multicolored	.50	.15
2717	A2065	29c multicolored	.50	.15
2718	A2066	29c multicolored	.50	.15
a.		Bkt. pane of 4, #2715-2718	2.25	
b.		As "a," imperf horiz.	—	
c.		As "a," imperf	—	
		Set value		.40

Self-Adhesive
Die Cut

2719	A2064	29c multicolored	.60	.15
		Booklet pane of 18	11.00	

Issued: #2710-2718, Oct. 22; #2719, Oct. 28.
"Greetings" is 27mm long on Nos. 2711-2714, 25mm long on Nos. 2715-2718 and 21½mm long on No. 2719. Nos. 2715-2719 differ in color from Nos. 2711-2714.

Chinese New Year

Year of the
Rooster
A2067

1992, Dec. 30   Litho. & Engr.   *Perf. 11*

2720	A2067	29c multicolored	.50	.15

American Music Series

Elvis Presley
A2068

Oklahoma!
A2069

Hank Williams
A2070

Elvis Presley
A2071

Bill Haley
A2072

Clyde
McPhatter
A2073

Ritchie Valens
A2074

Otis Redding
A2075

Buddy Holly
A2076

Dinah
Washington
A2077

1993, Jan. 8   Photo.   *Perf. 11*

2721	A2068	29c multicolored	.50	.15

1993, Mar. 30   Photo.   *Perf. 10*

2722	A2069	29c multicolored	.50	.15

1993

2723	A2070	29c multicolored	.50	.15
a.		Perf. 11.2x11.4	20.00	3.00
2724	A2071	29c multicolored	.50	.15
2725	A2072	29c multicolored	.50	.15
2726	A2073	29c multicolored	.50	.15
2727	A2074	29c multicolored	.50	.15
2728	A2075	29c multicolored	.50	.15
2729	A2076	29c multicolored	.50	.15
2730	A2077	29c multicolored	.50	.15
a.		Vertical strip of 7, #2724-2730	3.50	—
		Set value, #2724-2730		.60

Booklet Stamps
Perf. 11 Horiz.

2731	A2071	29c multicolored	.50	.15
2732	A2072	29c multicolored	.50	.15
2733	A2073	29c multicolored	.50	.15
2734	A2074	29c multicolored	.50	.15
2735	A2075	29c multicolored	.50	.15
2736	A2076	29c multicolored	.50	.15
2737	A2077	29c multicolored	.50	.15
a.		Booklet pane. 2 #2731. 1 each #2732-2737	4.50	—
b.		Booklet pane of 4, #2731, 2735-2737 + tab	2.50	—
		Set value		.60

Issued: No. 2723, June 9; others, June 16.
See Nos. 2769, 2771, 2775 and designs A2112-A2117.

Space Fantasy

A2086

A2087

A2088

A2089

A2090

Perf. 11 Vert. on 1 or 2 Sides
1993, Jan. 25   Photo.
Booklet Stamps

2741	A2086	29c multicolored	.50	.15
2742	A2087	29c multicolored	.50	.15
2743	A2088	29c multicolored	.50	.15
2744	A2089	29c multicolored	.50	.15
2745	A2090	29c multicolored	.50	.15
a.		Bklt. pane of 5. #2741-2745	2.50	2.00
		Set value		.45

Black Heritage

Percy Lavon Julian
(1899-1975),
Chemist — A2091

1993, Jan. 29   Litho. & Engr.   *Perf. 11*

2746	A2091	29c multicolored	.50	.15

Oregon Trail

A2092

1993, Feb. 12   Litho. & Engr.   *Perf. 11*

2747	A2092	29c multicolored	.50	.15

World University Games

A2093

1993, Feb. 25   Photo.   *Perf. 11*

2748	A2093	29c multicolored	.50	.15

Grace Kelly (1929-1982)

Actress, Princess of
Monaco — A2094

1993, Mar. 24   Engr.   *Perf. 11*

2749	A2094	29c blue	.50	.15

See Monaco No. 1851.

Circus

Clown — A2095

Ringmaster
A2096

Trapeze
Artist — A2097

Elephant
A2098

1993, Apr. 6   Litho.   *Perf. 11*
2750	A2095	29c multicolored	.50	.15
2751	A2096	29c multicolored	.50	.15
2752	A2097	29c multicolored	.50	.15
2753	A2098	29c multicolored	.50	.15
a.		Block of 4, #2750-2753	2.00	1.75
		Set value		.35

Cherokee Strip Land Run, Centennial

A2099

1993, Apr. 17   Litho. & Engr.   *Perf. 11*
2754	A2099	29c multicolored	.50	.15

Dean Acheson (1893-1971)

Secretary of State — A2100

1993, Apr. 21   Engr.   *Perf. 11*
2755	A2100	29c greenish gray	.50	.15

Sporting Horses

Steeplechase
A2101

Thoroughbred Racing
A2102

Harness Racing
A2103

Polo
A2104

Perf. 11x11 1/2

1993, May 1   Litho. & Engr.
2756	A2101	29c multicolored	.50	.15
2757	A2102	29c multicolored	.50	.15
2758	A2103	29c multicolored	.50	.15
2759	A2104	29c multicolored	.50	.15
a.		Block of 4, #2756-2759	2.00	1.75
b.		As "a." black (engr.) omitted	2,000.	
		Set value		.35

Garden Flowers

Hyacinth
A2105

Daffodil
A2106

Tulip — A2107

Iris — A2108

Lilac — A2109

Litho. & Engr.

1993, May 15   *Perf. 11 Vert.*
2760	A2105	29c multicolored	.50	.15
2761	A2106	29c multicolored	.50	.15
2762	A2107	29c multicolored	.50	.15
2763	A2108	29c multicolored	.50	.15
2764	A2109	29c multicolored	.50	.15
a.		Booklet pane of 5, #2760-2764	2.50	2.00
b.		As "a." black (engr.) omitted	400.00	
c.		As "a." imperf	3,000.	
		Set value		.45

World War II

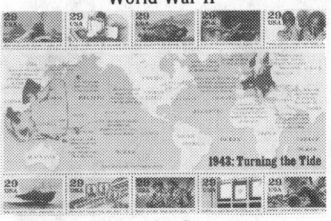

A2110

Designs and events of 1943: a, Destroyers (Allied forces battle German U-boats). b, Military medics treat the wounded. c, Amphibious landing craft on beach (Sicily attacked by Allied forces, July). d, B-24s hit Ploesti refineries, August. e, V-mail delivers letters from home. f, PT boat (Italy invaded by Allies, Sept.). g, Nos. WS7, WS8, savings bonds (Bonds and stamps help war effort). h, "Willie and Joe" keep spirits high. i, Banner in window (Gold Stars mark World War II losses). j, Marines assault Tarawa, Nov.

Central label is the size of 15 stamps and shows world map with extent of Axis control and Allied operations.

Illustration reduced.

1993, May 31   Litho. & Engr.   *Perf. 11*
2765	A2110	Block of 10 + label	5.25	4.50
a.-j.		29c any single	.50	.30

Joe Louis (1914-1981)

A2111

1993, June 22   Litho. & Engr.   *Perf. 11*
2766	A2111	29c multicolored	.50	.15

American Music Series
Oklahoma! Type and

Show Boat — A2112

Porgy & Bess — A2113

My Fair Lady — A2114

Perf. 11 Horiz. on 1 or 2 Sides
1993, July 14   Photo.
Booklet Stamps
2767	A2112	29c multicolored	.50	.15
2768	A2113	29c multicolored	.50	.15
2769	A2069	29c multicolored	.50	.15
2770	A2114	29c multicolored	.50	.15
a.		Booklet pane of 4, #2767-2770	2.50	2.00
		Set value		.35

No. 2769 has smaller design size, brighter colors and shorter inscription than No. 2722, as well as a frameline around the design and other subtle design differences.

Hank Williams Type and

Patsy Cline
A2115

The Carter Family
A2116

Bob Wills
A2117

1993, Sept. 25   Photo.   *Perf. 10*
2771	A2070	29c multicolored	.50	.15
2772	A2115	29c multicolored	.50	.15
2773	A2116	29c multicolored	.50	.15
2774	A2117	29c multicolored	.50	.15
a.		Block or horiz. strip of 4, #2771-2774	2.00	1.50
		Set value		1.75

Booklet Stamps
Perf. 11 Horiz.
With Black Frameline
2775	A2070	29c multicolored	.50	.15
2776	A2116	29c multicolored	.50	.15
2777	A2115	29c multicolored	.50	.15
2778	A2117	29c multicolored	.50	.15
a.		Booklet pane of 4, #2775-2778	2.50	2.00
		Set value		.35

Inscription at left measures 27mm on No. 2771, 27 1/2mm on No. 2723 and 22mm on No. 2775. No. 2723 shows only two tuning keys on guitar, while No. 2771 shows those two and parts of two others.

National Postal Museum

Independence Hall, Benjamin Franklin, Printing Press, Colonial Post Rider
A2118

Pony Express Rider, Civil War Soldier, Concord Stagecoach
A2119

JN-4H Biplane, Charles Lindbergh, Railway Mail Car, 1931 Model A Ford Mail Truck
A2120

California Gold Rush Miner's Letter, Nos. 39, 295, C3a, C13, Barcode and Circular Date Stamp
A2121

1993, July 30   Litho. & Engr.   *Perf. 11*
2779	A2118	29c multicolored	.50	.15
2780	A2119	29c multicolored	.50	.15
2781	A2120	29c multicolored	.50	.15
2782	A2121	29c multicolored	.50	.15
a.		Block or strip of 4, #2779-2782	2.00	1.75
b.		As "a." engr. maroon (USA/29) & black ("My Dear...") omitted	—	
c.		As "a." imperf	—	
		Set value		.35

American Sign Language

A2122

A2123

Designs:

1993, Sept. 20   Photo.   *Perf. 11 1/2*
2783	A2122	29c multicolored	.50	.15
2784	A2123	29c multicolored	.50	.15
a.		Pair, #2783-2784	1.00	.65

Classic Books

A2124

A2125

A2126

A2127

Designs: No. 2785, Rebecca of Sunnybrook Farm, by Kate Douglas Wiggin. No. 2786, Little House on the Prairie, by Laura Ingalls Wilder. No. 2787, The Adventures of Huckleberry Finn, by Mark Twain. No. 2788, Little Women, by Louisa May Alcott.

1993, Oct. 23 Litho. & Engr. Perf. 11
2785 A2124 29c multicolored .50 .15
2786 A2125 29c multicolored .50 .15
2787 A2126 29c multicolored .50 .15
2788 A2127 29c multicolored .50 .15
  a. Block or horiz. strip of 4, #2785-2788 2.00 1.75
  b. As "a," imperf —
     Set value .35

Christmas

Madonna and Child in a Landscape, by Giovanni Battista Cima — A2128

Jack-in-the-Box
A2129

Red-Nosed Reindeer
A2130

Snowman
A2131

Toy Soldier Blowing Horn
A2132

1993, Oct. 21 Litho. & Engr. Perf. 11
2789 A2128 29c multicolored .50 .15

Booklet Stamp
Size: 18x25mm
Perf. 11¹/₂x11 on 2 or 3 Sides
2790 A2128 29c multicolored .50 .15
  a. Booklet pane of 4 2.25 1.75
  b. Imperf pair —
  c. As "a," imperf —

No. 2790 has darker colors and smaller inscriptions than No. 2789.

1993 Photo. Perf. 11¹/₂
2791 A2129 29c multicolored .50 .15
2792 A2130 29c multicolored .50 .15
2793 A2131 29c multicolored .50 .15
2794 A2132 29c multicolored .50 .15
  a. Block or strip of 4, #2791-2794 2.00 1.75

Booklet Stamps
Size: 18x21mm
Perf. 11x10 on 2 or 3 Sides
2795 A2132 29c multicolored .50 .15
2796 A2131 29c multicolored .50 .15
2797 A2130 29c multicolored .50 .15
2798 A2129 29c multicolored .50 .15
  a. Booklet pane, 3 each #2795-2796, 2 each #2797-2798 5.00 4.00
  b. Booklet pane, 3 each #2797-2798, 2 each #2795-2796 5.00 —

Self-Adhesive
Size: 19¹/₂x26¹/₂mm
Die Cut
2799 A2131 29c multicolored .50 .15
2800 A2132 29c multicolored .50 .15
2801 A2129 29c multicolored .50 .15
2802 A2130 29c multicolored .50 .15
  a. Bklt. pane, 3 each 2799-2802 7.00

Size: 17x20mm
2803 A2131 29c multicolored .50 .15
  a. Booklet pane of 18 10.00
     Set value 1.05

Issue dates: Nos. 2791-2798, Oct. 21. Nos. 2799-2803, Oct. 28.
Snowman on Nos. 2793, 2799 has three buttons and seven snowflakes beneath nose (placement differs on both stamps). No. 2796 has two buttons and five snowflakes beneath nose. No. 2803 has two orange buttons and four snowflakes beneath nose.

Mariana Islands

A2133

1993, Nov. 4 Litho. & Engr. Perf. 11
2804 A2133 29c multicolored .50 .15

Columbus' Landing in Puerto Rico, 500th Anniv.

A2134

1993, Nov. 19 Photo. Perf. 11.2
2805 A2134 29c multicolored .50 .15

AIDS Awareness

A2135

1993, Dec. 1 Photo. Perf. 11.2
2806 A2135 29c black & red .50 .15
  a. Perf. 11 vert. on 1 or 2 sides .50 .15
  b. As "a," booklet pane of 5 2.50 2.00

Winter Olympics

Slalom — A2136

Luge — A2137

Ice Dancing
A2138

Cross-Country Skiing
A2139

Ice Hockey — A2140

1994, Jan. 6 Litho. Perf. 11.2
2807 A2136 29c multicolored .50 .15
2808 A2137 29c multicolored .50 .15
2809 A2138 29c multicolored .50 .15
2810 A2139 29c multicolored .50 .15
2811 A2140 29c multicolored .50 .15
  a. Strip of 5, 2807-2811 2.50 2.25
     Set value .45

Edward R. Murrow, Journalist (1908-65)

A2141

1994, Jan. 21 Engr. Perf. 11.2
2812 A2141 29c brown .50 .15

Love

A2142

A2143

A2144

1994 Litho. & Engr. Die Cut
Self-Adhesive (No. 2813)
2813 A2142 29c multicolored .50 .15
  a. Booklet pane of 18 11.00
Photo.
Perf. 10.9x11.1
2814 A2143 29c multicolored .50 .15
  a. Booklet pane of 10 5.75 3.50
Litho. & Engr.
Perf. 11.1
2814C A2143 29c multicolored .50 .15
Photo. & Engr.
Perf. 11.2
2815 A2144 52c multicolored 1.00 .20

Size of No. 2814C is 20x28mm. No. 2814 is 18x24¹/₂mm.
Issued: No. 2813, Jan. 27. Nos. 2814-2815, Feb. 14. No. 2814C, June 24.
Nos. 2813-2814 were issued in booklets only.

Black Heritage

Dr. Allison Davis (1902-83), Social Anthropologist, Educator — A2145

1994, Feb. 1 Engr. Perf. 11.2
2816 A2145 29c red brown & brown .50 .15

Chinese New Year

Year of the Dog — A2146

1994, Feb. 5 Photo. Perf. 11.2
2817 A2146 29c multicolored .50 .15

Buffalo Soldiers

Buffalo Soldiers A2147

Perf. 11.5x11.2
1994, Apr. 22 Litho. & Engr.
2818 A2147 29c multicolored .50 .15

Silent Screen Stars

Rudolph Valentino (1895-1926)
A2148

Clara Bow (1905-65)
A2149

Charlie Chaplin (1889-1977)
A2150

Lon Chaney (1883-1930)
A2151

John Gilbert (1895-1936)
A2152

Zasu Pitts (1898-1963)
A2153

Harold Lloyd
(1894-1971)
A2154

Keystone Cops
A2155

Theda Bara
(1885-1955)
A2156

Buster Keaton
(1895-1966)
A2157

Litho. & Engr.
1994, Apr. 27   *Perf. 11.2*

2819	A2148	29c red, blk & brt vio	.50	.15
2820	A2149	29c red, blk & brt vio	.50	.15
2821	A2150	29c red, blk & brt vio	.50	.15
2822	A2151	29c red, blk & brt vio	.50	.15
2823	A2152	29c red, blk & brt vio	.50	.15
2824	A2153	29c red, blk & brt vio	.50	.15
2825	A2154	29c red, blk & brt vio	.50	.15
2826	A2155	29c red, blk & brt vio	.50	.15
2827	A2156	29c red, blk & brt vio	.50	.15
2828	A2157	29c red, blk & brt vio	.50	.15
a.		Block of 10, #2819-2828	5.00	4.00
b.		As "a," black (litho.) omitted		—
c.		As "a," black, red & brt vio (litho.) omitted		—
		Set value		.80

Garden Flowers

Lily — A2158

Zinnia — A2159

Gladiola
A2160

Marigold
A2161

Rose — A2162

Perf. 10.9 Vert.
1994, Apr. 28   Litho. & Engr.
Booklet Stamps

2829	A2158	29c multicolored	.50	.15
2830	A2159	29c multicolored	.50	.15
2831	A2160	29c multicolored	.50	.15
2832	A2161	29c multicolored	.50	.15
2833	A2162	29c multicolored	.50	.15
a.		Booklet pane of 5, #2829-2833	2.50	
b.		As "a," imperf	2,500.	
c.		As "a," black (engr.) omitted	425.00	
		Set value		.40

1994 World Cup Soccer Championships

A2163

A2164

A2165

Design: 40c, Soccer player, diff.

1994, May 26   Photo.   *Perf. 11.1*

2834	A2163	29c multicolored	.50	.15
2835	A2163	40c multicolored	.80	.20
2836	A2164	50c multicolored	1.00	.20
		Nos. 2834-2836 (3)	2.30	.55

Souvenir Sheet

2837	A2165	Sheet of 3, #a.-c.	2.50	—

Nos. 2834-2836 are printed on phosphor-coated paper, while Nos. 2837a (29c), 2837b (40c), 2837c (50c) are block tagged. No. 2837c has a portion of the yellow map in the LR corner.

World War II

A2166

Designs and events of 1944: a, Allied forces retake New Guinea. b, P-51s escort B-17s on bombing raids. c, Troops running from landing craft (Allies in Normandy, D-Day, June 6). d, Airborne units spearhead attacks. e, Officer at periscope (Submarines shorten war in Pacific). f, Parade (Allies free Rome, June 4; Paris, Aug. 25). g, Soldier firing flamethrower (US troops clear Saipan bunkers). h, Red Ball Express speeds vital supplies. i, Battleship firing main battery (Battle for Leyte Gulf, Oct. 23-26). j, Soldiers in snow (Bastogne and Battle of the Bulge, Dec.).
Central label is size of 15 stamps and shows world map with extent of Axis control and Allied operations.
Illustration reduced.

Litho. & Engr.
1994, June 6   *Perf. 10.9*

2838	A2166	Block of 10 + label	5.25	4.50
a.-j.		29c any single	.50	.30

Norman Rockwell

A2167

A2168

Perf. 10.9x11.1
1994, July 1   Litho. & Engr.

2839	A2167	29c multicolored	.50	.15

Souvenir Sheet
Litho.

2840	A2168	Sheet of 4	4.00	—
a.		50c Freedom from Want	1.00	.65
b.		50c Freedom from Fear	1.00	.65
c.		50c Freedom of Speech	1.00	.65
d.		50c Freedom of Worship	1.00	.65

Moon Landing, 25th Anniv.

A2169

A2170

1994, July 20   Litho.   *Perf. 11.2x11.1*
Miniature Sheet

2841	A2169	Sheet of 12	7.50	—
a.		29c Single stamp	.60	.60

Litho. & Engr.
Perf. 10.7x11.1

2842	A2170	$9.95 multicolored	17.50	7.50

Locomotives

Hudson's
General
A2171

McQueen's
Jupiter
A2172

Eddy's
No. 242
A2173

Ely's No. 10
A2174

Buchanan's
No. 999
A2175

1994, July 28   Photo.   *Perf. 11 Horiz.*
Booklet Stamps

2843	A2171	29c multicolored	.50	.15
2844	A2172	29c multicolored	.50	.15
2845	A2173	29c multicolored	.50	.15
2846	A2174	29c multicolored	.50	.15
2847	A2175	29c multicolored	.50	.15
a.		Booklet pane of 5, #2843-2847	2.50	2.00
b.		As "a," imperf		.40
		Set value		.40

George Meany, Labor Leader (1894-1980)

A2176

1994, Aug. 16   Engr.   *Perf. 11.1x11*

2848	A2176	29c blue	.50	.15

American Music Series

Al Jolson
(1886-1950)
A2177

Bing Crosby
(1904-77)
A2178

Ethel Waters
(1896-1977)
A2179

Nat "King" Cole (1919-65)
A2180

Ethel Merman
(1908-84)
A2181

Bessie Smith
(1894-1937)
A2182

Muddy Waters
(1915-83)
A2183

Billie Holiday
(1915-59)
A2184

Robert Johnson (1911-38) A2185

Jimmy Rushing (1902-72) A2186

"Ma" Rainey (1886-1939) A2187

Mildred Bailey (1907-51) A2188

Howlin' Wolf (1910-76) A2189

1994   Photo.   Perf. 10.1x10.2

2849 A2177	29c multicolored	.50	.15
2850 A2178	29c multicolored	.50	.15
2851 A2179	29c multicolored	.50	.15
2852 A2180	29c multicolored	.50	.15
2853 A2181	29c multicolored	.50	.15
a.	Vert. strip of 5, #2849-2853	2.50	2.00
	Set value		.40

Perf. 11x10.8

Litho.

2854 A2182	29c multicolored	.50	.15
2855 A2183	29c multicolored	.50	.15
2856 A2184	29c multicolored	.50	.15
2857 A2185	29c multicolored	.50	.15
2858 A2186	29c multicolored	.50	.15
2859 A2187	29c multicolored	.50	.15
2860 A2188	29c multicolored	.50	.15
2861 A2189	29c multicolored	.50	.15
a.	Block of 9, #2854-2861 +1 additional stamp	4.50	3.50
	Set value		.65

Issued: Nos. 2849-2853, 9/1/94; Nos. 2854-2861, 9/17/94.

Literary Arts Series

James Thurber (1894-1961) — A2190

Litho. & Engr.

1994, Sept. 10   Perf. 11

2862 A2190	29c multicolored	.50	.15

Wonders Of The Sea

Diver, Motorboat A2191

Diver, Ship A2192

Diver, Ship's Wheel A2193

Diver, Coral A2194

1994, Oct. 3   Litho.   Perf. 11x10.9

2863 A2191	29c multicolored	.50	.15
2864 A2192	29c multicolored	.50	.15
2865 A2193	29c multicolored	.50	.15
2866 A2194	29c multicolored	.50	.15
a.	Block of 4, #2963-2966	2.00	1.50
b.	As "a," imperf	2,500.	
	Set value		.35

Cranes

Black-Necked A2195

Whooping A2196

Litho. & Engr.

1994, Oct. 9   Perf. 10.8x11

2867 A2195	29c multicolored	.50	.15
2868 A2196	29c multicolored	.50	.15
a.	Pair, #2867-2868	1.00	.65
b.	Black & magenta (engr.) omitted		
	Set value		.15

See People's Republic of China Nos. 2528-2529.

Legends Of The West
Miniature Pane

A2197

g. Bill Pickett (1870-1932) (Revised)

Designs: a, Home on the Range. b, Buffalo Bill Cody (1846-1917). c, Jim Bridger (1804-81). d, Annie Oakley (1860-1926). e, Native American Culture. f, Chief Joseph (c. 1840-1904). h, Bat Masterson (1853-1921). i, John C. Fremont (1813-90). j, Wyatt Earp (1848-1929). k, Nellie Cashman (c. 1849-1925). l, Charles Goodnight (1826-1929). m, Geronimo (1823-1909). n, Kit Carson (1809-68). o, Wild Bill Hickok (1837-76). p, Western Wildlife. q, Jim Beckwourth (c. 1798-1866). r, Bill Tilghman (1854-1924). s, Sacagawea (c. 1787-1812). t, Overland Mail.

1994, Oct. 18   Photo.   Perf. 10.1x10

2869 A2197	Pane of 20	12.00	—
a.-t.	29c any single	.60	.15
u.	As No. 2869, a.-e. imperf, f.-j. part perf.	—	

Legends Of The West (Recalled)
Miniature Pane

g. Bill Pickett (Recalled)

Nos. 2870b-2870d, 2870f-2870o, 2870q-2870s have a frameline around the vignette that is half the width of the frameline on similar stamps in No. 2869. Other design differences may exist.

1994   Photo.   Perf. 10.1x10

2870 A2197	29c Pane of 20	160.00	—

150,000 panes were made available through a drawing. Panes were delivered in an envelope. Value is for pane without envelope.

Christmas

Madonna and Child, by Elisabetta Sirani A2200

Stocking A2201

Santa Claus A2202

Cardinal in Snow A2203

Litho. & Engr.

1994, Oct. 20   Perf. 11.1

2871 A2200	29c multicolored	.50	.15
a.	Perf. 9.8x10.8	.50	.15
b.	As "a," booklet pane of 10	5.25	3.50
c.	As "a," imperf		

Litho.

2872 A2201	29c multicolored	.50	.15
a.	Booklet pane of 20	10.50	3.00

Booklet Stamps
Photo.
Die Cut
Self-Adhesive

2873 A2202	29c multicolored	.50	.15
a.	Booklet pane of 12	6.25	
2874 A2203	29c multicolored	.50	.15
a.	Booklet pane of 18	9.50	
	Set value, #2871-2874		.40

Bureau Of Engraving & Printing
Souvenir Sheet

A2204

1994, Nov. 3   Litho. & Engr.   Perf. 11

2875 A2204	Sheet of 4	15.00	—
a.	$2 Single stamp	3.00	1.25

Chinese New Year

Year of the Boar — A2205

1994, Dec. 30   Photo.   Perf. 11.2x11.1

2876 A2205	29c multicolored	.50	.15

A2206

A2207

A2208

A2209

A2210

A2208a

1994, Dec. 13   Litho.   Perf. 11x10.8
Untagged

2877 A2206	(3c) tan, bright blue & red	.15	.15

Perf. 10.8x10.9

2878 A2206	(3c) tan, dark blue & red	.15	.15
	Set value, #2877-2878		.15

Inscriptions on #2877 are in a thin typeface. Those on #2878 are in heavy, bold type.

Photo.
Perf. 11.2x11.1
Tagged

2879 A2207	(20c) black "G," yellow & multi	.40	.15

Perf. 11x10.9

2880 A2207	(20c) red "G," yellow & multi	.40	.15

Perf. 11.2x11.1

2881 A2208	(32c) black "G" & multi	.60	.15
a.	Booklet pane of 10	6.00	—

Perf. 11x10.9

2882 A2208	(32c) red "G" & multi	.60	.15
	Set value, #2879-2882		.35

Distance on #2882 from bottom of red G to top of flag immediately above is 13 3/4 mm. Illustration A2208a shows #2885 superimposed over #2882.

Booklet Stamps
Perf. 10x9.9 on 2 or 3 Sides
2883	A2208 (32c) black "G" & multi	.60	.15
a.	Booklet pane of 10	6.50	

Perf. 10.9 on 2 or 3 Sides
2884	A2208 (32c) blue "G" & multi	.60	.15
a.	Booklet pane of 10	6.00	
b.	As "a," imperf		

Perf. 11x10.9 on 2 or 3 Sides
2885	A2208a (32c) red "G" & multi	.60	.15
a.	Booklet pane of 10	6.00	
b.	Pair, imperf vert.	—	

Distance on #2885 from bottom of red G to top of flag immediately above is 13½mm. See note below #2882.

A2208b   A2208c

Self-Adhesive   Die Cut
2886	A2208b (32c) gray, blue, lt blue, red & blk	.60	.15
a.	Booklet pane of 18	11.00	

No. 2886 is printed on pre-phosphored paper and has only a small number of blue shading dots in the white stripes immediately below the flag's blue field.
2887	A2208c (32c) black, blue & red	.60	.15
a.	Booklet pane of 18	11.00	
	Set value, #2883-2887		.40

No. 2887 has noticeable blue shading in the white stripes immediately below the blue field and has overall tagging.

COIL STAMPS
1994-95   Perf. 9.8 Vert.
2888	A2209 (25c) black "G"	.50	.15
2889	A2208 (32c) black "G"	.60	.15
a.	Imperf., pair		
2890	A2208 (32c) blue "G"	.60	.15
2891	A2208 (32c) red "G"	.60	.15

Rouletted 9.8 Vert.
2892	A2208 (32c) red "G"	.60	.15

Perf. 9.8 Vert.
2893	A2210 (5c) green & multi	.15	.15
	Set value, #2888-2893		.50

Nos. 2888-2892 issued 12/13/94. No. 2893 was only available through the Philatelic Fulfillment Center after its announcement 1/12/95.

Eagle and Shield Type of 1993 and:

Flag Over Porch A2212

Butte A2217

Mountain A2218

Auto A2220

Auto Tail Fin A2223

Juke Box A2225

Flag Over Field — A2230

1995-97   Photo.   Perf. 10.4
2897	A2212 32c multicolored	.60	.15
a.	Imperf., vert. pair	300.00	

COIL STAMPS
Self-Adhesive (#2902B, 2904A-2904B, 2906-2907, 2910, 2912A-2912B, 2915-2915D, 2919-2921)
Photo.
Perf. 9.8 Vert.
2902	A2217 (5c) yel, red & bl	.15	.15
a.	Imperf., pair	750.00	

Serpentine Die Cut 11.5 Vert.
2902B	A2217 (5c) yellow, red & blue	.15	.15

Perf. 9.8 Vert.
2903	A2218 (5c) purple & multi	.20	.20

Letters of inscription "USA NONPROFIT ORG." outlined in purple on #2903.
2904	A2218 (5c) blue & multi	.20	.20
b.	Imperf., pair	700.00	

Letters of inscription have no outline on #2904.

Serpentine Die Cut 11.2 Vert.
2904A	A2218 (5c) pur & multi	.20	.20

Serpentine Die Cut 9.8 Vert.
2904B	A2218 (5c) pur & multi	.20	.20

Letters of inscription outlined in purple on #2904B, not outlined on No. 2904A.

Perf. 9.8 Vert.
2905	A2220 (10c) blk, red brn & brn	.20	.20

Serpentine Die Cut 11.5 Vert.
2906	A2220 (10c) blk, brn & red brn	.20	.20
2907	A1957 (10c) gold & multi	.20	.20

Perf. 9.8 Vert.
2908	A2223 (15c) dk org yel & multi	.30	.30

No. 2908 has dark, bold colors, heavy shading lines and heavily shaded chrome.
2909	A2223 (15c) buff & multi	.30	.30

No. 2909 has shinier chrome, more subdued colors and finer details than No. 2908.

Serpentine Die Cut 11.5 Vert.
2910	A2223 (15c) buff & multi	.30	.30

Perf. 9.8 Vert.
2911	A2225 (25c) dk red, dk yel grn & multi	.50	.50

No. 2911 has dark, saturated colors and dark blue lines in the music selection board.
2912	A2225 (25c) brt org red, brt yel grn & multi	.50	.50

No. 2912 has bright colors, less shading and light blue lines in the music selection board.

Serpentine Die Cut 11.5 Vert.
2912A	A2225 (25c) brt org red, brt yel grn & multi	.50	.50

Serpentine Die Cut 9.8 Vert.
2912B	A2225 (25c) dark red, dark yellow green & multi	.50	.50

Perf. 9.8 Vert.
2913	A2212 32c bl, tan, brn, red & lt bl	.60	.15
	Imperf., pair	75.00	

No. 2913 has pronounced light blue shading in the flag.
2914	A2212 32c bl, yel brn, red & gray	.60	.15

No. 2914 has pale gray shading in the flag.

Serpentine Die Cut 8.7 Vert.
2915	A2212 32c multicolored	.60	.30

Serpentine Die Cut 9.7 Vert.
2915A	A2212 32c dk bl, tan, brn, red & lt bl	.60	.15
h.	Imperf., pair		

Serpentine Die Cut 11.5 Vert.
2915B	A2212 32c As #2915A	.60	.15

Serpentine Die Cut 10.9 Vert.
2915C	A2212 32c As #2915A	.60	.15

Serpentine Die Cut 9.8 Vert.
2915D	A2212 32c dark blue, tan, brown, red & light blue	.60	.15

Die cutting on #2915D starts and ends with straight cuts and has 9 teeth between. Die cutting on #2915A has a straight cut at bottom and 11 teeth above. Stamps on multiples of No. 2915A touch, and are on a peelable backing the same size as the stamps, while those of No. 2915D are separated on the peelable backing, which is larger than the stamps.

Booklet Stamps
Perf. 10.8x9.8
2916	A2212 32c bl, tan, brn, red & lt bl	.60	.15
a.	Booklet pane of 10	6.00	
b.	As "a," imperf		

Die Cut
2919	A2230 32c multicolored	.60	.15
a.	Booklet pane of 18	11.00	
b.	Vert. pair, no die cutting btwn.		

Serpentine Die Cut 8.8
2920	A2212 32c multi, large date	.60	.15
a.	Booklet pane of 20+label	12.00	
b.	Small date	1.50	.15
c.	As "b," booklet pane of 20+label	30.00	
d.	Serpentine Die Cut 11.3	.60	.15
e.	As "d," booklet pane of 10	6.00	
f.	As No. 2920, pane of 15+label	9.00	—
g.	As "a," partial pane of 10, 3 stamps and parts of 7 stamps printed on backing liner	—	
h.	As 2920, booklet pane of 15	—	

No. 2920d is dated "1996." Date on No. 2920 is nearly twice as large as date on No. 2920b. No. 2920f comes in various configurations.

No. 2920h is a pane of 16 with one stamp removed. The missing stamp is the lower right stamp in the pane. No. 2920h cannot be made from No. 2920f, a pane of 15 + label. The label is located in the second or third row of the pane and is die cut. If the label is removed, an impression of the die cutting appears on the backing paper.

Serpentine Die Cut 9.8 on 2 or 3 Sides
2921	A2212 32c dk bl, tan, brn, red & lt bl	.60	.15
a.	Booklet pane of 10	6.00	
b.	Booklet pane of 5 + label	3.25	
c.	As "a." imperf	—	
	Set value, #2916-2921		.40

Date on No. 2920b is nearly twice as large as date on No. 2920.

No. 2920f comes in various configurations.

No. 2921 comes with either "1996" or "1997" below the design at left bottom corner. Values the same.

Issued: #2902, 2905, 3/10/95; #2908-2909, 2911-2912, 2919, 3/17/95; #2915, 2920, 4/18/95; #2897, 2913-2914, 2916, 5/19/95; #2920d, 1/20/96; #2904B, 2912B, 2915D 1/24/96; #2903-2904, 3/16/96; #2915A, 5/21/96; #2907, 2921, 5/21/96; #2902B, 2904A, 2906, 2910, 2912A, 2915B, 6/15/96; #2915C, 5/21/96; #2921b, 1/24/97.

See Nos. 3132-3133.

Great Americans Issue

A2248   A2249

A2253   A2255

A2258

1995-96   Engr.   Perf. 11.1
2933	A2248 32c brown	.60	.15
2934	A2249 32c green	.60	.15
2938	A2253 46c carmine	.90	.15
2940	A2255 55c green	1.10	.20
2943	A2258 78c brt purple	1.60	.20
	Nos. 2933-2943 (5)	4.80	.85

Issued: #2933, 9/13; 46c, 10/20; 55c, 7/11; 78c, 8/18; #2934, 5/26/96.

This is an expanding set. Nos. will change.

Love

Cherub from Sistine Madonna, by Raphael
A2263   A2264

Litho. & Engr.
1995, Feb. 1   Perf. 11.2
2948	A2263 (32c) multicolored	.60	.15

Self-Adhesive   Die Cut
2949	A2264 (32c) multicolored	.60	.15
a.	Booklet pane of 20 + label	12.00	
b.	As No. 2949, red (engr.) omitted	1,000.	
c.	As "a," red (engr.) omitted		
	Set value		.20

Florida Statehood, 150th Anniv. A2265

1995, Mar. 3   Litho.   Perf. 11.1
2950	A2265 32c multicolored	.60	.15

Earth Day

Earth Clean-Up A2266

Solar Energy A2267

Tree Planting A2268

Beach Clean-Up A2269

1995, Apr. 20   Litho.   Perf. 11.1x11
2951	A2266 32c multicolored	.60	.15
2952	A2267 32c multicolored	.60	.15
2953	A2268 32c multicolored	.60	.15
2954	A2269 32c multicolored	.60	.15
a.	Block of 4, #2951-2954	2.40	1.75
	Set value		.35

Richard M. Nixon

Richard M. Nixon, 37th President (1913-94) — A2270

Litho. & Engr.
1995, Apr. 26   Perf. 11.2
2955	A2270 32c multicolored	.60	.15
a.	Red (engr.) omitted	1,250.	

No. 2955 is known with red (engr. "Richard Nixon") inverted, and with red (engr.) omitted but only half of Nixon portrait present, both from printer's waste.

No. 2955a shows a complete Nixon portrait.

Black Heritage

Bessie Coleman (d. 1926), Aviator — A2271

1995, Apr. 27   Engr.   Perf. 11.2
2956 A2271 32c red & black   .60   .15

Love

A2272   A2273

Cherubs from Sistine Madonna, by Raphael — A2274

Litho. & Engr.
1995, May 12   Perf. 11.2
2957 A2272 32c multicolored   .60   .15
2958 A2273 55c multicolored   1.10   .15

BOOKLET STAMPS
Perf. 9.8x10.8
2959 A2272 32c multicolored   .60   .15
  a.   Booklet pane of 10   6.00
  b.   As "a," imperf

Self-Adhesive
Die Cut
2960 A2274 55c multicolored   1.10   .15
  a.   Booklet pane of 20 + label   22.50
      Set value   .45

Recreational Sports

Volleyball A2275

Softball A2276

Bowling A2277

Tennis A2278

Golf A2279

1995, May 20   Litho.   Perf. 11.2
2961 A2275 32c multicolored   .60   .15
2962 A2276 32c multicolored   .60   .15
2963 A2277 32c multicolored   .60   .15
2964 A2278 32c multicolored   .60   .15
2965 A2279 32c multicolored   .60   .15
  a.   Vert. strip of 5, #2961-2965   3.00   2.00
  b.   As "a," imperf
  c.   As "a," yellow omitted
  d.   As "a," yel, bl & mag omitted
      Set value   .40

Prisoners of War & Missing in Action

A2280

1995, May 29   Perf. 11.2
2966 A2280 32c multicolored   .60   .15

Legends of Hollywood

Marilyn Monroe (1926-62) — A2281

1995, June 1   Photo.   Perf. 11.1
2967 A2281 32c multicolored   .60   .15
  a.   Imperf., pair   600.00

Texas Statehood

A2282

1995, June 16   Litho.   Perf. 11.2
2968 A2282 32c multicolored   .60   .15

Great Lakes Lighthouses

Split Rock, Lake Superior A2283   St. Joseph, Lake Michigan A2284

Spectacle Reef, Lake Huron — A2285   Marblehead, Lake Erie — A2286

Thirty Mile Point, Lake Ontario — A2287

1995, June 17   Photo.   Perf. 11.2 Vert.
Booklet Stamps
2969 A2283 32c multicolored   .60   .15
2970 A2284 32c multicolored   .60   .15
2971 A2285 32c multicolored   .60   .15
2972 A2286 32c multicolored   .60   .15
2973 A2287 32c multicolored   .60   .15
  a.   Booklet pane of 5, #2969-2973   3.00   2.25
      Set value   .40

U.N., 50th Anniv.

A2288

1995, June 26   Engr.   Perf. 11.2
2974 A2288 32c blue   .60   .15

Civil War

A2289

Designs: a, Monitor and Virginia. b, Robert E. Lee. c, Clara Barton. d, Ulysses S. Grant. e, Battle of Shiloh. f, Jefferson Davis. g, David Farragut. h, Frederick Douglass. i, Raphael Semmes. j, Abraham Lincoln. k, Harriet Tubman. l, Stand Watie. m, Joseph E. Johnston. n, Winfield Hancock. o, Mary Chesnut. p, Battle of Chancellorsville. q, William T. Sherman. r, Phoebe Pember. s, "Stonewall" Jackson. t, Battle of Gettysburg.

1995, June 29   Photo.   Perf. 10.1
2975 A2289 Pane of 20   12.00   —
  a.-t.   32c any single   .60   .15
  u.   As "No. 2975," a.-e. imperf, f.-j. part perf   —
  v.   As "No. 2975," k.-t. imperf, f.-j. part perf   —
  w.   As "No. 2975," imperf   —
  x.   Block of 9 (f.-h., k.-m., p.-r.), k.-l., p.-q. imperf vert.   —

Carousel Horses

A2290   A2291

A2292   A2293

1995, July 21   Litho.   Perf. 11
2976 A2290 32c multicolored   .60   .15
2977 A2291 32c multicolored   .60   .15
2978 A2292 32c multicolored   .60   .15
2979 A2293 32c multicolored   .60   .15
  a.   Block of 4, #2976-2979   2.40   1.75
      Set value   .40

Woman Suffrage

A2294

Litho. & Engr.
1995, Aug. 26   Perf. 11.1x11
2980 A2294 32c multicolored   .60   .15
  a.   Black (engr.) omitted   600.00
  b.   Imperf, pair   1,600.

World War II

A2295

Designs and events of 1945: a, Marines raise flag on Iwo Jima. b, Fierce fighting frees Manila by March 3, 1945. c, Soldiers advancing (Okinawa, the last big battle). d, Destroyed bridge (US and Soviets link up at Elbe River). e, Allies liberate Holocaust survivors. f, Germany surrenders at Reims. g, Refugees (by 1945, World War II has uprooted millions). h, Truman announces Japan's surrender. i, Sailor kissing nurse (news of victory hits home). j, Hometowns honor their returning veterans.

Central label is size of 15 stamps and shows world map with extent of Axis control and Allied operations.

Illustration reduced.

Litho. & Engr.
1995, Sept. 2   Perf. 11.1
2981 A2295 Block of 10   6.00   4.50
  a.-j.   32c any single   .60   .30

American Music Series

Louis Armstrong (1901-71) A2296

Coleman Hawkins (1904-69) A2297

James P. Johnson (1894-1955) A2298

Jelly Roll Morton (1890-1941) A2299

Charlie Parker (1920-55) A2300

Eubie Blake
(1883-1983)
A2301

Charles
Mingus
(1922-79)
A2302

Thelonious
Monk (1917-
82)
A2303

John Coltrane
(1926-67)
A2304

Erroll Garner
(1921-77)
A2305

1995	**Litho.**		*Perf. 11.1x11*
2982 A2296	32c white denomination	.60	.15
2983 A2297	32c multicolored	.60	.15
2984 A2296	32c black denomination	.60	.15
2985 A2298	32c multicolored	.60	.15
2986 A2299	32c multicolored	.60	.15
2987 A2300	32c multicolored	.60	.15
2988 A2301	32c multicolored	.60	.15
2989 A2302	32c multicolored	.60	.15
2990 A2303	32c multicolored	.60	.15
2991 A2304	32c multicolored	.60	.15
2992 A2305	32c multicolored	.60	.15
a.	Vert. block of 10, #2983-2992, top selvage	6.00	—
b.	As "a," dark blue (inscriptions) omitted		
	Set value, #2982-2992		.90

Issued: No. 2982, 9/1/95; others, 9/16/95.

Garden Flowers

Aster	Chrysanthemum
A2306	A2307

Aster
A2306

Chrysanthemum
A2307

Dahlia
A2308

Hydrangea
A2309

Rudbeckia — A2310

Perf. 10.9 Vert.
1995, Sept. 19   Litho. & Engr.
Booklet Stamps

2993 A2306	32c multicolored	.60	.15
2994 A2307	32c multicolored	.60	.15
2995 A2308	32c multicolored	.60	.15
2996 A2309	32c multicolored	.60	.15
2997 A2310	32c multicolored	.60	.15
a.	Booklet pane of 5, #2993-2997	3.00	2.25
	Set value		.40

Eddie Rickenbacker (1890-1973), Aviator

A2311

1995, Sept. 25   Photo.   *Perf. 11.1*
2998 A2311	60c multicolored	1.25	.25

Republic of Palau

A2312

1995, Sept. 29   Litho.   *Perf. 11.1*
2999 A2312	32c multicolored	.60	.15

Comic Strips

A2313

Designs: a, The Yellow Kid. b, Katzenjammer Kids. c, Little Nemo in Slumberland. d, Bringing Up Father. e, Krazy Kat. f, Rube Goldberg's Inventions. g, Toonerville Folks. h, Gasoline Alley. i, Barney Google. j, Little Orphan Annie. k, Popeye. l, Blondie. m, Dick Tracy. n, Alley Oop. o, Nancy. p, Flash Gordon. q, Li'l Abner. r, Terry and the Pirates. s, Prince Valiant. t, Brenda Starr, Reporter.

1995, Oct. 1   Photo.   *Perf. 10.1*
3000 A2313	Pane of 20	12.00	
a.-t.	32c any single	.60	.15
u.	As No. 3000, a.-h. imperf., i.-l. part perf	—	
v.	As No. 3000, m.-t. imperf., i.-l. part perf	—	

Inscriptions on back of each stamp describe the comic strip.

U.S. Naval Academy, 150th Anniversary

A2314

1995, Oct. 10   Litho.   *Perf. 10.9*
3001 A2314	32c multicolored	.60	.15

Literary Arts Series

Tennessee
Williams
(1911-83)
A2315

1995, Oct. 13   Litho.   *Perf. 11.1*
3002 A2315	32c multicolored	.60	.15

Christmas

Madonna and Child, by
Giotto di
Bondone — A2316

Santa Claus
Entering
Chimney
A2317

Child Holding
Jumping Jack
A2318

Child Holding
Tree — A2319

Santa Claus
Working on
Sled — A2320

Midnight
Angel
A2321

Children
Sledding
A2322

1995   Litho. & Engr.   *Perf. 11.2*
3003 A2316	32c multicolored	.60	.15
a.	Perf. 9.8x10.8	.60	.15
b.	As "a." booklet pane of 10	6.00	4.00
c.	As #3003, black (engr. denomination) omitted		

Lithographed
3004 A2317	32c multicolored	.60	.15
3005 A2318	32c multicolored	.60	.15
3006 A2319	32c multicolored	.60	.15
3007 A2320	32c multicolored	.60	.15
a.	Block or strip of 4, #3004-3007	2.40	1.25
b.	Booklet pane of 10, 3 each #3004-3005, 2 each #3006-3007	6.00	4.00
c.	Booklet pane of 10, 2 each #3004-3005, 3 each #3006-3007	6.00	4.00
d.	As "a," imperf.	900.00	
	Set value		.32

Self-Adhesive Stamps
Photogravure
Serpentine Die Cut
3008 A2320	32c multicolored	.60	.15
3009 A2318	32c multicolored	.60	.15
3010 A2317	32c multicolored	.60	.15

3011 A2319	32c multicolored	.60	.15
a.	Booklet pane of 20, 5 each #3008-3011 + label	12.00	

Lithographed
3012 A2321	32c multicolored	.60	.15
a.	Booklet pane of 20 + label	12.00	
c.	Booklet pane of 15 + label	9.00	
d.	Booklet pane of 15		

Colors of No. 3012c are deeper than those on #3012a. Label on #3012c has die-cutting, not found on label of #3012a.

No. 3012d is a pane of 16 with one stamp removed. The missing stamp is from the second row, either from the top or bottom, of the pane. No. 3012d cannot be made from No. 3012c, a pane of 15 + label. The label is die cut. If the label is removed, an impression of the die cutting appears on the backing paper.

Photogravure
Die Cut
3013 A2322	32c multicolored	.60	.15
a.	Booklet pane of 18	11.00	

Self-Adhesive Coil Stamps
Serpentine Die Cut Vert.
3014 A2320	32c multicolored	.60	.30
3015 A2318	32c multicolored	.60	.30
3016 A2317	32c multicolored	.60	.30
3017 A2319	32c multicolored	.60	.30

Lithographed
3018 A2321	32c multicolored	.60	.30

Nos. 3014-3018 were only available through the Philatelic Fullfillment Center in Kansas City.
Issued: #3003, 3012-3013, 3018, 10/19; #3004-3011, 3014-3017, 9/30.

Antique Automobiles

1893 Duryea
A2323

1894 Haynes
A2324

1898 Columbia
A2325

1899 Winton
A2326

1901 White
A2327

1995, Nov. 3   Photo.   *Perf. 11.1*
3019 A2323	32c multicolored	.60	.15
3020 A2324	32c multicolored	.60	.15
3021 A2325	32c multicolored	.60	.15
3022 A2326	32c multicolored	.60	.15
3023 A2327	32c multicolored	.60	.15
a.	Vert. or horiz. strip of 5, #3019-3023	3.00	2.00
	Set value		.40

Vert. and horiz. strips are all in different order.

Utah Statehood Centenary

Delicate Arch, Arches
Natl. Park — A2328

1996, Jan. 4   Litho.   *Perf. 11.1*
3024 A2328	32c multicolored	.60	.15

Garden Flowers

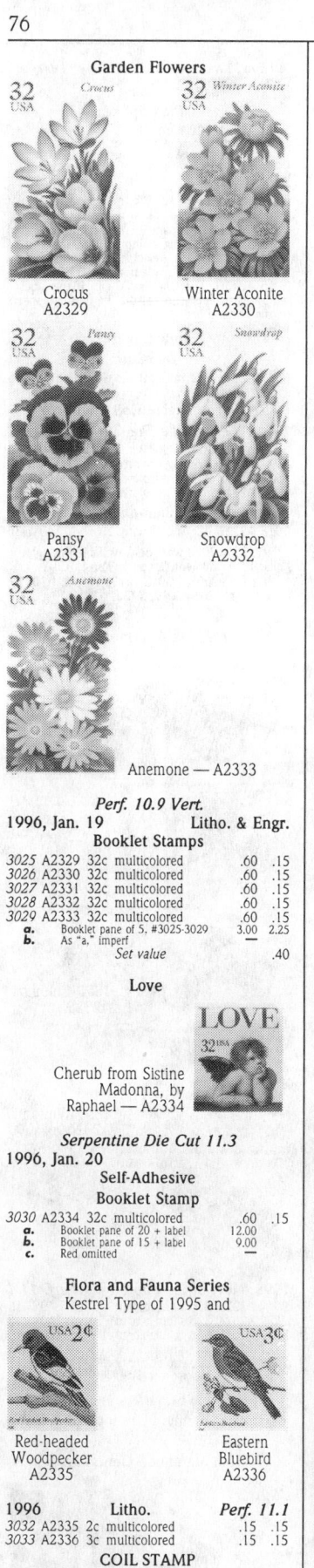

Crocus
A2329

Winter Aconite
A2330

Pansy
A2331

Snowdrop
A2332

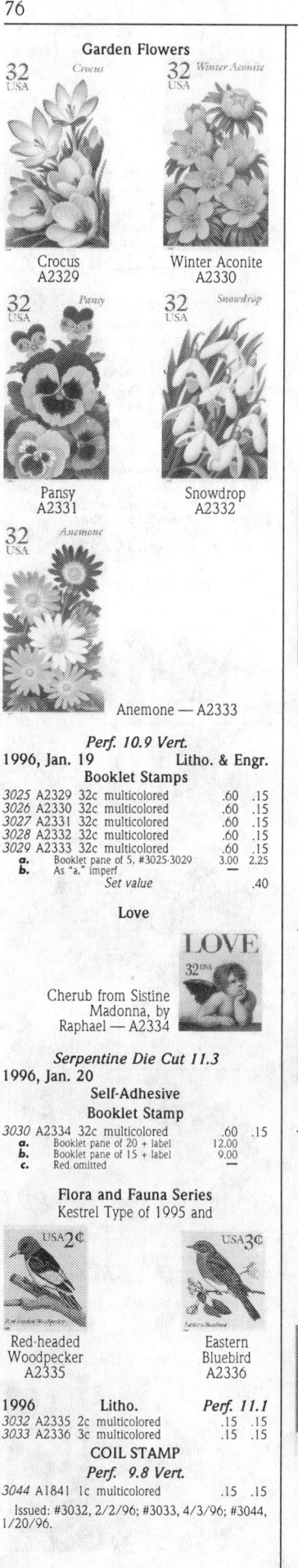

Anemone — A2333

Perf. 10.9 Vert.

1996, Jan. 19   Litho. & Engr.
Booklet Stamps
3025 A2329 32c multicolored   .60   .15
3026 A2330 32c multicolored   .60   .15
3027 A2331 32c multicolored   .60   .15
3028 A2332 32c multicolored   .60   .15
3029 A2333 32c multicolored   .60   .15
a.   Booklet pane of 5, #3025-3029   3.00 2.25
b.   As "a," imperf   —
         Set value   .40

Love

Cherub from Sistine
Madonna, by
Raphael — A2334

Serpentine Die Cut 11.3

1996, Jan. 20
Self-Adhesive
Booklet Stamp
3030 A2334 32c multicolored   .60   .15
a.   Booklet pane of 20 + label   12.00
b.   Booklet pane of 15 + label   9.00
c.   Red omitted

Flora and Fauna Series
Kestrel Type of 1995 and

Red-headed
Woodpecker
A2335

Eastern
Bluebird
A2336

1996   Litho.   *Perf. 11.1*
3032 A2335 2c multicolored   .15   .15
3033 A2336 3c multicolored   .15   .15
COIL STAMP
Perf. 9.8 Vert.
3044 A1841 1c multicolored   .15   .15
    Issued: #3032, 2/2/96; #3033, 4/3/96; #3044,
1/20/96.

Blue Jay & Rose Types of 1993-95
*Serpentine Die Cut 10.4x10.8 on 3
Sides*

1996-97   Photo.
Self-Adhesive
Booklet Stamp
3048 A1847 20c multicolored   .40   .15
a.   Booklet pane of 10   4.00

Serpentine Die Cut 11.3x11.7
3049 A1853 32c yellow, orange,
             green & black   .60   .15
a.   Booklet pane of 20 + label 12.00
b.   Booklet pane of 4   3.20
c.   Booklet pane of 5 + label   3.00
d.   Booklet pane of 6   3.60

Coil Stamps
Serpentine Die Cut 11.6 Vert.
3053 A1847 20c multicolored   .40   .15

Serpentine Die Cut 9.8 Vert.
Litho.
Self-Adhesive
3054 A1853 32c yel, org, blk & grn   .60   .15
a.   Imperf, pair
    Issued: #3048, 3053, 8/2/96; #3049,
10/24/96; #3054, 8/1/97.

Black Heritage

Ernest E. Just (1883-
1941), Marine
Biologist — A2358

1996, Feb. 1   Litho.   *Perf. 11.1*
3058 A2358 32c gray & black   .60   .15

Smithsonian Institution, 150th Anniversary

A2359

1996, Feb. 7   *Perf. 11.1*
3059 A2359 32c multicolored   .60   .15

Chinese New Year

Year of the
Rat — A2360

1996, Feb. 8   Photo.   *Perf. 11.1*
3060 A2360 32c multicolored   .60   .15

Pioneers of Communication

Eadweard
Muybridge
(1830-1904),
Photographer
A2361

Ottmar
Mergenthaler
(1854-99),
Inventor of
Linotype
A2362

Frederic E.
Ives (1856-
1937),
Developer of
Halftone
Process
A2363

William
Dickson
(1860-1935),
Co-developer
of Kinetoscope
A2364

1996, Feb. 22   Litho.   *Perf. 11.1x11*
3061 A2361 32c multicolored   .60   .15
3062 A2362 32c multicolored   .60   .15
3063 A2363 32c multicolored   .60   .15
3064 A2364 32c multicolored   .60   .15
a.   Block or strip of 4, #3061-3064 2.40 1.75
         Set value   .32

Fulbright Scholarships, 50th Anniversary

A2365

Litho. & Engr.
1996, Feb. 28   *Perf. 11.1*
3065 A2365 32c multicolored   .60   .15

Jacqueline Cochran (1910-80), Pilot

A2366

Litho. & Engr.
1996, Mar. 9   *Perf. 11.1*
3066 A2366 50c multicolored   1.00   .20
a.   Black (eng.) omitted   90.00

Marathon

A2367

1996, Apr. 11   Litho.   *Perf. 11.1*
3067 A2367 32c multicolored   .60   .15

1996 Summer Olympic Games

A2368

Designs: a, Decathlon (javelin). b, Canoeing. c,
Women's running. d, Women's diving. e, Cycling. f,
Freestyle wrestling. g, Women's gymnastics. h,
Women's sailboarding. i, Shot put. j, Women's soc-
cer. k, Beach volleyball. l, Rowing. m, Sprints. n,
Women's swimming. o, Women's softball. p, Hur-
dles. q, Swimming. r, Gymnastics (pommel horse).
s, Equestrian. t, Basketball.

1996, May 2   Photo.   *Perf. 10.1*
3068 A2368 Pane of 20   12.00   —
a.-t.   32c any single   .60   .15
u.   As No. 3068, imperf
v.   As No. 3068, back inscrip-
         tions omitted on a., f., k.,
         p., incorrect back inscrip-
         tions on others
    Inscription on back of each stamp describes the
sport shown.

Georgia O'Keeffe (1887-1986)

A2369

1996, May 23   Photo.   *Perf. 11.6x11.4*
3069 A2369 32c multicolored   .60   .15
a.   Imperf, pair   250.00

Tennessee Statehood Bicentennial

A2370

1996, May 31   Photo.   *Perf. 11.1*
3070 A2370 32c multicolored   .60   .15
Booklet Stamp
Self-Adhesive
Serpentine Die Cut 9.9x10.8
3071 A2370 32c multicolored   .60   .30
a.   Booklet pane of 20   12.00
b.   Horiz. pair, no die cutting btwn.

American Indian Dances

Fancy
A2371

Butterfly
A2372

Traditional
A2373

Raven
A2374

Hoop — A2375

1996, June 7   Litho.   *Perf. 11.1*
3072 A2371 32c multicolored   .60   .15
3073 A2372 32c multicolored   .60   .15
3074 A2373 32c multicolored   .60   .15
3075 A2374 32c multicolored   .60   .15
3076 A2375 32c multicolored   .60   .15
a.   Strip of 5, #3072-3076   3.00 1.75
         Set value   .40

Prehistoric Animals

Eohippus
A2376

Woolly Mammoth
A2377

Mastodon
A2378

Saber-tooth Cat — A2379

1996, June 8   Litho.   Perf. 11.1x11
3077 A2376 32c multicolored .60 .15
3078 A2377 32c multicolored .60 .15
3079 A2378 32c multicolored .60 .15
3080 A2379 32c multicolored .60 .15
a.   Block or strip of 4, #3077-3080   2.40 1.50
        Set value   .30

Breast Cancer Awareness

A2380

1996, June 15   Litho.   Perf. 11.1
3081 A2380 32c multicolored   .60 .15

Legends of Hollywood

James Dean (1931-55) — A2381

1996, June 24   Photo.   Perf. 11.1
3082 A2381 32c multicolored   .60 .15
a.   Imperf. pair   450.00
b.   As "a," red (USA 32c) omitted   —

Folk Heroes

MIGHTY CASEY   PAUL BUNYAN
A2382   A2383

JOHN HENRY   PECOS BILL
A2384   A2385

1996, July 11   Litho.   Perf. 11.1x11
3083 A2382 32c multicolored .60 .15
3084 A2383 32c multicolored .60 .15
3085 A2384 32c multicolored .60 .15
3086 A2385 32c multicolored .60 .15
a.   Block or strip of 4, #3083-3086   2.40 1.50
        Set value   .35

Centennial Olympic Games

Myron's Discobolus — A2386

1996, July 19   Engr.   Perf. 11.1
3087 A2386 32c brown   .60 .15

Sheet margin of the pane of 20 is lithographed.

Iowa Statehood, 150th Anniversary

Young Corn, by Grant Wood — A2387

1996, Aug. 1   Litho.   Perf. 11.1
3088 A2387 32c multicolored   .60 .15

Booklet Stamp
Self-Adhesive
Serpentine Die Cut 11.6x11.4
3089 A2387 32c multicolored   .60 .15
a.   Booklet pane of 20   12.00

Rural Free Delivery, Cent.

A2388

Litho. & Engr.
1996, Aug. 7   Perf. 11.2x11
3090 A2388 32c multicolored   .60 .15

Riverboats

Robt. E. Lee — A2389

Sylvan Dell — A2390

Far West A2391

Rebecca Everingham A2392

Bailey Gatzert A2393

Self-Adhesive
Serpentine Die Cut 11x11.1
1996, Aug. 22   Photo.
3091 A2389 32c multicolored .60 .15
3092 A2390 32c multicolored .60 .15
3093 A2391 32c multicolored .60 .15
3094 A2392 32c multicolored .60 .15
3095 A2393 32c multicolored .60 .15
a.   Vert. strip of 5, 3091-3095   3.00
b.   As "a," with special die cutting   —   —

The serpentine die cutting runs through the peel-able backing to which Nos. 3091-3095 are affixed. No. 3095a exists with stamps in different sequences.

On the long side of each stamp in No. 3095b, the die cutting is missing 3 "perforations" between the stamps, one near each end and one in the middle. This allows a complete strip to be removed from the backing paper for use on a first day cover.

American Music Series
Big Band Leaders

Count Basie A2394

Tommy & Jimmy Dorsey A2395

Glenn Miller A2396

Benny Goodman A2397

Songwriters

Harold Arlen A2398

Johnny Mercer A2399

Dorothy Fields A2400

Hoagy Carmichael A2401

1996, Sept. 11   Litho.   Perf. 11.1x11
3096 A2394 32c multicolored .60 .15
3097 A2395 32c multicolored .60 .15
3098 A2396 32c multicolored .60 .15
3099 A2397 32c multicolored .60 .15
a.   Block or strip of 4, 3096-3099   2.40 1.50
        Set value   .35
3100 A2398 32c multicolored .60 .15
3101 A2399 32c multicolored .60 .15
3102 A2400 32c multicolored .60 .15
3103 A2401 32c multicolored .60 .15
a.   Block or strip of 4, 3100-3103   2.40 1.50
        Set value   .35

Literary Arts

F. Scott Fitzgerald (1896-1940) A2402

1996, Sept. 27   Photo.   Perf. 11.1
3104 A2402 23c multicolored   .45 .15

Endangered Species

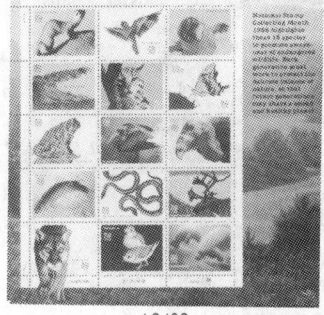

A2403

Designs: a, Black-footed ferret. b, Thick-billed parrot. c, Hawaiian monk seal. d, American crocodile. e, Ocelot. f, Schaus swallowtail butterfly. g, Wyoming toad. h, Brown pelican. i, California condor. j, Gila trout. k, San Francisco garter snake. l, Woodland caribou. m, Florida panther. n, Piping plover. o, Florida manatee.

1996, Oct. 2   Litho.   Perf. 11.1x11
3105 A2403 Pane of 15   9.00   —
a.-o.   32c any single   .60 .15
See Mexico No. 1995.

Computer Technology

A2404

Perf. 10.9x11.1
1996, Oct. 8   Litho. & Engr.
3106 A2404 32c multicolored   .60 .15

Christmas

Madonna and Child from
Adoration of the
Shepherds, by Paolo de
Matteis — A2405

Family at
Fireplace
A2406

Decorating
Tree
A2407

Dreaming of
Santa Claus
A2408

Holiday
Shopping
A2409

Skaters — A2410

1996 Litho. & Engr. *Perf. 11.1x11.2*
3107 A2405 32c multicolored   .60 .15
Litho.
Perf. 11.3
3108 A2406 32c multicolored   .60 .15
3109 A2407 32c multicolored   .60 .15
3110 A2408 32c multicolored   .60 .15
3111 A2409 32c multicolored   .60 .15
   a. Block or strip of 4, #3108-3111   2.40 1.50

Self-Adhesive Booklet Stamps
Litho. & Engr.
***Serpentine Die Cut 10 on 2, 3 or 4
Sides***
3112 A2405 32c multicolored   .60 .15
   a. Booklet pane of 20 + label   12.00

Litho.
***Serpentine Die Cut 11.8x11.5 on 2, 3
or 4 Sides***
3113 A2406 32c multicolored   .60 .15
3114 A2407 32c multicolored   .60 .15
3115 A2408 32c multicolored   .60 .15
3116 A2409 32c multicolored   .60 .15
   a. Booklet pane. 5 ea #3113-3116   12.00

Photo.
Die Cut
3117 A2410 32c multicolored   .60 .15
   a. Booklet pane of 18   11.00
Issued: #3108-3111, 3113-3117, 10/8; #3107,
3112, 11/1.

Hanukkah

A2411

Serpentine Die Cut 11.1
1996, Oct. 22   Photo.
Self-Adhesive
3118 A2411 32c multicolored   .60 .15
See Israel No. 1289

Cycling
Souvenir Sheet

A2412

1996, Nov. 1 Photo. *Perf. 11x11.1*
3119 A2412 Sheet of 2   2.00 2.00
   a. 50c orange & multi   1.00 1.00
   b. 50c blue green & multi   1.00 1.00

Chinese New Year

Year of the
Ox — A2413

1997, Jan. 5 Photo. *Perf. 11.2*
3120 A2413 32c multicolored   .60 .15

Black Heritage

Brig. Gen. Benjamin O.
Davis, Sr. (1880-
1970) — A2414

Self-Adhesive
Serpentine Die Cut 11.4
1997, Jan. 28   Litho.
3121 A2414 32c multicolored   .60 .15

Statue of Liberty Type of 1994
***Serpentine Die Cut 11 on 2, 3 or 4
Sides***
1997, Feb. 1   Photo.
Self-Adhesive
3122 A1951 32c red, lt bl, dk bl &
                  yel   .60 .15
   a. Booklet pane of 20 + label   12.00
   b. Booklet pane of 4   3.20
   c. Booklet pane of 5 + label   3.00
   d. Booklet pane of 6   3.60

***Serpentine Die Cut 11.5x11.8 on 2, 3
or 4 Sides***
1997   Photo.
Self-Adhesive
3122E A1951 32c red, lt bl, dk bl
                  & yel   .60 .15
   f. Booklet pane of 20 + label   12.00
   g. Booklet pane of 6   3.60

Love

Swans
A2415   A2416

***Serpentine Die Cut 11.8x11.6 on 2, 3
or 4 Sides***
1997, Feb. 7   Litho.
Self-Adhesive
3123 A2415 32c multicolored   .60 .15
   a. Booklet pane of 20 + label   12.00
   d. As "a." black omitted   —

***Serpentine Die Cut 11.6x11.8 on 2, 3
or 4 Sides***
3124 A2416 55c multicolored   1.10 .15
   a. Booklet pane of 20 + label   22.00

Helping Children Learn

A2417

Serpentine Die Cut 11.6x11.7
1997, Feb. 18   Photo.
Self-Adhesive
3125 A2417 32c multicolored   .60 .15

Merian Botanical Prints

Citron, Moth,
Larvae, Pupa,
Beetle
A2418

Flowering
Pineapple,
Cockroaches
A2419

No. 3128 (r), No. 3129 (l), No. 3128a
below

***Serpentine Die Cut 10.9x10.2 on 2, 3
or 4 Sides***
1997, Mar. 3   Photo.
Self-Adhesive
3126 A2418 32c multicolored   .60 .15
3127 A2419 32c multicolored   .60 .15
   a. Booklet pane of 20, 10 ea #3126-
           3127 + label   12.00

Size: 18.5x24mm
***Serpentine Die Cut 11.2x10.8 on 2 or
3 Sides***
3128 A2418 32c multicolored   .60 .15
   a. See footnote   .60 .15
   b. Booklet pane of 5. 2 ea #3128-
           3129, 1 #3128a   3.00
3129 A2419 32c multicolored   .60 .15
   a. See footnote   .60 .15
   b. Booklet pane of 5. 2 ea #3128-
           3129, 1 #3129a   3.00

Nos. 3128a-3129a are placed sideways on the
pane and are serpentine die cut 11.2 on top and
bottom, 10.8 on left side. The right side is 11.2
broken by a large perf where the stamp meets the
vertical perforations of the two stamps above it. See
illustration above.

Pacific '97

Sailing Ship — A2420

Stagecoach — A2421

1997, Mar. 13 Engr. *Perf. 11.2*
3130 A2420 32c blue   .60 .15
3131 A2421 32c red   .60 .15
   a. Pair, #3130-3131   1.25 .30

Juke Box and Flag Over Porch Types of
1995
COIL STAMPS
1997, Mar. 14 Photo. *Imperf.*
Self-Adhesive
3132 A2225 (25c) brt org red, brt yel
                  grn & multi   .50 .50
Tagged
Serpentine Die Cut 9.9 Vert.
3133 A2212 32c dk bl, tan, brn,
                  red & lt bl   .60 .15

Nos. 3132-3133 were issued without backing
paper. No. 3132 has simulated perforations ending
in black bars at the top and bottom edges of the
stamp.

Literary Arts

Thornton
Wilder (1897-
1975)
A2422

1997, Apr. 17 Litho. *Perf. 11.1*
3134 A2422 32c multicolored   .60 .15

Raoul Wallenberg (1912-47)

Wallenberg
and Jewish
Refugees
A2423

1997, Apr. 24 Litho. *Perf. 11.1*
3135 A2423 32c multicolored   .60 .15

Dinosaurs

A2424

Designs: a, Ceratosaurus. b, Camptosaurus. c,
Camarasaurus. d, Brachiosaurus. e, Goniopholis. f,
Stegosaurus. g, Allosaurus. h, Opisthias. i,
Edmontonia. j, Einiosaurus. k, Daspletosaurus. l,
Palaeosaniwa. m, Corythosaurus. n, Ornithominus.
o, Parasaurolophus.

1997, May 1 Litho. *Perf. 11x11.1*
3136 A2424 Sheet of 15   9.00 —
   a.-o. 32c any single   .60 .15

Bugs Bunny

A2425

Serpentine Die Cut 11
1997, May 22   Photo.
3137   Pane of 10   6.00
   a. A2425 32c single   .60 .15
   b. Booklet pane of 9   5.40
   c. Booklet pane of 1   .60

Die cutting on #3137b does not extend through
the backing paper.

3138   Pane of 10   250.00
   a. A2425 32c single   .60
   b. Booklet pane of 9   5.40
   c. Booklet pane of 1, imperf. 225.00

Die cutting on #3138b extends through the
backing paper.

An untagged promotional piece similar to No. 3137c exists on the same backing paper as the booklet pane, with the same design image, but without Bugs' signature and the single stamp. Replacing the stamp is an enlarged "32 / USA" in the same style as used on the stamp.

Pacific 97

Franklin
A2426

Washington
A2427

1997 Litho. & Engr. Perf. 10.5x10.4

3139	Sheet of 12	12.00	—
a.	A2426 50c single	1.00	.50
3140	Sheet of 12	14.50	—
a.	A2427 60c single	1.25	.60

Margins on Nos. 3139-3140 are lithographed.
Issued: No. 3139, 5/29, No. 3140, 5/30.

Marshall Plan, 50th Anniv.

Gen. George
C. Marshall,
Map of Europe
A2428

1997, June 4 Perf. 11.1

3141	A2428 32c multicolored	.60	.15

Classic American Aircraft

A2429

Designs: a, Mustang. b, Model B. c, Cub. d, Vega. e, Alpha. f, B-10. g, Corsair. h, Stratojet. i, GeeBee. j, Staggerwing. k, Flying Fortress. l, Stearman. m, Constellation. n, Lightning. o, Peashooter. p, Tri-Motor. q, DC-3. r, 314 Clipper. s, Jenny. t, Wildcat.

1997, July 19 Photo. Perf. 10.1

3142	A2429 Pane of 20	12.00	—
a.-t.	32c any single	.60	.15

Inscriptions on back of each stamp describe the airplane.

Football Coaches

Bear Bryant
A2430

Pop Warner
A2431

Vince
Lombardi
A2432

George Halas
A2433

1997 Litho. Perf. 11.2

3143	A2430 32c multicolored	.60	.15
3144	A2431 32c multicolored	.60	.15
3145	A2432 32c multicolored	.60	.15
3146	A2433 32c multicolored	.60	.15
a.	Block or strip of 4, #3143-3146	2.40	—
	Set value		.35

With Red Bar Above Coach's Name
Perf. 11

3147	A2432 32c multicolored	.60	.30
3148	A2430 32c multicolored	.60	.30
3149	A2431 32c multicolored	.60	.30
3150	A2433 32c multicolored	.60	.30

Issued: #3143-3146, 7/25; #3147, 8/5; #3148, 8/7; #3149, 8/8; #3150, 8/16.

American Dolls

A2434

Designs: a, "Alabama Baby," and doll by Martha Chase. b, "Columbian Doll." c, Johnny Gruelle's "Raggedy Ann." d, Doll by Martha Chase. e, "American Child." f, "Baby Coos." g, Plains Indian. h, Doll by Izannah Walker. i, "Babyland Rag." j, "Scootles." k, Doll by Ludwig Greiner. l, "Betsy McCall." m, Percy Crosby's "Skippy." n, "Maggie Mix-up." o, Dolls by Albert Schoenhut.

1997, July 28 Perf. 10.9x11.1

3151	A2434 Pane of 15	9.00	—
a.-o.	32c any single	.60	.15

Legends Of Hollywood

Humphrey Bogart (1899-1957) — A2435

1997, July 31 Photo. Perf. 11.1

3152	A2435 32c multicolored	.60	.15

Perforations in corner of each stamp are star-shaped.

"The Start and Stripes Forever!"

A2436

1997, Aug. 21 Perf. 11.1

3153	A2436 32c multicolored	.60	.15

American Music Series
Opera Singers

Lily Pons
A2437

Richard
Tucker
A2438

Lawrence
Tibbett
A2439

Rosa Ponselle
A2440

Classical Composers & Conductors

Leopold
Stokowski
A2441

Arthur
Fiedler
A2442

George Szell
A2443

Eugene
Ormandy
A2444

Samuel
Barber
A2445

Ferde Grofé
A2446

Charles Ives
A2447

Louis Moreau
Gottschalk
A2448

1997 Litho. Perf. 11

3154	A2437 32c multicolored	.60	.15
3155	A2438 32c multicolored	.60	.15
3156	A2439 32c multicolored	.60	.15
3157	A2440 32c multicolored	.60	.15
a.	Block or strip of 4, #3154-3157	2.40	—
	Set value		.35
3158	A2441 32c multicolored	.60	.15
3159	A2442 32c multicolored	.60	.15
3160	A2443 32c multicolored	.60	.15
3161	A2444 32c multicolored	.60	.15
3162	A2445 32c multicolored	.60	.15
3163	A2446 32c multicolored	.60	.15
3164	A2447 32c multicolored	.60	.15
3165	A2448 32c multicolored	.60	.15
a.	Block of 8, #3158-3165	4.80	—
	Set value		.70

Issued: #3154-3157, 9/10; #3158-3165, 9/12.

Padre Félix Varela (1788-1853)

A2449

1997, Sept. 15 Litho. Perf. 11.2

3166	A2449 32c purple	.60	.15

Department of the Air Force, 50th Anniv.

Thunderbirds
Aerial
Demonstration
Squadron
A2450

1997, Sept. 18 Litho. Perf. 11.2x11.1

3167	A2450 32c multicolored	.60	.15

Classic Movie Monsters

Lon Chaney as The
Phantom of the
Opera — A2451

Bela Lugosi as
Dracula — A2452

Boris Karloff as
Frankenstein's
Monster — A2453

Boris Karloff as The
Mummy — A2454

Lon Chaney, Jr. as
The Wolf
Man — A2455

1997, Sept. 30   **Photo.**   *Perf. 10.2*
3168 A2451 32c multicolored .60 .15
3169 A2452 32c multicolored .60 .15
3170 A2453 32c multicolored .60 .15
3171 A2454 32c multicolored .60 .15
3172 A2455 32c multicolored .60 .15
   a.   Strip of 5, #3168-3172   3.00
        Set value   .40

Beginning with No. 3172a, a hidden 3-D design can be seen on some stamps when they are viewed with a special viewer sold by the post office.

First Supersonic Flight, 50th Anniv.

A2456

Serpentine Die Cut 11.4
1997, Oct. 14   **Litho.**
Self-Adhesive
3173 A2456 32c multicolored .60 .15

Women In Military Service

A2457

1997, Oct. 18   **Litho.**   *Perf. 11.1*
3174 A2457 32c multicolored .60 .15

Kwanzaa

A2458

Serpentine Die Cut 11
1996, Oct. 22   **Photo.**
Self-Adhesive
3175 A2458 32c multicolored .60 .15

Christmas

Madonna and Child, by Sano di Pietro
A2459

Holly
A2460

Serpentine Die Cut 9.9 on 2, 3 or 4 Sides
1997   **Litho.**
Booklet Stamps
Self-Adhesive
3176 A2459 32c multicolored .60 .15
   a.   Booklet pane of 20 + label   12.00
Serpentine Die Cut 11.2x11.8 on 2, 3 or 4 Sides
3177 A2460 32c multicolored .60 .15
   a.   Booklet pane of 20 + label   12.00
   b.   Booklet pane of 4   2.50
   c.   Booklet pane of 5 + label   3.00
   d.   Booklet pane of 6   3.75
Issued: No. 3176, 10/27; No. 3177, 10/30.

Mars Pathfinder
Souvenir Sheet

Mars Rover Sojourner — A2461

1997, Dec. 10   **Photo.**   *Perf. 11x11.1*
3178 A2461 $3 multicolored 6.00 —
The perforations at the bottom of the stamp include the letters "USA." Vertical rouletting extends from the vertical perforations of the stamp to the bottom of the souvenir sheet.

Chinese New Year

Year of the Tiger
A2462

1998, Jan. 5   **Photo.**   *Perf. 11.2*
3179 A2462 32c multicolored .60 .15

Subject Index of Regular and Air Post Issues

AIR POST STAMPS

For prepayment of postage on all mailable matter sent by airmail.

Curtiss Jenny — AP1

Engraved (Flat Plate Printing)
1918　　　Unwmk.　　　Perf. 11

C1	AP1 6c orange	75.00	30.00
	Never hinged	110.00	
C2	AP1 16c green	105.00	35.00
	Never hinged	155.00	
C3	AP1 24c car rose & blue	105.00	35.00
	Never hinged	155.00	
a.	Center inverted	150,000.	
	Never hinged	175,000.	
	Nos. C1-C3 (3)	285.00	100.00

Wooden Propeller and Radiator AP2

Emblem of Air Service AP3

De Havilland Biplane — AP4

1923

C4	AP2 8c dark green	27.50	14.00
	Never hinged	40.00	
C5	AP3 16c dark blue	105.00	30.00
	Never hinged	155.00	
C6	AP4 24c carmine	120.00	30.00
	Never hinged	180.00	
	Nos. C4-C6 (3)	252.50	74.00

Map of US and Two Mail Planes AP5

1926-27

C7	AP5 10c dark blue	3.00	.35
	Never hinged	4.50	
C8	AP5 15c olive brown	3.50	2.50
	Never hinged	5.25	
C9	AP5 20c yellow green ('27)	9.00	2.00
	Never hinged	13.50	
	Nos. C7-C9 (3)	15.50	4.85

Lindbergh's Airplane "Spirit of St. Louis" — AP6

1927, June 18

C10	AP6 10c dark blue	8.50	2.50
	Never hinged	12.50	
a.	Booklet pane of 3	85.00	65.00
	Never hinged	120.00	

Singles from No. C10a are imperf. at sides or imperf. at sides and bottom.

Nos. C1-C10 were available for ordinary postage.

Beacon on Rocky Mountains AP7

1928, July 25　　　Perf. 11

C11	AP7 5c carmine & blue	5.25	.75
	Never hinged	8.00	
a.	Vertical pair, imperf. btwn.	5,500.	

Winged Globe AP8

1930, Feb. 10　　　Perf. 11
Size: 46½x19mm

C12	AP8 5c violet	11.00	.50
	Never hinged	16.50	
a.	Horiz. pair, imperf. btwn.	4,500.	

See Nos. C16-C17, C19.

Graf Zeppelin Issue

Zeppelin over Atlantic Ocean AP9

Zeppelin between Continents — AP10

Zeppelin Passing Globe AP11

1930, Apr. 19　　　Perf. 11

C13	AP9 65c green	275.00	160.00
	Never hinged	400.00	
C14	AP10 $1.30 brown	550.00	375.00
	Never hinged	750.00	
C15	AP11 $2.60 blue	850.00	575.00
	Never hinged	1,200.	
	Nos. C13-C15 (3)	1,675.	1,110.

Issued for use on mail carried on first Europe-Pan-America round-trip flight of Graf Zeppelin, May, 1930.

Type of 1930 Issue
Rotary Press Printing
1931-32　　　Perf. 10½x11
Size: 47½x19mm

C16	AP8 5c violet	5.50	.60
	Never hinged	8.25	
C17	AP8 8c olive bister ('32)	2.50	.40
	Never hinged	3.75	

Century of Progress Issue

Airship "Graf Zeppelin" AP12

Flat Plate Printing
1933, Oct. 2　　　Perf. 11

C18	AP12 50c green	80.00	70.00
	Never hinged	120.00	

Flight of the "Graf Zeppelin" in Oct. 1933, to Miami, Akron and Chicago, and from the last city to Europe.

> Catalogue values for unused stamps in this section, from this point to the end of the section, are for Never Hinged items.

Type of 1930 Issue
Rotary Press Printing
1934, June 30　　　Perf. 10½x11

C19	AP8 6c dull orange	3.50	.25

Transpacific Issues

The "China Clipper" over the Pacific — AP13

Flat Plate Printing
1935, Nov. 22　　　Perf. 11

C20	AP13 25c blue	1.40	1.00

Issued to pay postage on mail carried on the Transpacific air post service inaugurated Nov. 22, 1935.

The "China Clipper" over the Pacific AP14

1937, Feb. 15　　　Perf. 11

C21	AP14 20c green	11.00	1.75
C22	AP14 50c carmine	10.00	5.00

Eagle Holding Shield, Olive Branch and Arrows — AP15

1938, May 14　　　Perf. 11

C23	AP15 6c dk blue & carmine	.50	.15
a.	Vert. pair, imperf. horiz.	375.00	
b.	Horiz. pair, imperf. vert.	12,500.	

Transatlantic Issue

Winged Globe AP16

1939, May 16　　　Perf. 11

C24	AP16 30c dull blue	10.50	1.50

Twin-Motored Transport Plane — AP17

Rotary Press Printing
1941-44　　　Perf. 11x10½

C25	AP17 6c carmine	.15	.15
a.	Booklet pane of 3 ('43)	5.00	1.50
b.	Horiz. pair, imperf. between	1,750.	
C26	AP17 8c olive green ('44)	.20	.15
C27	AP17 10c violet	1.25	.20
C28	AP17 15c brown carmine	2.75	.35
C29	AP17 20c bright green	2.25	.30
C30	AP17 30c blue	2.50	.35
C31	AP17 50c orange	11.00	3.00
	Nos. C25-C31 (7)	20.10	4.50

Singles from No. C25a are imperf. at sides or imperf. at sides and bottom.

DC-4 Skymaster AP18

1946, Sept. 25　　　Perf. 11x10½

C32	AP18 5c carmine	.15	.15

DC-4 Skymaster — AP19

1947, Mar. 26　　　Perf. 10½x11

C33	AP19 5c carmine	.15	.15

See Nos. C37, C39, C41.

Pan American Union Building, Washington, DC — AP20

Statue of Liberty and New York Skyline AP21

Plane over San Francisco-Oakland Bay Bridge — AP22

1947　　　Perf. 11x10½

C34	AP20 10c black	.25	.15
C35	AP21 15c brt blue green	.35	.15
a.	Horiz. pair, imperf. between	2,000.	
C36	AP22 25c blue	.85	.15
	Nos. C34-C36 (3)	1.45	
	Set value		.25

Coil Stamp
1948, Jan. 15　　　Perf. 10 Horiz.

C37	AP19 5c carmine	1.00	.80

New York City Issue

Map of Five Boroughs, Circular Band and Planes — AP23

1948, July 31　　　Perf. 11x10½

C38	AP23 5c bright carmine	.15	.15

50th anniv. of the consolidation of the 5 boroughs of NYC.

Type of 1947
1949, Jan. 18　　　Perf. 10½x11

C39	AP19 6c carmine	.15	.15
a.	Booklet pane of 6	10.00	5.00

Alexandria Bicentennial Issue

Home of John Carlyle, Alexandria Seal and Gadsby's Tavern — AP24

Rotary Press Printing
1949, May 11　　　Perf. 11x10½

C40	AP24 6c carmine	.15	.15

Founding of Alexandria, Va, 200th anniv.

Type of 1947
Coil Stamp
1949, Aug. 25　　　Perf. 10 Horiz.

C41	AP19 6c carmine	3.00	.15

Universal Postal Union Issue

Post Office Department Building AP25

Globe and Doves Carrying Messages AP26

Boeing Stratocruiser and Globe — AP27

1949　　　Unwmk.　　　Perf. 11x10½

C42	AP25 10c violet	.20	.20
C43	AP26 15c ultramarine	.30	.25
C44	AP27 25c rose carmine	.50	.40
	Nos. C42-C44 (3)	1.00	.85

75th anniv. of the UPU.

Wright Brothers Issue

Wilbur and Orville Wright and their Plane — AP28

1949, Dec. 17   *Perf. 11x10½*
C45 AP28 6c magenta   .15   .15
46th anniv. of the Wright Brothers' 1st flight, Dec. 17, 1903.

Diamond Head, Honolulu, Hawaii — AP29

1952, Mar. 26   *Perf. 11x10½*
C46 AP29 80c brt red violet   5.00 1.25

First Plane and Modern Plane AP30   Eagle in Flight AP31

Powered Flight Issue

1953, May 29   *Perf. 11x10½*
C47 AP30 6c carmine   .15   .15
50th anniversary of powered flight.

For Domestic Post Cards
1954, Sept. 3   *Perf. 11x10½*
C48 AP31 4c bright blue   .15   .15
See No. C50.

Air Force Issue

B-52 Stratofortress and F-104 Starfighters AP32

Rotary Press Printing
1957, Aug. 1   *Perf. 11x10½*
C49 AP32 6c blue   .15   .15
50th anniv. of US Air Force.

Flying Eagle Type of 1954
For Domestic Post Cards
1958, July 31   *Perf. 11x10½*
C50 AP31 5c rose red   .15   .15

Silhouette of Jet Airliner — AP33

1958, July 31   *Perf. 10½x11*
C51 AP33 7c blue   .15   .15
a.   Booklet pane of 6   14.00   7.00

Coil Stamp
Perf. 10 Horizontally
C52 AP33 7c blue   2.25   .15
Set value   .15
See Nos. C60-C61.

Alaska Statehood Issue

Big Dipper, North Star and Map of Alaska — AP34

Rotary Press Printing
1959, Jan. 3   *Perf. 11x10½*
C53 AP34 7c dark blue   .15   .15
Alaska's admission to statehood.

Balloon Jupiter Issue

Balloon and Crowd — AP35

Giori Press Printing
1959, Aug. 17   *Perf. 11*
C54 AP35 7c dark blue & red   .15   .15
Cent. of the carrying of mail by the balloon Jupiter from Lafayette to Crawfordsville, Ind.

Hawaii Statehood Issue

Alii Warrior, Map of Hawaii and Star of Statehood AP36

Rotary Press Printing
1959, Aug. 21   *Perf. 11x10½*
C55 AP36 7c rose red   .15   .15
Hawaii's admission to statehood.

Pan American Games Issue

Runner Holding Torch — AP37

Giori Press Printing
1959, Aug. 27   *Perf. 11*
C56 AP37 10c violet blue & brt red   .25   .25
3rd Pan American Games, Chicago, Aug. 27-Sept. 7.

Liberty Bell — AP38

Statue of Liberty — AP39

Abraham Lincoln — AP40

Giori Press Printing
1959-66   *Perf. 11*
C57 AP38 10c blk & grn ('60)   1.25   .70
C58 AP39 15c black & orange   .35   .20
C59 AP40 25c blk & mar ('60)   .50   .15
a.   Tagged ('66)   .60   .30
Nos. C57-C59 (3)   2.10
Set value   .80

Luminescence
See note following No. 1053. "Tagged" varieties of untagged airmail stamps start with No. C59a and end with No. C67a.
Airmail stamps starting with No. C69 are tagged unless otherwise noted.

Type of 1958
Rotary Press Printing
1960, Aug. 12   *Perf. 10½x11*
C60 AP33 7c carmine   .15   .15
a.   Booklet pane of 6   17.50   8.00

Type of 1958
Coil Stamp
1960, Oct. 22   *Perf. 10 Horiz.*
C61 AP33 7c carmine   4.25   .25

Type of 1959-60 and

Statue of Liberty — AP41

Giori Press Printing
1961-67   *Perf. 11*
C62 AP38 13c black & red   .40   .15
a.   Tagged ('67)   .75   .50
C63 AP41 15c black & orange   .30   .15
a.   Tagged ('67)   .35   .20
b.   As "a," horiz. pair, imperf. vert.   15,000.
Set value   .15
No. C63 has a gutter between the two parts of the design; No. C58 has none.

Jet Airliner Over Capitol — AP42

Rotary Press Printing
1962, Dec. 5   *Perf. 10½x11*
C64 AP42 8c carmine   .15   .15
a.   Tagged ('63)   .15   .15
b.   Booklet pane 5 + label   7.00   3.00
c.   As "b," tagged ('64)   .20   .75
Three different messages are found on the label in No. C64b, and one on No. C64c.

Coil Stamp
Perf. 10 Horizontally
C65 AP42 8c carmine   .40   .15
a.   Tagged ('65)   .35   .15
Set value   .15
The 1st luminescent tagged US issue was No. C64a issued Aug. 1, 1963, at Dayton, OH. Initial experiments there used tagged stamps and an automated facer-canceler to extract airmail as an aid to dispatch.

Montgomery Blair — AP43   Bald Eagle — AP44

Montgomery Blair Issue
Giori Press Printing
1963, May 3   Unwmk.   *Perf. 11*
C66 AP43 15c car, dp claret & blue   .60   .55
Blair (1813-1883), Postmaster Gen. (1861-64), who called the 1st Intl. Postal Conf., Paris, 1863, forerunner of the UPU.

For Domestic Post Cards
Rotary Press Printing
1963, July 12   *Perf. 11x10½*
C67 AP44 6c red   .15   .15
a.   Tagged ('67)   3.00   2.50

Amelia Earhart Issue

Amelia Earhart and Lockheed Electra — AP45

Giori Press Printing
1963, July 24   *Perf. 11*
C68 AP45 8c carmine & maroon   .20   .15
Earhart (1898-1937), 1st woman to fly across the Atlantic.

Dr. Robert H. Goddard Issue

Robert H. Goddard, Atlas Rocket and Launching Tower, Cape Kennedy AP46

1964, Oct. 5   Unwmk.   Tagged
C69 AP46 8c blue, red & bister   .40   .15
Goddard (1882-1945), physicist and pioneer rocket researcher.

Tlingit Totem, Southern Alaska AP47   "Columbia Jays," by Audubon AP48

Alaska Purchase Issue
Giori Press Printing
1967, Mar. 30   *Perf. 11*
C70 AP47 8c brown   .25   .15
Cent. of the Alaska Purchase. The Tlingit totem is from the Alaska State Museum, Juneau.

1967, Apr. 26   *Perf. 11*
C71 AP48 20c multicolored   .80   .15
See note after No. 1241.

50-Star Runway — AP49

Rotary Press Printing
1968, Jan. 5   Unwmk.   *Perf. 11x10½*
C72 AP49 10c carmine   .20   .15
b.   Booklet pane of 8   2.00   .75
c.   Booklet pane of 5 + label   3.75   .75

Coil Stamp
Perf. 10 Vertically
C73 AP49 10c carmine   .30   .15
a.   Imperf., pair   600.00
Set value   .15

The $1 Air Lift stamp is listed as No. 1341.

Air Mail Service Issue

Curtiss Jenny — AP50

Lithographed, Engraved (Giori)
1968, May 15   *Perf. 11*
C74 AP50 10c blue, black & red   .25   .15
a.   Red (tail stripe) omitted
50th anniv. of regularly scheduled US air mail service.

USA and Jet — AP51

1968, Nov. 22   *Perf. 11*
C75 AP51 20c red, blue & black   .35   .15
See No. C81.

Moon Landing Issue

FIRST MAN ON THE MOON
First Man on the Moon — AP52

Litho. & Engr. (Giori)
1969, Sept. 9   *Perf. 11*
C76 AP52 10c multicolored   .25   .15
  a. Rose red (litho.) omitted   500.00

Man's 1st landing on the moon, July 20, 1969. US astronauts Neil A. Armstrong and Col. Edwin E. Aldrin, Jr., with Lieut. Col. Michael Collins piloting Apollo 11.

On No. C76a, the litho. rose red is missing from the entire vignette—the dots on top of the yellow areas as well as the flag shoulder patch.

Type of 1968 and:

Silhouette of Delta Wing Plane — AP53

Silhouette of Jet Airliner — AP54

Winged Airmail Envelope — AP55

Statue of Liberty AP56

Design: 21c, "USA" and jet (as C75).

Rotary Press Printing
1971-73   *Perf. 10½x11*
C77 AP53 9c red   .20   .15

Perf. 11x10½
C78 AP54 11c carmine   .20   .15
  a. Booklet pane of 4 + 2 labels   1.25   .75
  b. Untagged (Bureau precanceled)   .30
C79 AP55 13c carmine ('73)   .25   .15
  a. Booklet pane of 5 + label ('73) 1.50   .75
  b. Untagged (Bureau precanceled)   .30

Giori Press Printing
Perf. 11
C80 AP56 17c bluish black, red & dark green   .30   .15

Litho. & Engr. (Giori)
Perf. 11
C81 AP51 21c red, blue & black   .35   .15
  Nos. C77-C81 (5)   1.30
  Set value   .45

Issue dates: 9c, May 15; 11c, May 7; 17c, July 13; 21c, May 21, 1971; 13c, Nov. 16, 1973.
The 9c was for use on domestic postal cards.
No. C78b is precanceled "WASHINGTON D.C." (or "DC") and No. C79b "WASHINGTON DC" for the use of Congressmen and the public.

Coil Stamps
Rotary Press Printing
1971-73   *Perf. 10 Vertically*
C82 AP54 11c carmine   .25   .15
  a. Imperf., pair   250.00
C83 AP55 13c carmine ('73)   .30   .15
  a. Imperf., pair   80.00
  Set value   .15

Issue dates: 11c, May 7; 13c, Dec. 27.

National Parks Centennial Issue

Kii Statue and Temple, City of Refuge, Hawaii — AP57

Litho. & Engr. (Giori)
1972, May 3   *Perf. 11*
C84 AP57 11c orange & multi   .20   .15
  a. Blue & green (litho) omitted   1,100.

Cent. of the Natl. Parks system. No. C84 shows view of the City of Refuge Natl. Historical Park at Honaunau.

Olympic Games Issue

Skiing and Olympic Rings — AP58

Photogravure (Andreotti)
1972, Aug. 17   *Perf. 11x10½*
C85 AP58 11c multicolored   .20   .15

11th Winter Olympic Games, Sapporo, Japan, Feb. 3-13, and 20th Summer Olympic Games, Munich, Germany, Aug. 26-Sept. 11.

Electronics Progress Issue

De Forest Audions AP59

Progress in Electronics

Litho. & Engr. (Giori)
1973, July 10   *Perf. 11*
C86 AP59 11c multicolored   .20   .15
  a. Vermilion & olive (litho.) omitted 1,400.

Statue of Liberty AP60

Mt. Rushmore National Memorial AP61

1974   Giori Press Printing   Perf. 11
C87 AP60 18c car, black & ultra   .35   .25
C88 AP61 26c ultra, black & car   .50   .15

Issue dates: 18c, Jan. 11; 26c, Jan. 2.

Plane and Globes — AP62

Plane, Globes and Flag — AP63

Giori Press Printing
1976, Jan. 2   *Perf. 11*
C89 AP62 25c ultra, red & black   .45   .15
C90 AP63 31c ultra, red & black   .50   .15
  Set value   .25

Wright Brothers Issue

USAirmail 31c
Orville and Wilbur Wright, Flyer A — AP64

USAirmail 31c
Wright Brothers, Flyer A and Shed — AP65

Litho. & Engr.
1978, Sept. 23   *Perf. 11*
C91 AP64 31c ultra & multi   .60   .30
C92 AP65 31c ultra & multi   .60   .30
  a. Vert. pair, #C91-C92   1.20 1.10
  b. As "a," ultramarine & black (engr.) omitted   800.00

  c. As "a," black (engr.) omitted   —
  d. As "a," black, yellow, magenta, blue & brown (litho.) omitted   2,250.

75th anniv. of 1st powered flight, Kill Devil Hill, NC, Dec. 17, 1903.

Octave Chanute Issue

Chanute and Biplane Hangglider AP66

Biplane Hanggliders and Chanute AP67

Litho. & Engr.
1979, Mar. 29   *Perf. 11*
C93 AP66 21c ultra & multi   .70   .30
C94 AP67 21c ultra & multi   .70   .30
  a. Vert. pair, #C93-C94   1.40 1.10
  b. As "a," ultramarine & black (engr.) omitted   4,500.

Octave Chanute (1832-1910), civil engineer and aviation pioneer.

Wiley Post Issue

Wiley Post and "Winnie Mae" — AP68

NR-105 W, Post in Pressurized Suit, Portrait — AP69

Litho. & Engr.
1979, Nov. 20   *Perf. 11*
C95 AP68 25c ultra & multi   1.10   .35
C96 AP69 25c ultra & multi   1.10   .35
  a. Vert. pair, #C95-C96   2.25 1.25

Post (1899-1935), 1st man to fly around the world alone and high-altitude flying pioneer.

Olympic Games Issue

High Jump — AP70

1979, Nov. 1   Photo.   Perf. 11
C97 AP70 31c multicolored   .65   .30

22nd Olympic Games, Moscow, July 19-Aug. 3, 1980.

Philip Mazzei
Patriot Remembered

Philip Mazzei (1730-1816), Italian-born Political Writer — AP71   40c

1980, Oct. 13   Photo.   Perf. 11
C98 AP71 40c multicolored   .75   .15
  a. Perf. 10½x11   4.50
  b. Imperf., pair   3,500.
  c. Horiz. pair, imperf. vert.

Blanche Stuart Scott (1886-1970) Pioneer Pilot AP72

Glenn Curtiss (1878-1930) AP73

Glenn Curtiss Aviation Pioneer

1980, Dec. 30
C99 AP72 28c multicolored   .55   .15
C100 AP73 35c multicolored   .60   .15

Scott, 1st woman pilot, and Curtiss, aviation pioneer and aircraft designer.

1984 Olympic Games

USA 40c   AP81

1983, June 17   *Perf. 11*
C101 AP81 28c Gymnast   1.00   .30
C102 AP81 28c Hurdler   1.00   .30
C103 AP81 28c Basketball   1.00   .30
C104 AP81 28c Soccer   1.00   .30
  a. Block of 4, #C101-C104   4.50 2.00
  b. As "a," imperf. vert.   —

Nos. C101-C104 are vertical.

1983, Apr. 8
C105 AP81 40c Shot put   .90   .40
C106 AP81 40c Gymnast   .90   .40
C107 AP81 40c Swimmer   .90   .40
C108 AP81 40c Weightlifting   .90   .40
  a. Block of 4, #C105-C108   4.25 2.50
  b. As "a," imperf.   1,350.

1983, Nov. 4
C109 AP81 35c Women's fencing   .90   .50
C110 AP81 35c Cycling   .90   .50
C111 AP81 35c Women's volleyball .90   .50
C112 AP81 35c Pole vaulting   .90   .50
  a. Block of 4, #C109-C112   4.00 3.00

Alfred V. Verville AP86

Alfred V. Verville Aviation Pioneer   33

Lawrence and Elmer Sperry Aviation Pioneers   39
Lawrence and Elmer Sperry AP87

1985, Feb. 13   Photo.
C113 AP86 33c multicolored   .60   .20
  a. Imperf., pair   1,000.
C114 AP87 39c multicolored   .70   .25
  a. Imperf., pair   1,400.

Alfred V. Verville (1890-1970), aircraft designer, Lawrence Sperry (1892-1931), designer and pilot, and Elmer Sperry (1860-1930), inventor.

Transpacific Airmail AP88

1985, Feb. 15   Photo.
C115 AP88 44c multicolored   .80   .25
  a. Imperf., pair   1,000.

Fr. Junipero Serra (1713-84)
California Missionary

Junipero Serra USAirmail

Outline Map of Southern California, Portrait, San Gabriel Mission AP89   44

1985, Aug. 22   Photo.   *Perf. 11*
C116 AP89 44c multicolored   .90   .30
  a. Imperf., pair   1,600.

New Sweden 1638

Settling of New Sweden, 350th Anniv. AP90   USAirmail   44

Design: 17th Cent. European settler negotiating with two American Indians, map of New Sweden, the Swedish ships *Kalmar Nyckel* and *Fogel Grip*, based on an 18th cent. illustration from a Swedish book about the Colonies.

1988, Mar. 29 — Litho. & Engr.
C117 AP90 44c multicolored — 1.00 .25
See Finland No. 768 and Sweden No. 1672.

Samuel Pierpont Langley (1834-1906)
Astronomer, Aviation Pioneer and Inventor

Langley and Unmanned Aerodrome No. 5 — AP91

1988, May 14 — Litho. & Engr. Perf. 11
C118 AP91 45c multicolored — .85 .20

Igor Sikorsky (1889-1972)
Aeronautic Engineer

Sikorsky and VS300 Helicopter, 1939 — AP92

1988, June 23 — Photo. Perf. 11
C119 AP92 36c multicolored — .65 .20

French Revolution, Bicent.

Liberty, Equality and Fraternity — AP93

Perf. 11½x11
1989, July 14 — Litho. & Engr.
C120 AP93 45c multicolored — .85 .20
See France Nos. 2143-2145a.

Pre-Columbian America Issue

UPAE Emblem and Southeastern Figure, *Key Marco Cat,* Calusa Culture, Pre-Columbian Mississippian Period, A.D. 700-1450 — AP94

1989, Oct. 12 — Photo. Perf. 11
C121 AP94 45c multicolored — .85 .20
Discovery of America, 500th anniv. (in 1992).

Futuristic Mail Delivery

Spacecraft AP95	Air-suspended Hover Car AP96

Moon Rover AP97	Space Shuttle AP98

1989, Nov. 27 — Perf. 11
C122 AP95 45c multicolored — 1.00 .40
C123 AP96 45c multicolored — 1.00 .40
C124 AP97 45c multicolored — 1.00 .40

C125 AP98 45c multicolored — 1.00 .40
b. Block of 4, Nos. C122-C125 — 4.00 3.00
b. As "a," light blue (engr.) omitted — 1,350.

1989, Nov. 24 — Litho. & Engr. Imperf.
C126 Sheet of 4 — 4.25 3.25
a. AP95 45c multicolored — .90 .50
b. AP96 45c multicolored — .90 .50
c. AP97 45c multicolored — .90 .50
d. AP98 45c multicolored — .90 .50
World Stamp Expo '89, 20th UPU Congress. See Russia No. 5837.

Pre-Columbian America Issue

Tropical Coast AP99

1990, Oct. 12 — Photo. Perf. 11
C127 AP99 45c multicolored — .85 .20

Harriet Quimby, Bleriot Aircraft AP100

1991, Apr. 27 — Photo. Perf. 11
C128 AP100 50c multicolored — .90 .25
a. Vert. pair, imperf. horiz. — 2,000.
b. Perf. 11.2 ('93) — .90 .25

William T. Piper, Piper Cub AP101

1991, May 17
C129 AP101 40c multicolored — .80 .20
See No. C132.

Antarctic Treaty, 30th Anniv. AP102

1991, June 21 — Photo. Perf. 11
C130 AP102 50c multicolored — .90 .25

Pre-Columbian America Issue

First Americans Crossed Over From Asia — AP103

1991, Oct. 12 — Photo. Perf. 11
C131 AP103 50c multicolored — .90 .25

Piper Type of 1991
1993 — Photo. Perf. 11
C132 AP101 40c multicolored — .80 .20
Piper's hair touches top edge of design. Bullseye perf. 11.2.

AIR POST SPECIAL DELIVERY STAMPS

To provide for the payment of both the postage and the special delivery fee in one stamp.

Great Seal of United States — APSD1

Flat Plate Printing
1934 — Unwmk. Perf. 11
CE1 APSD1 16c dark blue — .60 .65
Never hinged — .80
For imperforate variety see No. 771.

1936
CE2 APSD1 16c red & blue — .40 .25
Never hinged — .50
a. Horiz. pair, imperf. vert. — 4,000.

SPECIAL DELIVERY STAMPS

When affixed to any letter or article of mailable matter, secure immediate delivery, between 7 A. M. and midnight, at any post office.

Messenger Running SD1

Flat Plate Printing
1885 — Unwmk. Perf. 12
E1 SD1 10c blue — 275.00 40.00
Never hinged — 465.00

Messenger Running SD2

1888
E2 SD2 10c blue — 250.00 15.00
Never hinged — 425.00

1893
E3 SD2 10c orange — 165.00 20.00
Never hinged — 275.00

Messenger Running SD3

Line under "Ten Cents"

1894
E4 SD3 10c blue — 600.00 25.00
Never hinged — 975.00

1895 — Wmk. 191
E5 SD3 10c blue — 140.00 3.25
Never hinged — 215.00
b. Printed on both sides

Messenger on Bicycle SD4

1902
E6 SD4 10c ultramarine — 90.00 3.00
Never hinged — 135.00

Helmet of Mercury and Olive Branch — SD5

1908
E7 SD5 10c green — 55.00 30.00
Never hinged — 85.00

1911 — Wmk. 190 Perf. 12
E8 SD4 10c ultramarine — 90.00 5.00
Never hinged — 140.00
b. 10c violet blue — 95.00 5.00
Never hinged — 140.00

1914 — Perf. 10
E9 SD4 10c ultramarine — 160.00 6.00
Never hinged — 240.00

1916 — Unwmk. Perf. 10
E10 SD4 10c pale ultra — 265.00 25.00
Never hinged — 400.00

1917 — Perf. 11
E11 SD4 10c ultramarine — 16.50 .50
b. 10c gray violet — 16.50 .50
Never hinged — 27.50
c. 10c blue — 45.00 2.50
Never hinged — 70.00

Postman and Motorcycle SD6

Post Office Truck — SD7

1922-25
E12 SD6 10c gray violet — 27.50 .40
Never hinged — 40.00
a. 10c deep ultramarine — 32.50 .50
Never hinged — 47.50
E13 SD6 15c deep orange ('25) — 25.00 .90
Never hinged — 37.50
E14 SD7 20c black ('25) — 1.75 1.40
Never hinged — 2.50
Nos. E12-E14 (3) — 54.25 2.70

No. E12 measures 36x21½mm
No. E15 measures 36½x21¾mm
No. E13 measures 36½x21½mm
No. E16 measures 36¾x22¼mm
No. E14 measures 35½x21½mm
No. E19 measures 36¼x22mm

Rotary Press Printing
1927-31 — Perf. 11x10½
E15 SD6 10c gray violet — .60 .15
Never hinged — .80
a. 10c red lilac — .60 .15
Never hinged — .80
b. 10c gray lilac — .60 .15
Never hinged — .80
c. Horiz. pair, imperf. btwn. — 300.00
E16 SD6 15c deep orange ('31) — .70 .15
Never hinged — .90
Set value — .15

> Catalogue values for unused stamps in this section, from this point to the end of the section, are for Never Hinged items.

1944-51

E17	SD6	13c blue	.60	.15
E18	SD6	17c orange yellow	2.75	1.75
E19	SD7	20c black ('51)	1.25	.15
		Nos. E17-E19 (3)	4.60	2.05

Special Delivery
Letter, Hand to
Hand — SD8

1954-57   Perf. 11x10½

E20	SD8	20c deep blue	.40	.15
E21	SD8	30c lake ('57)	.50	.15
		Set value		.15

Arrows — SD9

Giori Press Printing
1969-71   Perf. 11

E22	SD9	45c car & vio blue	1.25	.25
E23	SD9	60c vio blue & car ('71)	1.25	.20

Issue dates: 45c, Nov. 21; 60c, May 10.

REGISTRATION STAMP

Issued for the prepayment of registry fees; not usable for postage.

Eagle — RS1

Wmk. 190
1911, Dec. 1   Engr.   Perf. 12

F1	RS1	10c ultramarine	75.00	6.00
		Never hinged	115.00	

CERTIFIED MAIL STAMP

For use on first-class mail for which no indemnity value is claimed, but for which proof of mailing and proof of delivery are available at less cost than registered mail.

Catalogue values for unused stamps in this section are for Never Hinged items.

Letter Carrier — CM1

Rotary Press Printing
1955, June 6 Unwmk.   Perf. 10½x11

FA1	CM1	15c red	.40	.25

POSTAGE DUE STAMPS

For affixing, by a postal clerk to any piece of mailable matter, to denote the amount to be collected from the addressee because of insufficient prepayment of postage.

Unused Values for Nos. J1-J14 are for stamps with full original gum.

D1   D2

Printed by the American Bank Note Company

1879   Unwmk.   Engraved   Perf. 12

J1	D1	1c brown	45.00	8.50
J2	D1	2c brown	300.00	7.50
J3	D1	3c brown	40.00	4.50
J4	D1	5c brown	500.00	45.00
J5	D1	10c brown	525.00	25.00
a.		Imperf., pair	1,600.	
J6	D1	30c brown	250.00	50.00
J7	D1	50c brown	350.00	60.00
		Nos. J1-J7 (7)	2,010.	200.50

Special Printing
1879

J8	D1	1c deep brown	6,250.	
J9	D1	2c deep brown	4,250.	
J10	D1	3c deep brown	3,750.	
J11	D1	5c deep brown	3,500.	
J12	D1	10c deep brown	2,250.	
J13	D1	30c deep brown	2,400.	
J14	D1	50c deep brown	2,500.	

1884

J15	D1	1c red brown	45.00	4.50
J16	D1	2c red brown	55.00	4.50
J17	D1	3c red brown	825.00	175.00
J18	D1	5c red brown	385.00	25.00
J19	D1	10c red brown	385.00	17.50
J20	D1	30c red brown	175.00	50.00
J21	D1	50c red brown	1,500.	175.00
		Nos. J15-J21 (7)	3,370.	451.50

1891

J22	D1	1c bright claret	20.00	1.00
J23	D1	2c bright claret	25.00	1.00
J24	D1	3c bright claret	50.00	8.00
J25	D1	5c bright claret	60.00	8.00
J26	D1	10c bright claret	100.00	17.50
J27	D1	30c bright claret	350.00	150.00
J28	D1	50c bright claret	375.00	150.00
		Nos. J22-J28 (7)	980.00	335.50

See Die and Plate Proofs in the Scott U.S. Specialized for imperfs. on stamp paper.

Printed by the Bureau of Engraving and Printing

1894

J29	D2	1c vermilion	1,300.	325.
		Never hinged	1,800.	
J30	D2	2c vermilion	550.00	125.
		Never hinged	825.	

1894

J31	D2	1c deep claret	37.50	6.00
		Never hinged	55.00	
b.		Vert. pair, imperf. horiz.		
J32	D2	2c deep claret	35.00	4.00
		Never hinged	52.50	
J33	D2	3c deep claret	140.00	30.00
		Never hinged	210.00	
J34	D2	5c deep claret	200.00	35.00
		Never hinged	290.00	
J35	D2	10c deep claret	200.00	25.00
		Never hinged	290.00	
J36	D2	30c deep claret	350.00	90.00
		Never hinged	525.00	
a.		30c carmine	350.00	100.00
		Never hinged	525.00	
b.		30c pale rose	290.00	85.00
		Never hinged	440.00	
J37	D2	50c deep claret	925.00	250.00
		Never hinged	1,400.	
a.		50c pale rose	875.00	250.00
		Never hinged	1,350.	
		Nos. J31-J37 (7)	1,887.	440.00

Shades are numerous in the 1894 and later issues.

See Die and Plate Proofs in the Scott U.S. Specialized for 1c imperf. on stamp paper.

1895   Wmk. 191

J38	D2	1c deep claret	7.50	.75
		Never hinged	12.50	
J39	D2	2c deep claret	7.50	.70
		Never hinged	12.50	
J40	D2	3c deep claret	47.50	1.75
		Never hinged	72.50	
J41	D2	5c deep claret	50.00	1.75
		Never hinged	80.00	
J42	D2	10c deep claret	52.50	3.50
		Never hinged	82.50	
J43	D2	30c deep claret	450.00	50.00
		Never hinged	675.00	
J44	D2	50c deep claret	275.00	37.50
		Never hinged	425.00	
		Nos. J38-J44 (7)	890.00	95.95

1910-12   Wmk. 190

J45	D2	1c deep claret	27.50	3.00
		Never hinged	40.00	
a.		1c rose carmine	25.00	3.00
		Never hinged	37.50	

J46	D2	2c deep claret	27.50	1.00
		Never hinged	40.00	
a.		2c rose carmine	25.00	1.00
		Never hinged	37.50	
J47	D2	3c deep claret	450.00	30.00
		Never hinged	675.00	
J48	D2	5c deep claret	75.00	6.50
		Never hinged	120.00	
a.		5c rose carmine	—	—
J49	D2	10c deep claret	95.00	12.50
		Never hinged	150.00	
a.		10c rose carmine	—	—
J50	D2	50c deep claret ('12)	750.00	120.00
		Never hinged	1,150.	
		Nos. J45-J50 (6)	1,425.	173.00

1914   Perf. 10

J52	D2	1c carmine lake	50.00	11.00
		Never hinged	80.00	
a.		1c dull rose	60.00	11.00
		Never hinged	95.00	
J53	D2	2c carmine lake	40.00	.40
		Never hinged	65.00	
a.		2c dull rose	45.00	.40
		Never hinged	70.00	
b.		2c vermilion	45.00	.40
		Never hinged	70.00	
J54	D2	3c carmine lake	750.00	37.50
		Never hinged	1,125.	
a.		3c dull rose	750.00	37.50
		Never hinged	1,125.	
J55	D2	5c carmine lake	32.50	2.50
		Never hinged	50.00	
a.		5c dull rose	32.50	2.50
		Never hinged	50.00	
J56	D2	10c carmine lake	50.00	2.00
		Never hinged	80.00	
a.		10c dull rose	60.00	2.00
		Never hinged	95.00	
J57	D2	30c carmine lake	200.00	17.50
		Never hinged	275.00	
J58	D2	50c carmine lake	8,250.	650.00
		Never hinged	10,500.	
		Nos. J52-J58 (7)	9,372.	720.90

1916   Unwmk.   Perf. 10

J59	D2	1c rose	2,000.	300.00
		Never hinged	3,100.	
J60	D2	2c rose	150.00	20.00
		Never hinged	240.00	

1917   Perf. 11

J61	D2	1c carmine rose	2.50	.25
		Never hinged	3.75	
a.		1c rose red	2.50	.25
		Never hinged	3.75	
b.		1c deep claret	2.50	.25
		Never hinged	3.75	
J62	D2	2c carmine rose	2.25	.25
		Never hinged	3.50	
a.		2c rose red	2.25	.25
		Never hinged	3.50	
b.		2c deep claret	2.25	.25
		Never hinged	3.50	
J63	D2	3c carmine rose	10.00	.25
		Never hinged	17.50	
a.		3c rose red	10.00	.25
		Never hinged	17.50	
b.		3c deep claret	10.00	.35
		Never hinged	17.50	
J64	D2	5c carmine	10.00	.25
		Never hinged	17.50	
a.		5c rose red	10.00	.25
		Never hinged	17.50	
b.		5c deep claret	10.00	.25
		Never hinged	17.50	
J65	D2	10c carmine rose	15.00	.30
		Never hinged	27.50	
a.		10c rose red	15.00	.25
		Never hinged	27.50	
b.		10c deep claret	15.00	.25
		Never hinged	27.50	
J66	D2	30c carmine rose	80.00	.75
		Never hinged	120.00	
a.		30c deep claret	80.00	.75
		Never hinged	120.00	
J67	D2	50c carmine rose	100.00	.30
		Never hinged	150.00	
a.		50c rose red	100.00	.30
		Never hinged	150.00	
b.		50c deep claret	100.00	.30
		Never hinged	150.00	
		Nos. J61-J67 (7)	219.75	2.35

1925

J68	D2	½c dull red	1.00	.25
		Never hinged	1.50	

D3   D4

1930   Perf. 11

J69	D3	½c carmine	4.50	1.40
		Never hinged	6.00	
J70	D3	1c carmine	3.00	.25
		Never hinged	4.25	
J71	D3	2c carmine	4.00	.25
		Never hinged	5.75	
J72	D3	3c carmine	21.00	1.75
		Never hinged	32.50	
J73	D3	5c carmine	19.00	2.50
		Never hinged	30.00	
J74	D3	10c carmine	40.00	1.00
		Never hinged	65.00	
J75	D3	30c carmine	110.00	2.00
		Never hinged	160.00	
J76	D3	50c carmine	140.00	.75
		Never hinged	250.00	

J77	D4	$1 carmine	30.00	.25
		Never hinged	40.00	
a.		$1 scarlet	25.00	.25
		Never hinged	35.00	
J78	D4	$5 carmine	37.50	.25
		Never hinged	57.50	
a.		$5 scarlet	32.50	.25
		Never hinged	47.50	
		Nos. J69-J78 (10)	409.00	10.40

Rotary Press Printing
1931-56   Perf. 11x10½

J79	D3	½c dull carmine	.90	.15
		Never hinged	1.30	
J80	D3	1c dull carmine	.20	.15
		Never hinged	.30	
J81	D3	2c dull carmine	.20	.15
		Never hinged	.30	
J82	D3	3c dull carmine	.25	.15
		Never hinged	.40	
J83	D3	5c dull carmine	.40	.15
		Never hinged	.60	
J84	D3	10c dull carmine	1.10	.15
		Never hinged	1.60	
J85	D3	30c dull carmine	7.50	.25
		Never hinged	10.00	
J86	D3	50c dull carmine	10.00	.25
		Never hinged	15.00	
J79a	D3	½c scarlet	.90	.15
		Never hinged	1.30	
J80a	D3	1c scarlet	.20	.15
		Never hinged	.30	
J81a	D3	2c scarlet	.20	.15
		Never hinged	.30	
J82a	D3	3c scarlet	.25	.15
		Never hinged	.40	
J83a	D3	5c scarlet	.40	.15
		Never hinged	.60	
J84a	D3	10c scarlet	1.10	.15
		Never hinged	1.60	
J85a	D3	30c scarlet	7.50	.25
		Never hinged	10.00	
J86a	D3	50c scarlet	10.00	.25
		Never hinged	15.00	

Perf. 10½x11

J87	D4	$1 scarlet ('56)	35.00	.25
		Never hinged	52.50	
		Nos. J79-J87 (17)	55.55	
		Set value		1.05
		Nos. J79a-J86a (8)	20.55	
		Set value		.80

Catalogue values for unused stamps in this section, from this point to the end of the section, are for Never Hinged items.

D5

Denominations added by rubber plates in an operation similar to precanceling.

Rotary Press Printing
Perf. 11x10½
1959, June 19   Unwmk.
Denomination in Black

J88	D5	½c carmine rose	1.50	1.10
J89	D5	1c carmine rose	.15	.15
a.		"1 CENT" omitted	300.00	
b.		Pair, one without "1 CENT"	450.00	
J90	D5	2c carmine rose	.15	.15
J91	D5	3c carmine rose	.15	.15
a.		Pair, one without "3 CENTS"	750.00	
J92	D5	4c carmine rose	.15	.15
J93	D5	5c carmine rose	.15	.15
a.		Pair, one without "5 CENTS"		
J94	D5	6c carmine rose	.15	.15
a.		Pair, one without "6 CENTS"	800.00	
J95	D5	7c carmine rose	.20	.15
J96	D5	8c carmine rose	.20	.15
a.		Pair, one without "8 CENTS"	750.00	
J97	D5	10c carmine rose	.20	.15
J98	D5	30c carmine rose	.65	.15
J99	D5	50c carmine rose	1.10	.15

Straight Numeral Outlined in Black

J100	D5	$1 carmine rose	2.00	.15
J101	D5	$5 carmine rose	9.00	.20
		Nos. J88-J101 (14)	15.75	
		Set value		1.60

All single copies with value omitted are catalogued as No. J89a.

1978-85

Denomination in Black

J102	D5	11c carmine rose	.25	.20
J103	D5	13c carmine rose	.25	.20
J104	D5	17c carmine rose	.40	.35
		Nos. J102-J104 (3)	.90	.75
		Nos. J88-J104 (17)	16.65	

Issue dates: Jan. 2, 1978, June 10, 1985.

UNITED STATES OFFICES IN CHINA

Issued for sale by the postal agency at Shanghai, at their surcharged value in local currency. Valid to the amount of their original values for the prepayment of postage on mail dispatched from the US postal agency at Shanghai to addresses in the US.

SHANGHAI
2¢
CHINA

Nos. 498-499, 502-504, 506-510, 512, 514-518 Surcharged

1919		Unwmk.	Perf. 11	
K1	A140	2c on 1c green	22.50	27.50
		Never hinged	35.00	
K2	A140	4c on 2c rose, type I	22.50	27.50
		Never hinged	35.00	
K3	A140	6c on 3c vio, type II	45.00	65.00
		Never hinged	67.50	
K4	A140	8c on 4c brown	50.00	65.00
		Never hinged	75.00	
K5	A140	10c on 5c blue	55.00	65.00
		Never hinged	80.00	
K6	A140	12c on 6c red org	70.00	95.00
		Never hinged	105.00	
K7	A140	14c on 7c black	75.00	110.00
		Never hinged	120.00	
K8	A148	16c on 8c ol bis	55.00	70.00
		Never hinged	80.00	
a.		16c on 8c olive green	50.00	60.00
		Never hinged	75.00	
K9	A148	18c on 9c sal red	55.00	75.00
		Never hinged	80.00	
K10	A148	20c on 10c org yel	50.00	60.00
		Never hinged	75.00	
K11	A148	24c on 12c brn car	60.00	70.00
		Never hinged	90.00	
a.		24c on 12c claret brown	80.00	110.00
		Never hinged	140.00	
K12	A148	30c on 15c gray	75.00	125.00
		Never hinged	120.00	
K13	A148	40c on 20c dp ultra	110.00	190.00
		Never hinged	175.00	
K14	A148	60c on 30c org red	100.00	160.00
		Never hinged	150.00	
K15	A148	$1 on 50c lt vio	400.00	550.00
		Never hinged	600.00	
K16	A148	$2 on $1 vio brown	350.00	450.00
		Never hinged	500.00	
a.		Double surcharge	4,250.	4,750.
		Never hinged	5,750.	
		Nos. K1-K16 (16)	1,595.	2,205.

SHANGHAI
2 Cts.
CHINA

Nos. 498 and 528B Surcharged

1922, July 3				
K17	A140	2c on 1c green	110.00	110.00
		Never hinged	160.00	
K18	A140	4c on 2c carmine, type VII	95.00	95.00
		Never hinged	140.00	

OFFICIAL STAMPS

The franking privilege having been abolished, as of July 1, 1873, these stamps were provided for each of the departments of Government for the prepayment of postage on official matter.

These stamps were supplanted on May 1, 1879, by penalty envelopes and on July 5, 1884, were declared obsolete.

Designs, except Post Office, resemble those illustrated but are not identical. Each bears the name of Department. Portraits are as follows: 1c, Franklin; 2c, Jackson; 3c, Washington; 6c, Lincoln; 7c, Stanton; 10c, Jefferson; 12c, Clay; 15c, Webster; 24c, Scott; 30c, Hamilton; 90c, Perry.

Practically all Official stamps of the 1870's exist imperf.

O6

Grade, condition and original gum are very important in valuing #O1-O120 unused.

Printed by the Continental Bank Note Co.
Thin Hard Paper

O1

1873		Unwmk. Engr.	Perf. 12	

Dept. of Agriculture

O1	O1	1c yellow	150.00	110.00
O2	O1	2c yellow	125.00	45.00
O3	O1	3c yellow	110.00	8.50
O4	O1	6c yellow	120.00	35.00
O5	O1	10c yellow	240.00	140.00
O6	O1	12c yellow	325.00	175.00
O7	O1	15c yellow	275.00	160.00
O8	O1	24c yellow	275.00	140.00
O9	O1	30c yellow	350.00	200.00
		Nos. O1-O9 (9)	1,970.	1,013.

Special printings overprinted "SPECIMEN" follow No. O120.

Executive Dept.

O10	O1	1c carmine	525.00	300.00
O11	O1	2c carmine	350.00	150.00
O12	O1	3c carmine	425.00	150.00
a.		3c violet rose	425.00	150.00
O13	O1	6c carmine	625.00	375.00
O14	O1	10c carmine	575.00	450.00
		Nos. O10-O14 (5)	2,500.	1,425.

Special printings overprinted "SPECIMEN" follow No. O120.

Dept. of the Interior

O15	O1	1c vermilion	32.50	7.50
O16	O1	2c vermilion	27.50	5.00
O17	O1	3c vermilion	45.00	4.50
O18	O1	6c vermilion	32.50	4.50
O19	O1	10c vermilion	32.50	9.00
O20	O1	12c vermilion	47.50	7.00
O21	O1	15c vermilion	80.00	15.00
O22	O1	24c vermilion	57.50	12.50
a.		Double impression		—
O23	O1	30c vermilion	80.00	12.50
O24	O1	90c vermilion	180.00	32.50
		Nos. O15-O24 (10)	615.00	110.00

Special printings overprinted "SPECIMEN" follow No. O120.

Dept. of Justice

O25	O1	1c purple	100.00	70.00
O26	O1	2c purple	165.00	75.00
O27	O1	3c purple	165.00	15.00
O28	O1	6c purple	150.00	22.50
O29	O1	10c purple	170.00	50.00
O30	O1	12c purple	135.00	32.50
O31	O1	15c purple	260.00	110.00
O32	O1	24c purple	650.00	250.00
O33	O1	30c purple	550.00	150.00
O34	O1	90c purple	825.00	375.00
		Nos. O25-O34 (10)	3,170.	1,150.

Special printings overprinted "SPECIMEN" follow No. O120.

Navy Dept.

O35	O1	1c ultramarine	70.00	32.50
a.		1c dull blue	80.00	35.00
O36	O1	2c ultramarine	55.00	15.00
a.		2c dull blue	65.00	10.00
O37	O1	3c ultramarine	55.00	7.50
a.		3c dull blue	65.00	10.00
O38	O1	6c ultramarine	55.00	12.50
a.		6c dull blue	65.00	13.00
O39	O1	7c ultramarine	350.00	130.00
a.		7c dull blue	400.00	140.00
O40	O1	10c ultramarine	75.00	25.00
a.		10c dull blue	80.00	25.00
O41	O1	12c ultramarine	90.00	22.50
O42	O1	15c ultramarine	165.00	45.00
O43	O1	24c ultramarine	165.00	50.00
a.		24c dull blue	190.00	—
O44	O1	30c ultramarine	135.00	25.00
O45	O1	90c ultramarine	650.00	160.00
a.		Double impression		3,750.
		Nos. O35-O45 (11)	1,865.	525.00

Special printings overprinted "SPECIMEN" follow No. O120.

O6

Post Office Dept.

O47	O6	1c black	12.00	5.00
O48	O6	2c black	15.00	4.00
a.		Double impression	300.00	
O49	O6	3c black	5.00	1.25
a.		Printed on both sides		3,000.
O50	O6	6c black	15.00	3.00
a.		Diagonal half used as 3c on cover		3,000.
O51	O6	10c black	65.00	30.00
O52	O6	12c black	32.50	7.50
O53	O6	15c black	45.00	12.50
O54	O6	24c black	55.00	15.00
O55	O6	30c black	55.00	15.00
O56	O6	90c black	85.00	12.50
		Nos. O47-O56 (10)	389.00	105.75

Stamps of the POD are often on paper with a gray surface. This is due to insufficient wiping of the plates during printing.

Special printings overprinted "SPECIMEN" follow No. O120.

Seward — O8

Dept. of State

O57	O1	1c dark green	100.00	35.00
O58	O1	2c dark green	200.00	55.00
O59	O1	3c bright green	80.00	15.00
O60	O1	6c bright green	75.00	17.50
O61	O1	7c dark green	150.00	35.00
O62	O1	10c dark green	120.00	25.00
O63	O1	12c dark green	185.00	75.00
O64	O1	15c dark green	200.00	50.00
O65	O1	24c dark green	400.00	130.00
O66	O1	30c dark green	375.00	100.00
O67	O1	90c dark green	700.00	225.00
O68	O8	$2 green & black	850.00	600.00
O69	O8	$5 green & black	6,000.	3,000.
O70	O8	$10 green & black	4,000.	2,000.
O71	O8	$20 green & black	3,250.	1,500.

Special printings overprinted "SPECIMEN" follow No. O120.

Treasury Dept.

O72	O1	1c brown	35.00	4.00
O73	O1	2c brown	45.00	4.00
O74	O1	3c brown	30.00	1.50
a.		Double impression		
O75	O1	6c brown	40.00	3.50
O76	O1	7c brown	85.00	20.00
O77	O1	10c brown	85.00	7.00
O78	O1	12c brown	85.00	5.50
O79	O1	15c brown	80.00	7.00
O80	O1	24c brown	400.00	57.50
O81	O1	30c brown	135.00	8.00
O82	O1	90c brown	140.00	9.00
		Nos. O72-O82 (11)	1,160.	127.00

Special printings overprinted "SPECIMEN" follow No. O120.

War Dept.

O83	O1	1c rose	130.00	6.50
O84	O1	2c rose	120.00	8.50
O85	O1	3c rose	125.00	2.50
O86	O1	6c rose	400.00	5.50
O87	O1	7c rose	120.00	65.00
O88	O1	10c rose	40.00	10.00
O89	O1	12c rose	135.00	8.00
O90	O1	15c rose	35.00	10.00
O91	O1	24c rose	35.00	6.00
O92	O1	30c rose	37.50	6.00
O93	O1	90c rose	85.00	35.00
		Nos. O83-O93 (11)	1,262.	163.00

Special printings overprinted "SPECIMEN" follow No. O120.

Printed by the American Bank Note Co.

1879		Soft Porous Paper		

Dept. of Agriculture

O94	O1	1c yel, no gum	2,100.	
O95	O1	3c yellow	275.00	50.00

Dept. of the Interior

O96	O1	1c vermilion	200.00	175.00
O97	O1	2c vermilion	3.75	1.50
O98	O1	3c vermilion	3.25	1.00
O99	O1	6c vermilion	5.00	5.00
O100	O1	10c vermilion	60.00	50.00
O101	O1	12c vermilion	120.00	80.00
O102	O1	15c vermilion	275.00	200.00
O103	O1	24c vermilion	2,600.	—

Dept. of Justice

O106	O1	3c bluish purple	80.00	50.00
O107	O1	6c bluish purple	175.00	140.00

Post Office Dept.

O108	O6	3c black	14.00	4.50

Treasury Dept.

O109	O1	3c brown	42.50	6.00
O110	O1	6c brown	80.00	30.00
O111	O1	10c brown	120.00	35.00
O112	O1	30c brown	1,200.	250.00
O113	O1	90c brown	1,650.	250.00
		Nos. O109-O113 (5)	3,092.	571.00

War Dept.

O114	O1	1c rose red	3.25	2.50
O115	O1	2c rose red	4.75	2.75
O116	O1	3c rose red	4.75	1.40
b.		Double impression	750.00	
O117	O1	6c rose red	4.25	1.30
O118	O1	10c rose red	35.00	32.50
O119	O1	12c rose red	27.50	9.00
O120	O1	30c rose red	75.00	60.00
		Nos. O114-O120 (7)	154.50	109.45

SPECIAL PRINTINGS

Special printings of Official stamps were made in 1875 at the time the other Reprints, Re-issues and Special Printings were printed.

Although perforated, these stamps were sometimes (but not always) cut apart with scissors. As a result the perforations may be mutilated and the design damaged.

All values exist imperforate.

Printed by the Continental Bank Note Co.

Overprinted in Block Letters **SPECIMEN**

1875			Perf. 12

Thin, hard white paper
Type D

AGRICULTURE
Carmine Overprint

O1S	D	1c yellow	14.00
a.		"Sepcimen" error	700.00
b.		Small dotted "i" in "Specimen"	425.00
c.		Horiz. ribbed paper	20.00
O2S	D	2c yellow	27.50
a.		"Sepcimen" error	750.00
O3S	D	3c yellow	75.00
a.		"Sepcimen" error	3,000.
O4S	D	6c yellow	130.00
a.		"Sepcimen" error	5,500.
O5S	D	10c yellow	130.00
a.		"Sepcimen" error	3,250.
O6S	D	12c yellow	125.00
a.		"Sepcimen" error	3,250.
O7S	D	15c yellow	125.00
a.		"Sepcimen" error	3,250.
O8S	D	24c yellow	125.00
a.		"Sepcimen" error	3,250.

O9S	D	30c yellow	125.00
a.		"Specimen" error	3,250.
		Nos. O1S-O9S (9)	876.50

EXECUTIVE
Blue Overprint

O10S	D	1c carmine	14.00
a.		Small dotted "i" in "Specimen"	325.00
b.		Ribbed paper	20.00
O11S	D	2c carmine	27.50
O12S	D	3c carmine	27.50
O13S	D	6c carmine	27.50
O14S	D	10c carmine	27.50
		Nos. O10S-O14S (5)	124.00

INTERIOR
Blue Overprint

O15S	D	1c vermilion	27.50
O16S	D	2c vermilion	35.00
a.		"Sepcimen" error	3,750.
O17S	D	3c vermilion	475.00
O18S	D	6c vermilion	450.00
O19S	D	10c vermilion	450.00
O20S	D	12c vermilion	475.00
O21S	D	15c vermilion	475.00
O22S	D	24c vermilion	475.00
O23S	D	30c vermilion	475.00
O24S	D	90c vermilion	475.00
		Nos. O15S-O24S (10)	3,812.

JUSTICE
Blue Overprint

O25S	D	1c purple	15.00
a.		"Sepcimen" error	675.00
b.		Small dotted "i" in "Specimen"	275.00
c.		Horiz. ribbed paper	20.00
O26S	D	2c purple	30.00
a.		"Sepcimen" error	1,100.
O27S	D	3c purple	250.00
a.		"Sepcimen" error	3,750.
O28S	D	6c purple	250.00
O29S	D	10c purple	250.00
O30S	D	12c purple	250.00
a.		"Sepcimen" error	4,000.
O31S	D	15c purple	275.00
a.		"Sepcimen" error	4,000.
O32S	D	24c purple	300.00
a.		"Sepcimen" error	4,000.
O33S	D	30c purple	300.00
a.		"Sepcimen" error	4,000.
O34S	D	90c purple	325.00
		Nos. O25S-O34S (10)	2,245.

NAVY
Carmine Overprint

O35S	D	1c ultramarine	17.50
a.		"Sepcimen" error	550.00
O36S	D	2c ultramarine	35.00
a.		"Sepcimen" error	675.00
O37S	D	3c ultramarine	300.00
O38S	D	6c ultramarine	350.00
O39S	D	7c ultramarine	150.00
a.		"Sepcimen" error	2,000.
O40S	D	10c ultramarine	350.00
a.		"Sepcimen" error	4,250.
O41S	D	12c ultramarine	300.00
a.		"Sepcimen" error	4,000.
O42S	D	15c ultramarine	300.00
a.		"Sepcimen" error	4,250.
O43S	D	24c ultramarine	300.00
a.		"Sepcimen" error	4,000.
O44S	D	30c ultramarine	300.00
a.		"Sepcimen" error	4,500.
O45S	D	90c ultramarine	300.00
		Nos. O35S-O45S (11)	2,702.

POST OFFICE
Carmine Overprint

O47S	D	1c black	25.00
a.		"Sepcimen" error	650.00
b.		Inverted overprint	1,000.
O48S	D	2c black	65.00
a.		"Sepcimen" error	1,750.
O49S	D	3c black	450.00
a.		"Sepcimen" error	—
O50S	D	6c black	425.00
O51S	D	10c black	275.00
a.		"Sepcimen" error	4,250.
O52S	D	12c black	400.00
O53S	D	15c black	475.00
a.		"Sepcimen" error	4,250.
O54S	D	24c black	425.00
a.		"Sepcimen" error	4,250.
O55S	D	30c black	425.00
O56S	D	90c black	425.00
a.		"Sepcimen" error	8,000.
		Nos. O47S-O56S (10)	3,390.

STATE
Carmine Overprint

O57S	D	1c bluish green	15.00
a.		"Sepcimen" error	400.00
b.		Small dotted "i" in "Specimen"	400.00
c.		Horiz. ribbed paper	20.00
O58S	D	2c bluish green	30.00
a.		"Sepcimen" error	550.00
O59S	D	3c bluish green	45.00
a.		"Sepcimen" error	2,000.
O60S	D	6c bluish green	95.00
a.		"Sepcimen" error	2,250.
O61S	D	7c bluish green	47.50
a.		"Sepcimen" error	1,750.
O62S	D	10c bluish green	180.00
a.		"Sepcimen" error	7,500.
O63S	D	12c bluish green	190.00
a.		"Sepcimen" error	3,500.
O64S	D	15c bluish green	180.00
O65S	D	24c bluish green	180.00
a.		"Sepcimen" error	3,500.
O66S	D	30c bluish green	180.00
a.		"Sepcimen" error	3,750.
O67S	D	90c bluish green	180.00
a.		"Sepcimen" error	3,750.

O68S	D	$2 green & black	7,250.
O69S	D	$5 green & black	12,000.
O70S	D	$10 green & black	16,000.
O71S	D	$20 green & black	19,000.
		Nos. O57S-O67S (11)	1,322.

TREASURY
Blue Overprint

O72S	D	1c dark brown	27.50
O73S	D	2c dark brown	130.00
O74S	D	3c dark brown	475.00
O75S	D	6c dark brown	425.00
O76S	D	7c dark brown	250.00
O77S	D	10c dark brown	450.00
O78S	D	12c dark brown	475.00
O79S	D	15c dark brown	475.00
O80S	D	24c dark brown	375.00
O81S	D	30c dark brown	500.00
O82S	D	90c dark brown	500.00
		Nos. O72S-O82S (11)	4,082.

WAR
Blue Overprint

O83S	D	1c deep rose	17.50
a.		"Sepcimen" error	550.00
O84S	D	2c deep rose	35.00
a.		"Sepcimen" error	1,000.
O85S	D	3c deep rose	350.00
a.		"Sepcimen" error	4,000.
O86S	D	6c deep rose	350.00
a.		"Sepcimen" error	4,250.
O87S	D	7c deep rose	72.50
a.		"Sepcimen" error	1,900.
O88S	D	10c deep rose	325.00
a.		"Sepcimen" error	4,250.
O89S	D	12c deep rose	375.00
a.		"Sepcimen" error	4,250.
O90S	D	15c deep rose	375.00
a.		"Sepcimen" error	4,250.
O91S	D	24c deep rose	375.00
a.		"Sepcimen" error	4,250.
O92S	D	30c deep rose	375.00
a.		"Sepcimen" error	4,250.
O93S	D	90c deep rose	375.00
a.		"Sepcimen" error	4,750.
		Nos. O83S-O93S (11)	3,025.

SOFT POROUS PAPER
1881   EXECUTIVE
Blue Overprint

O10xS	D	1c violet rose	45.00

NAVY
Carmine Overprint

O35xS	D	1c gray blue	50.00
a.		Double overprint	850.00

STATE

O57xS	D	1c yellow green	180.00

Official Postal Savings Mail

These stamps were used to prepay postage on official correspondence of the Postal Savings Division of the POD. Discontinued Sept. 23, 1914.

O11

1911   Wmk. 191

O121	O11	2c black	13.00	1.50
		Never hinged	20.00	
O122	O11	50c dark green	130.00	40.00
		Never hinged	200.00	
O123	O11	$1 ultra	120.00	11.00
		Never hinged	180.00	

Wmk. 190

O124	O11	1c dark violet	7.00	1.50
		Never hinged	10.00	
O125	O11	2c black	40.00	5.50
		Never hinged	60.00	
O126	O11	10c carmine	15.00	1.60
		Never hinged	22.50	
		Nos. O121-O126 (6)	325.00	61.10

> Catalogue values for unused stamps in this section, from this point to the end of the section, are for Never Hinged items.

> Catalogue values for used stamps are for regularly used copies, not copies removed from first day covers.

Official Mail

USA 20c — O12

Official Mail USA — 15 — O13

Type O13 has frame line completely around blue design.

1983-85   Unwmk.   Perf. 11

O127	O12	1c red, bl & blk	.15	.15
O128	O12	4c red, bl & blk	.15	.25
O129	O12	13c red, bl & blk	.40	.75
O129A	O12	14c red, bl & blk ('85)	.40	.50
O130	O12	17c red, bl & blk	.45	.40
O132	O12	$1 red, bl & blk	2.00	1.00
O133	O12	$5 red, bl & blk	9.00	5.00
		Nos. O127-O133 (7)	12.55	8.05

Coil Stamps
Perf. 10 Vert.

O135	O12	20c red, bl & blk	1.75	2.00
a.		Imperf., pair	2,000.	
O136	O12	22c red, bl & blk ('85)	.70	2.00

No. O129A does not have a "c" after the "14."

Inscribed: Postal Card Rate D

1985, Feb. 4   Perf. 11

O138	O12	(14c) red, bl & blk	4.50	5.00

Coil Stamps

Inscribed: No. O139, Domestic Letter Rate D. No. O140, Domestic Mail E.

1985-88   Perf. 10 Vert.

O138A	O13	15c red, bl & blk	.40	.50
O138B	O13	20c red, bl & blk	.45	.30
O139	O12	(22c) red, bl & blk	4.50	3.00
O140	O13	(25c) red, bl & blk	.75	2.00
O141	O13	25c red, bl & blk	.65	.50
a.		Imperf., pair	2,000.	—
		Nos. O138A-O141 (5)	6.75	6.30

Issue dates: 1985; E, Mar. 22, 1988; 15c, June 11; 20c, May 19; 25c, June 11. See Nos. O143, O145-O151.

1989, July 5   Litho.   Perf. 11

O143	O13	1c red, blue & black	.15	.15

O14

1991, Jan. 22   Litho.   Perf. 10 Vert.
Coil Stamp

O144	O14	(29c) red, blue & black	.75	.50

Official Type of 1985
1991-93   Litho.   Perf. 10 Vert.
Coil Stamp

O145	O13	29c red, blue & black	.65	.30

Perf. 11

O146	O13	4c red, blue & black	.15	.30
O146A	O13	10c red, blue & black	.25	.30
O147	O13	19c red, blue & black	.40	.50
O148	O13	23c red, blue & black	.45	.30
a.		Imperf., pair	—	
O151	O13	$1 red, blue & black	2.00	.75

Nos. O146A, O151 have a line of microscopic printing below eagle. Nos. O147 and O148 have blue background made up of crosshatched lines, thicker lettering and thinner numerals.

Issue dates: No. O146, Apr. 6. Nos. O145, O147, O148, May 24. 10c, Oct. 19, 1993. No. O151, Sept. 1993.

COIL STAMP
1994, Dec. 13   Litho.   Perf. 9.8 Vert.

Inscribed: No. O152, For U.S. addresses only G.

O152	O14	(32c) red, blue & black	.65	—

Type of 1985
1995, May 9   Litho.   Perf. 9.8 Vert.
COIL STAMP

O153	O13	32c red, blue & black	.65	—

Perf. 11.2

O154	O13	1c red, blue & black	.15	—
O155	O13	20c red, blue & black	.40	—
O156	O13	23c red, blue & black	.45	—

Nos. O153-O156 have a line of microscopic text below the eagle.

NEWSPAPER STAMPS

For the prepayment of postage on bulk shipments of newspapers and periodicals. From 1875 on, the stamps were affixed to memorandums of mailing, canceled and retained by the post office. Discontinued on July 1, 1898.

Many used stamps are pen canceled. Handstamp cancellations are rare on Nos. PR1-PR4. Used values for issues from 1875 through 1897 are for stamps with handstamp cancellations. Stamps with pen cancels sell for about 50% of the listed values.

Washington N1

Franklin N2

Lincoln — N3

Printed by the National Bank Note Co.
Thin Hard Paper, No Gum

1865   Unwmk.   Typo.   Perf. 12
Size: 51x95mm
Colored Border

PR1	N1	5c dark blue	325.00	—
a.		5c light blue	350.00	
PR2	N2	10c blue green	130.00	—
a.		10c green	130.00	
b.		Pelure paper	150.00	
PR3	N3	25c orange red	175.00	—
a.		25c carmine red	200.00	
b.		Pelure paper	175.00	

White Border
Yellowish Paper

PR4	N1	5c light blue	80.00	—
a.		5c dark blue	80.00	
b.		Pelure paper	80.00	
		Nos. PR1-PR4 (4)	710.00	

Reprints of 1865 Issue
Printed by the National Bank Note Co.
Hard White Paper, Without Gum

1875

PR5	N1	5c dull blue	95.00	
a.		Printed on both sides		

PR6	N2	10c dk bluish green	100.00	
a.		Printed on both sides	*1,750.*	
PR7	N3	25c dark carmine	125.00	
		Nos. PR5-PR7 (3)	320.00	

The 5c has white border, 10c and 25c have colored borders.

Printed by the American Bank Note Co.
Soft Porous Paper
1880
White Border

PR8	N1	5c dark blue	225.

Statue of Freedom — N4   "Justice" — N5

Ceres — N6   "Victory" — N7

Clio — N8   Minerva — N9

Vesta — N10   "Peace" — N11

"Commerce" N12   Hebe N13

Indian Maiden — N14

Printed by the Continental Bank Note Co.
Engraved Thin Hard Paper
1875   Size: 24x35mm

PR9	N4	2c black	30.00	22.50
PR10	N4	3c black	35.00	25.00
PR11	N4	4c black	32.50	25.00
PR12	N4	6c black	40.00	25.00
PR13	N4	8c black	55.00	35.00
PR14	N4	9c black	110.00	80.00
PR15	N4	10c black	55.00	30.00
PR16	N5	12c rose	125.00	70.00
PR17	N5	24c rose	150.00	80.00
PR18	N5	36c rose	175.00	90.00

PR19	N5	48c rose	300.00	150.00
PR20	N5	60c rose	160.00	80.00
PR21	N5	72c rose	350.00	190.00
PR22	N5	84c rose	525.00	240.00
PR23	N5	96c rose	300.00	160.00
PR24	N6	$1.92 dark brn	400.00	200.00
PR25	N7	$3 vermilion	525.00	240.00
PR26	N8	$6 ultra	850.00	325.00
PR27	N9	$9 yellow	1,100.	400.00
PR28	N10	$12 blue grn	1,250.	525.00
PR29	N11	$24 dk gray vio	1,250.	525.00
PR30	N12	$36 brn rose	1,350.	625.00
PR31	N13	$48 red brn	1,850.	750.00
PR32	N14	$60 violet	1,850.	750.00

Special Printing of the 1875 Issue
Printed by the Continental Bank Note Co.
Hard White Paper
Without Gum

PR33	N4	2c gray black	150.	
a.		Horizontally ribbed paper	150.	
PR34	N4	3c gray black	160.	
a.		Horizontally ribbed paper	170.	
PR35	N4	4c gray black	180.	
PR36	N4	6c gray black	225.	
PR37	N4	8c gray black	275.	
PR38	N4	9c gray black	300.	
PR39	N4	10c gray black	375.	
a.		Horizontally ribbed paper	400.	
PR40	N5	12c pale rose	450.	
PR41	N5	24c pale rose	625.	
PR42	N5	36c pale rose	750.	
PR43	N5	48c pale rose	850.	
PR44	N5	60c pale rose	925.	
PR45	N5	72c pale rose	1,250.	
PR46	N5	84c pale rose	1,500.	
PR47	N5	96c pale rose	2,000.	
PR48	N6	$1.92 dk brown	5,000.	
PR49	N7	$3 vermilion	10,000.	
PR50	N8	$6 ultra	11,500.	
PR51	N9	$9 yellow	20,000.	
PR52	N10	$12 blue green	18,500.	
PR53	N11	$24 dk gray vio	—	
PR54	N12	$36 brown rose	—	
PR55	N13	$48 red brown	—	
PR56	N14	$60 violet	—	

Nos. PR33 to PR56 exist imperf. but were not regularly issued. (See the Scott U.S. Specialized Catalogue.)

Printed by the American Bank Note Co.
1879
Soft Porous Paper

PR57	N4	2c black	12.00	5.50
PR58	N4	3c black	15.00	7.00
PR59	N4	4c black	14.00	7.00
PR60	N4	6c black	27.50	15.00
PR61	N4	8c black	27.50	15.00
PR62	N4	10c black	27.50	15.00
PR63	N5	12c red	110.00	45.00
PR64	N5	24c red	110.00	45.00
PR65	N5	36c red	300.00	140.00
PR66	N5	48c red	250.00	100.00
PR67	N5	60c red	210.00	90.00
a.		Imperf., pair	600.00	
PR68	N5	72c red	400.00	180.00
PR69	N5	84c red	300.00	140.00
PR70	N5	96c red	200.00	90.00
PR71	N6	$1.92 pale brown	150.00	85.00
PR72	N7	$3 red ver	150.00	85.00
PR73	N8	$6 blue	250.00	140.00
PR74	N9	$9 orange	175.00	90.00
PR75	N10	$12 yellow grn	260.00	120.00
PR76	N11	$24 dk violet	325.00	160.00
PR77	N12	$36 Indian red	400.00	175.00
PR78	N13	$48 yellow brown	500.00	240.00
PR79	N14	$60 purple	500.00	240.00
		Nos. PR57-PR70 (14)	2,003.	894.50

See the Scott U.S. Specialized Catalogue Die and Plate Proof section for other imperforates.

Special Printing of the 1879 Issue
Printed by the American Bank Note Co.
1881

PR80	N4	2c intense black	375.00

1885

PR81	N4	1c black	15.00	7.50
PR82	N5	12c carmine	50.00	17.50
PR83	N5	24c carmine	52.50	20.00
PR84	N5	36c carmine	75.00	30.00
PR85	N5	48c carmine	110.00	45.00
PR86	N5	60c carmine	150.00	65.00
PR87	N5	72c carmine	160.00	70.00
PR88	N5	84c carmine	325.00	160.00
PR89	N5	96c carmine	250.00	120.00
		Nos. PR81-PR89 (9)	1,187.	535.00

See the Scott U.S. Specialized Catalogue Die and Plate Proof section for imperforates.

Printed by the Bureau of Engraving and Printing
1894   Soft Wove Paper

PR90	N4	1c intense black	125.00
PR91	N4	2c intense black	125.00
PR92	N4	4c intense black	135.00

PR93	N4	6c intense black	1,750.	
PR94	N4	10c intense black	250.00	
PR95	N5	12c pink	750.00	—
PR96	N5	24c pink	750.00	—
PR97	N5	36c pink	5,000.	
PR98	N5	60c pink	5,000.	
PR99	N5	96c pink	6,000.	
PR100	N7	$3 scarlet	7,500.	
PR101	N8	$6 pale blue	9,500.	

Statue of Freedom N15   "Justice" N16

"Victory" — N17   Clio — N18

Vesta — N19   "Peace" — N20

"Commerce" N21   Indian Maiden N22

1895   **Unwmk.**
Sizes: 1c-50c, 21x34mm,
$2-$100, 24x35mm

PR102	N15	1c black	45.00	12.50
		Never hinged	70.00	
PR103	N15	2c black	45.00	12.50
		Never hinged	70.00	
PR104	N15	5c black	60.00	20.00
		Never hinged	95.00	
PR105	N15	10c black	125.00	52.50
		Never hinged	190.00	
PR106	N16	25c carmine	175.00	55.00
		Never hinged	280.00	
PR107	N16	50c carmine	375.00	150.00
		Never hinged	600.00	
PR108	N17	$2 scarlet	450.00	110.00
		Never hinged	675.00	
PR109	N18	$5 ultra	650.00	225.00
		Never hinged	950.00	
PR110	N19	$10 green	600.00	250.00
		Never hinged	900.00	
PR111	N20	$20 slate	900.00	450.00
		Never hinged	1,350.	
PR112	N21	$50 dull rose	950.00	450.00
		Never hinged	1,400.	
PR113	N22	$100 purple	1,100.	525.00
		Never hinged	1,750.	
		Nos. PR102-PR113 (12)	5,475.	2,312.

1895-97   **Wmk. 191**

PR114	N15	1c black ('96)	5.00	4.00
		Never hinged	7.50	
PR115	N15	2c black	5.50	4.00
		Never hinged	8.25	
PR116	N15	5c black ('96)	8.00	6.50
		Never hinged	11.00	
PR117	N15	10c black	5.50	4.25
		Never hinged	8.25	
PR118	N16	25c carmine	10.00	10.00
		Never hinged	15.00	
PR119	N16	50c carmine	12.50	15.00
		Never hinged	20.00	
PR120	N17	$2 scar ('97)	16.00	22.50
		Never hinged	25.00	

PR121	N18	$5 dk blue ('96)	30.00	35.00
		Never hinged	45.00	
a.		$5 light blue	150.00	70.00
		Never hinged	240.00	
PR122	N19	$10 green ('96)	27.50	35.00
		Never hinged	40.00	
PR123	N20	$20 slate ('96)	30.00	37.50
		Never hinged	45.00	
PR124	N21	$50 dl rose ('97)	40.00	42.50
		Never hinged	65.00	
PR125	N22	$100 purple ('96)	45.00	47.50
		Never hinged	75.00	
		Nos. PR114-PR125 (12)	235.00	263.75

In 1899 the Government sold 26,989 sets of these stamps, but, as the stock of the high values was not sufficient to make up the required number, the $5, $10, $20, $50 and $100 were reprinted. These are virtually indistinguishable from earlier printings.

For overprints see Nos. R159-R160.

PARCEL POST STAMPS

Issued for the prepayment of postage on parcel post packages only.

Post Office Clerk — PP1

City Carrier — PP2

Railway Postal Clerk — PP3

Rural Carrier — PP4

Mail Train — PP5

Steamship and Mail Tender — PP6

Automobile Service — PP7

Airplane Carrying Mail — PP8

Manufacturing PP9

Dairying PP10

Harvesting
PP11

Fruit Growing
PP12

1913		Engr.	Wmk. 190	*Perf. 12*	
Q1	PP1	1c carmine rose		4.75	1.30
		Never hinged		7.00	
Q2	PP2	2c carmine rose		6.00	1.00
		Never hinged		9.00	
Q3	PP3	3c carmine		10.00	5.25
		Never hinged		15.00	
Q4	PP4	4c carmine rose		30.00	2.50
		Never hinged		45.00	
Q5	PP5	5c carmine rose		25.00	2.00
		Never hinged		37.50	
Q6	PP6	10c carmine rose		45.00	2.50
		Never hinged		67.50	
Q7	PP7	15c carmine rose		60.00	10.00
		Never hinged		90.00	
Q8	PP8	20c carmine rose		120.00	20.00
		Never hinged		175.00	
Q9	PP9	25c carmine rose		60.00	6.00
		Never hinged		87.50	
Q10	PP10	50c carmine rose		250.00	37.50
		Never hinged		375.00	
Q11	PP11	75c carmine rose		80.00	30.00
		Never hinged		120.00	
Q12	PP12	$1 carmine rose		325.00	25.00
		Never hinged		475.00	
		Nos. Q1-Q12 (12)		1,015.00	143.05

PARCEL POST POSTAGE DUE STAMPS

For affixing by a postal clerk, to any parcel post package, to denote the amount to be collected from the addressee because of insufficient prepayment of postage.

PPD1

1913		Engr.	Wmk. 190	*Perf. 12*	
JQ1	PPD1	1c dark green		9.00	4.00
		Never hinged		13.50	
JQ2	PPD1	2c dark green		70.00	16.00
		Never hinged		105.00	
JQ3	PPD1	5c dark green		12.50	5.25
		Never hinged		19.00	
JQ4	PPD1	10c dark green		150.00	40.00
		Never hinged		225.00	
JQ5	PPD1	25c dark green		85.00	4.75
		Never hinged		130.00	
		Nos. JQ1-JQ5 (5)		326.50	70.00

SPECIAL HANDLING STAMPS

For use on fourth-class mail to secure the same expeditious handling accorded to first-class mail matter.

PP13

1925-29		Unwmk.	Engr.	*Perf. 11*	
QE1	PP13	10c yellow grn ('28)		1.40	1.00
		Never hinged		2.00	
QE2	PP13	15c yellow grn ('28)		1.50	.90
		Never hinged		2.10	
QE3	PP13	20c yellow grn ('28)		2.25	1.50
		Never hinged		3.25	
QE4	PP13	25c yellow grn ('29)		19.00	7.50
		Never hinged		27.50	
a.		25c deep green ('25)		27.50	5.50
		Never hinged		40.00	
		Nos. QE1-QE4 (4)		24.15	10.90

COMPUTER VENDED POSTAGE

CVP1

CVP2

1989, Aug. 23   Tagged   *Guillotined*
Self-Adhesive
Washington, DC, Machine 82
Any Date Other Than 1st Day

1	CVP1	25c 1st Class	6.00	—
a.		1st day dated, serial #12501-15500	4.50	—
b.		1st day dated, serial #00001-12500	4.50	—
c.		1st day dated, serial over #27500	—	—
2	CVP1	$1 3rd Class	—	—
a.		1st day dated, serial #24501-27500	—	—
b.		1st day dated, serial over #27500	—	—
3	CVP2	$1.69 Parcel Post	—	—
a.		1st day dated, serial #21501-24500	—	—
b.		1st day dated, serial over #27500	—	—
4	CVP1	$2.40 Priority Mail	—	—
a.		1st day dated, serial #18501-21500	—	—
b.		Priority Mail ($2.74), with bar code (CVP2)	100.00	—
c.		1st day dated, serial over #27500	—	—
5	CVP1	$8.75 Express Mail	—	—
a.		1st day dated, serial #15501-18500	—	—
b.		1st day dated, serial over #27500	—	—
		Nos. 1a-5a (5)	82.50	

Washington, DC, Machine 83
Any Date Other Than 1st Day

6	CVP1	25c 1st Class	6.00	—
a.		1st day dated, serial #12501-15500	4.50	—
b.		1st day dated, serial #00001-12500	4.50	—
c.		1st day dated, serial over #27500	—	—
7	CVP1	$1 3rd Class	—	—
a.		1st day dated, serial #24501-27500	—	—
b.		1st day dated, serial over #27500	—	—
8	CVP2	$1.69 Parcel Post	—	—
a.		1st day dated, serial #21501-24500	—	—
b.		1st day dated, serial over #27500	—	—
9	CVP1	$2.40 Priority Mail	—	—
a.		1st day dated, serial #18501-21500	—	—
b.		1st day dated, serial over #27500	—	—
c.		Priority Mail ($2.74), with bar code (CVP2)	100.00	—
10	CVP1	$8.75 Express Mail	—	—
a.		1st day dated, serial #15501-18500	—	—
b.		1st day dated, serial over #27500	—	—
		Nos. 6a-10a (5)	57.50	

1989, Sept. 1
Kensington, MD, Machine 82
Any Date Other Than 1st Day

11	CVP1	25c 1st Class	6.00	—
a.		1st day dated, serial #12501-15500	4.50	—
b.		1st day dated, serial #00001-12500	4.50	—
c.		1st day dated, serial over #27500	—	—
12	CVP1	$1 3rd Class	—	—
a.		1st day dated, serial #24501-27500	—	—
b.		1st day dated, serial over #27500	—	—
13	CVP2	$1.69 Parcel Post	—	—
a.		1st day dated, serial #21501-24500	—	—
b.		1st day dated, serial over #27500	—	—
14	CVP1	$2.40 Priority Mail	—	—
a.		1st day dated, serial #18501-21500	—	—
b.		1st day dated, serial over #27500	—	—
c.		Priority Mail ($2.74), with bar code (CVP2)	100.00	—
15	CVP1	$8.75 Express Mail	—	—
a.		1st day dated, serial #15501-18500	—	—
b.		1st day dated, serial over #27500	—	—
		Nos. 11a-15a (5)	57.50	—
		Nos. 11b, 11b (2)	9.00	—

Kensington, MD, Machine 83
Any Date Other Than 1st Day

16	CVP1	25c 1st Class	6.00	—
a.		1st day dated, serial #12501-15500	4.50	—
b.		1st day dated, serial #00001-12500	4.50	—
c.		1st day dated, serial over #27500	—	—
17	CVP1	$1 3rd Class	—	—
a.		1st day dated, serial #24501-27500	—	—
b.		1st day dated, serial over #27500	—	—
18	CVP2	$1.69 Parcel Post	—	—
a.		1st day dated, serial #21501-24500	—	—
b.		1st day dated, serial over #27500	—	—
19	CVP1	$2.40 Priority Mail	—	—
a.		1st day dated, serial #18501-21500	—	—
b.		1st day dated, serial over #27500	—	—
c.		Priority Mail ($2.74), with bar code (CVP2)	100.00	—
20	CVP1	$8.75 Express Mail	—	—
a.		1st day dated, serial #15501-18500	—	—
b.		1st day dated, serial over #27500	—	—
		Nos. 16a-20a (5)	57.50	—
		Nos. 6b, 16b (2)	9.00	—

1989, Nov.
Washington, DC, Machine 11

21	CVP1	25c 1st Class	150.00	—
a.		1st Class, with bar code (CVP2)	—	—

Stamps in CVP1 design, probably certified 1st class, with $1.10 denominations exist.

22	CVP1	$1 3rd Class	500.00	—
23	CVP2	$1.69 Parcel Post	500.00	—
24	CVP1	$2.40 Priority Mail	500.00	—
a.		Priority Mail ($2.74), with bar code (CVP2)	—	—
25	CVP1	$8.75 Express Mail	500.00	—

Washington, DC, Machine 12

26	CVP1	25c 1st Class	150.00	—

A $1.10 certified 1st Class stamp, dated Nov. 20, exists on cover.

27	CVP1	$1 3rd Class	—	

A $1.40 Third Class stamp of type CVP2, dated Dec. 1 is known on a Dec. 2 cover.

28	CVP2	$1.69 Parcel Post	—	
29	CVP1	$2.40 Priority Mail	—	
a.		Priority Mail ($2.74), with bar code (CVP2)	—	
30	CVP1	$8.75 Express Mail	—	

An $8.50 Express Mail stamp, dated Dec. 2, exists on cover.

Type I — CVP3   Type II — CVP3

1992, Aug. 20   Engr.   *Perf. 10 Horiz.*
Coil Stamp

31	CVP3	29c red & blue, type I	.60	.25
c.		32c, type II ('94)	.65	.25

No. 31 was available in all denominations from 1c to $99.99. The listing is for the first class rate. Other denominations, se-tenant combinations, or "errors" will not be listed.

Type II denomination has large sans-serif numerals preceded by an asterisk measuring 2mm across. No. 31 has small numerals with serifs preceded by an asterisk 1½mm across.

CVP4

1994, Feb. 19   Photo.   *Perf. 9.9 Vert.*
Coil Stamp

32	CVP4	29c dark red & dark blue	.60	.25

No. 32 was available in all denominations from 19c to $99.99. The listing is for the first class rate at time of issue. Other denominations, se-tenant combinations, or "errors" will not be listed.

1996, Jan. 26   Photo.   *Perf. 9.9 Vert.*

33	CVP4	32c bright red & blue	.60	.25

Letters in "USA" on No. 33 are thicker than on No. 32. Numerous other design differences exist in the moire pattern and in the bunting.

For No. 33, the 32c value has been listed because it was the first class rate at time of issue. No. 33 has "1996" in the lower left corner; No. 32 has no date.

CARRIERS' STAMPS

OFFICIAL ISSUES

Issued by the US Government to facilitate payment of fees for delivering and collecting letters.

Franklin   Eagle
OC1   OC2

1851		Unwmk.	Engr.	*Imperf.*	
LO1	OC1	(1c) dull blue, *rose*		4,500.	5,000.
LO2	OC2	1c blue		22.50	40.00
1875					

REPRINT
Without Gum

LO3	OC1	(1c) blue, *rose*, imperf.		50.00	

SPECIAL PRINTING

LO4	OC1	(1c) blue, perf. 12		2,500.	

REPRINT

LO5	OC2	1c blue, imperf.		25.00	

SPECIAL PRINTING

LO6	OC2	1c blue, perf. 12		190.00	

Reprints of the Franklin Carrier are printed in dark blue, instead of the dull blue or deep blue of the originals. The reprints of the Eagle carrier are on hard white paper, ungummed and sometimes perforated, and also on a coarse wove paper. Originals are on yellowish paper with brown gum.

SEMI-OFFICIAL ISSUES

Issued by officials or employees of the US Government for the purpose of securing or indicating payment of carriers' fees.

Baltimore, Md.

C1

1850-55		Typo.		*Imperf.*	
1LB1	C1	1c red, *bluish*		130.	130.
1LB2	C1	1c blue, *bluish*		160.	115.
a.		Bluish laid paper			
1LB3	C1	1c blue		120.	80.
a.		Laid paper		190.	130.
1LB4	C1	1c green		—	600.
1LB5	C1	1c red		500.	400.

Ten varieties.

C2   C3

1856				Typo.	
1LB6	C2	1c blue		120.	80.
1LB7	C2	1c red		120.	80.

Shades exist of Nos. 1LB6-1LB7.

1857					
1LB8	C3	1c black		60.	45.
a.		"SENT"		90.	65.
b.		Short rays		90.	65.
1LB9	C3	1c red		90.	80.
a.		"SENT"		125.	100.
b.		Short rays		125.	100.

Ten varieties of C3.

BOSTON, MASS.

C6   C7

1849-50   **Typeset**
3LB1 C6 1c blue   375.   180.
3LB2 C7 1c blue (shades), *slate*   190.   100.

CHARLESTON, S. C.

C8   C10

1849   **Typo.**
4LB1 C8 2c black, *brn rose*   4,000. 2,500.
4LB2 C8 2c black, *yellow*   2,500.

1854   **Typeset**
4LB3 C10 2c black   1,000.

 C11

1849-50   **Typeset**
4LB5 C11 2c black, *bluish*,
         pelure   600.   450.
4LB7 C11 2c black, *yellow*   600.   750.
        Several varieties of C11.

C13   C14

C15

1851-58   **Typeset**
4LB8 C13 2c blk, *bluish*   225.   130.
 a.   Period after "Paid"   450.   200.
 b.   "Cens"   700.
 c.   "Conours" and "Bents"
4LB9 C13 2c blk, *bluish*,
          pelure   475.   525.
4LB11 C14 (2c) blk, *bluish*   325.
4LB12 C14 (2c) blk, *bluish*,
          pelure   325.
4LB13 C15 (2c) blk, *bluish*
          ('58)   425.   200.
 a.   Comma after "PAID"   1,000.
 b.   No period after "Post" 1,300.
        Several varieties of C13.

C16   C17

1851-58   **Typeset**
4LB14 C16 2c black, *bluish*   550.   625.
4LB15 C17 2c black, *bluish*   700.   700.
        Several varieties of each.

 C18

1858   **Typeset**
4LB16 C18 2c black, *bluish*   5,000.
        Several varieties.

Same as C19, but Inscribed "Beckmann's
City Post"

1860
4LB17 C19 2c black   —
        One copy exists, on cover.

C19   C20

1859   **Typeset**
4LB18 C19 2c black, *bluish*   3,000.
4LB19 C20 2c black, *bluish*   5,000.
4LB20 C20 2c black, *pink*   200.
4LB21 C20 2c black, *yellow*   175.

CINCINNATI, OHIO

C20a

1854   **Litho.**   **Wove Paper**
9LB1 C20a 2c brown   2,750. 2,750.

CLEVELAND, OHIO

C20b   C20c

1854   **Wove Paper**   **Litho.**
10LB1 C20b blue   2,000. 2,000.

            Vertically Laid Paper
10LB2 C20c 2c black, *bluish*   —   3,750.

LOUISVILLE, KY.

C21   C22

1857-58   **Litho.**
5LB1 C21 (2c) bluish green   90.
5LB2 C22 (2c) blue ('58)   175.   175.
5LB3 C22 (2c) black ('58)   700. 1,750.

NEW YORK, N.Y.

C23

1842   **Engr.**
6LB1 C23 3c black, *grayish*   1,250.

    Used copies are Carriers' stamps only when can-
celed with the regular government cancellation
"U.S." in octagonal frame (see illustration),
"U.S.CITY DESPATCH POST," or New York circu-
lar postmark. When canceled "FREE" in frame they
were used as local stamps (see No. 40L1 in the
Scott Specialized Catalogue of United States
Stamps).

C24

1842-45   **Engr.**
Unsurfaced Paper, Colored Through
6LB2 C24 3c black, *rosy buff*   800.
6LB3 C24 3c blk, *light blue*   500.   500.
6LB4 C24 3c black, *green*
    Some authorities consider No. 6LB2 to be an
essay, and No. 6LB4 to be a color changeling.

Glazed Paper, Surface Colored
6LB5 C24 3c black, *blue green*
         (shades)   175.   140.
 a.   Double impression   500.
 b.   3c, black, *blue*   650.   200.
 c.   As "b," double impression   750.
 d.   3c, black, *green*   1,000.   900.
 e.   As "d," double impression

No. 6LB5 Surcharged in
Red — C25

1846
6LB7 C25 2c on 3c, on cover   —
    The City Despatch 2c red is listed in the Scott
United States Specialized Catalogue as a Local
stamp.

C27

1849-50   **Typo.**
6LB9 C27 1c black, *rose*   90.   75.
6LB10 C27 1c black, *yellow*   90.   90.
6LB11 C27 1c black, *buff*   90.   75.
 a.   Pair, one stamp sideways 1,000.

PHILADELPHIA, PA.

C28   C29

1849-50   **Typeset**
7LB1 C28 1c blk, *rose* (with letters L.P.)   275.
7LB2 C28 1c black, *rose* (with letter S)   750.
7LB3 C28 1c blk, *rose* (with letter H)   275.
7LB4 C28 1c blk, *rose* (with letters L.S.)   275.
7LB5 C28 1c black, *rose* (with letters J.J.) 3,250.
7LB6 C29 1c black, *rose*   225.   190.
7LB7 C29 1c black, *blue*, glazed   800.
7LB8 C29 1c blk, *ver*, glazed   700.
7LB9 C29 1c blk, *yel*, glazed   3,000.
        Several varieties of each.
    Nos. 7LB1-7LB9 normally received no
cancellation.
    The 1c black on buff (unglazed), type C29, is
believed to be a color changeling.

C30   C31

C32

1850-52   **Litho.**
7LB11 C30 1c gold, *black*,
          glazed   140.   105.
7LB12 C30 1c blue   300.   225.
7LB13 C30 1c black   550.
        25 varieties of C30.

        Handstamped
7LB14 C31 1c blue, *buff*   2,250.
7LB16 C31 1c black   1,650.

1856(?)
7LB18 C32 1c black   900. 1,400.

P. O. PAID
    One Cent.

    Labels in these designs are not believed to
be Carrier stamps.

ST. LOUIS, MO.

C36   (Actual
             size) — C37

Several varieties.

1849   **Litho.**
8LB1 C36 2c black   4,000. 7,500.

1857   **Litho.**
8LB2 C37 2c blue   5,000.

    Carrier stamps Nos. 9LB1, 10LB1-10LB2 are
listed following No. 4LB21.

STAMPED ENVELOPES AND
WRAPPERS

VALUES

    Values are for cut squares in a grade
of very fine. Very fine cut squares will
have the design well centered within
moderately large margins. Precanceled
cut squares must include the entire precancellation. Values for unused entires
are for those without printed or manuscript address. Values for letter sheets
are for folded entires. Unfolded copies
sell for more. A "full corner" includes
back and side flaps and commands a
premium. (Entire envelopes and wrappers are listed in the Scott U.S. Specialized Catalogue.)
    Wrappers are listed with envelopes of
corresponding designs, and indicated by
prefix letter "W" instead of "U."
    Envelopes with the stamp printed by
error in colorless embossing from an
uninked die, are "albinos." They are
worth more than normal, inked impressions. Albinos of earlier issues, canceled
while current, are scarce.
    The papers of these issues vary
greatly in texture, and in color from yellowish to bluish white and from amber to
dark buff.
    "+" Some authorities claim that Nos.
U37, U48, U49, U110, U124, U125,
U130, U133A, U137A, U137B, U137C,
W138, U145, U162, U178A, U185,
U220, U285, U286, U298, U299, UO3,
UO32, UO38, UO45 and UO45A (each
with "+" before number) were not regularly issued and are not known to have
been used.

        Washington

U1   U2

U1 — "THREE" in short label with curved ends; 13mm wide at top.
U2 — "THREE" in short label with straight ends; 15½mm wide at top.

U3   U4

U3 — "THREE" in short label with octagon ends.
U4 — "THREE" in wide label with straight ends; 20mm wide at top.

U5   U6

U5 — "THREE" in medium wide label with curved ends; 14½mm wide at top.

U7   U8

U7 — "TEN" in short label; 15⅓mm wide at top.
U8 — "TEN" in wide label 20mm wide at top.

1853-55   On Diagonally Laid Paper

U1	U1	3c red	240.00	20.00
U2	U1	3c red, *buff*	80.00	11.00
U3	U2	3c red	900.00	35.00
U4	U2	3c red, *buff*	250.00	20.00
U5	U3	3c red ('54)	4,500.	375.00
U6	U3	3c red, *buff* ('54)	250.00	42.50
U7	U4	3c red	700.00	85.00
U8	U4	3c red, *buff*	1,500.	100.00
U9	U5	3c red ('54)	25.00	3.00
U10	U5	3c red, *buff* ('54)	15.00	3.00
U11	U6	6c red	170.00	65.00
U12	U6	6c red, *buff*	125.00	55.00
U13	U6	6c green	225.00	100.00
U14	U6	6c green, *buff*	185.00	80.00
U15	U7	10c green ('55)	200.00	70.00
U16	U7	10c green, *buff* ('55)	70.00	50.00
a.		10c pale green, *buff*	70.00	45.00
U17	U8	10c green ('55)	250.00	100.00
a.		10c pale green	225.00	100.00
U18	U8	10c green, *buff* ('55)	125.00	60.00
a.		10c pale green, *buff*	125.00	60.00

Nos. U9, U10, U11, U12, U13, U14, U17 and U18 have been reprinted on white and buff papers, wove or vertically laid, and are not known entire. The originals are on diagonally laid paper. Value of 8 reprints on laid, $225. Reprints on wove sell for more.

Franklin, Period after "POSTAGE."
U9   U10

U10 — Bust touches inner frame-line at front and back.

No period after   Washington
"POSTAGE"   U12
U11

Envelopes are on diagonally laid paper. Wrappers on vertically or horizontally laid paper.

1860-61

U19	U9	1c blue, *buff*	30.00	15.00
W20	U9	1c blue, *buff* ('61)	65.00	50.00
W21	U9	1c blue, *man* ('61)	45.00	40.00
W22	U9	1c blue, *org* ('61)	2,500.	
U23	U10	1c blue, *org*	450.00	350.00
U24	U11	1c blue, *buff*	225.00	90.00
W25	U11	1c blue, *man* ('61)	3,250.	2,100.
U26	U12	3c red	27.50	13.00
U27	U12	3c red, *buff*	20.00	12.50
U28	U12+9	3c + 1c red & blue	325.00	240.00
U29	U12+9	3c + 1c red & blue, *buff*	275.00	225.00
U30	U12	6c red	2,400.	1,250.
U31	U12	6c red, *buff*	2,000.	900.00
U32	U12	10c green	1,200.	350.00
U33	U12	10c green, *buff*	1,100.	250.00

Nos. U26, U27, U30 to U33 have been reprinted on the same vertically laid paper as the reprints of the 1853-55 issue, and are not known entire. Value, Nos. U26-U27, $160; Nos. U30-U33, $100.

U13   U14

Washington
U15   U16

Envelopes are on diagonally laid paper.

1861

U34	U13	3c pink	20.00	5.50
U35	U13	3c pink, *buff*	19.00	5.00
U36	U13	3c pink, *bl* (letter sheet)	75.00	50.00

+U37	U13	3c pink, *org*	3,000.	
U38	U14	6c pink	110.00	80.00
U39	U14	6c pink, *buff*	65.00	60.00
U40	U15	10c yellow green	32.50	30.00
a.		10c blue green	30.00	27.50
U41	U15	10c yel green, *buff*	27.50	27.50
a.		10c blue green, *buff*	27.50	27.50
U42	U16	12c red & brown, *buff*	180.00	160.00
a.		12c lake & brown, *buff*	800.00	
U43	U16	20c red & bl, *buff*	190.00	175.00
U44	U16	24c red & green, *buff*	200.00	175.00
a.		24c lake & green, *sal*	225.00	200.00
U45	U16	40c black & red, *buff*	300.00	300.00

Nos. U38 and U39 have been reprinted on the same papers as the reprints of the 1853-55 issue and are not known entire. Value of two reprints, $60.

Jackson — U17   Jackson — U18

"U.S. POSTAGE" above

U17 — The downstroke and tail of the "2" unite near the point.

U18 — The downstroke and tail of the "2" touch but do not merge.

Jackson — U19   Jackson — U20

"U.S. POST" above

U19 — Stamp measures 24 to 25mm in width.

U20 — Stamp measures 25½ to 26¼mm in width.

Envelopes are on diagonally laid paper. Wrappers on vertically or horizontally laid paper.

1863-64

U46	U17	2c black, *buff*	35.00	17.50
W47	U17	2c black, *dk man*	45.00	35.00
+U48	U18	2c black, *buff*	2,250.	
+U49	U18	2c black, *orange*	1,200.	
U50	U19	2c blk, *buff* ('64)	12.50	9.00
W51	U19	2c blk, *buff* ('64)	160.00	150.00
U52	U19	2c blk, *org* ('64)	11.00	9.00
W53	U19	2c black, *dk man* ('64)	37.50	25.00
U54	U20	2c blk, *buff* ('64)	12.50	9.00
W55	U20	2c blk, *buff* ('64)	75.00	55.00
U56	U20	2c blk, *org* ('64)	11.00	8.00
W57	U20	2c blk, *lt man* ('64)	12.50	11.50

Washington   Washington
U21   U22

1864-65

U58	U21	3c pink	7.00	1.50
U59	U21	3c pink, *buff*	5.00	1.00
U60	U21	3c brown ('65)	42.50	27.50
U61	U21	3c brn, *buff* ('65)	42.50	25.00
U62	U21	6c pink	60.00	27.50
U63	U21	6c pink, *buff*	32.50	27.50
U64	U21	6c purple ('65)	45.00	27.50
U65	U21	6c pur, *buff* ('65)	40.00	19.00
U66	U22	9c lem, *buff* ('65)	400.00	240.00
U67	U22	9c org, *buff* ('65)	100.00	80.00
a.		9c orange yellow, *buff*	90.00	85.00
U68	U22	12c brn, *buff* ('65)	350.00	225.00
U69	U22	12c red brn, *buff* ('65)	85.00	55.00
U70	U22	18c red, *buff* ('65)	90.00	90.00
U71	U22	24c bl, *buff* ('65)	95.00	80.00
U72	U22	30c grn, *buff* ('65)	65.00	60.00
a.		30c yellow green, *buff*	60.00	72.50
U73	U22	40c rose, *buff* ('65)	90.00	225.00

Reay Issue

The engravings in this issue are finely executed.

Franklin — U23   Jackson — U24

U23 — Bust points to the end of the "N" of "ONE".

U24 — Bust narrow at back. Small, thick figures of value.

Washington — U25   Lincoln — U26

U25 — Queue projects below bust.

U26 — Neck very long at the back.

Stanton — U27   Jefferson — U28

U27 — Bust pointed at the back, figures "7" are normal.

U28 — Queue forms straight line with the bust.

Clay — U29   Webster — U30

U29 — Ear partly concealed by hair, mouth large, chin prominent.

U30 — Has side whiskers.

Scott — U31   Hamilton — U32

U31 — Straggling locks of hair at top of head; ornaments around the inner oval end in squares.

U32 — Back of bust very narrow, chin almost straight; labels containing figures of value are exactly parallel.

Perry — U33

U33 — Front of bust very narrow and pointed; inner lines of shields project very slightly beyond the oval.

1870-71

U74	U23	1c blue	32.50	27.50
a.		1c ultramarine	55.00	32.50
U75	U23	1c blue, *amber*	32.50	27.50
a.		1c ultramarine, *amb*	50.00	30.00
U76	U23	1c blue, *org*	17.50	15.00
W77	U23	1c blue, *man*	40.00	35.00
U78	U24	2c brown	37.50	15.00
U79	U24	2c brown, *amb*	15.00	8.50
U80	U24	2c brown, *org*	9.00	6.00
W81	U24	2c brown, *man*	25.00	20.00
U82	U25	3c green	6.50	.85
U83	U25	3c green, *amb*	5.75	1.90
U84	U25	3c green, *cream*	8.50	4.00
U85	U26	6c dark red	20.00	16.00
a.		6c vermilion	15.00	16.00
U86	U26	6c dk red, *amber*	22.50	15.00
a.		6c vermilion, *amber*	21.00	15.00
U87	U26	6c dk red, *cr*	25.00	15.00
a.		6c vermilion, *cream*	22.50	15.00

U88	U27	7c ver, amb ('71)	45.00 180.00
U89	U28	10c olive black	475.00 425.00
U90	U28	10c ol blk, amb	475.00 425.00
U91	U28	10c brown	50.00 70.00
U92	U28	10c brn, amb	70.00 50.00
a.		10c dark brown, amb	60.00 60.00
U93	U29	12c plum	110.00 82.50
U94	U29	12c plum, amb	110.00 110.00
U95	U29	12c plum, cr	225.00 225.00
U96	U30	15c red orange	67.50 70.00
a.		15c orange	67.50
U97	U30	15c red org, amb	140.00 180.00
		15c orange, amber	140.00
U98	U30	15c red org, cr	240.00 225.00
a.		15c orange, cream	240.00
U99	U31	24c purple	120.00 120.00
U100	U31	24c pur, amb	175.00 300.00
U101	U31	24c pur, cream	175.00 300.00
U102	U32	30c black	80.00 100.00
U103	U32	30c blk, amb	190.00 250.00
U104	U32	30c blk, cream	210.00 400.00
U105	U33	90c carmine	140.00 225.00
U106	U33	90c car, amb	325.00 400.00
U107	U33	90c car, cream	375.00 650.00

Plimpton Issue

The profiles in this issue are inferior to the fine engraving of the Reay issue.

U34   U35

U34 — Bust forms an angle at the back near the frame. Lettering poorly executed. Distinct circle in "O" of "POSTAGE."

U35 — Lower part of bust points to the end of the "E" in "ONE." Head inclined downward.

U36   U37

U36 — Bust narrow at back. Thin figures of value. The head of the "P" in "POSTAGE" is very narrow. The bust at front is broad and ends in sharp corners.

U37 — Bust broad. Figures of value in long ovals.

U38   U39

U38 — Similar to die 2 but the figure "2" at the left touches the oval.

U39 — Similar to die 2 but the "O" of "TWO" has the center netted instead of plain. The "G" of "POSTAGE" and the "C" of "CENTS" have diagonal crossline.

U40   U41

U40 — Bust broad; numerals in ovals short and thick.

U41 — Similar to die 5 but the ovals containing the numerals are much heavier. A diagonal line runs from the upper part of the "U" to the white frame-line.

U42   U43

U42 — Similar to die 5 but the middle stroke of "N" in "CENTS" is as thin as the vertical strokes.

U43 — Bottom of bust cut almost semi-circularly.

U44   U45

U44 — Thin lettering, long thin figures of value.

U45 — Thick lettering, well-formed figures of value, queue does not project below bust.

U46

U46 — Top of head egg-shaped; knot of queue well marked and projects triangularly.

Taylor — U47

Die 1   Die 2

Die 1 — Figures of value with thick curved tops.

Die 2 — Figures of value with long, thin tops.

U48   U49

U48 — Neck very short at the back.

U49 — Figures of value turned up at the ends.

U50   U51

U50 — Very large head.

U51 — Knot of queue stands out prominently.

U52   U53

U52 — Ear prominent, chin receding.

U53 — No side whiskers, forelock projects above head.

U54   U55

U54 — Hair does not project; ornaments around the inner oval end in points.

U55 — Back of bust rather broad, chin slopes considerably; labels containing figures of value are not exactly parallel.

U56

U56 — Front of bust sloping; inner lines of shields project considerably into the inner oval.

1874-86

U34

U108	1c dark blue	95.00	70.00
a.	1c light blue	110.00	75.00
U109	1c dk blue, amb	120.00	75.00
+U110	1c dk blue, cr	900.00	
U111	1c dk blue, org	20.00	16.00
a.	1c light blue, org	22.50	15.00
W112	1c dk blue, man	50.00	40.00

U35

U113	1c light blue	1.50	.75
a.	1c dark blue	7.50	7.50
U114	1c lt blue, amb	4.00	4.00
a.	1c dark blue, amb	15.00	10.00
U115	1c blue, cr	4.25	4.50
a.	1c dark blue, cr	17.50	8.00
U116	1c lt blue, org	.75	.40
a.	1c dark blue, org	3.00	3.50
U117	1c lt bl, bl ('80)	5.75	5.25
U118	1c light blue, fawn ('79)	5.75	5.50
U119	1c lt blue, man ('86)	5.75	3.25
W120	1c dark blue, man	1.50	1.00
a.	1c dark blue, man	7.00	8.00
U121	1c lt blue, amb man ('86)	11.00	10.00

U36

U122	2c brown	90.00	37.50
U123	2c brown, amb	55.00	40.00
+U124	2c brown, cr	775.00	
+U125	2c brown, org	10,000.	
W126	2c brown, man	110.00	65.00
W127	2c ver, man	1,100.	250.00

U37

U128	2c brown	42.50	32.50
U129	2c brown, amb	65.00	37.50
+U130	2c brown, cr	20,000.	
W131	2c brown, man	15.00	15.00

U38

U132	2c brown	60.00	27.50
U133	2c brown, amb	190.00	55.00
+U133A	2c brown, cr	—	

U39

U134	2c brown	575.00	135.00
U135	2c brown, amb	400.00	110.00
U136	2c brown, org	45.00	27.50
W137	2c brown, man	60.00	35.00
+U137A	2c vermilion	18,500.	
+U137B	2c ver, amb	18,500.	
+U137C	2c ver, org	18,500.	
+W138	2c ver, man	7,000.	

U40

U139	2c brown ('75)	40.00	32.50
U140	2c brown, amb ('75)	75.00	62.50
U140A	2c brown, org ('75)	—	
W141	2c brown, man ('75)	35.00	25.00
U142	2c ver ('75)	5.50	2.75
a.	2c pink	8.50	6.50

U143	2c ver, amber ('75)	5.50	2.75
U144	2c ver, cr ('75)	12.50	6.00
+U145	2c ver, org ('75)	9,000.	
U146	2c ver, bl ('80)	125.00	30.00
U147	2c ver, fawn ('75)	6.00	4.50
W148	2c ver, man ('75)	3.50	3.50

U41

U149	2c ver ('78)	45.00	30.00
a.	2c pink	45.00	30.00
U150	2c ver, amber ('78)	22.50	17.50
U151	2c ver, bl ('80)	12.50	9.00
a.	2c pink, blue	10.00	9.00
U152	2c ver, fawn ('78)	10.00	4.50

U42

U153	2c ver ('76)	55.00	25.00
U154	2c ver, amb ('76)	275.00	85.00
W155	2c ver, man ('76)	19.00	9.50

U43

U156	2c ver ('81)	600.00	130.00
U157	2c ver, amb ('81)	15,000.	15,000.
W158	2c ver, man ('81)	80.00	62.50

U44

U159	3c green	22.50	6.50
U160	3c green, amb	27.50	10.00
U161	3c green, cr	35.00	12.50
+U162	3c green, blue	—	

U45

U163	3c green	1.25	.25
U164	3c green, amb	1.40	.65
U165	3c green, cr	7.50	6.75
U166	3c green, blue	8.00	6.00
U167	3c green, fawn ('75)	4.50	3.50

U46

U168	3c green ('81)	500.00	55.00
U169	3c green, amb ('81)	225.00	100.00
U170	3c grn, bl ('81)	8,000.	1,600.
U171	3c green, fawn ('81)	25,000.	1,500.

U47

U172	5c blue, die 1 ('75)	10.00	8.00
U173	5c blue, die 1, amb ('75)	10.00	9.00
U174	5c blue, die 1, cr ('75)	90.00	40.00
U175	5c blue, die 1, bl ('75)	25.00	15.00
U176	5c blue, die 1, fawn ('75)	110.00	55.00
U177	5c blue, die 2 ('75)	7.50	6.50
U178	5c blue, die 2, amb ('75)	8.00	7.50
+U178A	5c blue, die 2, cr ('76)	3,250.	
U179	5c blue, die 2, blue ('75)	15.00	9.00
U180	5c blue, die 2, fawn ('75)	100.00	45.00

U48

U181	6c red	6.75	6.00
a.	6c vermilion	5.75	5.50
U182	6c red, amber	10.00	6.00
a.	6c vermilion, amber	10.00	6.00
U183	6c red, cream	20.00	12.50
a.	6c vermilion, cream	20.00	12.50
U184	6c red, fawn ('75)	17.50	12.50

U49

+U185	7c vermilion	1,500.	
U186	7c ver, amber	95.00	60.00

U50

U187	10c brown	32.50	20.00
U188	10c brown, amb	60.00	32.50

U51

U189	10c choc ('75)	7.50	4.25
a.	10c bister brown	8.50	5.00
b.	10c yellow ocher	1,250.	
U190	10c choc, amb ('75)	8.50	7.50
a.	10c bister brown, amb	8.50	7.50
b.	10c yellow ocher, amb	1,050.	
U191	10c brn, oriental buff ('86)	10.00	8.50
U192	10c brn, bl ('86)	12.50	8.50
a.	10c gray black, blue	11.00	7.50
b.	10c red brown, blue	11.00	7.50
U193	10c brown, man ('86)	14.00	10.00
a.	10c red brown, man	12.50	9.00
U194	10c brown, amb man ('86)	15.00	9.00
a.	10c red brown, amber manila	17.50	9.00

U52

U195	12c plum	175.00	85.00
U196	12c plum, amb	160.00	150.00
U197	12c plum, cream	200.00	175.00

U53

U198	15c orange	45.00	37.50
U199	15c orange, amb	125.00	100.00
U200	15c org, cream	350.00	350.00

U54

U201	24c purple	150.00	125.00
U202	24c purple, amb	150.00	125.00
U203	24c pur, cream	150.00	125.00

U55

U204	30c black	60.00	27.50
U205	30c black, amb	70.00	60.00
U206	30c black, cream	375.00	375.00

U207	30c blk, *oriental buff* ('86)	95.00	80.00
U208	30c blk, *bl* ('86)	100.00	80.00
U209	30c black, *man* ('86)	90.00	80.00
U210	30c black, *amb man* ('86)	125.00	80.00

U56

U211	90c carmine ('75)	125.00	80.00
U212	90c car, *amb* ('75)	160.00	225.00
U213	90c car, *cr* ('75)	1,300.	
U214	90c car, *oriental buff* ('86)	200.00	275.00
U215	90c car, *bl* ('86)	180.00	250.00
U216	90c car, *man* ('86)	125.00	250.00
U217	90c car, *amb man* ('86)	115.00	200.00

See Nos. U336-U347.

United States Centennial Issue

Single line under "POSTAGE" — U57   Double line under "POSTAGE" — U58

1876

U218	U57 3c red	50.00	25.00
U219	U57 3c green	45.00	17.50
+U220	U58 3c red	22,500.	
U221	U58 3c green	52.50	22.50

Cent. of the US, and the World's Fair at Philadelphia.
See No. U582.

Garfield — U59   Washington — U60

1882-86

U222	U59 5c brown	4.00	2.75
U223	U59 5c brown, *amb*	4.50	3.25
U224	U59 5c brn, *oriental buff* ('86)	110.00	70.00
U225	U59 5c brown, *blue*	60.00	35.00
U226	U59 5c brown, *fawn*	240.00	

1883, Oct.

U227	U60 2c red	3.50	2.25
a.	2c brown (error), entire	3,000.	
U228	U60 2c red, *amber*	4.50	2.75
U229	U60 2c red, *blue*	6.50	5.00
U230	U60 2c red, *fawn*	7.50	5.25

Wavy lines fine and clear — U61   Wavy lines thick and blurred — U62

Four Wavy Lines in Oval

1883, Nov.

U231	U61 2c red	3.50	2.25
U232	U61 2c red, *amber*	4.50	3.75
U233	U61 2c red, *blue*	7.50	7.00
U234	U61 2c red, *fawn*	5.50	4.50
W235	U61 2c red, *manila*	15.00	6.00

1884, June

U236	U62 2c red	7.50	4.00
U237	U62 2c red, *amber*	11.00	10.00
U238	U62 2c red, *blue*	17.50	10.00
U239	U62 2c red, *fawn*	12.00	9.50

See Nos. U260-W269.

3½ links over left "2" — U63   2 links below right "2" — U64

Round "O" in "TWO" — U65

U240	U63 2c red	65.00	40.00
U241	U63 2c red, *amber*	700.00	325.00
U242	U63 2c red, *fawn*		6,500.
U243	U64 2c red	85.00	55.00
U244	U64 2c red, *amber*	160.00	75.00
U245	U64 2c red, *blue*	325.00	140.00
U246	U64 2c red, *fawn*	325.00	140.00
U247	U65 2c red	1,400.	350.00
U248	U65 2c red, *amber*	2,500.	850.00
U249	U65 2c red, *fawn*	600.00	375.00

See Nos. U270-U276.

Jackson — U66

Die 1 — Numeral at left is 2¾mm wide   Die 2 — Numeral at left is 3¼mm wide

1883-86

U250	U66 4c grn, die 1	3.50	3.50
U251	U66 4c grn, die 1, *amb*	4.25	3.50
U252	U66 4c grn, die 1, *oriental buff* ('86)	7.50	9.00
U253	U66 4c grn, die 1, *bl* ('86)	7.50	6.50
U254	U66 4c grn, die 1, *man* ('86)	8.50	7.50
U255	U66 4c grn, die 1, *amb man* ('86)	17.50	10.00
U256	U66 4c grn, die 2	5.00	5.00
U257	U66 4c grn, die 2, *amb*	10.00	7.00
U258	U66 4c grn, die 2, *man* ('86)	9.50	7.50
U259	U66 4c grn, die 2, *amb man* ('86)	10.00	7.50

1884, May

U260	U61 2c brown	12.00	5.75
U261	U61 2c brn, *amber*	11.00	6.75
U262	U61 2c brn, *blue*	12.00	9.50
U263	U61 2c brn, *fawn*	11.00	9.00
W264	U61 2c brn, *manila*	12.50	10.00

1884, June   Retouched Die

U265	U62 2c brown	14.00	6.00
U266	U62 2c brn, *amber*	60.00	40.00
U267	U62 2c brn, *blue*	12.00	6.00
U268	U62 2c brn, *fawn*	14.00	11.00
W269	U62 2c brn, *manila*	20.00	15.00

2 Links Below Right "2"

U270	U64 2c brown	85.00	37.50
U271	U64 2c brn, *amber*	200.00	90.00
U272	U64 2c brn, *fawn*	3,500.	1,250.

Round "O" in "Two"

U273	U65 2c brn	160.00	80.00
U274	U65 2c brn, *amber*	200.00	80.00
U275	U65 2c brn, *blue*		5,500.
U276	U65 2c brn, *fawn*	825.00	650.00

Washington
U67   U68

U67 — Extremity of bust below the queue forms a point.

U68 — Extremity of bust is rounded.

Similar to U61
Two wavy lines in oval

1884-86

U277	U67 2c brown	.45	.15
a.	2c brown lake	20.00	22.50
U278	U67 2c brn, *amber*	.60	.45
a.	2c brown lake, *amber*	30.00	12.50
U279	U67 2c brn, *oriental buff*	2.60	2.00
U280	U67 2c brn, *blue*	2.25	2.00
U281	U67 2c brn, *fawn*	2.75	2.25
U282	U67 2c brn, *man* ('86)	9.00	4.00
W283	U67 2c brn, *man*	5.00	5.00
U284	U67 2c brn, *amb man* ('86)	5.50	5.75
+U285	U67 2c red	550.00	
+U286	U67 2c red, *blue*	250.00	
W287	U67 2c red, *man*	110.00	
U288	U68 2c brown	150.00	35.00
U289	U68 2c brn, *amb*	14.00	12.50
U290	U68 2c brn, *blue*	750.00	140.00
U291	U68 2c brn, *fawn*	20.00	19.00
W292	U68 2c brn, *man*	20.00	17.50

Grant — US1

1886   Letter Sheet

U293	US1 2c green, entire	24.00	16.00

See the Scott U.S. Specialized Catalogue for perforation and inscription varieties..

Franklin
U69   Washington
U70

U70 — Bust points between 3rd and 4th notches of inner oval; "G" of "POSTAGE" has no bar.

U71   U72

U71 — Bust points between second and third notches of inner oval; "G" of "POSTAGE" has a bar; ear is indicated by one heavy line; one vertical line at corner of mouth.

U72 — Frame same as die 2; upper part of head more rounded; ear indicated by two curved lines with two locks of hair in front; two vertical lines at corner of mouth.

Jackson — U73

Grant — U74   U75

U74 — There is a space between the beard and the collar of the coat. A button is on the collar.

U75 — The collar touches the beard and there is no button.

1887-94

U294	U69 1c blue	.50	.20
U295	U69 1c dk bl ('94)	6.50	2.50
U296	U69 1c bl, *amb* ('94)	3.00	1.25
U297	U69 1c dk blue, *amb* ('94)	45.00	22.50
+U298	U69 1c bl, *oriental buff* ('94)	2,750.	
+U299	U69 1c bl, *bl* ('94)	4,750.	
U300	U69 1c bl, *man* ('94)	.65	.35
W301	U69 1c bl, *man* ('94)	.45	.30
U302	U69 1c dk blue, *man* ('94)	22.50	10.00
W304	U69 1c dk blue, *man* ('94)	12.00	9.50
U305	U70 2c green	10.00	9.00
U306	U70 2c grn, *amb*	22.50	14.00
U307	U70 2c grn, *oriental buff*	75.00	30.00
U308	U70 2c grn, *blue*	3,000.	700.00
U309	U70 2c grn, *man*	2,500.	500.00
U310	U70 2c grn, *amb man*	1,800.	550.00
U311	U71 2c green	.30	.15
U312	U71 2c grn, *amb*	.40	.20
U313	U71 2c grn, *oriental buff*	.55	.25
U314	U71 2c grn, *blue*	.60	.30
U315	U71 2c grn, *man*	1.60	.50
W316	U71 2c grn, *man*	3.00	2.50
U317	U71 2c grn, *amb man*	2.50	1.90
U318	U72 2c green	110.00	12.50
U319	U72 2c grn, *amb*	160.00	25.00
U320	U72 2c grn, *oriental buff*	155.00	40.00
U321	U72 2c grn, *blue*	175.00	65.00
U322	U72 2c grn, *man*	150.00	65.00
U323	U72 2c grn, *amb man*	325.00	72.50
U324	4c lake	2.25	1.75
a.	4c scarlet	2.50	2.00
b.	4c scarlet ('94)	2.75	2.00
U325	U73 4c car, *amb*	2.50	2.25
a.	4c lake, *amber*	3.00	2.50
b.	4c scarlet, *amber* ('94)	3.00	3.25
U326	U73 4c car, *oriental buff*	5.00	3.00
a.	4c lake, *oriental buff*	6.00	3.50
U327	U73 4c car, *blue*	4.50	4.00
a.	4c lake, *blue*	4.50	4.00
U328	U73 4c car, *man*	6.00	5.50
a.	4c lake, *manila*	7.25	6.00
b.	4c pink, *manila*	7.50	4.50
U329	U73 4c car, *amb man*	4.25	2.75
a.	4c lake, *amb manila*	4.50	3.25
b.	4c pink, *amb manila*	5.25	3.75
U330	U74 5c blue	3.25	4.00
U331	U74 5c bl, *amber*	4.00	2.25
U332	U74 5c bl, *oriental buff*	4.25	3.75
U333	U74 5c bl, *blue*	7.00	5.50
U334	U75 5c blue ('94)	11.00	5.50
U335	U75 5c bl, *amb* ('94)	10.00	5.50
U336	U55 30c red brown	37.50	37.50
a.	30c yellow brown	45.00	45.00
b.	30c chocolate	45.00	47.50
U337	U55 30c red brn, *amb*	42.50	42.50
a.	30c yellow brown, *amber*	42.50	42.50
b.	30c choc, *amber*	42.50	42.50
U338	U55 30c red brn, *oriental buff*	40.00	42.50
a.	30c yel brn. *oriental buff*	35.00	42.50
U339	U55 30c red brn, *bl*	40.00	42.50
a.	30c yellow brown, *blue*	35.00	42.50
U340	U55 30c red brn, *manila*	42.50	42.50
a.	30c brown, *manila*	40.00	37.50
U341	U55 30c red brown, *amb man*	47.50	27.50
a.	30c yel brn, *amb man*	47.50	27.50
U342	U56 90c purple	60.00	70.00
U343	U56 90c pur, *amb*	75.00	75.00
U344	U56 90c pur, *oriental buff*	75.00	80.00
U345	U56 90c pur, *blue*	80.00	85.00
U346	U56 90c pur, *man*	80.00	85.00
U347	U56 90c pur, *amb manila*	85.00	85.00

Columbian Exposition Issue

Columbus and Liberty — U76

1893

U348	U76 1c deep blue	2.00	1.10
U349	U76 2c violet	1.75	.50
a.	2c dark slate (error)	1,750.	
U350	U76 5c chocolate	8.50	7.50
a.	5c slate brown (error)	750.00	750.00
U351	U76 10c slate brown	30.00	25.00
	Nos. U348-U351 (4)	42.25	34.10

Franklin
U77

Washington
U78

U78 — Bust points to first notch of inner oval and is only slightly concave below.

U79

U80

U79 — Bust points to middle of second notch of inner oval and is quite hollow below. Queue has ribbon around it.

U80 — Same as die 2 but hair flowing and no ribbon around queue.

Lincoln — U81

Pointed but not draped.

U82

U83

U82 — Bust broad and draped.

U83 — Head larger, inner oval has no notches.

Grant — U84

Similar to designs of 1887-95 but smaller

1899

U352	U77	1c green	.55	.20
U353	U77	1c grn, *amb*	4.50	1.50
U354	U77	1c grn, *oriental buff*	10.00	2.75
U355	U77	1c grn, *bl*	11.00	7.50
U356	U77	1c grn, *man*	2.00	.95
W357	U77	1c grn, *man*	2.25	1.10
U358	U78	2c carmine	2.75	1.75
U359	U78	2c car, *amb*	17.50	14.00
U360	U78	2c car, *oriental buff*	17.50	8.00
U361	U78	2c car, *blue*	55.00	27.50
U362	U79	2c carmine	.30	.20
a.		2c dark lake	27.50	32.50
U363	U79	2c car, *amb*	1.00	.20
U364	U79	2c car, *oriental buff*	1.00	.20
U365	U79	2c car, *blue*	1.25	.55
W366	U79	2c car, *man*	6.00	3.25
U367	U80	2c carmine	4.00	2.75
U368	U80	2c car, *amber*	8.00	6.75
U369	U80	2c car, *oriental buff*	22.50	12.50
U370	U80	2c car, *blue*	11.00	10.00
U371	U81	4c brown	15.00	11.00
U372	U81	4c brn, *amb*	16.00	12.50
U373	U82	4c brown	6,250.	375.00
U374	U83	4c brown	10.00	8.00
U375	U83	4c brn, *amb*	37.50	17.50
W376	U83	4c brn, *man*	15.00	8.25
U377	U84	5c blue	9.50	9.50
U378	U84	5c blue, *amb*	12.50	10.00

Franklin
U85

Washington
U86

U86 — One short and two long vertical lines at right of "CENTS."

Grant — U87

Lincoln — U88

1903

U379	U85	1c green	.60	.20
U380	U85	1c green, *amb*	12.50	2.00
U381	U85	1c grn, *oriental buff*	12.50	2.50
U382	U85	1c green, *blue*	14.00	2.50
U383	U85	1c grn, *manila*	3.00	.90
W384	U85	1c grn, *manila*	1.25	.40
U385	U86	2c carmine	.35	.15
U386	U86	2c carmine, *amb*	1.50	.20
U387	U86	2c car, *oriental buff*	1.50	.30
U388	U86	2c carmine, *blue*	1.10	.50
W389	U86	2c car, *manila*	15.00	9.00
U390	U87	4c chocolate	18.00	11.00
U391	U87	4c choc, *amber*	17.50	12.50
W392	U87	4c choc, *manila*	16.00	12.50
U393	U88	5c blue	17.50	12.50
U394	U88	5c blue, *amber*	17.50	12.50

U89

The three lines at the right of "CENTS" and at the left of "TWO" are usually all short; the lettering is heavier and the ends of the ribbons slightly changed.

1904 **Re-cut Die**

U395	U89	2c carmine	.45	.20
U396	U89	2c car, *amber*	7.00	1.00
U397	U89	2c car, *oriental buff*	5.00	1.10
U398	U89	2c carmine, *blue*	3.25	.90
W399	U89	2c car, *manila*	11.00	9.50

Franklin — U90

Die 1

Die 2

Die 3

Die 4

Die 1. Wide "D" in "UNITED."
Die 2. Narrow "D" in "UNITED."
Die 3. Wide "S-S" in "STATES" (1910).
Die 4. Sharp angle at back of bust, "N" and "E" of "ONE" are parallel (1912).

1907-16 **Die 1**

U400	U90	1c green	.25	.15
a.		Die 2	.75	.25
b.		Die 3	.75	.35
c.		Die 4	.65	.30
U401	U90	1c green, *amber*	.75	.40
a.		Die 2	.85	.70
b.		Die 3	.95	.75
c.		Die 4	.80	.65
U402	U90	1c grn, *oriental buff*	4.00	1.00
a.		Die 2	5.00	1.50
b.		Die 3	6.00	1.50
c.		Die 4	4.25	1.50

U403	U90	1c green, *blue*	4.25	1.50
a.		Die 2	4.25	1.50
b.		Die 3	4.25	3.00
c.		Die 4	3.75	1.25
U404	U90	1c grn, *manila*	2.75	1.90
a.		Die 3	3.50	3.00
W405	U90	1c grn, *manila*	.40	.25
a.		Die 2	40.00	25.00
b.		Die 3	6.00	4.00
c.		Die 4	40.00	

Die 1, Washington — U91

Die 2

Die 3

Die 4

Die 5

Die 6

Die 7

Die 8

Die 1. Oval "O" in "TWO" and "C" in "CENTS," front of bust broad.
Die 2. Similar to 1 but hair in two distinct locks at top of head.
Die 3. Round "O" in "TWO" and "C" in "CENTS," coarse lettering.
Die 4. Similar to 3 but lettering fine and clear, hair lines clearly embossed. Inner oval thin and clear.
Die 5. All "S's" wide (1910).
Die 6. Similar to 1 but front of bust narrow (1913).
Die 7. Similar to 6 but upper corner of front of bust cut away (1916).
Die 8. Similar to 7 but lower stroke of "S" in "CENTS" is a straight line. Hair as in Die 2 (1916).

Die I

U406	U91	2c brown red	.70	.15
a.		Die 2	27.50	6.25
b.		Die 3	.50	.20
U407	U91	2c brn red, *amb*	4.50	2.00
a.		Die 2	100.00	45.00
b.		Die 3	2.75	1.00
U408	U91	2c brown red, *oriental buff*	6.50	1.50
a.		Die 2	125.00	55.00
b.		Die 3	6.00	2.50
U409	U91	2c brn red, *blue*	4.00	1.75
a.		Die 2	125.00	100.00
b.		Die 3	4.00	1.50
W410	U91	2c brn red, *man*	40.00	32.50
U411	U91	2c carmine	.20	.15
a.		Die 2	.40	.20
b.		Die 3	.65	.35
c.		Die 4	.35	.20
d.		Die 5	.45	.30
e.		Die 6	.35	.20
f.		Die 7	12.50	10.00
g.		Die 8	13.00	10.00
h.		Die 1, with added impression of 1c grn (#U400), entire	325.00	
i.		Die 1, with added impression of 4c blk (#U416a), entire	300.00	
U412	U91	2c carmine, *amb*	.20	.15
a.		Die 2	.40	.25
b.		Die 3	1.25	.45
c.		Die 4	.35	.25
d.		Die 5	.55	.35
e.		Die 6	.50	.35
f.		Die 7	11.00	8.00
U413	U91	2c car, *oriental buff*	.40	.20
a.		Die 2	.50	.45
b.		Die 3	6.00	3.00
c.		Die 4	.35	.20
d.		Die 5	2.75	1.25
e.		Die 6	.50	.35
f.		Die 7	35.00	17.50
g.		Die 8	11.00	8.50
U414	U91	2c carmine, *blue*	.40	.20
a.		Die 2	.40	.35
b.		Die 3	.75	.60
c.		Die 4	.40	.25
d.		Die 5	.50	.30
e.		Die 6	.45	.30
f.		Die 7	12.50	7.50
g.		Die 8	12.50	7.50
W415	U91	2c car, *manila*	4.00	2.00
a.		Die 2	4.00	1.10
b.		Die 3	4.00	2.25
c.		Die 7	40.00	35.00

"F" 1mm from left
"4" — Die 1

"F" 1¾mm from
left "4" — Die 2

U416	U90	4c black, die 2	3.50	2.25
a.		Die 1	4.25	3.00
U417	U90	4c black, *amb*, die 2	5.00	2.50
a.		Die 1	5.00	2.50

Die 1-Tall "F" in   Die 2-Short "F" in
"FIVE"   "FIVE"

U418	U91 5c blue, die 2	6.00	2.25
a.	Die 1	6.00	2.25
b.	5c blue, buff, die 2 (error)	1,000.	
c.	5c blue, blue, die 2 (error)	1,000.	
d.	5c blue, blue, die 1 (error)	1,100.	
U419	U91 5c blue, amber, die 2	12.00	11.00
a.	Die 1	12.00	11.00

Franklin — U92

Die 1   Die 2

Die 3   Die 4   Die 5

(The 1c and 4c dies are the same except for
figures of value.)
Die 1. UNITED nearer inner circle than outer
circle.
Die 2. Large U; large NT closely spaced.
Die 3. Knob of hair at back of neck. Large NT
widely spaced.
Die 4. UNITED nearer outer circle than inner
circle.
Die 5. Narrow oval C, (also O and G).

1916-32   Die 1

U420	U92 1c green	.15	.15
a.	Die 2	90.00	55.00
b.	Die 3	.30	.15
c.	Die 4	.40	.40
d.	Die 5	.40	.35
U421	U92 1c grn, amber	.35	.30
a.	Die 2	300.00	175.00
b.	Die 3	1.00	.65
c.	Die 4	1.15	.85
d.	Die 5	.90	.55
U422	U92 1c grn, oriental buff	1.75	.90
a.	Die 4	3.75	1.25
U423	U92 1c green, blue	.40	.35
a.	Die 2	.75	.45
b.	Die 4	1.25	.65
c.	Die 5	.65	.35
U424	U92 1c grn, (unglazed) manila	6.00	4.00
W425	U92 1c grn, (unglazed) manila	.20	.15
a.	Die 3	140.00	125.00
U426	U92 1c grn, (glazed) brown ('20)	30.00	15.00
W427	U92 1c grn, (glazed) brown ('20)	60.00	
U428	U92 1c grn, (unglazed) brown ('20)	7.50	7.50

Die 1, Washington — U93

Die 2

Die 3

Die 4

Die 5

Die 6

Die 7

Die 8

Die 9

(The 1½c, 2c, 3c, 5c, and 6c are the same
except for figures of value.)
Die 1. Letters broad. Numerals vertical. Large
head (9¼mm) from tip of nose to back of neck. E
closer to inner circle than N of cents.

Die 2. Similar to 1; but U far from left circle.
Die 3. Similar to 2; but all inner circles very thin
(Rejected Die).
Die 4. Similar to 1; but C very close to left circle.
Die 5. Small head (8¾mm) from tip of nose to
back of neck. T and S of CENTS close at bottom.
Die 6. Similar to 5; but T and S of CENTS far
apart at bottom. Left numeral slopes to right.
Die 7. Large head. Both numerals slope to right.
Clean cut lettering. All letters T have short top
strokes.
Die 8. Similar to 7; but all letters T have long top
strokes.
Die 9. Narrow oval C (also O and G).

Die 1

U429	U93 2c carmine	.15	.15
a.	Die 2	9.00	6.00
b.	Die 3	30.00	25.00
c.	Die 4	9.00	7.50
d.	Die 5	.50	.35
e.	Die 6	.60	.30
f.	Die 7	.65	.25
g.	Die 8	.45	.20
h.	Die 9	.40	.20
i.	2c grn. error, die 1. entire	8,000.	
j.	2c car. die 1 with added impression of 1c grn (#U420), die 1. entire	700.00	
k.	Die 1. with added impression of 4c blk (#U416a), entire	700.00	
l.	Die 1. with added impression of 1c grn (#U400), die 1, entire	500.00	
U430	U93 2c car, amber	.25	.15
a.	Die 2	9.25	7.50
b.	Die 4	20.00	10.00
c.	Die 5	1.10	.35
d.	Die 6	.95	.40
e.	Die 7	.70	.35
f.	Die 8	.60	.30
g.	Die 9	.50	.20
U431	U93 2c car, oriental buff	2.00	.65
a.	Die 2	100.00	40.00
b.	Die 4	30.00	30.00
c.	Die 5	2.75	1.75
d.	Die 6	3.00	2.00
e.	Die 7	2.75	1.75
U432	U93 2c carmine, blue	.20	.15
b.	Die 2	25.00	20.00
c.	Die 4	100.00	90.00
d.	Die 4	25.00	25.00
e.	Die 5	.80	.30
f.	Die 6	.85	.40
g.	Die 7	.75	.35
h.	Die 8	.60	.25
i.	Die 9	.90	.30
U432A	U93 2c car, manila, die 7, entire	25,000.	
W433	U93 2c car, manila	.20	.20
W434	U93 2c car, (glazed) brn ('20)	80.00	50.00
W435	U93 2c car, (unglazed) brn ('20)	85.00	50.00
U436	U93 3c dk violet	.50	.20
a.	3c purple ('32), die 1	.30	.15
b.	3c dark violet, die 5	1.65	.75
c.	3c dark violet, die 6	2.00	1.40
d.	3c dark violet, die 7	1.40	.95
e.	3c purple ('32), die 7	.60	.25
f.	3c purple ('32), die 9	.35	.20
g.	3c carmine (error), die 1	30.00	27.50
h.	3c carmine (error), die 5	32.50	30.00
i.	3c dk vio, die 1, with added impression of 1c grn (#U420), die 1. entire	600.00	
j.	3c dk vio, die 1, with added impression of 2c car (#U429), die 1, entire	700.00	—
U437	U93 3c dk violet, amb	3.00	1.25
a.	3c purple ('32), die 1	.30	.15
b.	3c dark vio, die 5	4.50	2.50
c.	3c dark vio, die 6	4.50	2.50
d.	3c dark vio, die 7	3.75	2.25
e.	3c purple ('32), die 7	.60	.15
f.	3c purple ('32), die 9	.50	.15
g.	3c carmine (error), die 5	375.00	275.00
h.	3c black (error), die 1	165.00	—
U438	U93 3c dk vio, oriental buff	20.00	1.50
a.	Die 5	20.00	1.00
b.	Die 6	30.00	1.65
c.	Die 7	30.00	3.50
U439	U93 3c dk violet, bl	6.00	2.00
a.	3c purple ('32), die 1	.25	.20
b.	3c dark violet, die 5	6.50	4.00
c.	3c dark violet, die 6	6.00	4.25
d.	3c dark violet, die 7	9.00	5.50
e.	3c purple ('32), die 7	.55	.25
f.	3c purple ('32), die 9	.50	.20
g.	3c carmine (error), die 5	300.00	300.00
U440	U92 4c black	1.00	.60
a.	4c black with added impression of 2c car (#U429), die 1, entire	250.00	
U441	U92 4c black, amb	2.75	.85
U442	U92 4c black, bl ('21)	.80	.85
U443	U93 5c blue	3.00	2.75
U444	U93 5c blue, amber	3.50	1.60
U445	U93 5c bl, blue ('21)	3.75	3.25

See Nos. U481-U485, U529-U531.

Listings of double or triple surcharges
of 1920-25 are for specimens with the
surcharges directly or partly upon the
stamp.

Surcharged Type 1

1920-21

U446	U93 2c on 3c dk vio (U436)	11.00	10.00
a.	Die 5	11.00	10.00

Surcharged Type 2

Rose Surcharge

U447	U93 2c on 3c dk vio (U436)	7.00	6.50
b.	Die 6	9.00	8.50

Black Surcharge

U447A	U93 2c on 2c car (U429)	—	
U447C	U93 2c on 2c car, amb (U430)	—	
U448	U93 2c on 3c dk vio (U436)	2.25	2.00
U449	U93 2c on 3c dk vio, amb (U437)	6.00	6.00
U450	U93 2c on 3c dk vio, oriental buff (U438)	15.00	14.00
U451	U93 2c on 3c dk vio, blue (U439)	11.00	10.00

Surcharged Type 3

Bars 2mm apart

U451A	U90 2c on 1c grn (U400)	2,000.	
U452	U92 2c on 1c grn (U420)	1,000.	
a.	Dbl. surch., type 3	1,050.	
U453	U91 2c on 2c car (U411)	1,100.	
a.	Die 4	1,100.	
U453B	U91 2c on 2c car, bl (U414e)	1,000.	
U453C	U91 2c on 2c car, oriental buff (U413e)	1,000.	650.00
d.	Die 1	1,000.	
U454	U93 2c on 2c car (U429)	77.50	
U455	U93 2c on 2c car, amb (U430)	1,250.	
U456	U93 2c on 2c car, oriental buff (U431)	175.00	
a.	Dbl. surch., Type 3	225.00	
U457	U93 2c on 2c car, bl (U432)	200.00	
U458	U93 2c on 3c dk vio (U436)	.45	.35
a.	Double surcharge	14.00	7.50
b.	Triple surcharge	35.00	
c.	Dbl. surch., one in mag	65.00	
d.	Dbl. surch., Types 2 & 3	100.00	
U459	U93 2c on 3c dk vio, amb (U437)	2.50	1.00
a.	Dbl. surch., Type 3	18.00	
b.	Dbl. surch., Types 2 & 3	80.00	
U460	U93 2c on 3c dk vio, oriental buff (U438)	2.50	1.00
a.	Double surcharge	12.50	
b.	Triple surcharge	27.50	
U461	U93 2c on 3c dk vio, bl (U439)	4.00	1.00
a.	Double surcharge	15.00	
U462	U87 2c on 4c choc (U390)	350.00	160.00
U463	U87 2c on 4c choc, amb (U391)	350.00	100.00
U463A	U90 2c on 4c blk (U416)	1,100.	375.00
U464	U93 2c on 5c bl (U443)	1,000.	

Surcharged Type 4

Similar to Type 3, but bars 1½mm apart.

U465	U92 2c on 1c grn (U420)	1,100.	
U466	U91 2c on 2c car (U411e)	3,750.	
U466A	U93 2c on 2c car (U429)	240.00	
c.	Die 5	375.00	
U466B	U93 2c on 2c car, amb (U430)	2,250.	
U467	U45 2c on 3c grn (U163)	225.00	
U468	U93 2c on 3c dk vio (U436)	.70	.45
a.	Double surcharge	15.00	
b.	Triple surcharge	20.00	
c.	Inverted surcharge	75.00	
d.	Dbl. surch., Types 2 & 4	75.00	
e.	2c on 3c car (error) (U436h)	450.00	
U469	U93 2c on 3c dk vio, amb (U437)	3.25	2.25
a.	Dbl. surch., Types 2 & 4	60.00	
U470	U93 2c on 3c dk vio, oriental buff (U438)	4.25	2.50
a.	Double surcharge, Type 4	18.50	
b.	Dbl. surch., Types 2 & 4	60.00	
U471	U93 2c on 3c dk vio, bl (U439)	3.75	1.75
a.	Double surcharge, Type 4	18.50	
b.	Dbl. surch., Types 2 & 4	150.00	
U472	U87 2c on 4c choc (U390)	11.00	8.00
a.	Double surcharge	37.50	
U473	U87 2c on 4c choc, amb (U391)	15.00	10.00

1 CENT

Dbl. Surch., Type 4 and as above

U474	U93 2c on 1c on 3c dk vio (U436)	225.00	
U475	U93 2c on 1c on 3c dk vio, amb (U437)	225.00	

Surcharged Type 5

2

U476	U93 2c on 3c dk vio, amb (U437)	120.00	
a.	Double surcharge		

Surcharged Type 6

2

U477	U93 2c on 3c dk vio (U436)	100.00	
U478	U93 2c on 3c dk vio, amb (U437)	200.00	

Handstamped Surcharge in Black or Violet—Type 7

2

U479	U93 2c on 3c dk vio (Bk) (U436)	275.00	
U480	U93 2c on 3c dk vio (V) (U436d)	1,500.	

Expertization by competent authorities is recommened for Nos. U479-U480.

Type of 1916-32 Issue

1925-34

U481	U93 1½c brown, die 1	.15	.15
a.	Die 8	.60	.25
b.	1½c pur, die 1 (error) ('34)	90.00	
U482	U93 1½c brown, die 1, amber	.90	.40
a.	Die 8	1.40	.75
U483	U93 1½c brn, die 1, bl	1.50	.95
a.	Die 8	1.75	1.25
U484	U93 1½c brown, die 1, manila	6.00	3.00
W485	U93 1½c brown, die 1, manila	.75	.15
a.	With added impression of No. W433	120.00	—

Surcharged Type 8

1½

1925

U486	U71 1½c on 2c grn (U311)	675.00	
U487	U71 1½c on 2c grn, amb (U312)	750.00	
U488	U77 1½c on 1c grn (U352)	550.00	
U489	U77 1½c on 1c grn, amb (U353)	90.00	60.00
U490	U90 1½c on 1c grn (U400)	3.75	3.50
a.	Die 2	12.00	9.00
b.	Die 4	6.00	2.50
U491	U90 1½c on 1c grn, amb (U401)	7.50	2.50
a.	Die 2	75.00	65.00
b.	Die 4	4.25	2.25
U492	U90 1½c on 1c grn, oriental buff (U402a)	200.00	80.00
a.	Die 4	200.00	80.00
U493	U90 1½c on 1c grn, bl (U403c)	75.00	52.50
a.	Die 2	75.00	52.50
U494	U90 1½c on 1c grn, man (U404)	210.00	72.50
U495	U92 1½c on 1c grn (U420)	.45	.25
a.	Die 3	1.50	.60
b.	Die 4	1.65	.75
c.	Double surcharge	4.00	1.90
U496	U92 1½c on 1c grn, amb (U421)	15.00	12.50
U497	U92 1½c on 1c grn, oriental buff (U422)	3.00	1.90
U498	U92 1½c on 1c grn, bl (U423)	1.10	.75
U499	U92 1½c on 1c grn, man (U424)	11.00	6.00
U500	U92 1½c on 1c grn, brn (unglazed) (U428)	55.00	30.00
U501	U93 1½c on 1c grn, brn (glazed) (U426)	55.00	25.00
U502	U93 1½c on 2c car (U429)	225.00	
U503	U93 1½c on 2c car, oriental buff (U431)	250.00	—
a.	Double surcharge		—
U504	U93 1½c on 2c car, bl (U432)	250.00	

On Envelopes of 1925

U505	U93 1½c on 1½c brn (U481)	400.00	
a.	Die 8	400.00	
U506	U93 1½c on 1½c brn, bl (U483)	325.00	

The paper of No. U500 is not glazed and appears to be the same as that used for wrappers of 1920.

Surcharged Type 9

1½

Black Surcharge

U507	U69 1½c on 1c bl (U294)	1,100.	
U508	U77 1½c on 1c grn, amb (U353)	50.00	
U508A	U85 1½c on 1c grn (U379)	1,750.	
U509	U85 1½c on 1c grn, amb (U380)	12.00	10.00
a.	Double surcharge	25.00	
U509B	U85 1½c on 1c grn, oriental buff (U381)	50.00	40.00
U510	U90 1½c on 1c grn (U400)	2.00	1.25
a.	Double surcharge	7.50	
b.	Die 2	6.00	4.00
c.	Die 3	16.00	8.00
d.	Die 4	3.00	1.25
U511	U90 1½c on 1c grn, amb (U401)	150.00	72.50
U512	U90 1½c on 1c grn, oriental buff (U402)	6.00	4.00
a.	Die 4	17.00	14.00
U513	U90 1½c on 1c grn, bl (U403)	5.00	2.50
a.	Die 4	5.00	4.00
U514	U90 1½c on 1c grn, man (U404)	22.50	9.00
a.	Die 3	50.00	37.50
U515	U92 1½c on 1c grn (U420)	.30	.20
a.	Double surcharge	6.00	
b.	Inverted surcharge	9.00	
c.	Triple surcharge	11.00	
d.	Double surcharge, one inverted, entire		—
U516	U92 1½c on 1c grn, amb (U421)	40.00	25.00
U517	U92 1½c on 1c grn, oriental buff (U422)	4.25	1.25
U518	U92 1½c on 1c grn, bl (U423)	4.25	1.25
a.	Double surcharge	9.00	
U519	U92 1½c on 1c grn, man (U424)	20.00	10.00
a.	Double surcharge	27.50	

U520	U93 1½c on 2c car (U429)	250.00	—

Magenta Surcharge

U521	U92 1½c on 1c grn	4.25	3.50
a.	Double surcharge	25.00	

Sesquicentennial Exposition Issue

Liberty Bell — U94

Die 1. The center bar of "E" of "POSTAGE" is shorter than top bar.
Die 2. The center bar of "E" of "POSTAGE" is of same length as top bar.

1926

U522	U94 2c carmine, die 1	1.10	.50
a.	Die 2	6.00	3.75

See note below No. 627.

Washington Bicentennial Issue

Mount Vernon — U95

2 cent:
Die 1. "S" of "POSTAGE" normal.
Die 2. "S" of "POSTAGE" raised.

1932

U523	U95 1c olive green	.90	.80
U524	U95 1½c chocolate	1.75	1.50
U525	U95 2c car, die 1	.40	.20
a.	Die 2	70.00	16.00
b.	Die 1, blue, entire (error)	27,500.	
U526	U95 3c violet	1.75	.35
U527	U95 4c black	18.00	16.00
U528	U95 5c dark blue	3.75	3.50
	Nos. U523-U528 (6)	26.55	22.35

Bicen. of the birth of Washington.

1932 — Die 7

U529	U93 6c orange	5.50	4.00
U530	U93 6c orange, amber	11.00	8.00
U531	U93 6c orange, blue	11.00	10.00

Franklin — U96   Washington — U97

Die 1

Die 2

Die 3

Die 1. Short (3½mm) and thick "1" in thick circle.
Die 2. Tall (4½mm) and thin "1" in thin circle; upper and lower bars of E in ONE long and 1mm from circle.
Die 3. As in Die 2, but E normal and 1½mm from circle.

1950

U532	U96 1c green, die 1	5.00	1.75
a.	Die 2	6.50	3.00
b.	Die 3	6.00	3.00
	Die 3, precanceled		.50

Die 1   Die 2
Die 3   Die 4

Die 1. Thick "2" in circle; toe of "2" is an acute angle.
Die 2. Thin "2" in thin circle; toe of "2" is almost right angle; line through stand of "E" in POSTAGE goes considerably below tip of chin; "N" of UNITED is tall; "O" of TWO is high.
Die 3. Thin "2" in thin circle; toe of "2" is almost right angle; short UN in UNITED: thin crossbar in A of STATES.
Die 4. Tall UN in UNITED; thick crossbar in A of STATES; otherwise like Die 3.

U533	U97 2c carmine, die 3	.75	.25
a.	Die 1	.75	.30
b.	Die 2	1.40	.85
c.	Die 4	1.30	.60

Die 1   Die 2

Die 3

Die 4   Die 5

Die 1. Thick and tall (4½mm) "3" in thick circle; long top bars and short stems in T's of STATES.
Die 2. Thin and tall (4½mm) "3" in medium circle; short top bars and long stems in T's of STATES.
Die 3. Thin and short (4mm) "3" in thin circle; lettering wider than Dies 1 and 2; line from left stand of N to stand of E is distinctly below tip of chin.
Die 4. Figure and letters as in Die 3. Line hits tip of chin; short N in UNITED and thin crossbar in A of STATES.
Die 5. Figure, letter and chin line as in Die 4; but tall N in UNITED and thick crossbar in A of STATES.

U534	U97 3c dk violet, die 4	.40	.20
a.	Die 2	2.00	.70
b.	Die 3	.75	.50
c.	Die 3	.50	.25
d.	Die 5	.80	.45

Washington — U98

1952
U535 U98 1½c brown   5.00 3.50
    Precanceled   .50

Die 1   Die 2

Die 3

Die 1. Head high in oval (2mm below T of STATES). Circle near (1mm) bottom of colored oval.
Die 2. Head low in oval (3mm). Circle 1½mm from edge of oval. Right leg of A of POSTAGE shorter than left. Short leg on P.
Die 3. Head centered in oval (2½mm). Circle as in Die 2. Legs of A of POSTAGE about equal. Long leg on P.

1958
U536 U96 4c red violet, die 1   .75   .20
  a.   Die 2   1.00   .20
  b.   Die 3   1.00   .20

Nos. U429, U429f,
U429h, U533, U533a-
U533c Surcharged in
Red at Left of Stamp - b

1958
U537 U93 2c + 2c car, die 1   3.00 1.50
  a.   2c + 2c carmine, die 7   10.00 7.00
  b.   2c + 2c carmine, die 9   5.00 5.00
U538 U97 2c + 2c car, die 1   .75   .20
  a.   2c + 2c carmine, die 2   1.00   —
  b.   2c + 2c carmine, die 3   .80   .25
  c.   2c + 2c carmine, die 4   .80   —

Nos. U436a, U436e-
U436f, U534a-U534d
Surcharged in Green at
Left of Stamp - a

U539 U93 3c + 1c pur, die 1   15.00 11.00
  a.   3c + 1c purple, die 7   12.00 9.00
  b.   3c + 1c purple, die 9   30.00 15.00
U540 U97 3c + 1c dk violet, die 3   .50   .15
  a.   3c + 1c dk violet, die 2, entire 1,000.
  b.   3c + 1c dark violet, die 4   .75   .15
  c.   3c + 1c dark violet, die 5   .75   .15

See No. U545.

Franklin   Washington
U99   U100

Die 1   Die 2

Dies of 1¼c
Die 1. The "4" is 3mm high. Upper leaf in left cluster 2mm from "U."
Die 2. The "4" is 3½mm high. Leaf clusters are larger. Upper leaf at left is 1mm from "U."

1960
U541 U99 1¼c turquoise, die 1   .70   .50
    Die 1, precanceled   .15
  a.   Die 2, precanceled   2.00
U542 U100 2½c dull blue   .80   .50
    Precanceled   .15

Precanceled Cut Squares
Precanceled envelopes do not normally receive another cancellation. Since the lack of a cancellation makes it impossible to distinguish between cut squares from used and unused envelopes, they are valued here as used only.

Pony Express Centennial Issue

Pony
Express
Rider
U101

Envelope White Outside, Blue Inside
1960, July 19
U543 U101 4c brown   .60   .30

Abraham Lincoln — U102

Die 1   Die 2

Die 3

Die 1. Center bar of E of POSTAGE is above the middle. Center bar of E of STATES slants slightly upward. Nose sharper, more pointed. No offset ink specks inside envelope on back of die impression.
Die 2. Center bar of E in POSTAGE in middle. P of POSTAGE has short stem. Ink specks on back of die impression.
Die 3. Fl of FIVE closer than Die 1 or 2. Second T of STATES seems taller than ES. Ink specks on back of die impression.

1962, Nov. 19
U544 U102 5c dark blue, die 2   .80   .20
  a.   Die 1   .85   .25
  b.   Die 3   .90   .35
  c.   Die 2 with albino impression of 4c (#U536)   50.00   —
  d.   Die 3 with albino impression of 4c (#U536)   70.00   —

No. U536 Surcharged Type "a" in Green at Left of Stamp
Two types of surcharge "a":
Type I. "U.S. POSTAGE" 18½mm high. Serifs on cross of T both diagonal. Two lines of shading in C of CENT.
Type II. "U.S. POSTAGE" 17½mm high. Right serif on cross of T is vertical. Three shading lines in C.

1962, Nov.
U545 U96 4c + 1c red vio, Type I   1.40   .50
  a.   Type II   1.00   .50

New York World's Fair (1964-65)

Globe with
Satellite
Orbit
U103

1964, Apr. 22
U546 U103 5c carmine rose   .60   .40

Liberty   Old
Bell — U104   Ironsides — U105

Eagle — U106   Head of Statue of
                    Liberty — U107

1965-69   **Tagged (6c)**
U547 U104 1¼c brown   .15
U548 U104 1⁴⁄₁₀c brown ('68)   .15
U548A U104 1⁶⁄₁₀c orange ('69)   .15
U549 U105 4c bright blue   .75   .15
U550 U106 5c bright purple   .75   .15
  a.   Tagged ('67)   1.25   .15
U551 U107 6c lt green ('68)   .70   .15
    Set value   .55

Issue dates: 5c, Jan. 5; 1¼c, Jan. 6; 6c, Jan. 4; 1⁴⁄₁₀c, Mar. 26; 1⁶⁄₁₀c, June 16.
No. U550a has a luminescent panel 9x29mm at left of stamp. It glows yellow green under ultraviolet light.

Nos. U549-U550 Surcharged Types "b" and "a" in Red or Green at Left of Stamp
1968, Feb. 5
U552 U105 4c + 2c brt blue (R)   3.75 2.00
U553 U106 5c + 1c brt purple (G)   3.50 2.50
  a.   Tagged   3.50 2.75

Tagging
Envelopes from No. U554 onward are tagged, with the tagging element in the ink unless otherwise noted.

Herman Melville Issue

Moby
Dick — U108

1970, Mar. 7
U554 U108 6c light blue   .50   .15
Herman Melville (1819-91), writer, and the whaling industry.

Youth Conference Issue

Youth
Conference
Emblem
U109

1971, Feb. 24
U555 U109 6c light blue   .75   .15
White House Conference on Youth, Estes Park, Colo., Apr. 18-22.

Bell Type of 1965-69 and

Eagle — U110

1971   **Untagged (1⁷⁄₁₀c)**
U556 U104 1⁷⁄₁₀c deep lilac   .15
U557 U110 8c bright ultra   .40   .15
    Set value   .15

Issue dates: 1⁷⁄₁₀c, May 10; 8c, May 6.

Nos. U551 and
U555 Surcharged in
Green at Left of
Stamp

1971, May 16
U561 U107 6c + (2c) light green   1.00   .30
U562 U109 6c + (2c) light blue   2.00 1.60

Bowling Issue

Bowling Ball and
Pin — U111

1971, Aug. 21
U563 U111 8c rose red   .50   .15
Salute to bowling and 7th World Tournament of the Intl. Bowling Fed., Milwaukee, WI.

Aging Conference Issue

Conference
Symbol — U112

1971, Nov. 5
U564 U112 8c light blue   .50   .15
White House Conference on Aging, Washington, DC, Nov. 28-Dec. 2, 1971.

International Transportation Exhibition Issue

Transportation
Exhibition
Emblem
U113

Illustration ⅖ actual size.

1972, May 2
U565 U113 8c ultra & rose red   .50   .15
US Intl. Transportation Exhib., Dulles Intl. Airport, Washington, May 27-June 4.

No. U557 Surcharged Type "b" in Ultramarine at Left of Stamp
1973, Dec. 1
U566 U110 8c + 2c bright ultra   .40   .15

Liberty
Bell — U114

1973, Dec. 5
U567 U114 10c emerald   .40   .15

"Volunteer Yourself" — U115

1974, Aug. 23   Untagged
U568 U115 1⁸/₁₀c blue green   .15

US Tennis Centenary Issue

Tennis Racquet — U116

1974, Aug. 31
U569 U116 10c yel, brt blue & lt grn   .30   .20

Bicentennial Era Issue

The Seafaring Tradition--Compass Rose — U118

The American Homemaker--Quilt Pattern — U119

The American Farmer--Sheaf of Wheat U120

The American Doctor — U121

The American Craftsman--Tools, c. 1750 — U122

Designs (in brown on left side of envelope): 10c, Norwegian sloop Restaurationen. No. U572, Spinning wheel. No. U573, Plow. No. U574, Colonial era medical instruments and bottle. No. U575, Shaker rocking chair.

Light Brown Diagonally Laid Paper

1975-76
U571 U118 10c brown & blue   .30   .15
  a. Brown ("10c/USA," etc.) omit-
    ted, entire   125.00
U572 U119 13c brn & bl grn   .35   .15
  a. Brown ("13c/USA," etc.) omit-
    ted, entire   125.00
U573 U120 13c brn & brt grn   .35   .15
  a. Brown ("13c/USA," etc.) omit-
    ted, entire   125.00
U574 U121 13c brown & orange   .35   .15
  a. Brown ("13c/USA," etc.) omit-
    ted, entire   —
U575 U122 13c brown & car   .35   .15
  a. Brown ("13c/USA," etc.) omit-
    ted, entire   125.00

Issue dates: 10c, Oct. 13, 1975. No. U572, Feb. 2, 1976. No. U573, Mar. 15, 1976. No. 574, June 30, 1976. No. U575, Aug. 6, 1976.

Liberty Tree, Boston, 1646 — U123

1975, Nov. 8
U576 U123 13c orange brown   .30   .15

Precanceled Cut Squares
See note following No. U542.

Star and Pinweel — U124

U125

U126

Eagle — U127

"Uncle Sam" — U128

1976-78
U577 U124   2c red, untagged ('76)   .15
U578 U125   2.1c yel grn, untagged
            ('77)   .15
U579 U126   2.7c grn, untagged ('78)   .15
U580 U127 (15c) orange ('78)   .40   .15
U581 U128   15c red ('78)   .40   .15
            Set value   .45

Issue dates: 2c, Sept. 10; 2.1c June 3; 2.7c, July 5; A, May 22; 15c, June 3.

Bicentennial Issue

Centennial Envelope, 1876 — U129

1976, Oct. 15
U582 U129 13c emerald   .35   .15
    See Nos. U218-U221.

Golf Issue

Golf Club in Motion and Golf Ball — U130

1977, Apr. 7
U583 U130 13c blk, bl & yel green   .45   .20
  a. Black omitted, entire
  b. Black and blue omitted, entire   550.00

Energy Issue

Energy Conservation U131

Energy Development U132

1977, Oct. 20
U584 U131 13c blk, red & yel   .40   .15
  a. Red & yel omitted, entire
  b. Yellow omitted, entire
  c. Black omitted, entire
  d. Black & red omitted, entire   475.00
U585 U132 13c blk, red & yel   .40   .15
  Nos. U584-U585 have a luminescent panel at left of stamp.

Olive Branch and Star — U133

1978, July 28
U586 U133 15c on 16c blue   .35   .15
  a. Surcharge omitted, entire   400.00
  b. Surcharge on #U581, entire

Auto Racing Issue

Indianapolis 500 Racing Car — U134

1978, Sept. 2
U587 U134 15c red, blue & black   .35   .15
  a. Black omitted, entire   140.00
  b. Black & blue omitted, entire
  c. Red omitted, entire
  d. Red & blue omitted, entire

No. U576 Surcharged at left of Stamp Like No. U586

1978, Nov. 28   Embossed
U588 U123 15c on 13c org brown   .35   .15

Precanceled Cut Squares
See note following No. U542.

U135

Weaver Violins — U136

U137

Eagle — U138

Star — U139

Eagle U140

1979-82   Untagged (3.1c, 3.5c, 5.9c)
U589 U135 3.1c ultramarine   .15
U590 U136 3.5c purple   .15
U591 U137 5.9c brown   .15
U592 U138 (18c) violet   .45   .20
U593 U139 18c dark blue   .45   .20
U594 U140 (20c) brown   .45   .15
        Set value   .80

Issue dates: 3.1c, May 18; 3.5c, June 23; 5.9c, Feb. 17, 1982; Mar. 15, 1981; #U592, Apr. 2, 1981; #U593, Oct. 11, 1981; #U594.

Veterinary Medicine Issue

Seal of Veterinarians U141

Design on left side of envelope shows 5 animals and a bird in brown and "Veterinary Medicine" in gray.

1979, July 24
U595 U141 15c brown & gray   .35   .15
  a. Gray omitted, untagged, entire 700.00
  b. Brown omitted, entire

Olympic Games Issue

U142

Design (multicolored on left side of envelope) shows two soccer players with ball.

1979, Dec. 10
U596 U142 15c red, green & black   .60   .15
  a. Red & green omitted, untagged,
    entire   225.00
  b. Blk omitted, untagged, entire   225.00
  c. Black & green omitted, entire   225.00
  d. Red omitted, untagged, entire

22nd Olympic Games, Moscow, July 19-Aug. 3, 1980.

Bicycling Issue

Highwheeler Bicycle — U143

Design (on left side of envelope) shows racing bicycle.

1980, May 16
U597 U143 15c bl & rose claret   .40   .15
  a. Blue ("15c USA") omitted   100.00

America's Cup Yacht Races Issue

Racing Yacht — U144

1980, Sept. 15
U598 U144 15c light blue   .40   .15

Italian
Honeybee
and Orange
Blossoms
U145

Bee & Petals Colorless Embossed
1980, Oct. 10
U599 U145 15c multicolored   .35   .15
a.   Brown ("USA 15c") omitted, en-
         tire   140.00

Design: Hand and braille colorless embossed

1981, Oct. 11
U600 U146 18c blue & red   .45   .20
a.   Blue omitted, untagged, entire

Capitol
Dome — U147

1981, Nov. 13
U601 U147 20c deep magenta   .45   .15

U148

Illustration reduced.

1982, June 15
U602 U148 20c dk blue, blk & mag   .45   .15
a.   Dark blue omitted, entire
b.   Dark blue & magenta omitted, en-
         tire   —

U149

1982, Aug. 6
U603 U149 20c purple & black   .45   .15

1983, Mar. 21   Untagged
U604 U150 5.2c orange   .15

U151

1983, Aug. 3
U605 U151 20c red, blue & black   .45   .15
a.   Red omitted, entire   —
b.   Blue omitted, entire   —
c.   Red & black omitted, entire   —
d.   Blue & black omitted, entire   —
e.   Black omitted, entire   350.00

Small Business USA 20c
U152

Design shows storefronts at lower left.
Stamp and design continue on back of envelope.

1984, May 7   Photo.
U606 U152 20c multicolored   .50   .15

U153

1985, Feb. 1   Embossed
U607 U153 (22c) deep green   .55   .15

Bison
U154

1985, Feb. 25   Embossed
U608 U154 22c violet brown   .55   .15
a.   Untagged, precanceled with 3 blue
         lines   .15

Frigate U.S.S.
Constitution, "Old
Ironsides" — U155

1985, May 3   Embossed   Untagged
U609 U155 6c green blue   .15

Mayflower — U156

1986, Dec. 4   Embossed   Untagged
Precanceled
U610 U156 8.5c black & gray   .15

Stars — U157

1988, Mar. 26   Embossed & Typo.
U611 U157 25c dk bl & dk red   .60   .15
a.   Dark red ("25") omitted, entire   85.00

Sea Gulls, Frigate USS
Constellation — U158

Embossed & Typo.
1988, Apr. 12   Untagged
U612 U158 8.4c black & brt blue   .15
a.   Black omitted, entire   600.00

First-Class
Snowflake — U159

"Holiday Greetings!" inscribed at lower left.

1988, Sept. 8   Typo.
U613 U159 25c dark red & green   .60   .25

Stars and "*Philatelic Mail*" Continuous
in Dark Red Below Vignette — U160

1989, Mar. 10   Typo.
U614 U160 25c dk red & dp bl   .50   .25

"USA" and Stars — U161

1989, July 10   Typo.   Unwmk.
U615 U161 25c dk red & dp bl   .50   .25
a.   Dark red omitted, entire

Love — U162

Litho. & Typo.
1989, Sept. 25   Unwmk.
U616 U162 25c dark red & blue   .50   .25

Shuttle Docking at Space Station — U163

1989, Dec. 3   Typo.   Unwmk.
U617 U163 25c ultramarine   .60   .30
a.   Ultramarine omitted, entire   750.00

A hologram, visible through the die cut window
to the right of "USA 25," is affixed to the inside of
the envelope. Available only in No. 9 size. No. 9
envelopes are 225mm by 100mm.
See Nos. U625, U639.

Vince Lombardi Trophy, Football
Players — U164

1990, Sept. 9   Litho.   Unwmk.
U618 U164 25c vermilion   .50   .25

A hologram, visible through the die cut window
to the right of "USA 25," is affixed to the inside of
the envelope.

Star — U165

Has embossed bars above and below the design.

1991, Jan. 24   Embossed & Typo.
U619 U165 29c ultra & rose   .60   .30
a.   Ultramarine omitted, entire
b.   Rose omitted, entire   —

Precanceled Cut Squares
See note following No. U542.

Birds — U166

Stamp and design continue on back of envelope.

1991, May 3   Typo.   Wmk.
Untagged
Precanceled
U620 U166 11.1c blue & red   .20

Love — U167

1991, May 9   Litho.
U621 U167 29c lt blue, maroon &
         brt rose   .60   .30
a.   Bright rose omitted, entire   500.00

Creating a Brighter World
Magazine Industry, 250th Anniv. — U168

Photo. & Typo.

1991, Oct. 7   **Unwmk.**
U622 U168 29c multicolored   .60   .30

The photogravure vignette, visible through the die cut window to the right of "USA 29," is affixed to the inside of the envelope. Available only in No. 10 size.

Star
U169

Stamp and design continue on back of envelope.

1991, July 20   **Typo.**
U623 U169 29c ultra & rose   .60   .30
  a.   Ultra omitted, entire   —
  b.   Rose omitted, entire   —

Lined with a blue design to provide security for enclosures. Available only in No. 9 size.

Country
Geese
U170

1991, Nov. 8   **Litho. & Typo.**   **Wmk.**
U624 U170 29c blue gray & yellow   .60   .60

Space Shuttle Type of 1989
1992, Jan. 21   **Typo.**   **Unwmk.**
U625 U163 29c yellow green   .60   .25

A hologram, visible through the die cut window to the right of "USA 29," is affixed to the inside of the envelope. Available only in No. 10 size.
See No. U617a for envelopes with hologram only.

Hillebrandia — U172

Illustration reduced.

1992, Apr. 22
U627 U172 29c multicolored   .60   .30

The lithographed vignette, visible through the die cut window to the right of "29 USA," is affixed to the inside of the envelope.

U173

Typo. & Embossed

1992, May 19   **Untagged**

Precanceled
U628 U173 19.8c red & blue   .40

Disabled Americans

U174

1992, July 22   **Typo.**   **Unwmk.**
U629 U174 29c red & blue   .60   .30

U175

Illustration reduced.

Typo. & Litho.
1993, Oct. 2   **Unwmk.**   **Die Cut**
U630 U175 29c multicolored   .60   .30

The lithographed vignette, visible through the die cut window to the right of "USA 29," is affixed to the inside of the envelope.

U176

Typo. & Embossed
1994, Sept. 17   **Unwmk.**
U631 U176 29c brown & black   —   .30
  a.   Black ("29/USA") omitted, entire
       See No. U638.

Liberty Bell — U177

Typo. & Embossed
1995, Jan. 3   **Unwmk.**
U632 U177 32c greenish blue & blue   .65   .30
  a.   Greenish blue omitted, entire

U178

Design size: 49x38mm (#U633), 53x44mm (#U634). Stamp and design continue on back of envelope.

1995   **Typo.**   **Unwmk.**
U633 U178 (32c) blue & red   .65   .30
U634 U178 (32c) blue & red   .65   .30
  a.   Red color and tagging omitted, entire
  b.   Blue omitted, entire

Originally, Nos. U633-U634 were only available through the Philatelic Fullfillment Center after their announcement 1/12/95.

U179

Design size: 58x25mm. Stamp and design continue on back of envelope.

1995, Mar. 10   **Typo.**   **Unwmk.**
Precanceled
U635 U179 (5c) green & red brown   .15

Graphic Eagle — U180

1995, Mar. 10   **Typo.**   **Unwmk.**
Precanceled
U636 U180 (10c) dark carmine &   blue   .15

Spiral Heart — U181

1995, May 12   **Typo.**   **Unwmk.**
U637 U181 32c red, *light blue*   .65   .30

Liberty Bell Type of 1995
1995, May 16   **Typo.**
U638 U177 32c greenish blue & blue   .65   .30

Space Shuttle Type of 1989
                 Unwmk.
1995, Sept. 22   **Typo.**   **Die Cut**
U639 U163 32c carmine rose   .65   .35

A hologram, visible through the die cut window to the right of "USA 32," is affixed to the inside of the envelope.

U182

Typo. & Litho.
1996, Apr. 20   **Unwmk.**   **Die Cut**
U640 U182 32c multicolored   .60   .30

The lithographed vignette, visible through the die cut window to the right of "USA 32c," is affixed to the inside of the envelope.

U183

1996, May 2
U641 U183 32c multicolored   .60   .30
  a.   Black & red omitted, entire   —
  b.   Blue & gold omitted, entire   —

AIR POST STAMPED ENVELOPES AND AIR LETTER SHEETS

UC1   UC2

UC1 — Vertical rudder is not semi-circular but slopes down to the left. The tail of the plane projects into the G of POSTAGE.

UC2 — Vertical rudder is semi-circular. The tail of the plane touches but does not project into the G of POSTAGE.

6c: Same as UC2 except 3 types of numeral.
Die 2a- Numeral "6" 6½mm wide.
Die 2b- Numeral "6" 6mm wide.
Die 2c- Numeral "6" 5½mm wide.
Die 3- Vertical rudder leans forward. S closer to O than to T of POSTAGE. E of POSTAGE has short center bar.

1929-44		**Embossed**	
UC1	UC1 5c blue	3.50	2.00
UC2	UC2 5c blue	11.00	5.00
UC3	UC2 6c org, die 2a ('34)	1.45	.40
a.	No. UC3 with added impression of 3c pur (#U436a), entire without border	3,000.	
UC4	UC2 6c org, die 2b ('42)	2.75	2.00
UC5	UC2 6c org, die 2c ('44)	.75	.30
UC6	UC2 6c org, die 3 ('42)	1.00	.35
a.	6c org, *blue* (error), entire	3,500.	2,400.
UC7	UC2 8c olive green ('32)	13.00	3.50

Surcharged in black on envelopes indicated by numbers in brackets.

1945			
UC8	U93 6c on 2c (U429)	1.25	.65
a.	6c on 1c grn, error, (U420)	1,750.	
b.	6c on 3c purple, error, (U436a)	1,750.	
c.	6c on 3c purple, error, amb (U437a)	3,000.	
d.	6c on 3c vio, error, (U526)	3,000.	
UC9	U95 6c on 2c (U525)	75.00	40.00

Nos. UC8a-UC8d are known only entire.

Surcharged in Black on 6c Orange Air Post Envelopes without borders

REVALUED 5¢ P.O.DEPT.

1946			
UC10	UC2 5c on 6c, die 2a	2.75	1.50
a.	Double surcharge	60.00	
UC11	UC2 5c on 6c, die 2b	9.00	5.50
UC12	UC2 5c on 6c, die 2c	.75	.50
a.	Double surcharge	60.00	60.00
UC13	UC2 5c on 6c, die 3	.80	.60
a.	Double surcharge	60.00	

The 6c borderless envelopes and the revalued envelopes were issued primarily for use to and from members of the armed forces.
The 5c rate came into effect Oct. 1, 1946.

DC-4 Skymaster UC3

Die 1. The end of the wing at the right is a smooth curve. The juncture of the front end of the plane and the engine forms an acute angle. The first T of STATES and the E's of UNITED STATES lean to the left.
Die 2. The end of the wing at the right is a straight line. The juncture of the front end of the plane and the engine is wide open. The first T of

STATES and the E's of UNITED STATES lean to the right.

1946   **Embossed**
UC14 UC3 5c carmine, die 1   .75   .20
UC15 UC3 5c carmine, die 2   .85   .25
     See Nos. UC18, UC26.

DC-4 Skymaster — UC4

Letter Sheet for Foreign Postage
"Air Letter" on face, 2-line inscription on back.

1947, Apr. 29   **Typo.**
UC16 UC4 10c brt red, *pale bl*,
     entire   7.50   6.00
   a. "Air Letter" on face, 4-line in-
     scription on back ('51), en-
     tire   16.00   14.00
   b. As "a," 10c chocolate, *pale bl*,
     entire   400.00
   c. "Air Letter" and "Aero-
     gramme" on face, 4-line in-
     scription on back ('53),
     entire   45.00   12.50
   d. "Air Letter" and "Aero-
     gramme" on face, 3-line in-
     scription on back ('55),
     entire   8.00   8.00

Washington and Franklin, Early and
Modern Mail-carrying Vehicles — UC5

Embossed, Rotary Press Printing
1947, May 21
UC17 UC5 5c car, (22¼mm high)   .40   .25
   a. Flat plate (21¼mm high)   .50   .30

Cent. of the 1st postage stamps issued by the US Government.

Type of 1946

Type I- 6's lean to right.
Type II- 6's upright.

1950, Sept. 22
UC18 UC3 6c carmine, Type I   .35   .15
   a. Type II   .75   .25

Several other types differ slightly from the two listed.

Nos. UC14, UC15,
UC18 Surcharged in
Red at Left of Stamp

REVALUED
6¢
P. O. DEPT.

1951
UC19 UC3 6c on 5c car, die 1   .85   .50
UC20 UC3 6c on 5c car, die 2   .80   .50
   a. 6c on 6c car, error, entire   1,500.00
   b. 6c on 5c, double surcharge   250.00   —

Nos. UC14, UC15
and UC17
Surcharged in Red at
Left of Stamp

REVALUED
6¢
P. O. DEPT.

1952
UC21 UC3 6c on 5c, die 1   27.50   17.50
UC22 UC3 6c on 5c, die 2   3.50   2.50
   a. Double surcharge   75.00
UC23 UC3 6c on 5c, entire   1,750.

The 6c on 4c black (No. U440) is believed to be a favor printing.

Eagle in Flight — UC6

1956, May 2   **Embossed**
UC25 UC6 6c red   .75   .50
   FIPEX, NYC, Apr. 28-May 6. Two types exist, differing mainly in the clouds at top.

Skymaster Type of 1946

1958, July 31
UC26 UC3 7c blue   .65   .50

Nos. UC3-UC5,
UC18 and UC25
Surcharged in Green
at Left of Stamp

1958
UC27 UC2 6c + 1c, die 2a   250.00   225.00
UC28 UC2 6c + 1c, die 2b   65.00   75.00
UC29 UC2 6c + 1c, die 2c   37.50   50.00
UC30 UC3 6c + 1c, type I   1.00   .50
   a. Type II   1.00   .50
UC31 UC6 6c + 1c   1.00   .50

Jet Airliner — UC7

Letter Sheet for Foreign Postage.

Two types:
Type I - Back inscription in 3 lines.
Type II - Back inscription in 2 lines.

1958-59   **Typo.**
UC32 UC7 10c bl & red, *bl*, II
     ('59), entire   6.00   5.00
   a. Type I ('58), entire   10.00   5.00
   b. Red omitted, II, entire   —
   c. Blue omitted, II, entire   —

Silhouette of Jet
Airliner — UC8

1958, Nov. 21   **Embossed**
UC33 UC8 7c blue   .60   .25

1960, Aug. 18
UC34 UC8 7c carmine   .60   .25

Jet Plane and
Globe — UC9

Letter Sheet for Foreign Postage

1961, Nov. 16   **Typo.**
UC35 UC9 11c red & bl, *bl*, entire   2.75   1.50
   a. Red omitted, entire   875.00
   b. Blue omitted, entire   875.00

UC10   UC11

1962, Nov. 17   **Embossed**
UC36 UC10 8c red   .55   .15

1965, Jan. 7
UC37 UC11 8c red   .35   .15
   a. Tagged ('67)   1.25   .30

No. UC37a has a luminescent panel ³/₈x1 inches at left of stamp. It glows orange red under ultraviolet light.

Pres. John F.
Kennedy and
Jet
Plane — UC12

Letter Sheets for Foreign Postage

1965-67   **Typo.**
UC38 UC12 11c red & dk bl, *blue*,
     entire   3.25   1.50
UC39 UC12 13c red & dk bl, *blue*,
     entire   3.00   1.50
   a. Red omitted   500.00
   b. Dark blue omitted   500.00

Issued: 11c, May 29, 1965; 13c, May 29, 1967.

UC13

1968, Jan. 8   **Tagged**   **Embossed**
UC40 UC13 10c red   .50   .15

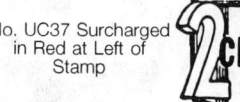

No. UC37 Surcharged
in Red at Left of
Stamp

1968, Feb. 5
UC41 UC11 8c + 2c red   .65   .15

Tagging
Envelopes and Letter Sheets from No.
UC42 onward are tagged unless otherwise noted.

Globes and Flock of Birds
UC14

Letter Sheet for Foreign Postage

1968, Dec. 3   **Photo.**
UC42 UC14 13c gray, brn, org &
     black, *blue*, en-
     tire   8.00   4.00
   a. Orange omitted, entire   —
   b. Brown omitted, entire   400.00
   c. Black omitted, entire   —

Intl. Human Rights Year, and 20th anniv. of the UN Declaration of Human Rights.

UC15

1971, May 6   **Embossed**
UC43 UC15 11c red & blue   .50   .15

Birds in Flight and "usa" — UC16

Letter Sheet for Foreign Postage
"postage 15c" in Gray

1971, May 28   **Photo.**
UC44 UC16 15c gray, red, white &
     blue, *blue*, entire   1.50   1.10
   a. "AEROGRAMME" added, entire   1.50   1.10

Folding instructions (2 steps) in capitals on No. UC44; (4 steps) in upper and lower case on No. UC44a. No. UC44a issued Dec. 13.
See No. UC46.

No. UC40
Surcharged in Green
at Left of Stamp

1971, June 28   **Embossed**
UC45 UC13 10c + (1c) red   1.50   .20

Letter Sheet for Foreign Postage
"usa" Type of 1971

Design: Three balloons and cloud at left in address section; no birds beside stamp.

"postage 15c" in Blue

1973, Feb. 10   **Photo.**
UC46 UC16 15c red, white & bl,
     blue, entire   .75   .40

Hot Air Ballooning World Championships, Albuquerque, NM, Feb. 10-17. Folding instructions as on No. UC44a, with "INTERNATIONAL HOT AIR BALLOONING" added to inscription.

Bird in
Flight — UC17

1973, Dec. 1   **Embossed**
UC47 UC17 13c rose red   .30   .15

Beginning with No. UC48 all letter sheets are for Foreign Postage unless noted otherwise.

UC18

1974, Jan. 4   **Photo.**
UC48 UC18 18c red & blue, *blue*,
     entire   .90   .30
   a. Red omitted, entire   —

UC19 postage 18c

Design: "NATO" and NATO emblem in multicolor at left in address section.

1974, Apr. 4   **Photo.**
UC49 UC19 18c red & blue, *blue*,
     entire   .90   .40

25th anniv. of NATO.

UC20

1976, Jan. 16   **Photo.**
UC50 UC20 22c red & blue, *blue*,
     entire   .90   .40

UC21   22c

1978, Nov. 3   **Photo.**
UC51 UC21 22c bl, *bl*, entire   .70   .25

UC22

Design (multicolored in bottom left corner) shows discus thrower.

1979, Dec. 5   **Photo.**
UC52 UC22 22c red, blk & grn, *blu-
    ish,* entire   1.50   .25

22nd Olympic Games, Moscow, July 19-Aug. 3, 1980.

UC23

Design shows Statue of Liberty at lower left. Inscribed "Tour the United States," folding area shows tourist attractions.

1980-81   **Photo.**
UC53 UC23 30c bl, red & brn, *bl,*
        entire   .65   .30
  a. Red ("30c") omitted, entire   75.00
UC54 UC23 30c yel, magenta, bl &
        blk, *bl,* entire
        ('81)   .65   .30

Issued: Dec. 29, 1980; Sept. 21, 1981.

UC24

"Made in USA . . . world's best buys."

1982, Sept. 16   **Photo.**
UC55 UC24 30c multi, *bl,* entire   .65   .30

World Communications Year Issue

World Map Showing Locations of Satellite Tracking Stations — UC25

1983, Jan. 7   **Photo.**
UC56 UC25 30c multi, *bl,* entire   .65   .30

1984 Olympics

Olympics 84
USA
30c

UC26

1983, Oct. 14   **Photo.**
UC57 UC26 30c multi, *bl,* entire   .65   .30

UC27

Design: Satellite over Earth at lower left, with Landsat photographs on folding area. Inscribed: Landsat views the Earth.

1985, Feb. 14   **Photo.**
UC58 UC27 36c multi, *bl,* entire   .70   .35

National Tourism Week

Urban Skyline
UC28

1985, May 21   **Photo.**
UC59 UC28 36c multi, *bl,* entire   .70   .35
  a. Black omitted, entire

Mark Twain (1835-1910) and Halley's Comet

Comet Tail Viewed
from Space — UC29

1985, Dec. 4   **Photo.**
UC60 UC29 36c multi, entire   .70   .35

UC30

1988, May 9   **Litho.**
UC61 UC30 39c multi, entire   .80   .40

Montgomery Blair and Pres.
Lincoln — UC31

Design: Mail bags and text at lower left. Globe, locomotive, bust of Blair, UPU emblem and text contained on reverse folding area.

1989, Nov. 20   **Litho.**
UC62 UC31 39c multi, entire   .80   .40

UC32

1991, May 17   **Litho.**
UC63 UC32 45c gray, red & blue,
        blue, entire   .90   .45
  a. White paper, entire   .90   .45

Thaddeus Lowe (1832-1913),
Balloonist — UC33

Letter Sheet for Foreign Postage

1995, Sept. 23   **Litho.**
UC64 UC33 50c multicolored, *blue*   1.00   .50

POSTAL CARDS
"R.F." CONTROL OVERPRINT
STAMPED ENVELOPES
are listed in the Scott Specialized Cat-
alogue of United States Stamps.
NEWSPAPER WRAPPERS
Included in listings of Stamped Enve-
lopes with prefix "W" instead of "U"
LETTER SHEETS Included with
Stamped Envelopes

OFFICIAL STAMPED ENVELOPES

Post Office Department

"2" 9mm   "3" 9mm
high — UO1   high — UO2

"6" 9½mm
high — UO3

1873
UO1 UO1 2c black, *lemon*   15.00   8.00
UO2 UO2 3c black, *lemon*   9.00   6.00
+UO3 UO2 3c black, *lemon*   6,750.
UO4 UO3 6c black, *lemon*   17.50 14.00

"2" 9¼mm   "3" 9¼mm
high — UO4   high — UO5

"6" 10½mm
high — UO6

1874-79
UO5 UO4 2c black, *lemon*   6.00   4.00
UO6 UO4 2c black   70.00 32.50
UO7 UO5 3c black, *lemon*   3.00   .75
UO8 UO5 3c black   1,100. 850.00
UO9 UO5 3c black, *amber*   45.00 35.00
UO10 UO5 3c black, *blue*   15,000.
UO11 UO5 3c blue, *blue*   14,000.
UO12 UO6 6c black, *lemon*   8.00   6.00
UO13 UO6 6c black   750.00

Postal Service

UO7

1877
UO14 UO7 black   6.00   3.75
UO15 UO7 black, *amber*   50.00 27.50
UO16 UO7 blue, *amber*   45.00 30.00
UO17 UO7 blue, *blue*   7.00   6.00
   Nos. UO14-UO17 (4)   108.00 67.25

War Department

Franklin — UO8   Jackson — UO9

UO8 — Bust points to the end of "N" of "ONE."

UO9 — Bust narrow at the back.

Washington   Lincoln
UO10   UO11

UO10 — Queue projects below the bust.

UO11 — Neck very long at the back.

Jefferson — UO12   Clay — UO13

UO12 — Queue forms straight line with bust.

UO13 — Ear partly concealed by hair, mouth large, chin prominent.

Webster — UO14   Scott — UO15

UO14 — Has side whiskers.

Hamilton — UO16

Back of bust very narrow, chin almost straight; the labels containing the letters "U S" are exactly parallel.

1873   Reay Issue
UO18 UO8 1c dark red   525.00 300.00
UO19 UO9 2c dark red   800.00 425.00
UO20 UO10 3c dark red   60.00 40.00
UO21 UO10 3c dark red,
               amb   12,000.
UO22 UO10 3c dark red, *cr* 450.00 225.00
UO23 UO11 3c dark red   210.00 90.00
UO24 UO11 6c dark red, *cr* 1,750. 425.00
UO25 UO12 10c dark red   2,750. 350.00
UO26 UO13 12c dark red   110.00 50.00
UO27 UO14 15c dark red   110.00 55.00
UO28 UO15 24c dark red   110.00 50.00
UO29 UO16 30c dark red   450.00 150.00

UO30 UO8 1c vermilion   135.00
WO31 UO8 1c ver., *man*   12.50 12.50
+UO32 UO9 2c vermilion   275.00
WO33 UO9 2c ver., *man*   200.00
UO34 UO10 3c vermilion   70.00 40.00
UO35 UO10 3c ver., *amb*   80.00

UO36	UO10	3c ver, *cr*	15.00	12.50
UO37	UO11	6c vermilion	70.00	
+UO38	UO11	6c ver, *cr*	325.00	
UO39	UO12	10c vermilion	200.00	
UO40	UO13	12c vermilion	135.00	
UO41	UO14	15c vermilion	210.00	
UO42	UO15	24c vermilion	375.00	
UO43	UO16	30c vermilion	375.00	

UO17   UO18

UO17--Bottom serif on "S" is thick and short, bust at bottom below hair forms sharp point.

UO18--Bottom serif on "S" is thick and short front part of bust is rounded.

UO19   UO20

UO19--Bottom serif on "S" is short, queue does not project below bust.

UO20--Neck very short at the back.

UO21   UO22

UO21--Knot of queue stands out prominently.

UO22--Ear prominent, chin receding.

UO23   UO24

UO23--Has no side whiskers, forelock projects above head.

UO24--Back of bust rather broad; chin slopes considerably; the labels containing letters "U S" are not exactly parallel.

1875
Plimpton Issue

UO44	UO17	1c red	120.00	80.00
+UO45	UO17	1c red, *amb*	750.00	
+UO45A	UO17	1c red, *org*	17,500.	
WO46	UO17	1c red, *man*	3.75	2.75
UO47	UO18	2c red	90.00	
UO48	UO18	2c red, *amb*	25.00	14.00
UO49	UO18	2c red, *org*	42.50	12.50
WO50	UO18	2c red, *man*	75.00	40.00
UO51	UO19	3c red	12.50	9.00
UO52	UO19	3c red, *amb*	14.00	9.00
UO53	UO19	3c red, *cr*	6.50	3.75
UO54	UO19	3c red, *bl*	3.50	2.75
UO55	UO19	3c red, *fawn*	4.50	2.75
UO56	UO20	6c red	40.00	30.00
UO57	UO20	6c red, *amb*	70.00	40.00
UO58	UO20	6c red, *cr*	175.00	87.50
UO59	UO21	10c red	150.00	82.50
UO60	UO21	10c red, *amb*	1,100.	
UO61	UO22	12c red	42.50	40.00
UO62	UO22	12c red, *amb*	625.00	
UO63	UO22	12c red, *cr*	600.00	
UO64	UO23	15c red	160.00	140.00
UO65	UO23	15c red, *amb*	700.00	
UO66	UO23	15c red, *cr*	675.00	
UO67	UO24	30c red	160.00	140.00
UO68	UO24	30c red, *amb*	900.00	
UO69	UO24	30c red, *cr*	900.00	

POSTAL SAVINGS STAMPED ENVELOPES

UO25

1911

UO70	UO25	1c green	60.00	20.00
UO71	UO25	1c grn, *oriental buff*	175.00	65.00
UO72	UO25	2c carmine	10.00	3.75
a.		2c carmine, *manila* (error)	1,900.	

Used Values
Catalogue values for regularly used entires. Those with first day cancels generally sell for much less.

OFFICIAL MAIL

UO26

1983, Jan. 12

UO73	UO26	20c blue, entire	1.00	30.00

UO27

1985, Feb. 26

UO74	UO27	22c blue, entire	.65	5.00

UO28

1987, Mar. 2   Typo.

UO75	UO28	22c blue, entire	.65	20.00

Used exclusively to mail US Savings Bonds.

UO29

1988, Mar. 22   Typo.

UO76	UO29	(25c) blk & bl, entire	.65	20.00

Used exclusively to mail US Saving Bonds.

UO30

1988, Apr. 11   Embossed & Typo.

UO77	UO30	25c blk & blue, entire	.65	5.00
a.		Denomination & lettering as No. UO78	—	

UO31

1988, Apr. 11   Typo.

UO78	UO31	25c black & blue, entire	.65	25.00
a.		Denomination & lettering as No. UO77	—	

Used exclusively to mail US Saving Bonds.

Used Values
The appearance in the marketplace of postally used examples of the entires used to mail passports (Nos. UO79-UO82, UO86-UO87) is so infrequent that it currently is not possible to establish accurate values.

1990, Mar. 17   Typo.

UO79	UO31	45c blk & bl, entire	1.25	—
UO80	UO31	65c blk & bl, entire	1.50	—

Used exclusively to mail US passports.

UO32

Type UO32: sharp impression, stars and "E Pluribus Unum" are clear and distinct. Official is 14½mm long, USA is 17mm long.

1990, Aug. 10   Typo.

UO81	UO32	45c blk & bl, entire	1.25	—
UO82	UO32	65c blk & bl, entire	1.50	—

Used exclusively to mail US passports.

UO33

1991, Jan. 22   Typo.   Wmk.

UO83	UO33	(29c) blk & bl, entire	1.00	20.00

Used exclusively to mail US Saving Bonds.

UO34

1991, Apr. 6   Typo. & Embossed

UO84	UO34	29c black & blue, entire	.70	2.00

UO35

1991, Apr. 17   Typo.   Wmk.

UO85	UO35	29c blk & bl, entire	.70	20.00

Used exclusively to mail US Saving Bonds.

Consular Service, Bicent. — UO36

1992, July 10   Litho.   Unwmk.

UO86	UO36	52c blue & red, entire	1.15
UO87	UO36	75c blue & red, entire	1.60

Used exclusively to mail US passports.

UO37

Typo. & Embossed

1995, May 9   Unwmk.

UO88	UO37	32c blue & red, entire	.75	5.00

OFFICIAL WRAPPERS
Included in listings of Official Stamped Envelopes with prefix letters "WO" instead of "UO"

REVENUE STAMPS

Nos. R1-R102 were used to pay taxes on documents and proprietary articles including playing cards. Until Dec. 25, 1862, the law stated that a revenue stamp could be used only for payment of the tax upon the particular instrument or article specified on its face. After that date stamps, except the Proprietary, could be used indiscriminately.

Values quoted are for pen-canceled copies. Stamps with handstamped cancellations sell at higher prices. Stamps canceled with cuts, punches or holes sell for less. See the Scott U.S. Specialized Catalogue.

General Issue
First Issue. Head of Washington in Oval. Various Frames as Illustrated.
Old Paper
Perf. 12

Nos. R1b to R42b, part perforate, occur perforated sometimes at sides only and sometimes at top and bottom only. The higher values, part perforate, are perforated at sides only. Imperforate and part perforate revenues often bring much more in pairs or blocks than as single copies.

The experimental silk paper is a variety of the old paper and has only a very few minute fragments of fiber.

Some of the stamps were in use eight years and were printed several times. Many color variations occurred, particularly when unstable pigments were used and the color was intended to be purple or violet, such as the 4c Proprietary, 30c and $2.50 stamps. Before 1868 dull colors predominate on these and the early red stamps. In later printings of the 4c Proprietary, 30c and $2.50 stamps, red predominates in the mixture, and on the dollar values the red is brighter. The early $1.90 stamp is dull purple, imperf. or perforated. In a later printing, perforated only, the purple is darker.

R1   R2

R3

R4   R5

1862-71   Engr.

R1	R1	1c Express, red		1.25
a.		Imperf.		55.00
b.		Part perf.		35.00
d.		Silk paper		85.00
R2	R1	1c Playing Cards, red		130.00
a.		Imperf.		1,000.
b.		Part perf.		700.00
R3	R1	1c Proprietary, red		.50
a.		Imperf.		725.00
b.		Part perf.		120.00
d.		Silk paper		20.00
R4	R1	1c Telegraph, red		11.00
a.		Imperf.		375.00
R5	R2	2c Bank Check, blue		.25
a.		Imperf.		1.00
b.		Part perf.		1.75
e.		Vertical pair, imperf. between, old paper		400.00
R6	R2	2c Bank Check, orange		.25
b.		Part perf.		55.00
d.		Silk paper		240.00
e.		Old paper, green		375.00
R7	R2	2c Certificate, blue		25.00
a.		Imperf.		12.50
R8	R2	2c Certificate, orange		25.00
R9	R2	2c Express, blue		.40
a.		Imperf.		12.50
b.		Part perf.		17.50
R10	R2	2c Express, orange		7.50
b.		Part perf.		55.00
d.		Silk paper		55.00
R11	R2	2c Playing Cards, blue		4.00
b.		Part perf.		165.00
R12	R2	2c Playing Cards, orange		35.00
R13	R2	2c Proprietary, blue		.40
a.		Imperf.		350.00
b.		Part perf.		120.00
d.		Silk paper		45.00
e.		Ultramarine		160.00
R14	R2	2c Proprietary, orange		35.00
R15	R2	2c U.S. Int. Rev., orange ('64)		.15
d.		Silk paper		.25
e.		Old paper, green		475.00
R16	R3	3c For. Exch., green		3.50
b.		Part perf.		250.00
d.		Silk paper		45.00
R17	R3	3c Playing Cards, green ('63)		120.00
a.		Imperf.		8,500.
R18	R3	3c Proprietary, green		3.25
b.		Part perf.		275.00
d.		Silk paper		27.50
e.		Printed on both sides, old paper		1,600.
R19	R3	3c Telegraph, green		2.75
a.		Imperf.		55.00
b.		Part perf.		20.00
R20	R3	4c Inland Exch., brown ('63)		1.75
d.		Silk paper		42.50
R21	R3	4c Playing Cards, slate ('63)		500.00
R22	R3	4c Proprietary, purple		6.50
b.		Part perf.		210.00
d.		Silk paper		55.00

Many shade and color variations of Nos. R21-R22. See foreword, "Revenue Stamps."

R23	R3	5c Agreement, red		.25
d.		Silk paper		1.50
R24	R3	5c Certificate, red		.25
a.		Imperf.		2.50
b.		Part perf.		11.00
d.		Silk paper		.35
R25	R3	5c Express, red		.30
a.		Imperf.		4.50
b.		Part perf.		5.00
R26	R3	5c Foreign Exchange, red		.30
b.		Part perf.		
d.		Silk paper		175.00
R27	R3	5c Inland Exch., red		.25
a.		Imperf.		5.00
b.		Part perf.		3.75
d.		Silk paper		12.50
R28	R3	5c Playing Cards, red ('63)		17.50
R29	R3	5c Proprietary, red ('64)		22.50
d.		Silk paper		90.00
R30	R3	6c Inland Exch., org ('63)		1.50
d.		Silk paper		60.00
R31	R3	6c Proprietary, orange ('71)		1,600.

Nearly all copies of No. R31 are faulty or repaired and poorly centered.

The Catalogue value is for a fine centered copy with minor faults which do not detract from its appearance.

R32	R3	10c Bill of Lading, blue		1.00
a.		Imperf.		45.00
b.		Part perf.		200.00
R33	R3	10c Certificate, blue		.25
a.		Imperf.		120.00
b.		Part perf.		200.00
d.		Silk paper		4.50
R34	R3	10c Contract, blue		.35
b.		Part perf.		150.00
d.		Silk paper		2.25
e.		Ultramarine, part perf.		400.00
f.		Ultramarine, old paper		1.00

R6

R7

R35	R3	10c For. Exch., blue		7.00
d.		Silk paper		9.00
e.		ultra, old paper		.15
R36	R3	10c Inland Exch., blue		.15
a.		Imperf.		175.00
b.		Part perf.		3.50
c.		Silk paper		27.50
R37	R3	10c Power of Attorney, blue		.50
a.		Imperf.		450.00
b.		Part perf.		20.00
R38	R3	10c Proprietary, blue ('64)		15.00
R39	R3	15c For. Exch., brown ('63)		14.00
R40	R3	15c Inland Exch., brown		1.25
a.		Imperf.		30.00
b.		Part perf.		12.50
R41	R3	20c For. Exch., red		32.50
a.		Imperf.		40.00
R42	R3	20c Inland Exch., red		.35
a.		Imperf.		15.00
b.		Part perf.		17.50
R43	R4	25c Bond, red		2.50
a.		Imperf.		145.00
b.		Part perf.		6.00
R44	R4	25c Certificate, red		.25
a.		Imperf.		10.00
b.		Part perf.		6.00
d.		Silk paper		2.75
e.		Printed on both sides, old paper		1,750.
f.		Impression of No. R48 on back, old paper		
R45	R4	25c Entry of Goods, red		.55
a.		Imperf.		17.50
b.		Part perf.		65.00
d.		Silk paper		22.50
R46	R4	25c Insurance, red		.25
a.		Imperf.		10.00
b.		Part perf.		10.00
d.		Silk paper		4.50
R47	R4	25c Life Insurance, red		6.50
a.		Imperf.		35.00
b.		Part perf.		200.00
R48	R4	25c Power of Attorney, red		.30
a.		Imperf.		6.00
b.		Part perf.		27.50
R49	R4	25c Protest, red		6.75
a.		Imperf.		30.00
b.		Part perf.		250.00
R50	R4	25c Warehouse Receipt, red		22.50
a.		Imperf.		42.50
b.		Part perf.		235.00
R51	R4	30c For. Exch., lilac		52.50
a.		Imperf.		72.50
b.		Part perf.		950.00
d.		Silk paper		
R52	R4	30c Inland Exch., lilac		3.50
a.		Imperf.		47.50
b.		Part perf.		60.00
d.		Silk paper		

Many shade and color variations of Nos. R51-R52. See foreword, "Revenue Stamps."

R53	R4	40c Inland Exch., brown		3.50
a.		Imperf.		575.00
b.		Part perf.		7.00
R54	R5	50c Conveyance, blue		.15
a.		Imperf.		14.00
b.		Part perf.		1.60
d.		Silk paper		3.00
e.		Ultramarine, old paper		.25
f.		Ultramarine, silk paper		
R55	R5	50c Entry of Goods, blue		.40
a.		Imperf.		12.00
b.		Part perf.		35.00
R56	R5	50c For. Exch., blue		5.00
a.		Imperf.		42.50
b.		Part perf.		40.00
R57	R5	50c Lease, blue		8.50
a.		Imperf.		24.00
b.		Part perf.		60.00
R58	R5	50c Life Insurance, blue		.90
a.		Imperf.		30.00
b.		Part perf.		45.00
R59	R5	50c Mortgage, blue		.50
a.		Imperf.		14.00
b.		Part perf.		2.50
d.		Silk paper		
R60	R5	50c Original Process, blue		.60
a.		Imperf.		3.00
b.		Part perf.		550.00
d.		Silk paper		1.60
R61	R5	50c Passage Ticket, blue		1.25
a.		Imperf.		72.50
b.		Part perf.		140.00
R62	R5	50c Probate of Will, blue		19.00
a.		Imperf.		35.00
b.		Part perf.		60.00
R63	R5	50c Surety Bond, blue		.30
a.		Imperf.		150.00
b.		Part perf.		2.50
e.		Ultramarine, old paper		.75
R64	R5	60c Inland Exch., org		6.00
a.		Imperf.		85.00
b.		Part perf.		47.50
d.		Silk paper		32.50
R65	R5	70c For. Exch., green		8.00
a.		Imperf.		325.00
b.		Part perf.		95.00
d.		Silk paper		47.50

R8   R9

R10

(Illustration sideways)
R11

Old Paper

R66	R6	$1 Conveyance, red		12.50
a.		Imperf.		12.00
b.		Part perf.		425.00
d.		Silk paper		75.00
R67	R6	$1 Entry of Goods, red		1.50
a.		Imperf.		32.50
d.		Silk paper		47.50
R68	R6	$1 For. Exch., red		.55
a.		Imperf.		60.00
d.		Silk paper		45.00
R69	R6	$1 Inland Exch., red		.40
a.		Imperf.		12.50
b.		Part perf.		300.00
d.		Silk paper		2.25

R70	R6	$1 Lease, red		2.00
a.		Imperf.		35.00
R71	R6	$1 Life Insurance, red		6.00
a.		Imperf.		150.00
R72	R6	$1 Manifest, red		25.00
a.		Imperf.		42.50
R73	R6	$1 Mortgage, red		160.00
a.		Imperf.		200.00
R74	R6	$1 Passage Ticket, red		190.00
a.		Imperf.		250.00
R75	R6	$1 Power of Attorney, red		2.00
a.		Imperf.		72.50
R76	R6	$1 Probate of Will, red		32.50
a.		Imperf.		70.00
R77	R7	$1.30 For. Exch., orange ('63)		50.00
a.		Imperf.		3,000.
R78	R7	$1.50 Inland Exch., blue		3.25
a.		Imperf.		22.50
R79	R7	$1.60 For. Exch., green ('63)		95.00
a.		Imperf.		900.00
R80	R7	$1.90 For. Exch., purple ('63)		75.00
a.		Imperf.		3,750.

Many shade and color variations of No. R80. See foreword, "Revenue Stamps."

R81	R8	$2 Conveyance, red		2.00
a.		Imperf.		100.00
b.		Part perf.		1,300.
R82	R8	$2 Mortgage, red		3.00
a.		Imperf.		100.00
d.		Silk paper		55.00
R83	R8	$2 Probate of Will, red ('63)		50.00
a.		Imperf.		3,250.
R84	R8	$2.50 Inland Exch., pur ('63)		6.50
a.		Imperf.		2,500.
d.		Silk paper		20.00
R85	R8	$3 Charter Party, green		4.25
a.		Imperf.		110.00
d.		Silk paper		80.00
f.		Printed on both sides		2,000.
g.		Impression of #RS208 on back		4,000.
R86	R8	$3 Manifest, green		25.00
a.		Imperf.		110.00
R87	R8	$3.50 Inland Exch., blue ('63)		45.00
a.		Printed on both sides		2,750.

Many shade and color variations of the $2.50. See foreword, "Revenue Stamps." The $3.50 has stars in upper corners.

R88	R9	$5 Charter Party, red		6.00
a.		Imperf.		240.00
d.		Silk paper		60.00
R89	R9	$5 Conveyance, red		6.00
a.		Imperf.		35.00
d.		Silk paper		60.00
R90	R9	$5 Manifest, red		77.50
a.		Imperf.		110.00
R91	R9	$5 Mortgage, red		17.00
a.		Imperf.		110.00
R92	R9	$5 Probate of Will, red		17.50
a.		Imperf.		475.00
R93	R9	$10 Charter Party, green		25.00
a.		Imperf.		550.00
R94	R9	$10 Conveyance, green		60.00
a.		Imperf.		90.00
R95	R9	$10 Mortgage, green		25.00
a.		Imperf.		350.00
R96	R9	$10 Probate of Will, green		27.50
a.		Imperf.		1,150.
R97	R10	$15 Mortgage, blue		120.00
a.		Imperf.		1,100.
e.		Ultramarine, old paper		190.00
R98	R10	$20 Conveyance, org		60.00
a.		Imperf.		115.00
d.		Silk paper		100.00
R99	R10	$20 Probate of Will, orange		1,050.
a.		Imperf.		1,200.
R100	R10	$25 Mortgage, red ('63)		115.00
a.		Imperf.		900.00
d.		Silk paper		175.00
e.		Horiz. pair, imperf. btwn., old paper		1,100.
R101	R10	$50 U.S. Int. Rev., green ('63)		90.00
a.		Imperf.		190.00
R102	R11	$200 U.S. Int. Rev., green & red ('64)		625.00
a.		Imperf.		1,400.

DOCUMENTARY STAMPS

Second Issue

After release of the First Issue revenue stamps, the Bureau of Internal Revenue received many reports of fraudulent cleaning and re-use. The Bureau ordered a Second Issue with new designs and colors, using a patented "chameleon" paper which is usually slightly violet or pinkish, with silk fibers.

R12   R12a

R13a   R13

R13b

Head of Washington in Black within Octagon. Various Frames and Numeral Arrangements.

1871			**Perf. 12**
R103	R12	1c blue & black	35.00
		Cut cancel	17.50
a.		Inverted center	950.00
R104	R12	2c blue & black	1.10
		Cut cancel	.20
a.		Inverted center	3,750.
R105	R12a	3c blue & black	15.00
		Cut cancel	8.50
R106	R12a	4c blue & black	60.00
		Cut cancel	30.00
R107	R12a	5c blue & black	1.50
		Cut cancel	.50
a.		Inverted center	1,650.
R108	R12a	6c blue & black	90.00
		Cut cancel	50.00
R109	R12a	10c blue & black	.90
		Cut cancel	.15
a.		Inverted center	1,650.
R110	R12a	15c blue & black	25.00
		Cut cancel	14.00
R111	R12a	20c blue & black	5.50
		Cut cancel	2.50
a.		Inverted center	8,000.

Head of Washington in Black within Circle
Various Frames

R112	R13	25c blue & black	.60
		Cut cancel	.15
a.		Inverted center	8,000.
b.		Sewing machine perf.	95.00
		Perf. 8	275.00
R113	R13	30c blue & black	65.00
		Cut cancel	35.00
R114	R13	40c blue & black	40.00
		Cut cancel	20.00
R115	R13a	50c blue & black	.60
		Cut cancel	.15
a.		Sewing machine perf.	75.00
b.		Inverted center	800.00
		Inverted center, punch cancellation	220.00
R116	R13a	60c blue & black	90.00
		Cut cancel	45.00
R117	R13a	70c blue & black	35.00
		Cut cancel	17.50
a.		Inverted center	2,750.
R118	R13b	$1 blue & black	3.00
		Cut cancel	1.25
a.		Inverted center	4,250.
		Invtd. center, punch cancel	750.
R119	R13b	$1.30 blue & black	275.00
		Cut cancel	150.00

R120	R13b	$1.50 blue & black	12.50
		Cut cancel	7.00
a.		Sewing machine perf.	450.00
R121	R13b	$1.60 blue & black	325.00
		Cut cancel	200.00
R122	R13b	$1.90 blue & black	165.00
		Cut cancel	90.00
R123	R13b	$2 blue & black	15.00
		Cut cancel	7.50
R124	R13b	$2.50 blue & black	27.50
		Cut cancel	15.00
R125	R13b	$3 blue & black	30.00
		Cut cancel	17.50
R126	R13b	$3.50 blue & black	150.00
		Cut cancel	75.00
R127	R13b	$5 blue & black	17.50
		Cut cancel	9.00
a.		Inverted center	2,200.
		Invtd. center, punch cancel	650.
R128	R13b	$10 blue & black	100.00
		Cut cancel	60.00
R129	R13b	$20 blue & black	325.00
		Cut cancel	200.00
R130	R13b	$25 blue & black	325.00
		Cut cancel	200.00
R131	R13b	$50 blue & black	350.00
		Cut cancel	225.00
R132	R13b	$200 red, blue & blk	4,750.
		Cut cancel	2,750.
R133	R13b	$500 red org, grn & blk	12,500.

Fraudulently produced inverted centers exist, some excellently made.

Value for No. R133 is for a very fine appearing example with a light cut cancel or with minor flaws.

Third Issue

Violet "Chameleon" Paper with Silk Fibers. Various Frames and Numeral Arrangements.

1871-72			**Perf. 12**
R134	R12	1c claret & blk ('72)	30.00
		Cut cancel	17.50
R135	R12	2c orange & blk	.20
		Cut cancel	.15
a.		2c vermilion & black (error)	550.00
b.		Inverted center	300.00
c.		Imperf., pair	—
R136	R12a	4c brown & blk ('72)	35.00
		Cut cancel	17.50
R137	R12a	5c orange & black	.25
		Cut cancel	.15
a.		Inverted center	3,250.
R138	R12a	6c orange & blk ('72)	35.00
		Cut cancel	17.50
R139	R12a	15c brown & blk ('72)	8.50
		Cut cancel	4.00
a.		Inverted center	8,000.
R140	R13	30c orange & blk ('72)	14.00
		Cut cancel	7.00
a.		Inverted center	2,250.
R141	R13	40c brown & blk ('72)	30.00
		Cut cancel	15.00
R142	R13	60c orange & blk ('72)	60.00
		Cut cancel	30.00
R143	R13	70c green & blk ('72)	40.00
		Cut cancel	20.00
R144	R13b	$1 green & blk ('72)	1.35
		Cut cancel	.50
a.		Inverted center	5,500.
R145	R13b	$2 ver & black ('72)	20.00
		Cut cancel	12.50
R146	R13b	$2.50 claret & blk ('72)	35.00
		Cut cancel	20.00
a.		Inverted center	13,500.
R147	R13b	$3 green & blk ('72)	35.00
		Cut cancel	20.00
R148	R13b	$5 ver & black ('72)	20.00
		Cut cancel	10.00
R149	R13b	$10 green & blk ('72)	75.00
		Cut cancel	40.00
R150	R13b	$20 orange & blk ('72)	475.00
		Cut cancel	250.00
a.		$20 vermilion & black (error)	600.00

1874			**Perf. 12**
R151	R12	2c orange & black, *green*	.20
		Cut cancel	.15
a.		Inverted center	350.00

Liberty — R14

1875-78			
R152	R14	2c blue, *blue*, silk paper	.15
b.		Wmk. 191R ('78)	.15
c.		Wmk. 191R, rouletted	32.50
d.		Vert. pair, imperf. horiz.	175.00
e.		As "b," imperf., pair	250.00

The rouletted stamps probably were introduced in 1881.

Nos. 279, 267 or 279B, 272-274 Overprinted in Red or Blue

1898	**Wmk. 191**		**Perf. 12**
R153	A87(a)	1c green (R)	3.00	2.50
R154	A87(b)	1c green (R)	.15	.15
a.		Overprint inverted	20.00	17.50
b.		Overprint on back instead of face, inverted		
c.		Pair, one without ovpt.		
R155	A88(b)	2c carmine (Bl)	.15	.15
a.		Overprint inverted	2.50	1.75
b.		Pair, one without ovpt.	750.00	
c.		Overprinted on back instead of face, inverted		

Handstamped Type "b"

R156	A93	8c vio brn	4,000.
R157	A94	10c dark green	4,000.
R158	A95	15c dark blue	4,750.

Nos. R156-R158 were emergency provisionals, privately prepared, not officially issued.

Privately Prepared Provisionals

No. 285 Overprinted **I. R.** in Red   **L. H. C.**

1898	**Wmk. 191**		**Perf. 12**
R158A	A100	1c dk yel grn	8,500.	7,750.

Same Overprinted "I.R./P.I.D. & Son" in Red

R158B	A100	1c dk yel grn	—	10,000.

Nos. R158A-R158B were overprinted with federal government permission by the Purvis Printing Co. upon order of Capt. L.H. Chapman of the Chapman Steamboat Line. Both the Chapman line and P.I. Daprix & Son operated freight-carrying steamboats on the Erie Canal. The Chapman Line touched at Syracuse, Utica, Little Falls and Fort Plain; the Daprix boat ran between Utica and Rome. 250 of each stamp were overprinted.

Dr. Kilmer & Co. provisional overprints are listed in the Scott Specialized Catalogue of United States Stamps under Private Die Medicine Stamps, Nos. RS307-RS315.

Newspaper Stamp No. PR121 Surcharged Vertically in Red

INT. REV. $5. DOCUMENTARY.

1898	**Wmk. 191**		**Perf. 12**
	Reading Down		
R159	N18	$5 on $5 dk blue	250.00	160.00
	Reading Up		
R160	N18	$5 on $5 dk blue	110.00	70.00

Battleship R15

Inscribed: "Series of 1898" and "Documentary."

1898	**Wmk. 191R**		**Rouletted 5½**	
R161	R15	½c orange	2.00	6.25
R162	R15	½c dark gray	.25	.15
a.		Vert. pair, imperf. horiz.	60.00	
R163	R15	1c pale blue	.15	.15
a.		Vert. pair, imperf. horiz.	7.50	
b.		Imperf., pair	300.00	
R164	R15	2c carmine rose	.25	.25
a.		Vert. pair, imperf. horiz.	47.50	
b.		Imperf., pair	160.00	
c.		Horiz. pair, imperf. vert.	—	
R165	R15	3c dark blue	1.25	.15
R166	R15	4c pale rose	.90	.15
a.		Vert. pair, imperf. horiz.	90.00	
R167	R15	5c lilac	.20	.15
a.		Pair, imperf. horiz. or vert.	175.00	125.00
b.		Horiz. pair, imperf. btwn.		300.00
R168	R15	10c dark brown	1.25	.15
a.		Vert. pair, imperf. horiz.	27.50	27.50
b.		Horiz. pair, imperf. vert.		
R169	R15	25c purple brown	1.25	.15
R170	R15	40c blue lilac	110.00	.60
		Cut cancellation		.30
R171	R15	50c slate violet	11.00	.15
a.		Imperf., pair	300.00	
R172	R15	80c bister	65.00	.25
				.15

No. R167b may not be genuine.

Hyphen Hole Perf. 7

R163p	1c		.25	.15
R164p	2c		.30	.15
R165p	3c		10.00	.50
R166p	4c		3.50	.90
R167p	5c		3.50	.15

R168p	10c		2.75	.15
R169p	25c		4.50	.25
R170p	40c		150.00	25.00
R171p	50c		17.50	.25
b.	Horiz. pair, imperf. btwn.		—	250.00
R172p	80c		150.00	30.00

Commerce — R16

1898			**Rouletted 5½**	
R173	R16	$1 dark green	8.00	.15
a.		Vert. pair, imperf. horiz.	—	
b.		Horiz. pair, imperf. vert.	—	300.00
p.		Hyphen hole perf. 7	15.00	.65
R174	R16	$3 dark brown	17.50	.85
a.		Cut cancellation		.15
		Horiz. pair, imperf. vert.		450.00
p.		Hyphen hole perf. 7	20.00	2.25
		Cut cancellation		.25
R175	R16	$5 orange red	22.50	1.40
		Cut cancellation		.20
R176	R16	$10 black	70.00	2.75
		Cut cancellation		.50
a.		Horiz. pair, imperf. vert.		
R177	R16	$30 red	210.00	110.00
		Cut cancellation		45.00
R178	R16	$50 gray brown	100.00	5.50
		Cut cancellation		2.00

There are 2 styles of rouletting for the 1898 proprietary and documentary stamps, an ordinary roulette 5½ and one where small rectangles of the paper are cut out, called hyphen hole perf. 7. Except for Nos. R161, R162 and R175-R178, all the stamps of the two series exist with both roulettes. See Nos. R182-R183.

John Marshall — R17

Alexander Hamilton R18

James Madison R19

Inscribed "Series of 1898"

1899		**Without Gum**	**Imperf.**	
R179	R17	$100 yel brn & black	110.00	30.00
		Cut cancellation		20.00
R180	R18	$500 car lake & black	650.00	500.00
		Cut cancellation		225.00
R181	R19	$1000 grn & blk	675.00	300.00
		Cut cancellation		110.00

See Nos. R224-R227, R246-R252, R282-R286.

Type of 1898

1900 — Hyphen-Hole Perf. 7

No.	Type	Description	Unused	Used
R182	R16	$1 carmine	15.00	.50
		Cut cancellation		.15
R183	R16	$3 lake	110.00	45.00
		Cut cancellation		7.00

Surcharged in Black

a   b

Surcharged type "a"

1900

No.	Type	Description	Unused	Used
R184	R16	$1 gray	10.00	.20
		Cut cancellation		.15
a.		Horiz. pair, imperf. vert.	—	
b.		Surcharge omitted	125.00	
		As "b", cut cancellation		80.00
R185	R16	$2 gray	6.00	.20
		Cut cancellation		.15
R186	R16	$3 gray	55.00	11.00
		Cut cancellation		2.00
R187	R16	$5 gray	37.50	6.50
		Cut cancellation		1.00
R188	R16	$10 gray	65.00	17.50
		Cut cancellation		3.00
R189	R16	$50 gray	650.00	400.00
		Cut cancellation		75.00

Surcharged type "b"

1902

No.	Type	Description	Unused	Used
R190	R16	$1 green	17.50	3.75
		Cut cancellation		.20
a.		Inverted surcharge	175.00	
R191	R16	$2 green	15.00	1.30
		Cut cancellation		.25
a.		Surcharged as #R185	75.00	75.00
b.		Surch. as #R185, in vio	1,300.	—
c.		Double surcharge	100.00	
d.		Triple surcharge	—	
R192	R16	$5 green	125.00	25.00
		Cut cancellation		4.00
a.		Surcharge omitted	140.00	
b.		Pair, one without surch.	325.00	
R193	R16	$10 green	325.00	125.00
		Cut cancellation		45.00
R194	R16	$50 green	950.00	800.00
		Cut cancellation		225.00

Warning: If Nos. R190-R194 are soaked, the center part of the surcharged numeral may wash off. Before surcharging, a square of soluble varnish was applied to the middle of some stamps.

R20   Liberty — R21

Inscribed "Series of 1914"

Offset Printing

1914 — Wmk. 190 — Perf. 10

No.	Type	Description	Unused	Used
R195	R20	½c rose	7.50	3.50
R196	R20	1c rose	1.40	.15
R197	R20	2c rose	2.00	.15
R198	R20	3c rose	47.50	30.00
R199	R20	4c rose	14.00	2.00
R200	R20	5c rose	4.00	.20
R201	R20	10c rose	3.25	.15
R202	R20	25c rose	27.50	.55
R203	R20	40c rose	17.50	1.00
R204	R20	50c rose	6.00	.15
R205	R20	80c rose	85.00	10.00
		Nos. R195-R205 (11)	215.65	47.85

Wmk. 191R

No.	Type	Description	Unused	Used
R206	R20	½c rose	1.50	.50
R207	R20	1c rose	.15	.15
R208	R20	2c rose	.15	.15
R209	R20	3c rose	1.40	.20
R210	R20	4c rose	3.50	.45
R211	R20	5c rose	1.75	.25
R212	R20	10c rose	.60	.15
R213	R20	25c rose	5.00	1.25
R214	R20	40c rose	65.00	12.50
		Cut cancellation		.45
R215	R20	50c rose	15.00	.25
R216	R20	80c rose	95.00	17.50
		Nos. R206-R216 (11)	189.05	33.35

Engr.

No.	Type	Description	Unused	Used
R217	R21	$1 green	30.00	.20
		Cut cancellation		.15
a.		$1 yellow green	—	.15
R218	R21	$2 carmine	45.00	.50
		Cut cancellation		.15
R219	R21	$3 purple	55.00	2.00
		Cut cancellation		.20
R220	R21	$5 blue	47.50	2.75
		Cut cancellation		.50
R221	R21	$10 orange	110.00	5.00
		Cut cancellation		.75
R222	R21	$30 vermilion	225.00	11.00
		Cut cancellation		.75
R223	R21	$50 violet	1,250.	800.00
		Cut cancellation		350.00

See #R240-R245, R257-R259, R276-R281.

Portrait Types of 1899 Inscribed "Series of 1915" (#R224), or "Series of 1914"

1914-15 — Without Gum — Perf. 12

No.	Type	Description	Unused	Used
R224	R19	$60 brn (Lincoln)	—	100.00
		Cut cancellation		45.00
R225	R17	$100 grn (Washington)	60.00	40.00
		Cut cancellation		15.00
R226	R18	$500 blue	—	450.00
		Cut cancellation		200.00
R227	R19	$1000 orange	—	350.00
		Cut cancellation		150.00

The stamps of types R17, R18 and R19 in this and subsequent issues are issued in vert. strips of 4 which are imperf. at the top, bottom and right side; therefore, single copies are always imperf. on 1 or 2 sides.

R22

Offset Printing

1917 — Wmk. 191R — Perf. 11 — Size: 21x18mm

No.	Type	Description	Unused	Used
R228	R22	1c carmine rose	.15	.15
R229	R22	2c carmine rose	.15	.15
R230	R22	3c carmine rose	1.25	.35
R231	R22	4c carmine rose	.50	.15
R232	R22	5c carmine rose	.20	.15
R233	R22	8c carmine rose	1.75	.30
R234	R22	10c carmine rose	.35	.15
R235	R22	20c carmine rose	.60	.15
R236	R22	25c carmine rose	1.10	.15
R237	R22	40c carmine rose	1.50	.40
R238	R22	50c carmine rose	2.00	.15
R239	R22	80c carmine rose	5.00	.15
		Nos. R228-R239 (12)	14.55	
		Set value		1.30

Type of 1914 without "Series 1914"

1917-33 — Engr. — Size: 18½x27½mm

No.	Type	Description	Unused	Used
R240	R21	$1 yellow green	6.50	.15
a.		$1 green	6.50	.15
R241	R21	$2 rose	11.00	.15
R242	R21	$3 violet	35.00	.75
		Cut cancellation		.15
R243	R21	$4 yellow brown ('33)	25.00	1.75
		Cut cancellation		.15
R244	R21	$5 dark blue	15.00	.25
		Cut cancellation		.15
R245	R21	$10 orange	30.00	.90
		Cut cancellation		.15

Portrait Types of 1899-1915 without "Series of" and Date

Portraits: $30, Grant. $100, Washington.

1917 — Without Gum — Perf. 12

No.	Type	Description	Unused	Used
R246	R17	$30 dp org. grn numerals	45.00	10.00
		Cut cancellation		1.00
a.		Imperf., pair	750.00	
b.		Numerals in blue	70.00	1.90
		As "b", cut cancellation		1.00
R247	R19	$60 brown	55.00	7.00
		Cut cancellation		.80
R248	R17	$100 green	32.50	1.00
		Cut cancellation		.35
R249	R18	$500 blue, red numerals	220.00	35.00
		Cut cancellation		10.00
a.		Numerals in orange	—	50.00
R250	R19	$1000 orange	125.00	12.50
		Cut cancellation		4.00
a.		Imperf., pair	900.00	

See note after No. R227.

1928-29 — Offset Printing — Perf. 10

No.	Type	Description	Unused	Used
R251	R22	1c carmine rose	2.00	1.50
R252	R22	2c carmine rose	.60	.20
R253	R22	4c carmine rose	5.50	3.75
R254	R22	5c carmine rose	1.25	.50
R255	R22	10c carmine rose	1.75	1.25
R256	R22	20c carmine rose	5.50	4.50
		Nos. R251-R256 (6)	16.60	11.70

Engr.

No.	Type	Description	Unused	Used
R257	R21	$1 green	85.00	30.00
		Cut cancellation		5.00
R258	R21	$2 rose	32.50	2.50
R259	R21	$10 orange	110.00	40.00
		Cut cancellation		25.00

1929 — Offset Printing — Perf. 11x10

No.	Type	Description	Unused	Used
R260	R22	2c carmine rose	2.75	2.50
R261	R22	5c carmine rose	2.00	1.75
R262	R22	10c carmine rose	7.50	6.50
R263	R22	20c carmine rose	15.00	8.00

Used values for Nos. R264-R734 are for copies which are neither cut nor perforated with initials. Copies with cut cancellations or perforated initials are valued in the Scott U. S. Specialized Catalogue.

Types of 1917-33   SERIES 1940
Overprinted in Black

1940 — Offset Printing — Perf. 11

No.	Type	Description	Unused	Used
R264	R22	1c rose pink	2.75	2.25
R265	R22	2c rose pink	2.75	1.75
R266	R22	3c rose pink	8.25	4.00
R267	R22	4c rose pink	3.50	.55
R268	R22	5c rose pink	3.75	.90
R269	R22	8c rose pink	14.00	12.50
R270	R22	10c rose pink	1.75	.90
R271	R22	20c rose pink	2.25	.60
R272	R22	25c rose pink	5.50	1.00
R273	R22	40c rose pink	5.50	.65
R274	R22	50c rose pink	6.00	.50
R275	R22	80c rose pink	10.00	.90
		Nos. R264-R275 (12)	66.00	26.05

Engr.

No.	Type	Description	Unused	Used
R276	R21	$1 green	32.50	.55
R277	R21	$2 rose	32.50	1.00
R278	R21	$3 violet	45.00	25.00
R279	R21	$4 yellow brown	80.00	30.00
R280	R21	$5 dark blue	45.00	11.00
R281	R21	$10 orange	110.00	27.50

Types of 1917 Handstamped in Green Like Nos. R264-R281

Without Gum — Perf. 12

No.	Type	Description	Unused	Used
R282	R17	$30 vermilion	450.	
a.		With black 2-line handstamp in larger type	—	
R283	R19	$60 brown	650.	
a.		As #R282a, cut cancel	—	
R284	R17	$100 green	950.	
R285	R18	$500 blue	1,400.	
a.		As #R282a	2,250.	2,000.
b.		Blue handstamp, double transfer	—	
R286	R19	$1000 orange	650.	

Alexander Hamilton — R23

Levi Woodbury — R24   Thomas Corwin — R25

Portraits: 2c, Oliver Wolcott, Jr. 3c, Samuel Dexter. 4c, Albert Gallatin. 5c, George Washington Campbell. 8c, Alexander Dallas. 10c, William H. Crawford. 20c, Richard Rush. 25c, Samuel D. Ingham. 40c, Louis McLane. 50c, William J. Duane. 80c, Walter Forward. $1, Robert J. Walker. $2, Thomas Ewing. $3, Walter Forward. $4, John Canfield Spencer. $5, George M. Bibb. $10, Robert J. Walker. $20, William M. Meredith. $50, James Guthrie. $60, Howell Cobb. $100, P. F. Thomas. $500, John Adams Dix. $1,000, Salmon P. Chase.

Overprinted in Black Like Nos. R264-R281

1940 — Size: 19x22mm — Perf. 11 — Various Portraits

No.	Type	Description	Unused	Used
R288	R23	1c carmine	4.00	3.00
R289	R23	2c carmine	4.50	2.75
R290	R23	3c carmine	17.50	9.00
R291	R23	4c carmine	40.00	20.00
R292	R23	5c carmine	3.00	.60
R293	R23	8c carmine	60.00	45.00
R294	R23	10c carmine	2.50	.45
R295	R23	20c carmine	3.75	2.50
R296	R23	25c carmine	2.75	.50
R297	R23	40c carmine	40.00	18.00
R298	R23	50c carmine	4.50	.40
R299	R23	80c carmine	85.00	60.00
		Nos. R288-R299 (12)	267.50	162.20

Size: 21½x36¼mm

No.	Type	Description	Unused	Used
R300	R24	$1 carmine	32.50	.50
R301	R24	$2 carmine	40.00	.75
R302	R24	$3 carmine	125.00	75.00
R303	R24	$4 carmine	65.00	30.00
R304	R24	$5 carmine	40.00	1.50
R305	R24	$10 carmine	70.00	5.00
R305A	R24	$20 carmine	1,500.	550.00
b.		Imperf., pair	600.00	

Size: 28½x42mm — Various Frame Designs — Perf. 12 — Without Gum

No.	Type	Description	Unused	Used
R306	R25	$30 carmine	110.00	40.00
R306A	R25	$50 carmine	—	1,250.
R307	R25	$60 carmine	225.00	45.00
a.		Vert. pair, imperf. between		1,450.
R308	R25	$100 carmine	160.00	10.00
R309	R25	$500 carmine	—	1,000.
R310	R25	$1000 carmine	—	425.00

The $30 to $1,000 denominations in this and following similar issues, and the $2,500, $5,000 and $10,000 stamps of 1952-58 have straight edges on one or two sides. They were issued without gum through No. R723.

Overprinted in Black "SERIES 1941"

1941 — Size: 19x22mm — Perf. 11

No.	Type	Description	Unused	Used
R311	R23	1c carmine	3.00	2.25
R312	R23	2c carmine	3.00	.90
R313	R23	3c carmine	7.50	3.50
R314	R23	4c carmine	5.00	1.25
R315	R23	5c carmine	1.00	.25
R316	R23	8c carmine	14.00	7.50
R317	R23	10c carmine	1.25	.15
R318	R23	20c carmine	3.00	.45
R319	R23	25c carmine	1.75	.20
R320	R23	40c carmine	10.00	2.50
R321	R23	50c carmine	2.50	.15
R322	R23	80c carmine	45.00	10.00
		Nos. R311-R322 (12)	97.00	29.10

Size: 21½x36¼mm

No.	Type	Description	Unused	Used
R323	R24	$1 carmine	8.50	.25
R324	R24	$2 carmine	10.00	.35
R325	R24	$3 carmine	17.50	2.50
R326	R24	$4 carmine	27.50	15.00
R327	R24	$5 carmine	32.50	.60
R328	R24	$10 carmine	50.00	3.00
R329	R24	$20 carmine	500.00	175.00

Size: 28½x42mm — Perf. 12 — Without Gum

No.	Type	Description	Unused	Used
R330	R25	$30 carmine	50.00	22.50
R331	R25	$50 carmine	175.00	150.00
R332	R25	$60 carmine	—	42.50
R333	R25	$100 carmine	45.00	17.50
R334	R25	$500 carmine	—	200.00
R335	R25	$1000 carmine	—	100.00

Overprinted in Black "SERIES 1942"

1942 — Size: 19x22mm — Perf. 11

No.	Type	Description	Unused	Used
R336	R23	1c carmine	.50	.45
R337	R23	2c carmine	.45	.45
R338	R23	3c carmine	.70	.60
R339	R23	4c carmine	1.20	.90
R340	R23	5c carmine	.45	.20
R341	R23	8c carmine	5.50	4.25
R342	R23	10c carmine	1.20	.25
R343	R23	20c carmine	1.20	.45
R344	R23	25c carmine	2.10	.45
R345	R23	40c carmine	4.75	1.20
R346	R23	50c carmine	3.00	.20
R347	R23	80c carmine	16.00	10.00
		Nos. R336-R347 (12)	37.05	19.40

Size: 21½x36¼mm

No.	Type	Description	Unused	Used
R348	R24	$1 carmine	7.50	.25
R349	R24	$2 carmine	9.00	.25
R350	R24	$3 carmine	15.00	2.00
R351	R24	$4 carmine	22.50	3.75
R352	R24	$5 carmine	25.00	.90
R353	R24	$10 carmine	55.00	2.50
R354	R24	$20 carmine	110.00	30.00

Size: 28½x42mm — Perf. 12 — Without Gum

No.	Type	Description	Unused	Used
R355	R25	$30 carmine	40.00	20.00
R356	R25	$50 carmine	325.00	250.00
R357	R25	$60 carmine	675.00	575.00
R358	R25	$100 carmine	150.00	100.00
R359	R25	$500 carmine	—	200.00
R360	R25	$1000 carmine	—	100.00

Overprinted in Black "SERIES 1943"

1943 — Size: 19x22mm — Perf. 11

No.	Type	Description	Unused	Used
R361	R23	1c carmine	.60	.50
R362	R23	2c carmine	.45	.35
R363	R23	3c carmine	2.50	2.50
R364	R23	4c carmine	1.00	1.00
R365	R23	5c carmine	.50	.30
R366	R23	8c carmine	4.00	3.00
R367	R23	10c carmine	.60	.25
R368	R23	20c carmine	1.75	.60
R369	R23	25c carmine	1.50	.25
R370	R23	40c carmine	5.00	2.00
R371	R23	50c carmine	1.25	.15
R372	R23	80c carmine	12.50	5.50
		Nos. R361-R372 (12)	31.65	16.40

Size: 21½x36¼mm

R373	R24	$1 carmine	5.00	.35
R374	R24	$2 carmine	10.00	.25
R375	R24	$3 carmine	17.50	2.00
R376	R24	$4 carmine	22.50	3.00
R377	R24	$5 carmine	27.50	.50
R378	R24	$10 carmine	45.00	3.00
R379	R24	$20 carmine	95.00	20.00

Size: 28½x42mm
Perf. 12
Without Gum

R380	R25	$30 carmine	35.00	18.00
R381	R25	$50 carmine	67.50	25.00
R382	R25	$60 carmine	—	70.00
R383	R25	$100 carmine	—	10.00
R384	R25	$500 carmine	—	175.00
R385	R25	$1000 carmine	—	150.00

Overprinted in Black "Series 1944"
1944   Size: 19x22mm   Perf. 11

R386	R23	1c carmine	.40	.35
R387	R23	2c carmine	.40	.35
R388	R23	3c carmine	.40	.35
R389	R23	4c carmine	.55	.50
R390	R23	5c carmine	.30	.15
R391	R23	8c carmine	1.75	1.25
R392	R23	10c carmine	.40	.15
R393	R23	20c carmine	.75	.20
R394	R23	25c carmine	1.40	.15
R395	R23	40c carmine	2.75	.60
R396	R23	50c carmine	3.00	.15
R397	R23	80c carmine	12.50	4.80
Nos. R386-R397 (12)			24.60	8.20

Size: 21½x36¼mm

R398	R24	$1 carmine	5.50	.20
R399	R24	$2 carmine	8.00	.25
R400	R24	$3 carmine	12.50	1.50
R401	R24	$4 carmine	17.50	10.00
R402	R24	$5 carmine	20.00	.25
R403	R24	$10 carmine	37.50	1.25
R404	R24	$20 carmine	80.00	15.00

Size: 28½x42mm
Perf. 12
Without Gum

R405	R25	$30 carmine	50.00	20.00
R406	R25	$50 carmine	20.00	10.00
R407	R25	$60 carmine	100.00	45.00
R408	R25	$100 carmine	—	8.00
R409	R25	$500 carmine	—	1,050.
R410	R25	$1000 carmine	—	165.00

Overprinted in Black "Series 1945"
1945   Size: 19x22mm   Perf. 11

R411	R23	1c carmine	.20	.20
R412	R23	2c carmine	.25	.20
R413	R23	3c carmine	.50	.45
R414	R23	4c carmine	.30	.30
R415	R23	5c carmine	.25	.15
R416	R23	8c carmine	4.25	2.00
R417	R23	10c carmine	.80	.15
R418	R23	20c carmine	4.50	1.00
R419	R23	25c carmine	1.10	.30
R420	R23	40c carmine	4.75	1.00
R421	R23	50c carmine	2.75	.20
R422	R23	80c carmine	17.50	8.00
Nos. R411-R422 (12)			37.15	13.95

Size: 21½x36¼mm

R423	R24	$1 carmine	7.00	.15
R424	R24	$2 carmine	7.50	.25
R425	R24	$3 carmine	15.00	2.25
R426	R24	$4 carmine	20.00	3.00
R427	R24	$5 carmine	20.00	.40
R428	R24	$10 carmine	40.00	1.25
R429	R24	$20 carmine	80.00	11.00

Size: 28½x42mm
Without Gum
Perf. 12

R430	R25	$30 carmine	60.00	20.00
R431	R25	$50 carmine	65.00	25.00
R432	R25	$60 carmine	110.00	40.00
R433	R25	$100 carmine	—	12.00
R434	R25	$500 carmine	200.00	150.00
R435	R25	$1000 carmine	100.00	82.50

Overprinted in Black "Series 1946"
1946   Wmk. 191R   Perf. 11
Size: 19x22mm

R436	R23	1c carmine	.20	.25
R437	R23	2c carmine	.35	.30
R438	R23	3c carmine	.35	.30
R439	R23	4c carmine	.60	.50
R440	R23	5c carmine	.30	.15
R441	R23	8c carmine	1.25	1.10
R442	R23	10c carmine	.70	.15
R443	R23	20c carmine	1.25	.40
R444	R23	25c carmine	4.00	.20
R445	R23	40c carmine	2.50	.75
R446	R23	50c carmine	3.00	.20
R447	R23	80c carmine	10.00	4.00
Nos. R436-R447 (12)			24.50	8.30

Size: 21½x36¼mm

R448	R24	$1 carmine	7.00	.20
R449	R24	$2 carmine	10.00	.20
R450	R24	$3 carmine	15.00	5.00
R451	R24	$4 carmine	20.00	10.00
R452	R24	$5 carmine	20.00	.45
R453	R24	$10 carmine	40.00	1.50
R454	R24	$20 carmine	80.00	10.00

Size: 28½x42mm
Without Gum
Perf. 12

R455	R25	$30 carmine	40.00	12.00
R456	R25	$50 carmine	20.00	9.00
R457	R25	$60 carmine	40.00	16.00
R458	R25	$100 carmine	45.00	10.00
R459	R25	$500 carmine	—	100.00
R460	R25	$1000 carmine	—	100.00

Overprinted in Black "Series 1947"
1947   Wmk. 191R   Perf. 11
Size: 19x22mm

R461	R23	1c carmine	.65	.50
R462	R23	2c carmine	.55	.50
R463	R23	3c carmine	.55	.50
R464	R23	4c carmine	.70	.60
R465	R23	5c carmine	.35	.30
R466	R23	8c carmine	1.20	.70
R467	R23	10c carmine	1.10	.25
R468	R23	20c carmine	1.80	.50
R469	R23	25c carmine	2.40	.60
R470	R23	40c carmine	3.75	.90
R471	R23	50c carmine	3.00	.25
R472	R23	80c carmine	8.00	6.00
Nos. R461-R472 (12)			24.05	11.60

Size: 21½x36¼mm

R473	R24	$1 carmine	5.75	.25
R474	R24	$2 carmine	9.00	.50
R475	R24	$3 carmine	10.00	5.00
R476	R24	$4 carmine	11.00	4.50
R477	R24	$5 carmine	17.50	.50
R478	R24	$10 carmine	40.00	2.00
R479	R24	$20 carmine	60.00	10.00

Size: 28½x42mm
Perf. 12
Without Gum

R480	R25	$30 carmine	60.00	17.50
R481	R25	$50 carmine	30.00	12.00
R482	R25	$60 carmine	75.00	35.00
R483	R25	$100 carmine	30.00	10.00
R484	R25	$500 carmine	—	150.00
R485	R25	$1000 carmine	—	80.00

Overprinted in Black "Series 1948"
1948   Wmk. 191R   Perf. 11
Size: 19x22mm

R486	R23	1c carmine	.25	.25
R487	R23	2c carmine	.35	.30
R488	R23	3c carmine	.45	.35
R489	R23	4c carmine	.40	.30
R490	R23	5c carmine	.35	.15
R491	R23	8c carmine	.75	.35
R492	R23	10c carmine	.60	.15
R493	R23	20c carmine	1.75	.30
R494	R23	25c carmine	1.50	.20
R495	R23	40c carmine	4.50	1.50
R496	R23	50c carmine	2.25	.15
R497	R23	80c carmine	7.00	4.50
Nos. R486-R497 (12)			20.15	8.50

Size: 21½x36¼mm

R498	R24	$1 carmine	7.00	.20
R499	R24	$2 carmine	10.00	.20
R500	R24	$3 carmine	14.00	2.50
R501	R24	$4 carmine	20.00	2.50
R502	R24	$5 carmine	17.50	.50
R503	R24	$10 carmine	40.00	1.00
a.		Pair, one dated "1946"	—	
R504	R24	$20 carmine	80.00	10.00

Size: 28½x42mm
Perf. 12
Without Gum

R505	R25	$30 carmine	40.00	20.00
R506	R25	$50 carmine	40.00	15.00
a.		Vert. pair, imperf. btwn.	—	
R507	R25	$60 carmine	60.00	25.00
a.		Vert. pair, imperf. btwn.	1,100	
R508	R25	$100 carmine	50.00	10.00
a.		Vert. pair, imperf. btwn.	850.00	
R509	R25	$500 carmine	125.00	100.00
R510	R25	$1000 carmine	80.00	60.00

Overprinted in Black "Series 1949"
1949   Wmk. 191R   Perf. 11
Size: 19x22mm

R511	R23	1c carmine	.25	.25
R512	R23	2c carmine	.55	.35
R513	R23	3c carmine	.40	.35
R514	R23	4c carmine	.60	.50
R515	R23	5c carmine	.35	.40
R516	R23	8c carmine	.70	.60
R517	R23	10c carmine	.40	.25
R518	R23	20c carmine	1.30	.60
R519	R23	25c carmine	1.80	.70
R520	R23	40c carmine	4.25	2.10
R521	R23	50c carmine	3.50	.30
R522	R23	80c carmine	8.50	4.75
Nos. R511-R522 (12)			22.60	10.95

Size: 21½x36¼mm

R523	R24	$1 carmine	7.00	.40
R524	R24	$2 carmine	9.00	2.00
R525	R24	$3 carmine	14.00	6.00
R526	R24	$4 carmine	17.50	6.00
R527	R24	$5 carmine	17.50	2.25
R528	R24	$10 carmine	40.00	2.50
R529	R24	$20 carmine	80.00	9.00

Size: 28½x42mm
Perf. 12
Without Gum

R530	R25	$30 carmine	50.00	22.50
R531	R25	$50 carmine	60.00	35.00
R532	R25	$60 carmine	—	40.00
R533	R25	$100 carmine	45.00	15.00
R534	R25	$500 carmine	—	180.00
R535	R25	$1000 carmine	—	110.00

Overprinted in Black "Series 1950"
1950   Wmk. 191R   Perf. 11
Size: 19x22mm

R536	R23	1c carmine	.20	.15
R537	R23	2c carmine	.30	.25
R538	R23	3c carmine	.35	.30
R539	R23	4c carmine	.50	.40
R540	R23	5c carmine	.30	.15
R541	R23	8c carmine	1.25	.65
R542	R23	10c carmine	.60	.20
R543	R23	20c carmine	1.00	.35
R544	R23	25c carmine	1.50	.35
R545	R23	40c carmine	3.25	1.75
R546	R23	50c carmine	4.00	.20
R547	R23	80c carmine	7.00	4.00
Nos. R536-R547 (12)			20.25	8.75

Size: 21½x36¼mm

R548	R24	$1 carmine	7.00	.20
R549	R24	$2 carmine	9.00	2.00
R550	R24	$3 carmine	10.00	4.00
R551	R24	$4 carmine	14.00	5.00
R552	R24	$5 carmine	17.50	.75
R553	R24	$10 carmine	40.00	7.50
R554	R24	$20 carmine	80.00	8.50

Size: 28½x42mm
Perf. 12
Without Gum

R555	R25	$30 carmine	65.00	40.00
R556	R25	$50 carmine	40.00	14.00
a.		Vert. pair, imperf. horiz.	—	
R557	R25	$60 carmine	—	50.00
R558	R25	$100 carmine	50.00	17.50
R559	R25	$500 carmine	—	100.00
R560	R25	$1000 carmine	—	75.00

Overprinted in Black "Series 1951"
1951   Wmk. 191R   Perf. 11
Size: 19x22mm

R561	R23	1c carmine	.15	.15
R562	R23	2c carmine	.30	.25
R563	R23	3c carmine	.25	.25
R564	R23	4c carmine	.30	.25
R565	R23	5c carmine	.30	.20
R566	R23	8c carmine	1.00	.35
R567	R23	10c carmine	.55	.20
R568	R23	20c carmine	1.25	.45
R569	R23	25c carmine	1.25	.40
R570	R23	40c carmine	3.00	1.25
R571	R23	50c carmine	2.50	.35
R572	R23	80c carmine	6.00	2.50
Nos. R561-R572 (12)			16.85	6.60

Size: 21½x36¼mm

R573	R24	$1 carmine	7.00	.20
R574	R24	$2 carmine	9.00	.50
R575	R24	$3 carmine	12.50	3.50
R576	R24	$4 carmine	17.50	5.00
R577	R24	$5 carmine	14.00	.60
R578	R24	$10 carmine	35.00	2.25
R579	R24	$20 carmine	75.00	8.50

Size: 28½x42mm
Perf. 12
Without Gum

R580	R25	$30 carmine	—	10.00
a.		Imperf. pair	750.00	
R581	R25	$50 carmine	50.00	15.00
R582	R25	$60 carmine	—	40.00
R583	R25	$100 carmine	40.00	12.50
R584	R25	$500 carmine	125.00	82.50
R585	R25	$1000 carmine	—	90.00

Overprinted in Black "Series 1952"

Designs: 55c, $1.10, $1.65, $2.20, $2.75, $3.30, L. J. Gage; $2500, William Windom; $5000, C. J. Folger; $10,000, W. Q. Gresham.

1952   Wmk. 191R   Perf. 11
Size: 19x22mm

R586	R23	1c carmine	.20	.15
R587	R23	2c carmine	.35	.25
R588	R23	3c carmine	.30	.25
R589	R23	4c carmine	.30	.25
R590	R23	5c carmine	.25	.15
R591	R23	8c carmine	.65	.45
R592	R23	10c carmine	.40	.20
R593	R23	20c carmine	1.00	.35
R594	R23	25c carmine	1.50	.40
R595	R23	40c carmine	3.00	1.00
R596	R23	50c carmine	2.75	.20
R597	R23	55c carmine	17.50	10.00
R598	R23	80c carmine	10.00	3.00
Nos. R586-R598 (13)			38.20	16.65

Size: 21½x36¼mm

R599	R24	$1 carmine	5.00	1.50
R600	R24	$1.10 carmine	35.00	25.00
R601	R24	$1.65 carmine	125.00	45.00
R602	R24	$2 carmine	9.00	.65
R603	R24	$2.20 carmine	100.00	60.00
R604	R24	$2.75 carmine	110.00	60.00
R605	R24	$3 carmine	20.00	4.00
a.		Horiz. pair, imperf. btwn.	500.00	
R606	R24	$3.30 carmine	100.00	60.00
R607	R24	$4 carmine	17.50	4.00
R608	R24	$5 carmine	17.50	1.25
R609	R24	$10 carmine	35.00	1.25
R610	R24	$20 carmine	55.00	9.00

Size: 28½x42mm
Perf. 12
Without Gum

R611	R25	$30 carmine	45.00	18.00
R612	R25	$50 carmine	40.00	12.00
R613	R25	$60 carmine	—	50.00
R614	R25	$100 carmine	35.00	8.00
R615	R25	$500 carmine	—	100.00
R616	R25	$1000 carmine	—	30.00
R617	R25	$2500 carmine	—	150.00
R618	R25	$5000 carmine	—	1,100.
R619	R25	$10,000 carmine	—	650.00

Overprinted in Black "Series 1953"
1953   Wmk. 191R   Perf. 11
Size: 19x22mm

R620	R23	1c carmine	.20	.15
R621	R23	2c carmine	.20	.15
R622	R23	3c carmine	.25	.20
R623	R23	4c carmine	.35	.25
R624	R23	5c carmine	.20	.15
R625	R23	8c carmine	.75	.35
R626	R23	10c carmine	.40	.20
R627	R23	20c carmine	.75	.40
R628	R23	25c carmine	1.00	.50
R629	R23	40c carmine	1.75	1.00
R630	R23	50c carmine	2.50	.20
R631	R23	55c carmine	3.50	2.00
a.		Horiz. pair, imperf. vert.	350.00	
R632	R23	80c carmine	6.00	2.00
Nos. R620-R632 (13)			17.85	7.55

Size: 21½x36¼mm

R633	R24	$1 carmine	4.00	.25
R634	R24	$1.10 carmine	7.00	2.25
a.		Horiz. pair, imperf. vert.	500.00	
b.		Imperf. pair	550.00	
R635	R24	$1.65 carmine	8.00	4.00
R636	R24	$2 carmine	6.00	.65
R637	R24	$2.20 carmine	10.00	6.00
R638	R24	$2.75 carmine	14.00	7.00
R639	R24	$3 carmine	8.00	3.00
R640	R24	$3.30 carmine	22.50	8.00
R641	R24	$4 carmine	16.00	7.50
R642	R24	$5 carmine	16.00	1.00
R643	R24	$10 carmine	35.00	1.75
R644	R24	$20 carmine	70.00	18.00

Size: 28½x42mm
Perf. 12
Without Gum

R645	R25	$30 carmine	40.00	12.00
R646	R25	$50 carmine	75.00	25.00
R647	R25	$60 carmine	300.00	140.00
R648	R25	$100 carmine	35.00	12.00
R649	R25	$500 carmine	250.00	115.00
R650	R25	$1000 carmine	125.00	57.50
R651	R25	$2500 carmine	475.00	475.00
R652	R25	$5000 carmine	—	1,250.
R653	R25	$10,000 carmine	—	1,000.

Types of 1940 without Overprint
1954   Wmk. 191R   Perf. 11
Size: 19x22mm

R654	R23	1c carmine	.15	.15
a.		Horiz. pair, imperf. vert.	—	
R655	R23	2c carmine	.15	.15
R656	R23	3c carmine	.15	.15
R657	R23	4c carmine	.15	.15
R658	R23	5c carmine	.15	.15
R659	R23	8c carmine	.25	.20
R660	R23	10c carmine	.25	.20
R661	R23	20c carmine	.50	.30
R662	R23	25c carmine	.60	.35
R663	R23	40c carmine	1.25	.60
R664	R23	50c carmine	1.65	.20
a.		Horiz. pair, imperf. vert	275.00	
R665	R23	55c carmine	1.50	1.25
R666	R23	80c carmine	2.25	1.75
Nos. R654-R666 (13)			9.00	5.60

Size: 21½x36¼mm

R667	R24	$1 carmine	1.50	.30
R668	R24	$1.10 carmine	3.25	2.50
R669	R24	$1.65 carmine	85.00	55.00
R670	R24	$2 carmine	1.75	.25
R671	R24	$2.20 carmine	4.50	3.75
R672	R24	$2.75 carmine	95.00	50.00
R673	R24	$3 carmine	3.00	2.00
R674	R24	$3.30 carmine	6.50	5.00
R675	R24	$4 carmine	4.00	3.50
R676	R24	$5 carmine	6.00	.40
R677	R24	$10 carmine	12.50	1.25
R678	R24	$20 carmine	20.00	5.25

Overprinted in Black "Series 1954"
Perf. 12
Size: 28½x42mm
Without Gum

R679	R25	$30 carmine	30.00	12.00
R680	R25	$50 carmine	40.00	15.00
R681	R25	$60 carmine	65.00	20.00
R682	R25	$100 carmine	30.00	7.00
R683	R25	$500 carmine	—	75.00
R684	R25	$1000 carmine	150.00	55.00

R685	R25	$2500 carmine	—	175.00
R686	R25	$5000 carmine	—	725.00
R687	R25	$10,000 carmine	—	500.00

Overprinted in Black "Series 1955"
Without Gum

1955   Wmk. 191R   Perf. 12
Size: 28½x42mm

R688	R25	$30 carmine	40.00	11.50
R689	R25	$50 carmine	40.00	13.50
R690	R25	$60 carmine	70.00	24.00
R691	R25	$100 carmine	35.00	7.00
R692	R25	$500 carmine	—	125.00
R693	R25	$1000 carmine	—	35.00
R694	R25	$2500 carmine	—	125.00
R695	R25	$5000 carmine	800.00	700.00
R696	R25	$10,000 carmine	—	500.00

Overprinted in Black "Series 1956"
Without Gum

1956   Size: 28½x42mm

R697	R25	$30 carmine	50.00	13.50
R698	R25	$50 carmine	55.00	17.00
R699	R25	$60 carmine	—	32.50
R700	R25	$100 carmine	50.00	12.50
R701	R25	$500 carmine	—	75.00
R702	R25	$1000 carmine	—	55.00
R703	R25	$2500 carmine	—	250.00
R704	R25	$5000 carmine	—	1,250.
R705	R25	$10,000 carmine	—	450.00

Overprinted in Black "Series 1957"
Without Gum

1957   Size: 28½x42mm

R706	R25	$30 carmine	65.00	27.50
R707	R25	$50 carmine	50.00	24.00
R708	R25	$60 carmine	—	150.00
R709	R25	$100 carmine	45.00	12.50
R710	R25	$500 carmine	175.00	85.00
R711	R25	$1000 carmine	—	80.00
R712	R25	$2500 carmine	—	525.00
R713	R25	$5000 carmine	—	600.00
R714	R25	$10,000 carmine	—	450.00

Overprinted in Black "Series 1958"
Without Gum

1958   Size: 28½x42mm

R715	R25	$30 carmine	75.00	20.00
R716	R25	$50 carmine	60.00	20.00
R717	R25	$60 carmine	—	25.00
R718	R25	$100 carmine	50.00	10.00
R719	R25	$500 carmine	125.00	55.00
R720	R25	$1000 carmine	—	67.50
R721	R25	$2500 carmine	—	600.00
R722	R25	$5000 carmine	—	1,350.
R723	R25	$10,000 carmine	—	650.00

Documentary Stamps and Type of 1940
Without Overprint
With Gum

1958   Size: 28½x42mm

R724	R25	$30 carmine	35.00	7.00
a.		Vert. pair, imperf. horiz.	—	
R725	R25	$50 carmine	37.50	7.00
a.		Vert. pair, imperf. horiz.	—	
R726	R25	$60 carmine	75.00	20.00
R727	R25	$100 carmine	17.50	4.75
R728	R25	$500 carmine	80.00	25.00
R729	R25	$1000 carmine	50.00	20.00
a.		Vert. pair, imperf. horiz.	—	600.00
R730	R25	$2500 carmine	—	140.00
R731	R25	$5000 carmine	—	150.00
R732	R25	$10,000 carmine	—	125.00

> Catalogue values for unused stamps in this section, from this point to the end of the section, are for Never Hinged items.

Internal Revenue Building, Washington, DC — R26

Giori Press Printing
1962, July 1   Unwmk.   Perf. 11

R733	R26	10c vio bl & brt grn	1.10	.35

Centenary of Internal Revenue Service.

"Established 1862" Removed

1963

R734	R26	10c vio blue & brt green	3.00	.35

Documentary revenue stamps were no longer required after Dec. 31, 1967.

PROPRIETARY STAMPS

Stamps for use on proprietary articles were included in the first general issue of 1862-71. They are Nos. R3, R13, R14, R18, R22, R29, R31 and R38.

Washington — RB1

Various Frames and Sizes
Violet or Green Paper with Silk Threads

1871-74   Engr.   Perf. 12
a. left column = Violet Paper (1871)
b. right column = Green Paper (1874)

RB1	RB1	1c green & blk	5.00	7.50
b.		Imperf.	80.00	
d.		Inverted center	2,500.	
RB2	RB1	2c green & blk	6.00	15.00
d.		Invtd. center, violet	40,000.	
d.		Invtd. center, green		8,500.
RB3	RB1	3c green & blk	15.00	45.00
c.		Sewing machine perf.	225.00	
d.		Inverted center	16,000.	
RB4	RB1	4c green & blk	10.00	15.00
c.		Inverted center	22,500.	
RB5	RB1	5c green & blk	130.00	140.00
c.		Inverted center	80,000.	
RB6	RB1	6c green & blk	35.00	85.00
RB7	RB1	10c green & blk ('73)	175.00	45.00
RB8	RB1	50c green & blk ('73)	500.00	900.00
RB9	RB1	$1 green & blk ('73)	1,000.	3,750.
RB10	RB1	$5 green & blk ('73)	3,000.	27,500.

Washington — RB2

Various Frames and Sizes
Green Paper

Wmk. 191R, Unwmkd. (Silk Paper)
1875-81
b. left column = Perf.
c. right column = Rouletted 6

RB11	RB2	1c green	.40	65.00
d.		Silk paper	1.90	
e.		Vert. pair, imperf btwn.		250.00
RB12	RB2	2c brown	1.40	80.00
		Silk paper	2.50	
RB13	RB2	3c orange	3.00	80.00
		Silk paper	12.50	
RB14	RB2	4c red brown	5.50	
		Silk paper		
RB15	RB2	4c red	4.50	125.00
RB16	RB2	5c black	90.00	1,250.
		Silk paper	110.00	
RB17	RB2	6c violet blue	20.00	225.00
		Silk paper	25.00	
RB18	RB2	6c violet	30.00	
RB19	RB2	10c blue ('81)	300.00	

Many fraudulent roulettes exist.

Battleship — RB3

Rouletted 5½
1898   Wmk. 191R   Engr.

RB20	RB3	⅛c yellow green	.15	.15
a.		Vert. pair, imperf. horiz.	.15	.15
RB21	RB3	¼c brown	.15	.15
a.		¼c red brown	.15	.15
b.		¼c yellow brown	.15	.15
c.		¼c orange brown	.15	.15
d.		¼c bister	.15	.15
e.		Vert. pair, imperf. horiz.	—	
f.		Printed on both sides	—	
RB22	RB3	⅜c deep orange	.15	.15
a.		Horiz. pair, imperf. vert.	11.00	
b.		Vert. pair, imperf. horiz.		
RB23	RB3	⅝c deep ultra	.15	.15
a.		Vert. pair, imperf. horiz.	60.00	
b.		Vert. pair, imperf. btwn.	250.00	
RB24	RB3	1c dark green	1.00	.15
a.		Vert. pair, imperf. horiz.		
RB25	RB3	1¼c violet	.15	.15
a.		1¼c brown violet	.15	
b.		Vert. pair, imperf. btwn.		
RB26	RB3	1⅞c dull blue	7.50	1.00
RB27	RB3	2c vio brown	.75	.20
a.		Vert. pair, imperf. horiz.	35.00	
RB28	RB3	2½c lake	2.50	.15
a.		Vert. pair, imperf. horiz.	125.00	

RB29	RB3	3¾c olive gray	30.00	7.00
RB30	RB3	4c purple	7.50	.75
RB31	RB3	5c brown org	7.50	.75
a.		Vert. pair, imperf. horiz.	—	300.00
b.		Horiz. pair, imperf. vert.	—	400.00
		Nos. RB20-RB31 (12)	57.50	10.75

Hyphen Hole Perf. 7

RB20p		⅛c	.15	.15
RB21p		¼c	.15	.15
g.		¼c yellow brown	.15	.15
h.		¼c orange brown	.15	.15
RB22p		⅜c	.25	.15
RB23p		⅝c	.25	.15
RB24p		1c	25.00	15.00
RB25p		1¼c	.20	.15
c.		1¼c brown violet	.20	.15
RB26p		1⅞c	20.00	6.75
RB27p		2c	4.00	.25
RB28p		2½c	2.50	.20
RB29p		3¾c	50.00	15.00
RB30p		4c	50.00	15.00
RB31p		5c	50.00	7.50

See note following No. R178.

RB4

RB5

Offset Printing
1914   Wmk. 190   Perf. 10

RB32	RB4	⅛c black	.20	.15
RB33	RB4	¼c black	1.75	1.00
RB34	RB4	⅜c black	.20	.15
RB35	RB4	⅝c black	3.50	1.75
RB36	RB4	1¼c black	2.50	.80
RB37	RB4	1⅞c black	35.00	15.00
RB38	RB4	2½c black	7.50	2.50
RB39	RB4	3⅛c black	80.00	50.00
RB40	RB4	3¾c black	35.00	20.00
RB41	RB4	4c black	50.00	27.50
RB42	RB4	4⅜c black	1,100.	
RB43	RB4	5c black	100.00	70.00
		Nos. RB32-RB41,RB43 (11)	325.65	188.85

Wmk. 191R

RB44	RB4	⅛c black	.20	.15
RB45	RB4	¼c black	.20	.15
RB46	RB4	⅜c black	.60	.30
RB47	RB4	½c black	3.00	2.75
RB48	RB4	⅝c black	.20	.15
RB49	RB4	1c black	4.25	4.00
RB50	RB4	1¼c black	.35	.25
RB51	RB4	1½c black	3.00	2.25
RB52	RB4	1⅞c black	1.00	.60
RB53	RB4	2c black	5.00	4.00
RB54	RB4	2½c black	1.25	.60
RB55	RB4	3c black	4.00	2.75
RB56	RB4	3⅛c black	5.00	3.00
RB57	RB4	3¾c black	11.00	7.50
RB58	RB4	4c black	.30	.20
RB59	RB4	4⅜c black	14.00	8.00
RB60	RB4	5c black	3.00	2.50
RB61	RB4	6c black	55.00	40.00
RB62	RB4	8c black	17.50	11.00
RB63	RB4	10c black	11.00	7.00
RB64	RB4	20c black	22.50	17.50
		Nos. RB44-RB64 (21)	162.35	115.05

1919   Perf. 11

RB65	RB5	1c dark blue	.15	.15
RB66	RB5	2c dark blue	.15	.15
RB67	RB5	3c dark blue	1.00	.60
RB68	RB5	4c dark blue	1.00	.50
RB69	RB5	5c dark blue	1.25	.60
RB70	RB5	8c dark blue	14.00	9.00
RB71	RB5	10c dark blue	5.00	2.00
RB72	RB5	20c dark blue	7.50	3.00
RB73	RB5	40c dark blue	45.00	10.00
		Nos. RB65-RB73 (9)	75.05	26.00

FUTURE DELIVERY STAMPS

Issued to facilitate the collection of a tax upon each sale, agreement of sale or agreement to sell any products or merchandise at any exchange or board of trade, or other similar place for future delivery.

Documentary Stamps Nos. R228 to R250 Overprinted in Black or Red

FUTURE

DELIVERY

Offset Printing
1918-34   Wmk. 191R   Perf. 11
Overprint Horizontal
(Lines 8mm apart)

RC1	R22	2c car rose	3.50	.15
RC2	R22	3c car rose ('34)	30.00	22.50
		Cut cancellation		12.50
RC3	R22	4c car rose	6.00	.15
RC3A	R22	5c car rose ('33)	75.00	5.00

RC4	R22	10c car rose	11.00	.15
a.		Double overprint	—	5.00
b.		"FUTURE" omitted	—	200.00
c.		"DELIVERY FUTURE"		35.00
RC5	R22	20c car rose	15.00	.15
a.		Double overprint	—	20.00
RC6	R22	25c car rose	35.00	.40
				.15
RC7	R22	40c car rose	40.00	.75
		Cut cancellation		.15
RC8	R22	50c car rose	8.50	.15
a.		"DELIVERY" omitted	—	100.00
RC9	R22	80c car rose	75.00	10.00
		Cut cancellation		1.00
a.		Double overprint		35.00
		Nos. RC1-RC9 (10)	299.00	39.40

Overprint Vertical, Reading Up (Lines 2mm apart)
Engr.

RC10	R21	$1 green (R)	30.00	.25
				.15
a.		Overprint reading down		275.00
b.		Black overprint		
		Cut cancellation		125.00
RC11	R21	$2 rose	35.00	.25
		Cut cancellation		.15
RC12	R21	$3 violet (R)	80.00	2.50
				.15
a.		Overprint reading down	—	50.00
RC13	R21	$5 dark blue (R)	50.00	.35
				.15
RC14	R21	$10 orange	80.00	.75
				.15
a.		"DELIVERY FUTURE"		100.00
RC15	R21	$20 olive bis	150.00	4.00
				.50
		Nos. RC10-RC15 (6)	425.00	8.10

Perf. 12
Overprint Horizontal
(Lines 11½mm apart)
Without Gum

RC16	R17	$30 ver, green numerals	70.00	3.50
		Cut cancellation		1.25
a.		Numerals in blue	60.00	3.50
		Cut cancellation		1.50
b.		As "a," imperf.		100.00
RC17	R19	$50 olive green	47.50	1.25
		Cut cancellation		.40
a.		$50 olive bister	47.50	.40
		Cut cancellation		.40
RC18	R19	$60 brown	70.00	2.25
		Cut cancellation		.75
a.		Vert. pair, imperf. horiz.		400.00
RC19	R17	$100 yel green ('34)	80.00	27.50
		Cut cancellation		7.00
RC20	R18	$500 blue, red numerals (R)	70.00	11.00
				4.50
a.		Numerals in orange	—	50.00
		Cut cancellation		11.00
RC21	R19	$1000 orange	75.00	5.50
				1.50
a.		Vert. pair, imperf. horiz.		900.00
		Nos. RC16-RC21 (6)	412.50	51.00

See note after No. R227.

1923-24   Offset Printing   Perf. 11
Overprint Horiz.
(Lines 2mm apart)

RC22	R22	1c carmine rose	1.00	.20
RC23	R22	80c carmine rose	65.00	1.75
		Cut cancellation		.35

FUTURE

Documentary Stamps of 1917 Overprinted in Red or Black

DELIVERY

1925-34   Engr.

RC25	R21	$1 green (R)	27.50	.75
				.15
RC26	R21	$10 orange (Bk) ('34)	90.00	15.00
		Cut cancellation		10.00

Overprinted like Nos. RC1-RC9

1928-29   Offset Printing   Perf. 10

RC27	R22	10c carmine rose		1,500.
RC28	R22	20c carmine rose		1,500.

STOCK TRANSFER STAMPS

Issued to facilitate the collection of a tax on all sales or agreements to sell, or memoranda of sales or delivery of, or transfers of legal title to shares or certificates of stock.

Documentary Stamps Nos. R228 to R259 Overprinted in Black or Red

STOCK

TRANSFER

Offset Printing
1918-29 Wmk. 191R Perf. 11
Overprint Horiz. (Lines 8mm apart)

No.	Type	Denom	Unused	Used
RD1	R22	1c car rose	.85	.15
a.		Double overprint		
RD2	R22	2c car rose	.20	.15
a.		Double overprint		5.00
		Cut cancellation		2.50
RD3	R22	4c car rose	.20	.15
a.		Double overprint		4.00
		Cut cancellation		2.00
b.		"STOCK" omitted		10.00
d.		Overprint lines 10mm apart		
RD4	R22	5c car rose	.25	.15
RD5	R22	10c car rose	.25	.15
a.		Double overprint		5.00
		Cut cancellation		2.50
b.		"STOCK" omitted		
RD6	R22	20c car rose	.50	.15
a.		Double overprint		6.00
b.		"STOCK" double		
RD7	R22	25c car rose	1.50	.20
		Cut cancellation		.15
RD8	R22	40c car rose ('22)	1.25	.15
RD9	R22	50c car rose	.65	.15
		Cut cancellation		.15
RD10	R22	80c car rose	3.00	.30
		Cut cancellation		.15
		Nos. RD1-RD10 (10)	8.65	
		Set value		.90

Overprint Vertical, Reading Up (Lines 2mm apart)
Engr.

No.	Type	Denom	Unused	Used
RD11	R21	$1 green (R)	70.00	20.00
		Cut cancellation		3.00
a.		Ovpt. reading down	125.00	20.00
		Cut cancellation		7.50
RD12	R21	$1 green (Bk)	2.50	.25
a.		Pair, one without ovpt.		150.00
b.		Ovptd. on back instead of face, inverted	—	100.00
c.		Ovpt. reading down		6.00
d.		$1 yellow green	2.75	.15
RD13	R21	$2 rose	2.50	.15
a.		Ovpt. reading down		10.00
		Cut cancellation		1.50
b.		Vert. pair, imperf. horiz.	500.00	
RD14	R21	$3 violet (R)	17.50	4.25
				.20
RD15	R21	$4 yellow brn	9.00	.15
				.15
RD16	R21	$5 dk blue (R)	6.00	.15
				.15
a.		Ovpt. reading down	20.00	1.00
				.16
RD17	R21	$10 orange	16.00	.30
				.15
RD18	R21	$20 ol bis ('21)	75.00	20.00
		Cut cancellation		3.00
		Nos. RD11-RD18 (8)	198.50	45.25

1918 Without Gum Perf. 12
Overprint Horizontal (Lines 11½mm apart)

No.	Type	Denom	Unused	Used
RD19	R17	$30 ver, green numerals	17.50	4.50
		Cut cancellation		1.00
a.		Numerals in blue		55.00
RD20	R19	$50 olive green, (Cleveland)	110.00	8.00
		Cut cancellation		20.00
RD21	R19	$60 brown	110.00	20.00
		Cut cancellation		9.00
RD22	R17	$100 green	22.50	5.50
		Cut cancellation		2.25
RD23	R18	$500 blue (R)	300.00	110.00
		Cut cancellation		65.00
a.		Numerals in orange		140.00
RD24	R19	$1000 orange	165.00	72.50
		Cut cancellation		25.00

See note after No. R227.

1928-32 Offset Printing Perf. 10
Overprint Horiz. (Lines 8mm apart)

No.	Type	Denom	Unused	Used
RD25	R22	2c carmine rose	2.50	.25
RD26	R22	4c carmine rose	2.50	.25
RD27	R22	10c carmine rose	2.00	.25
a.		Inverted overprint	1,000.	
RD28	R22	20c carmine rose	3.00	.25
RD29	R22	50c carmine rose	3.00	.25

Overprint Vertical, Reading Up (Lines 2mm apart)
Engr.

No.	Type	Denom	Unused	Used
RD30	R21	$1 car rose	30.00	.20
		$1 yellow green	—	—
RD31	R21	$2 car rose	30.00	.15
a.		Pair, one without overprint	200.00	175.00
RD32	R21	$10 orange	32.50	.35
		Cut cancellation		1.00
		Nos. RD25-RD32 (8)	106.00	1.95

STOCK
Overprinted Horiz. in Black
TRANSFER
1920-28 Offset Printing Perf. 11

No.	Type	Denom	Unused	Used
RD33	R22	2c carmine rose	7.50	.70
RD34	R22	10c carmine rose	1.25	.30
b.		Inverted overprint	1,500.	
RD35	R22	20c carmine rose	1.00	.20
d.		Inverted overprint (perf. initials)	—	
RD36	R22	50c carmine rose	3.00	.20

Engr.

No.	Type	Denom	Unused	Used
RD37	R21	$1 green	40.00	8.00
RD38	R21	$2 rose	35.00	8.00
		Nos. RD33-RD38 (6)	87.75	17.40

Shifted overprints on the 10c, 20c and 50c result in "TRANSFER STOCK," "TRANSFER" omitted, "STOCK" omitted, pairs, one without overprint and other varieties.

Perf. 10
Offset Printing

No.	Type	Denom	Unused	Used
RD39	R22	2c carmine rose	6.00	.50
RD40	R22	10c carmine rose	1.25	.50
RD41	R22	20c carmine rose	2.25	.25
		Nos. RD39-RD41 (3)	9.50	1.25

Used values for Nos. RD42-RD372 are for copies which are neither cut nor perforated with initials. Copies with cut cancellations or perforated initials are valued in the Scott U.S. Specialized Catalogue.

SERIES 1940

Documentary Stamps of 1917-33 Overprinted in Black

STOCK TRANSFER

1940 Perf. 11

No.	Type	Denom	Unused	Used
RD42	R22	1c rose pink	3.00	.45
a.		"Series 1940" inverted		225.00
RD43	R22	2c rose pink	3.00	.50
RD45	R22	4c rose pink	3.00	.20
RD46	R22	5c rose pink	3.50	.20
RD48	R22	10c rose pink	3.50	.20
RD49	R22	20c rose pink	7.50	.20
RD50	R22	25c rose pink	7.50	.60
RD51	R22	40c rose pink	5.00	.75
RD52	R22	50c rose pink	6.00	.25
RD53	R22	80c rose pink	90.00	50.00
		Nos. RD42-RD53 (10)	132.00	53.35

Engr.

No.	Type	Denom	Unused	Used
RD54	R21	$1 green	20.00	.35
RD55	R21	$2 rose	20.00	.60
RD56	R21	$3 violet	125.00	9.00
RD57	R21	$4 yel brown	40.00	1.00
RD58	R21	$5 dark blue	40.00	1.00
RD59	R21	$10 orange	100.00	6.00
RD60	R21	$20 olive bister	225.00	75.00
		Nos. RD54-RD60 (7)	570.00	92.95

Stock Transfer Stamps of 1918 Handstamped in Blue "Series 1940"

1940 Without Gum Perf. 12

No.	Type	Denom	Unused	Used
RD61	R17	$30 vermilion	900.	450.
RD62	R19	$50 olive green	900.	700.
a.		Dbl. ovpt. (perf. initials canc.)		350.
RD63	R19	$60 brown		1,000.
RD64	R17	$100 green		550.
RD65	R18	$500 blue		2,000.
RD66	R19	$1000 orange		2,250.

Alexander Hamilton — ST1

Levi Woodbury — ST2

Thomas Corwin — ST3

Portraits (see R23-R25): 2c, Wolcott. 4c, Gallatin. 5c, Campbell. 10c, Crawford. 20c, Rush. 25c, Ingham. 40c, McLane. 50c, Duane. 80c, Taney. $2, Ewing. $3, Forward. $4, Spencer. $5, Bibb. $10, Walker. $20, Meredith. $50, Guthrie. $60, Cobb. $100, Thomas. $500, Dix. $1,000, Chase.

Overprinted in Black **SERIES 1940**

1940 Wmk. 191R Perf. 11
Various Portraits
Size: 19x22mm

No.	Type	Denom	Unused	Used
RD67	ST1	1c brt green	9.00	2.75
RD68	ST1	2c brt green	5.50	1.40
RD70	ST1	4c brt green	10.00	3.75
RD71	ST1	5c brt green	6.00	1.40
a.		Without overprint (cut canc.)		250.00
RD73	ST1	10c brt green	8.50	1.75
RD74	ST1	20c brt green	10.00	2.00
RD75	ST1	25c brt green	27.50	8.00
RD76	ST1	40c brt green	55.00	30.00
RD77	ST1	50c brt green	8.50	1.75
RD78	ST1	80c brt green	70.00	50.00
		Nos. RD67-RD78 (10)	210.00	102.80

Size: 21½x36¼mm

No.	Type	Denom	Unused	Used
RD79	ST2	$1 brt green	30.00	3.50
a.		Without overprint (perf. initials canc.)		225.00
RD80	ST2	$2 brt green	35.00	8.50
RD81	ST2	$3 brt green	55.00	10.00
RD82	ST2	$4 brt green	250.00	200.00
RD83	ST2	$5 brt green	50.00	12.50
RD84	ST2	$10 brt green	125.00	35.00
RD85	ST2	$20 brt green	450.00	70.00

Perf. 12
Without Gum
Size: 28½x42mm
Various Frame Designs

No.	Type	Denom	Unused	Used
RD86	ST3	$30 brt green	—	125.00
RD87	ST3	$50 brt green	300.00	200.00
RD88	ST3	$60 brt green	—	300.00
RD89	ST3	$100 brt green	—	175.00
RD90	ST3	$500 brt green	—	850.00
RD91	ST3	$1000 brt green	—	750.00

Overprinted in Black "Series 1941" **SERIES 1941**

1941 Size: 19x22mm Perf. 11

No.	Type	Denom	Unused	Used
RD92	ST1	1c brt green	.65	.50
RD93	ST1	2c brt green	.45	.25
RD95	ST1	4c brt green	.40	.15
RD96	ST1	5c brt green	.35	.15
RD98	ST1	10c brt green	.75	.15
RD99	ST1	20c brt green	1.75	.25
RD100	ST1	25c brt green	1.75	.40
RD101	ST1	40c brt green	2.50	.75
RD102	ST1	50c brt green	3.75	.35
RD103	ST1	80c brt green	20.00	7.50
		Nos. RD92-RD103 (10)	32.35	10.50

Size: 21½x36¼mm

No.	Type	Denom	Unused	Used
RD104	ST2	$1 brt green	11.00	.20
RD105	ST2	$2 brt green	12.50	.25
RD106	ST2	$3 brt green	19.00	1.50
RD107	ST2	$4 brt green	35.00	6.50
RD108	ST2	$5 brt green	35.00	.60
RD109	ST2	$10 brt green	75.00	4.00
RD110	ST2	$20 brt green	140.00	55.00
		Nos. RD104-RD110 (7)	327.50	68.05

Perf. 12
Without Gum
Size: 28½x42mm

No.	Type	Denom	Unused	Used
RD111	ST3	$30 brt green	140.00	125.00
RD112	ST3	$50 brt green	225.00	140.00
RD113	ST3	$60 brt green	450.00	175.00
RD114	ST3	$100 brt green	—	75.00
RD115	ST3	$500 brt green	875.00	725.00
RD116	ST3	$1000 brt green	—	900.00

Overprinted in Black "Series 1942"

1942 Size: 19x22mm Perf. 11

No.	Type	Denom	Unused	Used
RD117	ST1	1c brt green	.50	.30
RD118	ST1	2c brt green	.40	.35
RD119	ST1	4c brt green	3.00	1.00
RD120	ST1	5c brt green	.40	.15
a.		Ovpt. inverted (cut cancel)		225.00
RD121	ST1	10c brt green	1.75	.15
RD122	ST1	20c brt green	2.00	.15
RD123	ST1	25c brt green	2.00	.15
RD124	ST1	40c brt green	4.00	.35
RD125	ST1	50c brt green	5.00	.20
RD126	ST1	80c brt green	17.50	5.25
		Nos. RD117-RD126 (10)	36.55	8.05

Size: 21½x36¼mm

No.	Type	Denom	Unused	Used
RD127	ST2	$1 brt green	11.00	.35
RD128	ST2	$2 brt green	16.00	.35
RD129	ST2	$3 brt green	22.50	1.00
RD130	ST2	$4 brt green	35.00	17.50
RD131	ST2	$5 brt green	30.00	.35
a.		Double overprint (perf. initials cancel)		
RD132	ST2	$10 brt green	60.00	7.50
RD133	ST2	$20 brt green	135.00	32.50
		Nos. RD127-RD133 (7)	309.50	59.55

Perf. 12
Without Gum
Size: 28½x42mm

No.	Type	Denom	Unused	Used
RD134	ST3	$30 brt green	90.00	45.00
RD135	ST3	$50 brt green	150.00	90.00
RD136	ST3	$60 brt green	—	110.00
RD137	ST3	$100 brt green	—	77.50
RD138	ST3	$500 brt green	—	8,000.
RD139	ST3	$1000 brt green	—	400.00

Overprinted in Black "Series 1943"
1943 Size: 19x22mm Perf. 11

No.	Type	Denom	Unused	Used
RD140	ST1	1c brt green	.40	.25
RD141	ST1	2c brt green	.50	.40
RD142	ST1	4c brt green	1.75	.25
RD143	ST1	5c brt green	.50	.15
RD144	ST1	10c brt green	1.00	.15
RD145	ST1	20c brt green	1.75	.15
RD146	ST1	25c brt green	3.50	.25
RD147	ST1	40c brt green	3.50	.25
RD148	ST1	50c brt green	3.50	.25
RD149	ST1	80c brt green	12.50	4.50
		Nos. RD140-RD149 (10)	28.90	6.50

Size: 21½x36¼mm

No.	Type	Denom	Unused	Used
RD150	ST2	$1 brt green	12.50	.15
RD151	ST2	$2 brt green	14.00	.35
RD152	ST2	$3 brt green	17.50	1.00
RD153	ST2	$4 brt green	35.00	15.00
RD154	ST2	$5 brt green	50.00	.35
RD155	ST2	$10 brt green	70.00	4.50
RD156	ST2	$20 brt green	125.00	35.00
		Nos. RD150-RD156 (7)	324.00	56.35

Perf. 12
Without Gum
Size: 28½x42mm

No.	Type	Denom	Unused	Used
RD157	ST3	$30 brt green	200.00	100.00
RD158	ST3	$50 brt green	275.00	125.00
RD159	ST3	$60 brt green	—	300.00
RD160	ST3	$100 brt green	—	50.00
RD161	ST3	$500 brt green	—	400.00
RD162	ST3	$1000 brt green	—	250.00

Overprinted in Black "Series 1944"
Portraits: $2,500, William Windom. $5,000, C. J. Folger. $10,000, Walter Q. Gresham.

1944 Wmk. 191R Perf. 11
Size: 19x22mm

No.	Type	Denom	Unused	Used
RD163	ST1	1c brt green	.65	.60
RD164	ST1	2c brt green	.45	.20
RD165	ST1	4c brt green	.60	.15
RD166	ST1	5c brt green	.50	.15
RD167	ST1	10c brt green	.75	.15
RD168	ST1	20c brt green	1.25	.20
RD169	ST1	25c brt green	2.00	.30
RD170	ST1	40c brt green	8.00	5.00
RD171	ST1	50c brt green	4.50	.20
RD172	ST1	80c brt green	7.50	4.50
		Nos. RD163-RD172 (10)	26.20	11.55

Size: 21½x36¼mm

No.	Type	Denom	Unused	Used
RD173	ST2	$1 brt green	7.50	.40
RD174	ST2	$2 brt green	30.00	.60
RD175	ST2	$3 brt green	25.00	1.25
RD176	ST2	$4 brt green	30.00	5.00
RD177	ST2	$5 brt green	27.50	.90
RD178	ST2	$10 brt green	60.00	4.50
RD179	ST2	$20 brt green	100.00	8.00
		Nos. RD173-RD179 (7)	280.00	20.65

Perf. 12
Without Gum
Size: 28½x42mm
Bright Green

No.	Type	Denom	Unused	Used
RD180	ST3	$30	125.00	60.00
RD181	ST3	$50	85.00	50.00
RD182	ST3	$60	150.00	100.00
RD183	ST3	$100	—	47.50
RD184	ST3	$500	—	400.00
RD185	ST3	$1000	—	
		(cut cancel)		225.00
RD185A	ST3	$2500	—	
RD185B	ST3	$5000	—	
RD185C	ST3	$10,000	—	
		(cut cancel)		1,250.

Overprinted in Black "Series 1945"
1945 Wmk. 191R Perf. 11
Size: 19x22mm

No.	Type	Denom	Unused	Used
RD186	ST1	1c brt green	.15	.15
RD187	ST1	2c brt green	.25	.20
RD188	ST1	4c brt green	.25	.20
RD189	ST1	5c brt green	.25	.15
RD190	ST1	10c brt green	.75	.35
RD191	ST1	20c brt green	.35	.30
RD192	ST1	25c brt green	2.00	.35
RD193	ST1	40c brt green	3.00	.20
RD194	ST1	50c brt green	3.50	.25
RD195	ST1	80c brt green	6.50	2.50
		Nos. RD186-RD195 (10)	17.90	4.65

Size: 21½x36¼mm

No.	Type	Denom	Unused	Used
RD196	ST2	$1 brt green	12.50	.25
RD197	ST2	$2 brt green	17.50	.45
RD198	ST2	$3 brt green	30.00	.60
RD199	ST2	$4 brt green	30.00	2.50
RD200	ST2	$5 brt green	20.00	.50
RD201	ST2	$10 brt green	45.00	6.50
RD202	ST2	$20 brt green	70.00	8.00

Perf. 12
Without Gum
Size: 28½x42mm
Bright green

No.	Type	Denom	Unused	Used
RD203	ST3	$30	90.00	45.00
RD204	ST3	$50	60.00	17.50
RD205	ST3	$60	150.00	125.00
RD206	ST3	$100	—	25.00
RD207	ST3	$500	—	400.00

RD208	ST3	$1000	—	475.00
RD208A	ST3	$2500	—	—
RD208B	ST3	$5000	—	—
RD208C	ST3	$10,000 cut canc.	—	1,500.

Overprinted in Black "Series 1946"
1946 Wmk. 191R Perf. 11
Size: 19x22mm

RD209	ST1	1c brt green	.20	.15
a.		Pair, one dated "1945"	475.00	
RD210	ST1	2c brt green	.35	.15
RD211	ST1	4c brt green	.30	.15
RD212	ST1	5c brt green	.35	.15
RD213	ST1	10c brt green	.75	.15
RD214	ST1	20c brt green	1.50	.20
RD215	ST1	25c brt green	1.50	.25
RD216	ST1	40c brt green	3.50	.60
RD217	ST1	50c brt green	4.50	.20
RD218	ST1	80c brt green	9.00	6.00
Nos. RD209-RD218 (10)			21.95	8.00

Size: 21 1/2x36 1/4mm

RD219	ST2	$1 brt green	8.00	.50
RD220	ST2	$2 brt green	9.00	.50
RD221	ST2	$3 brt green	17.50	1.25
RD222	ST2	$4 brt green	17.50	5.50
RD223	ST2	$5 brt green	25.00	1.00
RD224	ST2	$10 brt green	50.00	2.50
RD225	ST2	$20 brt green	80.00	35.00
Nos. RD219-RD225 (7)			207.00	46.25

Perf. 12
Without Gum
Size: 28 1/2x42mm

RD226	ST3	$30 brt grn	70.00	27.50
RD227	ST3	$50 brt grn	55.00	35.00
RD228	ST3	$60 brt grn	125.00	82.50
RD229	ST3	$100 brt grn	77.50	35.00
RD230	ST3	$500 brt grn	—	165.00
RD231	ST3	$1000 brt grn	—	140.00
RD232	ST3	$2500 brt grn (cut cancel)		4,500.
RD233	ST3	$5000 brt grn		5,500.
RD234	ST3	$10,000 brt grn (cut cancel)		2,000.

Overprinted in Black "Series 1947"
1947 Wmk. 191R Perf. 11
Size: 19x22mm

RD235	ST1	1c brt green	.65	.55
RD236	ST1	2c brt green	.60	.50
RD237	ST1	4c brt green	.50	.40
RD238	ST1	5c brt green	.45	.35
RD239	ST1	10c brt green	.60	.50
RD240	ST1	20c brt green	1.10	.50
RD241	ST1	25c brt green	1.75	.50
RD242	ST1	40c brt green	3.00	.75
RD243	ST1	50c brt green	4.00	.10
RD244	ST1	80c brt green	15.00	10.00
Nos. RD235-RD244 (10)			27.65	14.35

Size: 21 1/2x36 1/4mm

RD245	ST2	$1 brt green	6.00	.50
RD246	ST2	$2 brt green	12.50	.75
RD247	ST2	$3 brt green	20.00	1.50
RD248	ST2	$4 brt green	32.50	6.00
RD249	ST2	$5 brt green	27.50	1.50
RD250	ST2	$10 brt green	45.00	5.00
RD251	ST2	$20 brt green	85.00	30.00
Nos. RD245-RD251 (7)			228.50	45.25

Perf. 12
Without Gum
Size: 28 1/2x42mm

RD252	ST3	$30 brt grn	60.00	35.00
RD253	ST3	$50 brt grn	125.00	82.50
RD254	ST3	$60 brt grn	150.00	125.00
RD255	ST3	$100 brt grn	—	27.50
RD256	ST3	$500 brt grn	—	250.00
RD257	ST3	$1000 brt grn	—	85.00
RD258	ST3	$2500 brt grn (cut cancel)	—	350.00
RD259	ST3	$5000 brt grn (cut cancel)	—	300.00
RD260	ST3	$10,000 brt grn (cut cancel)	—	55.00
a.		Horiz. pair, imperf. vert. (cut cancel)	—	

Overprinted in Black "Series 1948"
1948 Wmk. 191R Perf. 11
Size: 19x22mm

RD261	ST1	1c brt green	.25	.25
RD262	ST1	2c brt green	.25	.25
RD263	ST1	4c brt green	.30	.30
RD264	ST1	5c brt green	.25	.24
RD265	ST1	10c brt green	.30	.25
RD266	ST1	20c brt green	1.40	.35
RD267	ST1	25c brt green	1.40	.40
RD268	ST1	40c brt green	1.75	.75
RD269	ST1	50c brt green	4.25	.30
RD270	ST1	80c brt green	12.50	6.00
Nos. RD261-RD270 (10)			22.65	9.09

Size: 21 1/2x36 1/4mm

RD271	ST2	$1 brt green	8.50	.40
RD272	ST2	$2 brt green	12.50	.60
RD273	ST2	$3 brt green	15.00	3.75
RD274	ST2	$4 brt green	17.50	9.00
RD275	ST2	$5 brt green	25.00	2.50
RD276	ST2	$10 brt green	45.00	4.50
RD277	ST2	$20 brt green	75.00	18.00
Nos. RD271-RD277 (7)			198.50	38.75

Perf. 12
Without Gum
Size: 28 1/2x42mm

RD278	ST3	$30 brt grn	90.00	40.00
RD279	ST3	$50 brt grn	60.00	40.00
RD280	ST3	$60 brt grn	150.00	100.00
RD281	ST3	$100 brt grn	—	17.50
RD282	ST3	$500 brt grn	—	210.00
RD283	ST3	$1000 brt grn	—	100.00
RD284	ST3	$2500 brt grn	300.00	275.00
RD285	ST3	$5000 brt grn	—	250.00
RD286	ST3	$10,000 brt grn (cut canc.)	—	55.00

Overprinted in Black "Series 1949"
1949 Wmk. 191R Perf. 11
Size: 19x22mm

RD287	ST1	1c brt green	.50	.45
RD288	ST1	2c brt green	.50	.45
RD289	ST1	4c brt green	.60	.50
RD290	ST1	5c brt green	.60	.50
RD291	ST1	10c brt green	1.30	.60
RD292	ST1	20c brt green	2.10	.50
RD293	ST1	25c brt green	3.00	.85
RD294	ST1	40c brt green	5.50	1.50
RD295	ST1	50c brt green	5.00	.25
RD296	ST1	80c brt green	12.50	6.50
Nos. RD287-RD296 (10)			31.60	12.10

Size: 21 1/2x36 1/4mm

RD297	ST2	$1 brt green	10.00	.65
RD298	ST2	$2 brt green	15.00	.90
RD299	ST2	$3 brt green	32.50	4.50
RD300	ST2	$4 brt green	30.00	7.50
RD301	ST2	$5 brt green	40.00	2.00
RD302	ST2	$10 brt green	50.00	4.00
RD303	ST2	$20 brt green	115.00	15.00
Nos. RD297-RD303 (7)			292.50	34.55

Perf. 12
Without Gum
Size: 28 1/2x42mm

RD304	ST3	$30 brt grn	—	40.00
RD305	ST3	$50 brt grn	140.00	55.00
RD306	ST3	$60 brt grn	165.00	140.00
RD307	ST3	$100 brt grn	—	55.00
RD308	ST3	$500 brt grn	—	200.00
RD309	ST3	$1000 brt grn	—	80.00
RD310	ST3	$2500 brt grn (cut canc.)	—	325.00
RD311	ST3	$5000 brt grn (cut canc.)	—	350.00
RD312	ST3	$10,000 brt grn	—	275.00
a.		Pair, one without ovpt. (cut cancel)		

Overprinted in Black "Series 1950"
1950 Wmk. 191R Perf. 11
Size: 19x22mm

RD313	ST1	1c brt green	.40	.35
RD314	ST1	2c brt green	.40	.30
RD315	ST1	4c brt green	.40	.35
RD316	ST1	5c brt green	.40	.20
RD317	ST1	10c brt green	2.00	.30
RD318	ST1	20c brt green	2.75	.50
RD319	ST1	25c brt green	4.00	.60
RD320	ST1	40c brt green	4.75	.90
RD321	ST1	50c brt green	7.50	.35
RD322	ST1	80c brt green	9.50	5.00
Nos. RD313-RD322 (10)			32.10	8.85

Size: 21 1/2x36 1/4mm

RD323	ST2	$1 brt green	10.00	.40
RD324	ST2	$2 brt green	17.50	.75
RD325	ST2	$3 brt green	27.50	4.00
RD326	ST2	$4 brt green	35.00	7.50
RD327	ST2	$5 brt green	35.00	1.75
RD328	ST2	$10 brt green	80.00	5.00
RD329	ST2	$20 brt green	110.00	25.00
Nos. RD323-RD329 (7)			315.00	44.40

Perf. 12
Without Gum
Size: 28 1/2x42mm

RD330	ST3	$30 brt grn	80.00	40.00
RD331	ST3	$50 brt grn	75.00	70.00
RD332	ST3	$60 brt grn	—	110.00
RD333	ST3	$100 brt grn	—	35.00
a.		Vert. pair, imperf betwn.		
RD334	ST3	$500 brt grn	—	165.00
RD335	ST3	$1000 brt grn	—	75.00
RD336	ST3	$2500 brt grn	—	1,000.
RD337	ST3	$5000 brt grn	—	550.00
RD338	ST3	$10,000 brt grn		

Overprinted in Black "Series 1951"
1951 Wmk. 191R Perf. 11
Size: 19x22mm

RD339	ST1	1c brt green	1.10	.35
RD340	ST1	2c brt green	1.10	.30
RD341	ST1	4c brt green	1.50	.50
RD342	ST1	5c brt green	1.10	.35
RD343	ST1	10c brt green	1.50	.30
RD344	ST1	20c brt green	3.75	.90
RD345	ST1	25c brt green	5.00	.90
RD346	ST1	40c brt green	8.00	2.00
RD347	ST1	50c brt green	8.50	.90
RD348	ST1	80c brt green	15.00	10.00
Nos. RD339-RD348 (10)			51.05	22.50

Size: 21 1/2x36 1/4mm

RD349	ST2	$1 brt green	17.50	.80
RD350	ST2	$2 brt green	25.00	1.25
RD351	ST2	$3 brt green	35.00	10.00
RD352	ST2	$4 brt green	40.00	12.00
RD353	ST2	$5 brt green	50.00	2.50
RD354	ST2	$10 brt green	80.00	8.50
RD355	ST2	$20 brt green	125.00	17.50
Nos. RD349-RD355 (7)			372.50	52.55

Perf. 12
Without Gum
Size: 28 1/2x42mm

RD356	ST3	$30 brt grn	—	45.00
RD357	ST3	$50 brt grn	—	50.00
RD358	ST3	$60 brt grn	—	450.00
RD359	ST3	$100 brt grn	—	55.00
RD360	ST3	$500 brt grn	—	140.00
RD361	ST3	$1000 brt grn	—	75.00
RD362	ST3	$2500 brt grn	—	950.00
RD363	ST3	$5000 brt grn	—	950.00
RD364	ST3	$10,000 brt grn	—	110.00

Overprinted in Black "Series 1952"
1952 Wmk. 191R Perf. 11
Size: 19x22mm

RD365	ST1	1c brt green	30.00	15.00
RD366	ST1	10c brt green	30.00	15.00
RD367	ST1	20c brt green	300.00	
RD368	ST1	25c brt green	400.00	
RD369	ST1	40c brt green	75.00	35.00

Size: 21 1/2x36 1/4mm

RD370	ST2	$4 brt green	700.	450.
RD371	ST2	$10 brt green	1,750.	
RD372	ST2	$20 brt green	2,750.	

Stock Transfer stamps were discontinued in 1952.

See the Scott United States Specialized Catalogue for other categories of Revenue stamps.

HUNTING PERMIT STAMPS

The receipts of the sales of these "Migratory Bird Hunting" stamps help to maintain waterfowl life in the United States.

> Catalogue values for unused stamps in this section are for Never Hinged items. Unused stamps with part or no gum sell for substantially less than the unused never hinged values.

Department of Agriculture

HP1

Various Designs
Inscribed "U. S. Department of Agriculture"
Engraved; Flat Plate Printing
1934 Unwmk. Perf. 11
"Void after June 30, 1935"

RW1	HP1	$1 blue	675.00	115.00
		Hinged	350.00	
		No gum	160.00	
a.		Imperf. pair		
b.		Vert. pair, imperf. horiz.		

Used copies are unsigned.

1935 "Void after June 30, 1936"

RW2		$1 Canvasback Ducks Taking to Flight	650.00	130.00
		Hinged	375.00	
		No gum	175.00	

1936 "Void after June 30, 1937"

RW3		$1 Canada Geese in Flight	325.00	65.00
		Hinged	190.00	
		No gum	95.00	

1937 "Void after June 30, 1938"

RW4		$1 Scaup Ducks Taking to Flight	275.00	47.50
		Hinged	150.00	
		No gum	75.00	

1938 "Void after June 30, 1939"

RW5		$1 Pintail Drake and Duck Alighting	350.00	47.50
		Hinged	190.00	
		No gum	75.00	

Department of the Interior

Green-Winged Teal — HP2

Various Designs
Inscribed: "U. S. Department of the Interior"

1939   **"Void after June 30, 1940"**
RW6   HP2 $1 chocolate   200.00 40.00
Hinged   110.00
No gum   50.00

1940   **"Void after June 30, 1941"**
RW7 $1 Black Mallards   200.00 40.00
Hinged   110.00
No gum   50.00

1941   **"Void after June 30, 1942"**
RW8 $1 Family of Ruddy
            Ducks   200.00 40.00
Hinged   110.00
No gum   50.00

1942   **"Void after June 30, 1943"**
RW9 $1 Baldpates   200.00 40.00
Hinged   110.00
No gum   50.00

1943   **"Void after June 30, 1944"**
RW10 $1 Wood Ducks   75.00 35.00
Hinged   50.00
No gum   42.50

1944   **"Void after June 30, 1945"**
RW11 $1 White-fronted Geese 85.00 25.00
Hinged   50.00
No gum   32.50

1945   **"Void after June 30, 1946"**
RW12 $1 Shoveller Ducks in
            Flight   60.00 22.50
Hinged   35.00
No gum   25.00

1946   **"Void after June 30, 1947"**
RW13 $1 Redhead Ducks   45.00 13.00
No gum   18.00

1947   **"Void after June 30, 1948"**
RW14 $1 Snow Geese   45.00 13.00
No gum   18.00

1948   **"Void after June 30, 1949"**
RW15 $1 Bufflehead Ducks in
            Flight   50.00 13.00
No gum   21.00

Goldeneye Ducks HP3

1949   **"Void after June 30, 1950"**
RW16   HP3 $2 bright green   55.00 13.00
No gum   22.00

1950   **"Void after June 30, 1951"**
RW17 $2 Trumpeter Swans in
            Flight   72.50 10.00
No gum   25.00

1951   **"Void after June 30, 1952"**
RW18 $2 Gadwall Ducks   72.50 10.00
No gum   25.00

1952   **"Void after June 30, 1953"**
RW19 $2 Harlequin Ducks   72.50 10.00
No gum   25.00

1953   **"Void after June 30, 1954"**
RW20 $2 Blue-winged Teal   75.00 10.00
No gum   25.00

1954   **"Void after June 30, 1955"**
RW21 $2 Ring-necked Ducks   75.00 9.00
No gum   25.00

1955   **"Void after June 30, 1956"**
RW22 $2 Blue Geese   75.00 9.00
No gum   25.00

1956   **"Void after June 30, 1957"**
RW23 $2 American Merganser   75.00 9.00
No gum   25.00

1957   **"Void after June 30, 1958"**
RW24 $2 American Eiders   75.00 9.00
No gum   25.00
   a. Back inscription inverted   —

1958   **"Void after June 30, 1959"**
RW25 $2 Canada Geese   72.50 9.00
No gum   25.00

Labrador Retriever Carrying Mallard Drake HP4

1959   **Giori Press Printing**
        "Void after June 30, 1960"
RW26   HP4 $3 blue, ocher & blk 92.50 9.00
No gum   35.00

Redhead Ducks HP5

1960   **"Void after June 30, 1961"**
RW27   HP5 $3 red brn, dk bl & bis-
            ter   80.00 9.00
No gum   35.00

1961   **"Void after June 30, 1962"**
RW28 $3 Mallard Hen and Duck-
            lings   82.50 9.00
No gum   37.50

Pintail Drakes Coming in for Landing HP6

1962   **"Void after June 30, 1963"**
RW29   HP6 $3 dk bl, dk red brn &
            black   95.00 9.00
No gum   62.50

1963   **"Void after June 30, 1964"**
RW30 $3 Pair of Brant landing 95.00 9.00
No gum   65.00

1964   **"Void after June 30, 1965"**
RW31 $3 Hawaiian Nene Geese   95.00 9.00
No gum   65.00

1965   **"Void after June 30, 1966"**
RW32 $3 3 Canvasback Drakes   92.50 9.00
No gum   62.50

Whistling Swans HP7

1966   **"Void after June 30, 1967"**
RW33   HP7 $3 ultra, sl grn & blk 95.00 9.00
No gum   42.50

1967   **"Void after June 30, 1968"**
RW34 $3 Old Squaw Ducks   100.00 9.00
No gum   42.50

1968   **"Void after June 30, 1969"**
RW35 $3 Hooded Mergansers   57.50 8.00
No gum   22.50

MIGRATORY BIRD HUNTING STAMP
White-winged Scoters — HP8

1969   **"Void after June 30, 1970"**
RW36   HP8 $3 gray, brn, indigo &
            brn red   57.50 7.00
No gum   22.50

1970   **Litho. & Engr.**
        "Void after June 30, 1971"
RW37 $3 Ross' Geese   57.50 6.50
No gum   22.50

1971   **"Void after June 30, 1972"**
RW38 $3 3 Cinnamon Teal   40.00 6.50
No gum   20.00

1972   **"Void after June 30, 1973"**
RW39 $5 Emperor Geese   25.00 6.50
No gum   12.50

1973   **"Void after June 30, 1974"**
RW40 $5 Steller's Eiders   21.00 6.00
No gum   12.00

1974   **"Void after June 30, 1975"**
RW41 $5 Wood Ducks   20.00 6.00
No gum   10.00

1975   **"Void after June 30, 1976"**
RW42 $5 Weathered canvasback
            duck decoy and flying
            ducks   15.00 5.50
No gum   7.50

1976   **Engr.**
        "Void after June 30, 1977"
RW43 $5 Family of Canada
            Geese   14.00 5.50
No gum   7.00

1977   **Engr. & Litho.**
        "Void after June 30, 1978"
RW44 $5 Ross' Geese, pair   15.00 5.50
No gum   7.50

Hooded Merganser HP9

1978   **"Void after June 30, 1979"**
RW45   HP9 $5 multicolored   12.50 5.50
No gum   7.50

1979   **"Void after June 30, 1980"**
RW46 $7.50 Green-winged teal 14.00 6.00
No gum   8.00

1980   **"Void after June 30, 1981"**
RW47 $7.50 Mallards   14.00 6.00
No gum   8.00

1981   **"Void after June 30, 1982"**
RW48 $7.50 Ruddy Ducks   14.00 6.00
No gum   8.00

1982   **"Void after June 30, 1983"**
RW49 $7.50 Canvasbacks   14.00 6.00
No gum   8.00
   a. Orange & violet omitted   —

1983   **"Void after June 30, 1984"**
RW50 $7.50 Pintails   15.00 6.00
No gum   8.00

1984   **"Void after June 30, 1985"**
RW51 $7.50 Widgeons   15.00 6.00
No gum   8.00

1985   **"Void after June 30, 1986"**
RW52 $7.50 Cinnamon Teal   14.00 6.00
No gum   8.00

1986   **"Void after June 30, 1987"**
RW53 $7.50 Fulvous Whistling
            Duck   15.00 6.00
No gum   8.00
   a. Black omitted   3,750.

1987   **Perf. 11¹/₂x11**
        "Void after June 30, 1988"
RW54 $10 Redheads   15.00 8.00
No gum   10.00

1988   **"Void after June 30, 1989"**
RW55 $10 Snow Goose   16.00 8.00
No gum   10.00

1989   **"Void after June 30, 1990"**
RW56 $12.50 Lesser Scaups   19.00 9.00
No gum   12.00

1990   **"Void after June 30, 1991"**
RW57 $12.50 Black Bellied
            Whistling Duck   19.00 9.00
No gum   12.00
   a. Back inscription omitted   425.00

The back inscription is on top of the gum so beware of copies with gum removed. Used examples of No. RW57a cannot exist.

King Eiders HP10

1991   **"Void after June 30, 1992"**
RW58   HP10 $15 multicolored   22.50 9.00
No gum   15.00
   a. Black (engr.) omitted   8,500.

1992   **"Void after June 30, 1993"**
RW59 $15 Spectacled Eider   22.50 9.00
No gum   15.00

1993   **"Void after June 30, 1994"**
RW60 $15 Canvasbacks   22.50 9.00
No gum   15.00
   a. Black (engr.) omitted   3,250.

1994   **"Void after June 30, 1995"**
RW61 $15 Red-breasted mergan-
            sers   21.00 9.00
No gum   15.00

1995   **"Void after June 30, 1996"**
RW62 $15 Mallards   21.00 9.00
No gum   15.00

1996   "Void after June 30, 1997"
RW63 $15 *Surf Scoters*   21.00   9.00
    No gum   15.00

1997   "Void after June 30, 1998"
RW64 $15 *Canada Goose*   21.00   9.00
    No gum   15.00

CONFEDERATE STATES

ABERDEEN, MISS.

E1   E1a

Handstamped
1XU1 E1   5c black   2,500.
1XU2 E1   10c (ms.) on 5c black   —

Abingdon, Va.

Handstamped
2XU1 E1a   2c black   11,000.
2XU2 E1a   5c black   850.
2XU3 E1a   10c black   2,200.   3,500.

No. 2XU1 is unique. The unused No. 2XU3 is a unique mint example, and the value represents the price realized in a 1997 auction sale..

Albany, Ga.

PAID
E1   E2

Handstamped
3XU1 E1   5c greenish blue   750.
3XU2 E1   10c greenish blue   2,000.
3XU3 E1   10c on 5c grnsh blue   2,500.
3XU5 E2   5c greenish blue   —
3XU6 E2   10c greenish blue   2,250.

E1   Two varieties — A1

Anderson Court House, S.C.
Handstamped
4XU1 E1   5c black   1,500.
4XU2 E1   10c (ms.) black   2,500.

Athens, Ga.

Typo.
5X1 A1   5c purple (shades)   900.   950.
   a.   Vertical tete beche pair   4,000.
5X2 A1   5c red   —   3,000.

Atlanta, Ga.

E1   E2

E3

Handstamped
6XU1 E1   5c red   3,500.
6XU2 E1   5c black   175.   600.
6XU3 E1   10c on 5c black   1,500.
6XU4 E2   2c black   2,500.
6XU5 E2   5c black   1,500.
6XU6 E2   10c black   850.
6XU7 E2   10c on 5c black   2,500.
6XU8 E3   5c black   3,500.
6XU9 E3   10c black ("10" up-
         right)   2,750.

Augusta, Ga.

E1

Handstamped
7XU1 E1   5c black   —
Provisional status questioned.

E1   E1a

Austin, Miss.
Typo.
8XU1 E1   5c red, *amber*   20,000.
No. 8XU1 is unique.

Austin, Texas

Handstamped
9XU1 E1a   10c black   1,500.

Autaugaville, Ala.

E1   E2

Handstamped
10XU1 E1   5c black   8,000.
10XU2 E2   5c black   11,000.

Baton Rouge, La.

A1   A2

A3   A4

Typeset
Ten varieties each of A1, A2 and A3
11X1 A1   2c green   5,000.   3,500.
   a.   "McCcrmick"   8,000.   7,500.
11X2 A2   5c green & car   1,250.   1,000.
   a.   "McCcrmick"   2,000.
11X3 A3   5c green & car   4,500.   1,750.
   a.   "McCcrmick"   3,250.
11X4 A4   10c blue   6,000.

Beaumont, Tex.

A1   A2

Typeset
Several varieties of A1
12X1 A1   10c black, *yellow*   —   4,500.
12X2 A1   10c black, *pink*   —   4,000.
12X3 A2   10c black, *yellow,* on
         cover   90,000.

A1   E1

Bridgeville, Ala.
Handstamped
13X1 A1   5c black & red   20,000.

Canton, Miss.
Handstamped
14XU1 E1   5c black   1,500.
14XU2 E1   10c (ms.) on 5c black   3,500.

Carolina City, N.C.

Carolina City, N. C

E1

Handstamped
118XU1 E1   5c black   5,000.

Chapel Hill, N.C.

E1

Handstamped
15XU1 E1   5c black   2,500.

Charleston, S.C.

A1   E1

E2

Litho.
16X1 A1   5c blue   900.   750.

Typographed from Woodcut
16XU1 E1   5c blue   1,100.   1,750.
16XU2 E1   5c blue, *amber*   1,100.   1,750.
16XU3 E1   5c blue, *orange*   1,100.   1,750.
16XU4 E1   5c blue, *buff*   1,100.   1,750.
16XU5 E1   5c blue, *blue*   1,100.   1,750.
16XU6 E2   10c blue, *orange*   77,500.

Handstamped
16XU7 E2   10c black   3,000.

The No. 16XU6 used entire is unique; value based on 1997 auction realization.

No. 16XU7 is unique. It is a cut-out, not an entire. It may not have been mailed from Charleston and may not have paid postage.

Chattanooga, Tenn.

E1

Handstamped
17XU2 E1   5c black   1,600.
17XU3 E1   5c on 2c black   3,250.

Christiansburg, Va.

E1

Typeset. Impressed at top right.
99XU1 E1   5c black, *blue*   2,000.
99XU2 E1   5c blue   1,400.
99XU3 E1   5c black, *orange*   2,000.
99XU4 E1   5c green, on US envelope
          #U27   4,500.
99XU5 E1   10c blue   3,500.

Colaparchee, Ga.

E1   Control

Handstamped
119XU1 E1   5c black   3,500.

Columbia, S.C.

E1

E2

Handstamped
18XU1	E1	5c blue	500.	750.
18XU2	E1	5c black	600.	750.
18XU3	E1	10c on 5c blue	3,000.	
18XU4	E2	5c blue (seal on front)	1,500.	
a.		Seal on back		700.
18XU5	E2	10c blue (seal on back)	2,000.	

Circular Seal similar to E2, 27mm diameter

18XU6	E2	5c blue (seal on back)	2,500.

E1

E1a

Columbia, Tenn.

Handstamped
113XU1	E1	5c red	3,500.

Columbus, Ga.

19XU1	E1a	5c blue	700.
19XU2	E1a	10c red	2,000.

E1

E1a

Courtland, Ala.

Handstamped from Woodcut
103XU1	E1	5c black	—
103XU2	E1	5c red	10,000.

Provisional status of No. 103XU1 questioned.

Dalton, Ga.

Handstamped
20XU1	E1a	5c black	500.
20XU2	E1a	10c black	700.
20XU3	E1a	10c (ms.) on 5c black	1,500.

Danville, Va.

A1

Design measures
60x37mm — E1

E2

E3

Wove Paper
Typeset
21X1	A1	5c red	5,500.
		Cut to shape	4,000.

Laid Paper
21X2	A1	5c red	6,500.

Two types: "SOUTHERN" in straight or curved line.

Typo.
21XU1	E1	5c black	5,500.
21XU2	E1	5c black, *amber*	5,500.
21XU3	E1	5c black, *dark buff*	5,250.

Handstamped
21XU4	E2	10c black	2,000.
21XU5	E2	10c blue	
21XU6	E3	10c black	2,750.

The existence of No. 21XU5 has been questioned.

Demopolis, Ala.

E1

Handstamped. Signature in ms.
22XU1	E1	5c black ("Jno. Y. Hall")	2,000.
22XU2	E1	5c black ("J. Y. Hall")	2,000.
22XU3	E1	5c (ms.) black ("J. Y. Hall")	2,500.

Eatonton, Ga.

E1

Handstamped
23XU1	E1	5c black	3,000.
23XU2	E1	5c + 5c black	1,250.

Emory, Va.

A1

E1

E2

Handstamped on sheet margins of US 1857 1c stamps
Perf. 15 on Three Sides
24X1	A1	5c blue	— 3,500.

No. 24X1 exists with "5" above or below "PAID."

Handstamped
24XU1	E1	5c blue	2,000.
24XU2	E2	10c blue	3,000.

E1

E1a

Fincastle, Va.

Typeset
104XU1	E1	10c black	20,000.

No. 104XU1 is unique.

Forsyth, Ga.

Handstamped
120XU1	E1a	10c black	1,350.

E1

A1

Franklin, N.C.

Typo.
25XU1	E1	5c blue, *buff*	30,000.

No. 25XU1 is unique.

Fredericksburg, Va.

Typeset. Ten varieties.
Thin Bluish Paper
26X1	A1	5c blue, *bluish*	250. 750.
26X2	A1	10c red (shades), *bluish*	900.

Gainesville, Ala.

E1

E2

Handstamped
27XU1	E1	5c black	5,000.
27XU2	E2	10c black	7,500.

Galveston, Tex.

E1

E2

Handstamped
98XU1	E1	5c black	500.	900.
98XU2	E1	10c black		1,750.
98XU3	E2	10c black	550.	2,400.
98XU4	E2	20c black		3,500.

Georgetown, S.C.

E1

Control

Handstamped
28XU1	E1	5c black	800.

Goliad, Tex.

A1

A2

Typeset
Several varieties of A1 and A2
29X1	A1	5c black	5,000.
29X2	A1	5c black, *gray*	4,500.
29X3	A1	5c black, *rose*	5,000.
29X4	A1	10c black	— 5,000.
29X5	A1	10c black, *rose*	5,000.

Type A1 stamps bear ms. control: "Clarke P.M."
29X6	A2	5c black, *gray*	5,000.
a.		"Goliad"	5,500.
29X7	A2	10c black, *gray*	5,000.
a.		"Goliad"	5,500.
29X8	A2	5c black, *dark blue*	6,000.
29X9	A2	10c black, *dark blue*	6,500.

Gonzales, Tex.

A1

30X1	A1	(5c) gold, *dark blue*	7,500.

No. 30X1 must bear double circle town cancel as validating control. All items of type A1 without this control are book labels.

Greensboro, Ala.

E1

E2

Handstamped
31XU1	E1	5c black	1,500.
31XU2	E1	10c black	2,750.
31XU3	E2	10c black	2,750.

Greensboro, N.C.

E1

Handstamped
32XU1	E1	10c red	1,250.

Greenville, Ala.

A1

A2

Typeset

33X1 A1 5c red & blue   22,500. 40,000.
33X2 A2 10c red & blue   — 40,000.

Two used examples each are known of Nos. 33X1-33X2. All are on covers, and the used values reflect this.

Greenville Court House, S.C.

E1   Control

Handstamped. Several Types.

34XU1 E1 5c black   1,800.
34XU2 E1 10c black   2,000.
34XU3 E1 20c (ms.) on 10c black   3,000.

Envelopes usually bear the black circle control on the back.

Greenwood Depot, Va.

A1

"PAID" Handstamped; value and signature ms.

Laid Paper

35X1 A1 10c black, gray blue   4,500. —

Griffin, Ga.

E1

Handstamped

102XU1 E1 5c black   1,750.

A1

Grove Hill, Ala.
Typo.

36X1 A1 5c black, on cover   75,000.

Hallettsville, Tex.

A1a

Handstamped
Ruled Letter Paper

37X1 A1a 10c black, gray blue, on cover   15,000.

Hamburgh, S.C.

E1

Handstamped

112XU1 E1 5c black   2,000.

A1

A1a

Helena, Tex.
Typeset
Several varieties

38X1 A1 5c black, buff   7,500. 6,000.
38X2 A1 10c black, gray   5,000.

Hillsboro, N.C.

Handstamped

39X1 A1a 5c black, on cover   15,000.

Houston, Tex.

E1

Handstamped

40XU1 E1 5c red   — 700.
40XU2 E1 10c red   — 1,250.
40XU3 E1 10c black   2,000.
40XU4 E1 5c + 10c red   2,500.
40XU5 E1 10c + 10c red   2,500.
40XU6 E1 10c (ms.) on 5c red   3,000.

Huntsville, Tex.

E1   Control

Handstamped

92XU1 E1 5c black   2,500.

No. 92XU1 exists with "5" outside or within control circle.

A1   E1

Independence, Tex.
Handstamped

41X1 A1 10c black, buff   3,250.
41X2 A1 10c black, dull rose   3,500.
41X3 A1 10c black, buff (small "10", "Pd" in ms.)   4,000.

No. 41X3 is known only cut to shape.

Iuka, Miss.

Typeset

42XU1 E1 5c black   1,600.

E1   E1a

Jackson, Miss.
Handstamped

43XU1 E1 5c black   500.
43XU2 E1 10c black   2,000.
43XU3 E1 10c on 5c black   2,750.
43XU4 E1 10c on 5c blue   2,750.

The 5c also exists on a lettersheet.

Jacksonville, Ala.

Handstamped

110XU1 E1a 5c black   — 1,500.

A1   E1

Jetersville, Va.
Typeset ("5"); ms. ("AHA.")
Laid Paper

44X1 A1 5c black, vert. pair on cover, uncanceled   16,000.

Jonesboro, Tenn.

Handstamped

45XU1 E1 5c black   3,750.
45XU2 E1 5c dark blue   6,500.

Kingston, Ga.

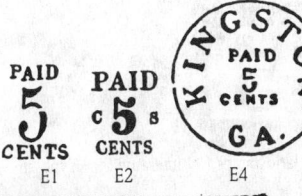

PAID 5 CENTS   PAID 5 CENTS

E1   E2   E4

E3

Typo. (E1-E3); Handstamped (E4)

46XU1 E1 5c black   2,000.
46XU2 E2 5c black   3,500.
  a. No "C" or "S" at sides of numeral
46XU3 E2 5c black, amber   2,750.
46XU4 E3 5c black
46XU5 E4 5c black   2,000.

Knoxville, Tenn.

A1

Grayish White Laid Paper

47X1 A1 5c brick red   1,250. 900.
47X2 A1 5c carmine   1,750. 1,500.
47X3 A1 10c green, on cover   57,750.

The 5c has been reprinted in red, brown and chocolate on white and bluish wove and laid paper.

The No. 47X3 cover is unique. Value is based on 1997 auction sale.

E1   E2

Typo.

47XU1 E1 5c blue   750. 1,500.
47XU2 E1 5c blue, orange   750. 1,500.
47XU3 E1 10c red (cut to shape)   1,800.
47XU4 E1 10c red, orange (cut to shape)   1,800.

Handstamped

47XU5 E2 5c black   750. 1,500.
47XU6 E2 10c on 5c black   3,500.

Type E2 exists with "5" above or below "PAID."

La Grange, Tex.

E1

Handstamped

48XU1 E1 5c black   — 2,000.
48XU2 E1 10c black   2,500.

Lake City, Fla.

E1   Control

Handstamped

96XU1 E1 10c black   2,000.

Envelopes have black circle control mark, or printed name of E.R. Ives, postmaster, on face or back.

Laurens Court House, S.C.

E1

Handstamped

116XU1 E1 5c black   —

---

120 CONFEDERATE STATES

Lenoir, N.C.

A1   E1

Handstamped from Woodcut
Paper has ruled lines in orange
49X1   A1   5c blue   3,250. 2,750.

Handstamped
49XU1   A1   5c black   3,500.
49XU2   A1   10c (5c + 5c) blue   3,500.
49XU3   E1   5c blue   2,500.
49XU4   E1   5c black
The existence of No. 49XU4 has been questioned.

Lexington, Miss.

E1

Handstamped
50XU1   E1   5c black   5,000.
50XU2   E1   10c black   5,000.

PAID
5cts.
A1   A1a

Liberty, Va.
Typeset. Laid Paper
74X1   A1   5c black   —
A cover with Salem, Va., postmark is known.

Limestone Springs, S.C.
Handstamped
121X1   A1a   5c black, on cover   4,000.
Stamps are round, square or rectangular. Covers are not postmarked.

Livingston, Ala.

A1

Litho.
51X1   A1   5c blue   7,000.

Lynchburg, Va.

A1   E1

Stereotype from Woodcut
52X1   A1   5c blue (shades)   600. 1,000.

Typo.
52XU1   E1   5c black   1,500.
52XU2   E1   5c black, amber   650. 1,500.
52XU3   E1   5c black, buff   1,500.
52XU4   E1   5c black, brown   900. 1,500.

Macon, Ga.

A1   A2   A3

E1

A4

Typeset. Wove Paper.
Several varieties of each. Ten of A2.
53X1   A1   5c blk, lt blue green (shades)   850. 600.
53X3   A2   5c black, yellow   2,500. 800.
53X4   A3   5c blk, yel (shades)   2,750. 1,250.
   a.   Vertical tete beche pair   12,000.
53X5   A4   2c black, gray green   6,500.

Laid Paper
53X6   A2   5c black, yellow   3,000. 3,500.
53X7   A2   5c black, yellow   6,000.
53X8   A1   5c blk, lt blue green   1,750. 2,000.

Handstamped
Two types of "PAID" and "5"
53XU1   E1   5c black   250. 500.

Marietta, Ga.

E1   E2

Handstamped
Two types of "PAID" and numerals
54XU1   E1   5c black   300.
54XU2   E1   10c on 5c black   1,750.
54XU3   E1   10c black
54XU4   E2   5c black   2,000.
The existence of No. 54XU3 is questioned.

Marion, Va.

A1

Handstamped Numeral within Typeset Frame
Wove Paper
55X1   A1   5c black   5,000.
55X2   A1   10c black   16,500. 8,000.
Bluish Laid Paper
55X3   A1   5c black   —
The 2c, 3c, 15c and 20c are believed to be bogus.

Memphis, Tenn.

A1   A2

Stereotype from Woodcut
56X1   A1   2c blue (shades)   80. 1,250.
56X2   A2   5c red (shades)   140. 175.
   a.   Tete beche pair
   b.   Pair, one sideways   750. 1,500.
   c.   Pelure paper   —

Typo.
56XU1   A2   5c red   2,500.
56XU2   A2   5c red, amber   2,500.
56XU3   A2   5c red, orange   2,250.

Micanopy, Fla.

E1

Handstamped
105XU1   E1   5c black   11,500.

Milledgeville, Ga.

E1

E2   E3

Handstamped
57XU1   E1   5c black   250.
57XU2   E1   5c blue   800.
57XU3   E1   10c on 5c black   1,000.
57XU4   E2   10c black   225. 1,000.
57XU5   E3   10c black   750.

Mobile, Ala.

A1

Litho.
58X1   A1   2c black   1,500. 950.
58X2   A1   5c blue   275. 225.

Montgomery, Ala.

E1   E2

E3

Handstamped
59XU1   E1   5c red   750.
59XU2   E1   5c blue   400. 900.
59XU3   E1   10c red   800.
59XU4   E1   10c blue   900.
59XU5   E1   10c black   800.
59XU6   E1   10c on 5c red   2,500.
The 10c design is larger than the 5c.

59XU7   E2   2c red   2,500.
59XU7A   E2   2c blue   3,500.
59XU8   E2   5c black   2,250.
59XU9   E3   10c black   2,750.
59XU10   E3   10c red   1,500.

Mt. Lebanon, La.

A1

Woodcut, Design Reversed
60X1   A1   5c red brown, on cover   100,000.
No. 60X1 is unique.

Nashville, Tenn.

A1   A2

E1

Typeset (5 varieties of 3c)
61X1   A1   3c carmine   150.
No. 61X1 was not placed in use.

Stereotype from Woodcut
Gray Blue Ribbed Paper
61X2   A2   5c carmine (shades)   850. 500.
   a.   Vertical tete beche pair   2,000.
61X3   A2   5c brick red   850. 450.
61X4   A2   5c gray (shades)   850. 625.
61X5   A2   5c violet brown   750. 475.
   a.   Vertical tete beche pair   3,500. 2,500.
61X6   A2   10c green   3,000. 3,000.

Handstamped
61XU1   E1   5c blue   750.
61XU2   E1   5c + 10c blue   2,400.

New Orleans, La.

A1   A2

J.L.RIDDELL,P.M
PD 5 CTS
N O.P.O

E1

Stereotype from Woodcut
62X1   A1   2c blue   150. 500.
   a.   Printed on both sides   1,500.
62X2   A1   2c red (shades)   125. 1,000.
62X3   A2   5c brown, white   250. 150.
   a.   Printed on both sides   1,500.
   b.   5c ocher   650. 600.
62X4   A2   5c red brown, bluish   280. 175.
   a.   Printed on both sides   2,750.
62X5   A2   5c yellow brown, off white   125. 225.
62X6   A2   5c red   — 7,500.
62X7   A2   5c red, bluish   10,000.

		Handstamped		
62XU1	E1	5c black		3,500.
62XU2	E1	10c black		5,000.

"J L. RIDDELL, P.M." omitted

62XU3	E1	2c black	7,500.

 A1   A1a

New Smyrna, Fla.
Handstamped

63X1	A1	10c ("01") on 5c black	45,000.

No. 63X1 is unique.

Oakway, S.C.
Handstamped

115X1	A1a	5c black, on cover	— 66,000.

Two used examples of No. 115X1 are recorded, both on cover. Value represents 1997 auction sale realization for the cover on which the stamp is tied.

 E1   A1

Pensacola, Fla.
Handstamped

106XU1	E1	5c black	3,750.
106XU2	E1	10c (ms.) on 5c black	4,250.

Petersburg, Va.
Typeset (10 varieties)

65X1	A1	5c red (shades)	1,500.	450.

 A1   A1a

Pittsylvania Court House, Va.
Typeset
Wove Paper

66X1	A1	5c red	6,000.	5,000.
		Octagonally cut		3,000.

Laid Paper

66X2	A1	5c red	6,500.
		Octagonally cut	5,500.

Pleasant Shade, Va.
Typeset (5 varieties)

67X1	A1a	5c blue	2,500. 5,000.

 A1   E1

Port Lavaca, Tex.
Typeset

107X1	A1	10c black	25,000.

No. 107X1 is unique.

Raleigh, N.C.
Handstamped

68XU1	E1	5c red	450.
68XU2	E1	5c blue	2,250.

 A1   E1

Rheatown, Tenn.
Typeset. Three varieties.

69X1	A1	5c red	2,000.	2,750.
		Pen canceled		2,000.

Richmond, Tex.
Handstamped

70XU1	E1	5c red	1,500.
70XU2	E1	10c red	1,000.
70XU3	E1	10c on 5c red	5,000.
70XU4	E1	15c (ms.) on 10c red	5,000.

 E1   E1a

Ringgold, Ga.
Handstamped

71XU1	E1	5c blue black	2,500.

Rutherfordton, N.C.
Handstamped; "Paid 5cts" in ms.

72X1	E1a	5c black, cut round	25,000.

No. 72X1 is on cover, uncanceled and possibly unique.

Salem, N.C.

"Paid 5" in Ms.
E1

"Paid 5" Handstamped
E2

Handstamped

73XU1	E1	5c black	1,150.
73XU2	E1	10c black	1,500.
73XU3	E2	5c black	1,500.
73XU4	E2	10c on 5c black	2,800.

Reprints exist on various papers. They either lack the "Paid" and value or have them counterfeited.

Salisbury, N.C.

SALISBURY
N. C.
POSTAGE

FIVE CENTS
P.M. E1

Typo.
Impressed at top left

75XU1	E1	5c black, *greenish*	5,000.

One example known with part of envelope torn away, leaving part of design missing. Illustration E1 partly suppositional.

San Antonio, Tex.

 E1   E2

Control

Handstamped

76XU1	E1	10c black	275.	2,000.
76XU2	E2	10c black		2,500.

Black circle control mark is on front or back.

Savannah, Ga.

 E1   Control

PAID 10
E2

Handstamped

101XU1	E1	5c black	225.
101XU2	E2	5c black	450.
101XU3	E1	10c black	600.
101XU4	E2	10c black	600.
101XU5	E1	10c on 5c black	1,500.
101XU6	E2	20c on 5c black	2,000.

Envelope must bear octagonal control mark. One example is known of No. 101XU6.

 E1   E1a

Selma, Ala.
Handstamped; Signature in ms.

77XU1	E1	5c black	1,000.
77XU2	E1	10c black	2,500.
77XU3	E1	10c on 5c black	3,000.

Sparta, Ga.
Handstamped

93XU1	E1a	5c red	— 1,000.
93XU2	E1a	10c red	2,250.

Spartanburg, S.C.

 A1   A2

Handstamped on Ruled or Plain Wove Paper

78X1	A1	5c black	3,500.
a.		"5" omitted	
78X2	A2	5c black, *bluish*	4,000.
78X3	A2	5c black, *brown*	4,000.

Most examples of Nos. 78X1-78X3 are cut round. Cut square examples are worth much more.

Statesville, N.C.

 E1

Handstamped

79XU1	E1	5c black	175.	450.
79XU2	E1	10c on 5c black		2,000.

Sumter, S.C.

 E1

Handstamped

80XU1	E1	5c black	300.
80XU2	E1	10c black	300.
80XU3	E1	10c on 5c black	800.
80XU4	E1	2c (ms.) on 10c black	1,100.

Used examples of Nos. 80XU1-80XU2 are indistinguishable from handstamped "Paid" covers.

 E1   A1

Talbotton, Ga.
Handstamped

94XU1	E1	5c black	750.
94XU2	E1	10c black	500.
94XU3	E1	10c on 5c black	2,000.

Tellico Plains, Tenn.

		Typeset	Laid Paper
81X1	A1	5c red	1,250.
81X2	A1	10c red	2,500.

Thomasville, Ga.

 E1

Control   E2

Handstamped

82XU1	E1	5c black	500.
82XU2	E2	5c black	900.

Tullahoma, Tenn.

E1   Control

Handstamped

111XU1	E1	10c black	2,000.

E1   E1a

Tuscaloosa, Ala.

Handstamped

83XU1	E1	5c black	250.
83XU2	E1	10c black	250.

Used examples of Nos. 83XU1-83XU2 are indistinguishable from handstamped "Paid" covers.

Tuscumbia, Ala.

Handstamped

84XU1	E1a	5c black	2,250.
84XU2	E1a	5c red	3,000.
84XU3	E1a	10c black	3,500.

See US Postmasters' Provisional No. 12XU1.

Union City, Tenn.

E1

The use of E1 to produce provisional envelopes is doubtful.

A1   A1a

Uniontown, Ala.

Typeset in settings of four (2x2)
Four varieties of each value
Laid Paper

86X1	A1	2c dk blue, *gray blue*	9,500.	
86X2	A1	2c dark blue	5,500.	
86X3	A1	5c green, *gray blue*	2,750.	2,000.
86X4	A1	5c green	2,750.	2,000.
86X5	A1	10c red, *gray blue*	10,000.	7,500.

Unionville, S.C.

Handstamped
Wove Paper with Blue Ruled Lines

87X1	A1a	5c black, *grayish*	17,500.

Valdosta, Ga.

E1   Control

Handstamped

100XU1	E1	10c black	2,000.

The black control is usually on back of envelope.

A1   E1

Victoria, Tex.

Typeset

88X1	A1	5c red brown, *green*	4,000.	
88X2	A1	10c red brown, *green*	5,000.	4,500.

Pelure Paper

88X3	A1	10c red brown, *green* ("10" in bold face type)	6,250.	6,250.

Walterborough, S.C.

Typeset

108XU1	E1	10c black, *buff*	3,750.	
108XU2	E1	10c carmine	2,500.	

Warrenton, Ga.

E1

Handstamped

89XU1	E1	5c black	1,250.
89XU2	E1	10c (ms.) on 5c black	850.

E1   E1a

Washington, Ga.

Handstamped

117XU1	E1	10c black	2,000.

Weatherford, Tex.

Woodcut with "PAID" inserted in type.
Handstamped

109XU1	E1a	5c black	2,000.
109XU2	E1a	5c + 5c black	11,000.

No. 109XU2 is unique.

Winnsborough, S.C.

PAID 5
E1   Control

Handstamped

97XU1	E1	5c black	1,500.
97XU2	E1	10c black	2,000.

Envelopes must bear black circle control on front or back.

Wytheville, Va.

5 PAID
E1   Control

Handstamped

114XU1	E1	5c black	900.

For later additions, listed out of numerical sequence, see:

No. 74X1,	Liberty, Va.
No. 92XU1,	Huntsville, Tex.
No. 93XU1,	Sparta, Ga.
No. 94XU1,	Talbotton, Ga.
No. 96XU1,	Lake City, Fla.
No. 97XU1,	Winnsborough, S.C.
No. 98XU1,	Galveston, Tex.
No. 99XU1,	Christiansburg, Va.
No. 100XU1,	Valdosta, Ga.
No. 101XU1,	Savannah, Ga.
No. 102XU1,	Griffin, Ga.
No. 103XU1,	Courtland, Ala.
No. 104XU1,	Fincastle, Va.
No. 105XU1,	Micanopy, Fla.
No. 106XU1,	Pensacola, Fla.
No. 107X1,	Port Lavaca, Tex.
No. 108XU1,	Walterborough, S.C.
No. 109XU1,	Weatherford, Tex.
No. 110XU1,	Jacksonville, Ala.
No. 111XU1,	Tullahoma, Tenn.
No. 112XU1,	Hamburgh, S.C.
No. 113XU1,	Columbia, Tenn.
No. 114XU1,	Wytheville, Va.
No. 115X1,	Oakway, S.C.
No. 116XU1,	Laurens Court House, S.C.
No. 117XU1,	Washington, Ga.
No. 118XU1,	Carolina City, N.C.
No. 119XU1,	Colapatchee, Ga.
No. 120XU1,	Forsyth, Ga.
No. 121XU1,	Limestone Springs, S.C.

GENERAL ISSUES

Jefferson Davis   Thomas Jefferson
A1   A2

1861   Unwmk.   Litho.   *Imperf.*

1	A1	5c green	225.00	150.00
		No gum	165.00	
a.		5c light green	225.00	150.00
		No gum	165.00	
b.		5c dark green	240.00	175.00
		No gum	175.00	
c.		5c olive green	260.00	175.00
		No gum	185.00	
2	A2	10c blue	280.00	190.00
		No gum	220.00	
a.		10c light blue	280.00	190.00
		No gum	220.00	
b.		10c dark blue	525.00	240.00
		No gum	400.00	
c.		10c indigo	*2,750.*	*2,250.*
		No gum	*2,000.*	
d.		Printed on both sides	—	—
e.		10c greenish blue	475.00	300.00
		No gum	350.00	

The earliest printings of No. 2 were made by Hoyer & Ludwig, the later ones by J. T. Paterson & Co. Stamps of the later printings usually have a small colored dash below the lowest point of the upper left spandrel.
See Nos. 4-5.

Andrew Jackson — A3   Jefferson Davis — A4

1862

3	A3	2c green	700.00	650.00
		No gum	550.00	
a.		2c bright yellow green	*1,750.*	—
		No gum	*1,400.*	
4	A1	5c blue	180.00	110.00
		No gum	135.00	
a.		5c dark blue	225.00	160.00
		No gum	160.00	
b.		5c light milky blue	270.00	200.00
		No gum	190.00	
5	A2	10c rose	1,250.00	500.00
		No gum	950.00	
a.		10c carmine	*2,800.*	*1,750.*
		No gum	*2,100.*	

Typo.

6	A4	5c lt blue (London print)	10.00	25.00
		No gum	7.50	
7	A4	5c blue (local print)	13.00	17.50
		No gum	10.00	
a.		5c deep blue	14.00	27.50
		No gum	10.50	
b.		Printed on both sides	*2,500.*	850.00

No. 6 has fine, clear impression. No. 7 has coarser impression and the color is duller and often blurred.
Both 2c and 10c stamps, types A4 and A10, were privately printed in various colors.

Andrew Jackson — A5

1863   *Engr.*

8	A5	2c brown red	70.00	350.00
		No gum	55.00	
a.		2c pale red	90.00	*450.00*
		No gum	70.00	

Jefferson Davis
A6   A6a

Thick or Thin Paper

9	A6	10c blue	800.	550.
		No gum	625.	
a.		10c milky blue	800.	550.
		No gum	625.	
b.		10c gray blue	850.	650.
		No gum	650.	
10	A6a	10c blue (with frame line)	3,750.	1,250.
		No gum	3,000.	
a.		10c milky blue	3,750.	1,250.
		No gum	3,000.	
b.		10c greenish blue	4,250.	1,350.
		No gum	3,400.	
c.		10c dark blue	4,250.	1,350.
		No gum	3,400.	

Values of Nos. 10, 10a, 10b and 10c are for copies showing parts of lines on at least three sides.

Column 1 (top, partial)

A7

A8

There are many slight differences between A7 and A8, the most noticeable being the additional line outside the ornaments at the corners of A8.

11	A7 10c blue	9.00	12.50
	No gum	7.50	
a.	10c milky blue	22.50	37.50
	No gum	19.00	
b.	10c dark blue	18.50	25.00
	No gum	15.00	
c.	10c greenish blue	17.50	17.50
	No gum	12.50	
d.	10c green	70.00	75.00
	No gum	60.00	
e.	Perforated	290.00	275.00
12	A8 10c blue	11.00	15.00
	No gum	9.00	
a.	10c milky blue	25.00	35.00
	No gum	20.00	
b.	10c light blue	11.00	15.00
	No gum	9.00	
c.	10c greenish blue	20.00	45.00
	No gum	16.50	
d.	10c dark blue	11.00	20.00
	No gum	9.00	
e.	10c green	90.00	110.00
	No gum	75.00	
f.	Perforated	290.00	275.00

The paper of Nos. 11 and 12 varies from thin hard to thick soft. The so-called laid paper is probably due to thick streaky gum.

George Washington A9

John C. Calhoun A10

13	A9 20c green	37.50	400.00
	No gum	27.50	
a.	20c yellow green	60.00	450.00
	No gum	40.00	
b.	20c dark green	65.00	500.00
	No gum	42.50	
c.	Diagonal half used as 10c on cover		2,000.
d.	Horiz. half used as 10c on cover		2,250.

1862   **Typo.**

14	A10 1c orange	80.00	
	No gum	70.00	
a.	1c deep orange	110.00	
	No gum	85.00	

The 1c was never put in use.

CANAL ZONE

kə-'nal 'zōn

LOCATION — A strip of land 10 miles wide, extending through the Republic of Panama, between the Atlantic and Pacific Oceans.

GOVT. — From 1904-79 a US Government Reservation; from 1979 under control of the Republic of Panama.

AREA — 552.8 sq. mi.

POP. — 41,800 (est. 1976)

The Canal Zone, site of the Panama Canal, was leased in perpetuity to the US for a cash payment of $10,000,000 and a yearly rental. Treaties between the two countries provided for transfer of control of this area to Panama in 1979, including the postal service.

100 Centavos = 1 Peso
100 Centesimos = 1 Balboa
100 Cents = 1 Dollar

> Catalogue values for unused stamps in this country are for Never Hinged items, beginning with Scott 118 in the regular postage section and Scott C6 in the air post section.

Watermarks

Wmk. 190- "USPS" in Single-lined Capitals

Wmk. 191- Double-lined "USPS" in Capitals

Map of Panama — A1

Violet to Violet-blue Handstamp, "CANAL ZONE," on Panama Nos. 72-72c, 78 and 79

1904   **Unwmk.**   **Perf. 12**

1	A1 2c rose, both "PANA-MA" up or down	550.00	425.00
a.	"CANAL ZONE" inverted	850.00	850.00
b.	"CANAL ZONE" double	2,000.	2,000.
c.	"CANAL ZONE" double, both inverted	15,000.	
d.	"PANAMA" reading down and up	700.00	650.00
e.	As "d," "CANAL ZONE" inverted	6,500.	6,500.
f.	Vert. pair, "Panama" reading up on top 2c, down on other	2,000.	2,000.
2	A1 5c blue	225.00	175.00
a.	"CANAL ZONE" inverted	600.00	600.00
b.	"CANAL ZONE" double	2,250.	1,500.
c.	Pair, one without "CANAL ZONE"	5,000.	5,000.
d.	"CANAL ZONE" diagonal, running down to right	700.00	700.00
3	A1 10c yellow	375.00	225.00
a.	"CANAL ZONE" inverted	625.00	600.00
b.	"CANAL ZONE" double		12,500.
c.	Pair, one without "CANAL ZONE"	6,000.	5,000.
	Nos. 1-3 (3)	1,150.	825.00

On the 2c stamp "PANAMA" is normally about 13mm; on the 5c and 10c about 15mm.

Varieties of "PANAMA" overprint exist on the 2c with inverted "V" for "A," accent on "A," inverted "N," etc.

Counterfeit "CANAL ZONE" overprints exist.

US Nos. 300, 319, 304, 306 and 307 Overprinted in Black

CANAL ZONE (vertical)   **PANAMA** (vertical)

1904   **Wmk. 191**

4	A115 1c blue green	32.50	22.50
5	A129 2c carmine	30.00	25.00
a.	2c scarlet	32.50	25.00
6	A119 5c blue	100.00	65.00
7	A121 8c violet black	175.00	85.00
8	A122 10c pale red brown	150.00	90.00
	Nos. 4-8 (5)	487.50	287.50

Beware of fake overprints.

A2

A3

CANAL ZONE Regular Type

CANAL ZONE Antique Type

Black Overprint on Stamps of Panama

1904-06   **Unwmk.**

9	A2 1c green	2.75	2.25
a.	"CANAL" in antique type	100.00	100.00
b.	"ZONE" in antique type	70.00	70.00
c.	Inverted overprint	—	2,250.
d.	Double overprint	1,250.	1,000.
10	A2 2c rose	4.50	2.50
a.	Inverted overprint	225.00	275.00
b.	"L" of "CANAL" sideways	2,500.	2,000.

Overprinted "CANAL ZONE" Black, "PANAMA" and Bar in Red on Panama Nos. 77-79 "PANAMA" 15mm long

11	A3 2c rose	7.50	5.00
a.	"ZONE" in antique type	175.00	175.00
b.	"PANAMA" inverted, bar at bottom	350.00	350.00

12	A3 5c blue	8.00	3.75
a.	"CANAL" in antique type	75.00	65.00
b.	"ZONE" in antique type	75.00	65.00
c.	"CANAL ZONE" double	600.00	600.00
d.	"PANAMA" ovpt. dbl.	1,050.	850.00
e.	"PANAMA" inverted, bar at bottom		1,000.
13	A3 10c yellow	22.50	12.50
a.	"CANAL" in antique type	200.00	200.00
b.	"ZONE" in antique type	175.00	160.00
c.	"PANAMA" ovpt. dbl.	600.00	600.00
d.	"PANAMA" overprint in red brown	27.50	27.50
	Nos. 11-13 (3)	38.00	21.25

With Added Surcharge in Red on Panama No. 81

8 cts

14	A3 8c on 50c bis brn	30.00	20.00
a.	"ZONE" in antique type	1,000.	1,000.
b.	"CANAL ZONE" invtd.	425.00	400.00
c.	Rose brown overprint	40.00	40.00
d.	As "c," "CANAL" in antique type	2,250.	
e.	As "c," "ZONE" in antique type	2,250.	
f.	As "c," "8 cts" double	850.00	
g.	As "c," "8" omitted	4,250.	

Panama No. 74 Overprinted "CANAL ZONE" in Regular Type in Black and Surch. Like No. 14 in Red. Both "PANAMA" Reading Up. "PANAMA" 13mm long

1905

15	A3 8c on 50c bis brn	3,000.	4,500.
a.	"PANAMA" reading down & up	6,500.	—

On No. 15 with original gum the gum is always disturbed.

Panama Nos. 19 and 21 Surcharged in Black:

a

b

CANAL ZONE 1 ct. (with PANAMA on sides)

CANAL ZONE 1 ct.

CANAL ZONE 1 ct.
c

CANAL ZONE 2 cts.
d

CANAL ZONE 2 cts.
e

CANAL ZONE 2 cts.
f

There were 3 printings of each denomination differing mainly in the relative position of the various parts of the surcharges. Varieties occur with invtd. "V" for the 3rd "A" in "PANAMA," "CA spaced, "ZO" spaced, "2c" spaced, accents in various positions, and with bars shifted so that 2 bars appear on top or bottom of the stamp (either with or without the corresponding bar on top or bottom) and sometimes with only 1 bar at top or bottom.

1906

16	A4 1c on 20c vio, type a	1.90	1.60
a.	Surcharge type b	1.90	1.60
b.	Surcharge type c	2.00	1.60
17	A4 2c on 1p lake, type d	2.75	2.75
a.	Surcharge type e	2.75	2.75
b.	Surcharge type f	20.00	20.00

Panama No. 74 Overprinted "CANAL ZONE" in Regular Type in Black and Surcharged in Red

8 cts. b   **8 cts** c

Both "PANAMA" reading up

1905-06

18	A3 (b) 8c on 50c bis brn	55.00	50.00
a.	"ZONE" in antique type	200.00	180.00
b.	"PANAMA" down & up	175.00	160.00
19	A3 (c) 8c on 50c bis brn ('06)	55.00	45.00
a.	"CANAL" in antique type	200.00	180.00
b.	"ZONE" in antique type	200.00	180.00
c.	"8 cts." double	1,100.	1,100.
d.	"PANAMA" down & up	100.00	90.00

On Nos. 18-19 with original gum the gum is usually disturbed.

Panama No. 81 Overprinted "CANAL ZONE" in Regular Type in Black and Surcharged in Red Type "c" plus Period. "PANAMA" reading up and down

20	A3 8c on 50c bis brn	45.00	40.00
a.	"CANAL" in antique type	200.00	180.00
b.	"ZONE" in antique type	200.00	180.00
c.	"8 cts" omitted	750.00	750.00
d.	"8 cts" double	1,500.	

Numerous minor varieties of all these surcharges exist. Nos. 14, 18, 19 and 20 exist without CANAL ZONE overprint but were not regularly issued.

Vasco Nunez de Balboa — A5

Francisco Hernandez de Cordoba — A6

Justo Arosemena A7

Manuel J. Hurtado A8

Jose de Obaldia — A9

Stamps of Panama Ovptd. in Black

1906-07

Overprint Reading Up

21	A6 2c red & black	27.50	27.50
a.	"Canal" only	4,000.	

Overprint Reading Down

22	A5 1c green & black	2.25	1.25
a.	Horiz. pair, imperf. btwn.	1,250.	1,250.
b.	Vert. pair, imperf. btwn.	1,750.	1,750.
c.	Vert. pair, imperf. horiz.	1,750.	1,750.
d.	Invtd. ovpt., reading up	550.00	550.00
e.	Double overprint	275.00	275.00
f.	Dbl. ovpt., one reading up	1,350.	1,350.
g.	Inverted center and ovpt. reading up	3,250.	2,750.
23	A6 2c red & black	3.25	1.40
a.	Horiz. pair, imperf. btwn.	1,750.	1,750.
b.	Vertical pair, one without overprint	1,750.	1,750.
c.	Double overprint	450.00	450.00
d.	Dbl. ovpt., one diagonal	750.00	750.00
e.	Pair, Nos. 23, 23d	1,750.	
f.	2c carmine red & black	5.00	2.75
g.	As "f," inverted center and overprint reading up		5,000.
h.	As "d," one "ZONE CANAL"	4,000.	
i.	"CANAL" double	3,250.	
24	A7 5c ultra & black	6.50	2.25
c.	Double overprint	450.00	350.00
d.	"CANAL" only	3,500.	
e.	"ZONE CANAL"	4,500.	

25	A8	8c purple & black	22.50	8.00
a.		Horizontal pair, imperf. between and at left margin	2,000.	—
26	A9	10c violet & black	20.00	8.00
a.		Dbl. ovpt., one reading up	3,250.	
b.		Overprint reading up	3,500.	
		Nos. 22-26 (5)	54.50	20.90

Nos. 22 to 25 occur with "CA" spaced.

Cordoba
A11

Arosemena
A12

Hurtado — A13

Jose de Obaldia — A14

1909

Overprint Reading Down

27	A11	2c vermilion & black	12.50	6.50
a.		Horiz. pair, one without ovpt.	2,600.	
b.		Vert. pair, one without ovpt.	2,750.	
28	A12	5c deep blue & black	45.00	12.50
29	A13	8c violet & black	40.00	14.00
30	A14	10c violet & black	40.00	15.00
a.		Horiz. pair, one without ovpt.	2,400.	
b.		Vert. pair, one without ovpt.	2,600.	
		Nos. 27-30 (4)	137.50	48.00

Nos. 27 to 30 occur with "CA" spaced.
See Nos. 32-35, 39-41, 47-48, 53-54, 56-57.

Vasco Nunez de Balboa — A15

Type I

Black Overprint, Reading Up

Type I Overprint: "C" with serifs both top and bottom. "L" "Z" and "E" with slanting serif.

Compare Type I overprint with Types II to V illustrated before Nos. 38, 46, 52 and 55. Illustrations of Types I to V are considerably enlarged and do not show actual spacing between lines of overprint.

1909-10

31	A15	1c dk green & blk	4.00	1.60
a.		Inverted center and overprint reading down		15,000.
c.		Bklt. pane of 6 handmade, perf. margins	575.00	
32	A11	2c vermilion & blk	4.50	1.60
a.		Vert. pair, imperf. horiz.	1,000.	1,000.
c.		Bklt. pane of 6, handmade, perf. margins	750.00	
d.		Double overprint		—
33	A12	5c dp blue & blk	15.00	4.00
a.		Double overprint	375.00	375.00
34	A13	8c violet & blk ('10)	11.00	5.25
a.		Vert. pair, one without ovpt.	1,500.	
35	A14	10c violet & black	50.00	20.00
		Nos. 31-35 (5)	84.50	32.45

See Nos. 38, 46, 52, 55.

A16

A17

Black Surcharge

1911

36	A16	10c on 13c gray	6.00	2.25
a.		"10 cts." inverted	250.00	250.00
b.		"10 cts." omitted	250.00	

1914

37	A17	10c gray	55.00	12.50

Type II: "C" with serif at top only. "L" and "E" with vertical serifs. "O" tilts to left

CANAL ZONE

1912-16

38	A15	1c green & blk ('13)	11.00	3.00
a.		Vert. pair, one without ovpt.	1,500.	1,500.
b.		Booklet pane of 6	600.00	
c.		As "b," handmade, perf. margins	1,000.	
39	A11	2c vermilion & blk	8.50	1.40
a.		Horiz. pair, right stamp without ovpt.	1,250.	
b.		Horiz. pair, left stamp without ovpt.	1,750.	
c.		Booklet pane of 6	500.00	
d.		Overprint reading down	175.00	
e.		As "d," inverted center	700.00	750.00
f.		As "e," booklet pane of 6 handmade, perf. margins	6,500.	
g.		As "c," handmade, perf. margins	1,000.	
h.		As #39, "CANAL" only		1,100.
40	A12	5c dp blue & blk	22.50	3.25
a.		With portrait of 2c	8,000.	
41	A14	10c violet & blk ('16)	47.50	8.50
		Nos. 38-41 (4)	89.50	16.15

Map of Panama Canal — A18

Balboa Takes Possession of the Pacific Ocean — A19

Gatun Lock — A20

Culebra Cut — A21

Blue Overprint, Type II

1915

42	A18	1c dark green & black	8.50	6.50
43	A19	2c carmine & black	10.00	4.25
44	A20	5c blue & black	11.00	5.75
45	A21	10c orange & black	22.50	11.00
		Nos. 42-45 (4)	52.00	27.50

Type III: Similar to Type I but letters appear thinner, particularly the lower bar of "L," "Z" and "E." Impressions are often light, rough and irregular

CANAL ZONE

1915-20

46	A15	1c green & black	160.00	95.00
a.		Overprint reading down	375.00	
b.		Double overprint	300.00	
c.		"ZONE" double	4,250.	
d.		Dbl. ovpt., one "ZONE CANAL"	1,750.	
47	A11	2c orange ver & blk	3,000.	100.00
48	A12	5c dp blue & black	550.00	175.00
		Nos. 46-48 (3)	3,710.	370.00

S.S. "Panama" in Culebra Cut — A22

S.S. "Panama" in Culebra Cut — A23

S.S. "Cristobal" in Gatun Locks — A24

Blue Overprint, Type II

1917

49	A22	12c purple & black	17.50	5.50
50	A23	15c brt blue & black	55.00	22.50
51	A24	24c yel brown & black	50.00	14.00
		Nos. 49-51 (3)	122.50	42.00

Type IV: "C" thick at bottom, "E" with center bar same length as top and bottom bars

CANAL ZONE

Black Overprint, Reading Up

1918-20

52	A15	1c green & black	32.50	11.00
a.		Overprint reading down	175.00	—
b.		Booklet pane of 6	650.00	
c.		Bklt. pane of 6, left vert. row of 3 without ovpt.	7,500.	
d.		Bklt. pane of 6, right vert. row of 3 with dbl. ovpt.	7,500.	
e.		Horiz. bklt. pair, left stamp without overprint	3,000.	
f.		Horiz. bklt. pair, right stamp with dbl. overprint	3,000.	
53	A11	2c vermilion & blk	115.00	7.00
a.		Overprint reading down	150.00	150.00
b.		Horizontal pair, right stamp without overprint	2,000.	
c.		Booklet pane of 6	1,000.	
d.		Bklt. pane of 6, left vert. row of 3 without ovpt.	8,000.	
e.		Horiz. bklt. pair, left stamp without overprint	3,000.	4,500.
54	A12	5c dp blue & black ('20)	200.00	35.00
		Nos. 52-54 (3)	347.50	53.00

Normal spacing between words of overprint on Nos. 52 and 53 is 9¼mm. On No. 54 and the booklet printings of Nos. 52 and 53, the normal spacing is 9mm. Minor spacing varieties are known. No. 53e used is unique and is on cover.

Type V: Smaller block type 1¾mm high. "A" with flat top

CANAL ZONE

Black Overprint, Reading Up

1920-21

55	A15	1c lt green & black	22.50	3.50
a.		Overprint reading down	250.00	225.00
b.		Horiz. pair, right stamp without ovpt.	1,500.	
c.		Horiz. pair, left stamp without ovpt.	1,000.	
d.		"ZONE" only	2,750.	
e.		Booklet pane of 6	1,750.	
f.		"CANAL" double	1,250.	
56	A11	2c orange ver & blk	8.50	2.25
a.		Double overprint	575.00	
b.		Double overprint, one reading down	650.00	
c.		Horiz. pair, right stamp without ovpt.	1,500.	
d.		Horiz. pair, left stamp without ovpt.	1,000.	
e.		Vert. pair, one without overprint	1,500.	
f.		"ZONE" double	1,000.	
g.		Booklet pane of 6	850.00	
h.		"CANAL" double	1,000.	
57	A12	5c dp blue & black	325.00	55.00
a.		Horiz. pair, right stamp without ovpt.	2,250.	
b.		Horiz. pair, left stamp without ovpt.	2,250.	
		Nos. 55-57 (3)	356.00	60.75

Drydock at Balboa — A25

Ship in Pedro Miguel Locks — A26

Black Overprint, Type V

1920

58	A25	50c orange & black	275.00	160.00
59	A26	1b dk violet & blk	160.00	65.00

Jose Vallarino
A27

The "Land Gate"
A28

Bolivar's Tribute — A29

Municipal Building in 1821 and 1921 — A30

Statue of Balboa — A31

Tomas Herrera — A32

Jose de Fabrega — A33

Black or Red Overprint, Type V

1921

60	A27	1c green	3.75	1.40
a.		"CANAL" double	2,500.	
b.		Booklet pane of 6	900.00	
61	A28	2c carmine	3.00	1.50
a.		Overprint reading down	225.00	225.00
b.		Double overprint	900.00	
c.		Vert. pair, one without overprint	3,500.	
d.		"CANAL" double	1,900.	
f.		Booklet pane of 6	2,100.	
62	A29	5c blue (R)	11.00	4.50
a.		Overprint reading down (R)	60.00	
63	A30	10c violet	18.00	7.50
a.		Overprint reading down	100.00	
64	A31	15c light blue	47.50	17.50
65	A32	24c black brown	70.00	22.50
66	A33	50c black	150.00	100.00
		Nos. 60-66 (7)	303.25	154.90

Experts question the status of the 5c blue with a small type V overprint in red or black.

Type III Ovpt. in Black, Reading Up

1924

67	A27	1c green	500.	200.
a.		"ZONE CANAL" reading down	850.	
b.		"ZONE" reading down	1,900.	

Coat of Arms — A34

Black Overprint

1924

68	A34	1c dark green	11.00	4.50
69	A34	2c carmine	8.25	2.75

The 5c to 1b values were prepared but never issued. See listing in the Scott U.S. Specialized Catalogue.

US Nos. 551-554, 557, 562, 564-566, and 569-571 Overprinted in Red or Black

CANAL

Type A

ZONE

Letters "A" with Flat Tops

1924-25 Flat Plate Printing Perf. 11

70	A154	½c olive brown (R)	1.25	.75
71	A155	1c deep green	1.40	.90
a.		Inverted overprint	500.00	500.00
b.		"ZONE" inverted	350.00	325.00
c.		"CANAL" only	1,750.	
d.		"ZONE CANAL"	450.00	
e.		Booklet pane of 6	100.00	
72	A156	1½c yellow brown	1.90	1.70
73	A157	2c carmine	7.50	1.70
a.		Booklet pane of 6	175.00	
74	A160	5c dark blue	19.00	8.50
75	A165	10c orange	45.00	22.50
76	A167	12c brown violet	35.00	32.50
a.		"ZONE" inverted	3,750.	3,000.
77	A168	14c dark blue	30.00	22.50
78	A169	15c gray	50.00	35.00
79	A172	30c olive brown	35.00	22.50
80	A173	50c lilac	75.00	45.00
81	A174	$1 violet brown	225.00	90.00
	Nos. 70-81 (12)		526.05	283.55

The space between the two lines of the overprint, on both type A and B, varies on some settings.

US Nos. 554, 555, 557, 562, 564-567, 569-571 and 623 Overprinted in Black or Red

CANAL

Type B

ZONE

Letters "A" with Sharp Pointed Tops

1925-26

84	A157	2c carmine	30.00	7.50
a.		"CANAL" ONLY	1,500.	
b.		"ZONE CANAL"	350.00	
c.		Horiz. pair, one without overprint	3,500.	
d.		Booklet pane of 6	175.00	
85	A158	3c violet	4.00	3.25
a.		"ZONE ZONE"	600.00	550.00
86	A160	5c dark blue	4.00	2.25
a.		"ZONE ZONE"	1,100.	
b.		"CANAL" inverted	950.00	
c.		Inverted overprint	500.00	
d.		Pair, one without overprint	3,250.	
e.		"ZONE CANAL"	325.00	
f.		"ZONE" only	2,000.	
g.		Pair, one without ovpt., other ovpt. invtd.	2,250.	
h.		"CANAL" only	2,250.	
87	A165	10c orange	35.00	11.00
a.		"ZONE ZONE"	3,000.	
88	A167	12c brown violet	22.50	12.50
a.		"ZONE ZONE"	5,250.	
89	A168	14c dark blue	20.00	16.00
90	A169	15c gray	7.00	4.00
a.		"ZONE ZONE"	5,500.	
91	A187	17c black (R)	4.25	3.25
a.		"ZONE" only	800.00	
b.		"CANAL" only	1,700.	
c.		"ZONE CANAL"	175.00	
92	A170	20c carmine rose	7.25	3.25
a.		"CANAL" inverted	3,600.	
b.		"ZONE" inverted	3,850.	
c.		"ZONE CANAL"	3,600.	
93	A172	30c olive brown	5.00	4.00
94	A173	50c lilac	225.00	165.00
95	A174	$1 violet brown	125.00	90.00
	Nos. 84-95 (12)		489.00	292.00

Overprint Type B on US Sesquicentennial Stamp No. 627

1926

96	A188	2c carmine rose	4.50	3.75

On this stamp there is a space of 5mm between the two words of the overprint.

Overprint Type B on US Nos. 583, 584 and 591

1927 Rotary Press Printings Perf. 10

97	A157	2c carmine	42.50	11.00
a.		Pair, one without overprint	3,250.	
b.		Booklet pane of 6	650.00	
c.		"CANAL" only	2,000.	
d.		"ZONE" only	2,750.	
98	A158	3c violet	8.00	4.25
99	A165	10c orange	17.50	7.25
	Nos. 97-99 (3)		68.00	22.50

Overprint Type B on US Nos. 632, 634, 635, 637 and 642

Rotary Press Printings

1927-31 Perf. 11x10½

100	A155	1c green	2.25	1.40
a.		Pair, one without overprint	3,000.	
101	A157	2c carmine	2.50	1.00
a.		Booklet pane of 6	175.00	
102	A158	3c violet	4.25	2.75
a.		Booklet pane of 6, handmade, perf. margins	6,500.	
103	A160	5c dark blue	30.00	10.00
104	A165	10c orange	17.50	10.00
	Nos. 100-104 (5)		56.50	25.15

Wet and Dry Printings

Canal Zone stamps printed by both the "wet" and "dry" process are Nos. 105, 108-109, 111-114, 117, 138-140, C21-C24, C26, J25, J27. Starting with Nos. 147 and C27, the Bureau of Engraving and Printing used the "dry" method exclusively. See note following US Scott 1029.

 Maj. Gen. William Crawford Gorgas — A35

 Maj. Gen. George Washington Goethals — A36

 Gaillard Cut — A37

 Maj. Gen. Harry Foote Hodges — A38

 Lt. Col. David D. Gaillard — A39

 Maj. Gen. William L. Sibert — A40

 Jackson Smith — A41

 Rear Adm. Harry H. Rousseau — A42

  Col. Sydney B. Williamson — A43

 J.C.S. Blackburn — A44

1928-40 Flat Plate Printing Perf. 11

105	A35	1c green	.15	.15
106	A36	2c carmine	.16	.15
a.		Booklet pane of 6	15.00	20.00
107	A37	5c blue ('29)	1.00	.40
108	A38	10c orange ('32)	.20	.20
109	A39	12c violet brown ('29)	.75	.60
110	A40	14c blue ('37)	.85	.85
111	A41	15c gray ('32)	.40	.35
112	A42	20c olive brown ('32)	.60	.20
113	A43	30c brown black ('40)	.80	.70
114	A44	50c lilac ('29)	1.50	.65
	Nos. 105-114 (10)		6.41	4.25

For surcharges & overprints see #J21-J24, O1-O8.

United States Nos. 720 and 695 Overprinted type B

Rotary Press Printing

1933 Perf. 11x10½

115	A226	3c deep violet	2.75	.25
b.		"CANAL" only	2,600.	
c.		Bklt. pane of 6, handmade, perf. margins	225.00	
116	A168	14c dark blue	4.50	3.50
a.		"ZONE CANAL"	1,500.	

 Gen. George Washington Goethals — A45

Flat Plate Printing

1934, Aug. 15 Perf. 11

117	A45	3c deep violet	.15	.15
a.		Booklet pane of 6	45.00	32.50
b.		As "a," handmade, perf. margins	225.00	

20th anniv. of the Panama Canal opening.

See No. 153.

Catalogue values for unused stamps in this section, from this point to the end of the section, are for Never Hinged items.

US Nos. 803 and 805 Overprinted in Black

CANAL ZONE

Rotary Press Printing

1939 Perf. 11x10½

118	A275	½c deep orange	.15	.15
119	A277	1½c bister brown	.15	.15
	Set value		.25	.25

Panama Canal Anniversary Issue

 Balboa-Before — A46

 Balboa-After — A47

 Gaillard Cut-Before — A48

 Gaillard Cut-After — A49

 Bas Obispo-Before — A50

 Bas Obispo-After — A51

 Gatun Locks-Before — A52

 Gatun Locks-After — A53

 Canal Channel-Before — A54

 Canal Channel-After — A55

 Gamboa-Before — A56

 Gamboa-After — A57

 Pedro Miguel Locks-Before A58

 Pedro Miguel Locks-After A59

 Gatun Spillway-Before — A60

 Gatun Spillway-After A61

Flat Plate Printing

1939, Aug. 15 Perf. 11

120	A46	1c yellow green	.65	.30
121	A47	2c rose carmine	.65	.35
122	A48	3c purple	.65	.15
123	A49	5c dark blue	1.60	1.25
124	A50	6c red orange	3.00	3.00
125	A51	7c black	3.25	3.00
126	A52	8c green	4.75	3.50
127	A53	10c ultramarine	3.50	3.00
128	A54	11c blue green	8.00	8.50
129	A55	12c brown carmine	7.50	8.00
130	A56	14c dark violet	7.50	8.00
131	A57	15c olive green	10.00	6.00
132	A58	18c rose pink	10.00	8.50
133	A59	20c brown	12.50	7.50
134	A60	25c orange	17.50	17.50
135	A61	50c violet brown	22.50	6.00
	Nos. 120-135 (16)		113.55	84.55

25th anniv. of the Panama Canal.

 Maj. Gen. George W. Davis — A62

 Gov. Charles E. Magoon — A63

 Theodore Roosevelt — A64

 John F. Stevens — A65

 John F. Wallace — A66

1946-49 Size: 19x22mm Perf. 11

136	A62	½c bright red ('48)	.40	.25
137	A63	1½c chocolate ('48)	.40	.25
138	A64	2c rose carmine ('49)	.15	.15
139	A65	5c deep blue	.35	.20
140	A66	25c yellow green ('48)	.85	.55
	Nos. 136-140 (5)		2.15	1.40

See #155, 162, 164. For overprint see #O9.

 Map of Biological Area and Coati-Mundi A67

1948, Apr. 17 Perf. 11

141	A67	10c black	1.10	.80

25th anniv. of the establishment of the Canal Zone Biological Area on Barro Colorado Is.

"Forty-niners" Arriving at Chagres — A68

Journey by "Bungo" to Las Cruces — A69

Las Cruces Trail to Panama — A70

Departure for San Francisco — A71

1949, June 1   *Perf. 11*
142 A68   3c blue   .50   .25
143 A69   6c violet   .65   .30
144 A70 12c bright green   1.10   .90
145 A71 18c deep red lilac   2.00 1.50
   Nos. 142-145 (4)   4.25 2.95
Centenary of the California Gold Rush.

Workers in Culebra Cut — A72

Early Railroad Scene — A73

1951, Aug. 15
146 A72 10c carmine   2.25 1.50
Contribution of West Indian laborers in the construction of the Canal.

1955, Jan. 28   *Perf. 11*
147 A73   3c violet   .60   .50
Cent. of the completion of the Panama Railroad and the 1st transcontinental railroad trip in Americas.

Gorgas Hospital and Ancon Hill — A74

1957, Nov. 17
148 A74   3c black, *blue green*   .40   .35
75th anniv. of Gorgas Hospital. Printed on two shades of blue green paper.

S.S. Ancon — A75

1958, Aug. 30   Engr.   Unwmk.
149 A75   4c greenish blue   .35   .30

Roosevelt Medal and Map — A76

1958, Nov. 15   *Perf. 11*
150 A76   4c brown   .40   .30
Theodore Roosevelt (1858-1919).

Canal Zone stamps can be mounted in the Scott U.S. Possessions album.

Boy Scout Badge — A77

Administration Building — A78

Giori Press Printing
1960, Feb. 8   *Perf. 11*
151 A77   4c dk blue, red & bister   .45   .40
Boy Scouts of America, 50th anniv.

1960, Nov. 1   Engr.   Perf. 11
152 A78   4c rose lilac   .20   .15

Types of 1934, 1960 and 1946
Coil Stamps
1960-62   *Perf. 10 Vert.*
153 A45   3c deep violet   .15   .15
          Perf. 10 Horizontally
154 A78   4c deep rose lilac   .20   .15
          Perf. 10 Vertically
155 A65   5c deep blue   .25   .20
   Nos. 153-155 (3)   .60   .50
Issue dates: 3c, 4c, 1960. 5c, Feb. 10, 1962.

Girl Scout Badge and Camp at Gatun Lake — A79

Giori Press Printing
1962, Mar. 12   *Perf. 11*
156 A79   4c blue, dk green & bister   .40   .30
50th anniv. of Girl Scouts.

Thatcher Ferry Bridge and Map of Western Hemisphere A80

1962, Oct. 12
157 A80   4c black & silver   .30   .25
   a.   Silver (bridge) omitted   7,000.
Opening of the Thatcher Ferry Bridge, spanning the Panama Canal.

Goethals Memorial, Balboa — A81

Fort San Lorenzo — A82

Giori Press Printing
1968-71   *Perf. 11*
158 A81   6c green & ultra   .30   .30
159 A82   8c multicolored   .35   .20
Issued: 6c, Mar. 15, 1968; 8c, July 14, 1971.

Portrait Type of 1928-48
Coil Stamps
1975, Feb. 14   Engr.   Perf. 10 Vert.
160 A35   1c green   .15   .15
161 A38 10c orange   .70   .40
162 A66 25c yellow green   2.75 2.75
   Nos. 160-162 (3)   3.60 3.30

Dredge Cascadas A83

Giori Press Printing
1976, Feb. 23   *Perf. 11*
163 A83 13c multicolored   .35   .20
   a.   Booklet pane of 4   3.00   —

Stevens Type of 1946
Rotary Press Printing
1977   *Perf. 11x10½*
          Size: 19x22½mm
164 A65   5c deep blue   .60   .85
   a.   Tagged   9.50   —

Towing Locomotive, Ship in Lock — A84

1978, Oct. 25   Engr.   Perf. 11
165 A84 15c dp green & blue green   .35   .20

AIR POST STAMPS

AIR MAIL

Nos. 105-106 Surcharged in Dark Blue

25 CENTS 25

Type I- Flag of "5" pointing up **15**

Type II- Flag of "5" curved **15**

Flat Plate Printing
1929   Unwmk.   Perf. 11
C1 A35 15c on 1c green, I   8.00 5.50
C2 A35 15c on 1c green, II   85.00 75.00
C3 A36 25c on 2c carmine   3.50 2.00
   Nos. C1-C3 (3)   96.50 82.50

AIR MAIL

Nos. 114 and 106 Surcharged

≡10c

1929, Dec. 31
C4 A44 10c on 50c lilac   7.50 6.50
C5 A36 20c on 2c carmine   5.00 1.75
   a.   Dropped "2" in surcharge   80.00 60.00

Catalogue values for unused stamps in this section, from this point to the end of the section, are for Never Hinged items.

Gaillard Cut — AP1

1931-49   *Engr.*
C6 AP1   4c red violet ('49)   .75   .70
C7 AP1   5c yellow green   .60   .45
C8 AP1   6c yellow brown ('46)   .75   .35
C9 AP1 10c orange   1.00   .35
C10 AP1 15c blue   1.25   .30
C11 AP1 20c red violet   2.00   .30
C12 AP1 30c rose lake ('41)   3.50 1.00
C13 AP1 40c yellow   3.50 1.10
C14 AP1 $1 black   8.50 1.90
   Nos. C6-C14 (9)   21.85 6.45
For overprints see Nos. CO1-CO14.

Douglas Plane over Sosa Hill — AP2

Planes and Map of Central America — AP3

Pan American Clipper and Scene near Fort Amador — AP4

Pan American Clipper at Cristobal Harbor — AP5

Pan American Clipper over Gaillard Cut — AP6

Pan American Clipper Landing — AP7

1939, July 15
C15 AP2   5c greenish black   3.75 2.25
C16 AP3 10c dull violet   3.00 2.25
C17 AP4 15c light brown   4.25 1.25
C18 AP5 25c blue   13.00 8.00
C19 AP6 30c rose carmine   12.00 6.75
C20 AP7 $1 green   35.00 22.50
   Nos. C15-C20 (6)   71.00 43.00
10th anniv. of Air Mail service and the 25th anniv. of the opening of the Panama Canal.

Globe and Wing — AP8

1951, July 16   Unwmk.   Perf. 11
C21 AP8   4c red violet   .75   .35
C22 AP8   6c brown   .50   .30
C23 AP8 10c red orange   .90   .45
C24 AP8 21c blue   7.50 4.00
C25 AP8 31c cerise   7.50 3.75
   a.   Horiz. pair, imperf. vert.   1,000.
C26 AP8 80c gray black   4.50 1.50
   Nos. C21-C26 (6)   21.65 10.35

1958, Aug. 16
C27 AP8   5c yellow green   1.00   .65
C28 AP8   7c olive   1.00   .55
C29 AP8 15c brown violet   3.75 2.75
C30 AP8 25c orange yellow   10.00 2.75
C31 AP8 35c dark blue   6.25 2.75
   Nos. C27-C31 (5)   22.00 9.45
   Nos. C21-C31 (11)   43.65 19.80
See No. C34.

Emblem of US Army Caribbean School — AP9

Giori Press Printing
1961, Nov. 21   *Perf. 11*
C32 AP9 15c red & dk blue   1.25   .75

Malaria Eradication Emblem and Mosquito AP10

1962, Sept. 24   Unwmk.   Perf. 11
C33 AP10 7c yellow & black   .45   .40
WHO drive to eradicate malaria.

Type of 1951
Rotary Press Printing
1963, Jan. 7   *Perf. 10½x11*
C34 AP8 8c carmine   .50 .30

Alliance
Emblem
AP11

Giori Press Printing
1963, Aug. 17   **Unwmk.**   *Perf. 11*
C35 AP11 15c gray, green & dk ultra   1.10 .85

2nd anniv. of the Alliance for Progress, which aims to stimulate economic growth and raise living standards in Latin America.

Jet over
Cristobal
AP12

Designs: 8c, Gatun Locks. 15c, Madden Dam. 20c, Gaillard Cut. 30c, Miraflores Locks. 80c, Balboa.

1964, Aug. 15   *Perf. 11*
C36 AP12 6c green & black   .45 .35
C37 AP12 8c rose red & black   .45 .35
C38 AP12 15c blue & black   1.00 .75
C39 AP12 20c rose lilac & blk   1.50 1.00
C40 AP12 30c redsh brown & blk   2.25 2.25
C41 AP12 80c ol bister & black   3.75 3.00
    Nos. C36-C41 (6)   9.40 7.70

50th anniv. of the Panama Canal.

Seal and Jet
Plane — AP13

1965, July 15   **Unwmk.**   *Perf. 11*
C42 AP13 6c green & black   .35 .30
C43 AP13 8c rose red & black   .45 .15
C44 AP13 15c blue & black   .50 .20
C45 AP13 20c lilac & black   .55 .30
C46 AP13 30c redsh brn & blk   .80 .30
C47 AP13 80c bister & black   2.00 .75
    Nos. C42-C47 (6)   4.65 2.00

1968-76
C48 AP13 10c dull orange & blk   .25 .15
   a.   Booklet pane of 4 ('70)   4.25
C49 AP13 11c gray olive & blk   .25 .20
   a.   Booklet pane of 4   3.50
C50 AP13 13c emerald & black   .80 .30
   a.   Booklet pane of 4   6.00
C51 AP13 22c violet & black   .75 2.00
C52 AP13 25c pale yel green & blk   .60 .70
C53 AP13 35c salmon & black   .90 2.00
    Nos. C48-C53 (6)   3.55 5.35

Issued: 10c, 25c, 3/15/68; 11c, 9/24/71; 13c, 2/11/74; 22c, 35c, 5/10/76.

AIR POST OFFICIAL STAMPS

Officials and Air Post Officials were sold to the public only with a Balboa Heights, Canal Zone wavy line parcel post cancel while current. After being withdrawn from use, unused copies (except for Nos. CO8-CO12, O3 and O8) were sold at face value for three months beginning Jan. 2, 1952.

Used values are for the CTO copies, postally used copies being worth more.

Nos. C7, C9-C14   **OFFICIAL**
Overprinted in Black   **PANAMA CANAL**

Two Types of Overprint
1941-42   **Unwmk.**   *Perf. 11*
"PANAMA CANAL" 19-20mm
CO1 AP1 5c yellow green   5.50 1.50
CO2 AP1 10c orange   8.50 2.00
CO3 AP1 15c blue   11.00 2.00
CO4 AP1 20c red violet   12.50 4.00
CO5 AP1 30c rose lake ('42)   17.50 5.00

CO6 AP1 40c yellow   17.50 7.50
CO7 AP1 $1 black   20.00 10.00
    Nos. CO1-CO7 (7)   92.50 32.00

Overprint varieties occur on Nos. CO1-CO7 and CO14: "O" over "N" of "PANAMA" (entire 3rd row). "O" broken at top (pos. 31). "O" over 2nd "A" of "PANAMA" (pos. 45). 1st "F" of "OFFICIAL" over 2nd "A" of "PANAMA" (pos. 50).

1941
"PANAMA CANAL" 17mm long
CO8 AP1 5c light green   — 160.00
CO9 AP1 10c orange   — 275.00
CO10 AP1 20c red violet   — 175.00
CO11 AP1 30c rose lake   — 65.00
CO12 AP1 40c yellow   — 180.00
    Nos. CO8-CO12 (5)   855.00

Same Overprint on No. C8

1947, Nov.
"PANAMA CANAL" 19-20mm long
CO14 AP1 6c yellow brown   12.50 5.00
   a.   Inverted overprint   2,500.

POSTAGE DUE STAMPS

Postage Due Stamps of the US Nos. J45a, J46a and J49a Overprinted in Black

CANAL ZONE

1914, Mar.   **Wmk. 190**   *Perf. 12*
J1 D2 1c rose carmine   85.00 15.00
J2 D2 2c rose carmine   250.00 45.00
J3 D2 10c rose carmine   850.00 40.00
    Nos. J1-J3 (3)   1,185. 100.00

Castle Gate (See footnote) — D1

Statue of
Columbus
D2

Pedro J. Sosa
D3

Blue Overprint, Type II, on Postage Due Stamps of Panama

1915   **Unwmk.**
J4 D1 1c olive brown   12.50 5.00
J5 D2 2c olive brown   200.00 17.50
J6 D3 10c olive brown   50.00 10.00
    Nos. J4-J6 (3)   262.50 32.50

The 1c was intended to show a gate of San Lorenzo Castle, Chagres. By error the stamp actually shows the main gate of San Geronimo Castle, Portobelo.

Experts believe that the 1c with overprint type V, reading up or down, is bogus.

Surcharged in Red

CANAL 2 ZONE

J7 D1 1c on 1c olive brn   105.00 15.00
J8 D2 2c on 2c olive brn   25.00 7.00
J9 D3 10c on 10c olive brn   22.50 5.00
    Nos. J7-J9 (3)   152.50 27.00

Columbus
Statue — D4

Capitol, Panama
City — D5

Carmine Surcharge
1919
J10 D4 2c on 2c olive brown   30.00 12.50
J11 D5 4c on 4c olive brown   35.00 15.00
   a.   "ZONE" omitted   7,500.
   b.   "4" omitted   7,500.

US Postage Due Stamps Nos. J61, J62b and J65b Overprinted in Black

CANAL

Type A

ZONE

Letters "A" with Flat Tops
1924   *Perf. 11*
J12 D2 1c carmine rose   110.00 27.50
J13 D2 2c deep claret   60.00 10.00
J14 D2 10c deep claret   250.00 50.00
    Nos. J12-J14 (3)   420.00 87.50

US Postage Stamps Nos. 552, 554 and 562 Overprinted Type A and additional Overprint in Red or Blue

POSTAGE DUE

1925
J15 A155 1c deep green   90.00 13.00
J16 A157 2c carmine (Bl)   22.50 7.00
J17 A165 10c orange   50.00 11.00
   a.   "POSTAGE DUE" double   450.00
   b.   "E" of "POSTAGE" missing   450.00
   c.   As "a" and "b"   3,250.
    Nos. J15-J17 (3)   162.50 31.00

"CANAL ZONE" Type B Overprinted on US Nos. J61, J62, J65, J65a
Letters "A" with Sharp Pointed Tops
1925
J18 D2 1c carmine rose   8.00 3.00
   a.   "ZONE ZONE"   1,250.
J19 D2 2c carmine rose   15.00 4.00
   a.   "ZONE ZONE"   1,500.
J20 D2 10c carmine rose   150.00 20.00
   a.   Pair, one without overprint   1,750.
   b.   10c rose red   250.00 100.00
   c.   As "b," double overprint   425.00
    Nos. J18-J20 (3)   173.00 27.00

No. 107 Surcharged in Black

POSTAGE DUE
10
≡ ≡

1929-30
J21 A37 1c on 5c blue   4.50 1.75
   a.   "POSTAGE DUE" omitted   5,000.
J22 A37 2c on 5c blue   7.50 2.50
J23 A37 5c on 5c blue   7.50 2.75
J24 A37 10c on 5c blue   7.50 2.75
    Nos. J21-J24 (4)   27.00 9.75

On No. J23 the horizontal bars in the lower corners of the surcharge are omitted.

Canal Zone Seal — D6

1932-41
J25 D6 1c claret   .15 .15
J26 D6 2c claret   .15 .20
J27 D6 5c claret   .35 .20
J28 D6 10c claret   1.40 1.50
J29 D6 15c claret ('41)   1.10 1.00
    Nos. J25-J29 (5)   3.15 3.05

The 1c and 5c are found in both "wet" and "dry" printings. (See note after US No. 1029.) The dry printings are in red violet.

OFFICIAL STAMPS

See note at beginning of Air Post Official Stamps.

Regular Issues of 1928-34 Overprinted in Black:

OFFICIAL	**OFFICIAL**
PANAMA	**PANAMA CANAL**
CANAL	Type 2
Type 1	

Type 1 - "PANAMA" 10mm long.
Type 1A - "PANAMA" 9mm long.

1941   **Unwmk.**   *Perf. 11*
O1 A35 1c yellow green (1)   2.25 .40
O2 A45 3c deep violet (1)   4.00 .75
O3 A37 5c blue (2)   1,000. 32.50
O4 A38 10c orange (1)   7.00 1.90
O5 A41 15c gray (1)   12.50 2.25
O6 A42 20c olive brown (1)   15.00 2.75
O7 A44 50c lilac (1)   37.50 5.50
O8 A44 50c rose lilac (1A)   625.00

Same Overprint on No. 139
1947
O9 A65 5c deep blue (1)   9.00 3.50

CUBA
'kyü-bə

LOCATION — The largest island of the West Indies; south of Florida.
GOVT. — socialist; under US military governor 1899-1902 and US provisional governor 1906-1909.
AREA — 44,206 sq. mi.
POP. — 9,710,000 (1981)
CAPITAL — Havana

Formerly a Spanish possession, Cuba's attempts to gain freedom led to US intervention in 1898. Under Treaty of Paris of that year, Spain relinquished the island to US trust. In 1902, a republic was established and Cuban Congress took over government from US military authorities.

100 Cents = 1 Dollar

Watermark

Wmk. 191- Double-lined "USPS" in Capitals

Values for Nos. 176-220 are for stamps in the grade of fine and in sound condition where such exist. Values for Nos. 221-J4 are for very fine examples.

King Alfonso XIII
A19   N2
United States Administration
Puerto Principe Issue
Issues of Cuba of 1898 and 1896
Surcharged:

HABILITADO   **HABILITADO**
1   # 1
cent.   **cents.**
a   b

HABILITADO 2 cents. c

HABILITADO 2 cents. d

HABILITADO 3 cents. e

HABILITADO 3 cents. f

HABILITADO 5 cents. g

HABILITADO 5 cents. h

HABILITADO 5 cents. i

HABILITADO 5 cents. j

HABILITADO 3 cents. k

HABILITADO 3 cents. l

HABILITADO 10 cents. m

Types a, c, d, e, f, g and h are 17½mm high, the others are 19½mm high.

Black Surcharge on #156-158, 160
1898-99

176	(a)	1c on 1m org brn	45.	30.
177	(b)	1c on 1m org brn	45.	35.
a.		Broken figure "1"	75.	65.
b.		Inverted surcharge		200.
d.		As "a," inverted		250.
178	(c)	2c on 2m org brn	22.50	18.
a.		Inverted surcharge	250.	50.
179	(d)	2c on 2m org brn	40.	35.
a.		Inverted surcharge	350.	100.
179B	(k)	3c on 1m org brn	300.	175.
c.		Double surcharge	1,500.	750.
179D	(l)	3c on 1m org brn	1,500.	675.
e.		Double surcharge	—	
179F	(e)	3c on 2m org brn		1,500.

Value for No. 179F is for copies with minor faults.

179G	(f)	3c on 2m org brn	—	2,000.

Value for No. 179G is for copies with minor faults.

180	(e)	3c on 3m org brown	27.50	30.
a.		Inverted surcharge		100.
181	(f)	3c on 3m org brown	75.	75.
a.		Inverted surcharge		200.
182	(g)	5c on 1m org brown	700.	200.
a.		Inverted surcharge		500.
183	(h)	5c on 1m org brown	1,300.	500.
a.		Inverted surcharge		700.
184	(g)	5c on 2m org brown	750.	250.
185	(h)	5c on 2m org brown	1,500.	500.
186	(g)	5c on 3m org brown		165.
a.		Inverted surcharge		700.
187	(h)	5c on 3m org brown		400.
a.		Inverted surcharge		1,000.
188	(g)	5c on 5m org brown	70.	60.
a.		Inverted surcharge	400.	200.
b.		Double surcharge		
189	(h)	5c on 5m org brown	350.	250.
a.		Double surcharge	—	400.

Values for Nos. 188, 189 are for the 1st printing. The 2nd printing was surcharged using a shiny ink.

189C	(i)	5c on 5m org brown		7,500.

Black Surcharge on No. P25

190	(g)	5c on ½m blue grn	250.	75.
a.		Inverted surcharge	500.	150.
b.		Pair, one without surch.		

Value for No. 190b is for pair with unsurcharged copy at right. Exists with unsurcharged stamp at left.

191	(h)	5c on ½m blue grn	300.	90.
a.		Inverted surcharge		200.
192	(i)	5c on ½m blue grn	550.	200.
a.		Dbl. surch., one diagonal		11,500.
193	(j)	5c on ½m blue grn	700.	300.

Red Surcharge on No. 161

196	(k)	3c on 1c black violet	60.	35.
a.		Inverted surcharge		300.
197	(l)	3c on 1c black violet	125.	55.
a.		Inverted surcharge		300.
198	(i)	5c on 1c black violet	20.	25.
a.		Inverted surcharge		125.
b.		Vert. surch., reading up		3,500.
c.		Double surcharge	400.	600.
d.		Double invtd. surcharge		

No. 198b exists reading down.

199	(j)	5c on 1c black vio	50.	50.
a.		Inverted surcharge		250.
b.		Vertical surcharge		2,000.
c.		Double surcharge	1,000.	600.
200	(m)	10c on 1c black vio	20.	50.
a.		Broken figure "1"	40.	100.

Black Surcharge on Nos. P26-P30

201	(k)	3c on 1m blue green	350.	350.
a.		Inverted surcharge		450.
b.		"EENTS"	550.	450.
c.		As "b," inverted		850.
202	(l)	3c on 1m blue green	500.	400.
a.		Inverted surcharge		850.
203	(k)	3c on 2m blue green	850.	350.
b.		Inverted surcharge	1,250.	850.
c.		As "a," inverted		950.
204	(l)	3c on 2m blue green	1,250.	600.
a.		Inverted surcharge		750.
205	(k)	3c on 3m blue green	900.	350.
a.		Inverted surcharge		500.
b.		"EENTS"	1,250.	450.
c.		As "b," inverted		700.
206	(l)	3c on 3m blue green	1,200.	550.
a.		Inverted surcharge		700.
211	(i)	5c on 1m blue green	—	1,800.
212		"EENTS"	—	2,250.
213	(i)	5c on 2m blue green	—	1,800.
a.		"EENTS"		1,900.
214	(i)	5c on 2m blue green		1,750.
215	(i)	5c on 3m blue green		500.
a.		"EENTS"		1,000.
216	(i)	5c on 3m blue green		1,000.
217	(i)	5c on 4m blue green	2,500.	900.
a.		"EENTS"	3,000.	1,500.
b.		Inverted surcharge		2,000.
c.		As "a," inverted		2,000.
218	(j)	5c on 4m blue green		1,250.
a.		"EENTS"		2,000.
219	(i)	5c on 8m blue green	2,500.	1,250.
a.		Inverted surcharge		1,500.
b.		"EENTS"	—	1,800.
c.		As "b," inverted		2,500.
220	(j)	5c on 8m blue green		2,000.
a.		Inverted surcharge		2,500.

CUBA

US Nos. 279, 267, 279B, 268, 281, 282C and 283 Surcharged in Black

1 c. de PESO.

1899		**Wmk. 191**	*Perf. 12*	
221	A87	1c on 1c yellow green	5.25	.35
222	A88	2c on 2c car	5.75	.40
a.		2c on 2c red	6.50	.30
c.		Inverted surcharge	3,500.	3,500.
223	A88	2½c on 2c carmine	3.50	.50
a.		2½c on 2c red	4.00	1.60
224	A89	3c on 3c purple	10.00	1.75
a.		"CUBA"	35.00	35.00
225	A91	5c on 5c blue	10.00	2.00
226	A94	10c on 10c brn, type I	20.00	6.50
b.		"CUBA" omitted	4,000.	4,000.
226A	A94	10c on 10c brn, type II	6,000.	
		Nos. 221-226 (6)	54.50	11.50

The 2½c was sold and used as a 2c stamp.
Excellent counterfeits of this and the preceding issue exist, especially inverted and double surcharges.

Issues of the Republic under US Military Rule

Statue of Columbus A20

Royal Palms A21

"Cuba" — A22

Ocean Liner — A23

Cane Field — A24

Wmk. U S-C (191C)

1899		**Engr.**	*Perf. 12*	
227	A20	1c yellow green	3.50	.15
228	A21	2c carmine	3.50	.15
a.		2c scarlet	3.50	.15
b.		Booklet pane of 6	2,000.	
229	A22	3c purple	3.50	.15
230	A23	5c blue	4.50	.20
231	A24	10c brown	11.00	.50
		Nos. 227-231 (5)	26.00	1.15

Unwatermarked stamps of designs A20-A24 were re-engraved and issued by the Cuban Republic. See Volume 2 for details of the re-engraving.

SPECIAL DELIVERY STAMPS

United States Administration

CUBA.

US No. E5 Surcharged in Red

10c. de PESO

1899		**Wmk. 191**	*Perf. 12*	
E1	SD3	10c on 10c blue	130.00	100.00
a.		No period after "CUBA"	450.00	400.00

Issues of the Republic under US Military Rule

Special Delivery Messenger SD2

Inscribed: "Immediata"

1899		**Wmk. 191C**	**Engr.**	
E2	SD2	10c orange	45.00	15.00

POSTAGE DUE STAMPS

United States Administration

Postage Due Stamps of the US Nos. J38, J39, J41 and J42 Surcharged in Black Like Nos. 221-226A

1899		**Wmk. 191**	*Perf. 12*	
J1	D2	1c on 1c dp claret	45.00	5.25
J2	D2	2c on 2c dp claret	45.00	5.25
a.		Inverted surcharge		2,500.
J3		5c on 5c dp claret	45.00	5.25
J4	D2	10c on 10c dp claret	27.50	2.50
		Nos. J1-J4 (4)	162.50	18.25

DANISH WEST INDIES

'dä-nish 'west 'in-dēs

LOCATION — Group of islands in the West Indies, lying east of Puerto Rico
GOVT. — Danish colony
AREA — 132 sq. mi.
POP. — 27,086 (1911)
CAPITAL — Charlotte Amalie

The US bought these islands in 1917 and they became the US Virgin Islands, using US stamps and currency.

100 Cents = 1 Dollar
100 Bit = 1 Franc (1905)

Watermarks

Wmk. 111- Small Crown

Wmk. 112- Crown

Wmk. 113- Crown

Wmk. 114- Multiple Crosses

Coat of Arms — A1

Yellowish Paper
Yellow Wavy-line Burelage, UL to LR

1856		**Wmk. 111**	**Typo.**	*Imperf.*
1	A1	3c dk car, brown gum	150.	185.
a.		3c dark carmine, yellow gum	160.	200.
b.		3c carmine, white gum	3,000.	3,000.

Reprint: 1981, carmine, back-printed across two stamps ("Reprint by Dansk Post og Telegrafmuseum 1978"), value, pair, $10.

White Paper
Yellow Wavy-line Burelage, UR to LL

1866				
2	A1	3c rose	50.00	40.00

No. 2 reprints unwatermarked: 1930 carmine, value $100. 1942 rose carmine, back-printed across each row ("Nytryk 1942 G. A. Hagemann Danmark og Dansk Vestindiens Friemaerker Bind 2"), value $50.

1872			*Perf. 12½*	
3	A1	3c rose	75.00	125.00

1873

Without Burelage

4	A1	4c dull blue	100.00	250.00
a.		Imperf., pair	600.00	
b.		Horiz. pair, imperf. vert.	500.00	

#4 reprints, unwatermarked, imperf.: 1930, ultramarine, value $100. 1942, blue back-printed like 1942 reprint of #2, value $50.

A2

Normal Frame   Inverted Frame

The arabesques in the corners have a main stem and a branch. When the frame is in normal position, in the upper left corner the branch leaves the main stem half way between two little leaflets. In the lower right corner the branch starts at the foot of the second leaflet. When the frame is inverted the corner designs are, of course, transposed.

White Wove Paper, Varying from Thin to Thick

1874-79		**Wmk. 112**	*Perf. 14x13½*	
5	A2	1c green & brn red	17.50	10.00
a.		1c grn & rose lilac, thin paper	75.00	75.00
b.		1c grn & red violet, medium paper	40.00	40.00
c.		1c green & violet, thick paper	17.50	10.00
e.		Inverted frame	17.50	10.00

6	A2	3c blue & carmine	17.50	10.00
d.		Imperf., pair	300.00	
e.		Inverted frame	17.50	10.00
7	A2	4c brn & dull blue	15.00	15.00
b.		4c brown & ultramarine	250.00	100.00
c.		Diagonal half used as 2c on cover		100.00
d.		Inverted frame	1,500.	1,500.
8	A2	5c green & gray ('76)	20.00	15.00
b.		Inverted frame		100.00
9	A2	7c lilac & orange	20.00	35.00
a.		7c lilac & yellow	40.00	50.00
b.		Inverted frame	30.00	60.00
10	A2	10c blue & brn ('76)	20.00	10.00
b.		"cent.s"	25.00	17.50
c.		Inverted frame	20.00	10.00
11	A2	12c red lilac & yel green ('77)	22.50	37.50
a.		12c lilac & deep green	75.00	75.00
12	A2	14c lilac & green	350.00	500.00
a.		Inverted frame	2,000.	2,500.
13	A2	50c violet, thin paper ('79)	65.00	75.00
a.		50c gray violet, thick porous paper	100.00	150.00
		Nos. 5-13 (9)	547.50	707.50

The central element in the fan-shaped scrollwork at the outside of the lower left corner of Nos. 5a and 7b looks like an elongated diamond.
See Nos. 16-20. For surcharges see Nos. 14-15, 23-28, 40.

Nos. 9 and 13 Surcharged in Black
10 CENTS

1 CENT
1895

1887-95

14	A2	1c on 7c lilac & org	50.00	90.00
a.		1c on 7c lilac & yellow	75.00	125.00
b.		Double surcharge	200.00	300.00
c.		Inverted frame	65.00	90.00
15	A2	10c on 50c violet, thin paper ('95)	20.00	50.00

Type of 1874-79

			Perf. 13	
1896-1901				
16	A2	1c green & red vio ('98)	8.00	8.00
a.		Normal frame	200.00	300.00
17	A2	3c blue & lake ('98)	8.00	8.00
a.		Normal frame	225.00	250.00
18	A2	4c bister & dull blue ('01)	9.00	9.00
a.		Diagonal half used as 2c on cover		25.00
b.		Inverted frame	35.00	30.00
c.		As "b," diagonal half used as 2c on cover		250.00
19	A2	5c green & gray	35.00	20.00
a.		Normal frame	600.00	900.00
20	A2	10c blue & brown ('01)	55.00	75.00
a.		Inverted frame	900.00	1,300.
b.		"cent.s"	60.00	95.00
		Nos. 16-20 (5)	115.00	120.00

Arms — A5

1900

21	A5	1c light green	2.00	2.00
22	A5	5c light blue	8.00	12.00

See Nos. 29-30. For surcharges see Nos. 41-42.

Nos. 6, 17, 20 Surcharged:
2 CENTS 1902 c   **8 Cents 1902** d

Surcharge "c" in Black

			Perf. 14x13½	
1902				
23	A2	2c on 3c blue & car	500.00	400.00
a.		"2" in date with straight tail	525.00	450.00
b.		Normal frame	2,500.	—

			Perf. 13	
24	A2	2c on 3c blue & lake	8.00	12.50
a.		"2" in date with straight tail	15.00	20.00
b.		Dated "1901"	325.00	400.00
c.		Normal frame	150.00	175.00
d.		Dark green surcharge	1,250.	
e.		As "d" & "a"	1,500.	
f.		As "d" & "c"	6,000.	
25	A2	8c on 10c blue & brn	15.00	20.00
a.		"2" with straight tail	15.00	22.50
b.		On No. 20b	15.00	25.00
c.		Inverted frame	250.00	300.00

Only one copy of No. 24f can exist.

Surcharge "d" in Black

27	A2	2c on 3c blue & lake	8.00	17.00
a.		Normal frame	200.00	300.00
28	A2	8c on 10c blue & brn	7.00	7.00
a.		On No. 20b	9.00	9.00
b.		Inverted frame	200.00	250.00
		Nos. 23-28 (5)	538.00	456.50

			Wmk. 113	
1903				
29	A5	2c carmine	8.00	10.00
30	A5	8c brown	17.50	20.00

King Christian IX — A8
St. Thomas Harbor — A9

			Perf. 13	
1905		**Typo.**		
31	A8	5b green	3.00	2.00
32	A8	10b red	4.00	2.00
33	A8	20b green & blue	10.00	8.00
34	A8	25b ultramarine	7.00	7.00
35	A8	40b red & gray	8.00	8.00
36	A8	50b yellow & gray	7.00	9.00

Frame Typo., Center Engr.
Wmk. Two Crowns (113)

			Perf. 12	
37	A9	1fr green & blue	15.00	22.50
38	A9	2fr org red & brown	30.00	50.00
39	A9	5fr yellow & brown	75.00	150.00
		Nos. 31-39 (9)	159.00	

Favor cancels exist on #37-39. Value 25% less.

Nos. 18, 22, 30 Surcharged in Black
5 BIT 1905

			Perf. 13	
1905		**Wmk. 112**		
40	A2	5b on 4c bis & dull blue	9.00	17.50
a.		Inverted frame	30.00	45.00
41	A5	5b on 5c light blue	8.00	14.00

			Wmk. 113	
42	A5	5b on 8c brown	8.00	15.00
		Nos. 40-42 (3)	25.00	46.50

Favor cancels exist on #40-42. Value 25% less.

Frederik VIII — A10
Christian X — A11

Frame Typo., Center Engr.

			Perf. 13	
1907-08		**Wmk. 113**		
43	A10	5b green	1.50	1.00
44	A10	10b red	1.50	1.00
45	A10	15b violet & brown	3.50	3.50
46	A10	20b green & blue	30.00	15.00
47	A10	25b blue & dk blue	1.50	1.00
48	A10	30b claret & slate	40.00	35.00
49	A10	40b ver & gray	4.00	4.00
50	A10	50b yellow & brown	4.00	5.00
		Nos. 43-50 (8)	86.00	65.50

			Perf. 14x14½	
1915		**Wmk. 114**		
51	A11	5b yellow green	2.00	5.00
52	A11	10b red	2.00	35.00
53	A11	15b lilac & red brown	2.00	35.00
54	A11	20b green & blue	2.00	35.00
55	A11	25b blue & dark blue	2.00	5.00
56	A11	30b claret & black	2.00	35.00
57	A11	40b orange & black	2.50	35.00
58	A11	50b brown & green	2.50	35.00
		Nos. 51-58 (8)	17.00	

Forged and favor cancellations exist.

POSTAGE DUE STAMPS

Royal Cipher, "Christian 9 Rex" — D1

			Perf. 11½	
1902		**Unwmk. Litho.**		
J1	D1	1c dark blue	5.00	10.00
J2	D1	4c dark blue	6.00	15.00
J3	D1	6c dark blue	25.00	45.00
J4	D1	10c dark blue	15.00	20.00
		Nos. J1-J4 (4)	51.00	90.00

There are five types of each value. On the 4c they may be distinguished by differences in the figures "4"; on the other values the differences are minute.
Used values of Nos. J1-J4 are for canceled copies.
Uncanceled examples without gum have probably been used. Value 60% of unused.
Counterfeits of Nos. J1-J4 exist.

D2

			Perf. 13	
1905-13				
J5	D2	5b red & gray	4.00	5.00
J6	D2	20b red & gray	10.00	12.50
J7	D2	30b red & gray	7.00	12.50
J8	D2	50b red & gray	9.00	9.00
a.		Perf. 14x14½ ('13)	35.00	110.00
b.		Perf. 11½	500.00	
		Nos. J5-J8 (4)	30.00	39.00

All values of this issue are known imperforate, but were not regularly issued.
Used values of Nos. J5-J8 are for canceled copies.
Uncanceled examples without gum have probably been used. Value 60% of unused.
Counterfeits of Nos. J5-J8 exist.
Danish West Indies stamps were replaced by those of the US in 1917, after the US bought the islands.

GUAM
'gwäm

LOCATION — One of the Mariana Islands in the Pacific Ocean, about 1450 miles east of the Philippines
GOVT. — United States Possession
AREA — 206 sq. mi.
POP. — 9,000 (est. 1899)
CAPITAL — Agaña

Formerly a Spanish possession, Guam was ceded to the United States in 1898 following the Spanish-American War. Stamps overprinted "Guam" were superseded by the regular postage stamps of the United States in 1901.

100 Cents = 1 Dollar

US Nos. 279, 267, 268, 280a, 281, 282, 272, 282C, 283, 284, 275, 275a, 276 and 276A
Overprinted in Black (1c-50c) or Red ($1)

GUAM

			Perf. 12	
1899		**Wmk. 191**		
1	A87	1c deep green	20.00	25.00
2	A88	2c red	17.50	25.00
a.		2c rose carmine	22.50	30.00
3	A89	3c purple	125.00	175.00
4	A90	4c lilac brown	135.00	175.00
5	A91	5c blue	30.00	45.00
6	A92	6c lake	125.00	200.00
7	A93	8c violet brown	125.00	200.00
8	A94	10c brown, type I	45.00	55.00
9	A94	10c brown, type II	3,500.	
10	A95	15c olive green	150.00	175.00
11	A96	50c orange	300.00	375.00
a.		50c red orange	500.00	
12	A97	$1 black, type I	350.00	400.00
13	A97	$1 black, type II	3,750.	
		Nos. 1-8,10-12 (11)	1,422.	1,850.

SPECIAL DELIVERY STAMP

United States No. E5 Overprinted in Red **GUAM**

			Perf. 12	
1899		**Wmk. 191**		
E1	SD3	10c blue	150.00	200.00

Guam Guard Mail stamps of 1930 are listed in the Scott Specialized United States Catalogue.

HAWAII
hə-'wä-yē

LOCATION — Group of 20 islands in the Pacific Ocean, about 2,000 miles southwest of San Francisco.
GOVT. — Former Kingdom and Republic
AREA — 6,435 sq. mi.
POP. — 150,000 (est. 1899)
CAPITAL — Honolulu

Until 1893 an independent kingdom, from 1893 to 1898 a republic, the Hawaiian Islands were annexed to the US in 1898. The Territory of Hawaii achieved statehood in 1959.

100 Cents = 1 Dollar

Values for Nos. 1-4 are for examples with minor damage that has been skillfully repaired.

A1   A2

A3

Pelure Paper

		1851-52 Unwmk.	**Typeset**	*Imperf.*
1	A1	2c blue	660,000.	200,000.
2	A1	5c blue	45,000.	25,000.
3	A2	13c blue	22,500.	17,500.
4	A3	13c blue	40,000.	27,500.

Two varieties of each.
No. 1 unused is unique.

King Kamehameha III
A4   A5

Thick White Wove Paper

		1853		**Engr.**
5	A4	5c blue	1,250.	950.
a.		Line through "Honolulu" (Pos. 2)	2,250.	1,250.
6	A5	13c dark red	600.	1,000.

See #8-9. See Special Printings section, #10-11.

A6

1857

| 7 | A6 | 5c on 13c dark red | 6,750. | 9,000. |

1857

Thin White Wove Paper

8	A4	5c blue	600.	575.
a.		Line through "Honolulu" (Pos. 2)	1,050.	1,000.
b.		Double impression	2,500.	3,500.

1861

Thin Bluish Wove Paper

| 9 | A4 | 5c blue | 350. | 250. |
| a. | | Line through "Honolulu" (Pos. 2) | 750. | 1,000. |

For Re-issues and Reprints of Types A4-A5 see Special Printings section.

Unused values for the Numeral stamps, Nos. 12-26, are for examples without gum.

A7

A8   A9

1859-62   **Typeset**

12	A7	1c lt blue, *bluish white*	7,000.	5,500.
a.		"1 Ce" omitted		15,000.
b.		"nt" omitted		
13	A7	2c lt blue, *bluish white*	6,000.	3,500.
a.		2c dark blue, *grayish white*	6,500.	3,750.
b.		Comma after "Cents"		6,000.
c.		No period after "Leta"		
14	A7	2c blk, *grnsh blue* ('62)	6,000.	3,500.
		"2-Cents."		

1863

15	A7	1c black, *grayish*	450.	1,000.
a.		Tete beche pair	3,500.	
b.		"NTER"		
		Period omitted after "Postage"	700.	
16	A7	2c black, *grayish*	800.	600.
a.		"2" at top of rectangle	3,500.	2,500.
b.		Printed on both sides		20,000.
c.		"NTER"	3,000.	3,000.
d.		2c black, *grayish white*	675.	575.
e.		Period omitted after "Cents"		
f.		Overlapping impressions		
g.		"TAGE.		
17	A7	2c dk blue, *bluish*	7,500.	6,500.
		"ISL"		
18	A7	2c black, *blue gray*	2,750.	4,500.

1864-65

19	A7	1c black	475.	1,000.
20	A7	2c black	650.	1,150.
21	A8	5c blue, *blue* ('65)	675.	475.
a.		Tete beche pair	7,500.	
b.		5c bluish black, *grayish white*	12,000.	
22	A9	5c blue, *blue* ('65)	500.	750.
a.		Tete beche pair	5,000.	
b.		5c blue, *grayish white*		—
c.		Overlapping impressions		

1864   **Laid Paper**

23	A7	1c black	250.	2,000.
a.		HA instead of HAWAIIAN	2,500.	
b.		Tete beche pair	6,000.	
c.		Tete beche pair, #23, 23a	17,500.	
24	A7	2c black	250.	1,000.
a.		"NTER"	2,250.	
b.		"S" of "POSTAGE" omitted	1,000.	
c.		Tete beche pair	5,000.	

A10

1865   **Wove Paper**

25	A10	1c dark blue	250.	
a.		Double impression		
b.		With inverted impression of #21	6,500.	
26	A10	2c dark blue	250.	

Nos. 12 to 26 were typeset and were printed in settings of ten, each stamp differing from the others.

King Kamehameha IV — A11

1861-63   **Litho.**

Horizontally Laid Paper

| 27 | A11 | 2c pale rose | 275. | 250. |
| a. | | 2c carmine rose ('63) | 1,750. | 2,000. |

Vertically Laid Paper

| 28 | A11 | 2c pale rose | 275. | 150. |
| a. | | 2c carmine rose ('63) | 275. | 325. |

For Re-issues and Reprints of Type A11 see Special Printings section.

Princess Victoria   King Kamehameha
Kamamalu — A12   IV — A13

King Kamehameha V
A14   A15

Mataio Kekuanaoa — A16

1864-86   **Wove Paper**   **Engr.**   **Perf. 12**

30	A12	1c purple ('71)	9.00	7.50
a.		1c mauve	35.00	15.00
b.		1c violet	15.00	10.00
31	A13	2c vermilion ('86)	15.00	9.00
a.		2c rose vermilion ('64)	35.00	12.50
b.		Half used as 1c on cover		8,500.
32	A14	5c blue ('66)	150.00	30.00
33	A15	6c yellow green ('71)	25.00	9.00
a.		6c bluish green ('79)	25.00	9.00
34	A16	18c dull rose ('71)	85.00	35.00
		Without gum	17.50	
		Nos. 30-34 (5)	284.00	90.50

No. 32 has traces of rectangular frame lines surrounding the design. Nos. 39 and 52C have no such frame lines.
For overprints see #53, 58-60, 65, 66C, 71.

King David   Prince William Pitt
Kalakaua   Leleiohoku
A17   A18

1875

| 35 | A17 | 2c brown | 7.50 | 3.00 |
| 36 | A18 | 12c black | 55.00 | 27.50 |

See Nos. 38, 43, 46. For overprints see Nos. 56, 62-63, 66, 69.

Princess   King David
Likelike — A19   Kalakaua — A20

Queen   Statue of King
Kapiolani — A21   Kamehameha
   I — A22

King William   Queen Emma
Lunalilo   Kaleleonalani
A23   A24

1882

37	A19	1c blue	6.00	10.00
38	A17	2c lilac rose	125.00	45.00
39	A14	5c ultramarine	15.00	3.25
a.		Vert. pair, imperf. horiz.	4,250.	4,250.
40	A20	10c black	35.00	20.00
41	A21	15c red brown	55.00	25.00
		Nos. 37-41 (5)	236.00	103.25

1883-86

42	A19	1c green	2.75	1.90
43	A17	2c rose ('86)	4.00	1.00
a.		2c dull red	60.00	20.00
44	A20	10c red brown ('84)	30.00	10.00
45	A20	10c vermilion	32.50	12.50
46	A18	12c red lilac	75.00	32.50
47	A22	25c dark violet	125.00	55.00
48	A23	50c red	150.00	82.50
49	A24	$1 rose red	225.00	135.00
		Maltese cross cancellation		75.00
		Nos. 42-49 (8)	644.25	330.40

Other fiscal cancellations exist on No. 49. For overprints see Nos. 54-55, 57, 61-61B, 64, 67-68, 70, 72-73.
For Reproduction and Reprint of the 2c see Special Printings section.

Queen Liliuokalani — A25

1890-91   *Perf. 12*

52	A25	2c dull violet ('91)	4.50	1.50
a.		Vert. pair, imperf. horiz.	3,750.	
52C	A14	5c deep indigo	105.00	135.00

Stamps of 1864-91   **Provisional**
Overprinted in Red   **GOVT.**
               1893

1893

53	A12	1c purple	7.50	12.50
a.		"189" instead of "1893"	400.00	
b.		No period after "GOVT"	200.00	200.00
54	A19	1c blue	6.00	12.50
b.		No period after "GOVT"	135.00	135.00

55	A19	1c green	1.50	3.00
		Pair, one without ovpt.	10,000.	
b.		Double overprint	600.00	450.00
56	A17	2c brown	10.00	20.00
a.		No period after "GOVT"	300.00	
57	A25	2c dull violet	1.50	1.25
a.		Inverted overprint	4,000.	3,500.
b.		Double overprint	850.00	650.00
c.		"18 3" instead of "1893"	600.00	500.00
58	A14	5c deep indigo	10.00	25.00
a.		No period after "GOVT"	225.00	250.00
59	A14	5c ultra	6.00	2.50
a.		Inverted overprint	1,250.	1,250.
b.		Double overprint	5,000.	
60	A15	6c green	15.00	25.00
a.		Double overprint	1,250.	
61	A20	10c black	9.00	15.00
a.		Double overprint	700.00	100.00
61B	A20	10c red brown	15,000.	30,000.
62	A18	12c black	9.00	17.50
a.		Double overprint	2,000.	
63	A18	12c red lilac	150.00	250.00
64	A22	25c dark violet	25.00	40.00
a.		No period after "GOVT"	300.00	300.00
		Nos. 53-61,62-64 (12)	250.50	424.25

Overprinted in Black

65	A13	2c vermilion	65.00	75.00
a.		No period after "GOVT"	250.00	250.00
66	A17	2c rose	1.25	2.25
a.		Double overprint	2,500.	
b.		No period after "GOVT"	50.00	60.00
66C	A15	6c green	15,000.	30,000.
67	A20	10c vermilion	15.00	30.00
68	A20	10c red brown	7.50	12.50
69	A18	12c red lilac	275.00	500.00
70	A21	15c red brown	20.00	30.00
a.		Double overprint	2,000.	
71	A16	18c dull rose	25.00	35.00
a.		Double overprint	350.00	
b.		Pair, one without ovpt.	2,500.	
c.		No period after "GOVT"	300.00	300.00
d.		"18 3" instead of "1893"	375.00	375.00
72	A23	50c red	60.00	90.00
a.		No period after "GOVT"	400.00	400.00
73	A24	$1 rose red	110.00	175.00
a.		No period after "GOVT"	425.00	400.00
		Nos. 65-66,67-73 (9)	578.75	949.75

Coat of   View of
Arms — A26   Honolulu — A27

Statue of   Stars and
Kamehameha   Palms — A29
I — A28

S. S.   Pres. Sanford
"Arawa" — A30   Ballard
   Dole — A31

Statue of King
Kamehameha I — A32

1894

74	A26	1c yellow	2.00	1.25
75	A27	2c brown	2.25	.60
76	A28	5c rose lake	4.00	1.50
77	A29	10c yellow green	6.00	4.50
78	A30	12c blue	12.50	17.50
79	A31	25c deep blue	12.50	17.50
		Nos. 74-79 (6)	39.25	42.85

1899

80	A26	1c dark green	1.50	1.25
81	A27	2c rose	1.35	1.00
a.		2c salmon	1.50	1.25
b.		Vert. pair, imperf. horiz.	4,500.	
82	A32	5c blue	5.50	3.00
		Nos. 80-82 (3)	8.35	5.25

OFFICIAL STAMPS

Lorrin Andrews
Thurston — O1

1896			Unwmk.	Engr.	Perf. 12	
O1	O1	2c green			35.00	17.50
O2	O1	5c black brown			35.00	17.50
O3	O1	6c deep ultra			35.00	17.50
O4	O1	10c bright rose			35.00	17.50
O5	O1	12c orange			35.00	17.50
O6	O1	25c gray violet			35.00	17.50
		Nos. O1-O6 (6)			210.00	105.00

Used values for Nos. O1-O6 are for copies canceled to order "FOREIGN OFFICE/HONOLULU H.I." in double circle without date.

The stamps of Hawaii were replaced by those of the United States.

SPECIAL PRINTINGS

Re-issues

1868

Ordinary White Wove Paper

10	A4	5c blue	25.00	
a.		Line through "Honolulu" (Pos. 2)	50.00	
11	A5	13c dull rose	250.00	

Reprints:

5c. Originals have two small dots near the left side of the square in the upper right corner. These dots are missing in the reprints.

13c. The bottom of the 3 of 13 in the upper left corner is flattened in the originals and rounded in the reprints. The "t" of "Cts" on the left side is as tall as the "C" in the reprints, but shorter in the originals.

On August 19, 1892, the remaining supply of reprints was overprinted in black "REPRINT." The reprints (both with and without overprint) were sold at face value. See the Scott U.S. Specialized Catalogue.

1869 **Engr.** **Thin Wove Paper**

29	A11	2c red	45.00	—

No. 29 was sold only at the Honolulu post office, at first without overprint and later with overprint "CANCELLED."

See note following No. 51.

Reproduction and Reprint
Yellowish Wove Paper

1886-89 **Imperf.**

50	A11	2c orange vermilion	150.00	
51	A11	2c carmine ('89)	25.00	

In 1885 the Postmaster General wished to have on sale complete sets of Hawaii's stamps as far back as type A11, but was unable to find either the stone from which Nos. 27 and 28, or the plate from which No. 29 was printed. He therefore sent a copy of No. 29 to the American Bank Note Co., with an order to engrave a new plate and print 10,000 stamps, of which 5000 were overprinted "Specimen" in blue.

The original No. 29 was printed in sheet of 15 (5x3), but the plate of these "Official Imitations" was made up of 50 stamps (10x5). Later, in 1887, the original die for No. 29 was discovered, and after retouching, a new plate was made and 37,500 stamps were printed. These, like the originals, were printed in sheets of 15. They were delivered during 1889 and 1890. In 1892 all remaining unsold in the Post Office were overprinted "Reprint."

No. 29 is red in color, and printed on very thin white wove paper. No. 50 is orange vermilion in color, on medium, white to buff paper. In No. 50 the vertical line on the left side of the portrait touches the horizontal line over the label "Elua Keneta", while in the other two varieties, Nos. 29 and 51, it does not touch the horizontal line by half a millimeter. In No. 51 there are three parallel lines on the left side of the King's nose, while in No. 29 and No. 50 there are no such lines.

It is claimed that both Nos. 50 and 51 were available for postage, although not made to fill a postal requirement.

PHILIPPINES

ˌfi-lə-ˈpēnz

LOCATION — Group of 7,100 islands and islets in the Malay Archipelago, north of Borneo, in the North Pacific Ocean
GOVT. — US Admin., 1898-1946
AREA — 115,748 sq. mi.
POP. — 16,971,100 (est. 1941)
CAPITAL — Quezon City

The islands were ceded to the US by Spain in 1898. On Nov. 15, 1935, they were given their independence, subject to a transition period which ended July 4, 1946. On that date the Commonwealth became the "Republic of the Philippines."

100 Cents = 1 Dollar (1899)
100 Centavos = 1 Peso (1906)

Watermarks

Wmk. 191PI-   Wmk. 190PI-
Double-lined PIPS   Single-lined PIPS

Wmk. 257- Curved Wavy Lines

Issued under US Administration

Issues of the US
Overprinted in Black

On No. 260

1899-1900		Unwmk.	Perf. 12	
212	A96	50c orange	400.00	250.00

On Nos. 279, 279d, 267, 268, 281, 282C, 283, 284, 275 and 275a

Wmk. 191

213	A87	1c yellow green	3.00	.60
a.		Inverted overprint	13,500.	
214	A88	2c orange red, type III	1.25	.60
a.		2c carmine, type III	1.90	.90
b.		Booklet pane of 6 ('00)	300.00	150.00
215	A89	3c purple	5.75	1.25
216	A91	5c blue	5.50	.90
a.		Inverted overprint		3,750.
217	A94	10c brown, type I	17.50	4.00
217A	A94	10c org brown, type II	200.00	32.50
218	A95	15c olive green	32.50	8.00
219	A96	50c orange	140.00	37.50
a.		50c red orange	275.00	
		Nos. 213-219 (8)	405.50	85.35

No. 216a is valued in the grade of fine.

On Nos. 280b, 282 and 272

1901

220	A90	4c orange brown	22.50	4.50
221	A92	6c lake	27.50	7.00
222	A93	8c violet brown	27.50	7.50
		Nos. 220-222 (3)	77.50	19.00

On Nos. 276, 276A, 277a and 278

Red Overprint

223	A97	$1 black, type I	425.	240.
223A	A97	$1 black, type II	2,250.	675.
224	A98	$2 dark blue	475.	250.
225	A99	$5 dark green	850.	650.

On Nos. 300-313 and shades

1903-04

Black Overprint

226	A115	1c blue green	4.00	.30
227	A116	2c carmine	7.50	1.10
228	A117	3c bright violet	67.50	12.50
229	A118	4c brown ('04)	75.00	12.50
a.		4c orange brown	75.00	20.00
230	A119	5c blue	11.00	1.00
231	A120	6c brownish lake ('04)	80.00	22.50
232	A121	8c vio blk ('04)	40.00	12.50
233	A122	10c pale red brown ('04)	20.00	2.25
a.		10c red brown	25.00	3.00
b.		Pair, one without ovpt.		1,500.

234	A123	13c purple black	32.50	17.50
a.		13c brown violet	32.50	17.50
235	A124	15c olive green	60.00	15.00
236	A125	50c orange	130.00	35.00
		Nos. 226-236 (11)	527.50	142.15

Red Overprint

237	A126	$1 black	450.	250.
238	A127	$2 dk blue ('04)	750.	750.
239	A128	$5 dk blue ('04)	1,000.	900.

On Nos. 319, 319c in Black

1904

240	A129	2c carmine	5.50	2.25
a.		Booklet pane of 6	1,100.	
b.		2c scarlet	6.25	2.75

Jose Rizal — A40   Arms of
                      Manila — A41

Designs: 4c, McKinley. 6c, Magellan. 8c, Miguel Lopez de Legaspi. 10c, Gen. Henry W. Lawton. 12c, Lincoln. 16c, Adm. William T. Sampson. 20c, Washington. 26c, Francisco Carriedo. 30c, Franklin.

Each Inscribed "Philippine Islands/United States of America"

1906, Sept. 8		Engr.	Wmk. 191PI	
241	A40	2c deep green	.25	.15
a.		2c yellow green ('10)	.40	.15
b.		Booklet pane of 6	425.00	
242	A40	4c carmine	.30	.15
a.		4c carmine lake ('10)	.60	.15
b.		Booklet pane of 6	600.00	
243	A40	6c violet	1.25	.20
244	A40	8c brown	2.50	.65
245	A40	10c blue	1.75	.20
246	A40	12c brown lake	5.00	2.00
247	A40	16c violet black	3.75	.20
248	A40	20c orange brown	4.00	.30
249	A40	26c violet brown	6.00	2.25
250	A40	30c olive green	4.75	1.50
251	A41	1p orange	27.50	7.00
252	A41	2p black	35.00	1.25
253	A41	4p dark blue	100.00	15.00
254	A41	10p dark green	225.00	70.00
		Nos. 241-254 (14)	417.05	100.85

Change of Colors

1909-13			Perf. 12	
255	A40	12c red orange	8.50	2.50
256	A40	16c olive green	3.50	.75
257	A40	20c yellow	7.50	1.25
258	A40	26c blue green	1.75	.75
259	A40	30c ultramarine	10.00	3.25
260	A41	1p pale violet	30.00	5.00
260A	A41	2p vio brown ('13)	85.00	2.75
		Nos. 255-260A (7)	146.25	16.25

1911		Wmk. 190PI	Perf. 12	
261	A40	2c green	.65	.15
a.		Booklet pane of 6	475.00	
262	A40	4c carmine lake	2.50	.15
a.		4c carmine		
b.		Booklet pane of 6	525.00	
263	A40	6c deep violet	2.00	.15
264	A40	8c brown	8.50	.45
265	A40	10c blue	3.25	.15
266	A40	12c orange	2.50	.45
267	A40	16c olive green	2.50	.15
268	A40	20c yellow	2.00	.15
a.		20c orange	2.00	.15
269	A40	26c blue green	3.00	.20
270	A40	30c ultramarine	3.50	.45
271	A41	1p pale violet	22.50	.55
272	A41	2p violet brown	27.50	.75
273	A41	4p deep blue	625.00	80.00
274	A41	10p deep green	225.00	25.00
		Nos. 261-274 (14)	930.40	108.75

1914				
275	A40	30c gray	10.00	.40

1914-23			Perf. 10	
276	A40	2c green	1.75	.15
a.		Booklet pane of 6	400.00	
277	A40	4c carmine	1.75	.15
a.		Booklet pane of 6	400.00	
278	A40	6c light violet	37.50	9.00
a.		6c deep violet	42.50	6.00
279	A40	8c brown	40.00	10.00
280	A40	10c dark blue	25.00	.20
281	A40	16c olive green	75.00	4.50
282	A40	20c orange	22.50	.85
283	A40	30c gray	55.00	2.75
284	A41	1p pale violet	110.00	3.00
		Nos. 276-284 (9)	368.50	30.60

1918-26			Perf. 11	
285	A40	2c green	20.00	4.25
a.		Booklet pane of 6	650.00	
286	A40	4c carmine	25.00	2.50
a.		Booklet pane of 6	1,250.	
287	A40	6c deep violet	35.00	1.75
287A	A40	8c light brown	200.00	25.00
288	A40	10c dark brown	52.50	1.50

289	A40	16c olive green	90.00	6.75
289A	A40	20c orange	60.00	7.50
289C	A40	30c gray	55.00	12.50
289D	A41	1p pale violet	70.00	14.00
		Nos. 285-289D (9)	607.50	75.75

1917-25		Unwmk.	Perf. 11	
290	A40	2c yellow green	.15	.15
a.		2c dark green	.15	.15
b.		Vert. pair, imperf. horiz.	1,500.	
c.		Horiz. pair, imperf. btwn.	1,500.	
d.		Vert. pair, imperf. btwn.	1,750.	
e.		Booklet pane of 6	27.50	
291	A40	4c carmine	.15	.15
a.		4c light rose	.15	.15
b.		Booklet pane of 6	17.50	
292	A40	6c deep violet	.30	.15
a.		6c lilac	.35	.15
b.		6c red violet	.35	
c.		Booklet pane of 6	550.00	
293	A40	8c yellow brown	.20	.15
a.		8c orange brown	.20	.15
294	A40	10c deep blue	.20	.15
295	A40	12c red orange	.30	.15
296	A40	16c light olive green	55.00	.25
a.		16c olive bister	55.00	.40
297	A40	20c orange yellow	.30	.15
298	A40	26c green	.45	.45
a.		26c blue green	.55	.25
299	A40	30c gray	.55	.15
300	A41	1p pale violet	27.50	1.00
a.		1p red lilac	27.50	1.00
b.		1p pale rose lilac	27.50	1.10
301	A41	2p violet brown	25.00	.75
302	A41	4p blue	22.50	.45
a.		4p dark blue	22.50	.45
		Nos. 290-302 (13)	132.60	
		Set value		3.75

1923-26

Design: 16c, Adm. George Dewey.

303	A40	16c olive bister	.90	.15
a.		16c olive green	1.30	.20
304	A41	10p deep green ('26)	45.00	5.00

See Nos. 326-353. For surcharges see Nos. 368-369, 450. For overprints see Nos. C1-C28, C36-C46, C54-C57, O5-O14.

Legislative
Palace — A42

1926, Dec. 20		Unwmk.	Perf. 12	
319	A42	2c green & black	.40	.25
a.		Horiz. pair, imperf. btwn.	275.00	
b.		Vert. pair, imperf. btwn.	500.00	
320	A42	4c car & black	.40	.35
a.		Horiz. pair, imperf. btwn.	275.00	
b.		Vert. pair, imperf. between	500.00	
321	A42	16c ol grn & black	.75	.65
a.		Horiz. pair, imperf. btwn.	350.00	
b.		Vert. pair, imperf. btwn.	550.00	
c.		Double impression of center	575.00	
322	A42	18c lt brn & black	.85	.50
a.		Double impression of center	575.00	
b.		Vert. pair, imperf. btwn.	550.00	
323	A42	20c orange & black	1.20	.80
a.		20c orange & brown	500.00	
b.		Imperf., pair	450.00	450.00
c.		As "a," imperf., pair	850.00	
d.		Vert. pair, imperf. between	550.00	
324	A42	24c gray & black	.85	.55
a.		Vert. pair, imperf. btwn.	550.00	
325	A42	1p rose lilac & blk	45.00	30.00
a.		Vert. pair, imperf. btwn.	625.00	
		Nos. 319-325 (7)	49.45	33.10

Opening of the Legislative Palace.
For overprints see Nos. O1-O4.

Coil Stamp
Rizal Type of 1906

1928		Perf. 11 Vertically	
326	A40	2c green	7.50	15.00

Types of 1906-23

1925-31		Unwmk.	Imperf.	
340	A40	2c yel grn ('31)	.15	.15
a.		green ('25)	.25	.15
341	A40	4c car rose ('31)	.15	.15
a.		carmine ('25)	.40	.20
342	A40	6c violet ('31)	1.00	1.00
a.		deep violet ('25)	8.00	4.00
343	A40	8c brown ('31)	.90	.90
a.		yellow brown ('25)	6.00	3.00
344	A40	10c blue ('31)	1.00	1.00
a.		deep blue ('25)	10.00	5.00
345	A40	12c dp orange ('31)	1.50	1.50
a.		red orange ('25)	10.00	5.00
346	A40	16c olive green (Dewey) ('31)	1.10	1.10
a.		bister green ('25)	8.50	4.00
347	A40	20c orange yel ('31)	1.10	1.10
a.		yellow ('25)	8.50	4.00
348	A40	26c green ('31)	1.10	1.10
a.		blue green ('25)	10.00	5.00
349	A40	30c light gray ('31)	1.25	1.00
a.		gray ('25)	10.00	5.00
350	A41	1p lt violet ('31)	4.00	4.00
a.		violet ('25)	70.00	30.00
351	A41	2p brn vio ('31)	10.00	10.00
a.		violet brown ('25)	150.00	50.00
352	A41	4p blue ('31)	30.00	30.00
a.		deep blue ('25)	700.00	300.00

353	A41 10p green ('31)	90.00	90.00
a.	deep green ('25)	1,000.	500.00
	Nos. 340-353 (14)	143.25	143.25

Mount Mayon, Luzon — A43

Post Office, Manila — A44

Pier No. 7, Manila Bay A45

(See footnote) A46

Rice Planting — A47

Rice Terraces — A48

Baguio Zigzag — A49

1932, May 3   Perf. 11

354	A43 2c yellow green	.40	.20
355	A44 4c rose carmine	.35	.25
356	A45 12c orange	.50	.50
357	A46 18c red orange	17.50	9.00
358	A47 20c yellow	.65	.55
359	A48 24c deep violet	1.00	.65
360	A49 32c olive brown	1.00	.70
	Nos. 354-360 (7)	21.40	11.85

The 18c vignette was intended to show Pagsanjan Falls in Laguna, central Luzon, and is so labeled. Through error the stamp pictures Vernal Falls in Yosemite Natl. Park, CA.
For overprints see #C29-C35, C47-C51, C63.

Nos. 302, 302a
Surcharged in Orange
or Red

1932

368	A41 1p on 4p blue (O)	2.00	.45
a.	1p on 4p dark blue (O)	2.75	1.30
369	A41 2p on 4p dark blue (R)	3.50	.75
a.	2p on 4p blue (R)	3.50	.75

Baseball — A50

Tennis — A51

Basketball — A52

1934, Apr. 14   Typo.   Perf. 11½

380	A50 2c yellow brown	1.50	.80
381	A51 6c ultramarine	.25	.20
a.	Vert. pair, imperf. between	1,250.	
382	A52 16c violet brown	.50	.50
a.	Vert. pair, imperf. horiz.	1,250.	

Tenth Far Eastern Championship Games.

Jose Rizal — A53

Woman and Carabao — A54

La Filipina — A55

Pearl Fishing — A56

Fort Santiago — A57

Salt Spring — A58

Magellan's Landing, 1521 A59

"Juan de la Cruz" A60

Rice Terraces — A61

"Blood Compact," 1565 — A62

Barasoain Church, Malolos — A63

Battle of Manila Bay, 1898 — A64

Montalban Gorge — A65

George Washington — A66

1935, Feb. 15   Engr.   Perf. 11

383	A53 2c rose	.15	.15
384	A54 4c yellow green	.20	.15
385	A55 6c dark brown	.15	.15
386	A56 8c violet	.15	.15
387	A57 10c rose carmine	.16	.15
388	A58 12c black	.15	.15
389	A59 16c dark blue	.15	.15
390	A60 20c light olive green	.20	.15
391	A61 26c indigo	.25	.25
392	A62 30c orange red	.25	.25
393	A63 1p red orange & black	1.65	1.25
394	A64 2p bister brn & black	4.00	1.25
395	A65 4p blue & black	4.00	2.75
396	A66 5p green & black	8.00	2.00
	Nos. 383-396 (14)	19.46	8.95

For overprints see Nos. 411-424, 433-446, 463-466, 468, 472-474, 478-484, 485-494, C52-C53, O15-O36, O38, O40-O43, N2-N3, NO6. For surcharges see Nos. 449, N4-N9, N28, NO2-NO5.

Commonwealth Issues

The Temples of Human Progress A67

1935, Nov. 15

397	A67 2c carmine rose	.15	.15
398	A67 6c deep violet	.20	.15
399	A67 16c blue	.20	.15
400	A67 36c yellow green	.35	.30
401	A67 50c brown	.55	.55
	Nos. 397-401 (5)	1.45	1.30

Inauguration of the Philippine Commonwealth, Nov. 15th, 1935.

Jose Rizal — A68

President Manuel L. Quezon — A69

1936, June 19   Perf. 12

402	A68 2c yellow brown	.15	.15
403	A68 6c slate blue	.15	.15
a.	Horiz. pair, imperf. vert.	1,350.	
404	A68 36c red brown	.50	.45
	Nos. 402-404 (3)	.80	
	Set value		.60

75th anniv. of the birth of Jose Rizal.

1936, Nov. 15   Perf. 11

408	A69 2c orange brown	.15	.15
409	A69 6c yellow green	.15	.15
410	A69 12c ultramarine	.15	.15
	Set value		.30	.25

1st anniv. of the Commonwealth.
For overprints see Nos. 467, 475.

Nos. 383-396 Overprinted in Black

COMMON-WEALTH a		COMMONWEALTH b	

1936-37   Perf. 11

411	A53 (a) 2c rose	.15	.15
a.	Booklet pane of 6	2.50	.65
412	A54 (b) 4c yel grn ('37)	.50	
413	A55 (a) 6c dark brown	.20	.15
414	A56 (b) 8c violet ('37)	.25	.20
415	A57 (b) 10c rose carmine	.20	.15
a.	"COMMONWEALT"		
416	A58 (b) 12c black ('37)	.20	.15
417	A59 (b) 16c dark blue	.20	.15
418	A60 (b) 20c lt ol grn ('37)	.65	.40
419	A61 (b) 26c indigo ('37)	.45	.35
420	A62 (b) 30c orange red	.35	.15
421	A63 (b) 1p red org & black	.65	.20
422	A64 (b) 2p bister brn & black ('37)	5.00	2.75

423	A65 (b) 4p blue & blk ('37)	17.50	3.00
424	A66 (b) 5p green & black ('37)	1.75	1.25
	Nos. 411-424 (14)	28.05	
	Nos. 411,413-424 (13)		9.05

Map of Philippines A70

Arms of Manila A71

1937, Feb. 3

425	A70 2c yellow green	.15	.15
426	A70 6c light brown	.15	.15
427	A70 12c sapphire	.15	.15
428	A70 20c deep orange	.25	.15
429	A70 36c deep violet	.55	.40
430	A70 50c carmine	.65	.35
	Nos. 425-430 (6)	1.90	
	Set value		1.00

33rd Eucharistic Congress.

1937, Aug. 27   Perf. 11

431	A71 10p gray	4.25	2.00
432	A71 20p henna brown	2.25	1.40

For overprints see Nos. 495-496. For surcharges see Nos. 451, C58.

Nos. 383-396 Overprinted in Black

COMMON-WEALTH a	COMMONWEALTH b

1938-40   Perf. 11

433	A53 (a) 2c rose ('39)	.15	.15
a.	Booklet pane of 6	3.50	.65
b.	"WEALTH COMMON-"	4,000.	
c.	Hyphen omitted		
434	A54 (b) 4c yel grn ('40)	1.25	—
435	A55 (b) 6c dk brn ('39)	.15	.15
a.	6c golden brown	.15	.15
436	A56 (b) 8c violet ('39)	.15	.15
a.	"COMMONWEALT"	65.00	
437	A57 (b) 10c rose car ('39)	.15	.15
a.	"COMMONWEALT"		
438	A58 (b) 12c black ('40)	.15	.15
439	A59 (b) 16c dark blue	.15	.15
440	A60 (a) 20c lt ol grn ('39)	.15	.15
441	A61 (b) 26c indigo ('40)	.20	.20
442	A62 (b) 30c org red ('39)	1.40	.70
443	A63 (b) 1p red org & blk	.40	.20
444	A64 (b) 2p bis brn & blk	2.75	.75
445	A65 (b) 4p bl & blk ('40)	100.00	75.00
446	A66 (b) 5p grn & blk ('40)	4.50	2.75
	Nos. 433-446 (14)	111.55	
	Nos. 433,435-446 (13)		80.65

Overprint "b" measures 18½x1¾mm. No. 433b occurs in booklet pane, No. 433a, position 5; all copies are straight-edged, left and bottom.

Stamps of 1917-37 Surcharged in Red, Violet or Black

FIRST FOREIGN	TRADE WEEK
	2 CENTAVOS
MAY 21-27, 1939	
FIRST FOREIGN TRADE WEEK	**50** CENTAVOS **50**
	FIRST FOREIGN TRADE WEEK
MAY 21-27, 1939 **6** CENTAVOS **6**	MAY 21-27, 1939

1939, July 5

449	A54 2c on 4c yel green (R)	.15	.15
450	A40 6c on 26c blue grn (V)	.15	.15
a.	6c on 26c deep	.65	.30
451	A71 50c on 20p henna brn (Bk)	1.00	1.00
	Nos. 449-451 (3)	1.30	1.30

Foreign Trade Week.

Triumphal Arch — A72

Malacanan Palace — A73

1939, Nov. 15
452	A72	2c yellow green	.15	.15
453	A72	6c carmine	.15	.15
454	A72	12c bright blue	.20	.15
		Set value	.35	.20

For overprints see Nos. 469, 476.

1939, Nov. 15
455	A73	2c green	.15	.15
456	A73	6c orange	.15	.15
457	A73	12c carmine	.20	.15
		Set value	.35	.20

#452-457 for 4th anniv. of the Commonwealth.
For overprint see No. 470.

Quezon Taking Oath of Office — A74

Jose Rizal — A75

1940, Feb. 8
458	A74	2c dark orange	.15	.15
459	A74	6c dark green	.15	.15
460	A74	12c purple	.25	.15
	Nos. 458-460 (3)		.55	
		Set value		.25

4th anniversary of Commonwealth.
For overprints see Nos. 471, 477.

Rotary Press Printing
1941, Apr. 14   *Perf. 11x10½*
Size: 19x22½mm
461	A75	2c apple green	.15	.15

Flat Plate Printing
1941-43   *Perf. 11*
Size: 18¾x22mm
462	A75	2c apple green ('43)	.15	.15
a.	2c pale apple green		.20	.15
b.	Bklt. pane of 6 (apple green, '43)		1.25	1.25
c.	Bklt. pane of 6 (pale apple green)		2.50	2.75

No. 462 was issued only in booklet panes and all copies have straight edges.
Further printings were made in 1942 and 1943 in different shades from the first supply of stamps sent to the islands.
For type A75 overprinted see Nos. 464, O37, O39, N1, NO1.

Philippine Stamps of 1935-41, Handstamped in Violet   **VICTORY**

1944   *Perf. 11, 11x10½*
463	A53	2c (#411)	260.00	95.00
a.	Booklet pane of 6		2,000.	
463B	A53	2c (#433)	1,200.	1,200.
464	A75	2c (#461)	2.50	2.25
465	A54	4c (#384)	25.00	25.00
466	A55	6c (#385)	1,500.	1,350.
467	A69	6c (#409)	110.00	85.00
468	A55	6c (#413)	650.00	600.00
469	A72	6c (#453)	135.00	110.00
470	A73	6c (#456)	600.00	550.00
471	A74	6c (#459)	160.00	150.00
472	A56	8c (#436)	15.00	20.00
473	A57	10c (#415)	110.00	75.00
474	A57	10c (#437)	135.00	110.00
475	A69	12c (#410)	400.00	175.00
476	A72	12c (#454)	3,500.	2,000.
477	A74	12c (#460)	190.00	135.00
478	A59	16c (#389)	700.00	
479	A59	16c (#417)	450.00	325.00
480	A59	16c (#439)	160.00	100.00
481	A60	20c (#440)	27.50	27.50
482	A62	30c (#420)	225.00	160.00
483	A62	30c (#442)	325.00	250.00
484	A63	1p (#443)	5,500.	4,000.

Nos. 463-484 are valued in the grade of fine to very fine.

Types of 1935-37 Overprinted

VICTORY   **VICTORY**

COMMON-WEALTH	COMMONWEALTH
a	b

1945   *Perf. 11*
485	A53 (a)	2c rose	.15	.15
486	A54 (b)	4c yellow green	.15	.15
487	A55 (b)	6c golden brown	.15	.15
488	A56 (b)	8c violet	.15	.15
489	A57 (b)	10c rose carmine	.15	.15
490	A58 (b)	12c black	.20	.15
491	A59 (b)	16c dark blue	.25	.15

492	A60 (a)	20c lt olive green	.30	.15
493	A62 (b)	30c orange red	.40	.35
494	A63 (b)	1p red org & black	1.10	.25

Nos. 431-432 Overprinted in Black   **VICTORY**
495	A71	10p gray	40.00	13.50
496	A71	20p henna brown	35.00	15.00
	Nos. 485-496 (12)		78.00	30.30

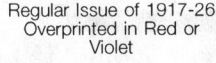

Jose Rizal — A76

Rotary Press Printing
1946, May 28   *Perf. 11x10½*
497	A76	2c sepia	.15	.15

For overprints see No. 503 (Philippines, Vol. 4) and No. O44.

Succeeding issues, released by the Philippine Republic on and after July 4, 1946, are listed in Vol. 5.

AIR POST STAMPS

Madrid-Manila Flight Issue

Regular Issue of 1917-26 Overprinted in Red or Violet

1926, May 13   **Unwmk.**   *Perf. 11*
C1	A40	2c green (R)	7.50	3.50
C2	A40	4c carmine	10.00	4.25
a.	Inverted overprint		2,000.	
C3	A40	6c lilac (R)	47.50	14.00
C4	A40	8c org brown	47.50	14.00
C5	A40	10c deep blue (R)	47.50	14.00
C6	A40	12c red orange	47.50	25.00
C7	A40	16c lt olive green (Sampson)	1,650.	1,550.
C8	A40	16c ol bister (Sampson) (R)	3,250.	2,600.
C9	A40	16c olive green (Dewey)	55.00	25.00
C10	A40	20c orange yellow	55.00	25.00
C11	A40	26c blue green	55.00	27.50
C12	A40	30c gray	55.00	27.50
C13	A41	2p vio brown (R)	475.00	260.00
C14	A41	4p dark blue (R)	675.00	450.00
C15	A41	10p deep green	1,050.	625.00

Same Overprint on No. 269
Wmk. 190PI
Perf. 12
C16	A40	26c blue green		2,400.

Same Overprint on No. 284
Perf. 10
C17	A41	1p pale violet	175.00	100.00

Flight of Spanish aviators Gallarza and Loriga from Madrid to Manila.

London-Orient Flight Issue

Regular Issue of 1917-25 Overprinted in Red   **L.O.F.**
1928

1928, Nov. 9   **Unwmk.**   *Perf. 11*
C18	A40	2c green	.40	.25
C19	A40	4c carmine	.50	.40
C20	A40	6c violet	1.75	1.40
C21	A40	8c orange brown	1.90	1.60
C22	A40	10c deep blue	1.90	1.60
C23	A40	12c red orange	2.75	2.25
C24	A40	16c ol green (Dewey)	2.00	1.50
C25	A40	20c orange yellow	2.75	2.25
C26	A40	26c blue green	8.00	5.50
C27	A40	30c gray	8.00	5.50

Same Overprint on No. 271
Wmk. 190PI
Perf. 12
C28	A41	1p pale violet	45.00	25.00
	Nos. C18-C28 (11)		74.95	47.25

Flight from London to Manila.

Nos. 354-360 Overprinted

ROUND-THE-WORLD FLIGHT
VON GRONAU
1932

1932, Sept. 27   **Unwmk.**   *Perf. 11*
C29	A43	2c yellow green	.40	.30
C30	A44	4c rose carmine	.40	.30
C31	A45	12c orange	.60	.50
C32	A46	18c red orange	3.50	3.25
C33	A47	20c yellow	1.75	1.50
C34	A48	24c deep violet	1.75	1.50
C35	A49	32c olive green	1.75	1.50
	Nos. C29-C35 (7)		10.15	8.85

Visit of Capt. Wolfgang von Gronau on his round-the-world flight.

Regular Issue of 1917-25 Overprinted
F. REIN
MADRID-MANILA
FLIGHT-1933

1933, Apr. 11
C36	A40	2c green	.40	.35
C37	A40	4c carmine	.45	.35
C38	A40	6c deep violet	.80	.75
C39	A40	8c orange brown	2.50	1.50
C40	A40	10c dark blue	2.25	1.00
C41	A40	12c orange	2.00	1.00
C42	A40	16c ol green (Dewey)	2.00	1.00
C43	A40	20c yellow	2.00	1.00
C44	A40	26c gray	2.25	1.50
a.	26c blue green		3.00	1.80
C45	A40	30c gray	3.00	1.75
	Nos. C36-C45 (10)		17.65	10.20

Flight from Madrid to Manila of aviator Fernando Rein y Loring.

Stamp of 1917 Overprinted

1933, May 26   **Unwmk.**   *Perf. 11*
C46	A40	2c green	.50	.40

Regular Issue of 1932 Overprinted

C47	A44	4c rose carmine	.20	.15
C48	A45	12c orange	.30	.15
C49	A47	20c yellow	.30	.20
C50	A48	24c deep violet	.40	.25
C51	A49	32c olive brown	.50	.35
	Nos. C46-C51 (6)		2.20	1.50

Nos. 387 and 392 Overprinted in Gold   **P.I.-U.S. INITIAL FLIGHT**
December · 1935

1935, Dec. 2
C52	A57	10c rose carmine	.30	.20
C53	A62	30c orange red	.50	.35

China Clipper flight from Manila to San Francisco, Dec. 2-5, 1935.

Regular Issue of 1917-25 Surcharged in Various Colors
MANILA-MADRID
ARNACAL
FLIGHT-1936
2 CENTAVOS 2

1936, Sept. 6   *Perf. 11*
C54	A40	2c on 4c carmine (Bl)	.15	.15
C55	A40	6c on 12c red org (V)	.15	.15
C56	A40	16c on 26c blue green (Bk)	.25	.20
a.	16c on 26c green (Bk)		1.25	.70
		Set value	.40	.35

Manila-Madrid flight by aviators Antonio Arnaiz and Juan Calvo.

Regular Issue of 1917-37 Surcharged in Black or Red
FIRST AIR MAIL EXHIBITION
Feb 17 to 19, 1939
8 CENTAVOS 8

1939, Feb. 17
C57	A40	8c on 26c blue green	.75	.40
a.	8c on 26c green		1.60	.55
C58	A71	1p on 10p gray (R)	3.00	2.25

1st Air Mail Exhib., Feb. 17-19, 1939.

Moro Vinta and Clipper — AP1

1941, June 30
C59	AP1	8c carmine	1.00	.60
C60	AP1	20c ultramarine	1.20	.45
C61	AP1	60c blue green	1.75	1.00
C62	AP1	1p sepia	.70	.50
	Nos. C59-C62 (4)		4.65	2.55

For overprint see No. NO7. For surcharges see Nos. N10-N11, N35-N36.

No. C47 Handstamped in Violet   **VICTORY**

1944, Dec. 3   **Unwmk.**   *Perf. 11*
C63	A44	4c rose carmine	1,600.	1,600.

SPECIAL DELIVERY STAMPS

US No. E5 Overprinted in Red   **PHILIPPINES**

1901, Oct. 15   **Wmk. 191**   *Perf. 12*
E1	SD3	10c dark blue	110.00	100.00

Special Delivery Messenger SD2

1906   **Engr.**   **Wmk. 191PI**
E2	SD2	20c ultramarine	30.00	7.50
b.	20c pale ultramarine		30.00	7.50

See Nos. E3-E6. For overprints see Nos. E7-E10, EO1.

Special Printing
Ovptd. in Red as #E1 on US #E6
1907
E2A	SD4	10c ultramarine		2,250.

1911   **Wmk. 190PI**
E3	SD2	20c deep ultramarine	20.00	1.75

1916   *Perf. 10*
E4	SD2	20c deep ultra	175.00	50.00

1919   **Unwmk.**   *Perf. 11*
E5	SD2	20c ultramarine	.60	.20
a.	20c pale blue		.75	.20
b.	20c dull violet		.60	.20

Type of 1906 Issue

1925-31   *Imperf.*
E6	SD2	20c dull violet ('31)	20.00	17.50

Type of 1919 Overprinted in Black   **COMMONWEALTH**

1939   *Perf. 11*
E7	SD2	20c blue violet	.25	.20

Nos. E5b and E7, Handstamped in Violet   **VICTORY**

1944   *Perf. 11*
E8	SD2	20c (On #E5b)	700.00	500.00
E9	SD2	20c (On #E7)	190.00	150.00

Type SD2 Overprinted "VICTORY" As No. 486

1945
E10	SD2	20c blue violet	.70	.55
a.	"IC" close together		3.25	2.75

SPECIAL DELIVERY OFFICIAL STAMP

Type of 1906 Issue
Overprinted **O. B.**

1931		Unwmk.		Perf. 11	
EO1	SD2	20c dull violet		.65	.40
a.		No period after "B"		20.00	15.00
b.		Double overprint			

POSTAGE DUE STAMPS

Postage Due Stamps of
the US Nos. J38-J44
Overprinted in Black

1899, Aug. 16		Wmk. 191		Perf. 12	
J1	D2	1c deep claret		5.75	1.25
J2	D2	2c deep claret		6.00	1.10
J3	D2	5c deep claret		15.00	2.25
J4	D2	10c deep claret		19.00	4.75
J5	D2	50c deep claret		200.00	90.00

No. J1 was used to pay regular postage Sept. 5-19, 1902.

1901, Aug. 31					
J6	D2	3c deep claret		17.50	6.00
J7	D2	30c deep claret		225.00	95.00
		Nos. J1-J7 (7)		488.25	200.35

Post Office Clerk — D3

		Unwmk.			
1928, Aug. 21		Engr.		Perf. 11	
J8	D3	4c brown red		.15	.15
J9	D3	6c brown red		.15	.15
J10	D3	8c brown red		.15	.15
J11	D3	10c brown red		.15	.15
J12	D3	12c brown red		.15	.15
J13	D3	16c brown red		.15	.15
J14	D3	20c brown red		.15	.15
		Set value		.90	.90

For overprints see Nos. O16-O22, NJ1. For surcharge see No. J15.

No. J8 Surcharged in **3 CVOS. 3**
Blue

1937					
J15	D3	3c on 4c brown red		.20	.15

Nos. J8-J14
Handstamped in **VICTORY**
Violet

1944					
J16	D3	4c brown red		125.00	—
J17	D3	6c brown red		80.00	—
J18	D3	8c brown red		85.00	—
J19	D3	10c brown red		80.00	—
J20	D3	12c brown red		80.00	—
J21	D3	16c brown red		85.00	—
J22	D3	20c brown red		85.00	—
		Nos. J16-J22 (7)		620.00	

OFFICIAL STAMPS

Official Handstamped Overprints

"Officers purchasing stamps for government business may, if they so desire, overprint them with the letters "O.B." either in writing with black ink or by rubber stamps but in such a manner as not to obliterate the stamp that postmasters will be unable to determine whether the stamps have been previously used." C. M. Cotterman, Director of Posts, Dec. 26, 1905.

Beginning with Jan. 1, 1906, all branches of the Insular Government used postage stamps to prepay postage instead of franking them as before. Some officials used manuscript, some utilized typewriting machines, some made press-printed overprints, but by far the larger number provided themselves with rubber stamps. The majority of these read "O.B." but other forms were: "OFFICIAL BUSINESS" or "OFFICIAL MAIL" in 2 lines, with variations on many of these.

These "O.B." overprints are known on US 1899-1901 stamps; on 1903-06 stamps in red and blue; on 1906 stamps in red, blue, black, yellow and green.

"O.B." overprints were also made on the centavo and peso stamps of the Philippines, per order of May 25, 1907.

Beginning in 1926, the Bureau of Posts issued press-printed official stamps, but many government offices continued to handstamp ordinary postage stamps "O.B."

Regular Issue of 1926 **OFFICIAL**
Overprinted in Red

1926, Dec. 20		Unwmk.		Perf. 12	
O1	A42	2c green & black		2.25	1.00
O2	A42	4c carmine & black		2.25	1.20
a.		Vertical pair, imperf. between		750.00	
O3	A42	18c lt brown & black		7.00	4.00
O4	A42	20c orange & black		6.75	1.75
		Nos. O1-O4 (4)		18.25	7.95

Opening of the Legislative Palace.

Regular Issue of 1917-26 **O.B.**
Overprinted

1931				Perf. 11	
O5	A40	2c green		.15	.15
a.		No period after "B"		15.00	5.00
b.		No period after "O"			
O6	A40	4c carmine		.15	.15
a.		No period after "B"		15.00	5.00
O7	A40	6c deep violet		.20	.15
O8	A40	8c yellow brn		.20	.15
O9	A40	10c deep blue		.30	.15
O10	A40	12c red orange		.25	.15
a.		No period after "B"		32.50	
O11	A40	16c lt ol green (Dewey)		.25	.15
a.		16c olive bister		1.25	.20
O12	A40	20c orange yellow		.25	.15
a.		No period after "B"		22.50	15.00
O13	A40	26c green		.40	.30
a.		26c blue green		1.00	.65
O14	A40	30c gray		.30	.25
		Nos. O5-O14 (10)		2.45	
		Set value			1.25

Same Overprint on Nos. 383-392

1935					
O15	A53	2c rose		.15	.15
a.		No period after "B"		15.00	5.00
O16	A54	4c yellow green		.15	.15
a.		No period after "B"		15.00	8.50
O17	A55	6c dark brown		.15	.15
a.		No period after "B"		20.00	17.50
O18	A56	8c violet		.15	.15
O19	A57	10c rose carmine		.20	.15
O20	A58	12c black		.20	.15
O21	A59	16c dark blue		.20	.15
O22	A60	20c lt olive green		.20	.15
O23	A61	26c indigo		.25	.20
O24	A62	30c orange red		.30	.25
		Set value		1.60	1.00

Same Overprint on Nos. 411 and 418

1937-38				Perf. 11	
O25	A53	2c rose		.15	.15
a.		No period after "B"		4.25	2.25
O26	A60	20c lt olive green ('38)		.65	.50
		Set value		.70	.55

Nos. 383-392 Overprinted in Black:

O. B.

	COMMON-	**O.**	**B.**
	WEALTH		
	a		b

1938-40					
O27	A53 (a)	2c rose		.15	.15
a.		Hyphen omitted		20.00	20.00
b.		No period after "B"		25.00	25.00
O28	A54 (b)	4c yellow green		.15	.15
O29	A55 (a)	6c dark brown		.15	.15
O30	A56 (b)	8c violet		.15	.15
O31	A57 (b)	10c rose carmine		.15	.15
a.		No period after "O"		30.00	30.00
O32	A58 (b)	12c black		.15	.15
O33	A59 (b)	16c dark blue		.20	.15
O34	A60 (a)	20c lt ol green ('40)		.25	.25
O35	A61 (b)	26c indigo		.30	.30
O36	A62 (b)	30c orange red		.25	.25
		Set value		1.60	1.25

No. 461 Overprinted in **O. B.**
Black

			Perf. 11x10½		
1941, Apr. 14		Unwmk.			
O37	A75	2c apple green		.15	.15

Official Stamps
Handstamped in **VICTORY**
Violet

1944			Perf. 11, 11x10½		
O38	A53	2c #O27		200.00	110.00
O39	A75	2c #O37		6.50	3.00
O40	A54	4c #O16		37.50	25.00
O40A	A55	6c #O29		4,250.	

O41	A57	10c #O31		135.00	
a.		No period after "O"		—	
O42	A60	20c #O22		6,000.	
O43	A60	20c #O26		1,550.	

No. 497 Overprinted Like No. O37 in
Black

			Perf. 11x10½		
1946, June 19		Unwmk.			
O44	A76	2c sepia		.15	.15

OCCUPATION STAMPS

Issued under Japanese Occupation

Nos. 461, 438 and 439 Overprinted with
Bars in Black

1942-43		Unwmk.	Perf. 11x10½, 11		
N1	A75	2c apple green		.15	.15
a.		Pair, one without overprint		—	
N2	A58	12c black ('43)		.15	.15
N3	A59	16c dark blue		5.00	3.75
		Nos. N1-N3 (3)		5.30	4.05

Nos. 435, 442, 443 and 423 Surcharged
in Black

a

b

16   16

50 CENTAVOS 50

c

1   1

● ONE PESO ●

d

			Perf. 11		
N4	A55	5c on 6c golden brn		.15	.15
a.		Top bar shorter, thinner		.20	.20
b.		5c on 6c dark brown		.20	.20
c.		As "b" and "a"		.20	.20
N5	A62	16c on 30c orange red ('43)		.25	.25
N6	A63	50c on 1p red org & black ('43)		.60	.60
a.		Double surcharge		300.00	
N7	A65	1p on 4p blue & black ('43)		110.00	120.00
		Nos. N4-N7 (4)		111.00	121.00

On Nos. N4 and N4b, the top bar measures 1½x22½mm. On Nos. N4a and N4c, the top bar measures 1x21mm and the "5" is smaller and thinner.

No. 384 Surcharged in Black

CONGRATULATIONS
FALL OF
BATAAN AND
CORREGIDOR
1942
2

1942, May 18					
N8	A54	2c on 4c yellow green		6.00	6.00

Japan's capture of Bataan and Corregidor. The American-Filipino forces finally surrendered May 7, 1942.

No. 384 Surcharged in Black

1942, Dec. 8					
N9	A54	5c on 4c yellow green		.50	.50

1st anniv. of the "Greater East Asia War."

Nos. C59 and C62 Surcharged in Black

ヒトー ギョー セイフ
イッシューオン キネン
1-23-43
2

1943, Jan. 23					
N10	AP1	2(c) on 8c carmine		.25	.25
N11	AP1	5c on 1p sepia		.50	.50

1st anniv. of the Philippine Executive Commission.

Nipa Hut — OS1   Rice Planting — OS2

Mt. Mayon and Mt. Fuji — OS3   Moro Vinta — OS4

		Engr., Typo. (2, 6, 25c)			
1943-44		Wmk. 257		Perf. 13	
N12	OS1	1c deep orange		.15	.15
N13	OS2	2c bright green		.15	.15
N14	OS1	4c slate green		.15	.15
N15	OS3	5c orange brown		.15	.15
N16	OS2	6c red		.15	.15
N17	OS3	10c blue green		.15	.15
N18	OS4	12c steel blue		1.00	1.00
N19	OS4	16c dark brown		.15	.15
N20	OS1	20c rose violet		1.25	1.25
N21	OS2	21c violet		.15	.15
N22	OS3	25c pale brown		.15	.15
N23	OS3	1p deep carmine		.75	.75
N24	OS2	2p dull violet		5.00	5.00
N25	OS4	5p dark olive		8.50	8.50
		Nos. N12-N25 (14)		17.85	17.85

For surcharges see Nos. NB5-NB7.

Map of Manila
Bay Showing
Bataan and
Corregidor
OS5

1943, May 7		Photo.		Unwmk.	
N26	OS5	2c carmine red		.15	.15
N27	OS5	5c bright green		.25	.25
		Set value		.35	.35

Fall of Bataan and Corregidor, 1st anniv.

No. 440 Surcharged in Black

12   12

1943, June 20   Engr.   *Perf. 11*
N28 A60 12c on 20c lt olive green .20 .20
a.   Double surcharge

350th anniv. of the printing press in the Philippines. "Limbagan" is Tagalog for "printing press."

Rizal Monument, Filipina and Philippine Flag — OS6

1943, Oct. 14   Photo.   *Perf. 12*
N29 OS6 5c light blue .15 .15
a.   Imperf. .15 .15
N30 OS6 12c orange .15 .15
a.   Imperf. .15 .15
N31 OS6 17c rose pink .20 .20
a.   Imperf. .20 .20
Set value .35 .35
Set value, imperf. .35 .35

"Independence of the Philippines." Japan granted "independence" Oct. 14, 1943, when the puppet republic was founded.
The imperforate stamps were issued without gum.

Jose Rizal — OS7

Rev. Jose Burgos — OS8

Apolinario Mabini — OS9

1944, Feb. 17   Litho.   *Perf. 12*
N32 OS7 5c blue .20 .20
a.   Imperf. .15 .15
N33 OS8 12c carmine .15 .15
a.   Imperf. .15 .15
N34 OS9 17c deep orange .15 .15
a.   Imperf. .15 .15
Set value .30 .30
Set value, imperf. .35 .35

Nos. C60 and C61 Surcharged in Black

REPÚBLICA NG PILIPINAS 5-7-44

1944, May 7   *Perf. 11*
N35 AP1 5c on 20c ultra .50 .35
N36 AP1 12c on 60c blue green 1.25 .85

Fall of Bataan and Corregidor, 2nd anniv.

Jose P. Laurel — OS10

Without Gum

1945, Jan. 12   Litho.   *Imperf.*
N37 OS10 5c dull violet brown .15 .15
N38 OS10 7c blue green .15 .15
N39 OS10 20c chalky blue .15 .15
Set value .25 .20

1st anniv. of the puppet Philippine Republic (Oct. 14, 1944). "S" stands for "sentimos."

OCCUPATION SEMI-POSTAL STAMPS

Woman, Farming and Cannery — OSP1

Unwmk.

1942, Nov. 12   Litho.   *Perf. 12*
NB1 OSP1 2c + 1c pale violet .15 .15
NB2 OSP1 5c + 1c brt green .25 .15
NB3 OSP1 16c + 2c orange 25.00 25.00
Nos. NB1-NB3 (3) 25.40 25.30

Campaign to produce and conserve food. The surtax aided the Red Cross.

Souvenir Sheet

OSP2

Without Gum

1943, Oct. 14   *Imperf.*
NB4 OSP2 Sheet of 3 45.00 6.00

"Independence of the Philippines."
No. NB4 contains Nos. N29a-N31a. Lower inscription from Rizal's "Last Farewell." Sold for 2.50p.

BAHÂ 1943 +21

Nos. N18, N20 and N21 Surcharged in Black

1943, Dec. 8   Wmk. 257   *Perf. 13*
NB5 OS4 12c + 21c steel blue .15 .15
NB6 OS1 20c + 36c rose violet .15 .15
NB7 OS3 21c + 40c violet .15 .15
Set value .30 .30

The surtax was for the benefit of victims of a Luzon flood. "Baha" is Tagalog for "flood."

Souvenir Sheet

OSP3

Without Gum

1944, Feb. 9 Unwmk. Litho. *Imperf.*
NB8 OSP3 Sheet of 3 5.00 3.00

No. NB8 contains Nos. N32a-N34a.
Sheet sold for 1p, surtax going to a fund for the care of heroes' monuments.

OCCUPATION POSTAGE DUE STAMP

No. J15 Ovptd. with Bar in Blue

1942, Oct. 14   Unwmk.   *Perf. 11*
NJ1 D3 3c on 4c brown red 35.00 20.00

On copies of No. J15, two lines were drawn in India ink with a ruling pen across "United States of America" by employees of the Short Paid Section of the Manila Post Office to make a provisional 3c postage due stamp which was used from Sept. 1, 1942, (when the letter rate was raised from 2c to 5c) until Oct. 14 when No. NJ1 went on sale.

OCCUPATION OFFICIAL STAMPS

Nos. 461, 413, 435, 435a and 442 Overprinted or Surcharged in Black with Bars and

1943-44 Unwmk. *Perf. 11x10½, 11*
NO1 A75 2c apple green .15 .15
a.   Double overprint 500.00
NO2 A55 5c on 6c dk brown
(#413, '44) 35.00 35.00
NO3 A55 5c on 6c gldn brn
(No. 435a) .15 .15
a.   Narrower spacing btwn. bars .15 .15
b.   5c on 6c dark brown (#435) .15 .15
c.   As "b," narrower spacing between bars .15 .15
d.   Double surcharge
NO4 A62 16c on 30c orange red .30 .30
a.   Wider spacing between bars .30 .30
Nos. NO1-NO4 (4) 35.60 35.60

On Nos. NO3 and NO3b, the bar deleting "United States of America" is 9¾-10mm above the bar deleting "Common-." On Nos. NO3a and NO3c, the spacing is 8-8½mm.
On No. NO4 the center bar is 19mm long, 3½mm below the top bar and 6mm above the Japanese characters. On No. NO4a, the center bar is 20½mm long, 9mm below the top bar and 1mm above the Japanese characters.
"K. P." (Kagamitang Pampamahalaan) is Tagalog for "Official Business."

Nos. 435 and 435a Surcharged in Black

REPUBLIKA NG PILIPINAS (K. P.)

1944   *Perf. 11*
NO5 A55 5c on 6c golden brown .15 .15
a.   5c on 6c dark brown .15 .15

Nos. O34 and C62 Overprinted in Black

Pilipinas REPUBLIKA

a

K. P.

REPUBLIKA NG PILIPINAS

b

(K. P.)

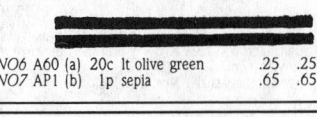

NO6 A60 (a) 20c lt olive green .25 .25
NO7 AP1 (b) 1p sepia .65 .65

PUERTO RICO

ˌpwer-tə-ˈrē-(ˌ)kō

(Porto Rico)

LOCATION — Large island in the West Indies, east of Hispaniola
GOVT. — Former Spanish possession
AREA — 3,435 sq. mi.
POP. — 953,243 (1899)
CAPITAL — San Juan

The island was ceded to the US by the Treaty of 1898.
Spanish issues of 1855-73 used in both Puerto Rico and Cuba are listed as Cuba Nos. 1-4, 9-14, 18-21, 32-34, 35A-37, 39-41, 43-45, 47-49, 51-53, 55-57.
Spanish issues of 1873-1898 for Puerto Rico only are listed in Vol. 4 of this Catalogue.

100 Cents = 1 Dollar (1898)

Issued under US Administration
Ponce Issue

A11

1898   Unwmk.   *Imperf.*
200 A11 5c violet, yellowish 7,000.

The only way No. 200 is known used is hand-stamped on envelopes. Both unused stamps and used envelopes have a violet control mark.
Counterfeits exist of Nos. 200-201.

Coamo Issue

A12

1898   Unwmk.   *Imperf.*
201 A12 5c black 650. 1,050.

There are ten varieties in the setting (see the Scott United States Specialized Catalogue). The stamps bear the control mark "F. Santiago" in violet.

US Nos. 279, 267, 281, 272 and 282C Overprinted in Black at 36 degree angle

1899   Wmk. 191   *Perf. 12*
210 A87 1c yellow green 5.00 1.40
a.   Ovpt. at 25 degree angle 7.50 2.25
211 A88 2c car, type III 4.25 1.25
a.   Ovpt. at 25 degree angle 5.50 2.25
212 A91 5c blue 9.00 2.50
213 A93 8c violet brown 27.50 17.50
a.   Ovpt. at 25 degree angle 32.50 18.50
c.   "PÖRTO RIC" 125.00 110.00
214 A94 10c brown, type I 17.50 6.00
Nos. 210-214 (5) 63.25 28.65

Misspellings of the overprint, actually broken letters (PÖRTO RICU, PORTU RICO, FORTO RICO), are found on 1c, 2c, 8c and 10c.

US Nos. 279 and 267 Overprinted Diagonally in Black

1900
215 A87 1c yellow green 6.00 1.40
216 A88 2c red 4.75 1.25
a.   2c orange red 5.25 1.25
b.   Inverted overprint 8,250.

POSTAGE DUE STAMPS

US Nos. J38, J39, J42 Overprinted like Nos. 210-214

1899   Wmk. 191   *Perf. 12*
J1 D2 1c deep claret 22.50 5.50
a.   Overprint at 25 degree angle 22.50 7.50
J2 D2 2c deep claret 11.00 6.00
a.   Overprint at 25 degree angle 15.00 7.00
J3 D2 10c deep claret 160.00 60.00
a.   Overprint at 25 degree angle 180.00 85.00
Nos. J1-J3 (3) 193.50 71.50

Stamps of Puerto Rico were replaced by those of the US.

Puerto Rico, U.S. issues, stamps can be mounted in the Scott U.S. Possessions album.

RYUKYU ISLANDS

LOCATION — Chain of 63 islands between Japan and Formosa, separating the East China Sea from the Pacific Ocean

GOVT. — Semi-autonomous under United States administration

AREA — 848 sq. mi.

POP. — 945,465 (1970)

CAPITAL — Naha, Okinawa

The Ryukyus were part of Japan until American forces occupied them in 1945. The islands reverted to Japan May 15, 1972.

Before the general issue of 1948, a number of provisional stamps were used. These included a mimeographed-handstamped adhesive for Kume Island, and various current stamps of Japan handstamped with chops by the postmasters of Okinawa, Amami, Miyako and Yaeyama. Although authorized by American authorities, these provisionals were local in nature, so are omitted in the listings that follow. They are listed in the Scott United States Specialized Catalogue.

100 Sen = 1 Yen

100 Cents = 1 Dollar (1958)

Catalogue values for all unused stamps in this country are for Never Hinged items.

Watermark

Wmk. 257

Cycad — A1

Lily — A2

Sailing Ship — A3

Farmer — A4

Wmk. 257

1949, July 18   Typo.   *Perf. 13*

Second Printing

1	A1	5s magenta	1.40	1.50
2	A2	10s yellow green	5.50	5.50
3	A1	20s yellow green	2.50	2.50
4	A3	30s vermilion	1.40	1.50
5	A2	40s magenta	1.40	1.50
6	A3	50s ultra	3.00	3.25
7	A4	1y ultra	5.50	5.50
		Nos. 1-7 (7)	20.70	21.25

First Printing

1a	A1	5s magenta	2.25	3.50
2a	A2	10s yellow green	1.40	2.00
3a	A1	20s yellow green	1.40	2.00
4a	A3	30s vermilion	2.25	3.25
5a	A2	40s magenta	50.00	50.00
6a	A3	50s ultramarine	2.25	3.50
7a	A4	1y ultramarine	450.00	290.00
		Nos. 1a-7a (7)	509.55	354.25

First printing: thick yellow gum, dull colors, rough perforations, grayish paper. Second printing: white gum, sharp colors, cleancut perforations, white paper.

Roof Tiles — A5   Ryukyu University — A6

Designs: 1y, Ryukyu girl. 2y, Shuri Castle. 3y, Guardian dragon. 4y, Two women. 5y, Sea shells.

Perf. 13x13½

1950, Jan. 21   Unwmk.   Photo.

8	A5	50s dark carmine rose	.20	.20
a.		White paper	.50	.50
9	A5	1y deep blue	2.50	2.00
10	A5	2y rose violet	11.00	6.00
11	A5	3y carmine rose	25.00	11.00
12	A5	4y grnsh gray	15.00	11.00
13	A5	5y blue green	7.50	5.00
		Nos. 8-13 (6)	61.20	35.20

No. 8a is on whiter paper with colorless gum. Issued Sept. 6, 1958. No. 8 is on toned paper with yellowish gum.

For surcharges see Nos. 16-17.

1951, Feb. 12   *Perf. 13½x13*

14	A6	3y red brown	55.00	20.00

Opening of Ryukyu University, Feb. 12.

Pine Tree — A7

1951, Feb. 19   *Perf. 13*

15	A7	3y dark green	50.00	20.00

Reforestation Week, Feb. 18-24.

Nos. 8 and 10 Surcharged in Black

Three types of 10y surcharge:
I - Narrow-spaced rules, "10" normal spacing.
II - Wide-spaced rules, "10" normal spacing.
III - Rules and "10" both wide-spaced.

1952   *Perf. 13x13½*

16	A5	10y on 50s, type II	9.00	9.00
a.		Type I	35.00	35.00
b.		Type III	40.00	40.00
17	A5	100y on 2y rose vio	1,900.	1,200.

Surcharge forgeries are known of No. 17. Authentication by competent experts is recommended.

Dove, Bean Sprout and Map — A8

Madanbashi Bridge — A9

1952, Apr. 1   *Perf. 13½x13*

18	A8	3y deep plum	120.00	35.00

Establishment of the Government of the Ryukyu Islands (GRI), Apr. 1, 1952.

1952-53

Designs: 2y, Main Hall, Shuri Castle. 3y, Shurei Gate. 6y, Stone Gate, Sogenji temple, Naha. 10y, Benzaiten-do temple. 30y, Sonohan Utaki (altar) at Shuri Castle. 50y, Tamaudum (royal mausoleum), Shuri. 100y, Stone Bridge, Hosho Pond.

19	A9	1y red	.20	.20
20	A9	2y green	.25	.25
21	A9	3y aqua	.35	.35
22	A9	6y blue	1.75	1.75
23	A9	10y crimson rose	2.50	.90
24	A9	30y olive green	11.00	6.50
a.		30y light olive green ('58)	30.00	
25	A9	50y rose violet	15.00	8.25
26	A9	100y claret	20.00	6.25
		Nos. 19-26 (8)	51.05	24.45

Issued: 1y, 2y, 3y, 11/20/52; others, 1/20/53.

Reception at Shuri Castle — A10

Perry and American Fleet A11

Perf. 13½x13, 13x13½

1953, May 26

27	A10	3y deep magenta	12.50	6.50
28	A11	6y dull blue	1.25	1.25

Centenary of the arrival of Commodore Matthew Calbraith Perry at Naha, Okinawa.

Chofu Ota and Pencil-shaped Matrix — A12

Shigo Toma and Pen — A13

1953, Oct. 1   *Perf. 13½x13*

29	A12	4y yellow brown	10.00	5.00

3rd Newspaper Week.

1954, Oct. 1

30	A13	4y blue	13.00	7.50

4th Newspaper Week.

Ryukyu Pottery A14

Noguni Shrine and Sweet Potato Plant A15

Designs: 15y, Lacquerware. 20y, Textile design.

1954-55   Photo.   *Perf. 13*

31	A14	4y brown	1.00	.60
32	A14	15y vermilion	4.00	2.00
33	A14	20y yellow orange	2.25	2.00
		Nos. 31-33 (3)	7.25	4.60

Issue dates: June 25, 1954, June 20, 1955. For surcharges see Nos. C19, C21, C23.

1955, Nov. 26

34	A15	4y blue	11.00	7.00

350th anniv. of the introduction of the sweet potato to the Ryukyu Islands.

Stylized Trees — A16

Willow Dance — A17

1956, Feb. 18   Unwmk.

35	A16	4y bluish green	10.00	5.00

Arbor Week, Feb. 18-24.

1956, May 1   *Perf. 13*

Design: 8y, Straw hat dance. 14y, Dancer in warrior costume with fan.

36	A17	5y rose lilac	.90	.60
37	A17	8y violet blue	2.00	1.65
38	A17	14y reddish brown	3.00	2.00
		Nos. 36-38 (3)	5.90	4.25

For surcharges see Nos. C20, C22.

Telephone A18

1956, June 8

39	A18	4y violet blue	15.00	7.00

Establishment of dial telephone system.

Garland of Pine, Bamboo and Plum — A19

Map of Okinawa and Pencil Rocket — A20

1956, Dec. 1   *Perf. 13½x13*

40	A19	2y multicolored	2.00	1.00

New Year, 1957.

1957, Oct. 1   Photo.   *Perf. 13½x13*

41	A20	4y deep violet blue	.75	.75

7th annual Newspaper Week, Oct. 1-7.

Phoenix — A21

1957, Dec. 1   Unwmk.   *Perf. 13*
42 A21 2y multicolored   .25 .25
New Year, 1958.

Ryukyu Stamps — A22

1958, July 1   *Perf. 13½*
43 A22 4y multicolored   .80 .80
10th anniversary of first Ryukyu stamps.

Yen Symbol and Dollar
Sign — A23

1958, Sept. 16   Typo.   *Perf. 11*
Without Gum
44 A23 ½c orange   .90   .90
  a. Imperf., pair   950.00
  b. Horiz. pair, imperf. btwn.   100.00
  c. Vert. pair, imperf. btwn.   150.00
  d. Vert. strip of 4, imperf. btwn.   500.00
45 A23 1c yellow green   1.40 1.40
  a. Horiz. pair, imperf. btwn.   150.00
  b. Vert. pair, imperf. btwn.   110.00
  c. Vert. strip of 3, imperf. btwn.   450.00
  d. Vert. strip of 4, imperf. btwn.   500.00
  e. Block of 4, imperf. btwn. vert &   —
    horiz.
46 A23 2c dark blue   2.25 2.25
  a. Horiz. pair, imperf. btwn.   150.00
  b. Vert. pair, imperf. btwn.   1,500.00
  c. Horiz. strip of 3, imperf. btwn.   300.00
  d. Horiz. strip of 4, imperf. btwn.   500.00
47 A23 3c deep carmine   1.75 1.50
  a. Horiz. pair, imperf. btwn.   150.00
  b. Vert. pair, imperf. btwn.   110.00
  c. Vert. strip of 3, imperf. btwn.   300.00
  d. Vert. strip of 4, imperf. btwn.   550.00
  e. Block of 4, imperf. btwn. vert &
    horiz.
48 A23 4c bright green   2.25 2.25
  a. Horiz. pair, imperf. btwn.   500.00
  b. Vert. pair, imperf. btwn.   150.00
49 A23 5c orange   4.25 3.75
  a. Horiz. pair, imperf. btwn.   150.00
  b. Vert. pair, imperf. btwn.   750.00
50 A23 10c aqua   5.75 4.75
  a. Horiz. pair, imperf. btwn.   200.00
  b. Vert. pair, imperf. btwn.   150.00
  c. Vert. strip of 3, imperf. btwn.   550.00
51 A23 25c brt vio blue   8.00 6.00
  a. Gummed paper ('61)   9.50   8.50
  b. Horiz. pair, imperf. btwn.   1,400.00
  d. Vert. strip of 3, imperf. btwn.   600.00
52 A23 50c gray   17.50 10.00
  a. Gummed paper ('61)   10.50   10.00
  b. Horiz. pair, imperf. btwn.   1,200.00
53 A23 $1 rose lilac   12.50 5.50
  a. Horiz. pair, imperf. btwn.   400.00
  b. Vert. pair, imperf. btwn.   1,750.00
  Nos. 44-53 (10)   56.55 38.30

Printed locally. Perforation, paper and shade varieties exist.
Nos. 51a, 52a are on off-white paper and perf 10.3.

Gate of Courtesy — A24

1958, Oct. 15   Photo.   *Perf. 13½*
54 A24 3c multicolored   1.25 1.00
Restoration of Shureimon, Gate of Courtesy, on
road leading to Shuri City.
Counterfeits exist.

Lion Dance
A25

Trees and
Mountains
A26

1958, Dec. 10   Unwmk.   *Perf. 13½*
55 A25 1½c multicolored   .25 .20
New Year, 1959.

1959, Apr. 30   Litho.   *Perf. 13½x13*
56 A26 3c bl, yel grn, grn & red   .70 .60
"Make the Ryukyus Green" movement.

Yonaguni
Moth
A27

1959, July 23   Photo.   *Perf. 13*
57 A27 3c multicolored   1.10 .90
Meeting of the Japanese Biological Education
Society in Okinawa.

Hibiscus
A28

Toy (Yakaji)
A29

3c, Fish (Moorish idol). 8c, Sea shell (Phalium
bandatum). 13c, Butterfly (Kallima Inachus
Eucerca), denomination at left, butterfly going up.
17c, Jellyfish (Dactylometra pacifera Goette).

Inscribed   琉球郵便

1959, Aug. 10   *Perf. 13x13½*
58 A28 ½c multicolored   .20 .20
59 A28 3c multicolored   .75 .40
60 A28 8c lt ultra, blk & ocher   10.00 5.50
61 A28 13c lt bl, gray & org   2.50 1.75
62 A28 17c vio bl, red & yel   20.00 9.00
  Nos. 58-62 (5)   33.45 16.85

Four-character inscription measures 10x2mm on
½c; 12x3mm on 3c, 8c; 8½x2mm on 13c, 17c.
See Nos. 76-80.

1959, Dec. 1   Litho.
63 A29 1½c gold & multi   .55 .38
New Year, 1960.

University
Badge
A30

1960, May 22   Photo.   *Perf. 13*
64 A30 3c multicolored   .95 .50
Opening of Ryukyu University, 10th anniv.

Dancer — A31

Designs: Various Ryukyu Dances.

1960, Nov. 1   Photo.   *Perf. 13*
Dark Gray Background
65 A31 1c yellow, red & vio   1.10 .80
66 A31 2½c crimson, bl & yel   2.50 1.00
67 A31 5c dk blue, yel & red   .65 .50
68 A31 10c dk blue, yel & car   .80 .65
  Nos. 65-68 (4)   5.05 2.95
See Nos. 81-87, 220.

Torch and
Nago
Bay — A32

Runners at
Starting
Line — A33

1960, Nov. 8
72 A32 3c lt bl, grn & red   5.25 2.25
73 A33 8c orange & slate grn   .75 .75
8th Kyushu Inter-Prefectural Athletic Meet,
Nago, Northern Okinawa, Nov. 6-7.

Little Egret
and Rising
Sun — A34

1960, Dec. 1   Unwmk.   *Perf. 13*
74 A34 3c redsh brown   5.50 2.50
National census.

Okinawa Bull
Fight — A35

1960, Dec. 10   *Perf. 13½*
75 A35 1½c bis, dk bl & red brn   1.75 .65
New Year, 1961.

Type of 1959 With Japanese Inscription
Redrawn:

琉 球 郵 便

1960-61   Photo.   *Perf. 13x13½*
76 A28 ½c multi ('61)   .45 .45
77 A28 3c multi ('61)   .90 .35
78 A28 8c lt ultra, blk & ocher   .90 .80
79 A28 13c blue, brn & red   1.10 .90
80 A28 17c vio bl, red & yel   15.00 6.00
  Nos. 76-80 (5)   18.35 8.50

Size of Japanese inscription on Nos. 78-80 is
10½x11½mm. On No. 79 the denomination is at
right, butterfly going down.
Issued: 8c-17c, July 1; 3c, Aug. 23; ½c, Oct.

Dancer Type of 1960 with "RYUKYUS"
Added in English

1961-64   *Perf. 13*
81 A31 1c multi   .15 .15
82 A31 2½c multi ('62)   .20 .15
83 A31 5c multi ('62)   .25 .25
84 A31 10c multi ('62)   .45 .40
84A A31 20c multi ('64)   3.00 1.40
85 A31 25c multi ('62)   .90 .90
86 A31 50c multi   2.25 1.40
87 A31 $1 multi   6.00 .25
  Nos. 81-87 (8)   13.20 4.90

Issue dates: 50c, $1, Sept. 1. 1c, Dec. 5. 25c,
Feb. 1. 2½c, 5c, 10c, June 20. 20c, Jan. 20.

Pine Tree — A36

1961, May 1   Photo.   *Perf. 13*
88 A36 3c yellow grn & red   1.50 1.25
"Make the Ryukyus Green" movement.

Naha,
Steamer and
Sailboat
A37

1961, May 20
89 A37 3c aqua   2.10 1.10
40th anniversary of Naha.

White Silver
Temple — A38

Books and
Bird — A39

1961, Oct. 1   Typo.   *Perf. 11*
90 A38 3c red brown   2.00 1.50
  a. Horiz. pair, imperf. between   500.00
  b. Vert. pair, imperf. between   600.00
Merger of townships Takamine, Kanegushiku
and Miwa with Itoman.

1961, Nov. 12   Litho.   *Perf. 13*
91 A39 3c multicolored   1.10 .90
Issued for Book Week.

Rising Sun and Eagles — A40

Symbolic Steps, Trees and Government Building — A41

1961, Dec. 10   **Photo.**   *Perf. 13¹/₂*
92 A40 1½c gold, ver & blk   2.00 1.50
New Year, 1962.

1962, Apr. 1   **Unwmk.**   *Perf. 13¹/₂*
Design: 3c, Government Building.
93 A41 1½c multicolored   .60 .60
94 A41 3c brt grn, red & gray   .80 .80
10th anniv. of the Government of the Ryukyu Islands (GRI).

Anopheles Hyrcanus Sinensis — A42
8c, Malaria eradication emblem & Shurei gate.

1962, Apr. 7   *Perf. 13¹/₂x13*
95 A42 3c multicolored   .60 .60
96 A42 8c multicolored   .90 .75
WHO drive to eradicate malaria.

Dolls and Toys — A43

Linden or Sea Hibiscus — A44

1962, May 5   **Litho.**   *Perf. 13¹/₂*
97 A43 3c red, blk, bl & buff   1.10 .75
Issued for Children's Day.

1962, June 1   **Photo.**
Flowers: 3c, Indian coral tree. 8c, Iju (Schima liukiuensis Nakai). 13c, Touch-me-not (garden balsam). 17c, Shell flower (Alpinia speciosa).
98 A44 ½c multicolored   .15 .15
99 A44 3c multicolored   .35 .15
100 A44 8c multicolored   .40 .40
101 A44 13c multicolored   .60 .55
102 A44 17c multicolored   1.00 .80
    Nos. 98-102 (5)   2.50 2.05
See #107, 114 for 1½c and 15c flower stamps.
For surcharge see No. 190.

Earthenware A45

1962, July 5   *Perf. 13¹/₂x13*
103 A45 3c multicolored   3.25 2.50
Issued for Philatelic Week.

Japanese Fencing (Kendo) A46

1962, July 25   *Perf. 13*
104 A46 3c multicolored   4.00 3.00
All-Japan Kendo Meeting, Okinawa, July 25.

Rabbit Playing near Water, Bingata Cloth Design — A47

Young Man and Woman, Stone Relief — A48

1962, Dec. 10   *Perf. 13x13¹/₂*
105 A47 1½c gold & multi   1.00 .80
New Year, 1963.

1963, Jan. 15   **Photo.**   *Perf. 13¹/₂*
106 A48 3c gold, black & blue   .90 .65
Issued for Adult Day.

Gooseneck Cactus A49

Trees and Wooded Hills A50

1963, Apr. 5   *Perf. 13x13¹/₂*
107 A49 1½c dk bl, grn, yel & pink   .15 .15
1963, Mar. 25   *Perf. 13¹/₂x13*
108 A50 3c ultra, grn & red brn   .90 .80
"Make the Ryukyus Green" movement.

Map of Okinawa A51

Hawks over Islands A52

1963, Apr. 30   **Unwmk.**   *Perf. 13¹/₂*
109 A51 3c multicolored   1.25 1.00
Opening of the Round Road on Okinawa.

1963, May 10   **Photo.**
110 A52 3c multicolored   1.10 .95
Issued for Bird Day, May 10.

Shioya Bridge — A53

1963, June 5
111 A53 3c multicolored   1.10 .95
Opening of Shioya Bridge over Shioya Bay.

Tsuikin-wan Lacquerware Bowl — A54

1963, July 1   **Unwmk.**   *Perf. 13¹/₂*
112 A54 3c multicolored   3.00 2.50
Issued for Philatelic Week.

Map of Far East and JCI Emblem — A55

1963, Sept. 16   **Photo.**   *Perf. 13¹/₂*
113 A55 3c multicolored   .70 .50
Meeting of the Intl. Junior Chamber of Commerce (JCI), Naha, Okinawa, Sept. 16-19.

Mamaomoto A56

Site of Nakagusuku Castle A57

1963, Oct. 15   *Perf. 13x13¹/₂*
114 A56 15c multicolored   1.50 .80
1963, Nov. 1   *Perf. 13¹/₂x13*
115 A57 3c multicolored   .70 .45
Protection of national cultural treasures.

Flame — A58

Dragon (Bingata Pattern) — A59

1963, Dec. 10   *Perf. 13¹/₂*
116 A58 3c red, dk bl & yel   .70 .45
15th anniversary of the Universal Declaration of Human Rights.

1963, Dec. 10   **Photo.**
117 A59 1½c multicolored   .50 .30
New Year, 1964.

Carnation A60

Pineapples and Sugar Cane A61

1964, May 10   *Perf. 13¹/₂*
118 A60 3c bl, yel, blk & car   .40 .35
Issued for Mother's Day.

1964, June 1
119 A61 3c multicolored   .40 .35
Agricultural census.

Minsah Obi (Sash Woven of Kapok) — A62

1964, July 1   **Unwmk.**   *Perf. 13¹/₂*
120 A62 3c dp bl, rose pink & ocher   .55 .45
   a.   3c dp bl, dp car & ocher   .70 .60
Issued for Philatelic Week.

Girl Scout and Emblem — A63

1964, Aug. 31   **Photo.**
121 A63 3c multicolored   .40 .30
10th anniversary of Ryukyuan Girl Scouts.

Shuri Relay Station — A64

Parabolic Antenna and Map — A65

1964, Sept. 1   **Unwmk.**   *Perf. 13¹/₂*
Black Overprint
122 A64 3c deep green   .65 .65
   a.   Figure "1" inverted   27.50 27.50
123 A65 8c ultra   1.25 1.25
Opening of the Ryukyu Islands-Japan microwave system carrying telephone and telegraph messages between the Ryukyus and Japan. Nos. 122-123 not issued without overprint.

Gate of Courtesy, Olympic Torch and Emblem — A66

1964, Sept. 7   **Photo.**   *Perf. 13¹/₂x13*
124 A66 3c ultra, yellow & red   .20 .15
Relaying of the Olympic torch on Okinawa en route to Tokyo.

"Naihanchi," Karate Stance — A67

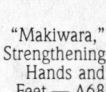
"Makiwara," Strengthening Hands and Feet — A68

"Kumite," Simulated Combat — A69

1964-65   **Photo.**   *Perf. 13¹/₂*
125 A67 3c dull claret, yel & blk   .50 .30
126 A68 3c yellow & multi ('65)   .40 .30
127 A69 3c gray, red & blk ('65)   .40 .30
    Nos. 125-127 (3)   1.30 .90
Karate, Ryukyuan self-defense sport.
Issued: #125, 10/5; #126, 2/5; #127, 6/5.

Miyara Dunchí — A70

Snake and Iris (Bingata) — A71

1964, Nov. 1 *Perf. 13½*
128 A70 3c multicolored .25 .20
Protection of national cultural treasures. Miyara Dunchi was built as a residence by Miyara-pechin Toen in 1819.

1964, Dec. 10 Photo.
129 A71 1½c multicolored .25 .20
New Year, 1965.

Boy Scouts — A72

1965, Feb. 6 *Perf. 13½*
130 A72 3c lt blue & multi .45 .30
10th anniversary of Ryukyuan Boy Scouts.

Main Stadium, Onoyama A73

1965, July 1 *Perf. 13x13½*
131 A73 3c multicolored .20 .20
Inauguration of the main stadium of the Onoyama athletic facilities.

Samisen of King Shoko — A74

1965, July 1 Photo. *Perf. 13½*
132 A74 3c buff & multi .45 .30
Issued for Philatelic Week.

Kin Power Plant — A75

ICY Emblem, Ryukyu Map — A76

1965, July 1
133 A75 3c green & multi .20 .20
Completion of Kin power plant.

1965, Aug. 24 Photo. *Perf. 13½*
134 A76 3c multicolored .20 .15
UN, 20th anniv.; Intl. Cooperation Year, 1964-65.

Naha City Hall — A77

1965, Sept. 18 Unwmk. *Perf. 13½*
135 A77 3c blue & multi .20 .15
Completion of Naha City Hall.

Chinese Box Turtle A78

Horse (Bingata) A79

Turtles: No. 137, Hawksbill turtle (denomination at top, country name at bottom). No. 138, Asian terrapin (denomination and country name on top).

1965-66 Photo. *Perf. 13½*
136 A78 3c gldn brn & multi .30 .30
137 A78 3c black, yel & brn .30 .30
138 A78 3c gray & multi .30 .30
Nos. 136-138 (3) .90 .90
Issue dates: No. 136, Oct. 20, 1965. No. 137, Jan. 20, 1966. No. 138, Apr. 20, 1966.

1965, Dec. 10 Photo. *Perf. 13½*
139 A79 1½c multicolored .15 .15
a. Gold omitted 1,200. 1,200.
New Year, 1966.

Noguchi's Okinawa Woodpecker A80

Sika Deer A81

1966 Photo. *Perf. 13½*
140 A80 3c shown .20 .20
141 A81 3c shown .25 .25
142 A81 3c Dugong .25 .25
Nos. 140-142 (3) .70 .70
Nature conservation.
Issued: #140, Feb. 15; #141, Mar. 15; #142, Apr. 20.

Ryukyu Bungalow Swallow — A82

1966, May 10 Photo. *Perf. 13½*
143 A82 3c sky blue, blk & brn .15 .15
4th Bird Week, May 10-16.

Lilies and Ruins A83

1966, June 23 *Perf. 13x13½*
144 A83 3c multicolored .15 .15
Memorial Day, commemorating the end of the Battle of Okinawa, June 23, 1945.

University of the Ryukyus A84

1966, July 1
145 A84 3c multicolored .15 .15
Transfer of the University of the Ryukyus from US authority to the Ryukyu Government.

Lacquerware, 18th Century — A85

Tile-Roofed House and UNESCO Emblem — A86

1966, Aug. 1 *Perf. 13½*
146 A85 3c gray & multi .15 .15
Issued for Philatelic Week.

1966, Sept. 20 Photo. *Perf. 13½*
147 A86 3c multicolored .15 .15
UNESCO, 20th anniv.

Government Museum and Dragon Statue — A87

1966, Oct. 6
148 A87 3c multicolored .15 .15
Completion of the GRI (Government of the Ryukyu Islands) Museum, Shuri.

Tomb of Nakasone-Tuimya Genga, Ruler of Miyako — A88

1966, Nov. 1 Photo. *Perf. 13½*
149 A88 3c multicolored .15 .15
Protection of national cultural treasures.

Ram in Iris Wreath (Bingata) A89

Clown Fish A90

1966, Dec. 10 Photo. *Perf. 13½*
150 A89 1½c dk blue & multi .15 .15
New Year, 1967.

1966-67

Fish: No. 152, Young boxfish (white numeral at lower left). No. 153, Forceps fish (pale buff numeral at lower right). No. 154, Spotted triggerfish (orange numeral). No. 155, Saddleback butterflyfish (carmine numeral, lower left).

151 A90 3c org red & multi .20 .15
152 A90 3c org yel & multi ('67) .20 .15
153 A90 3c multi ('67) .30 .25
154 A90 3c multi ('67) .30 .25
155 A90 3c multi ('67) .30 .25
Nos. 151-155 (5) 1.30 1.05
Issue dates: #151, Dec. 20. #152, Jan. 10. #153, Apr. 10. #154, May 25. #155, June 10.

Tsuboya Urn — A91

Episcopal Miter — A92

1967, Apr. 20
156 A91 3c yellow & multi .20 .20
Issued for Philatelic Week.

1967-68 Photo. *Perf. 13½*
Seashells: No. 158, Venus comb murex. No. 159, Chiragra spider. No. 160, Green turban. No. 161, Euprotomus bulla.

157 A92 3c lt green & multi .20 .15
158 A92 3c grnsh bl & multi .20 .15
159 A92 3c emerald & multi .25 .20
160 A92 3c lt blue & multi .30 .20
161 A92 3c brt blue & multi .60 .35
Nos. 157-161 (5) 1.55 1.05
Issued: 1967, #157, July 20; #158, Aug. 30. 1968; #159, Jan. 18; #160, Feb. 20; #161, June 5.

Red-tiled Roofs and ITY Emblem — A93

1967, Sept. 11 Photo. *Perf. 13½*
162 A93 3c multicolored .20 .20
International Tourist Year.

Mobile TB Clinic — A94

1967, Oct. 13 Photo. *Perf. 13½*
163 A94 3c lilac & multi .20 .20
Anti-Tuberculosis Society, 15th anniv.

Hojo Bridge, Enkaku Temple, 1498 — A95

1967, Nov. 1
164 A95 3c blue grn & multi .20 .20
Protection of national cultural treasures.

Monkey (Bingata) — A96

TV Tower and Map — A97

1967, Dec. 11 Photo. *Perf. 13½*
165 A96 1½c silver & multi .20 .20
New Year 1968.

1967, Dec. 22
166 A97 3c multicolored .25 .20
Opening of Miyako and Yaeyama television stations.

Dr. Kijin Nakachi and Helper — A98

Pill Box (Inro) — A99

1968, Mar. 15　Photo.　Perf. 13½
167 A98 3c multicolored　　　　.25 .20
120th anniv. of the first vaccination in the Ryukyu Islands, performed by Dr. Kijin Nakachi.

1968, Apr. 18
168 A99 3c gray & multi　　　　.45 .45
Philatelic Week.

Young Man, Library, Book and Map of Ryukyu Islands — A100

1968, May 13
169 A100 3c multicolored　　　　.30 .25
10th International Library Week.

Mailmen's Uniforms and Stamp of 1948 A101

1968, July 1　Photo.　Perf. 13x13½
170 A101 3c multicolored　　　　.30 .25
1st Ryukyuan postage stamps, 20th anniv.

Main Gate, Enkaku Temple — A102

Photo. & Engr.
1968, July 15　　　　　　Perf. 13½
171 A102 3c multicolored　　　　.30 .25
Restoration of the main gate of the Enkaku Temple, built 1492-1495, and destroyed during WWII.

Old Man's Dance — A103

1968, Sept. 15　Photo.　Perf. 13½
172 A103 3c gold & multi　　　　.30 .25
Issued for Old People's Day.

Mictyris Longicarpus A104

Crabs: No. 174, Uca dubia stimpson. No. 175, Saptozius vinosus. No. 176, Cardisoma carnifex. No. 177, Ocypode ceratophthalma pallas.

1968-69　　Photo.　　Perf. 13½
173 A104 3c blue, ocher & blk　　.30 .25
174 A104 3c lt bl grn & multi　　.35 .25
175 A104 3c lt green & multi　　.35 .25

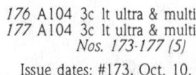

176 A104 3c lt ultra & multi　　.45 .30
177 A104 3c lt ultra & multi　　.45 .30
　　Nos. 173-177 (5)　　1.90 1.35
Issue dates: #173, Oct. 10. #174, Feb. 5, 1969. #175, Mar. 5, 1969. #176, May 15, 1969; #177, June 2, 1969.

Saraswati Pavilion — A105

1968, Nov. 1　Photo.　Perf. 13½
178 A105 3c multicolored　　　　.30 .20
Restoration of the Saraswati Pavilion (in front of Enkaku Temple), destroyed during WWII.

Tennis Player A106

Cock and Iris (Bingata) A107

1968, Nov. 3　Photo.　Perf. 13½
179 A106 3c green & multi　　　　.40 .30
35th All-Japan East-West Men's Soft-ball Tennis Tournament, Naha City, Nov. 23-24.

1968, Dec. 10
180 A107 1½c orange & multi　　.20 .15
New Year, 1969.

Boxer — A108

Ink Slab Screen — A109

1969, Jan. 3
181 A108 3c gray & multi　　　　.40 .25
20th All-Japan Amateur Boxing Championships, University of the Ryukyus, Jan. 3-5.

1969, Apr. 17　Photo.　Perf. 13½
182 A109 3c salmon, indigo & red　.40 .20
Philatelic Week.

Box Antennas and Map of Radio Link A110

Gate of Courtesy and Emblems A111

1969, July 1　Photo.　Perf. 13½
183 A110 3c multicolored　　　　.25 .20
Opening of the UHF (radio) circuit system between Okinawa and the outlying Miyako-Yaeyama Islands.

1969, Aug. 1　Photo.　Perf. 13½
184 A111 3c Prus bl, gold & ver　.25 .20
22nd All-Japan Formative Education Study Conference, Naha, Aug. 1-3.

Tug of War Festival A112

Hari Boat Race A113

Izaiho Ceremony, Kudaka Island A114

Mortardrum Dance — A115

Sea God Dance A116

1969-70　　　Photo.　　Perf. 13
185 A112 3c multicolored　　　.30 .25
186 A113 3c multicolored　　　.35 .25
187 A114 3c multicolored　　　.35 .25
188 A115 3c multicolored ('70)　.50 .35
189 A116 3c multicolored ('70)　.50 .35
　　Nos. 185-189 (5)　　2.00 1.45
Folklore. Issue dates: #185, Aug. 1; #186, Sept. 5; #187, Oct. 3; #188, Jan. 20; #189, Feb. 27.

No. 99 Surcharged　改訂½¢

1969, Oct. 15　Photo.　Perf. 13½
190 A44　½c on 3c multi　　　.90 .90

Nakamura-ke Farm House, Built 1713-51 A117

1969, Nov. 1　Photo.　Perf. 13½
191 A117 3c multicolored　　　.20 .15
Protection of national cultural treasures.

Statue of Kyuzo Toyama, Maps of Hawaiian and Ryukyu Islands — A118

1969, Dec. 5　Photo.　Perf. 13½
192 A118 3c lt ultra & multi　　.35 .35
a.　Without overprint　　　2,500.
b.　Wide-spaced bars　　　725.00
Ryukyu-Hawaii emigration led by Kyuzo Toyama, 70th anniversary.
The overprint - "1969" at lower left and bars across "1970" at upper right - was applied before No. 192 was issued.

Dog and Flowers (Bingata) A119

Sake Flask Made from Coconut A120

1969, Dec. 10
193 A119 1½c pink & multi　　.15 .15
New Year, 1970.

1970, Apr. 15　Photo.　Perf. 13½
194 A120 3c multicolored　　　.25 .20
Philatelic Week.

Classic Opera Issue

"The Bell" (Shushin Kaneiri) — A121

Child and Kidnapper (Chunusudu) A122

Robe of Feathers (Mekarushi) A123

Vengeance of Two Young Sons (Nidotichiuchi) A124

The Virgin and the Dragon (Kokonomaki) A125

1970　　　　Photo.　　Perf. 13½
195 A121 3c dull bl & multi　　.40 .40
196 A122 3c lt blue & multi　　.40 .40
197 A123 3c bluish grn & multi　.40 .40
198 A124 3c dull bl grn & multi　.40 .40
199 A125 3c multicolored　　　.40 .40
　　Nos. 195-199 (5)　　2.00 2.00
195a-199a, 5 sheets of 4　20.00 20.00
Issue dates: #195, Apr. 28. #196, May 29. #197, June 30. #198, July 30. #199, Aug. 25.

Underwater Observatory and Tropical Fish — A126

1970, May 22
200 A126 3c blue grn & multi　　.30 .25
Completion of the underwater observatory at Busena-Misaki, Nago.

Noboru Jahana (1865-1908), Politician A127

Map of Okinawa and People A128

Portraits: No. 202, Saion Gushichan Bunjaku (1682-1761), statesman. No. 203, Choho Giwan (1823-1876), regent and poet.

1970-71   Engr.   Perf. 13½
201 A127 3c rose claret   .50 .30
202 A127 3c dull blue green   .75 .55
203 A127 3c black   .50 .30
    Nos. 201-203 (3)   1.75 1.15

Issue dates: No. 201, Sept. 25, 1970. No. 202, Dec. 22, 1970. No. 203, Jan. 22, 1971.

1970, Oct. 1   Photo.
204 A128 3c red & multi   .25 .15
          Oct. 1, 1970 census.

Great Cycad of Une — A129

1970, Nov. 2   Photo.   Perf. 13½
205 A129 3c gold & multi   .25 .20
     Protection of national treasures.

Japanese Flag, Diet and Map of Ryukyus A130

Wild Boar and Cherry Blossoms (Bingata) A131

1970, Nov. 15   Photo.   Perf. 13½
206 A130 3c ultra & multi   .80 .50

Citizens' participation in national administration according to Japanese law of Apr. 24, 1970.

1970, Dec. 10
207 A131 1½c multicolored   .15 .15
          New Year, 1971.

Low Hand Loom (Jibata) — A132

Farmer Wearing Palm Bark Raincoat and Kuba Leaf Hat — A133

Fisherman's Wooden Box and Scoop — A134

Designs: No. 209, Woman running a filature (reel). No. 211, Woman hulling rice with cylindrical "Shiri-ushi."

1971   Photo.   Perf. 13½
208 A132 3c lt blue & multi   .30 .25
209 A132 3c pale grn & multi   .30 .25
210 A133 3c lt blue & multi   .35 .25
211 A132 3c yellow & multi   .40 .30
212 A134 3c gray & multi   .35 .25
    Nos. 208-212 (5)   1.70 1.30

Issue dates: #208, Feb. 16; #209, Mar. 16; #210, Apr. 30; #211, May 20; #212, June 15.

Water Carrier (Taku) — A135

1971, Apr. 15   Photo.   Perf. 13½
213 A135 3c blue grn & multi   .35 .25
          Philatelic Week.

Old and New Naha, and City Emblem A136

1971, May 20   Perf. 13
214 A136 3c ultra & multi   .25 .20
50th anniversary of Naha as a municipality.

Caesalpinia Pulcherrima — A137

Design: 2c, Madder (Sandanka).

1971   Photo.   Perf. 13
215 A137 2c gray & multi   .15 .15
216 A137 3c gray & multi   .20 .15
     Issue dates: 2c, Sept. 30; 3c, May 10.

View from Mabuni Hill — A138

Mt. Arashi from Haneji Sea — A139

Yabuchi Island from Yakena Port — A140

1971-72
217 A138 3c green & multi   .20 .15
218 A139 3c blue & multi   .20 .15
219 A140 4c multi ('72)   .25 .15
    Nos. 217-219 (3)   .65 .45

Government parks. Issue dates: No. 217, July 30; No. 218, Aug. 30, 1971; No. 219, Jan. 20, 1972.

Dancer — A141

Deva King, Torinji Temple — A142

1971, Nov. 1   Photo.   Perf. 13
220 A141 4c Prus blue & multi   .20 .15

1971, Dec. 1
221 A142 4c dp blue & multi   .20 .20
  Protection of national cultural treasures.

Rat and Chrysanthemums A143

Student Nurse A144

1971, Dec. 10
222 A143 2c brown org & multi   .15 .15
          New Year 1972.

1971, Dec. 24
223 A144 4c lilac & multi   .20 .15
     Nurses' training, 25th anniversary.

Birds on Seashore A145

Sun over Islands A147

Coral Reef — A146

1972   Photo.   Perf. 13
224 A145 5c brt blue & multi   .40 .25
225 A146 5c gray & multi   .40 .25
226 A147 5c ocher & multi   .40 .25
    Nos. 224-226 (3)   1.20 .75

Issue dates: No. 224, Apr. 14; No. 225, Mar. 30; No. 226, Mar. 21.

Dove, US and Japanese Flags — A148

1972, Apr. 17   Photo.   Perf. 13
227 A148 5c brt blue & multi   .60 .45

Ratification of the Reversion Agreement with US under which the Ryukyu Islands were returned to Japan.

Antique Sake Pot (Yushibin) — A149

1972, Apr. 20
228 A149 5c ultra & multi   .50 .35
          Philatelic Week.
Ryukyu stamps were replaced by those of Japan after May 15, 1972.

AIR POST STAMPS

Dove and Map of Ryukyus — AP1

Perf. 13x13½
1950, Feb. 15   Unwmk.   Photo.
C1 AP1 8y bright blue   120.00 50.00
C2 AP1 12y green   35.00 20.00
C3 AP1 16y rose carmine   15.00 15.00
   Nos. C1-C3 (3)   170.00 85.00

Heavenly Maiden AP2

1951-54
C4 AP2 13y blue   2.25 1.50
C5 AP2 18y green   3.25 2.25
C6 AP2 30y cerise   6.00 1.75
C7 AP2 40y red violet   7.00 5.50
C8 AP2 50y yellow orange   9.00 6.50
   Nos. C4-C8 (5)   27.50 17.50

Issue dates: Oct. 1, 1951, Aug. 16, 1954.

Heavenly Maiden Playing Flute — AP3

1957, Aug. 1   Engr.   Perf. 13½
C9 AP3 15y blue green   8.00 3.50
C10 AP3 20y rose carmine   12.00 5.50
C11 AP3 35y yellow green   14.00 6.50
C12 AP3 45y reddish brown   16.00 8.00
C13 AP3 60y gray   18.00 10.00
    Nos. C9-C13 (5)   68.00 33.50

Same Surcharged in Brown Red or Light Ultramarine   改訂 9¢

1959, Dec. 20
C14 AP3 9c on 15y (BrR)   2.50 1.50
a.   Inverted surcharge   850.00
C15 AP3 14c on 20y (LU)   3.00 3.00
C16 AP3 19c on 35y (BrR)   7.00 5.00
C17 AP3 27c on 45y (LU)   15.00 6.00
C18 AP3 35c on 60y (BrR)   15.00 9.00
    Nos. C14-C18 (5)   42.50 24.50

改訂

Nos. 31-33, 36 and 38 Surcharged in Black, Brown, Red, Blue or Green

9¢

1960, Aug. 3   Photo.   Perf. 13
C19 A14 9c on 4y   3.00   1.00
a.   Inverted surcharge   12,000. 15,000.
C20 A17 14c on 5y (Br)   3.50   1.75
C21 A14 19c on 15y (R)   2.25   1.50
C22 A17 27c on 14y (Bl)   7.50   2.75
C23 A14 35c on 20y (G)   6.00   3.75
    Nos. C19-C23 (5)   22.25 10.75

Wind God — AP4

Designs: 9c, Heavenly Maiden (as on AP2). 14c, Heavenly Maiden (as on AP3). 27c, Wind God at right. 35c, Heavenly Maiden over treetops.

1961, Sept. 21   Photo.   Perf. 13½
C24 AP4 9c multicolored   .30   .20
C25 AP4 14c multicolored   .70   .60
C26 AP4 19c multicolored   .70   .70
C27 AP4 27c multicolored   .30   .60
C28 AP4 35c multicolored   1.50 1.25
    Nos. C24-C28 (5)   6.20 3.35

Jet over Gate of Courtesy — AP5

Jet Plane — AP6

1963, Aug. 28   Perf. 13x13½
C29 AP5 5½c multicolored   .25   .25
C30 AP6 7c multicolored   .25   .25

SPECIAL DELIVERY STAMP

Dragon and Map of
Ryukyus — SD1

Perf. 13x13½

1950, Feb. 15   Unwmk.   Photo.
E1   SD1 5y bright blue   27.50 16.00

UNITED NATIONS

yu–ˌnī–təd 'nā–shənz

LOCATION — Headquarters in New York City

United Nations stamps are used on UN official mail sent from UN Headquarters, NY, or from the UN Offices in Geneva, Switzerland, and Vienna, Austria to points throughout the world. They may be used on private correspondence sent through the UN post offices, and are valid only at the individual UN post offices.

UN mail is carried by the US, Swiss and Austrian postal systems.

The UN stamps issued for use in Geneva and Vienna are listed in separate sections at the end of the NY issues. They are denominated in centimes and francs, and are valid only in Geneva or Vienna. The UN stamps issued for use in New York, denominated in cents and dollars, are valid only in New York.

Letters bearing Nos. 170-174 provide an exception as they were carried by the Canadian postal system.

See Switzerland Nos. 7O1-7O39 in Volume 6 for stamps issued by the Swiss Government for official use of the UN European Office in Geneva.

The 1962 UN Temporary Executive Authority (UNTEA) overprints on stamps of Netherlands New Guinea are listed under West Irian in Volume 6.

> Catalogue values for all unused stamps in this country are for Never Hinged items.

> Stamps are inscribed in English, French or Spanish or are multi-lingual.

Watermark

Wmk. 309- Wavy Lines

Peoples of the
World — A1

UN Headquarters
Building — A2

"Peace, Justice,
Security" — A3

UN Flag — A4

UN Children's
Fund — A5

World Unity — A6

Perf. 13x12½, 12½x13, 12½x13½
(2c, 5c)

1951   Unwmk.   Engr. & Photo.

1	A1	1c magenta	.15	.15
2	A2	1½c blue green	.15	.15
3	A3	2c purple	.15	.15
4	A4	3c magenta & blue	.15	.15
5	A5	5c blue	.15	.15
6	A1	10c chocolate	.25	.20
7	A4	15c violet & blue	.25	.20
8	A6	20c dark brown	.40	.20
9	A4	25c ol gray & blue	.40	.20
10	A2	50c indigo	3.50	1.50
11	A3	$1 red	1.60	.65
		Nos. 1-11 (11)	7.15	3.70

See Offices in Geneva Nos. 4, 14.

Veteran's War
Memorial
Building, San
Francisco
A7

1952, Oct. 24   Engr.   Perf. 12
12   A7 5c blue   .20   .20
7th anniv. of the signing of the UN charter.

Globe and
Encircled
Flame — A8

1952, Dec. 10   Perf. 13½x14
13   A8 3c deep green   .15   .15
14   A8 5c blue   .25   .25
      Set value   .30
Fourth anniv. of the adoption of the Universal Declaration of Human Rights.

Refugee Family — A9

1953, Apr. 24   Perf. 12½x13
15   A9 3c dk red brn & rose brn   .15   .15
16   A9 5c indigo & blue   .35   .30
"Protection for Refugees."

Envelope, UN
Emblem and
Map — A10

1953, June 12   Unwmk.   Perf. 13
17   A10 3c black brown   .15   .15
18   A10 5c dark blue   .75   .60
Issued to honor the UPU.

Gearwheels and
UN
Emblem — A11

1953, Oct. 24   Perf. 13x12½
19   A11 3c dark gray   .20   .15
20   A11 5c dark green   .40   .40
UN activities in the field of technical assistance.

Hands Reaching
Toward
Flame — A12

Ear of
Wheat — A13

1953, Dec. 10   Perf. 12½x13
21   A12 3c bright blue   .20   .15
22   A12 5c rose red   1.25   1.00
Human Rights Day.

1954, Feb. 11
23   A13 3c dark green & yellow   .40   .35
24   A13 8c indigo & yellow   1.00   .70
Issued to honor the FAO.

UN Emblem and
Anvil — A14

1954, May 10   Perf. 12½x13
25   A14 3c brown   .20   .15
26   A14 8c magenta   1.40   1.10
Honoring the ILO.

UN European
Office,
Geneva
A15

1954, Oct. 25   Perf. 14
27   A15 3c dark blue violet   2.25   1.00
28   A15 8c red   .30   .25
UN Day.

Mother and
Child — A16

1954, Dec. 10   Perf. 14
29   A16 3c red orange   7.50   2.00
30   A16 8c olive green   .25   .25
Human Rights Day.

Symbol of
Flight — A17

1955, Feb. 9   Perf. 13½x14
31   A17 3c blue   2.25   .50
32   A17 8c rose carmine   .75   .90
International Civil Aviation Organization.

UNESCO
Emblem
A18

1955, May 11   Perf. 13½x14
33   A18 3c lilac rose   .25   .20
34   A18 8c light blue   .20   .20
Honoring the UN Educational, Scientific and Cultural Organization.

UN Charter
A19

1955, Oct. 24   Perf. 13½x14
35   A19 3c deep plum   1.50   .40
36   A19 4c dull green   .70   .15
37   A19 8c bluish black   .20   .20
      Nos. 35-37 (3)   2.40   .75
10th anniv. of the UN.

Souvenir Sheet
Wmk. 309   *Imperf.*

38	Sheet of 3	110.00	35.00
a.	A19 3c deep plum	10.00	1.50
b.	A19 4c dull green	10.00	1.50
c.	A19 8c bluish black	10.00	1.50

Two printings were made of No. 38. The first may be distinguished by the broken line of background shading on the 8c. It leaves a small white spot below the left leg of the "n" of "Unies." For the 2nd printing, the broken line was retouched, eliminating the white spot.

Hand Holding Torch — A20

1955, Dec. 9 Unwmk.   *Perf. 14x13¹/₂*
39	A20 3c ultra	.15	.15
40	A20 8c green	.20	.20

Human Rights Day, Dec. 10.

Symbols of Telecommunication — A21

1956, Feb. 17   *Perf. 14*
41	A21 3c turquoise blue	.20	.15
42	A21 8c deep carmine	.40	.30

Honoring the ITU.

Globe and Caduceus — A22

1956, Apr. 6   *Perf. 14*
43	A22 3c bright greenish blue	.15	.15
44	A22 8c golden brown	.30	.25

Honoring the World Health Organization.

General Assembly A23

1956, Oct. 24   *Perf. 14*
45	A23 3c dark blue	.15	.15
46	A23 8c gray olive	.15	.15
	Set value	.20	.15

UN Day, Oct. 24.

Flame and Globe — A24

1956, Dec. 10   *Perf. 14*
47	A24 3c plum	.15	.15
48	A24 8c dark blue	.15	.15
	Set value	.20	.15

Human Rights Day.

Weather Balloon — A25

1957, Jan. 28   *Perf. 14*
49	A25 3c violet blue	.15	.15
50	A25 8c dark carmine rose	.15	.15
	Set value	.20	.15

Honoring the World Meteorological Organization.

Badge of UN Emergency Force — A26   UN Emblem and Globe — A27

1957, Apr. 8   *Perf. 14x12¹/₂*
51	A26 3c light blue	.15	.15
52	A26 8c rose carmine	.15	.15
	Set value	.20	.15

UN Emergency Force.

Re-engraved

1957, Apr.-May
53	A26 3c blue	.15	.15
54	A26 8c rose carmine	.20	.20
	Set value	.25	.20

On Nos. 53-54 the background within and around the circles is shaded lightly, giving a halo effect. The letters are more distinct with a line around each letter.

1957, Oct. 24 Engr.   *Perf. 12¹/₂x13*
55	A27 3c orange brown	.15	.15
56	A27 8c dark blue green	.15	.15

Honoring the Security Council.

Flaming Torch — A28

1957, Dec. 10   *Perf. 14*
57	A28 3c red brown	.15	.15
58	A28 8c black	.15	.15
	Set value	.20	.15

Human Rights Day.

Atom and UN Emblem A29   Central Hall, Westminster A30

1958, Feb. 10   *Perf. 12*
59	A29 3c olive	.15	.15
60	A29 8c blue	.15	.15
	Set value	.20	.15

Honoring the International Atomic Energy Agency.

1958, Apr. 14   *Perf. 12*
61	A30 3c violet blue	.15	.15
62	A30 8c rose claret	.15	.15
	Set value	.20	.15

Central Hall, Westminster, London, was the site of the first session of the UN General Assembly 1946.

UN Seal A31   Gearwheels A32

1958   *Perf. 13¹/₂x14*
63	A31 4c red orange	.15	.15

Perf. 13x14
64	A31 8c bright blue	.15	.15
	Set value	.20	.20

Issue dates: 4c, Oct. 24; 8c, June 2.

1958, Oct. 24 Engr.   *Perf. 12*
65	A32 4c dark blue green	.15	.15
66	A32 8c vermilion	.15	.15
	Set value	.25	.20

Honoring the Economic and Social Council.

Hands Upholding Globe — A33

1958, Dec. 10   *Unwmk.*
67	A33 4c yellow green	.15	.15
68	A33 8c red brown	.15	.15
	Set value	.25	.20

Human Rights Day and the 10th anniv. of the signing of the Universal Declaration of Human Rights.

New York City Building, Flushing Meadows A34

1959, Mar. 30   *Perf. 12*
69	A34 4c light lilac rose	.15	.15
70	A34 8c aqua	.15	.15
	Set value	.25	.20

Site of many General Assembly meetings, 1946-50.

UN Emblems and Symbols of Agriculture, Industry and Trade — A35   Figure Adapted from Rodin's "Age of Bronze" — A36

1959, May 18   *Perf. 12*
71	A35 4c blue	.15	.15
72	A35 8c red orange	.25	.20
	Set value		.20

Honoring the UN Economic Commission for Europe.

1959, Oct. 23 Engr.   *Perf. 12*
73	A36 4c bright red	.15	.15
74	A36 8c dark olive green	.15	.15
	Set value	.25	.20

Honor the Trusteeship Council.

World Refugee Year Emblem — A37

1959, Dec. 10   *Unwmk.*
75	A37 4c olive & red	.15	.15
76	A37 8c olive & brt greenish blue	.15	.15
	Set value	.20	.15

World Refugee Year, July 1, 1959-June 30, 1960.

Chaillot Palace, Paris — A38

1960, Feb. 29   *Perf. 14*
77	A38 4c rose lilac & blue	.15	.15
78	A38 8c dull green & brown	.20	.15
	Set value	.25	.20

Chaillot Palace in Paris was the site of General Assembly meetings in 1948 and 1951.

Map of Far East and Steel Beam — A39

1960, Apr. 11 Photo.   *Perf. 13x13¹/₂*
79	A39 4c dp cl, bl grn & dl yel	.15	.15
80	A39 8c ol green, blue & rose	.20	.15
	Set value	.25	.20

Honoring the Economic Commission for Asia and the Far East (ECAFE).

Tree, FAO and UN Emblems — A40

1960, Aug. 29   *Perf. 13¹/₂*
81	A40 4c green, dk blue & org	.15	.15
a.	Imperf., pair		
82	A40 8c yel green, black & org	.15	.15
	Set value	.25	.20

5th World Forestry Congress, Seattle, Wash., Aug. 29-Sept. 10.

UN Headquarters and Preamble to UN Charter — A41

1960, Oct. 24 Engr.   *Perf. 11*
83	A41 4c blue	.15	.15
84	A41 8c gray	.15	.15
	Set value	.20	.15

Souvenir Sheet
Imperf
85	Sheet of 2	.65	.55
a.	A41 4c blue	.30	.30
b.	A41 8c gray	.30	.15

15th anniv. of the UN.

Block and Tackle — A42   Scales of Justice — A43

1960, Dec. 9   Photo.   Perf. 13½x13
86 A42 4c multicolored   .15 .15
87 A42 8c multicolored   .15 .15
a.   Imperf., pair
        Set value   .25 .20

Honoring the International Bank for Reconstruction and Development.
No. 86 exists imperf.

1961, Feb. 13   Unwmk.
88 A43 4c yel, org brn & blk   .15 .15
89 A43 8c yellow, green & black   .15 .15
        Set value   .25 .20

Honoring the International Court of Justice. The design was taken from Raphael's "Stanze."
Nos. 88-89 exist imperf.

Seal of
International
Monetary
Fund — A44

1961, Apr. 17   Perf. 13x13½
90 A44 4c bright bluish green   .15 .15
91 A44 7c fawn & yellow   .15 .15
        Set value   .25 .20

Honoring the International Monetary Fund.
No. 90 exists imperf.

Abstract Group
of Flags — A45

1961, June 5   Perf. 11½
92 A45 30c multicolored   .35 .15

See Offices in Geneva No. 10.

Cogwheel and Map
of Latin
America — A46

1961, Sept. 18   Perf. 13½
93 A46 4c blue, red & citron   .15 .15
94 A46 11c green, lilac & org ver   .30 .20

Honoring the Economic Commission for Latin America.

Africa House,
Addis Ababa,
and Map — A47

1961, Oct. 24   Photo.   Perf. 11½
95 A47 4c ultra, org, yel & brown   .15 .15
96 A47 11c emer, org, yel & brown   .25 .15
        Set value   .25

Honoring the Economic Commission for Africa.

Mother Bird Feeding
Young and UNICEF
Seal — A48

1961, Dec. 4   Unwmk.   Perf. 11½
97 A48 3c brown, gold, org & yel   .15 .15
98 A48 4c blue, gold, bl & emer   .15 .15
99 A48 13c deep green, gold, purple &
             pink   .20 .20
        Set value   .35 .30

15th anniv. of the UN Children's Fund.

Family and
Symbolic
Buildings
A49

1962, Feb. 28   Photo.   Perf. 14½x14
Central design multicolored
100 A49 4c bright blue   .15 .15
a.   Black omitted   —
b.   Yellow omitted   —
c.   Brown omitted   —
101 A49 7c orange brown   .15 .15
a.   Red omitted   —
b.   Black omitted   —
        Set value   .25 .20

UN program for housing and urban development.

"The World Against
Malaria" — A50

1962, Mar. 30   Perf. 14x14½
Word frame in gray
102 A50 4c org, yel, green & black   .15 .15
103 A50 11c green, yel, brn & indigo   .25 .15
        Set value   .30 .20

Honoring the WHO and to call attention to the international campaign to eradicate malaria from the world.

"Peace" — A51

UN Flag — A52

Hands
Combining
"UN" and
Globe — A53

UN Emblem
over
Globe — A54

Photogravure; Engraved (5c)
1962, May 25   Perf. 14x14½
104 A51 1c ver, blue, black & gray   .15 .15
105 A52 3c lt green, Prus blue, yel &
             gray   .15 .15
                Perf. 12
            Size: 36½x23½mm
106 A53 5c dark carmine rose   .15 .15
                Perf. 12½
107 A54 11c dk & lt blue & gold   .25 .20
        Set value   .60 .35

See #167 and UN Offices in Geneva #2, 6.

Flag at Half-mast
and UN
Headquarters
A55

World Map Showing
Congo
A56

1962, Sept. 17   Unwmk.   Perf. 11½
108 A55 5c black, lt blue & blue   .15 .15
109 A55 15c black, gray ol & blue   .25 .20

1st anniv. of the death of Dag Hammarskjold, Secretary General of the UN 1953-61, in memory of those who died in the service of the UN.

1962, Oct. 24
110 A56 4c olive, org, black & yel   .15 .15
111 A56 11c bl grn, org, blk & yel   .30 .20

UN Operation in the Congo.

Globe in Universe
and Palm
Frond — A57

1962, Dec. 3   Engr.   Perf. 14x13½
112 A57 4c violet blue   .15 .15
113 A57 11c rose claret   .20 .15
        Set value   .30 .20

Honoring the Committee on Peaceful Uses of Outer Space.

Development Decade
Emblem — A58

                Perf. 11½
1963, Feb. 4   Unwmk.   Photo.
114 A58 5c pale grn, mar, dk blue &
             Prus blue   .15 .15
115 A58 11c yel, mar, dk blue & Prus
             blue   .20 .15
        Set value   .30 .20

UN Development Decade and the UN Conference on the Application of Science and Technology for the Benefit of the Less Developed Areas, Geneva, Feb. 4-20.

Stalks of
Wheat — A59

1963, Mar. 22   Perf. 11½
116 A59 5c ver, green & yellow   .15 .15
117 A59 11c ver, dp claret & yel   .25 .15
        Set value   .30 .20

"Freedom from Hunger" campaign of the FAO.

Bridge over Map
of New
Guinea — A60

1963, Oct. 1   Unwmk.   Perf. 11½
118 A60 25c blue, green & gray   .45 .20

1st anniv. of the UN Temporary Executive Authority (UNTEA) in West New Guinea (West Irian).

General Assembly
Building, New
York — A61

1963, Nov. 4   Photo.   Perf. 13
119 A61 5c violet blue & multi   .15 .15
120 A61 11c green & multi   .20 .15
        Set value   .30 .20

Since Oct. 1955 all sessions of the General Assembly have been held in the General Assembly Hall, UN Headquarters, N.Y.

Flame — A62

1963, Dec. 10   Perf. 13
121 A62 5c green, gold, red & yel   .15 .15
122 A62 11c car, gold, blue & yel   .20 .15
        Set value   .20

15th anniv. of the signing of the Universal Declaration of Human Rights.

Ships at Sea and
IMCO
Emblem — A63

1964, Jan. 13   Perf. 11½
123 A63 5c blue, ol, ocher & yel   .15 .15
124 A63 11c bl, dk grn, emer & yel   .20 .15
        Set value   .30 .20

Honoring the Intergovernmental Maritime Consultative Organization.

Map of the
World — A64

UN
Emblem — A65

Three Men United
Before Globe — A66

Stylized Globe
and Weather
Vane — A67

1964-71   Unwmk.   Photo.   Perf. 14
125 A64 2c lt bl, dk blue, org & yel
             green   .15 .15
a.   Perf. 13x13½ ('71)   .20 .15
                Perf. 11½
126 A65 7c dk bl, org brn & blk   .20 .15
127 A66 10c blue grn, ol grn & blk   .20 .15
128 A67 50c multicolored   .75 .40
        Set value   .65

Dates of issue: 2c, 7c, 10c, May 29; 50c, Mar. 6, 1964. See UN Offices in Geneva Nos. 3, 12.

Arrows
Showing
Global Flow
of
Trade — A68

1964, June 15   *Perf. 13*
129 A68 5c black, red & yellow   .15 .15
130 A68 11c black, olive & yellow   .20 .15
    Set value   .30 .20

UN Conference on Trade and Development, Geneva, Mar. 23-June 15.

Poppy Capsule and Hands — A69

1964, Sept. 21   Engr.   *Perf. 12*
131 A69 5c rose red & black   .15 .15
132 A69 11c emerald & black   .20 .15
    Set value   .30 .20

International efforts and achievements in the control of narcotics.

Padlocked Atomic Blast — A70   "Education for Progress" — A71

Photogravure and Engraved
1964, Oct. 23   *Perf. 11x11 1/2*
133 A70 5c dark red & dk brown   .15 .15

Signing of the nuclear test ban treaty pledging an end to nuclear explosions in the atmosphere, outer space and under water.

1964, Dec. 7   Photo.   *Perf. 12 1/2*
134 A71 4c multicolored   .15 .15
135 A71 5c multicolored   .15 .15
136 A71 11c multicolored   .20 .15
    Set value   .30 .20

UNESCO world campaign for universal literacy and for free compulsory primary education.

Progress Chart of Special Fund, Key and Globe A72   Leaves and View of Cyprus A73

Perf. 13 1/2x13
1965, Jan. 25   Unwmk.
137 A72 5c multicolored   .15 .15
138 A72 11c multicolored   .20 .15
   a. Black omitted (UN emblem on key)   —
    Set value   .25 .15

Special Fund Program, which aims to speed economic growth and social advancement in low-income countries.

1965, Mar. 4   Photo.   *Perf. 11 1/2*
139 A73 5c org, olive & black   .15 .15
140 A73 11c yel grn, blue grn & blk   .20 .15
    Set value   .25 .15

UN Peace-keeping Force on Cyprus.

"From Semaphore to Satellite" — A74

1965, May 17   Unwmk.   *Perf. 11 1/2*
141 A74 5c multicolored   .15 .15
142 A74 11c multicolored   .20 .15
    Set value   .25 .15

Cent. of the ITU.

ICY Emblem — A75

1965, June 26   Engr.   *Perf. 14x13 1/2*
143 A75 5c dark blue   .15 .15
144 A75 15c lilac rose   .25 .15
    Set value   .15

Souvenir Sheet
145 A75   Sheet of 2, #143-144   .35 .20

20th anniv. of the UN and Intl. Cooperation Year.

"Peace" — A76   Opening Words, UN Charter — A77

UN Headquarters and Emblem — A78   UN Emblem — A79

UN Emblem — A80

1965-66   Photo.   *Perf. 13 1/2*
146 A76 1c ver, bl, blk & gray   .15 .15
      Perf. 14
147 A77 15c ol bis, dull yel, blk & dp claret   .25 .15
      Perf. 12
148 A78 20c dk bl, bl, red & yel   .30 .20
   a. Yellow omitted   —

Lithographed and Embossed
      Perf. 14
149 A79 25c lt bl & dk blue   .35 .20
      Photo.
      Perf. 11 1/2
150 A80 $1 aqua & sapphire   1.60 1.10
    Nos. 146-150 (5)   2.65 1.80

Issue dates: 1c, 25c, Sept. 20, 1965. 15c, 20c, Oct. 25, 1965. $1, Mar. 25, 1966.
See UN Offices in Geneva Nos. 5, 9 and 11.

Fields and People A81   Globe and Flags of UN Members A82

1965, Nov. 29   Photo.   *Perf. 12*
151 A81 4c multicolored   .15 .15
152 A81 5c multicolored   .15 .15
153 A81 11c multicolored   .20 .15

Emphasize the importance of the world's population growth and its problems and to call attention to population trends and developments.

1966, Jan. 31   Photo.   *Perf. 11 1/2*
154 A82 5c multicolored   .15 .15
155 A82 15c multicolored   .20 .15
    Set value   .30 .20

World Federation of UN Associations.

WHO Headquarters, Geneva — A83

1966, May 26   Photo.   *Perf. 12 1/2x12*
      Granite Paper
156 A83 5c multicolored   .20 .15
157 A83 11c multicolored   .30 .15
    Set value   .15

WHO Headquarters, Geneva.

Coffee — A84

1966, Sept. 19   *Perf. 13 1/2x13*
158 A84 5c multicolored   .15 .15
159 A84 11c multicolored   .20 .15
    Set value   .25 .15

International Coffee Agreement of 1962.

UN Observer — A85   Children of Various Races — A86

1966, Oct. 24   Photo.   *Perf. 11 1/2*
      Granite Paper
160 A85 15c multicolored   .25 .15

Peace Keeping UN Observers.

1966, Nov. 28   Litho.   *Perf. 13x13 1/2*

Designs: 5c, Children riding locomotive and tender. 11c, Children in open railroad car playing medical team.

161 A86 4c pink & multi   .15 .15
162 A86 5c pale green & multi   .15 .15
   a. Yellow omitted   —
163 A86 11c ultra & multi   .20 .15
   a. Imperf., pair   —
   b. Dark blue omitted   —
    Set value   .30 .20

20th anniv. of UNICEF.

Hand Rolling up Sleeve and Chart Showing Progress — A87

1967, Jan. 23   Photo.   *Perf. 12 1/2*
164 A87 5c multicolored   .15 .15
165 A87 11c multicolored   .20 .15
    Set value   .25 .20

UN Development Program.

Type of 1962 and

UN Headquarters, New York and World Map — A88

1967   Photo.   *Perf. 11 1/2*
166 A88 1 1/2c ultra, blk, org & ocher   .15 .15
      Size: 33x23mm
167 A53 5c red brn, brn & org yel   .15 .15
    Set value   .15 .15

Issue dates: 1 1/2c, Mar. 17; 5c, Jan. 23. See UN Offices in Geneva No. 1.

Fireworks — A89

1967, Mar. 17   *Perf. 14x14 1/2*
168 A89 5c dark blue & multi   .15 .15
169 A89 11c brown lake & multi   .20 .15
    Set value   .25 .20

Honoring all nations which gained independence since 1945.

"Peace" A90   UN Pavilion, EXPO '67 A91

Litho. & Engr.; Litho. (8c)
1967, Apr. 28   *Perf. 11*
170 A90 4c shown   .15 .15
171 A90 5c Justice   .15 .15
172 A91 8c shown   .15 .15
173 A90 10c Fraternity   .20 .20
174 A90 15c Truth   .20 .20
    Set value   .70 .70

Montreal World's Fair, EXPO '67, Apr. 28-Oct. 27. Under special agreement with the Canadian Government Nos. 170-174 were valid for postage only on mail posted at the UN pavilion during the fair. The denominations are expressed in Canadian currency.

Luggage Tags and UN Emblem A92

1967, June 19   Unwmk.   *Perf. 14*
      Litho.
175 A92 5c multicolored   .15 .15
176 A92 15c multicolored   .25 .15
    Set value   .30 .20

International Tourist Year, 1967.

Quotation from Isaiah 2:4 — A93

1967, Oct. 24   Photo.
177 A93 6c multicolored   .15 .15
178 A93 13c multicolored   .20 .15
    Set value   .30 .20

UN General Assembly's resolutions on general and complete disarmament and for suspension of nuclear and thermonuclear tests.

Art at UN Issue
Miniature Sheet

Memorial Window, by Marc Chagall — A94

"The Kiss of Peace" by
Marc Chagall — A95

1967, Nov. 17 Litho.   Rouletted 9
179 A94   Sheet of 6   .40 .20
  a. 6c multi, 41x46mm   .15 .15
  b. 6c multi, 24x46mm   .15 .15
  c. 6c multi, 41x33½mm   .15 .15
  d. 6c multi, 36x33½mm   .15 .15
  e. 6c multi, 29x33½mm   .15 .15
  f. 6c multi, 41½x47mm   .15 .15

Perf. 12½x13½
180 A95 6c multicolored   .15 .15

No. 179 is divisible into six 6c stamps, each
rouletted on 3 sides, imperf. on fourth side. Size:
124x80mm. On Nos. 179a-179c, "United Nations.
6c" appears at top; on Nos. 179d-179f, at bottom.
No. 179f includes name "Marc Chagall."

Globe and Major
UN
Organs — A96

1968, Jan. 16 Photo.   Perf. 11½
181 A96 6c multicolored   .15 .15
182 A96 13c multicolored   .15 .15
  Set value   .25 .20

Honoring the UN Secretariat.

Statue by   Factories and Chart
Henrik Starcke   A98
A97

Art at UN Issue
1968, Mar. 1 Photo.   Perf. 11½
183 A97 6c blue & multi   .15 .15
184 A97 75c rose lake & multi   1.10 .85

The 6c is part of the "Art at UN" series. The 75c
belongs to the definitive series. The 6c exists
imperforate.
The Starcke statue represents mankind's search
for freedom and happiness.
See UN Offices in Geneva No. 13.

1968, Apr. 18 Litho.   Perf. 12
185 A98 6c multicolored   .15 .15
186 A98 13c multicolored   .20 .15
  Set value   .30 .20

UN Industrial Development Organization.

UN Headquarters — A99

1968, May 31 Litho.   Perf. 13½
187 A99 6c multicolored   .15 .15

Radarscope
and Globes
A100

1968, Sept. 19 Photo.   Perf. 13x13½
188 A100 6c green & multi   .15 .15
189 A100 20c lilac & multi   .30 .20
  Set value   .40 .30

World Weather Watch, a new weather system
directed by the World Meterological Organization.

Human Rights   Books and UN
Flame — A101   Emblem — A102

Photogravure; Foil Embossed
1968, Nov. 22   Perf. 12½
190 A101 6c brt bl, dp ultra & gold   .15 .15
191 A101 13c rose red, dk red & gold   .20 .15
  Set value   .30 .20

International Human Rights Year.

1969, Feb. 10 Litho.   Perf. 13½
192 A102 6c yel green & multi   .15 .15
193 A102 13c bluish lilac & multi   .20 .15
  Set value   .25 .20

UN Institute for Training and Research (UNITAR).

UN Building,
Santiago,
Chile — A103

1969, Mar. 14 Litho.   Perf. 14
194 A103 6c lt blue, vio bl & lt grn   .15 .15
195 A103 15c pink, cr & red brown   .25 .20
  Set value   .30 .25

The UN Building in Santiago, Chile is the seat of
the UN Economic Commission for Latin America
and of the Latin American Institute for Economic
and Social Planning.

"UN" and UN   UN Emblem and
Emblem   Scales of Justice
A104   A105

1969, Mar. 14 Photo.   Perf. 13½
196 A104 13c brt blue, black & gold   .20 .15

See UN Offices in Geneva No. 7.

1969, Apr. 21 Photo.   Perf. 11½
Granite Paper
197 A105 6c brt green, ultra & gold   .15 .15
198 A105 13c crim, lilac & gold   .20 .15
  Set value   .25 .20

20th anniv. session of the UN Intl. Law
Commission.

Allegory of
Labor,
Emblems of
UN and
ILO — A106

1969, June 5 Photo.   Perf. 13
199 A106 6c blue, dp bl, yel & gold   .15 .15
200 A106 20c org ver, mag, yel & gold   .25 .20
  Set value   .35 .30

"Labor and Development" and the 50th anniv. of
the ILO.

Art at UN Issue

Ostrich, Tunisian
Mosaic, 3rd
Century — A107

Design: 13c, Pheasant.

1969, Nov. 21 Photo.   Perf. 14
201 A107 6c blue & multi   .15 .15
202 A107 13c red & multi   .20 .15
  Set value   .25 .20

Art at UN Issue

Peace Bell, Gift of
Japanese — A108

1970, Mar. 13 Photo.   Perf. 13½x13
203 A108 6c vio blue & multi   .15 .15
204 A108 25c claret & multi   .30 .25
  Set value   .35

Mekong River,
Power Lines and
Map of
Delta — A109

1970, Mar. 13   Perf. 14
205 A109 6c dk blue & multi   .15 .15
206 A109 13c dp plum & multi   .20 .15
  Set value   .25 .20

Lower Mekong Basin, Viet Nam, Development
project under UN auspices.

"Fight
Cancer" — A110

1970, May 22 Litho.   Perf. 14
207 A110 6c blue & black   .15 .15
208 A110 13c olive & black   .20 .15
  Set value   .25 .20

Fight against cancer in connection with the 10th
Intl. Cancer Congress of the International Union
Against Cancer, Houston, Texas, May 22-29.

UN Emblem and Olive   UN Emblem
Branch   A112
A111

1970, June 26 Photo.   Perf. 11½
209 A111 6c red, gold, dk & lt blue   .15 .15
210 A111 13c dk bl, gold, grn & red   .20 .15
Perf. 12½
211 A112 25c dk blue, gold & lt blue   .35 .25
  Set value   .45

Souvenir Sheet
Imperf
212   Sheet of 3   .60 .60
  a. A111 6c multicolored   .15 .15
  b. A111 13c multicolored   .20 .15
  c. A112 25c multicolored   .30 .20

25th anniv. of the UN.

Scales, Olive   Sea Bed, Fish,
Branch,   Underwater
Progress Symbol   Research
A113   A114

1970, Nov. 20 Photo.   Perf. 13½
213 A113 6c gold & multi   .15 .15
214 A113 13c silver & multi   .20 .15
  Set value   .20

Issued to publicize "Peace, Justice and Progress"
in connection with the 25th anniv. of the UN.

Photogravure and Engraved
1971, Jan. 25   Perf. 13
215 A114 6c blue & multi   .15 .15

Peaceful uses of the sea bed. See Offices in
Geneva No. 15.

Refugees, Sculpture   Wheat and
by Kaare K.   Globe — A116
Nygaard — A115

1971, Mar. 12 Litho.   Perf. 13x12½
216 A115 6c brown, ocher & black   .15 .15
217 A115 13c ultra, grnsh blue & blk   .20 .15
  Set value   .30 .20

International support for refugees. See Offices in
Geneva No. 16.

1971, Apr. 13 Photo.   Perf. 14
218 A116 13c brn red, gold & green   .20 .15

Publicizing the UN World Food Program. See
Offices in Geneva No. 17.

UPU
Headquarters,
Bern — A117

1971, May 28 Photo.   Perf. 11½
219 A117 20c brown org & multi   .25 .20

Opening of new UPU Headquarters, Bern. See
Offices in Geneva No. 18.

"Eliminate Racial
Discrimination" — A118

A119

1971, Sept. 21 Photo.   Perf. 13½
220 A118 8c yel green & multi   .15 .15
221 A119 13c blue & multi   .20 .15
  Set value   .30 .20

International Year Against Racial Discrimination.
See Offices in Geneva Nos. 19-20.

UN Headquarters, New York — A120

UN Emblem and Symbolic Flags A121

1971, Oct. 22   Perf. 13¹/₂; 13 (60c)
222 A120   8c vio blue & multi   .15   .15
223 A121   60c ultra & multi   .75   .60

Maia by Pablo Picasso — A122

1971, Nov. 19   Photo.   Perf. 11¹/₂
224 A122   8c olive & multi   .15   .15
225 A122   21c ultra & multi   .30   .20

UN Intl. School. See Offices in Geneva No. 21.

Letter Changing Hands A123

1972, Jan. 5   Litho.   Perf. 14
226 A123   95c blue & multi   1.40 1.25

"No More Nuclear Weapons" A124

1972, Feb. 14   Photo.   Perf. 13¹/₂x14
227 A124   8c dull rose, blk, bl & gray   .15   .15

To promote non-proliferation of nuclear weapons. See Offices in Geneva No. 23.

Proportions of Man (c. 1509), by Leonardo da Vinci A125

"Human Environment" A126

Lithographed and Engraved
1972, Apr. 7   Perf. 13x13¹/₂
228 A125   15c black & multi   .30   .20

World Health Day, Apr. 7. See Offices in Geneva No. 24.

Lithographed and Embossed
1972, June 5   Perf. 12¹/₂x14
229 A126   8c multicolored   .15   .15
230 A126   15c multicolored   .25   .20
          Set value   .25

UN Conference on Human Environment, Stockholm, June 5-16, 1972. See Offices in Geneva Nos. 25-26.

"Europe" and UN Emblem A127

The Five Continents, by José María Sert A128

1972, Sept. 11   Litho.   Perf. 13x13¹/₂
231 A127   21c yel brown & multi   .35   .20

Economic Commission for Europe, 25th anniv. See Offices in Geneva No. 27.

Art at UN Issue
1972, Nov. 17   Photo.   Perf. 12x12¹/₂
232 A128   8c gold, brn & gldn brn   .15   .15
233 A128   15c gold, brn & blue grn   .30   .20
          Set value   .25

See Offices in Geneva Nos. 28-29.

Olive Branch and Broken Sword — A129

1973, Mar. 9   Litho.   Perf. 13¹/₂x13
234 A129   8c blue & multi   .20   .15
235 A129   15c lilac rose & multi   .40   .20
          Set value   .25

Disarmament Decade, 1970-79. Nos. 234-235 exist imperf. See Offices in Geneva Nos. 30-31.

Poppy Capsule and Skull — A130

Honeycomb — A131

1973, Apr. 13   Photo.   Perf. 13¹/₂
236 A130   8c multicolored   .15   .15
237 A130   15c multicolored   .35   .35

Fight against drug abuse. See Offices in Geneva No. 32.

1973, May 25   Photo.   Perf. 14
238 A131   8c olive bister & multi   .20   .15
239 A131   21c gray blue & multi   .45   .20
          Set value   .30

5th anniv. of the UN Volunteer Program. See UN Offices in Geneva No. 33.

Map of Africa with Namibia — A132

1973, Oct. 1   Photo.   Perf. 13¹/₂
240 A132   8c emerald & multi   .15   .15
241 A132   15c brt rose & multi   .35   .20
          Set value   .30

To publicize Namibia (South-West Africa), for which the UN General Assembly ended the mandate of South Africa and established the UN Council for Namibia to administer the territory until independence. See Offices in Geneva No. 34.

UN Emblem, Human Rights Flame — A133

1973, Nov. 16   Photo.   Perf. 13¹/₂
242 A133   8c dp carmine & multi   .15   .15
243 A133   21c blue green & multi   .35   .20

25th anniv. of the adoption and proclamation of the Universal Declaration of Human Rights. See Offices in Geneva Nos. 35-36.

ILO Headquarters, Geneva — A134

1974, Jan. 11   Photo.   Perf. 14
244 A134   10c ultra & multi   .20   .15
245 A134   21c blue green & multi   .35   .20

New Headquarters of Intl. Labor Organization. See Offices in Geneva Nos. 37-38.

Post Horn Encircling Globe — A135

1974, Mar. 22   Photo.   Perf. 14
246 A135   10c multicolored   .25   .15

Centenary of UPU. See Offices in Geneva Nos. 39-40.

Art at UN Issue

Peace Mural, by Candido Portinari — A136

1974, May 6   Photo.   Perf. 14
247 A136   10c gold & multi   .20   .15
248 A136   18c ultra & multi   .40   .30

See Offices in Geneva Nos. 41-42.

Dove and UN Emblem A137

UN Headquarters A138

Globe, UN Emblem, Flags — A139

1974, June 10   Photo.   Perf. 14
249 A137   2c dk bl & lt blue   .15   .15
250 A138   10c multicolored   .20   .15
251 A139   18c multicolored   .30   .20
          Set value   .35

Children of the World — A140

Law of the Sea — A141

1974, Oct. 18   Photo.   Perf. 14
252 A140   10c lt blue & multi   .20   .15
253 A140   18c lilac & multi   .40   .20
          Set value   .30

World Population Year. See Offices in Geneva Nos. 43-44.

1974, Nov. 22   Photo.   Perf. 14
254 A141   10c green & multi   .20   .15
255 A141   26c multicolored   .35   .25

UN General Assembly declared the sea bed common heritage of mankind, exempt from arms race. See Offices in Geneva No. 45.

Satellite and Globe — A142

1975, Mar. 14   Litho.   Perf. 13
256 A142   10c multicolored   .20   .15
257 A142   26c multicolored   .35   .25

Peaceful uses of outer space (meteorology, industry, fishing, communications). See Offices in Geneva Nos. 46-47.

Equality Between Men and Women — A143

1975, May 9   Litho.   Perf. 15
258 A143   10c multicolored   .20   .15
259 A143   18c multicolored   .40   .20
          Set value   .30

International Women's Year 1975. See Offices in Geneva Nos. 48-49.

UN Flag and "XXX" — A144

1975, June 26   Litho.   Perf. 13
260 A144   10c multicolored   .15   .15
261 A144   26c purple & multi   .50   .25

Souvenir Sheet
Imperf
262   Sheet of 2   .65   .20
 a.   A144 10c olive bister & multi .20   .15
 b.   A144 26c purple & multi   .40   .15

30th anniv. of the UN. See Offices in Geneva Nos. 50-52.

Hand Reaching up over Map of Africa and Namibia — A145

Wild Rose Growing from Barbed Wire — A146

1975, Sept. 22   Photo.   Perf. 13¹/₂
263 A145   10c multicolored   .20   .15
264 A145   18c multicolored   .35   .20
          Set value   .30

"Namibia—United Nations direct responsibility." See note after No. 241. See Offices in Geneva Nos. 53-54.

1975, Nov. 21   Engr.   Perf. 12¹/₂
265 A146   13c ultramarine   .25   .15
266 A146   26c rose carmine   .50   .45

UN Peace-keeping Operations. See Offices in Geneva Nos. 55-56.

Symbolic Flags Forming
Dove
A147

UN Emblem
A149

People of All
Races
A148

UN
Flag — A150

Dove and
Rainbow — A151

Perf. 13x13¹/₂, 13¹/₂x13, 14 (9c)

1976   **Litho.; Photo. (9c)**
267 A147 3c multicolored   .15   .15
268 A148 4c multicolored   .15   .15
269 A149 9c multicolored   .15   .15
270 A150 30c blue, emer & black   .40   .35
271 A151 50c multicolored   .70   .65
        Nos. 267-271 (5)   1.55
        Set value   1.25

Issue dates: 9c, Nov. 19. Others, Jan. 9.
See Offices in Vienna No. 8.

Interlocking
Bands — A152

1976, Mar. 12   Photo.   *Perf. 14*
272 A152 13c blue, green & black   .20   .15
273 A152 26c green & multi   .35   .30

World Federation of UN Association. See Offices
in Geneva No. 57.

Cargo, Globe and
Graph — A153

Houses Around
Globe — A154

1976, Apr. 23   Photo.   *Perf. 11¹/₂*
274 A153 13c multicolored   .20   .15
275 A153 31c multicolored   .40   .30

UN Conference on Trade and Development
(UNCTAD), Nairobi, Kenya, May 1976. See Offices
in Geneva No. 58.

1976, May 28   Photo.   *Perf. 14*
276 A154 13c multicolored   .20   .15
277 A154 25c green & multi   .40   .30

Habitat, UN Conference on Human Settlements,
Vancouver, Canada, May 31-June 11. See Offices in
Geneva Nos. 59-60.

Grain — A156

Magnifying Glass,
Sheet of Stamps, UN
Emblem — A155

1976, Oct. 8   Photo.   *Perf. 11¹/₂*
278 A155 13c blue & multi   .20   .20
279 A155 31c green & multi   1.75 1.50

UN Postal Administration, 25th anniv. Sheets of
20. See Offices in Geneva #61-62.

1976, Nov. 19   Litho.   *Perf. 14¹/₂*
280 A156 13c multicolored   .35   .15

World Food Council. See Offices in Geneva No.
63.

WIPO
Headquarters,
Geneva
A157

1977, Mar. 11   Photo.   *Perf. 14*
281 A157 13c citron & multi   .15   .15
282 A157 31c brt green & multi   .45   .30

World Intellectual Property Organization. See
Geneva No. 64.

Drops of Water Falling
into Funnel — A158

1977, Apr. 22   Photo.   *Perf. 13¹/₂x13*
283 A158 13c yellow & multi   .20   .15
284 A158 25c salmon & multi   .45   .25

UN Water Conf., Mar del Plata, Argentina, Mar.
14-25. See Offices in Geneva #65-66.

Burning Fuse
Severed — A159

1977, May 27   Photo.   *Perf. 14*
285 A159 13c purple & multi   .15   .15
286 A159 31c dk blue & multi   .45   .30

UN Security Council. See Geneva #67-68.

"Combat
Racism"
A160

1977, Sept. 19   Litho.   *Perf. 13¹/₂x13*
287 A160 13c black & yellow   .15   .15
288 A160 31c black & vermilion   .40   .25

Fight against racial discrimination. See Geneva
Nos. 69-70.

Atom, Grain, Fruit and
Factory — A161

1977, Nov. 18   Photo.
289 A161 13c yellow bister & multi   .20   .15
290 A161 18c dull green & multi   .30   .20

Peaceful uses of atomic energy. See Geneva Nos.
71-72.

Opening Words
of UN
Charter — A162

"Live Together
in
Peace" — A163

People of the
World — A164

1978, Jan. 27   Litho.   *Perf. 14¹/₂*
291 A162 1c gold, brown & red   .15   .15
292 A163 25c multicolored   .35   .30
293 A164 $1 multicolored   1.25 1.25

See Offices in Geneva No. 73.

Smallpox
Virus — A165

1978, Mar. 31   Photo.   *Perf. 12x11¹/₂*
294 A165 13c rose & black   .15   .15
295 A165 31c blue & black   .45   .40

Global eradication of smallpox. See Offices in
Geneva Nos. 74-75.

Open Handcuff
A166

Multicolored
Bands and Clouds
A167

1978, May 5   Photo.   *Perf. 12*
296 A166 13c multicolored   .20   .15
297 A166 18c multicolored   .30   .20

Liberation, justice and cooperation for Namibia.
See Offices in Geneva No. 76.

1978, June 12   Photo.   *Perf. 14*
298 A167 13c multicolored   .20   .15
299 A167 25c multicolored   .45   .40

International Civil Aviation Organization for
"Safety in the Air." See Offices in Geneva #77-78.

General
Assembly
A168

1978, Sept. 15   Photo.   *Perf. 13¹/₂*
300 A168 13c multicolored   .20   .15
301 A168 18c multicolored   .30   .25

See Offices in Geneva Nos. 79-80.

Hemispheres as
Cogwheels
A169

1978, Nov. 17   Photo.   *Perf. 14*
302 A169 13c multicolored   .25   .20
303 A169 31c multicolored   .65   .55

Technical Cooperation Among Developing Countries Conf., Buenos Aires, Argentina, Sept. 1978.
See Offices in Geneva No. 81.

Hand Holding
Olive
Branch — A170

Tree of Various
Races — A171

Globe, Dove with
Olive
Branch — A172

Birds and
Globe — A173

1979, Jan. 19   Photo.   *Perf. 14*
304 A170 5c multicolored   .15   .15
305 A171 14c multicolored   .20   .15
306 A172 15c multicolored   .30   .25
307 A173 20c multicolored   .30   .25
        Nos. 304-307 (4)   .95   .80

UNDRO Against
Fire and
Water — A174

1979, Mar. 9   Photo.   *Perf. 14*
308 A174 15c multicolored   .30   .20
309 A174 20c multicolored   .40   .30

Office of the UN Disaster Relief Coordinator. See
Offices in Geneva Nos. 82-83.

Child and ICY
Emblem — A175

1979, May 4   Photo.   *Perf. 14*
310 A175 15c multicolored   .20   .20
311 A175 31c multicolored   .45   .40

International Year of the Child. See Offices in
Geneva Nos. 84-85.

Map of Namibia,
Olive
Branch — A176

Scales and Sword of
Justice — A177

1979, Oct. 5   Litho.   *Perf. 13¹/₂*
312 A176 15c multicolored   .20   .20
313 A176 31c multicolored   .40   .40

For a free and independent Namibia. See Offices
in Geneva No. 86.

1979, Nov. 9   Litho.   Perf. 13x13½
314 A177 15c multicolored .... .20 .20
315 A177 20c multicolored .... .40 .35
Intl. Court of Justice, The Hague, Netherlands. See Offices in Geneva Nos. 87-88.

Graph of Economic Trends — A178

Key — A179

1980, Jan. 11   Perf. 15x14½
316 A178 15c multicolored .... .20 .20
317 A179 31c multicolored .... .45 .35
New International Economic Order. See Offices in Geneva No. 89; Vienna No. 7.

Women's Year Emblems A180

1980, Mar. 7   Litho.   Perf. 14½x15
318 A180 15c multicolored .... .20 .20
319 A180 20c multicolored .... .30 .25
UN Decade for Women. See Offices in Geneva Nos. 90-91; Vienna Nos. 9-10.

UN Emblem and "UN" on Helmet A181

Arrows and UN Emblem A182

1980, May 16   Litho.   Perf. 14x13
320 A181 15c black & brt blue .... .25 .20
321 A182 31c multicolored .... .45 .40
UN Peace-keeping Operations. See Offices in Geneva No. 92; Vienna No. 11.

"35" and Flags — A183

Globe and Laurel — A184

1980, June 26   Litho.   Perf. 13
322 A183 15c multicolored .... .20 .20
323 A184 20c multicolored .... .40 .30

Souvenir Sheet
Imperf
324   Sheet of 2 .... .50 .45
  a. A183 15c multicolored .... .15
  b. A184 31c multicolored .... .35
35th anniv. of the UN. See Offices in Geneva Nos. 93-95; Vienna Nos. 12-14.

Flag of Turkey A185

1980, Sept. 26   Litho.   Perf. 12
Granite Paper
325 A185 15c shown .... .20 .15
326 A185 15c Luxembourg .... .20 .15
327 A185 15c Fiji .... .20 .15
328 A185 15c Viet Nam .... .20 .15
  a. Se-tenant block of 4 .... 1.25
329 A185 15c Guinea .... .20 .15
330 A185 15c Surinam .... .20 .15
331 A185 15c Bangladesh .... .20 .15
332 A185 15c Mali .... .20 .15
  a. Se-tenant block of 4 .... 1.25
333 A185 15c Yugoslavia .... .20 .15
334 A185 15c France .... .20 .15
335 A185 15c Venezuela .... .20 .15
336 A185 15c El Salvador .... .20 .15
  a. Se-tenant block of 4 .... 1.25
337 A185 15c Madagascar .... .20 .15
338 A185 15c Cameroon .... .20 .15
339 A185 15c Rwanda .... .20 .15
340 A185 15c Hungary .... .20 .15
  a. Se-tenant block of 4 .... 1.25
     Nos. 325-340 (16) 3.20
     Set value 1.60

Issued in 4 sheets of 16. Each sheet contains 4 blocks of 4 (Nos. 325-328, 329-332, 333-336, 337-340). A se-tenant block of 4 designs centers each sheet.
See #350-365, 374-389, 399-414, 425-440, 450-465, 477-492, 499-514, 528-543, 554-569, 690-697.

Symbolic Flowers A186

Symbols of Progress A187

1980, Nov. 21   Litho.   Perf. 13½x13
341 A186 15c multicolored .... .30 .25
342 A187 20c multicolored .... .40 .35
Economic and Social Council (ECOSOC). See Offices in Geneva Nos. 96-97; Vienna Nos. 15-16.

Inalienable Rights of the Palestinian People A188

1981, Jan. 30   Photo.
343 A188 15c multicolored .... .30 .25
See Offices in Geneva #98; Vienna #17.

Interlocking Puzzle Pieces — A189

Stylized Person — A190

1981, Mar. 6   Photo.
344 A189 20c multicolored .... .35 .20
345 A190 35c multicolored .... .50 .40
Intl. Year of the Disabled. See Offices in Geneva Nos. 99-100; Vienna Nos. 18-19.

Divislava and Sebastocrator Kaloyan, Bulgarian Mural, 1259, Boyana Church, Sofia — A191

1981, Apr. 15   Photo.   Perf. 11½
Granite Paper
346 A191 20c multicolored .... .30 .30
347 A191 31c multicolored .... .45 .40
See Offices in Geneva #101; Vienna #20.

Solar Energy — A192

Conference Emblem — A193

1981, May 29   Litho.   Perf. 13
348 A192 20c multicolored .... .35 .30
349 A193 40c multicolored .... .60 .50
Conference on New and Renewable Sources of Energy, Nairobi, Aug. 10-21. See Offices in Geneva No. 102; Vienna No. 21.

Flag Type of 1980
1981, Sept. 25   Litho.
Granite Paper
350 A185 20c Djibouti .... .25 .25
351 A185 20c Sri Lanka .... .25 .25
352 A185 20c Bolivia .... .25 .25
353 A185 20c Equatorial Guinea .... .25 .25
  a. Se-tenant block of 4 .... 1.50
354 A185 20c Malta .... .25 .25
355 A185 20c Czechoslovakia .... .25 .25
356 A185 20c Thailand .... .25 .25
357 A185 20c Trinidad & Tobago .... .25 .25
  a. Se-tenant block of 4 .... 1.50
358 A185 20c Ukrainian SSR .... .25 .25
359 A185 20c Kuwait .... .25 .25
360 A185 20c Sudan .... .25 .25
361 A185 20c Egypt .... .25 .25
  a. Se-tenant block of 4 .... 1.50
362 A185 20c US .... .25 .25
363 A185 20c Singapore .... .25 .25
364 A185 20c Panama .... .25 .25
365 A185 20c Costa Rica .... .25 .25
  a. Se-tenant block of 4 .... 1.50
     Nos. 350-365 (16) 4.00 4.00
See note after No. 340.

Seedling and Tree Cross Section — A194

"10" and Symbols of Progress — A195

1981, Nov. 13   Litho.
366 A194 18c multicolored .... .30 .25
367 A195 28c multicolored .... .55 .45
UN Volunteers Program, 10th anniv. See Offices in Geneva #103-104; Vienna #22-23.

Respect for Human Rights — A196

Independence of Colonial Countries and People — A197

Second Disarmament Decade — A198

1982, Jan. 22   Perf. 11½x12
368 A196 17c multicolored .... .30 .15
369 A197 28c multicolored .... .45 .25
370 A198 40c multicolored .... .75 .40
     Nos. 368-370 (3) .... 1.50 .80

10th Anniv. of UN Environment Program
A199   A200

1982, Mar. 19   Litho.   Perf. 13½x13
371 A199 20c multicolored .... .30 .25
372 A200 40c multicolored .... .85 .65

UN Emblem and Olive Branch in Outer Space — A201

1982, June 11   Litho.   Perf. 13 x 13½
373 A201 20c multicolored .... .55 .45
Exploration and Peaceful Uses of Outer Space. See Offices in Geneva Nos. 109-110; Vienna No. 27.

Flag Type of 1980
1982, Sept. 24   Litho.   Perf. 12
Granite Paper
374 A185 20c Austria .... .30 .25
375 A185 20c Malaysia .... .30 .25
376 A185 20c Seychelles .... .30 .25
377 A185 20c Ireland .... .30 .25
  a. Se-tenant block of 4 .... 2.00
378 A185 20c Mozambique .... .30 .25
379 A185 20c Albania .... .30 .25
380 A185 20c Dominica .... .30 .25
381 A185 20c Solomon Islands .... .30 .25
  a. Se-tenant block of 4 .... 2.00
382 A185 20c Philippines .... .30 .25
383 A185 20c Swaziland .... .30 .25
384 A185 20c Nicaragua .... .30 .25
385 A185 20c Burma .... .30 .25
  a. Se-tenant block of 4 .... 2.00
386 A185 20c Cape Verde .... .30 .25
387 A185 20c Guyana .... .30 .25
388 A185 20c Belgium .... .30 .25
389 A185 20c Nigeria .... .30 .25
  a. Se-tenant block of 4 .... 2.00
     Nos. 374-389 (16) 4.80 4.00
See note after No. 340.

Conservation and Protection of Nature — A202

1982, Nov. 19   Photo.   *Perf. 14*
390 A202 20c Leaf   .40   .35
391 A202 28c Butterfly   .55   .50
   See Offices in Geneva Nos. 111-112; Vienna Nos. 28-29.

World Communications Year A203

World Communications Year — A204

1983, Jan. 28   Litho.   *Perf. 13*
392 A203 20c multicolored   .35   .25
393 A204 40c multicolored   .75   .65
   See Offices in Geneva #113; Vienna #30.

Safety at Sea
A205   A206

1983, Mar. 18   Litho.   *Perf. 14¹/₂*
394 A205 20c multicolored   .40   .25
395 A206 37c multicolored   .75   .65
See Offices in Geneva #114-115; Vienna #31-32.

World Food
Program
A207

1983, Apr. 22   Engr.   *Perf. 13¹/₂*
396 A207 20c rose lake   .45   .35
   See Offices in Geneva #116; Vienna #33-34.

Trade and Development
A208   A209

1983, June 6   Litho.   *Perf. 14*
397 A208 20c multicolored   .40   .25
398 A209 28c multicolored   .75   .65
   See Offices in Geneva Nos. 117-118; Vienna Nos. 35-36.

Flag Type of 1980
1983, Sept. 23   Photo.   *Perf. 12*
Granite Paper
399 A185 20c Great Britain   .30   .25
400 A185 20c Barbados   .30   .25
401 A185 20c Nepal   .30   .25
402 A185 20c Israel   .30   .25
  a. Se-tenant block of 4   1.65
403 A185 20c Malawi   .30   .25
404 A185 20c Byelorussian SSR   .30   .25
405 A185 20c Jamaica   .30   .25
406 A185 20c Kenya   .30   .25
  a. Se-tenant block of 4   1.65
407 A185 20c People's Republic of
        China   .30   .25
408 A185 20c Peru   .30   .25
409 A185 20c Bulgaria   .30   .25
410 A185 20c Canada   .30   .25
  a. Se-tenant block of 4   1.65
411 A185 20c Somalia   .30   .25
412 A185 20c Senegal   .30   .25
413 A185 20c Brazil   .30   .25

414 A185 20c Sweden   .30   .25
  a. Se-tenant block of 4   1.65
    Nos. 399-414 (16)   4.80 4.00
   See note after No. 340.

35th Anniv. of the Universal Declaration
of Human Rights
A210   A211

Photogravure and Engraved
1983, Dec. 9   *Perf. 13¹/₂*
415 A210 20c Window Right   .40   .30
416 A211 40c Peace Treaty with Na-
      ture   .85   .75
See Offices in Geneva #119-120, Vienna #37-38.

Intl. Population
Conference
A212

1984, Feb. 3   Litho.   *Perf. 14*
417 A212 20c multicolored   .30   .25
418 A212 40c multicolored   .75   .75
   See Offices in Geneva #121; Vienna #39.

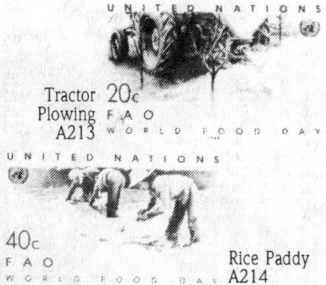

Tractor
Plowing
A213

Rice Paddy
A214

1984, Mar. 15   Litho.   *Perf. 14¹/₂*
419 A213 20c multicolored   .30   .25
420 A214 40c multicolored   .75   .65
   World Food Day, Oct. 16. See Offices in Geneva Nos. 122-123; Vienna Nos. 40-41.

Grand Canyon
A215

Ancient City of
Polonnaruwa,
Sri
Lanka — A216

1984, Apr. 18   Litho.   *Perf. 14*
421 A215 20c multicolored   .30   .25
422 A216 50c multicolored   .85   .75
   World Heritage (protection of world cultural and natural sites). See #601-602; Offices in Geneva #124-125, 211-212; Vienna #42-43, 125-126.

A217   A218

1984, May 29   Photo.   *Perf. 11¹/₂*
423 A217 20c multicolored   .45   .35
424 A218 50c multicolored   1.00   .85
   Future for Refugees. See Offices in Geneva Nos. 126-127; Vienna Nos. 44-45.

Flag Type of 1980
1984, Sept. 21   Photo.   *Perf. 12*
Granite Paper
425 A185 20c Burundi   .55   .20
426 A185 20c Pakistan   .55   .20
427 A185 20c Benin   .55   .20
428 A185 20c Italy   .55   .20
  a. Se-tenant block of 4   3.00
429 A185 20c Tanzania   .55   .20
430 A185 20c United Arab Emirates   .55   .20
431 A185 20c Ecuador   .55   .20
432 A185 20c Bahamas   .55   .20
  a. Se-tenant block of 4   3.00
433 A185 20c Poland   .55   .20
434 A185 20c Papua New Guinea   .55   .20
435 A185 20c Uruguay   .55   .20
436 A185 20c Chile   .55   .20
  a. Se-tenant block of 4   3.00
437 A185 20c Paraguay   .55   .20
438 A185 20c Bhutan   .55   .20
439 A185 20c Central African Re-
      public   .55   .20
440 A185 20c Australia   .55   .20
  a. Se-tenant block of 4   3.00
    Nos. 425-440 (16)   8.80 3.20
   See note after No. 340.

Intl. Youth
Year — A219

ILO Turin
Center — A220

1984, Nov. 15   Litho.   *Perf. 13¹/₂*
441 A219 20c multicolored   .45   .30
442 A219 35c multicolored   1.00   .65
   See Offices in Geneva #128; Vienna #46-47.

1985, Feb. 1   Engr.
443 A220 23c Turin Center emblem   .65   .45
   See Offices in Geneva #129-130; Vienna #48.

UN
University
A221

1985, Mar. 15   Photo.   *Perf. 13¹/₂*
444 A221 50c multicolored   1.25   .85
   See Offices in Geneva #131-132; Vienna #49.

Peoples of the
World — A222

Painting UN
Emblem — A223

1985, May 10   Litho.   *Perf. 14*
445 A222 22c multicolored   .35   .30
446 A223 $3 multicolored   4.00 3.50
See Offices in Geneva #133-134; Vienna #50-51.

The Corner
A224

Alvaro
Raking Hay
A225

   Oil paintings (details) by American artist Andrew Wyeth.

1985, June 26   Photo.   *Perf. 12x11¹/₂*
447 A224 22c multicolored   .50   .35
448 A225 45c multicolored   1.00   .85
Souvenir Sheet
Imperf
449   Sheet of 2   1.90 1.50
 a. A224 22c multicolored   .50   —
 b. A225 45c multicolored   1.00   —
   40th anniv. of the UN. No. 449 has multicolored margin with inscription and UN emblem. Size: 75x83mm. See Offices in Geneva Nos. 135-137; Vienna Nos. 52-54.

Flag Type of 1980
1985, Sept. 20   Photo.   *Perf. 12*
Granite Paper
450 A185 22c Grenada   .60   .50
451 A185 22c Federal Republic of
      Germany   .60   .50
452 A185 22c Saudi Arabia   .60   .50
453 A185 22c Mexico   .60   .50
  a. Se-tenant block of 4   4.00
454 A185 22c Uganda   .60   .50
455 A185 22c St. Thomas & Prince   .60   .50
456 A185 22c USSR   .60   .50
457 A185 22c India   .60   .50
  a. Se-tenant block of 4   4.00
458 A185 22c Liberia   .60   .50
459 A185 22c Mauritius   .60   .50
460 A185 22c Chad   .60   .50
461 A185 22c Dominican Republic   .60   .50
  a. Se-tenant block of 4   4.00
462 A185 22c Sultanate of Oman   .60   .50
463 A185 22c Ghana   .60   .50
464 A185 22c Sierra Leone   .60   .50
465 A185 22c Finland   .60   .50
  a. Se-tenant block of 4   4.00
    Nos. 450-465 (16)   9.60 8.00
   See note after No. 340.

A226   A227

Photoravure and Engraved
1985, Nov. 22   *Perf. 13¹/₂*
466 A226 22c Asian child   .45   .30
467 A226 33c Breastfeeding   .75   .60
   UNICEF Child Survival Campaign. See Offices in Geneva #138-139; Vienna #55-56.

1986, Jan. 31   Photo.   *Perf. 11¹/₂*
468 A227 22c Abstract Painting by
      Wosene Kosrof   .60   .45
   Africa in Crisis, campaign against hunger. See Offices in Geneva #140; Vienna #57.

Water Resources
A228

1986, Mar. 14   Photo.   *Perf. 13¹/₂*
469 A228 22c Dam   1.60 1.25
470 A228 22c Irrigation   1.60 1.25
471 A228 22c Hygiene   1.60 1.25
472 A228 22c Well   1.60 1.25
  a. Block of 4, #469-472   6.75 5.50
   UN Development program. No. 472a has continuous design. See Offices in Geneva #141-144; Vienna #58-61.

Human Rights
Stamp of
1954 — A229

Stamp collecting: 44c, Engraver.

1986, May 22   Engr.   Perf. 12¹/₂
473 A229 22c dk violet & brt blue   .35   .35
474 A229 44c brown & emer green   .90   .85

See Offices in Geneva #146-147; Vienna #62-63.

Birds Nest in
Tree — A230

Peace in Seven
Languages
A231

Photo. & Embossed
1986, June 20   Perf. 13¹/₂
475 A230 22c multicolored   .90   .45
476 A231 33c multicolored   2.25 1.50

Intl. Peace Year. See Offices in Geneva Nos. 148-149; Vienna Nos. 64-65.

Flag Type of 1980
1986, Sept. 19   Photo.   Perf. 12
Granite Paper
477 A185 22c New Zealand   .60   .45
478 A185 22c Lao PDR   .60   .45
479 A185 22c Burkina Faso   .60   .45
480 A185 22c Gambia   .60   .45
   a.   Se-tenant block of 4   3.25
481 A185 22c Maldives   .60   .45
482 A185 22c Ethiopia   .60   .45
483 A185 22c Jordan   .60   .45
484 A185 22c Zambia   .60   .45
   a.   Se-tenant block of 4   3.25
485 A185 22c Iceland   .60   .45
486 A185 22c Antigua & Barbuda   .60   .45
487 A185 22c Angola   .60   .45
488 A185 22c Botswana   .60   .45
   a.   Se-tenant block of 4   3.25
489 A185 22c Romania   .60   .45
490 A185 22c Togo   .60   .45
491 A185 22c Mauritania   .60   .45
492 A185 22c Colombia   .60   .45
   a.   Se-tenant block of 4   3.25
   Nos. 477-492 (16)   9.60 7.20

See note after No. 340.

Souvenir Sheet

World Federation of UN
Associations, 40th
Anniv. — A232

Designs: 22c, Mother Earth, by Edna Hibel, US. 33c, Watercolor by Salvador Dali (b. 1904), Spain. 39c, New Dawn, by Dong Kingman, US. 44c, Watercolor by Chaim Gross, US.

1986, Nov. 14   Litho.   Perf. 13x13¹/₂
493   Sheet of 4   4.50 1.65
   a. A232 22c multicolored   .50   —
   b. A232 33c multicolored   .80   —
   c. A232 39c multicolored   .95   —
   d. A232 44c multicolored   1.10 —

See Offices in Geneva #150; Vienna #66.

Trygve Halvdan Lie
(1896-1968), 1st
Secretary-General
A233

Photogravure and Engraved
1987, Jan. 30   Perf. 13¹/₂
494 A233 22c multicolored   1.00   .20

See Offices in Geneva #151; Vienna #67.

Intl. Year of
Shelter for
the
Homeless
A234

Perf. 13¹/₂x12¹/₂
1987, Mar. 13   Litho.
495 A234 22c Surveying, blueprint   .50   .20
496 A234 44c Cutting lumber   1.40   .45

See Offices in Geneva #154-155; Vienna #68-69.

YES TO LIFE · NO TO DRUGS

Fight Drug
Abuse
A235

1987, June 12   Litho.   Perf. 14¹/₂x15
497 A235 22c Construction   .65   .20
498 A235 33c Education   1.25   .35

See Offices in Geneva #156-157; Vienna #70-71.

Flag Type of 1980
1987, Sept. 18   Photo.   Perf. 12
Granite Paper
499 A185 22c Comoros   .65   .50
500 A185 22c Yemen PDR   .65   .50
501 A185 22c Mongolia   .65   .50
502 A185 22c Vanuatu   .65   .50
   a.   Se-tenant block of 4   3.00
503 A185 22c Japan   .65   .50
504 A185 22c Gabon   .65   .50
505 A185 22c Zimbabwe   .65   .50
506 A185 22c Iraq   .65   .50
   a.   Se-tenant block of 4   3.00
507 A185 22c Argentina   .65   .50
508 A185 22c Congo   .65   .50
509 A185 22c Niger   .65   .50
510 A185 22c St. Lucia   .65   .50
   a.   Se-tenant block of 4   3.00
511 A185 22c Bahrain   .65   .50
512 A185 22c Haiti   .65   .50
513 A185 22c Afghanistan   .65   .50
514 A185 22c Greece   .65   .50
   a.   Se-tenant block of 4   3.00
   Nos. 499-514 (16)   10.40 8.00

See note after No. 340.

UN
Day — A236

Designs: Multinational people in various occupations.

1987, Oct. 23   Litho.   Perf. 14¹/₂x15
515 A236 22c multicolored   .50   .35
516 A236 39c multicolored   .80   .70

See Offices in Geneva Nos. 158-159; Vienna Nos. 74-75.

Immunize Every
Child — A237

1987, Nov. 20   Litho.   Perf. 15x14¹/₂
517 A237 22c Measles   .90   .50
518 A237 44c Tetanus   2.25 1.50

See Offices in Geneva Nos. 160-161; Vienna Nos. 76-77.

IFAD
FOR A WORLD
WITHOUT HUNGER   22c

UNITED NATIONS

Intl. Fund for Agricultural Development
(IFAD) — A238

1988, Jan. 29   Litho.   Perf. 13¹/₂
519 A238 22c Fishing   .55   .40
520 A238 33c Farming   1.10   .85

See Offices in Geneva Nos. 162-163; Vienna Nos. 78-79.

UNITED NATIONS - FOR A BETTER WORLD

3c   A239

1988, Jan. 29   Photo.   Perf. 13¹/₂x14
521 A239 3c multicolored ('88)   .15   .15

SURVIVAL OF THE FORESTS
UNITED NATIONS   25c

Survival of
the Forests
A240

1988, Mar. 18   Litho.   Perf. 14x15
522 A240 25c multicolored   2.25 1.75
523 A240 44c multicolored   3.75 3.25
   a.   Pair, #522-523   6.25 5.25

No. 523a has continuous design. See Offices in Geneva Nos. 165-166; Vienna Nos. 80-81.

Intl. Volunteer
Day — A241

1988, May 6   Perf. 13x14, 14x13
524 A241 25c Education, vert.   .55   .40
525 A241 50c Vocational training   1.25 1.00

See Offices in Geneva Nos. 167-168; Vienna Nos. 82-83.

Health in
Sports
A242

HEALTH IN SPORTS

Perf. 13¹/₂x13, 13x13¹/₂
1988, June 17   Litho.
526 A242 25c Cycling, vert.   .55   .45
527 A242 38c Marathon   1.40 1.10

See Offices in Geneva Nos. 169-170; Vienna Nos. 84-85.

Flag Type of 1980
1988, Sept. 16   Photo.   Perf. 12
Granite Paper
528 A185 25c Spain   .60   .45
529 A185 25c St. Vincent & Grena-
               dines   .60   .45
530 A185 25c Ivory Coast   .60   .45
531 A185 25c Lebanon   .60   .45
   a.   Se-tenant block of 4   3.00
532 A185 25c Yemen (Arab Republic)   .60   .45
533 A185 25c Cuba   .60   .45

534 A185 25c Denmark   .60   .45
535 A185 25c Libya   .60   .45
   a.   Se-tenant block of 4   3.00
536 A185 25c Qatar   .60   .45
537 A185 25c Zaire   .60   .45
538 A185 25c Norway   .60   .45
539 A185 25c German Democratic
               Republic   .60   .45
   a.   Se-tenant block of 4   3.00
540 A185 25c Iran   .60   .45
541 A185 25c Tunisia   .60   .45
542 A185 25c Samoa   .60   .45
543 A185 25c Belize   .60   .45
   a.   Se-tenant block of 4   3.00
   Nos. 528-543 (16)   9.60 7.20

See note after No. 340.

HUMAN RIGHTS
A243

25c
UNITED NATIONS
WORLD
BANK
A244

1988, Dec. 9   Photo. & Engr.
544 A243 25c multicolored   .60   .40

Souvenir Sheet
545 A243 $1 multicolored   1.75 1.40

Universal Declaration of Human Rights, 40th anniv.
See Offices in Geneva Nos. 171-172; Vienna Nos. 86-87.

1989, Jan. 27   Litho.   Perf. 13x14
546 A244 25c Energy and nature   .80   .45
547 A244 45c Agriculture   1.70 1.00

World Bank. See Offices in Geneva Nos. 173-174; Vienna Nos. 88-89.

NOBEL PEACE PRIZE 1988

UNITED NATIONS
PEACE-KEEPING
FORCES

25c

UN Peace-Keeping
Force, 1988 Nobel
Peace Prize
Winner — A245

1989, Mar. 17   Litho.   Perf. 14x13¹/₂
548 A245 25c multicolored   .75   .40

See Offices in Geneva #175, Vienna #90.

UNITED NATIONS   45c

Aerial Photograph of New York
Headquarters — A246

1989, Mar. 17   Perf. 14¹/₂x14
549 A246 45c multicolored   .80   .60

WORLD WEATHER WATCH

World Weather Watch,
25th Anniv. (in
1988) — A247

United Nations   25c

Satellite photographs: 25c, Storm system off the East Coast, US. 36c, Typhoon Abby in the North-West Pacific.

1989, Apr. 21   Litho.   Perf. 13x14
550 A247 25c multicolored   .80   .50
551 A247 36c multicolored   1.75 1.25

See Offices in Geneva Nos. 176-177; Vienna Nos. 91-92.

A248

A249

Photo. & Engr., Photo.

1989, Aug. 23   *Perf. 14*

552 A248 25c multicolored   3.25   .50
553 A249 90c multicolored   2.25 1.75

Offices in Vienna, 10th anniv. See Offices in Geneva Nos. 178-179; Vienna Nos. 93-94.

Flag Type of 1980

1989, Sept. 22   **Photo.**   *Perf. 12*
Granite Paper

554 A185 25c Indonesia   .75   .55
555 A185 25c Lesotho   .75   .55
556 A185 25c Guatemala   .75   .55
557 A185 25c Netherlands   .75   .55
   a.   Se-tenant block of 4   3.50
558 A185 25c South Africa   .75   .55
559 A185 25c Portugal   .75   .55
560 A185 25c Morocco   .75   .55
561 A185 25c Syrian Arab Republic .75   .55
   a.   Se-tenant block of 4   3.50
562 A185 25c Honduras   .75   .55
563 A185 25c Kampuchea   .75   .55
564 A185 25c Guinea-Bissau   .75   .55
565 A185 25c Cyprus   .75   .55
   a.   Se-tenant block of 4   3.50
566 A185 25c Algeria   .75   .55
567 A185 25c Brunei   .75   .55
568 A185 25c St. Kitts and Nevis .75   .55
569 A185 25c United Nations   .75   .55
   a.   Se-tenant block of 4   3.50
     Nos. 554-569 (16)   12.00 8.80

See note after No. 340.

Declaration of
Human Rights,
40th Anniv. (in
1988) — A250

Paintings: 25c, *The Table of Universal Brotherhood*, by Jose Clemente Orozco. 45c, *Study for Composition II*, by Vassily Kandinsky.

1989, Nov. 17   **Litho.**   *Perf. 13½*

570 A250 25c multicolored   .60   .45
571 A250 45c multicolored   1.10   .85

Printed in sheets of 12+12 se-tenant labels containing Articles 1 (25c) or 2 (45c) inscribed in English, French or German.
See Nos. 582-583, 599-600, 616-617, 627-628; Offices in Geneva Nos. 180-181, 193-194, 209-210, 224-225, 234-235; Vienna Nos. 95-96, 108-109, 123-124, 139-140, 150-151.

Intl. Trade
Center — A251

1990, Feb. 2   **Litho.**   *Perf. 14½x15*

572 A251 25c multicolored   1.60 1.10

See Offices in Geneva #182; Vienna #97.

Fight AIDS
Worldwide
A252

Perf. 13½x12½
1990, Mar. 16   **Litho.**

573 A252 25c shown   .65   .55
574 A252 40c Shadow over crowd 1.50 1.25

See Offices in Geneva Nos. 184-185; Vienna Nos. 99-100.

Medicinal
Plants — A253

1990, May 4   **Photo.**   *Perf. 11½*
Granite Paper

575 A253 25c *Catharanthus roseus*   .60   .45
576 A253 90c *Panax quinquefolium* 2.25 1.50

See Offices in Geneva Nos. 186-187; Vienna Nos. 101-102.

United
Nations,
45th
Anniv.
A254

1990, June 26   **Litho.**   *Perf. 14½x13*
577 A254 25c shown   1.00   .70
578 A254 45c "45," emblem   2.75   .85

Souvenir Sheet
579   Sheet of 2, #577-578   9.50 2.00

See Offices in Geneva Nos. 188-189; Vienna Nos. 103-104.

Crime
Prevention — A255

1990, Sept. 13   **Photo.**   *Perf. 14*
580 A255 25c Crimes of youth   1.00   .60
581 A255 36c Organized crime   2.25 1.00

See Offices in Geneva Nos. 191-192; Vienna Nos. 106-107.

Human Rights Type of 1989

Artwork: 25c, Fragment from the sarcophagus of Plotinus, c. 270 A.D. 45c, Combined Chambers of the High Court of Appeal by Charles Paul Renouard.

1990, Nov. 16   **Litho.**   *Perf. 13½*
582 A250 25c black, gray & tan   .50   .35
583 A250 45c black & brown   1.00   .75

See Offices in Geneva Nos. 193-194; Vienna Nos. 108-109.
Printed in sheets of 12+12 se-tenant labels containing Articles 7 (25c) or 8 (45c) inscribed in English, French or German.

Economic
Commission for
Europe
A256

1991, Mar. 15   **Litho.**   *Perf. 14*
584 A256 30c Two storks   1.25   .90
585 A256 30c Woodpecker, ibex 1.25   .90
586 A256 30c Capercaille, plover 1.25   .90
587 A256 30c Falcon, marmot   1.25   .90
   a.   Block of 4, #584-587   5.00 3.75

Namibian
Independence
A257

1991, May 10   **Litho.**   *Perf. 14*
588 A257 30c Dunes, Namib Desert .85   .60
589 A257 50c Savanna   2.00 1.40

See Offices in Geneva Nos. 199-200; Vienna Nos. 114-115.

A258

The Golden Rule by
Norman
Rockwell — A259

1991, Sept. 11   **Litho.**   *Perf. 13½*
590 A258 30c multicolored   .60   .55

Photo.
Perf. 12x11½
591 A259 50c multicolored   1.00 1.00

UN Headquarters, New
York — A260

1991, May 10   **Engr.**   *Perf. 13½*
592 A260 $2 dark blue   3.00 2.50

Rights of the
Child
A261

1991, June 14   **Litho.**   *Perf. 14½*
593 A261 30c Children, globe   1.25   .50
594 A261 70c Houses, rainbow 2.75 1.50

See Offices in Geneva Nos. 203-204; Vienna Nos. 117-118.

Banning
of Chemical
Weapons
A262

Design: 90c, Hand holding back chemical drums.

1991, Sept. 11   **Litho.**   *Perf. 13½*
595 A262 30c multicolored   1.25   .65
596 A262 90c multicolored   3.00 2.25

See Offices in Geneva Nos. 205-206; Vienna Nos. 119-120.

UN Postal
Administration,
40th
Anniv. — A263

1991, Oct. 24   **Litho.**   *Perf. 14x15*
597 A263 30c No. 1   1.25   .60
598 A263 40c No. 3   1.75 1.10

See Offices in Geneva Nos. 207-208; Vienna Nos. 121-122.

Human Rights Type of 1989

Artwork: 30c, The Last of England, by Ford Madox Brown. 50c, The Emigration to the East, by Tito Salas.

1991, Nov. 20   **Litho.**   *Perf. 13½*
599 A250 30c multicolored   .90   .30
600 A250 50c multicolored   1.50   .50

See Offices in Geneva Nos. 209-210; Vienna Nos. 123-124.
Printed in sheets of 12+12 se-tenant labels containing Articles 13 (30c) or 14 (50c) inscribed in English, French or German.

World Heritage Type of 1984

Designs: 30c, Uluru Natl. Park, Australia. 50c, The Great Wall of China.

1992, Jan. 24   **Litho.**   *Perf. 13*
Size: 35x28mm

601 A215 30c multicolored   .85   .60
602 A215 50c multicolored   1.75 1.00

See Offices in Geneva Nos. 211-212; Vienna Nos. 125-126.

Clean Oceans
A264

1992, Mar. 13   **Litho.**   *Perf. 14*
603 A264 29c Ocean surface   .75   .70
604 A264 29c Ocean bottom   .75   .70
   a.   Pair, #603-604   1.50 1.40

Printed in sheets of 12 containing 6 #604a.

Earth Summit
A265

Designs: No. 605, Globe at LR. No. 606, Globe at LL. No. 607, Globe at UR. No. 608, Globe at UL.

1992, May 22   **Photo.**   *Perf. 11½*
605 A265 29c multicolored   .65   .50
606 A265 29c multicolored   .65   .50
607 A265 29c multicolored   .65   .50
608 A265 29c multicolored   .65   .50
   a.   Block of 4, #605-608   2.60 2.00

See Offices in Geneva Nos. 216-219, Vienna Nos. 129-132.

Mission to Planet Earth — A266

Designs: No. 609, Satellites over city, sailboats, fishing boat. No. 610, Satellite over coast, passenger liner, dolphins, whale, volcano.

1992, Sept. 4   **Photo.**   *Rouletted 8*
Granite Paper

609 A266 29c multicolored   3.50   .60
610 A266 29c multicolored   3.50   .60
   a.   Pair, #609-610   7.50 1.25

See Offices in Geneva Nos. 220-221, Vienna Nos. 133-134.

Science and
Technology
for
Development
A267

Design: 50c, Animal, man drinking.

1992, Oct. 2   **Litho.**   *Perf. 14*
611 A267 29c multicolored   .60   .45
612 A267 50c multicolored   1.00   .70

See Offices in Geneva Nos. 222-223, Vienna Nos. 135-136.

UN University Building, Tokyo A268 4c

UN Headquarters A269

Design: 40c, UN University Building, Tokyo, diff.

Perf. 14, 13½x13 (29c)
1992, Oct. 2   Litho.
613 A268	4c multicolored	.15	.15
614 A269	29c multicolored	.60	.55
615 A268	40c multicolored	.80	.75
	Nos. 613-615 (3)	1.55	1.45

Human Rights Type of 1989
Artwork: 29c, Lady Writing a Letter With her Maid, by Vermeer. 50c, The Meeting, by Ester Almqvist.

1992, Nov. 20   Litho.   *Perf. 13½*
616 A250	29c multicolored	.90	.55
617 A250	50c multicolored	1.25	1.00

See Offices in Geneva Nos. 224-225; Vienna Nos. 139-140.
Printed in sheets of 12+12 se-tenant labels containing Articles 19 (29c) and 20 (50c) inscribed in English, French or German.

Aging With Dignity — A270

Designs: 29c, Elderly couple, family. 52c, Old man, physician, woman holding fruit basket.

1993, Feb. 5   Litho.   *Perf. 13*
618 A270	29c multicolored	1.00	.55
619 A270	52c multicolored	1.90	1.00

See Offices in Geneva Nos. 226-227; Vienna Nos. 141-142.

Endangered Species A271

Designs: No. 620, Hairy-nosed wombat. No. 621, Whooping crane. No. 622, Giant clam. No. 623, Giant sable antelope.

1993, Mar. 3   Litho.   *Perf. 13x12½*
620 A271	29c multicolored	.65	.50
621 A271	29c multicolored	.65	.50
622 A271	29c multicolored	.65	.50
623 A271	29c multicolored	.65	.50
a.	Block of 4, #620-623	2.75	2.50

See Nos. 639-642, 657-660, 674-677, 700-703; Offices in Geneva Nos. 228-231, 246-249, 264-267, 280-283, 298-301; Vienna Nos. 143-146, 162-165, 180-183, 196-199; 214-217.

Healthy Environment A272

Designs: 29c, Personal. 50c, Family.

1993, May 7   Litho.   *Perf. 15x14½*
624 A272	29c Man	.75	.45
625 A272	52c Family	1.25	.75

WHO, 45th anniv.
See Offices in Geneva Nos. 232-233; Vienna Nos. 147-148.

A273

1993, May 7   Litho.   *Perf. 15x14*
626 A273	5c multicolored	.15	.15

Human Rights Type of 1989
Artwork: 29c, Shocking Corn, by Thomas Hart Benton. 35c, The Library, by Jacob Lawrence.

1993, June 11   Litho.   *Perf. 13½*
627 A250	29c multicolored	1.10	.65
628 A250	35c multicolored	1.40	.80

See Offices in Geneva Nos. 234-235; Vienna Nos. 150-151.
Printed in sheets of 12 + 12 se-tenant labels containing Articles 25 (29c) and 26 (35c) inscribed in English, French or German.

Intl. Peace Day — A274

Denomination at: No. 629, UL. No. 630, UR. No. 631, LL. No. 632, LR.

Rouletted 12½
1993, Sept. 21   Litho. & Engr.
629 A274	29c blue & multi	2.00	.75
630 A274	29c blue & multi	2.00	.75
631 A274	29c blue & multi	2.00	.75
632 A274	29c blue & multi	2.00	.75
a.	Block of 4, #629-632	9.00	7.00

See Offices in Geneva Nos. 236-239; Vienna Nos. 152-155.

Environment-Climate — A275

Designs: No. 633, Chameleon. No. 634, Palm trees, top of funnel cloud. No. 635, Bottom of funnel cloud, deer, antelope. No. 636, Bird of paradise.

1993, Oct. 29   Litho.   *Perf. 14½*
633 A275	29c multicolored	.70	.55
634 A275	29c multicolored	.70	.55
635 A275	29c multicolored	.70	.55
636 A275	29c multicolored	.70	.55
a.	Strip of 4, #633-636	3.00	2.25

See Offices in Geneva Nos. 240-243; Vienna Nos. 156-159.

Intl. Year of the Family — A276

Designs: 29c, Mother holding child, two children, woman. 45c, People tending crops.

1994, Feb. 4   Litho.   *Perf. 13.1*
637 A276	29c green & multi	1.40	.75
638 A276	45c blue & multi	2.00	1.10

See Offices in Geneva Nos. 244-245; Vienna Nos. 160-161.

Endangered Species Type of 1993
Designs: No. 639, Chimpanzee. No. 640, St. Lucia Amazon. No. 641, American crocodile. No. 642, Dama gazelle.

1994, Mar. 18   Litho.   *Perf. 12.7*
639 A271	29c multicolored	.65	.50
640 A271	29c multicolored	.65	.50
641 A271	29c multicolored	.65	.50
642 A271	29c multicolored	.65	.50
a.	Block of 4, #639-642	2.75	2.25

See Offices in Geneva Nos. 246-249; Vienna Nos. 162-165.

Protection for Refugees — A277

1994, Apr. 29   Litho.   *Perf. 14.3x14.8*
643 A277	50c multicolored	1.40	.70

See Offices in Geneva No. 250; Vienna No. 166.

Dove of Peace — A278

Sleeping Child, by Stanislaw Wyspianski A279

Mourning Owl, by Vanessa Isitt A280

1994, Apr. 29   Litho.   *Perf. 12.9*
644 A278	10c multicolored	.20	.15
645 A279	19c multicolored	.40	.35

Engr.
Perf. 13.1
646 A280	$1 red brown	2.00	1.75

Intl. Decade for Natural Disaster Reduction A281

Earth viewed from space, outline map of: No. 647, North America. No. 648, Eurasia. No. 649, South America, No. 650, Australia and South Asia.

1994, May 27   Litho.   *Perf. 13.9x14.2*
647 A281	29c multicolored	1.75	.60
648 A281	29c multicolored	1.75	.60
649 A281	29c multicolored	1.75	.60
650 A281	29c multicolored	1.75	.60
a.	Block of 4, #647-650	8.00	3.00

See Offices in Geneva Nos. 251-254; Vienna Nos. 170-173.

Population and Development — A282

Designs: 29c, Children playing. 52c, Family with house, car, other possessions.

1994, Sept. 1   Litho.   *Perf. 13.2x13.6*
651 A282	29c multicolored	.85	.60
652 A282	52c multicolored	1.30	1.00

See Offices in Geneva Nos. 258-259; Vienna Nos. 174-175.

UNCTAD, 30th Anniv. — A283

1994, Oct. 28
653 A283	29c multicolored	.65	.50
654 A283	50c multi, diff.	1.10	.70

See Offices in Geneva Nos. 260-261; Vienna Nos. 176-177.

UN, 50th Anniv. — A284

Social Summit, Copenhagen — A285

1995, Jan. 1   Litho. & Engr.   *Perf. 13.4*
655 A284	32c multicolored	1.25	.90

See Offices in Geneva No. 262; Vienna No. 178.

Perf. 13.6x13.9
1995, Feb. 3   Photo. & Engr.
656 A285	50c multicolored	1.00	1.00

See Offices in Geneva No. 263; Vienna No. 179.

Endangered Species Type of 1993
Designs: No. 657, Giant armadillo. No. 658, American bald eagle. No. 659, Fijian/Tongan banded iguana. No. 660, Giant panda.

1995, Mar. 24   Litho.   *Perf. 13x12½*
657 A271	32c multicolored	.70	.55
658 A271	32c multicolored	.70	.55
659 A271	32c multicolored	.70	.55
660 A271	32c multicolored	.70	.55
a.	Block of 4, 657-660	3.00	2.25

See Offices in Geneva Nos. 264-267; Vienna Nos. 180-183.

Intl. Youth Year, 10th Anniv. — A286

32c, Seated child. 55c, Children cycling.

1995, May 26   Litho.   *Perf. 14.4x14.7*
661 A286	32c multicolored	.75	.45
662 A286	55c multicolored	1.25	.85

See Offices in Geneva Nos. 268-269; Vienna Nos. 184-185.

UN, 50th Anniv. — A287

Designs: 32c, Hand with pen signing UN Charter, flags. 50c, Veterans' War Memorial, Opera House, San Francisco.

1995, June 26   Engr.   *Perf. 13.3x13.6*
663 A287	32c black	.75	.45
664 A287	50c maroon	1.10	.70

Souvenir Sheet
Litho. & Engr.
Imperf
665	Sheet of 2, #663-664	2.50	2.00
a.	A287 32c black	.95	.75
b.	A287 50c maroon	1.35	1.10

See Offices in Geneva Nos. 270-271; Vienna Nos. 186-187.

4th World
Conference on
Women,
Beijing — A288

Designs: 32c, Mother and child. 40c, Seated
woman, cranes flying above.

1995, Sept. 5   Photo.   Perf. 12
666 A288 32c multicolored   .80   .40
       Size: 28x50mm
667 A288 40c multicolored   1.10   .50
   See Offices in Geneva Nos. 273-274; Vienna
Nos. 189-190.

UN
Headquarters
A289

1995, Sept. 5   Litho.   Perf. 15
668 A289 20c multicolored   .40   .20

       Miniature Sheet

United Nations, 50th Anniv. — A290

   Designs: #669a-669 l, Various people in continuous design (2 blocks of six stamps with gutter
between).

1995, Oct. 24   Litho.   Perf. 14
669   Sheet of 12   9.00 5.00
  a.-l. A290 32c any single   .70   .40

670   Souvenir booklet   10.00
  a. A290 32c Booklet pane of 3, vert.
       strip of 3 from UL of sheet   2.50 2.50
  b. A290 32c Booklet pane of 3, vert.
       strip of 3 from UR of sheet   2.50 2.50
  c. A290 32c Booklet pane of 3, vert.
       strip of 3 from LL of sheet   2.50 2.50
  d. A290 32c Booklet pane of 3, vert.
       strip of 3 from LR of sheet   2.50 2.50
   See Offices in Geneva Nos. 275-276; Vienna
Nos. 190-191.

WFUNA, 50th
Anniv. — A291

1996, Feb. 2   Litho.   Perf. 13x13½
671 A291 32c multicolored   .65   .30
   See Offices in Geneva No. 277; Vienna No. 193.

Mural, by
Fernand
Leger — A292

1996, Feb. 2   Litho.   Perf. 14½x15
672 A292 32c multicolored   .65   .30
673 A292 60c multi, diff.   1.25   .60

   Endangered Species Type of 1993
   Designs: No. 674, Masdevallia veitchiana. No.
675, Saguaro cactus. No. 676, West Australian
pitcher plant. No. 677, Encephalartos horridus.

1996, Mar. 14   Litho.   Perf. 12½
674 A271 32c multicolored   .65   .30
675 A271 32c multicolored   .65   .30
676 A271 32c multicolored   .65   .30
677 A271 32c multicolored   .65   .30
  a.   Block of 4, #674-677   2.60   —
   See Offices in Geneva Nos. 280-283; Vienna
Nos. 196-199.

City Summit
(Habitat II) — A293

   Designs: No. 678, Deer. No. 679, Man, child,
dog sitting on hill, overlooking town. No. 680, People walking in park, city skyline. No. 681, Tropical
park, Polynesian woman, boy. No. 682, Polynesian
village, orchids, bird.

1996, June 3   Litho.   Perf. 14x13½
678 A293 32c multicolored   .70   .30
679 A293 32c multicolored   .70   .30
680 A293 32c multicolored   .70   .30
681 A293 32c multicolored   .70   .30
682 A293 32c multicolored   .70   .30
  a.   Strip of 5, #678-682   3.50   —
   See Offices in Geneva Nos. 284-288; Vienna
Nos. 200-204.

Sport and the Environment — A294

   1996 Summer Olympic Games, Atlanta, GA:
32c, Men's basketball, vert. 50c, Women's
volleyball.

       Perf. 14x14½, 14½x14
1996, July 19   Litho.
683 A294 32c multicolored   .65   .30

684 A294 50c multicolored   1.00   .50
       Souvenir Sheet
685 A294   Sheet of 2, #683-684   1.90 1.65
   See Offices in Geneva Nos. 289-291; Vienna
Nos. 205-207.

Plea for
Peace — A295

   Designs: 32c, Doves. 60c, Stylized dove.

       Perf. 14½x15, 15x14½
1996, Sept. 17   Litho.
686 A295 32c multicolored   .65   .30
687 A295 60c multicolored   1.25   .60
   See Offices in Geneva Nos. 292-293; Vienna
Nos. 208-209.

UNICEF, 50th
Anniv. — A296

   Fairy Tales: 32c, Yeh-Shen, China. 60c, The Ugly
Duckling, by Hans Christian Andersen.

1996, Nov. 20   Litho.   Perf. 14½x15
688 A296 32c multicolored   .65   .30
689 A296 60c multicolored   1.25   .60
       Panes of 8 + label.
   See Offices in Geneva Nos. 294-295; Vienna
Nos. 210-211.

       Flag Type of 1980
1997, Feb. 12   Photo.   Perf. 12
       Granite Paper
690 A185 32c Tadjikistan   .65   .30
691 A185 32c Georgia   .65   .30
692 A185 32c Armenia   .65   .30
693 A185 32c Namibia   .65   .30
  a.   Block of 4, #690-693   2.60 1.20
694 A185 32c Liechtenstein   .65   .30
695 A185 32c South Korea   .65   .30
696 A185 32c Kazakhstan   .65   .30
697 A185 32c Latvia   .65   .30
  a.   Block of 4, #694-697   2.60 1.20

       See note after No. 340.

Cherry Blossoms, UN
Headquarters — A297

Peace
Rose — A298

1997, Feb. 12   Litho.   Perf. 14½
698 A297 8c multicolored   .15   .15
699 A297 55c multicolored   1.10   .55

   Endangered Species Type of 1993
   Designs: No. 700, African elephant. No. 701,
Major Mitchell's cockatoo. No. 702, Black-footed
ferret. No. 703, Cougar.

1997, Mar. 13   Litho.   Perf. 12½
700 A271 32c multicolored   .65   .30
701 A271 32c multicolored   .65   .30
702 A271 32c multicolored   .65   .30
703 A271 32c multicolored   .65   .30
  a.   Block of 4, #700-703   2.60 1.20
   See Offices in Geneva Nos. 298-301; Vienna
Nos. 214-217.

Earth Summit,
5th Anniv.
A299

   Designs: No. 704, Sailboat. No. 705, Three sailboats. No. 706, Two people watching sailboat, sun.
No. 707, Person, sailboat.
   $1, Combined design similar to Nos. 704-707.

1997, May 30   Photo.   Perf. 11.5
       Granite Paper
704 A299 32c multicolored   .65   .30
705 A299 32c multicolored   .65   .30
706 A299 32c multicolored   .65   .30
707 A299 32c multicolored   .65   .30
  a.   Block of 4, #704-707   2.60 1.20
       Souvenir Sheet
708 A299 $1 multicolored   2.00 2.00
  a.   Ovptd. in sheet margin   2.00 2.00
   See Offices in Geneva Nos. 302-306; Vienna
Nos. 218-222.
   No. 708 contains one 60x43mm stamp. Overprint in sheet margin of No. 708a reads "PACIFIC
97 / World Philatelic Exhibition / San Francisco,
California / 29 May - 8 June 1997."

Transportation
A300

   Ships: No. 709, Clipper ship. No. 710, Paddle
steamer. No. 711, Ocean liner. No. 712, Hovercraft. No. 713, Hydrofoil.

1997, Aug. 29   Litho.   Perf. 14x14½
709 A300 32c multicolored   .65   .30
710 A300 32c multicolored   .65   .30
711 A300 32c multicolored   .65   .30
712 A300 32c multicolored   .65   .30
713 A300 32c multicolored   .65   .30
  a.   Strip of 5, #709-713   3.25 1.50
   See Offices in Geneva Nos. 307-311; Vienna
Nos. 223-227.
   No. 713a has continuous design.

Philately — A301

   Designs: 32c, No. 473. 50c, No. 474.

1997, Oct. 14   Litho.   Perf. 13½x14
714 A301 32c multicolored   .65   .30
715 A301 50c multicolored   1.00   .50
   See Offices in Geneva Nos. 312-313; Vienna
Nos. 228-229.

World Heritage
Convention, 25th
Anniv. — A302

   Terracotta warriors of Xian: 32c, Single warrior.
60c, Massed warriors. No. 718a, like #716. No.
718b, like #717. No. 718c, like Geneva #314. No.
718d, like Geneva #315. No. 718e, like Vienna
#230. No. 718f, like Vienna #231.

1997, Nov. 19   Litho.   *Perf. 13½*

716	A302	32c multicolored	.65	.30
717	A302	60c multicolored	1.25	.60
718		Souvenir booklet	6.50	
a.-f.		A302 8c any single	.15	.15
g.		Booklet pane of 4 #718a	.60	.60
h.		Booklet pane of 4 #718b	.60	.60
i.		Booklet pane of 4 #718c	.60	.60
j.		Booklet pane of 4 #718d	.60	.60
k.		Booklet pane of 4 #718e	.60	.60
l.		Booklet pane of 4 #718f	.60	.60

See Offices in Geneva Nos. 314-316; Vienna Nos. 230-232.

AIR POST STAMPS

Plane and Gull — AP1

Swallows and UN Emblem AP2

1951, Dec. 14   Engr.   *Perf. 14* *Unwmk.*

C1	AP1	6c henna brown	.15	.15
C2	AP1	10c bright blue green	.15	.20
C3	AP2	15c deep ultra	.20	.25
C4	AP2	25c gray black	.90	.35
		Nos. C1-C4 (4)	1.40	.95

The 6c, 15c and 25c exist imperforate.

Airplane Wing and Globe — AP3

1957, May 27   *Perf. 12½x14*

C5	AP3	4c maroon	.15	.15

1959, Feb. 9   *Perf. 12½x13½*

C6	AP3	5c rose red	.15	.15

UN Flag and Plane — AP4

1959, Feb. 9   *Perf. 13½x14*

C7	AP4	7c ultramarine	.15	.15

Outer Space — AP5

UN Emblem — AP6

"Flight Across Globe" — AP8

Bird of Laurel Leaves — AP7

Jet Plane and Envelope — AP9

1963-64   Photo.   *Perf. 11½*

C8	AP5	6c blk, blue & yel grn	.15	.15
C9	AP6	8c yel, ol green & red	.15	.15

Perf. 12½x12

C10	AP7	13c ultra, aqua, gray & car	.20	.20

Perf. 11½x12, 12x11½

C11	AP8	15c violet, buff, gray & pale grn ('64)	.35	.20
a.		Gray omitted		
C12	AP9	25c yel, org, gray, blue & red ('64)	.65	.30
		Nos. C8-C12 (5)	1.50	1.00

Dates of issue: 6c, 8c, 13c, June 17, 1963; 15c, 25c, May 1. See Offices in Geneva No. 8.

Jet Plane and UN Emblem — AP10

1968, Apr. 18   Litho.   *Perf. 13*

C13	AP10	20c multicolored	.30	.25

Wings, Envelopes and UN Emblem — AP11

1969, Apr. 21   Litho.

C14	AP11	10c org ver, org, yel & black	.20	.20

UN Emblem and Stylized Wing — AP12

Birds in Flight — AP13

Clouds AP14

"UN" and Plane — AP15

Lithograved and Engraved

1972, May 1   *Perf. 13x13½*

C15	AP12	9c lt blue, dark red & vio blue	.15	.15

Photo.   *Perf. 14x13½*

C16	AP13	11c blue & multi	.20	.15

Perf. 13½x14

C17	AP14	17c yel, red & orange	.25	.20

Perf. 13

C18	AP15	21c silver & multi	.30	.25
		Nos. C15-C18 (4)	.90	
		Set value		.60

Globe and Jet — AP16

Pathways Radiating from UN Emblem AP17

Bird in Flight, UN Headquarters AP18

Perf. 13, 12½x13 (18c)

1974, Sept. 16   Litho.

C19	AP16	13c multicolored	.20	.15
C20	AP17	18c multicolored	.25	.20
C21	AP18	26c blue & multi	.35	.30
		Nos. C19-C21 (3)	.80	.65

Winged Airmail Letter — AP19

Symbolic Globe and Plane — AP20

1977, June 27   Photo.   *Perf. 14*

C22	AP19	25c grnsh blue & multi	.35	.25
C23	AP20	31c magenta	.40	.30

OFFICES IN GENEVA, SWITZERLAND

For use only on mail posted at the Palais des Nations (UN European Office), Geneva. Inscribed in French unless otherwise stated.

100 Centimes = 1 Franc

Types of UN Issues 1961-69 and

UN European Office, Geneva — G1

Designs: 5c, UN Headquarters, New York, and world map. 10c, UN flag. 20c, Three men united before globe. 50c, Opening words of UN Charter. 60c, UN emblem over globe. 70c, "UN" and UN emblem. 75c, "Flight Across Globe." 80c, UN Headquarters and emblem. 90c, Abstract group of flags. 1fr, UN Emblem. 2fr, Stylized globe and weather vane. 3fr, Statue by Henrik Starcke. 10fr, "Peace, Justice, Security."

Perf. 13 (5c, 70c, 90c); Perf. 12½x12 (10c); Perf. 11½ (20c-60c, 3fr); Perf. 11½x12 (75c); Perf. 13½x14 (80c); Perf. 14 (1fr); Perf. 12x11½ (2fr); Perf. 12 (10fr)

Photogravure; Lithographed & Embossed (1fr); Engraved (10fr)

1969-70   Unwmk.

1	A88	5c purple & multi	.15	.15
a.		Green omitted		
2	A52	10c salmon & multi	.15	.15
3	A66	20c black & multi	.15	.15
4	G1	30c dk blue & multi	.15	.15
5	A77	50c ultra & multi	.20	.20
6	A54	60c dk brown, sal & gold	.25	.25
7	A104	70c red, black & gold	.25	.25
8	AP8	75c car rose & multi	.30	.30
9	A78	80c blue grn, red & yel	.30	.30
10	A45	90c blue & multi	.30	.30
11	A79	1fr lt & dk green	.35	.35
12	A67	2fr blue & multi	.70	.70

13	A97	3fr olive & multi	1.10	1.10
14	A3	10fr deep blue	3.50	3.50
		Nos. 1-14 (14)	7.85	7.85

The 20c, 80c and 90c are inscribed in French. The 75c and 10fr carry French inscription at top, English at bottom.

Issue dates: 60c and 10fr, Apr. 17, 1970; 70c, 80c, 90c, 2fr, Sept. 22, 1970. Others, Oct. 4, 1969.

Sea Bed Type

Photogravure and Engraved

1971, Jan. 25   *Perf. 13*

15	A114	30c green & multi	.20	.20

Refugee Type

1971, Mar. 12   Litho.   *Perf. 13x12½*

16	A115	50c dp car, dp org & black	.20	.30

Food Program Type

1971, Apr. 13   Photo.   *Perf. 14*

17	A116	50c dk purple, gold & grn	.20	.30

UPU Headquarters Type

1971, May 28   Photo.   *Perf. 11½*

18	A117	75c green & multi	.30	.30

Eliminate Discrimination Types

1971, Sept. 21   Photo.   *Perf. 13½*

19	A118	30c blue & multi	.20	.20
20	A119	50c multicolored	.30	.30

Picasso Type

1971, Nov. 19   Photo.   *Perf. 11½*

21	A122	1.10fr carmine & multi	.75	.65

Palais des Nations, Geneva G2

1972, Jan. 5   Photo.   *Perf. 11½*

22	G2	40c olive & multi	.20	.25

Nuclear Weapons Type

1972, Feb. 14   Photo.   *Perf. 13½x14*

23	A124	40c yel green, blk, rose & gray	.25	.45

World Health Day Type

Lithographed and Engraved

1972, Apr. 7   *Perf. 13x13½*

24	A125	80c black & multi	.40	.50

Environment Type

Lithographed and Embossed

1972, June 5   *Perf. 12½x14*

25	A126	40c multicolored	.35	.30
26	A126	80c multicolored	.75	.70

ECE Type

1972, Sept. 11   Litho.   *Perf. 13x13½*

27	A127	1.10fr red & multi	1.00	.90

Art at UN Type

1972, Nov. 17   Photo.   *Perf. 12x12½*

28	A128	40c gold, brown & red	.40	.35
29	A128	80c gold, brown & olive	.70	.70

Disarmament Type

1973, Mar. 9   Litho.   *Perf. 13½x13*

30	A129	60c violet & multi	.40	.35
31	A129	1.10fr olive & multi	.85	.75

Nos. 30-31 exist imperf.

Drug Abuse Type

1973, Apr. 13   Photo.   *Perf. 13½*

32	A130	60c blue & multi	.45	.40

Volunteers Type

1973, May 25   Photo.   *Perf. 14*

33	A131	80c multicolored	.45	.70

Namibia Type

1973, Oct. 1   Photo.   *Perf. 13½*

34	A132	60c red & multi	.55	.45

Human Rights Type

1973, Nov. 16   Photo.   *Perf. 13½*

35	A133	40c ultra & multi	.30	.30
36	A133	80c olive & multi	.60	.60

ILO Headquarters Type

1974, Jan. 11　　Photo.　　Perf. 14
37	A134	60c violet & multi	.50　.45
38	A134	80c brown & multi	.85　.60

UPU Type

1974, Mar. 22　　Photo.　　Perf. 14
39	A135	30c multicolored	.20　.20
40	A135	60c multicolored	.40　.40

Art at UN Type

1974, May 6　　Photo.　　Perf. 14
41	A136	60c dark red & multi	.40　.40
42	A136	1fr green & multi	.70　.70

WPY Type

1974, Oct. 18　　Photo.　　Perf. 14
43	A140	60c brt green & multi	.45　.45
44	A140	80c brown & multi	.55　.55

Law of the Sea Type

1974, Nov. 22　　Photo.　　Perf. 14
45	A141	1.30fr blue & multi	.95　.95

Outer Space Type

1975, Mar. 14　　Litho.　　Perf. 13
46	A142	60c multicolored	.35　.35
47	A142	90c multicolored	.55　.55

IWY Type

1975, May 9　　Litho.　　Perf. 15
48	A143	60c multicolored	.45　.40
49	A143	90c multicolored	.65　.55

30th Anniv. Type

1975, June 26　　Litho.　　Perf. 13
50	A144	60c green & multi	.45　.40
51	A144	90c violet & multi	.65　.60

Souvenir Sheet
Imperf
52		Sheet of 2	.50　1.00
a.		A144 60c green & multi	.35　.35
b.		A144 90c violet & multi	.55　.55

Namibia Type

1975, Sept. 22　　Photo.　　Perf. 13½
53	A145	50c multicolored	.30　.30
54	A145	1.30fr multicolored	1.00　.70

Peace-keeping Operations Type

1975, Nov. 21　　Engr.　　Perf. 12½
55	A146	60c greenish blue	.40　.40
56	A146	70c bright violet	.75　.50

WFUNA Type

1976, Mar. 12　　Photo.　　Perf. 14
57	A152	90c multicolored	1.00　.65

UNCTAD Type

1976, Apr. 23　　Photo.　　Perf. 11½
58	A153	1.10fr multicolored	1.00　.80

Habitat Type

1976, May 28　　Photo.　　Perf. 14
59	A154	40c multicolored	.30　.30
60	A154	1.50fr violet & multi	1.00　1.00

UN Emblem, Post Horn and Rainbow — G3

1976, Oct. 8　　Photo.　　Perf. 11½
61	G3	80c tan & multi	.60　.60
62	G3	1.10fr lt green & multi	1.90　1.90

Sheets of 20.

Food Council Type

1976, Nov. 19　　Litho.　　Perf. 14½
63	A156	70c multicolored	.60　.55

WIPO Type

1977, Mar. 11　　Photo.　　Perf. 14
64	A157	80c red & multi	.60　.55

Drop of Water and Globe — G4

1977, Apr. 22　　Photo.　　Perf. 13½x13
65	G4	80c ultra & multi	.60　.50
66	G4	1.10fr dark car & multi	.85　.75

UN Water Conference, Mar del Plata, Argentina, Mar. 14-25.

Hands Protecting UN Emblem — G5

1977, May 24　　Photo.　　Perf. 14
67	G5	80c blue & multi	.60　.50
68	G5	1.10fr emerald & multi	.85　.75

UN Security Council.

Colors of Five Races Spun into One Firm Rope — G6

1977, Sept. 19　　Litho.　　Perf. 13
69	G6	40c multicolored	.30　.30
70	G6	1.10fr multicolored	.85　.85

Fight against racial discrimination.

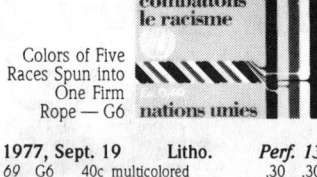

Atomic Energy Turning Partly into Olive Branch — G7

1977, Nov. 18　　Photo.
71	G7	80c dark car & multi	.50　.50
72	G7	1.10fr Prus blue & multi	.75　.75

Peaceful uses of atomic energy.

"Tree" of Doves — G8

1978, Jan. 27　　Litho.　　Perf. 14½
73	G8	35c multicolored	.15　.15

Globes with Smallpox Distribution — G9

1978, Mar. 31　　Photo.　　Perf. 12x11½
74	G9	80c yellow & multi	.50　.50
75	G9	1.10fr lt green & multi	.75　.75

Global eradication of smallpox.

Namibia Type

1978, May 5　　Photo.　　Perf. 12
76	A166	80c multicolored	.75　.60

Women's Year Emblem G15

Jets and Flight Patterns — G10

1978, June 12　　Photo.　　Perf. 14
77	G10	70c multicolored	.40　.30
78	G10	80c multicolored	.75　.50

International Civil Aviation Organization for "Safety in the Air."

General Assembly, Flags and Globe G11

1978, Sept. 15　　Photo.　　Perf. 13½
79	G11	70c multicolored	.60　.55
80	G11	1.10fr multicolored	1.00　.60

Technical Cooperation Type

1978, Nov. 17　　Photo.　　Perf. 14
81	A169	80c multicolored	.85　.55

Seismograph Recording Earthquake G12

1979, Mar. 9　　Photo.　　Perf. 14
82	G12	80c multicolored	.50　.40
83	G12	1.50fr multicolored	.85　.85

Office of the UN Disaster Relief Coordinator (UNDRO).

Children and Rainbow — G13

1979, May 4　　Photo.　　Perf. 14
84	G13	80c multicolored	.50　.50
85	G13	1.10fr multicolored	.90　.90

International Year of the Child.

Namibia Type

1979, Oct. 5　　Litho.　　Perf. 13½
86	A176	1.10fr multicolored	.60　.60

International Court of Justice, Scales — G14

1979, Nov. 9　　Litho.　　Perf. 13x13½
87	G14	80c multicolored	.40　.40
88	G14	1.10fr multicolored	.60　.60

International Court of Justice, The Hague, Netherlands.

Economic Order Type

1980, Jan. 11　　　　Perf. 15x14½
89	A179	80c multicolored	.70　.60

1980, Mar. 7　　Litho.　　Perf. 14½x15
90	G15	40c multicolored	.35　.60
91	G15	70c multicolored	.75　.55

UN Decade for Women.

Peace-keeping Operations Type

1980, May 16　　Litho.　　Perf. 14x13
92	A181	1.10fr blue & green	.70　.70

35th Anniv. Type and

Dove and "35" — G16

1980, June 26　　Litho.　　Perf. 13
93	G16	40c multicolored	.30　.30
94	A183	70c multicolored	.50　.50

Souvenir Sheet
Imperf
95		Sheet of 2	.60　.60
a.		G16 40c multicolored	.20　—
b.		A183 70c multicolored	.40　—

35th anniv. of the UN.

ECOSOC Type and

Family Climbing Line Graph — G17

1980, Nov. 21　　Litho.　　Perf. 13½x13
96	A186	40c multicolored	.25　.25
97	G17	70c multicolored	.50　.50

Palestinian Rights Type

1981, Jan. 30　　　　Photo.
98	A188	80c multicolored	.60　.60

Disabled Type of UN, Vienna

1981, Mar. 6　　　　Photo.
99	A190	40c multicolored	.25　.25
100	V4	1.50fr multicolored	1.00　1.00

Art Type

1981, Apr. 15　　Photo.　　Perf. 11½
101	A191	80c multicolored	.60　.60

Energy Type

1981, May 29　　Litho.　　Perf. 13
102	A192	1.10fr multicolored	.75　.75

Volunteers Program Type and Symbols of Science, Agriculture and Industry — G18

1981, Nov. 13　　Litho.　　Perf. 13½x13
103	A194	40c multicolored	.35　.30
104	G18	70c multicolored	.60　.55

Fight Against Apartheid — G19　　Flower of Flags — G20

1982, Jan. 22　　Photo.　　Perf. 11½x12
105	G19	30c multicolored	.20　.15
106	G20	1fr multicolored	.70　.65

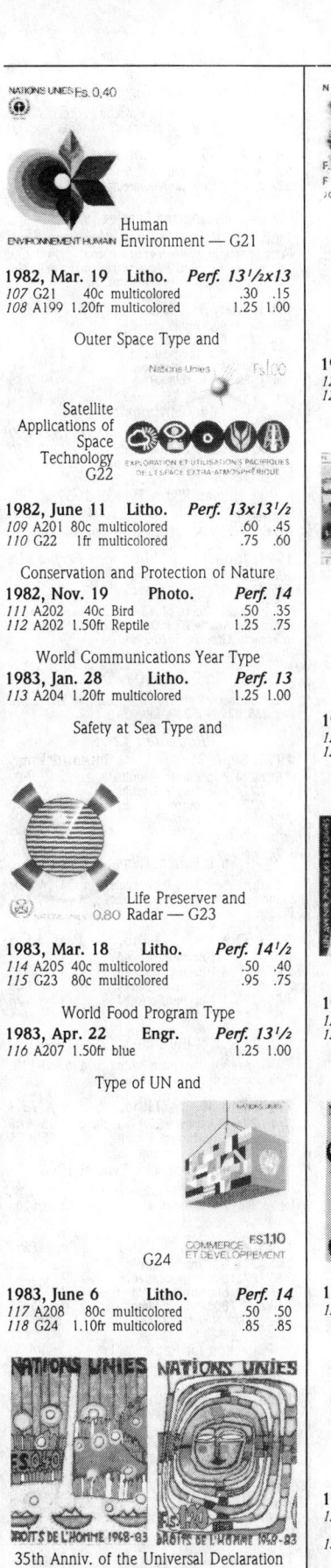

Human Environment — G21

1982, Mar. 19   Litho.   Perf. 13¹/₂x13
107 G21   40c multicolored   .30   .15
108 A199   1.20fr multicolored   1.25 1.00

Outer Space Type and

Satellite Applications of Space Technology G22

1982, June 11   Litho.   Perf. 13x13¹/₂
109 A201   80c multicolored   .60   .45
110 G22   1fr multicolored   .75   .60

Conservation and Protection of Nature

1982, Nov. 19   Photo.   Perf. 14
111 A202   40c Bird   .50   .35
112 A202   1.50fr Reptile   1.25   .75

World Communications Year Type

1983, Jan. 28   Litho.   Perf. 13
113 A204   1.20fr multicolored   1.25 1.00

Safety at Sea Type and

Life Preserver and Radar — G23

1983, Mar. 18   Litho.   Perf. 14¹/₂
114 A205   40c multicolored   .50   .40
115 G23   80c multicolored   .95   .75

World Food Program Type

1983, Apr. 22   Engr.   Perf. 13¹/₂
116 A207   1.50fr blue   1.25 1.00

Type of UN and

G24

1983, June 6   Litho.   Perf. 14
117 A208   80c multicolored   .50   .50
118 G24   1.10fr multicolored   .85   .85

35th Anniv. of the Universal Declaration of Human Rights
G25   G26

Perf. 13¹/₂
1983, Dec. 9   Photo.   Engr.
119 G25   40c Homo Humus
                  Humanitas   .45   .45
120 G26   1.20fr Right to Create   .95   .90

Intl. Population Conference Type

1984, Feb. 3   Litho.   Perf. 14
121 A212   1.20fr multicolored   1.00   .85

Fishing G27

Women Farm Workers, Africa G28

1984, Mar. 15   Litho.   Perf. 14¹/₂
122 G27   50c multicolored   .40   .30
123 G28   80c multicolored   .70   .55

World Food Day.

Valletta, Malta — G29

Los Glaciares Natl. Park, Argentina G30

1984, Apr. 18   Litho.   Perf. 14
124 G29   50c multicolored   .60   .60
125 G30   70c multicolored   .85   .80

World Heritage. See Nos. 211-212.

G31   G32

1984, May 29   Photo.   Perf. 11¹/₂
126 G31   35c multicolored   .35   .20
127 G32   1.50fr multicolored   1.25   .75

Refugees.

International Youth Year — G33

1984, Nov. 15   Litho.   Perf. 13¹/₂
128 G33   1.20fr multicolored   1.25 1.00

ILO Type of UN and

Turin Center — G34

1985, Feb. 1   Engr.
129 A220   80c Turin Center em-
                  blem   .60   .45
130 G34   1.20fr U Thant Pavilion   .90   .70

UN University Type

1985, Mar. 15   Photo.   Perf. 13¹/₂
131 A221   50c Farmer, discussion
                  group   .50   .40
132 A221   80c As above   .80   .60

Postman — G35

Doves — G36

1985, May 10   Litho.   Perf. 14
133 G35   20c multicolored   .20   .15
134 G36   1.20fr multicolored   1.25 1.00

40th Anniv. Type

1985, June 26   Photo.   Perf. 12x11¹/₂
135 A224   50c multicolored   .45   .35
136 A225   70c multicolored   .65   .50

Souvenir Sheet
Imperf
137   Sheet of 2   1.50 1.10
  a.   A224 50c multicolored   .70   —
  b.   A225 70c multicolored   —   —

UNICEF Child Survival Campaign
Photo. & Engr.
1985, Nov. 22   Perf. 13¹/₂
138 A226   50c Three girls   .60   .20
139 A226   1.20fr Infant drinking   1.25 1.00

Africa in Crisis Type
Abstract painting by Alemayehou Gabremedhin.

1986, Jan. 31   Photo.   Perf. 11¹/₂
140 A227   1.40fr Mother, hungry
                  children   1.40 1.00

UN Development Program Type

1986, Mar. 14   Photo.   Perf. 13¹/₂
141 A228   35c Erosion control   2.00 1.50
142 A228   35c Logging   2.00 1.50
143 A228   35c Lumber transport   2.00 1.50
144 A228   35c Nursery   2.00 1.50
  a.   Block of 4, #141-144   8.50 6.00

No. 144a has a continuous design.

Doves and Sun — G37

1986, Mar. 14   Litho.   Perf. 15x14¹/₂
145 G37   5c multicolored   .15   .15

UN Stamp Collecting Type
Designs: 50c, UN Human Rights stamp. 80c, UN stamps.

1986, May 22   Engr.   Perf. 12¹/₂
146 A229   50c dk green & hn brn   .50   .40
147 A229   80c dk green & yel org   .90   .70

Flags and Globe as Dove — G38

Peace in French — G39

Photo. & Embossed
1986, June 20   Perf. 13¹/₂
148 G38   45c multicolored   .60   .45
149 G39   1.40fr multicolored   1.75 1.25

Intl. Peace Year.

WFUNA Anniv. Type
Souvenir Sheet
Designs: 35c, Abstract by Benigno Gomez, Honduras. 45c, Abstract by Alexander Calder (1898-1976), US. 50c, Abstract by Joan Miro (b. 1893), Spain. 70c, Sextet with Dove, by Ole Hamann, Denmark.

1986, Nov. 14   Litho.   Perf. 13x13¹/₂
150   Sheet of 4   4.25 2.00
  a.   A232 35c multicolored   .55   —
  b.   A232 45c multicolored   .75   —
  c.   A232 50c multicolored   .95   —
  d.   A232 70c multicolored   1.25   —

Trygve Lie Type
Photo. & Engr.
1987, Jan. 30   Perf. 13¹/₂
151 A233   1.40fr multicolored   1.25 1.00

Sheaf of Colored Bands, by Georges Mathieu — G40

Armillary Sphere, Palais des Nations — G41

Photo., Photo. & Engr. (No. 153)
Perf. 11¹/₂x12, 13¹/₂ (No. 153)
1987, Jan. 30
152 G40   90c multicolored   .70   .60
153 G41   1.40fr multicolored   1.10   .90

Perf. 13¹/₂x12¹/₂
1987, Mar. 13   Litho.
154 A234   50c Construction   .70   .55
155 A234   90c Finishing interior   1.20   .90

Fight Drug Abuse Type
1987, June 12   Litho.   Perf. 14¹/₂
156 A235   80c Mother and child   .70   .55
157 A235   1.20fr Workers in rice
                  paddy   1.25 1.00

UN Day Type
Designs: Multinational people in various occupations.

1987, Oct. 23   Litho.   Perf. 14¹/₂x15
158 A236   35c multicolored   .65   .50
159 A236   50c multicolored   1.00   .75

Immunize Every Child Type
1987, Nov. 20   Litho.   Perf. 15x14¹/₂
160 A237   90c Whooping cough   1.50 1.00
161 A237   1.70fr Tuberculosis   2.75 1.15

IFAD Type
1988, Jan. 29   Litho.   Perf. 13¹/₂
162 A238   35c Flocks   .45   .35
163 A238   1.40fr Fruit   1.75 1.40

G42

1988, Jan. 29   Photo.   Perf. 14
164 G42   50c multicolored   1.00   .70

Survival of the Forests Type
1988, Mar. 18   Litho.   Perf. 14x15
165 A240   50c Pine forest   1.75 1.50
166 A240   1.10fr as 50c   4.75 4.25
  a.   Pair, #165-166   6.50 6.00

No. 166a has a continuous design.

Intl. Volunteer Day Type
Perf. 13x14, 14x13
1988, May 6   Litho.
167 A241   80c Agriculture, vert.   .95   .60
168 A241   90c Veterinary medicine   1.00   .70

Health in Sports Type
Perf. 13¹/₂x13, 13x13¹/₂

1988, June 17   Litho.
169 A242   50c Soccer, vert.   .60   .40
170 A242   1.40fr Swimming   1.60 1.25

Human Rights Declaration Anniv. Type
1988, Dec. 9   Photo. & Engr.   Perf. 12
171 A243   90c multicolored   1.10   .85
Souvenir Sheet
172 A243   2fr multicolored   2.75 2.25

World Bank Type
1989, Jan. 27   Litho.   Perf. 13x14
173 A244   80c Telecommunications 1.00   .75
174 A244   1.40fr Industry   2.25 1.75

Peace-Keeping Force Type
1989, Mar. 17   Litho.   Perf. 14x13¹/₂
175 A245   90c multicolored   1.10 1.00

World Weather Watch Anniv. Type
Satellite photographs: 90c, Europe under the influence of Arctic air. 1.10fr, Surface temperatures of sea, ice and land surrounding the Kattegat between Denmark and Sweden.

1989, Apr. 21   Litho.   Perf. 13x14
176 A247   90c multicolored   1.25 1.00
177 A247   1.10fr multicolored   2.00 1.50

G43   G44

Photo. & Engr., Photo.
Perf. 14
1989, Aug. 23
178 G43   50c multicolored   1.25   .70
179 G44   2fr multicolored   4.00 2.50

Offices in Vienna, 10th anniv.

Human Rights Type of 1989
Paintings and sculpture: 35c, *Young Mother Sewing,* by Mary Cassatt. 80c, *The Unknown Slave,* sculpture by Albert Mangones.

1989, Nov. 17   Litho.   Perf. 13¹/₂
180 A250   35c multicolored   .40   .40
181 A250   80c multicolored   1.10 1.10

Printed in sheets of 12+12 se-tenant labels containing Articles 3 (35c) or 4 (80c) inscribed in French, German or English.

Intl. Trade Center Type
1990, Feb. 2   Litho.   Perf. 14¹/₂x15
182 A251   1.50fr multicolored   2.50 2.00

G45

1990, Feb. 2   Photo.   Perf. 14x13¹/₂
183 G45   5fr multicolored   5.00 4.00

G46

Fight AIDS Worldwide
G46a

Perf. 13¹/₂x12¹/₂
1990, Mar. 16   Litho.
184 G46   50c multicolored   1.25 1.00
185 G46a   80c multicolored   2.00   .50

Medicinal Plants Type
1990, May 4   Photo.   Perf. 11¹/₂
Granite Paper
186 A253   90c *Plumeria rubra*   1.25   .70
187 A253   1.40fr *Cinchona officinalis* 2.25 1.50

UN 45th Anniv. Type
"45," emblem and: 90c, Symbols of clean environment, transportation and industry. 1.10fr, Dove in silhouette.

1990, June 26   Litho.   Perf. 14¹/₂x13
188 A254   90c multicolored   1.25   .45
189 A254   1.10fr multicolored   2.25 1.50
Souvenir Sheet
190 A254   Sheet of 2, #188-189   6.00 2.65

Crime Prevention Type
1990, Sept. 13   Photo.   Perf. 14
191 A255   50c Official corruption 1.00   .70
192 A255   2fr Environmental crime 2.75 2.25

Human Rights Type of 1989
Paintings: 35c, The Prison Courtyard by Vincent Van Gogh. 90c, Katho's Son Redeems the Evil Doer From Execution by Albrecht Durer.

1990, Nov. 16   Litho.   Perf. 13¹/₂
193 A250   35c multicolored   .55   .25
194 A250   90c black & brown   1.50   .60

Printed in sheets of 12+12 se-tenant labels containing Articles 9 (35c) or 10 (90c) inscribed in French, German or English.

Economic Commission for Europe Type
1991, Mar. 15   Litho.   Perf. 14
195 A256   90c Owl, gull   1.25   .60
196 A256   90c Bittern, otter   1.25   .60
197 A256   90c Swan, lizard   1.25   .60
198 A256   90c Great crested grebe 1.25   .60
a.   Block of 4, #195-198   5.50 2.40

Namibian Independence Type
1991, May 10   Litho.   Perf. 14
199 A257   70c Mountains   1.25 1.00
200 A257   90c Baobab tree   2.25 1.75

Ballots Filling Ballot Box — G47

UN Emblem — G48

1991, May 10   Litho.   Perf. 15x14¹/₂
201 G47   80c multicolored   1.25 1.00
202 G48   1.50fr multicolored   2.50 2.00

G49

Rights of the Child — G50

Litho.
Perf. 14¹/₂
Perf. 15x14¹/₂
1991, June 14
203 G49   80c Hands holding infant 1.60 1.00
204 G50   1.10fr Children, flowers 2.00 1.50

G51   NATIONS UNIES   0.80

Banning of Chemical Weapons G52

1991, Sept. 11   Litho.   Perf. 13¹/₂
205 G51   80c multicolored   1.50 1.00
206 G52   1.40fr multicolored   2.75 1.50

UN Postal Administration, 40th Anniv. Type
1991, Oct. 24   Litho.   Perf. 14x15
207 A263   50c UN NY #7   .85   .70
208 A263   1.60fr UN NY #10   2.50 2.00

Human Rights Type of 1989
Artwork: 50c, Early Morning in Ro...1925, by Paul Klee. 90c, The Marriage of Giovanni Arnolfini and Fiovanna Cenami, by Jan Van Eyck.

1991, Nov. 20   Litho.   Perf. 13¹/₂
209 A250   50c multicolored   1.00   .70
210 A250   90c multicolored   1.75 1.25

Printed in sheets of 12+12 se-tenant labels containing Articles 15 (50c) and 16 (90c) inscribed in French, German or English.

World Heritage Type of 1984
Designs: 50c, Sagarmatha Natl. Park, Nepal. 1.10fr, Stonehenge, United Kingdom.

1992, Jan. 24   Litho.   Perf. 13
Size: 35x28mm
211 G29   50c multicolored   1.25 1.00
212 G29   1.10fr multicolored   2.75 1.65

G53   NATIONS UNIES

1992, Jan. 24   Perf. 15x14¹/₂
213 G53   3fr multicolored   3.50 3.00

Clean Oceans Type
1992, Mar. 13   Litho.   Perf. 14
214 A264   80c Ocean surface, diff. 1.10   .75
215 A264   80c Ocean bottom, diff. 1.10   .75
a.   Pair, #214-215   2.25 1.75

Printed in sheets of 12 containing 6 #215a.

Earth Summit Type
Designs: No. 216, Rainbow. No. 217, Faces shaped as clouds. No. 218, Two sailboats. No. 219, Woman with parasol, sailboat, flowers.

1992, May 22   Photo.   Perf. 11¹/₂
216 A265   75c multicolored   1.10   .75
217 A265   75c multicolored   1.10   .75
218 A265   75c multicolored   1.10   .75
219 A265   75c multicolored   1.10   .75
a.   Block of 4, #216-219   4.50 3.00

Mission to Planet Earth Type
Designs: No. 220, Space station. No. 221, Probes near Jupiter.

1992, Sept. 4   Photo.   Rouletted 8
Granite Paper
220 A266   1.10fr multicolored   2.50 2.00
221 A266   1.10fr multicolored   2.50 2.00
a.   Pair, #220-221   5.00 4.00

Science and Technology Type
Designs: 90c, Doctor, nurse. 1.60fr, Graduate seated before computer.

1992, Oct. 2   Litho.   Perf. 14
222 A267   90c multicolored   1.40   .90
223 A267   1.60fr multicolored   2.50 1.75

Human Rights Type of 1989
Artwork: 50c, The Oath of the Tennis Court, by Jacques Louis David. 90c, Rocking Chair I, by Henry Moore.

1992, Nov. 20   Litho.   Perf. 13¹/₂
224 A250   50c multicolored   1.25   .90
225 A250   90c multicolored   2.25 1.75

Printed in sheets of 12+12 se-tenant labels containing Articles 21 (50c) and 22 (90c) inscribed in French, German or English.

Aging With Dignity Type
Designs: 50c, Older man coaching soccer. 1.50fr, Older man working at computer terminal.

1993, Feb. 5   Litho.   Perf. 13
226 A270   50c multicolored   .90   .60
227 A270   1.50fr multicolored   2.75 1.75

Endangered Species Type
Designs: No. 228, Pongidae (gorilla). No. 229, Falco peregrinus (peregrine falcon). No. 230, Trichechus inunguis (Amazonian manatee). No. 231, Panthera uncia (snow leopard).

1993, Mar. 3   Litho.   Perf. 13x12¹/₂
228 A271   80c multicolored   1.25   .90
229 A271   80c multicolored   1.25   .90
230 A271   80c multicolored   1.25   .90
231 A271   80c multicolored   1.25   .90
a.   Block of 4, #228-231   5.00 4.00

Healthy Environment Type
1993, May 7   Litho.   Perf. 15x14¹/₂
232 A272   50c Neighborhood   1.10   .70
233 A272   1fr Urban skyscrapers   2.40 1.50

Human Rights Type of 1989
Artwork: 50c, Three Musicians, by Pablo Picasso. 90c, Voice of Space, by Rene Magritte.

1993, June 11   Litho.   Perf. 13¹/₂
234 A250   50c multicolored   1.25   .90
235 A250   90c multicolored   2.25 1.75

Printed in sheets of 12 + 12 se-tenant labels containing Article 27 (50c) and 28 (90c) inscribed in French, German or English.

Intl. Peace Day Type
Denomination at: No. 236, UL. No. 237, UR. No. 238, LL. No. 239, LR.

Rouletted 12¹/₂
1993, Sept. 21   Litho. & Engr.
236 A274   60c purple & multi   2.10   .90
237 A274   60c purple & multi   2.10   .90
238 A274   60c purple & multi   2.10   .90
239 A274   60c purple & multi   2.10   .90
a.   Block of 4, #236-239   9.00 3.75

Environment-Climate Type
Designs: No. 240, Polar bears. No. 241, Whale sounding. No. 242, Elephant seal. No. 243, Penguins.

1993, Oct. 29   Litho.   Perf. 14¹/₂
240 A275   1.10fr multicolored   1.50 1.25
241 A275   1.10fr multicolored   1.50 1.25
242 A275   1.10fr multicolored   1.50 1.25
243 A275   1.10fr multicolored   1.50 1.25
a.   Strip of 4, #240-243   6.00 5.00

Intl. Year of the Family Type of 1993
Designs: 80c, Parents teaching child to walk. 1fr, Two women and child picking plants.

1994, Feb. 4   Litho.   Perf. 13.1
244 A276   80c rose violet & multi 1.35 1.00
245 A276   1fr brown & multi   1.75 1.25

Endangered Species Type of 1993
Designs: No. 246, Mexican prairie dog. No. 247, Jabiru. No. 248, Blue whale. No. 249, Golden lion tamarin.

1994, Mar. 18   Litho.   Perf. 12.7
246 A271   80c multicolored   1.10   .85
247 A271   80c multicolored   1.10   .85
248 A271   80c multicolored   1.10   .85
249 A271   80c multicolored   1.10   .85
a.   Block of 4, #246-249   4.50 3.50

Protection for Refugees Type of 1994
Design: 1.20fr, Hand lifting figure over chasm.

1994, Apr. 29   Litho.   Perf. 14.3x14.8
250 A277   1.20fr multicolored   3.00 2.25

Intl. Decade for Natural Disaster Reduction Type of 1994
Earth seen from space, outline map of: No. 251, North America. No. 252, Eurasia. No. 253, South America. No. 254, Australia and South Pacific region.

1994, May 27   Litho.   Perf. 13.9x14.2
251 A281   60c multicolored   1.50   .50
252 A281   60c multicolored   1.50   .50
253 A281   60c multicolored   1.50   .50
254 A281   60c multicolored   1.50   .50
a.   Block of 4, #251-254   7.00 2.00

Palais des
Nations,
Geneva
G54

Creation of the
World, by Oili
Maki — G55

1994, Sept. 1   Litho.   Perf. 14.3x14.6
255 G54 60c multicolored   .75   .55
256 G55 80c multicolored   1.00   .70
257 G54 1.80fr multi. diff.   2.25 1.75

Population and Development Type of 1994
Designs: 60c, People shopping at open-air market. 80c, People on vacation crossing bridge.

1994, Sept. 1   Litho.   Perf. 13.2x13.6
258 A282 60c multicolored   1.25   .70
259 A282 80c multicolored   1.75 1.00

UNCTAD Type of 1994
1994, Oct. 28
260 A283 80c multi. diff.   1.25 1.00
261 A283 1fr multi. diff.   1.65 1.40
a.   Grayish green omitted   —

UN 50th Anniv. Type of 1995
1995, Jan. 1   Litho. & Engr.   Perf. 13.4
262 A284 80c multicolored   1.40 1.25

Social Summit Type of 1995
Perf. 13.6x13.9
1995, Feb. 3   Photo. & Engr.
263 A285 1fr multi. diff.   1.75 1.25

Endangered Species Type of 1993
Designs: No. 264, Crowned lemur, Lemur coronatus. No. 265, Giant Scops owl, Otus gurneyi. No. 266, Zetek's frog, Atelopus varius zeteki. No. 267, Wood bison, Bison bison athabascae.

1995, Mar. 24   Litho.   Perf. 13x12¹/₂
264 A271 80c multicolored   1.40 1.10
265 A271 80c multicolored   1.40 1.10
266 A271 80c multicolored   1.40 1.10
267 A271 80c multicolored   1.40 1.10
a.   Block of 4, 264-267   7.00 4.50

Intl. Youth Year Type of 1995
Designs: 80c, Farmer on tractor, fields at harvest time. 1fr, Couple standing by fields at night.

1995, May 26   Litho.   Perf. 14.4x14.7
268 A286 80c multicolored   1.50 1.10
269 A286 1fr multicolored   1.90 1.40

UN, 50th Anniv. Type of 1995
Designs: 60c, Like No. 663. 1.80fr, Like No. 664.

1995, June 26   Engr.   Perf. 13.3x13.6
270 A287 60c maroon   1.00   .60
271 A287 1.80fr green   3.25 1.75
Souvenir Sheet
Litho. & Engr.
Imperf
272   Sheet of 2, #270-271   4.25 4.25
a.   A287 60c maroon   1.00 1.00
b.   A287 1.80fr green   3.25 3.25

Conference on Women Type of 1995
Designs: 60c, Black woman, cranes flying above. 1fr, Women, dove.

1995, Sept. 5   Photo.   Perf. 12
273 A288 60c multicolored   1.50   .50
Size: 28x50mm
274 A288 1fr multicolored   2.50   .85

UN People, 50th Anniv. Type of 1995
1995, Oct. 24   Litho.   Perf. 14
275   Sheet of 12   15.00 9.00
a.-l. A290 30c any single   1.20   .70
276   Souvenir booklet   16.00
a.   A290 30c Booklet pane of 3,
      strip of 3 from UL of sheet 3.75 3.50
b.   A290 30c Booklet pane of 3,
      strip of 3 from UR of sheet 3.75 3.50
c.   A290 30c Booklet pane of 3,
      strip of 3 from LL of sheet 3.75 3.50
d.   A290 30c Booklet pane of 3,
      strip of 3 from LR of sheet 3.75 3.50

WFUNA, 50th Anniv. Type of 1996
1996, Feb. 2   Litho.   Perf. 13x13¹/₂
277 A291 80c multicolored   1.50   .65

The Galloping Horse Treading on a Flying Swallow, Chinese Bronzework, Eastern Han Dynasty (25-220 A.D.) — G56

Palais des
Nations,
Geneva
G57

1996, Feb. 2   Litho.   Perf. 14¹/₂x15
278 G56 40c multicolored   .65   .30
279 G57 70c multicolored   1.10   .55

Endangered Species Type of 1993
Designs: No. 280, Paphiopedilum delenatii. No. 281, Pachypodium baronii. No. 282, Sternbergia lutea. No. 283, Darlingtonia californica.

1996, Mar. 14   Litho.   Perf. 12¹/₂
280 A271 80c multicolored   1.30   .65
281 A271 80c multicolored   1.30   .65
282 A271 80c multicolored   1.30   .65
283 A271 80c multicolored   1.30   .65
a.   Block of 4, #280-283   6.50   —

City Summit Type of 1996
Designs: No. 284, Asian family. No. 285, Oriental garden. No. 286, Fruit, vegetable vendor, mosque. No. 287, Boys playing ball. No. 288, Couple reading newspaper.

1996, June 3   Litho.   Perf. 14x13¹/₂
284 A293 70c multicolored   1.10   .30
285 A293 70c multicolored   1.10   .30
286 A293 70c multicolored   1.10   .30
287 A293 70c multicolored   1.10   .30
288 A293 70c multicolored   1.10   .30
a.   Strip of 5, #284-288   5.50   —

Sport and the Environment Type of 1996
Designs: 70c, Cycling, vert. 1.10fr, Sprinters.

Perf. 14x14¹/₂, 14¹/₂x14
1996, July 19   Litho.
289 A294 70c multicolored   1.25   .55
290 A294 1.10fr multicolored   1.75   .85
Souvenir Sheet
291 A294 Sheet of 2, #289-290   3.00 2.85

Plea for Peace Type of 1996
Designs: 90c, Tree filled with birds, vert. 1.10fr, Bouquet of flowers in rocket tail vase, vert.

1996, Sept. 17   Litho.   Perf. 15x14¹/₂
292 A295 90c multicolored   1.40   .70
293 A295 1.10fr multicolored   1.75   .85

UNICEF Type of 1996
Fairy Tales: 70c, The Sun and the Moon, South America. 1.80fr, Ananse, Africa.

1996, Nov. 20   Litho.   Perf. 14¹/₂x15
294 A296 70c multicolored   1.10   .55
295 A296 1.80fr multicolored   2.75 1.40
Panes of 8 + label.

UN
Flag — G58

Palais des
Nations Under
Construction,
by Massimo
Campigli
G59

1997, Feb. 12   Litho.   Perf. 14¹/₂
296 G58 10c multicolored   .15   .15
297 G59 1.10fr multicolored   1.50   .75

Endangered Species Type of 1993
Designs: No. 298, Ursus maritimus (polar bear). No. 299, Goura cristata (blue-crowned pigeon). No. 300, Amblyrhynchus cristatus (marine iguana). No. 703, Lama guanicoe (guanaco).

1997, Mar. 13   Litho.   Perf. 12¹/₂
298 A271 80c multicolored   1.10   .55
299 A271 80c multicolored   1.10   .55
300 A271 80c multicolored   1.10   .55
301 A271 80c multicolored   1.10   .55
a.   Block of 4, #298-301   4.50 2.25

Earth Summit Anniv. Type of 1997
Designs: No. 302, Person flying over mountain. No. 303, Mountain, person's face. No. 304, Person standing on mountain, sailboats. No. 305, Person, mountain, trees.
1.10fr, Combined design similar to Nos. 302-305.

1997, May 30   Photo.   Perf. 11.5
Granite Paper
302 A299 45c multicolored   .65   .30
303 A299 45c multicolored   .65   .30
304 A299 45c multicolored   .65   .30
305 A299 45c multicolored   .65   .30
a.   Block of 4, #302-305   2.60 1.20
Souvenir Sheet
306 A299 1.10fr multicolored   1.50 1.50

Transportation Type of 1997
Air transportation: No. 307, Zeppelin, Fokker trimotor. No. 308, Boeing 314 Clipper, Lockheed Constellation. No. 309, DeHavilland Comet. No. 310, Boeing 747, Illyushin jet. No. 311, Concorde.

1997, Aug. 29   Litho.   Perf. 14x14¹/₂
307 A300 70c multicolored   1.00   .50
308 A300 70c multicolored   1.00   .50
309 A300 70c multicolored   1.00   .50
310 A300 70c multicolored   1.00   .50
311 A300 70c multicolored   1.00   .50
a.   Strip of 5, #307-311   5.00 2.50
No. 311a has continuous design.

Philately Type of 1997
Designs: 70c, No. 146. 1.10fr, No. 147.

1997, Oct. 14   Litho.   Perf. 13¹/₂x14
312 A301 70c multicolored   1.00   .50
313 A301 1.10fr multicolored   1.50   .75

World Heritage Convention Type of 1997
Terracotta warriors of Xian: 45c, Single warrior. 70c, Massed warriors. No. 316a, like #716. No. 316b, like #717. No. 316c, like Geneva #314. No. 316d, like Geneva #315. No. 316e, like Vienna #230. No. 316f, like Vienna #231.

1997, Nov. 19   Litho.   Perf. 13¹/₂
314 A302 45c multicolored   .60   .30
315 A302 70c multicolored   1.00   .50
316   Souvenir booklet   3.75
a.-f. A302 10c any single   .15   .15
g.   Booklet pane of 4 #316a   .60   .60
h.   Booklet pane of 4 #316b   .60   .60
i.   Booklet pane of 4 #316c   .60   .60
j.   Booklet pane of 4 #316d   .60   .60
k.   Booklet pane of 4 #316e   .60   .60
l.   Booklet pane of 4 #316f   .60   .60

OFFICES IN VIENNA, AUSTRIA

For use only on mail posted at the Vienna International Center for the UN and the International Atomic Energy Agency.

100 Groschen = 1 Schilling

Type of Geneva 1978, UN Types of 1961-72 and

Donaupark,
Vienna — V1

Aerial View — V2

1979, Aug. 24   Photo.   Unwmk.
Granite Paper
1 G8   50g multicolored   .15   .15
2 A52 1s multicolored   .15   .15
3 V1   4s multicolored   .20   .20
4 AP13 5s multicolored   .25   .25
5 V2   6s multicolored   .35   .30
6 A45 10s multicolored   .50   .45
      Nos. 1-6 (6)   1.60 1.50
No. 6 has no frame.

Economic Order Type
1980, Jan. 11   Litho.   Perf. 15x14¹/₂
7 A178 4s multicolored   .70   .50

Dove Type
1980, Jan. 11   Litho.   Perf. 13x13¹/₂
8 A147 2.50s multicolored   .30   .20

Women's Year
Emblem on
World
Map — V3

1980, Mar. 7   Litho.   Perf. 14¹/₂x15
9 V3 4s lt green & dk green   .50   .25
10 V3 4s bister brown   .85   .45
UN Decade for Women.

Peace-keeping Operations Type
1980, May 16   Litho.   Perf. 14x13
11 A182 6s multicolored   .60   .50

35th Anniv. Types of Geneva and UN
1980, June 26   Litho.   Perf. 13
12 G16 4s multicolored   .40   .25
13 A184 6s multicolored   .70   .45
Souvenir Sheet
Imperf
14   Sheet of 2   .65   .70
a.   G14 4s multicolored   .20   —
b.   A184 6s multicolored   .40   —
35th anniv. of the UN.

ECOSOC Types of UN and Geneva
1980, Nov. 21   Litho.   Perf. 13¹/₂x13
15 A187 4s multicolored   .32   .20
16 G17 6s multicolored   .55   .20

Palestinian Rights Type
1981, Jan. 30   Photo.
17 A188 6s multicolored   .50   .45

Disabled Type of UN and

Interlocking
Stitches — V4

1981, Mar. 6   Photo.
18 A189 4s multicolored   .40   .35
19 V4   6s multicolored   .60   .50

Art Type
1981, Apr. 15   Photo.   Perf. 11¹/₂
20 A191 6s multicolored   .75   .50

Energy Type
1981, May 29   Litho.   Perf. 13
21 A193 7.50s multicolored   .70   .50

Volunteers Program Types of UN and Geneva
1981, Nov. 13   Litho.   Perf. 13¹/₂x13
22 A195 5s multicolored   .55   .35
23 G18 7s multicolored   1.10   .65

"For a Better World" — V5

1982, Jan. 22   Photo.   Perf. 11½x12
24   V5   3s multicolored   .35   .20

Human Environment Types of UN and Geneva

1982, Mar. 19   Litho.   Perf. 13½x13
25   A200   5s multicolored   .45   .40
26   G21   7s multicolored   .90   .55

Outer Space Type of Geneva

1982, June 11   Litho.   Perf. 13x13½
27   G22   5s multicolored   .70   .60

Conservation and Protection of Nature Type

1982, Nov. 19   Photo.   Perf. 14
28   A202   5s Fish   .45   .40
29   A202   7s Animal   .65   .60

World Communications Year Type

1983, Jan. 28   Litho.   Perf. 13
30   A203   4s multicolored   .50   .40

Safety at Sea Types of Geneva and UN

1983, Mar. 18   Litho.   Perf. 14½
31   G23   4s multicolored   .45   .30
32   A206 6s multicolored   .65   .55

World Food Program Type

1983, Apr. 22   Engr.   Perf. 13½
33   A207   5s green   .50   .35
34   A207   7s brown   .70   .55

Trade and Development Types of Geneva and UN

1983, June 6   Litho.   Perf. 14
35   G24   4s multicolored   .45   .25
36   A209   8.50s multicolored   .75   .65

35th Anniv. of the Universal Declaration of Human Rights
V6   V7

Photogravure and Engraved
1983, Dec. 9   Perf. 13½
37   V6   5s The Second Skin   .50   .40
38   V7   7s Right to Think   .80   .70

Intl. Population Conference Type

1984, Feb. 3   Litho.   Perf. 14
39   A212   7s multicolored   .65   .50

Field Irrigation — V8

Pest Control V9

1984, Mar. 15   Litho.   Perf. 14½
40   V8   4.50s multicolored   .50   .40
41   V9   6s multicolored   .70   .60

World Food Day.

Serengeti Park, Tanzania — V10

Ancient City of Shiban, People's Democratic Rep. of Yemen — V11

1984, Apr. 18   Litho.   Perf. 14
42   V10   3.50s multicolored   .40   .25
43   V11   15s multicolored   1.40 1.00

World Heritage. See Nos. 125-126.

V12   V13

1984, May 29   Photo.   Perf. 11½
44   V12   4.50s multicolored   .55   .45
45   V13   8.50s multicolored   1.40 .85

Refugees.

International Youth Year — V14

1984, Nov. 15   Litho.   Perf. 13½
46   V14   3.50s multicolored   .50   .40
47   V14   6.50s multicolored   .80   .65

ILO Type of Geneva

1985, Feb. 1   Engr.   Perf. 13½
48   G34   7.50s U Thant Pavilion   .85   .65

UN University Type

1985, Mar. 15   Photo.   Perf. 13½
49   A221   8.50s Rural scene, scientist   1.00   .80

Ship of Peace — V15

Sharing Umbrella — V16

1985, May 10   Litho.   Perf. 14
50   V15   4.50s multicolored   .35   .30
51   V16   15s multicolored   2.50 2.25

40th Anniv. Type

1985, June 26   Photo.   Perf. 12x11½
52   A224   6.50s multicolored   1.00   .55
53   A225   8.50s multicolored   1.50 1.00

Souvenir Sheet
Imperf
54   Sheet of 2   3.00 2.00
a.   A224   6.50s multicolored   .70   .60
b.   A225   8.50s multicolored   .90   .75

UNICEF Child Survival Campaign
Photogravure and Engraved
1985, Nov. 22   Perf. 13½
55   A226   4s Spoonfeeding children   .90   .65
56   A226   6s Mother hugging infant   1.50 1.25

Africa in Crisis Type
Abstract painting by Tesfaye Tessema.

1986, Jan. 31   Photo.   Perf. 11½
57   A227   8s multicolored   .85   .70

UN Development Program Type

1986, Mar. 14   Photo.   Perf. 13½
58   A228   4.50s Developing corp strains   2.00   .25
59   A228   4.50s Animal husbandry   2.00   .25
60   A228   4.50s Technical instruction   2.00   .25
61   A228   4.50s Nutrition education   2.00   .25
a.   Block of 4, #58-61   9.00 1.00

No. 61a has a continuous design.

UN Stamp Collecting Type
Designs: 3.50s, UN stamps. 6.50s, Engraver.

1986, May 22   Engr.   Perf. 12½
62   A229   3.50s dk ultra & dk brown   .50   .35
63   A229   6.50s int blue & brt rose   1.00   .85

Olive Branch, Rainbow, Earth — V17

Photogravure and Embossed
1986, June 20   Perf. 13½
64   V17   5s shown   .85   .60
65   V17   6s Doves, UN emblem   1.00   .70

Intl. Peace Year.

WFUNA Anniv. Type
Souvenir Sheet
Designs: 4c, White Stallion, by Elisabeth von Janota-Bzowski, Germany. 5s, Surrealistic landscape by Ernst Fuchs, Austria. 6s, Geometric abstract by Victor Vasarely (b. 1908), France. 7s, Mythological abstract by Wolfgang Hutter (b. 1928), Austria.

1986, Nov. 14   Litho.   Perf. 13x13½
66   Sheet of 4   4.25 4.00
a.   A232   4s multicolored   .75   .60
b.   A232   5s multicolored   .85   .70
c.   A232   6s multicolored   1.00   .80
d.   A232   7s multicolored   1.25 1.00

Trygve Lie Type
Photogravure and Engraved
1987, Jan. 30   Perf. 13½
67   A233   8s multicolored   .90   .75

Shelter for the Homeless Type
Perf. 13½x12½
1987, Mar. 13   Litho.
68   A234   4s Family, homes   .55   .40
69   A234   9.50s Entering home   1.40 1.10

Fight Drug Abuse Type

1987, June 12   Litho.   Perf. 14½x15
70   A235   5s Soccer players   .65   .50
71   A235   8s Family   1.10   .85

Donaupark, Vienna — V18

Peace Embracing the Earth — V19

1987, June 12   Perf. 14½x15
72   V18   2s multicolored   .30   .25
73   V19   17s multicolored   1.75 1.50

UN Day Type

1987, Oct. 23   Litho.   Perf. 14½x15
74   A236   5s multicolored   .80   .65
75   A236   6s multicolored   1.25 1.00

Immunize Every Child Type

1987, Nov. 20   Perf. 15x14½
76   A237   4s Polio   1.00   .35
77   A237   9.50s Diphtheria   2.25   .75

IFAD Type

1988, Jan. 29   Litho.   Perf. 13½
78   A238   4s Grains   .75   .55
79   A238   6s Vegetables   1.10   .90

Survival of the Forests Type
Deciduous forest in fall.

1988, Mar. 18   Litho.   Perf. 14x15
80   A240   4s multicolored   2.75 2.25
81   A240   5s multicolored   4.25 3.25
a.   Pair, #80-81   7.25 6.00

No. 81a has a continuous design.

Intl. Volunteer Day Type
Perf. 13x14, 14x13
1988, May 6   Litho.
82   A241   6s Medical care, vert.   1.00   .70
83   A241   7.50s Construction   1.50 1.10

Health in Sports Type
Perf. 13½x13, 13x13½
1988, June 17   Litho.
84   A242   6s Skiing, vert.   1.00   .70
85   A242   8s Tennis   1.50 1.25

Human Rights Declaration Anniv. Type

1988, Dec. 9   Photo. & Engr.   Perf. 12
86   A243   5s multicolored   .75   .65

Souvenir Sheet
87   A243   11s multicolored   1.25   .50

World Bank Type

1989, Jan. 27   Litho.   Perf. 13x14
88   A244   5.50s Transportation   1.10   .75
89   A244   8s Health care, education   2.25 1.75

Peace-Keeping Force Type

1989, Mar. 17   Litho.   Perf. 14x13½
90   A245   6s multicolored   1.10   .80

World Weather Watch Anniv. Type
Designs: 4s, Helical cloud formation over Italy, the eastern Alps and parts of Yugoslavia. 9.50s, Rainfall in Tokyo, Japan.

1989, Apr. 21   Litho.   Perf. 13x14
91   A247   4s multicolored   1.10   .75
92   A247   9.50s multicolored   2.75 2.25

V20   V21

Photo. & Engr., Photo.
1989, Aug. 23   Perf. 14
93   V20   5s multicolored   4.50   .50
94   V21   7.50s multicolored   1.00   .70

Offices in Vienna, 10th anniv.

Human Rights Type
Paintings: 4s, The Prisoners, by Kathe Kollwitz. 6s, Justice, by Raphael.

1989, Nov. 17   Litho.   Perf. 13½
95   A250   4s multicolored   .80   .60
96   A250   6s multicolored   1.20   .90

Printed in sheets of 12+12 se-tenant labels containing Articles 5 (4s) or 6 (6s) inscribed in German, English or French.

Intl. Trade Center Type

1990, Feb. 2   Litho.   Perf. 14½x15
97   A251   12s multicolored   1.50 1.25

Painting by Kurt Regschek V22

1990, Feb. 2   Litho.   Perf. 13x13½
98   V22   1.50s multicolored   .30   .20

Fight AIDS
Worldwide
V23

VEREINTE NATIONEN $11

Perf. 13½x12½
1990, Mar. 16   Litho.
99   V23   5s "AIDS"   1.00   .75
100 V23   11s Stylized figures, ink blot   2.50 2.00

Medicinal Plants Type
1990, May 4   Photo.   Perf. 11½
Granite Paper
101 A253 4.50s Bixa orellana   1.00   .75
102 A253 9.50s Momordica charan-
tia   2.50 2.00

UN 45th Anniv. Type
"45" and emblem.
1990, June 26 Litho.   Perf. 14½x13
103 A254 7s multicolored   1.25 1.00
104 A254 9s multi, diff.   2.25 1.75
Souvenir Sheet
105 A254 Sheet of 2, #103-104   5.00 3.00

Crime Prevention Type
1990, Sept. 13   Photo.   Perf. 14
106 A255 6s Domestic violence   1.25 1.00
107 A255 8s Crime against cultural
heritage   2.35 1.75

Human Rights Type of 1989
Paintings: 4.50s, Before the Judge by Sandor
Bihari. 7s, Young Man Greeted by a Woman Writing a Poem by Suzuki Harunobu.
1990, Nov. 16   Perf. 13½
108 A250 4.50s multicolored   .90   .65
109 A250 7s multicolored   2.25 1.50
Printed in sheets of 12+12 se-tenant labels containing Articles 11 (4.50s) or 12 (7s) inscribed in
German, English or French.

Economic Commission for Europe Type
1991, Mar. 15   Litho.   Perf. 14
110 A256 5s Weasel, hoopoe   1.00   .75
111 A256 5s Warbler, swans   1.00   .75
112 A256 5s Badgers, squirrel   1.00   .75
113 A256 5s Fish   1.00   .75
a.   Block of 4, #110-113   4.75 3.00

Namibian Independence Type
1991, May 10   Litho.   Perf. 14
114 A257   6s Mountain, clouds   1.25   .75
115 A257 9.50s Dune, Namib Desert   2.75 2.00

$20
V24   VEREINTE NATIONEN

1991, May 10 Litho. Perf. 15x14½
116 V24 20s multicolored   3.25 2.50

V25

Rights of the
Child — V26

1991, June 14   Litho.   Perf. 14½
117 V25 7s Stick drawings   1.50 1.25
118 V26 9s Child, clock, fruit   2.00 1.65

VEREINTE NATIONEN   s5 V27

$10

Banning of
Chemical
Weapons
V28

1991, Sept. 11   Litho.   Perf. 13½
119 V27 5s multicolored   1.25   .75
120 V28 10s multicolored   2.25 1.50

UN Postal Administration, 40th Anniv. Type
1991, Oct. 24   Litho.   Perf. 14x15
121 A263 5s UN NY No. 8   1.00   .75
122 A263 8s UN NY No. 5   2.25 1.90

Human Rights Type of 1989
Artwork: 4.50s, Pre-columbian Mexican pottery,
c. 600 A.D. 7s, Windows, 1912, by Robert
Delaunay.
1991, Nov. 20   Litho.   Perf. 13½
123 A250 4.50s black & brown   .80   .75
124 A250 7s multicolored   1.50 1.25
Printed in sheets of 12+12 se-tenant labels containing Articles 17 (4.50s) and 18 (7s) inscribed in
German, English or French.

World Heritage Type of 1984
Designs: 5s, Iguacu Natl. Park, Brazil. 9s, Abu
Simbel, Egypt.
1992, Jan. 24   Litho.   Perf. 13
Size: 35x28mm
125 V10 5s multicolored   1.25 1.00
126 V10 9s multicolored   2.25 1.75

Clean Oceans Type
1992, Mar. 13   Litho.   Perf. 14
127 A264 7s Ocean surface, diff.   1.25   .60
128 A264 7s Ocean bottom, diff.   1.25   .60
a.   Pair, #127-128   2.50 1.20
Printed in sheets of 12 containing 6 #128a.

Earth Summit Type
1992, May 22   Photo.   Perf. 11½
129 A265 5.50s Man in space   1.25 1.00
130 A265 5.50s Sun   1.25 1.00
131 A265 5.50s Man fishing   1.25 1.00
132 A265 5.50s Sailboat   1.25 1.00
a.   Block of 4, #129-132   5.00 4.25

Mission to Planet Earth Type
Designs: No. 133, Satellite, person's mouth. No.
134, Satellite, person's ear.
1992, Sept. 4   Photo.   Rouletted 8
Granite Paper
133 A266 10s multicolored   2.75 1.00
134 A266 10s multicolored   2.75 1.00
a.   Pair, #133-134   5.50 2.00

Science and Technology Type
Designs: 5.50s, Woman emerging from computer
screen. 7s, Green thumb growing flowers.
1992, Oct. 2   Litho.   Perf. 14
135 A267 5.50s multicolored   .90   .75
136 A267 7s multicolored   1.75 1.50

V29

Intl. Center,
Vienna — V30

1992, Oct. 2   Litho.   Perf. 13x13½
137 V29 5.50s multicolored   1.00   .75
Perf. 13½x13
138 V30 7s multicolored   2.00 1.50

Human Rights Type of 1989
Artwork: 6s, Les Constructeurs, by Fernand
Leger. 10s, Sunday Afternoon on the Island of La
Grande Jatte, by Georges Seurat.
1992, Nov. 20   Litho.   Perf. 13½
139 A250 6s multicolored   1.25   .85
140 A250 10s multicolored   2.00 1.50
Printed in sheets of 12+12 se-tenant labels con-
taining Articles 23 (6s) and 24 (10s) inscribed in
German, English or French.

Aging With Dignity Type
Designs: 5.50s, Elderly couple, family working in
garden. 7s, Older woman teaching.
1993, Feb. 5   Litho.   Perf. 13
141 A270 5.50s multicolored   1.25 1.00
142 A270   7s multicolored   2.00 1.50

Endangered Species Type
Designs: No. 143, Equus grevyi (Grevy's zebra).
No. 144, Spheniscus humboldti (Humboldt's penguins). No. 145, Varanus griseus (desert monitor).
No. 146, Canis lupus (gray wolf).
1993, Mar. 3   Litho.   Perf. 13x12½
143 A271 7s multicolored   1.25 1.00
144 A271 7s multicolored   1.25 1.00
145 A271 7s multicolored   1.25 1.00
146 A271 7s multicolored   1.25 1.00
a.   Block of 4, #143-146   5.00 4.00

Healthy Environment Type
1993, May 7   Litho.   Perf. 15x14½
147 A272 6s Wave in ocean   1.50   .75
148 A272 10s Globe   2.50 1.50

VEREINTE
NATIONEN s13 V31

1993, May 7   Photo.   Perf. 11½
Granite Paper
149 V31 13s multicolored   2.50 2.25

Human Rights Type of 1989
Artwork: 5s, Lower Austrian Peasants' Wedding,
by Ferdinand G. Waldmuller. 6s, Outback, by Sally
Morgan.
1993, June 11   Litho.   Perf. 13½
150 A250 5s multicolored   1.00   .75
151 A250 6s multicolored   2.25   .50
Printed in sheets of 12 + 12 se-tenant labels
containing Article 29 (5s) and 30 (6s) inscribed in
German, English or French.

Intl. Peace Day Type
Denomination at: No. 152, UL. No. 153, UR.
No. 154, LL. No. 155, LR.
Rouletted 12½
1993, Sept. 21   Litho. & Engr.
152 A274 5.50s green & multi   2.00   .90
153 A274 5.50s green & multi   2.00   .90
154 A274 5.50s green & multi   2.00   .90
155 A274 5.50s green & multi   2.00   .90
a.   Block of 4, #152-155   8.50 3.75

Environment-Climate Type
Designs: No. 156, Monkeys. No. 157, Bluebird,
industrial pollution, volcano. No. 158, Volcano,
nuclear power plant, tree stumps. No. 159, Cactus,
tree stumps, owl.
1993, Oct. 29   Litho.   Perf. 14½
156 A275 7s multicolored   1.50 1.25
157 A275 7s multicolored   1.50 1.25
158 A275 7s multicolored   1.50 1.25
159 A275 7s multicolored   1.50 1.25
a.   Strip of 4, #156-159   6.00 5.00

Intl. Year of the Family Type of 1993
Designs: 5.50s, Adults, children holding hands.
8s, Two adults, child planting crops.
1994, Feb. 4   Litho.   Perf. 13.1
160 A276 5.50s blue green & multi   1.25 1.00
161 A276   8s red & multi   2.00 1.50

Endangered Species Type of 1993
Designs: No. 162, Ocelot. No. 163, White-
breasted silver-eye. No. 164, Mediterranean monk
seal. No. 165, Asian elephant.

1994, Mar. 18   Litho.   Perf. 12.7
162 A271 7s multicolored   1.40 1.25
163 A271 7s multicolored   1.40 1.25
164 A271 7s multicolored   1.40 1.25
165 A271 7s multicolored   1.40 1.25
a.   Block of 4, #162-165   5.75 5.00

Protection for Refugees Type of 1994
Design: 12s, Protective hands surround group of
refugees.
1994, Apr. 29   Litho.   Perf. 14.3x14.8
166 A277 12s multicolored   2.00 1.50

V32   V33

V34

1994, Apr. 29   Litho.   Perf. 12.9
167 V32 50g multicolored   .15   .15
168 V33 4s multicolored   .70   .50
169 V34 30s multicolored   5.00 4.00
Nos. 167-169 (3)   5.85 4.65

Intl. Decade for Natural Disaster Reduction Type of 1994
Earth seen from space, outline map of: No. 170,
North America. No. 171, Eurasia. No. 172, South
America. No. 173, Australia and South Asia.
1994, May 27   Litho.   Perf. 13.9x14.2
170 A281 6s multicolored   1.75   .80
171 A281 6s multicolored   1.75   .80
172 A281 6s multicolored   1.75   .80
173 A281 6s multicolored   1.75   .80
a.   Block of 4, #170-173   7.50 3.50

Population and Development Type of 1994
Designs: 5.50s, Women teaching, running
machine tool, coming home to family. 7s, Family on
tropical island.
1994, Sept. 1   Litho.   Perf. 13.2x13.6
174 A282 5.50s multicolored   1.40   .75
175 A282   7s multicolored   1.65 1.25

UNCTAD Type of 1994
1994, Oct. 28
176 A283 6s multi, diff.   1.40   .55
177 A283 7s multi, diff.   1.60   .65

UN 50th Anniv. Type of 1995
1995, Jan. 1   Litho. & Engr.   Perf. 13.4
178 A284 7s multicolored   1.75   .75

Social Summit Type of 1995
Perf. 13.6x13.9
1995, Feb. 3   Photo. & Engr.
179 A285 14s multi, diff.   2.50 1.50

Endangered Species Type of 1993
Designs: No. 180, Black rhinoceros, Diceros
bicornis. No. 181, Golden conure, Aratinga
guarouba. No. 182, Douc langur, Pygathrix
nemaeus. No. 183, Arabian oryx, Oryx leucoryx.
1995, Mar. 24   Litho.   Perf. 13x12½
180 A271 7s multicolored   1.40 1.25
181 A271 7s multicolored   1.40 1.25
182 A271 7s multicolored   1.40 1.25
183 A271 7s multicolored   1.40 1.25
a.   Block of 4, 180-183   6.25 5.00

Intl. Youth Year Type of 1995
Designs: 6s, Village in winter. 7s, Teepees.
1995, May 26   Litho.   Perf. 14.4x14.7
184 A286 6s multicolored   1.40 1.00
185 A286 7s multicolored   1.65 1.25

UN, 50th Anniv. Type of 1995
Designs: 7s, Like No. 663. 10s, Like No. 664.

1995, June 26 Engr.   *Perf. 13.3x13.6*
186 A287   7s green   1.40 1.25
187 A287 10s black   2.00 1.50

Souvenir Sheet
Litho. & Engr.
Imperf
188   Sheet of 2, #186-187   4.00 4.00
 a. A287 7s green   1.40 1.40
 b. A287 10s black   2.00 2.00

Conference on Women Type of 1995

Designs: 5.50s, Women amid tropical plants. 6s, Woman reading, swans on lake.

1995, Sept. 5   Photo.   *Perf. 12*
189 A288 5.50s multicolored   1.40   .55
Size: 28x50mm
190 A288 6s multicolored   1.75   .65

UN People, 50th Anniv. Type of 1995

1995, Oct. 24   Litho.   *Perf. 14*
191   Sheet of 12   16.00 11.00
 a.-l. A290 3s any single   1.25   .85
192   Souvenir booklet   16.00
 a. A290 3s Booklet pane of 3, vert.
     strip of 3 from UL of sheet   3.50 3.00
 b. A290 3s Booklet pane of 3, vert.
     strip of 3 from UR of sheet   3.50 3.00
 c. A290 3s Booklet pane of 3, vert.
     strip of 3 from LL of sheet   3.50 3.00
 d. A290 3s Booklet pane of 3, vert.
     strip of 3 from LR of sheet   3.50 3.00

WFUNA, 50th Anniv. Type of 1996

Design: 7s, Harlequin holding dove.

1996, Feb. 2   Litho.   *Perf. 13x13¹/₂*
193 A291 7s multicolored   1.50   .65

UN Flag — V35   Abstract, by Karl
                     Korab — V36

1996, Feb. 2   Litho.   *Perf. 15x14¹/₂*
194 V35   1s multicolored   .20   .15
195 V36 10s multicolored   2.00 1.00

Endangered Species Type of 1993

Designs: No. 196, Cypripedium calceolus. No. 197, Aztekium ritteri. No. 198, Euphorbia cremersii. No. 199, Dracula bella.

1996, Mar. 14   Litho.   *Perf. 12¹/₂*
196 A271 7s multicolored   1.30   .65
197 A271 7s multicolored   1.30   .65
198 A271 7s multicolored   1.30   .65
199 A271 7s multicolored   1.30   .65
 a.   Block of 4, #196-199   5.25

City Summit Type of 1996

Designs: No. 200, Arab family selling fruits, vegetables. No. 201, Woman beside stream, camels. No. 202, Woman carrying bundle on head, city skyline. No. 203, Woman threshing grain, yoke of oxen in field. No. 204, Native village, elephant.

1996, June 3   Litho.   *Perf. 14x13¹/₂*
200 A293 6s multicolored   1.25   .30
201 A293 6s multicolored   1.25   .30
202 A293 6s multicolored   1.25   .30
203 A293 6s multicolored   1.25   .30
204 A293 6s multicolored   1.25   .30
 a.   Strip of 5, #200-204   6.50

Sport and the Environment Type of 1996

Designs: 6s, Men's parallel bars (gymnastics), vert. 7s, Hurdles.

Perf. 14x14¹/₂x14¹/₂x14
1996, July 19   Litho.
205 A294 6s multicolored   1.25   .55
206 A294 7s multicolored   1.50   .65
Souvenir Sheet
207 A294 Sheet of 2, #205-206   2.75 2.40

Plea for Peace Type of 1996

7s, Dove & butterflies. 10s, Stylized dove, diff.

1996, Sept. 17 Litho.   *Perf. 14¹/₂x15*
208 A295 7s multicolored   1.40   .65
209 A295 10s multicolored   2.00   .95

UNICEF Type of 1996

Fairy Tales: 5.50s, Hansel and Gretel, by the Brothers Grimm. 8s, How Maui Stole Fire from the Gods, South Pacific.

1996, Nov. 20   Litho.   *Perf. 14¹/₂x15*
210 A296 5.50s multicolored   1.10   .50
211 A296 8s multicolored   1.75   .75
Panes of 8 + label.

V37   Phoenixes Flying
               Down (Detail),
               by Sagenji
               Yoshida — V38

1997, Feb. 12   Litho.   *Perf. 14¹/₂*
212 V37   5s multicolored   .85   .40
213 V38   6s multicolored   1.00   .50

Endangered Species Type of 1993

No. 214, Macaca sylvanus (Barbary macaque). No. 215, Anthropoides paradisea (blue crane). No. 216, Equus przewalskii (Przewalski horse). No. 217, Myrmecophaga tridactyla (giant anteater).

1997, Mar. 13   Litho.   *Perf. 12¹/₂*
214 A271 7s multicolored   1.10   .55
215 A271 7s multicolored   1.10   .55
216 A271 7s multicolored   1.10   .55
217 A271 7s multicolored   1.10   .55
 a.   Block of 4, #214-217   4.50 2.25

Earth Summit Anniv. Type of 1997

Designs: No. 218, Person running. No. 219, Hills, stream, trees. No. 220, Tree with orange leaves. No. 221, Tree with pink leaves.
11s, Combined design similar to Nos. 218-221.

1997, May 30   Photo.   *Perf. 11.5*
Granite Paper
218 A299 3.50s multicolored   .60   .30
219 A299 3.50s multicolored   .60   .30
220 A299 3.50s multicolored   .60   .30
221 A299 3.50s multicolored   .60   .30
 a.   Block of 4, #218-221   2.50 1.25
Souvenir Sheet
222 A299 11s multicolored   1.75 1.75

Transportation Type of 1997

Ground transportation: No. 223, 1829 Rocket, 1901 Darraque. No. 224, Steam engine from Vladikawska Railway, trolley. No. 225, Double-decker bus. No. 226, 1950s diesel locomotive, semi-trailer. No. 227, High-speed train, electric car.

1997, Aug. 29   Litho.   *Perf. 14x14¹/₂*
223 A300 7s multicolored   1.10   .55
224 A300 7s multicolored   1.10   .55
225 A300 7s multicolored   1.10   .55
226 A300 7s multicolored   1.10   .55
227 A300 7s multicolored   1.10   .55
 a.   Strip of 5, #223-227   5.50 2.75

No. 227a has continuous design.

Philately Type of 1997

Designs: 6.50s, No. 62. 7s, No. 63.

1997, Oct. 14   Litho.   *Perf. 13¹/₂x14*
228 A301 6.50s multicolored   1.00   .50
229 A301 7s multicolored   1.10   .55

World Heritage Convention Type of 1997

Terracotta warriors of Xian: 3s, Single warrior. 6s, Massed warriors. No. 232a, like #716. No. 232b, like #717. No. 232c, like Geneva #314. No. 232d, like Geneva #315. No. 232e, like Vienna #230. No. 232f, like Vienna #231.

1997, Nov. 19   Litho.   *Perf. 13¹/₂*
230   A302 3s multicolored   .50   .25
231   A302 6s multicolored   1.00   .50
232   Souvenir booklet   4.00
 a.-f. A302 3s any single   .15   .15
 g.   Booklet pane of 4 #232a   .65   .65
 h.   Booklet pane of 4 #232b   .65   .65
 i.   Booklet pane of 4 #232c   .65   .65
 j.   Booklet pane of 4 #232d   .65   .65
 k.   Booklet pane of 4 #232e   .65   .65
 l.   Booklet pane of 4 #232f   .65   .65

ABU DHABI

ä-bü-'thä-bē

LOCATION — Arabia, on Persian Gulf
GOVT. — Sheikdom under British
protection

POP. — 25,000 (estimated)
CAPITAL — Abu Dhabi

Abu Dhabi is one of six Persian Gulf sheikdoms to join the United Arab Emirates, which proclaimed its independence Dec. 2, 1971. See United Arab Emirates.

100 Naye Paise = 1 Rupee
1000 Fils = 1 Dinar (1966)

> **Catalogue values for all unused stamps in this country are for Never Hinged items.**

Sheik Shakbut   Palace — A2
bin
Sultan — A1

Designs: 40np, 50np, 75np, Gazelle. 5r, 10r, Oil rig and camels.

Perf. 14¹/₂
1964, Mar. 30   Photo.   Unwmk.
1 A1   5np brt yellow green   .15   .15
2 A1 15np brown   .30   .15
3 A1 20np brt ultra   .40   .20
4 A1 30np red orange   .50   .25
5 A1 40np brt violet   .65   .35
6 A1 50np brown olive   .75   .35
7 A1 75np gray   1.25   .55

Engr.   *Perf. 13x13¹/₂*
8 A2   1r light green   1.75   .75
9 A2   2r black   4.00 1.75
10 A2   5r carmine rose   10.00 4.75
11 A2 10r dark blue   22.50 12.00
   Nos. 1-11 (11)   42.25 21.25
For surcharges see Nos. 15-25.

Falcon Perched on
Wrist — A3

40np, Falcon facing left. 2r, Falcon facing right.

1965, Mar. 30   Photo.   *Perf. 14¹/₂*
12 A3 20np chlky blue & brn   1.50   .50
13 A3 40np ultra & brown   3.50 2.00
14 A3   2r brt blue grn & gray
        brn   15.00 15.00
   Nos. 12-14 (3)   20.00 17.50

Nos. 1-11 Surcharged

5Fils ٥ فلس   Fils فلس
  a   b

100   ١٠٠
Fils   فلس
      c

1966, Oct. 1   Photo.   *Perf. 14¹/₂*
15 A1 (a)   5f on 5np   .20   .20
16 A1 (a) 15f on 15np   .65   .45
17 A1 (a) 20f on 20np   .90   .60
18 A1 (a) 30f on 30np   1.00   .75
19 A1 (b) 40f on 40np   1.75 1.00
20 A1 (b) 50f on 50np   7.50 9.00
21 A1 (b) 75f on 75np   .75   .75

Engr.
Perf. 13x13¹/₂
22 A2 (c) 100f on 1r   9.00 6.00
23 A2 (c) 200f on 2r   20.00 12.50
24 A2 (c) 500f on 5r   45.00 42.50
25 A2 (c) 1d on 10r   87.50 95.00
   Nos. 15-25 (11)   182.50 177.00

Overprint on No. 25 has "1 Dinar" on 1 line and 3 bars through old denomination.

Sheik Zaid bin Sultan al Nahayan
A4   A6

Dorcas Gazelle — A5

Designs: 5f, 15f, 20f, 35f, Crossed flags of Abu Dhabi. 200f, Falcon. 500f, 1d, Palace.

Engr.; Flags Litho.
1967, Apr. 1   *Perf. 13x13¹/₂*
26 A4   5f dull grn & red   .15   .15
27 A4 15f dk brown & red   .30   .20
28 A4 20f dk blue & red   .35   .25
29 A4 35f purple & red   .65   .45
Engr.
30 A4 40f green   .75   .55
31 A4 50f brown   1.00   .70
32 A4 60f blue   1.30   .80
33 A4 100f car rose   2.25 1.50
Litho.
34 A5 125f green & brn ol   2.75 1.90
35 A5 200f sky blue & brn   4.50 3.00
36 A5 500f org & brt pur   11.00 7.50
37 A5   1d green & vio bl   25.00 15.00
   Nos. 26-37 (12)   50.00 32.00

In 1969, the 15f was surcharged "25" in Arabic in black with a numbering machine.

1967, Aug. 6   Photo.   *Perf. 14¹/₂x14*
38 A6 40f Prussian green   1.40 1.10
39 A6 50f brown   1.40   .75
40 A6 60f blue   2.25 1.00
41 A6 100f carmine rose   4.00 1.90
   Nos. 38-41 (4)   9.05 4.75

Human
Rights
Flame
and Sheik
Zaid
A6a

Perf. 14¹/₂x14
1968, Apr. 1   Photo.   Unwmk.
Emblem in Red and Green
42 A6a 35f peacock bl & gold   1.25   .60
43 A6a 60f dk blue & gold   2.00   .75
44 A6a 150f dk brown & gold   4.75 1.75
   Nos. 42-44 (3)   8.00 3.10

International Human Rights Year.

Sheik
Zaid
and
Coat of
Arms
A7

Perf. 14x14¹/₂
1968, Aug. 6   Photo.   Unwmk.
45 A7   5f green, sil, red & blk   .40   .15
46 A7 10f brn org, sil, red & blk   .60   .20
47 A7 10f lilac, gold, red & blk   3.75 1.50
48 A7 125f lt blue, gold, red &
        blk   5.50 2.25
   Nos. 45-48 (4)   10.25 4.10

Accession of Sheik Zaid, 2nd anniversary.

Abu Dhabi Airport A8

5f, Buildings under construction and earth-moving equipment. 35f, New bridge and falcon. Each stamp shows different portrait of Sheik Zaid.

Perf. 12, 12¹/₂x13 (10f)
1969, Mar. 28   **Litho.**
Size: 5f, 35f, 59x34mm

49	A8	5f multicolored	1.00	.25
50	A8	10f multicolored	1.50	.60
51	A8	35f multicolored	6.00	2.50
		Nos. 49-51 (3)	8.50	3.35

Issued to publicize progress made in Abu Dhabi during preceding 2 years.

Sheik Zaid and Abu Dhabi Petroleum Co. — A9

Designs: 60f, Abu Dhabi Marine Areas drilling platform and helicopter. 125f, Zakum Field separator at night. 200f, Tank farm.

1969, Aug. 6   **Litho.**   **Perf. 14x13¹/₂**

52	A9	35f olive grn & multi	.65	.25
53	A9	60f yel brown & multi	1.25	.55
54	A9	125f multicolored	2.75	1.10
55	A9	200f red brown & multi	5.00	2.00
		Nos. 52-55 (4)	9.65	3.90

Accession of Sheik Zaid, 3rd anniversary.

Sheik Zaid — A10

Sheik Zaid and Stallion A11

Designs: 5f, 25f, 60f, 90f, Oval frame around portrait. 150f, Gazelle and Sheik. 500f, Fort Jahili and Sheik. 1d, Grand Mosque and Sheik.

1970-71   **Litho.**   **Perf. 14**

56	A10	5f lt green & multi	.15	.15
57	A10	10f bister & multi	.30	.15
58	A10	25f lilac & multi	.65	.20
59	A10	35f violet & multi	.90	.30
60	A10	50f sepia & multi	1.50	.40
61	A10	60f violet & multi	1.75	.45
62	A10	70f rose red & multi	2.25	.60
63	A10	90f car rose & multi	2.50	.70
64	A11	125f multi ('71)	3.00	.85
65	A11	150f multi ('71)	3.50	1.00
66	A11	500f multi ('71)	11.00	3.50
67	A11	1d multi ('71)	22.50	6.50
		Nos. 56-67 (12)	50.00	14.80

For surcharge see No. 80.

25 ABU DHABI

Sheik Zaid and Mt. Fuji — A12

1970, Aug.   **Litho.**   **Perf. 13¹/₂x13**

68	A12	25f multicolored	1.75	1.00
69	A12	35f multicolored	2.00	1.25
70	A12	60f multicolored	3.75	1.75
		Nos. 68-70 (3)	7.50	4.00

Issued to publicize EXPO '70 International Exhibition, Osaka, Japan, Mar. 15-Sept. 13.

Abu Dhabi Airport A13

Designs: 60f, Airport entrance. 150f, Aerial view of Abu Dhabi Town, vert.

Perf. 14x13¹/₂, 13¹/₂x14
1970, Sept. 22   **Litho.**

71	A13	25f multicolored	1.25	.50
72	A13	60f multicolored	4.00	1.25
73	A13	150f multicolored	7.25	3.00
		Nos. 71-73 (3)	12.50	4.75

Accession of Sheik Zaid, 4th anniversary.

Gamal Abdel Nasser — A14

1971, May 3   **Litho.**   **Perf. 14**

74	A14	25f deep rose & blk	2.75	2.00
75	A14	35f rose violet & blk	4.00	3.00

In memory of Gamal Abdel Nasser (1918-1970), President of UAR.

Scout Cars — A15

Designs: 60f, Patrol boat. 125f, Armored car in desert. 150f, Meteor jet fighters.

1971, Aug. 6   **Litho.**   **Perf. 13**

76	A15	35f multicolored	2.25	1.00
77	A15	60f multicolored	3.25	1.50
78	A15	125f multicolored	4.50	2.25
79	A15	150f multicolored	5.00	3.00
		Nos. 76-79 (4)	15.00	7.75

Accession of Sheik Zaid, 5th anniversary.

No. 60 Surcharged in Green

5 Fils

1971, Dec. 8   **Perf. 14**

80	A10	5f on 50f multi	65.00	30.00

Dome of the Rock, Jerusalem — A16

Designs: Different views of Dome of the Rock.

1972, June 3   **Perf. 13**

81	A16	35f lt violet & multi	8.50	2.00
82	A16	60f lt violet & multi	12.50	2.50
83	A16	125f lilac & multi	24.00	5.50
		Nos. 81-83 (3)	45.00	10.00

Nos. 80-83 were issued after Abu Dhabi joined the United Arab Emirates Dec. 2, 1971. Stamps of UAE replaced those of Abu Dhabi. UAE Nos. 1-12 were used only in Abu Dhabi except the 10f and 25f which were issued later in Dubai and Sharjah.

ADEN

'ä–d²n

LOCATION — Southern Arabia
GOVT. — Former British colony and protectorate
AREA — 112,075 sq. mi.
POP. — 220,000 (est. 1964)
CAPITAL — Aden

Aden used India stamps before 1937.
In January, 1963, the colony of Aden (the port) and the sheikdoms and emirates of the Western Aden Protectorate formed the Federation of South Arabia. This did not include the Eastern Aden Protectorate with Kathiri and Qu'aiti States. Stamps of Aden, except those of Kathiri and Qu'aiti States, were replaced Apr. 1, 1965, by those of the Federation of South Arabia. See South Arabia, Vol. 1B, and People's Democratic Republic of Yemen, Vol. 5.

12 Pies = 1 Anna
16 Annas = 1 Rupee
100 Cents = 1 Shilling (1951)

> Catalogue values for unused stamps in this country are for Never Hinged items, beginning with Scott 28 in the regular postage section and for all of the items in the states' sections.

Dhow — A1

Perf. 13x11¹/₂
1937, Apr. 1   **Engr.**   **Wmk. 4**

1	A1	¹/₂a lt green	.35	.25
2	A1	9p dark green	.50	.40
3	A1	1a black brown	.50	.35
4	A1	2a red	.90	.70
5	A1	2¹/₂a blue	1.10	.75
6	A1	3a carmine rose	2.25	2.25
7	A1	3¹/₂a gray blue	1.75	1.40
8	A1	8a rose lilac	3.00	2.75
9	A1	1r brown	6.50	4.75
10	A1	2r orange yellow	11.00	8.00
11	A1	5r rose violet	52.50	40.00
12	A1	10r olive green	160.00	125.00
		Nos. 1-12 (12)	240.35	186.60
		Set, never hinged	325.00	

> Common Design Types pictured following the introduction.

Coronation Issue
Common Design Type
1937, May 12   **Perf. 13¹/₂x14**

13	CD302	1a black brown	.40	.40
14	CD302	2¹/₂a blue	.75	.75
15	CD302	3¹/₂a gray blue	1.25	1.25
		Nos. 13-15 (3)	2.40	2.40
		Set, never hinged	3.50	

Aidrus Mosque — A2

Designs: ³/₄a, 5r, Camel Corpsman. 1a, 2r, Aden Harbor. 1¹/₂a, 1r, Adenese dhow. 2¹/₂a, 8a, Mukalla. 3a, 14a, 10r, Capture of Aden, 1839.

1939-45   **Engr. Wmk. 4**   **Perf. 12¹/₂**

16	A2	¹/₂a green	.25	.15
17	A2	³/₄a brown violet	.25	.15
18	A2	1a lt blue	.25	.15
19	A2	1¹/₂a red	.55	.15
20	A2	2a dark brown	.35	.15
21	A2	2¹/₂a brt ultra	.55	.15
22	A2	3a orange car & dk brn	.55	.15
23	A2	8a orange	1.00	.15
23A	A2	14a lt bl & brn blk ('45)	1.10	.80
24	A2	1r bright green	1.25	.85
25	A2	2r rose vio & indigo	4.50	1.25
26	A2	5r ol grn & red brn	12.00	5.50
27	A2	10r dk pur & vio brn	14.00	11.00
		Nos. 16-27 (13)	36.60	20.60
		Set, never hinged	55.00	

> Catalogue values for unused stamps in this section, from this point to the end of the section, are for Never Hinged items.

Peace Issue
Common Design Type
Perf. 13¹/₂x14
1946, Oct. 15   **Engr.**   **Wmk. 4**

28	CD303	1¹/₂a carmine	.15	.15
29	CD303	2¹/₂a deep blue	.30	.15

Return to peace at end of World War II.

Silver Wedding Issue
Common Design Types
1949, Jan. 17 Photo.   **Perf. 14x14¹/₂**

30	CD304	1¹/₂a scarlet	.40	.40

Engraved; Name Typographed
Perf. 11¹/₂x11

31	CD305	10r purple	25.00	25.00

25th anniv. of the marriage of King George VI and Queen Elizabeth.

UPU Issue
Common Design Types
Surcharged with New Values in Annas and Rupees
Engr.; Name typo. on Nos. 33-34
1949, Oct. 10   **Perf. 13¹/₂, 11x11¹/₂**

32	CD306	2¹/₂a on 20c dp ultra	.35	.35
33	CD307	3a on 30c dp car	.75	.75
34	CD308	8a on 50c org	1.65	1.65
35	CD309	1r on 1sh blue	2.75	2.75
		Nos. 32-35 (4)	5.50	5.50

75th anniv. of the formation of the UPU.

Nos. 18 and 20-27 Surcharged with New Values in Black or Carmine

1951, Oct. 1   **Wmk. 4**   **Perf. 12¹/₂**

36	A2	5c on 1a	.30	.30
37	A2	10c on 2a	.40	.40
38	A2	15c on 2¹/₂a	.55	.55
a.		Double surcharge	500.00	
39	A2	20c on 3a	1.10	1.10
40	A2	30c on 8a (C)	1.10	1.10
41	A2	50c on 8a	1.10	.85
42	A2	70c on 14a	1.40	1.40
43	A2	1sh on 1r	1.75	1.40
44	A2	2sh on 2r	7.00	6.00
45	A2	5sh on 5r	11.00	11.50
46	A2	10sh on 10r	22.50	22.50
		Nos. 36-46 (11)	48.20	47.10

Surcharge on No. 40 includes 2 bars.

Coronation Issue
Common Design Type
1953, June 2   **Engr.**   **Perf. 13¹/₂x13**

47	CD312	15c dark green & black	.35	.35

Minaret — A10   Camel Transport — A11

15c, Crater. 25c, Mosque. 35c, Dhow. 50c, Map. 70c, Salt works. 1sh, Dhow building. 1sh, 25c, Colony Badge. 2sh, Aden Protectorate levy. 5sh, Crater Pass. 10sh, Tribesman. 20sh, Aden in 1572.

Perf. 12, 12x13¹/₂ ('56)
1953-58   **Engr.**   **Wmk. 4**
Size: 29x23, 23x29mm

48	A10	5c grn, perf.		
		12x13¹/₂ ('56)	.15	.15
a.	Perf. 12		.15	.15

No.	Type	Description	Unused	Used
49	A11	10c orange	.15	.15
50	A11	15c blue green	.90	.50
51	A11	25c carmine	.60	.35
52	A10	35c ultra, perf. 12	1.75	1.75
a.		35c dp bl, perf. 12x13½ ('58)	3.00	2.00
53	A10	50c blue, perf. 12	.15	.15
a.		Perf. 12x13½ ('56)	.55	.15
54	A10	70c gray, perf. 12	.15	.15
a.		Perf. 12x13½ ('56)	.60	.15
55	A11	1sh pur & sepia	.20	.15
55A	A11	1sh vio & black ('55)	1.10	.15
56	A10	1sh25c blk & lt blue ('56)	1.65	.50
57	A10	2sh car rose & sep	.90	.40
57A	A10	2sh car & black ('56)	4.25	.40
58	A10	5sh blue & sepia	.90	.40
58A	A10	5sh dk blue & blk ('56)	3.75	.50
59	A10	10sh olive & sepia	1.25	6.75
60	A10	10sh ol gray & blk ('54)	9.50	1.10

Size: 36½x27mm
Perf. 13½x13

No.	Type	Description	Unused	Used
61	A11	20sh rose vio & dk brn	4.75	8.50
61A	A11	20sh lt vio & blk ('57)	30.00	12.00
		Nos. 48-61A (18)	62.10	34.05

Various shades from two or more printings exist.
No. 60 has heavier shading on tribesman's lower garment than No. 59.
See #66-75. For overprints see #63-64.

Type of 1953
Inscribed: "Royal Visit 1954"
1954, Apr. 27   Perf. 12

62	A11	1sh purple & sepia	.40	.40

Nos. 50 and 56 Overprinted in Red

تعديل
الدستور
١٩٥٩
No. 63

REVISED
CONSTITUTION
1959
No. 64

1959, Jan. 26   Perf. 12, 12x13½

63	A11	15c dark blue green	.25	.25
64	A10	1sh25c black & light blue	.70	.70

Introduction of a revised constitution.

Freedom from Hunger Issue
Common Design Type
Perf. 14x14½
1963, June 4   Photo.   Wmk. 314

65	CD314	1sh25c green	.85	.65

Types of 1953-57
Perf. 12x13½, 12 (#67-69, 73)
1964-65   Engr.   Wmk. 314

66	A10	5c green ('65)	.20	.25
67	A11	10c orange	.25	.15
68	A11	15c Prus green	.30	.25
69	A11	25c carmine	.50	.25
70	A10	35c dk blue	2.50	.75
71	A10	50c dull blue	2.50	.75
72	A10	70c gray	2.75	1.25
73	A11	1sh vio & black	2.75	1.25
74	A10	1sh25c blk & lt blue	5.50	7.25
75	A10	2sh car & blk ('65)	10.00	14.00
		Nos. 66-75 (10)	27.25	26.15

KATHIRI STATE OF SEIYUN

LOCATION — In Eastern Aden Protectorate
GOVT. — Sultanate
CAPITAL — Seiyun

Catalogue values for unused stamps in this section are for Never Hinged items.

Sultan Ja'far bin Mansur al Kathiri — A1

Seiyun — A2

Minaret at Tarim — A3

Designs: 2½a, Mosque at Seiyun. 3a, Palace at Tarim. 8a, Mosque at Seiyun, horiz. 1r, South Gate, Tarim. 2r, Kathiri House. 5r, Mosque at Tarim.

1942   Engr.   Wmk. 4   Perf. 14

1	A1	½a dark green	.15	.25
2	A1	¾a copper brown	.15	.25
3	A1	1a deep blue	.20	.40

Perf. 13x11½, 11½x13

4	A3	1½a dark car rose	.30	.45
5	A3	2a black brown	.30	.45
6	A3	2½a deep blue	.50	.45
7	A2	3a dk car rose & dull brn	.85	.55
8	A2	8a orange red	.35	1.10
9	A3	1r green	1.40	1.75
10	A2	2r rose vio & dk blue	6.50	8.00
11	A3	5r gray green & fawn	16.00	13.00
		Nos. 1-11 (11)	26.70	26.65

For surcharges see Nos. 20-27.

Nos. 4, 6 Ovptd. in Black or Red:

VICTORY	VICTORY
ISSUE	ISSUE
8TH JUNE 1946	8TH JUNE 1946
a	b

1946, Oct. 15   Perf. 13x11½, 11½x13   Wmk. 4

12	A2 (a)	1½a dark car rose	.15	.15
13	A3 (b)	2½a deep blue (R)	.25	.25
a.		Inverted overprint	425.00	

Victory of the Allied Nations in WWII.

Silver Wedding Issue
Common Design Types
1949, Jan. 17   Photo.   Perf. 14x14½

14	CD304	1½a scarlet	.35	.35

Engraved; Name Typo.
Perf. 11½x11

15	CD305	5r green	11.00	11.00

25th anniv. of the marriage of King George VI and Queen Elizabeth.

UPU Issue
Common Design Types
Surcharged with New Values in Annas and Rupees
Engr.; Name Typo. on Nos. 17-18
1949, Oct. 10   Perf. 13½, 11x11½

16	CD306	2½a on 20c dp ultra	.15	.15
17	CD307	3a on 30c dp car	.20	.20
18	CD308	8a on 50c orange	.65	.65
19	CD309	1r on 1sh blue	1.25	1.25
		Nos. 16-19 (4)	2.25	2.25

75th anniv. of the formation of the UPU.

Nos. 3 and 5-11 Surcharged with New Values in Carmine or Black
Perf. 14, 13x11½, 11½x13
1951, Oct. 1   Engr.   Wmk. 4

20	A1	5c on 1a (C)	.15	.15
21	A3	10c on 2a	.20	.15
22	A3	15c on 2½a	.60	.55
23	A2	20c on 3a	.25	.25
24	A2	50c on 8a	.35	.30
25	A3	1sh on 1r	1.10	.80
26	A2	2sh on 2r	4.00	2.50
27	A3	5sh on 5r	9.00	6.00
		Nos. 20-27 (8)	15.65	10.70

Coronation Issue
Common Design Type
1953, June 2   Perf. 13½x13

28	CD312	15c dk green & blk	.25	.25

Sultan Hussein A10

Qarn Adh Dhabi A11

Designs: 15c, Seiyun scene, horiz. 25c, Minaret at Tarim. 35c, Mosque at Seiyun. 50c, Palace at Tarim, horiz. 1sh, Mosque at Seiyun, horiz. 2sh, South Gate, Tarim. 5sh, Kathiri house, horiz. 10sh, Mosque entrance, Tarim.

1954, Jan. 15   Engr.   Perf. 12½

29	A10	5c dark brown	.15	.15
30	A10	10c deep blue	.15	.15

Perf. 13x11½, 11½x13

31	A11	15c dk blue green	.15	.15
32	A11	25c dk car rose	.15	.15
33	A11	35c deep blue	.15	.15
34	A11	50c dk car rose & dk brn	.15	.15
35	A11	1sh deep orange	.35	.30
36	A11	2sh gray green	1.00	.85
37	A11	5sh vio & dk blue	2.50	3.25
38	A11	10sh vio & yel brn	5.50	6.50
		Nos. 29-38 (10)	10.80	11.80

Perf. 11½x13, 13x11½
1964, July 1   Wmk. 314
Designs: 1sh25c, Seiyun, horiz. 1sh50c, View of Gheil Ömer, horiz.

39	A11	70c black	.35	.35
40	A11	1sh25c bright green	.60	.60
41	A11	1sh50c purple	.80	.80
		Nos. 39-41 (3)	1.75	1.75

QUAITI STATE OF SHIHR AND MUKALLA

LOCATION — In Eastern Aden Protectorate
GOVT. — Sultanate
CAPITAL — Mukalla

Catalogue values for unused stamps in this section are for Never Hinged items.

Sultan Sir Saleh bin Ghalib al Qu'aiti — A1

Mukalla Harbor — A2

Buildings at Shibam — A3

Designs: 2a, Gateway of Shihr. 3a, Outpost of Mukalla. 8a, View of 'Einat. 1r, Governor's Castle, Du'an. 3r, Mosque in Hureidha. 5r, Meshhed.

1942   Engr.   Wmk. 4   Perf. 14

1	A1	½a dark green	.50	.15
2	A1	¾a copper brown	.50	.15
3	A1	1a deep blue	.60	.15

Perf. 13x11½, 11½x13

4	A2	1½a dk car rose	.70	.15
5	A2	2a black brown	.70	.15
6	A2	2½a deep blue	.40	.15
7	A3	3a dk car rose & dl brn	.70	.15
8	A3	8a orange red	.40	.35
9	A2	1r green	1.50	.50
10	A3	2r rose vio & dk blue	9.50	2.00
11	A3	5r gray green & fawn	12.50	2.00
		Nos. 1-11 (11)	28.00	7.15

For surcharges see Nos. 20-27.

Nos. 4, 6 Ovptd. in Black or Carmine like Kathiri Nos. 12-13
Perf. 11½x13, 13x11½
1946, Oct. 15

12	A2 (b)	1½a dk car rose	.15	.15
13	A3 (a)	2½a deep blue (C)	.25	.25

Victory of the Allied Nations in WWII.

Silver Wedding Issue
Common Design Types
1949, Jan. 17   Photo.   Perf. 14x14½

14	CD304	1½a scarlet	.30	.30

Engraved; Name Typo.
Perf. 11½x11

15	CD305	5r green	11.00	11.00

25th anniv. of the marriage of King George VI and Queen Elizabeth.

UPU Issue
Common Design Types
Surcharged with New Values in Annas and Rupees
Engr.; Name Typo. on Nos. 17 and 18
1949, Oct. 10   Perf. 13½, 11x11½

16	CD306	2½a on 20c dp ultra	.15	.15
17	CD307	3a on 30c dp car	.35	.35
18	CD308	8a on 50c org	.90	.90
19	CD309	1r on 1sh blue	2.50	2.50
a.		Surcharge omitted	1,300.	
		Nos. 16-19 (4)	3.90	3.90

Nos. 3 and 5-11 Surcharged with New Values in Carmine or Black
Perf. 14, 13x11½, 11½x13
1951, Oct. 1   Engr.   Wmk. 4

20	A1	5c on 1a (C)	.15	.15
21	A2	10c on 2a	.15	.15
22	A3	15c on 2½a	.15	.15
23	A2	20c on 3a	.15	.15
24	A3	50c on 8a	.15	.15
25	A2	1sh on 1r	.30	.30
26	A3	2sh on 2r	4.00	6.00
27	A3	5sh on 5r	6.50	8.00
		Nos. 20-27 (8)	11.55	15.05

Coronation Issue
Common Design Type
1953, June 2   Engr.   Perf. 13½x13

28	CD312	15c dk blue & black	.40	.40

Qu'aiti State in Hadhramaut

Metal Work — A10

Fisheries — A11

Designs: 10c, Mat making. 15c, Weaving. 25c, Pottery. 35c, Building. 50c, Date cultivation. 90c, Agriculture. 1sh25c, 10sh, Lime burning. 2sh, Dhow building. 5sh, Agriculture.

Perf. 11½x13, 13½x14
1955, Sept. 1   Engr.   Wmk. 4

29	A10	5c greenish blue	.15	.15
30	A10	10c black	.15	.15
31	A10	15c dk green	.15	.15
32	A10	25c carmine	.15	.15
33	A10	35c ultra	.15	.15
34	A10	50c red orange	.35	.35
35	A10	90c brown	.50	.50
36	A11	1sh purple & blk	.60	.60
37	A11	1sh25c red org & blk	.70	.70
38	A11	2sh dk blue & blk	1.25	1.25
39	A11	5sh green & blk	3.25	3.25
40	A11	10sh car & black	7.00	7.00
		Nos. 29-40 (12)	14.40	14.40

Types of 1955 with Portrait of Sultan Awadh Bin Saleh El-Qu'aiti
Design: 70c, Agriculture. Others as before.

1963, Oct. 20   Wmk. 314

41	A10	5c greenish blue	.15	.15
42	A10	10c black	.15	.15
43	A10	15c dark green	.15	.15
44	A10	25c carmine	.15	.15
45	A10	35c ultra	.25	.25

46	A10	50c red orange	.35	.35
47	A10	70c brown	.60	.60
48	A11	1sh purple & blk	.85	.85
49	A11	1sh25c red org & blk	1.10	1.10
50	A11	2sh dk blue & blk	1.75	1.75
51	A11	5sh green & blk	4.25	4.50
52	A11	10sh carmine & blk	9.50	10.00
		Nos. 41-52 (12)	19.25	20.00

AFARS AND ISSAS
French Territory of the

'ä–,fär(z) and ē–'sä(z)

LOCATION — East Africa
GOVT. — French Overseas Territory
AREA — 8,880 sq. mi.
POP. — 150,000 (est. 1974)
CAPITAL — Djibouti (Jibuti)

The French overseas territory of Somali Coast was renamed the French Territory of the Afars and Issas in 1967. It became the Djibouti Republic (which see) on June 27, 1977.

100 Centimes = 1 Franc

Catalogue values for all unused stamps in this country are for Never Hinged items.

Imperforates
Most stamps of Afars and Issas exist imperforate in issued and trial colors, and also in small presentation sheets in issued colors.

Grayheaded
Kingfisher
A48

1967	**Engr.**	**Unwmk.**	**Perf. 13**	
310	A48	10fr Halcyon leucocephala	1.50	1.25
311	A48	15fr Haematopus ostralegus	2.00	1.50
312	A48	50fr Tringa nebularia	7.75	4.50
313	A48	55fr Coracias abyssinicus	9.50	5.25
314	A48	60fr Xerus rutilus	13.00	10.00
		Nos. 310-314 (5)	33.75	22.50

Issued: 10fr, 55fr, Aug. 21; 15fr, 50fr, 60fr, Sept. 25. See No. C50.

Soccer — A49

1967, Dec. 18	**Engr.**	**Perf. 13**		
315	A49	25fr shown	1.90	1.50
316	A49	30fr Basketball	2.50	2.00

Common Design Types
Pictured in section at front of book.

WHO Anniversary Issue
Common Design Type

1968, May 4	**Engr.**	**Perf. 13**		
317	CD126	15fr multicolored	1.25	1.00

20th anniv. of WHO.

Damerdjog
Fortress — A50

Administration Buildings: 25fr, Ali Adde. 30fr, Dorra. 40fr, Assamo.

1968, May 17	**Engr.**	**Perf. 13**		
318	A50	20fr slate, brn & emer	.90	.50
319	A50	25fr brt grn, bl & brn	.95	.50
320	A50	30fr brn ol, brn org & sl	1.10	.75
321	A50	40fr brn ol, sl & brt grn	2.00	1.50
		Nos. 318-321 (4)	4.95	3.25

Human Rights Year Issue
Common Design Type

1968, Aug. 10	**Engr.**	**Perf. 13**		
322	CD127	10fr purple, ver & org	.75	.60
323	CD127	70fr green, pur & org	1.50	1.10

International Human Rights Year.

Radio-television Station, Djibouti — A52

High Commission Palace, Djibouti — A53

Designs: 2fr, Justice Building. 5fr, Chamber of Deputies. 8fr, Great Mosque. 15fr, Monument of Free French Forces, vert. 40fr, Djibouti Post Office. 70fr, Residence of Gov. Léonce Lagarde at Obock. No. 332, Djibouti Harbormaster's Building. No. 333, Control tower, Djibouti Airport.

1968-70	**Engr.**	**Perf. 13**		
324	A52	1fr dk red, sky bl & ind	.25	.15
325	A52	2fr green, bl & indigo	.25	.15
326	A52	5fr brn, sky bl & grn	.35	.20
327	A52	8fr choc, emer & gray	.40	.20
328	A52	15fr grn, sky bl & yel brn	3.00	2.00
329	A52	40fr green, brn & slate	2.00	1.00
330	A53	60fr multicolored	2.25	1.50
331	A53	70fr dl grn, gray & ol bis	3.00	1.50
332	A53	85fr multicolored	4.00	2.00
333	A53	85fr dk grn, bl & gray	4.50	2.50
		Nos. 324-333 (10)	20.00	11.20

Issue years: 1968 - 60fr; 1969 - 1fr-15fr, 70fr, 85fr; 1970 - 40fr, 85fr.

Locust — A54

Designs: 50fr, Pest control by helicopter. 55fr, Pest control by plane.

1969, Oct. 6	**Engr.**	**Perf. 13**		
334	A54	15fr brn, grn & slate	2.50	1.00
335	A54	50fr dk grn, bl & ol brn	1.50	1.00
336	A54	55fr red brn, bl & brn	2.00	1.50
		Nos. 334-336 (3)	6.00	3.50

Campaign against locusts.

ILO Issue
Common Design Type

1969, Nov. 24	**Engr.**	**Perf. 13**		
337	CD131	30fr orange, gray & lilac	1.25	.80

Afar Dagger in
Ornamental
Scabbard
A56

1970, Apr. 3	**Engr.**	**Perf. 13**		
338	A56	10fr yel grn, dk grn & org brn	.50	.35
339	A56	15fr yel grn, bl & org brn	.60	.35
340	A56	20fr yel grn, red & org brn	.80	.55
341	A56	25fr yel grn, plum & org brn	1.10	.55
		Nos. 338-341 (4)	3.00	1.80

See No. 364.

UPU Headquarters Issue
Common Design Type

1970, May 20	**Engr.**	**Perf. 13**		
342	CD133	25fr brn, brt grn & choc	1.00	.60

Trapshooting
A57

Motorboats
A58

Designs: 50fr, Steeplechase. 55fr, Sailboat, vert. 60fr, Equestrians.

1970	**Engr.**	**Perf. 13**		
343	A57	30fr dp brn, yel grn & brt bl	1.65	.90
344	A58	48fr blue & multi	1.75	.90
345	A58	50fr cop red, bl & pur	2.25	1.25
346	A58	55fr red brn, bl & ol	1.75	1.25
347	A58	60fr ol, blk & red brn	2.75	1.75
		Nos. 343-347 (5)	10.15	6.05

Issued: 30fr, June 5; 48fr, Oct. 9; 50fr, 60fr, Nov. 6.

Automatic
Ferry,
Tadjourah
A59

1970, Nov. 25				
348	A59	48fr blue, brn & grn	2.25	1.40

Volcanic
Geode — A60

Diabase and
Chrysolite
A61

10fr, Doleritic basalt. 15fr, Olivine basalt.

1971	**Photo.**	**Perf. 13**		
349	A61	10fr black & multi	1.25	.50
350	A61	15fr black & multi	1.65	.50
351	A60	25fr black, crim & brn	3.50	1.50
352	A61	40fr black & multi	6.50	2.00
		Nos. 349-352 (4)	12.90	4.50

Issued: 10fr, 11/22; 15fr, 10/8; 25fr, 4/26; 40fr, 1/25.

A62

A63

1971, July 1	**Photo.**	**Perf. 12x12½**		
353	A62	4fr Manta birostris	1.25	.50
354	A62	9fr Coryphaena hippurus	1.25	.50
355	A62	9fr Pristis pectinatus	2.50	1.50
		Nos. 353-355 (3)	5.00	2.50

See No. C60.

De Gaulle Issue
Common Design Type

Designs: 60fr, Gen. Charles de Gaulle, 1940. 85fr, Pres. de Gaulle, 1970.

1971, Nov. 9	**Engr.**	**Perf. 13**		
356	CD134	60fr dk vio bl & blk	2.00	1.50
357	CD134	85fr dk vio bl & blk	2.50	1.50

1972, Mar. 8	**Photo.**	**Perf. 12½x13**		

Shells: 4fr, Strawberry Top. 9fr, Cypraea pantherina. 20fr, Bull-mouth helmet. 50fr, Ethiopian volute.

358	A63	4fr olive & multi	1.25	.40
359	A63	9fr dk blue & multi	1.50	.60
360	A63	20fr dp green & multi	3.75	1.00
361	A63	50fr dp claret & multi	7.50	1.50
		Nos. 358-361 (4)	14.00	3.50

Shepherd — A64

Design: 10fr, Dromedary breeding.

1973, Apr. 11	**Photo.**	**Perf. 13**		
362	A64	9fr blue & multi	1.00	.30
363	A64	10fr blue & multi	1.00	.30

Afar Dagger — A65

1974, Jan. 29	**Engr.**	**Perf. 13**		
364	A65	30fr slate grn & dk brn	1.10	.65

For surcharge see No. 379.

Flamingos, Lake Abbe — A66

Designs: Flamingos and different views of Lake Abbe.

1974, Feb. 22	**Photo.**	**Perf. 13**		
370	A66	5fr multicolored	1.25	.30
371	A66	15fr multicolored	.60	.30
372	A66	50fr multicolored	1.90	1.25
		Nos. 370-372 (3)	3.75	2.05

Soccer Ball — A67

1974, May 24	**Engr.**	**Perf. 13**		
373	A67	25fr black & emerald	1.25	.80

World Cup Soccer Championship, Munich, June 13-July 7.

Letters Around
UPU Emblem
A68

Oleo Chrysophylla
A69

1974, Oct. 9	**Engr.**	**Perf. 13**		
374	A68	20fr multicolored	1.00	.50
375	A68	100fr multicolored	2.50	2.00

Centenary of Universal Postal Union.

1974, Nov. 22   **Photo.**
376 A69 10fr shown   .75   .40
377 A69 15fr *Ficus species*   1.10 .60
378 A69 20fr *Solanum adoense*   2.25 1.00
        Nos. 376-378 (3)   4.10 2.00
            Day Primary Forest.

No. 364 Surcharged with New Value and
        Two Bars in Red
1975, Jan. 1   **Engr.**   *Perf. 13*
379 A65 40fr on 30fr multi   1.50 .90

Treasury — A70

Design: 25fr, Government buildings.

1975, Jan. 7   **Engr.**   *Perf. 13*
380 A70 8fr blue, gray & red   .40   .30
381 A70 25fr red, blue & indigo   .75   .60

Ranella Spinosa — A71

Sea Shells: No. 382, Darioconus textile. No. 383,
Murex palmarosa. 10fr, Conus sumatrensis. 15fr,
Cypraea pulchra. No. 386, 45fr, Murex scolopax.
No. 387, Cypraea exhusta. 55fr, Cypraea erythraen-
sis. 60fr, Conus taeniatus.

1975-76   **Engr.**   *Perf. 13*
382 A71 5fr blue grn & brn   1.25   .40
383 A71 5fr blue & multi ('76)   .90   .20
384 A71 10fr lilac, blk & brn   1.25   .40
385 A71 15fr blue, indigo & brn   2.25   .60
386 A71 20fr purple & lt brn   3.00 1.65
387 A71 20fr brt grn & multi ('76)   1.10   .40
388 A71 40fr green & brown   6.00 1.00
389 A71 45fr green, bl & bister   5.00 1.00
390 A71 55fr turq & multi ('76)   3.00 1.25
391 A71 60fr buff & sepia ('76)   6.00 1.75
        Nos. 382-391 (10)   29.75 8.65

Hypolimnas
Misippus
A72

Butterflies: 40fr, Papilio nireus. 50fr, Acraea
anemosa. 65fr, Holocerina smilax menieri. 70fr,
Papilio demodocus. No. 397, Papilio dardanus. No.
398, Balachowsky gonimbrasca. 150fr, Vanessa
cardui.

1975-76   **Photo.**   *Perf. 13*
392 A72 25fr emerald & multi   1.90 1.00
393 A72 40fr yellow & multi   2.00 1.00
394 A72 50fr ultra & multi ('76)   2.25 1.50
395 A72 65fr olive & multi ('76)   3.25 1.50
396 A72 70fr violet & multi   4.25 2.00
397 A72 100fr blue & multi   5.50 2.00
398 A72 100fr Prus bl & multi
             ('76)   4.25 2.00
399 A72 150fr green & multi ('76)   6.00 2.00
        Nos. 392-399 (8)   29.40 13.00

A73

Perf. 13x12½, 12½x13
1975-76   **Photo.**
400 A73 10fr Hyaena hyaena   .55   .30
401 A73 15fr Cercopithecus
             aethiops   1.10   .50
402 A73 15fr Equus asinus
             somalicus   .90   .50

---

403 A73 30fr Dorcatragus
             megalotis   1.65   .90
404 A73 50fr Ichneumia albi-
             cauda   2.25 1.00
405 A73 60fr Hystrix galasta   2.75 1.25
406 A73 70fr Ictonyx striatus   4.00 1.75
407 A73 200fr Orycteropus afar   6.75 4.00
        Nos. 400-407 (8)   19.95 10.20
        Issued: 10fr, 15fr, 30fr, 1976.

A74   A75

1975-76   **Photo.**   *Perf. 12½x13*
413 A74 20fr Vidua macroura   1.25   .80
414 A74 25fr Psittacula krameri   1.25   .40
415 A74 50fr Cinnyris venustus   2.50 1.50
416 A74 60fr Ardea goliath   3.50 1.75
417 A74 100fr Scopus umbretta   4.50 2.50
418 A74 100fr Oena capensis   3.50 1.65
419 A74 300fr Platalea alba   9.00 4.00
        Nos. 413-419 (7)   25.50 12.60
        Issued: 25fr, No. 418, 300fr, 1976.

1975, Dec. 19   **Engr.**   *Perf. 13*
421 A75 20fr Palms   1.00   .40

Satellite and Alexander Graham
Bell — A76

1976, Mar. 10   **Engr.**   *Perf. 13*
422 A76 200fr dp bl, org & sl grn   4.00 2.25
    Centenary of the first telephone call by Alexan-
der Graham Bell, Mar. 10, 1876.

Basketball
A77

1976, July 7   **Litho.**   *Perf. 12½*
423 A77 10fr shown   .45   .20
424 A77 15fr Bicycling   .60   .30
425 A77 40fr Soccer   1.10   .50
426 A77 60fr Running   1.40   .80
        Nos. 423-426 (4)   3.55 1.80
    21st Olympic Games, Montreal, Canada, July 17-
Aug. 1.

Pterois Radiata — A78

1976, Aug. 10   **Photo.**   *Perf. 13x13½*
428 A78 45fr blue & multi   2.50 1.00

Psammophis Elegans — A79

Design: 70fr, Naja nigricollis, vert.
Perf. 13x13½, 13½x13
1976, Sept. 27   **Photo.**
430 A79 70fr ocher & multi   2.75 1.50
431 A79 80fr emerald & multi   3.25 1.75

Motorcyclist — A80

1977, Jan. 27   **Litho.**   *Perf. 12x12½*
432 A80 200fr multicolored   5.25 2.75
        Moto-Cross motorcycle race.

Conus Betulinus — A81

Sea Shells: 5fr, Cyprea tigris. 70fr, Conus
striatus. 85fr, Cyprea mauritiana.

1977   **Engr.**   *Perf. 13*
433 A81 5fr multicolored   .90   .50
434 A81 30fr multicolored   1.40   .60
435 A81 70fr multicolored   4.75 1.75
436 A81 85fr multicolored   5.00 2.00
        Nos. 433-436 (4)   12.05 4.85

Gaterin
Gaterinus
A82

1977, Apr. 15   **Photo.**   *Perf. 13x12½*
437 A82 15fr shown   1.10   .40
438 A82 65fr Barracudas   3.25 1.10

AIR POST STAMPS

AP16   AP17

Unwmk.
1967, Aug. 21   **Engr.**   *Perf. 13*
C50 AP16 200fr Aquila rapax belisa-
              rius   15.00 7.50

1968   **Engr.**   *Perf. 13*
    48fr, Parachutists. 85fr, Water skier & skin diver.
C51 AP17 48fr brn ol, Prus bl & brn   2.75 1.50
C52 AP17 85fr dk brn, ol & Prus bl   3.75 2.50
        Issue dates: 48fr, Jan. 5; 85fr, Mar. 15.

Aerial Map of the Territory — AP18

1968, Nov. 15   **Engr.**   *Perf. 13*
C53 AP18 500fr bl, dk brn & ocher   26.00 8.00

    Buildings Type of Regular Issue
Designs: 100fr, Cathedral, vert. 200fr, Sayed
Hassan Mosque, vert.

1969   **Engr.**   *Perf. 13*
C54 A53 100fr multicolored   2.25 1.50
C55 A53 200fr multicolored   5.25 3.00
    Issue dates: 100fr, Apr. 4; 200fr, May 8.

Concorde Issue
Common Design Type
1969, Apr. 17
C56 CD129 100fr org red & olive   17.50 10.00

Arta Ionospheric   Japanese Sword
Station — AP19   Guard, Fish
                        Design — AP20

1970, May 8   **Engr.**   *Perf. 13*
C57 AP19 70fr multicolored   3.00 2.00

    Gold embossed
1970, Sept. 29   *Perf. 12½*
    200fr, Japanese sword guard, horse design.
C58 AP20 100fr multicolored   7.50 5.00
C59 AP20 200fr multicolored   9.50 5.50
    EXPO '70 International Exposition, Osaka, Japan,
Mar. 15-Sept. 13.

Scarus
vetula
AP21

1971, July 1   **Photo.**   *Perf. 12½*
C60 AP21 30fr black & multi   4.00 2.50

Djibouti
Harbor
AP22

1971, Nov. 26
C61 AP22 100fr blue & multi   4.00 2.25
        New Djibouti harbor.

PTEROCLES LICHTENSTEINI
AP23

AP24

1972   Photo.   Perf. 12¹/₂x13

C62	AP23	30fr Pterocles lichten-		
		steini	1.90	1.40
C63	AP23	49fr Uppupa epops	4.50	2.50
C64	AP23	66fr Capella media	5.75	3.25
C65	AP23	500fr Francolinus		
		ochropectus	24.00	9.00
		Nos. C62-C65 (4)	36.15	16.15

Issue dates: #C65, Nov. 3, others Apr. 21.

1972, June 8   Engr.   Perf. 13

Olympic Rings and: 5fr, Running. 10fr, Basket-ball. 55fr, Swimming, horiz. 60fr, Olympic torch and Greek frieze, horiz.

C66	AP24	5fr multicolored	.45	.30
C67	AP24	10fr multicolored	.55	.40
C68	AP24	55fr multicolored	1.75	1.10
C69	AP24	60fr multicolored	2.25	1.25
		Nos. C66-C69 (4)	5.00	3.05

20th Olympic Games, Munich, Aug. 26-Sept. 11.

Louis Pasteur — AP25

Design: 100fr, Albert Calmette and C. Guérin.

1972, Oct. 5   Engr.   Perf. 13

| C70 | AP25 | 20fr multicolored | 1.25 | .50 |
| C71 | AP25 | 100fr multicolored | 4.00 | 2.50 |

Pasteur, Calmette, Guerin, chemists and bacteri-ologists, benefactors of mankind.

Map and Views of Territory — AP26

200fr, Woman and Mosque of Djibouti, vert.

1973, Jan. 15   Photo.   Perf. 13

| C72 | AP26 | 30fr brown & multi | 4.50 | 3.50 |
| C73 | AP26 | 200fr multicolored | 8.00 | 6.00 |

Visit of Pres. Georges Pompidou of France, Jan. 15-17.

AP27

1973, Feb. 26   Photo.   Perf. 13x12¹/₂

C74	AP27	30fr Oryx beisa	2.00	1.00
C75	AP27	50fr Madogua saltiana	2.75	1.50
C76	AP27	66fr Felis caracal	3.75	2.00
		Nos. C74-C76 (3)	8.50	4.50

See Nos. C94-C96.

Celts — AP28

Various pre-historic flint tools. 40fr, 60fr, horiz.

1973   Perf. 13

C77	AP28	20fr yel grn, blk & brn	2.25	1.50
C78	AP28	40fr yellow & multi	2.75	2.00
C79	AP28	49fr lilac & multi	5.00	3.00
C80	AP28	60fr blue & multi	3.75	2.50
		Nos. C77-C80 (4)	13.75	9.00

Issued: 20fr, 49fr, Mar. 16; 40fr, 60fr, Sept. 7.

Octopus macropus — AP29

1973, Mar. 16

| C81 | AP29 | 40fr shown | 3.00 | 1.00 |
| C82 | AP29 | 60fr Halicore dugong | 5.00 | 2.50 |

AP30   AP31

Copernicus: 8fr, Nicolaus Copernicus, Polish astronomer. 9fr, William C. Roentgen, physicist, X-ray discoverer. No. C85, Edward Jenner, physician, discoverer of vaccination. No. C86, Marie Curie, discoverer of radium and polonium. 49fr, Robert Koch, physician and bacteriologist. 50fr, Clement Ader (1841-1925), French aviation pioneer. 55fr, Guglielmo Marconi, Italian electrical engineer, inventor. 85fr, Moliere, French playwright. 100fr, Henri Farman (1874-1937), French aviation pio-neer. 150fr, Andre-Marie Ampere (1775-1836), French physicist. 250fr, Michelangelo Buonarroti (1475-1564), Italian sculptor, painter and architect.

1973-75   Engr.   Perf. 13

C83	AP30	8fr multicolored	.65	.30
C84	AP30	9fr multicolored	1.00	.40
C85	AP30	10fr multicolored	.90	.50
C86	AP30	10fr multicolored	.75	.40
C87	AP30	49fr multicolored	3.25	1.65
C88	AP30	50fr multicolored	2.50	1.25
C89	AP30	55fr multicolored	1.90	1.00
C90	AP30	85fr multicolored	3.75	1.75
C91	AP30	100fr multicolored	3.75	2.00
C92	AP30	150fr multicolored	3.75	2.00
C93	AP30	250fr multicolored	6.50	3.50
		Nos. C83-C93 (11)	28.70	14.75

Issued: 8fr, 85fr, 5/9/73; 9fr, #C85, 49fr, 10/12/73; 100fr, 1/29/74; 55fr, 3/22/74; #C86, 8/23/74; 150fr, 7/24/75; 250fr, 6/26/75; 50fr, 9/25/75.

Perf. 12¹/₂x13, 13x12¹/₂

1973, Dec. 12   Photo.

C94	AP31	20fr Papio anubis	1.25	.60
C95	AP31	50fr Genetta tigrina, horiz.	2.50	.90
C96	AP31	66fr Lapus habessinicus	4.00	1.50
		Nos. C94-C96 (3)	7.75	3.00

Spearfishing — AP32

1974, Apr. 14   Engr.   Perf. 13

C97 AP32 200fr multicolored   7.50 4.50

No. C97 was prepared for release in Nov. 1972, for the 3rd Underwater Spearfishing Contest in the Red Sea. Dates were obliterated with a rectangle and the stamp was not issued without this obliteration.

Rock Carvings, Balho — AP33

1974, Apr. 26

C98 AP33 200fr carmine & slate   7.00 5.00

Lake Assal AP34

Designs (Lake Assal): 50fr, Rock formations on shore. 85fr, Crystallized wood.

1974, Oct. 25   Photo.   Perf. 13

C99	AP34	49fr multicolored	1.25	.75
C100	AP34	50fr multicolored	1.75	1.00
C101	AP34	85fr multicolored	3.50	2.25
		Nos. C99-C101 (3)	6.50	4.00

Columba guinea — AP35

1975, May 23   Photo.   Perf. 13

C102 AP35 500fr multicolored   18.00 6.50

Djibouti Airport — AP36

1977, Mar. 1   Litho.   Perf. 12

C103 AP36 500fr multicolored   10.00 7.50

Opening of new Djibouti Airport.

Thomas A. Edison and Phonograph — AP37

Design: 75fr, Alexander Volta, electric train, lines and light bulb.

1977, May 5   Engr.   Perf. 13

| C104 | AP37 | 55fr multicolored | 3.00 | 1.50 |
| C105 | AP37 | 75fr multicolored | 4.50 | 2.50 |

Famous inventors: Thomas Alva Edison and Alexander Volta (1745-1827).

POSTAGE DUE STAMPS

Nomad's Milk Jug — D3

Perf. 14x13

1969, Dec. 15   Engr.   Unwmk.

J49	D3	1fr red brn, red lil & slate	.20	.20
J50	D3	2fr red brn, emer & slate	.20	.20
J51	D3	5fr red brn, bl & slate	.30	.30
J52	D3	10fr red brn, brn & slate	.80	.80
		Nos. J49-J52 (4)	1.50	1.50

AFGHANISTAN

af-'ga-nə-,stan

LOCATION — Central Asia, bounded by Iran, Russian Turkestan, Pakistan, Balu-chistan and China
GOVT. — Republic
AREA — 251,773 sq. mi.
POP. — 17,150,000 (1984 est.)
CAPITAL — Kabul

Afghanistan changed from a constitu-tional monarchy to a republic in July 1973.

12 Shahi = 6 Sanar = 3 Abasi =
2 Krans = 1 Rupee Kabuli
60 Paisas = 1 Rupee (1921)
100 Pouls = 1 Rupee Afghani (1927)

Catalogue values for unused stamps in this country are for Never Hinged items, beginning with Scott 364 in the regular postage section, Scott B1 in the semi-postal section, Scott C7 in the airpost section, Scott O8 in officials section, and Scott RA6 in the postal tax section.

From 1871 to 1892 and 1898 the Mos-lem year date appears on the stamp. Numer-als as follows:

1886-88
Colored Wove Paper
155	A12	1ab black, *magenta*	27.50
156	A12	1ab claret brn, *org*	20.00
156A	A12	1ab red, *org*	2.00
156B	A14	2ab red, *org*	4.75
156C	A15	1rup red, *org*	3.50

Laid Batonné Paper
157	A12	1ab black, *lavender*	2.75
158	A12	1ab cl brn, *grn*	6.50
159	A13	1ab black, *pink*	17.50
160	A14	2ab black, *pink*	35.00
161	A15	1rup black, *pink*	20.00

Laid Paper
162	A12	1ab black, *pink*	6.50
163	A14	2ab black, *pink*	6.50
164	A15	1rup black, *pink*	6.50
165	A12	1ab brown, *yel*	6.50
166	A14	2ab brown, *yel*	6.50
167	A15	1rup brown, *yel*	6.50
168	A12	1ab black, *grn*	6.50
169	A14	2ab black, *grn*	6.50
170	A15	1rup blue, *grn*	6.50

1891
Colored Wove Paper
175	A12	1ab green, *rose*	22.50
176	A15	1rup pur, *grn batonne*	22.50

Nos. 109-176 fall into three categories:

1. Those regularly issued and in normal postal use from 1881 on, handstamped on thin white laid or wove paper in strip sheets containing 12 or more impressions of the same denomination arranged in two irregular rows, with the impressions often touching or overlappng.

2. The 1884 postal issues provisionally printed on smooth or ribbed colored wove paper to supplement low stocks of the normal white paper stamps.

3. The "special" printings made in a range of colors on several types of laid or wove colored papers, most of which were never used for normal printings. These were produced periodically from 1886 to 1891 to meet philatelic demands. Although nominally valid for postage, most of the special printings were exported directly to fill dealers' orders, and few were ever postally used. Many of the sheets contained all three denominations with impressions separated by ruled lines. Sometimes different colors were used, so se-tenant multiples of denomination or color exist. Many combinations of stamp and paper colors exist besides those listed.

Various shades of each color exist.

Type A12 is known dated "1297."

Counterfeits, lithographed or typographed, are plentiful.

Kingdom of Afghanistan

A16   A17

A18

Dated "1309"

1891   Pelure Paper   Litho.
177	A16	1ab slate blue	.85	.85
a.		Tete beche pair	14.00	
178	A17	2ab slate blue	6.00	5.00
179	A18	1rup slate blue	12.25	10.00
		Nos. 177-179 (3)	19.10	15.85

Revenue stamps of similar design exist in various colors.

Nos. 177-179 were printed in panes on the same sheet, so se-tenant gutter pairs exist. Examples in black or red are proofs.

A Mosque Gate and Crossed Cannons (National Seal) — A19

Dated "1310" in Upper Right Corner

1892
Flimsy Wove Paper
180	A19	1ab black, *green*	2.00	1.60
181	A19	1ab black, *orange*	2.50	2.50
182	A19	1ab black, *yellow*	2.00	1.60
183	A19	1ab black, *pink*	2.50	1.60
184	A19	1ab black, *lil rose*	2.50	2.50
185	A19	1ab black, *blue*	4.25	3.50
186	A19	1ab black, *salmon*	2.00	2.00
187	A19	1ab black, *magenta*	2.50	2.50
188	A19	1ab black, *violet*	2.50	2.50
188A	A19	1ab black, *scarlet*	2.50	1.75

Many shades exist.

A20

A21

Undated

1894
Flimsy Wove Paper
189	A20	2ab black, *green*	6.50	6.50
190	A21	1rup black, *green*	10.00	10.00

24 varieties of the 2 abasi and 12 varieties of the rupee.

Nos. 189-190 and F3 were printed se-tenant in the same sheet. Pairs exist.

A21a

Dated "1316"

1898
Flimsy Wove Paper
191	A21a	2ab black, *pink*	2.50
192	A21a	2ab black, *magenta*	2.50
193	A21a	2ab black, *yellow*	1.10
193A	A21a	2ab black, *salmon*	3.00
194	A21a	2ab black, *green*	1.40
195	A21a	2ab black, *purple*	1.75
195A	A21a	2ab black, *blue*	17.50
		Nos. 191-195A (7)	29.75

Nos. 191-195A were not regularly issued. Genuinely used copies are scarce. No. 195A was found in remainder stocks and probably was never released.

A22   A23

A24

1907   Engr.   Imperf.
Medium Wove Paper
196	A22	1ab blue green	3.75	2.50
a.		1ab emerald	8.50	5.00
197	A22	1ab brt blue	10.00	10.00
198	A23	2ab deep blue	1.85	1.25
199	A24	1rup green	3.00	2.50
a.		1rup blue green	6.00	6.00

Zigzag Roulette 10
200	A22	1ab green	60.00
201	A23	2ab blue	80.00
201A	A24	1rup blue green	110.00

1908   Perf. 12
202	A22	1ab green	10.00	6.25
203	A23	2ab deep blue	1.25	1.25
204	A24	1rup blue green	3.00	3.00
		Nos. 202-204 (3)	14.25	10.50

Twelve varieties of the 1 abasi, 6 of the 2 abasi, 4 of the 1 rupee.

Nos. 196-204 were issued in small sheets containing 3 or 4 panes. Gutter pairs, normal and tête bêche, exist.

A25   A26

A27

1909-19   Typo.   Perf. 12
205	A25	1ab ultra	.35	.25
a.		Imperf., pair	5.00	
206	A25	1ab red ('16)	.25	.15
a.		Imperf.		
207	A25	1ab rose ('18)	.25	.15
208	A26	2ab green	.50	.30
a.		Imperf., pair	3.00	
b.		Horiz. pair, imperf. btwn.		
208C	A26	2ab yellow ('16)	1.25	1.25
209	A26	2ab bis ('18-'19)	.90	.90
210	A27	1rup lilac brn	1.50	1.50
a.		1rup red brown	2.50	2.00
211	A27	1rup ol bis ('16)	1.50	1.50
		Nos. 205-211 (8)	6.50	6.00

A28

1913
212	A28	2pa drab brown	1.25	1.25
a.		2pa red brown	1.25	1.25

No. 212 is inscribed "Tiket waraq dak" (Postal card stamps). It was usable only on postcards and not accepted for postage on letters.

Nos. 196-212 sometimes show letters of a papermaker's watermark, "Howard & Jones, London."

Royal Star — A29

1920, Aug. 24   Perf. 12
Size: 39x47mm
214	A29	10pa rose	20.00	12.00
215	A29	20pa red brown	45.00	18.00
216	A29	30pa green	90.00	60.00
		Nos. 214-216 (3)	155.00	90.00

Issued in sheets of two.

1921, Mar.
Size: 22½x28¼mm
217	A29	10pa rose	.35	.15
a.		Perf. 11 ('27)	.65	1.00
218	A29	20pa red brown	1.00	.50
219	A29	30pa yel green	1.00	.50
a.		Tete beche pair	6.00	5.50
b.		30pa green	1.50	.75
c.		As "b," Tete beche pair	6.50	6.50
		Nos. 217-219 (3)	2.35	1.15

Two types of the 10pa, three of the 20pa.

Crest of King Amanullah — A32

A30   A32

1924, Feb. 26   Perf. 12
220	A30	10pa chocolate	10.00	6.00
a.		Tete beche pair	20.00	16.00

6th Independence Day.
Printed in sheets of four consisting of two tete beche pairs, and in sheets of two. Two types exist.

Some authorities believe that Nos. Q15-Q16 were issued as regular postage stamps.

1925, Feb. 26   Perf. 12
Size: 29x37mm
222	A32	10pa light brown	10.00	6.00

7th Independence Day.
Printed in sheets of 8 (two panes of 4).

1926, Feb. 28
Wove Paper
Size: 26x33mm
224	A32	10pa dark blue	1.40	1.40
a.		Imperf., pair	6.00	
b.		Horiz. pair, imperf. btwn.	8.00	
c.		Vert. pair, imperf. btwn.	8.00	
d.		Laid paper	6.50	5.00

7th anniv. of Independence. Printed in sheets of 4, and in sheets of 8 (two panes of 4). Tete beche gutter pairs exist.

Tughra and Crest of Amanullah — A33

1927, Feb.
225	A33	10pa magenta	10.00	4.25
a.		Vertical pair, imperf. between	20.00	

Dotted Background
226	A33	10pa magenta	5.50	4.25
a.		Horiz. pair, imperf. between	15.00	

The surface of No. 226 is covered by a net of fine dots.

8th anniv. of Independence. Printed in sheets of 8 (two panes of 4). Tete beche gutter pairs exist.

National Seal — A34   A35

A35a   A36

1927, Oct.   Imperf.
227	A34	15p pink	.35	.35
228	A35	30p Prus green	.80	.40
229	A36	60p light blue	1.50	1.50
a.		Tete beche pair	4.50	
		Nos. 227-229 (3)	2.65	2.25

1927-30   Perf. 11, 12
230	A34	15p pink	.25	.15
231	A34	15p ultra ('29)	.50	.30
232	A35	30p Prus green	.35	.35
233	A35a	30p dp green ('30)	.75	.70
234	A36	60p bright blue	1.50	1.00
a.		Tete beche pair	5.00	
235	A36	60p black ('29)	1.40	.65
		Nos. 230-235 (6)	4.75	3.15

Nos. 230, 232 and 234 are usually imperforate on one or two sides.

No. 233 has been redrawn. A narrow border of pearls has been added and "30," in European and Arabic numerals, inserted in the upper spandrels.

Tughra and
Crest of
Amanullah
A37

1928, Feb. 27
236 A37 15p pink   2.00 2.00
  a. Tete beche pair   7.50
  b. Horiz. pair, imperf. vert.   6.00
  c. As "a," imperf. vert., block of 4   10.00

9th anniv. of Independence. This stamp is
always imperforate on one or two sides.
A 15p blue of somewhat similar design was prepared for the 10th anniv., but was not issued due to
Amanullah's dethronement. Value, $15.

A38

A39   A40

A41   A42

1928-30   *Perf. 11, 12*
237 A38 2p dull blue   2.50 1.60
  a. Vertical pair, imperf. between
238 A38 2p lt rose ('30)   .25   .25
239 A39 10p gray green   .25   .15
  a. Tete beche pair   5.00 5.00
  b. Vert. pair, imperf. horiz.   .65
  c. Vertical pair, imperf. between   1.00
240 A40 10p choc ('30)   .50   .50
  a. 10p brown purple ('29)   10.00 2.50
241 A40 25p car rose   .35   .25
242 A40 25p Prus green ('29)   .75   .60
243 A41 40p ultra   .40   .35
  a. Tete beche pair   5.00
244 A41 40p rose ('29)   1.00 1.00
  a. Tete beche pair   7.00
  b. Vert. pair, imperf. horiz.   3.50
245 A42 50p red   .30   .30
246 A42 50p dk blue ('29)   1.50 1.00
  Nos. 237-246 (10)   7.80 6.00

The sheets of these stamps are often imperforate
at the outer margins.
Nos. 237-238 are newspaper stamps.

This handstamp was used for ten
months by the Revolutionary Gov't in
Kabul as a control mark on outgoing
mail. It occasionally fell on the stamps
but there is no evidence that it was officially used as an overprint. Unused copies were privately made.

Independence
Monument — A46

Wmk. Large Seal in the Sheet
1931, Aug.   Litho.   *Perf. 12*
Laid Paper
Without Gum
262 A46 20p red   1.00 .60
13th Independence Day.

National Assembly
Chamber — A47

A48   A50

National
Assembly
Building
A49

National
Assembly
Chamber
A51

National
Assembly
Building — A52

1932   Unwmk.   Typo.   *Perf. 12*
Wove Paper
263 A47 40p olive   1.00   .40
264 A48 60p violet   .65   .50
265 A49 80p dark red   1.00   .80
266 A50 1af black   10.00 4.25
267 A51 2af ultra   3.50 2.75
268 A52 3af gray green   4.25 3.50
  Nos. 263-268 (6)   20.40 12.20

Formation of the Natl. Council. Imperforate or
perforated examples on ungummed chalky paper
are proofs.
See Nos. 304-305.

Mosque at
Balkh — A53   Kabul Fortress — A54

Parliament House,
Darul
Funun — A55

Parliament House,
Darul
Funun — A56

Arch of Qalai
Bist — A57

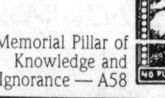

Memorial Pillar of
Knowledge and
Ignorance — A58

Independence
Monument — A59

Minaret at
Herat — A60

Arch of
Paghman — A61

Ruins at
Balkh — A62

Minarets of
Herat — A63

Great Buddha
at
Bamian — A64

1932   Typo.   *Perf. 12*
269 A53 10p brown   .50   .15
270 A54 15p dk brown   .60   .15
271 A55 20p red   .30   .15
272 A56 25p dk green   .75   .15
273 A57 30p red   .40   .30
274 A58 40p orange   .65   .35
275 A59 50p blue   .80   .35
  a. Tete beche pair   5.50
276 A60 60p blue   1.50   .50
277 A61 80p violet   1.75 1.00
278 A62 1af dark blue   2.75   .60
279 A63 2af dk red violet   3.75 2.00
280 A64 3af claret   4.25 2.50
  Nos. 269-280 (12)   18.00 8.20

Counterfeits of types A53-A65 exist.
See Nos. 290-295, 298-299, 302-303.

Entwined 2's — A65

Two types:
Type I - Numerals shaded. Size about 21x29mm.
Type II - Numerals unshaded. Size about
21-3/4x30mm.

1931-38   *Perf. 12, 11x12*
281 A65 2p red brn (I)   .25   .15
282 A65 2p olive blk (I) ('34)   .25   .15
283 A65 2p grnsh gray (I) ('34)   .35   .15
283A A65 2p black (II) ('36)   .35   .15
284 A65 2p salmon (II) ('38)   .25   .15

284A A65 2p rose (I) ('38)   .25   .15
  b. Imperf., pair   3.00

Imperf
285 A65 2p black (II) ('37)   .75   .15
286 A65 2p salmon (II) ('38)   .25   .15
  Nos. 281-286 (8)   2.70
  Set value   .70

The newspaper rate was 2 pouls.

Independence
Monument — A66

1932, Aug.   *Perf. 12*
287 A66 1af deep rose   2.75 1.50
14th Independence Day.

1929 Liberation
Monument, Kabul — A67

1932, Oct.   Typo.
288 A67 80p red brown   .85   .50

Arch of
Paghman
A68

1933, Aug.
289 A68 50p light ultra   1.25 1.25
15th Independence Day.

Types of 1932 and

Royal Palace,
Kabul — A69

Darrah- Shikari
Pass, Hindu
Kush — A70

1934-38   Typo.   *Perf. 12*
290 A53 10p deep violet   .15   .15
291 A54 15p turq green   .20   .15
292 A55 20p magenta   .25   .15
293 A56 25p deep rose   .30   .15
294 A57 30p orange   .40   .20
295 A58 40p blue black   .75   .15
296 A69 45p dark blue   1.50 1.00
297 A69 45p red ('38)   .50   .15
298 A59 50p orange   .30   .15
299 A60 50p purple   .85   .15
300 A70 75p red   1.00   .35
301 A70 75p dk blue ('38)   .60   .40
302 A61 80p brown vio   1.00   .50
303 A62 1af red violet   1.65 1.00
304 A51 2af gray black   3.00 2.00
305 A52 3af ultra   5.00 3.00
  Nos. 290-305 (16)   17.45 9.80

Nos. 290, 292, 300, 304, 305 exist imperf.

Independence Monument — A71

1934, Aug.   Litho.
Without Gum
306 A71 50p pale green   2.50 1.25
  a. Tete beche pair   10.00 3.50

16th year of Independence. Each sheet of 40 (4x10) included 4 tete beche pairs as lower half of sheet was inverted.

Independence Monument A74

Fireworks Display A75

1935, Aug. 15
Laid Paper
309 A74 50p dark blue   1.25 1.25
17th year of Independence.

1936, Aug. 15   Perf. 12
Wove Paper
310 A75 50p red violet   1.25 1.00
18th year of Independence.

Independence Monument and Nadir Shah — A76

1937
311 A76 50p vio & bis brn   1.00 .60
  a. Imperf., pair   2.25
19th year of Independence.

Mohammed Nadir Shah
A77   A78

1938   Perf. 11x12
Without Gum
315 A77 50p brt blue & sepia   5.00 2.50
  a. Imperf. pair   20.00
20th year of Independence.

1939   Perf. 11, 12x11
317 A78 50p deep salmon   1.75 1.00
21st year of Independence.

National Arms A79

Parliament House, Darul Funun A80

Royal Palace, Kabul A81

Independence Monument A82

Independence Monument and Nadir Shah — A83

Mohammed Zahir Shah — A84

Mohammed Zahir Shah — A85

Perf. 11, 11x12, 12x11, 12
1939-61   Typo.
318	A79	2p intense blk	.15 .15
318A	A79	2p brt pink ('61)	1.50 .50
319	A80	10p brt purple	.15 .15
320	A80	15p brt green	.15 .15
321	A80	20p red lilac	.15 .15
322	A81	25p rose red	1.00 .25
322A	A81	25p green ('41)	.50 .15
323	A81	30p orange	.20 .15
324	A81	40p dk gray	.20 .15
325	A82	45p brt carmine	.20 .15
326	A82	50p dp orange	.30 .20
327	A82	60p violet	.60 .20
328	A83	75p ultra	3.00 .75
328A	A83	75p red vio ('41)	.75 .30
328C	A83	75p brt red ('44)	3.00 3.00
328D	A83	75p chnt brn ('49)	4.00 3.00
329	A83	80p chocolate	.50 .50
	a.	80p dull red violet (error)	
330	A84	1af brt red violet	1.50 .75
330A	A85	1af brt red vio ('44)	3.00 1.50
331	A85	2af copper red	1.75 .50
	a.	2af dp rose red	2.50 1.35
332	A84	3af deep blue	3.75 1.60
		Nos. 318-332 (21)	26.35 14.25

Many shades exist in this issue.
On No. 332 the King faces slightly left.
No. 318A issued with and without gum.
See #795A-795B. For similar design see #907A.

Mohammed Nadir Shah — A86

1940, Aug. 23   Perf. 11
333 A86 50p gray green   .75 .60
22nd year of Independence.

Independence Monument A87   Arch of Paghman A88

1941, Aug. 23   Perf. 12
334 A87 15p gray green   8.00 2.75
335 A88 50p red brown   1.25 .85
23rd year of Independence.

Sugar Factory, Baghlan — A89

1942, Apr.   Perf. 12
336 A89 1.25af blue (shades)   2.00 1.00
  a. 1.25af ultra   2.00 1.00

In 1949, a 1.50af brown, type A89, was sold for 3af by the Philatelic Office, Kabul. It was not valid for postage. Value $3.50.

Independence Monument A90

Mohammed Nadir Shah and Arch of Paghman A91

1942, Aug. 23   Perf. 12
337 A90 35p bright green   2.75 2.00
338 A91 125p chalky blue   1.40 1.10
24th year of Independence.

Independence Monument and Nadir Shah — A92

Mohammed Nadir Shah — A93

Perf. 11x12, 12x11
1943, Aug. 25   Typo.   Unwmk.
339 A92 35p carmine   18.00 6.00
340 A93 1.25af dark blue   3.00 1.75
25th year of Independence.

Tomb of Gohar Shad, Herat — A94

Ruins of Qalai Bist — A95

1944, May 1   Perf. 12, 11x12
341 A94 35p orange   .50 .30
342 A95 70p violet   1.00 .60
  a. 70p rose lilac   3.50 .75

A96   A97

1944, Aug.   Perf. 12
343 A96 35p crimson   .80 .60
344 A97 1.25af ultra   1.40 1.10
26th year of Independence.

A98   A99

1945, July
345 A98 35p dp red lil   .75 .65
346 A99 1.25af blue   1.75 1.50
27th year of Independence.

Mohammed Zahir Shah A100   Independence Monument A101

Mohammed Nadir Shah — A102

1946, July
347 A100 15p emerald   .45 .35
348 A101 20p dp red lilac   .70 .55
349 A102 125p blue   1.75 1.75
  Nos. 347-349 (3)   2.90 2.65
28th year of Independence.

Zahir Shah and Ruins of Qalai Bist — A103

A104   A105

1947, Aug.
350 A103 15p yellow green   .30 .15
351 A104 35p plum   .40 .20
352 A105 125p deep blue   1.40 1.40
  Nos. 350-352 (3)   2.10 1.75
29th year of Independence.

Begging Child — A106

A107

1948, May Unwmk. Typo. Perf. 12
353 A106 35p yel green   3.00 2.00
354 A107 125p gray blue   3.00 2.25

Children's Day, May 29, 1948, and valid only on that day. Proceeds were used for Child Welfare.

Foreign postal stationery (stamped envelopes, postal cards and air letter sheets) is beyond the scope of this catalogue.

A108

A109

A110

1948, Aug.
355 A108 15p green   .20 .15
356 A109 20p magenta   .40 .15
357 A110 125p dark blue   .75 .70
      Nos. 355-357 (3)   1.35 1.00
      30th year of Independence.

United Nations Emblem A111

1948, Oct. 24
358 A111 125p dk violet blue   7.00 7.00
UN, 3rd anniv. Valid one day only. Sheets of 9.

Maiwand Victory Column, Kandahar — A112

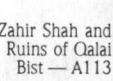
Zahir Shah and Ruins of Qalai Bist — A113

Independence Monument and Nadir Shah — A114

359 A112 25p green   .25 .15
360 A113 35p magenta   .35 .25
361 A114 1.25af blue   .90 .75
      Nos. 359-361 (3)   1.50 1.15
      31st year of Independence.

> Catalogue values for unused stamps in this section, from this point to the end of the section, are for Never Hinged items.

Nadir Shah — A117

1950, Aug.
364 A117 35p red brown   .30 .30
365 A117 125p blue   .65 .65
      32nd year of Independence.

Medical School and Nadir Shah A119

1950, Dec. 22   Typo.   Perf. 12
Size: 38x25mm
367 A119 35p emerald   .60 .60
Size: 46x30mm
368 A119 1.25af deep blue   1.90 1.90
      a. 1.25af black (error)   6.00
19th anniv. of the founding of Afghanistan's Faculty of Medicine. On sale and valid for use on Dec. 22-28, 1950.

Minaret, Herat — A120

Zahir Shah — A121

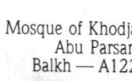
Mosque of Khodja Abu Parsar, Balkh — A122

A123   A124

20p, Buddha at Bamian. 40p, Ruined arch. 45p, Maiwand Victory ournent. 50p, View of Kandahar. 60p, Ancient tower. 70p, Afghanistan flag. 80p, 1af, Profile of Zahir Shah in uniform.

Photogravure, Engraved and Lithographed
Perf. 12, 12½, 13x12½, 13½
1951, Mar. 21   Unwmk.
Imprint: "Waterlow & Sons Limited, London"

369 A120 10p yellow & brn   .15 .15
370 A120 15p blue & brn   .15 .15
371 A120 20p black   5.00 2.75
372 A121 25p green   .15 .15
373 A122 30p cerise   .20 .15
374 A121 35p violet   .20 .15
375 A122 40p chestnut brn   .25 .15
376 A120 45p deep blue   .20 .15
377 A122 50p olive black   .45 .15
378 A120 60p black   1.50 .75
379 A122 70p dk grn, blk, red & grn .25 .15
380 A123 75p cerise   .75 .35
381 A123 80p carmine & blk   .65 .35
382 A123 1af dp grn & vio   .45 .35
383 A124 1.25af rose lil & blk 5.00 .35
384 A124 2af ultra   1.10 .35
385 A124 3af ultra & blk   .50 .90
      Nos. 369-385 (17)   18.95 7.50

Nos. 372, 374 and 381 to 385 are engraved, No. 379 is engraved and lithographed.
Imperfs. exist of the photogravure stamps.
See Nos. 445-451, 453, 552A-552D. For surcharges see Nos. B1-B2.

Arch of Paghman — A125

Nadir Shah and Independence Monument A126

Overprint in Violet

Perf. 13½x13, 13
1951, Aug. 25   Engr.
386 A125 35p dk green & blk   .60 .35
387 A126 1.25af deep blue   1.40 .85
Overprint reads "Sol 33 Istiqlal" or "33rd Year of Independence." Overprint measures about 11mm wide.
See Nos. 398-399B, 441-442.

Proposed Flag of Pashtunistan — A127

Design: 125p, Flag and Pashtunistan warrior.

1951, Sept. 2   Litho.   Perf. 11½
388 A127 35p dull chocolate   .80 .65
389 A127 125p blue   2.00 1.75
      Issued to publicize "Free Pashtunistan" Day.

Imperforates
From 1951 to 1958, quantities of nearly all locally-printed stamps were left imperforate and sold by the government at double face. From 1959 until March, 1964, many of the imperforates were sold for more than face value.

Avicenna — A128

1951, Nov. 4   Typo.   Perf. 11½
390 A128 35p deep claret   .50 .35
391 A128 125p blue   1.40 1.10
20th anniv. of the founding of the natl. Graduate School of Medicine.

A129

Dove and UN Symbols — A130

1951, Oct. 24
392 A129 35p magenta   1.40 1.00
393 A130 125p blue   3.50 2.75
      7th anniv. of the UN.

Amir Sher Ali Khan and Tiger Head Stamp — A131

Nos. 395, 397, Zahir Shah and stamp.

1951, Dec. 23   Litho.
394 A131 35p chocolate   .35 .35
395 A131 35p rose lilac   .35 .35
396 A131 125p ultra   .65 .60
      a. Cliche of 35p in plate of 125p 80.00 80.00
397 A131 125p aqua   .65 .60
      Nos. 394-397 (4)   2.00 1.90
      76th anniv. of the UPU.

Stamps of 1951 Without Overprint
Perf. 13½x13, 13
1952, Aug. 24   Engr.
398 A125 35p dk green & blk   1.25 1.25
399 A126 1.25af deep blue   1.25 1.25
      For overprints see #399A-399B, 441-442.

Same Overprinted in Violet

399A A125 35p dk grn & blk   .60 .40
399B A126 1.25af deep blue   1.60 1.00
      #398-399B issued for 34th Independence Day.

Globe — A132

Perf. 11½
1952, Oct. 25   Unwmk.   Litho.
400 A132 35p rose   .55 .45
401 A132 125p aqua   1.10 1.00
      Issued to honor the United Nations.

Symbol of Medicine — A134

Tribal Warrior, Natl. Flag — A135

1952, Nov.   Perf. 11½
403 A134 35p chocolate   .40 .15
404 A134 125p violet blue   1.10 1.10
21st anniv. of the natl. Graduate School of Medicine.
No. 404 is inscribed in French with white letters on a colored background.

1952, Sept. 1   Perf. 11
405 A135 35p red   .30 .30
406 A135 125p dark blue   .60 .60
No. 406 is inscribed in French "Pashtunistan Day, 1952."

Flags of Afghanistan & Pashtunistan A139

Badge of Pashtunistan A140

Perf. 10½x11, 11
1953, Sept. 1   Unwmk.
411 A139 35p vermilion   .20 .15
412 A140 125p blue   .60 .45
      Issued to publicize "Free Pashtunistan" Day.

Nadir Shah and Flag Bearer — A141

A142

1953, Aug. 24   Perf. 11
413 A141 35p green   .20 .15
414 A142 125p violet   .75 .60
      35th anniv. of Independence.

United Nations
Emblem — A143

1953, Oct. 24
415 A143 35p lilac   .60 .60
416 A143 125p violet blue   1.50 1.20
United Nations Day, 1953.

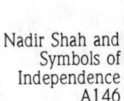

Nadir Shah
A144   A145

1953, Nov. 29
417 A144 35p orange   .65 .65
418 A145 125p chalky blue   1.50 1.50
22nd anniv. of the founding of the natl. Graduate
School of Medicine.

Redrawn

35p. Original- Right character in
second line of Persian inscription:

Redrawn- Persian character:

125p: Original- Inscribed "XXIII," "MADECINE"
and "ANNIVERAIRE"
Redrawn- Inscribed "XXII," "MEDECINE" and
"ANNIVERSAIRE"

1953
419 A144 35p deep orange   3.50
420 A145 125p chalky blue   4.25

Nadir Shah and
Symbols of
Independence
A146

1954, Aug.   Typo.   Perf. 11
421 A146 35p carmine rose   .35 .30
422 A146 125p violet blue   1.00 .80
36th year of Independence.

Raising Flag of
Pashtunistan
A147

1954, Sept.   Perf. 11½
423 A147 35p chocolate   .35 .30
424 A147 125p blue   1.00 .80
Issued to publicize "Free Pashtunistan" Day.

UN Flag and
Map — A148

1954, Oct. 24   Perf. 11
425 A148 35p carmine rose   .65 .65
426 A148 125p dk violet blue   2.00 2.00
9th anniv. of the United Nations.

UN Symbols — A149

Design: 125p, UN emblem & flags.

1955, June 26   Litho.   Perf. 11
Size: 26½x36mm
427 A149 35p dark green   .45 .40
Size: 28½x36mm
428 A149 125p aqua   1.10 .90
10th anniv. of the UN charter.

Nadir Shah
(center) and
Brothers — A150

1929 Civil War Scene   Tribal Elders'
and Zahir   Council and
Shah — A151   Pashtun
                          Flag — A152

1955, Aug.   Unwmk.   Perf. 11
429 A150 35p brt pink   .30 .30
430 A150 35p violet blue   .30 .30
431 A151 125p rose lilac   .90 .75
432 A151 125p light violet   .90 .75
Nos. 429-432 (4)   2.40 2.10
37th anniv. of Independence.

1955, Sept. 5
433 A152 35p orange brown   .20 .20
434 A152 125p yellow green   .90 .65
Issued for "Free Pashtunistan" Day.

UN
Flag — A153   A154

1955, Oct. 24   Unwmk.   Perf. 11
435 A153 35p orange brown   .75 .60
436 A153 125p brt ultra   1.40 1.10
10th anniv. of the United Nations.

1956, Aug.   Litho.
437 A154 35p lt green   .25 .20
438 A154 140p lt violet blue   .90 .75
38th anniv. of Independence.

Jesh'n Exhibition
Hall — A155

1956, Aug. 25
439 A155 35p chocolate   .25 .20
440 A155 50p lt violet blue   .25 .20
International Exposition at Kabul.
Of the 50p face value, only 35p paid postage.
The remaining 15p went to the Exposition.

Nos. 398-399 Handstamped in Violet

a   b

1957, Aug.   Engr.   Perf. 13½x13, 13
441 A125 (a) 35p dk green & blk   .40 .20
442 A126 (b) 1.25af deep blue   .60 .50
Arabic overprint measures 19mm.
39th year of independence.

Pashtunistan
Flag — A156

1957, Sept. 1   Litho.   Perf. 11
443 A156 50p pale lilac rose   .60 .60
444 A156 155p light violet   .90 .75
Issued for "Free Pashtunistan" Day. French
inscription on No. 444. 15p of each stamp went to
the Pashtunistan Fund.

Types of 1951 and

Game of
Buzkashi
A157

**Perf. 12, 12½, 12½x13, 13, 13x12,
13x12½, 13½x14**
Photo., Engr., Engr.& Litho.
1957, Nov. 23   Unwmk.
**Imprint: "Waterlow & Sons Limited,
London"**
445 A122 30p brown   .15 .15
446 A122 40p rose red   .20 .15
447 A122 50p yellow   .35 .15
448 A122 60p ultra   .40 .15
449 A123 75p brt violet   .50 .15
450 A123 80p violet & brn   .50 .15
451 A123 1af carmine & ultra   1.00 .15
452 A157 140p olive & dp claret   2.00 .50
453 A124 3af orange & blk   2.50 .50
Nos. 445-453 (9)   7.60 2.05
No. 452 lacks imprint.

Nadir Shah and
Flag-bearer
A158

1958, Aug. 25   Perf. 13½x14
454 A158 35p dp yellow green   .15 .15
455 A158 140p brown   .40 .35
40th year of Independence.

Exposition
Buildings — A159

1958, Aug. 23   Litho.   Perf. 11
456 A159 35p brt blue green   .15 .15
457 A159 140p vermilion   .50 .40
International Exposition at Kabul.

Pres. Celal Bayar   Flags of UN and
of Turkey   Afghanistan
A160   A161

1958, Sept. 13   Unwmk.
458 A160 50p lt blue   .20 .15
459 A160 100p brown   .35 .30
Visit of President Celal Bayar of Turkey.

1958, Oct. 24 Photo.   Perf. 14x13½
Flags in Original Colors
460 A161 50p dark gray   .60 .60
461 A161 100p green   1.10 .90
United Nations Day, Oct. 24.

Atomic Energy
Encircling the
Hemispheres
A162

1958, Oct. 20   Perf. 13½x14
462 A162 50p blue   .35 .35
463 A162 100p dp red lilac   .55 .55
Issued to promote Atoms for Peace.

UNESCO
Building,
Paris — A163

1958, Nov. 3
464 A163 50p dp yellow grn   .50 .40
465 A163 100p brown olive   .75 .60
UNESCO Headquarters in Paris opening, Nov. 3.

Globe and
Torch — A164

Perf. 13½x14
1958, Dec. 10   Unwmk.
466 A164 50p lilac rose   .35 .35
467 A164 100p maroon   .65 .65
10th anniv. of the signing of the Universal Declaration of Human Rights.

Nadir Shah and
Flags — A165

1959, Aug. Litho. Perf. 11 Rough
468 A165 35p light vermilion   .20 .20
469 A165 165p light violet   .65 .40
41st year of Independence.

Uprooted Oak
Emblem — A166

1960, Apr. 7   Perf. 11
470 A166 50p deep orange   .15 .15
471 A166 165p blue   .35 .30
Issued to publicize World Refugee Year, July 1,
1959-June 30, 1960.
Two imperf. souvenir sheets exist. Both contain a
50p and a 165p, type A166, with marginal inscriptions and WRY emblem in maroon. On one sheet
the stamps are in the colors of Nos. 470-471 (size
108x81mm). On the other, the 50p is blue and the
165p is deep orange (size 107x80mm). Value $4
each.
For surcharges see Nos. B35-B36.

Buzkashi
A167

1960, May 4   *Perf. 11, Imperf.*
472 A167 25p rose red   .22 .15
473 A167 50p bluish green   .50 .35
a.   Cliche of 25p in plate of 50p   20.00 20.00
See Nos. 549-550A.

Independence
Monument — A168

1960, Aug.   *Perf. 11, 12*
474 A168 50p light blue   .15 .15
475 A168 175p bright pink   .40 .40
42nd Independence Day.

Globe and
Flags — A169

1960, Oct. 24   Litho.   *Perf. 11, 12*
476 A169 50p rose lilac   .25 .20
477 A169 175p ultra   .75 .65
UN Day.
An imperf. souvenir sheet contains one each of Nos. 476-477 with marginal inscriptions ("La Journée des Nations Unies 1960" in French and Persian) and UN emblem in light blue. Size: 127x85½mm. Value $4.
This sheet was surcharged "+20ps" in 1962. Value $8.50.

Teacher
Pointing to
Globe — A170

1960, Oct. 23   *Perf. 11*
478 A170 50p brt pink   .20 .15
479 A170 100p brt green   .70 .45
Issued to publicize Teacher's Day.

Mohammed Zahir Shah — A171

1960, Oct. 15
480 A171 50p red brown   .30 .15
481 A171 150p dk car rose   .90 .30
Honoring the King on his 46th birthday.

Buzkashi
A172

1960, Nov. 9   *Perf. 11*
482 A172 175p lt red brown   1.00 .40
See Nos. 551-552.

No. 482 Overprinted "1960" and Olympic Rings in Bright Green.

1960, Dec. 24
483 A172 175p red brown   2.00 1.75
a.   Souv. sheet of 1, imperf.   7.00
17th Olympic Games, Rome, Aug. 25-Sept. 11.

Mir Wais — A173

1961, Jan. 5   Unwmk.   *Perf. 10½*
484 A173 50p brt rose lilac   .20 .15
485 A173 175p ultra   .60 .60
a.   Souv. sheet of 2, #484-485, imperf.   2.00 2.00
Mir Wais (1665-1708), national leader.

No Postal Need
existed for the 1p-15p denominations issued with sets of 1961-63 (between Nos. 486 and 649, B37 and B65). The lowest denomination actually used for non-philatelic postage in that period was 25p (except for the 2p newspaper rate for which separate stamps were provided).

Horse, Sheep
and
Camel — A174

#487, 175p, Rock partridge. 10p, 100p, Afghan hound. 15p, 150p, Grain & grasshopper, vert.

1961, Mar. 29   Photo.   *Perf. 13½x14*
486 A174 2p maroon & buff
487 A174 2p ultra & org
488 A174 5p brown & yel
489 A174 10p black & salmon
490 A174 15p blue grn & yel
491 A174 25p black & pink
492 A174 50p black & citron
493 A174 100p black & pink
494 A174 150p green & yel
495 A174 175p ultra & pink
Nos. 486-495 (10)   2.00
Two souvenir sheets, perf. and imperf., contain 2 stamps, 1 each of #492-493. Value $2 each.

Afghan Fencing
A175

Designs: No. 497, 5p, 25p, 50p, Wrestlers. 10p, 100p, Man with Indian clubs. 15p, 150p, Afghan fencing. 175p, Children skating.

1961, July 6   *Perf. 13½x14*
496 A175 2p green & rose lil
497 A175 2p brown & citron
498 A175 5p gray & rose
499 A175 10p blue & bister
500 A175 15p sl bl & dl lil
501 A175 25p black & dl bl
502 A175 50p sl grn & bis brn
503 A175 100p brown & bl grn
504 A175 150p brown & org yel
505 A175 175p black & blue
Nos. 496-505 (10)   1.50
Issued for Children's Day.
A souvenir sheet exists, perf. and imperf., containing one each of Nos. 502-503. Value $3.50 each.
For surcharges see Nos. B37-B41.

Bande Amir
Lakes — A176

1961, Aug. 7   Photo.   *Perf. 13½x14*
506 A176 3af brt blue   .35 .30
507 A176 10af rose claret   1.10 1.00

Nadir
Shah — A177

Girl Scout — A178

1961, Aug. 23   *Perf. 14x13½*
508 A177 50p rose red & blk   .50 .40
509 A177 175p brt grn & org brn   1.00 .80
43rd Independence Day.
Two souvenir sheets, perf. and imperf., contain one each of Nos. 508-509. Value, each $2.50.

     Perf. 14x13½
1961, July 23   *Unwmk.*
510 A178 50p dp car & dk gray   .30 .15
511 A178 175p dp grn & rose brn   .60 .40
Issued for Women's Day.
Two souvenir sheets exist, perf. and imperf., containing one each of Nos. 510-511. Value $3 each.

Exhibition Hall,
Kabul — A179

1961, Aug. 23   *Perf. 13½x14*
512 A179 50p yel brn & yel grn   .15 .15
513 A179 175p blue & brn   .40 .30
International Exhibition at Kabul.

Pathan with
Pashtunistan
Flag — A180

1961, Aug. 31   Photo.   *Perf. 14x13½*
514 A180 50p blk, lil & red   .15 .15
515 A180 175p brn, grnsh bl & red   .35 .30
Issued for "Free Pashtunistan Day."
Souvenir sheets exist perf. and imperf. containing one each of Nos. 514-515. Value $2 each.

Assembly
Building
A181

1961, Sept. 10   *Perf. 12*
516 A181 50p dk gray & brt grn   .15 .15
517 A181 175p ultra & brn   .45 .30
Anniv. of the founding of the Natl. Assembly.
Souvenir sheets exist, perf. and imperf., containing one each of Nos. 516-517. Value $1 each.

Exterminating
Anopheles
Mosquito
A182

1961, Oct. 5   *Perf. 13½x14*
518 A182 50p blk & brn lil   .50 .30
519 A182 175p maroon & brt grn   1.10 .50
Anti-Malaria campaign. Souvenir sheets exist, perf. and imperf., containing one each of Nos. 518-519. Value $4 each.

Zahir Shah — A183

1961, Oct. 15   *Perf. 13½*
520 A183 50p lilac & blue   .15 .15
521 A183 175p emerald & red brn   .40 .35
Issued to honor King Mohammed Zahir Shah on his 47th birthday.
See Nos. 609-612.

Pomegranates
A184

Fruit: No. 523, 5p, 25p, 50p, Grapes. 10p, 150p, Apples. 15p, 175p, Pomegranates. 100p, Melons.

1961, Oct. 16   *Perf. 13½x14*
Fruit in Natural Colors
522 A184 2p black
523 A184 2p green
524 A184 5p lilac rose
525 A184 10p lilac
526 A184 15p dk blue
527 A184 50p dull red
528 A184 50p purple
529 A184 100p brt blue
530 A184 150p brown
531 A184 175p olive gray
Nos. 522-531 (10)   1.75
For Afghan Red Crescent Society.
Souvenir sheets exist, perf. and imperf., containing one each of Nos. 528-529. Value $1.50 each.
For surcharges see Nos. B42-B46.

UN
Headquarters,
NY — A185

1961, Oct. 24   *Perf. 13½x14*
Vertical Borders in Emerald, Red and Black
532 A185 1p rose lilac
533 A185 2p slate
534 A185 3p brown
535 A185 4p ultra
536 A185 50p rose red
537 A185 75p gray
538 A185 175p brt green
Nos. 532-538 (7)   1.25
16th anniv. of the UN. Souvenir sheets exist, perf. and imperf., containing one each of Nos. 536-538. Value $2 each.

Children Giving
Flowers to
Teacher — A186

People Raising
UNESCO
Symbol — A187

#540, 5p, 25p, 50p, Tulips. 10p, 100p, Narcissus. 15p, 150p, Children giving flowers to teacher. 175p, Teacher with children in front of school.

1961, Oct. 26   Photo.   *Perf. 12*
539 A186 2p multicolored
540 A186 2p multicolored
541 A186 5p multicolored
542 A186 10p multicolored
543 A186 15p multicolored
544 A186 25p multicolored
545 A186 50p multicolored
546 A186 100p multicolored

547 A186 150p multicolored
548 A186 175p multicolored
  Nos. 539-548 (10)   1.75

Issued for Teacher's Day.
Souvenir sheets exist, perf. and imperf. containing one each of Nos. 545-546. Value, 2 sheets, $4. For surcharges see Nos. B47-B51.

Buzkashi Types of 1960
1961-72   Litho.   Perf. 10½, 11
549 A167 25p violet   .15 .15
  b.   25p brt vio. typo. ('72)   .15 .15
550 A167 30p blue   .30 .15
550A A167 50p yel org ('69)   .15 .15
551 A172 100p citron   .45 .15
551A A172 150p orange ('64)   .30 .15
552 A172 2af lt green   1.10 .45
  Nos. 549-552 (7)   2.65
    Set value   .85

Zahir Shah Types of 1951
Photo., Engr., Engr. & Litho.
1962   Perf. 13x12, 13
Imprint: "Thomas De La Rue & Co. Ltd."
552A A123 75p brt purple   1.10 .25
552B A123 1af car & ultra   1.40 .35
552C A124 2af blue   1.75 .75
552D A124 3af orange & blk   4.00 1.10
  Nos. 552A-552D (4)   8.25 2.45

1962, July 2   Photo.   Perf. 14x13½
553 A187 2p rose lil & brn
554 A187 2p ol bis & brn
555 A187 5p dp org & dk grn
556 A187 10p gray & mag
557 A187 15p blue & brn
558 A187 25p org yel & pur
559 A187 50p lt grn & pur
560 A187 75p brt cit & brn
561 A187 100p dp org & brn
  Nos. 553-561 (9)   1.25

15th anniv. of UNESCO. Souvenir sheets exist, perf. and imperf. One contains Nos. 558-559; the other contains one. Value, $3 each.
For surcharges see Nos. B52-B60.

Ahmad Shah — A188   Afghan Hound — A189

1962, Feb. 24   Photo.   Perf. 13½
562 A188 50p red brn & gray   .15 .15
563 A188 75p green & salmon   .25 .20
564 A188 100p claret & bister   .40 .30
  Nos. 562-564 (3)   .80 .65

Ahmad Shah (1724-73), founded the Afghan kingdom in 1747 and ruled until 1773.

1962, Apr. 21   Perf. 14x13½
Designs: 5p, 75p, Afghan cock. 10p, 100p, Kondjid plant. 15p, 125p, Astrakhan skins.
565 A189 1p rose & brn
566 A189 2p lt green & brn
567 A189 5p dp rose & claret
568 A189 10p lt grn & sl grn
569 A189 15p blue grn & blk
570 A189 25p blue & brn
571 A189 50p gray & brn
572 A189 75p rose lil & lil
573 A189 100p gray & dl grn
574 A189 125p rose brn & blk
  Nos. 565-574 (10)   2.00

Agriculture Day. Perf. and imperf. souvenir sheets exist. Set of 4 sheets, value $4.

Athletes with Flag and Nadir Shah A190   Woman in National Costume A191

1962, Aug. 23   Perf. 12
575 A190 25p multicolored   .15 .15
576 A190 50p multicolored   .20 .15
577 A190 150p multicolored   .25 .15
  Nos. 575-577 (3)   .60
    Set value   .20
44th Independence Day.

1962, Aug. 30   Perf. 11½x12
578 A191 25p lilac & brn   .15 .15
579 A191 50p green & brn   .25 .15
    Set value   .20

Issued for Women's Day. For souvenir sheet see note after No. C16.

Man and Woman with Flag — A192   Malaria Eradication Emblem and Swamp — A193

1962, Aug. 31   Photo.
580 A192 25p black, pale bl & red   .15 .15
581 A192 50p black, grn & red   .20 .15
582 A192 150p black, pink & red   .45 .15
  Nos. 580-582 (3)   .80
    Set value   .30
Issued for "Free Pashtunistan Day."

1962, Sept. 5   Perf. 14x13½
583 A193 2p dk grn & ol gray
584 A193 2p dk green & sal
585 A193 5p red brn & ol
586 A193 10p red brn & brt grn
587 A193 15p red brn & gray
588 A193 25p brt bl & bluish grn
589 A193 50p brt bl & rose lil
590 A193 75p black & blue
591 A193 100p black & brt pink
592 A193 150p black & bis brn
593 A193 175p black & orange
  Nos. 583-593 (11)   2.00

WHO drive to eradicate malaria. Perf. and imperf. souvenir sheets exist. Set of 4 sheets, value $6.50.
For surcharges see Nos. B61-B71.

National Assembly Building A194

Perf. 10½, 11 (100p)
1962, Sept. 10   Unwmk.   Litho.
594 A194 25p lt green   .35 .25
595 A194 50p blue   .55 .35
596 A194 75p rose   .70 .55
597 A194 100p violet   1.10 .90
598 A194 125p ultra   1.20 1.10
  Nos. 594-598 (5)   3.90 3.15
Establishment of the National Assembly.

Horse Racing — A195

Designs: 2p, Pole vaulting. 3p, Wrestling. 4p, Weight lifting. 5p, Soccer.

1962, Sept. 22   Photo.   Perf. 12
Black Inscriptions
599 A195 1p lt ol & red brn
600 A195 2p lt grn & red brn
601 A195 3p yellow & dk pur
602 A195 4p pale bl & grn
603 A195 5p bluish grn & dk brn
  Nos. 599-603, C17-C22 (11)   2.50

4th Asian Games, Djakarta, Indonesia. Two souvenir sheets exist. A perforated one contains a 125p blue, dark blue and brown stamp in horse racing design. An imperf. one contains a 2af buff, purple and black stamp in soccer design. Value, $3.50 each.

Runners A196

1p, 2p, Diver, vert. 4p, Peaches. 5p, Iris, vert.

Perf. 11½x12, 12x11½
1962, Oct. 2   Unwmk.
604 A196 1p rose lil & brn
605 A196 2p blue & brn
606 A196 3p brt blue & lil
607 A196 4p ol gray & multi
608 A196 5p gray & multi
  Nos. 604-608, C23-C25 (8)   2.00
Issued for Children's Day.

King Type of 1961, Dated "1962"
1962, Oct. 15   Perf. 13½
Various Frames
609 A183 25p lilac rose & brn   .15 .15
610 A183 50p orange brn & grn   .15 .15
611 A183 75p blue & lake   .15 .15
612 A183 100p green & red brn   .20 .20
    Set value   .50 .50
Issued to honor King Mohammed Zahir Shah on his 48th birthday.

Grapes A197

1962, Oct. 16   Perf. 12
613 A197 1p shown
614 A197 2p Grapes
615 A197 3p Pears
616 A197 4p Wistaria
617 A197 5p Blossoms
  Nos. 613-617, C26-C28 (8)   1.00
For the Afghan Red Crescent Society.

UN Headquarters, NY and Flags of UN and Afghanistan A198

1962, Oct. 24   Unwmk.
618 A198 1p multicolored
619 A198 2p multicolored
620 A198 3p multicolored
621 A198 4p multicolored
622 A198 5p multicolored
  Nos. 618-622, C29-C31 (8)   1.50

UN Day. Souvenir sheets exist. One contains a single 4af ultramarine stamp, perforated; the other, a 4af ocher stamp, imperf. Value, 2 sheets, $5.

Boy Scout — A199   Pole Vault — A200

1962, Oct. 18   Photo.   Perf. 12
623 A199 1p yel, dk grn & sal
624 A199 2p dl yel, slate & sal
625 A199 3p rose, blk & sal
626 A199 4p multicolored
  Nos. 623-626, C32-C35 (8)   1.50
Issued to honor the Boy Scouts.

1962, Oct. 25   Unwmk.   Perf. 12
3p, High jump. 4p, 5p, Different blossoms.
627 A200 1p lilac & dk grn
628 A200 2p yellow grn & brn
629 A200 3p bister & vio

630 A200 4p sal pink, grn & ultra
631 A200 5p yellow, grn & bl
  Nos. 627-631, C36-C37 (7)   1.25
Issued for Teacher's Day.

Rockets A201

1962, Nov. 29
632 A201 50p pale lil & dk bl   .40
633 A201 100p lt blue & red brn   .80

UN World Meteorological Day. A souvenir sheet contains one 5af pink and green stamp. Value $6.

Ansari Mausoleum, Herat — A202

Perf. 13½
1963, Jan. 3   Unwmk.   Photo.
634 A202 50p purple & green   .15 .15
635 A202 75p gray & magenta   .20 .20
636 A202 100p orange brn & brn   .30 .30
  Nos. 634-636 (3)   .65 .65

Khwaja Abdullah Ansari, Sufi, religious leader and poet, on the 900th anniv. of his death.

Sheep — A203

Silkworm, Cocoons, Moth and Mulberry Branch A204

1963, Mar. 1   Perf. 12
637 A203 1p grnsh blue & blk
638 A203 2p yellow grn & blk
639 A203 3p lilac rose & blk
640 A204 4p gray, grn & brn
641 A204 5p red lil, grn & brn
  Nos. 637-641, C42-C44 (8)   1.50
Issued for the Day of Agriculture.

Rice — A205

Designs: 3p, Corn. 300p, Wheat emblem.

1963, Mar. 27   Unwmk.   Perf. 14
642 A205 2p gray, claret & grn   .15 .15
643 A205 3p green, yel & ocher   .15 .15
644 A205 300p dk blue & yel   .30 .30
    Set value   .45 .45
FAO "Freedom from Hunger" campaign.

Meteorological Measuring Instrument A206

Designs: 3p, 10p, Weather station. 4p, 5p, Rockets in space.

1963, May 23　Photo.　Perf. 13½x14
645　A206　1p dp magenta & brn
646　A206　2p brt blue & brn
647　A206　3p red & brown
648　A206　4p orange & lilac
649　A206　5p green & dl vio
　　　　　　Imperf
650　A206　10p red brn & grn
　Nos. 645-650, C46-C50 (11)　　7.50

3rd UN World Meteorological Day, Mar. 23.

Independence
Monument — A207

1963, Aug. 23　Litho.　Perf. 10½
651　A207　25p lt green　　　.15　.15
652　A207　50p orange　　　.15　.15
653　A207　150p rose carmine　.35　.20
　　　　　　Set value　　.55　.35

45th Independence Day.

Pathans in
Forest — A208

1963, Aug. 31　Unwmk.　Perf. 10½
654　A208　25p pale violet　　.15　.15
655　A208　50p sky blue　　　.15　.15
655A　A208　150p dull red brn　.40　.35
　　Nos. 654-655A (3)　　　.70
　　　　　　Set value　　　　.50

Issued for "Free Pashtunistan Day."

4th Asian
Games, Djakarta
A208a

Designs: 2p, 250p, 300p, Wrestling. 3p, 10p, Tennis. 4p, 500p, Javelin. 5p, 9af, Shot put.

1963, Sept. 3　Litho.　Perf. 12
656　A208a　2p rose vio & brn
656A　A208a　3p olive grn & brn
656B　A208a　4p blue & brn
656C　A208a　5p yel grn & brn
656D　A208a　10p lt bl grn & brn
656E　A208a　300p yellow & vio
656F　A208a　500p lt yel bis & brn
656G　A208a　9af pale grn & vio
　　　　Souvenir Sheets
656H　A208a　250p lilac & vio
656I　A208a　300p blue & blk

Nos. 656-656F are airmail. Nos. 656-656I exist imperf.

National
Assembly
Building
A209

1963, Sept. 10　　　Perf. 11
657　A209　25p gray　　　.15　.15
658　A209　50p dull red　　.15　.15
659　A209　75p brown　　　.20　.15
660　A209　100p olive　　　.30　.15
661　A209　125p lilac　　　.40　.20
　　Nos. 657-661 (5)　　1.20
　　　　　　Set value　　.65

Issued to honor the National Assembly.

Balkh Gate
A210

1963, Oct. 8
662　A210　3af choc (screened margins)　.40　.30
　a.　White margins　　　1.00　.35

In the original printing a halftone screen extended across the plate, covering the space between the stamps. A retouch removed the screen between the stamps (No. 662a).

Intl. Red
Cross, Cent.
A210a

4p, 5p, 200p, 3af, Nurse holding patient, vert. 10p, 4af, 6af, Crown Prince Ahmed Shah.

1963, Oct. 9　　　Perf. 13½
662B　A210a　2p olive, blk & red
662C　A210a　3p blue, blk & red
662D　A210a　4p lt grn, blk & red
662E　A210a　5p lt vio, blk & red
662F　A210a　10p gray grn, red & blk
662G　A210a　100p dull bl grn, red & blk
662H　A210a　200p lt brn, blk & red
662I　A210a　4af brt bl grn, red & blk
662J　A210a　6af lt brn, red & blk
　　　　Souvenir Sheet
662K　A210a　3af dl blue, blk & red

Nos. 662G-662K are airmail. Nos. 662B-662K exist imperf.

Zahir Shah — A211　　Kemal
　　　　　　　　　　　Ataturk — A212

1963, Oct. 15　　　Perf. 10½
663　A211　25p green　　　.15　.15
663A　A211　50p gray　　　.15　.15
663B　A211　75p carmine rose　.20　.15
663C　A211　100p dull redsh brn　.30　.15
　　Nos. 663-663C (4)　　.80
　　　　　　Set value　　.35

King Mohammed Zahir Shah, 49th birthday.

1963, Oct. 10　　　Perf. 10½
664　A212　1af blue　　　.15　.15
665　A212　3af rose lilac　　.40　.35

25th anniv. of the death of Kemal Ataturk, president of Turkey.

Protection of
Nubian
Monuments
A213

Designs: 5af, 7.50af, 10af, Ruins, vert.

Perf. 12, Imperf. (150p, 250p, 10af)
1963, Nov. 16　　　Photo.
666　A213　100p lil rose & blk
666A　A213　150p rose lil & blk
666B　A213　200p brown & blk
666C　A213　250p ultra & blk
666D　A213　500p green & blk
666E　A213　5af greenish blue & gray bl
666F　A213　7.50af red brn & gray bl
666G　A213　10af ver & gray bl

#666E-666G are airmail. #666D exists imperf.

Women's　　　　Boy and Girl
Day — A213a　　Scouts — A213c

A213b

Intl. Red
Cross, Cent.

1964, Jan. 5　　　Perf. 14x13½
667　A213a　2p multicolored
667A　A213a　3p multicolored
667B　A213a　4p multicolored
667C　A213a　5p multicolored
667D　A213a　10p multicolored
　　　　Exist imperf.

1964, Jan. 5　Perf. 13½x14, 14x13½
#668F-668G, 668K-668M, Girl with flag.

668　A213b　2p multi
668A　A213b　3p multi
668B　A213b　4p multi
668C　A213b　5p multi
668D　A213b　10p multi
668E　A213c　2af multi
668F　A213c　2af multi
668G　A213c　2.50af multi
668H　A213c　3af multi
668I　A213c　4af multi
668J　A213c　6af multi
668K　A213c　12af multi
　　　　Souvenir Sheets
668L　A213c　5af multi
668M　A213c　6af multi
668N　A213c　6af multi
668O　A213c　6af multi

Nos. 668E-668O are airmail. Nos 668-668K, 668N-668O exist imperf.

Children — A213d

1964, Jan. 22　　　Perf. 12
669　A213d　2p Playing ball
669A　A213d　3p like #669
669B　A213d　4p Swinging, jumping rope, vert.
669C　A213d　5p Skiing, vert.
669D　A213d　10p like #669
669E　A213d　200p like #669C
669F　A213d　300p like #669B

Nos. 669E-669F are airmail. All exist imperf.

Red Crescent Society — A213e

Designs: 100p, 200p, Pierre and Marie Curie, physicists. 2.50af, 7.50af Nurse examining child. 3.50af, 5af, Nurse and patients.

Perf. 14, Imperf. (#670A, 670C-670D)
1964, Feb. 8
670　A213e　100p multi
670A　A213e　100p multi
670B　A213e　200p multi
670C　A213e　2.50af multi
670D　A213e　5af multi
670E　A213e　5af multi
670F　A213e　7.50af multi

Nos. 670B-670D are airmail.

Teachers'
Day — A213f

Flowers: 2p, 3p, 3af, 4af, Tulips. 4p, 5p, 3.50af, 6af, Flax. 10p, 1.50af, 2af, Iris.

Perf. 12, Imperf. (1.50af, 2af)
1964, Mar. 3
671　A213f　2p multicolored
671A　A213f　3p multicolored
671B　A213f　4p multicolored
671C　A213f　5p multicolored
671D　A213f　10p multicolored
671E　A213f　1.50af multicolored
671F　A213f　2af multicolored
671G　A213f　3af multicolored
671H　A213f　3.50af multicolored
　　　　Souvenir Sheets
671I　A213f　4af multicolored
671J　A213f　6af multi, imperf

#671E-671J are airmail. #671-671D exist imperf.

A213g

UN Day: 5p, 10p, 2af, 3af, 4af, Doctor and nurse, vert.

1964, Mar. 9　　　Perf. 14
672　A213g　2p multicolored
672A　A213g　3p multicolored
672B　A213g　4p multicolored
672C　A213g　5p multicolored
672D　A213g　10p multicolored
672E　A213g　100p multicolored
672F　A213g　2af multicolored
672G　A213g　3af multicolored
　　　　Souvenir Sheets
672H　A213g　4af multi, imperf.
672I　A213g　5af multicolored

Nos. 672E-672G are airmail. Nos. 672-672G exist imperf.
For surcharges see Nos. B71A-B71J.

UNICEF
A213h

Design: 5af, 7.50af, 10af, Children eating.

Perf. 14x13½, Imperf. (150p, 250p, 10af)
1964, Mar. 15
673　A213h　100p multicolored
673A　A213h　150p multicolored
673B　A213h　200p multicolored
673C　A213h　250p multicolored
673D　A213h　5af multicolored
673E　A213h　7.50af multicolored
673F　A213h　10af multicolored

Nos. 673D-673F are airmail.

Eradication
of Malaria
A213i

Designs: 4p, 5p, 5af, 10af Spraying mosquitoes.

1964, Mar. 15　　　Perf. 13½
674　A213i　2p lt red brn & yel grn
674A　A213i　3p olive grn & buff
674B　A213i　4p dk vio & bl grn
674C　A213i　5p brn & grn
674D　A213i　2af Prus bl & ver
　h.　Souvenir sheet of 1

674E A213i 5af dk grn & lt red brn, imperf.
 i. Souv. sheet of 1, imperf.
674F A213i 10af red brn & grnsh bl

 10 PS

674G A213i 10p on 4p Prus bl & rose

No. 674G not issued without surcharge. Nos. 674-674C, 674G exist imperf. Nos. 674D-674F are airmail.

Exists imperf.

"Tiger's Head" of 1878 — A214

1964, Mar. 22   Photo.   Perf. 12
675 A214 1.25af gold, grn & blk   .20 .15
676 A214 5af gold, rose car & blk   .50 .35

Issued to honor philately.

Unisphere and Flags — A215

1964, May 3   Perf. 13¹/₂x14
677 A215 6af crimson, gray & grn   .30 .20

New York World's Fair, 1964-65.

Hand Holding Torch — A216

1964, May 12   Photo.   Perf. 14x13¹/₂
678 A216 3.75af multicolored   .20 .20

1st UN Seminar on Human Rights in Kabul, May 1964. The denomination in Persian at right erroneously reads "3.25" but the stamp was sold and used as 3.75af.

Kandahar Airport A217

1964, Apr.   Litho.   Perf. 10¹/₂, 11
679 A217 7.75af dk red brown   .40 .20
680 A217 9.25af lt green   .50 .20
681 A217 10.50af lt green   .50 .30
682 A217 13.75af carmine rose   .70 .40
    Nos. 679-682 (4)   2.10 1.10

Inauguration of Kandahar Airport.

Snow Leopard A218

50p, Ibex, vert. 75p, Head of argali. 5af, Yak.

1964, June 25   Photo.   Perf. 12
683 A218 25p yellow & blue   .15 .15
684 A218 50p dl red & grn   .15 .15
685 A218 75p Prus bl & lil   .15 .15
686 A218 5af brt grn & dk brn   .30 .30
    Set value   .55 .55

View of Herat — A219

Flag and Map of Afghanistan A220

Tourist publicity: 75p, Tomb of Queen Gowhar Shad, vert.

Perf. 13¹/₂x14, 14x13¹/₂
1964, July 12
687 A219 25p sepia & bl   .15 .15
688 A219 75p dp blue & buff   .15 .15
689 A220 3af red, blk & grn   .30 .15
    Set value   .40 .20

Wrestling A221

25p, Hurdling, vert. 1af, Diving, vert. 5af, Soccer.

1964, July 26   Perf. 12
690 A221 25p ol bis, blk & car   .15 .15
691 A221 1af bl grn, blk & car   .15 .15
692 A221 3.75af yel grn, blk & car   .20 .20
693 A221 5af brn, blk & car   .30 .30
 a. Souv. sheet of 4, #690-693, imperf.   .90 .90
    Nos. 690-693 (4)   .80 .80

18th Olympic Games, Tokyo, Oct. 10-25, 1964. No. 693a sold for 15af. The additional 5af went to the Afghanistan Olympic Committee.

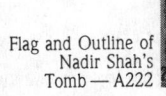

Flag and Outline of Nadir Shah's Tomb — A222

1964, Aug. 24   Photo.
695 A222 25p multicolored   .15 .15
696 A222 75p multicolored   .15 .15
    Set value   .20 .20

Independence Day. The stamps were printed with an erroneous inscription in upper left corner: "33rd year of independence." This was locally obliterated with a typographed gold bar.

Pashtunistan Flag — A223   Zahir Shah — A225

1964, Sept. 1   Unwmk.
697 A223 100p gold, blk, red, bl & grn   .15 .15

Issued for "Free Pashtunistan Day."

1964, Oct. 17   Perf. 14x13¹/₂
699 A225 1.25af gold & yel grn   .15 .15
700 A225 3.75af gold & rose   .20 .15
701 A225 50af gold & gray   2.00 1.75
    Nos. 699-701 (3)   2.35 2.05

King Mohammed Zahir Shah, 50th birthday.

Coat of Arms of Afghanistan and UN Emblem — A226

1964, Oct. 24   Perf. 13¹/₂x14
702 A226 5af gold, blk & dl bl   .20 .15

Issued for United Nations Day.

Emblem of Afghanistan Women's Association A227

1964, Nov. 9   Photo.   Unwmk.
703 A227 25p pink, dk bl & emer   .50 .25
704 A227 75p aqua, dk bl & emer   .75 .35
705 A227 1af sil, dk bl & emer   1.00 .50
    Nos. 703-705 (3)   2.25 1.10

Issued for Women's Day.

Poet Mowlana Nooruddin Abdul Rahman Jami (1414-1492) — A228

1964, Nov. 23   Litho.   Perf. 11 Rough
706 A228 1.50af blk, emer & yel   .85 .85

Woodpecker A229

Birds: 3.75af, Black-throated jay, vert. 5af, Impeyan pheasant, vert.

Perf. 13¹/₂x14, 14x13¹/₂
1965, Apr. 20   Photo.   Unwmk.
707 A229 1.25af multi   1.00 .50
708 A229 3.75af multi   1.75 .75
709 A229 5af multi   2.50 1.00
    Nos. 707-709 (3)   5.25 2.25

ITU Emblem, Old and New Communication Equipment A230

1965, May 17   Perf. 13¹/₂x14
710 A230 5af lt bl, blk & red   .35 .35

Cent. of the ITU.

"Red City," Bamian — A231

Designs: 3.75af, Ruins of ancient Bamian city. 5af, Bande Amir, mountain lakes.

1965, May 30   Perf. 13x13¹/₂
711 A231 1.25af pink & multi   .15 .15
712 A231 3.75af lt blue & multi   .20 .20
713 A231 5af yellow & multi   .30 .30
    Nos. 711-713 (3)   .65 .65

Issued for tourist publicity.

ICY Emblem A232

1965, June 25   Perf. 13¹/₂x13
714 A232 5af multicolored   .25 .25

International Cooperation Year, 1965.

ARIANA Air Lines Emblem and DC-3 — A233

Designs: 5af, DC-6 at right. 10af, DC-3 on top.

Perf. 13¹/₂x14
1965, July 15   Photo.   Unwmk.
715 A233 1.25af brt bl, gray & blk   .15 .15
716 A233 5af red lil, blk & bl   .30 .30
717 A233 10af bis, blk, bl gray & grn   .75 .75
 a. Souv. sheet of 3, #715-717, imperf.   1.00 1.00
    Nos. 715-717 (3)   1.20 1.20

10th anniv. of Afghan Air Lines, ARIANA.

Nadir Shah — A234

1965, Aug. 23   Perf. 14x13¹/₂
718 A234 1af dl grn, blk & red brn   .25 .15

For the 47th Independence Day.

Flag of Pashtunistan A235

Perf. 13¹/₂x14
1965, Aug. 31   Photo.   Unwmk.
719 A235 1af multicolored   .25 .15

Issued for "Free Pashtunistan Day."

Zahir Shah Signing Constitution — A236

1965, Sept. 11   Perf. 13x13¹/₂
720 A236 1.50af brt grn & blk   .25 .25

Promulgation of the new Constitution.

Zahir Shah and Oak Leaves — A237

1965, Oct. 14   Perf. 14x13¹/₂
721 A237 1.25af blk, ultra & salmon   .15 .15
722 A237 6af blk, lt bl & rose lil   .40 .35

King Mohammed Zahir Shah, 51st birthday.

Flags of UN
and
Afghanistan
A238

1965, Oct. 24   *Perf. 13½x14*
723 A238 5af multicolored   .20 .20
Issued for United Nations Day.

Dappled Ground
Gecko — A239

Designs: 4af, Caucasian agamid (lizard). 8af, Horsfield's tortoise.

Perf. 13½x14
1966, May 10   Photo.   Unwmk.
724 A239 3af tan & multi   .75 .35
725 A239 4af brt grn & multi   .85 .40
726 A239 8af violet & multi   1.50 .75
  Nos. 724-726 (3)   3.10 1.50

Soccer Player and
Globe — A240

1966, July 31   Litho.   *Perf. 14x13½*
727 A240 2af rose red & blk   .60 .20
728 A240 6af violet bl & blk   1.10 .25
729 A240 12af bister brn & blk   2.25 .60
  Nos. 727-729 (3)   3.95 1.05

World Cup Soccer Championship, Wembley,
England, July 11-30.

Cotton Flower
and
Boll — A241

5af, Silkworm. 7af, Farmer plowing with oxen.

1966, July 31   *Perf. 13½x14*
730 A241 1af multicolored   .50 .15
731 A241 5af multicolored   1.00 .30
732 A241 7af multicolored   1.40 .40
  Nos. 730-732 (3)   2.90 .85
Issued for the Day of Agriculture.

Independence
Monument
A242

1966, Aug. 23   Photo.   *Perf. 13½x14*
733 A242 1af multicolored   .25 .15
734 A242 3af multicolored   .75 .25
Issued to commemorate Independence Day.

Flag of
Pashtunistan
A243

1966, Aug. 31   Litho.   *Perf. 11 Rough*
735 A243 1af bright blue   .50 .15
"Free Pashtunistan Day."

Bagh-i-Bala
Park
Casino — A244

Tourist publicity: 2af, Map of Afghanistan. 8af,
Tomb of Abd-er-Rahman. The casino on 4af is the
former summer palace of Abd-er-Rahman near
Kabul.

1966, Oct. 3   Photo.   *Perf. 13½x14*
736 A244 2af red & multi   .20 .15
737 A244 4af multicolored   .40 .30
738 A244 8af multicolored   .65 .60
  a. Souvenir sheet of 3, #736-738, imperf.   3.50 3.50
  Nos. 736-738 (3)   1.25 1.05

Zahir   UNESCO
Shah — A245   Emblem — A246

1966, Oct. 14   *Perf. 14x13½*
739 A245 1af dk slate grn   .20 .15
740 A245 5af red brown   .50 .25
King Mohammed Zahir Shah, 52nd birthday. See
Nos. 760-761.

1967, Mar. 6   Litho.   *Perf. 12*
741 A246 2af multicolored   .60 .15
742 A246 6af multicolored   .75 .15
743 A246 12af multicolored   1.50 .30
  Nos. 741-743 (3)   2.85 .60
20th anniv. of UNESCO.

Zahir Shah and
UN Emblem
A247

1967   Photo.
744 A247 5af multicolored   .40 .15
745 A247 10af multicolored   .75 .30
UN Intl. Org. for Refugees, 20th anniv.

New Power
Station — A248

Designs: 5af, Carpet, vert. 8af, Cement factory.

1967, Jan. 7   Photo.   *Perf. 13½x14*
746 A248 2af red lil & ol grn   .15 .15
747 A248 5af multicolored   .20 .15
748 A248 8af blk, dk bl & tan   .40 .25
  Nos. 746-748 (3)   .75 .55
Issued to publicize industrial development.

International
Tourist Year
Emblem — A249

Designs: 6af, International Tourist Year emblem
and map of Afghanistan.

1967, May 11   Photo.   *Perf. 12*
749 A249 2af yel, blk & lt bl   .15 .15
750 A249 6af bis brn, blk & lt bl   .40 .20
  a. Souvenir sheet of 2, #749-750, imperf.   1.00 1.00
  Set value   .30
Intl. Tourist Year, 1967. No. 750a sold for 10af.

Power Dam, Dorunta   Macaque
A250   A251

6af, Sirobi Dam, vert. 8af, Reservoir at Jalalabad.

1967, July 2   Photo.   *Perf. 12*
751 A250 1af dk green & lil   .15 .15
752 A250 6af red brn & grnsh bl   .35 .35
753 A250 8af plum & dk bl   .50 .50
  Nos. 751-753 (3)   1.00 1.00
Progress in agriculture through electricity.

1967, July 28   Photo.   *Perf. 12*
Designs: 6af, Striped hyena, horiz. 12af, Persian
gazelles, horiz.
754 A251 2af dull yel & indigo   .25 .15
755 A251 6af lt green & sepia   .70 .35
756 A251 12af lt bl & red brn   1.50 .75
  Nos. 754-756 (3)   2.45 1.25

Pashtun
Dancers — A252

1967, Sept. 1   Photo.   *Perf. 12*
757 A252 2af magenta & violet   .50 .15
Issued for "Free Pashtunistan Day."

Retreat of British at   Fireworks and
Maiwand   UN Emblem
A253   A254

1967, Aug. 24
758 A253 1af dk brn & org ver   .25 .15
759 A253 2af dk brn & brt pink   .50 .15
  Set value   .20
Issued to commemorate Independence Day.

King Type of 1966
1967, Oct. 15   Photo.   *Perf. 14x13½*
760 A245 2af brown red   .15 .15
761 A245 8af dark blue   .50 .25
Issued to honor King Mohammed Zahir Shah on
his 53rd birthday.

1967, Oct. 24   Litho.   *Perf. 12*
762 A254 10af violet bl & multi   .65 .35
Issued for United Nations Day.

Greco-Roman Wrestlers   Said
A255   Jamalluddin
                           Afghan
                           A256

Design: 6af, Free style wrestlers.

1967, Nov. 20   Photo.
763 A255 4af ol grn & rose lil   .50 .15
764 A255 6af dp carmine & brn   .80 .20
  a. Souvenir sheet of 2, #763-764, imperf.   5.00 5.00
1968 Olympic Games.

765 A256 1af magenta   .15 .15
766 A256 5af brown   .35 .20
  Set value   .30
Said Jamalluddin Afghan, politician (1839-97).

Bronze Vase,   WHO Emblem
11th-12th   A258
Centuries
A257

Design: 7af, Bronze vase, Ghasnavide era, 11th-
12th centuries.

1967, Dec. 23   Photo.   *Perf. 12*
767 A257 3af lt green & brn   .20 .15
768 A257 7af yel & slate grn   .40 .30
  a. Souvenir sheet of 2, #767-768, imperf.   2.50 2.50

1968, Apr. 7   Photo.   *Perf. 12*
769 A258 2af citron & brt bl   .15 .15
770 A258 7af rose & brt bl   .30 .20
  Set value   .30
20th anniv. of the WHO.

Karakul — A259

1968, May 20   Photo.   *Perf. 12*
771 A259 1af yellow & blk   .25 .15
772 A259 6af lt blue & blk   .70 .20
773 A259 12af ultra & dk brn   1.25 .40
  Nos. 771-773 (3)   2.20 .75
Issued for the Day of Agriculture.

Map of Afghanistan   Victory Tower,
A260   Ghazni
                          A261

Design: 16af, Mausoleum, Ghazni.

1968, June 3   *Perf. 13½x14, 12*
774 A260 2af red, blk, lt bl & grn   .15 .15
775 A261 3af yel, dk brn & lt bl   .20 .15
776 A261 16af pink & multi   .95 .50
  Nos. 774-776 (3)   1.30
  Set value   .70
Issued for tourist publicity.

Cinereous
Vulture — A262

Birds: 6af, Eagle owl. 7af, Greater flamingoes.

1968, July 3   *Perf. 12*
777 A262 1af sky blue & multi   .75 .15
778 A262 6af yellow & multi   1.50 .20
779 A262 7af multicolored   1.75 .30
  Nos. 777-779 (3)   4.00 .65

Game of
"Pegsticking"
A263

2af, Olympic flame & rings, vert. 12af, Buzkashi.

1968, July 20   Photo.   Perf. 12
780 A263 2af multicolored   .15 .15
781 A263 8af orange & multi   .65 .30
782 A263 12af multicolored   1.00 .45
    Nos. 780-782 (3)   1.80 .90

19th Olympic Games, Mexico City, Oct. 12-27.

Flower-decked Armored Car — A264

1968, Aug. 23
783 A264 6af multicolored   .40 .20

Issued to commemorate Independence Day.

Flag of Pashtunistan A265

1968 Aug. 31   Photo.   Perf. 12
784 A265 3af multicolored   .25 .15

Issued for "Free Pashtunistan Day."

Zahir Shah — A266   Human Rights Flame — A267

1968, Oct. 14   Photo.   Perf. 12
785 A266 2af ultra   .15 .15
786 A266 8af brown   .45 .30
    Set value   .35

King Mohammed Zahir Shah, 54th birthday.

1968, Oct. 24
787 A267 1af multicolored   .15 .15
788 A267 2af violet, bis & blk   .20 .15
789 A267 6af vio blk, bis & vio   .40 .15
    Nos. 787-789 (3)   .75
    Set value   .25

Souvenir Sheet
Imperf
790 A267 10af plum, bis & red org   1.50 1.50

International Human Rights Year.

Maolana Djalalodine Balkhi — A268   Kushan Mural — A269

1968, Nov. 26   Photo.   Perf. 12
791 A268 4af dk green & mag   .25 .15

Balkhi (1207-73), historian.

1969, Jan. 2   Perf. 12
Design: 3af, Jug shaped like female torso.
792 A269 1af dk grn, mar & yel   .25 .15
793 A269 3af violet, gray & mar   .75 .15
    a. Souv. sheet of 2, #792-793, imperf. 1.50 1.50

Archaeological finds at Bagram, 1st cent. B.C. to 2nd cent. A.D.

ILO Emblem A270

1969, Mar. 23   Photo.   Perf. 12
794 A270 5af lt yel, lemon & blk   .30 .20
795 A270 8af lt bl, grnsh bl & blk .50 .30

50th anniv. of the ILO.

Arms Type of 1939
1969, May (?)   Typo.
795A A79 100p dark green   .15 .15
795B A79 150p deep brown   .25 .15
    Set value   .15

Nos. 795A-795B were normally used as newspaper stamps.

Badakhshan Scene — A271

Tourist Publicity: 2af, Map of Afghanistan. 7af, Three men on mules ascending the Pamir Mountains.

1969, July 6   Photo.   Perf. 13½x14
796 A271 2af ocher & multi   .20 .15
797 A271 4af multicolored   .30 .15
798 A271 7af multicolored   .75 .20
    a. Souvenir sheet of 3, #796-798, imperf. 1.75 1.75
    Nos. 796-798 (3)   1.25 .50

No. 798a sold for 15af.

Bust, from Hadda Treasure, 3rd-5th Centuries — A272   Zahir Shah and Queen Humeira — A273

Designs: 5af, Vase and jug. 10af, Statue of crowned woman. 5af and 10af from Bagram treasure, 1st-2nd centuries.

1969, Aug. 3   Photo.   Perf. 14x13½
799 A272 1af olive grn & gold   .15 .15
800 A272 5af purple & gold   .20 .15
801 A272 10af dp blue & gold   .40 .30
    Nos. 799-801 (3)   .75
    Set value   .50

1969, Aug. 23   Perf. 12
802 A273 5af gold, dk bl & red brn .35 .20
803 A273 10af gold, dp lil & bl grn .65 .35

Issued to commemorate Independence Day.

Map of Pashtunistan and Rising Sun — A274

1969, Aug. 31   Typo.   Perf. 10½
804 A274 2af lt blue & red   .15 .15

Issued for "Free Pashtunistan Day."

Zahir Shah — A275

1969, Oct. 14   Photo.   Perf. 12
Portrait in Natural Colors
805 A275 2af dk brown & gold   .15 .15
806 A275 6af brown & gold   .45 .20
    Set value   .25

King Mohammed Zahir Shah, 55th birthday.

UN Emblem and Flag of Afghanistan A276

1969, Oct. 24   Litho.   Perf. 13½
807 A276 5af blue & multi   .25 .15

Issued for United Nations Day.

ITU Emblem — A277   Wild Boar — A278

1969, Nov. 12
808 A277 6af ultra & multi   .30 .20
809 A277 12af rose & multi   .60 .35

Issued for World Telecommunications Day.

1969, Dec. 7   Photo.   Perf. 12
1af, Long-tailed porcupine. 8af, Red deer.
810 A278 1af yellow & multi   .25 .20
811 A278 3af blue & multi   .75 .50
812 A278 8af pink & multi   2.00 1.00
    Nos. 810-812 (3)   3.00 1.70

Man's First Footprints on Moon, and Earth — A279

1969, Dec. 28   Perf. 13½x14
813 A279 1af yel grn & multi   .15 .15
814 A279 3af yellow & multi   .25 .15
815 A279 6af blue & multi   .40 .20
816 A279 10af rose & multi   .65 .30
    Nos. 813-816 (4)   1.45
    Set value   .65

Moon landing. See note after Algeria #427.

Anti-cancer Symbol — A280   Mirza Abdul Quader Bedel — A281

1970, Apr. 7   Photo.   Perf. 14
817 A280 2af dk grn & rose car   .15 .15
818 A280 6af dk bl & rose claret   .40 .20
    Set value   .25

Issued to publicize the fight against cancer.

1970, May 6   Perf. 14x13½
819 A281 5af multicolored   .25 .15

Mirza Abdul Quader Bedel (1643-1720), poet.

Education Year Emblem A282   Mother and Child A283

1970, June 7   Photo.   Perf. 12
820 A282 1af black   .15 .15
821 A282 6af deep rose   .35 .20
822 A282 12af green   .75 .35
    Nos. 820-822 (3)   1.25
    Set value   .60

International Education Year 1970.

1970, June 15   Perf. 13½
823 A283 6af yellow & multi   .25 .20

Issued for Mother's Day.

UN Emblem, Scales of Justice, Spacecraft A284

1970, June 26
824 A284 4af yel, dk bl & dp bl   .20 .15
825 A284 6af pink, dk bl & brt bl   .35 .20

25th anniversary of United Nations.

Mosque of the Amir of the two Swords, Kabul — A285

2af, Map of Afghanistan. 7af, Arch of Paghman.

1970, July 6   Perf. 12
Size: 30½x30½mm
826 A285 2af lt bl, blk & cit   .15 .15
Size: 36x26mm
827 A285 3af pink & multi   .20 .15
828 A285 7af yellow & multi   .40 .20
    Nos. 826-828 (3)   .75
    Set value   .35

Issued for tourist publicity.

Zahir Shah Reviewing Troops A286

1970, Aug. 23   Photo.   Perf. 13½
829 A286 8af multicolored   .60 .25

Issued to commemorate Independence Day.

Pathans — A287

1970, Aug. 31   Typo.   *Perf. 10¹/₂*
830 A287 2af ultra & red   .15 .15
Issued for "Free Pashtunistan Day."

Quail — A288

4af, Golden eagle. 6af, Ringnecked pheasant.

1970, Sept.   Photo.   *Perf. 12*
831 A288 2af multicolored   .50 .25
832 A288 4af multicolored   1.00 .50
833 A288 6af multicolored   1.50 .75
    Nos. 831-833 (3)   3.00 1.50

Zahir Shah   Red Crescents
A289   A290

1970, Oct. 14   Photo.   *Perf. 14x13¹/₂*
834 A289 3af green & vio   .20 .15
835 A289 7af dk bl & vio brn   .60 .25
King Mohammed Zahir Shah, 56th birthday.

1970, Oct. 16   Typo.   *Perf. 10¹/₂*
836 A290 2af black, gold & red   .15 .15
Issued for the Red Crescent Society.

UN Emblem
and Charter
A291

1970, Oct. 24   Photo.   *Perf. 14*
837 A291 1af gold & multi   .15 .15
838 A291 5af gold & multi   .20 .15
    Set value   .30 .20
United Nations Day.

Tiger Heads of
1871 — A292

1970, Nov. 10   *Perf. 12*
839 A292 1af sal, lt grnsh bl & blk   .25 .15
840 A292 4af lt ultra, yel & blk   .50 .15
841 A292 8af lilac, lt bl & blk   .85 .35
    Nos. 839-841 (3)   1.60
    Set value
Cent. of the 1st Afghan postage stamps. The postal service was established in 1870, but the 1st stamps were issued in May, 1871.

Globe and
Waves
A293

1971, May 17   Photo.   *Perf. 13¹/₂*
842 A293 12af green, blk & bl   .60 .35
3rd World Telecommunications Day.

Callimorpha
Principalis
A294

Designs: 3af, Epizygaenella species. 5af, Parnassius autocrator.

1971, May 30   *Perf. 13¹/₂x14*
843 A294 1af vermilion & multi   1.00 .50
844 A294 2af yellow & multi   2.25 1.00
845 A294 5af ultra & multi   3.00 1.50
    Nos. 843-845 (3)   6.25 3.00

"UNESCO" and Half
of Ancient Kushan
Statue — A295

1971, June 26   Photo.   *Perf. 13¹/₂*
846 A295 6af ocher & vio   .40 .20
847 A295 10af lt blue & mar   .65 .30
UNESCO-sponsored Intl. Kushani Seminar.

Tughra and Independence
Monument — A296

1971, Aug. 23
848 A296 7af rose red & multi   .40 .20
849 A296 9af red orange & multi .65 .30
Independence Day.

Pashtunistan Square,
Kabul — A297

1971, Aug. 31   Typo.   *Perf. 10¹/₂*
850 A297 5af deep rose lilac   .27 .15
"Free Pashtunistan Day."

Zahir Shah — A298   A299

1971, Oct. 14   Photo.   *Perf. 12¹/₂x12*
851 A298 9af lt green & multi   .40 .30
852 A298 17af yellow & multi   .75 .55
King Mohammed Zahir Shah, 57th birthday.

1971, Oct. 16   *Perf. 14x13¹/₂*
Design: Map of Afghanistan, red crescent, various activities.
853 A299 8af lt bl, red, grn & blk .45 .25
For Afghan Red Crescent Society.

Equality Year
Emblem
A300

1971, Oct. 24   *Perf. 12*
854 A300 24af brt blue   1.25 .70
International Year Against Racial Discrimination and United Nations Day.

"Your Heart is   Tulip — A302
your
Health" — A301

1972, Apr. 7   Photo.   *Perf. 14*
855 A301 9af pale yellow & multi .75 .30
856 A301 12af gray & multi   1.50 .35
World Health Day.

1972, June 5   Photo.   *Perf. 14*
Designs: 10af, Rock partridge, horiz. 12af, Lynx, horiz. 18af, Allium stipitatum (flower).
857 A302 7af green & multi   .50 .25
858 A302 10af blue & multi   .75 .35
859 A302 12af lt green & multi 1.00 .35
860 A302 18af blue grn & multi 1.25 .60
    Nos. 857-860 (4)   3.50 1.55

Buddhist
Shrine, Hadda
A302a

Designs: 7af, Greco-Bactrian animal seal, 250 B.C. 9af, Greco-Oriental temple, Ai-Khanoum, 3rd-2nd centuries B.C.

1972, July 16   Photo.   *Perf. 12*
861 A302a 3af brown & dl bl   .50 .15
862 A302a 7af rose claret & dl grn .80 .20
863 A302a 9af green & lilac   1.10 .30
    Nos. 861-863 (3)   2.40 .65
Tourist publicity.

King and Queen Reviewing
Parade — A303

1972, Aug. 23   Photo.   *Perf. 13¹/₂*
864 A303 25af gold & multi   4.00 1.00
Independence Day.
Used as a provisional in 1978 with king and queen portion removed.

Wrestling
A304

10af, 19af, 21af, Wrestling, different hold.

1972, Aug. 26
865 A304 4af ol bis & multi   .25 .15
866 A304 8af lt blue & multi   .50 .25
867 A304 10af yel grn & multi   .60 .30
868 A304 19af multicolored   1.25 .40
869 A304 21af lilac & multi   1.40 .45
    a. Souv. sheet of 5, #865-869, imperf. 3.00 3.00
    Nos. 865-869 (5)   4.00 1.55
20th Olympic Games, Munich, Aug. 26-Sept. 11.
No. 869a sold for 60af.

Pathan and View of   Zahir
Tribal   Shah — A306
Territory — A305

1972, Aug. 31   *Perf. 12¹/₂x12*
870 A305 5af ultra & multi   .25 .15
Pashtunistan day.

1972, Oct. 14   Photo.   *Perf. 14x13¹/₂*
871 A306 7af gold, blk & Prus bl 1.50 .30
872 A306 14af gold, blk & lt brn 2.50 .50
58th birthday of King Mohammed Zahir Shah.

City Destroyed by Earthquake,
Refugees — A307

1972, Oct. 16   *Perf. 13¹/₂*
873 A307 7af lt bl, red & blk   .40 .20
For Afghan Red Crescent Society.

UN Emblem
A308

1972, Oct. 24
874 A308 12af lt ultra & blk   .65 .35
UN Economic Commission for Asia and the Far East (ECAFE), 25th anniv.

Ceramics
A309

Designs: 9af, Leather coat, vert. 12af, Metal ware, vert. 16af, Inlaid artifacts.

1972, Dec. 10   Photo.   *Perf. 12*
875 A309 7af gold & multi   .40 .20
876 A309 9af gold & multi   .55 .30
877 A309 12af gold & multi   .70 .35
878 A309 16af gold & multi   1.00 .50
    a. Souv. sheet of 4, #875-878, imperf. 2.25 2.25
    Nos. 875-878 (4)   2.65 1.35
Handicraft industries. No. 878a sold for 45af.

WMO and National Emblems — A310

1973, Apr. 3   Photo.   Perf. 14
879 A310   7af lt lil & dk grn   .40 .20
880 A310   14af lt bl & dp claret   .85 .45
Cent. of intl. meteorological cooperation.

Abu Rayhan al-Biruni — A311

Family — A312

1973, June 16   Photo.   Perf. 13½
881 A311   10af multicolored   .55 .30
Millennium of birth (973-1048), philosopher and mathematician.

1973, June 30   Photo.   Perf. 13½
882 A312   9af orange & red lil   .50 .30
Intl. Family Planning Fed., 21st anniv.

Republic

Impeyan Pheasant
A313

Birds: 9af, Great crested grebe. 12af, Himalayan snow cock.

1973, July 29   Photo.   Perf. 12x12½
883 A313   8af yellow & multi   1.25 .25
884 A313   9af blue & multi   1.75 .30
885 A313   12af multicolored   2.00 .35
   Nos. 883-885 (3)   5.00 .90

Stylized Buzkashi Horseman A314

1973, Aug.   Perf. 13½
886 A314   8af black   .30 .25
Tourist publicity.

Fireworks A315

1973, Aug. 23   Photo.   Perf. 12
887 A315   12af multicolored   .45 .35
55th Independence Day.

Lake Abassine, Pashtunistan Flag — A316

1973, Aug. 31   Perf. 14x13½
888 A316   9af multicolored   .50 .30
Pashtunistan Day.

Red Crescent — A317

1973, Oct. 16   Perf. 13½
889 A317   10af red, blk & gold   .60 .30
Red Crescent Society.

Kemal Ataturk — A318

1973, Oct. 28   Litho.   Perf. 10½
890 A318   1af blue   .15 .15
891 A318   7af reddish brown   .40 .20
   Set value   .25
50th anniversary of the Turkish Republic.

Human Rights Flame, Arms of Afghanistan A319

1973, Dec. 10   Photo.   Perf. 12
892 A319   12af sil, blk & lt bl   .45 .35
25th anniversary of the Universal Declaration of Human Rights.

Asiatic Black Bears — A320

1974, Mar. 26   Litho.   Perf. 12
893 A320   5af shown   .35 .15
894 A320   7af Afghan hound   .50 .20
895 A320   10af Persian goat   .70 .20
896 A320   12af Leopard   .90 .35
  a. Souv. sheet of 4, #893-896, imperf. 5.00 5.00
   Nos. 893-896 (4)   2.45 1.00

Worker and Farmer A321

1974, May 1 Photo. Perf. 13½x12½
897 A321   9af rose red & multi   .40 .25
International Labor Day, May 1.

Independence Monument and Arch — A322

1974, May 27   Photo.   Perf. 12
898 A322   4af blue & multi   .15 .15
899 A322   11af gold & multi   .35 .30
56th Independence Day.

Arms of Afghanistan and Symbol of Cooperation A323

Pres. Mohammad Daoud Khan — A324

Designs: 5af, Flag of Republic of Afghanistan. 15af, Soldiers and coat of arms of the Republic.

1974, July 25   Perf. 13½x12½, 14
Sizes: 4af, 15af, 36x22mm; 5af, 7af, 36x26, 26x36mm
900 A323   4af multicolored   .20 .15
901 A323   5af multicolored   .25 .15
902 A324   7af green, brn & blk   .30 .20
  a. Souv. sheet of 2, #901-902, imperf.   .70 .70
903 A323   15af multicolored   .65 .40
  a. Souv. sheet of 2, #900, 903, imperf. 1.00 1.00
   Nos. 900-903 (4)   1.40 .90
1st anniv. of the Republic of Afghanistan.

Lesser Spotted Eagle — A325

Birds: 6af, White-fronted goose, ruddy shelduck and gray-lag goose. 11af, European coots and European crane.

1974, Aug. 6   Photo.   Perf. 13½x13
904 A325   1af car rose & multi   .25 .15
905 A325   6af blue & multi   .75 .20
906 A325   11af yellow & multi   1.50 .40
  a. Strip of 3, #904-906   1.00 1.00
   Nos. 904-906 (3)   2.50
   Set value   .65

Flags of Pashtunistan and Afghanistan A326

1974, Aug. 31   Photo.   Perf. 14
907 A326   5af multicolored   .25 .15
Pashtunistan Day.

Natl. Arms A326a

1974, Aug.   Typo.   Rough Perf. 11
907A A326a 100p green

Coat of Arms — A327

1974, Oct. 9
908 A327   7af gold, grn & blk   .25 .20
Centenary of Universal Postal Union.

"un" and UN Emblem A328

1974, Oct. 24   Photo.   Perf. 14
909 A328   5af lt ultra & dk bl   .25 .15
United Nations Day.

Minaret of Jam — A329   Buddha, Hadda — A330

14af, Lady riding griffin, 2nd century, Bagram.

1975, May 5   Photo.   Perf. 13½
910 A329   7af multicolored   .25 .15
911 A330   14af multicolored   .60 .30
912 A330   15af multicolored   .65 .30
  a. Souvenir sheet of 3, #910-912, imperf. 3.50 3.50
   Nos. 910-912 (3)   1.50 .75
South Asia Tourism Year 1975.

New Flag of Afghanistan A331

1975, May 27   Photo.   Perf. 12
913 A331   16af multicolored   .75 .35
57th Independence Day.

Celebrating Crowd A332

1975, July 17   Photo.   Perf. 13½
914 A332   9af blue & multi   .45 .20
915 A332   12af carmine & multi   .55 .30
Second anniversary of the Republic.

Women's Year Emblems — A333

1975, Aug. 24   Photo.   Perf. 12
916 A333   9af car, lt bl & blk   .30 .20
International Women's Year 1975.

Pashtunistan Flag, Sun Rising Over Mountains A334

Mohammed Akbar Khan A335

1975, Aug. 31   *Perf. 13½*
917 A334 10af multicolored   .30 .25
Pashtunistan Day.

1976, Feb. 4   **Photo.**   *Perf. 14*
918 A335 15af lt brown & multi   .45 .35
Mohammed Akbar Khan (1816-1846), warrior son of Amir Dost Mohammed Khan.

Pres. Mohammad Daoud Khan
A336   A337

1974-78   **Photo.**   *Perf. 14*
919 A336 10af multi   .55   .20
920 A336 16af multi ('78)   2.00   .75
921 A336 19af multi   .75   .40
922 A336 21af multi   1.10   .45
923 A336 22af multi ('78)   3.00 1.60
924 A336 30af multi ('78)   4.00 2.25
925 A337 50af multi ('75)   2.25 1.10
926 A337 100af multi ('75)   4.50 2.00
       Nos. 919-926 (8)   18.15 8.75

Arms of Republic, Independence Monument — A338

1976, June 1   **Photo.**   *Perf. 14*
927 A338 22af blue & multi   .65 .45
58th Independence Day.

Flag Raising — A339

1976, July 17   **Photo.**   *Perf. 14*
928 A339 30af multicolored   .90 .75
Republic Day.

Mountain Peaks and Flag of Pashtunistan A340

1976, Aug. 31   **Photo.**   *Perf. 14*
929 A340 16af multicolored   .50 .40
Pashtunistan Day.

Coat of Arms — A340a

1976, Sept.   **Litho.**   *Perf. 11 Rough*
930 A340a 25p salmon   .25 .15
931 A340a 50p lt green   .25 .15
932 A340a 1af ultra   .25 .15
       Nos. 930-932 (3)   .75 .45

Flag and Views on Open Book — A341

1977, May 27   **Photo.**   *Perf. 14*
937 A341 20af green & multi   .60 .50
59th Independence Day.

Pres. Daoud and National Assembly — A342

President Taking Oath of Office — A343

Designs: 10af, Inaugural address. 18af, Promulgation of Constitution.

1977, June 22
938 A342 7af multicolored   .65   .45
939 A343 8af multicolored   .70   .60
940 A343 10af multicolored   .90   .75
941 A342 18af multicolored   1.65 1.25
   a. Souvenir sheet of 4   3.00 3.00
       Nos. 938-941 (4)   3.90 3.05

Election of 1st Pres. and promulgation of Constitution. No. 941a contains 4 imperf. stamps similar to Nos. 938-941.

Jamalluddin Medal A344

1977, July 6   **Photo.**   *Perf. 14*
942 A344 12af blue, blk & gold   .35 .30
Sajo Jamalluddin Afghani, reformer, 80th death anniversary.

Afghanistan Flag over Crowd — A345

1977, July 17
943 A345 22af multicolored   .65 .55

Dancers, Fountain, Pashtunistan Flag — A346

1977, Aug. 31
944 A346 30af multicolored   .90 .75
Pashtunistan Day.

Arms and Carrier Pigeon A346a

1977, Oct. 30   **Litho.**   *Perf. 11*
944A A346a 1af black & blue   .15 .15

Members of Parliament Congratulating Pres. Daoud — A347

1978, Feb. 5   **Litho.**   *Perf. 14*
945 A347 20af multicolored   1.75
Election of first president, first anniversary.

Map of Afghanistan, UPU Emblem A348

1978, Apr. 1   **Photo.**   *Perf. 14*
946 A348 10af green, blk & gold   .30 .25
Afghanistan's UPU membership, 50th anniv.

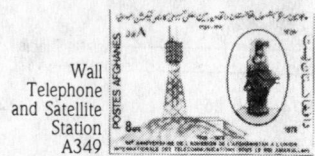

Wall Telephone and Satellite Station A349

1978, Apr. 12
947 A349 8af multicolored   .25 .20
Afghanistan's ITU membership, 50th anniv.

Democratic Republic

Arrows Pointing to Crescent, Cross and Lion — A350

1978, July 6   **Litho.**   *Perf. 11 Rough*
948 A350 3af black   1.00 .50
50th anniv. of Afghani Red Crescent Soc.

Khalq Party Emblem A350a

1978, Aug.   **Litho.**   *Perf. 11*
948A A350a 1af rose red & gold   1.25 .50
948B A350a 4af rose red & gold   1.75 .75

Qalai Bist Arch A351

1978, Aug. 19   *Perf. 14*
949 A351 16af Bamian Buddha   1.00 .40
949A A351 22af shown   1.25 .55
949B A351 30af Hazara Women   1.75 .90
       Nos. 949-949B (3)   4.00 1.85

Men with Pashtunistan Flag — A352   Coat of Arms and Emblems — A353

1978, Aug. 31   *Perf. 11 Rough*
950 A352 7af ultra & red   .20 .15
Pashtunistan Day.

1978, Sept. 8   *Perf. 11*
951 A353 20af rose red   .60 .50
World Literacy Day.

A354

Perf. 11½ Rough
1978, Oct. 25   **Litho.**
952 A354 18af light green   .55 .45
Hero of Afghanistan.

Khalq Party Flag — A355

1978, Oct. 19   Photo.   Perf. 11½
953 A355 8af black, red & gold   .25 .20
954 A355 9af black, red & gold   .30 .20
"The mail serving the people."

Nour Mohammad Taraki — A356

1979, Jan. 1   Litho.   Perf. 12
955 A356 12af multicolored   .35 .15

Nour Mohammad Taraki, founder of People's Democratic Party of Afghanistan, installation as president.

Woman Breaking Chain — A357

1979, Mar. 8   Litho.   Perf. 11
956 A357 14af red & ultra   1.50 .50
Women's Day. Inscribed "POSSTES."

Map of Afghanistan, Census Emblem A358

1979, Mar. 25   Litho.   Perf. 12
957 A358 3af multicolored   .75 .50
First comprehensive population census.

Farmers A359

1979, Mar. 21
958 A359 1af multicolored   .50 .25
Agricultural advances.

Pres. Taraki Reading First Issue of Khalq — A360

1979, Apr. 11   Perf. 12½x12
959 A360 2af multicolored   .25 .15

Khalq, newspaper of People's Democratic Republic of Afghanistan.

Pres. Noor Mohammad Taraki — A361

Plaza with Tank Monument and Fountain — A362

House where Revolution Started — A363

Designs: 50p, Taraki, tank. 12af, House where 1st Khalq Party Congress was held.

Perf. 12, 12½x12 (A362)
1979, Apr. 27   Litho.
959A A363 50p multicolored   .15 .15
960 A361 4af multicolored   .15 .15
961 A362 5af multicolored   .25 .15
962 A363 6af multicolored   .30 .25
963 A363 12af multicolored   .50 .45
   Nos. 959A-963 (5)   1.35 1.15
1st anniversary of revolution.

Carpenter and Blacksmith A364

1979, May 1   Perf. 12
964 A364 10af multicolored   .30 .25
Int'l Labor Day.

Children, Flag and Map of Afghanistan — A366

1979, June 1   Litho.   Perf. 12½x12
966 A366 16af multicolored   1.50 .75
International Year of the Child.

Doves Circling Asia in Globe A366a

1979   Litho.   Perf. 11x10½
966A A366a 2af red & blue   1.00 .20

Armed Afghans, Kabul Memorial and Arch — A367

Pashtunistan Citizens, Flag — A368

1979, Aug. 19   Litho.   Perf. 12
967 A367 30af multicolored   1.25 .75
60th independence day.

1979, Aug. 31
968 A368 9af multicolored   .30 .20
Pashtunistan Day.

UPU Day — A369

1979, Oct. 9   Litho.   Perf. 12
969 A369 15af multicolored   .45 .38

Tombstone — A369a

1979, Oct. 25   Litho.   Perf. 12½x12
969A A369a 22af multicolored   2.00 1.00

International Women's Day — A370

1980, Mar. 8   Litho.   Perf. 12
970 A370 8af multicolored   3.00 3.00

Farmers' Day — A371

1980, Mar. 21   Litho.   Perf. 11½x12
971 A371 2af multicolored   .50 .25

Non-smoker and Smoker — A372

1980, Apr. 7   Perf. 11½
972 A372 5af multicolored   .25 .15
Anti-smoking campaign; World Health Day.

Lenin, 110th Birth Anniversary A373

1980, Apr. 22   Perf. 12x12½
973 A373 12af multicolored   .35 .30

People and Fist on Map of Afghanistan A374

1980, Apr. 27   Litho.   Perf. 12½x12
974 A374 1af multicolored   .25 .25
Saur Revolution, 2nd anniversary.

International Workers' Solidarity Day — A375

1980, May 1
975 A375 9af multicolored   .30 .20

Wrestling, Moscow '80 Emblem A376

Perf. 12x12½, 12½x12½
1980, July 19
976 A376 3af Soccer, vert.   .60 .25
977 A376 6af shown   1.00 .45
978 A376 9af Buzkashi   1.65 .60
979 A376 10af Pegsticking   1.75 .75
   Nos. 976-979 (4)   5.00 2.05
22nd Summer Olympic Games, Moscow, July 19-Aug. 3.

61st Anniversary of Independence — A377

1980, Aug. 19   Litho.   Perf. 12½x12
980 A377 3af multicolored   .25 .15

Pashtunistan Day — A378

1980, Aug. 30
981 A378 25af multicolored   .80 .65

Intl. UPU
Day — A379

1980, Oct. 9　Litho.　Perf. 12½x12
982 A379　20af multicolored　　　　.60 .50

International
Women's
Day — A381

1981, Mar. 9　Litho.　Perf. 12½x12
984 A381　15af multicolored　　　　.45 .40

Farmers' Day — A382

1981, Mar. 20　Litho.　Perf. 12½x12
985 A382　1af multicolored　　　　.25 .25

Bighorn
Mountain Sheep
(Protected
Species) — A383

1981, Apr. 4　　　　Perf. 12x12½
986 A383　12af multicolored　　　1.00 .75

Saur Revolution,
3rd Anniversary
A384

Intl. Workers'
Solidarity Day
A385

1981, Apr. 27　　　　Perf. 11
987 A384　50p brown　　　　　.15 .15

1981, May 1　　　　Perf. 12½x12
988 A385　10af multicolored　　　.30 .25

13th World
Telecommunications
Day — A387

1981, May 17　Litho.　Perf. 12½x12
990 A387　9af multicolored　　　　.30 .20

Intl. Children's
Day — A388

1981, June 1　　　　Perf. 12x12½
991 A388　15af multicolored　　　.45 .40

People's
Independence
Monument
62nd Anniv.
of
Independence
A389

1981, Aug. 19
992 A389　4af multicolored　　　　.15 .15

Pashtunistan
Day — A390

1981, Aug. 31　Litho.　Perf. 12
992A A390　2af multicolored　　　.25 .15

Intl. Tourism
Day — A391

1981, Sept. 27　　　　Perf. 12½x12
993 A391　5af multicolored　　　　.25 .15

World Food
Day — A392

1981, Oct. 16
995 A392　7af multicolored　　　　.35 .15

Asia-Africa
Solidarity
Meeting
A393

1981, Nov. 18　Litho.　Perf. 11
996 A393　8af blue　　　　　　.25 .20

Struggle
Against
Apartheid
A394

1300th Anniv. of
Bulgaria
A395

1981, Dec. 1　　　　Perf. 12½x12
997 A394　4af multicolored　　　.30 .20

1981, Dec. 9　　　　Perf. 12x12½
998 A395　20af multicolored　　1.25 1.00

Buzkashi
Game
A395a

1980　　Photo.　　Perf. 14
998A A395a　50af multicolored　3.00 1.00
998B A395a　100af multicolored　6.00 2.00

Intl. Women's
Day — A396

1982, Mar. 8　Litho.　Perf. 12
999 A396　6af multicolored　　　.50 .25

Farmers'
Day — A397

1982, Mar. 21
1000 A397　4af multicolored　　　.25 .15

Rhubarb
Plant — A398

Saur Revolution,
4th
Anniv. — A399

Designs: Various local plants.

1982, Apr. 9　Litho.　Perf. 12
1001 A398　3af Judas trees　　　.25 .15
1002 A398　4af Rose of Sharon　.35 .15
1003 A398　16af shown　　　　1.00 .40
　　Nos. 1001-1003 (3)　　　1.60
　　　Set value　　　　　　.60

1982, Apr. 27
1004 A399　1af multicolored　　　.25 .15

George Dimitrov (1882-
1947), First Prime
Minister of
Bulgaria — A400

Intl. Workers'
Solidarity
Day — A401

1982, Apr. 30
1005 A400　30af multicolored　　.90 .75

1982, May 1
1006 A401　10af multicolored　　.30 .25

Storks — A402

1982, May 31
1007 A402　6af shown　　　　　.50 .25
1008 A402　11af Nightingales　1.00 .45

Hedgehogs
A403

1982, July 6　Litho.　Perf. 12
1009 A403　3af shown　　　　.25 .15
1010 A403　14af Cobra　　　.75 .50
　　See Nos. 1020-1022.

63rd Anniv. of
Independence
A404

1982, Aug. 19
1011 A404　20af multicolored　　.60 .50

Pashtunistan
Day — A405

1982, Aug. 31
1012 A405　32af multicolored　1.00 .80

World Tourism
Day — A406

1982, Sept. 27　Litho.　Perf. 12
1013 A406　9af multicolored　　.75 .50

UPU
Day — A407

1982, Oct. 9
1014 A407　4af multicolored　　.50 .25

World Food
Day — A408

1982, Oct. 16
1015 A408　9af multicolored　　.30 .20

37th Anniv. of
UN — A409

1982, Oct. 24
1016 A409　15af multicolored　　.45 .40

ITU Plenipotentiaries Conference, Nairobi, Sept. — A410

1982, Oct. 26
1017 A410 8af multicolored .25 .20

TB Bacillus Centenary A411

Human Rights Declaration, 34th Anniv. A412

1982, Nov. 24 Litho. *Perf. 12*
1018 A411 7af multicolored .25 .20

1982, Dec. 10
1019 A412 5af multicolored .25 .15

Animal Type of 1982

1982, Dec. 16
1020 A403 2af Lions .25 .15
1021 A403 7af Donkeys .75 .20
1022 A403 12af Marmots, vert. 1.00 .25
Nos. 1020-1022 (3) 2.00
Set value .50

Intl. Women's Day — A413

Mir Alicher Nawai Research Decade — A414

1983, Mar. 8
1023 A413 3af multicolored .25 .15

1983, Mar. 19
1024 A414 22af multicolored .70 .50

Farmers' Day — A415

1983, Mar. 21 Litho. *Perf. 12*
1025 A415 10af multicolored .30 .25

5th Anniv. of Saur Revolution A416

1983, Apr. 27 Litho. *Perf. 12*
1026 A416 15af multicolored 1.00 .50

Intl. Workers' Solidarity Day — A417

1983, May 1
1027 A417 2af multicolored .60 .50

World Communications Year — A418

1983, May 17
1028 A418 4af Modes of communication .25 .15
1029 A418 11af Building .75 .30

Intl. Children's Day — A419

1983, June 1 Litho. *Perf. 12*
1030 A419 25af multicolored 1.50 1.50

2nd Anniv. of National Front — A420

1983, June 15
1031 A420 1af multicolored .15 .15

Local Butterflies A421

Various butterflies. 9af, 13af vert.

1983, July 6
1032 A421 9af multicolored .55 .55
1033 A421 13af multicolored .80 .80
1034 A421 21af multicolored 1.25 1.25
Nos. 1032-1034 (3) 2.60 2.60

Struggle Against Apartheid — A422

1983, Aug. 1 Litho. *Perf. 12*
1035 A422 10af multicolored .60 .60

64th Anniv of Independence A423

1983, Aug. 19
1036 A423 6af multicolored .35 .35

Parliament House A423a

1983, Sept. Litho. *Perf. 12*
1036A A423a 50af shown 3.00 3.00
1036B A423a 100af Afghan Woman, Camel 6.00 6.00

A424

World Tourism Day — A425

1983, Sept. 27 Litho. *Perf. 12*
1037 A424 5af shown .30 .30
1038 A425 7af shown .45 .45
1039 A424 12af Golden statues .75 .75
1040 A425 16af Stone carving 1.00 1.00
Nos. 1037-1040 (4) 2.50 2.50

World Communications Year — A426

1983, Oct. 9 Litho. *Perf. 12*
1041 A426 14af Dish antenna, dove .85 .85
1042 A426 15af .90 .90

World Food Day A427

1983, Oct. 16 Litho. *Perf. 12*
1043 A427 14af multicolored .85 .85

Boxing A428

1983, Nov. 1 Litho. *Perf. 12*
1044 A428 1af Running .15 .15
1045 A428 18af shown 1.10 1.10
1046 A428 21af Wrestling 1.25 1.25
Nos. 1044-1046 (3) 2.50 2.50

Pashtunistan Day — A428a

1983, Nov. Litho. *Perf. 12*
1046A A428a 3af Pathans Waving Flag .20 .20

Handicrafts A429

1983, Nov. 22
1047 A429 2af Jewelry .15 .15
1048 A429 8af Stone ashtrays, dishes .50 .50
1049 A429 19af Furniture 1.10 1.10
1050 A429 30af Leather goods 1.90 1.90
Nos. 1047-1050 (4) 3.65 3.65

UN Declaration of Human Rights, 35th Anniv. A430

1983, Dec. 10 Litho. *Perf. 12*
1051 A430 20af multicolored 1.25 1.25

Kabul Polytechnical Institute, 20th Anniv. — A431

1983, Dec. 28 *Perf. 12½x12*
1052 A431 30af multicolored 1.90 1.90

1984 Winter Olympics A432

1984, Jan. *Perf. 12*
1053 A432 5af Figure skating .30 .30
1054 A432 9af Skiing .55 .55
1055 A432 11af Speed skating .65 .65
1056 A432 15af Hockey .90 .90
1057 A432 18af Biathlon 1.10 1.10
1058 A432 20af Ski jumping 1.25 1.25
1059 A432 22af Bobsledding 1.40 1.40
Nos. 1053-1059 (7) 6.15 6.15

Intl. Women's Day — A433

1984, Mar. 8
1060 A433 4af multicolored .25 .25

Farmers' Day — A434

Various agricultural scenes.

1984, Mar. 21 Litho. *Perf. 12*
1061 A434 2af multicolored .15 .15
1062 A434 4af multicolored .25 .25
1063 A434 7af multicolored .40 .40
1064 A434 9af multicolored .55 .55
1065 A434 15af multicolored .95 .95
1066 A434 18af multicolored 1.10 1.10
1067 A434 20af multicolored 1.25 1.25
Nos. 1061-1067 (7) 4.65 4.65

World Aviation Day — A435

1984, Apr. 12
1068 A435 5af Luna 1 .30 .30
1069 A435 8af Luna 2 .50 .50
1070 A435 11af Luna 3 .70 .70
1071 A435 17af Apollo 11 1.00 1.00
1072 A435 22af Soyuz 6 1.40 1.40
1073 A435 28af Soyuz 7 1.75 1.75
1074 A435 34af Soyuz 6, 7, 8 2.00 2.00
Nos. 1068-1074 (7) 7.65 7.65

Souvenir Sheet
Perf. 12x12½
1075 A435 25af S. Koroliov   1.50 1.50

No. 1075 contains one 30x41mm stamp.

Saur
Revolution,
6th Anniv.
A436

1984, Apr. 27   *Perf. 12*
1076 A436 3af multicolored   .25 .25

65th Anniv. of
Independence
A437

1984, Aug. 19   *Litho.*   *Perf. 12*
1077 A437 6af multicolored   .40 .40

Pashto's and
Balutchi's
Day — A438

1984, Aug. 31
1078 A438 3af Symbolic sun, tribal
         terr.   .25 .25

Wildlife
A439

Perf. 12½x12, 12x12½
1984, May 5   Litho.
1079 A439   1af Cape hunting dog,
         vert.   .15 .15
1080 A439   2af Argali sheep, vert.   .15 .15
1081 A439   6af Przewalski's horse   .40 .40
1082 A439   8af Wild boar, vert.   .50 .50
1083 A439 17af Snow leopard   1.00 1.00
1084 A439 19af Tiger   1.25 1.25
1085 A439 22af Indian elephant,
         vert.   1.40 1.40
     Nos. 1079-1085 (7)   4.85 4.85

19th UPU
Congress,
Hamburg
A440

1984, June 18   *Perf. 12x12½*
1086 A440 25af German postman,
         17th cent.   1.50 1.50
1087 A440 35af Postrider, 16th cent. 2.00 2.00
1088 A440 40af Carrier pigeon, letter 2.50 2.50
     Nos. 1086-1088 (3)   6.00 6.00

Souvenir Sheet
1089 A440 50af Hamburg No. 3 in
         black   4.00 4.00

No. 1089 contains one 30x40mm stamp.

Natl. Aviation,
40th Anniv.
A441

Soviet civil aircraft.

1984, June 29
1090 A441   1af Antonov AN-2   .15 .15
1091 A441   2af Ilyushin IL-12   .25 .25
1092 A441   9af Tupolev TU-104   .55 .55
1093 A441 10af Ilyushin IL-18   .60 .60
1094 A441 13af Tupolev TU-134   .80 .80

1095 A441 17af Ilyushin IL-62   1.00 1.00
1096 A441 21af Ilyushin IL-28   1.25 1.25
     Nos. 1090-1096 (7)   4.60 4.60

Ettore Bugatti
(1881-1947),
Type 43,
Italy — A442

Classic automobiles and their designers: 5af,
Henry Ford, 1903 Model A, US. 8af, Rene Panhard
(1841-1908), 1899 Landau, France. 11af, Gottlieb
Daimler (1834-1900), 1935 Daimler-Benz, Germany. 12af, Carl Benz (1844-1929), 1893 Victoris,
Germany. 15af, Armand Peugeot (1848-1915),
1892 Vis-a-Vis, France. 22af, Louis Chevrolet
(1879-1941), 1925 Sedan, US.

1984, June 30
1097 A442   2af multicolored   .15 .15
1098 A442   5af multicolored   .30 .30
1099 A442   8af multicolored   .50 .50
1100 A442 11af multicolored   .70 .70
1101 A442 12af multicolored   .75 .75
1102 A442 15af multicolored   .90 .90
1103 A442 22af multicolored   1.40 1.40
     Nos. 1097-1103 (7)   4.70 4.70

Qalai Bist
Arch — A443

World Tourism Day: 2af, Ornamental buckled
harness. 5af, Victory Monument and Memorial
Arch, Kabul. 9af, Standing sculpture of Afghani
ruler and attendants. 15af, Buffalo riders in snow.
19af, Camel driver, tent, camel in caparison. 21af,
Horsemen playing buzkashi.

1984, Sept. 27
1104 A443   1af multicolored   .15 .15
1105 A443   2af multicolored   .15 .15
1106 A443   5af multicolored   .30 .30
1107 A443   9af multicolored   .55 .55
1108 A443 15af multicolored   .60 .60
1109 A443 19af multicolored   1.10 1.10
1110 A443 21af multicolored   1.25 1.25
     Nos. 1104-1110 (7)   4.10 4.10

UN World Food
Day — A444

Fruit-bearing trees.

1984, Oct. 16
1111 A444   2af multicolored   .15 .15
1112 A444   4af multicolored   .25 .25
1113 A444   6af multicolored   .40 .40
1114 A444   9af multicolored   .55 .55
1115 A444 13af multicolored   .80 .80
1116 A444 15af multicolored   .90 .90
1117 A444 26af multicolored   1.65 1.65
     Nos. 1111-1117 (7)   4.70 4.70

People's
Democratic
Party, 20th
Anniv.
A445

1985, Jan. 1
1118 A445 25af multicolored   1.50 1.50

Farmer's
Day — A446

1985, Mar. 2
1119 A446   1af Oxen   .15 .15
1120 A446   3af Mare, foal   .20 .20
1121 A446   7af Brown horse   .40 .40

1122 A446   8af White horse, vert.   .50 .50
1123 A446 15af Sheep, sheepskins   .90 .90
1124 A446 16af Shepherd, cattle,
         sheep   1.00 1.00
1125 A446 25af Family, camels   1.50 1.50
     Nos. 1119-1125 (7)   4.65 4.65

Geologist's
Day — A447

1985, Apr. 5
1126 A447   4af multicolored   .25 .25

Lenin Leading
Red Army,
1917 — A448

Lenin and: 10af, Soviet Workers' Party deputies,
Smolny. 15af, Revolutionaries, 1917, Leningrad.
50af, Portrait.

1985, Apr. 21   *Perf. 12x12½*
1127 A448 10af multicolored   .60 .60
1128 A448 15af multicolored   .90 .90
1129 A448 25af multicolored   1.50 1.50
     Nos. 1127-1129 (3)   3.00 3.00

Souvenir Sheet
1130 A448 50af multicolored   4.00 4.00

Saur Revolution, 7th
Anniv. — A449

1985, Apr. 27
1131 A449 21af multicolored   1.25 1.25

Berlin-Treptow Soviet War Memorial, Red
Army at Siege of Berlin, 1945 — A450

Designs: 9af, Victorious Motherland monument,
fireworks over Kremlin. 10af, Caecilienhof, site of
Potsdam Treaty signing, flags of Great Britain, USSR
and US.

1985, May 9   *Perf. 12½x12*
1132 A450   6af multicolored   .40 .40
1133 A450   9af multicolored   .55 .55
1134 A450 10af multicolored   .65 .65
     Nos. 1132-1134 (3)   1.60 1.60

End of World War II, defeat of Nazi Germany,
40th anniv.

INTELSAT,
20th Anniv.
A451

Designs: 6af, INTELSAT satellite orbiting Earth.
9af, INTELSAT III. 10af, Rocket launch, Baikanur
Space Center, vert.

Perf. 12x12½, 12½x12
1985, Apr. 6   Litho.
1135 A451   6af multicolored   .40 .40
1136 A451   9af multicolored   .55 .55
1137 A451 10af multicolored   .60 .60
     Nos. 1135-1137 (3)   1.55 1.55

12th World Youth
Festival,
Moscow — A452

1985, May 5
1138 A452   7af Olympic stadium,
         Moscow   .50 .50
1139 A452 12af Festival emblem   .75 .75
1140 A452 13af Kremlin   .80 .80
1141 A452 18af Folk doll, emblem   1.10 1.10
     Nos. 1138-1141 (4)   3.15 3.15

Intl. Child
Survival
Campaign
A453

1985, June 1
1142 A453   1af Weighing child   .15 .15
1143 A453   2af Immunization   .15 .15
1144 A453   4af Breastfeeding   .25 .25
1145 A453   5af Mother, child   .30 .30
     Nos. 1142-1145 (4)   .85 .85

Flowers
A454

1985, July 5
1146 A454   2af Oenothera affinis   .15 .15
1147 A454   4af Erythrina crista-
         galli   .25 .25
1148 A454   8af Tillandsia aer-
         anthos   .50 .50
1149 A454 13af Vinca major   .80 .80
1150 A454 18af Mirabilis jalapa   1.10 1.10
1151 A454 25af Cypella herbertii   1.50 1.50
1152 A454 30af Clytostoma callis-
         tegioides   1.90 1.90
     Nos. 1146-1152 (7)   6.20 6.20

Souvenir Sheet
Perf. 12½x11½
1153 A454 75af Sesbania punicea,
         horiz.   6.00 6.00

ARGENTINA '85.

Independence,
66th Anniv.
A455

1985, Aug. 19   *Perf. 12x12½*
1154 A455 33af Mosque   2.00 2.00

Pashto's and
Balutchi's
Day — A456

1985, Aug. 30
1155 A456 25af multicolored   1.50 1.50

UN Decade for
Women
A457

1985, Sept. 22
1156 A457 10af Emblems   .60 .60

World
Tourism Day,
10th Anniv.
A457a

1985, Sept. 27   Litho.   Perf. 12
1156A A457a 1af Guldara Stupa   .15 .15
1156B A457a 2af Mirwais Tomb,
              vert.   .15 .15
1156C A457a 10af Statue of Bamy-
              an, vert.   .60 .60
1156D A457a 13af No Gumbad
              Mosque, vert.   .80 .80
1156E A457a 14af Pule Kheshti
              Mosque   .85 .85
1156F A457a 15af Bost Citadel   .90 .90
1156G A457a 20af Ghazni Minaret,
              vert.   1.25 1.25
    Nos. 1156A-1156G (7)   4.70 4.70

Sports
A457b

Perf. 12x12½, 12½x12
1985, Oct. 3   Litho.
1156H A457b 1af Boxing   .15 .15
1156I A457b 2af Volleyball   .15 .15
1156J A457b 3af Soccer, vert.   .20 .20
1156K A457b 12af Buzkashi   .90 .90
1156L A457b 14af Weight lifting   1.00 1.00
1156M A457b 18af Wrestling   1.25 1.25
1156N A457b 25af Peg sticking   1.90 1.90
    Nos. 1156H-1156N (7)   5.55 5.55

World Food
Day — A457c

1985, Oct. 16
1156O A457c 25af multicolored   1.50 1.50

UN 40th
Anniv. — A458

Birds — A459

1985, Oct. 24   Perf. 12½x12
1157 A458 22af multicolored   1.40 1.40

Perf. 12½x12, 12x12½
1985, Oct. 25
1158 A459 2af Jay   .15 .15
1159 A459 4af Plover, hummingbird   .25 .25
1160 A459 8af Pheasant   .50 .50
1161 A459 13af Hoopoe   1.10 1.10
1162 A459 18af Falcon   1.10 1.10

1163 A459 25af Partridge   1.50 1.50
1164 A459 30af Pelicans, horiz.   1.90 1.90
    Nos. 1158-1164 (7)   6.20 6.20
Souvenir Sheet
Perf. 12x12½
1165 A459 75af Parakeets   6.00 6.00

Mushrooms — A460

1985, June 10   Litho.   Perf. 12½x12
1165A A460 3af Tricholomopsis ru-
              tilans   .20 .20
1166 A460 4af Boletus miniato-
              porus   .25 .25
1167 A460 7af Amanita rubescens   .45 .45
1168 A460 11af Boletus scaber   .65 .65
1169 A460 12af Coprinus atra-
              mentarius   .75 .75
1170 A460 18af Hypholoma   1.10 1.10
1171 A460 20af Boletus aurantiacus 1.25 1.25
    Nos. 1165A-1171 (7)   4.65 4.65

World Wildlife Fund — A461

1985, Nov. 25
1172 A461 2af Leopard, cubs   .15 .15
1173 A461 9af Adult's head   .55 .55
1174 A461 11af Adult   .70 .70
1175 A461 15af Cub   .90 .90
    Nos. 1172-1175 (4)   2.30 2.30

Motorcycle, Cent. — A462

Designs: Different makes and landmarks.

1985, Dec. 16
1176 A462 2af multicolored   .15 .15
1177 A462 4af multicolored   .25 .25
1178 A462 8af multicolored   .50 .50
1179 A462 13af multicolored   .75 .75
1180 A462 18af multicolored   1.00 1.00
1181 A462 25af multicolored   1.50 1.50
1182 A462 30af multicolored   1.75 1.75
    Nos. 1176-1182 (7)   5.90 5.90
Souvenir Sheet
Perf. 11½x12½
1183 A462 75af multicolored   6.00 6.00

People's Democratic Party, 21st
Anniv. — A463

1986, Jan. 1   Perf. 12½x12
1184 A463 2af multicolored   .25 .25

27th Soviet Communist Party
Congress — A464

1986, Mar. 31
1185 A464 25af Lenin   1.50 1.50

First Man in Space, 25th Anniv. — A465

Designs: 3af, Spacecraft. 7af, Soviet space
achievement medal, vert. 9af, Rocket lift-off, vert.
11af, Yuri Gagarin, military decorations, vert. 13af,
Gagarin, cosmonaut. 15af, Gagarin, politician. 17af,
Gagarin wearing flight suit, vert.

Perf. 12½x12, 12x12½
1986, Apr. 12   Litho.
1186 A465 3af multicolored
1187 A465 7af multicolored
1188 A465 9af multicolored
1189 A465 11af multicolored
1190 A465 13af multicolored
1191 A465 15af multicolored
1192 A465 17af multicolored
    Nos. 1186-1192 (7)   4.50 4.50

Loya Jirgah (Grand Assembly) of the
People's Democratic Republic, 1st Anniv.
A465a

1986, Apr. 23   Litho.   Perf. 12½x12
1192A A465a 3af multicolored   .25 .25

Intl. Day of Labor
Solidarity — A465b

1986, May 1   Perf. 12½x12
1192B A465b 5af multicolored   .30 .30

Intl. Red
Crescent Day
A465c

1986, May 8   Perf. 12x12½
1192C A465c 7af multicolored   .45 .45

Intl. Children's
Day — A466

1986, June 1   Perf. 12
1193 A466 1af Mother, children, vert. .15 .15
1194 A466 3af Mother, child, vert.   .25 .25
1195 A466 3af Children, map   .40 .40
    Nos. 1193-1195 (3)   .80 .80

World Youth
Day — A466a

1986, July 31   Perf. 12x12½
1195A A466a 15af multicolored   .90 .90

Pashtos' and
Baluchis'
Day — A467

1986, Aug. 31   Perf. 12x12½
1196 A467 4af multicolored   .25 .25

Intl. Peace
Year — A468

1986, Sept. 30 Photo. Perf. 12½x12
1197 A468 12af black & Prus blue   .75 .75

A469

1986 World Cup Soccer Championships,
Mexico — A470

Various soccer plays.

1986, Apr. 15   Litho.   Perf. 12
1198 A469 3af multi, vert.
1199 A469 4af multicolored
1200 A469 7af multicolored
1201 A469 11af multi, vert.
1202 A469 12af multicolored
1203 A469 18af multi, vert.
1204 A469 20af multi, vert.
    Nos. 1198-1204 (7)   4.50 4.50
Souvenir Sheet
Perf. 12½x12
1205 A470 75af multicolored   6.00 6.00

A471

A472

1986, Apr. 21   Perf. 12½x12
1206 A471 16af Lenin   1.00 1.00

1986, Apr. 27   Litho.   Perf. 12½x12
1207 A472 8af multicolored   .50 .50
    Saur revolution, 8th anniv.

Natl. Independence,
67th Anniv. — A473

1986, Aug. 19   Litho.   Perf. 12½x12
1208 A473 10af multicolored   .65 .65

Literacy
Day — A474

1986, Sept. 18   Perf. 12x12½
1209 A474 2af multicolored   .25 .25

Dogs — A475

Lizards — A476

1986, May 19   Litho.   Perf. 12x12½
1210 A475 5af St. Bernard
1211 A475 7af Collie
1212 A475 8af Pointer
1213 A475 9af Golden retriever
1214 A475 11af German shepherd
1215 A475 15af Bulldog
1216 A475 20af Afghan hound
    Nos. 1210-1216 (7)   4.50 4.50

1986, July 7   Perf. 12x12½, 12½x12
1217 A476 3af Cobra
1218 A476 4af shown
1219 A476 5af Praying mantis
1220 A476 8af Beetle
1221 A476 9af Tarantula
1222 A476 10af Python
1223 A476 11af Scorpions
    Nos. 1217-1223 (7)   3.00 3.00
    Nos. 1217, 1219, 1221-1223 horiz.

STOCKHOLMIA '86 — A477

Ships.

1986, Aug. 28   Perf. 12½x12
1224 A477 4af multicolored
1225 A477 5af multicolored
1226 A477 6af multicolored
1227 A477 7af multicolored
1228 A477 8af multicolored
1229 A477 9af multicolored
1230 A477 11af multicolored
    Nos. 1224-1230 (7)   3.00 3.00

Souvenir Sheet
1231 A477 50af Galley   4.00 4.00

A479   A480

1986, Sept. 14   Perf. 12
1232 A479 3af lt blue, blk & olive gray   .25 .25
Reunion of Afghan tribes under the Supreme Girgah.

1986, Oct. 25   Perf. 12½x12
1233 A480 3af black & brt ver   .25 .25
Natl. youth solidarity.

Locomotives — A481

1986, June 21   Perf. 12½x12
1234 A481 4af multicolored
1235 A481 5af multicolored
1236 A481 6af multicolored
1237 A481 7af multicolored
1238 A481 8af multicolored
1239 A481 9af multicolored
1240 A481 11af multicolored
    Nos. 1234-1240 (7)   3.00 3.00

Fish
A482

Various fish.

1986, May 25
1241 A482 5af multicolored
1242 A482 7af multicolored
1243 A482 8af multicolored
1244 A482 9af multicolored
1245 A482 11af multicolored
1246 A482 15af multicolored
1247 A482 20af multicolored
    Nos. 1241-1247 (7)   4.50 4.50

Saur
Revolution,
9th Anniv.
A483

1987, Apr. 27   Perf. 12
1248 A483 3af multicolored   .25 .25

Natl.
Reconciliation
A484

1987, May 27   Perf. 12x12½
1249 A484 3af multicolored   .25 .25

A485

A486

UN Child Survival
Campaign — A487

1987, June 1   Perf. 12
1250 A485 1af multicolored   .15 .15
1251 A486 5af multicolored   .30 .30
1252 A487 9af multicolored   .55 .55
    Nos. 1250-1252 (3)   1.00 1.00

Conference
of
Clergymen
and Ulema,
1st Anniv.
A488

1987, June 30
1253 A488 5af multicolored   .30 .30

Butterflies — A489   A490

1987, July 3
1254 A489 7af multicolored
1255 A489 9af multi, diff.
1256 A489 10af multi, diff.
1257 A489 12af multi, diff.
1258 A489 15af multi, diff.
1259 A489 22af multi, diff.
1260 A489 25af multi, diff.
    Nos. 1254-1260 (7)   6.00 6.00
    10af, 15af and 22af horiz.

1987, Aug. 11
1261 A490 1af multicolored   .25 .25
1st election of local representatives for State
Power and Administration.

Natl. Independence, 68th Anniv. — A490a

1987, Aug. 19
1261A A490a 3af multicolored   .25 .25

1st Artificial Satellite
(Sputnik), 30th
Anniv. — A491

1987, Oct. 4   Litho.   Perf. 12½x12
1262 A491 10af Sputnik
1263 A491 15af Rocket launch
1264 A491 25af Soyuz
    Nos. 1262-1264 (3)   3.00 3.00

World Post
Day — A492

1987, Oct. 9   Perf. 12x12½
1265 A492 22af multicolored   1.40 1.40

Intl. Communications and Transport
Day — A493

1987, Oct. 24   Perf. 12½x12
1266 A493 42af multicolored   2.50 2.50

October Revolution
in Russia, 70th
Anniv. — A494

Mice — A495

1987, Nov. 7
1267 A494 25af Lenin   1.50 1.50

1987, Dec. 6   Perf. 12½x12, 12x12½
Various mice. Nos. 1269-1272 horiz.
1268 A495 2af multicolored
1269 A495 4af multi, diff.
1270 A495 8af multi, diff.
1271 A495 16af multi, diff.
1272 A495 20af multi, diff.
    Nos. 1268-1272 (5)   3.00 3.00

Medicinal
Plants — A496

Pashto's and
Baluchis'
Day — A497

1987, Nov. 11   Litho.   Perf. 12
1273 A496 3af Castor bean   .20 .20
1274 A496 6af Licorice   .35 .35
1275 A496 9af Chamomile   .55 .55
1276 A496 14af Datura   .80 .80
1277 A496 18af Dandelion   1.00 1.00
    Nos. 1273-1277 (5)   2.90 2.90

1987, Aug. 30
1278 A497 4af multicolored   .25 .25

Dinosaurs
A498

Pashtos' and
Baluchis' Day
A499

Perf. 12½x12, 12x12½
1988, June 6   Litho.
1279 A498 3af Mesosaurus   .20 .20
1280 A498 5af Styracosaurus   .30 .30
1281 A498 10af Uinatherium   .60 .60
1282 A498 15af Protoceratops   .90 .90
1283 A498 20af Stegosaurus   1.25 1.25
1284 A498 25af Ceratosaurus   1.50 1.50
1285 A498 30af Dinornis maximus   1.90 1.90
    Nos. 1279-1285 (7)   6.65 6.65
    Nos. 1280-1283 horiz.

1988, Aug. 30   Perf. 12½x12
1286 A499 23af multicolored   1.40 1.40

Afghan-Soviet
Joint Space
Flight — A500

Valentina
Tereshkova, 1st
Woman in Space,
25th
Anniv. — A501

1988, Aug. 30
1287 A500 32af multicolored 2.00 2.00

Perf. 12x12½, 12½x12
1988, Oct. 16
1288	A501	10af Portrait, rocket, horiz.	.60	.60
1289	A501	15af Lift-off, dove	.90	.90
1290	A501	25af Spacecraft, Earth, horiz.	1.50	1.50
		Nos. 1288-1290 (3)	3.00	3.00

Traditional
Crafts — A502

Precious and
Semiprecious
Gems — A503

Perf. 12x12½, 12½x12
1988, Nov. 9 Litho.
1291	A502	2af Pitcher, bowls	.15	.15
1292	A502	4af Vases	.25	.25
1293	A502	5af Dress	.30	.30
1294	A502	9af Mats, napkins	.55	.55
1295	A502	15af Pocketbooks	.90	.90
1296	A502	23af Jewelry	1.40	1.40
1297	A502	50af Furniture	3.00	3.00
		Nos. 1291-1297 (7)	6.55	6.55

Nos. 1291-1292, 1294-1297 horiz.

1988, Dec. 5 Perf. 12½x12
1298	A503	13af Emeralds	.80	.80
1299	A503	37af Lapiz lazuli	2.25	2.25
1300	A503	40af Rubies	2.50	2.50
		Nos. 1298-1300 (3)	5.55	5.55

1988 Winter Olympics,
Calgary — A504

1988, Dec. 25
1301	A504	2af Women's figure skating	.15	.15
1301A	A504	5af Skiing	.30	.30
1301B	A504	9af Bobsledding	.55	.55
1301C	A504	22af Biathlon	1.40	1.40
1301D	A504	37af Speed skating	2.25	2.25

Size: 80x60mm
| 1302 | A504 | 75af Ice hockey | 4.50 | 4.50 |
| | | Nos. 1301-1302 (6) | 9.15 | 9.15 |

A510

A511

A512

A513

A513a

Flowers — A514

Various flowering plants.

Perf. 12x12½, 12½x12
1988, Jan. 27 Litho.
1303	A510	3af multicolored	.15	.15
1304	A511	5af multicolored	.30	.30
1305	A511	7af multi, vert.	.40	.40
1306	A512	9af multicolored	.50	.50
1307	A513	12af multicolored	.75	.75
1308	A513a	15af multicolored	.90	.90
1309	A514	24af multicolored	1.50	1.50
		Nos. 1303-1309 (7)	4.50	4.50

Traditional
Musical
Instruments
A515

String and percussion instruments.

1988, Jan. 15 Litho. Perf. 12
1310	A515	1af shown	.15	.15
1311	A515	3af drums	.20	.20
1312	A515	5af multi, diff.	.30	.30
1313	A515	15af multi, diff.	.90	.90
1314	A515	18af multi, diff.	1.10	1.10
1315	A515	25af multi, diff.	1.50	1.50
1316	A515	33af multi, diff.	2.00	2.00
		Nos. 1310-1316 (7)	6.15	6.15

Admission of
Afghanistan to the ITU
and UPU, 60th
Anniv. — A516

1988, Apr. 13 Litho. Perf. 12
1317 A516 20af multicolored 1.25 1.25

Saur
Revolution,
10th Anniv.
A517

1988, Apr. 23
1318 A517 10af multicolored .65 .65

Fruit — A518

1988, July 18 Litho. Perf. 12
1319	A518	2af Baskets, compote	.15	.15
1320	A518	4af Four baskets	.25	.25
1321	A518	7af Basket	.45	.45
1322	A518	8af Grapes, vert.	.50	.50
1323	A518	16af Market	1.00	1.00
1324	A518	22af Market, diff.	1.40	1.40
1325	A518	25af Vendor, vert.	1.50	1.50
		Nos. 1319-1325 (7)	5.25	5.25

Jawaharlal Nehru
(1889-1964), 1st Prime
Minister of Independent
India — A519

1988, Nov. 14
1326 A519 40af multicolored 2.50 2.50

Natl.
Independence,
69th Anniv.
A520

1988, Aug. 1
1327 A520 24af multicolored 1.50 1.50

Intl. Red Cross and Red
Crescent Organizations,
125th Annivs. — A521

1988, Sept. 26
1328 A521 10af multicolored .60 .60

Natl. Reconciliation Institute, 2nd
Anniv. — A522

1989, Jan. 4
1329 A522 4af multicolored .25 .25

Chess
A523

Boards, early matches and hand-made chessmen.

1989, Feb. 2 Litho. Perf. 12x12½
1330	A523	2af Bishop	.15	.15
1331	A523	3af Queen	.20	.20
1332	A523	4af King (bust)	.25	.25
1333	A523	7af King, diff.	.40	.40
1334	A523	16af Knight	1.00	1.00
1335	A523	24af Pawn	1.50	1.50
1336	A523	45af Bishop, diff.	2.75	2.75
		Nos. 1330-1336 (7)	6.25	6.25

Paintings by
Picasso — A524

Fauna — A525

Designs: 4af, *The Old Jew.* 6af, *The Two Mountebanks.* 8af, *Portrait of Ambrouse Vollar.* 22af, *Woman of Majorca.* 35af, *Acrobat on the Ball.* 75af, *Usine a Horta de Ebro.*

1989, Feb. 13 Litho. Perf. 12½x12
1341	A524	4af multicolored	.25	.25
1342	A524	6af multicolored	.35	.35
1343	A524	8af multicolored	.50	.50
1344	A524	22af multicolored	1.40	1.40
1345	A524	35af multicolored	2.25	2.25

Size: 71x90mm
Imperf
| 1346 | A524 | 75af multicolored | 4.50 | 4.50 |
| | | Nos. 1341-1346 (6) | 9.25 | 9.25 |

1989, Feb. 20 Litho. Perf. 12½x12
1347	A525	3af *Allactaga euphratica*	.15	.15
1348	A525	4af *Equus hemionus*	.25	.25
1349	A525	14af *Felis lynx*	.85	.85
1350	A525	35af *Gypaetus barbatus*	2.25	2.25
1351	A525	44af *Capra falconeri*	2.75	2.75

Size: 71x91mm
Imperf
| 1352 | A525 | 100af *Naja oxiana* | 6.00 | 6.00 |
| | | Nos. 1347-1352 (6) | 12.25 | 12.25 |

Intl. Women's
Day — A526

1989, Mar. 8 Perf. 12½x12
1353 A526 8af multicolored .50 .50

Restoration and Development of San'a, Yemen
A527

1988, Dec. 27 *Litho.* *Perf. 12*
1354 A527 32af multicolored 2.00 2.00

Agriculture Day — A528

1989, Mar. 21
1355 A528 1af Cattle .15 .15
1356 A528 2af Old and new plows .15 .15
1357 A528 3af Field workers .20 .20
Set value .35 .35

World Meteorology Day — A529

1989, Mar. 23
1358 A529 27af shown 1.65 1.65
1359 A529 32af Emblems 2.00 2.00
1360 A529 40af Weather station, balloon, vert. 2.50 2.50
Nos. 1358-1360 (3) 6.15 6.15

Saur Revolution, 11th Anniv. A530

1989, Apr. 27
1361 A530 20af multicolored 1.25 1.25

Classic Automobiles — A531

1989, Dec. 30 *Litho.* *Perf. 12¹/₂x12*
1362 A531 5af 1910 Duchs, Germany
1363 A531 10af 1911 Ford, US
1364 A531 20af 1911 Renault, France
1365 A531 25af 1911, Russo-Balte, Russia
1366 A531 30af 1926 Fiat, Italy

Asia-Pacific Telecommunity, 10th Anniv. — A532

1989, Aug. 3 *Perf. 12*
1367 A532 3af shown
1368 A532 27af Emblem, satellite dish

Teacher's Day — A533

1989, May 30 *Litho.* *Perf. 12*
1369 A533 42af multicolored 1.25

French Revolution, Bicent. — A534

1989, July *Litho.* *Perf. 12*
1370 A534 25af multicolored .80

Natl. Independence, 70th Anniv. A535

1989, Aug. 18 *Litho.* *Perf. 12*
1371 A535 25af multicolored .80

A536

Birds — A537

1989, Aug. 30
1372 A536 3af multicolored .15
Pashtos' and Baluchis' Day.

1989, Dec. 5 *Litho.* *Perf. 12*
1373 A537 3af Platalea leucorodia .15
1374 A537 5af Porphyrio porhyrio .15
1375 A537 10af Botaurus stellaris, horiz. .30
1376 A537 15af Pelecanus onocrotalus .45
1377 A537 20af Netta rufina .60
1378 A537 25af Cygnus olor .75
1379 A537 30af Phalacrocorax carbo, horiz. .90
Nos. 1373-1379 (7) 3.30

Tourism — A538

Mushrooms — A539

1989, Dec.
1380 A538 1af Mosque .15
1381 A538 2af Minaret .15
1382 A538 3af Buzkashi, horiz. .15
1383 A538 4af Jet over Hendo Kush, horiz. .15
Set value .30

1996, July 20 *Litho.* *Perf. 12¹/₂x13*
Designs: 100af, Suillus luteus. 300af, Russula virescens. 400af, Clitocybe inversa. 500af, Volvariella bombycina. 600af, Macrolepiota procera. 800af, Cystoderma cinnabarinum. 4000af, Lycoperdon umbrinum.

1384 A539 100af multicolored .25
1385 A539 300af multicolored .70
1386 A539 400af multicolored .95

1387 A539 500af multicolored 1.10
1388 A539 600af multicolored 1.40
1389 A539 800af multicolored 1.75
Nos. 1384-1389 (6) 6.15
Souvenir Sheet
1390 A539 4000af multicolored 5.25
No. 1390 contains one 32x40mm stamp.

Bears A540

Designs: 500af, Ursus americanus, vert. 600af, Ursus maritimus. 800af, Helarctos malayanus. 900af, Ursus arctos horribilis. 1000af, Ursus arctos pyreneicus, vert. 4000af, Ursus arctos syriacus, vert.

Perf. 12¹/₂x13, 13x12¹/₂
1996, Aug. 15 *Litho.*
1391 A540 500af multicolored .75
1392 A540 600af multicolored .90
1393 A540 800af multicolored 1.25
1394 A540 900af multicolored 1.40
1395 A540 1000af multicolored 1.50
Nos. 1391-1395 (5) 5.80
Souvenir Sheet
Perf. 13
1396 A540 4000af multicolored 6.15
No. 1396 contains one 32x40mm stamp.

1998 World Cup Soccer Championships, France — A541

Various soccer players.

1996, Sept. 18 *Litho.* *Perf. 13*
Background Color
1397 A541 500af green .75
1398 A541 600af purple .90
1399 A541 700af brown 1.00
Size: 28x42mm
1400 A541 800af yellow 1.20
1401 A541 900af blue 1.35
1402 A541 1000af vermilion 1.50
Nos. 1397-1402 (6) 6.70
Souvenir Sheet
Perf. 12¹/₂
1403 A541 4000d multicolored 6.00
No. 1403 contains one 32x40mm stamp.

Silkworms A542

Designs: 300af, Arctia caja. 400af, Sphinx ligustri. 500af, Zerynthia polyxema. 600af, Papilio machaon. 700af, Cerura vinula. 800af, Celerio euphorbiae. 3000af, Abraxes grossulariata.

1996 *Perf. 12¹/₂*
1404 A542 300af multicolored .45
1405 A542 400af multicolored .60
1406 A542 500af multicolored .75
1407 A542 600af multicolored .90
1408 A542 700af multicolored 1.00
1409 A542 800af multicolored 1.20
Nos. 1404-1409 (6) 4.90
Souvenir Sheet
Perf. 13
1410 A542 3000af multicolored 4.60
No. 1410 contains one 40x32mm stamp.

Domestic Cats — A543

Designs: 200af, American shorthair. 500af, Japanese bobtail. 600af, British shorthair. 800af, Devon rex. 1000af, Colorpoint shorthair. 1200af, Somali. 4000af, Sphinx.

1996 *Litho.* *Perf. 12¹/₂*
1411 A543 200af multicolored .30
1412 A543 500af multicolored .75
1413 A543 600af multicolored .90
1414 A543 800af multicolored 1.20
1415 A543 1000af multicolored 1.50
1416 A543 1200af multicolored 1.75
Nos. 1411-1416 (6) 6.40
Souvenir Sheet
1417 A543 4000af multicolored 6.00
No. 1417 contains one 40x32mm stamp.

Horses A544

1996
1418 A544 200af Eohippus .45
1419 A544 300af Miohippus .65
1420 A544 400af Merychippus .90
1421 A544 500af Pliohippus 1.10
1422 A544 600af Equus 1.30
Nos. 1418-1422 (5) 4.40
Souvenir Sheet
Perf. 13
1423 A544 3000af Trotter, sulky 6.00
No. 1423 contains one 40x32mm stamp. Inscription on No. 1418 reads "Echippus."

Tulips — A545

Designs: 300af, Jewel of Spring. 400af, Mrs. John Scheepers. 500af, Absalon. 600af, Queen of Sheba. 800af, Marlette. 1000af, Mary Housley, 3000af, Fosteriana Purissima.

1997 *Litho.* *Perf. 12¹/₂*
1424 A545 300af multicolored .45
1425 A545 400af multicolored .60
1426 A545 500af multicolored .70
1427 A545 600af multicolored .90
1428 A545 800af multicolored 1.15
1429 A545 1000af multicolored 1.45
Nos. 1424-1429 (6) 5.25
Souvenir Sheet
1430 A545 3000af multicolored 4.25
No. 1430 contains one 32x40mm stamp.

Llamas and Camels A546

Designs: 400af, Lama vicugna, vert. 600af, Lama guanicoe. 800af, Camelus dromedarius. 1000af, Lama guanicoe pacos, vert. 1200af, Lama guanicoe glama. 1500af, Camelus ferus bactrianus. 4000af, Camelus dromedarius, vert.

1997

1431	A546	400af multicolored	.60
1432	A546	600af multicolored	.85
1433	A546	800af multicolored	1.15
1434	A546	1000af multicolored	1.45
1435	A546	1200af multicolored	1.70
1436	A546	1500af multicolored	2.20
	Nos. 1431-1436 (6)		7.95

Souvenir Sheet

1437	A546	4000af multicolored	5.75

No. 1437 contains one 32x40mm stamp.

Islamic Revolution, 4th Anniv. — A547

Design: 1500af, Farmer plowing beside stream.

1996   Litho.   Perf. 13

1438	A547	800af multicolored	1.50
1439	A547	1500af multicolored	3.00

Independence, 77th Anniv. — A548

In Honor of Prophet Mohammed A549

1996

1440	A548	700af multicolored	1.40
1441	A549	1500af multicolored	3.00

Domestic Cats A550

Designs: 30af, Norwegian forest. 50af, Ragdoll. 100af, Longhair Scottish fold. 200af, Oriental longhair. 300af, Manx. 500af, Sphinx. 1200af, Manx, diff.

1997   Perf. 12½

1442	A550	30af multicolored	.15
1443	A550	50af multicolored	.20
1444	A550	100af multicolored	.40
1445	A550	200af multicolored	.80
1446	A550	300af multicolored	1.25
1447	A550	500af multicolored	2.00
	Nos. 1442-1447 (6)		4.80

Souvenir Sheet
Perf. 13

1448	A550	1200af multicolored	4.50

No. 1448 contains one 40x32mm stamp.

Wildflowers A551

Designs: 50af, Nymphaea odorata. 100af, Nymphaea lotus. 200af, Aponogeton distachyus. 500af, Nymphaea capensis. 800af, Numphaea rubra. 1000af, Pontederia cordata. 3000af, Nymphaea daubenyana, horiz.

1997   Litho.   Perf. 12½

1449	A551	50af multicolored	.15
1450	A551	100af multicolored	.15
1451	A551	200af multicolored	.25
1452	A551	500af multicolored	.65
1453	A551	800af multicolored	1.00
1454	A551	1000af multicolored	1.25
	Nos. 1449-1454 (6)		3.45

Souvenir Sheet

1455	A551	3000af multicolored	3.80

No. 1455 contains one 40x32mm stamp.

Early Sailing Ships — A552

Designs: 400af, Hanseatic cog. 600af, Northern Europe dromond. 800af, Venetian cargo ship. 1000af, Northern Europe merchant ship. 1200af, Ladia Russian war ship. 1500af, Genoa merchant ship.
4000af, Egyptian merchant ship.

1997   Litho.   Perf. 12½

1456	A552	400af multicolored	.45
1457	A552	600af multicolored	.70
a.	Pair, #1456-1457		1.15
1458	A552	800af multicolored	.95
1459	A552	1000af multicolored	1.15
a.	Pair, #1458-1459		2.10
1460	A552	1200af multicolored	1.40
1461	A552	1500af multicolored	1.75
a.	Pair, #1460-1461		3.15
	Nos. 1456-1461 (6)		6.40

Souvenir Sheet

1462	A552	4000af multicolored	4.60

SEMI-POSTAL STAMPS

Catalogue values for unused stamps in this section are for Never Hinged items.

No. 373 Surcharged in Violet

MILLIEME ANNIVERSAIRE
DE BOALI SINAI BALKI
125 POULS

40 POULS

1952, July 12   Unwmk.   Perf. 12½

B1	A122	40p + 30p cerise	10.00 1.50
B2	A122	125p + 30p cerise	12.50 2.00

1000th anniv. of the birth of Avicenna.

Children at Play — SP1

1955, July 3   Typo.   Perf. 11

B3	SP1	35p + 15p dk green	.50 .35
B4	SP1	125p + 25p purple	1.00 .85

The surtax was for child welfare.

Amir Sher Ali Khan, Tiger Head Stamp and Zahir Shah — SP2

Children at Play — SP3

1955, July 2   Litho.

B5	SP2	35p + 15p carmine	.40 .30
B6	SP2	125p + 25p pale vio bl	.85 .55

85th anniv. of the Afghan post.

1956, June 20   Typo.

B7	SP3	35p + 15p brt vio bl	.75 .25
B8	SP3	140p + 15p dk org brn	1.25 .75

Issued for Children's Day. The surtax was for child welfare. No. B8 inscribed in French.

Pashtunistan Monument, Kabul — SP4

1956, Sept. 1   Litho.

B9	SP4	35p + 15p dp violet	.20 .20
B10	SP4	140p + 15p dk brown	.60 .60

"Free Pashtunistan" Day. The surtax aided the "Free Pashtunistan" movement.
No. B9 measures 30½x19½mm; No. B10, 29x19mm. On sale and valid for use only on Sept. 1-2.

Globe and Sun — SP5   Children on Seesaw — SP6

1956, Oct. 24   Perf. 11

B11	SP5	35p + 15p ultra	.65 .60
B12	SP5	140p + 15p red brown	1.25 1.00

Afghanistan's UN admission, 10th anniv.

1957, June 20   Unwmk.

B13	SP6	35p + 15p brt rose	.75 .25
B14	SP6	140p + 15p ultra	1.50 .90

Children's Day. Surtax for child welfare.

UN Headquarters and Emblems — SP7

1957, Oct. 24   Perf. 11 Rough

B15	SP7	35p + 15p red brown	.35 .20
B16	SP7	140p + 15p lt ultra	.65 .55

United Nations Day.

Swimming Pool and Children — SP8

1958, June 22   Perf. 11

B17	SP8	35p + 15p rose	.25 .20
B18	SP8	140p + 15p dl red brn	.75 .60

Children's Day. Surtax for child welfare.

Pashtunistan Flag — SP9

1958, Aug. 31

B19	SP9	35p + 15p lt blue	.20 .20
B20	SP9	140p + 15p red brown	.60 .60

Issued for "Free Pashtunistan Day."

Children Playing Tug of War — SP10

1959, June 23   Litho.   Perf. 11

B21	SP10	35p + 15p brown vio	.50 .20
B22	SP10	165p + 15p brt pink	1.00 .60

Children's Day. Surtax for child welfare.

Pathans in Tribal Dance — SP11

1959, Sept.   Unwmk.   Perf. 11 Rough

B23	SP11	35p + 15p green	.50 .20
B24	SP11	165p + 15p orange	1.00 .60

Issued for "Free Pashtunistan Day."

Afghan Cavalryman with UN Flag — SP12

1959, Oct. 24   Perf. 11 Rough

B25	SP12	35p + 15p green	.20 .15
B26	SP12	165p + 15p lt bl grn	.45 .40

Issued for United Nations Day.

Children SP13

1960, Oct. 23   Litho.

B27	SP13	75p + 25p lt ultra	.75 .20
B28	SP13	175p + 25p lt green	1.50 .35

Children's Day. Surtax for child welfare.

Man with Spray Gun — SP14

1960, Sept. 6   Perf. 11 Rough

B29	SP14	50p + 50p orange	.80 1.00
B30	SP14	175p + 50p red brown	2.25 2.25

11th anniversary of the WHO malaria control program in Afghanistan.

SP15

1960, Sept. 1   Unwmk.

B31	SP15	50p + 50p rose	.25 .20
B32	SP15	175p + 50p dk blue	.55 .45

Issued for "Free Pashtunistan Day."

Ambulance — SP16

1960, Oct. 16   Perf. 11

Crescent in Red

B33	SP16	50p + 50p violet	.40 .30
B34	SP16	175p + 50p blue	.90 .75

Issued for the Red Crescent Society.

Nos. 470-471 Surcharged in Blue or Orange

1960, Dec. 31   Litho.   *Perf. 11*

B35	A166	50p + 25p dp org (Bl)	1.50 1.50
B36	A166	165p + 25p blue (O)	1.50 1.50

The souvenir sheets described after No. 471 were surcharged in carmine "+25 Ps" on each stamp. Value $5 each.

See general note after No. 485.

Nos. 496-500 Surcharged

UNICEF
يونيسيف
+25PS

1961   Unwmk.   Photo.   *Perf. 13½x14*

B37	A175	2p + 25p green & rose lil	
B38	A175	2p + 25p brown & cit	
B39	A175	5p + 25p gray & rose	
B40	A175	10p + 25p blue & bis	
B41	A175	15p + 25p sl bl & dl lil	
		Nos. B37-B41 (5)	1.50

UNICEF. The same surcharge was applied to an imperf. souvenir sheet like that noted after No. 505. Value $4.50.

Nos. 522-526 Surcharged "+25PS" and Crescent in Red

1961, Oct. 16   *Perf. 13½x14*

B42	A184	2p + 25p black	
B43	A184	2p + 25p green	
B44	A184	5p + 25p lilac rose	
B45	A184	10p + 25p lilac	
B46	A184	15p + 25p dk blue	
		Nos. B42-B46 (5)	2.00

Issued for the Red Crescent Society.

Nos. 539-543 Surcharged in Red: "UNESCO + 25PS"

1962   *Perf. 12*

B47	A186	2p + 25p multi	
B48	A186	2p + 25p multi	
B49	A186	5p + 25p multi	
B50	A186	10p + 25p multi	
B51	A186	15p + 25p multi	
		Nos. B47-B51 (5)	1.50

UNESCO. The same surcharge was applied to the souvenir sheets mentioned after No. 548. Value, 2 sheets, $3.50.

Nos. 553-561 Surcharged: "Dag Hammarskjöld +20PS"

1962, Sept. 17   *Perf. 14x13½*

B52	A187	2p + 20p	
B53	A187	2p + 20p	
B54	A187	5p + 20p	
B55	A187	10p + 20p	
B56	A187	15p + 20p	
B57	A187	25p + 20p	
B58	A187	50p + 20p	
B59	A187	75p + 20p	
B60	A187	100p + 20p	
		Nos. B52-B60 (9)	2.00

In memory of Dag Hammarskjold, Sec. Gen. of the UN, 1953-61. Perf. and imperf. souvenir sheets exist. Value, 2 sheets, $3.

Nos. 583-593 Surcharged "+15PS"

1963, Mar. 15   *Perf. 14x13½*

B61	A193	2p + 15p	
B62	A193	3p + 15p	
B63	A193	5p + 15p	
B64	A193	10p + 15p	
B65	A193	15p + 15p	
B66	A193	25p + 15p	
B67	A193	50p + 15p	
B68	A193	75p + 15p	
B69	A193	100p + 15p	
B70	A193	150p + 15p	
B71	A193	175p + 15p	
		Nos. B61-B71 (11)	7.50

WHO drive to eradicate malaria.

Postally used copies of Nos. B37-B71 are uncommon and command a considerable premium over the values for unused copies.

Nos. 672-672G, 672I Surcharged in Various Positions

15e ANNIVERSAIRE DES DROITS HUMAINS

+50 POULS

1964, Mar. 9

B71A	A213g	2p + 50p	
B71B	A213g	3p + 50p	
B71C	A213g	4p + 50p	
B71D	A213g	5p + 50p	

B71E	A213g	10p + 50p	
B71F	A213g	100p + 50p	
B71G	A213g	2af + 50p	
B71H	A213g	3af + 50p	

Souvenir Sheet

B71J	A213g	5af + 50p	

Nos. B71E-B71G are airmail semi-postals.

Blood Transfusion Kit — SP17

1964, Oct. 18   Litho.   *Perf. 10½*

B72	SP17	1af + 50p black & rose	.50 .15

Issued for the Red Crescent Society and Red Crescent Week, Oct. 18-24.

First Aid Station — SP18

1965, Oct.   Photo.   *Perf. 13½x14*

B73	SP18	1.50af + 50p multi	1.00 .50

Issued for the Red Crescent Society.

Children Playing — SP19

1966, Nov. 28   Photo.   *Perf. 13½x14*

B74	SP19	1af + 1af yel grn & cl	.35 .15
B75	SP19	3af + 2af yel & brn	.75 .20
B76	SP19	7af + 3af rose lil & grn	1.25 .40
		Nos. B74-B76 (3)	2.35 .75

Children's Day.

Nadir Shah Presenting Society Charter — SP20

1967   Photo.   *Perf. 13x14*

B77	SP20	2af + 1af red & dk grn	.25 .15
B78	SP20	5af + 1af lil rose & brn	.50 .25

Issued for the Red Crescent Society.

Vaccination SP21   Red Crescent SP22

1967, June 6   Photo.   *Perf. 12*

B79	SP21	2af + 1af yellow & blk	.75 .15
B80	SP21	5af + 2af pink & brn	1.00 .25

The surtax was for anti-tuberculosis work.

**1967, Oct. 18   Photo.   *Perf. 12*
Crescent in Red**

B81	SP22	3af + 1af gray ol & blk	.50 .15
B82	SP22	5af + 1af dl bl & blk	.75 .20

Issued for the Red Crescent Society.

Queen Humeira SP23   Red Crescent SP24

1968, June 14   Photo.   *Perf. 12*

B83	SP23	2af + 2af red brown	.25 .20
B84	SP23	7af + 2af dull green	.75 .50

Issued for Mother's Day.

1968, Oct. 16   Photo.   *Perf. 12*

B85	SP24	4af + 1af yel, blk & red	.45 .25

Issued for the Red Crescent Society.

Red Cross, Crescent, Lion and Sun Emblems — SP25   Mother and Child — SP26

1969, May 5   Litho.   *Perf. 14x13½*

B86	SP25	3af + 1af multicolored	.75 .20
B87	SP25	5af + 1af multicolored	1.25 .30

League of Red Cross Societies, 50th anniv.

1969, June 14   Photo.   *Perf. 12*

B88	SP26	1af + 1af yel org & brn	.25 .15
B89	SP26	4af + 1af rose lil & pur	.40 .25
a.		Souvenir sheet of 2	1.00 1.00

Mother's Day. No. B89a contains 2 imperf. stamps similar to Nos. B88-B89. Sold for 10af.

Red Crescent — SP27

1969, Oct. 16   Photo.   *Perf. 12*

B90	SP27	6af + 1af multi	.75 .30

Issued for the Red Crescent Society.

UN and FAO Emblems, Farmer SP28

1973, May 24   Photo.   *Perf. 13½*

B91	SP28	14af + 7af grnsh bl & lil	1.10 .75

World Food Program, 10th anniversary.

Dome of the Rock, Jerusalem — SP29

1977, Sept. 11   Photo.   *Perf. 14*

B92	SP29	12af + 3af multi	1.50 .35

Surtax for Palestinian families and soldiers.

15 Cent. (lunar) of Islamic Pilgrimage (Hegira) — SP30

1981, Jan. 17   Litho.   *Perf. 12½x12*

B93	SP30	13af + 2af multi	.45 .40

Red Crescent Aid Programs — SP31

1981, May 8   *Perf. 12x12½*

B94	SP31	1af + 4af multi	1.00 1.00

Intl. Year of the Disabled — SP32

1981, Oct. 12   *Perf. 12x12½*

B95	SP32	6af + 1af multi	.35 .25

AIR POST STAMPS

Plane over Kabul — AP1

Perf. 12, 12x11, 11

1939, Oct. 1   Typo.   Unwmk.

C1	AP1	5af orange	3.75 2.25
a.		Imperf., pair ('47)	22.50 22.50
b.		Horiz. pair, imperf. vert.	20.00
C2	AP1	10af blue	3.75 1.75
a.		10af lt bl	5.00 5.00
b.		Imperf., pair ('47)	22.50
c.		Horiz. pair, imperf. vert.	20.00
C3	AP1	20af emerald	7.50 5.00
a.		Imperf., pair ('47)	22.50
b.		Horiz. pair, imperf. vert.	20.00
c.		Vert. pair, imperf. horiz.	22.50
		Nos. C1-C3 (3)	15.00 9.00

These stamps come with clean-cut or rough perforations. Counterfeits exist.

1948, June 14   *Perf. 12x11½*

C4	AP1	5af emerald	15.00 15.00
C5	AP1	10af red orange	15.00 15.00
C6	AP1	20af blue	15.00 15.00
		Nos. C4-C6 (3)	45.00 45.00

Imperforates exist.

Catalogue values for unused stamps in this section, from this point to the end of the section, are for Never Hinged items.

Plane over Palace Grounds, Kabul — AP2

1951-54   Engr.   *Perf. 13½*
Imprint: "Waterlow & Sons, Limited, London"**

C7	AP2	5af henna brn	2.50 .55
C8	AP2	5af dp grn ('54)	3.50 .50
C9	AP2	10af gray	4.00 1.40
C10	AP2	20af dark blue	6.50 2.25

1957

C11	AP2	5af ultra	.90 .35
C12	AP2	10af dark vio	1.75 .75
		Nos. C7-C12 (6)	19.15 5.80

See No. C38.

Ariana Plane
over Hindu
Kush — AP3

Perf. 11, Imperf.
1960-63   Litho.   Unwmk.
C13 AP3 75p light vio   .30   .30
C14 AP3 125p blue   .40   .45
      Perf. 10¹⁄₂, 11
C14A AP3 5af citron ('63)   1.10 1.10
      Nos. C13-C14A (3)   1.80 1.85

POSTES AFGHANES Girl Scout — AP4

1962, Aug. 30 Photo.   Perf. 11¹⁄₂x12
C15 AP4 100p ocher & brn   .60   .60
C16 AP4 175p brt yel grn & brn .85   .85
   Women's Day. A souvenir sheet exists contain-
ing one each of #578-579, C15-C16. Value $3.

Sports Type of Regular Issue, 1962
   Designs: 25p, 50p, Horse racing. 75p, 100p,
Wrestling. 150p, Weight lifting. 175p, Soccer.

1962, Sept. 25 Unwmk.   Perf. 12
      Black Inscriptions
C17 A195 25p rose & red brn
C18 A195 50p gray & red brn
C19 A195 75p pale vio & dk grn
C20 A195 100p gray ol & dk pur
C21 A195 150p rose lil & grn
C22 A195 175p sal & brn
      Nos. C17-C22   2.25

Children's Day Type of Regular Issue
      Perf. 11¹⁄₂x12, 12x11¹⁄₂
1962, Oct. 14   Unwmk.
C23 A196 75p Runners
C24 A196 150p Peaches
C25 A196 200p Iris, vert.
   A souvenir sheet contains one each of Nos. C23-
C25. Value $2.50.

Red Crescent Type of Regular Issue
1962, Oct. 16   Perf. 12
   **Fruit and Flowers in Natural Colors;
        Carmine Crescent**
C26 A197 25p Grapes
C27 A197 50p Pears
C28 A197 100p Wistaria
   Two souvenir sheets exist. One contains a 150p
gray brown stamp in blossom design, the other a
200p gray stamp in wistaria design, imperf. Value,
each $5.

UN Type of Regular Issue
1962, Oct. 24   Photo.
   **Flags in Original Colors, Black
          Inscriptions**
C29 A198 75p blue
C30 A198 100p lt brn
C31 A198 175p brt grn

Boy Scout Type of Regular Issue
1962, Oct. 25 Unwmk.   Perf. 12
C32 A199 25p gray, blk, dl grn & sal
C33 A199 50p grn, brn & sal
C34 A199 75p grn, red brn & sal
C35 A199 100p bl, slate & sal

Teacher's Day Type of Regular Issue
1962, Oct. 25
C36 A200 100p Pole vault
C37 A200 150p High jump
   A souvenir sheet contains one 250p pink and
slate green stamp in design of 150p. Value $2.50.

Type of 1951-54
1962   Engr.   Perf. 13¹⁄₂
   **Imprint: "Thomas De La Rue & Co.
              Ltd."**
C38 AP2 5af ultra   6.00 1.00

Agriculture Types of Regular Issue
         Unwmk.
1963, Mar. 1   Photo.   Perf. 12
C42 A204 100p dk car, grn & brn
C43 A203 150p ocher & blk
C44 A204 200p ultra, grn & brn

Hands
Holding
Wheat
Emblem
AP5

POSTES AFGHANES

1963, Mar. 27   Photo.   Perf. 14
C45 A5 500p lil, lt brn & brn   1.75 .60
   FAO "Freedom from Hunger" campaign.
   Two souvenir sheets exist. One contains a
1000p blue green, light brown and brown, type
AP5, imperf. The other contains a 200p brown and
green and 300p ultramarine, yellow and ocher in
rice and corn designs, type A205. Values $6 and
$2.50.

Meteorological Day Type of Regular Issue
   Designs: 100p, 500p, Meteorological measuring
instrument. 200p, 400p, Weather station. 300p,
Rockets in space.
1963, May 23   Imperf.
C46 A206 100p brn & bl
         Perf. 13¹⁄₂x14
C47 A206 200p brt grn & lil
C48 A206 300p dk bl & rose
C49 A206 400p bl & dl red brn
C50 A206 500p car rose & gray grn
   Nos. C47 and C50 printed se-tenant.
   Two souvenir sheets exist. One contains a 125p
red and brown stamp in rocket design. The other
contains a 100p blue and dull red brown in "rock-
ets in space" design. Values $5 and $7.50.

POSTES AFGHANES

Kabul
International
Airport — AP8

         Perf. 12x11¹⁄₂
1964, Apr.   Unwmk.   Photo.
C57 AP8 10af red lil & grn   .55   .20
C58 AP8 20af dk grn & red lil   .80   .40
   a.   Perf. 12 ('68)   5.00 3.00
C59 AP8 50af dk bl & grnsh bl 2.25 1.00
   a.   Perf. 12 ('68)   8.00 1.00
      Nos. C57-C59 (3)   3.60 1.60
   Inauguration of Kabul Airport Terminal.
   Nos. C58a-C59a are 36mm wide. Nos. C58-
C59 are 35¹⁄₂mm wide.

POSTES AFGHANES

Zahir Shah and Kabul Airport — AP9

   Design: 100af, Zahir Shah and Ariana Plane.
1971   Photo.   Perf. 12¹⁄₂x13¹⁄₂
C60 AP9 50af multi   10.00 8.00
C61 AP9 100af blk, red & grn   5.00 3.00
   Remainders of No C60 were used, starting in
1978, with king's portrait removed.

REGISTRATION STAMPS

R1

      Dated "1309"
1891   Unwmk.   Litho.   Imperf.
      Pelure Paper
F1   R1 1r slate blue   2.00
   a.   Tete beche pair   12.50
   Genuinely used copies of No. F1 are rare. Counterfeit cancellations exist.

R2

      Dated "1311"
1893   Thin Wove Paper
F2   R2 1r black, green   1.60
   Genuinely used copies of No. F2 are rare. Counterfeit cancellations exist.

R3

      Undated
1894
F3   R3 2ab black, green   8.00 10.00
   12 varieties. See note below Nos. 189-190.

R4

      Undated
1898-1900
F4   R4 2ab black, deep rose   4.00 4.00
F5   R4 2ab black, lilac rose   4.00 4.00
F6   R4 2ab black, magenta   6.00 4.00
F7   R4 2ab black, salmon   2.50 4.00
F8   R4 2ab black, orange   6.00 4.00
F9   R4 2ab black, yellow   2.50 4.00
F10 R4 2ab black, green   6.00 4.00
      Nos. F4-F10 (7)   31.00 28.00
   Many shades of paper.
   Nos. F4-F10 come in two sizes, measured
between outer frame lines: 52x36mm, 1st printing;
46x33mm, 2nd printing. The outer frame line (not
pictured) is 3-6mm from inner frame line.
   Used on P.O. receipts.

OFFICIAL STAMPS

(Used only on interior mail.)

Coat of
Arms — O1

1909   Unwmk.   Typo.   Perf. 12
         Wove Paper
O1   O1 red   .75 1.00
   a.   Carmine ('19?)   1.25 1.25
   Later printings of No. O1 in scarlet, vermilion,
claret, etc., on various types of paper, were issued
until 1927.

Coat of Arms — O2

1939-68?   Typo.   Perf. 11, 12
O3   O2 15p emerald   .35   .15
O4   O2 30p ocher ('40)   .50   .50
O5   O2 45p dark carmine   .40   .35
O6   O2 50p brt car ('68)   .30   .30
   a.   50p carmine rose ('55)   .50   .40
O7   O2 1af brt red violet   .80   .80
      Nos. O3-O7 (5)   2.35 2.10
   Size of 50p, 24x31mm, others 22¹⁄₂x28mm.

> Catalogue values for unused
> stamps in this section, from this
> point to the end of the section, are
> for Never Hinged items.

1964-65   Litho.   Perf. 11
O8   O2 50p rose   .75   .75
   a.   50p salmon ('65)   1.50 1.50

Stamps of this type are revenues.

PARCEL POST STAMPS

Coat of
Arms — PP1

PP2

PP3

PP4

1909   Unwmk.   Typo.   Perf. 12
Q1   PP1 3sh bister   .85 1.00
   a.   Imperf., pair   1.00
Q2   PP2 1kr olive gray   1.10 1.25
   a.   Imperf., pair   1.40
Q3   PP3 1r orange   5.00 3.75
Q4   PP3 1r olive green   2.00 4.00
Q5   PP4 2r red   6.00 4.00
      Nos. Q1-Q5 (5)   14.95 14.00

1916-18
Q6   PP1 3sh green   5.00 2.50
Q7   PP2 1kr pale red   2.50 1.25
   a.   1kr rose red ('18)   3.25 3.25
Q8   PP3 1r brown org   2.00 1.25
   a.   1r deep brown ('18)   2.50 2.50
Q9   PP4 2r blue   5.00 3.00
      Nos. Q6-Q9 (4)   14.50 10.00
   Nos. Q1-Q9 sometimes show letters of the
papermaker's watermark "HOWARD & JONES
LONDON."
   Ungummed copies are remainders. They sell for
one-third the price of mint examples.

Old Habibia
College, Near
Kabul — PP5

1921

Wove Paper

Q10	PP5	10pa chocolate	3.00	1.75
a.		Tete beche pair	6.25	
Q11	PP5	15pa light brn	4.50	2.50
a.		Tete beche pair	6.25	
Q12	PP5	30pa red violet	5.75	2.75
a.		Tete beche pair	8.75	
b.		Laid paper	15.00	7.50
Q13	PP5	1r brt blue	7.25	5.50
a.		Tete beche pair	20.00	
		Nos. Q10-Q13 (4)	20.50	12.50

Stamps of this issue are usually perforated on one or two sides only.

The laid paper of No. Q12b has a papermaker's watermark in the sheet.

PP6

1924-26

Wove Paper

Q15	PP6	5kr ultra ('26)	35.00	15.00
Q16	PP6	5r lilac	8.75	8.75

A 15r rose exists, but is not known to have been placed in use.

PP7

PP8

1928-29   *Perf. 11, 11xImperf.*

Q17	PP7	2r yellow orange	10.00	3.00
Q18	PP7	2r green ('29)	3.00	3.00
Q19	PP8	3r deep green	7.50	4.00
Q20	PP8	3r brown ('29)	5.00	5.00
		Nos. Q17-Q20 (4)	25.50	15.00

POSTAL TAX STAMPS

Aliabad
Hospital near
Kabul — PT1

Pierre
and
Marie
Curie
PT2

Perf. 12x11½, 12

1938, Dec. 22   Typo.   Unwmk.

RA1	PT1	10p peacock grn	1.50	2.75
RA2	PT2	15p dull blue	1.50	2.75

Obligatory on all mail Dec. 22-28, 1938. The money was used for the Aliabad Hospital. See note with CD80.

Begging Child
PT3   PT4

1949, May 28   Typo.   *Perf. 12*

RA3	PT3	35p red orange	1.60	1.60
RA4	PT4	125p ultra	2.50	2.00

United Nations Children's Day, May 28. Obligatory on all foreign mail on that date. Proceeds were used for child welfare.

Paghman Arch
and UN
Emblem
PT5

1949, Oct. 24

RA5	PT5	125p dk blue green	10.00	6.00

4th anniv. of the UN. Valid one day only. Issued in sheets of 9 (3x3).

> **Catalogue values for unused stamps in this section, from this point to the end of the section, are for Never Hinged items.**

Zahir Shah and Map of Afghanistan — PT6

1950, Mar. 30   Typo.

RA6	PT6	125p blue green	2.00	1.25

Return of Zahir Shah from a trip to Europe for his health. Valid for two weeks. The tax was used for public health purposes.

Hazara Youth — PT7

1950, May 28   Typo.   *Perf. 11½*

RA7	PT7	125p dk blue green	2.00	1.50

Tax for Child Welfare. Obligatory and valid only on May 28, 1950, on foreign mail.

Ruins
of Qalai
Bist and
Globe
PT8

1950, Oct. 24

RA8	PT8	1.25af ultramarine	7.50	4.00

5th anniv. of the UN. Proceeds went to Afghanistan's UN Projects Committee.

Zahir Shah
and Medical
Center
PT9

1950, Dec. 22   Typo.   *Perf. 11½*
Size: 38x25mm

RA9	PT9	35p carmine	1.00	1.00
RA10	PT9	1.25af black	4.50	2.25

The tax was for the national Graduate School of Medicine.

Koochi Girl with
Lamb — PT10

Kohistani Boy
and
Sheep — PT11

1951, May 28

RA11	PT10	35p emerald	.75	.65
RA12	PT11	1.25af ultramarine	.75	.65

The tax was for Child Welfare.

Distributing Gifts to
Children — PT12

Qandahari Boys
Dancing the
"Attan" — PT13

1952, May 28   Litho.

RA13	PT12	35p chocolate	.25	.25
RA14	PT13	125p violet	.75	.75

The tax was for Child Welfare.

Soldier Receiving First
Aid — PT14

1952, Oct.

RA15	PT14	10p light green	.50	.35

Stretcher-bearers and Wounded — PT15

Soldier
Assisting
Wounded
PT16

1953, Oct.

RA16	PT15	10p yel grn & org red	.50	.40
RA17	PT16	10p vio brn & org red	.50	.40

Prince
Mohammed
Nadir — PT17   Map and Young
Musicians — PT18

1953, May 28

RA18	PT17	35p orange yellow	.20	.15
RA19	PT17	125p chalky blue	.55	.55

No. RA19 is inscribed in French "Children's Day." The tax was for child welfare.

1954, May 28   Unwmk.   *Perf. 11*

RA20	PT18	35p purple	.30	.15
RA21	PT18	125p ultra	1.10	1.10

No. RA21 is inscribed in French. The tax was for child welfare.

Red Crescent
PT19   PT20

1954, Oct. 17   *Perf. 11½*

RA22	PT19	20p blue & red	.25	.20

1955, Oct. 18   *Perf. 11*

RA23	PT20	20p dull grn & car	.50	.25

Zahir Shah and Red
Crescent — PT21

1956, Oct. 18

RA24	PT21	20p lt grn & rose car	.25	.20

Red Crescent Headquarters, Kabul — PT22

1957, Oct. 17
RA25 PT22 20p lt ultra & car   .75 .50

Map and Crescent — PT23

1958, Oct.   Unwmk.   Perf. 11
RA26 PT23 25p yel grn & red   .30 .30

PT24

1959, Oct. 17   Litho.   Perf. 11
RA27 PT24 25p lt violet & red   .20 .15

The tax on Nos. RA15-RA17, RA22-RA27 was for the Red Crescent Society. Use of these stamps was required for one week.

AGUERA, LA

LOCATION — An administrative district in southern Rio de Oro on the northwest coast of Africa.
GOVT. — Spanish possession
AREA — Because of indefinite political boundaries, figures for area and population are not available.

100 Centimos = 1 Peseta

Type of 1920 Issue of   **LA AGÜERA**
Rio de Oro Overprinted

1920, June   Unwmk.   Perf. 13

1	A8	1c blue green	1.65	1.65
2	A8	2c olive brown	1.65	1.65
3	A8	5c deep green	1.65	1.65
4	A8	10c light red	1.65	1.65
5	A8	15c yellow	1.65	1.65
6	A8	20c lilac	1.65	1.65
7	A8	25c deep blue	1.65	1.65
8	A8	30c dark brown	1.65	1.65
9	A8	40c pink	1.65	1.65
10	A8	50c bright blue	4.50	4.00
11	A8	1p red brown	8.00	6.50
12	A8	4p dark violet	25.00	19.00
13	A8	10p orange	50.00	45.00
		Nos. 1-13 (13)	102.35	89.35

King Alfonso XIII — A2

1922, June   Typo.

14	A2	1c turquoise blue	.75	.75
15	A2	2c dark green	.75	.75
16	A2	5c blue green	.75	.75
17	A2	10c red	.75	.75
18	A2	15c red brown	.75	.75
19	A2	20c yellow	.75	.75
20	A2	25c deep blue	.75	.75
21	A2	30c dark brown	.75	.75
22	A2	40c rose red	1.00	1.00
23	A2	50c red violet	3.50	2.50
24	A2	1p rose	7.00	5.00
25	A2	4p violet	15.00	11.00
26	A2	10p orange	22.50	17.00
		Nos. 14-26 (13)	55.00	42.50

For later issues see Spanish Sahara.

AITUTAKI

ĭt-ə-'täk-ē

LOCATION — One of the larger Cook Islands, in the South Pacific Ocean northeast of New Zealand
GOVT. — A dependency of the British dominion of New Zealand
AREA — 7 sq. mi.
POP. — 2,335 (1981)

The Cook Islands were attached to New Zealand in 1901. Stamps of Cook Islands were used in 1932-72.

Aitutaki acquired its own postal service in August 1972, though remaining part of Cook Islands.

12 Pence = 1 Shilling
100 Cents = 1 Dollar (1972)

> Catalogue values for unused stamps in this country are for Never Hinged items, beginning with Scott 37.

Watermark

Wmk. 61· Single-lined NZ and Star Close Together

Stamps of New Zealand Surcharged in Red or Blue:

AITUTAKI.   **AITUTAKI.**

Ava Pene.   **Tai Pene.**
a   b

1903   Engr.   Wmk. 61   Perf. 14
1 A18(a) ½p green (R)   3.00 6.00
2 A35(b) 1p rose (Bl)   5.00 6.25

AITUTAKI.

Rua Pene Ma Te Ava.
c

AITUTAKI. AITUTAKI. AITUTAKI.

Toru Pene.   Ono Pene.   Tai Tiringi.
d   e   f

Perf. 11
3 A22(c) 2½p blue (R)   3.75 8.25
4 A23(d) 3p yellow brn (Bl)   8.50 11.00
5 A26(e) 6p red (Bl)   25.00 27.50
6 A29(f) 1sh scarlet (Bl)   55.00 57.50
a. 1sh orange red (Bl)   65.00 85.00

1912   Typo.   Perf. 14x15
7 A41(a) ½p yellow grn (R)   1.00 2.25

Engr.
Perf. 14
9 A22(c) 2½p deep blue (R)   5.00 6.50

AITUTAKI.   **AITUTAKI.**

Ono Pene.   Tai Tiringi.
g   h

1913-16   Typo.
10 A42(b) 1p rose (Bl)   1.50 2.75

Engr.
12 A41(a) 6p car rose (Bl) ('16)   35.00 45.00
13 A41(h) 1sh ver (Bl) ('14)   55.00 67.50

1916-17   Perf. 14x13½, 14x14½
17 A45(g) 6p car rose (Bl)   10.00 19.00
18 A45(h) 1sh ver (Bl) ('17)   27.50 45.00
| | Nos. 1-18 (13) | 235.25 | 304.50 |

New Zealand Stamps of 1909-19 Overprinted in Red or Dark Blue   **AITUTAKI.**

1917-20   Typo.   Perf. 14x15
19 A43 ½p yellow grn ('20)   .60 2.00
20 A42 1p car (Bl) ('20)   .90 2.50
21 A47 1½p gray black   1.75 6.00
22 A47 1½p brown org ('19)   1.40 5.25
23 A43 3p choc (Bl) ('19)   3.75 7.25

Perf. 14x13½, 14x14½
Engr.
24 A44 2½p dull blue ('18)   1.40 6.00
25 A45 3p vio brn (Bl) ('18)   1.75 8.00
26 A45 6p car rose (Bl)   3.75 12.00
27 A45 1sh vermilion (Bl)   10.00 21.00
| | Nos. 19-27 (9) | 25.30 | 70.00 |

Landing of Capt. Cook A15   Avarua Waterfront A16

Capt. James Cook — A17   Palm — A18

Houses at Arorangi — A19   Avarua Harbor — A20

1920   Engr.   Unwmk.   Perf. 14
28 A15 ½p green & black   .95 2.50
29 A16 1p carmine & black   1.25 3.75
30 A17 1½p brown & blk   2.00 6.00
31 A18 3p dp blue & blk   2.00 7.50
32 A19 6p slate & red brn   6.25 15.00
33 A20 1sh claret & blk   8.25 26.00
| | Nos. 28-33 (6) | 20.70 | 60.75 |

Inverted centers, double frames, etc. are from printers waste.

Rarotongan Chief (Te Po) — A21

1926-27   Wmk. 61   Perf. 14
34 A15 ½p green & blk ('27)   1.50 1.65
35 A16 1p carmine & blk   1.50 1.65
36 A21 2½p blue & blk ('27)   6.00 6.75
| | Nos. 34-36 (3) | 9.00 | 10.05 |

> Catalogue values for unused stamps in this section, from this point to the end of the section, are for Never Hinged items.

Cook Islands Nos. 199-200, 202, 205-206, 210, 212-213, 215-217 Overprinted   **Aitutaki**

1972   Photo.   Unwmk.   Perf. 14x13½
37 A34 ½c gold & multi   .45 .70
38 A34 1c gold & multi   .80 1.25
39 A34 2½c gold & multi   5.25 6.00
40 A34 4c gold & multi   .75 .85
41 A34 5c gold & multi   6.00 7.00
42 A34 10c gold & multi   5.25 5.25
43 A34 20c gold & multi   .80 .90
44 A34 25c gold & multi   .80 .90
45 A34 50c gold & multi   4.00 2.75

---

46 A35 $1 gold & multi   6.00 6.00
47 A35 $2 gold & multi   1.10 .75
| | Nos. 37-47 (11) | 31.20 | 32.35 |

Overprint horizontal on Nos. 46-47. On $2, overprint is in capitals of different font; size: 21x3mm.
Issued: Nos. 37-46, Aug. 9; No. 47, Nov. 24.

Same Overprint Horizontal in Silver On Cook Islands Nos. 330-332

1972, Oct. 27   Perf. 13½
48 A53 1c gold & multi   .15 .15
49 A53 5c gold & multi   .25 .25
50 A53 10c gold & multi   .45 .45
| | Nos. 48-50 (3) | .85 | .85 |

Fluorescence

Starting in 1972, stamps carry a "fluorescent security underprinting" in a multiple pattern of New Zealand's coat of arms with "Aitutaki" above, "Cook Islands" below and two stars at each side.

Silver Wedding Type of Cook Islands

1972, Nov. 20   Photo.   Perf. 13½
Size: 29x40mm
51 A54 5c silver & multi   4.75 3.50
Size: 66x40mm
52 A54 15c silver & multi   2.00 1.65

25th anniversary of the marriage of Queen Elizabeth II and Prince Philip. Nos. 51-52 printed in sheets of 5 stamps and one label.

Flower Issue of Cook Islands Overprinted   **AITUTAKI**

1972, Dec. 11   Photo.   Perf. 14x13½
53 A34 ½c on #199   .15 .15
54 A34 1c on #200   .15 .15
55 A34 2½c on #202   .15 .15
56 A34 4c on #205   .15 .15
57 A34 5c on #206   .20 .20
58 A34 10c on #210   .30 .30
59 A34 20c on #212   .70 .70
60 A34 25c on #213   .90 .90
61 A34 50c on #215   1.75 1.75
62 A35 $1 on #216   3.75 3.75
| | Nos. 53-62 (10) | 8.20 | 8.20 |

See Nos. 73-76.

The Passion of Christ, by Mathias Grunewald — A22

Paintings: No. 63b, St. Veronica, by Rogier van der Weyden. No. 63c, Crucifixion, by Raphael. No. 63d, Resurrection, by della Francesca. No. 64a, Last Supper, by Master of Amiens. No. 64b, Condemnation of Christ, by Hans Holbein, the Elder. No. 64c, Crucifixion, by Rubens. No. 64d, Resurrection, by El Greco. No. 65a, Passion of Christ, by El Greco. No. 65b, St. Veronica, by Jakob Cornelisz. No. 65c, Crucifixion, by Rubens. No. 65d, Resurrection, by Dierik Bouts.

Perf. 13½
1973, Apr. 6   Photo.   Unwmk.
63 Block of 4   .20 .20
a.-d. A22 1c any single   .15 .15
64 Block of 4   .65 .65
a.-d. A22 5c any single   .15 .15
65 Block of 4   1.50 1.50
a.-d. A22 10c any single   .35 .35
| | Nos. 63-65 (3) | 2.35 | 2.35 |

Easter. Printed in blocks of 4 in sheets of 40. Design descriptions in top and bottom margins.

Coin Type of Cook Islands

Queen Elizabeth II Coins: 1c, Taro leaf. 2c, Pineapples. 5c, Hibiscus. 10c, Oranges. 20c, Fairy terns. 50c, Bonito. $1, Tangaroa, Polynesian god of creation, vert.

1973, May 14   Perf. 13x13½
Size: 37x24mm

66	A55	1c dp car & multi	.15	.15
67	A55	2c blue & multi	.15	.15
68	A55	5c green & multi	.15	.15

Size: 46x30mm

69	A55	10c vio blue & multi	.30	.30
70	A55	20c green & multi	.60	.60
71	A55	50c dp car & multi	1.40	1.40

Size: 32x54½mm

72	A55	$1 blue, blk & sil	2.75	2.75
		Nos. 66-72 (7)	5.50	5.50

Cook Islands coinage commemorating silver wedding anniv. of Queen Elizabeth II.
Printed in sheets of 20 stamps and label showing Westminster Abbey.

Cook Islands Nos. 208, 210, 212 and 215 Overprinted Like Nos. 53-62 and: "TENTH ANNIVERSARY/ CESSATION/ OF/ NUCLEAR TESTING/ TREATY"

1973, July   Photo.   Perf. 14x13½

73	A34	8c gold & multi	.30	.30
74	A34	10c gold & multi	.40	.40
75	A34	20c gold & multi	.90	.90
76	A34	50c gold & multi	2.00	2.00
		Nos. 73-76 (4)	3.60	3.60

Nuclear Test Ban Treaty, 10th anniv., protest against French nuclear testing on Mururoa Atoll.

Princess Anne, Hibiscus A23

Design: 30c, Mark Phillips and hibiscus.

1973, Nov. 14   Photo.   Perf. 13½x14

77	A23	25c gold & multi	.40	.40
78	A23	30c gold & multi	.60	.60
a.		Souvenir sheet of 2, #77-78	1.10	1.10

Wedding of Princess Anne and Capt. Mark Phillips.

Virgin and Child, by Il Perugino — A24

Paintings of the Virgin and Child by various masters.

1973, Dec.   Photo.   Perf. 13

79		Block of 4	.20	.20
a.	A24	1c Van Dyck	.15	.15
b.	A24	1c Bartolommeo Montagna	.15	.15
c.	A24	1c Carlo Crivelli	.15	.15
d.	A24	1c Il Perugino	.15	.15
80		Block of 4	.60	.60
a.	A24	5c Cima da Conegliano	.15	.15
b.	A24	5c Memling	.15	.15
c.	A24	5c Veronese	.15	.15
d.	A24	5c Veronese	.15	.15
81		Block of 4	1.50	1.50
a.	A24	10c Raphael	.35	.35
b.	A24	10c Lorenzo Lotto	.35	.35
c.	A24	10c Del Colle	.35	.35
d.	A24	10c Memling	.35	.35
		Nos. 79-81 (3)	2.30	2.30

Christmas. Printed in blocks of 4 in sheets of 48. Design descriptions in margins.

Murex Ramosus A25

Terebra Maculata — A26

Pacific Shells: 1c, Nautilus macromphalus. 2c, Harpa major. 3c, Phalium strigatum. 4c, Cyprea

talpa. 5c, Mitra stictica. 8c, Charonia tritonis. 10c, Murex triremis. 20c, Oliva sericea. 25c, Tritonalia rubeta. 60c, Strombus latissimus. $1, Biplex perca. $5, Cypraea hesitata.

1974-75   Photo.   Perf. 13

82	A25	½c silver & multi	.40	.40
83	A25	1c silver & multi	.40	.40
84	A25	2c silver & multi	.40	.40
85	A25	3c silver & multi	.40	.40
86	A25	4c silver & multi	.40	.40
87	A25	5c silver & multi	.40	.40
88	A25	8c silver & multi	.90	.50
89	A25	10c silver & multi	.90	.50
90	A25	20c silver & multi	1.25	1.00
91	A25	25c silver & multi	1.50	1.00
92	A25	60c silver & multi	5.00	1.50
93	A25	$1 silver & multi	4.00	3.00

Perf. 14

94	A26	$2 silver & multi	7.50	7.50
95	A26	$5 silver & multi	27.50	27.50
		Nos. 82-95 (14)	50.95	45.15

Issue dates: Nos. 82-93, Jan. 31, 1974; $2, Jan. 20, 1975; $5, Feb. 28, 1975.
For overprints see Nos. O1-O16.

William Bligh and "Bounty" A27

1974, Apr. 11   Photo.   Perf. 13
Size: 38x22mm

96	A27	1c shown	.15	.15
97	A27	1c "Bounty" at sea	.15	.15
98	A27	5c Bligh and "Bounty" off Aitutaki	.32	.32
99	A27	5c Chart of Aitutaki, 1856	.32	.32
100	A27	5c James Cook and "Resolution"	.65	.65
101	A27	8c Maps of Aitutaki and Pacific Ocean	.65	.65
		Nos. 96-101,C1-C6 (12)	6.94	6.94

Capt. William Bligh (1754-1817), European discoverer of Aitutaki, Apr. 11, 1789. Stamps of same denomination printed se-tenant in sheets of 32.

Aitutaki Nos. 1 & 2 Map and UPU Emblem A28

Design: 50c, Aitutaki Nos. 4 and 28, map of Aitutaki and UPU emblem.

1974, July 15   Photo.   Perf. 13½

102	A28	25c blue & multi	.80	.80
103	A28	50c blue & multi	1.60	1.60
a.		Souvenir sheet of 2, #102-103	2.50	2.50

UPU, cent. Printed in sheets of 5 plus label showing UPU emblem.

A29   A30

Designs: Paintings of the Virgin and Child.

1974, Oct. 11   Photo.   Perf. 13½

104	A29	1c Van der Goes	.15	.15
105	A29	5c Giovanni Bellini	.15	.15
106	A29	8c Gerard David	.20	.20
107	A29	10c Antonello da Messina	.25	.25
108	A29	25c Joos van Cleve	.70	.70
109	A30	30c Maitre de St. Catherine	.80	.80
a.		Souvenir sheet of 6, #104-109	3.00	3.00
		Nos. 104-109 (6)	2.25	2.25

Christmas. #104-109 printed in sheets of 15 stamps and corner label. See #B1-B6.

1974, Nov. 29   Photo.   Perf. 14

Designs: Churchill portraits.

110	A30	10c Dublin, Age 5	.22	.15
111	A30	25c As young man	.55	.35
112	A30	30c Inspecting troops, WWII	.65	.38
113	A30	50c Painting	1.40	.80
114	A30	$1 Giving V sign	2.75	1.65
a.		Souvenir sheet of 5, #110-114 + label, perf. 13½	6.50	3.33
		Nos. 110-114 (5)	5.57	3.33

Sir Winston Churchill (1874-1965). Nos. 110-114 printed in sheets of 5 stamps and corner label.

Emblem US & USSR Flags A31

Design: 50c, Icarus and Apollo Soyuz spacecraft.

1975, July 24   Photo.   Perf. 13x14½

115	A31	25c multicolored	.75	.75
116	A31	50c multicolored	1.75	1.75
a.		Souvenir sheet of 2	2.50	2.50

Apollo Soyuz space test project (Russo-American cooperation), launching July 15; link-up July 17. Nos. 115 and 116 each printed in sheets of 5 stamps and one label showing area of Apollo splashdowns. No. 116a contains one each of Nos. 115-116 with gold and black border and inscription.

Madonna and Child, by Pietro Lorenzetti — A32

Paintings: 7c, Adoration of the Kings, by Rogier van der Weyden. 15c, Madonna and Child, by Bartolommeo Montagna. 20c, Adoration of the Shepherds.

1975, Nov. 24   Photo.   Perf. 14x13½

117	A32	Strip of 3	.32	.32
a.		6c St. Francis	.15	.15
b.		6c Madonna and Child	.15	.15
c.		6c St. John the Evangelist	.15	.15
118	A32	Strip of 3	.35	.35
a.		7c One King	.15	.15
b.		7c Madonna and Child	.15	.15
c.		7c Two Kings	.15	.15
119	A32	Strip of 3	.80	.80
a.		15c St. Joseph	.26	.26
b.		15c Madonna and Child	.26	.26
c.		15c St. John the Baptist	.26	.26
120	A32	Strip of 3	1.40	1.40
a.		20c One Shepherd	.42	.42
b.		20c Madonna and Child	.42	.42
c.		20c Two Shepherds	.42	.42
d.		Souv. sheet of 12, #117-120, perf. 13½	4.25	4.25
		Nos. 117-120 (4)	2.87	2.87

Christmas. Nos. 117-120 printed in sheets of 30 (10 strips of 3).
For surcharges see Nos. B7-B10.

Descent from the Cross, detail — A33

Designs (Painting, Flemish School, 16th Century): 30c, Virgin Mary, disciple and body of Jesus. 35c, Mary Magdalene and disciple.

1976, Apr. 5   Photo.   Perf. 13½

121	A33	15c gold & multi	.18	.18
122	A33	30c gold & multi	.48	.48
123	A33	35c gold & multi	1.25	1.25
a.		Souvenir sheet of 3	2.25	2.25
		Nos. 121-123 (3)	1.91	1.91

Easter. No. 123a contains 3 stamps similar to Nos. 121-123, perf. 13, in continuous design without gold frames and white margins.

Declaration of Independence — A34

Paintings by John Trumbull: 35c, Surrender of Cornwallis at Yorktown. 50c, Washington's Farewell Address. a, "1976 BICENTENARY." b, "UNITED STATES." c, "INDEPENDENCE 1776."

1976, June 1   Photo.   Perf. 13½

124	A34	Strip of 3	1.65	1.65
a.-c.		30c any single	.52	.52
125	A34	Strip of 3	2.25	2.25
a.-c.		35c any single	.75	.75
126	A34	Strip of 3	3.00	3.00
a.-c.		50c any single	.95	.95
d.		Souvenir sheet of 9 (3x3)	7.00	7.00
		Nos. 124-126 (3)	6.90	6.90

American Bicentennial. Nos. 124-126 printed in sheets of 5 strips of 3 and 3-part corner label showing portrait of John Trumbull, commemorative inscription and portraits of Washington (30c), John Adams (35c) and Jefferson (50c). No. 126d contains 3 strips similar to Nos. 124-126.

Bicycling A35

Montreal Olympic Games Emblem and: 35c, Sailing. 60c, Field hockey. 70c, Running.

1976, July 15   Photo.   Perf. 13x14

127	A35	15c multicolored	.30	.30
128	A35	35c multicolored	.70	.70
129	A35	60c multicolored	1.10	1.10
130	A35	70c multicolored	1.40	1.40
a.		Souvenir sheet of 4	4.00	4.00
		Nos. 127-130 (4)	3.50	3.50

21st Olympic Games, Montreal, Canada, July 17-Aug. 1. Nos. 127-130 printed in sheets of 5 stamps and label showing coat of Arms and Montreal Olympic Games emblem. No. 130a contains 4 stamps similar to Nos. 127-130 with gold margin around each stamp.

Nos. 127-130a Overprinted Diagonally: "ROYAL VISIT JULY 1976"

1976, July 30

131	A35	15c multicolored	.30	.30
132	A35	35c multicolored	.75	.75
133	A35	60c multicolored	1.10	1.10
134	A35	70c multicolored	1.50	1.50
a.		Souvenir sheet of 4	4.25	4.25
		Nos. 131-134 (4)	3.65	3.65

Visit of Queen Elizabeth II to Montreal and official opening of the Games. Each stamp of No. 134a has diagonal overprint. Sheet margin has additional overprint: "ROYAL VISIT OF H.M. QUEEN ELIZABETH II/OFFICIALLY OPENED 17 JULY 1976."

Annunciation
A36   A37

Designs: Nos. 137-138, Angel appearing to the shepherds. Nos. 139-140, Nativity. Nos. 141-142, Three Kings.

1976, Oct. 18   Perf. 13½x13

135	A36	6c dk green & gold	.15	.15
136	A37	6c dk green & gold	.15	.15
137	A36	7c dk brown & gold	.15	.15
138	A37	7c dk brown & gold	.15	.15
139	A36	15c dk blue & gold	.35	.35
140	A37	15c dk blue & gold	.35	.35
141	A36	20c purple & gold	.45	.45
142	A37	20c purple & gold	.45	.45
a.		Souvenir sheet of 8	2.50	2.50
		Nos. 135-142 (8)	2.20	2.20

Christmas. Stamps of same denomination printed se-tenant in sheets of 50. No. 142a contains 8 stamps similar to Nos. 135-142 with white margin around each pair of stamps.

A. G. Bell and 1876 Telephone A38

Design: 70c, Satellite and radar.

1977, Mar. 3   Photo.   Perf. 13¹/₂x13
143 A38 25c rose & multi   .45   .45
144 A38 70c violet & multi   1.50 1.50
a.   Souvenir sheet of 2   2.00 2.00

Centenary of first telephone call by Alexander Graham Bell, Mar. 10, 1876. No. 144a contains a 25c in colors of 70c and 70c in colors of 25c.

Calvary (detail), by Rubens A39

Paintings by Rubens: 20c, Lamentation. 35c, Descent from the Cross.

1977, Mar. 31   Photo.   Perf. 13¹/₂x14
145 A39 15c gold & multi   .38   .38
146 A39 20c gold & multi   .45   .45
147 A39 35c gold & multi   .65   .65
a.   Souv. sheet of 3, #145-147, perf. 13 1.75 1.75
      Nos. 145-147 (3)   1.48 1.48

Easter, and 400th birth anniv. of Peter Paul Rubens (1577-1640), Flemish painter.

Capt. Bligh, "Bounty" and George III — A40

Designs: 35c, Rev. John Williams, George IV, First Christian Church. 50c, British flag, map of Aitutaki, Queen Victoria. $1, Elizabeth II and family on balcony after coronation.

1977, Apr. 21   Perf. 13¹/₂
148 A40 25c gold & multi   .55   .55
149 A40 35c gold & multi   1.10 1.10
150 A40 50c gold & multi   1.50 1.50
151 A40 $1 gold & multi   3.00 3.00
a.   Souvenir sheet of 4, #148-151 7.50 7.50
      Nos. 148-151 (4)   6.15 6.15

Reign of Queen Elizabeth II, 25th anniv. For overprint and surcharge see Nos. O11, O15.

Annunciation
A41   A42

Designs: No. 154, Virgin, Child and ox. No. 155, Joseph and donkey (Nativity). No. 156, Three Kings. No. 157, Virgin and Child. No. 158, Joseph. No. 159, Virgin, Child and donkey (Flight into Egypt).

1977, Oct. 14   Photo.   Perf. 13¹/₂x14
152 A41 6c multicolored   .15   .15
153 A42 6c multicolored   .15   .15
154 A41 7c multicolored   .15   .15
155 A42 7c multicolored   .15   .15
156 A41 15c multicolored   .28   .28
157 A42 15c multicolored   .28   .28
158 A41 20c multicolored   .40   .40
159 A42 20c multicolored   .40   .40
a.   Souvenir sheet of 8, #152-159 2.50 2.50
      Nos. 152-159 (8)   1.96 1.96

Christmas. Stamps of same denomination printed se-tenant in sheets of 32.
For surcharges see Nos. B19-B26a.

Hawaiian Wood Figurine — A43

Designs: 50c, Talbot hunting dog, figure-head of "Resolution", horiz. $1, Temple figure.

1978, Jan. 19   Litho.   Perf. 13¹/₂
160 A43 35c multicolored   .60   .60
161 A43 50c multicolored   .80   .80
162 A43 $1 multicolored   1.50 1.50
a.   Souvenir sheet of 3, #160-162 3.50 3.50
      Nos. 160-162 (3)   2.90 2.90

Bicentenary of Capt. Cook's arrival in Hawaii. Nos. 160-162 issued in sheets of 6.

Avignon Pietà, 15th Century A44

Paintings: 15c, Jesus Carrying Cross, by Simone di Martini. 35c, Christ at Emmaus, by Rembrandt.

1978, Mar. 17   Photo.   Perf. 13¹/₂x14
163 A44 15c gold & multi   .25   .25
164 A44 20c gold & multi   .40   .40
165 A44 35c gold & multi   .60   .60
a.   Souvenir sheet of 3   1.50 1.50
      Nos. 163-165 (3)   1.25 1.25

Easter. No. 165a contains one each of Nos. 163-165, perf. 13¹/₂, and label showing Louvre, Paris. See Nos. B27-B29.

Elizabeth II — A45

Virgin and Child, by Dürer — A46

Souvenir Sheets

1978, June 15   Photo.   Perf. 13¹/₂x13
166   Sheet of 6   7.00 7.00
a.   A45 $1 Yale of Beaufort   1.10 1.10
b.   A45 $1 shown   1.10 1.10
c.   A45 $1 Ancestral statue   1.10 1.10
d.   Souvenir sheet of 6   7.00 7.00

25th anniv. of coronation of Queen Elizabeth II. No. 166 contains 2 each of Nos. 166a-166c, silver marginal inscription and coats of arms. No. 166d contains 2 strips of Nos. 166a-166c separated by horizontal slate green gutter showing Royal family on balcony, silver marginal inscription.

1978, Dec. 4   Photo.   Perf. 14¹/₂x13
Designs: Various paintings of the Virgin and Child by Albrecht Dürer.
167 A46 15c multicolored   .22   .22
168 A46 17c multicolored   .30   .30
169 A46 30c multicolored   .55   .55
170 A46 35c multicolored   .70   .70
      Nos. 167-170 (4)   1.77 1.77

Christmas; 450th death anniv. of Albrecht Dürer (1471-1528), German painter. Nos. 167-170 issued in sheets of 5 stamps and corner label. See No. B30.

Capt. Cook, by Nathaniel Dance — A47

Boy Holding Hibiscus, IYC Emblem — A48

Design: 75c, "Resolution" and "Adventure," by William Hodges.

1979, July 20   Photo.   Perf. 14x13¹/₂
171 A47 50c multicolored   1.10 1.10
172 A47 75c multicolored   1.50 1.50
a.   Souvenir sheet of 2, #171-172 3.00 3.00

Capt. James Cook (1728-1779), explorer, death bicentenary.

1979, Oct. 1   Photo.   Perf. 14x13¹/₂
IYC Emblem and: 35c, Boy playing guitar. 65c, Boys in outrigger canoe.
173 A48 30c multicolored   .50   .50
174 A48 35c multicolored   .55   .55
175 A48 65c multicolored   1.10 1.10
      Nos. 173-175 (3)   2.15 2.15

See No. B31.

Aitutaki No. 102, Hill, Penny Black A49

Designs: Nos. 176, 178-179, 181, paintings of letter writers, Flemish School, 17th century.

1979, Nov. 14   Photo.   Perf. 13
176 A49 50c Gabriel Metsu   .75   .75
177 A49 50c shown   .75   .75
178 A49 50c Jan Vermeer   .75   .75
179 A49 65c Gerard Terborch   .90   .90
180 A49 65c No. 103 (like No. 177) .90 .90
181 A49 65c Jan Vermeer   .90   .90
      Nos. 176-181 (6)   4.95 4.95

Souvenir Sheet
182   Sheet of 6   3.00 3.00
a.   A49 30c like No. 176   .42   .42
b.   A49 30c like No. 177   .42   .42
c.   A49 30c like No. 178   .42   .42
d.   A49 30c like No. 179   .42   .42
e.   A49 30c like No. 180   .42   .42
f.   A49 30c like No. 181   .42   .42

Sir Rowland Hill (1795-1879), originator of penny postage. Nos. 176-178 and 179-181 printed se-tenant in sheets of 9 (3x3).

Descent from the Cross, Detail — A50

Albert Einstein — A51

Easter: 30c, 35c, Descent from the Cross, by Quentin Metsys (details).

1980, Apr. 3   Photo.   Perf. 13x13¹/₂
183 A50 20c multicolored   .30   .30
184 A50 30c multicolored   .45   .45
185 A50 35c multicolored   .55   .55
      Nos. 183-185 (3)   1.30 1.30

See No. B32.

1980, July 21   Photo.   Perf. 14
186 A51 12c shown   .22   .22
187 A51 12c Formula, atom structure .22 .22
188 A51 15c Portrait, diff.   .25   .25
189 A51 15c Atomic blast   .25   .25
190 A51 20c Portrait, diff.   .35   .35

191 A51 20c Atomic blast, trees   .35   .35
a.   Souv. sheet of 6, #186-191, perf. 13 2.50 2.50
      Nos. 186-191 (6)   1.64 1.64

Albert Einstein (1879-1955), theoretical physicist. Stamps of same denomination se-tenant.

A52   A53

1980, Sept. 26   Photo.   Perf. 14
192 A52 6c Ancestral Figure, Aitutaki .15 .15
193 A52 6c God image staff, Rarotonga .15 .15
194 A52 6c Trade adze, Mangaia   .15   .15
195 A52 6c Tangaroa carving, Rarotonga .15 .15
196 A52 12c Wooden image, Aitutaki .18 .18
197 A52 12c Hand club, Rarotonga .18   .18
198 A52 12c Carved mace, Mangaia .18   .18
199 A52 12c Fisherman's god, Rarotonga .18 .18
200 A52 15c Ti'i image, Aitutaki .22   .22
201 A52 15c Fisherman's god, diff. .22 .22
202 A52 15c Carved mace, Cook Islands .22 .22
203 A52 15c Tangaroa, diff.   .22   .22
204 A52 20c Chief's headdress, Aitutaki .30 .30
205 A52 20c Carved mace, diff.   .30   .30
206 A52 20c God image staff, diff. .30 .30
207 A52 20c like #195   .30   .30
a.   Souvenir sheet of 16, #192-207 3.50
      Nos. 192-207 (16)   3.40 3.40

Third South Pacific Arts Festival, Port Moresby, Papua New Guinea. Stamps of same denomination se-tenant.

1980, Nov. 21   Photo.   Perf. 13x13¹/₂
Virgin and Child, Sculptures.
208 A53 15c 13th cent.   .22   .22
209 A53 20c 14th cent.   .30   .30
210 A53 25c 15th cent.   .38   .38
211 A53 35c 15th cent., diff.   .55   .55
      Nos. 208-211 (4)   1.45 1.45

Christmas. See No. B33.

Mourning Virgin, by Pedro Roldan — A54

Sturnus Vulgaris — A55

Easter (Roldan Sculptures): 40c, Christ. 50c, Mourning St. John.

1981, Mar. 31   Photo.   Perf. 14
212 A54 30c green & gold   .45   .45
213 A54 40c brt purple & gold   .55   .55
214 A54 50c dk blue & gold   .70   .70
      Nos. 212-214 (3)   1.70 1.70

See No. B34.

1981-82   Perf. 14x13¹/₂, 13¹/₂x14
215 A55 1c shown   .25   .15
216 A55 1c Poephila gouldiae   .25   .15
217 A55 2c Petroica multicolor   .35   .15
218 A55 2c Pachycephala pectoralis .35 .15
219 A55 3c Falco peregrinus   .40   .15
220 A55 3c Rhipidura rufifrous   .40   .15
221 A55 4c Tyto alba   .45   .15
222 A55 4c Padda oryzivora   .45   .15
223 A55 5c Artamus leucorhynchus .50 .15
224 A55 5c Vini peruviana   .50   .15
225 A55 6c Columba livia   .60   .20
226 A55 6c Porphyrio porphyria   .60   .20
227 A55 10c Geopelia striata   .90   .35
228 A55 10c Lonchura castaneothorax .90 .35
229 A55 12c Acridotheres tristis .90 .40
230 A55 12c Egretta sacra   .90   .40
231 A55 15c Diomeda melanophris 1.00 .50

232	A55 15c	Numenius phaeopus	1.00 .50
233	A55 20c	Gygis alba	1.10 .70
234	A55 20c	Pluvialis dominica	1.10 .70
235	A55 25c	Sula leucogaster	1.25 .90
236	A55 25c	Anas superciliosa	1.25 .90
237	A55 30c	Anas acuta	2.00 1.00
238	A55 30c	Fregata minor	2.00 1.00
239	A55 35c	Stercorarius pomarinus	2.25 1.25
240	A55 35c	Conopoderas caffra	2.25 1.25
241	A55 40c	Lalage maculosa	2.50 1.25
242	A55 40c	Gallirallus philippensis	2.50 1.25
243	A55 50c	Vini stepheni	2.75 1.65
244	A55 50c	Diomedea epomophora	2.75 1.65
245	A55 70c	Ptilinopus victor	5.50 2.25
246	A55 70c	Erythrura cyaneovirens	5.50 2.25

Photo. *Perf. 13½*
Size: 35x47mm

246A	A55 $1	Myiagra azureo-capilla	6.75 4.25
246B	A55 $2	Myiagra vanikoren-sis	11.50 9.00
246C	A55 $4	Amandava amandava	19.00 15.00
246D	A55 $5	Halcyon recurviros-tris	20.00 18.00
		Nos. 215-246D (36)	102.65 68.65

Issue dates: Nos. 215-230, Apr. 6; Nos. 231-238, May 8; Nos. 239-246, Jan. 14, 1982; Nos. 246A-246B, Feb. 15, 1982. Stamps of same denomination se-tenant. Nos. 231-246 horiz.

For surcharges and overprint see Nos. 293-306, 452-454, O40-O41.

Prince Charles and Lady Diana — A56

Perf. 13x13½, 13½x13

1981, June 10 **Photo.**

247	A56 60c	Charles, vert.	.75 .75
248	A56 80c	Lady Diana, vert.	1.00 1.00
249	A56 $1.40	Shown	1.75 1.75
		Nos. 247-249 (3)	3.50 3.50

Royal Wedding. Issued in sheets of 4.
For overprints and surcharges see Nos. 265-267, 307, 309, 355, 405-407, B35-B37.

1982 World Cup Soccer — A57

Designs: Various soccer players.

1981, Nov. 30 **Photo.** *Perf. 14*

250	A57 12c	Pair, #250a-250b	.40 .40
251	A57 15c	Pair, #251a-251b	.48 .48
252	A57 20c	Pair, #252a-252b	.65 .65
253	A57 25c	Pair, #253a-253b	.80 .80
		Nos. 250-253 (4)	2.33 2.33

See No. B38.

Christmas A58

Rembrandt Etchings: 15c, Holy Family, 1632, vert. 30c, Virgin with Child, 1634, vert. 40c, Adoration of the Shepherds, 1654. 50c, Holy Family with Cat, 1644.

1981, Dec. 10 *Perf. 14*

254	A58 15c	gold & dk brown	.22 .22
255	A58 30c	gold & dk brown	.45 .45
256	A58 40c	gold & dk brown	.60 .60
257	A58 50c	gold & dk brown	.75 .75
		Nos. 254-257 (4)	2.02 2.02

Souvenir Sheets

258	A58 80c + 5c like #254		1.10 1.10
259	A58 80c + 5c like #255		1.10 1.10
260	A58 80c + 5c like #256		1.10 1.10
261	A58 80c + 5c like #257		1.10 1.10

Nos. 258-261 have multicolored margins showing entire etching. Surtax on Nos. 258-261 was for local charities.

21st Birthday of Princess Diana — A59

1982, June 24 **Photo.** *Perf. 14*

262	A59 70c	shown	.75 .75
263	A59 $1	Wedding portrait	1.00 1.00
264	A59 $2	Diana, diff.	2.25 2.25
a.		Souvenir sheet of 3, #262-264	4.50 4.50
		Nos. 262-264 (3)	4.00 4.00

See No. 268-270a. For surcharges see #308, 310.

Nos. 247-249 Overprinted: "21 June 1982 PRINCE WILLIAM OF WALES" or "COMMEMORATING THE ROYAL BIRTH"

1982, July 13 *Perf. 13x13½, 13½x13*

265	A56 60c	multicolored	1.00 1.00
266	A56 80c	multicolored	1.50 1.50
267	A56 $1.40	multicolored	2.50 2.50
		Nos. 265-267 (3)	5.00 5.00

Nos. 262-264a Inscribed: "ROYAL BIRTH 21 JUNE 1982 PRINCE WILLIAM OF WALES"

1982, Aug. 5 *Perf. 14*

268	A59 70c	multicolored	1.10 1.10
269	A59 $1	multicolored	1.50 1.50
270	A59 $2	multicolored	3.00 3.00
a.		Souvenir sheet of 3	5.25 5.25
		Nos. 268-270 (3)	5.60 5.60

Christmas — A60

Madonna and Child Sculptures, 12th-15th Cent.

1982, Dec. 10 **Photo.** *Perf. 13*

271	A60 18c	multicolored	.25 .25
272	A60 36c	multicolored	.55 .55
273	A60 48c	multicolored	.90 .90
274	A60 60c	multicolored	.90 .90
		Nos. 271-274 (4)	2.45 2.45

Souvenir Sheet

275		Sheet of 4	2.75 2.75
a.	A60 18c + 2c like 18c		.30 .30
b.	A60 36c + 2c like 36c		.55 .55
c.	A60 48c + 2c like 48c		.75 .75
d.	A60 60c + 2c like 60c		.90 .90

Surtax was for children's charities.

Commonwealth Day — A61

1983, Mar. 14 **Photo.** *Perf. 13x13½*

276	A61 48c	Bananas	1.25 1.25
277	A61 48c	Ti'i statuette	1.25 1.25
278	A61 48c	Boys canoeing	1.25 1.25
279	A61 48c	Capt. William Bligh, Bounty	1.25 1.25
a.		Block of 4, #276-270	5.00 5.00

Scouting Year — A62

1983, Apr. 18 **Photo.** *Perf. 14*

280	A62 36c	Campfire	.55 .55
281	A62 48c	Salute	.75 .75
282	A62 60c	Hiking	.90 .90
		Nos. 280-282 (3)	2.20 2.20

Souvenir Sheet
Perf. 13½

283		Sheet of 3	3.00 3.00
a.	A62 36c + 3c like #280		.75 .75
b.	A62 48c + 3c like #281		.90 .90
c.	A62 60c + 3c like #282		1.20 1.20

Surtax was for benefit of Scouting.

Nos. 280-283 Overprinted: "15th WORLD SCOUT JAMBOREE"

1983, July 11 **Photo.** *Perf. 14*

284	A62 36c	multicolored	.55 .55
285	A62 48c	multicolored	.75 .75
286	A62 60c	multicolored	.90 .90
		Nos. 284-286 (3)	2.20 2.20

Souvenir Sheet

287		Sheet of 3	3.00 3.00
a.	A62 36c + 3c like #284		.75 .75
b.	A62 48c + 3c like #285		.90 .90
c.	A62 60c + 3c like #286		1.20 1.20

A63　　　　　　A64

Manned Flight Bicentenary: Modern sport balloons.

1983, July 22 **Photo.** *Perf. 14x13*

288	A63 18c	multicolored	.25 .25
289	A63 36c	multicolored	.55 .55
290	A63 48c	multicolored	.75 .75
291	A63 60c	multicolored	.90 .90
		Nos. 288-291 (4)	2.45 2.45

Souvenir Sheet

292	A63 $2.50	multicolored	3.50 3.50

Nos. 233-246, 246D, 248-249, 263-264 Surcharged

1983, Sept. 22

293	A55	18c on 20c, #233	.90 .36
294	A55	18c on 20c, #234	.90 .36
295	A55	36c on 25c, #235	1.25 .72
296	A55	36c on 25c, #236	1.25 .72
297	A55	36c on 30c, #237	1.25 .72
298	A55	36c on 30c, #238	1.25 .72
299	A55	36c on 35c, #239	1.25 .72
300	A55	36c on 35c, #240	1.25 .72
301	A55	48c on 40c, #241	2.00 .95
302	A55	48c on 40c, #242	2.00 .95
303	A55	48c on 50c, #243	2.00 .95
304	A55	48c on 50c, #244	2.00 .95
305	A55	72c on 70c, #245	3.00 1.45
306	A55	72c on 70c, #246	3.00 1.45
307	A56	96c on 80c, #248	5.50 1.90
308	A59	96c on $1, #263	5.50 1.90
309	A56	$1.20 on 1.40, #249	6.50 2.40
310	A59	$1.20 on $2, #264	6.50 2.40

Size: 35x47mm

311	A55	$5.60 on $5, #246D	16.00 11.00
		Nos. 293-311 (19)	63.30 31.34

Nos. 293-306 printed in se-tenant pairs. Nos. 307-308, 310-311 vert.

1983, Sept. 29 **Photo.** *Perf. 14*

312	A64 48c	shown	.65 .65
313	A64 60c	Communications satellite	.85 .85
314	A64 96c	Global coverage	1.50 1.50
a.		Souvenir sheet of 3, #312-314	3.00 3.00
		Nos. 312-314 (3)	3.00 3.00

World Communications Year.

Christmas A65

Raphael Paintings.

1983, Nov. 21 **Photo.** *Perf. 13½x14*

315	A65 36c	Madonna of the Chair	.48 .48
316	A65 48c	Alba Madonna	.65 .65
317	A65 60c	Connestabile Madonna	.80 .80
		Nos. 315-317 (3)	1.93 1.93

Souvenir Sheet

318		Sheet of 3	2.50 2.50
a.	A65 36c + 3c like #315		.60 .60
b.	A65 48c + 3c like #316		.75 .75
c.	A65 60c + 3c like #317		.90 .90

1983, Dec. 15 *Imperf.*
Size: 46x46mm

319	A65 85c + 5c like #315		1.25 1.25
320	A65 85c + 5c like #316		1.25 1.25
321	A65 85c + 5c like #317		1.25 1.25
		Nos. 319-321 (3)	3.75 3.75

Surtax was for children's charities.

Local Birds — A66

1984 **Photo.** *Perf. 14*

322	A66 2c	as No. 216	.25 .25
323	A66 3c	as No. 215	.25 .25
324	A66 5c	as No. 217	.25 .25
325	A66 10c	as No. 218	.25 .25
326	A66 12c	as No. 220	.35 .35
327	A66 18c	as No. 219	.45 .45
328	A66 24c	as No. 221	.65 .65
329	A66 30c	as No. 222	.75 .75
330	A66 36c	as No. 223	.90 .90
331	A66 48c	as No. 224	1.25 1.25
332	A66 50c	as No. 225	.90 .90
333	A66 60c	as No. 226	1.25 1.25
334	A66 72c	as No. 227	1.50 1.50
335	A66 96c	as No. 228	2.00 2.00
336	A66 $1.20	as No. 229	2.25 2.25
337	A66 $2.10	as No. 2230	4.00 4.00
338	A66 $3	as No. 246A	5.75 5.75
339	A66 $4.20	as No. 246B	7.00 7.00
340	A66 $5.60	as No. 246C	7.50 7.50
341	A66 $9.60	as No. 246D	12.50 12.50
		Nos. 322-341 (20)	50.00 50.00

For overprints and surcharges see Nos. O17-O39.

1984 Summer Olympics — A67

1984, July 24 **Photo.** *Perf. 13x13½*

342	A67 36c	Javelin	.32 .32
343	A67 48c	Shot put	.45 .45
344	A67 60c	Hurdles	.55 .55
345	A67 $2	Handball	1.75 1.75
		Nos. 342-345 (4)	3.07 3.07

Souvenir Sheet

346		Sheet of 4	3.50 3.50
a.	A67 36c + 5c like #342		.38 .38
b.	A67 48c + 5c like #343		.50 .50
c.	A67 60c + 5c like #344		.60 .60
d.	A67 $2 + 5c like #345		1.75 1.75

Surtax was for benefit of local sports.

Nos. 342-345 Overprinted in Gold on Black with Winners' Names, Event, Nationality

1984, Aug. 21 **Photo.** *Perf. 13x13½*

347	A67 36c	multicolored	.32 .32
348	A67 48c	multicolored	.45 .45
349	A67 60c	multicolored	.55 .55
350	A67 $2	multicolored	1.75 1.75
		Nos. 347-350 (4)	3.07 3.07

Ausipex '84 — A68

1984, Sept. 14 **Photo.** *Perf. 14*

351	A68 60c	William Bligh, map	.55 .55
352	A68 96c	Bounty, map	.85 .85
353	A68 $1.40	Stamps, map	1.25 1.25
		Nos. 351-353 (3)	2.65 2.65

Souvenir Sheet

354	Sheet of 3	3.25	3.25
a.	A68 60c + 5c like #351	.65	.65
b.	A68 96c + 5c like #352	1.00	1.00
c.	A68 $1.40 + 5c like #353	1.40	1.40

For overprint see No. 399.

No. 247 Surcharged with Black Bar and
New Value in Gold and: "15.9.84
Birth/Prince Henry"

1984, Oct. 10   Photo.   Perf. 13x13¹/₂

355	A56 $3 multicolored	3.00	3.00

Issued in sheets of 4.

A69   A70

1984, Nov. 16   Photo.   Perf. 13

356	A69 36c Annunciation	.32	.32
357	A69 48c Nativity	.45	.45
358	A69 60c Epiphany	.55	.55
359	A69 96c Flight into Egypt	.90	.90
	Nos. 356-359 (4)	2.22	2.22

**Souvenir Sheets
Size: 45x53mm
Imperf**

360	A69 90c + 7c like #356	.90	.90
361	A69 90c + 7c like #357	.90	.90
362	A69 90c + 7c like #358	.90	.90
363	A69 90c + 7c like #359	.90	.90

Christmas.

1984, Dec. 10   Photo.   Perf. 13¹/₂x14

364	A70 48c Diana, Henry	.75	.75
365	A70 60c William, Henry	.90	.90
366	A70 $2.10 Family	2.75	2.75
	Nos. 364-366 (3)	4.40	4.40

Souvenir Sheet

367	Sheet of 3	4.50	4.50
a.	A70 96c + 7c like #364	1.40	1.40
b.	A70 96c + 7c like #365	1.40	1.40
c.	A70 96c + 7c like #366	1.40	1.40

Christmas, Birth of Prince Henry, Sept. 15.
Surtax was for benefit of local children's
charities.

Audubon Birth
Bicentenary — A71

Illustrations of bird species by John J. Audubon.

1985, Mar. 22   Litho.   Perf. 13

368	A71 55c Gray kingbird	.52	.52
369	A71 65c Bohemian waxwing	.60	.60
370	A71 75c Summer tanager	.75	.75
371	A71 95c Cardinal	.95	.95
372	A71 $1.15 White-winged cross-bill	1.10	1.10
	Nos. 368-372 (5)	3.92	3.92

Queen
Mother,
85th
Birthday
A72

Photographs: 55c, Lady Elizabeth Bowes-Lyon,
age 7. 65c, Engaged to the Duke of York, 75c,
Duchess of York with daughter, Elizabeth. $1.30,
Holding the infant Prince Charles. $3, Portrait
taken on 63rd birthday.

1985-86   Perf. 13¹/₂x13

373	A72 55c multicolored	.50	.50
374	A72 65c multicolored	.60	.60
375	A72 75c multicolored	.70	.70
376	A72 $1.30 multicolored	1.20	1.20
a.	Souvenir sheet of 4, #373-376	3.25	3.25
	Nos. 373-376 (4)	3.00	3.00

Souvenir Sheet

377	A72 $3 multicolored	2.25	2.25

Nos. 373-376 printed in sheets of 4.
Issued: #376a, 8/4/86; others, 6/14/85.

Intl. Youth
Year
A73

Designs: 75c, The Calmady Children, by Thomas
Lawrence (1769-1830). 90c, Madame Charpen-
tier's Children, by Renoir (1841-1919). $1.40,
Young Girls at Piano, by Renoir.

1985, Sept. 16   Photo.   Perf. 13

378	A73 75c multicolored	.65	.65
379	A73 90c multicolored	.75	.75
380	A73 $1.40 multicolored	1.25	1.25
	Nos. 378-380 (3)	2.65	2.65

Souvenir Sheet

381	Sheet of 3	3.75	3.75
a.	A73 75c + 10c like #378	.95	.95
b.	A73 90c + 10c like #379	1.10	1.10
c.	A73 $1.40 + 10c like #380	1.70	1.70

Surcharged for children's activities.

Adoration of the Magi, by Giotto di
Bondone (1276-1337) — A74

1985, Nov. 15   Photo.   Perf. 13¹/₂x13

382	A74 95c multicolored	1.10	1.10
383	A74 95c multicolored	1.10	1.10
384	A74 $1.15 multicolored	1.40	1.40
385	A74 $1.15 multicolored	1.40	1.40
	Nos. 382-385 (4)	5.00	5.00

**Souvenir Sheet
Imperf**

386	A74 $6.40 multicolored	7.50	7.50

Christmas, return of Halley's Comet, 1985-86.
Stamps of the same denomination se-tenant.

Halley's
Comet
A75

Designs: 90c, Halley's Comet, A.D. 684, wood
engraving, Nuremberg Chronicles. $1.25, Sighting
of 1066, Bayeux Tapestry, detail, c. 1092, France.
$1.75, The Comet Inflicting Untold Disasters,
1456, Lucerne Chronicles, by Diebolt Schilling.
$4.20, Melancolia I, engraving by Durer.

1986, Feb. 25   Photo.   Perf. 13¹/₂x13

387	A75 90c multicolored	1.00	1.00
388	A75 $1.25 multicolored	1.40	1.40
389	A75 $1.75 multicolored	2.00	2.00
	Nos. 387-389 (3)	4.40	4.40

Souvenir Sheets

390	Sheet of 3 + label	3.30	3.30
a.	A75 95c, like #387	1.10	1.10
b.	A75 95c, like #388	1.10	1.10
c.	A75 95c, like #389	1.10	1.10

Imperf

391	A75 $4.20 multicolored	4.75	4.75

Elizabeth II, 60th
Birthday — A76

1986, Apr. 21   Perf. 14

392	A76 95c Coronation portrait	1.15	1.15

**Souvenir Sheet
Perf. 13¹/₂**

393	A76 $4.20 Portrait, diff.	5.00	5.00

No. 392 printed in sheets of 5 with label picturing U.K. flag and Queen's flag for New Zealand.

Statue of
Liberty,
Cent.
A77

1986, June 27   Photo.   Perf. 14

394	A77 $1 Liberty head	1.15	1.15
395	A77 $2.75 Statue	3.10	3.10

**Souvenir Sheet
Perf. 13¹/₂**

396	Sheet of 2	2.80	2.80
a.	A77 $1.25 like $1	1.40	1.40
b.	A77 $1.25 like $2.75	1.40	1.40

For surcharges see Nos B44, B49.

Wedding of Prince
Andrew and Sarah
Ferguson — A78

1986, July 23   Perf. 14

397	A78 $2 multicolored	2.30	2.30

**Souvenir Sheet
Perf. 13¹/₂**

398	A78 $5 multicolored	5.75	5.75

No. 397 printed in sheets of 5 plus label picturing Westminster Abbey.
For surcharge see No. B48.

No. 354 Ovptd. with Gold Circle over
AUSIPEX Emblem, Black and Gold
STAMPEX '86 Emblem

1986, Aug. 4   Photo.   Perf. 14

399	Sheet of 3	3.35	3.35
a.	A68 60c + 5c like #351	.70	.70
b.	A68 96c + 5c like #352	1.10	1.10
c.	A68 $1.40 + 5c like #353	1.55	1.55

STAMPEX '86, Adelaide, Aug. 4-10.

Christmas — A79

Paintings by Albrecht Durer: 75c, No. 404a, St.
Anne with Virgin and Child. $1.35, No. 404b, Vir-
gin and Child. $1.95, No. 404c, Adoration of the
Magi. $2.75, No. 404d, Rosary Festivity.

1986, Nov. 21   Litho.   Perf. 13¹/₂

400	A79 75c multicolored	.80	.80
401	A79 $1.35 multicolored	1.45	1.45
402	A79 $1.95 multicolored	2.10	2.10
403	A79 $2.75 multicolored	2.95	2.95
	Nos. 400-403 (4)	7.30	7.30

Souvenir Sheet

404	Sheet of 4	7.00	7.00
a.-d.	A79 $1.65 any single	1.75	1.75

For surcharges see Nos. B39-B44, B46-B47, B50-
B54.

Nos. 247-249 Surcharged in Gold and
Black

1987, Nov. 20   Photo.   Perf. 13x12¹/₂

405	A56 $2.50 on 60c No. 247	3.00	3.00
406	A56 $2.50 on 80c No. 248	3.00	3.00
407	A56 $2.50 on $1.40 No. 249	3.00	3.00
	Nos. 405-407 (3)	9.00	9.00

Issued in sheets of 4 with margin inscriptions
overprinted with gold bar and "40th Anniversary of
the Royal Wedding / 1947-1987" in black; "OVER-
PRINTED BY NEW ZEALAND GOVERNMENT
PRINTER, / WELLINGTON, NOVEMBER 1987"
at left.

A80

The Virgin with Garland, by
Rubens — A81

Painting details.

1987, Dec. 10   Photo.   Perf. 13x13¹/₂

408	A80 70c UL	.90	.90
409	A80 85c UR	1.10	1.10
410	A80 $1.50 LL	1.95	1.95
411	A80 $1.85 LR	2.35	2.35
	Nos. 408-411 (4)	6.30	6.30

Souvenir Sheets

412	Sheet of 4	5.00	5.00
a.	A80 95c like No. 408	1.25	1.25
b.	A80 95c like No. 409	1.25	1.25
c.	A80 95c like No. 410	1.25	1.25
d.	A80 95c like No. 411	1.25	1.25

Perf. 13

413	A81 $6 multicolored	7.75	7.75

Christmas.

1988 Summer Olympics, Seoul — A82

Flags of Korea, Aitutaki, ancient and modern
events, and Seoul Games emblem or $50 silver coin
issued to commemorate the participation of Aitutaki
athletes in the Olympics for the 1st time: 70c, No.
418a, Obverse of silver coin, chariot race, running.
85c, Emblem, running, soccer. 95c, Emblem, boxing, handball. $1.40, No. 418b, Reverse of coin,
spearmen, women's tennis.

Christmas — A96

Religious sculpture: 80c, Madonna and Child, by Nino Pisano. 90c, Virgin on Rosebush, by Luca Della Robbia. $1.15, Virgin with Child and St. John, by Juan Francisco Rustici. $1.95, Virgin with Child, by Michelangelo. $3, Madonna and Child, by Jacopo Della Quercia.

1993, Oct. 29   Litho.   *Perf. 14*
483	A96	80c multicolored	.90	.90
484	A96	90c multicolored	1.00	1.00
485	A96	$1.15 multicolored	1.25	1.25
486	A96	$1.95 multicolored	2.25	2.25

Size: 32x47mm
Perf. 13¹/₂
487	A96	$3 multicolored	3.50	3.50
		Nos. 483-487 (5)	8.90	8.90

1994 Winter Olympics, Lillehammer — A97

Designs: a, Ice hockey. b, Ski jumping. c, Cross-country skiing.

1994, Feb. 11   Litho.   *Perf. 14*
488	A97	$1.15 Strip of 3, #a.-c.	4.00	4.00

Flowers — A98

Hibiscus A98a

1994-97   Litho.   *Perf. 13¹/₂*
489	A98	5c Prostrate morning glory	.15	.15
490	A98	10c White frangipani	.15	.15
491	A98	15c Red hibiscus	.16	.16
492	A98	20c Yellow allamanda	.22	.22
493	A98	25c Royal poinciana	.28	.28
494	A98	30c White gardenia	.35	.35
495	A98	50c Pink frangipani	.55	.55
496	A98	80c Morning glory	.90	.90
497	A98	85c Yellow mallow	.95	.95
498	A98	90c Red coral tree	1.00	1.00
499	A98	$1 Cup of gold	1.10	1.10
500	A98	$2 Red cordia	2.25	2.25
501	A98a	$3 multicolored	3.75	3.75
502	A98a	$5 multicolored	6.25	6.25
503	A98a	$8 multicolored	10.00	10.00
		Nos. 489-503 (15)	28.06	28.06

Issued: 5c-90c, 2/17; $1, $2, 4/29; $3, $5, 11/18; $8, 11/21/97. This is an expanding set. Numbers may change.

First Manned Moon Landing, 25th Anniv. A99

Designs: No. 506, Astronauts Collins, Armstrong, Aldrin. No. 507, Splash down in South Pacific.

1994, July 20   Litho.   *Perf. 14*
506	A99	$2 multicolored	2.25	2.25
507	A99	$2 multicolored	2.25	2.25

Christmas — A100

Paintings: No. 508a, The Madonna of the Basket, by Corregio. b, Virgin & Child with Saints, by Hans Memling. c, The Virgin & Child with Flowers, by Dolci. d, Virgin & Child with Angels, by Bergognone.
No. 509a, The Adoration of the Kings, by Dosso. b, The Virgin & Child, by Bellini. c, The Virgin & Child, by Schiavone. d, Adoration of the Kings, by Dolci.

1994, Nov. 30   Litho.   *Perf. 14*
508	A100	85c Block of 4, #a.-d.	3.75	3.75
509	A100	90c Block of 4, #a.-d.	4.00	4.00

End of World War II, 50th Anniv. — A101

Designs: a, Battle of Britain, 1940. b, Battle of Midway, June 1942.

1995, Sept. 4   Litho.   *Perf. 13¹/₂x13*
510	A101	$4 Pair, #a.-b.	10.50	10.50

No. 510 issued in sheets of 4 stamps.

Queen Mother, 95th Birthday A102

1995, Sept. 14   Litho.   *Perf. 13x13¹/₂*
511	A102	$4 multicolored	5.25	5.25

UN, 50th Anniv. — A103

1995, Oct. 18   Litho.   *Perf. 13¹/₂*
512	A103	$4.25 multicolored	5.50	5.50

Year of the Sea Turtle A104

1995, Dec. 1   Litho.   *Perf. 14x13¹/₂*
513	A104	95c Green turtle	1.25	1.25
514	A104	$1.15 Leatherback turtle	1.50	1.50
515	A104	$1.50 Olive Ridley turtle	2.00	2.00
516	A104	$1.75 Loggerhead turtle	2.25	2.25
		Nos. 513-516 (4)	7.00	7.00

Queen Elizabeth II, 70th Birthday A105

1996, June 24   Litho.   *Perf. 14*
517	A105	$4.50 multicolored	6.00	6.00

No. 517 was issued in sheets of 4.

Modern Olympic Games, Cent. A106

Designs: No. 518, Pierre de Coubertin, Olympic torch, parading athletes, 1896. No. 519, Modern sprinters, US flag, Atlanta, 1996.

1996, July 11   Litho.   *Perf. 14*
518	A106	$2 multicolored	2.75	2.75
519	A106	$2 multicolored	2.75	2.75
a.		Pair, #518-519	5.50	5.50

SEMI-POSTAL STAMPS

Christmas Type of 1974

Designs: 1c+1c, like #104. 5c+1c, like #105. 8c+1c, like #106. 10c+1c, like #107. 25c+1c, like #108. 30c+1c, like #109.

1974, Dec. 2   Photo.   *Perf. 13¹/₂*
B1	A29	1c + 1c multicolored	.15	.15
B2	A29	5c + 1c multicolored	.15	.15
B3	A29	8c + 1c multicolored	.20	.20
B4	A29	10c + 1c multicolored	.30	.30
B5	A29	25c + 1c multicolored	.70	.70
B6	A29	30c + 1c multicolored	.75	.75
		Nos. B1-B6 (6)	2.25	2.25

Surtax was for child welfare.

Nos. 117-120 Surcharged in Silver

1975, Dec. 19   Photo.   *Perf. 14x13¹/₂*
B7	A32	Strip of 3	.45	.45
a.-c.		6c+1c any single	.15	.15
B8	A32	Strip of 3	.52	.52
a.-c.		7c+1c any single	.16	.16
B9	A32	Strip of 3	1.25	1.25
a.-c.		15c+1c any single	.40	.40
B10	A32	Strip of 3	1.90	1.90
a.-c.		20c+1c any single	.50	.50
		Nos. B7-B10 (4)	4.12	4.12

Christmas. The surtax was for children's activities during holiday season.

Nos. 135-142a Surcharged in Silver

1976, Nov. 19   Photo.   *Perf. 13¹/₂x13*
B11	A36	6c + 1c multicolored	.15	.15
B12	A37	6c + 1c multicolored	.15	.15
B13	A36	7c + 1c multicolored	.15	.15
B14	A37	7c + 1c multicolored	.15	.15
B15	A36	15c + 1c multicolored	.35	.35
B16	A37	15c + 1c multicolored	.35	.35
B17	A36	20c + 1c multicolored	.50	.50
B18	A37	20c + 1c multicolored	.50	.50
a.		Souvenir sheet of 8	3.50	3.50
		Nos. B11-B18 (8)	2.30	2.30

Surtax was for child welfare. Stamps of No. B18a each surcharged 2c.

Nos. 152-159a Surcharged in Black

1977, Nov. 15   *Perf. 13¹/₂x14*
B19	A41	6c + 1c multicolored	.15	.15
B20	A42	6c + 1c multicolored	.15	.15
B21	A41	7c + 1c multicolored	.15	.15
B22	A42	7c + 1c multicolored	.15	.15

B23	A41	15c + 1c multicolored	.35	.35
B24	A42	15c + 1c multicolored	.35	.35
B25	A41	20c + 1c multicolored	.50	.50
B26	A42	20c + 1c multicolored	.50	.50
a.		Souvenir sheet of 8	3.25	3.25
		Nos. B19-B26 (8)	2.30	2.30

Surtax was for child welfare. Stamps of No. B26a each surcharged 2c.

Easter Type of 1978
Souvenir Sheets

Paintings: No. B27, like No. 163. No. B28, like No. 164. No. B29, like No. 165.

1978, Mar. 17   Photo.   *Perf. 14*
B27	A44	50c + 5c multicolored	.90	.90
B28	A44	50c + 5c multicolored	.90	.90
B29	A44	50c + 5c multicolored	.90	.90

Nos. B27-B29 contain one stamp 33x25mm.

Christmas Type of 1978
Souvenir Sheet

1978, Dec. 4   Photo.   *Perf. 14¹/₂x13*
B30		Sheet of 4	2.00	2.00
a.		A46 15c + 2c like #167	.28	.28
b.		A46 17c + 2c like #168	.30	.30
c.		A46 30c + 2c like #169	.52	.52
d.		A46 35c + 2c like #170	.60	.60

Year of the Child Type
Souvenir Sheet

1979, Oct. 1   Photo.   *Perf. 14x13¹/₂*
B31		Sheet of 3	2.50	2.50
a.		A48 30c + 3c like #173	.55	.55
b.		A48 35c + 3c like #174	.60	.60
c.		A48 65c + 3c like #175	1.10	1.10

Easter Type of 1980
Souvenir Sheet

Designs: No. B32 shows entire painting in continuous design. Nos. B32a-B32c similar to Nos. B183-185. Size of Nos. B32a-B32c: 25x50mm.

1980, Apr. 3   Photo.   *Perf. 13x13¹/₂*
B32		Sheet of 3	1.50	1.50
a.		A50 20c + 2c multicolored	.35	.35
b.		A50 30c + 2c multicolored	.50	.50
c.		A50 35c + 2c multicolored	.60	.60

Christmas Type of 1980
Souvenir Sheet

1980, Nov. 21   Photo.   *Perf. 13x13¹/₂*
B33		Sheet of 4	1.75	1.75
a.		A53 15c + 2c like #208	.28	.28
b.		A53 20c + 2c like #209	.35	.35
c.		A53 25c + 2c like #210	.45	.45
d.		A53 35c + 2c like #211	.60	.60

Easter Type of 1981
Souvenir Sheet

1981, Mar. 31   Photo.   *Perf. 13¹/₂*
B34		Sheet of 3	2.00	2.00
a.		A54 30c + 2c like #212	.45	.45
b.		A54 40c + 2c like #213	.60	.60
c.		A54 50c + 2c like #214	.80	.80

Nos. 247-249 Surcharged

1981, Nov. 23   Photo.   *Perf. 13x13¹/₂*
B35	A56	60 + 5c multi	1.00	1.00
B36	A56	80 + 5c multi	1.25	1.25
B37	A56	$1.40 + 5c multi	2.25	2.25
		Nos. B35-B37 (3)	4.50	4.50

Intl. Year of the Disabled. Surtax was for the handicapped.

Soccer Type of 1981
Souvenir Sheet

1981, Nov. 30   *Perf. 14*
B38	A57	Sheet of 8, multi	2.50	2.50

No. B38 contains stamps with 2c surtax similar to Nos. 250-253. Surtax was for local sports.

Nos. 400-404 Surcharged
"NOVEMBER/21-24 1986/FIRST VISIT TO SOUTH/PACIFIC" and 10c in Silver

1986, Nov. 25   Litho.   *Perf. 13¹/₂*
B39	A79	75c + 10c multi	1.25	1.25
B40	A79	$1.35 + 10c multi	2.00	2.00
B41	A79	$1.95 + 10c multi	3.00	3.00
B42	A79	$2.75 + 10c multi	4.00	4.00
		Nos. B39-B42 (4)	10.25	10.25

Souvenir Sheet
B43		Sheet of 4	13.00	13.00
a.-d.		A79 $1.65 +10c on #404a-404d	3.25	3.25

State visit of Pope John Paul II.
For surcharges see Nos. B51-B54.

Nos. 394-395, 397 and 400-403
Surcharged "HURRICANE RELIEF/ + 50c"
in Silver or Black

1987, Apr. 29   Litho.   Perf. 13¹/₂, 14

B44	A79	75c + 50c #400	2.00	2.00
B45	A77	$1 + 50c #394 (B)	2.50	2.50
B46	A79	$1.35 + 50c #401	3.00	3.00
B47	A79	$1.95 + 50c #402	3.25	3.25
B48	A78	$2 + 50c #397	3.25	3.25
B49	A79	$2.75 + 50c #395 (B)	4.25	4.25
B50	A79	$2.75 + 50c #403	4.25	4.25
		Nos. B44-B50 (7)	22.50	22.50

Nos. B39-B42 Surcharged "HURRICANE
RELIEF / +50c" in Silver

1987, Apr. 29   Litho.   Perf. 13¹/₂

B51	A79	75c + 50c No. B39	2.50	2.50
B52	A79	$1.35 + 50c No. B40	3.00	3.00
B53	A79	$1.95 + 50c No. B41	3.50	3.50
B54	A79	$2.75 + 50c No. B42	4.25	4.25
		Nos. B51-B54 (4)	13.25	13.25

AIR POST STAMPS

Capt. Bligh Type of 1974

1974, Sept. 9   Litho.   Perf. 13
Size: 46x26mm

C1	A27	10c Bligh and "Bounty"	.40	.40
C2	A27	10c "Bounty" at sea	.40	.40
C3	A27	25c Bligh and "Bounty"	.85	.85
C4	A27	25c Chart, 1856	.85	.85
C5	A27	30c Cook and "Resolution"	1.10	1.10
C6	A27	30c Maps	1.10	1.10
		Nos. C1-C6 (6)	4.70	4.70

Stamps of same denomination printed se-tenant
in sheets of 20. See note after No. 101.

OFFICIAL STAMPS

Nos. 83-90, 92-95,
150-151 Overprinted **O.H.M.S.**
or Surcharged in
Black, Silver or Gold

1978-79   Photo.   Perf. 13x13¹/₂

O1	A25	1c multi	.15	.15
O2	A25	2c multi	.15	.15
O3	A25	3c multi	.15	.15
O4	A25	4c multi (G)	.15	.15
O5	A25	5c multi	.15	.15
O6	A25	8c multi	.15	.15
O7	A25	10c multi	.15	.15
O8	A25	15c on 60c multi	.22	.20
O9	A25	18c on 60c multi	.28	.25
O10	A25	20c multi (G)	.30	.28
O11	A40	50c multi	.75	.70
O12	A25	60c multi	.90	.80
O13	A25	$1 multi	1.40	1.25
O14	A26	$2 multi	3.00	2.75
O15	A40	$4 on $1 multi (S)	6.00	5.50
O16	A26	$5 multi	7.25	6.50
		Nos. O1-O16 (16)	21.15	19.28

Overprint on 4c, 20c, $1 diagonal.
Issued: #O14-O16, 2/20/79; others, 11/3/78.

Stamps of 1983-84 Ovptd. or Surcharged
in Green

O.H.M.S.

or Gold (#O29-O32)

75c ▬

O.H.M.S.

1985, Aug. 9   Perf. 14, 13x13¹/₂

O17	A66	2c No. 322	.15	.15
O18	A66	5c No. 324	.15	.15
O19	A66	10c No. 325	.15	.15
O20	A66	12c No. 326	.15	.15
O21	A66	18c No. 327	.20	.20
O22	A66	20c on 24c No. 328	.22	.22
O23	A66	30c No. 329	.35	.35
O24	A66	40c on 36c No. 330	.45	.45
O25	A66	50c No. 332	.55	.55
O26	A66	55c on 48c No. 331	.62	.62
O27	A66	60c No. 333	.68	.68
O28	A66	65c on 72c No. 334	.72	.72
O29	A61	75c on 48c No. 276	.85	.85
O30	A61	75c on 48c No. 277	.85	.85
O31	A61	75c on 48c No. 278	.85	.85

O32	A61	75c on 48c No. 279	.85	.85
a.		Block of 4, Nos. O29-O32	3.50	3.50
O33	A66	80c on No. 335	.90	.90
		Nos. O17-O33 (17)	8.69	8.69

Nos. 336-341, 246C-246D Overprinted or
Surcharged Like Nos. O17-O28, O33 in
Metallic Green or Blue

1986, Oct. 1   Perf. 14

O34	A66	$3 multi	3.10	3.10
O35	A66	$4.20 multi	4.35	4.35
O36	A66	$5.60 multi	5.80	5.80
O37	A66	$9.60 multi	10.00	10.00

1988-91   Perf. 14

O38	A66	$1.20 multi	1.50	1.50
O39	A66	$2.10 multi	2.50	2.50

Perf. 13¹/₂

O40	A55	$14 on $4 (B)	17.50	17.50
O41	A55	$18 on $5 (B)	22.50	22.50
		Nos. O34-O41 (8)	67.25	67.25

Issue dates: July 2, 1991. Others, June 15.

AJMAN
äj-'man

LOCATION — Oman Peninsula, Arabia, on
Persian Gulf
GOVT. — Sheikdom under British
Protection
AREA — 100 sq. mi.
POP. — 4,400
CAPITAL — Ajman

Ajman is one of six Persian Gulf sheikdoms to join the United Arab Emirates,
which proclaimed its independence Dec. 2,
1971. See United Arab Emirates.

100 Naye Paise = 1 Rupee

┌─────────────────────────────────┐
│ Catalogue values for all unused   │
│ stamps in this country are for Never │
│ Hinged items.   │
└─────────────────────────────────┘

Sheik Rashid
bin Humaid
al Naimi and
Arab
Stallion — A1

Designs: 2np, 50np, Regal angelfish. 3np, 70np,
Camel. 4np, 1r, Angelfish. 5np, 1.50r, Green turtle. 10np, 2r, Jewelfish. 15np, 3r, White storks.
20np, 5r, White-eyed gulls. 30np, 10r, Lanner falcon. 40np as 1np.

Photo. & Litho.
1964   Unwmk.   Perf. 14
Size: 35x22mm

1	A1	1np gold & multi	.15	.15
2	A1	2np gold & multi	.15	.15
3	A1	3np gold & multi	.15	.15
4	A1	4np gold & multi	.15	.15
5	A1	5np gold & multi	.15	.15
6	A1	10np gold & multi	.15	.15
7	A1	15np gold & multi	.15	.15
8	A1	20np gold & multi	.15	.15
9	A1	30np gold & multi	.15	.15

Size: 42x27mm

10	A1	40np gold & multi	.15	.15
11	A1	50np gold & multi	.15	.15
12	A1	70np gold & multi	.15	.15
13	A1	1r gold & multi	.30	.15
14	A1	1.50r gold & multi	.40	.15
15	A1	2r gold & multi	.75	.15

Size: 53x33¹/₂mm

16	A1	3r gold & multi	.80	.15
17	A1	5r gold & multi	1.25	.40
18	A1	10r gold & multi	3.00	.75
		Nos. 1-18 (18)	8.30	
		Set value		2.25

Issued: #1-9, 6/20; #10-15, 9/7; #16-18, 11/4.

Pres. and Mrs. John
F. Kennedy with
Caroline — A2

Pres. Kennedy: 10np, As a boy in football uniform. 15np, Diving. 50np, As navy lieutenant,
receiving Navy and Marine Corps Medal from Capt.
Frederic L. Conklin. 1r, Sailing with Jacqueline
Kennedy. 2r, With Eleanor Roosevelt. 5r, With Lyndon B. Johnson and Hubert H. Humphrey. 10r,
Portrait.

1964, Dec. 15   Photo.   Perf. 13¹/₂x14

19	A2	10np grn & red lil	.15	.15
20	A2	15np Prus bl & vio	.15	.15
21	A2	50np org brn & dk bl	.15	.15
22	A2	1r brn & Prus grn	.50	.15
23	A2	2r red lil & dp ol	.70	.15
24	A2	3r grn & red brn	1.00	.20
25	A2	5r vio & brn	1.75	.30
26	A2	10r dk bl & red brn	3.50	.50
		Nos. 19-26 (8)	7.90	
		Set value		1.50

John F. Kennedy (1917-63). A souvenir sheet
contains one each of Nos. 23-26.

Runners at
Start — A3

10np, 1.50r, Boxing. 25np, 2r, Judo. 50np, 5r,
Gymnast on vaulting horse. 1r, 3r, Sailing yacht.

1965, Jan. 12   Photo.   Perf. 13¹/₂x14

27	A3	5np red brn, brt pink & Prus grn	.15	.15
28	A3	10np dk ol grn, bl gray & red brn	.15	.15
29	A3	15np dk vio, grn & sep	.15	.15
30	A3	25np bl sal pink & blk	.15	.15
31	A3	50np mar, bl & ind	.15	.15
32	A3	1r dk grn, lil & ultra	.35	.15
33	A3	1.50r lil, grn & brn	.55	.15
34	A3	2r red org, bis & dk bl	.75	.20
35	A3	3r dk brn, grnsh bl & lil	1.00	.25
36	A3	5r grn, yel & red brn	2.00	.40
		Nos. 27-36 (10)	5.40	
		Set value		1.35

18th Olympic Games, Tokyo, Oct. 10-25, 1964.
A souvenir sheet contains four stamps similar to
Nos. 33-36 in changed colors.

Stanley Gibbons Catalogue, 1865, US No.
1X2 — A4

Designs: 10np, Austria, Scarlet Mercury 1856.
15np, British Guiana 1c, 1856. 25np, Canada 12p,
1851. 50np, Hawaii 2c, 1851. 1r, Mauritius 2p,
1847. 3r, Switzerland, Geneva 10c, 1843. 5r,
Tuscany 31, 1860. 5np, 15np, 50np and 3r show
first edition of Stanley Gibbons Catalogue; 10np,
25np, 1r and 5r show 1965 Elizabethan Catalogue.

1965, May 6   Unwmk.   Perf. 13

37	A4	5np multi	.15	.15
38	A4	10np multi	.15	.15
39	A4	15np multi	.15	.15
40	A4	25np multi	.15	.15
41	A4	50np multi	.15	.15
42	A4	1r multi	.45	.15
43	A4	3r multi	.75	.20
a.		Souv. sheet of 4, #38-39, 42-43	2.00	
44	A4	5r multi	1.25	.30
a.		Souv. sheet of 4, #37, 40-41, 44	2.25	
		Set value		2.75	.75

Gibbons Catalogue Cent. Exhib., London, Feb.
17-20. Nos. 43a and 44a for 125th anniv. of 1st
postage stamp. Sheets exist imperf.
Stamps of Ajman were replaced in 1972 by those
of United Arab Emirates.

AIR POST STAMPS

Type of Regular Issue, 1964

Designs: 15np, Arab stallion. 25np, Regal angelfish. 35np, Camel. 50np, Angelfish. 75np, Green
turtle. 1r, Jewelfish. 2r, White storks. 3r, White-
eyed gulls. 5r, Lanner falcon.

Photo. & Litho.
1965   Unwmk.   Perf. 14
Size: 42x25¹/₂mm

C1	A1	15np silver & multi	.15	.15
C2	A1	25np silver & multi	.15	.15
C3	A1	35np silver & multi	.15	.15
C4	A1	50np silver & multi	.15	.15
C5	A1	75np silver & multi	.15	.15
C6	A1	1r silver & multi	.40	.15

Size: 53x33¹/₂mm

C7	A1	2r silver & multi	.60	.15
C8	A1	3r silver & multi	1.25	.20
C9	A1	5r silver & multi	2.50	.30
		Nos. C1-C9 (9)	5.50	
		Set value		1.00

Issue dates: #C1-C6, Nov. 15, C7-C9, Dec 18.

AIR POST OFFICIAL STAMPS

Type of Regular Issue, 1964

Designs: 75np, Jewelfish. 2r, White storks. 3r,
White-eyed gulls. 5r, Lanner falcon.

Photo. & Litho.
1965, Dec. 18   Unwmk.   Perf. 14
Size: 42x25¹/₂mm

CO1	A1	75np gold & multi	.35	.15

Size: 53x33¹/₂mm

CO2	A1	2r gold & multi	1.00	.15
CO3	A1	3r gold & multi	1.50	.20
CO4	A1	5r gold & multi	3.00	.35
		Nos. CO1-CO4 (4)	5.85	.85

OFFICIAL STAMPS

Type of Regular Issue, 1964

25np, Arab stallion. 40np, Regal angelfish. 50np,
Camel. 75np, Angelfish. 1r, Green turtle.

Photo. & Litho.
1965, Dec. 1   Unwmk.   Perf. 14
Size: 42x25¹/₂mm

O1	A1	25np gold & multi	.15	.15
O2	A1	40np gold & multi	.15	.15
O3	A1	50np gold & multi	.15	.15
O4	A1	75np gold & multi	.20	.15
O5	A1	1r gold & multi	.25	.15
		Set value		.75	.25

ALAOUITES
'al-aú-,wītz

LOCATION — A division of Syria, in West-
ern Asia
GOVT. — Under French Mandate
AREA — 2,500 sq. mi.
POP. — 278,000 (approx. 1930)
CAPITAL — Latakia

This territory became an independent
state in 1924, although still administered
under the French Mandate. In 1930 it was
renamed Latakia and Syrian stamps overprinted "Lattaquie" superseded the stamps
of Alaouites. For these and subsequent
issues see Latakia and Syria.

100 Centimes = 1 Piastre

Issued under French Mandate
Stamps of France Surcharged:

ALAOUITES	**ALAOUITES**
0 P. 25	**2 PIASTRES**
العلويين	العلويين
١/٤ الغرش	غروش ٢
Nos. 1-6, 16-18	Nos. 7-15, 19-21

1925		**Unwmk.**	***Perf. 14x13¹/₂***	
1	A16	10c on 2c vio brn	1.10	1.10
2	A22	25c on 5c orange	.85	.85
3	A20	75c on 15c gray brn	1.50	1.50
4	A22	1p on 20c red brn	1.00	1.00
5	A22	1.25p on 25c blue	1.25	1.25
6	A22	1.50p on 30c red	4.50	4.50
7	A22	2p on 35c violet	1.00	1.00
8	A18	2p on 40c red & pale bl	2.00	2.00
9	A18	2p on 45c grn & bl	4.50	4.50
10	A18	3p on 60c vio & ultra	2.25	2.25
11	A20	3p on 60c lt vio	4.50	4.50
12	A20	4p on 85c vermilion	.80	.80
13	A18	5p on 1fr cl & ol grn	3.00	3.00
14	A18	10p on 2fr org & pale bl	4.00	4.00
15	A18	20p on 5fr bl & buff	5.50	5.50
		Nos. 1-15 (15)	37.75	37.75

For overprints see Nos. C1-C4.

Same Surcharges on Pasteur Stamps of France

16	A23	50c on 10c green	.80	.80
17	A23	75c on 15c red	.80	.80
18	A23	1.50p on 30c red	1.00	1.00
19	A23	2p on 45c red	1.40	1.40
20	A23	2.50p on 50c blue	1.50	1.50
21	A23	4p on 75c blue	2.00	2.00
		Nos. 16-21 (6)	7.50	7.50

Stamps of Syria, 1925, Overprinted in Red, Black or Blue:

Alaouites   **ALAOUITES**

العلوين   العلوين
On A3, A5   On A4

1925, Mar. 1			***Perf. 12¹/₂, 13¹/₂***	
25	A3	10c dk violet (R)	.30	.30
a.		Double overprint	15.00	15.00
26	A4	25c olive black (R)	.55	.55
a.		Inverted overprint	10.00	10.00
b.		Blue overprint	20.00	20.00
27	A4	50c yellow green	.45	.45
a.		Inverted overprint	10.00	10.00
b.		Blue overprint	20.00	20.00
c.		Red overprint	17.50	17.50
28	A4	75c brown orange	.50	.50
a.		Inverted overprint	9.00	9.00
29	A5	1p magenta	.75	.75
30	A4	1.25p deep green	.55	.55
a.		Red overprint	17.50	17.50
31	A4	1.50p rose red (Bl)	.50	.50
a.		Inverted overprint	10.00	10.00
b.		Black overprint	20.00	20.00
32	A4	2p dk brown (R)	.55	.55
a.		Blue overprint	25.00	25.00
33	A4	2.50p pck blue (R)	.65	.65
a.		Black overprint	25.00	25.00
34	A4	3p orange brown	.55	.55
a.		Inverted overprint	6.50	6.50
b.		Blue overprint	25.00	25.00
35	A4	5p violet	.70	.70
a.		Red overprint	25.00	25.00
36	A4	10p violet brown	1.00	1.00
37	A4	25p ultra (R)	2.50	2.50
		Nos. 25-37 (13)	9.55	9.55

For overprints see Nos. C5-C19.

Stamps of Syria, 1925, Surcharged in Black or Red:

ALAOUITES
الملوين
Nos. 38-42

Alaouites
العلوين
Nos. 43-45

1926				
38	A4	3.50p on 75c brn org	.75	.60
a.		Surcharged on face and back	5.00	4.50
39	A4	4p on 25c ol blk (R)	1.00	.60
40	A4	6p on 2.50p pck bl (R)	.80	.60
41	A4	12p on 1.25p dp grn	.70	.60
a.		Inverted surcharge	10.00	10.00
42	A4	20p on 1.25p dp grn	1.25	1.10
43	A4	4.50p on 75c brn org	2.50	1.25
a.		Inverted surcharge	25.00	
44	A4	7.50p on 2.50p pck bl	1.75	1.25
45	A4	15p on 25p ultra	3.25	2.00
		Nos. 38-45 (8)	12.00	8.00

For overprint see No. C21.

Syria #199 Ovptd. like #25 in Red

1928				
46	A3	5c on 10c dk violet	.30	.30
a.		Double surcharge	13.00	

Syria Nos. 178 and 174 Surcharged like Nos. 43-45 in Red

47	A4	2p on 1.25p dp green	6.00	3.50
48	A4	4p on 25c olive black	3.25	2.50

For overprint see No. C20.

ALAOUITES
العلوين

49	A4	4p on 25c olive black	35.00	30.00
a.		Double impression		
		Nos. 46-49 (4)	44.55	36.30

AIR POST STAMPS

Nos. 8, 10, 13 & 14 with Additional Overprint in Black

1925, Jan. 1		**Unwmk.**	***Perf. 14x13¹/₂***	
C1	A18	2p on 40c	3.50	3.50
a.		Overprint reversed	60.00	
C2	A18	3p on 60c	5.25	5.25
a.		Overprint reversed	60.00	60.00
C3	A18	5p on 1fr	3.50	3.50
C4	A18	10p on 2fr	3.50	3.50
		Nos. C1-C4 (4)	15.75	15.75

Nos. 32, 34, 35 & 36 With Additional Overprint in Green

AVION

1925, Mar. 1			***Perf. 13¹/₂***	
C5	A4	2p dark brown	1.00	1.00
C6	A4	3p orange brown	1.00	1.00
C7	A4	5p violet	1.00	1.00
C8	A4	10p violet brown	1.00	1.00
		Nos. C5-C8 (4)	4.00	4.00

Nos. 32, 34, 35 & 36 With Additional Overprint in Red

1926, May 1				
C9	A4	2p dark brown	1.40	1.40
C10	A4	3p orange brown	1.40	1.40
C11	A4	5p violet	1.40	1.40
C12	A4	10p violet brown	1.40	1.40
		Nos. C9-C12 (4)	5.60	5.60

No. C9 has the original overprint in black.
Double or inverted overprints, original or plane, are known on most of Nos. C9-C12. Value, $8-$10.
The red plane overprint was also applied to Nos. C5-C8. These are believed to have been essays, and were not regularly issued.

Nos. 27, 29, and 37 With Additional Overprint of Airplane in Red or Black

1929, June-July				
C17	A4	50c yel grn (R)	.75	.75
a.		Plane overprint double	15.00	
b.		Plane ovpt. on face and back	11.00	
c.		Pair with plane overprint tete beche	35.00	
C18	A5	1p magenta (Bk)	2.75	2.75
C19	A4	25p ultra (R)	17.50	10.00
a.		Plane overprint inverted	60.00	60.00
		Nos. C17-C19 (3)	21.00	13.50

Nos. 47 and 45 With Additional Overprint of Airplane in Red

1929-30				
C20	A4	2p on 1.25p ('30)	1.20	1.20
a.		Surcharge inverted	4.00	
b.		Double surcharge	3.50	
C21	A4	15p on 25p (Bk + R)	17.50	14.00
a.		Plane overprint inverted	35.00	35.00

POSTAGE DUE STAMPS

Postage Due Stamps of France, 1893-1920, Surcharged Like No. 1 (Nos. J1-J2) or No. 7 (Nos. J3-J5)

1925		**Unwmk.**	***Perf. 14x13¹/₂***	
J1	D2	50c on 10c choc	1.90	1.90
J2	D2	1p on 20c ol grn	1.90	1.90
J3	D2	2p on 30c red	1.90	1.90
J4	D2	3p on 50c vio brn	1.90	1.90
J5	D2	5p on 1fr red brn, *straw*	1.90	1.90
		Nos. J1-J5 (5)	9.50	9.50

Postage Due Stamps of Syria, 1925, Overprinted Like No. 26 (Type D5) or No. 25 (Type D6) in Black, Blue or Red

1925			***Perf. 13¹/₂***	
J6	D5	50c brown, *yel*	.55	.55
J7	D6	1p vio, *rose* (Bl)	.55	.55
a.		Black overprint	9.00	9.00
b.		Double overprint (Bk + Bl)	14.00	14.00
J8	D5	2p blk, *blue* (R)	.90	.90
J9	D5	3p blk, *red org*	1.25	1.25
J10	D5	5p blk, *bl grn* (R)	1.75	1.75
		Nos. J6-J10 (5)	5.00	5.00

The stamps of Alaouites were superseded in 1930 by those of Latakia.

ALBANIA

al-ˈbā-nē-ə

LOCATION — Southeastern Europe
GOVT. — Republic
AREA — 11,101 sq. mi.
POP. — 2,750,000 (1982 est.)
CAPITAL — Tirana

After the outbreak of World War I, the country fell into a state of anarchy when the Prince and all members of the International Commission left Albania. Subsequently General Ferrero in command of Italian troops declared Albania an independent country. A constitution was adopted and a republican form of government was instituted which continued until 1928 when, by constitutional amendment, Albania was declared to be a monarchy. The President of the republic, Ahmed Zogu, became king of the new state. Many unlisted varieties or surcharges and lithographed labels are said to have done postal duty in Albania and Epirus during this unsettled period.

In March 1939, Italy invaded Albania. King Zog fled but did not abdicate. The King of Italy acquired the crown.

Germany occupied Albania from September, 1943, until late 1944 when it became an independent state. The People's Republic began in January, 1946.

40 Paras = 1 Piaster = 1 Grossion
100 Centimes = 1 Franc (1917)
100 Qintar = 1 Franc
100 Qintar (Qindarka) = 1 Lek (1947)

> Catalogue values for unused stamps in this country are for Never Hinged items, beginning with Scott 458 in the regular postage section, Scott B34 in the semi-postal section, and Scott C67 in the airpost section.

Watermarks

Wmk. 125-   Wmk. 220- Double
Lozenges   Headed Eagle

Stamps of Turkey Handstamped

SHQIPËNIA

Handstamped on Issue of 1908
Perf. 12, 13¹/₂ and Compound

			Unwmk.	
1	A19	2¹/₂pi violet brown	350.00	300.00

1913, June

With Additional Overprint in ب Carmine

2	A19	10pa blue green	200.00	175.00

The eagle handstamp was applied to other Turkish stamps of 1908: 25pi green and 50 pi red brown. The 5pa ocher, Albania No. 4, was surcharged "2 paras." These three stamps were retained by officials. Values, $2,250, $5,500, $375.

Handstamped on Issue of 1909

4	A21	5pa ocher	175.00	175.00
5	A21	10pa blue green	175.00	100.00
6	A21	20pa car rose	140.00	100.00
7	A21	1pi ultra	125.00	100.00
8	A21	2pi blue black	225.00	175.00
10	A21	5pi dark violet	500.00	450.00
11	A21	10pi dull red	1,750.	1,750.

For surcharge see No. 19.

With Additional Overprint in Blue ب or Carmine

14	A21	20pa car rose (Bl)	350.00	350.00
15	A21	1pi brt blue (C)	700.00	650.00

Handstamped on Newspaper Stamp of 1911

17	A21	2pa olive green	140.00	125.00

Handstamped on Postage Due Stamp of 1908

18	A19	1pi black, *dp rose*	900.00	650.00

No. 18 was used for regular postage.

No. 6 Surcharged With New Value

19	A21	10pa on 20pa car rose	325.00	300.00

The overprint on #1-19 was handstamped and is found inverted, double, etc.

Nos. 6, 7 and 8 exist with the handstamp in red, blue or violet, but these varieties are not known to have been regularly issued.

Excellent counterfeits exist of Nos. 1 to 19.

A1

1913, July				***Imperf.***

Handstamped on White Laid Paper Without Eagle and Value

20	A1	(1pi) black	140.00	275.00
		Cut to shape	65.00	65.00
a.		Sewing machine perf.	200.00	175.00

1913, Aug.

Value Typewritten in Violet With Eagle

21	A1	10pa violet	8.00	6.00
22	A1	20pa red & black	9.00	7.50
23	A1	1gr black	9.00	9.00
24	A1	2gr blue & violet	10.00	8.50

25	A1	5gr violet & blue	14.00	12.00
26	A1	10gr blue	14.00	12.00
		Nos. 21-26 (6)	64.00	55.00

Nos. 21-26 exist with the eagle inverted or omitted and with numerous errors in the figures of value and the spelling of the word "grosh."

A2   Skanderbeg (George Castriota) — A3

1913, Nov.   Perf. 11½
Handstamped on White Laid Paper
Eagle and Value in Black

27	A2	10pa green	3.00	2.00
b.		Eagle and value in green	25.00	
c.		10pa red (error)	20.00	20.00
d.		10pa violet (error)	20.00	20.00
29	A2	20pa red	4.00	3.00
b.		20pa green (error)	20.00	20.00
30	A2	30pa violet	4.00	3.00
a.		30pa ultramarine (error)	20.00	20.00
b.		30pa red (error)	20.00	20.00
31	A2	1gr ultramarine	5.00	4.00
a.		1gr green (error)	20.00	20.00
b.		1gr black (error)	20.00	20.00
c.		1gr violet (error)	20.00	20.00
33	A2	2gr black	8.00	7.00
a.		2gr violet (error)	20.00	20.00
b.		2gr blue (error)	20.00	20.00
		Nos. 27-33 (5)	24.00	19.00

The stamps of this issue are known with eagle or value inverted or omitted.
1st anniv. of Albanian independence.

1913, Dec.   Typo.   Perf. 14

35	A3	2q orange brn & buff	1.00	1.00
36	A3	5q green & blue grn	1.00	1.00
37	A3	10q rose red	1.00	1.00
38	A3	25q dark blue	1.00	1.00
39	A3	50q violet & red	3.00	2.00
40	A3	1fr deep brown	7.00	6.00
		Nos. 35-40 (6)	14.00	12.00

For overprints and surcharges see Nos. 41-52, 105, J1-J9.

7.Mars

Nos. 35-40 Handstamped in Black or Violet

RROFTË MBRETI .1914

1914, Mar. 7

41	A3	2q orange brn & buff	20.00	18.00
42	A3	5q grn & bl grn (V)	20.00	18.00
43	A3	10q rose red	20.00	18.00
44	A3	25q dark blue (V)	20.00	18.00
45	A3	50q violet & red	20.00	18.00
46	A3	1fr deep brown	20.00	18.00
		Nos. 41-46 (6)	120.00	108.00

Issued to celebrate the arrival of Prince Wilhelm zu Wied on Mar. 7, 1914.

Nos. 35-40 Surcharged in Black:

5 PARA -   **1 GROSH**
   a   b

1914, Apr. 2

47	A3 (a)	5pa on 2q	1.10	1.10
48	A3 (a)	10pa on 5q	1.10	1.10
49	A3 (a)	20pa on 10q	2.00	1.50
50	A3 (b)	1gr on 25q	2.50	2.00
51	A3 (b)	2gr on 50q	2.50	2.00
52	A3 (b)	5gr on 1fr	13.00	11.00
		Nos. 47-52 (6)	22.20	18.70

For overprints see Nos. 105, J6-J9.

Inverted Surcharge

47a	A3 (a)	5pa on 2q	5.00	5.00
48a	A3 (a)	10pa on 5q	5.00	5.00
49a	A3 (a)	20pa on 10q	5.00	5.00
50a	A3 (b)	1gr on 25q	6.50	6.50
51a	A3 (b)	2gr on 50q	7.50	7.50
52b	A3 (b)	5gr on 1fr	21.00	21.00
		Nos. 47a-52b (6)	50.00	50.00

Korce (Korytsa) Issues

A4

1914   Handstamped   Imperf.

52A	A4	10pa violet & red	90.00	90.00
c.		10pa black & red	90.00	90.00
53	A4	25pa violet & red	90.00	90.00
a.		25pa black & red	150.00	150.00

Nos. 52A-53a originally were handstamped directly on the cover, so the paper varies. Later they were also produced in sheets; these are rarely found. Nos. 52A-53a were issued by Albanian military authorities.

A5   A6

1917   Typo. & Litho.   Perf. 11½

54	A5	1c dk brown & grn	9.00	6.50
55	A5	2c red & green	9.00	6.50
56	A5	3c gray grn & grn	9.00	6.50
57	A5	5c green & black	7.00	4.25
58	A5	10c rose red & black	7.00	4.25
59	A5	25c blue & black	7.00	4.25
60	A5	50c violet & black	8.50	6.00
61	A5	1fr brown & black	8.50	6.00
		Nos. 54-61 (8)	65.00	44.25

1917-18

62	A6	1c dk brown & grn	2.75	2.50
63	A6	2c red brown & grn	2.75	2.50
a.		"CTM" for "CTS"	30.00	30.00
64	A6	3c black & green	2.75	2.50
a.		"CTM" for "CTS"	30.00	30.00
65	A6	5c green & black	2.75	2.75
66	A6	10c dull red & black	2.75	2.75
67	A6	50c violet & black	7.50	6.00
68	A6	1fr red brn & black	10.00	8.00
		Nos. 62-68 (7)	31.25	27.00

Counterfeits abound of Nos. 54-68, 80-81.

QARKU

I

KORÇES

No. 65 Surcharged in Red

25 CTS

1918

80	A6	25c on 5c green & blk	55.00	45.00

A7

1918

81	A7	25c blue & black	35.00	30.00

General Issue

A8   A9

Handstamped in Rose   or Blue

1919   Perf. 12½

84	A8	(2)q on 2h brown	4.25	4.25
85	A8	5q on 16h green	4.25	4.25
86	A8	10q on 8h rose (Bl)	4.25	4.25
87	A8	25q on 64h blue	4.25	4.25
88	A9	25q on 64h blue	200.00	200.00
89	A8	50q on 32h violet	4.25	4.25
90	A8	1fr on 1.28k org, bl	6.00	6.00
		Nos. 84-90 (7)	227.25	227.25

See Nos. J10-J13. Compare with types A10-A14. For overprints see Nos 91-104.

Handstamped in Rose or Blue

1919, Jan. 16

91	A8	(2)q on 2h brown	8.50	8.50
92	A8	5q on 16h green	8.50	8.50
93	A8	10q on 8h rose (Bl)	8.50	8.50
94	A8	25q on 64h blue	26.00	26.00
95	A9	25q on 64h blue	21.00	21.00
96	A8	50q on 32h violet	8.50	8.50
97	A8	1fr on 1.28k org, bl	4.50	4.50
		Nos. 91-97 (7)	85.50	85.50

Handstamped in Violet

1919

98	A8	(2)q on 2h brown	10.00	10.00
99	A8	5q on 16h green	10.00	10.00
100	A8	10q on 8h rose	10.00	10.00
101	A8	25q on 64h blue	10.00	10.00
102	A9	25q on 64h blue	100.00	90.00
103	A8	50q on 32h violet	10.00	10.00
104	A8	1fr on 1.28k org, bl	10.00	10.00
		Nos. 98-104 (7)	160.00	150.00

No. 50 Overprinted in Violet

SHKODER · 1919

1919   Perf. 14

105	A3	1gr on 25q blue	5.00	5.00

A10   A11

1919, June 5   Perf. 11½, 12½

106	A10	10q on 2h brown	3.50	3.50
107	A11	15q on 8h rose	3.50	3.50
108	A11	20q on 16h green	3.50	3.50
109	A10	25q on 64h blue	3.50	3.50
110	A11	50q on 32h violet	3.50	3.50
111	A11	1fr on 96h orange	3.50	3.50
112	A10	2fr on 1.60k vio, buff	14.00	14.00
		Nos. 106-112 (7)	35.00	35.00

Nos. 106-108, 110 exist with inverted surcharge.

A12   A13

Black or Violet Surcharge

1919

113	A12	10q on 8h car	3.50	3.50
114	A12	15q on 8h car (V)	3.50	3.50
115	A13	20q on 16h green	3.50	3.50
116	A13	25q on 35h violet	3.50	3.50
117	A13	50q on 64h green	9.25	9.25
118	A13	1fr on 96h orange	4.75	4.75
119	A12	2fr on 1.60k vio, buff	7.00	7.00
		Nos. 113-119 (7)	35.00	35.00

A14   A15

Overprinted in Blue or Black Without New Value

1920   Perf. 12½

120	A14	1q gray (Bl)	22.50	22.50
121	A14	10q rose (Bk)	1.75	2.75
a.		Double overprint	24.00	27.50
122	A14	20q brown (Bl)	11.00	11.00
123	A14	25q blue (Bk)	110.00	110.00
124	A14	50q brown vio (Bk)	14.00	16.00
		Nos. 120-124 (5)	159.25	162.25

Counterfeit overprints exist of Nos. 120-128.

Surcharged with New Value

125	A14	2q on 10q rose (R)	4.25	4.25
126	A14	5q on 10q rose (G)	4.25	4.25
127	A14	25q on 10q rose (Bl)	4.25	4.25
128	A14	50q on 10q rose (Br)	4.25	4.25
		Nos. 125-128 (4)	17.00	17.00

Stamps of type A14 (Portrait of the Prince zu Wied) were not placed in use without overprint or surcharge.

Post Horn Overprinted in Black

1920   Perf. 14x13

129	A15	2q orange	3.75	3.25
130	A15	5q deep green	6.25	6.00
131	A15	10q red	11.00	11.00
132	A15	25q light blue	20.00	11.00
133	A15	50q gray green	4.25	4.00
134	A15	1fr claret	4.25	4.00
		Nos. 129-134 (6)	49.50	39.25

Type A15 was never placed in use without post horn or "Besa" overprint.

Stamps of Type A15 (No Post Horn) Overprinted   **BESA**

1921

135	A15	2q orange	3.25	3.25
136	A15	5q deep green	4.50	4.50
137	A15	10q red	7.75	7.75
138	A15	25q light blue	17.50	14.00
139	A15	50q gray green	5.75	5.75
140	A15	1fr claret	4.75	4.75
		Nos. 135-140 (6)	43.50	40.00

For surcharge & overprints see #154, 156-157.

Stamps of these types, and with "TAKSE" overprint, were unauthorized and never placed in use. They are common.

Gjirokaster A18

Korcha — A19

Designs: 5q, Kanina. 10q, Berati. 25q, Bridge at Vezirit. 50q, Rozafat. 2fr, Dursit.

1923   Typo.   Perf. 12½, 11½

147	A18	2q orange	.60	.60
148	A18	5q yellow green	.50	.50
149	A18	10q carmine	.50	.50
150	A18	25q dark blue	.50	.50
151	A18	50q dark green	.50	.50
152	A19	1fr dark violet	.65	.65
153	A19	2fr olive green	1.75	1.75
		Nos. 147-153 (7)	5.00	5.00

For overprints & surcharges see #158-185, B1-B8.

No. 135 Surcharged

1922 Perf. 14x13
154 A15 1q on 2q orange 3.00 3.00

Stamps of Type A15 (No Post Horn) Overprinted [BESA]

1922
156 A15 5q deep green 3.00 2.50
157 A15 10q red 3.00 2.50

Nos. 147-151 Overprinted (top line in Black; diamond in Violet)

1924, Jan. Perf. 12½
158 A18 2q red orange 4.00 3.75
159 A18 5q yellow green 4.00 3.75
160 A18 5q carmine 4.00 3.75
161 A18 25q dark blue 4.00 3.75
162 A18 50q dark green 4.00 3.75
Nos. 158-162 (5) 20.00 18.75

The words "Mbledhje Kushtetuese" are in taller letters on the 25q than on the other values. Opening of the Constituent Assembly.

No. 147 Surcharged

=>=| 1 |<=

1924
163 A18 1q on 2q red orange 2.25 2.25

Nos. 163, 147-152 Overprinted

Triumf' i legalitetit 24 Dhetuer 1924

1924
164 A18 1q on 2q orange 1.75 2.50
165 A18 2q orange 1.75 2.50
166 A18 5q yellow green 1.75 2.50
167 A18 10q carmine 1.75 2.50
168 A18 25q dark blue 1.75 2.50
169 A18 50q dark green 1.75 2.50
170 A19 1fr dark violet 1.75 2.50
Nos. 164-170 (7) 12.25 17.50

Issued to celebrate the return of the Government to the Capital after a revolution.

Nos. 163, 147-152 Overprinted

Republika Shqiptare

21 Kallnduer 1925

1925
171 A18 1q on 2q orange 1.75 2.50
172 A18 2q orange 1.75 2.50
173 A18 5q yellow green 1.75 2.50
174 A18 10q carmine 1.75 2.50
175 A18 25q dark blue 1.75 2.50
176 A18 50q dark green 1.75 2.50
177 A19 1fr dark violet 1.75 2.50
Nos. 171-177 (7) 12.25 17.50

Proclamation of the Republic, Jan. 21, 1925. The date "1921" instead of "1925" occurs once in each sheet of 50.

Nos. 163, 147-153 Overprinted

1925
178 A18 1q on 2q orange .55 .75
a. Inverted overprint 7.00 7.00
179 A18 2q orange .55 .75
180 A18 5q yellow green .55 .75
a. Inverted overprint 7.00 7.00
181 A18 10q carmine .55 .75
182 A18 25q dark blue .55 .75
183 A18 50q dark green .55 .75
184 A19 1fr dark violet .65 .90
185 A19 2fr olive green .65 .90
Nos. 178-185 (8) 4.60 6.30

President Ahmed Zogu
A25   A26

1925 Perf. 13½, 13½x13
186 A25 1q orange .15 .15
187 A25 2q red brown .15 .15
188 A25 5q green .15 .15
189 A25 10q rose red .15 .15
190 A25 15q gray brown 1.50 1.50
191 A25 25q dark blue .15 .15
192 A25 50q blue green .55 .55
193 A26 1fr red & ultra .95 .95
194 A26 2fr green & orange .95 .95
195 A26 3fr brown & violet 1.50 1.50
196 A26 5fr violet & black 3.75 3.75
Nos. 186-196 (11) 9.95 9.95

No. 193 in ultramarine and brown, and No. 194 in gray and brown were not regularly issued. Value, both $15.
For overprints & surcharges see #197-209, 238-248.

Nos. 186-196 Overprinted in Various Colors

1927
197 A25 1q orange (V) .60 .40
198 A25 2q red brn (G) .25 .15
199 A25 5q green (R) 1.25 .15
200 A25 10q rose red (Bl) .25 .15
201 A25 15q gray brn (G) 7.50 7.50
202 A25 25q dk blue (R) .60 .15
203 A25 50q blue grn (Bl) .60 .15
204 A26 1fr red & ultra (Bk) 1.25 .15
205 A26 2fr green & org (Bk) 1.25 .15
206 A26 3fr brown & vio (Bk) 2.00 .55
207 A26 5fr violet & blk (Bk) 3.00 .95
Nos. 197-207 (11) 18.55 10.45

No. 200 exists perf. 11.
For surcharges see Nos. 208-209, 238-240.

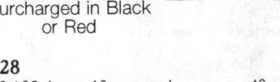

Nos. 200, 202 Surcharged in Black or Red

1928
208 A25 1q on 10q rose red .40 .30
a. Inverted surcharge 3.75 3.75
209 A25 5q on 25q dk blue (R) .40 .30
a. Inverted surcharge 3.75 3.75

King Zog I
A27   A28
Black Overprint

1928 Perf. 14x13½
210 A27 1q orange brown 2.25 2.25
211 A27 2q slate 2.25 2.25
212 A27 5q blue green 2.25 2.25
213 A27 10q rose red 2.25 2.25
214 A27 15q bister 12.00 12.00
215 A27 25q dark blue 1.75 1.75
216 A27 50q lilac rose 2.25 2.25

Red Overprint
Perf. 13½x14
217 A28 1fr blue & slate 2.50 2.50
Nos. 210-217 (8) 27.50 27.50

Compare with types A29-A32.

A29   A30

Zog Bridge — A35

Black or Red Overprint
1928 Perf. 14x13½
218 A29 1q orange brown 8.25 8.25
219 A29 2q slate (R) 8.25 8.25
220 A29 5q blue green 7.00 7.00
221 A29 10q rose red 4.50 4.50
222 A29 15q bister 4.75 4.75
223 A29 25q deep blue (R) 4.75 4.75
224 A29 50q lilac rose 5.25 5.25

Perf. 13½x14
225 A30 1fr blue & slate (R) 7.75 7.75
226 A30 2fr green & slate (R) 9.50 9.50
Nos. 218-226 (9) 60.00 60.00

Proclamation of Ahmed Zogu as King of Albania.

A31   A32

Black Overprint
1928 Perf. 14x13½
227 A31 1q orange brown .35 .35
228 A31 2q slate .35 .25
229 A31 5q blue green 2.25 .35
230 A31 10q rose red .35 .25
231 A31 15q bister 9.00 8.00
232 A31 25q deep blue .35 .25
233 A31 50q lilac rose .60 .25

Perf. 13½x14
234 A32 1fr blue & slate 1.25 1.10
235 A32 2fr green & slate 1.25 1.25
236 A32 3fr dk red & ol bis 3.50 1.75
237 A32 5fr dull vio & gray 4.50 4.50
Nos. 227-237 (11) 23.75 18.30

The overprint reads "Kingdom of Albania."

Mbr. Shqiptare

Nos. 203, 202, 200 Surcharged in Black

■ 5 ■

1929
238 A25 1q on 50q blue green .35 .35
239 A25 5q on 25q dark blue .35 .35
240 A25 15q on 10q rose red .55 .50
Nos. 238-240 (3) 1.25 1.20

RROFT-MBRETI

Nos. 186-189, 191-194 Overprinted in Black or Red

8 X 1929.

1929 Perf. 11½, 13½
241 A25 1q orange 4.00 4.00
242 A25 2q red brown 4.00 4.00
243 A25 5q green 4.00 4.00
244 A25 10q rose red 4.00 4.00
245 A25 25q dark blue 4.00 4.00
246 A25 50q blue green (R) 4.75 4.75
247 A26 1fr red & ultra 7.00 7.00
248 A26 2fr green & orange 8.75 8.75
Nos. 241-248 (8) 40.50 40.50

34th birthday of King Zog. The overprint reads "Long live the King."

Lake Butrinto — A33   King Zog I — A34

Ruin at Zog Manor — A36

Perf. 14, 14½
1930, Sept. 1 Photo. Wmk. 220
250 A33 1q slate .15 .15
251 A33 2q orange red .15 .15
252 A34 5q yellow green .15 .15
253 A34 10q carmine .15 .15
254 A34 15q dark brown .15 .15
255 A34 25q dark ultra .20 .15
256 A33 50q slate green .30 .30
257 A35 1fr violet .75 .75
258 A35 2fr indigo .85 .85
259 A36 3fr gray green 1.90 1.90
260 A36 5fr orange brown 3.25 3.25
Nos. 250-260 (11) 8.00 7.95

2nd anniversary of accession of King Zog I.
For overprints see Nos. 261-270, 299-309, J39.
For surcharges see Nos. 354-360.

	1 9 2 4 – 24Dhetuer – 4	1 9 2 3

Nos. 250-259 Overprinted in Black

1934, Dec. 24
261 A33 1q slate 2.00 2.00
262 A33 2q orange red 2.00 2.00
263 A34 5q yellow green 2.00 2.00
264 A34 10q carmine 2.00 2.00
265 A34 15q dark brown 2.00 2.00
266 A34 25q dark ultra 2.00 2.00
267 A33 50q slate green 2.00 2.00
268 A35 1fr violet 4.50 4.50
269 A35 2fr indigo 9.00 9.00
270 A36 3fr gray green 12.50 12.50
Nos. 261-270 (10) 40.00 40.00

Tenth anniversary of the Constitution.

Allegory of Death of Skanderbeg A37

Albanian Eagle in Turkish Shackles A38

5q, 25q, 40q, 2fr, Eagle with wings spread.

1937 Unwmk. Perf. 14
271 A37 1q brown violet .15 .15
272 A38 2q brown .15 .15
273 A38 5q lt green .22 .22
274 A37 10q olive brown .30 .30
275 A38 15q rose red .38 .38
276 A38 25q blue .70 .70
277 A38 50q deep green .95 .95
278 A38 1fr violet 1.65 1.65
279 A38 2fr orange brown 4.25 4.25
Nos. 271-279 (9) 8.75 8.75

Souvenir Sheet
280 Sheet of 3 13.00 12.00
a. A37 20q red violet 2.50 2.50
b. A38 30q olive brown 2.50 2.50
c. A38 40q red 2.50 2.50

25th anniv. of independence from Turkey, proclaimed Nov. 26, 1912.

Queen Geraldine and King Zog — A40

1938 Perf. 14
281 A40 1q slate violet .15 .15
282 A40 2q red brown .15 .15
283 A40 5q green .15 .15
284 A40 10q olive brown .35 .35
285 A40 15q rose red .50 .50
286 A40 25q blue .85 .85
287 A40 50q Prus green 2.50 2.50
288 A40 1fr purple 5.25 5.25
Nos. 281-288 (8) 9.90 9.90

Souvenir Sheet
289 Sheet of 4 18.00 18.00
a. A40 20q dark red violet 1.75 1.75
b. A40 30q brown olive 1.75 1.75

Wedding of King Zog and Countess Geraldine Apponyi, Apr. 27, 1938.
No. 289 contains 2 each of Nos. 289a, 289b.

Queen
Geraldine — A42

National
Emblems — A43

Designs: 10q, 25q, 30q, 1fr, King Zog.

1938

290	A42	1q dp red violet	.15	.15
291	A43	2q red orange	.15	.15
292	A42	5q deep green	.20	.20
293	A42	10q red brown	.20	.20
294	A42	15q deep rose	.55	.55
295	A42	25q deep blue	.70	.70
296	A43	50q gray black	1.75	1.75
297	A42	1fr slate green	6.00	6.00
		Nos. 290-297 (8)	9.70	9.70

Souvenir Sheet

298	Sheet of 3	18.00	18.00
b.	A43 20q Prussian green	2.00	2.00
c.	A42 30q deep violet	2.00	2.00

10th anniv. of royal rule. They were on sale for 3 days (Aug. 30-31, Sept. 1) only, during which their use was required on all mail.
No. 298 contains Nos. 294, 298b, 298c.

Issued under Italian Dominion

Nos. 250-260
Overprinted in Black

Mbledhja
Kushtetuëse
12-IV-1939
XVII

1939   Wmk. 220   Perf. 14

299	A33	1q slate	.15	.15
300	A33	2q orange red	.15	.15
301	A34	5q yellow green	.15	.15
302	A34	10q carmine	.20	.20
303	A34	25q dark brown	.20	.20
304	A34	25q dark ultra	.30	.30
305	A33	50q slate green	.45	.45
306	A35	1fr violet	.85	.85
307	A35	2fr indigo	1.25	1.25
308	A36	3fr gray green	2.50	2.50
309	A36	5fr orange brown	3.50	3.50
		Nos. 299-309 (11)	9.70	9.70

Resolution adopted by the Natl. Assembly, Apr. 12, 1939, offering the Albanian Crown to Italy.

Native Costumes
A46   A47   A48

King Victor Emmanuel III
A49   A50

Native
Costume
A51

Monastery
A52

Designs: 2fr, Bridge at Vezirit. 3fr, Ancient Columns. 5fr, Amphitheater.

1939   Unwmk.   Photo.   Perf. 14

310	A46	1q blue gray	.15	.15
311	A47	2q olive green	.15	.15
312	A48	3q golden brown	.15	.15
313	A49	5q green	.15	.15
314	A50	10q brown	.20	.15
315	A50	15q crimson	.25	.20
316	A50	25q sapphire	.40	.25
317	A50	30q brt violet	.55	.35
318	A51	50q dull purple	.70	.35
319	A49	65q red brown	1.00	1.00
320	A52	1fr myrtle green	1.25	1.25
321	A52	2fr brown lake	3.00	3.00
322	A52	3fr brown black	5.75	5.75
323	A52	5fr gray violet	12.00	12.00
		Nos. 310-323 (14)	25.70	24.90

For overprints and surcharges see Nos. 331-353.

King Victor
Emmanuel III — A56

1942   Photo.

324	A56	5q green	.15	.15
325	A56	10q brown	.15	.15
326	A56	15q rose red	.20	.20
327	A56	25q blue	.45	.45
328	A56	65q red brown	.65	.65
329	A56	1fr myrtle green	1.25	1.25
330	A56	2fr gray violet	2.75	2.75
		Nos. 324-330 (7)	5.60	5.60

Conquest of Albania by Italy, 3rd anniv.

No. 311 Surcharged in   1 QIND
Black

331	A47	1q on 2q olive green	1.00	1.00

Issued under German Administration

Stamps of 1939
Overprinted in Carmine or
Brown

14
Shtator
1943

1943

332	A47	2q olive green	1.10	1.40
333	A48	3q golden brown	1.10	1.40
334	A49	5q green	1.10	1.40
335	A50	10q brown	1.10	1.40
336	A50	15q crimson (Br)	1.10	1.40
337	A50	25q sapphire	1.10	1.40
338	A50	30q brt violet	1.10	1.40
339	A49	65q red brown	1.25	2.25
340	A52	1fr myrtle green	7.75	10.00
341	A52	2fr brown lake	10.50	20.00
342	A52	3fr brown black	45.00	52.50

Surcharged with New Values

343	A49	1q on 3q gldn brn	1.10	1.40
344	A49	50q on 65q red brn	1.25	2.25
		Nos. 332-344 (13)	74.55	98.20

Proclamation of Albanian independence.
The overprint "14 Shtator 1943" on Nos. 324 to 328 is private and fraudulent.

Independent State

Nos. 312 to 317 and
319 to 321
Surcharged with New
Value and Bars in
Black or Carmine,
and:

QEVERIJA
DEMOKRAT.
E SHQIPERISE
22-X-1944

1945

345	A48	30q on 3q gldn brn	3.50	3.50
346	A49	40q on 5q green	3.50	3.50
347	A50	50q on 10q brown	3.50	3.50
348	A50	60q on 15q crimson	3.50	3.50
349	A50	80q on 25q saph (C)	3.50	3.50
350	A50	1fr on 30q brt vio	3.50	3.50
351	A49	2fr on 65q red brn	3.50	3.50
352	A52	3fr on 1fr myr grn	3.50	3.50
353	A52	5fr on 2fr brn lake	3.50	3.50
		Nos. 345-353 (9)	31.50	31.50

"DEMOKRATIKE" is not abbreviated on Nos. 352 and 353.

Nos. 250, 251, 256
and 258 Surcharged
in Black or Carmine,
and

1943 1945
J.N.Ç.L.SHQ.
10 KORRIK.
FR.SHQ. 5
≡ ≡

1945   Wmk. 220

354	A33	30q on 1q slate	1.25	1.25
355	A33	60q on 1q slate	1.50	1.50
356	A33	80q on 1q slate	1.65	1.65
357	A33	1fr on 1q slate	2.50	2.50
358	A33	2fr on 2q org red	3.25	3.25
359	A33	3fr on 50q sl grn	8.50	8.50
360	A35	5fr on 2fr indigo	11.00	11.00
		Nos. 354-360 (7)	29.65	29.65

Albanian Natl. Army of Liberation, 2nd anniv.
The surcharge on No. 360 is condensed to fit the size of the stamp.

Country House,
Labinot — A57

40q, 60q, Bridge at Berat. 1fr, 3fr, Permet.

Unwmk.
1945, Nov. 28   Typo.   Perf. 11

361	A57	20q bluish green	.20	.20
362	A57	30q deep orange	.40	.40
363	A57	40q brown	.40	.40
364	A57	60q red violet	.60	.60
365	A57	1fr rose red	1.25	1.25
366	A57	3fr dark blue	6.00	6.00
		Nos. 361-366 (6)	8.85	8.85

Counterfeits exist. See note after No. B33.
For overprints and surcharges see Nos. 367-378, 418-423, B28-B33.

ASAMBLEJA
KUSHTETUESE

Nos. 361 to 366
Overprinted in Black

10 KALLHUER 1946

1946

367	A57	20q bluish green	.60	.60
368	A57	30q deep orange	.60	.60
369	A57	40q brown	.95	.95
370	A57	60q red violet	1.75	1.75
371	A57	1fr rose red	4.75	4.75
372	A57	3fr dark blue	7.50	7.50
		Nos. 367-372 (6)	16.15	16.15

Convocation of the Constitutional Assembly, Jan. 10, 1946.

People's Republic

Nos. 361 to
366
Overprinted in
Black

REPUBLIKA POPULLORE
E
SHQIPERISE

1946

373	A57	20q bluish green	.75	.75
374	A57	30q deep orange	1.25	1.25
375	A57	40q brown	1.65	1.65
376	A57	60q red violet	2.75	2.75
377	A57	1fr rose red	5.00	5.00
378	A57	3fr dark blue	8.50	8.50
		Nos. 373-378 (6)	19.90	19.90

Proclamation of the Albanian People's Republic.
For surcharges see Nos. 418-423.

Globe, Dove and
Olive
Branch — A60

Perf. 11½, Imperf.
1946, Mar. 8   Typo.

Denomination in Black

379	A60	20q lilac & dull red	.15	.15
380	A60	40q dp lilac & dull red	.35	.35
381	A60	50q violet & dull red	.50	.50
382	A60	1fr lt blue & red	.80	.80
383	A60	2fr dk blue & red	1.65	1.65
		Nos. 379-383 (5)	3.45	3.45

International Women's Congress.

Athletes with
Shot and
Indian
Club — A61

Perf. 11½
1946, Oct. 6   Litho.   Unwmk.

384	A61	1q grnsh black	6.00	6.00
385	A61	2q green	6.00	6.00
386	A61	5q brown	6.00	6.00
387	A61	10q crimson	6.00	6.00
388	A61	20q ultra	6.00	6.00
389	A61	40q rose violet	6.00	6.00
390	A61	1fr deep orange	10.00	10.00
		Nos. 384-390 (7)	46.00	46.00

Balkan Games, Tirana, Oct. 6-13.

Qemal Stafa — A62

1947, May 5   Perf. 12½x11½

391	A62	20q brn & yel brn	1.75	1.75
392	A62	28q dk blue & blue	1.75	1.75
393	A62	40q brn blk & gray brn	3.00	3.00
a.	Souvenir sheet, #391-393	6.50	6.50
	Nos. 391-393 (3)	6.50	6.50

5th anniv. of the death of Qemal Stafa.

Young Railway
Laborers
A64

1947, May 16   Perf. 11½

395	A64	1q brn blk & gray brn	1.25	.60
396	A64	4q dk green & green	1.25	.60
397	A64	10q blk brn & bis brn	1.25	.60
398	A64	15q dk red & red	1.50	.60
399	A64	20q indigo & bl gray	2.00	.90
400	A64	28q dk blue & blue	3.00	.90
401	A64	40q brn vio & rose vio	7.75	4.25
402	A64	68q dk brn & org brn	12.00	7.75
		Nos. 395-402 (8)	30.00	16.20

Issued to publicize the construction of the Durres Elbasan Railway by Albanian youths.

Citizens Led by
Hasim
Zeneli — A65

Enver Hoxha and
Vasil Shanto — A66

Vojo Kushi — A68

Inauguration of
Vithkuq
Brigade — A67

1947, July 10   Litho.

403	A65	16q brn org & red brn	3.25	3.25
404	A66	20q org brn & dk brn	3.25	3.25
405	A67	28q blue & dk blue	3.50	3.50
406	A68	40q lilac & dk brn	5.00	5.00
		Nos. 403-406 (4)	15.00	15.00

4th anniv. of the formation of Albania's army, July 10, 1943.

Conference Building
Ruins, Peza — A69

Disabled
Soldiers — A70

1947, Sept. 16
407	A69	2 l red violet	2.25	2.00
408	A69	2.50 l deep blue	2.25	2.00

Peza Conf., Sept. 16, 1942, 5th anniv.

1947, Nov. 17   Perf. 12½x11½
408A	A70	1 l red	3.50	3.50

Disabled War Veterans Cong., Nov. 14-20, 1947.

A71

A73

Designs: 2 l, Banquet. 2.50 l, Peasants rejoicing.

Perf. 11½x12½, 12½x11½
1947, Nov. 17   Unwmk.
409	A71	1.50 l dull violet	2.50	2.50
410	A71	2 l brown	2.50	2.50
411	A71	2.50 l blue	2.50	2.50
412	A73	3 l rose red	2.50	2.50
		Nos. 409-412 (4)	10.00	10.00

Agrarian reform law of Nov. 17, 1946, 1st anniv.

Burning Farm Buildings A74

Designs: 2.50 l, Trench scene. 5 l, Firing line. 8 l, Winter advance. 12 l, Infantry column.

1947, Nov. 29   Perf. 11½x12½
413	A74	1.50 l red	1.65	1.65
414	A74	2.50 l rose brown	2.00	2.00
415	A74	5 l blue	2.50	2.50
416	A74	8 l purple	4.00	4.00
417	A74	12 l brown	6.00	6.00
		Nos. 413-417 (5)	16.15	16.15

3rd anniv. of Albania's liberation.

Nos. 373 to 378 Surcharged with New Value and Bars in Black
1948, Feb. 22   Perf. 11
418	A57	50q on 30q deep org	.25	.25
419	A57	1 l on 20q bluish grn	.50	.50
420	A57	2.50 l on 60q red vio	1.00	1.00
421	A57	3 l on 1fr rose red	1.25	1.25
422	A57	5 l on 3fr dark blue	2.25	2.25
423	A57	12 l on 40q brown	4.75	4.75
		Nos. 418-423 (6)	10.00	10.00

The two bars consist of four type squares each set close together.

Map, Train and Construction Workers A75

1948, June 1   Litho.   Perf. 11½
424	A75	50q dk car rose	1.10	.55
425	A75	1 l lt green & blk	1.25	.55
426	A75	1.50 l deep rose	1.25	.55
427	A75	2.50 l org brn & dk brn	1.25	.55
428	A75	5 l dull blue	2.00	1.10
429	A75	8 l salmon & dk brn	4.75	2.00
430	A75	12 l red vio & dk vio	6.50	2.25
431	A75	20 l olive gray	12.50	5.50
		Nos. 424-431 (8)	30.60	12.55

Issued to publicize the construction of the Durres-Tirana Railway.

Marching Soldiers A76

Design: 8 l, Battle scene.

1948, July 10
432	A76	2.50 l yellow brown	1.25	1.25
433	A76	5 l dark blue	1.65	1.65
434	A76	8 l violet gray	3.25	3.25
		Nos. 432-434 (3)	6.15	6.15

5th anniv. of the formation of Albania's army.

Bricklayer, Flag, Globe and "Industry" A77

Map and Soldier A78

1949, May 1   Photo.   Perf. 12½x12
435	A77	2.50 l olive brown	.30	.30
436	A77	5 l blue	.70	.70
437	A77	8 l violet brown	1.10	1.10
		Nos. 435-437 (3)	2.10	2.10

Issued to publicize Labor Day, May 1, 1949.

1949, July 10   Unwmk.
438	A78	2.50 l brown	.50	.50
439	A78	5 l light ultra	.75	.75
440	A78	8 l brown orange	1.50	1.50
		Nos. 438-440 (3)	2.75	2.75

6th anniv. of the formation of Albania's army.

Enver Hoxha A79

Albanian Citizen and Spasski Tower, Kremlin A80

1949, Oct. 16   Engr.   Perf. 12½
441	A79	50q purple	.15	.15
442	A79	1 l dull green	.15	.15
443	A79	1.50 l car lake	.20	.15
444	A79	2 l brown	.30	.15
445	A79	5 l violet blue	.65	.15
446	A79	8 l sepia	1.10	.90
447	A79	12 l rose lilac	2.50	1.50
448	A79	20 l gray blue	5.00	2.50
		Nos. 441-448 (8)	10.05	5.65

1949, Sept. 10   Photo.   Perf. 12½x12
449	A80	2.50 l orange brown	.50	.50
450	A80	5 l deep ultra	1.00	1.00

Albanian-Soviet friendship.

Albanian Soldier and Flag — A81

Battle Scene — A82

1949, Nov. 29   Unwmk.   Perf. 12
451	A81	2.50 l brown	.25	.25
452	A82	3 l dark red	.50	.50
453	A81	5 l violet	.60	.60
454	A82	8 l black	1.65	1.65
		Nos. 451-454 (4)	3.00	3.00

Fifth anniversary of Albania's liberation.

Joseph V. Stalin — A83

Symbols of UPU and Postal Transport — A84

1949, Dec. 21
455	A83	2.50 l dark brown	.45	.55
456	A83	5 l violet blue	1.25	1.25
457	A83	8 l rose brown	2.00	2.25
		Nos. 455-457 (3)	3.70	4.05

70th anniv. of the birth of Joseph V. Stalin.

Canceled to Order
Beginning in 1950, Albania sold some issues in sheets canceled to order. Values in second column when much less than unused are for "CTO" copies. Postally used stamps are valued at slightly less than, or the same as, unused.

> Catalogue values for unused stamps in this section, from this point to the end of the section, are for Never Hinged items.

1950, July 1   Photo.   Perf. 12x12½
458	A84	5 l blue	2.25	1.25
459	A84	8 l rose brown	3.25	1.75
460	A84	12 l sepia	4.00	2.25
		Nos. 458-460 (3)	9.50	5.25

75th anniv. (in 1949) of the UPU.

Sami Frasheri — A85

Arms and Albanian Flags — A86

Authors: 2.50 l, Andon Zako. 3 l, Naim Frasheri. 5 l, Kostandin Kristoforidhi.

1950, Nov. 5   Perf. 14
461	A85	2 l dark green	.70	.15
462	A85	2.50 l red brown	.95	.20
463	A85	3 l brown carmine	1.40	.25
464	A85	5 l deep blue	2.00	.60
		Nos. 461-464 (4)	5.05	1.20

"Jubilee of the Writers of the Renaissance."

1951, Jan. 11   Engr.   Perf. 14x13½
465	A86	2.50 l brown carmine	1.10	.25
466	A86	5 l deep blue	2.00	.50
467	A86	8 l sepia	3.00	1.00
		Nos. 465-467 (3)	6.10	1.75

5th anniv. of the formation of the Albanian People's Republic.

Skanderbeg A87

Enver Hoxha and Congress of Permet A88

1951, Mar. 1
468	A87	2.50 l brown	.75	.25
469	A87	5 l violet	1.50	.50
470	A87	8 l olive bister	2.50	1.00
		Nos. 468-470 (3)	4.75	1.75

483rd anniv. of the death of George Castriota (Skanderbeg).

1951, May 24   Photo.   Perf. 12
471	A88	2.50 l dark brown	.45	.20
472	A88	3 l rose brown	.70	.30
473	A88	5 l violet blue	1.10	.50
474	A88	8 l rose lilac	1.90	.80
		Nos. 471-474 (4)	4.15	1.80

Congress of Permet, 7th anniversary.

Child and Globe — A89

Weighing Baby — A90

1951, July 16
475	A89	2 l green	1.00	.30
476	A90	2.50 l brown	1.50	.40
477	A90	3 l red	2.00	.50
478	A89	5 l blue	3.00	.80
		Nos. 475-478 (4)	7.50	2.00

Intl. Children's Day, June 1, 1951.

Enver Hoxha and Birthplace of Albanian Communist Party — A91

1951, Nov. 8   Photo.   Perf. 14
479	A91	2.50 l olive brown	.30	.25
480	A91	3 l rose brown	.45	.35
481	A91	5 l dark slate blue	.70	.60
482	A91	8 l black	1.00	.85
		Nos. 479-482 (4)	2.45	2.05

Albanian Communist Party, 10th anniv.

Battle Scene — A92

Designs: 5 l, Schoolgirl, "Agriculture and Industry." 8 l, Four portraits.

1951, Nov. 28   Perf. 12x12½
483	A92	2.50 l brown	.40	.15
484	A92	5 l blue	.65	.40
485	A92	8 l brown carmine	1.40	.75
		Nos. 483-485 (3)	2.45	1.30

Albanian Communist Youth Org., 10th anniv.

Albanian Heroes (Haxhija, Lezhe, Giyebegej, Mezi and Dedej) — A93

Nos. 486-489 each show five "Heroes of the People"; No. 490 shows two (Stafa and Shanto).

1950, Dec. 25   Unwmk.   Perf. 14
486	A93	2 l dark green	.65	.15
487	A93	2.50 l purple	.80	.15
488	A93	3 l scarlet	.95	.25
489	A93	5 l brt blue	1.50	.35
490	A93	8 l olive brown	3.75	1.00
		Nos. 486-490 (5)	7.65	1.90

6th anniv. of Albania's liberation.

Tobacco Factory, Shkoder — A94

Composite, Lenin Hydroelectric Plant — A95

Designs: 1 l, Canal. 2.50 l, Textile factory. 3 l, "8 November" Cannery. 5 l, Motion Picture Studio,

Tirana. 8 l, Stalin Textile Mill, Tirana. 20 l, Central Hydroelectric Dam.

1953, Aug. 1 *Perf. 12x12½, 12½x12*
491	A94	50q red brown	.15	.15
492	A94	1 l dull green	.15	.15
493	A94	2.50 l brown	.60	.15
494	A94	3 l rose brown	.85	.15
495	A94	5 l blue	1.25	.15
496	A94	8 l brown olive	2.25	.15
497	A95	12 l deep plum	3.50	.35
498	A94	20 l slate blue	6.25	.50
		Nos. 491-498 (8)	15.00	
		Set value		1.30

Liberation Scene — A96

1954, Nov. 29 *Perf. 12x12½*
499	A96	50q brown violet	.15	.15
500	A96	1 l olive green	.25	.15
501	A96	2.50 l yellow brown	.65	.15
502	A96	3 l carmine rose	.80	.15
503	A96	5 l gray blue	1.10	.15
504	A96	8 l rose brown	2.00	.55
		Nos. 499-504 (6)	4.95	
		Set value		1.00

10th anniversary of Albania's liberation.

School — A97

Pandeli Sotiri, Petro Nini Luarasi, Nuci Naci — A98

1956, Feb. 23 *Unwmk.*
505	A97	2 l rose violet	.35	.15
506	A98	2.50 l lt green	.50	.15
507	A98	5 l ultra	1.10	.20
508	A97	10 l brt grnsh blue	2.25	.35
		Nos. 505-508 (4)	4.20	
		Set value		.70

Opening of the 1st Albanian school, 70th anniv.

Flags — A99

Designs: 5 l, Labor Party headquarters, Tirana. 8 l, Marx and Lenin.

1957, June 1 *Engr.* *Perf. 11½x11*
509	A99	5 l brown	.45	.15
510	A99	5 l lt violet blue	.90	.15
511	A99	8 l rose lilac	2.00	.20
		Nos. 509-511 (3)	3.35	
		Set value		.40

Albania's Labor Party, 15th anniv.

Congress Emblem A100

1957, Oct. 4 *Unwmk.* *Perf. 11½*
512	A100	2.50 l gray brown	.50	.15
513	A100	3 l rose red	.70	.15
514	A100	5 l dark blue	.90	.15
515	A100	8 l green	1.65	.15
		Nos. 512-515 (4)	3.75	
		Set value		.65

4th Intl. Trade Union Cong., Leipzig, Oct. 4-15.

Lenin and Cruiser "Aurora" — A101

1957, Nov. 7 *Litho.* *Perf. 10½*
516	A101	2.50 l violet brown	.45	.15
517	A101	5 l violet blue	.95	.15
518	A101	8 l gray	1.25	.30
		Nos. 516-518 (3)	2.65	.60

40th anniv. of the Russian Revolution.

Albanian Fighter Holding Flag A102 — Naum Veqilharxhj A103

1957, Nov. 28 *Perf. 10½*
519	A102	1.50 l magenta	.40	.15
520	A102	2.50 l brown	.60	.15
521	A102	5 l blue	1.00	.15
522	A102	8 l green	2.00	.30
		Nos. 519-522 (4)	4.00	
		Set value		.60

Proclamation of independence, 45th anniv.

1958, Feb. 1 *Unwmk.*
523	A103	2.50 l dark brown	.50	.15
524	A103	5 l violet blue	1.00	.15
525	A103	8 l rose lilac	2.00	.30
		Nos. 523-525 (3)	3.50	.60

160th anniv. of the birth of Naum Veqilharxhj, patriot and writer.

Luigi Gurakuqi A104 — Soldiers A105

1958, Apr. 15 *Photo.* *Perf. 10½*
526	A104	1.50 l dark green	.30	.15
527	A104	2.50 l brown	.40	.15
528	A104	5 l blue	.75	.15
529	A104	8 l sepia	1.50	.20
		Nos. 526-529 (4)	2.95	
		Set value		.50

Transfer of the ashes of Luigi Gurakuqi.

1958, July 10 *Litho.*
2.50 l, 11 l, Airman, sailor, soldier and tank.
530	A105	1.50 l blue green	.20	.15
531	A105	2.50 l dark red brown	.30	.15
532	A105	5 l rose red	.95	.15
533	A105	11 l bright blue	1.50	.25
		Nos. 530-533 (4)	2.95	
		Set value		.50

15th anniversary of Albanian army.

Cerciz Topulli and Mihal Grameno — A106 — Buildings and Tree — A107

1958, July 1
534	A106	2.50 l dk olive bister	.35	.15
535	A107	3 l green	.45	.15
536	A106	5 l blue	.75	.15
537	A107	8 l red brown	1.25	.20
		Nos. 534-537 (4)	2.80	
		Set value		.50

50th anniversary, Battle of Mashkullore.

Ancient Amphitheater and Goddess of Butrinto — A108

1959, Jan. 25 *Litho.* *Perf. 10½*
538	A108	2.50 l redsh brown	.65	.15
539	A108	6.50 l lt blue green	1.65	.15
540	A108	11 l dark blue	2.50	.40
		Nos. 538-540 (3)	4.80	
		Set value		.60

Cultural Monuments Week.

Frederic Joliot-Curie and World Peace Congress Emblem A109 — Basketball A110

1959, July 1 *Unwmk.*
541	A109	1.50 l carmine rose	1.00	.20
542	A109	2.50 l rose violet	1.75	.30
543	A109	11 l blue	5.00	1.50
		Nos. 541-543 (3)	7.75	2.00

10th anniv. of the World Peace Movement.

1959, Nov. 20 *Perf. 10½*
Sports: 2.50 l, Soccer. 5 l, Runner. 11 l, Man and woman runners with torch and flags.
544	A110	1.50 l bright violet	.40	.15
545	A110	2.50 l emerald	.55	.15
546	A110	5 l carmine rose	1.50	.25
547	A110	11 l ultra	4.00	1.75
		Nos. 544-547 (4)	6.45	2.30

1st Albanian Spartacist Games.

Fighter and Flags A111 — Mother and Child, UN Emblem A112

Designs: 2.50 l, Miner with drill standing guard. 3 l, Farm woman with sheaf of grain. 6.50 l, Man and woman in laboratory.

1959, Nov. 29
548	A111	1.50 l brt carmine	.50	.15
549	A111	2.50 l red brown	.70	.15
550	A111	3 l brt blue green	.90	.15
551	A111	6.50 l bright red	2.00	.25
a.		Souvenir sheet	6.00	6.00
		Nos. 548-551 (4)	4.10	
		Set value		.45

15th anniversary of Albania's liberation.
No. 551a contains one each of Nos. 548-551, imperf. and all in bright carmine. Inscribed ribbon frame of sheet and frame lines for each stamp are blue green.

1959, Dec. 5 *Unwmk.*
552	A113	5 l lt grnsh blue	3.00	.55
a.		Miniature sheet	3.00	3.00

10th anniv. (in 1958) of the signing of the Universal Declaration of Human Rights.
No. 552a contains one imperf. stamp similar to No. 552; ornamental border.

Woman with Olive Branch A113 — Alexander Moissi A114

1960, Mar. 8 *Litho.* *Perf. 10½*
553	A113	2.50 l chocolate	.45	.15
554	A113	11 l rose carmine	2.00	.30

50th anniv. of Intl. Women's Day, Mar. 8.

1960, Apr. 20
555	A114	3 l deep brown	.35	.15
556	A114	11 l Prus green	1.40	.25

80th anniversary of the birth of Alexander Moissi (Moisiu) (1880-1935), German actor.

Lenin A115 — School Building A116

1960, Apr. 22
557	A115	4 l Prus blue	1.65	.15
558	A115	11 l lake	3.50	.20
		Set value		.25

90th anniversary of birth of Lenin.

1960, May 30 *Litho.* *Perf. 10½*
559	A116	5 l green	1.25	.20
560	A116	6.50 l plum	1.25	.20

1st Albanian secondary school, 50th anniv.

Soldier on Guard Duty — A117 — Liberation Monument, Tirana, Family and Policeman — A118

1960, May 12 *Unwmk.* *Perf. 10½*
561	A117	1.50 l carmine rose	.30	.15
562	A117	11 l Prus blue	1.65	.20
		Set value		.25

15th anniversary of the Frontier Guards.

1960, May 14
563	A118	1.50 l green	.30	.15
564	A118	8.50 l brown	1.65	.25
		Set value		.30

15th anniversary of the People's Police.

Congress Site — A119 — Pashko Vasa — A120

1960, Mar. 25
565	A119	2.50 l sepia	.25	.15
566	A119	7.50 l dull blue	1.00	.25

40th anniversary, Congress of Louchnia.

1960, May 5
Designs: 1.50 l, Jani Vreto. 6.50 l, Sami Frasheri. 11 l, Page of statutes of association.
567	A120	1 l gray olive	.35	.15
568	A120	1.50 l brown	.50	.15
569	A120	6.50 l blue	1.10	.15
570	A120	11 l rose red	2.00	.20
		Nos. 567-570 (4)	3.95	
		Set value		.35

80th anniv. (in 1959) of the Association of Albanian Authors.

Albanian Fighter and Cannon A121 — TU-104 Plane, Clock Tower, Tirana, and Kremlin, Moscow A122

1960, Aug. 2 *Litho.* *Perf. 10½*
571	A121	1.50 l olive brown	.40	.15
572	A121	2.50 l maroon	.50	.15
573	A121	5 l dark blue	1.25	.20
		Nos. 571-573 (3)	2.15	
		Set value		.35

Battle of Viona (against Italian troops), 40th anniv.

1960, Aug. 18

574	A122	1 1 redsh brown	.40	.15
575	A122	7.50 1 brt grnsh blue	1.50	.35
576	A122	11.50 1 gray	2.75	.60
		Nos. 574-576 (3)	4.65	1.10

TU-104 flights, Moscow-Tirana, 2nd anniv.

Rising Sun and
Federation Emblem
A123

Ali Kelmendi
A124

1960, Nov. 10   Unwmk.   Perf. 10½

577	A123	1.50 1 ultra	.30	.15
578	A123	8.50 1 red	1.10	.20
		Set value		.25

Intl. Youth Federation, 15th anniv.

1960, Dec. 5   Litho.   Perf. 10½

579	A124	1.50 1 pale gray grn	.30	.15
580	A124	11 1 dull rose lake	.70	.20
		Set value		.25

Ali Kelmendi, communist leader, 60th birthday.

Flags of Russia and
Albania and Clasped
Hands
A125

Marx and
Lenin
A126

1961, Jan. 10   Unwmk.   Perf. 10½

581	A125	2 1 violet	.30	.15
582	A125	8 1 dull red brown	.70	.20
		Set value		.25

15th anniv. of the Albanian-Soviet Friendship
Society.

1961, Feb. 13   Litho.

583	A126	2 1 rose red	.30	.15
584	A126	8 1 violet blue	1.10	.20
		Set value		.25

Fourth Communist Party Congress.

Man from
Shkoder
A127

Otter
A128

Costumes: 1.50 1, Woman from Shkoder. 6.50 1,
Man from Lume. 11 1, Woman from Mirdite.

1961, Apr. 28   Perf. 10½

585	A127	1 1 slate	.35	.15
586	A127	1.50 1 dull claret	.60	.15
587	A127	6.50 1 ultra	1.90	.20
588	A127	11 1 red	3.25	.35
		Nos. 585-588 (4)	6.10	
		Set value		.65

1961, June 25   Unwmk.   Perf. 10½

Designs: 6.50 1, Badger. 11 1, Brown bear.

589	A128	2 1 grayish blue	2.00	.15
590	A128	6.50 1 blue green	4.50	.50
591	A128	11 1 dark red brown	8.00	.85
		Nos. 589-591 (3)	14.50	1.60

Dalmatian
Pelicans
A129

Cyclamen
A130

1961, Sept. 30   Perf. 14

592	A129	1.50 1 shown	2.00	.20
593	A129	7.50 1 Gray herons	4.00	.40
594	A129	11 1 Little egret	6.00	.60
		Nos. 592-594 (3)	12.00	1.20

1961, Oct. 27   Litho.

595	A130	1.50 1 shown	2.00	.15
596	A130	8 1 Forsythia	3.50	.20
597	A130	11 1 Lily	4.50	.40
		Nos. 595-597 (3)	10.00	.75

Milosh G.
Nikolla — A131

Flag with Marx
and
Lenin — A132

1961, Oct. 30   Perf. 14

598	A131	50q violet brown	.30	.15
599	A131	8.50 1 Prus green	1.25	.25
		Set value		.25

50th anniv. of the birth of Milosh Gjergi Nikolla,
poet.

1961, Nov. 8

600	A132	2.50 1 vermilion	.50	.15
601	A132	7.50 1 dull red brn	1.00	.25
		Set value		.30

20th anniv. of the founding of Albania's Communist Party.

Worker, Farm
Woman and
Emblem
A133

Yuri Gagarin and
Vostok 1
A134

1961, Nov. 23   Unwmk.   Perf. 14

602	A133	2.50 1 violet blue	.50	.15
603	A133	7.50 1 rose claret	1.00	.30

20th anniv. of the Albanian Workers' Party.

1962, Feb. 15   Unwmk.   Perf. 14

604	A134	50q blue	.35	.15
605	A134	4 1 red lilac	1.65	.15
606	A134	11 1 dk slate grn	3.25	.65
		Nos. 604-606 (3)	5.25	.95

1st manned space flight, made by Yuri A.
Gagarin, Soviet astronaut, Apr. 12, 1961.
Nos. 604-606 were overprinted with an over-all
yellow tint and with "POSTA AJRORE" (Air Mail)
in maroon in 1962. Value, set $50.

Petro Nini
Luarasi — A135

Malaria
Eradication
Emblem — A136

1962, Feb. 28   Litho.

607	A135	50q Prus blue	.25	.15
608	A135	8.50 1 olive gray	1.50	.15
		Set value		.30

50th anniv. (in 1961) of the death of Petro Nini
Luarasi, Albanian patriot.

1962, Apr. 30   Unwmk.   Perf. 14

609	A136	1.50 1 brt green	.15	.15
610	A136	2.50 1 brown red	.15	.15
611	A136	10 1 red lilac	.55	.25
612	A136	11 1 blue	.90	.35
		Nos. 609-612 (4)	1.75	
		Set value		.75

WHO drive to eradicate malaria.
Souvenir sheets, perf. and imperf., contain one
each of Nos. 609-612. Value $14.00 each. Nos.
609-612 imperf., value, set $14.00.

Camomile
A137

Woman Diver
A138

Medicinal plants.

1962, May 10

613	A137	50q shown	.20	.15
614	A137	8 1 Linden	.75	.25
615	A137	11.50 1 Garden sage	1.75	.50
		Nos. 613-615 (3)	2.70	.90

Value, imperf. set $12.

1962, May 31   Perf. 14

2.50 1, Pole vault. 3 1, Mt. Fuji & torch, horiz. 9 1,
Woman javelin thrower. 10 1, Shot putting.

616	A138	50q brt grnsh bl & blk	.15	.15
617	A138	2.50 1 gldn brn & sepia	.20	.15
618	A138	3 1 blue & gray	.40	.15
619	A138	9 1 rose car & dk brn	1.10	.25
620	A138	10 1 olive & blk	1.25	.30
		Nos. 616-620 (5)	3.10	
		Set value		.75

1964 Olympic Games, Tokyo. Value, imperf. set
$25. A 15 1 (like 3 1) exists in souv. sheet, perf. and
imperf.

Globe and
Orbits — A139

Dog Laika and Sputnik
2 — A140

Designs: 1.50 1, Rocket to the sun. 20 1, Lunik 3
photographing far side of the moon.

1962, June   Unwmk.   Perf. 14

621	A139	50q violet & org	.20	.15
622	A140	1 1 blue grn & brn	.35	.15
623	A140	1.50 1 yellow & ver	.50	.15
624	A139	20 1 magenta & bl	3.50	.80
		Nos. 621-624 (4)	4.55	
		Set value		1.05

Russian space explorations.
#621-624 exist imperforate in changed colors.
Two miniature sheets exist, containing one 14-
lek picturing Sputnik 1. The perforated 14-lek is
yellow and brown; the imperf. red and brown.

Soccer Game,
Map of South
America — A141

2.50 1, 15 1, Soccer game and globe as ball.

1962, July   Litho.

625	A141	1 1 org & dk pur	.15	.15
626	A141	2.50 1 emer & bluish grn	.25	.15
627	A141	6.50 1 lt brn & pink	.90	.15
628	A141	15 1 bluish grn & mar	1.50	.35
		Nos. 625-628 (4)	2.80	
		Set value		.55

Issued to commemorate the World Soccer Championships, Chile, May 30-June 17.
Exist imperforate in changed colors.
Two miniature sheets exist, each containing a
single 20-lek in design similar to A141. The perf.
sheet is brown and green; the imperf., brown and
orange.

Map of Europe
and
Albania — A142

Woman of
Dardhe — A143

Designs: 1 1, 2.50 1, Map of Adriatic Sea and
Albania and Roman statue.

1962, Aug.

630	A142	50q multicolored	.40	.35
631	A142	1 1 ultra & red	1.00	.80
632	A142	2.50 1 blue & red	3.00	2.50
633	A142	11 1 multicolored	6.00	5.00
		Nos. 630-633 (4)	10.40	8.65

Tourist propaganda. Imperforates in changed colors exist.
Miniature sheets containing a 7 1 and 8 1 stamp,
perf. and imperf., exist.

1962, Sept.

Regional Costumes: 1 1, Man from Devoll. 2.50 1,
Woman from Lunxheri. 14 1, Man from Gjirokaster.

635	A143	50q car, bl & pur	.15	.15
636	A143	1 1 red brn & ocher	.15	.15
637	A143	2.50 1 vio, yel grn & blk	.65	.15
638	A143	14 1 red brn & pale grn	2.25	.50
		Nos. 635-638 (4)	3.20	

Value, imperf. set $18.

Chamois
A144

Ismail Qemali
A145

Animals: 1 1, Lynx, horiz. 1.50 1, Wild boar,
horiz. 15 1, 20 1, Roe deer.

1962, Oct. 24   Unwmk.   Perf. 14

639	A144	50q sl grn & dk pur	.60	.15
640	A144	1 1 orange & blk	1.10	.15
641	A144	1.50 1 red brn & blk	1.50	.15
642	A144	15 1 yel ol & red brn	7.75	1.00
		Nos. 639-642 (4)	10.95	1.45

Miniature Sheet

643	A144	20 1 yel ol & red brn	15.00	15.00

Imperfs. in changed colors, value #639-642 $25,
#643 $25.

1962, Dec. 28   Litho.

Designs: 1 1, Albania eagle. 16 1, Eagle over fortress formed by "RPSH."

644	A145	1 1 red & red brn	.30	.15
645	A145	3 1 org brn & blk	.55	.15
646	A145	16 1 dk car rose & blk	3.50	.50
		Nos. 644-646 (3)	4.35	
		Set value		.65

50th anniv. of independence. Imperfs. in
changed colors, value, set $12.50.

---

*The lack of a value for a listed item
does not necessarily indicate rarity.*

Monument of October Revolution A146

Henri Dunant, Cross, Globe and Nurse A147

1963, Jan. 5   Unwmk.   Perf. 14
647 A146   5 l shown   .50   .15
648 A146 10 l Lenin statue   1.25   .25
         Set value   .30

October Revolution (Russia, 1917), 45th anniv.

1963, Jan 25   Unwmk.   Perf. 14
649 A147   1.50 l rose lake, red & blk   .25   .15
650 A147   2.50 l lt bl, red & blk   .30   .15
651 A147   6 l emerald, red & blk   .75   .25
652 A147   10 l dull yel, red & blk   1.40   .35
         Nos. 649-652 (4)   2.70
         Set value   .75

Cent. of the Geneva Conf., which led to the establishment of the Intl. Red Cross in 1864. Imperfs. in changed colors, value, set $20.

Stalin and Battle of Stalingrad A148

Andrian G. Nikolayev A149

1963, Feb. 2
653 A148   8 l dk green & slate   4.00   .50

Battle of Stalingrad, 20th anniv. See #C67.

1963, Feb. 28   Litho.
Designs: 7.50 l, Vostoks 3 and 4 and globe, horiz. 20 l, Pavel R. Popovich. 25 l, Nikolayev, Popovich and globe with trajectories.
654 A149   2.50 l vio bl & sepia   .40   .15
655 A149   7.50 l lt blue & blk   .75   .15
656 A149   20 l violet & sepia   2.25   .70
         Nos. 654-656 (3)   3.40 1.00

Miniature Sheet
657 A149   25 l vio bl & sepia   12.00 12.00

1st group space flight of Vostoks 3 and 4, Aug. 11-15, 1962. Imperfs. in changed colors, value #654-656 $12, #657 $12.

"Albania" Decorating Police Officer — A150

Polyphylla Fullo — A151

1963, Mar. 20   Unwmk.   Perf. 14
658 A150   2.50 l crim, mag & blk   .40   .15
659 A150   7.50 l org ver, dk red & blk 1.40   .25

20th anniversary of the security police.

1963, Mar. 20
Beetles: 1.50 l, Lucanus cervus. 8 l, Procerus gigas. 10 l, Cicindela Albanica.
660 A151   50q ol grn & brn   .25   .15
661 A151   1.50 l blue & brn   .55   .15
662 A151   8 l dl rose & blk vio   2.75 1.10
663 A151   10 l brt citron & blk   3.00 1.25
         Nos. 660-663 (4)   6.55 2.65

1913 Stamp and Postmark — A152

Design: 10 l, Stamps of 1913, 1937 and 1962.

1963, May 5
664 A152   5 l yel, buff, bl & blk   .70   .25
665 A152 10 l car rose, grn & blk   1.40   .45

50th anniversary of Albanian stamps.

Boxer — A153

Crested Grebe — A154

Designs: 3 l, Basketball baskets. 5 l, Volleyball. 6 l, Bicyclists. 9 l, Gymnast. 15 l, Hands holding torch, and map of Japan.

1963, May 25   Perf. 13½
666 A153   2 l yel, blk & red brn   .25   .15
667 A153   3 l ocher, brn & bl   .35   .15
668 A153   5 l gray bl, red brn & brn .60   .15
669 A153   6 l gray, dk gray & grn   .80   .25
670 A153   9 l rose, red brn & bl   1.50   .30
         Nos. 666-670 (5)   3.50 1.00

Miniature Sheet
671 A153   15 l lt bl, car, blk & brn 9.00 9.00

1964 Olympic Games in Tokyo. Value, imperfs. #666-670 $7.50, #671 $8.

1963, Apr. 20   Litho.   Perf. 14
Birds: 3 l, Golden eagle. 6.50 l, Gray partridges. 11 l, Capercaillie.
672 A154   50q multicolored   .20   .15
673 A154   3 l multicolored   1.10   .25
674 A154 6.50 l multicolored   2.50   .55
675 A154   11 l multicolored   4.00   .85
         Nos. 672-675 (4)   7.80 1.80

Soldier and Building A155

Designs: 2.50 l, Soldier with pack, ship and plane. 5 l, Soldier in battle. 6 l, Soldier and bulldozer.

1963, July 10   Unwmk.   Perf. 12
676 A155   1.50 l brick red, yel & blk .30   .15
677 A155   2.50 l bl, ocher & brn   .40   .15
678 A155   5 l bluish grn, gray & blk .90 .15
679 A155   6 l red brn, buff & bl   1.25   .25
         Nos. 676-679 (4)   2.85
         Set value   .50

Albanian army, 20th anniversary.

Maj. Yuri A. Gagarin A156

Designs: 5 l, Maj. Gherman Titov. 7 l, Maj. Andrian G. Nikolayev. 11 l, Lt. Col. Pavel R. Popovich. 14 l, Lt. Col. Valeri Bykovski. 20 l, Lt. Valentina Tereshkova.

1963, July 30
Portraits in Yellow and Black
680 A156   3 l brt purple   .45   .15
681 A156   5 l dull blue   .65   .15
682 A156   7 l gray   .90   .15
683 A156   11 l deep claret   1.50   .35
684 A156   14 l blue green   2.25   .55
685 A156   20 l ultra   3.25 1.00
         Nos. 680-685 (6)   9.00 2.35

Man's conquest of space. Value, imperf. set $18.

Volleyball — A157

1963, Aug. 31   Perf. 12x12½
686 A157   2 l shown   .15   .15
687 A157   3 l Weight lifting   .35   .15
688 A157   5 l Soccer   .65   .15

---

689 A157   7 l Boxing   .80   .25
690 A157   8 l Rowing   1.50   .30
         Nos. 686-690 (5)   3.45 1.00

European championships. Imperfs. in changed colors, value set $16.

Papilio Podalirius A158

1963, Sept. 29   Litho.
Various Butterflies and Moths in Natural Colors
691 A158   1 l red   .15   .15
692 A158   2 l blue   .30   .15
693 A158   4 l dull lilac   .50   .25
694 A158   5 l pale green   .90   .40
695 A158   8 l bister   1.10   .55
696 A158   10 l light blue   1.65   .70
         Nos. 691-696 (6)   4.60 2.20

Oil Refinery, Cerrik — A159

Flag and Shield — A160

2.50 l, Food processing plant, Tirana, horiz. 30 l, Fruit canning plant. 50 l, Tannery, horiz.

1963, Nov. 15   Unwmk.   Perf. 14
697 A159   2.50 l rose red, pnksh   .40   .15
698 A159   20 l slate grn, grnsh   1.40   .20
699 A159   30 l dull pur, grysh   3.25   .50
700 A159   50 l ocher, yel   3.50   .75
         Nos. 697-700 (4)   8.55 1.60

Industrial development in Albania.

1963, Nov. 24   Perf. 12½x12
701 A160   2 l grnsh bl, blk, ocher & red   .35   .15
702 A160   8 l blue, blk, ocher & red   1.00   .50
         Set value   .55

1st Congress of Army Aid Assn.

Chinese, Caucasian and Negro Men — A161

1963, Dec. 10   Perf. 12x11½
703 A161   3 l bister & blk   .50   .15
704 A161   5 l bister & ultra   .95   .20
705 A161   7 l bister & vio   1.50   .30
         Nos. 703-705 (3)   2.95   .65

15th anniv. of the Universal Declaration of Human Rights.

Slalom Ascent — A162

Designs: 50q, Bobsled, horiz. 6.50 l, Ice hockey, horiz. 12.50 l, Women's figure skating. No. 709A, Ski jumper.

1963, Dec. 25   Perf. 14
706 A162   50q grnsh bl & blk   .15   .15
707 A162   2.50 l red, gray & blk   .30   .15
708 A162   6.50 l blk & gray   .75   .20
709 A162 12.50 l red, blk & yel grn 1.75   .50
         Nos. 706-709 (4)   2.95

         Set value   .80

Miniature Sheet
709A A162 12.50 l multi   4.25 4.25

9th Winter Olympic Games, Innsbruck, Jan. 29-Feb. 9, 1964. Imperfs. in changed colors, value #706-709 $25, #709A $30.

1964, Jan. 21   Perf. 12½x12
710 A163   5 l gray & bister   .35   .15
711 A163 10 l gray & ocher   .65   .30

40th anniversary, death of Lenin.

Hurdling A164

Fish A165

Designs: 3 l, Track, horiz. 6.50 l, Rifle shooting, horiz. 8 l, Basketball.

Perf. 12½x12, 12x12½
1964, Jan. 30   Litho.
712 A164   2.50 l pale vio & ultra   .30   .15
713 A164   3 l grn & red brn   .45   .15
714 A164   6.50 l blue & claret   .90   .20
715 A164   8 l lt blue & ocher   1.25   .20
         Nos. 712-715 (4)   2.90
         Set value   .60

1st Games of the New Emerging Forces, GANEFO, Jakarta, Indonesia, Nov. 10-22, 1963.

1964, Feb. 26   Unwmk.   Perf. 14
716 A165   50q Sturgeon   .15   .15
717 A165   1 l Gilthead   .15   .15
718 A165   1.50 l Striped mullet   .40   .15
719 A165   2.50 l Carp   .60   .15
720 A165   6.50 l Mackerel   1.65   .40
721 A165   10 l Lake Ohrid trout 3.00   .50
         Nos. 716-721 (6)   5.95
         Set value   1.25

Wild Animals A166

1964, Mar. 28   Perf. 12½x12
722 A166   1 l Red Squirrel   .15   .15
723 A166   1.50 l Beech marten   .15   .15
724 A166   2 l Red fox   .50   .15
725 A166   2.50 l Hedgehog   .55   .15
726 A166   3 l Hare   .65   .15
727 A166   5 l Jackal   1.10   .25
728 A166   7 l Wildcat   1.65   .35
729 A166   8 l Wolf   2.00   .50
         Nos. 722-729 (8)   6.75
         Set value   1.50

Lighting Olympic Torch — A167

Designs: 5 l, Torch and globes. 7 l, 15 l, Olympic flag and Mt. Fuji. 10 l, National Stadium, Tokyo.

1964, May 18   Perf. 12x12½
730 A167   3 l lt yel grn, yel & buff   .25   .15
731 A167   5 l red & vio blue   .35   .15
732 A167   7 l lt bl, ultra & yel   .55   .20
733 A167 10 l orange, bl & vio   .75   .25
         Nos. 730-733 (4)   1.90
         Set value   .55

Miniature Sheet
734 A167 15 l lt bl, ultra & org   12.50 12.50

18th Olympic Games, Tokyo, Oct. 10-25, 1964. No. 734 contains one 49x62mm stamp. Imperfs. in changed colors, value #730-733 $11, #734 $14. See No. 745.

Partisans — A168

Designs: 5 l, Arms of Albania. 8 l, Enver Hoxha.

Perf. 12¹/₂x12

1964, May 24		**Litho.**	**Unwmk.**	
735	A168	2 l	orange, red & blk	.50 .15
736	A168	5 l	multicolored	1.25 .15
737	A168	8 l	red brn, blk & red	2.50 .20
	Nos. 735-737 (3)			4.25
	Set value			.35

20th anniv. of the Natl. Anti-Fascist Cong. of Liberation, Permet, May 24, 1944. The label attached to each stamp, without perforations between, carries a quotation from the 1944 Congress.

Albanian Flag and Revolutionists A169

Full Moon A170

Perf. 12¹/₂x12

1964, June 10		**Litho.**	**Unwmk.**	
738	A169	2.50 l	red & gray	.15 .15
739	A169	7.50 l	lilac rose & gray	.60 .20

Albanian revolution of 1924, 40th anniv.

1964, June 27   **Perf. 12x12¹/₂**

Designs: 5 l, New moon. 8 l, Half moon. 11 l, Waning moon. 15 l, Far side of moon.

740	A170	1 l	purple & yel	.25 .15
741	A170	5 l	violet & yel	.60 .15
742	A170	8 l	blue & yel	1.10 .30
743	A170	11 l	green & yel	1.75 .45
	Nos. 740-743 (4)			3.70 1.05

Miniature Sheet
Perf. 12 on 2 sides

744	A170	15 l	ultra & yel	12.50 12.50

No. 744 contains one stamp, size: 35x36mm, perforated at top and bottom. Imperfs. in changed colors, value #740-743 $12.50, #744 $12.50.

No. 733 with Added Inscription: "Rimini 25-VI-64"

1964   **Perf. 12x12¹/₂**

745	A167	10 l	orange, bl & vio	3.50 3.00

"Toward Tokyo 1964" Phil. Exhib. at Rimini, Italy, June 25-July 6.

Wren — A171

Birds: 1 l, Penduline titmouse. 2.50 l, Green woodpecker. 3 l, Tree creeper. 4 l, Nuthatch. 5 l, Great titmouse. 6 l, Goldfinch. 18 l, Oriole.

1964, July 31			**Perf. 12x12¹/₂**	
746	A171	50q	multi	.15 .15
747	A171	1 l	orange & multi	.15 .15
748	A171	2.50 l	multi	.25 .15
749	A171	3 l	blue & multi	.35 .15
750	A171	4 l	yellow & multi	.45 .15
751	A171	5 l	blue & multi	.55 .15
752	A171	6 l	lt vio & multi	.80 .30
753	A171	18 l	pink & multi	2.25 .85
	Nos. 746-753 (8)			4.95
	Set value			1.60

Running and Gymnastics A172

Sport: 2 l, Weight lifting, judo. 3 l, Equestrian, bicycling. 4 l, Soccer, water polo. 5 l, Wrestling, boxing. 6 l, Pentathlon, hockey. 7 l, Swimming, sailing. 8 l, Basketball, volleyball. 9 l, Rowing, canoeing. 10 l, Fencing, pistol shooting. 20 l, Three winners.

Perf. 12x12¹/₂

1964, Sept. 25		**Litho.**	**Unwmk.**	
754	A172	1 l	lt bl, rose & emer	.15 .15
755	A172	2 l	bis brn, bluish grn & vio	.15 .15
756	A172	3 l	vio, red org & ol bis	.20 .15
757	A172	4 l	grnsh bl, ol & ultra	.20 .15
758	A172	5 l	grnsh bl, car & pale lil	.30 .15
759	A172	6 l	dk bl, org & lt bl	.35 .15
760	A172	7 l	dk bl, lt ol & org	.35 .15
761	A172	8 l	emerald, gray & yel	.50 .20
762	A172	9 l	bl, yel & lil rose	.65 .30
763	A172	10 l	brt grn, org brn & yel grn	1.65 .50
	Nos. 754-763 (10)			4.50
	Set value			1.60

Miniature Sheet
Perf. 12

764	A172	20 l	violet & lemon	10.00 5.00

18th Olympic Games, Tokyo, Oct. 10-25. No. 764 contains one stamp, size: 41x68mm, Imperfs. in changed colors, value #754-763 $12.50, #764 $12.50.

SHQIPERIA

Arms of People's Republic of China — A173

Mao Tse-tung and Flag A174

1964, Oct. 1   **Perf. 11¹/₂x12, 12x11¹/₂**

765	A173	7 l	black, red & yellow	2.00 .30
766	A174	8 l	black, red & yellow	3.00 .40

People's Republic of China, 15th anniv.

Karl Marx A175

Jeronim de Rada A176

Designs: 5 l, St. Martin's Hall, London. 8 l, Friedrich Engels.

1964, Nov. 5			**Perf. 12x11¹/₂**	
767	A175	2 l	red, lt vio & blk	.55 .15
768	A175	5 l	gray blue	1.10 .20
769	A175	8 l	ocher, blk & red	2.25 .30
	Nos. 767-769 (3)			3.90 .65

Centenary of First Socialist International.

1964, Nov. 15			**Perf. 12¹/₂x11¹/₂**	
770	A176	7 l	slate green	1.10 .30
771	A176	8 l	dull violet	1.65 .35

Birth of Jeronim de Rada, poet, 150th anniv.

Arms of Albania — A177

Factories A178

Designs: 3 l, Combine harvester. 4 l, Woman chemist. 10 l, Hands holding Constitution, hammer and sickle.

Perf. 11¹/₂x12, 12x11¹/₂

1964, Nov. 29				
772	A177	1 l	multicolored	.35 .15
773	A178	2 l	red, yel & vio bl	.45 .15
774	A178	3 l	red, yel & brn	.85 .15
775	A178	4 l	red, yel & gray grn	1.00 .15
776	A177	10 l	red, bl & blk	1.65 .45
	Nos. 772-776 (5)			4.30
	Set value			.80

20th anniversary of liberation.

Planet Mercury — A179

Planets: 2 l, Venus and rocket. 3 l, Earth, moon and rocket. 4 l, Mars and rocket. 5 l, Jupiter. 6 l, Saturn. 7 l, Uranus. 8 l, Neptune. 9 l, Pluto. 15 l, Solar system and rocket.

1964, Dec. 15			**Perf. 12x12¹/₂**	
777	A179	1 l	yellow & pur	.15 .15
778	A179	2 l	multicolored	.15 .15
779	A179	3 l	multicolored	.20 .15
780	A179	4 l	multicolored	.25 .15
781	A179	5 l	yel, dk pur & brn	.45 .15
782	A179	6 l	lt grn, vio brn & yel	.60 .15
783	A179	7 l	yellow & grn	.70 .20
784	A179	8 l	yellow & vio	.85 .25
785	A179	9 l	lt grn, yel & blk	1.25 .35
	Nos. 777-785 (9)			4.60
	Set value			1.30

Miniature Sheet
Perf. 12 on 2 sides

786	A179	15 l	car, bl, yel & grn	17.50 17.50

No. 786 contains one stamp, size: 62x51mm, perforated at top and bottom. Imperfs. in changed colors. Value #777-785, $15; #786, $17.50.

European Chestnut A180

Symbols of Industry A181

1965, Jan. 25			**Perf. 11¹/₂x12**	
787	A180	1 l	shown	.15 .15
788	A180	2 l	Medlars	.25 .15
789	A180	3 l	Persimmon	.50 .15
790	A180	4 l	Pomegranate	.55 .15
791	A180	5 l	Quince	.80 .20
792	A180	10 l	Orange	1.65 .35
	Nos. 787-792 (6)			3.90
	Set value			.90

1965, Feb. 20

Designs: 5 l, Books, triangle and compass. 8 l, Beach, trees and hotel.

793	A181	2 l	blk, car rose & pink	1.75 .40
794	A181	5 l	yel, gray & blk	3.50 .85
795	A181	8 l	blk, vio bl & lt bl	5.75 1.60
	Nos. 793-795 (3)			11.00 2.85

Professional trade associations, 20th anniv.

Water Buffalo A182

Various designs: Water buffalo.

1965, Mar.			**Perf. 12x11¹/₂**	
796	A182	1 l	lt yel grn, yel & brn blk	.35 .15
797	A182	2 l	lt bl, dk gray & blk	.85 .15
798	A182	3 l	yellow, brn & grn	1.10 .15
799	A182	7 l	brt grn, yel & brn blk	2.75 .35
800	A182	12 l	pale lil, dk brn & ind	4.00 .65
	Nos. 796-800 (5)			9.05 1.45

Mountain View, Valbona — A183

Views: 1.50 l, Seashore. 3 l, Glacier and peak, vert. 4 l, Gorge, vert. 5 l, Mountain peaks. 9 l, Lake and hills.

1965, Mar.		**Litho.**	**Perf. 12**	
801	A183	1.50 l	multi	1.40 .15
802	A183	2.50 l	multi	1.75 .20
803	A183	3 l	multi	2.75 .25
804	A183	4 l	multi	3.00 .40
805	A183	5 l	multi	5.00 .50
806	A183	9 l	multi	8.00 .75
	Nos. 801-806 (6)			21.90 2.25

Frontier Guard — A184

Small-bore Rifle Shooting, Prone — A185

1965, Apr. 25			**Unwmk.**	
807	A184	2.50 l	lt blue & multi	.85 .15
808	A184	12.50 l	lt ultra & multi	3.50 .90

20th anniversary of the Frontier Guards.

1965, May 10

Designs: 2 l, Rifle shooting, standing. 3 l, Target over map of Europe, showing Bucharest. 4 l, Pistol shooting. 15 l, Rifle shooting, kneeling.

809	A185	1 l	lil, car rose, blk & brn	.15 .15
810	A185	2 l	bl, blk, brn & vio bl	.35 .15
811	A185	3 l	pink & car rose	.45 .15
812	A185	4 l	bis, blk & vio brn	.60 .15
813	A185	15 l	brt grn, brn & vio brn	2.25 .50
	Nos. 809-813 (5)			3.80
	Set value			.90

European Shooting Championships, Bucharest.

ITU Emblem, Old and New Communications Equipment — A186

Col. Pavel Belyayev — A187

1965, May 17   *Perf. 12¹/₂x12*

814 A186	2.50 l brt grn, blk & lil rose	.50	.15
815 A186	12.50 l vio, blk & brt bl	3.25	.30
	Set value		.35

Centenary of the ITU.

1965, June 15   *Perf. 12*

Designs: 2 l, Voskhod II. 6.50 l, Lt. Col. Alexei Leonov. 20 l, Leonov floating in space.

816 A187	1.50 l lt blue & brn	.15	.15
817 A187	2 l dk bl, lt vio & lt ultra	.20	.15
818 A187	6.50 l lilac & brn	.70	.15
819 A187	20 l chlky bl, yel & blk	1.90	.35
	Nos. 816-819 (4)	2.95	
	Set value		.60

Miniature Sheet
Perf. 12 on 2 sides

820 A187	20 l brt bl, org & blk	6.00	6.00

Space flight of Voskhod II and 1st man walking in space, Lt. Col. Alexei Leonov. No. 820 contains one stamp, size: 51x59¹/₂mm, perforated at top and bottom. Imperf., brt grn background, value $6.

Marx and Lenin — A188   Mother and Child — A189

1965, June 21   *Perf. 12*

821 A188	2.50 l dk brn, red & yel	.85	.15
822 A188	7.50 l sl grn, org ver & buff	2.25	.25

6th Conf. of Postal Ministers of Communist Countries, Peking, June 21-July 15.

Perf. 12¹/₂x12, 12x12¹/₂
1965, June 29   Litho.   Unwmk.

Designs: 2 l, Pioneers. 3 l, Boy and girl at play, horiz. 4 l, Child on beach. 15 l, Girl with book.

823 A189	1 l brt bl, rose lil & blk	.15	.15
824 A189	2 l salmon, vio & blk	.35	.15
825 A189	3 l green, org & vio	.50	.15
826 A189	4 l multicolored	.70	.15
827 A189	15 l lil rose, brn & ocher	2.25	.40
	Nos. 823-827 (5)	3.95	
	Set value		.70

Issued for International Children's Day.

Statue of Magistrate A190   Flowers A191

Designs: 1 l, Amphora. 2 l, Illyrian armor. 3 l, Mosaic, horiz. 15 l, Torso, Apollo statue.

1965, July 20   *Perf. 12*

828 A190	1 l ol, org & brn	.15	.15
829 A190	2 l gray grn, grn & brn	.25	.15
830 A190	3 l tan, brn, car & lil	.50	.15
831 A190	4 l green, bis & brn	.70	.20
832 A190	15 l gray & pale claret	1.75	.65
	Nos. 828-832 (5)	3.35	
	Set value		1.00

1965, Aug. 11   *Perf. 12¹/₂x12*

833 A191	1 l Fuchsia	.15	.15
834 A191	2 l Cyclamen	.30	.15
835 A191	3 l Tiger lily	.50	.15
836 A191	3.50 l Iris	.60	.15
837 A191	4 l Dahlia	.70	.15
838 A191	4.50 l Hydrangea	.80	.15
839 A191	5 l Rose	1.00	.20
840 A191	7 l Tulips	1.90	.30
	Nos. 833-840 (8)	5.95	
	Set value		1.10

Nos. 698-700 Surcharged New Value and Two Bars

1965, Aug. 16   *Perf. 14*

841 A159	5q on 30 l	.15	.15
842 A159	15q on 30 l	.30	.15
843 A159	25q on 50 l	.45	.15
844 A159	80q on 50 l	.90	.20
845 A159	1.10 l on 20 l	1.50	.30
846 A159	2 l on 20 l	2.75	.60
	Nos. 841-846 (6)	6.05	
	Set value		1.30

White Stork — A192   "Homecoming," by Bukurosh Sejdini — A193

Migratory Birds: 20q, Cuckoo. 30q, Hoopoe. 40q, European bee-eater. 50q, European nightjar. 1.50 l, Quail.

1965, Aug. 31   *Perf. 12*

847 A192	10q yellow, blk & gray	.20	.15
848 A192	20q brt pink, blk & dk bl	.35	.15
849 A192	30q violet, blk & bis	.65	.15
850 A192	40q emer, blk yel & org	1.40	.15
851 A192	50q ultra, brn & red brn	1.65	.25
852 A192	1.50 l bis, red brn & dp org	4.50	.75
	Nos. 847-852 (6)	8.75	
	Set value		1.35

1965, Sept. 26   Litho.   *Perf. 12x12¹/₂*

853 A193	25q olive black	1.75	.15
854 A193	65q blue black	4.25	.35
855 A193	1.10 l black	6.50	.60
	Nos. 853-855 (3)	12.50	1.10

Second war veterans' meeting.

Hunting — A194   Oleander — A195

1965, Oct. 6   Litho.   Unwmk.

856 A194	10q Capercaillie	.25	.15
857 A194	20q Deer	.40	.15
858 A194	30q Pheasant	.70	.20
859 A194	40q Mallards	1.10	.20
860 A194	50q Boar	1.25	.25
861 A194	1 l Rabbit	3.75	.55
	Nos. 856-861 (6)	7.45	1.50

1965, Oct. 26   *Perf. 12¹/₂x12*

Flowers: 20q, Forget-me-nots. 30q, Pink. 40q, White water lily. 50q, Bird's foot. 1 l, Corn poppy.

862 A195	20q brt bl, grn & car rose	.20	.15
863 A195	20q org red, bl, brn & grn	.40	.15
864 A195	30q vio, car rose & grn	.60	.15
865 A195	40q emerald, yel & blk	.80	.20
866 A195	20q grn brn, yel & grn	1.00	.20
867 A195	1 l yel grn, blk & rose red	2.00	.70
	Nos. 862-867 (6)	5.00	1.55

Hotel Turizmi, Fier — A196   Freighter "Teuta" — A197

Buildings: 10q, Hotel, Peshkopi. 15q, Sanatorium, Tirana. 25q, Rest home, Pogradec. 65q, Partisan Sports Arena, Tirana. 80q, Rest home, Mali Dajt. 1.10 l, Culture House, Tirana. 1.60 l, Hotel Adriatik, Durres. 2 l, Migjeni Theater, Shkoder. 3 l, Alexander Moissi House of Culture, Durres.

1965, Oct.   *Perf. 12x12¹/₂*

868 A196	5q blue & blk	.15	.15
869 A196	10q ocher & blk	.15	.15
870 A196	15q dull grn & blk	.15	.15
871 A196	25q violet & blk	.20	.15

---

872 A196	65q lt brn & blk	.70	.15
873 A196	80q yel grn & blk	.90	.15
874 A196	1.10 l lilac & blk	1.25	.20
875 A196	1.60 l lt vio bl & blk	1.90	.35
876 A196	2 l dull rose & blk	2.50	.50
877 A196	3 l gray & blk	4.00	.70
	Nos. 868-877 (10)	11.90	
	Set value		2.15

1965, Nov. 16

Ships: 20q, Raft. 30q, Sailing ship, 19th cent. 40q, Sailing ship, 18th cent. 50q, Freighter "Vlora." 1 l, Illyric galleys.

878 A197	10q brt grn & dk grn	.15	.15
879 A197	20q ol bis & dk grn	.20	.15
880 A197	30q lt & dp ultra	.35	.15
881 A197	40q vio & dp vio	.60	.20
882 A197	50q pink & dk red	.75	.20
883 A197	1 l bister & brn	1.50	.45
	Nos. 878-883 (6)	3.55	1.30

Brown Bear — A198   Basketball and Players — A199

Various Albanian bears. 50q, 55q, 60q, horiz.

1965, Dec. 7   *Perf. 11¹/₂x12*

884 A198	10q bister & dk brn	.30	.15
885 A198	20q pale brn & dk brn	.40	.15
886 A198	30q bis, dk brn & car	.65	.15
887 A198	35q pale brn & dk brn	.80	.15
888 A198	40q bister & dk brn	1.25	.20
889 A198	50q bister & dk brn	1.50	.20
890 A198	55q bister & dk brn	1.50	.20
891 A198	60q pale brn, dk brn & car	1.65	.45
	Nos. 884-891 (8)	8.05	1.75

1965, Dec. 15   Litho.   *Perf. 12¹/₂x12*

Designs: 10q, Games' emblem (map of Albania and basket). 30q, 50q, Players with ball (diff. designs). 1.40 l, Basketball medal on ribbon.

892 A199	10q blue, yel & car	.15	.15
893 A199	20q rose lil, lt brn & blk	.35	.15
894 A199	30q bis, lt brn, red & blk	.45	.15
895 A199	50q lt grn, lt brn & blk	.95	.15
896 A199	1.40 l rose, blk, brn & yel	1.75	.50
	Nos. 892-896 (5)	3.65	
	Set value		.80

7th Balkan Basketball Championships, Tirana, Dec. 15-19.

Arms of Republic and Smokestacks — A200

Designs (Arms and): 10q, Book. 30q, Wheat. 60q, Book, hammer and sickle. 80q, Factories.

1966, Jan. 11   Litho.   *Perf. 11¹/₂x12*
Coat of Arms in Gold

897 A200	10q crimson & brn	.15	.15
898 A200	20q blue & vio bl	.15	.15
899 A200	30q org yel & brn	.35	.15
900 A200	60q yel grn & brt grn	.50	.20
901 A200	80q crimson & brn	1.10	.25
	Nos. 897-901 (5)	2.25	
	Set value		.60

Albanian People's Republic, 20th anniv.

Cow — A201

Perf. 12¹/₂x12, 12x12¹/₂
1966, Feb. 25

902 A201	10q shown	.20	.15
903 A201	20q Pig	.35	.15
904 A201	25q Ewe & lamb	.45	.15
905 A201	35q Ram	.65	.15
906 A201	40q Dog	.95	.15
907 A201	50q Cat, vert.	1.00	.15
908 A201	55q Horse, vert.	1.25	.25
909 A201	60q Ass, vert.	1.50	.30
	Nos. 902-909 (8)	6.35	
	Set value		1.20

Soccer Player and Map of Uruguay — A202   Andon Zako Cajupi — A203

5q, Globe in form of soccer ball. 15q, Player, map of Italy. 20q, Goalkeeper, map of France. 25q, Player, map of Brazil. 30q, Player, map of Switzerland. 35q, Player, map of Sweden. 40q, Player, map of Chile. 50q, Player, map of Great Britain. 70q, World Championship cup & ball.

1966, Mar. 20   Litho.   *Perf. 12*

910 A202	5q gray & dp org	.15	.15
911 A202	10q lt brn, bl & vio	.15	.15
912 A202	15q cit, dk bl & brt bl	.25	.15
913 A202	20q org, vio bl & brt bl	.25	.15
914 A202	25q salmon & sepia	.30	.15
915 A202	30q lt yel grn & brn	.30	.15
916 A202	35q lt ultra & emer	.35	.15
917 A202	40q pink & brown	.55	.15
918 A202	50q pale grn, mag & rose red	.55	.15
919 A202	70q gray, brn, yel & blk	.70	.25
	Nos. 910-919 (10)	3.45	
	Set value		1.00

World Cup Soccer Championship, Wembley, England, July 11-30.

1966, Mar. 27   Unwmk.

920 A203	40q bluish blk	.50	.15
921 A203	1.10 l dark green	1.50	.15
	Set value		.25

Andon Zako Cajupi, poet, birth centenary .

Painted Lady — A204   WHO Headquarters, Geneva, and Emblem — A205

Designs: 20q, Blue dragonfly. 30q, Cloudless sulphur butterfly. 35q, 40q, Splendid dragonfly. 50q, Machaon swallow-tail. 55q, Sulphur butterfly. 60q, Whitemarbled butterfly.

1966, Apr. 21   Litho.   *Perf. 11¹/₂x12*

922 A204	10q multicolored	.25	.15
923 A204	20q yellow & multi	.40	.15
924 A204	30q yellow & multi	.65	.15
925 A204	35q sky blue & multi	.80	.15
926 A204	40q multicolored	.85	.15
927 A204	50q rose & multi	1.10	.15
928 A204	55q multicolored	1.25	.15
929 A204	60q multicolored	2.00	.15
	Nos. 922-929 (8)	7.30	
	Set value		.70

Perf. 12x12¹/₂, 12¹/₂x12
1966, May 3   Litho.

Designs (WHO Emblem and): 35q, Ambulance and stretcher bearers, vert. 60q, Albanian mother and nurse weighing infant, vert. 80q, X-ray machine and hospital.

930 A205	25q lt blue & blk	.30	.15
931 A205	35q salmon & ultra	.55	.15
932 A205	60q lt grn, bl & red	.90	.15
933 A205	80q yel, bl, grn & lt brn	1.25	.20
	Nos. 930-933 (4)	3.00	
	Set value		.45

Inauguration of the WHO Headquarters, Geneva.

Bird's Foot
Starfish — A206

Designs: 25q, Starfish. 35q, Brittle star. 45q, Butthorn starfish. 50q, Starfish. 60q, Sea cucumber. 70q, Sea urchin.

1966, May 10   *Perf. 12x12½*

934	A206	15q multicolored	.25	.15
935	A206	25q multicolored	.45	.15
936	A206	35q multicolored	.65	.15
937	A206	45q multicolored	.90	.15
938	A206	50q multicolored	1.10	.20
939	A206	60q multicolored	1.25	.20
940	A206	70q multicolored	1.90	.35
		Nos. 934-940 (7)	6.50	
		Set value		1.10

Luna 10 — A207

30q, 80q, Trajectory of Luna 10, earth & moon.

1966, June 10   *Perf. 12x12½*

941	A207	20q blue, yel & blk	.35	.15
942	A207	30q yel grn, blk & bl	.45	.15
943	A207	70q vio, yel & blk	.90	.20
944	A207	80q yel, vio, grn & blk	1.25	.20
		Nos. 941-944 (4)	2.95	.70

Launching of the 1st artificial moon satellite, Luna 10, Apr. 3, 1966.

Jules Rimet
Cup and
Soccer
A208

Designs: Various scenes of soccer play.

1966, July 12   Litho.   *Perf. 12x12½*
Black Inscriptions

945	A208	10q ocher & lilac	.15	.15
946	A208	20q lt blue & cit	.15	.15
947	A208	30q brick red & Prus bl	.25	.15
948	A208	35q lt ultra & rose	.30	.15
949	A208	40q yel grn & lt red brn	.35	.15
950	A208	50q lt red brn & yel grn	.60	.15
951	A208	55q rose lil & yel grn	.65	.15
952	A208	60q dp rose & ocher	1.25	.25
		Nos. 945-952 (8)	3.70	
		Set value		.80

World Cup Soccer Championship, Wembley, England, July 11-30.

Water Level Map of
Albania — A209

30q, Water measure & fields. 70q, Turbine & pylon. 80q, Hydrological decade emblem.

1966, July   *Perf. 12½x12½*

953	A209	20q brick red, blk & org	.30	.15
954	A209	30q emer, blk & lt brn	.50	.15
955	A209	70q brt violet & blk	1.10	.15
956	A209	80q brt bl, org, yel & blk	1.25	.30
		Nos. 953-956 (4)	3.15	.85

Hydrological Decade (UNESCO), 1965-74.

Greek Turtle — A210

Designs: 15q, Grass snake. 25q, European pond turtle. 30q, Wall lizard. 35q, Wall gecko. 45q, Emerald lizard. 50q, Slowworm. 90q, Horned viper (or sand viper).

1966, Aug. 10   Litho.   *Perf. 12½x12*

957	A210	10q gray & multi	.15	.15
958	A210	15q yellow & multi	.20	.15
959	A210	25q ultra & multi	.30	.15
960	A210	30q multicolored	.45	.20
961	A210	35q multicolored	.60	.20
962	A210	45q multicolored	.70	.25
963	A210	50q orange & multi	.80	.30
964	A210	90q lilac & multi	1.75	.55
		Nos. 957-964 (8)	4.95	1.95

Persian Cat
A211

Cats: 10q, Siamese, vert. 15q, European tabby, vert. 25q, Black kitten. 60q, 65q, 80q, Various Persians.

Perf. 12x12½, 12½x12

1966, Sept. 20   Litho.

965	A211	10q multicolored	.15	.15
966	A211	15q blk, sepia & car	.25	.15
967	A211	25q blk, dk & lt brn	.30	.15
968	A211	45q blk, org & yel	.60	.15
969	A211	60q blk, brn & yel	.75	.20
970	A211	65q multicolored	.90	.20
971	A211	80q blk, gray & yel	1.50	.30
		Nos. 965-971 (7)	4.45	
		Set value		1.00

Pjeter Budi,
Writer — A212

1966, Oct. 5   *Perf. 12x12½*

972	A212	25q buff & slate grn	.25	.15
973	A212	1.75 l gray & dull claret	1.75	.45

UNESCO
Emblem
A213

Designs (UNESCO Emblem and): 15q, Open book, rose and school. 25q, Male folk dancers. 1.55 l, Jug, column and old building.

1966, Oct. 20   Litho.   *Perf. 12*

974	A213	5q lt gray & multi	.15	.15
975	A213	15q dp blue & multi	.25	.15
976	A213	25q gray & multi	.50	.15
977	A213	1.55 l multi	2.00	.50
		Nos. 974-977 (4)	2.90	
		Set value		.75

20th anniv. of UNESCO.

Hand Holding Book
with Pictures of Marx,
Engels, Lenin and Stalin
A214

Hammer and
Sickle, Party
Emblem in
Sunburst
A215

Designs: 25q, Map of Albania, hammer and sickle, symbols of agriculture and industry. 65q, Symbolic grain and factories. 95q, Fists holding rifle, spade, axe, sickle and book.

1966, Nov. 1   Litho.   *Perf. 11½x12*

978	A214	15q vermilion & gold	.35	.15
979	A214	25q multicolored	.55	.15
980	A214	65q brn, brn org & gold	1.25	.15
981	A214	95q yellow & multi	1.90	.35
		Nos. 978-981 (4)	4.05	
		Set value		.60

Albanian Communist Party, 5th Cong.

1966, Nov. 8

Designs: 25q, Partisan and sunburst. 65q, Steel worker and blast furnace. 95q, Combine harvester, factories, and pylon.

982	A215	15q orange & multi	.30	.15
983	A215	25q red & multi	.40	.15
984	A215	65q multicolored	1.10	.15
985	A215	95q blue & multi	1.50	.35
		Nos. 982-985 (4)	3.30	
		Set value		.60

25th anniv. of the founding of the Albanian Workers Party.

Russian Wolfhound — A216

Dogs: 15q, Sheep dog. 25q, English setter. 45q, English springer spaniel. 60q, Bulldog. 65q, Saint Bernard. 80q, Dachshund.

1966   Litho.   *Perf. 12½x12*

986	A216	10q green & multi	.20	.15
987	A216	15q multicolored	.30	.15
988	A216	25q lilac & multi	.40	.15
989	A216	45q rose & multi	.75	.35
990	A216	60q brown & multi	1.00	.40
991	A216	65q ultra & multi	1.10	.45
992	A216	80q blue grn & multi	1.50	.50
		Nos. 986-992 (7)	5.25	2.15

Ndre Mjeda
A217

Proclamation
A218

1966   *Perf. 12½x12½*

993	A217	25q brt bl & dk brn	.50	.15
994	A217	1.75 l brt grn & dk brn	2.00	.65

Birth Centenary of the priest Ndre Mjeda.

1966   *Perf. 11½x12, 12x11½*

Designs: 10q, Banner, man and woman holding gun and axe, horiz. 1.85 l, man with axe and banner and partisan with gun.

995	A218	5q lt brn, red & blk	.15	.15
996	A218	10q red, blk, gray & bl	.20	.15
997	A218	1.85 l red, blk & salmon	1.50	.30
		Nos. 995-997 (3)	1.85	
		Set value		.40

25th anniv. of the Albanian Communist Party.

Golden Eagle — A219

Birds of Prey: 15q, European sea eagle. 25q, Griffon vulture. 40q, Common sparrowhawk. 50q, Osprey. 70q, Egyptian vulture. 90q, Kestrel.

1966, Dec. 20   Litho.   *Perf. 11½x12*

998	A219	10q gray & multi	.20	.15
999	A219	15q multicolored	.25	.15
1000	A219	25q citron & multi	.45	.15
1001	A219	40q multicolored	.80	.20
1002	A219	50q multicolored	.95	.25
1003	A219	70q yellow & multi	1.40	.35
1004	A219	90q multicolored	1.90	.45
		Nos. 998-1004 (7)	5.95	1.70

Hake
A220

Fish: 15q, Red mullet. 25q, Opah. 40q, Atlantic wolf fish. 65q, Lumpfish. 80q, Swordfish. 1.15 l, Shorthorn sculpin.

1967, Jan.   Photo.   *Perf. 12x11½*
Fish in Natural Colors

1005	A220	10q blue	.15	.15
1006	A220	15q lt yellow grn	.25	.15
1007	A220	25q Prus blue	.35	.15
1008	A220	40q emerald	.85	.20
1009	A220	65q brt blue grn	.95	.25
1010	A220	80q blue	1.40	.35
1011	A220	1.15 l brt green	1.75	.60
		Nos. 1005-1011 (7)	5.70	1.85

White
Pelican — A221

Designs: Various groups of pelicans.

1967, Feb. 22   Litho.   *Perf. 12*

1012	A221	10q pink & multi	.15	.15
1013	A221	15q pink & multi	.25	.15
1014	A221	25q pink & multi	.55	.15
1015	A221	50q pink & multi	1.00	.25
1016	A221	2 l pink & multi	3.75	.75
		Nos. 1012-1016 (5)	5.70	
		Set value		1.05

Camellia — A222

Flowers: 10q, Chrysanthemum. 15q, Hollyhock. 25q, Flowering Maple. 35q, Peony. 65q, Gladiolus. 80q, Freesia. 1.15 l, Carnation.

Unwmk.
1967, Apr. 12   Litho.   *Perf. 12*
Flowers in Natural Colors

1017	A222	5q pale brown	.15	.15
1018	A222	10q lt lilac	.15	.15
1019	A222	15q gray	.25	.15
1020	A222	25q ultra	.40	.15
1021	A222	35q lt blue	.70	.15
1022	A222	65q lt blue grn	1.00	.15
1023	A222	80q lt bluish gray	1.50	.25
1024	A222	1.15 l dull yellow	2.00	.40
		Nos. 1017-1024 (8)	6.15	
		Set value		1.00

A223

Rose — A224

Design: Congress emblem and power station.

1967, Apr. 24 **Litho.** **Perf. 12**
1025	A223	25q multi	.25	.15
1026	A223	1.75 l multi	2.25	.45

Cong. of the Union of Professional Workers, Tirana, Apr. 24.

1967, May 15 **Perf. 12x12½**
Various Roses in Natural Colors.
1027	A224	5q blue gray	.15	.15
1028	A224	10q brt blue	.15	.15
1029	A224	15q rose violet	.20	.15
1030	A224	25q lemon	.35	.15
1031	A224	35q brt grnsh blue	.45	.15
1032	A224	65q gray	.85	.15
1033	A224	80q brown	1.10	.50
1034	A224	1.65 l gray green	2.50	.45
		Nos. 1027-1034 (8)	5.75	
		Set value		1.10

Seashore, Bregdet Borsh — A225

Views: 15q, Buthrotum, vert. 25q, Shore, Fshati Piqeras. 45q, Shore, Bregdet. 50q, Shore, Bregdet Himare. 65q, Ship, Sarande (Santi Quaranta). 80q, Shore, Dhermi. 1 l, Sunset, Bregdet, vert.

Perf. 12x12½, 12½x12
1967, June 10
1035	A225	15q multicolored	.20	.15
1036	A225	20q multicolored	.25	.15
1037	A225	25q multicolored	.30	.15
1038	A225	45q multicolored	.80	.15
1039	A225	50q multicolored	.90	.15
1040	A225	65q multicolored	1.25	.20
1041	A225	80q multicolored	1.40	.25
1042	A225	1 l multicolored	1.90	.35
		Nos. 1035-1042 (8)	7.00	
		Set value		1.25

Fawn
A226

Roe Deer: 20q, Stag, vert. 25q, Doe, vert. 30q, Young stag and doe. 35q, Doe and fawn. 40q, Young stag, vert. 65q, Stag and doe, vert. 70q, Running stag and does.

Perf. 12½x12, 12x12½
1967, July 20 **Litho.**
1043	A226	15q multicolored	.35	.15
1044	A226	20q multicolored	.35	.15
1045	A226	25q multicolored	.55	.15
1046	A226	30q multicolored	.65	.15
1047	A226	35q multicolored	.80	.15
1048	A226	40q multicolored	1.00	.15
1049	A226	65q multicolored	1.65	.30
1050	A226	70q multicolored	1.65	.35
		Nos. 1043-1050 (8)	7.00	
		Set value		1.15

Man and Woman from Madhe
A227

Regional Costumes: 20q, Woman from Zadrimes. 25q, Dancer and drummer, Kukesit. 45q, Woman spinner, Dardhes. 50q, Farm couple, Myseqese. 65q, Dancer with tambourine, Tirana. 80q, Man and woman, Dropullit. 1 l, Piper, Laberise.

1967, Aug. 25 **Perf. 12**
1051	A227	15q tan & multi	.15	.15
1052	A227	20q lt yellow grn	.20	.15
1053	A227	25q multicolored	.20	.15
1054	A227	45q sky blue & multi	.35	.20
1055	A227	50q lemon & multi	.55	.25
1056	A227	65q pink & multi	.60	.35
1057	A227	80q multicolored	.80	.40
1058	A227	1.10 l multi	1.10	.55
		Nos. 1051-1058 (8)	3.95	2.20

Fighters and Newspaper — A228

Designs: 75q, Printing plant, newspapers and microphone. 2 l, People holding newspaper.

1967, Aug. 25 **Perf. 12½x12**
1059	A228	25q multicolored	.40	.15
1060	A228	75q pink & multi	.85	.15
1061	A228	2 l multicolored	2.25	.35
		Nos. 1059-1061 (3)	3.50	
		Set value		.50

Issued for the Day of the Press.

Street Scene, by Kolé Idromeno A229

Hakmarrja Battalion, by Sali Shijaku — A230

Designs: 20q, David, fresco by Onufri, 16th century, vert. 45q, Woman's head, ancient mosaic, vert. 50q, Men on horseback from 16th century icon, vert. 65q, Farm Women, by Zef Shoshi. 80q, Street Scene, by Vangjush Mio. 1 l, Bride, by Kolé Idromeno, vert.

Perf. 12, 12x12½, (A230)
1967, Oct. 25 **Litho.**
1062	A229	15q multicolored	.40	.15
1063	A229	20q multicolored	.45	.15
1064	A230	25q multicolored	.55	.15
1065	A229	45q multicolored	1.10	.15
1066	A229	50q multicolored	1.40	.15
1067	A230	65q multicolored	1.90	.25
1068	A230	80q multicolored	1.90	.25
1069	A230	1 l multicolored	2.50	.30
		Nos. 1062-1069 (8)	9.95	
		Set value		1.00

Lenin at Storming of Winter Palace — A231

Rabbit — A232

Designs: 15q, Lenin and Stalin, horiz. 50q, Lenin and Stalin addressing meeting. 1.10 l, Storming of the Winter Palace, horiz.

1967, Nov. 7 **Perf. 12**
1070	A231	15q red & multi	.25	.15
1071	A231	25q slate grn & blk	.55	.15
1072	A231	50q brn, blk & brn vio	.85	.15
1073	A231	1.10 l lilac, gray & blk	2.75	.25
		Nos. 1070-1073 (4)	4.40	
		Set value		.45

50th anniv. of the Russian October Revolution.

1967, Nov. 25
Designs: Various hares and rabbits. The 15q, 25q, 35q, 40q and 1 l are horizontal.
1074	A232	15q orange & multi	.20	.15
1075	A232	20q brt yel & multi	.20	.15
1076	A232	25q lt brn & multi	.25	.15
1077	A232	35q multicolored	.35	.15
1078	A232	40q yellow & multi	.65	.15
1079	A232	50q pink & multi	.75	.15
1080	A232	65q multicolored	1.25	.30
1081	A232	1 l lilac & multi	2.00	.45
		Nos. 1074-1081 (8)	5.65	
		Set value		1.20

University, Torch and Book — A233

1967 **Litho.** **Perf. 12**
1082	A233	25q multi	.25	.15
1083	A233	1.75 l multi	1.40	.30
		Set value		

10th anniv. of the founding of the State University, Tirana.

Coat of Arms and Soldiers A234

Designs: 65q, Arms, Factory, grain, flag, gun and radio tower. 1.20 l, Arms and hand holding torch.

1967 **Perf. 12x11½**
1084	A234	15q multi	.20	.15
1085	A234	65q multi	.55	.15
1086	A234	1.20 l multi	1.00	.15
		Nos. 1084-1086 (3)	1.75	
		Set value		.35

25th anniversary of the Democratic Front.

Turkey — A235

Designs: 20q, Duck. 25q, Hen. 45q, Rooster. 50q, Guinea fowl. 65q, Goose, horiz. 80q, Mallard, horiz. 1 l, Chicks, horiz.

Perf. 12x12½, 12½x12
1967, Nov. 25 **Photo.**
1087	A235	15q gold & multi	.25	.15
1088	A235	20q gold & multi	.25	.15
1089	A235	25q gold & multi	.30	.15
1090	A235	45q gold & multi	.50	.15
1091	A235	50q gold & multi	.75	.15
1092	A235	65q gold & multi	.95	.20
1093	A235	80q gold & multi	1.75	.30
1094	A235	1 l gold & multi	2.25	.40
		Nos. 1087-1094 (8)	7.00	
		Set value		1.25

Skanderbeg A236

Designs: 10q, Arms of Skanderbeg. 25q, Helmet and sword. 30q, Kruje Castle. 35q, Petreles Castle. 65q, Berati Castle. 80q, Skanderbeg addressing national chiefs. 90q, Battle of Albulenes.

1967, Dec. 10 **Litho.** **Perf. 12x12½**
Medallion in Bister and Dark Brown
1095	A236	10q gold & violet	.15	.15
1096	A236	15q gold & rose car	.15	.15
1097	A236	25q gold & vio bl	.20	.15
1098	A236	30q gold & dk blue	.25	.15
1099	A236	35q gold & maroon	.35	.15
1100	A236	65q gold & green	.60	.15
1101	A236	80q gold & gray brn	.95	.15
1102	A236	90q gold & ultra	1.75	.20
		Nos. 1095-1102 (8)	4.40	
		Set value		.70

500th anniv. of the death of Skanderbeg (George Castriota), national hero.

Ice Hockey — A237

Designs: 15q, 2 l, Winter Olympics emblem. 30q, Women's figure skating. 50q, Slalom. 80q, Downhill skiing. 1 l, Ski jump.

1967-68
1103	A237	15q multicolored	.15	.15
1104	A237	25q multicolored	.15	.15
1105	A237	30q multicolored	.15	.15
1106	A237	50q multicolored	.30	.15
1107	A237	80q multicolored	.60	.20
1108	A237	1 l multicolored	.85	.25
		Nos. 1103-1108 (6)	2.20	
		Set value		.65

Miniature Sheet
Imperf
1109	A237	2 l red, gray & brt bl ('68)	6.00	6.00

10th Winter Olympic Games, Grenoble, France, Feb. 6-18.
Nos. 1103-1108 issued Dec. 29, 1967.

Skanderbeg Monument, Kruje — A238

Designs: 10q, Skanderbeg monument, Tirana. 15q, Skanderbeg portrait, Uffizi Galleries, Florence. 25q, engraved portrait of Gen. Tanush Topia. 35q, Portrait of Gen. Gjergj Arianti, horiz. 65q, Portrait bust of Skanderbeg by O. Paskali. 80q, Title page of "The Life of Skanderbeg." 90q, Skanderbeg battling the Turks, painting by S. Rrota, horiz.

Perf. 12x12½, 12½x12
1968, Jan. 17 **Litho.**
1110	A238	10q multicolored	.15	.15
1111	A238	15q multicolored	.25	.15
1112	A238	25q blk, yel & lt bl	.35	.15
1113	A238	30q multicolored	.40	.15
1114	A238	35q lt vio, pink & blk	.65	.15
1115	A238	65q multicolored	1.00	.15
1116	A238	80q pink, blk & yel	1.25	.20
1117	A238	90q beige & multi	1.75	.25
		Nos. 1110-1117 (8)	5.80	
		Set value		.85

500th anniv. of the death of Skanderbeg (George Castriota), national hero.

Carnation A239

1968, Feb. 15   *Perf. 12*
Various Carnations in Natural Colors
1118	A239	15q green	.15	.15
1119	A239	20q dk brown	.15	.15
1120	A239	25q brt blue	.15	.15
1121	A239	50q gray olice	.30	.15
1122	A239	80q bluish gray	.75	.15
1123	A239	1.10 l violet gray	1.00	.25
		Nos. 1118-1123 (6)	2.50	
		Set value		.60

R.P. SHQIPERISE

"Electrification"
A240

65q, Farm tractor, horiz. 1.10 l, Cow & herd.

1968, Mar. 5   Litho.   *Perf. 12*
1124	A240	65q multi	.25	.15
1125	A240	65q multi	.70	.15
1126	A240	1.10 l multi	1.00	.20
		Nos. 1124-1126 (3)	1.95	
		Set value		.35

Fifth Farm Cooperatives Congress.

Goat
A241

Various goats. 15q, 20q, 25q are vertical.

Perf. 12x12½, 12½x12
1968, Mar. 25
1127	A241	15q multi	.15	.15
1128	A241	20q multi	.15	.15
1129	A241	25q multi	.20	.15
1130	A241	30q multi	.30	.15
1131	A241	40q multi	.40	.15
1132	A241	50q multi	.45	.15
1133	A241	80q multi	.80	.20
1134	A241	1.40 l multi	2.00	.35
		Nos. 1127-1134 (8)	4.45	
		Set value		.90

Zef N.   Physician and
Jubani — A242   Hospital — A243

1968, Mar. 30   *Perf. 12*
1135	A242	25q yellow & choc	.25	.15
1136	A242	1.75 l violet & blk	1.10	.30
		Set value		.40

Sesquicentennial of the birth of Zef N. Jubani, writer and scholar.

Perf. 12½x12, 12x12½
1968, Apr. 7   Litho.
Designs (World Health Organization Emblem and): 65q, Hospital and microscope, horiz. 1.10 l, Mother feeding child.
1137	A243	25q green & claret	.15	.15
1138	A243	65q black, yel & bl	.55	.15
1139	A243	1.10 l black & dp org	.80	.20
		Nos. 1137-1139 (3)	1.50	
		Set value		.35

20th anniv. of WHO.

Scientist
A244

Women: 15q, Militia member. 60q, Farm worker. 1 l, Factory worker.

1968, Apr. 14   *Perf. 12*
1140	A244	15q ver & dk red	.35	.15
1141	A244	25q blue grn & grn	.50	.15
1142	A244	60q dull yel & brn	.80	.15
1143	A244	1 l lt vio & vio	2.00	.30
		Nos. 1140-1143 (4)	3.65	
		Set value		.55

Albanian Women's Organization, 25th anniv.

Karl
Marx — A245

Designs: 25q, Marx lecturing to students. 65q, "Das Kapital," "Communist Manifesto" and marching crowd. 95q, Full-face portrait.

1968, May 5   Litho.   *Perf. 12*
1144	A245	15q gray, dk bl & bis	.25	.15
1145	A245	25q brn vio, dk brn & dl yel	.50	.15
1146	A245	65q gray, blk, brn & car	1.25	.20
1147	A245	95q gray, ocher & blk	2.00	.35
		Nos. 1144-1147 (4)	4.00	
		Set value		.65

Karl Marx, 150th birth anniversary.

Heliopsis — A246

Flowers: 20q, Red flax. 25q, Orchid. 30q, Gloxinia. 40q, Turk's-cap lily. 80q, Amaryllis. 1.40 l, Red magnolia.

1968, May 10   *Perf. 12x12½*
1148	A246	15q gold & multi	.15	.15
1149	A246	20q gold & multi	.15	.15
1150	A246	25q gold & multi	.15	.15
1151	A246	30q gold & multi	.15	.15
1152	A246	40q gold & multi	.45	.15
1153	A246	80q gold & multi	.55	.15
1154	A246	1.40 l gold & multi	.85	.30
		Nos. 1148-1154 (7)	2.45	
		Set value		.70

Proclamation
of Prizren
A247

25q, Abdyl Frasheri. 40q, House in Prizren.

1968, June 10   Litho.   *Perf. 12*
1155	A247	25q emerald & blk	.20	.15
1156	A247	40q multicolored	.45	.15
1157	A247	85q yellow & multi	.85	.25
		Nos. 1155-1157 (3)	1.50	
		Set value		.40

League of Prizren against the Turks, 90th anniv.

Shepherd, by A.
Kushi — A248

Paintings from Tirana Art Gallery: 20q, View of Tirana, by V. Mio, horiz. 25q, Mountaineer, by G. Madhi. 40q, Refugees, by A. Buza. 80q, Guerrillas of Shahin Matrakut, by S. Xega. 1.50 l, Portrait of an Old Man, by S. Papadhimitri. 1.70 l, View of

Scutari, by S. Rrota. 2.50 l, Woman in Scutari Costume, by Z. Colombi.

1968, June 20   *Perf. 12x12½*
1158	A248	15q gold & multi	.15	.15
1159	A248	20q gold & multi	.20	.15
1160	A248	25q gold & multi	.25	.15
1161	A248	40q gold & multi	.45	.15
1162	A248	80q gold & multi	.75	.15
1163	A248	1.50 l gold & multi	1.25	.25
1164	A248	1.70 l gold & multi	1.50	.50
		Nos. 1158-1164 (7)	4.55	
		Set value		1.10

Miniature Sheet
Perf. 12½xImperf.
1165	A248	2.50 l multi	2.00	.90

No. 1165 contains one stamp, size: 50x71mm.

Soldier and Guns — A249

Designs: 25q, Sailor and warships. 65q, Aviator and planes, vert. 95q, Militiamen and woman.

1968, July 10   Litho.   *Perf. 12*
1166	A249	15q multicolored	.30	.15
1167	A249	25q multicolored	.45	.15
1168	A249	65q multicolored	1.25	.15
1169	A249	95q multicolored	2.50	.20
		Nos. 1166-1169 (4)	4.50	
		Set value		.45

25th anniversary of the People's Army.

Squid — A250

Designs: 20q, Crayfish. 25q, Whelk. 50q, Crab. 70q, Spiny lobster. 80q, Shore crab. 90q, Norway lobster.

1968, Aug. 20
1170	A250	15q multicolored	.15	.15
1171	A250	20q multicolored	.20	.15
1172	A250	25q multicolored	.25	.15
1173	A250	50q multicolored	.45	.15
1174	A250	70q multicolored	.70	.25
1175	A250	80q multicolored	.90	.30
1176	A250	90q multicolored	1.25	.35
		Nos. 1170-1176 (7)	3.90	
		Set value		1.10

Women's Relay Race — A251

Sport: 20q, Running. 25q, Women's discus. 30q, Equestrian. 40q, High jump. 50q, Women's hurdling. 80q, Soccer. 1.40 l, Woman diver. 2 l, Olympic stadium.

1968, Sept. 23   Photo.   *Perf. 12*
1177	A251	15q multicolored	.15	.15
1178	A251	20q multicolored	.15	.15
1179	A251	25q multicolored	.15	.15
1180	A251	30q multicolored	.20	.15
1181	A251	40q multicolored	.25	.15
1182	A251	50q multicolored	.35	.15
1183	A251	80q multicolored	.55	.15
1184	A251	1.40 l multicolored	.95	.35
		Nos. 1177-1184 (8)	2.75	
		Set value		.85

Souvenir Sheet
Perf. 12½ Horizontally
1185	A251	2 l multicolored	2.25	.75

19th Olympic Games, Mexico City, Oct. 12-27. No. 1185 contains one rectangular stamp, size: 64x54mm. Value of imperfs., #1177-1184 $7, #1185 $5.

Enver Hoxha — A252

1968, Oct. 16   Litho.   *Perf. 12*
1186	A252	25q blue gray	.35	.15
1187	A252	35q rose brown	.50	.20
1188	A252	80q violet	.90	.35
1189	A252	1.10 l brown	1.10	.50
		Nos. 1186-1189 (4)	2.85	1.20

Souvenir Sheet
Imperf
1190	A252	1.50 l rose red, bl vio & gold	55.00	40.00

60th birthday of Enver Hoxha, First Secretary of the Central Committee of the Communist Party of Albania.

Book and
Pupils — A253

1968, Nov. 14   Photo.
1191	A253	15q maroon & slate grn	.45	.15
1192	A253	85q gray olive & sepia	2.75	.20
		Set value		.25

60th anniv. of the Congress of Monastir, Nov. 14-22, 1908, which adopted a unified Albanian alphabet.

Waxwing — A254

Birds: 20q, Rose-colored starling. 25q, Kingfishers. 50q, Long-tailed tits. 80q, Wallcreeper. 1.10 l, Bearded tit.

1968, Nov. 15   Litho.
Birds in Natural Colors
1193	A254	15q lt blue & blk	.15	.15
1194	A254	20q bister & blk	.15	.15
1195	A254	25q pink & blk	.30	.15
1196	A254	50q lt yel grn & blk	.35	.15
1197	A254	80q bis brn & blk	.80	.20
1198	A254	1.10 l pale green & blk	1.00	.25
		Nos. 1193-1198 (6)	2.75	
		Set value		.75

Mao Tse-tung — A255

1968, Dec. 26   Litho.   *Perf. 12½x12*
1199	A255	25q gold, red & blk	.40	.15
1200	A255	1.75 l gold, red & blk	2.00	.30

75th birthday of Mao Tse-tung, Chairman of the Communist Party of the People's Republic of China.

Adem Reka and Crane — A256

Portraits: 10q, Pjeter Lleshi and power lines. 15q, Mohammed Shehu and Myrteza Kepi. 25q, Shkurte Vata and women railroad workers. 65q, Agron Elezi, frontier guard. 80q, Ismet Bruçaj and mountain road. 1.30 l, Fuat Cela, blind revolutionary.

1969, Feb. 10   Litho.   Perf. 12x12½

1201	A256	5q multicolored	.15	.15
1202	A256	10q multicolored	.15	.15
1203	A256	15q multicolored	.15	.15
1204	A256	25q multicolored	.15	.15
1205	A256	65q multicolored	.40	.15
1206	A256	80q multicolored	.75	.15
1207	A256	1.30 l multicolored	1.25	.20
		Nos. 1201-1207 (7)	3.00	
		Set value		.55

Issued to honor a contemporary heroine and heroes.

Meteorological Instruments A257

Designs: 25q, Water gauge. 1.60 l, Radar, balloon and isobars.

1969, Feb. 25   Perf. 12

1208	A257	15q multicolored	.25	.15
1209	A257	25q ultra, org & blk	.45	.15
1210	A257	1.60 l rose vio, yel & blk	2.50	.25
		Nos. 1208-1210 (3)	3.20	
		Set value		.35

20th anniv. of Albanian hydrometeorology.

Partisans, 1944, by F. Haxmiu — A258

Paintings: 5q, Student Revolutionists, by P. Mele, vert. 65q, Steel Mill, by C. Ceka. 80q, Reconstruction, by V. Kilica. 1.10 l, Harvest, by N. Jonuzi. 1.15 l, Terraced Landscape, by S. Kaceli. 2 l, Partisans' Meeting.

Perf. 12x12½, 12½x12

1969, Apr. 25   Litho.

Size: 31½x41½mm

1211	A258	5q buff & multi	.15	.15

Size: 51½x30½mm

1212	A258	25q buff & multi	.15	.15

Size: 40½x32mm

1213	A258	65q buff & multi	.35	.15

Size: 51½x30½mm

1214	A258	80q buff & multi	.65	.15
1215	A258	1.10 l buff & multi	.70	.15
1216	A258	1.15 l buff & multi	.95	.20
		Nos. 1211-1216 (6)	2.95	
		Set value		.65

Miniature Sheet
Imperf

Size: 111x90mm

1217	A258	2 l ocher & multi	1.75	1.75

Leonardo da Vinci, Self-portrait A259

Designs (after Leonardo da Vinci): 35q, Lilies. 40q, Design for a flying machine, horiz. 1 l, Portrait of Beatrice. No. 1222, Portrait of a Noblewoman. No. 1223, Mona Lisa.

Perf. 12x12½, 12½x12

1969, May 2   Litho.

1218	A259	25q gold & sepia	.20	.15
1219	A259	35q gold & sepia	.40	.15
1220	A259	40q gold & sepia	.45	.15
1221	A259	1 l gold & multi	1.25	.20
1222	A259	2 l gold & sepia	2.25	.55
		Nos. 1218-1222 (5)	4.55	
		Set value		1.00

Miniature Sheet
Imperf

1223	A259	2 l gold & multi	3.25	2.25

Leonardo da Vinci (1452-1519), painter, sculptor, architect and engineer.

First Congress Meeting Place — A260

Designs: 1 l, Albanian coat of arms. 2.25 l, Two partisans with guns and flag.

1969, May 24   Perf. 12

1224	A260	25q lt grn, blk & red	.35	.15
1225	A260	2.25 l multi	2.50	.85

Souvenir Sheet

1226	A260	1 l gold, bl, blk & red	30.00	12.50

25th anniversary of the First Anti-Fascist Congress of Permet, May 24, 1944.

Albanian Violet — A261

Designs: Violets and Pansies.

1969, June 30   Litho.   Perf. 12x12½

1227	A261	5q gold & multi	.15	.15
1228	A261	10q gold & multi	.15	.15
1229	A261	15q gold & multi	.15	.15
1230	A261	20q gold & multi	.20	.15
1231	A261	25q gold & multi	.35	.15
1232	A261	80q gold & multi	.50	.30
1233	A261	1.95 l gold & multi	1.40	.65
		Nos. 1227-1233 (7)	2.90	
		Set value		1.25

Plum, Fruit and Blossoms — A262

Designs: Blossoms and Fruits.

1969, Aug. 10   Litho.   Perf. 12

1234	A262	10q shown	.15	.15
1235	A262	15q Lemon	.20	.15
1236	A262	25q Pomegranate	.30	.15
1237	A262	50q Cherry	.60	.15
1238	A262	80q Peach	.95	.20
1239	A262	1.20 l Apple	1.75	.35
		Nos. 1234-1239 (6)	3.95	
		Set value		.75

Basketball — A263

Designs: 10q, 80q, 2.20 l, Various views of basketball game. 25q, Hand aiming ball at basket and map of Europe, horiz.

1969, Sept. 15   Litho.   Perf. 12

1240	A263	10q multi	.15	.15
1241	A263	15q buff & multi	.15	.15
1242	A263	25q blue & multi	.25	.15
1243	A263	80q multi	.65	.15
1244	A263	2.20 l multi	1.65	.50
		Nos. 1240-1244 (5)	2.85	
		Set value		.80

16th European Basketball Championships, Naples, Italy, Sept. 27-Oct. 5.

Runner — A264

Designs: 5q, Games' emblem. 10q, Woman gymnast. 20q, Pistol shooting. 25q, Swimmer at start. 80q, Bicyclist. 95q, Soccer.

1969, Sept. 30

1245	A264	5q multicolored	.15	.15
1246	A264	10q multicolored	.15	.15
1247	A264	15q multicolored	.15	.15
1248	A264	20q multicolored	.30	.15
1249	A264	25q multicolored	.40	.15
1250	A264	80q multicolored	.80	.15
1251	A264	95q multicolored	1.25	.20
		Set value	1.40	.50

Second National Spartakiad.

Electronic Technicians, Steel Ladle — A265

Designs: 25q, Mao Tse-tung with microphones, vert. 1.40 l, Children holding Mao's red book, vert.

1969, Oct. 1   Litho.   Perf. 12

1252	A265	25q multi	.40	.15
1253	A265	85q multi	1.00	.15
1254	A265	1.40 l multi	1.65	.30
		Nos. 1252-1254 (3)	3.05	.60

People's Republic of China, 20th anniv.

Enver Hoxha — A266

Designs: 80q, Pages from Berat resolution. 1.45 l, Partisans with flag.

1969, Oct. 20   Litho.   Perf. 12

1255	A266	25q multicolored	.20	.15
1256	A266	80q gray & multi	.50	.15
1257	A266	1.45 l ocher & multi	.80	.30
		Nos. 1255-1257 (3)	1.50	.60

25th anniv. of the 2nd reunion of the Natl. Antifascist Liberation Council, Berat.

Soldiers — A267

Designs: 30q, Oil refinery. 35q, Combine harvester. 45q, Hydroelectric station and dam. 55q, Militia woman, man and soldier. 1.10 l, Dancers and musicians.

1969, Nov. 29

1258	A267	25q multi	.25	.15
1259	A267	30q multi	.25	.15
1260	A267	35q multi	.25	.15
1261	A267	45q multi	.30	.15
1262	A267	55q multi	.80	.15
1263	A267	1.10 l multi	1.65	.15
		Nos. 1258-1263 (6)	3.50	
		Set value		.40

25th anniv. of the socialist republic.

Joseph V. Stalin, (1879-1953), Russian Political Leader — A268

1969, Dec. 21   Litho.   Perf. 12

1264	A268	15q lilac	.15	.15
1265	A268	25q slate blue	.20	.15
1266	A268	1 l brown	.75	.15
1267	A268	1.10 l violet red	1.25	.20
		Nos. 1264-1267 (4)	2.35	
		Set value		.45

Head of Woman — A269

Greco-Roman Mosaics: 25q, Geometrical floor design, horiz. 80q, Bird and tree, horiz. 1.10 l, Floor with birds and grapes, horiz. 1.20 l, Fragment with corn within oval design.

1969, Dec. 25   Perf. 12½x12

1268	A269	15q gold & multi	.15	.15
1269	A269	25q gold & multi	.15	.15
1270	A269	80q gold & multi	.45	.15
1271	A269	1.10 l gold & multi	.70	.15
1272	A269	1.20 l gold & multi	.95	.30
		Nos. 1268-1272 (5)	2.40	
		Set value		.60

Cancellation of
1920 — A270

Design: 25q, Proclamation and congress site.

1970, Jan. 21   Litho.   Perf. 12
1273 A270   25q red, gray & blk   .20   .15
1274 A270   1.25 l dk grn, yel & blk   1.25 1.25
            Set value   .20

Congress of Louchnia, 50th anniversary.

Worker,
Student
and Flag
A271

1970, Feb. 11   Perf. 12¹/₂x12
1275 A271   25q red & multi   .20   .15
1276 A271   1.75 l red & multi   1.25   .25
            Set value   .30

Vocational organizations in Albania, 25th anniv.

Turk's-cap
Lily — A272

Lilies: 5q, Cernum, vert. 15q, Madonna, vert.
25q, Royal, vert. 1.10 l, Tiger. 1.15 l, Albanian.

Perf. 11¹/₂x12, 12x11¹/₂
1970, Mar. 10   Litho.
1277 A272   5q multi   .15   .15
1278 A272   15q multi   .15   .15
1279 A272   25q multi   .30   .15
1280 A272   80q multi   .75   .15
1281 A272   1.10 l multi   1.10 .15
1282 A272   1.15 l multi   1.40 .25
    Nos. 1277-1282 (6)   3.85
            Set value   .65

Lenin
A273

Designs (Lenin): 5q, Portrait, vert. 25q, As volunteer construction worker. 95q, Addressing crowd.
1.10 l, Saluting, vert.

1970, Apr. 22   Litho.   Perf. 12
1283 A273   5q multi   .15   .15
1284 A273   15q multi   .15   .15
1285 A273   25q multi   .20   .15
1286 A273   95q multi   .60   .15
1287 A273   1.10 l multi   1.10 .15
    Nos. 1283-1287 (5)   2.20
            Set value   .40

Centenary of birth of Lenin (1870-1924).

Frontier
Guard
A274

1970, Apr. 25
1288 A274   25q multi   .45   .15
1289 A274   1.25 l multi   2.50 .20
            Set value   .25

25th anniversary of Frontier Guards.

Soccer Players — A275

Designs: 5q, Jules Rimet Cup and globes. 10q,
Aztec Stadium, Mexico City. 25q, Defending goal.
65q, 80q, No. 1296, Two soccer players in various
plays. No. 1297, Mexican horseman and volcano
Popocatepetl.

1970, May 15   Litho.   Perf. 12¹/₂x12
1290 A275   5q multicolored   .15   .15
1291 A275   10q multicolored   .15   .15
1292 A275   15q multicolored   .15   .15
1293 A275   25q lt green & multi   .15   .15
1294 A275   65q pink & multi   .30   .15
1295 A275   80q lt blue & multi   .55   .15
1296 A275   2 l yellow & multi   1.50 .25
    Nos. 1290-1296 (7)   2.95
            Set value   .65

Souvenir Sheet
Perf 12 x Imperf
1297 A275   2 l multicolored   2.25 .80

World Soccer Championships for the Jules Rimet
Cup, Mexico City, May 31-June 21, 1970. No.
1297 contains one large horizontal stamp. Nos.
1290-1297 exist imperf.

UPU Headquarters and Monument,
Bern — A276

1970, May 30   Litho.   Perf. 12¹/₂x12
1298 A276   25q ultra, gray & blk   .15   .15
1299 A276   1.10 l orange, buff & blk   .65   .20
1300 A276   1.15 l green, gray & blk   .90   .25
    Nos. 1298-1300 (3)   1.70 .60

Inauguration of the new UPU Headquarters in
Bern.

Bird and
Grapes
Mosaic
A277

Mosaics, 5th-6th centuries, excavated near
Pogradec: 10q, Waterfowl and grapes. 20q, Bird
and tree stump. 25q, Bird and leaves. 65q, Fish.
2.25 l, Peacock, vert.

Perf. 12¹/₂x12, 12x12¹/₂
1970, July 10
1301 A277   5q multi   .15   .15
1302 A277   10q multi   .15   .15
1303 A277   20q multi   .20   .15
1304 A277   25q multi   .30   .15
1305 A277   65q multi   .55   .15
1306 A277   2.25 l multi   1.75 .35
    Nos. 1301-1306 (6)   3.10
            Set value   .65

Fruit Harvest
and Dancers
A278

Designs: 25q, Contour-plowed fields and conference table. 80q, Cattle and newspapers. 1.30 l,
Wheat harvest.

1970, Aug. 28   Litho.   Perf. 12x11¹/₂
1307 A278   15q brt violet & blk   .15   .15
1308 A278   25q dp blue & blk   .20   .15
1309 A278   80q dp brown & blk   .60   .15
1310 A278   1.30 l org brn & blk   .90   .15
    Nos. 1307-1310 (4)   1.85
            Set value   .35

25th anniv. of the agrarian reform law.

Attacking
Partisans — A279

Designs: 25q, Partisans with horses and flag.
1.60 l, Partisans.

1970, Sept. 3   Perf. 12
1311 A279   15q org brn & blk   .15   .15
1312 A279   25q brn, yel & blk   .15   .15
1313 A279   1.60 l dp grm & blk   1.25 .30
    Nos. 1311-1313 (3)   1.55
            Set value   .40

50th anniversary of liberation of Vlona.

Miners, by Nexhmedin Zajmi — A280

Paintings from the National Gallery, Tirana: 5q,
Bringing in the Harvest, by Isuf Sulovari, vert. 15q,
The Activists, by Dhimitraq Trebicka, vert. 65q,
Instruction of Partisans, by Hasan Nallbani. 95q,
Architectural Planning, by Vilson Kilica. No. 1319,
Woman Machinist, by Zef Shoshi, vert. No. 1320,
Partisan Destroying Tank, by Sali Shijaku, vert.

Perf. 12¹/₂x12, 12x12¹/₂
1970, Sept. 25   Litho.
1314 A280   5q multicolored   .15   .15
1315 A280   15q multicolored   .15   .15
1316 A280   25q multicolored   .20   .15
1317 A280   65q multicolored   .25   .15
1318 A280   95q multicolored   .45   .15
1319 A280   2 l multicolored   1.75 .30
    Nos. 1314-1319 (6)   2.95
            Set value   .60

Miniature Sheet
Imperf
1320 A280   2 l multicolored   1.50 .95

Electrification Map of
Albania — A281

Designs: 25q, Light bulb, hammer and sickle
emblem, map of Albania and power graph. 80q,
Linemen at work. 1.10 l, Use of electricity on the
farm, in home and business.

1970, Oct. 25   Litho.   Perf. 12
1321 A281   15q multi   .15   .15
1322 A281   25q multi   .15   .15
1323 A281   80q multi   .70   .15
1324 A281   1.10 l multi   1.00 .15
    Nos. 1321-1324 (4)   2.00
            Set value   .35

Albanian village electrification completion.

Friedrich
Engels — A282

Designs: 1.10 l, Engels as young man. 1.15 l,
Engels addressing crowd.

1970, Nov. 28   Litho.   Perf. 12x12¹/₂
1325 A282   25q bister & dk bl   .20   .15
1326 A282   1.10 l bister & dp claret   .60   .20
1327 A282   1.15 l bister & dk ol grn   .70   .25
    Nos. 1325-1327 (3)   1.50
            Set value   .50

150th anniv. of the birth of Friedrich Engels
(1820-95), German socialist, collaborator with Karl
Marx.

Ludwig van
Beethoven — A283

Designs: 5q, Birthplace, Bonn. 25q, 65q, 1.10 l,
various portraits. 1.80 l, Scene from Fidelio, horiz.

1970, Dec. 16   Litho.   Perf. 12
1328 A283   5q dp plum & gold   .15   .15
1329 A283   25q brt rose lil & sil   .15   .15
1330 A283   25q green & gold   .15   .15
1331 A283   65q magenta & sil   .30   .15
1332 A283   1.10 l dk blue & gold   .60   .25
1333 A283   1.80 l black & sil   1.40 .45
    Nos. 1328-1333 (6)   2.75
            Set value   .90

Bicentenary of the birth of Ludwig van Beethoven (1770-1827), composer.

Coat of
Arms
A284

Designs: 25q, Proclamation. 80q, Enver Hoxha
reading proclamation. 1.30 l, Young people and
proclamation.

1971, Jan. 11   Litho.   Perf. 12
1334 A284   15q lt bl, gold, blk & red   .15   .15
1335 A284   25q rose lil, blk, gold &
                    gray   .20   .15
1336 A284   80q emerald, blk & gold   .55   .15
1337 A284   1.30 l yel org, blk & gold   .85   .25
    Nos. 1334-1337 (4)   1.75
            Set value   .45

Declaration of the Republic, 25th anniv.

"Liberty"
A285

Black Men
A286

Designs: 50q, Women's brigade. 65q, Street battle, horiz. 1.10 l, Execution, horiz.

Perf. 12x11¹/₂, 11¹/₂x12
1971, Mar. 18   Litho.
1338 A285   25q dk bl & bl   .15   .15
1339 A285   50q slate green   .35   .15
1340 A285   65q dk brn & chestnut   .50   .15
1341 A285   1.10 l purple   .75   .15
    Nos. 1338-1341 (4)   1.75
            Set value   .40

Centenary of the Paris Commune.

1971, Mar. 21   Perf. 12x12¹/₂
1.10 l, Men of 3 races. 1.15 l, Black protest.

1342 A286   25q blk & bis brn   .15   .15
1343 A286   1.10 l blk & rose car   .60   .15
1344 A286   1.15 l blk & ver   .70   .15
    Nos. 1342-1344 (3)   1.45
            Set value   .35

Intl. year against racial discrimination.

Tulip — A287

Horseman, by
Dürer — A288

Designs: Various tulips.

1971, Mar. 25
1345	A287	5q multi	.15	.15
1346	A287	10q yellow & multi	.15	.15
1347	A287	15q pink & multi	.15	.15
1348	A287	20q lt blue & multi	.15	.15
1349	A287	25q multi	.25	.15
1350	A287	80q multi	.50	.15
1351	A287	1 l multi	.75	.20
1352	A287	1.45 l citron & multi	1.10	.25
		Nos. 1345-1352 (8)	3.20	
		Set value		.75

Perf. 11½x12, 12x11½
1971, May 15   **Litho.**

Art Works by Dürer: 15q, Three peasants. 25q, Dancing peasant couple. 45q, The bagpiper. 65q, View of Kalkrebut, horiz. 2.40 l, View of Trent, horiz. 2.50 l, Self-portrait.

1353	A288	10q black & pale grn	.15	.15
1354	A288	15q black & pale lil	.15	.15
1355	A288	25q black & pale bl	.25	.15
1356	A288	45q black & pale rose	.40	.15
1357	A288	65q black & multi	.60	.15
1358	A288	2.40 l black & multi	2.25	.35
		Nos. 1353-1358 (6)	3.80	
		Set value		.65

Miniature Sheet
Imperf

1359	A288	2.50 l multi	3.00	.80

Albrecht Dürer (1471-1528), German painter and engraver.

Satellite Orbiting
Globe — A289

Designs: 1.20 l, Government Building, Tirana, and Red Star emblem. 2.20 l, like 60q, 2.50 l, Flag of People's Republic of China forming trajectory around globe.

1971, June 10   Litho.   *Perf. 12x12½*
1360	A289	60q purple & multi	.40	.15
1361	A289	1.20 l ver & multi	1.00	.25
1362	A289	2.20 l green & multi	1.60	.45

Imperf
1363	A289	2.50 l vio blk & multi	2.50	.90
		Nos. 1360-1363 (4)	5.50	1.75

Space developments of People's Republic of China.

Mao Tse-
tung — A290

Designs: 1.05 l, House where Communist Party was founded, horiz. 1.20 l, Peking crowd with placards, horiz.

1971, July 1   *Perf. 12x12½, 12½x12*
1364	A290	25q silver & multi	.30	.15
1365	A290	1.05 l silver & multi	.95	.15
1366	A290	1.20 l silver & multi	1.25	.25
		Nos. 1364-1366 (3)	2.50	
		Set value		.45

50th anniv. of Chinese Communist Party.

5q

Crested Titmouse — A291

1971, Aug. 15   Litho.   Perf. 12½x12
1367	A291	5q shown	.15	.15
1368	A291	10q European serin	.15	.15
1369	A291	15q Linnet	.15	.15
1370	A291	25q Firecrest	.15	.15
1371	A291	45q Rock thrush	.40	.15
1372	A291	60q Blue tit	.60	.25
1373	A291	2.40 l Chaffinch	2.00	.60
a.		Block of 7, #1367-1373 + label	3.00	3.00
		Set value		1.15

Continuous design with bird's nest label at upper left.

Olympic Rings and Running — A292

Designs (Olympic Rings and): 10q, Hurdles. 15q, Canoeing. 25q, Gymnastics. 80q, Fencing. 1.05 l, Soccer. 2 l, Runner at finish line. 3.60 l, Diving, women's.

1971, Sept. 15
1374	A292	5q green & multi	.15	.15
1375	A292	10q multicolored	.15	.15
1376	A292	15q blue & multi	.15	.15
1377	A292	25q violet & multi	.15	.15
1378	A292	80q lilac & multi	.35	.15
1379	A292	1.05 l multicolored	.45	.15
1380	A292	3.60 l multicolored	2.50	.50
		Nos. 1374-1380 (7)	3.90	
		Set value		1.00

Souvenir Sheet
Imperf

1381	A292	2 l brt blue & multi	2.50	.75

20th Olympic Games, Munich, Aug. 26-Sept. 10, 1972.

Workers with
Flags — A293

Designs: 1.05 l, Party Headquarters, Tirana, and Red Star. 1.20 l, Rifle, star, flag and "VI," vert.

1971, Nov. 1   *Perf. 12*
1382	A293	25q gold, sil, red & bl	.20	.15
1383	A293	1.05 l gold, sil, red & bl	.65	.15
1384	A293	1.20 l gold, sil, red & blk	.80	.25
		Nos. 1382-1384 (3)	1.65	
		Set value		.40

6th Congress of Workers' Party.

Factories and
Workers
A294

Designs: 80q, "XXX" and flag, vert. 1.55 l, Enver Hoxha and flags.

1971, Nov. 8
1385	A294	15q gold, sil, lil & yel	.20	.15
1386	A294	80q gold, sil & red	.70	.15
1387	A294	1.55 l gold, sil, red & brn	1.40	.25
		Nos. 1385-1387 (3)	2.30	
		Set value		.40

30th anniversary of Workers' Party.

Construction Work, by M.
Fushekati — A295

Contemporary Albanian Paintings: 5q, Young Man, by R. Kuci, vert. 25q, Partisan, by D. Jukniu, vert. 80q, Fliers, by S. Kristo. 1.20 l, Girl in Forest, by A. Sadikaj. 1.55 l, Warriors with Spears and Shields, by S. Kamberi. 2 l, Freedom Fighter, by I. Lulani.

Perf. 12x12½, 12½x12
1971, Nov. 20
1388	A295	5q gold & multi	.15	.15
1389	A295	15q gold & multi	.15	.15
1390	A295	25q gold & multi	.15	.15
1391	A295	80q gold & multi	.40	.15
1392	A295	1.20 l gold & multi	.90	.20
1393	A295	1.55 l gold & multi	1.10	.25
		Nos. 1388-1393 (6)	2.85	
		Set value		.65

Miniature Sheet
Imperf

1394	A295	2 l gold & multi	2.25	.70

Young Workers'
Emblem — A296

1971, Nov. 23   *Perf. 12x12½*
1395	A296	15q lt blue & multi	.15	.15
1396	A296	1.35 l grnsh gray & multi	1.10	.25
		Set value		.30

Albanian Young Workers' Union, 30th anniv.

"Halili and Hajria" Ballet — A297

Scenes from "Halili and Hajria" Ballet: 10q, Brother and sister. 15q, Hajria before Sultan Suleiman. 50q, Hajria and husband. 80q, Execution of Halili. 1.40 l, Hajria killing her husband.

1971, Dec. 27   *Perf. 12½x12*
1397	A297	5q silver & multi	.15	.15
1398	A297	10q silver & multi	.15	.15
1399	A297	15q silver & multi	.15	.15
1400	A297	50q silver & multi	.45	.15
1401	A297	80q silver & multi	.70	.15
1402	A297	1.40 l silver & multi	1.10	.35
		Nos. 1397-1402 (6)	2.70	
		Set value		.75

Albanian ballet Halili and Hajria after drama by Kol Jakova.

Biathlon and Olympic Rings — A298

Designs (Olympic Rings and): 10q, Sledding. 15q, Ice hockey. 20q, Bobsledding. 50q, Speed skating. 1 l, Slalom. 2 l, Ski jump. 2.50 l, Figure skating, pairs.

1972, Feb. 10
1403	A298	5q lt olive & multi	.15	.15
1404	A298	10q lt violet & multi	.15	.15
1405	A298	15q multicolored	.15	.15
1406	A298	20q pink & multi	.15	.15
1407	A298	50q lt blue & multi	.30	.15
1408	A298	1 l ocher & multi	.75	.20
1409	A298	2 l lilac & multi	1.50	.35
		Set value	2.00	.75

Souvenir Sheet
Imperf

1410	A298	2.50 l blue & multi	2.25	.50

11th Winter Olympic Games, Sapporo, Japan, Feb. 3-13.

Wild
Strawberries
A299

Wild Fruits and Nuts: 10q, Blackberries. 15q, Hazelnuts. 20q, Walnuts. 25q, Strawberry-tree fruit. 30q, Dogwood berries. 2.40 l, Rowan berries.

1972, Mar. 20   Litho.   *Perf. 12*
1411	A299	5q lt grn & multi	.15	.15
1412	A299	10q yellow & multi	.15	.15
1413	A299	15q lt vio & multi	.15	.15
1414	A299	20q pink & multi	.20	.15
1415	A299	25q multi	.25	.15
1416	A299	30q multi	.35	.15
1417	A299	2.40 l multi	1.75	.45
		Nos. 1411-1417 (7)	3.00	
		Set value		.85

"Your Heart is your
Health" — A300

Worker and
Student — A301

World Health Day: 1.20 l, Cardiac patient and electrocardiogram.

1972, Apr. 7   *Perf. 12x12½*
1418	A300	1.10 l multicolored	.55	.15
1419	A300	1.20 l rose & multi	.70	.25

Perf. 11½x12½
1972, Apr. 24   Litho.

7th Trade Union Cong., May 8: 2.05 l, Assembly Hall, dancers and emblem.

1420	A301	25q multi	.25	.15
1421	A301	2.05 l blue & multi	1.50	.40
		Set value		.45

Qemal
Stafa
A302

Designs: 15q, Memorial flame. 25q, Monument "Spirit of Defiance," vert.

1972, May 5   *Perf. 12½x12, 12x12½*
1422	A302	15q gray & multi	.15	.15
1423	A302	25q sal rose, blk & gray	.15	.15
1424	A302	1.90 l dull yel & blk	1.10	.30
		Nos. 1422-1424 (3)	1.40	
		Set value		.45

30th anniversary of the murder of Qemal Stafa and of Martyrs' Day.

SHQIPERIA   Camellia — A303

Designs: Various camellias.

1972, May 10   Perf. 12x12½
Flowers in Natural Colors
1425	A303	5q lt blue & blk	.15	.15
1426	A303	10q citron & blk	.15	.15
1427	A303	15q grnsh gray & blk	.15	.15
1428	A303	25q pale sal & blk	.15	.15
1429	A303	45q gray & blk	.30	.15
1430	A303	50q sal pink & blk	.45	.15
1431	A303	2.50 l bluish gray & blk	1.90	.75
		Nos. 1425-1431 (7)	3.25	
		Set value		1.10

High Jump — A304

Designs (Olympic and Motion Emblems and): 10q, Running. 15q, Shot put. 20q, Bicycling. 25q, Pole vault. 50q, Hurdles, women's. 5q, Hockey. 2 l, Swimming. 2.50 l, Diving, women's.

1972, June 30   Litho.   Perf. 12½x12
1432	A304	5q multicolored	.15	.15
1433	A304	10q lt brn & multi	.15	.15
1434	A304	15q lt lil & multi	.15	.15
1435	A304	20q multicolored	.15	.15
1436	A304	25q lt vio & multi	.25	.15
1437	A304	50q lt grn & multi	.40	.15
1438	A304	75q multicolored	.80	.15
1439	A304	2 l multicolored	1.50	.30
		Nos. 1432-1439 (8)	3.45	
		Set value		.75

Miniature Sheet
Imperf
1440	A304	2.50 l multi	1.50	.85

20th Olympic Games, Munich, Aug. 26-Sept. 11. Nos. 1432-1439 each issued in sheets of 8 stamps and one label (3x3) showing Olympic rings in gold.

Autobus
A305

Designs: 25q, Electric train. 80q, Ocean liner Tirana. 1.05 l, Automobile. 1.20 l, Trailer truck.

1972, July 25   Litho.   Perf. 12
1441	A305	15q org brn & multi	.15	.15
1442	A305	25q gray & multi	.15	.15
1443	A305	80q dp grn & multi	.40	.15
1444	A305	1.05 l multi	.55	.15
1445	A305	1.20 l multi	.65	.15
		Nos. 1441-1445 (5)	1.90	
		Set value		.45

Arm Wrestling
A306

Folk Games: 10q, Piggyback ball game. 15q, Women's jumping. 25q, Rope game (srum). 90q, Leapfrog. 2 l, Women throwing pitchers.

1972, Aug. 18
1446	A306	5q multi	.15	.15
1447	A306	10q lt bl & multi	.15	.15
1448	A306	15q rose & multi	.15	.15
1449	A306	25q lt bl & multi	.15	.15

1450	A306	90q ocher & multi	.65	.15
1451	A306	2 l lt grn & multi	1.25	.25
		Set value	2.10	.55

1st National Festival of People's Games.

Mastheads — A307

30th Press Day: 25q, Printing press. 1.90 l, Workers reading paper.

1972, Aug. 25
1452	A307	15q lt bl & blk	.15	.15
1453	A307	25q red, grn & blk	.20	.15
1454	A307	1.90 l lt vio & blk	1.25	.35
		Nos. 1452-1454 (3)	1.60	
		Set value		.45

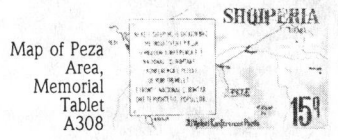

Map of Peza Area, Memorial Tablet
A308

1972, Sept. 16
1455	A308	15q shown	.20	.15
1456	A308	25q Guerrillas with flag	.30	.15
1457	A308	1.90 l Peza Conference memorial	1.75	.35
		Nos. 1455-1457 (3)	2.25	
		Set value		.45

30th anniversary, Conference of Peza.

Partisans, by Sotir Capo — A309

Paintings: 10q, Woman, by Ismail Lulani, vert. 15q, "Communists," by Lec Shkreli, vert. 20q, View of Nendorit, 1941, by Sali Shijaku, vert. 50q, Woman with Sheaf, by Zef Shoshi, vert. 1 l, Landscape with Children, by Dhimitraq Trebicka. 2 l, Women on Bicycles, by Vilson Kilica, 2.30 l, Folk Dance, by Abdurrahim Buza.

Perf. 12½x12, 12x12½
1972, Sept. 25   Litho.
1458	A309	5q gold & multi	.15	.15
1459	A309	10q gold & multi	.15	.15
1460	A309	15q gold & multi	.15	.15
1461	A309	20q gold & multi	.15	.15
1462	A309	50q gold & multi	.35	.15
1463	A309	1 l gold & multi	.70	.15
1464	A309	2 l gold & multi	1.50	.35
		Nos. 1458-1464 (7)	3.15	
		Set value		.75

Miniature Sheet
Imperf
1465	A309	2.30 l gold & multi	2.00	.80

No. 1465 contains one 41x68mm stamp.

Congress Emblem — A310

Design: 2.05 l, Young worker with banner.

1972, Oct. 23   Litho.   Perf. 12
1466	A310	25q silver, red & gold	.15	.15
1467	A310	2.05 l silver & multi	1.65	.45
		Set value		.50

Union of Working Youth, 6th Congress.

Hammer and Sickle — A311   Ismail Qemali — A312

Design: 1.20 l, Lenin as orator.

1972, Nov. 7   Litho.   Perf. 11½x12
1468	A311	1.10 l multi	.55	.20
1469	A311	1.20 l multi	.60	.25

55th anniv. of the Russian October Revolution.

Perf. 12x11½, 11½x12
1972, Nov. 29

Designs: 15q, Albanian fighters, horiz. 65q, Rally, horiz. 1.25 l, Coat of arms.

1470	A312	15q red, brt bl & blk	.15	.15
1471	A312	25q yel, blk & red	.20	.15
1472	A312	65q red, sal & blk	.50	.15
1473	A312	1.25 l dl red & blk	.95	.25
		Nos. 1470-1473 (4)	1.80	
		Set value		.45

60th anniv. of independence.

Cock, Mosaic A313

Mosaics, 2nd-5th centuries, excavated near Buthrotium and Apollonia: 10q, Bird, vert. 15q, Partridges, vert. 25q, Warrior's legs. 45q, Nymph riding dolphin, vert. 50q, Fish, vert. 2.50 l, Warrior with helmet.

Perf. 12½x12, 12x12½
1972, Dec. 10
1474	A313	5q silver & multi	.15	.15
1475	A313	10q silver & multi	.15	.15
1476	A313	15q silver & multi	.15	.15
1477	A313	25q silver & multi	.15	.15
1478	A313	45q silver & multi	.20	.15
1479	A313	50q silver & multi	.30	.15
1480	A313	2.50 l silver & multi	1.25	.40
		Set value	2.00	.70

Nicolaus Copernicus — A314

Designs: 10q, 25q, 80q, 1.20 l, Various portraits of Copernicus. 1.60 l, Heliocentric solar system.

1973, Feb. 19   Litho.   Perf. 12x12½
1481	A314	5q lilac rose & multi	.15	.15
1482	A314	10q dull olive & multi	.15	.15
1483	A314	25q multicolored	.20	.15
1484	A314	80q lt violet & multi	.60	.15
1485	A314	1.20 l blue & multi	.85	.25
1486	A314	1.60 l gray & multi	1.25	.35
		Nos. 1481-1486 (6)	3.20	
		Set value		.85

500th anniversary of the birth of Nicolaus Copernicus (1473-1543), Polish astronomer.

Flowering Cactus — A315

Designs: Various flowering cacti.

1973, Mar. 25   Litho.   Perf. 12
1487	A315	10q multicolored	.15	.15
1488	A315	15q multicolored	.15	.15
1489	A315	20q beige & multi	.15	.15
1490	A315	25q gray & multi	.20	.15
1491	A315	30q beige & multi	.30	.15
1492	A315	65q gray & multi	.75	.15
1493	A315	80q multicolored	.95	.15
1494	A315	2 l multicolored	2.50	.30
a.		Block of 8, #1487-1494	5.00	3.00
		Nos. 1487-1494 (8)	5.15	
		Set value		.70

Nos. 1487-1494 printed se-tenant.

Guard and Factories
A316

Design: 1.80 l, Guard and guards with prisoner.

1973, Mar. 20   Litho.   Perf. 12½x12
1495	A316	25q ultra & blk	.30	.15
1496	A316	1.80 l dk red & multi	1.40	.40
		Set value		.45

30th anniv. of the State Security Branch.

Common Tern
A317

Sterna hirundo

Sea Birds: 15q, White-winged black terns, vert. 25q, Black-headed gull, vert. 45q, Great black-headed gull. 80q, Slender-billed gull, vert. 2.40 l, Sandwich terns.

Perf. 12½x12, 12x12½
1973, Apr. 30
1497	A317	5q gold & multi	.15	.15
1498	A317	15q gold & multi	.15	.15
1499	A317	25q gold & multi	.30	.15
1500	A317	45q gold & multi	.35	.15
1501	A317	80q gold & multi	.80	.20
1502	A317	2.40 l gold & multi	2.50	.50
		Nos. 1497-1502 (6)	4.25	
		Set value		.90

Letters, 1913 Cancellation and Post Horn
A318

Design: 1.80 l, Mailman, 1913 cancel.

1973, May, 5   Litho.   Perf. 12x11½
1503	A318	25q red & multi	.40	.15
1504	A318	1.80 l red & multi	2.50	.50

60th anniversary of Albanian stamps.

Farmer, Worker, Soldier
A319

Design: 25q, Woman and factory, vert.

1973, June 4   Perf. 12
1505	A319	25q carmine rose	.25	.15
1506	A319	1.80 l yel, dp org & blk	1.50	.45

7th Congress of Albanian Women's Union.

Buying Sets

It is often less expensive to purchase complete sets than individual stamps that make up the set. Set values are provided for many such sets.

Creation of General Staff, by G. Madhi — A320

Designs: 40q, "August 1949," sculpture by Sh. Haderi, vert. 60q, "Generation after Generation," sculpture by H. Dule, vert. 80q, "Defend Revolutionary Victories," by M. Fushekati.

1973, July 10   Litho.   Perf. 12¹/₂x12
1507 A320 25q gold & multi   3.25 .15
1508 A320 40q gold & multi   5.00 .15
1509 A320 60q gold & multi   7.50 .25
1510 A320 80q gold & multi   9.25 .25
    Nos. 1507-1510 (4)   25.00 .80

30th anniversary of the People's Army.

"Electrification," by S. Hysa — A321

Albanian Paintings: 10q, Woman Textile Worker, by N. Nallbani. 15q, Gymnasts, by M. Fushekati. 50q, Aviator, by F. Stamo. 80q, Fascist Prisoner, by A. Lakuriqi. 1.20 l, Workers with Banner, by P. Mele. 1.30 l, Farm Woman, by Zef Shoshi. 2.05 l, Battle of Tenda, by F. Haxhiu. 10q, 50q, 80q, 1.20 l, 1.30 l, vertical.

Perf. 12¹/₂x12, 12x12¹/₂
1973, Aug. 10
1511 A321   5q gold & multi   .15 .15
1512 A321 10q gold & multi   .15 .15
1513 A321 15q gold & multi   .15 .15
1514 A321 50q gold & multi   .25 .15
1515 A321 80q gold & multi   .55 .15
1516 A321 1.20 l gold & multi   .90 .15
1517 A321 1.30 l gold & multi   .95 .20
    Nos. 1511-1517 (7)   3.10
    Set value   .60

Souvenir Sheet
Imperf
1518 A321 2.05 l multi   2.25 .65

Mary Magdalene, by Caravaggio A322

Paintings by Michelangelo da Caravaggio: 10q, The Lute Player, horiz. 15q, Self-portrait. 50q, Boy Carrying Fruit and Flowers. 80q, Still Life, horiz. 1.20 l, Narcissus. 1.30 l, Boy Peeling Apple. 2.05 l, Man with Feathered Hat.

Perf. 12x12¹/₂, 12¹/₂x12
1973, Sept. 28
1519 A322   5q gold & multi   .15 .15
1520 A322 10q gold & multi   .15 .15
1521 A322 15q gold, blk & gray .15 .15
1522 A322 50q gold & multi   .25 .15
1523 A322 80q gold & multi   .60 .15
1524 A322 1.20 l gold & multi   .80 .25
1525 A322 1.30 l gold & multi   .90 .25
    Nos. 1519-1525 (7)   3.00
    Set value   .75

Souvenir Sheet
Imperf
1526 A322 2.05 l multi   3.75 .60

Michelangelo da Caravaggio (Merisi; 1573?-1609), Italian painter. No. 1526 contains one stamp, size: 63x73mm.

Soccer — A323

Designs: 5q-1.25 l, Various soccer scenes. 2.05 l, Ball in goal and list of cities where championships were held.

1973, Oct. 30   Litho.   Perf. 12¹/₂x12
1527 A323   5q multi   .15 .15
1528 A323 10q multi   .15 .15
1529 A323 15q multi   .15 .15
1530 A323 20q multi   .15 .15
1531 A323 25q multi   .20 .15
1532 A323 90q multi   .65 .15
1533 A323 1.20 l multi   .95 .15
1534 A323 1.25 l multi 1.10 .20
    Nos. 1527-1534 (8)   3.50
    Set value   .65

Minature Sheet
Imperf
1535 A323 2.05 l multi   2.00 .60

World Soccer Cup, Munich 1974.

Weight Lifter — A324

Designs: Various stages of weight lifting. 1.20 l, 1.60 l, horiz.

1973, Oct. 30   Litho.   Perf. 12
1536 A324   5q multi   .15 .15
1537 A324 10q multi   .15 .15
1538 A324 25q multi   .20 .15
1539 A324 90q multi   .55 .20
1540 A324 1.20 l multi   .45 .15
1541 A324 1.60 l multi   .95 .15
    Nos. 1536-1541 (6)   2.45
    Set value   .55

Weight Lifting Championships, Havana, Cuba.

Ballet — A325   Harvester
                       Combine — A326

Designs: 5q, Cement factory, Kavaje. 10q, Ali Kelmendi truck factory and tank cars, horiz. 25q, "Communication." 35q, Skiers and hotel, horiz. 60q, Resort, horiz. 80q, Mountain lake. 1 l, Mao Tse-tung textile mill. 1.20 l, Steel workers. 2.40 l, Welder and pipe. 3 l, Skanderbeg Monument, Tirana. 5 l, Roman arches, Durres.

Perf. 12¹/₂x12, 12x12¹/₂
1973-74   **Litho.**
1543 A325   5q gold & multi   .15 .15
1544 A325   10q gold & multi   .15 .15
1545 A325   15q gold & multi   .15 .15
1545A A326   20q gold & multi   .15 .15
1546 A326   25q gold & multi   .20 .15
1547 A326   35q gold & multi   .20 .15
1548 A326   60q gold & multi   .35 .15
1549 A326   80q gold & multi   .50 .15
1549A A326   1 l gold & multi   .45 .15
1549B A326 1.20 l gold & multi   .75 .15
1549C A326 2.40 l gold & multi 1.50 .35
1550 A326   3 l gold & multi 1.75 .35
1551 A326   5 l gold & multi 2.75 .60
    Nos. 1543-1551 (13)   9.05
    Set value   1.95

Issue dates: Nos. 1545-1546, 1549-1550, Dec. 5, 1973; others, 1974.

Mao Tse-tung — A327

80th birthday of Mao Tse-tung: 1.20 l, Mao Tse-tung addressing crowd.

1973, Dec. 26   Perf. 12
1552 A327 85q gold, red & sepia .80 .15
1553 A327 1.20 l gold, red & sepia 1.25 .20

Old Man and Dog, by Gericault — A328

Paintings by Jean Louis André Theodore Gericault: 10q, Horse's Head. 15q, Male Model. 25q, Head of Black Man. 1.20 l, Self-portrait. 2.05 l, Raft of the Medusa, horiz. 2.20 l, Battle of the Giants.

Perf. 12x12¹/₂, 12x12¹/₂
1974, Jan. 18   **Litho.**
1554 A328 10q gold & multi   .15 .15
1555 A328 15q gold & multi   .15 .15
1556 A328 20q gold & multi   .15 .15
1557 A328 25q gold & blk   .25 .15
1558 A328 1.20 l gold & multi   .90 .15
1559 A328 2.20 l gold & multi 1.75 .35
    Nos. 1554-1559 (6)   3.35
    Set value   .65

Souvenir Sheet
Imperf
1560 A328 2.05 l gold & multi 1.50 .45

No. 1560 contains one 87x78mm stamp.

Lenin, by Pandi Mele — A329

Designs: 25q, Lenin with Sailors on Cruiser Aurora, by Dhimitraq Trebicka, horiz. 1.20 l, Lenin, by Vilson Kilica.

Perf. 12¹/₂x12, 12x12¹/₂
1974, Jan. 21
1561 A329 25q gold & multi   .20 .15
1562 A329 60q gold & multi   .50 .15
1563 A329 1.20 l gold & multi 1.10 .25
    Nos. 1561-1563 (3)   1.80
    Set value   .40

50th anniv. of the death of Lenin.

Swimming Duck, Mosaic — A330

Designs: Mosaics from the 5th-6th Centuries A.D., excavated near Buthrotium, Pogradec and Apollonia.

1974, Feb. 20   Litho.   Perf. 12¹/₂x12
1564 A330   5q shown   .15 .15
1565 A330 10q Bird and flower .15 .15
1566 A330 15q Vase and grapes .15 .15
1567 A330 25q Duck   .20 .15
1568 A330 40q Donkey and bird .30 .15
1569 A330 2.50 l Sea horse 1.50 .35
    Nos. 1564-1569 (6)   2.45
    Set value   .60

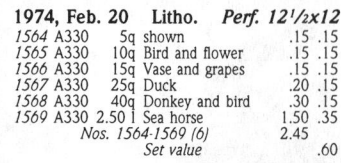

Soccer — A331

Various scenes from soccer. 2.05 l, World Soccer Cup & names of participating countries.

1974, Apr. 25   Litho.   Perf. 12¹/₂x12
1570 A331 10q gold & multi   .15 .15
1571 A331 15q gold & multi   .15 .15
1572 A331 20q gold & multi   .15 .15
1573 A331 25q gold & multi   .15 .15
1574 A331 40q gold & multi   .30 .15
1575 A331 80q gold & multi   .55 .15
1576 A331   1 l gold & multi   .85 .25
1577 A331 1.20 l gold & multi 1.10 .35
    Nos. 1570-1577 (8)   3.40
    Set value   1.00

Souvenir Sheet
Imperf
1578 A331 2.05 l gold & multi 2.50 .90

World Cup Soccer Championship, Munich, June 13-July 7. No. 1578 contains one stamp (60x60mm) with simulated perforations. Nos. 1570-1577 exist imperf, No. 1578 with simulated perfs omitted.

Arms of Albania, Soldier — A332

Design: 1.80 l, Soldier and front page of 1944 Congress Book.

1974, May 24   Litho.   Perf. 12
1579 A332 25q multicolored   .20 .15
1580 A332 1.80 l multicolored 1.25 .25
    Set value   .30

30th anniversary of the First Anti-Fascist Liberation Congress of Permet.

Medicinal Plants — A333

40q, 80q, 2.20 l, horiz.

1974, May 5   Perf. 12x12¹/₂
1581 A333 10q Bittersweet   .15 .15
1582 A333 15q Arbutus   .15 .15
1583 A333 20q Lilies of the valley .15 .15
1584 A333 25q Autumn crocus .20 .15
1585 A333 40q Borage   .25 .15
1586 A333 80q Soapwort   .85 .15
1587 A333 2.20 l Gentian   1.90 .40
    Nos. 1581-1587 (7)   3.65
    Set value   .80

Revolutionaries with Albanian Flag — A334

1.80 l, Portraits of 5 revolutionaries, vert.

1974, June 10 *Perf. 12¹/₂x12, 12x12¹/₂*
1588	A334	25q	red, blk & lil	.15 .15
1589	A334	1.80 l	yel, red & blk	.80 .25
			Set value	.30

50th anniversary Albanian Bourgeois Democratic Revolution.

European Redwing — A335

Designs: Songbirds; Nos. 1597-1600 vert.

1974, July 15 *Perf. 12¹/₂x12, 12x12¹/₂* Litho.
1594	A335	10q	shown	.15 .15
1595	A335	15q	European robin	.15 .15
1596	A335	20q	Greenfinch	.15 .15
1597	A335	25q	Bullfinch	.15 .15
1598	A335	40q	Hawfinch	.35 .15
1599	A335	80q	Blackcap	.85 .20
1600	A335	2.20 l	Nightingale	1.90 .45
		Nos. 1594-1600 (7)		3.70
			Set value	.90

SHQIPERIA Globe — A336

Cent. of UPU: 1.20 l, UPU emblem. 2.05 l, Jet over globe.

1974, Aug. 25 Litho. *Perf. 12x12¹/₂*
1601	A336	85q	green & multi	.80 .15
1602	A336	1.20 l	vio & ol grn	1.25 .20

Miniature Sheet
Imperf
1603	A336	2.05 l	blue & multi	12.00 12.00

Widows, by Sali Shijaku — A337

Albanian Paintings: 15q, Drillers, by Danish Jukniu, vert. 20q, Workers with Blueprints, by Clirim Ceka. 25q, Call to Action, by Spiro Kristo, vert. 40q, Winter Battle, by Sabaudin Xhaferi. 80q, Comrades, by Clirim Ceka, vert. 1 l, Aiding the Partisans, by Guri Madhi. 1.20 l, Teacher with Pupils, by Kleo Nini Brezat. 2.05 l, Comrades in Arms, by Guri Madhi.

1974, Sept. 25 *Perf. 12¹/₂x12, 12x12¹/₂*
1604	A337	10q	silver & multi	.15 .15
1605	A337	15q	silver & multi	.15 .15
1606	A337	20q	silver & multi	.20 .15
1607	A337	25q	silver & multi	.20 .15
1608	A337	40q	silver & multi	.40 .15
1609	A337	80q	silver & multi	.75 .15
1610	A337	1 l	silver & multi	.95 .15
1611	A337	1.20 l	silver & multi	1.00 .20
		Nos. 1604-1611 (8)		3.80
			Set value	.65

Miniature Sheet
Imperf
1612	A337	2.05 l	silver & multi	2.00 .40

Crowd on Tien An Men Square A338

Design: 1.20 l, Mao Tse-tung, vert.

1974, Oct. 1 *Perf. 12*
1613	A338	85q	gold & multi	.80 .15
1614	A338	1.20 l	gold & multi	1.25 .15
			Set value	.25

25th anniversary of the proclamation of the People's Republic of China.

Women's Volleyball A339

Designs (Spartakiad Medal and): 15q, Women hurdlers. 20q, Women gymnasts. 25q, Mass exercises in Stadium. 40q, Weight lifter. 80q, Wrestlers. 1 l, Military rifle drill. 1.20 l, Soccer.

1974, Oct. 9 *Perf. 12x12¹/₂*
1615	A339	10q	multi	.15 .15
1616	A339	15q	multi	.15 .15
1617	A339	20q	multi	.15 .15
1618	A339	25q	gray & multi	.15 .15
1619	A339	40q	multi	.15 .15
1620	A339	80q	multi	.45 .15
1621	A339	1 l	multi	.50 .15
1622	A339	1.20 l	tan & multi	.60 .20
		Nos. 1615-1622 (8)		2.30
			Set value	.70

National Spartakiad, Oct. 9-17.

View of Berat — A340

Designs: 80q, Enver Hoxha addressing Congress, bas-relief, horiz. 1 l, Hoxha and leaders leaving Congress Hall.

Perf. 12x12¹/₂, 12¹/₂x12
1974, Oct. 20 Litho.
1623	A340	25q	rose car & blk	.30 .15
1624	A340	80q	yel, brn & blk	.60 .15
1625	A340	1 l	dp lilac & blk	.90 .15
		Nos. 1623-1625 (3)		1.80
			Set value	.35

30th anniversary of 2nd Congress of Berat.

Anniversary Emblem, Factory Guards A341

Designs (Anniversary Emblem and): 35q, Chemical industry. 50q, Agriculture. 80q, Arts. 1 l, Atomic diagram and computer. 1.20 l, Youth education. 2.05 l, Anniversary emblem: Crowd and History Book.

1974, Nov. 29 Litho. *Perf. 12¹/₂x12*
1626	A341	25q	green & multi	.15 .15
1627	A341	35q	ultra & multi	.15 .15
1628	A341	50q	brown & multi	.25 .15
1629	A341	80q	multicolored	.40 .15
1630	A341	1 l	violet & multi	.50 .15
1631	A341	1.20 l	multicolored	.50 .20
		Nos. 1626-1631 (6)		1.90
			Set value	.70

Miniature Sheet
Imperf
1632	A341	2.05 l	gold & multi	2.00 .50

30th anniv. of liberation from Fascism.

Artemis, from Apolloni — A342

1974, Dec. 25 Photo. *Perf. 12x12¹/₂*
1633	A342	10q	shown	.15 .15
1634	A342	15q	Zeus statue	.15 .15
1635	A342	20q	Poseidon statue	.15 .15
1636	A342	25q	Illyrian helmet	.15 .15
1637	A342	40q	Amphora	.20 .15
1638	A342	80q	Agrippa	.50 .15
1639	A342	1 l	Demosthenes	.60 .15
1640	A342	1.20 l	Head of Bilia	.70 .20
		Nos. 1633-1640 (8)		2.60
			Set value	.65

Miniature Sheet
Imperf
1641	A342	2.05 l	Artemis & amphora	2.00 .60

Archaeological discoveries in Albania.

Workers and Factories A343

Design: 25q, Handshake, tools and book, vert.

1975, Feb. 11 Litho. *Perf. 12*
1642	A343	25q	brown & multi	.15 .15
1643	A343	1.80 l	yellow & multi	1.10 .20
			Set value	.35

Albanian Trade Unions, 30th anniversary.

Chicory A344

1975, Feb. 15
1644	A344	5q	shown	.15 .15
1645	A344	10q	Houseleek	.15 .15
1646	A344	15q	Columbine	.15 .15
1647	A344	20q	Anemone	.15 .15
1648	A344	25q	Hibiscus	.15 .15
1649	A344	30q	Gentian	.15 .15
1650	A344	35q	Hollyhock	.15 .15
1651	A344	2.70 l	Iris	1.20 .40
			Set value	1.75 .75

Protected flowers.

Jesus, from Doni Madonna — A345

Works by Michelangelo: 10q, Slave, sculpture. 15q, Head of Dawn, sculpture. 20q, Awakening Giant, sculpture. 25q, Cumaenian Sybil, Sistine Chapel. 30q, Lorenzo di Medici, sculpture. 1.20 l,

David, sculpture. 2.05 l, Self-portrait. 3.90 l, Delphic Sybil, Sistine Chapel.

1975, Mar. 20 Litho. *Perf. 12x12¹/₂*
1652	A345	5q	gold & multi	.15 .15
1653	A345	10q	gold & multi	.15 .15
1654	A345	15q	gold & multi	.15 .15
1655	A345	20q	gold & multi	.15 .15
1656	A345	25q	gold & multi	.15 .15
1657	A345	30q	gold & multi	.15 .15
1658	A345	1.20 l	gold & multi	.35 .20
1659	A345	3.90 l	gold & multi	1.50 .50
			Set value	2.25 .90

Miniature Sheet
Imperf
1660	A345	2.05 l	gold & multi	1.10 .50

Michelangelo Buonarroti (1475-1564), Italian sculptor, painter and architect.

Two-wheeled Cart — A346

Albanian Transportation of the Past: 5q, Horseback rider. 15q, Lake ferry. 20q, Coastal threemaster. 25q, Phaeton. 3.35 l, Early automobile on bridge.

1975, Apr. 15 Litho. *Perf. 12¹/₂x12*
1661	A346	5q	bl grn & multi	.15 .15
1662	A346	10q	ol & multi	.15 .15
1663	A346	15q	lil & multi	.15 .15
1664	A346	20q	multi	.15 .15
1665	A346	25q	multi	.15 .15
1666	A346	3.35 l	ocher & multi	1.50 .50
			Set value	1.90 .75

Guard at Frontier Stone — A347   Guardsman and Militia — A348

1975, Apr. 25 *Perf. 12*
1667	A347	25q	multi	.15 .15
1668	A348	1.80 l	multi	1.10 .20
			Set value	.25

30th anniversary of Frontier Guards.

Posting Illegal Poster — A349

Designs: 60q, Partisans in battle. 1.20 l, Partisan killing German soldier, and Albanian coat of arms.

1975, May 9 *Perf. 12¹/₂x12*
1669	A349	25q	multi	.15 .15
1670	A349	60q	multi	.25 .15
1671	A349	1.20 l	red & multi	.75 .25
		Nos. 1669-1671 (3)		1.15
			Set value	.40

30th anniversary of victory over Fascism.

European Widgeons — A350

Waterfowl: 10q, Red-crested pochards. 15q, White-fronted goose. 20q, Northern pintails. 25q, Red-breasted merganser. 30q, Eider ducks. 35q, Whooper swan. 2.70 l, Shovelers.

1975, June 15   Litho.   Perf. 12
1672	A350	5q brt blue & multi	.15 .15
1673	A350	10q yel grn & multi	.15 .15
1674	A350	15q brt rose lil & multi	.15 .15
1675	A350	20q bl grn & multi	.15 .15
1676	A350	25q multicolored	.15 .15
1677	A350	30q multicolored	.15 .15
1678	A350	35q orange & multi	.15 .15
1679	A350	2.70 l multi	1.65 .35
		Set value	2.25 .60

Shyqyri Kanapari, by Musa Qarri — A351

Albanian Paintings: 10q, Woman Saving Children in Sea, by Agim Faja. 15q, "November 28, 1912" (revolution), by Petrit Ceno, horiz. 20q, "Workers Unite," by Sali Shijaku. 25q, The Partisan Shota Galica, by Ismail Lulani. 30q, Victorious Resistance Fighters, 1943, by Nestor Jonuzi. 80q, Partisan Couple in Front of Red Flag, by Vilson Halimi. 2.05 l, Dancing Procession, by Abdurahim Buza. 2.25 l, Republic Day Celebration, by Fatmir Haxhiu, horiz.

Perf. 12x12¹/₂, 12¹/₂x12
1975, July 15   Litho.
1680	A351	5q gold & multi	.15 .15
1681	A351	10q gold & multi	.15 .15
1682	A351	15q gold & multi	.15 .15
1683	A351	20q gold & multi	.15 .15
1684	A351	25q gold & multi	.15 .15
1685	A351	30q gold & multi	.20 .15
1686	A351	80q gold & multi	.35 .15
1687	A351	2.25 l gold & multi	1.25 .30
		Nos. 1680-1687 (8)	2.55
		Set value	.60

Miniature Sheet
Imperf
1688	A351	2.05 l gold & multi	1.65 .50

Nos. 1680-1687 issued in sheets of 8 stamps and gold center label showing palette and easel.

Farmer Holding Reform Law — A352

Design: 2 l, Produce and farm machinery.

1975, Aug. 28   Perf. 12
1689	A352	15q multicolored	.15 .15
1690	A352	1.10 l multicolored	1.10 .35
		Set value	.40

Agrarian reform, 30th anniversary.

Alcynonium Palmatum — A353

Corals: 10q, Paramuricea chamaeleon. 20q, Coralium rubrum. 25q, Eunicella covalini. 3.70 l, Cladocora cespitosa.

1975, Sept. 25   Litho.   Perf. 12
1691	A353	5q blue, ol & blk	.15 .15
1692	A353	10q blue & multi	.15 .15
1693	A353	20q blue & multi	.15 .15
1694	A353	25q blue & blk	.20 .15
1695	A353	3.70 l blue & blk	2.00 .50
		Nos. 1691-1695 (5)	2.65
		Set value	.65

Bicycling — A354

Designs (Montreal Olympic Games Emblem and): 10q, Canoeing. 15q, Fieldball. 20q, Basketball. 25q, Water polo. 30q, Hockey. 1.20 l, Pole vault. 2.05 l, Fencing. 2.15 l, Montreal Olympic Games emblem and various sports.

1975, Oct. 20   Litho.   Perf. 12¹/₂
1696	A354	5q multi	.15 .15
1697	A354	10q multi	.15 .15
1698	A354	15q multi	.15 .15
1699	A354	20q multi	.15 .15
1700	A354	25q multi	.15 .15
1701	A354	30q multi	.15 .15
1702	A354	1.20 l multi	.40 .15
1703	A354	2.05 l multi	.85 .25
		Set value	1.65 .65

Miniature Sheet
Imperf
1704	A354	2.15 l org & multi	2.75 1.75

21st Olympic Games, Montreal, July 18-Aug. 8, 1976. Nos. 1696-1703 exist imperf.

Power Lines Leading to Village — A355

Designs: 25q, Transformers and insulators. 80q, Dam and power station. 85q, Television set, power lines, grain and cogwheel.

1975, Oct. 25   Perf. 12x12¹/₂
1705	A355	15q ultra & yel	.15 .15
1706	A355	25q brt vio & pink	.15 .15
1707	A355	80q lt grn & gray	.40 .15
1708	A355	85q ocher & brn	.40 .15
		Nos. 1705-1708 (4)	1.10
		Set value	.35

General electrification, 5th anniversary.

Child, Rabbit and Teddy Bear Planting Tree — A356

Fairy Tales: 10q, Mother fox. 15q, Ducks in school. 20q, Little pigs building house. 25q, Animals watching television. 30q, Rabbit and bear at work. 35q, Working and playing ants. 2.70 l, Wolf in sheep's clothes.

1975, Dec. 25   Litho.   Perf. 12¹/₂x12
1709	A356	5q black & multi	.15 .15
1710	A356	10q black & multi	.15 .15
1711	A356	15q black & multi	.15 .15
1712	A356	20q black & multi	.15 .15
1713	A356	25q black & multi	.15 .15
1714	A356	30q black & multi	.15 .15
1715	A356	35q black & multi	.20 .15
1716	A356	2.70 l black & multi	1.25 .30
		Set value	1.90 .60

Arms, People, Factories A357

Design: 1.90 l, Arms, government building, celebrating crowd.

1976, Jan. 11   Litho.   Perf. 12
1717	A357	25q gold & multi	.15 .15
1718	A357	1.90 l gold & multi	.85 .25
		Set value	.30

30th anniversary of proclamation of Albanian People's Republic.

Ice Hockey, Olympic Games' Emblem — A358

Designs: 10q, Speed skating. 15q, Biathlon. 50q, Ski jump. 1.20 l, Slalom. 2.15 l, Figure skating, pairs. 2.30 l, One-man bobsled.

1976, Feb. 4
1719	A358	5q silver & multi	.15 .15
1720	A358	10q silver & multi	.15 .15
1721	A358	15q silver & multi	.15 .15
1722	A358	50q silver & multi	.25 .15
1723	A358	1.20 l silver & multi	.60 .15
1724	A358	2.30 l silver & multi	1.40 .35
		Nos. 1719-1724 (6)	2.70
		Set value	.65

Miniature Sheet
Perf. 12 on 2 sides x Imperf.
1725	A358	2.15 l silver & multi	1.90 .80

12th Winter Olympic Games, Innsbruck, Austria, Feb. 4-15.

Meadow Saffron — A359

Medicinal Plants: 10q, Deadly night-shade. 15q, Yellow gentian. 20q, Horse chestnut. 70q, Shield fern. 80q, Marshmallow. 2.30 l, Thorn apple.

1976, Apr. 10   Litho.   Perf. 12x12¹/₂
1726	A359	5q black & multi	.15 .15
1727	A359	10q black & multi	.15 .15
1728	A359	15q black & multi	.15 .15
1729	A359	20q black & multi	.15 .15
1730	A359	70q black & multi	.25 .15
1731	A359	80q black & multi	.45 .15
1732	A359	2.30 l black & multi	1.25 .35
		Set value	2.25 .70

Bowl and Spoon — A360

15q, Flask, vert. 20q, Carved handles, vert. 25q, Pistol and dagger. 80q, Wall hanging, vert. 1.20 l, Earrings and belt buckle. 1.40 l, Jugs, vert.

1976   Litho.   Perf. 12¹/₂x12, 12x12¹/₂
1733	A360	10q lilac & multi	.15 .15
1734	A360	15q gray & multi	.15 .15
1735	A360	20q multi	.15 .15
1736	A360	25q car & multi	.15 .15
1737	A360	80q yellow & multi	.35 .15
1738	A360	1.20 l multi	.50 .15
1739	A360	1.40 l tan & multi	.65 .25
		Nos. 1733-1739 (7)	2.10
		Set value	.70

Natl. Ethnographic Conf., Tirana, June 28. For surcharge see No. 1873.

Founding of Cooperatives, by Zef Shoshi — A361

Paintings: 10q, Going to Work, by Agim Zajmi, vert. 25q, Crowd Listening to Loudspeaker, by Vilson Kilica. 40q, Woman Welder, by Sabaudin Xhaferi, vert. 50q, Factory, by Isuf Sulovari, vert. 1.20 l, 1942 Revolt, by Lec Shkreli, vert. 1.60 l, Coming Home from Work, by Agron Dine. 2.05 l, Honoring a Young Pioneer, by Andon Lakuriqi.

Perf. 12¹/₂x12, 12x12¹/₂
1976, Aug. 8   Litho.
1740	A361	5q gold & multi	.15 .15
1741	A361	10q gold & multi	.15 .15
1742	A361	25q gold & multi	.15 .15
1743	A361	40q gold & multi	.15 .15
1744	A361	50q gold & multi	.15 .15
1745	A361	1.20 l gold & multi	.50 .15
1746	A361	1.60 l gold & multi	.75 .30
		Nos. 1740-1746 (7)	2.00
		Set value	.70

Miniature Sheet
Perf. 12 on 2 sides x Imperf.
1747	A361	2.05 l gold & multi	1.10 .45

Red Flag, Agricultural Symbols — A362   Enver Hoxha, Partisans and Albanian Flag — A363

Design: 1.20 l, Red flag and raised pickax.

1976, Nov. 1
1748	A362	25q multi	.20 .15
1749	A362	1.20 l multi	.80 .20
		Set value	.25

7th Workers Party Congress.

1976, Oct. 28   *Perf. 12x12½*
1.90 l, Demonstrators with Albanian flag.

1750	A363	25q multi	.15 .15
1751	A363	1.90 l multi	1.00 .30
		Set value	.35

Anti-Fascist demonstrations, 35th anniv.

Attacking Partisans, Meeting House — A364

Designs (Red Flag and): 25q, Partisans, pickax and gun. 80q, Workers, soldiers, pickax and gun. 1.20 l, Agriculture and industry. 1.70 l, Dancers, symbols of science and art.

1976, Nov. 8   *Litho.*   *Perf. 12x12½*

1752	A364	10q gold & multi	.15 .15
1753	A364	25q gold & multi	.15 .15
1754	A364	80q gold & multi	.30 .15
1755	A364	1.20 l gold & multi	.50 .15
1756	A364	1.70 l gold & multi	1.00 .20
		Nos. 1752-1756 (5)	2.10
		Set value	.50

35th anniv. of 1st Workers Party Cong.

Young Workers and Track A365

Design: 1.25 l, Young soldiers and Albanian flag.

1976, Nov. 23   *Perf. 12*

1757	A365	80q yellow & multi	.55 .15
1758	A365	1.25 l carmine & multi	.75 .20

Union of Young Communists, 35th anniv.

"Cuca e Maleve" Ballet A366

Designs: Scenes from ballet "Mountain Girl."

1976, Dec. 14   *Perf. 12*

1759	A366	10q gold & multi	.15 .15
1760	A366	15q gold & multi	.15 .15
1761	A366	20q gold & multi	.15 .15
1762	A366	25q gold & multi	.15 .15
1763	A366	80q gold & multi	.55 .15
1764	A366	1.20 l gold & multi	.75 .20
1765	A366	1.40 l gold & multi	.95 .25
		Nos. 1759-1765 (7)	2.85
		Set value	.65

Miniature Sheet
Perf. 12 on 2 sides x Imperf.
1766 A366 2.05 l gold & multi   1.75 .45

Bashtoves Castle A367

Albanian Castles: 15q, Gjirokastres. 20q, Ali Pash Tepelenes. 25q, Petreles. 80q, Beratit. 1.20 l, Durresit. 1.40 l, Krujes.

1976, Dec. 30   *Litho.*   *Perf. 12*

1767	A367	10q black & dull bl	.15 .15
1768	A367	15q black & grn	.15 .15
1769	A367	20q black & gray	.15 .15
1770	A367	25q black & brn	.15 .15
1771	A367	80q black & rose	.40 .15
1772	A367	1.20 l black & vio	.45 .15
1773	A367	1.40 l black & brn red	.90 .15
		Nos. 1767-1773 (7)	2.35
		Set value	.60

Skanderbeg's Shield and Spear — A368

Skanderbeg's Weapons: 80q, Helmet, sword and scabbard. 1 l, Halberd, quiver with arrows, crossbow and spear.

1977, Jan. 28   *Litho.*   *Perf. 12*

1774	A368	15q silver & multi	.50 .15
1775	A368	80q silver & multi	2.25 .20
1776	A368	1 l silver & multi	3.25 .25
		Nos. 1774-1776 (3)	6.00
		Set value	.50

Skanderbeg (1403-1468), national hero.

Ilia Oiqi, Messenger in Storm — A369

Modern Heroes: 10q, Ilia Dashi, sailor in battle. 25q, Fran Ndue Ivanaj, fisherman in storm. 80q, Zeliha Allmetaj, woman rescuing child. 1 l, Ylli Zaimi, rescuing goats from flood. 1.90 l, Isuf Plloci, fighting forest fire.

1977, Feb. 28   *Litho.*   *Perf. 12x12½*

1777	A369	5q brown & multi	.15 .15
1778	A369	10q ultra & multi	.15 .15
1779	A369	25q blue & multi	.15 .15
1780	A369	80q ocher & multi	.50 .15
1781	A369	1 l brown & multi	.80 .15
1782	A369	1.90 l brown & multi	1.40 .20
		Nos. 1777-1782 (6)	3.15
		Set value	.50

Polyvinylchloride Plant, Vlore — A370

6th Five-year plan: 25q, Naphtha fractioning plant, Ballsh. 65q, Hydroelectric station and dam, Fjerzes. 1 l, Metallurgical plant and blast furance, Elbasan.

1977, Mar. 29   *Litho.*   *Perf. 12½x12*

1783	A370	15q silver & multi	.15 .15
1784	A370	25q silver & multi	.30 .15
1785	A370	65q silver & multi	.65 .15
1786	A370	1 l silver & multi	1.10 .15
		Nos. 1783-1786 (4)	2.20
		Set value	.35

Qerime Halil Galica — A371   Victory Monument, Tirana — A372

Design: 1.25 l, Qerime Halil Galica "Shota" and father Azem Galica.

1977, Apr. 20   *Litho.*   *Perf. 12*

1787	A371	80q dark red	.65 .15
1788	A371	1.25 l gray blue	1.10 .15
		Set value	.25

"Shota" Galica, communist fighter.

1977, May 5   *Litho.*   *Perf. 12*

Designs (Red Star and): 80q, Clenched fist, Albanian flag. 1.20 l, Bust of Qemal Stafa and poppies.

1789	A372	25q multi	.30 .15
1790	A372	80q multi	.90 .15
1791	A372	1.20 l multi	1.50 .20
		Nos. 1789-1791 (3)	2.70
		Set value	.35

35th anniversary of Martyrs' Day.

Physician Visiting Farm, Mobile Clinic — A373

Designs: 10q, Cowherd and cattle ranch. 20q, Militia woman helping with harvest, rifle and combine. 80q, Modern village, highway and power lines. 2.95 l, Tractor and greenhouses.

1977, June 18

1792	A373	5q multi	.15 .15
1793	A373	10q multi	.15 .15
1794	A373	20q multi	.15 .15
1795	A373	80q multi	.40 .15
1796	A373	2.95 l multi	2.50 .40
		Nos. 1792-1796 (5)	3.35
		Set value	.60

"Socialist transformation of the villages."

Armed Workers, Flag and Factory — A374

1.80 l, Workers with proclamation and flags.

1977, June 20

1797	A374	25q multi	.20 .15
1798	A374	1.80 l multi	1.25 .20
		Set value	.25

9th Labor Unions Congress.

Kerchief Dance — A375

Designs: Various folk dances.

1977, Aug. 20   *Litho.*   *Perf. 12*

1799	A375	5q multi	.15 .15
1800	A375	10q multi	.15 .15
1801	A375	15q multi	.15 .15
1802	A375	25q multi	.15 .15
1803	A375	80q multi	.30 .15
1804	A375	1.20 l multi	.60 .20
1805	A375	1.55 l multi	.75 .25
		Set value	1.90 .75

Miniature Sheet
Perf. 12 on 2 sides x Imperf.
1806 A375 2.05 l multi   1.25 .40
See Nos. 1836-1840, 1884-1888.

Attack A376

Designs: 25q, Enver Hoxha addressing Army. 80q, Volunteers and riflemen. 1 l, Volunteers, hydrofoil patrolboat and MiG planes. 1.90 l, Volunteers and Albanian flag.

1977, July 10   *Litho.*   *Perf. 12*

1807	A376	15q gold & multi	.15 .15
1808	A376	25q gold & multi	.15 .15
1809	A376	80q gold & multi	.45 .15
1810	A376	1 l gold & multi	.70 .15
1811	A376	1.90 l gold & multi	1.25 .25
		Nos. 1807-1811 (5)	2.70
		Set value	.50

"One People-One Army."

Armed Workers, Article 3 of Constitution A377

Design: 1.20 l, Symbols of farming and fertilizer industry, Article 25 of Constitution.

1977, Oct.

1812	A377	25q red, gold & blk	.25 .15
1813	A377	1.20 l red, gold & blk	.95 .20
		Set value	.25

New Constitution.

Picnic — A378

Film Frames: 15q, Telephone lineman in winter. 25q, Two men and a woman. 80q, Workers. 1.20 l, Boys playing in street. 1.60 l, Harvest.

1977, Oct. 25   *Litho.*   *Perf. 12½x12*

1814	A378	10q blue green	.15 .15
1815	A378	15q multi	.15 .15
1816	A378	25q black	.15 .15
1817	A378	80q multi	.55 .15
1818	A378	1.20 l deep claret	.95 .15
1819	A378	1.60 l multi	1.25 .20
		Nos. 1814-1819 (6)	3.20
		Set value	.55

Albanian films.

Farm Workers in Field, by V. Mio A379

Paintings by V. Mio: 10q, Landscape in Snow. 15q, Grazing Sheep under Walnut Tree in Spring. 25q, Street in Korce. 80q, Horseback Riders on Mountain Pass. 1 l, Boats on Shore. 1.75 l, Tractors Plowing Fields. 2.05 l, Self-portrait.

1977, Dec. 25   *Litho.*   *Perf. 12½x12*

1820	A379	5q gold & multi	.15 .15
1821	A379	10q gold & multi	.15 .15
1822	A379	15q gold & multi	.15 .15
1823	A379	25q gold & multi	.15 .15
1824	A379	80q gold & multi	.40 .15
1825	A379	1 l gold & multi	.45 .15
1826	A379	1.75 l gold & multi	.80 .15
		Set value	2.00 .55

Miniature Sheet
Imperf.; Perf. 12 Horiz. between Vignette and Value Panel
1827 A379 2.05 l gold & multi   2.00 .35

Pan Flute — A380   Albanian Flag, Monument and People — A381

Folk Musical Instruments: 25q, Single-string goat's-head fiddle. 80q, Woodwind. 1.20 l, Drum. 1.70 l, Bagpipe. Background shows various woven folk patterns.

1978, Jan. 20   *Perf. 12x12½*

1828	A380	15q multi	.15 .15
1829	A380	25q multi	.25 .15
1830	A380	80q multi	.70 .15
1831	A380	1.20 l multi	1.10 .15
1832	A380	1.70 l multi	1.50 .20
		Nos. 1828-1832 (5)	3.70
		Set value	.55

1978   *Perf. 12½x12, 12x12½*

Designs: 25q, Ismail Qemali and fighters, horiz. 1.65 l, People dancing around Albanian flag, horiz.

1833	A381	15q multi	.20 .15
1834	A381	25q multi	.25 .15
1835	A381	1.65 l multi	1.50 .20
		Nos. 1833-1835 (3)	1.95
		Set value	.30

65th anniversary of independence.

Folk Dancing Type of 1977

Designs: Various dances.

1914 A398 1.20 l Soccer .50 .15
1915 A398 1.40 l High jump .65 .25
    Nos. 1911-1915 (5)   1.70
    Set value   .50

Liberation Spartakiad, 35th anniversary.

1979, Oct. 12

Albanian Literary Society Centenary: 25q, Seal and charter. 80q, Founder. 1.55 l, 1879 Headquarters. 1.90 l, Founders.

1916 A399 25q multi .15 .15
1917 A399 80q multi .40 .15
1918 A399 1.20 l multi .60 .15
1919 A399 1.55 l multi .75 .20
    Nos. 1916-1919 (4)   1.90
    Set value   .45

Miniature Sheet

Perf. 12½ on 2 sides x Imperf.

1920 A399 1.90 l multi 2.00 .40

Congress Statute, Coat of Arms — A400

1979, Oct. 20 Photo. *Perf. 12x12½*
1921 A400 25q multi .50 .15
1922 A400 1.65 l multi 2.50 .25
    Set value   .30

2nd Congress of Berat, 35th anniversary.

Children Entering School, Books — A401

1979 Litho. *Perf. 12½x12*
1923 A401 5q shown .15 .15
1924 A401 10q Communications .15 .15
1925 A401 15q Steel workers .15 .15
1926 A401 20q Dancers, instruments .15 .15
1927 A401 25q Newspapers, radio, television .20 .15
1928 A401 60q Textile worker .40 .15
1929 A401 80q Armed forces .55 .15
1930 A401 1.20 l Industry .80 .20
1931 A401 1.60 l Transportation 1.00 .30
1932 A401 2.40 l Agriculture 1.50 .35
1932A A401 3 l Medicine 1.90 .50
    Nos. 1923-1932A (11)   6.95
    Set value   1.75

Workers and Factory A402

Worker, Red Flag and: 80q, Hand holding sickle and rifle. 1.20 l, Red star and open book. 1.55 l, Open book and cogwheel.

1979, Nov. 29
1933 A402 25q multi .15 .15
1934 A402 80q multi .20 .15
1935 A402 1.20 l multi .50 .15
1936 A402 1.55 l multi .60 .15
    Nos. 1933-1936 (4)   1.45
    Set value   .45

35th anniversary of independence.

Joseph Stalin — A403

Design: 1.10 l, Stalin on dais, horiz.

1979, Dec. 21 Litho. *Perf. 12*
1937 A403 80q red & dk bl .75 .15
1938 A403 1.10 l red & dk bl 1.00 .15
    Set value   .30

Joseph Stalin (1879-1953), birth centenary.

Fireplace and Pottery, Korcar A404

Home Furnishings: 80q, Cupboard bed, dagger, pistol, ammunition pouch, Shkodar. 1.20 l, Stool, pot, chair, Mirdit. 1.35 l, Chimney, dagger, jacket, Gjirokaster.

1980, Feb. 27 Litho. *Perf. 12*
1939 A404 25q multi .15 .15
1940 A404 80q multi .35 .15
1941 A404 1.20 l multi .55 .20
1942 A404 1.35 l multi .60 .30
    Nos. 1939-1942 (4)   1.65
    Set value   .65

See Nos. 1985-1988.

Pipe, Painted Flask — A405

1980, Mar. 4
1943 A405 25q shown .15 .15
1944 A405 80q Leather handbags .35 .15
1945 A405 1.20 l Carved eagle, embroidered rug .55 .20
1946 A405 1.35 l Lace .60 .30
    Nos. 1943-1946 (4)   1.65
    Set value   .65

Prof. Aleksander Xhuvanit Birth Centenary — A406

1980, Mar. 14
1947 A406 80q multi .55 .15
1948 A406 1 l multi .70 .20

Revolutionaries on Horseback — A407

Insurrection at Kosove, 70th Anniversary: 1 l, Battle scene.

1980, Apr. 4
1949 A407 80q red & black .60 .15
1950 A407 1 l red & black .75 .20

Soldiers and Workers Laboring to Aid the Stricken Populations, by D. Jukinui and I. Lulani — A408

1980, Apr. 15 Litho. *Perf. 12½*
1951 A408 80q lt blue & multi .60 .15
1952 A408 1 l lt blue grn & multi .75 .20

Lenin, 110th Birth Anniversary — A409

1980, Apr. 22
1953 A409 80q multi .90 .15
1954 A409 1 l multi 1.10 .20

Misto Mame and Ali Demi, War Martyrs A410

War Martyrs: 80q, Sadik Staveleci, Vojo Kusji, Hoxhi Martini. 1.20 l, Bule Naipi, Persefoni Kokedhima. 1.35 l, Ndoc Deda, Hydajet Lezha, Naim Gyylbegu, Ndoc Mazi, Ahmed Haxha.

1980, May 5
1955 A410 25q multi .15 .15
1956 A410 80q multi .40 .15
1957 A410 1.20 l multi .55 .20
1958 A410 1.35 l multi .70 .30
    Nos. 1955-1958 (4)   1.80
    Set value   .65

See Nos. 2012A-2012D, 2025-2028, 2064-2067, 2122-2125, 2171-2174, 2207-2209.

Scene from "Mirela" A411

1980, June 7
1959 A411 15q shown .15 .15
1960 A411 25q The Scribbler .15 .15
1961 A411 80q Circus Bears .35 .15
1962 A411 2.40 l Waterdrops 1.00 .35
    Nos. 1959-1962 (4)   1.65
    Set value   .55

Carrying Iron Castings in the Enver Hoxha Tractor Combine, by S. Shijaku and M. Fushekati — A412

Paintings (Gallery of Figurative Paintings, Tirana): 80q, The Welder, by Harilla Dhima. 1.20 l, Steel Erectors, by Petro Kokushta. 1.35 l, Pandeli Lena, 1.80 l, Communists, by Vilson Kilica.

1980, July 22
1963 A412 25q multi .15 .15
1964 A412 80q multi .35 .15
1965 A412 1.20 l multi .50 .15
1966 A412 1.35 l multi .65 .25
    Nos. 1963-1966 (4)   1.65
    Set value   .55

Souvenir Sheet

1967 A412 1.80 l multi 1.40 .40

Gate, Parchment Miniature, 11th Cent. — A413

Bas reliefs of the Middle Ages: 80q, Eagle, 13th cent. 1.20 l, Heraldic lion, 14th cent. 1.35 l, Pheasant, 14th cent.

1980, Sept. 27 Litho. *Perf. 12*
1968 A413 25q gold & blk .15 .15
1969 A413 80q gold & blk .25 .15
1970 A413 1.20 l gold & blk .45 .15
1971 A413 1.35 l gold & blk .55 .25
    Nos. 1968-1971 (4)   1.40
    Set value   .55

Divjaka National Park — A414

1980, Nov. 6
1972 A414 80q shown .50 .15
1973 A414 1.20 l Lura .85 .25
1974 A414 1.60 l Thethi 1.10 .25
    Nos. 1972-1974 (3)   2.45 .65

Souvenir Sheet

Perf. 12½

1975 A414 1.80 l Llogara Park 2.00 .75

Citizens, Flag and Arms of Albania A415

1981, Jan. 11 Litho. *Perf. 12*
1976 A415 80q shown .50 .15
1977 A415 1 l People's Party Headquarters, Tirana .75 .25

35th anniversary of the Republic.

Child's Bed — A416

1981, Mar. 20 Litho. *Perf. 12*
1978 A416 25q shown .15 .15
1979 A416 80q Wooden bucket, brass bottle .35 .20
1980 A416 1.20 l Shoes .55 .25
1981 A416 1.35 l Jugs .60 .30
    Nos. 1978-1981 (4)   1.65 .90

A417   A419

1981, Apr. 20
1982 A417 80q Soldiers .40 .20
1983 A417 1 l Sword combat .60 .25

Souvenir Sheet

Perf. 12½ Vert.

1984 A417 1.80 l Soldier with pistol 1.25 .80

Battle of Shtimje centenary.

Home Furnishings Type of 1980

1981, Feb. 25 Litho. *Perf. 12*
1985 A404 25q House interior, Labara .15 .15
1986 A404 80q Labara, diff. .35 .20
1987 A404 1.20 l Mat .55 .25
1988 A404 1.35 l Dibres .55 .30
    Nos. 1985-1988 (4)   1.60 .90

1981, June *Perf. 12*

Designs: Children's circus.

1989 A419 15q multi .15 .15
1990 A419 25q multi .15 .15
1991 A419 80q multi .35 .20
1992 A419 2.40 l multi 1.00 .60
    Nos. 1989-1992 (4)   1.65
    Set value   .65

Soccer Players
A420

1982 World Cup Soccer Elimination Games: Various soccer players.

1981, Mar. 31		Litho.	Perf. 12	
1993	A420	25q multi	.25	.15
1994	A420	80q multi	1.90	.40
1995	A420	1.20 l multi	2.75	.65
1996	A420	1.35 l multi	3.50	.80
		Nos. 1993-1996 (4)	8.40	2.00

Allies, by
S. Hysa
A421

Paintings: 80q, Warriors, by A. Buza. 1.20 l, Rallying to the Flag, Dec. 1911, by A. Zajmi, vert. 1.35 l, My Flag is My Heart, by L. Cefa, vert. 1.80 l, Circling the Flag in a Common Cause, by N. Vasia.

1981, July 10		Perf. 12¹/₂x12		
1997	A421	25q multi	.15	.15
1998	A421	80q multi	.35	.20
1999	A421	1.20 l multi	.50	.25
2000	A421	1.35 l multi	.55	.30
		Nos. 1997-2000 (4)	1.55	.90

Souvenir Sheet

2001	A421	1.80 l multi	1.40	.85

No. 2001 contains one stamp, size: 55x55mm.

Rifleman
A422

1981, Aug. 30			Perf. 12	
2002	A422	25q shown	.15	.15
2003	A422	80q Weight lifting	.40	.20
2004	A422	1.20 l Volleyball	.55	.25
2005	A422	1.35 l Soccer	.65	.35
		Nos. 2002-2005 (4)	1.75	.95

Albanian
Workers' Party,
8th Congress
A423

1981, Nov. 1				
2006	A423	80q Flag, star	.30	.20
2007	A423	1 l Flag, hammer & sickle	.40	.25

Albanian Workers'
Party, 40th
Anniv. — A424

Communist Youth
Org., 40th
Anniv. — A425

1981, Nov. 8				
2008	A424	80q Symbols of industrialization	.35	.25
2009	A424	2.80 l Fist, emblem	1.25	.70

Souvenir Sheet

2010	A424	1.80 l Enver Hoxha, Memoirs	2.00	.85

1981, Nov. 23				
2011	A425	80q Star, ax, map	.65	.20
2012	A425	1 l Flags, star	.85	.25

War Martyrs Type of 1980

Portraits: 25q, Perlat Rexhepi (1919-42) and Branko Kadia (1921-42). 80q, Xheladin Beqiri (1908-44) and Hajdar Dushi (1916-44). 1.20 l, Koci Bako (1905-41), Vasil Laci (1923-41) and Mujo Ulqinaku (1898-1939). 1.35 l, Mine Peza (1875-1942) and Zoja Cure (1920-44).

1981, May 5		Litho.	Perf. 12	
2012A	A410	25q silver & multi	.20	.15
2012B	A410	80q gold & multi	.75	.40
2012C	A410	1.20 l silver & multi	1.25	.55
2012D	A410	1.35 l gold & multi	1.40	.60
		Nos. 2012A-2012D (4)	3.60	1.70

Fan S. Noli, Writer,
Birth
Centenary — A426

1982, Jan. 6		Litho.	Perf. 12	
2013	A426	80q lt ol grn & gold	.40	.20
2014	A426	1.10 l lt red brn & gold	.60	.25

Traditional Houses Type of 1979

1982, Feb.			Perf. 12¹/₂x12	
2015	A392	25q Bulqize	.30	.20
2016	A392	80q Lebush	.35	.20
2017	A392	1.20 l Bicaj	.55	.30
2018	A392	1.55 l Klos	.80	.40
		Nos. 2015-2018 (4)	2.00	1.10

TB Bacillus
Centenary
A428

1982, Mar. 24			Perf. 12	
2019	A428	80q Globe	1.00	.25
2020	A428	1.10 l Koch	1.40	.35

Albanian
League
House,
Prizren,
by K.
Buza
A429

Kosova Landscapes: 25q, Castle at Prizrenit, by G. Madhi. 1.20 l, Mountain Gorge at Rogove, by K. Buza. 1.55 l, Street of the Hadhji at Zekes, by G. Madhi. 25q, 1.20 l, 1.55 l vert.

		Perf. 12x12¹/₂, 12¹/₂x12		
1982, Apr. 15			Litho.	
2021	A429	25q multi	.20	.15
2022	A429	80q multi	.50	.15
2023	A429	1.20 l multi	.70	.20
2024	A429	1.55 l multi	1.00	.30
		Nos. 2021-2024 (4)	2.40	
		Set value		.65

War Martyr Type of 1980

Designs: 25q, Hibe Palikuqi, Liri Gero. 80q, Mihal Duri, Kajo Karafili. 1.20 l, Fato Dudumi, Margarita Tutulani, Shejnaze Juka. 1.55 l, Memo Meto, Gjok Doci.

1982, May			Perf. 12	
2025	A410	25q multi	.15	.15
2026	A410	80q multi	.35	.20
2027	A410	1.20 l multi	.60	.30
2028	A410	1.55 l multi	.85	.45
		Nos. 2025-2028 (4)	1.95	1.10

Loading
Freighter
A430

Children's Paintings.

1982, June 15		Perf. 12¹/₂x12		
2029	A430	15q shown	.15	.15
2030	A430	80q Forest	.55	.20
2031	A430	1.20 l City	.90	.30
2032	A430	1.65 l Park	1.25	.45
		Nos. 2029-2032 (4)	2.85	1.10

9th Congress
of Trade
Unions
A431

1982, June 6		Litho.	Perf. 12	
2033	A431	80q Workers, factories	.80	.20
2034	A431	1.10 l Emblem, flag	1.10	.25

Alpine
Village
Festival,
by Danish
Jukniu
A432

Industrial Development Paintings: 80q, Hydroelectric Station Builders, by Ali Miruku. 1.20 l, Steel Workers, by Clirim Ceka. 1.55 l, Oil drillers, by Pandeli Lena. 1.90 l, Trapping the Furnace, by Jorgji Gjikopulli.

1982, July		Perf. 12¹/₂		
2035	A432	25q multi	.15	.15
2036	A432	80q multi	.50	.15
2037	A432	1.20 l multi	.75	.20
2038	A432	1.55 l multi	1.00	.30
		Nos. 2035-2038 (4)	2.40	.80

Souvenir Sheet
Perf. 12

2039	A432	1.90 l multi	1.65	.40

No. 2039 contains one 54x48mm stamp.

Communist Party
Newspaper "Voice of
the People," 40th
Anniv. — A432a

1982, Aug. 25		Litho.	Perf. 12	
2039A	A432a	80q Newspapers		
2039B	A432a	1.10 l Paper, press		

40th Anniv. of
Democratic
Front — A433

1982, Sept. 16			Perf. 12	
2040	A433	80q Glory to the Heroes of Peza Monument	.80	.20
2041	A433	1.10 l Marchers	1.10	.25

8th Youth
Congress — A434

Handmade
Shoulder
Bags — A435

1982, Oct. 4				
2042	A434	80q multi	.80	.20
2043	A434	1.10 l multi	1.10	.25

1982, Nov.				
2044	A435	25q Rug, horiz.	.15	.15
2045	A435	80q shown	.40	.15
2046	A435	1.20 l Wooden pots, bowls, horiz.	.60	.20
2047	A435	1.55 l Jug	.80	.30
		Nos. 2044-2047 (4)	1.95	
		Set value		.65

70th Anniv. of
Independence A436

1982, Nov. 28				
2048	A436	20q Ishamil Qemali	.15	.15
2049	A436	1.20 l Partisans	.60	.20
2050	A436	2.40 l Partisans, diff.	1.25	.40
		Nos. 2048-2050 (3)	2.00	.75

Souvenir Sheet

2051	A436	1.90 l Independence Monument, Tirana	1.65	.40

Dhermi Beach
A437

1982, Dec. 20				
2052	A437	25q shown	.15	.15
2053	A437	80q Sarande	.50	.20
2054	A437	1.20 l Ksamil	.75	.25
2055	A437	1.55 l Lukove	1.00	.35
		Nos. 2052-2055 (4)	2.40	.95

Handkerchief
Dancers
A438

Folkdancers.

1983, Feb. 20		Litho.	Perf. 12	
2056	A438	25q shown	.15	.15
2057	A438	80q With kerchief, drum	.40	.20
2058	A438	1.20 l With guitar, flute, tambourine	.60	.25
2059	A438	1.55 l Women	.80	.35
		Nos. 2056-2059 (4)	1.95	.95

A439   A440

1983, Mar. 14		Litho.	Perf. 12	
2060	A439	80q multi	1.10	.20
2061	A439	1.10 l multi	1.50	.25

Karl Marx (1818-83).

1983, Apr. 20				
2062	A440	80q Electricity generation	.40	.20
2063	A440	1.10 l Gas & oil production	.55	.25

Energy development.

War Martyr Type of 1980

Designs: 25q, Asim Zeneli (1916-43), Nazmi Rushiti (1919-42). 80q, Shyqyri Ishmi (1922-42), Shyqyri Alimerko (1923-43), Myzafer Asqeriu (1918-42). 1.20 l, Oybra Sokoli (1924-44), Qeriba Derri (1905-44), Ylbere Bilibashi (1928-44). 1.55 l, Themo Vasi (1915-44), Abaz Shehu (1905-42).

1983, May 5		Litho.	Perf. 12	
2064	A410	25q multi	.15	.15
2065	A410	80q multi	.40	.20
2066	A410	1.20 l multi	.60	.25
2067	A410	1.55 l multi	.80	.35
		Nos. 2064-2067 (4)	1.95	.95

Women's Union, 9th Congress — A441

1983, June 1   Litho.   Perf. 12x12½
2068 A441   80q red & gold   .85 .20
2069 A441   1.10 l blue & gold   1.10 .25

Bicycling A442

1983, June 20   Perf. 12
2070 A442   25q shown   .15 .15
2071 A442   80q Chess   .40 .20
2072 A442   1.20 l Gymnastics   .60 .20
2073 A442   1.55 l Wrestling   .80 .35
    Nos. 2070-2073 (4)   1.95 .95

40th Anniv. of People's Army — A443

1983, July 10
2074 A443   20q Armed services   .15 .15
2075 A443   1.20 l Soldier, gun barrels   .85 .25
2076 A443   2.40 l Factory guard, crowd   1.65 .50
    Nos. 2074-2076 (3)   2.65 .90

Sunny Day, by Myrteza Fushekati A444

Paintings: 80q, Messenger of the Grasp, by Niko Progi. 1.20 l, 29 November 1944, by Harilla Dhimo. 1.55 l, Fireworks, by Pandi Mele. 1.90 l, Partisan Assault, by Sali Shijaku and M. Fushekati.

1983, Aug. 28   Litho.   Perf. 12½x12
2077 A444   25q multi   .15 .15
2078 A444   80q multi   .40 .20
2079 A444   1.20 l multi   .60 .25
2080 A444   1.55 l multi   .80 .35
    Nos. 2077-2080 (4)   1.95 .95
Souvenir Sheet
Perf. 12
2081 A444   1.90 l multi   4.00 .50

Folklore Festival Type of 1978
Gjirokaster Folklore Festival: folkdances.

1983, Oct. 6   Litho.   Perf. 12
2082 A388   25q Sword dance   .15 .15
2083 A388   80q Kerchief dance   .50 .20
2084 A388   1.20 l Shepherd flautists   .75 .25
2085 A388   1.55 l Garland dance   1.00 .35
    Nos. 2082-2085 (4)   2.40 .95

World Communications Year — A446

1983, Nov. 10
2086 A446   60q multi   .40 .15
2087 A446   1.20 l multi   .85 .25

75th Birthday of Enver Hoxha — A447

1983, Oct. 16   Litho.   Perf. 12½
2088 A447   80q multi   .40 .20
2089 A447   1.20 l multi   .60 .25
2090 A447   1.80 l multi   .90 .40
    Nos. 2088-2090 (3)   1.90 .85
Souvenir Sheet
Perf. 12
2091 A447   1.90 l multi   1.40 .50

The Right to a Joint Triumph, by J. Keraj A448

Era of Skanderbeg in Figurative Art: 80q, The Heroic Center of the Battle of Krujes, by N. Bakalli. 1.20 l, The Rights of the Enemy after our Triumph, by N. Progri. 1.55 l, The Discussion at Lezhes, by B. Ahmeti. 1.90 l, Victory over the Turks, by G. Madhi.

1983, Dec. 10   Perf. 12½x12
2092 A448   25q multi   .20 .15
2093 A448   80q multi   .60 .20
2094 A448   1.20 l multi   .90 .25
2095 A448   1.55 l multi   1.25 .35
    Nos. 2092-2095 (4)   2.95 .95
Souvenir Sheet
Perf. 12
2096 A448   1.90 l multi   2.25 .50

Greco-Roman Ruins of Illyria — A449

1983, Dec. 28   Perf. 12
2097 A449   80q Amphitheater, Buthroxtum   .65 .20
2098 A449   1.20 l Colonnade, Apollonium   .95 .25
2099 A449   1.80 l Vaulted gallery, amphitheater at Epidamnus   1.40 .40
    Nos. 2097-2099 (3)   3.00 .85

Archeological Discoveries A450

Designs: Apollo, 3rd cent. 25q, Tombstone, Korce, 3rd cent. 80q, Apollo, diff. 1st cent. 1.10 l, Earthenware pot (child's head), Tren, 1st cent. 1.20 l, Man's head, Dyrrah, 2.20 l, Eros with Dolphin, statue Bronze Dyrrah, 3rd cent.

1984, Feb. 25   Perf. 12x12½
2100 A450   15q multi   .15 .15
2101 A450   25q multi   .15 .15
2102 A450   80q multi   .40 .20
2103 A450   1.10 l multi   .55 .20
2104 A450   1.20 l multi   .60 .25
2105 A450   2.20 l multi   1.10 .50
    Nos. 2100-2105 (6)   2.95
    Set value   1.25

Clock Towers — A451

1984, Mar. 30   Litho.   Perf. 12
2106 A451   15q Gjirokaster   .15 .15
2107 A451   25q Kavaje   .15 .15
2108 A451   80q Elbasan   .40 .20
2109 A451   1.10 l Tirana   .55 .20
2110 A451   1.20 l Peqin   .60 .20
2111 A451   2.20 l Kruje   1.10 .50
    Nos. 2106-2111 (6)   2.95
    Set value   1.25

40th Anniv. of Liberation A452

1984, Apr. 20   Litho.   Perf. 12
2112 A452   15q Student & microscope   .15 .15
2113 A452   25q Guerrilla with flag   .15 .15
2114 A452   80q Children with flag   .40 .20
2115 A452   1.10 l Soldier   .55 .20
2116 A452   1.20 l Workers with flag   .60 .25
2117 A452   2.20 l Militia at dam   1.10 .50
    Nos. 2112-2117 (6)   2.95
    Set value   1.25

Children — A453

1984, May   Litho.   Perf. 12
2118 A453   15q Children reading   .15 .15
2119 A453   25q Young pioneers   .25 .15
2120 A453   60q Gardening   .60 .15
2121 A453   2.80 l Kite flying   2.75 .60
    Nos. 2118-2121 (4)   3.75
    Set value   .85

War Martyr Type of 1980

Designs: 15q, Manush Almani, Mustafa Matohiti, Kastriot Muco. 25q, Zaho Koka, Reshit Collaku, Maliq Muco. 1.20 l, Lefter Talo, Tom Kola, Fuat Babani. 2.20 l, Myslysm Shyri, Dervish Hexali, Skender Caci.

1984, May 5   Litho.   Perf. 12
2122 A410   15q multi   .15 .15
2123 A410   25q multi   .15 .15
2124 A410   1.20 l multi   .95 .30
2125 A410   2.20 l multi   1.75 .60
    Nos. 2122-2125 (4)   3.00
    Set value   1.00

A454

A455

1984, May 24   Litho.   Perf. 12
2126 A454   80q Enver Hoxha   .80 .20
2127 A454   1.10 l Resistance fighter   1.25 .30
40th anniv. of Permet Congress.

1984, June 12   Litho.   Perf. 12
2128 A455   15q Goalkeeper   .15 .15
2129 A455   25q Referee   .20 .15
2130 A455   1.20 l Map of Europe   .90 .45
2131 A455   2.20 l Field diagram   1.75 .90
    Nos. 2128-2131 (4)   3.00 1.65

European soccer championships.

Freedom Came, by Myrteza Fushekati A456

Paintings, Tirana Gallery of Figurative Art: 25q, Morning, by Zamir Mati, vert. 80q, My Darling, by Agim Zajmi, vert. 2.60 l, For the Partisans, by Arben Basha. 1.90 l, Eagle, by Zamir Mati, vert.

1984, June 12   Perf. 12½
2132 A456   15q multi   .15 .15
2133 A456   25q multi   .25 .15
2134 A456   80q multi   .80 .25
2135 A456   2.60 l multi   2.75 .80
    Nos. 2132-2135 (4)   3.95 1.35
Souvenir Sheet
Perf. 12 Horiz.
2136 A456   1.90 l multi   3.00 .60

Flora — A457

1984, Aug. 20   Litho.   Perf. 12
2137 A457   15q Moraceae L.   .35 .15
2138 A457   25q Plantaginaceae L.   .60 .15
2139 A457   1.20 l Hypericaceae L.   2.75 .60
2140 A457   2.20 l Leontopodium alpinum   5.25 1.10
    Nos. 2137-2140 (4)   8.95 2.00

AUSIPEX '84, Melbourne, Sept. 21-30 — A458

1984, Sept. 21   Litho.   Perf. 12 Horiz.
2141 A458   1.90 l Sword dancers, emblem   1.50 .75

A459

A460

Forestry, logging, UNFAO emblem.

1984, Sept. 25   Perf. 12
2142 A459   15q Beech trees, transport   .15 .15
2143 A459   25q Pine forest, logging cable   .20 .15
2144 A459   1.20 l Firs, sawmill   .90 .45

2145 A459 2.20 l Forester clearing
woods　　　1.75　.90
Nos. 2142-2145 (4)　3.00 1.65

1984, Oct. 13　　*Perf. 12½*
2146 A460 1.20 l View of Gjirokaster 2.00 .45
　　　EURPHILA '84, Rome.

5th National
Spartakiad — A461

1984, Oct. 19　　*Perf. 12*
2147 A461　15q Soccer　　.15　.15
2148 A461　25q Women's track &
field　　.20　.15
2149 A461　80q Weight lifting　.60　.30
2150 A461 2.20 l Pistol shooting　1.75　.90
Nos. 2147-2150 (4)　2.70 1.50
Souvenir Sheet
Perf. 12 Horiz.
2151 A461 1.90 l Opening ceremony, red flags　　2.00　.75

November 29
Revolution,
40th Anniv.
A462

1984, Nov. 29　　*Perf. 12*
2152 A462　80q Industrial reconstruction　　1.25　.30
2153 A462 1.10 l Natl. flag, partisans 1.65 .40
Souvenir Sheet
Perf. 12 Horiz.
2154 A462 1.90 l Gen. Enver Hoxha
reading 1944 dec-
laration　　2.00　.75

Archaeological
Discoveries from
Illyria — A463

Designs: 15q, Iron Age water container. 80q,
Terra-cotta woman's head, 6th-7th cent. B.C.
1.20 l, Aphrodite, bust, 3rd cent. B.C. 1.70 l, Nike,
A.D. 1st-2nd cent. bronze statue.

1985, Feb. 25　　*Perf. 12x12½*
2155 A463　15q multi　　.15　.15
2156 A463　80q multi　　.80　.40
2157 A463 1.20 l multi　　1.10　.55
2158 A463 1.70 l multi　　1.75　.85
Nos. 2155-2158 (4)　3.80 1.95

Hysni Kapo (1915-
1980), Natl. Labor
Party Leader — A464

1985, Mar. 4　　*Perf. 12*
2159 A464　90q red & blk　　.85　.45
2160 A464 1.10 l chlky bl & blk　1.10　.55

OLYMPHILEX
'85, Lausanne
A465

1985, Mar. 18
2161 A465　25q Women's track &
field　　.25　.15
2162 A465　60q Weight lifting　.60　.30
2163 A465 1.20 l Soccer　　1.10　.55
2164 A465 1.50 l Women's pistol
shooting　　1.25　.65
Nos. 2161-2164 (4)　3.20 1.65

Johann Sebastian
Bach — A466

1985, Mar. 31
2165 A466　80q Portrait, manuscript 2.00 .40
2166 A466 1.20 l Eisenach, birthplace 3.00 .55

Gen. Enver
Hoxha (1908-
1985)
A467

1985, Apr. 11　　*Perf. 12½*
2167 A467　80q multicolored　.80　.40
Souvenir Sheet
Imperf
2168 A467 1.90 l multicolored　2.00 1.00

Natl. Frontier
Guards, 40th
Anniv.
A468

1985, Apr. 25　　*Perf. 12*
2169 A468　25q Guardsman, family　.35　.15
2170 A468　80q At frontier post　1.10　.40

War Martyrs Type of 1980

Cameo portraits: 25q, Mitro Xhani (1916-44),
Nimete Progonati (1929-44), Kozma Nushi (1909-
44). 40q, Ajet Xhindoli (1922-43), Mustafa Kacaci
(1903-44), Estref Caka Osaja (1919-44). 60q, Celo
Sinani (1929-44), Lt. Ambro Andoni (1920-44),
Meleq Gosnishti (1913-44). 1.20 l, Thodhori Mas-
tora (1920-44), Fejzi Micoli (1919-45), Hysen Cino
(1920-44).

1985, May 5
2171 A410　25q multi　　.25　.15
2172 A410　40q multi　　.40　.20
2173 A410　60q multi　　.60　.30
2174 A410 1.20 l multi　　1.25　.55
Nos. 2171-2174 (4)　2.50 1.20

Victory over
Fascism
A469

Designs: 25q, Rifle, red flag, inscribed May 9.
80q, Hand holding rifle, globe, broken swastika.

1985, May 9
2175 A469　25q multi　　.65　.15
2176 A469　80q multi　　2.00　.40
End of World War II, 40th anniv.

Primary
School, by
Thoma
Malo
A470

Paintings, Tirana Gallery of Figurative Art: 80q,
The Heroes, by Hysen Devolli, vert. 90q, In Our
Days, by Angjelin Dodmasej, vert. 1.20 l, Going Off
to Sow, by Ksenofon Dilo. 1.90 l, Foundry Workers,
by Mikel Gurashi.

1985, June 25　　*Perf. 12½*
2177 A470　25q multi　　.25　.15
2178 A470　80q multi　　.80　.40
2179 A470　90q multi　　.85　.45
2180 A470 1.20 l multi　　1.10　.55
Nos. 2177-2180 (4)　3.00 1.55
Souvenir Sheet
Perf. 12 Horiz.
2181 A470 1.90 l multi　　2.00 1.00

Basketball
Championships,
Spain — A471

Fruits — A472

Various plays.

1985, July 20　　Litho.　*Perf. 12*
2182 A471　25q dull bl & blk　.25　.15
2183 A471　80q dull grn & blk　.80　.40
2184 A471 1.20 l dl vio & blk　1.10　.60
2185 A471 1.60 l dl rose & blk　1.50　.75
Nos. 2182-2185 (4)　3.65 1.90

1985, Aug. 20
2186 A472　25q Oranges　　.25　.15
2187 A472　80q Plums　　.80　.40
2188 A472 1.20 l Apples　　1.10　.60
2189 A472 1.60 l Cherries　　1.50　.75
Nos. 2186-2189 (4)　3.65 1.90

Architecture
A473

1985, Sept. 20
2190 A473　25q Kruja　　.25　.15
2191 A473　80q Gjirokastra　.80　.40
2192 A473 1.20 l Berati　　1.10　.60
2193 A473 1.60 l Shkodera　1.50　.75
Nos. 2190-2193 (4)　3.65 1.90

Natl. Folk Theater
Festival — A474

Various scenes from folk plays.

1985, Oct. 6
2194 A474　25q multi　　.25　.15
2195 A474　80q multi　　.80　.40
2196 A474 1.20 l multi　　1.10　.60
2197 A474 1.60 l multi　　1.50　.75
Size: 56x82mm
Imperf
2198 A474 1.90 l multi　　3.50 1.90
Nos. 2194-2198 (5)　7.15 3.80

Socialist
People's
Republic,
40th
Anniv.
A475

1986, Jan. 11　Litho.　*Perf. 12½*
2199 A475　25q Natl. crest, vert.　.70　.15
2200 A475　80q Proclamation, 1946　2.25　.40

A476　　A477

Designs: 25q, Dam, River Drin, Melgun. 80q,
Bust of Enver Hoxha, dam power house.

1986, Feb. 20　　*Perf. 12*
2201 A476　25q multi　　1.25　.15
2202 A476　80q multi　　3.75　.40
Enver Hoxha hydro-electric power station,
Koman.

1986, Mar. 20　Litho.　*Perf. 12*
Flowers.
2203 A477　25q Gymnospermium
shqipetarum　　.35　.15
2204 A477 1.20 l Leucojum valen-
tinum　　1.90　.60
　a.　Pair. #2203-2204　2.25 1.00
No. 2204a sold only in booklets of 2; exists
imperf.

A478

Famous Men — A479

Designs: 25q, Maxim Gorky, Russian author.
80q, Andre Marie Ampere, French physicist. 1.20 l,
James Watt, English inventor of modern steam
engine. 2.40 l, Franz Liszt, Hungarian composer.

1986, Apr. 20
2205　　Strip of 4　4.40 2.20
　a.　A478 25q dull red brown　.25　.15
　b.　A478 80q dull violet　.75　.40
　c.　A478 1.20 l blue green　1.10　.60
　d.　A478 2.40 l dull lilac rose　2.25　.60
Size: 88x72mm
Imperf
2206 A479 1.90 l multi　　1.75　.88
No. 2206 has central area picturing Gorky,
Ampere, Watt and Liszt, perf. 12½.

War Martyrs Type of 1980

Portraits: 25q, Ramiz Aranitasi (1923-43), Inajete
Dumi (1924-44) and Laze Nuro Ferraj (1897-
1944). 80q, Dine Kalenja (1919-44), Kozma Naska
(1921-44), Met Hasa (1929-44) and Fahri
Ramadani (1920-44). 1.20 l, Hiqmet Buzi (1927-
44), Bajram Tusha (1922-42), Mumin Selami
(1923-42) and Hajrfdin Bylyshi (1923-42).

1986, May 5 — *Perf. 12*

2207	A410	25q multi	.65	.15
2208	A410	80q multi	2.25	.40
2209	A410	1.20 l multi	3.00	.55
	Nos. 2207-2209 (3)		5.90	1.10

1986 World Cup Soccer Championships, Mexico — A481

1986, May 31 — *Litho.* — *Perf. 12*

2210	A480	25q Globe, world cup	.25	.15
2211	A480	1.20 l Player, soccer ball	1.25	.60

Size: 97x64mm
Imperf

2212	A481	1.90 l multi	1.75	.90
	Nos. 2210-2212 (3)		3.25	1.65

No. 2212 has central label, perf. 12½.

Transportation Workers' Day, 40th Anniv. — A482

1986, Aug. 10 — *Litho.* — *Perf. 12*

2213	A482	1.20 l multi	3.00	.60

Prominent Albanians A483

Designs: 30q, Naim Frasheri (1846-1900), poet. 60q, Ndre Mjeda (1866-1937), poet. 90q, Petro Nini Luarasi (1865-1911), poet, journalist. 1 l, Andon Zako Cajupi (1866-1930), poet. 1.20 l, Millosh Gjergj Nikolla Migjeni (1911-1938), novelist. 2.60 l, Urani Rumbo (1884-1936), educator.

1986, Sept. 20 — *Litho.* — *Perf. 12*

2214	A483	30q multi	.30	.15
2215	A483	60q multi	.60	.30
2216	A483	90q multi	.90	.45
2217	A483	1 l multi	.95	.50
2218	A483	1.20 l multi	1.10	.60
2219	A483	2.60 l multi	2.50	1.25
	Nos. 2214-2219 (6)		6.35	3.25

Albanian Workers' Party, 9th Congress, Tirana A484

1986, Nov. 3 — *Litho.* — *Perf. 12*

2220	A484	30q multi	1.90	.25

A485   A486

Albanian Workers' Party, 45th Anniv.: 30q, Handstamp, signature of Hoxha. 1.20 l, Marx, Engels, Lenin and Stalin, party building.

1986, Nov. 8

2221	A485	30q multi	.60	.15
2222	A485	1.20 l multi	2.25	.60

1986, Nov. 29 — *Perf. 12x12½*

Statue of Mother Albania.

2223	A486	10q peacock blue	.15	.15
2224	A486	20q henna brn	.20	.15
2225	A486	30q vermilion	.30	.15
2226	A486	50q dk olive bis	.50	.25
2227	A486	60q lt olive grn	.60	.30
2228	A486	80q rose	.80	.40
2229	A486	90q ultra	.90	.45
2230	A486	1.20 l green	1.10	.60
2231	A486	1.60 l red vio	1.50	.75
2232	A486	2.20 l myrtle grn	2.00	1.10
2233	A486	3 l brn org	2.75	1.40
2234	A486	6 l yel bister	5.50	2.25
	Nos. 2223-2234 (12)		16.30	7.95

For surcharges see Nos. 2435-2439.

Artifacts A487

Designs: 30q, Head of Aesoulapius, 5th cent. B.C. Byllis, marble. 80q, Aphrodite, 3rd cent. B.C., Fier, terracotta. 1 l, Pan, 3rd-2nd cent. B.C., Byllis, bronze. 1.20 l, Jupiter, A.D. 2nd cent., Tirana, limestone.

1987, Feb. 20

2235	A487	30q multi	.30	.15
2236	A487	80q multi	.75	.40
2237	A487	1 l multi	.95	.45
2238	A487	1.20 l multi	1.10	.60
	Nos. 2235-2238 (4)		3.10	1.60

1st Albanian School, Cent. — A488

Famous Men — A489

Gun, quill pen, book of the alphabet and: 30q, Monument, vert. 80q, School, Korca. 1.20 l, Students.

1987, Mar. 7 — *Perf. 12*

2239	A488	30q multi	.35	.15
2240	A488	80q multi	.85	.40
2241	A488	1.20 l multi	1.25	.60
	Nos. 2239-2241 (3)		2.45	1.15

1987, Apr. 20

Designs: 30q, Victor Hugo, French author. 80q, Galileo Galilei, Italian mathematician, philosopher. 90q, Charles Darwin, British biologist. 1.30 l, Miguel Cervantes, Spanish novelist.

2242	A489	30q multi	.30	.15
2243	A489	80q multi	.75	.40
2244	A489	90q multi	.90	.45
2245	A489	1.30 l multi	1.25	.80
	Nos. 2242-2245 (4)		3.20	1.80

World Food Day — A490

10th Trade Unions Cong. — A491

1987, May 20

2246	A490	30q Forsythia europaea	.30	.15
2247	A490	90q Moltkia doerfleri	.85	.45
2248	A490	2.10 l Wulfenia baldacii	2.00	1.00
	Nos. 2246-2248 (3)		3.15	1.60

1987, June 25

2249	A491	1.20 l multi	2.25	.60

Sowing, by Bujar Asllani — A492

Paintings in the Eponymous Museum, Tirana: 30q, The Sustenance of Industry, by Myrteza Fushekati, vert. 80q, The Gifted Partisan, by Skender Kokobobo, vert. 1.20 l, At the Forging Block, by Clirim Ceka.

Perf. 12x12½, 12½x12

1987, July 20 — *Litho.*

2250	A492	30q multi	.30	.15
2251	A492	80q multi	.80	.40
2252	A492	1 l shown	1.00	.50
2253	A492	1.20 l multi	1.25	.60
	Nos. 2250-2253 (4)		3.35	1.65

A493

OLYMPHILEX '87, Rome, Aug. 29-Sept. 6 — A494

Illustration A494 reduced.

1987, Aug. 29 — *Litho.* — *Perf. 12½*

2254	A493	30q Hammer throw	.30	.15
2255	A493	90q Running	.90	.45
2256	A493	1.10 l Shot put	1.25	.60

Size: 85x60mm

2257	A494	1.90 l Runner, globe	2.00	1.00
	Nos. 2254-2257 (4)		4.45	2.20

Famous Men — A495

Designs: 30q, Themistokli Germenji (1871-1917), author, politician. 80q, Bajram Curri (1862-1925), founder of the Albanian League. 90q, Aleks Stavre Drenova (1872-1947), poet. 1.30 l, Gjerasim D. Qiriazi (1861-1894), teacher, journalist.

1987, Sept. 30 — *Perf. 12*

2258	A495	30q multi	.30	.15
2259	A495	80q multi	.80	.40
2260	A495	90q multi	.90	.45
2261	A495	1.30 l multi	1.30	.65
	Nos. 2258-2261 (4)		3.30	1.65

Albanian Labor Party Congress, Tirana A496

1987, Oct. 22 — *Litho.* — *Perf. 12*

2262	A496	1.20 l multi	1.90	.60

Natl. Independence, 75th Anniv. — A497

Postal Administration, 75th Anniv. — A498

1987, Nov. 27

2263	A497	1.20 l State flag	1.90	.60

1987, Dec. 5

2264	A498	90q P.O. emblem	2.00	.45
2265	A498	1.20 l State seal	2.50	.60

Art & Literature — A499

WHO, 40th Anniv. — A500

Portraits: 30q, Lord Byron (1788-1824), English Poet. 1.20 l, Eugene Delacroix (1798-1863), French painter.

1988, Mar. 10

2266	A499	30q org brn & blk	1.00	.15
2267	A499	1.20 l pale vio & blk	4.00	.60

1988, Apr. 7

2268	A500	90q multi	2.00	.45
2269	A500	1.20 l multi	2.50	.60

Flowers — A501

1988, May 20

Booklet Stamps

2270	A501	30q Sideritis raeseri	.75	.15
2271	A501	90q Lunaria telekiana	2.25	.45
2272	A501	2.10 l Sanguisorba albanica	5.50	1.10
a.	Bklt. pane of 3, plus label		8.50	
	Nos. 2270-2272 (3)		8.50	1.70

10th Women's Federation Congress A502

1988, June 6

2273	A502	90q blk, red & dark org	2.50	.45

European Soccer Championships — A503

Various athletes.
1.90 l, Goalie designs of Nos. 2274-2276.

1988, June 10
2274	A503	30q multicolored	.30	.15
2275	A503	80q multicolored	.80	.40
2276	A503	1.20 l multicolored	1.25	.60

Size: 79x68mm
Imperf
2277	A503	1.90 l multicolored	1.90	.95
		Nos. 2274-2277 (4)	4.25	2.10

Migjeni
(1911-1938),
Poet — A507

1988, Aug. 26　Litho.　Perf. 12
2285	A507	90q silver & brown	2.50	.50

Ballads — A508

1988, Sept. 5
2286	A508	30q Dede Skurra	1.00	.15
2287	A508	90q Omeri Iri	3.00	.65
2288	A508	1.20 l Gjergj Elez Alia	4.00	.65
		Nos. 2286-2288 (3)	8.00	1.30

Folklore Festival Type of 1978

1988, Oct. 6
2289	A388	30q Kerchief Dance	1.25	.15
2290	A388	1.20 l Dancers with raised arm	4.75	.65

Enver
Hoxha
Museum
A510

Perf. 12x12¹/₂, 12¹/₂x12
1988, Oct. 16　　　　　　Litho.
2291	A510	90q Portrait, vert.	1.10	.35
2292	A510	1.20 l shown	1.40	.50

Enver Hoxha (1908-1985), Communist leader.

Locomotives, Map Showing Rail
Network — A512

1989, Feb. 28　Litho.　Perf. 12¹/₂x12
2295	A512	30q 1947	.20	.15
2296	A512	90q 1949	.65	.35
2297	A512	1.20 l 1978	.85	.40
2298	A512	1.80 l 1985	1.25	.65
2299	A512	2.40 l 1988	1.65	.85
		Nos. 2295-2299 (5)	4.60	2.40

Archaeological
Treasures
A513

30q, Illyrian grave. 90q, Warrior on horseback.

1989, Mar. 10　Litho.　Perf. 12
2300	A513	30q blk & tan	.20	.15
2301	A513	90q blk & dl grn	.65	.35
2302	A513	2.10 l shown	1.50	.75
		Nos. 2300-2302 (3)	2.35	1.25

Folklore — A514

1989, Apr. 5　Litho.　Perf. 12x12¹/₂
2303	A514	30q multicolored	.20	.15
2304	A514	80q multi, diff.	.55	.30
2305	A514	1 l multi, diff.	.70	.35
2306	A514	1.20 l multi, diff.	.85	.45
		Nos. 2303-2306 (4)	2.30	1.25

Flowers — A515　　Famous
　　　　　　　　　People — A516

Designs: 30q, *Aster albanicus.* 90q, *Orchis x
paparisti.* 2.10 l, *Orchis albanica.*

1989, May 10　　　　　Perf. 12
2307	A515	30q multicolored	.20	.15
2308	A515	90q multicolored	.65	.35
2309	A515	2.10 l multicolored	1.50	.75
		Nos. 2307-2309 (3)	2.35	1.25

1989, June 3
Designs: 30q, Johann Strauss the Younger (1825-
1899), composer. 80q, Marie Curie (1867-1834),
chemist. 1 l, Federico Garcia Lorca (1898-1936),
poet. 1.20 l, Albert Einstein (1879-1955), physicist.
2310	A516	30q gold & blk brn	.20	.15
2311	A516	80q gold & blk brn	.60	.30
2312	A516	1 l gold & blk brn	.75	.35
2313	A516	1.20 l gold & blk brn	.85	.45
		Nos. 2310-2313 (4)	2.40	1.25

6th Congress
of Albanian
Democratic
Front
A517

1989, June 26
2314	A517	1.20 l multicolored	1.50	.65

French Revolution, Bicent. — A518

90q, Storming of the Bastille. 1.20 l, Statue.

1989, July 7　Litho.　Perf. 12¹/₂
2315	A518	90q multicolored	.75	.40
2316	A518	1.20 l shown	1.00	.50

Illyrian
Ship — A519

1989, July 25　　　　　Perf. 12
2317	A519	30q shown	.25	.15
2318	A519	80q Caravel	.60	.30
2319	A519	90q 3-masted schooner	.65	.35
2320	A519	1.30 l Modern cargo ship	1.00	.50
		Nos. 2317-2320 (4)	2.50	1.30

A520　　　　　A521

Famous Men: 30q, Pjeter Bogdani (1625-1689),
writer. 80q, Gavril Dara (1826-1889), poet. 90q,
Thimi Mitko (1820-1890), writer. 1.30 l, Kole
Idromeno (1860-1939), painter.

1989, Aug. 30　Litho.　Perf. 12
2321	A520	30q multicolored	.30	.15
2322	A520	80q multicolored	.80	.40
2323	A520	90q multicolored	.90	.45
2324	A520	1.30 l multicolored	1.25	.65
		Nos. 2321-2324 (4)	3.25	1.65

1989, Sept. 29
2325	A521	30q shown	.70	.35
2326	A521	1.20 l Workers	.95	.50

First Communist International, 125th anniv.

Spartakiad
Games — A522

1989, Oct. 27　　　　Perf. 12x12¹/₂
2327	A522	30q Gymasnastics	.20	.15
2328	A522	80q Soccer	.55	.30
2329	A522	1 l Cycling	.70	.35
2330	A522	1.20 l Running	.85	.45
		Nos. 2327-2330 (4)	2.30	1.25

Miniature Sheet

45th Anniv. of Liberation — A523

1989, Nov. 29　　　　Perf. 12x12¹/₂
2331		Sheet of 4	2.50	1.25
a.	A523	30q Revolutionary	.20	.15
b.	A523	80q "45"	.55	.30
c.	A523	1 l Coat of arms	.70	.35
d.	A523	1.20 l Workers	.85	.45

Rupicapra
Rupicapra — A524

1990, Mar. 15　　　　　Perf. 12
2332	A524	10q Two adults	.15	.15
2333	A524	30q Adult, kid	.30	.15
2334	A524	80q Adult	.80	.40
2335	A524	90q Adult head	.90	.40
a.		Block of 4, #2332-2335	2.10	1.10

World Wildlife Fund.

Tribal
Masks — A525

1990, Apr. 4　　　　Perf. 12x12¹/₂
2336	A525	30q shown	.30	.15
2337	A525	90q multi, diff.	.95	.50
2338	A525	1.20 l multi, diff.	1.25	.65
2339	A525	1.80 l multi, diff.	1.90	.95
		Nos. 2336-2339 (4)	4.40	2.25

Mushrooms
A526

1990, Apr. 28　Litho.　Perf. 12
2340	A526	30q Amanita caesarea	.25	.15
2341	A526	90q Lepiota procera	.75	.40
2342	A526	1.20 l Boletus edulis	1.00	.50
2343	A526	1.80 l Clathrus cance-latus	1.50	.75
		Nos. 2340-2343 (4)	3.50	1.80

First Postage
Stamp, 150th
Anniv.
A527

1990, May 6　　　　　Perf. 12
2344	A527	90q shown	.95	.50
2345	A527	1.20 l Post rider	1.25	.60
2346	A527	1.80 l Carriage	1.75	.95
a.		Bklt. pane of 3, #2344-2346 + label	4.25	
		Nos. 2344-2346 (3)	3.95	2.05

World Cup
Soccer,
Italy — A528

1990, June　　Litho.　Perf. 12
2347	A528	30q multicolored	.50	.25
2348	A528	90q multi, diff.	1.40	.75
2349	A528	1.20 l multi, diff.	2.00	1.00

Size: 80x63mm
Imperf
2350	A528	3.30 l multi, diff.	5.30	2.65
		Nos. 2347-2350 (4)	9.20	4.65

Vincent Van
Gogh, Death
Cent.
A529

Self portraits and: 30q, Details from various
paintings. 90q, Woman in field. 2.10 l, Asylum.
2.40 l, Self-portrait.

1990, July 27
2351	A529	30q multicolored	.50	.25
2352	A529	90q multicolored	1.40	.75
2353	A529	2.10 l multicolored	3.50	1.75

Size: 87x73mm
Imperf

2354	A529	2.40 l multicolored	1.90	.95
		Nos. 2351-2354 (4)	7.30	3.70

Albanian Folklore — A530

Scenes from medieval folktale of "Gjergj Elez Alia": 30q, Alia lying wounded. 90q, Alia being helped onto horse. 1.20 l, Alia fighting Bajloz. 1.80 l, Alia on horseback over severed head of Bajloz.

1990, Aug. 30   *Perf. 12¹/₂x12*

2355	A530	30q multicolored	.50	.25
2356	A530	90q multicolored	1.40	.70
2357	A530	1.20 l multicolored	2.00	.95
2358	A530	1.80 l multicolored	3.00	1.50
		Nos. 2355-2358 (4)	6.90	3.40

Founding of Berat, 2400th Anniv.
A531

Designs: 30q, Xhamia E Plumbit. 90q, Kisha E Shen Triadhes. 1.20 l, Ura E Beratit. 1.80 l, Onufri-Piktor Mesjetar. 2.40 l, Nikolla-Piktor Mesjetar.

1990, Sept. 20   *Perf. 12¹/₂*

2359		Block of 5 + 4 labels	4.25	2.10
a.	A531	30q multi	.20	.15
b.	A531	90q multi	.65	.30
c.	A531	1.20 l multi	.70	.35
d.	A531	1.80 l multi	1.25	.65
e.	A531	2.40 l multi	1.40	.70

No. 2359 was sold in souvenir folders for 9.90 l.

Illyrian Heroes — A532

1990, Oct. 20   *Perf. 12*

2360	A532	30q Pirroja	.50	.25
2361	A532	90q Teuta	1.40	.70
2362	A532	1.20 l Bato	2.00	.95
2363	A532	1.80 l Bardhyli	3.00	1.50
		Nos. 2360-2363 (4)	6.90	3.40

Intl. Literacy Year — A533

1990, Oct. 30

2364	A533	90q lt bl & multi	1.40	.70
2365	A533	1.20 l pink & multi	2.00	.95

Albanian Horseman by Eugene Delacroix
A534

Designs: 1.20 l, Albanian Woman by Camille Corot. 1.80 l, Skanderbeg by unknown artist.

1990, Nov. 30   *Perf. 12x12¹/₂*

2366	A534	30q multicolored	.50	.25
2367	A534	1.20 l multicolored	1.90	.95
2368	A534	1.80 l multicolored	3.00	1.50
		Nos. 2366-2368 (3)	5.40	2.70

Isa Boletini (1864-1916), Freedom Fighter — A535

1991, Jan. 23   *Perf. 12x12¹/₂*

2369	A535	90q Portrait	.65	.30
2370	A535	1.20 l shown	.90	.45

Pierre Auguste Renoir (1841-1919), Painter — A537

Paintings: 30q, Girl Reading, 1876, vert. 90q, The Swing, 1876, vert. 1.20 l, Boating Party, 1868-1869. 1.80 l, Flowers and grapes, 1878. 3 l, Self-portrait.

1991, Feb. 25   *Perf. 12¹/₂x12*

2373	A537	30q multicolored	.20	.15
2374	A537	90q multicolored	.65	.30
2375	A537	1.20 l multicolored	.90	.45
2376	A537	1.80 l multicolored	1.25	.65

Size: 95x75mm
Imperf

2377	A537	3 l multicolored	4.75	2.50
		Nos. 2373-2377 (5)	7.75	4.05

Flowers — A538

1991, Mar. 30   *Perf. 12*

2378	A538	30q Cistus albanicus	.50	.25
2379	A538	90q Trifolium pilczii	1.40	.75
2380	A538	1.80 l Lilium albanicum	3.00	1.50
		Nos. 2378-2380 (3)	4.90	2.50

Legend of Rozafa — A539

Various scenes from legend.

1991, Sept. 30   *Litho.*   *Perf. 12x12¹/₂*

2381	A539	30q multicolored	.50	.25
2382	A539	90q multicolored	1.40	.70
2383	A539	1.20 l multicolored	2.00	.95
2384	A539	1.80 l multicolored	3.00	1.50
		Nos. 2381-2384 (4)	6.90	3.40

Wolfgang Amadeus Mozart, Death Bicent. — A540

1991, Oct. 5   *Litho.*   *Perf. 12*

2385	A540	90q Conducting	.70	.35
2386	A540	1.20 l Portrait	.90	.45
2387	A540	1.80 l Playing piano	1.40	.70

Size: 89x70mm
Imperf

2388	A540	3 l Medal, score	4.00	4.00
		Nos. 2385-2388 (4)	7.00	5.50

Airplanes — A541

Designs: 30q, Glider, Otto Lilienthal, 1896. 80q, Avion III, Clement Ader, 1897. 90q, Flyer, Wright Brothers, 1903. 1.20 l, Concorde. 1.80 l, Tupolev 114. 2.40 l, Dornier 31 E.

1992, Jan. 27   *Litho.*   *Perf. 12¹/₂x12*

2389	A541	30q multicolored	.50	.25
2390	A541	80q multicolored	1.25	.65
2391	A541	90q multicolored	1.40	.70
2392	A541	1.20 l multicolored	2.00	.95
2393	A541	1.80 l multicolored	3.00	1.50
2394	A541	2.40 l multicolored	4.00	2.00
		Nos. 2389-2394 (6)	12.15	6.05

No. 2393 misidentifies a Tupolev 144.

Explorers — A542

1992, Jan. 10

2395	A542	30q Bering	.50	.25
2396	A542	90q Columbus	1.40	.70
2397	A542	1.80 l Magellan	3.00	1.50
		Nos. 2395-2397 (3)	4.90	2.45

1992 Winter Olympics, Albertville
A543

1992, Feb. 15   *Litho.*   *Perf. 12¹/₂*

2398	A543	30q Ski jumping	.25	.15
2399	A543	90q Cross country skiing	.70	.35
2400	A543	1.20 l Pairs figure skating	.95	.50
2401	A543	1.80 l Luge	1.40	.70
		Nos. 2398-2401 (4)	3.30	1.70

Participation of Albania in Conference on Security and Cooperation in Europe, Berlin (1991) — A544

1992, Mar. 31   *Litho.*   *Perf. 12¹/₂x12*

2402	A544	90q shown	.95	.95
2403	A544	1.20 l Flags, map	1.25	1.25
a.		Pair, #2402-2403		

Dated 1991. Issued in sheets containing 2 #2403a, 3 each #2402-2403 + 2 labels.

Albanian Admission to CEPT
A545

1992, Apr. 25   *Litho.*   *Perf. 12¹/₂*

2404	A545	90q Envelopes, CEPT emblem	.90	.90
2405	A545	1 l shown	1.25	1.25
a.		Pair, #2404-2405	2.25	2.25

Issued in sheets containing 2 #2405a, 3 each #2404-2405 and 2 labels.

Martyrs' Day — A546

1992, May 5   *Perf. 12x12¹/₂*

2406	A546	90q Freedom flame, vert.	1.00	1.00

Perf. 12¹/₂x12

2407	A546	4.10 l Flowers	4.50	4.50

European Soccer Championships, Sweden'92 — A547

Various stylized designs of soccer plays.

1992, June 10   *Litho.*   *Perf. 12*

2408	A547	30q green & lt grn	.15	.15
2409	A547	90q blue & pink	.25	.25
2410	A547	10.80 l henna & tan	3.00	3.00

Size: 90x70mm
Imperf

2411	A547	5 l tan, lt green & pink	1.40	1.40
		Nos. 2408-2411 (4)	4.80	4.80

1992 Summer Olympics, Barcelona
A548

1992, June 14   *Litho.*   *Perf. 12*

2412	A548	30q Tennis	.35	.35
2413	A548	90q Baseball	1.00	1.00
2414	A548	1.80 l Table tennis	2.00	2.00

Size: 90x70mm
Imperf

2415	A548	5 l Torch bearer	1.45	1.45
		Nos. 2412-2415 (4)	4.80	4.80

United Europe
A549

1992, July 10   *Litho.*   *Perf. 12*

2416	A549	1.20 l multicolored	.90	.45

Horses
A550

1992, Aug. 10   Litho.   Perf. 12
2417 A550   30q Native   .15 .15
2418 A550   90q Nonius   .25 .25
2419 A550   1.20 l Arabian, vert.   .35 .35
2420 A550   10.60 l Haflinger, vert. 2.75 2.75
    Nos. 2417-2420 (4)   3.50 3.50

Discovery of America, 500th Anniv.
A551

Map of North and South America and: 60q, Columbus, sailing ships. 3.20 l, Columbus meeting natives.

1992, Aug. 20
2421 A551   60q blk, bl & gray   .25 .25
2422 A551   3.20 l blk, brn & gray   1.25 1.25

Size: 90x70mm
Imperf
2423 A551   5 l Map, Columbus

A552   A553

Mother Theresa, infant.

1992, Oct. 4   Litho.   Perf. 12x12½
2424 A552   40q fawn   .15 .15
2425 A552   60q brown   .15 .15
2426 A552   1 l violet   .15 .15
2427 A552   1.80 l gray   .25 .25
2428 A552   2 l red   .30 .30
2429 A552   2.40 l green   .35 .35
2430 A552   3.20 l blue   .50 .50
2431 A552   5.60 l rose violet 1.00 1.00
2432 A552   7.20 l olive   1.05 1.05
2433 A552   10 l orange brown 1.50 1.50
    Nos. 2424-2433 (10)   5.40 5.40

See Nos. 2472-2476.

1993, Apr. 25   Litho.   Perf. 12
2434 A553   16 l multicolored   2.50 2.50

Visit of Pope John Paul II.

POSTA SHQIPTARE

Nos. 2223-2226, 2229 Surcharged

3 Lekë

1993, May 2   Litho.   Perf. 12x12½
2435 A486   3 l on 10q   .60 .60
2436 A486   6.50 l on 20q   1.25 1.25
2437 A486   13 l on 30q   2.50 2.50
2438 A486   20 l on 90q   4.00 4.00
2439 A486   30 l on 50q   5.75 5.75
    Nos. 2435-2439 (5)   14.10 14.10

Lef Nosi (1873-1945), Minister of Posts — A554

1993, May 5   Litho.   Perf. 12
2440 A554   6.50 l olive brown & bister .90 .90

First Albanian postage stamps, 80th anniv.

Europa
A555

Contemporary paintings by: 3 l, A. Zajmi, vert. 7 l, E. Hila. 20 l, B. Ahmeti-Peizazh.

1993, May 28   Litho.   Perf. 12
2441 A555   3 l multicolored   .55 .55
2442 A555   7 l multicolored   1.25 1.25

Size: 116x122mm
2443 A555   20 l multicolored   3.75 3.75
    Nos. 2441-2443 (3)   5.55 5.55

1993 Mediterranean Games, France
A556

1993, June 20   Litho.   Perf. 12
2444 A556   3 l Running   .55 .55
2445 A556   16 l Kayaking   1.60 1.60
2446 A556   21 l Cycling   3.75 3.75

Size: 111x78mm
Imperf
2447 A556   20 l Mediterranean map   3.50 3.50
    Nos. 2444-2447 (4)   10.80 10.80

Frang Bardhi, Author, 350th Death Anniv. — A557

1993, Aug. 20   Litho.   Perf. 12x12½
2448 A557   6.50 l shown   1.10 1.10

Size: 89x101mm
Imperf
2449 A557   20 l Writing at desk   3.50 3.50

A558   A559

1994, July 17   Litho.   Perf. 12
2450 A558   42 l shown   1.50 1.50
2451 A558   68 l Mascot, ball, US map   2.50 2.50

1994 World Cup Soccer Championships, US.

1994, Dec. 31   Litho.   Perf. 14
European Inventors, Discoveries: 50 l, Gjovalin Gjadri, engineer. 100 l, Karl von Ghega, Austrian engineer. 150 l, Sketch of road project.
2452 A559   50 l multicolored   2.00 2.00
2453 A559   100 l multicolored   4.00 4.00

Size: 50x70mm
Imperf
2454 A559   150 l multicolored   6.00 6.00
    Nos. 2452-2454 (3)   12.00 12.00

Europa (#2454).

Ali Pasa of Tepelene (Lion of Janina) (1744-1822)
A560

1995, Jan. 28   Perf. 14
2455 A560   60 l shown   2.50 2.50

Size: 70x50mm
Imperf
2456 A560   100 l Tepelene Palace   4.00 4.00

80 Lekë
POSTA SHQIPTARE

Intl. Olympic Committee, Cent. — A561

1995, Feb. 2   Imperf.
2457 A561   80 l multicolored   3.25 3.25

POSTA SHQIPTARE

Karl Benz (1844-1929), Automobile Pioneer — A562

Designs: 5 l, Automobile company emblem, Benz. 10 l, Modern Mercedes Benz automobile. 60 l, First four-wheel Benz 1886 motor car. 125 l, Pre-war Mercedes touring car.

1995, Jan. 21   Perf. 14
2458 A562   5 l multicolored   .15 .15
2459 A562   10 l multicolored   .30 .30
2460 A562   60 l multicolored   1.65 1.65
2461 A562   125 l multicolored   3.50 3.50
    Nos. 2458-2461 (4)   5.60 5.60

Liberation, 50th Anniv. (in 1994)
A563

1995, Jan. 28   Litho.   Perf. 14
2462 A563   50 l black, gray & red   2.00 2.00

Dated 1994.

Miniature Sheet

Albania '93 — A564

Composers: a, 3 l, Wagner. b, 6.50 l, Grieg. c, 11 l, Gounod. d, 20 l, Tchaikovsky.

1995, Jan. 26   Perf. 12
2463 A564   Sheet of 4, #a.-d.   2.00 2.00

Veskopoja Academy, 250th Anniv. — A565

Buildings of Veskopoja.

1995, Feb. 2
2464 A565   42 l multicolored   1.50 1.50
2465 A565   68 l multicolored   2.50 2.50
    a.   Pair, #2464-2465   4.00 4.00

Bleta Apricula — A566   Peace & Freedom — A567

1995, Aug. 20   Litho.   Perf. 12
2466 A566   5 l On flower   .20 .20
2467 A566   10 l Honeycomb, bee .40 .40
2468 A566   25 l Emerging from cell of honeycomb   1.00 1.00
    Nos. 2466-2468 (3)   1.60 1.60

1995, Aug. 10   Perf. 13½x14
Stylized hands reaching for: 50 l, Olive branch. 100 l, Peace dove. 150 l, Stylized person.
2469 A567   50 l multicolored   1.50 1.50
2470 A567   100 l multicolored   3.25 3.25

Size: 80x60mm
Imperf
2471 A567   150 l multicolored   4.75 4.75
    Nos. 2469-2471 (3)   9.50 9.50

Europa.

Mother Teresa Type of 1992

1994-95   Perf. 12x12½
2472 A552   5 l violet   .25 .25
2473 A552   18 l orange   .85 .85
2474 A552   20 l rose lilac .95 .95
2475 A552   25 l green   1.10 1.10
2476 A552   60 l olive   2.75 2.75
    Nos. 2472-2476 (5)   5.90 5.90

Issued: 20 l, 1994; 60 l, 1995; others, 7/94.

Arctic Explorers — A568

Designs: a, Fridtjof Nansen (1861-1930), Norway. b, James Cook (1728-79), England. c, Roald

Amundsen (1872-1928), Norway. d, Robert F. Scott (1872-1928), Great Britain.

1995, Sept. 14   Litho.   Perf. 13¹/₂x14
2477 A568 25 l Block of 4, #a.-d.   4.25 4.25

UN, 50th Anniv. A569

1995, Sept. 14   Litho.   Perf. 14x13¹/₂
2478 A569   2 l shown   .15 .15
2479 A569 100 l like #2478, flags streaming to right 4.25 4.25

Poets — A570

1995   Perf. 13¹/₂x14
2480 A570 25 l Pol Elyar   1.10 1.10
2481 A570 50 l Sergej Esnin   2.25 2.25
  a. Pair, #2480-2481   3.50 3.50

Entry into Council of Europe A571

Designs: 25 l, Doves flying from headquarters, Strasbourg. 85 l, Albanian eagle over map of Europe.

1995   Perf. 14x13¹/₂
2482 A571 25 l multicolored   1.10 1.10
2483 A571 85 l multicolored   3.75 3.75

Jan Kukuzeli, Composer A572

Stylized figure: 18 l, Writing. 20 l, Holding hand to head. 100 l, Holding up scroll of paper.

1995, Oct. 17   Perf. 13¹/₂x14
2484 A572 18 l multicolored   .85 .85
2485 A572 20 l multicolored   .95 .95

Size: 74x74mm
2486 A572 100 l multicolored   4.50 4.50
      Nos. 2484-2486 (3)   6.30 6.30

World Tourism Organization, 20th Anniv. — A573

Stylized designs: 18 l, Church, saint holding scroll. 20 l, City, older buildings. 42 l, City, modern buildings.

1995, Oct. 17
2487 A573 18 l multicolored   1.00 1.00
2488 A573 20 l multicolored   1.10 1.10
2489 A573 42 l multicolored   2.50 2.50
      Nos. 2487-2489 (3)   4.60 4.60

Fables of Jean de la Fontaine (1621-95) A574

Designs: 2 l, Raptor, turtle, wolf, goose, mouse, lion, rats. 3 l, Crow, goose, dog, foxes. 25 l, Insect, doves, frogs.
60 l, Drawings of Da la Fontaine, animals, birds.

1995, Aug. 20   Litho.   Perf. 14x13¹/₂
2490 A574   2 l multicolored   .15 .15
2491 A574   3 l multicolored   .15 .15
2492 A574 25 l multicolored   .95 .95

Imperf
Size: 73x56mm
2493 A574 60 l multicolored   2.70 2.70
      Nos. 2490-2493 (4)   3.95 3.95

Folklore Festival, Berat — A575   Motion Pictures, Cent. — A576

Stylized designs: 5 l, Men's choir. 50 l, Costumed woman seated in chair.

1995, Oct. 17   Litho.   Perf. 13¹/₂x14
2494 A575   5 l multicolored   .20 .20
2495 A575 50 l multicolored   2.25 2.25

1995, Nov. 17
2496 A576 10 l Louis Lumiere   .45 .45
2497 A576 85 l Auguste Lumiere 3.75 3.75
  a. Pair, #2496-2497   4.20 4.20

Elvis Presley (1935-77) A577

1995, Nov. 20   Litho.   Perf. 14x13¹/₂
2498 A577   3 l orange & multi   .15 .15
2499 A577 60 l green & multi   2.50 2.50

A578   A579

1995, Nov. 25   Perf. 13¹/₂x14
2500 A578 10 l 1925 Bank notes   .45 .45
2501 A578 25 l 1995 Bank notes 1.10 1.10
      National Bank, 70th anniv.

1995, Nov. 27   Litho.   Perf. 13¹/₂x14
2502 A579   5 l shown   .20 .20
2503 A579 50 l Maiden planting tree 2.25 2.25
      Democracy, 5th anniv.

A580   Mother Teresa — A581

Designs: 25 l, Soccer ball, British flag, map of Europe, stadium. 100 l, Soccer ball, player.

1996, June 4   Perf. 14
2504 A580 25 l multicolored   1.10 1.10
2505 A580 100 l multicolored   4.50 4.50
      Euro '96, European Soccer Championships, Great Britain.

1996, May 5   Perf. 13¹/₂x14
2506 A581 25 l blue & multi   1.10 1.10
2507 A581 100 l red & multi   4.50 4.50

Size: 52x74mm
Imperf
2508 A581 150 l Mother Teresa, diff.   6.75 6.75
      Nos. 2506-2508 (3)   12.35 12.35
      Europa. For overprint see No. 2551.

GSM Cellular Telephone Transmission A582

Designs: 10 l, Satellite transmitting signals. 60 l, Uses for cellular telephone, vert.

Perf. 13x13¹/₂, 13¹/₂x13
1996, Aug. 1   Litho.
2509 A582 10 l multicolored   .45 .45
2510 A582 60 l multicolored   2.50 2.50

1996 Summer Olympic Games, Atlanta — A583

Stylized designs.

1996, Aug. 3   Litho.   Perf. 13x14
2511 A583   5 l Runners   .20 .20
2512 A583 25 l Throwers   1.00 1.00
2513 A583 60 l Jumpers   2.40 2.40

Size: 52x37mm
Imperf
2514 A583 100 l Emblem, US flag 4.00 4.00
      Nos. 2511-2514 (4)   7.60 7.60

Gottfried Wilhelm Leibniz (1646-1716), Mathematician — A584

Designs: 85 l, René Descartes (1596-1650), mathematician.

1996, Sept. 20   Litho.   Perf. 14
2515 A584 10 l multicolored   .40 .40
2516 A584 85 l multicolored   3.50 3.50

Paintings by Francisco Goya (1746-1828) A585

Designs: 10 l, The Naked Maja. 60 l, Dona Isabel Cobos de Porcel. 100 l, Self portrait.

1996, Sept. 25   Perf. 14x13¹/₂
2517 A585 10 l multicolored   .40 .40
2518 A585 60 l multicolored   2.50 2.50

Souvenir Sheet
2519 A585 100 l multicolored   4.00 4.00

Religious Engravings — A586   UNICEF, 50th Anniv. — A587

Designs: a, 5 l, Book cover showing crucifixion, angels. b, 25 l, Medallion of crucifixion. c, 85 l, Book cover depicting life of Christ.

1996, Nov. 5   Perf. 13x13¹/₂
2520 A586 Block of 3, #a.-c. + label 4.75 4.75

1996, Nov. 11   Perf. 13¹/₂
Children's paintings: 5 l, Fairy princess. 10 l, Doll, sun. 25 l, Sea life. 50 l, House, people.

2521 A587   5 l multicolored   .20 .20
2522 A587 10 l multicolored   .45 .45
2523 A587 25 l multicolored   1.10 1.10
2524 A587 50 l multicolored   2.25 2.25
      Nos. 2521-2524 (4)   4.00 4.00

Gjergj Fishta (1871-1940), Writer, Priest A588   Omar Khayyam A589

1996, Dec. 20   Perf. 13¹/₂x14
2525 A588 10 l shown   .40 .40
2526 A588 60 l Battle scene, portrait 2.50 2.50

1997, Mar. 6   Perf. 14
2527 A589 20 l shown   .70 .70
2528 A589 50 l Portrait, diff.   1.75 1.75

A590   A591

1997, Mar. 20   Perf. 14x14¹/₂
2529 A590 20 l Portrait   .70 .70
2530 A590 60 l Printing press   2.15 2.15
  a. Pair, #2529-2530   2.85 2.85
      Johannes Gutenberg (1397?-1468).

1997, May 5   Litho.   Perf. 13x14
The Azure Eye (Stories and Legends): 30 l, Dragon on rock looking at warrior, donkey. 100 l, Dragon drinking water from pond, warrior.

2531 A591 30 l multicolored   1.20 1.20
2532 A591 100 l multicolored   4.00 4.00
      Europa.

A592   A593

1997, Apr. 10   **Perf. 14**
2533	A592	10 l Pelicanus Crispus	.40	.40
2534	A592	80 l Pelicans, diff.	3.00	3.00
a.		Pair, #2533-2534	3.40	3.40

No. 2534a is a continuous design.

1997, June 25   **Litho.**   **Perf. 14**
2535	A593	10 l black & dark brown	.40	.40
2536	A593	25 l black & blue black	1.00	1.00

Souvenir Sheet
2537	A593	80 l gray brown	2.90	2.90

Faik Konica (1875-1942), writer and politician.
No. 2537 contains one 22x26mm stamp.

A594   Skanderbeg — A595

1997 Mediterranean Games, Bari: 20 l, Man running. 30 l, Woman running, 3-man canoe. 100 l, Man breaking finish line, silhouettes of man and woman.

1997, July 17
2538	A594	20 l Man running	.75	.75
2539	A594	30 l Woman running, canoe	1.10	1.10

Size: 52x74mm
Imperf
2540	A594	100 l multicolored	3.60	3.60

1997   **Litho.**   **Perf. 13**
2541	A595	5 l red brn & red	.20	.20
2542	A595	10 l dp ol & ol	.40	.40
2543	A595	20 l dp green & grn	.80	.80
2544	A595	25 l dp mag & red lil	1.00	1.00
2545	A595	30 l dk violet & vio	1.20	1.20
2546	A595	50 l black	2.00	2.00
2547	A595	60 l brown & lt brn	2.40	2.40
2548	A595	80 l dk brown & brn	3.20	3.20
2549	A595	100 l dk red brown & red brn	3.90	3.90
2550	A595	110 l dark blue	4.30	4.30
		Nos. 2541-2550 (10)	19.40	19.40

No. 2507 Ovptd. in Silver
"HOMAZH / 1910-1997"

1997   **Perf. 13½x14**
2551	A581	100 l red & multi	6.50	6.50

SEMI-POSTAL STAMPS

Nos. 148-151 Surcharged
in Red and Black

5 qind.

1924, Nov. 1
B1	A18	5q + 5q yel grn	5.00	6.50
B2	A18	10q + 5q carmine	5.00	6.50
B3	A18	25q + 5q dark blue	5.00	6.50
B4	A18	50q + 5q dark grn	5.00	6.50
		Nos. B1-B4 (4)	20.00	26.00

Nos. B1 to B4 with
Additional Surcharge
in Red and Black

+ 5 qind.

1924
B5	A18	5q + 5q + 5q yel grn	5.00	6.50
B6	A18	10q + 5q + 5q car	5.00	6.50
B7	A18	25q + 5q + 5q dk bl	5.00	6.50
B8	A18	50q + 5q + 5q dk grn	5.00	6.50
		Nos. B5-B8 (4)	20.00	26.00

Issued under Italian Dominion

Nurse and
Child — SP1

Unwmk.

1943, Apr. 1   **Photo.**   **Perf. 14**
B9	SP1	5q + 5q dark grn	.25	.25
B10	SP1	10q + 10q olive brn	.25	.25
B11	SP1	15q + 15q rose red	.35	.35
B12	SP1	25q + 15q saphire	.50	.50
B13	SP1	30q + 20q violet	.60	.60
B14	SP1	50q + 25q dk org	.75	.75
B15	SP1	65q + 30q grnsh blk	1.10	1.10
B16	SP1	1fr + 40q chestnut	2.50	2.50
		Nos. B9-B16 (8)	6.30	6.30

The surtax was for the control of tuberculosis.
For surcharges see Nos. B24-B27.

Issued under German Administration

War
Victims — SP2

1944, Sept. 22
B17	SP2	5q + 5(q) dp grn	2.10	2.75
B18	SP2	10q + 5(q) dp brn	2.10	2.75
B19	SP2	15q + 5(q) car lake	2.10	2.75
B20	SP2	25q + 10(q) dp blue	2.10	2.75
B21	SP2	1fr + 50q dk olive	2.10	2.75
B22	SP2	2fr + 1(fr) purple	2.10	2.75
B23	SP2	3fr + 1.50(fr) dk org	2.10	2.75
		Nos. B17-B23 (7)	14.70	19.25

Surtax for victims of World War II.

Independent State

Nos. B9 to
B12
Surcharged
in Carmine

1945, May 4   **Unwmk.**   **Perf. 14**
B24	SP1	30q +15q on 5q+5q	1.75	1.75
B25	SP1	50q +25q on 10q+10q	1.75	1.75
B26	SP1	1fr +50q on 15q+15q	5.00	5.00
B27	SP1	2fr +1fr on 25q+15q	8.75	8.75
		Nos. B24-B27 (4)	17.25	17.25

The surtax was for the Albanian Red Cross.

People's Republic

Nos. 361 to 366
Overprinted in Red (cross)
and Surcharged in Black

KONGRESI
K.K.SH.
24-25-11-46
+0.10

1946, July 16   **Perf. 11**
B28	A57	20q + 10q bluish grn	6.50	6.50
B29	A57	30q + 15q dp org	6.50	6.50
B30	A57	40q + 20q brown	6.50	6.50
B31	A57	60q + 30q red vio	6.50	6.50
B32	A57	1fr + 50q rose red	6.50	6.50
B33	A57	3fr + 1.50fr dk bl	6.50	6.50
		Nos. B28-B33 (6)	39.00	39.00

To honor and benefit the Congress of the Albanian Red Cross.

Counterfeits: lithographed, dull gum. Genuine: typographed, shiny gum.

> Catalogue values for unused stamps in this section, from this point to the end of the section, are for Never Hinged items.

SP3   SP4

First Aid and Red Cross: 25q+5q, Nurse carrying child on stretcher. 65q+25q, Symbolic blood transfusion. 80q+40q, Mother and child.

1967, Dec. 1   **Litho.**   **Perf. 11½x12**
B34	SP3	15q + 5q blk, red & brn	.90	.45
B35	SP3	25q + 5q multi	1.00	.60
B36	SP3	65q + 25q multi	3.00	.65
B37	SP3	80q + 40q multi	5.00	1.50
		Nos. B34-B37 (4)	9.90	3.20

6th congress of the Albanian Red Cross.

1996, Aug. 5   **Litho.**   **Perf. 13½x13**
B38	SP4	50 l +10 l multi	2.50	2.50

Albanian Red Cross, 75th anniv.

AIR POST STAMPS

Airplane Crossing
Mountains
AP1

Wmk. 125

1925, May 30   **Typo.**   **Perf. 14**
C1	AP1	5q green	.50	.50
C2	AP1	10q rose red	.50	.50
C3	AP1	25q deep blue	.450	.50
C4	AP1	50q dark green	1.00	1.00
C5	AP1	1fr dk vio & blk	1.90	1.90
C6	AP1	2fr ol grn & vio	3.00	3.00
C7	AP1	3fr brn org & dk grn	5.25	5.25
		Nos. C1-C7 (7)	16.65	12.65

Nos. C1-C7 exist imperf.
For overprint see Nos. C8-C28.

Nos. C1-C7
Overprinted

1927, Jan. 18
C8	AP1	5q green	3.00	3.00
a.		Dbl. overprint, one invtd.	35.00	
C9	AP1	10q rose red	3.00	3.00
a.		Inverted overprint	30.00	
b.		Dbl. overprint, one invtd.	35.00	
C10	AP1	25q deep blue	1.60	1.60
a.		Inverted overprint	30.00	
C11	AP1	50q dark grn	1.60	1.60
a.		Inverted overprint	30.00	
C12	AP1	1fr dk vio & blk	1.60	1.60
a.		Inverted overprint	30.00	
b.		Double overprint	30.00	
C13	AP1	2fr ol grn & vio	1.60	1.60
C14	AP1	3fr brn org & dk grn	2.75	2.75
		Nos. C8-C14 (7)	15.15	15.15

REP. SHQYPTARE
Fluturim' i I-ar

Nos. C1-C7
Overprinted

Vlonë--Brindisi
21. IV. 1928

1928, Apr. 21
C15	AP1	5q green	1.25	1.25
a.		Inverted overprint	20.00	
C16	AP1	10q rose red	1.25	1.25
C17	AP1	25q deep blue	1.25	1.25
C18	AP1	50q dark green	1.25	1.25
C19	AP1	1fr dk vio & blk	18.00	18.00

C20	AP1	2fr ol grn & vio	18.00	18.00
C21	AP1	3fr brn org & dk grn	18.00	18.00
		Nos. C15-C21 (7)	59.00	59.00

First flight across the Adriatic, Valona to Brindisi, Apr. 21, 1928.
The variety "SHQYRTARE" occurs once in the sheet for each value. Value 3 times normal.

Nos. C1-C7
Overprinted in
Red Brown

1929, Dec. 1
C22	AP1	5q green	3.25	3.25
C23	AP1	10q rose red	3.25	3.25
C24	AP1	25q deep blue	3.50	3.50
C25	AP1	50q dk grn	15.00	17.50
C26	AP1	1fr dk vio & blk	150.00	165.00
C27	AP1	2fr ol grn	150.00	165.00
C28	AP1	3fr brn org & dk grn	150.00	165.00
		Nos. C22-C28 (7)	475.00	522.50

Excellent counterfeits exist.

King Zog and
Airplane over
Tirana — AP2

AP3

1930, Oct. 8   **Photo.**   **Unwmk.**
C29	AP2	5q yellow green	.30	.30
C30	AP2	15q rose red	.40	.40
C31	AP2	20q slate blue	.55	.55
C32	AP2	50q olive green	.75	.75
C33	AP3	1fr dark blue	1.65	1.65
C34	AP3	2fr olive brown	5.25	5.25
C35	AP3	3fr purple	7.00	7.00
		Nos. C29-C35 (7)	15.90	15.90

For overprints and surcharges see Nos. C36-C45.

Nos. C29-C35
Overprinted

TIRANE-ROME
6 KORRIK 1931

1931, July 6
C36	AP2	5q yellow grn	1.75	1.75
a.		Double overprint	65.00	
C37	AP2	15q rose red	1.75	1.75
C38	AP2	20q slate blue	1.75	1.75
C39	AP2	50q olive grn	1.75	1.75
C40	AP3	1fr dark blue	14.00	14.00
C41	AP3	2fr olive brn	14.00	14.00
C42	AP3	3fr purple	14.00	14.00
a.		Inverted overprint	175.00	
		Nos. C36-C42 (7)	49.00	49.00

1st air post flight from Tirana to Rome.
Only a very small part of this issue was sold to the public. Most of the stamps were given to the Aviation Company to help provide funds for conducting the service.

Issued under Italian Dominion

Nos. C29-C30
Overprinted in Black

Mbledhja
Kushtetuëse
12-IV-1939
XVII

1939, Apr. 19   **Unwmk.**   **Perf. 14**
C43	AP2	5q yel green	.75	.75
C44	AP2	15q rose red	.75	.75

No. C32 With Additional Surcharge
C45	AP2	20q on 50q ol grn	1.50	1.50
a.		Inverted overprint		
		Nos. C43-C45 (3)	3.00	3.00

See note after No. 309.

King Victor
Emmanuel III
and Plane
over
Mountains
AP4

1939, Aug. 4   **Photo.**
C46	AP4	20q brown	12.00	4.00

Shepherds
AP5

Map of Albania Showing
Air Routes — AP6

Designs: 20q, Victor Emmanuel III and harbor view. 50q, Woman and river valley. 1fr, Bridge at Vezirit. 2fr, Ruins. 3fr, Women waving to plane.

1940, Mar. 20   **Unwmk.**

C47	AP5	5q green	.25	.25
C48	AP6	15q rose red	.25	.25
C49	AP6	20q deep blue	.25	.25
C50	AP6	50q brown	.65	.65
C51	AP6	1fr myrtle green	1.25	1.50
C52	AP6	2fr brown black	4.25	5.00
C53	AP6	3fr rose violet	12.50	14.00
		Nos. C47-C53 (7)	19.40	21.90

People's Republic

Vuno-Himare
AP12

Albanian Towns: 1 l, 10 l, Rozafat-Shkoder. 2 l, 20 l, Keshtjelle-Butrinto.

1950, Dec. 15   **Engr.**   **Perf. 12½x12**

C54	AP12	50q gray black	.25	.25
C55	AP12	1 l red brown	.25	.25
C56	AP12	2 l ultra	.45	.45
C57	AP12	5 l deep green	.95	.95
C58	AP12	10 l deep blue	2.25	2.25
C59	AP12	20 l purple	5.75	5.75
		Nos. C54-C59 (6)	9.90	9.90

Nos. C56-C58 Surcharged with New Value
and Bars in Red or Black

1952-53

C60	AP12	50q on 2 l (R)	40.00	40.00
C61	AP12	50q on 5 l	10.00	5.00
C62	AP12	2.50 l on 5 l (R)	60.00	60.00
C63	AP12	2.50 l on 10 l	10.00	5.00
		Nos. C60-C63 (4)	120.00	110.00

Issued: #C60, C62, 12/26/52; #C61, C63, 3/14/53.

> Catalogue values for unused stamps in this section, from this point to the end of the section, are for Never Hinged items.

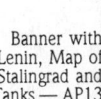

Banner with
Lenin, Map of
Stalingrad and
Tanks — AP13

1963, Feb. 2   **Litho.**   **Perf. 14**

C67	AP13	7 l grn & dp car	3.00	.60

20th anniversary, Battle of Stalingrad.

Sputnik and
Sun — AP14

Designs: 3 l, Lunik 4. 5 l, Lunik 3 photographing far side of the Moon. 8 l, Venus space probe. 12 l, Mars 1.

1963, Oct. 31   **Unwmk.**   **Perf. 12**

C68	AP14	2 l org, yel & blk	.25	.30
C69	AP14	3 l multi	.50	.30
C70	AP14	5 l rose lil, yel & blk	.90	.45

C71	AP14	8 l multi	1.25	.85
C72	AP14	12 l blue & org	2.25	2.50
		Nos. C68-72 (5)	5.15	4.40

Russian interplanetary explorations.

Nos. C68 and C71 Overprinted: "Riccione 23-8-1964"

1964, Aug. 23

C73	AP14	2 l org, yel & blk	8.00	3.50
C74	AP14	8 l multicolored	12.00	5.25

Intl. Space Exhib. in Riccione, Italy.

Plane over
Berat
AP15

1975, Nov. 25   **Litho.**   **Perf. 12**

C75	AP15	20q multi	.15	.15
C76	AP15	40q Gjirokaster	.15	.15
C77	AP15	60q Sarande	.20	.15
C78	AP15	90q Durres	.50	.15
C79	AP15	1.20 l Kruje	.75	.15
C80	AP15	2.40 l Boga	1.65	.35
C81	AP15	4.05 l Tirana	2.50	.70
		Nos. C75-C81 (7)	5.90	
		Set value		1.50

SPECIAL DELIVERY STAMPS

Issued under Italian Dominion

King Victor
Emmanuel
III — SD1

1940   **Unwmk.**   **Photo.**   **Perf. 14**

E1	SD1	25q bright violet	.40	.40
E2	SD1	50q red orange	1.25	1.50

Issued under German Administration

No. E1 Overprinted in
Carmine

**14
Shtator
1943**

1943

E3	SD1	25q bright violet	15.00	17.50

Proclamation of Albanian independence.

POSTAGE DUE STAMPS

Nos. 35-39
Handstamped in Various
Colors

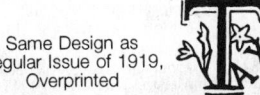

1914, Feb. 23   **Unwmk.**   **Perf. 14**

J1	A3	2q org brn & buff (Bl)	6.00	1.65
J2	A3	5q green (R)	6.00	2.50
J3	A3	10q rose red (Bl)	8.00	1.65
J4	A3	25q dark blue (R)	10.00	1.65
J5	A3	50q vio & red (Bk)	14.00	5.00
		Nos. J1-J5 (5)	44.00	12.45

The two parts of the overprint are handstamped separately. Stamps exist with one or both handstamps inverted, double, omitted or in wrong color.

Nos. 48-51 Overprinted in
Black   **TAKSË**

1914, Apr. 16

J6	A3	(a) 10pa on 5q green	2.75	2.25
J7	A3	(a) 20pa on 10q rose red	2.75	2.25
J8	A3	(b) 1gr on 25q blue	2.75	2.25
J9	A3	(b) 2gr on 50q vio & red	2.75	2.25
		Nos. J6-J9 (4)	11.00	9.00

Same Design as
Regular Issue of 1919,
Overprinted

Fortress at
Scutari — D3   D5

1919, Feb. 10   **Perf. 11½, 12½**

J10	A8	(4)q on 4h rose	5.00	4.50
J11	A8	(10)q on 10k red, grn	5.00	4.50
J12	A8	20q on 2k org, gray	5.00	4.50
J13	A8	50q on 5k brn, yel	5.00	4.50
		Nos. J10-J13 (4)	20.00	18.00

Post Horn Overprinted in Black

1920, Apr. 1   **Perf. 14x13**

J14	D3	4q olive green	.40	.40
J15	D3	10q rose red	.85	.85
J16	D3	20q bister brn	.85	.85
J17	D3	50q black	2.00	2.00
		Nos. J14-J17 (4)	4.10	4.10

1922   **Perf. 12½, 11½**
Background of Red Wavy Lines

J23	D5	4q black, red	1.00	1.00
J24	D5	10q black, red	1.00	1.00
J25	D5	20q black, red	1.00	1.00
J26	D5	50q black, red	1.00	1.00
		Nos. J23-J26 (4)	4.00	4.00

Same Overprinted in
White

1925

J27	D5	4q black, red	1.00	1.00
J28	D5	10q black, red	1.00	1.00
J29	D5	20q black, red	1.00	1.00
J30	D5	50q black, red	1.00	1.00
		Nos. J27-J30 (4)	4.00	4.00

The 10q with overprint in gold was a trial printing. It was not put in use.

D7   Coat of
Arms — D8

Overprinted "QINDAR" in Red

1926, Dec. 24   **Perf. 13½x13**

J31	D7	10q dark blue	.25	.20
J32	D7	20q green	.50	.40
J33	D7	30q red brown	.80	.60
J34	D7	50q dark brown	1.25	1.00
		Nos. J31-J34 (4)	2.80	2.20

Wmk. Double Headed Eagle (220)

1930, Sept. 1   **Photo.**   **Perf. 14, 14½**

J35	D8	10q dark blue	4.75	4.75
J36	D8	20q rose red	1.25	1.25
J37	D8	30q violet	1.25	1.25
J38	D8	50q dark green	1.50	1.50
		Nos. J35-J38 (4)	8.75	8.75

Nos. J36-J38 exist with overprint "14 Shtator 1943" (see Nos. 332-344) which is private and fraudulent on these stamps.

No. 253 Overprinted   **Taksë**

1936   **Perf. 14**

J39	A34	10q carmine	3.50	4.75

Issued under Italian Dominion

Coat of
Arms — D9

1940   **Unwmk.**   **Photo.**   **Perf. 14**

J40	D9	4q red orange	22.50	18.00
J41	D9	10q bright violet	22.50	18.00
J42	D9	20q brown	22.50	18.00

J43	D9	30q dark blue	22.50	18.00
J44	D9	50q carmine rose	22.50	18.00
		Nos. J40-J44 (5)	112.50	90.00

ALEXANDRETTA

ˌa–lig–(ˌ)zan–'dre–tə

LOCATION — A political territory in northern Syria, bordering on Turkey
GOVT. — French mandate
AREA — 10,000 sq. mi. (approx.)
POP. — 270,000 (approx.)

Included in the Syrian territory mandated to France under the Versailles Treaty, the name was changed to Hatay in 1938. The following year France returned the territory to Turkey in exchange for certain concessions. See Hatay.

100 Centimes = 1 Piaster

Stamps of Syria, 1930-36, Overprinted or Surcharged in Black or Red:

1938   **Unwmk.**   **Perf. 12x12½**

1	A6 (a)	10c vio brn	.35	.35
2	A6 (a)	20c brn org	.35	.35

          Perf. 13½

3	A9 (b)	50c vio (R)	.35	.35
4	A10 (b)	1p bis brn	.50	.50
5	A9 (b)	2p dk vio (R)	.60	.60
6	A13 (b)	3p yel grn (R)	1.75	1.75
7	A10 (b)	4p yel org	1.75	1.75
8	A16 (b)	6p grnsh blk (R)	2.00	2.00
9	A18 (b)	25p vio brn	4.75	4.75
10	A15 (c)	75c dark green	.50	.50
11	A10 (d)	2.50p on 4p yel org	.90	.90
12	AP2 (e)	12.50p on 15p org red	2.50	2.50
		Nos. 1-12 (12)	16.30	16.30

Issue dates: #1-9, Apr. 14. #10-12, Sept. 2.

Nos. 4, 7, 10-12 Overprinted in Black

1938, Nov. 10

13	A15	75c	30.00	30.00
14	A10	1p	20.00	18.00
15	A10	2.50p on 4p	12.50	11.00
16	A10	4.50p	15.00	13.50
17	AP2	12.50p on 15p	30.00	30.00
		Nos. 13-17 (5)	107.50	102.50

Death of Kemal Ataturk, pres. of Turkey.

AIR POST STAMPS

Air Post Stamps of Syria, 1937,
Overprinted Type "b" in Red or Black

1938, Apr. 14   **Unwmk.**   **Perf. 13**

C1	AP14	½p dark vio (R)	.75	.75
C2	AP15	1p black (R)	.35	.35
C3	AP14	2p blue grn (R)	1.50	1.50
C4	AP15	3p deep ultra	1.75	1.75

C5	AP14	5p rose lake	4.50	4.50
C6	AP14	10p red brown	5.00	5.00
C7	AP14	15p lake brown	5.75	5.75
C8	AP15	25p dk blue (R)	7.50	7.50
		Nos. C1-C8 (8)	27.10	27.10

POSTAGE DUE STAMPS

Postage Due Stamps of Syria, 1925-31, Ovptd. Type "b" in Black or Red

1938, Apr. 14   Unwmk.   Perf. 13½

J1	D5	50c brown, yel	1.00	.80
J2	D6	1p violet, rose	1.75	1.10
J3	D5	2p blk, blue (R)	1.75	1.60
J4	D5	3p blk, red org	3.50	3.25
J5	D5	5p blk, bl grn (R)	5.50	5.00
J6	D7	8p blk, gray bl (R)	6.00	5.00
		Nos. J1-J6 (6)	19.00	16.75

On No. J2, the overprint is vertical, reading up, other denominations, horizontal.

Stamps of Alexandretta were discontinued in 1938 and replaced by those of Hatay.

ALGERIA

al-'jir-ē-ə

LOCATION — North Africa
GOVT. — Republic
AREA — 919,595 sq. mi.
POP. — 21,463,000 (1984 est.)
CAPITAL — Algiers

The former French colony of Algeria became an integral part of France on Sept. 1, 1958, when French stamps replaced Algerian stamps. Algeria became an independent country July 3, 1962.

100 Centimes = 1 Franc
100 Centimes = 1 Dinar (1964)

Catalogue values for unused stamps in this country are for Never Hinged items, beginning with Scott 109 in the regular postage section, Scott B27 in the semi-postal section, Scott C1 in the airpost section, Scott CB1 in the airpost semi-postal section, and Scott J25 in the postage due section.

Stamps of France Overprinted in Red, Blue or Black:

ALGÉRIE
a

ALGÉRIE
b

ALGÉRIE
c

ALGÉRIE
d

1924-26   Unwmk.   Perf. 14x13½

1	A16(a)	1c dk gray (R)	.15	.15
2	A16(a)	2c violet brn	.15	.15
3	A16(a)	3c orange	.15	.15
4	A16(a)	4c yel brn (Bl)	.15	.15
5	A22(a)	5c orange (Bl)	.15	.15
6	A16(a)	5c green ('25)	.15	.15
7	A23(a)	10c green	.15	.15
b.		Booklet pane of 10	1.50	
8	A22(a)	10c green ('25)	.50	.15
9	A20(a)	15c slate grn	.15	.15
10	A23(a)	15c green ('25)	.15	.15
11	A22(a)	15c red brn (Bl) ('26)	.15	.15
12	A22(a)	20c red brn (Bl)	.15	.15
13	A22(a)	25c blue (R)	.15	.15
a.		Booklet pane of 10	3.00	
14	A23(a)	30c red (Bl)	.15	.15
15	A22(a)	30c cerise ('25)	.50	.15
16	A22(a)	30c lt bl (R) ('25)	.15	.15
a.		Booklet pane of 10	2.00	
17	A22(a)	35c violet	.15	.15
18	A18(b)	40c red & pale bl	.15	.15
19	A22(a)	40c ol brn (R) ('25)	.75	.20
20	A18(b)	45c grn & bl (R)	.25	.15
21	A23(a)	45c red (Bl) ('25)	.30	.15
22	A23(a)	50c blue (R)	.15	.15
23	A20(a)	60c lt violet	.15	.15
a.		Inverted overprint		250.00
24	A23(a)	65c rose (Bl)	.15	.15
25	A23(a)	75c blue (R)	.25	.15
a.		Double overprint	65.00	
26	A20(a)	80c ver ('26)	.40	.15
27	A20(a)	85c ver (Bl)	.25	.15
28	A18(b)	1fr cl & ol grn	1.00	.15
29	A23(a)	1.05fr ver ('26)	.55	.25
30	A18(c)	2fr org & pale bl	.40	.30

31	A18(b)	3fr vio & bl ('26)	3.00	.55
32	A18(d)	5fr bl & buff (R)	8.00	4.00
		Nos. 1-32 (32)	19.00	
		Set value		7.50

No. 15 was issued precanceled only. Values for precanceled stamps in first column are for those which have not been through the post and have original gum. Values in second column are for postally used, gumless stamps.
For surcharges see Nos. 75, P1.

Street in Kasbah, Algiers
A1

Mosque of Sidi Abd-er-Rahman
A2

La Pêcherie Mosque
A3

Marabout of Sidi Yacoub
A4

1926-39   Typo.   Perf. 14x13½

33	A1	1c olive	.15	.15
34	A1	2c red brown	.15	.15
35	A1	3c orange	.15	.15
36	A1	5c blue green	.15	.15
37	A1	10c brt violet	.15	.15
a.		Booklet pane of 10	3.25	
38	A2	15c orange brn	.15	.15
39	A2	20c green	.15	.15
40	A2	20c deep rose	.15	.15
41	A2	25c blue grn	.15	.15
42	A2	25c blue ('27)	.40	.15
43	A2	25c vio bl ('39)	.15	.15
44	A2	30c blue	.25	.15
45	A2	30c bl grn ('27)	.80	.30
46	A2	35c dp violet	1.00	.65
47	A2	40c olive green	.15	.15
a.		Booklet pane of 10	2.25	
48	A3	45c violet brn	.25	.20
49	A3	50c blue	.25	.15
a.		Booklet pane of 10	3.50	
50	A3	50c dk red ('30)	.15	.15
a.		Booklet pane of 10	4.75	
51	A3	60c yellow grn	.15	.15
52	A3	65c blk brn ('27)	1.25	.85
53	A3	65c ultra ('38)	.25	.15
a.		Booklet pane of 10	1.75	
54	A3	75c carmine	.30	.25
55	A3	75c blue ('29)	2.25	.15
56	A3	80c orange red	.45	.25
57	A3	90c red ('27)	5.00	2.75
58	A3	1fr gray grn & red brn	.65	.20
59	A3	1.05fr lt brown	.55	.30
60	A3	1.10fr mag ('27)	5.00	1.75
61	A4	1.25fr dk bl & ultra	1.00	.80
62	A4	1.50fr dk bl & ultra ('27)	2.25	.15
63	A4	2fr Prus bl & blk brn	1.90	.20
64	A4	3fr violet & org	.35	.25
65	A4	5fr red & violet	6.00	2.00
66	A4	10fr ol brn & rose ('27)	40.00	20.00
67	A4	20fr vio & grn ('27)	5.00	4.00
		Nos. 33-67 (35)	80.00	38.00

Type A4, 50c blue and rose red, inscribed "CENTENAIRE-ALGERIE" is France No. 255.
See design A24. For stamps and types surcharged see Nos. 68-74, 131, 136, 187, B1-B13, J27, P2.

Stamps of 1926 Surcharged with New Values

1927

68	A2	10c on 35c dp violet	.15	.15
69	A2	25c on 30c blue	.15	.15
70	A3	30c on 25c blue grn	.15	.15
71	A3	65c on 60c yel grn	.75	.35
72	A3	90c on 80c org red	.50	.20
73	A3	1.10fr on 1.05fr lt brn	.30	.15
74	A4	1.50fr on 1.25fr dk bl & ultra	1.25	.45
		Nos. 68-74 (7)	3.25	1.60

Bars cancel the old value on #68, 69, 73, 74.

No. 4 Surcharged

5c

1927

75	A16	5c on 4c yellow brown	.75	.25

Bay of Algiers — A5

1930, May 4   Engr.   Perf. 11, 12½

78	A5	10fr red brown	9.50	7.50
a.		Imperf., pair	25.00	

Cent. of Algeria and for Intl. Phil. Exhib. of North Africa, May, 1930.
One copy of No. 78 was sold with each 10fr admission.
For surcharges see Nos. 75, P1.

Travel across the Sahara — A6

Arch of Triumph, Lambese — A7

Admiralty Building, Algiers — A8

Kings' Tombs near Touggourt — A9

El-Kebir Mosque, Algiers — A10

Oued River at Colomb-Bechar
A11

Sidi Bon Medine Cemetery at Tlemcen
A13

View of Ghardaia
A12

1936-41   Engr.   Perf. 13

79	A6	1c ultra	.15	.15
80	A11	2c dk violet	.15	.15
81	A7	3c dk blue grn	.15	.15
82	A12	5c red violet	.15	.15
83	A8	10c emerald	.15	.15
84	A9	15c red	.15	.15
85	A13	20c dk blue grn	.15	.15
86	A10	25c rose vio	.32	.15
87	A12	30c yellow grn	.28	.15
88	A9	40c brown vio	.15	.15
89	A13	45c deep ultra	.65	.40
90	A8	50c red	.40	.15
91	A6	65c red brn	2.50	1.75
92	A6	65c rose car ('37)	.35	.15
93	A6	70c red brn ('39)	.15	.15
94	A11	75c slate bl	.18	.15
95	A7	90c henna brn	.65	.45
96	A10	1fr brown	.18	.15
97	A8	1.25fr lt violet	.35	.18
98	A8	1.25fr car rose ('39)	.30	.15
99	A11	1.50fr turq blue	.90	.18
99A	A11	1.50fr rose ('40)	.35	.15
100	A12	1.75fr henna brn	.15	.15
101	A7	2fr dk brown	.15	.15
102	A6	2.25fr yellow grn	8.00	6.50
103	A12	2.50fr dk ultra ('41)	.28	.26
104	A13	3fr magenta	.26	.15
105	A10	3.50fr pck blue	1.90	1.40
106	A8	5fr slate blue	.28	.15
107	A11	10fr henna brn	.32	.20
108	A9	20fr turq blue	.60	.35
		Nos. 79-108 (31)	20.70	
		Set value		13.00

See Nos. 124-125, 162.
Nos. 82 and 100 with surcharge "E. F. M. 30frs" (Emergency Field Message) were used in 1943 to pay cable tolls for US and Canadian servicemen.

For other surcharges see Nos. 122, B27.

Catalogue values for unused stamps in this section, from this point to the end of the section, are for Never Hinged items.

Algerian Pavilion — A14

1937   Perf. 13

109	A14	40c brt green	.40	.35
110	A14	50c rose carmine	.25	.15
111	A14	1.50fr blue	.60	.25
112	A14	1.75fr brown black	.65	.50
		Nos. 109-112 (4)	1.90	1.25

Paris International Exposition.

Constantine in 1837 — A15

1937

113	A15	65c deep rose	.30	.15
114	A15	1fr brown	3.25	.50
115	A15	1.75fr blue green	.25	.20
116	A15	2.15fr red violet	.20	.15
		Nos. 113-116 (4)	4.00	1.00

Taking of Constantine by the French, cent.

Ruins of a Roman Villa — A16

1938

117	A16	30c green	.50	.30
118	A16	65c ultra	.15	.15
119	A16	75c rose violet	.55	.40
120	A16	3fr carmine rose	1.40	1.40
121	A16	5fr yellow brown	2.25	2.25
		Nos. 117-121 (5)	4.85	4.50

Centenary of Philippeville.

No. 90 Surcharged in Black

0,25

1938

122	A8	25c on 50c red	.15	.15
a.		Double surcharge	35.00	30.00
b.		Inverted surcharge	20.00	18.00

Types of 1936

1939

Numerals of Value on Colorless Background

124	A7	90c henna brown	.15	.15
125	A10	2.25fr blue green	.20	.20
		Set value		.25	.25

For surcharge, see No. B38.

American Export Liner Unloading Cargo — A17

1939

126	A17	20c green	.65	.65
127	A17	40c red violet	.65	.50
128	A17	90c brown black	.35	.20
129	A17	1.25fr rose	2.25	.80
130	A17	2.25fr ultra	.65	.60
		Nos. 126-130 (5)	4.55	2.75

New York World's Fair.

Type of 1926, Surcharged in Black **1F**

Two types of surcharge:
I - Bars 6mm
II - Bars 7mm

1939-40   Perf. 14x13½
131 A1 1fr on 90c crimson (I)   .15 .15
a. Booklet pane of 10
b. Double surcharge (I)   35.00
c. Inverted surcharge (I)   22.50
d. Pair, one without surch. (I)   800.00
e. Type II ('40)   1.50 .15
f. Inverted surcharge (II)   27.50
g. Pair, one without surch. (II)   800.00

View of Algiers — A18

1941   Typo.
132 A18 30c ultra   .15 .15
133 A18 70c sepia   .15 .15
134 A18 1fr carmine rose   .15 .15
Nos. 132-134 (3)   .45
Set value   .15
See No. 163.

Marshal Pétain
A19   A20

1941   Engr.   Perf. 13
135 A19 1fr dark blue   .30 .15
For stamp and type surcharged see #B36-B37.

No. 53 Surcharged in Black with New Value and Bars

1941   Perf. 14x13½
136 A1 50c on 65c ultra   .30 .15
a. Booklet pane of 10
b. Inverted surcharge   21.00
c. Pair, one without surch.   52.50

1942   Perf. 14x13
137 A20 1.50fr orange red   .15 .15

Four other denominations of type A20 exist (4, 5, 10, 20fr), but were not placed in use.

Constantine   Oran
A21   A22

Arms of Algiers — A23

Engraver's Name at Lower Left

1942-43   Photo.   Perf. 12
138 A21 40c dark vio ('43)   .15 .15
139 A22 60c rose ('43)   .15 .15
140 A21 1.20fr yel grn ('43)   .15 .15
141 A23 1.50fr car rose   .15 .15
142 A22 2fr sapphire   .20 .15
143 A21 2.40fr rose ('43)   .15 .15
144 A23 3fr sapphire   .20 .15
145 A21 4fr blue ('43)   .15 .15
146 A22 5fr yel grn ('43)   .15 .15
Set value   .90 .60

For type surcharged see No. 166.

Imperforates

Nearly all of Algeria Nos. 138-285, B39-B96, C1-C12 and CB1-CB3 exist imperforate. See note after France No. 395.

Without Engraver's Name

1942-45   Typo.   Perf. 14x13½
147 A23 10c dull brn vio ('45)   .15 .15
148 A22 30c dp bl grn ('45)   .15 .15
149 A21 40c dull brn vio ('45)   .15 .15
150 A22 60c rose ('45)   .15 .15
151 A21 70c deep bl ('45)   .15 .15
152 A23 80c dk bl grn ('45)   .22 .22
153 A21 1.20fr dp bl grn ('45)   .20 .15
154 A23 1.50fr brt rose ('43)   .15 .15
155 A22 2fr dp blue ('45)   .20 .15
156 A21 2.40fr rose ('45)   .30 .22
157 A23 3fr dp blue ('45)   .15 .15
158 A22 4.50fr brown vio   .20 .15
Set value   1.50 1.00

For surcharge see No. 190.

La Pêcherie Mosque — A24

1942   Typo.
159 A24 50c dull red   .15 .15
a. Booklet pane of 10   2.75

1942   Photo.   Perf. 12
160 A24 40c gray green   .15 .15
161 A24 50c red   .15 .15
Set value   .20 .15

Types of 1936-41, Without "RF"

1942   Engr.   Perf. 13
162 A11 1.50fr rose   .30 .15

Typo.   Perf. 14x13½
163 A18 30c ultra   .15 .15

"One Aim Alone - Victory"
A25   A26

1943   Litho.   Perf. 12
164 A25 1.50fr deep rose   .15 .15
165 A26 1.50fr dark blue   .15 .15
Set value   .20 .15

Type of 1942-3 Surcharged with New Value in Black

1943   Photo.
166 A22 2fr on 5fr red orange   .15 .15
a. Surcharge omitted   140.00

Summer Palace, Algiers — A27

1944, Dec. 1   Litho.
167 A27 15fr slate   .80 .80
168 A27 20fr lt blue grn   .60 .40
169 A27 50fr dk carmine   .60 .50
170 A27 100fr deep blue   1.50 1.25
171 A27 200fr dull bis brn   2.50 1.40
Nos. 167-171 (5)   6.00 4.35

Marianne
A28
Gallic Cock
A29

1944-45
172 A28 10c gray   .15 .15
173 A28 30c red violet   .15 .15
174 A29 40c rose car ('45)   .15 .15
175 A28 50c red   .15 .15
176 A28 80c emerald   .15 .15
177 A29 1fr green ('45)   .15 .15
178 A28 1.20fr rose lilac   .15 .15

179 A28 1.50fr dark blue   .15 .15
a. Double impression   20.00
180 A29 2fr red   .15 .15
a. Double impression   22.50
181 A28 2fr dk brown ('45)   .15 .15
182 A28 2.40fr rose red   .15 .15
183 A28 3fr purple   .15 .15
184 A29 4fr ultra ('45)   .15 .15
185 A29 4.50fr olive blk   .30 .25
186 A29 10fr grnsh blk ('45)   .50 .35
Set value   1.90 1.40

No. 38 Surcharged in Black   **0f.30**

1944   Perf. 14x13½
187 A2 30c on 15c orange brn   .15 .15
a. Inverted surcharge   10.00 4.00

This stamp exists precanceled only. See note below No. 32.

No. 154 Surcharged "RF" and New Value

1945
190 A23 50c on 1.50fr brt rose   .15 .15
a. Inverted surcharge   15.00

Stamps of France, 1944, Overprinted Type "a" of 1924 in Black

1945-46
191 A99 80c yellow grn   .15 .15
192 A99 1fr grnsh blue   .15 .15
193 A99 1.20fr violet   .15 .15
194 A99 2fr violet brown   .25 .15
195 A99 2.40fr carmine rose   .25 .15
196 A99 3fr orange   .25 .15
Set value   1.00 .75

Same Overprint on Stamps of France, 1945-47, in Black, Red or Carmine

1945-47
197 A145 40c lilac rose   .15 .15
198 A145 50c violet bl (R)   .15 .15
199 A146 60c brt ultra (R)   .25 .15
200 A146 1fr rose red ('47)   .20 .15
201 A146 1.50fr rose lilac ('47)   .15 .15
202 A147 2fr myr grn (R) ('46)   .15 .15
203 A147 3fr deep rose   .15 .15
204 A147 4.50fr ultra (C) ('47)   .55 .15
205 A147 5fr lt green ('46)   .15 .15
206 A147 10fr ultra   .50 .25
Set value   1.75 .75

Same Overprint on France No. 383 and New Value Surcharged in Black

1946
207 A99 2fr on 1.50fr henna brn   .15 .15
a. Without "2F"   110.00

Same Overprint on France Nos. 562 and 564, in Carmine or Blue

1947
208 A153 10c dp ultra & blk (C)   .25 .25
209 A155 50c brown, yel & red (Bl)   .30 .30
Set value   .27 .27

Constantine   Algiers
A30   A31

Arms of Oran — A32

Perf. 14x13½
1947-49   Unwmk.   Typo.
210 A30 10c dk grn & brt red   .15 .15
211 A31 50c black & orange   .15 .15
212 A32 1fr ultra & yellow   .15 .15
213 A30 1.30fr blk & grnsh bl   .55 .35
214 A31 1.50fr pur & org yel   .15 .15
215 A32 2fr blk & brt grn   .15 .15
216 A30 2.50fr blk & brt red   .35 .30
217 A31 3fr vio brn & grn   .15 .15
218 A32 3.50fr lt grn & rose lil   .15 .15
219 A30 4fr dk brn & brt grn   .15 .15
220 A31 4.50fr ultra & scar   .15 .15
221 A31 5fr blk & grnsh bl   .15 .15
222 A32 6fr brown & scarlet   .15 .15
223 A32 8fr choc & ultra ('48)   .20 .15
224 A30 10fr car & choc ('48)   .35 .15
225 A31 15fr black & red ('49)   .35 .15
Set value   2.75 1.35

See Nos. 274-280, 285.

Peoples of the World — A33

1949, Oct. 24   Engr.   Perf. 13
226 A33 5fr green   1.25 1.00
227 A33 15fr scarlet   1.25 1.00
228 A33 25fr ultra   2.75 2.75
Nos. 226-228 (3)   5.25 4.75
75th anniv. of the UPU.

Grapes
A34
Apollo of Cherchell
A35

Designs: 25fr, Dates. 40fr, Oranges and lemons.

1950, Feb. 25
229 A34 20fr multicolored   1.25 .35
230 A34 25fr multicolored   1.40 .40
231 A34 40fr multicolored   2.75 .80
Nos. 229-231 (3)   5.40 1.55

1952   Unwmk.   Perf. 13
Designs: 12fr, 18fr, Isis statue, Cherchell. 15fr, 20fr, Child with eagle.
240 A35 10fr gray black   .25 .15
241 A35 12fr orange brn   .35 .15
242 A35 15fr deep blue   .25 .15
243 A35 18fr deep red   .35 .25
244 A35 20fr deep green   .35 .15
245 A35 30fr deep blue   .65 .35
Nos. 240-245 (6)   2.20
Set value   .85

War Memorial, Algiers — A38
Fossilized Nautilus — A39

Phonolite Dike — A40

1952, Apr. 11
246 A38 12fr dark green   .50 .35
Issued to honor the French Africa Army.

1952, Aug. 11
247 A39 15fr brt crimson   .85 .60
248 A40 30fr deep ultra   .90 .65
19th Intl. Geological Cong., Algiers, Sept. 8-15.

French and Algerian Soldiers and Camel — A41

1952, Nov. 30
249 A41 12fr chestnut brown   1.00 .60
50th anniv. of the establishment of the Sahara Companies.

Eugène
Millon — A42

François C.
Maillot — A43

Oranges — A44

Portrait: 50fr, Alphonse Laveran.

1954, Jan. 4   Unwmk.   Engr.   *Perf. 13*
250 A42 25fr dk grn & choc   1.10 .18
251 A43 40fr org brn & brn car   1.75 .60
252 A42 50fr ultra & indigo   1.75 .22
    Nos. 250-252 (3)   4.60 1.00
Military Health Service.

1954, May 8
253 A44 15fr indigo & blue   .70 .40
3rd Intl. Cong. on Agronomy, Algiers, 1954.

Type of France, 1954 Overprinted type "a"
in Black
Unwmk.
1954, June 6   Engr.   *Perf. 13*
254 A240 15fr rose carmine   .55 .45
Liberation of France, 10th anniversary.

Darguinah
Hydroelectric
Works
A45

Patio of
Bardo
Museum
A46

1954, June 19
255 A45 15fr lilac rose   .65 .45
Opening of Darguinah hydroelectric works.

1954   Typo.   *Perf. 14x13½*
257 A46 12fr red brn & brn org   .60 .25
258 A46 15fr dk blue & blue   .60 .25
    See Nos. 267-271.

Type of France, 1954, Overprinted type
"a" in Carmine
1954   Engr.   *Perf. 13*
260 A247 12fr dark green   .50 .45
150th anniv. of the 1st Legion of Honor awards
at Camp de Boulogne.

St. Augustine — A47

1954, Nov. 11
261 A47 15fr chocolate   .75 .65
1600th anniv. of the birth of St. Augustine.

Aesculapius
Statue and El
Kattar
Hospital,
Algiers — A48

1955, Apr. 3   Unwmk.   *Perf. 13*
262 A48 15fr red   .50 .35
Issued to publicize the 30th French Congress of
Medicine, Algiers, April 3-6, 1955.

Chenua
Mountain and
View of
Tipasa — A49

1955, May 31
263 A49 50fr brown carmine   .50 .20
2000th anniv. of the founding of Tipasa.

Type of France, 1955 Overprinted type "a"
in Red
1955, June 13
264 A251 30fr deep ultra   .60 .45
Rotary Intl., 50th anniv.

Marianne
A50

Great Kabylia Mountains
A51

Perf. 14x13½
1955, Oct. 3   Typo.   Unwmk.
265 A50 15fr carmine   .40 .25
    See No. 284.

1955, Dec. 17   Engr.   *Perf. 13*
266 A51 100fr indigo & ultra   2.00 .20

Bardo Type of 1954,
"Postes" and "Algerie" in White
Perf. 14x13½
1955-57   Unwmk.   Typo.
267 A46 10fr dk brown & lt brown   .25 .15
268 A46 12fr red brn & brn org ('56) .20 .15
269 A46 18fr crimson & ver ('57)   .45 .20
270 A46 20fr grn & yel grn ('57)   .35 .25
271 A46 25fr purple & brt purple   .50 .15
    Nos. 267-271 (5)   1.75
    Set value   .60

Marshal
Franchet
d'Esperey
A52

1956, May 25   Engr.   *Perf. 13*
272 A52 15fr sapphire & indigo   .70 .60
Birth cent. of Marshal Franchet d'Esperey.

Marshal
Jacques
Leclerc — A53

1956, Nov. 29
273 A53 15fr red brown & sepia   .50 .50
Death of Marshal Leclerc.
For type surcharged see No. B90.

Type of 1947-49 and

Arms of Bône — A54

Arms: 2fr, Tizi-Ouzou. 3fr, Mostaganem. 5fr,
Tlemcen. 10fr, Setif. 12fr, Orleansville.

1956-58   Typo.   *Perf. 14x13½*
274 A54 1fr green & ver   .15 .15
275 A54 2fr ver & ultra ('58)   .35 .20
276 A54 3fr ultra & emer ('58)   .35 .15
277 A54 5fr ultra & yellow   .15 .15
278 A31 6fr red & grn ('57)   .35 .25
279 A54 10fr dp cl & emer ('58)   .40 .25
280 A54 12fr ultra & red ('58)   .40 .25
    Nos. 274-280 (7)   2.15 1.40
Nos. 275 and 279 are inscribed "Republique
Francaise." See No. 285.

View of
Oran — A55

1956-58   Engr.   *Perf. 13*
281 A55 30fr dull purple   .45 .18
282 A55 35fr car rose ('58)   .75 .45

Electric Train
Crossing
Bridge — A56

1957, Mar. 25
283 A56 40fr dk blue grn & emer   .60 .18

Marianne Type of 1955
Inscribed "Algerie" Vertically
Perf. 14x13½
1957, Dec. 2   Typo.   Unwmk.
284 A50 20fr ultra   .40 .15

Arms Type of 1947-49 Inscribed
"Republique Francaise"
1958, July
285 A31 6fr red & green   10.00 10.00

Independent State
France Nos. 939, 968, 945-946 and 1013
Overprinted "EA" and Bars, Handstamped
or Typographed, in Black or Red
1962, July 2
286 A336 10c brt green   .25 .20
  a. Typographed overprint   .30 .20
287 A349 25c lake & gray   .20 .15
  a. Handstamped overprint   .25 .15
288 A339 45c brt vio & ol gray   3.50 3.00
  a. Handstamped overprint   15.00 10.00
289 A339 50c sl grn & lt claret   5.00 3.00
  a. Handstamped overprint   15.00 12.00
290 A372 1fr dk bl, sl & bis   2.75 1.00
  a. Handstamped overprint   4.00 1.50
    Nos. 286-290 (5)   11.70 7.35

Post offices were authorized to overprint their
stock of these 5 French stamps. The size of the
letters was specified as 3x6mm each, but various
sizes were used. The post offices had permission to
make their own rubber stamps. Typography, pen or
pencil were also used. Many types exist. Colors of
handstamped overprints include black, red, blue,
violet. "EA" stands for Etat Algérien.

Mosque, Tlemcen — A57

Roman Gates
of Lodi,
Médéa — A58

Designs: 5c, Kerrata Gorge. 10c, Dam at Foum el
Gherza. 95c, Oil field, Hassi Messaoud.

1962, Nov. 1   Engr.   *Perf. 13*
291 A57 5c Prus grn, grn & choc   .15 .15
292 A58 10c ol blk & dk bl   .15 .15
293 A57 25c sl grn, brn & ver   .40 .15

294 A57 95c dk bl, blk & bis   1.50 .55
295 A58 1fr green & blk   1.50 1.10
    Nos. 291-295 (5)   3.70
    Set value   1.75
The designs of Nos. 291-295 are similar to
French issues of 1959-61 with "Republique Alger-
ienne" replacing "Republique Francaise."

Flag, Rifle, Olive
Branch — A59

Design: Nos. 300-303, Broken chain and rifle
added to design A59.

1963, Jan. 6   Litho.   *Perf. 12½*
Flag in Green and Red
296 A59 5c bister brown   .15 .15
297 A59 10c blue   .15 .15
298 A59 25c vermilion   1.00 .15
299 A59 95c violet   .90 .45
300 A59 1fr green   .75 .45
301 A59 2fr brown   2.00 .45
302 A59 5fr lilac   3.00 1.25
303 A59 10fr gray   11.50 7.00
    Nos. 296-303 (8)   19.45 9.75
Nos. 296-299 for the successful revolution and
Nos. 300-303 the return of peace.

Men of
Various Races,
Wheat
Emblem and
Globe — A60

1963, Mar. 21   Engr.   *Perf. 13*
304 A60 25c maroon, dl grn & yel   .28 .15
FAO "Freedom from Hunger" campaign.

Map of Algeria and
Emblems — A61

Physicians from
13th Century
Manuscript — A62

1963, July 5   Unwmk.   *Perf. 13*
305 A61 25c bl, dk brn, grn & red   .40 .22
1st anniv. of Algeria's independence.

1963, July 29   Engr.
306 A62 25c brn red, grn & bis   1.00 .35
2nd Congress of the Union of Arab physicians.

Orange and
Blossom
A63

Scales and Scroll
A64

1963   *Perf. 14x13*
307 A63 8c gray grn & org   .65 .65
308 A63 20c slate & org red   .75 .75
309 A63 40c grnsh bl & org   1.00 1.00
310 A63 55c ol grn & org red   2.00 2.00
    Nos. 307-310 (4)   4.40 4.40
Nos. 307-310 issued precanceled only. See note
below No. 32.

1963, Oct. 13   Unwmk.   *Perf. 13*
311 A64 25c blk, grn & rose red   .42 .28
Issued to honor the new constitution.

Guerrillas
A65

Centenary
Emblem
A66

1963, Nov. 1
312 A65 25c dk brn, yel grn & car .55 .25
9th anniversary of Algerian revolution.

1963, Dec. 8   Photo.   Perf. 12
313 A66 25c lt vio bl, yel & dk red .55 .28
Centenary of International Red Cross.

UNESCO Emblem,
Scales and
Globe — A67

Workers — A68

1963, Dec. 16   Unwmk.   Perf. 12
314 A67 25c lt blue & blk .55 .25
15th anniv. of the Universal Declaration of
Human Rights.

1964, May 1   Engr.   Perf. 13
315 A68 50c dull red, red org & bl .90 .50
Issued for the Labor Festival.

Map of Africa
and
Flags — A69

1964, May 25   Unwmk.   Perf. 13
316 A69 45c blue, orange & car .55 .28
Africa Day on the 1st anniv. of the Addis Ababa
charter on African unity.

Ramses II Battling the Hittites (from Abu
Simbel) — A70

Design: 30c, Two statues of Ramses II.

1964, June 28   Engr.   Perf. 13
317 A70 20c choc, red & vio bl .55 .32
318 A70 30c brn, red & grnsh bl .65 .40
UNESCO world campaign to save historic monuments in Nubia.

A71

A72

Designs: 5c, 25c, 85c, Tractors. 10c, 30c, 65c,
Men working with lathe. 12c, 15c, 45c, Electronics
center and atom symbol. 20c, 50c, 95c, Draftsman
and bricklayer.

1964-65   Typo.   Perf. 14x13½
319 A71 5c red lilac .15 .15
320 A71 10c brown .15 .15
321 A71 12c emerald ('65) .38 .15

322 A71 15c dk blue ('65) .25 .15
323 A71 20c yellow .42 .15
324 A71 25c red .50 .15
325 A71 30c purple ('65) .42 .15
326 A71 45c rose car .50 .18
327 A71 50c ultra .62 .15
328 A71 65c orange .80 .18
329 A71 85c green 1.40 .22
330 A71 95c car rose 1.75 .26
    Nos. 319-330 (12) 7.34
    Set value 1.40
For surcharges see Nos. 389, 424.

1964, Aug. 30   Engr.   Perf. 13
331 A72 85c Communications tower 1.50 .75
Inauguration of the Hertzian cable telephone line
Algiers-Annaba.

Industrial &
Agricultural
Symbols — A73

Gas Flames
and
Pipes — A74

1964, Sept. 26   Typo.   Perf. 13½x14
332 A73 25c lt ultra, yel & red .60 .45
1st Intl. Fair at Algiers, Sept. 26-Oct. 11.

1964, Sept. 27
333 A74 30c violet, blue & yel .45 .35
Arzew natural gas liquification plant opening.

Planting Trees
A75

Children and
UNICEF
Emblem
A76

1964, Nov. 29   Unwmk.
334 A75 25c slate grn, yel & car .28 .20
National reforestation campaign.

1964, Dec. 13   Perf. 13½x14
335 A76 15c pink, vio bl & lt grn .25 .20
Issued for Children's Day.

Decorated Camel
Saddle — A77

1965, May 29   Typo.   Perf. 13½x14
336 A77 20c blk, red, emer & brn .22 .15
Handicrafts of Sahara.

ICY Emblem
A78

1965, Aug. 29   Engr.   Perf. 13
337 A78 30c blk, mar & bl grn .45 .32
338 A78 60c blk, brt bl & bl grn .85 .38
International Cooperation Year, 1965.

ITU Emblem
A79

1965, Sept. 19
339 A79 60c purple, emer & buff .45 .30
340 A79 95c dk brn, mar & buff .65 .35
Cent. of the ITU.

Musicians
A80

Miniatures by Mohammed Racim: 60c, Two
female musicians. 5d, Algerian princess and
antelope.

1965, Dec. 27   Photo.   Perf. 11½
341 A80 30c multicolored .70 .55
342 A80 60c multicolored 1.10 .70
343 A80 5d multicolored 8.00 5.25
    Nos. 341-343 (3) 9.80 6.50

Bulls,
Painted
in 6000
B.C.
A81

Wall Paintings from Tassili-N-Ajjer, c. 6000 B.C.:
No. 345, Shepherd, vert. 2d, Fleeing ostriches. 3d,
Two girls, vert.

1966, Jan. 29   Photo.   Perf. 11½
344 A81 1d brn, bis & red brn 2.75 1.90
345 A81 1d gray, blk, ocher & dk
        brn 2.75 1.90
346 A81 2d brn, ocher & red brn 6.50 3.00
347 A81 3d buff, blk, ocher & brn
        red 8.00 4.25
    Nos. 344-347 (4) 20.00 11.05
    See Nos. 365-368.

Pottery — A82

Handicrafts from Great Kabylia: 50c, Weaving,
woman at loom, horiz. 70c, Jewelry.

1966, Feb. 26   Engr.   Perf. 13
348 A82 40c Prus bl, brn red & blk .28 .22
349 A82 50c dk red, ol & ocher .38 .28
350 A82 70c vio bl, blk & red .65 .40
    Nos. 348-350 (3) 1.31 .90

Weather
Balloon,
Compass Rose
and
Anemometer
A83

1966, Mar. 23   Engr.   Unwmk.
351 A83 1d claret, brt bl & grn .85 .38
World Meteorological Day.

Book, Grain, Cogwheel
and UNESCO
Emblem — A84

Design: 60c, Grain, cogwheel, book and
UNESCO emblem.

1966, May 2   Typo.   Perf. 13x14
352 A84 30c yellow bis & blk .22 .20
353 A84 60c dk red, gray & blk .40 .22
Literacy as basis for development.

WHO
Headquarters,
Geneva
A85

1966, May 30   Engr.   Perf. 13
354 A85 30c multicolored .35 .30
355 A85 60c multicolored .70 .40
Inauguration of the WHO Headquarters, Geneva.

Algerian Scout
Emblem — A86

Arab Jamboree
Emblem — A87

1966, July 23   Photo.   Perf. 12x12½
356 A86 30c multicolored .65 .50
357 A87 1d multicolored 1.75 1.25

No. 356 commemorates the 30th anniv. of the
Algerian Mohammedan Boy Scouts. No. 357, the
7th Arab Boy Scout Jamboree, held at Good Daim,
Libya, Aug. 12.

Map of Palestine
and Victims
A88

Abd-el-Kader
A89

1966, Sept. 26   Typo.   Perf. 10½
358 A88 30c red & black .80 .40
Deir Yassin Massacre, Apr. 9, 1948.

1966, Nov. 2   Photo.   Perf. 11½
359 A89 30c multicolored .38 .15
360 A89 95c multicolored 1.10 .35
Transfer from Damascus to Algiers of the ashes of
Abd-el-Kader (1807?-1883), Emir of Mascara. See
Nos. 382-387.

UNESCO
Emblem — A90

1966, Nov. 19   Typo.   Perf. 10½
361 A90 1d multicolored 1.00 .35
20th anniv. of UNESCO.

Horseman
A91

Miniatures by Mohammed Racim: 1.50d, Woman at her toilette. 2d, The pirate Barbarossa in front of the Admiralty.

1966, Dec. 17   Photo.   Perf. 11½
Granite Paper

362	A91	1d multicolored	3.25	1.40
363	A91	1.50d multicolored	4.25	2.00
364	A91	2d multicolored	7.00	3.50
		Nos. 362-364 (3)	14.50	6.90

Wall Paintings Type of 1966

Wall Paintings from Tassili-N-Ajjer, c. 6000 B.C.: 1d, Cow. No. 366, Antelope. No. 367, Archers. 3d, Warrior, vert.

1967, Jan. 28   Photo.   Perf. 11½

365	A81	1d brn, bis & dl vio	2.75	1.90
366	A81	2d brn, ocher & red brn	5.00	3.25
367	A81	2d brn, yel & red brn	5.00	3.25
368	A81	3d blk, gray, yel & red brn	7.75	5.00
		Nos. 365-368 (4)	20.50	13.40

Bardo Museum
A92

La Kalaa
Minaret — A93

Design: 1.30d, Ruins at Sedrata.

1967, Feb. 27   Photo.   Perf. 13

369	A93	35c multicolored	.20	.15
370	A93	95c multicolored	.45	.28
371	A93	1.30d multicolored	.75	.40
		Nos. 369-371 (3)	1.40	.83

Moretti and International Tourist Year Emblem — A94

Design: 70c, Tuareg riding camel, Tassili, and Tourist Year Emblem, vert.

1967, Apr. 29   Litho.   Perf. 14

372	A94	40c multi	.50	.22
373	A94	70c multi	1.00	.35

International Tourist Year, 1967.

Spiny-tailed
Agamid — A95

Designs: 20c, Ostrich, vert. 40c, Slender-horned gazelle, vert. 70c, Fennec.

1967, June 24   Photo.   Perf. 11½

374	A95	5c bister & blk	.60	.50
375	A95	20c ocher, blk & pink	1.25	.80
376	A95	40c ol bis, blk & red brn	2.00	1.00
377	A95	70c gray, blk & dp org	3.50	2.00
		Nos. 374-377 (4)	7.35	4.30

Dancers — A96

Typographed and Engraved
1967, July 4   Perf. 10½

378	A96	50c gray vio, yel & blk	.45	.32

National Youth Festival.

Map of the Mediterranean and Sport Scenes — A97

1967, Sept. 2   Typo.   Perf. 10½

379	A97	30c black, red & blue	.25	.20

Issued to publicize the 5th Mediterranean Games, Tunis, Sept. 8-17.

Skiers — A98

Olympic Emblem and Sports — A99

1967, Oct. 21   Engr.   Perf. 13

380	A98	30c brt blue & ultra	.32	.20
381	A99	95c brn org, pur & brt grn	.80	.52

Issued to publicize the 10th Winter Olympic Games, Grenoble, Feb. 6-18, 1968.

Abd-el-Kader Type of 1966
Lithographed, Photogravure
1967-71   Perf. 13½, 11½

382	A89	5c dull pur ('68)	.15	.15
383	A89	10c green	.85	.35
383A	A89	10c sl grn (litho., '69)	.15	.15
383B	A89	25c orange ('71)	.18	.15
384	A89	30c black ('68)	.50	.20
385	A89	30c lt violet ('68)	.75	.30
386	A89	50c rose claret	.65	.18
387	A89	70c violet blue	.85	.22
		Nos. 382-387 (8)	4.08	
		Set value		1.40

No. 383, 50c and 70c, issued Nov. 13, 1967, are on granite paper, photo. The 5c, No.383A, 25c and 30c are litho., perf. 13½; others, perf. 11½.

The three 1967 stamps (No. 383, 50c, 70c) have numerals thin, narrow and close together; the Arabic inscription at lower right is 2mm high. The 5 litho. stamps are redrawn, with numerals thicker and spaced more widely; Arabic at lower right 3mm high.

Boy Scouts Holding Jamboree Emblem
A100

1967, Dec. 23   Engr.   Perf. 13

388	A100	1d multicolored	1.00	.80

12th Boy Scout World Jamboree, Farragut State Park, Idaho, Aug. 1-9.

No. 324 Surcharged
1967   Typo.   Perf. 14x13½

389	A71	30c on 25c red	.50	.20

Mandolin — A101

1968, Feb. 17   Photo.   Perf. 12½x13

390	A101	30c shown	.35	.22
391	A101	40c Lute	.40	.25
392	A101	1.30d Rebec	1.40	.65
		Nos. 390-392 (3)	2.15	1.12

Nememcha Rug — A102

Algerian Rugs: 70c, Guergour. 95c, Djebel-Amour. 1.30d, Kalaa.

1968, Apr. 13   Photo.   Perf. 11½

393	A102	30c multi	.75	.75
394	A102	70c multi	1.50	1.50
395	A102	95c multi	2.00	2.00
396	A102	1.30d multi	2.50	2.50
		Nos. 393-396 (4)	6.75	6.75

Human Rights Flame
A103

1968, May 18   Typo.   Perf. 10½

397	A103	40c blue, red & yel	.40	.28

International Human Rights Year, 1968.

WHO Emblem
A104

1968, May 18

398	A104	70c blk, lt bl & yel	.55	.28

20th anniv. of the WHO.

Welder — A105   Athletes, Olympic Flame and Rings — A106

1968, June 15   Engr.   Perf. 13

399	A105	30c gray, brn & ultra	.25	.18

Algerian emigration to Europe.

Perf. 12½x13, 13x12½
1968, July 4   Photo.

50c, Soccer player. 1d, Mexican pyramid, emblem, Olympic flame, rings & athletes, horiz.

400	A106	30c green, red & yel	.35	.28
401	A106	50c rose car & multi	.60	.32
402	A106	1d dk grn, org, brn & red	1.10	.65
		Nos. 400-402 (3)	2.05	1.25

19th Olympic Games, Mexico City, Oct. 12-27.

Scouts and Emblem
A107   Barbary Sheep
A108

1968, July 4   Perf. 13

403	A107	30c multicolored	.50	.18

8th Arab Boy Scout Jamboree, Algiers, 1968.

1968, Oct. 19   Photo.   Perf. 11½

404	A108	40c shown	.48	.25
405	A108	1d Red deer	1.25	.60

Hunting Scenes, Djemila
A109   "Industry"
A110

Design: 95c, Neptune's chariot, Timgad, horiz. Both designs are from Roman mosaics.

Perf. 12½x13, 13x12½
1968, Nov. 23   Photo.

406	A109	40c gray & multi	.35	.22
407	A109	95c gray & multi	.85	.50

1968, Dec. 14   Perf. 11½

Designs: No. 409, Miner with drill. 95c, "Energy" (circle and rays).

408	A110	30c dp orange & sil	.25	.18
409	A110	30c brown & multi	.25	.18
410	A110	95c silver, red & blk	.75	.35
		Nos. 408-410 (3)	1.25	.71

Issued to publicize industrial development.

Opuntia Ficus Indica — A111

Flowers: 40c, Carnations. 70c, Roses. 95c, Bird-of-paradise flower.

1969, Jan. Photo. Perf. 11½
Flowers in Natural Colors

411	A111	25c pink & blk	.52 .25
412	A111	40c yellow & blk	.65 .32
413	A111	70c gray & blk	1.25 .45
414	A111	95c brt blue & blk	2.00 .80
		Nos. 411-414 (4)	4.42 1.82

See Nos. 496-499.

Irrigation Dam at Djorf Torba-Oued Guir A112

Design: 1.50d, Truck on Highway No. 51 and camel caravan.

1969, Feb. 22 Photo. Perf. 11½

415	A112	30c multi	.24 .18
416	A112	1.50d multi	1.25 .65

Public works in the Sahara.

Mail Coach A113

1969, Mar. 22 Photo. Perf. 11½

417	A113	1d multicolored	1.10 .60

Issued for Stamp Day, 1969.

Capitol, Timgad — A114

Design: 1d, Septimius Temple, Djemila, horiz.

1969, Apr. 5 Photo. Perf. 13x12½

418	A114	30c gray & multi	.35 .18
419	A114	1d gray & multi	.85 .35

Second Timgad Festival, Apr. 4-8.

ILO Emblem — A115   Arabian Saddle — A116

1969, May 24 Photo. Perf. 11½

420	A115	95c dp car, yel & blk	1.00 .38

50th anniv. of the ILO.

1969, June 28 Photo. Perf. 12x12½

Algerian Handicrafts: 30c, Bookcase. 60c, Decorated copper plate.

Granite Paper

421	A116	30c multicolored	.28 .20
422	A116	60c multicolored	.55 .25
423	A116	1d multicolored	1.00 .45
		Nos. 421-423 (3)	1.83 .90

No. 321 Surcharged

0,20

1969 Typo. Perf. 14x13½

424	A71	20c on 12c emerald	.22 .15

Pan-African Culture Festival Emblem — A117   African Development Bank Emblem — A118

1969, July 19 Photo. Perf. 12½

425	A117	30c multicolored	.32 .18

Issued to commemorate the First Pan-African Culture Festival, Algiers, July 21-Aug. 1.

1969, Aug. 23 Typo. Perf. 10½

426	A118	30c dull blue, yel & blk	.32 .20

5th anniversary of the African Development Bank.

Astronauts and Landing Module on Moon — A119

Perf. 12½x11½
1969, Aug. 23 Photo.

427	A119	50c gold & multi	.60 .35

Man's 1st landing on the moon, July 20, 1969. US astronauts Neil A. Armstrong and Col. Edwin E. Aldrin, Jr., with Lieut. Col. Michael Collins piloting Apollo 11.

Algerian Women, by Dinet — A120

1.50d, The Watchmen, by Etienne Dinet.

1969, Nov. 29 Photo. Perf. 14½

428	A120	1d multi	1.75 .90
429	A120	1.50d multi	2.75 1.40

Mother and Child — A121

1969, Dec. 27 Photo. Perf. 11½

430	A121	30c multicolored	.32 .24

Issued to promote mother and child protection.

Agricultural Growth Chart, Tractor and Dam — A122

Designs: 30c, Transportation and development. 50c, Abstract symbols of industrialization.

1970, Jan. 31 Photo. Perf. 12½
Size: 37x23mm

431	A122	25c dk brn, yel & org	.16 .15

Litho. Perf. 14
Size: 49x23mm

432	A122	30c blue & multi	.24 .18

Photo. Perf. 12½
Size: 37x23mm

433	A122	50c rose lilac & multi	.28 .20
		Nos. 431-433 (3)	.68 .53

Four-Year Development Plan.

Old and New Mail Delivery A123   Spiny Lobster A124

1970, Feb. 28 Photo. Perf. 11½
Granite Paper

434	A123	30c multicolored	.28 .18

Issued for Stamp Day.

1970, Mar. 28

Designs: 40c, Mollusks. 75c, Retepora cellulosa. 1d, Red coral.

435	A124	30c ocher & multi	.35 .18
436	A124	40c multicolored	.50 .22
437	A124	75c ultra & multi	.90 .35
438	A124	1d lt blue & multi	1.25 .48
		Nos. 435-438 (4)	3.00 1.23

Oranges, EXPO '70 Emblem — A125

Designs (EXPO '70 Emblem and): 60c, Algerian pavilion. 70c, Grapes.

1970, Apr. 25 Photo. Perf. 12½x12

439	A125	30c lt blue, grn & org	.50 .15
440	A125	60c multicolored	.65 .18
441	A125	70c multicolored	1.00 .32
		Nos. 439-441 (3)	2.15 .65

EXPO '70 International Exhibition, Osaka, Japan, Mar. 15-Sept. 13, 1970.

Olives, Oil Bottle — A126   Saber — A127

1970, May 16 Photo. Perf. 12½x12

442	A126	1d yellow & multi	1.00 .65

Olive Year, 1969-1970.

Common Design Types pictured following the introduction.

UPU Headquarters Issue
Common Design Type

1970, May 30 Perf. 13
Size: 36x26mm

443	CD133	75c multicolored	.50 .40

1970, June 27 Photo. Perf. 12½

Designs: 40c, Guns, 18th century, horiz. 1d, Pistol, 18th century, horiz.

444	A127	40c yellow & multi	.65 .22
445	A127	75c red & multi	.80 .40
446	A127	1d multicolored	1.25 .50
		Nos. 444-446 (3)	2.70 1.12

Map of Arab Countries and Arab League Flag — A128

Typographed and Engraved
1970, July 25 Perf. 10½

447	A128	30c grn, ocher & lt bl	.30 .20

25th anniversary of the Arab League.

Lenin — A129

1970, Aug. 29 Litho. Perf. 11½x12

448	A129	30c brown & buff	.25 .20

Lenin (1870-1924), Russian communist leader.

Exhibition Hall and Algiers Fair Emblem — A130

1970, Sept. 11 Engr. Perf. 14x13½

449	A130	60c lt olive green	.40 .30

New Exhibition Hall for Algiers International Fair.

Education Year Emblem, Blackboard, Atom Symbol A131

Koran Page — A132

1970, Oct. 24 Photo. Perf. 14

450	A131	30c pink, blk, gold & lt bl	.22 .18
451	A132	3d multicolored	2.50 1.50

Issued for International Education Year.

Great Mosque, Tlemcen — A133

Design: 40c, Ketchaoua Mosque, Algiers, vert. 1d, Mosque, Sidi-Okba, vert.

1970-71   **Litho.**   *Perf. 14*
456 A133 30c multicolored   .22 .15
457 A133 40c sepia & lemon ('71)   .25 .15
458 A133 1d multicolored   .65 .28
    Nos. 456-458 (3)   1.12 .58

Symbols of the Arts — A134

1970, Dec. 26   **Photo.**   *Perf. 13x12½*
459 A134 1d grn, lt grn & org   .80 .45

Main Post Office, Algiers — A135

1971, Jan. 23   *Perf. 11½*
460 A135 30c multicolored   .32 .20
    Stamp Day, 1971.

Hurdling A136

40c, Vaulting, vert. 75c, Basketball, vert.

1971, Mar. 7   **Photo.**   *Perf. 11½*
461 A136 20c lt blue & slate   .25 .20
462 A136 40c lt grn & slate   .35 .35
463 A136 75c salmon pink & slate   .65 .50
    Nos. 461-463 (3)   1.25 1.05

Mediterranean Games, Izmir, Turkey, Oct. 1971.

Symbolic Head — A137

1971, Mar. 27   *Perf. 12½*
464 A137 60c car rose, blk & sil   .32 .20

Intl. year against racial discrimination.

Emblem and Technicians A138

1971, Apr. 24   **Photo.**   *Perf. 12½x12*
465 A138 70c claret, org & bluish blk   .40 .30

Founding of the Institute of Technology.

Woman from Aurès — A139

Regional Costumes: 70c, Man from Oran. 80c, Man from Algiers. 90c, Woman from Amour Mountains.

1971, Oct. 16   *Perf. 11½*
466 A139 50c gold & multi   1.50 .65
467 A139 70c gold & multi   1.65 1.00
468 A139 80c gold & multi   2.25 1.10
469 A139 90c gold & multi   2.50 1.25
    Nos. 466-469 (4)   7.90 4.00

See Nos. 485-488, 534-537.

UNICEF Emblem, Birds and Plants — A140

1971, Dec. 6   *Perf. 11½*
470 A140 60c multicolored   .55 .32

25th anniv. of UNICEF.

Lion of St. Mark A141

Design: 1.15d, Bridge of Sighs, Venice, vert.

1972, Jan. 24   **Litho.**   *Perf. 12*
471 A141 80c multi   .60 .32
472 A141 1.15d multi   .90 .52

UNESCO campaign to save Venice.

Javelin A142

Book and Book Year Emblem A143

Designs: 25c, Bicycling, horiz. 60c, Wrestling. 1d, Gymnast on rings.

1972, Mar. 25   **Photo.**   *Perf. 11½*
473 A142 25c maroon & multi   .30 .20
474 A142 40c ocher & multi   .35 .25
475 A142 60c ultra & multi   .40 .40
476 A142 1d rose & multi   1.00 .50
    Nos. 473-476 (4)   2.05 1.35

20th Olympic Games, Munich, Aug. 26-Sept. 11.

1972, Apr. 15
477 A143 1.15d bister, brn & red   .65 .48

International Book Year 1972.

Mailmen A144

Flowers A145

1972, Apr. 22
478 A144 40c gray & multi   .25 .15

Stamp Day 1972.

1972, May 27
479 A145 50c Jasmine   .65 .28
480 A145 60c Violets   .75 .35
481 A145 1.15d Tuberose   1.50 .55
    Nos. 479-481 (3)   2.90 1.18

Olympic Stadium, Chéraga — A146

1972, June 10
482 A146 50c gray, choc & grn   .60 .32

New Day, Algerian Flag — A147

1972, July 5
483 A147 1d green & multi   .65 .42

10th anniversary of independence.

Festival Emblem — A148

Mailing a Letter — A149

1972, July 5   **Litho.**   *Perf. 10½*
484 A148 40c grn, dk brn & org   .22 .15

1st Arab Youth Festival, Algiers, July 5-11.

Costume Type of 1971

Regional Costumes: 50c, Woman from Hoggar. 60c, Kabyle woman. 70c, Man from Mzab. 90c, Woman from Tlemcen.

1972, Nov. 18   **Photo.**   *Perf. 11½*
485 A139 50c gold & multi   .80 .70
486 A139 60c gold & multi   1.10 .90
487 A139 70c gold & multi   1.25 1.10
488 A139 90c gold & multi   1.75 1.25
    Nos. 485-488 (4)   4.90 3.95

1973, Jan. 20   **Photo.**   *Perf. 11*
489 A149 40c orange & multi   .40 .20

Stamp Day.

Ho Chi Minh, Map of Viet Nam — A150

1973, Feb. 17   **Photo.**   *Perf. 11½*
490 A150 40c multicolored   .75 .50

To honor the people of Viet Nam.

Embroidery from Annaba — A151

Designs: 60c, Tree of Life pattern from Algiers. 80c, Constantine embroidery.

1973, Feb. 24
491 A151 40c gray & multi   .75 .40
492 A151 60c blue and multi   1.00 .60
493 A151 80c dk red, gold & blk   1.50 .80
    Nos. 491-493 (3)   3.25 1.80

Stylized Globe and Wheat — A152

1973, Mar. 26   **Photo.**   *Perf. 11½*
494 A152 1.15d brt rose lil, org & grn   .75 .40

World Food Program, 10th anniversary.

Soldier and Flag A153

1973, Apr. 23   **Photo.**   *Perf. 14x13½*
495 A153 40c multicolored   .25 .18

Honoring the National Service.

Flower Type of 1969

Flowers: 30c, Opuntia ficus indica. 40c, Roses. 1d, Carnations. 1.15d, Bird-of-paradise flower.

1973, May 21   **Photo.**   *Perf. 11½*
Flowers in Natural Colors
496 A111 30c pink & blk   .40 .18
497 A111 40c gray & blk   .50 .20
498 A111 1d yellow & multi   .90 .40
499 A111 1.15d multi   1.25 .50
    Nos. 496-499 (4)   3.05 1.28

For overprints and surcharges see #518-519, 531.

OAU Emblem — A154

1973, May 28   **Photo.**   *Perf. 12½x13*
500 A154 40c multicolored   .40 .20

Org. for African Unity, 10th anniv.

Desert and Fruitful Land, Farmer and Family A155

1973, June 18   *Perf. 11½*
501 A155 40c gold & multi   .50 .40

Agricultural revolution.

ALGERIA

Map of Africa, Scout Emblem — A156

1973, July 16   Litho.   Perf. 10½
502 A156 80c purple   1.00 .50
24th Boy Scout World Conference (1st in Africa), Nairobi, Kenya, July 16-21.

Algerian PTT Emblem — A157

1973, Aug. 6   Perf. 14
503 A157 40c blue & orange   .22 .15
Adoption of new emblem for Post, Telegraph and Telephone System.

Conference Emblem — A158

Perf. 13½x12½   Photo.
504 A158 40c dp rose & multi   .18 .15
505 A158 80c blue grn & multi   .52 .26
4th Summit Conference of Non-aligned Nations, Algiers, Sept. 5-9.

Port of Skikda A159

1973, Sept. 29   Perf. 11½
506 A159 80c ocher, blk & ultra   .48 .25
New port of Skikda.

Young Workers — A160

1973, Oct. 22   Photo.   Perf. 13
507 A160 40c multicolored   .22 .15
Voluntary work service.

Arms of Algiers A161

1973, Dec. 22   Photo.   Perf. 13
508 A161 2d gold & multi   1.60 1.10
Millennium of Algiers.

Infant — A162

1974, Jan. 7   Litho.   Perf. 10½x11
509 A162 80c orange & multi   .60 .35
Fight against tuberculosis.

Man and Woman, Industry and Transportation A163

1974, Feb. 18   Photo.   Perf. 11½
510 A163 80c multicolored   .48 .20
Four-year plan.

A164

1974, Feb. 25   Photo.   Perf. 11½
511 A164 1.50d multi   1.10 .65
Millennium of the birth of abu-al-Rayhan al-Biruni (973-1048), philosopher and mathematician.

Map and Colors of Algeria, Tunisia, Morocco A165

1974, Mar. 4   Photo.   Perf. 13
512 A165 40c gold & multi   .28 .20
Maghreb Committee for Coordination of Posts and Telecommunications.

Hand Holding Rifle A166

Mother and Children A167

1974, Mar. 25   Perf. 11½
513 A166 80c red & black   .30 .20
Solidarity with the struggle of the people of South Africa.

1974, Apr. 8   Perf. 13½
514 A167 85c multicolored   .35 .22
Honoring Algerian mothers.

Village A168

Designs: 80c, Harvest. 90c, Tractor and sun. Designs after children's drawings.

1974, June 15
   Size: 45x26mm
515 A168 70c multicolored   .40 .18
   Size: 48x33mm
516 A168 80c multicolored   .48 .28
517 A168 90c multicolored   .60 .42
   Nos. 515-517 (3)   1.48 .88

Nos. 498-499 Overprinted "FLORALIES/1974"

1974, June 22   Photo.   Perf. 11½
518 A111 1d multi   .65 .35
519 A111 1.15d multi   .70 .40
1974 Flower Show.

Stamp Vending Machine — A169

1974, Oct. 7   Photo.   Perf. 13
520 A169 80c multicolored   .42 .20
Stamp Day 1974.

UPU Emblem and Globe — A170

1974, Oct. 14   Perf. 14
521 A170 80c multicolored   .50 .28
Centenary of Universal Postal Union.

"Revolution" — A171

Soldiers and Mountains — A172

Raising New Flag — A173

Design: 1d, Algerian struggle for independence (people, sun and fields).

1974, Nov. 4   Photo.   Perf. 14
522 A171 40c multicolored   .28 .18
523 A172 70c multicolored   .40 .22
524 A173 95c multicolored   .48 .22
525 A171 1d multicolored   .60 .28
   Nos. 522-525 (4)   1.76 .90
20th anniv. of the start of the revolution.

"Horizon 1980" — A174

Ewer and Basin — A175

1974, Nov. 23   Photo.   Perf. 13
526 A174 95c ocher, dk red & blk   .55 .25
10-year development plan, 1971-1980.

1974, Dec. 21   Perf. 11½
527 A175 50c shown   .22 .15
528 A175 60c Coffee pot   .28 .24
529 A175 95c Sugar bowl   .45 .30
530 A175 1d Bath tub   .50 .35
   Nos. 527-530 (4)   1.45 1.00
17th century Algerian copperware.

No. 497 Surcharged with New Value and Heavy Bar

1975, Jan. 4
531 A111 50c on 40c multi   .50 .40

Mediterranean Games' Emblem — A176

1975, Jan. 27   Perf. 13½
532 A176 50c purple, yel & grn   .28 .18
533 A176 1d orange, bl & mar   .60 .22
Mediterranean Games, Algiers, 1975.

Costume Type of 1971
Regional Costumes: No. 534, Woman from Hoggar. No. 535, Woman from Algiers. No. 536, Woman from Oran. No. 537, Man from Tlemcen.

1975, Feb. 22   Photo.   Perf. 11½
534 A139 1d gold & multi   1.00 .80
535 A139 1d gold & multi   1.00 .80
536 A139 1d gold & multi   1.00 .80
537 A139 1d gold & multi   1.00 .80
   Nos. 534-537 (4)   4.00 3.20

Map of Arab Countries, ALO Emblem A177

1975, Mar. 10   Litho.   Perf. 10½x11
538 A177 50c red brown   .25 .15
Arab Labor Organization, 10th anniversary.

Blood Transfusion A178

1975, Mar. 15   Perf. 14
539 A178 50c car rose & multi   .32 .18
Blood donation and transfusions.

15-Cent Minimum Value
The minimum value for a single stamp is 15 cents. This value reflects the costs of handling inexpensive stamps.

Post Office, Al-
Kantara
A179

Policeman and Map
of Algeria
A180

1975, May 10   Photo.   Perf. 11½
Granite Paper
540 A179 50c multicolored   .25 .15
Stamp Day 1975.

1975, June 1   Photo.   Perf. 13
541 A180 50c multicolored   .75 .40
Natl. Security and 10th Natl. Police Day.

Ground
Receiving
Station
A181

Designs: 1d, Map of Algeria with locations of
radar sites, transmission mast and satellite. 1.20d,
Main and subsidiary stations.

1975, June 28   Photo.   Perf. 13
542 A181 50c blue & multi   .28 .15
543 A181   1d blue & multi   .55 .20
544 A181 1.20d blue & multi   .60 .22
      Nos. 542-544 (3)   1.43 .57
National satellite telecommunications network.

Revolutionary with
Flag — A182

1975, Aug. 20   Photo.   Perf. 11½
545 A182 1d multicolored   .50 .25
August 20th Revolutionary Movement (Skikda),
20th anniversary.

Swimming and
Games'
Emblem
A183

Perf. 13x13½, 13½x13
1975, Aug. 23   Photo.
546 A183 25c shown   .15 .15
547 A183 50c Judo, map   .25 .18
548 A183 70c Soccer, vert.   .48 .22
549 A183   1d Running, vert.   .55 .25
550 A183 1.20d Handball, vert.   .70 .38
  a. Souv. sheet of 5, #546-550, perf 13 4.50 4.50
      Nos. 546-550 (5)   2.13 1.18
7th Mediterranean Games, Algiers, 8/23-9/46.
No. 550a sold for 4.50d. Exists imperf., same
value.

Setif, Guelma,
Kherrata — A184

1975   Litho.   Perf. 13½x14
551 A184   5c orange & blk   .15 .15
552 A184 10c emerald & blk   .15 .15
553 A184 25c dl blue & blk   .15 .15
554 A184 30c lemon & blk   .15 .15
555 A184 50c brt grn & blk   .22 .15
556 A184 70c fawn & blk   .35 .15
557 A184   1d vermilion & blk   .50 .25
      Nos. 551-557 (7)   1.67
      Set value   .60
30th anniv. of victory in World War II.
Issue dates: 50c, 1d, Nov. 3; others, Dec. 17.
For surcharge see No. 611.

Map of
Maghreb and
APU Emblem
A185

1975, Nov. 20   Photo.   Perf. 11½
558 A185 1d multicolored   .55 .28
10th Cong. of Arab Postal Union, Algiers.

Mosaic, Bey
Constantine's
Palace — A186

Dey-Alger Palace — A187

Famous buildings: 2d, Prayer niche, Medersa
Sidi-Boumediene, Tlemcen.

1975, Dec. 22
559 A186   1d lt blue & multi   .60 .22
560 A186   2d buff & multi   1.10 .60
561 A187 2.50d buff & blk   1.60 .90
      Nos. 559-561 (3)   3.30 1.72

Al-Azhar
University
A188

Perf. 11½x12½
1975, Dec. 29   Litho.
562 A188 2d multicolored   1.10 .60
Millennium of Al-Azhar University.

Red-billed
Firefinch — A189

Birds: 1.40d, Black-headed bush shrike, horiz.
2d, Blue tit. 2.50d, Blackbellied sandgrouse, horiz.

1976, Jan. 24   Photo.   Perf. 11½
563 A189 50c multi   .35 .18
564 A189 1.40d multi   .85 .55
565 A189   2d multi   1.10 .65
566 A189 2.50d multi   1.50 .90
      Nos. 563-566 (4)   3.80 2.28
      See Nos. 595-598.

Telephones 1876
and 1976 — A190

Map of Africa
with Angola and
its Flag — A191

1976, Feb. 23   Photo.   Perf. 13½x13
567 A190 1.40d rose, dk & lt bl   .65 .38
Centenary of first telephone call by Alexander
Graham Bell, Mar. 10, 1876.

1976, Feb. 23   Perf. 11½
568 A191 50c brown & multi   .25 .15
Algeria's solidarity with the People's Republic of
Angola.

A192   A193

Sahraoui flag and child, map of former Spanish
Sahara.

1976, Mar. 15   Photo.   Perf. 11½
569 A192 50c multicolored   .25 .15
Algeria's solidarity with Sahraoui Arab Democratic Republic, former Spanish Sahara.

1976, Mar. 22
570 A193 1.40d Mailman   .60 .32
Stamp Day 1976.

Microscope,
Slide with TB
Bacilli,
Patients
A194

1976, Apr. 26   Perf. 13x13½
571 A194 50c multicolored   .40 .20
Fight against tuberculosis.

"Setif, Guelma,
Kherrata" — A195

1976, May 24   Photo.   Perf. 13½x13
572 A195 50c blue & yellow   .35 .15
  a. Booklet pane of 6   4.75
  b. Booklet pane of 10   4.00
No. 572 was issued in booklets only.

Ram's Head over
Landscape — A196

People Holding
Torch, Map of
Algeria — A197

1976, June 17   Photo.   Perf. 11½
573 A196 50c multicolored   .40 .20
Livestock breeding.

1976, June 29   Photo.   Perf. 14x13½
574 A197 50c multicolored   .25 .15
National Charter.

Palestine Map and
Flag — A198

Map of
Africa — A199

1976, July 12   Perf. 11½
Granite Paper
575 A198 50c multicolored   2.00 1.00
Solidarity with the Palestinians.

1976, Oct. 3   Litho.   Perf. 10½x11
576 A199 2d dk blue & multi   1.00 .50
2nd Pan-African Commercial Fair, Algiers.

Blind
Brushmaker
A200

The
Blind,
by Dinet
A201

1976, Oct. 23   Photo.   Perf. 14½
577 A200 1.20d blue & multi   .65 .35
578 A201 1.40d gold & multi   1.50 .75
Rehabilitation of the blind.

"Constitution 1976" — A202

1976, Nov. 19   Photo.   Perf. 11½
579 A202 2d multicolored   1.00 .55
    New Constitution.

Soldiers Planting
Seedlings — A203

1976, Nov. 25   Litho.   Perf. 12
580 A203 1.40d multicolored   .75 .35
    Green barrier against the Sahara.

Ornamental
Border and
Inscription
A204

1976, Dec. 18   Photo.   Perf. 11½
            Granite Paper
581 A204 2d multicolored   1.25 .75
    Re-election of Pres. Houari Boumediene.
    See No. 627.

Map with Charge
Zones and Dials
A205

People and
Buildings
A206

1977, Jan. 22   Perf. 13
582 A205 40c silver & multi   .28 .15
    Inauguration of automatic national and interna-
tional telephone service.

1977, Jan. 29   Photo.   Perf. 11½
583 A206 60c on 50c multi   .35 .18
    2nd General Population and Buildings Census.
No. 583 was not issued without the typographed
red brown surcharge, date, and bars.

Sahara Museum,
Uargla — A207

1977, Feb. 12   Litho.   Perf. 14
584 A207 60c multicolored   .35 .20

El-Kantara Gorge — A208

        Perf. 12½x13½
1977, Feb. 19   Photo.
585 A208 20c green & yellow   .15 .15
  a. Bklt. pane, 3 #585, 4 #586 + label   8.00
  b. Bklt. pane, 5 #585, 2 #587 + label   6.50
586 A208 60c brt lilac & yel   .18 .15
587 A208 1d brown & yellow   .40 .15
    Set value   .63 .30

National Assembly — A209

1977, Feb. 27   Perf. 11½
588 A209 2d multicolored   1.00 .60

People and   Soldier and
Flag — A210   Flag — A211

        Perf. 13½, 11½ (3d)
1977, Mar. 12   Photo.
589 A210 2d multicolored   1.25 .40
590 A211 3d multicolored   1.75 .65
    Solidarity with the peoples of Zimbabwe (Rhode-
sia), 2d; Namibia, 3d.

Winter, Roman
Mosaic — A212

    The Seasons from Roman Villa, 2nd century
A.D.: 1.40d, Fall. 2d, Summer. 3d, Spring.

1977, Apr. 21   Photo.   Perf. 11½
            Granite Paper
591 A212 1.20d multi   .95 .52
592 A212 1.40d multi   1.25 .52
593 A212 2d multi   1.65 .95
594 A212 3d multi   2.50 1.65
  a. Souv. sheet of 4, #591-594, perf.,
        imperf.   10.00 10.00
    Nos. 591-594 (4)   6.35 3.64

    No. 594a sold for 8d.

        Bird Type of 1976
    Birds: 60c, Tristram's warbler. 1.40d, Moussier's
redstart, horiz. 2d, Temminck's horned lark, horiz.
3d, Eurasian hoopoe.

1977, May 21   Photo.   Perf. 11½
595 A189 60c multi   .75 .22
596 A189 1.40d multi   1.25 .40
597 A189 2d multi   1.75 .65
598 A189 3d multi   2.50 1.10
    Nos. 595-598 (4)   6.25 2.37

Horseman — A213

    Design: 5d, Attacking horsemen, horiz.

1977, June 25   Photo.   Perf. 11½
599 A213 2d multicolored   1.65 .75
600 A213 5d multicolored   3.50 2.00

Flag Colors, Games
Emblem — A214 0.60

Wall Painting,
Games Emblem
A215

1977, Sept. 24   Photo.   Perf. 11½
601 A214 60c multi   .35 .22
602 A215 1.40d multi   .80 .45
    3rd African Games, Algiers 1978.

Village and
Tractor
A216

1977, Nov. 12   Perf. 14x13
603 A216 1.40d multi   .90 .65
    Socialist agricultural village.

Almohades Dirham, 12th Century — A217

    Ancient Coins: 1.40d, Almohades coin, 12th
century. 2d, Almoravides dinar, 11th century.

1977, Dec. 17   Photo.   Perf. 11½
604 A217 60c ultra, sil & blk   .50 .35
605 A217 1.40d green, gold & brn   1.10 .50
606 A217 2d red brn, gold & brn   1.50 .90
    Nos. 604-606 (3)   3.10 1.75

Flowering Trees — A218

1978, Feb. 11   Photo.   Perf. 11½
607 A218 60c Cherry   .35 .24
608 A218 1.20d Peach   .85 .50
609 A218 1.30d Almond   .85 .50
610 A218 1.40d Apple   .90 .55
    Nos. 607-610 (4)   2.95 1.79

    No. 555 Surcharged with New Value and
            Bar
1978, Feb. 11   Litho.   Perf. 13½x14
611 A184 60c on 50c   .50 .16

Children with
Traffic Signs
and
Car — A219   0.60

1978, Apr. 29   Photo.   Perf. 11½
612 A219 60c multicolored   .28 .15
    Road safety and protection of children.

Sports and
Games
Emblems
A220

    Designs (Games Emblem and): 60c, Rower, vert.
1.20d, Flag colors. 1.30d, Fireworks, vert. 1.40d,
Map of Africa and dancers, vert.

1978, July 13   Photo.   Perf. 11½
613 A220 40c multi   .18 .15
614 A220 60c multi   .28 .18
615 A220 1.20d multi   .60 .28
616 A220 1.30d multi   .60 .35
617 A220 1.40d multi   .65 .35
    Nos. 613-617 (5)   2.31 1.31
    3rd African Games, Algiers, July 13-28.

TB
Patient
Returning
to Family
A221

1978, Oct. 5   Photo.   Perf. 13½x14
618 A221 60c multicolored   .35 .16
    Anti-tuberculosis campaign.

Holy Kaaba — A222

1978, Oct. 28   Photo.   Perf. 11½
619 A222 60c multicolored   .28 .15
    Pilgrimage to Mecca.

National
Servicemen
Building
Road — A223

1978, Nov. 4
620 A223 60c multicolored   .28 .15
    African Unity Road from El Goleah to In Salah,
inauguration.

Fibula
A224

Pres. Boumediene
A225

Jewelry: 1.35d, Pendant. 1.40d, Ankle ring.

1978, Dec. 21   Photo.   Perf. 12x11¹/₂
621 A224 1.20d multi   .65   .28
622 A224 1.35d multi   .70   .28
623 A224 1.40d multi   1.10 1.10
        Nos. 621-623 (3)   2.45 1.66

1979, Jan. 7   Photo.   Perf. 12x11¹/₂
624 A225 60c green, red & brown   .28   .15
Houari Boumediene, pres. of Algeria 1965-1978.

Torch and
Books
A226

1979, Jan. 27   Photo.   Perf. 11¹/₂
625 A226 60c multicolored   .28   .18
Natl. Front of Liberation Party Cong.

Pres.
Boumediene
A227

1979, Feb. 4   Photo.   Perf. 11¹/₂
626 A227 1.40d multi   .65   .28
40 days after death of Pres. Houari Boumediène.

Ornamental Type of 1976

Proclamation of new President.

1979, Feb. 10
627 A204 2d multicolored   1.00   .35
Election of Pres. Chadli Bendjedid.

A229   A230

1979, Apr. 18   Photo.   Perf. 11¹/₂
628 A229 60c multicolored   .28   .15
Sheik Abdul-Hamid Ben Badis (1889-1940).

1979, May 19   Photo.   Perf. 13¹/₂x14
Designs: 1.20d, Telephone dial, map of Africa.
1.40d, Symbolic Morse key and waves.

629 A230 1.20d multi   .55   .22
630 A230 1.40d multi   .60   .22
Telecom '79 Exhib., Geneva, Sept. 20-26.

Harvest, IYC
Emblem — A231

Design: 1.40d, Dancers and IYC emblem, vert.

Perf. 11¹/₂x11, 11x11¹/₂
1979, June 21
631 A231 60c multi   .40   .20
632 A231 1.40d multi   .60   .45
International Year of the Child.

A232   A233

1979, Oct. 20   Photo.   Perf. 11¹/₂
633 A232 1.40d Nuthatch   .90   .40

1979, Nov. 1   Photo.   Perf. 12¹/₂
Designs: 1.40d, Flag, soldiers and workers. 3d,
Revolutionaries and emblem.

634 A233 1.40d multi   .90   .22

Size: 37x48mm
Perf. 11¹/₂
635 A233 3d multi   2.25   .65
November 1 revolution, 25th anniversary.

Hegira, 1500
Anniv.
A234

1979, Dec. 2   Photo.   Perf. 11¹/₂
636 A234 3d multicolored   1.25   .65

Camels, Lion,
Men and
Slave — A235

Dionysian Procession (Setif Mosaic): 1.35d, Elephants, tigers and women. Men in tiger-drawn cart.
No. 639a has continuous design.

1980, Feb. 16   Photo.   Perf. 11¹/₂
Granite Paper
637 A235 1.20d multi   .55   .22
638 A235 1.35d multi   .60   .35
639 A235 1.40d multi   .65   .55
  a.   Strip of 3, #637-639   1.80 1.25

Science Day — A236

1980, Apr. 19   Photo.   Perf. 12
640 A236 60c multicolored   .28   .20

Dam and
Workers — A237

1980, June 17   Photo.   Perf. 11¹/₂
641 A237 60c multicolored   .28   .15
Extraordinary Congress of the National Liberation Front Party.

Olympic
Sports,
Moscow '80
Emblem
A238

1980, June 28
642 A238 50c Flame, rings, vert.   .22   .15
643 A238 1.40d shown   .65   .35
22nd Summer Olympic Games, Moscow, July
19-Aug. 3.

20th Anniversary of OPEC — A239

Perf. 11x10¹/₂, 10¹/₂x11
1980, Sept. 15   Engr.
644 A239   60c Men holding OPEC
                emblem, vert.   .28   .15
645 A239 1.40d shown   .65   .35

Aures
Valley
A240

1980, Sept. 25   Litho.   Perf. 13¹/₂x14
646 A240   50c shown   .22   .15
647 A240   1d El Oued Oasis   .40   .18
648 A240 1.40d Tassili Rocks   .60   .22
649 A240   2d View of Algiers   .90   .40
        Nos. 646-649 (4)   2.12   .95
World Tourism Conf., Manila, Sept. 27.

Avicenna (980-
1037),
Philosopher and
Physician
A241

1980, Oct. 25   Photo.   Perf. 12
650 A241 2d multicolored   1.50   .75

Ruins of
El
Asnam
A242

1980, Nov. 13   Photo.   Perf. 12
651 A242 3d multicolored   1.25   .45
Earthquake relief.

Crown
A243

1980, Dec. 20   Photo.   Perf. 12
Granite Paper
652 A243   60c Necklace, vert.   .28   .18
653 A243 1.40d Earrings, bracelet,
                vert.   .60   .28
654 A243   2d shown   .80   .45
        Nos. 652-654 (3)   1.68   .91
        See Nos. 705-707.

1980-1984 Five-Year
Plan — A244

1981, Jan. 29   Litho.   Perf. 14
655 A244 60c multicolored   .25   .15

Basket Weaving — A245

1981, Feb. 19   Photo.   Perf. 12¹/₂
Granite Paper
656 A245   40c shown   .20   .15
657 A245   60c Rug weaving   .28   .15
658 A245   1d Coppersmith   .40   .18
659 A245 1.40d Jeweler   .60   .32
        Nos. 656-659 (4)   1.48   .80

Cedar
Tree — A246

Arbor Day: 1.40d, Cypress tree, vert.

1981, Mar. 19   Photo.   Perf. 12
Granite Paper
660 A246   60c multi   .30   .15
661 A246 1.40d multi   .60   .32

Mohamed Bachir
el Ibrahimi (1869-
1965)
A247

Children Going
to
School — A248

1981, Apr. 16
Granite Paper
662 A247 60c multicolored .25 .15
663 A248 60c multicolored .25 .15
Set value .17
Science Day.

12th International
Hydatidological
Congress,
Algiers — A249

1981, Apr. 23 *Perf. 14x13½*
664 A249 2d multicolored .80 .32

13th World Telecommunications
Day — A250

1981, May 14 Photo. *Perf. 14x13½*
665 A250 1.40d multi .60 .20

Disabled
People
and
Hand
Offering
Flower
A251

Perf. 12½x13, 13x12½
1981, June 20 Litho.
666 A251 1.20d Symbolic globe, vert. .55 .18
667 A251 1.40d shown .60 .18
Intl. Year of the Disabled.

Papilio
Machaon
A252

1981, Aug. 20 Photo. *Perf. 11½*
Granite Paper
668 A252 60c shown .25 .15
669 A252 1.20d Rhodocera rhamni .55 .20
670 A252 1.40d Charaxes jasius .60 .25
671 A252 2d Papilio podalirius .80 .40
Nos. 668-671 (4) 2.20 1.00

Monk Seal — A253

1981, Sept. 17 *Perf. 14x13½*
672 A253 60c shown .25 .15
673 A253 1.40d Macaque .60 .35

World Food
Day — A254

Cave Drawings of
Tassili — A255

1981, Oct. 16 Photo. *Perf. 14x14½*
674 A254 2d multicolored .65 .35

1981, Nov. 21 *Perf. 11½*
Designs: Various cave drawings. 1.60d, 2d horiz.
675 A255 60c multi .30 .15
676 A255 1d multi .50 .18
677 A255 1.60d multi .75 .32
678 A255 2d multi .90 .40
Nos. 675-678 (4) 2.45 1.05

Galley, 17-
18th Cent.
A256

1981, Dec. 17 Photo. *Perf. 11½*
679 A256 60c shown .40 .18
680 A256 1.60d Ship, diff. .90 .35

1982 World
Cup Soccer
A257

Designs: Various soccer players.
Perf. 13x12½x 12½x13
1982, Feb. 25 Litho.
681 A257 80c multi, vert. .35 .15
682 A257 2.80d multi 1.10 .50

TB Bacillus
Centenary — A258

1982, Mar. 20 Photo. *Perf. 14½x14*
683 A258 80c multi .35 .15

Painted
Stand
A259

1982, Apr. 24 Photo. *Perf. 11½*
Granite Paper
684 A259 80c Mirror, vert. .35 .18
685 A259 2d shown .80 .40

Size: 48x33mm
686 A259 2.40d Chest 1.00 .55
Nos. 684-686 (3) 2.15 1.13

Djamaaal Djadid
Mosque,
Algiers — A260

1982, May 15 Litho. *Perf. 14*
687 A260 80c shown .35 .15
688 A260 2.40d Sidi Boumediene
Mosque, Tlemcen 1.00 .50
689 A260 3d Garden of Dey, Algiers 1.25 .55
Nos. 687-689 (3) 2.60 1.20
See Nos. 731-734, 745-747, 774, 778-783.

Callitris
Articulata
A261

Independence,
20th Anniv.
A262

Designs: Medicinal plants.

1982, May 27 Photo. *Perf. 11½*
Granite Paper
690 A261 50c shown .20 .15
691 A261 80c Artemisia herba-alba .25 .15
692 A261 1d Ricinus communis .50 .20
693 A261 2.40d Thymus fontanesii .90 .45
Nos. 690-693 (4) 1.85 .95

1982, July 5
Granite Paper
694 A262 50c Riflemen .20 .15
695 A262 80c Soldiers, horiz. .32 .18
696 A262 2d Symbols, citizens,
horiz. .80 .45
Nos. 694-696 (3) 1.32 .78
Souvenir Sheet
697 A262 5d Emblem 2.00 2.00
No. 697 contains one 32x39mm stamp.

Soummam
Congress
A263

1982, Aug. 20 Litho.
698 A263 80c Congress building .35 .15

Scouting
Year — A264

1982, Oct. 21 Photo.
Granite Paper
699 A264 2.80d multi 1.10 .45

Palestinian
Child — A265

Chlamydotis
Undulata — A266

1982, Nov. 25 Litho. *Perf. 10½*
700 A265 1.60d multi 2.00 .75

Perf. 15x14, 14x15
1982, Dec. 23 Photo.
Protected birds. 50c, 2d horiz.
701 A266 50c Geronticus eremita .40 .15
702 A266 80c shown .65 .18
703 A266 2d Aguila rapax 1.25 .40
704 A266 2.40d Gypaetus barbatus 1.75 .45
Nos. 701-704 (4) 4.05 1.18

Jewelry Type of 1980
1983, Feb. 10 *Perf. 11½*
Granite Paper
705 A243 50c Picture frame .18 .15
706 A243 1d Flaska .38 .28
707 A243 2d Brooch, horiz. .75 .45
Nos. 705-707 (3) 1.31 .88

A267

A268

1983, Mar. 17 Photo.
Granite Paper
708 A267 80c Abies numidica, vert. .32 .15
709 A267 2.80d Acacia raddiana 1.10 .60
Intl. Arbor Day.

Perf. 12x12½, 12½x12
1983, Apr. 21 Photo.
Various minerals. 1.20d, 2.40d horiz.
Granite Paper
710 A268 70c multi .28 .15
711 A268 80c multi .32 .20
712 A268 1.20d multi .50 .30
713 A268 2.40d multi 1.00 .60
Nos. 710-713 (4) 2.10 1.25

30th Anniv. of
Intl. Customs
Cooperation
Council
A269

1983, May 14 Photo. *Perf. 11½*
Granite Paper
714 A269 80c multi .35 .18

Emir Abdelkader Death
Centenary — A270

1983, May 22 Photo. *Perf. 12*
Granite Paper
715 A270 4d multi 1.60 .75

A271

A272

Local mushrooms.

1983, July 21 *Perf. 14x15*
716 A271 50c Amanita muscaria .20 .15
717 A271 80c Amanita phalloides .32 .18
718 A271 1.40d Pleurotus eryngi .55 .35
719 A271 2.80d Tefezia leonis 1.00 .60
Nos. 716-719 (4) 2.07 1.28

1983, Sept. 1 Photo. *Perf. 11½*
720 A272 80c multi .35 .15
ibn-Khaldun, historian, philosopher.

World
Communications
Year — A273

Perf. 11½x12½

1983, Sept. 22   **Litho.**
721 A273 80c Post Office, Algiers   .35 .15
722 A273 2.40d Telephone, circuit
              box   1.00 .38

Goat and
Tassili
Mountains
A274

1983, Oct. 20 Litho.   Perf. 12½x13
723 A274 50c shown   .20 .15
724 A274 80c Tuaregs in native
              costume   .32 .18
725 A274 2.40d Animals, rock paint-
              ing   1.00 .40
726 A274 2.80d Rock formation   1.00 .60
          Nos. 723-726 (4)   2.52 1.33

Sloughi Dog — A275

Perf. 14x14½, 14½x14

1983, Nov. 24   **Photo.**
727 A275 80c shown   .60 .40
728 A275 2.40d Sloughi, horiz.   1.50 .75

Natl. Liberation Party, 5th
Congress — A276

1983, Dec. 19   Photo.   Perf. 11½
729 A276 80c Symbols of develop-
             ment   .35 .22

Souvenir Sheet

730 A276 5d Emblem   3.00 2.50
No. 730 contains one 32x38mm stamp.

View Type of 1982

1984, Jan. 26   **Litho.   Perf. 14**
731 A260 10c View of Oran, 1830   .15 .15
732 A260 1d Sidi Abderahman and
             Taalibi Mosques   .40 .18
733 A260 2d Bejaia, 1830   .80 .35
734 A260 4d Constantine, 1830   1.75 .60
          Nos. 731-734 (4)   3.10 1.28
          See Nos. 745-747, 781, 783.

Pottery
A278

Perf. 11½x12, 12x11½

1984, Feb. 23   **Photo.**
                Granite Paper
735 A278 80c Jug, vert.   .35 .22
736 A278 1d Platter   .40 .22
737 A278 2d Oil lamp, vert.   .80 .45
738 A278 2.40d Pitcher   1.00 .60
          Nos. 735-738 (4)   2.55 1.49

Fountains of Old   1984 Summer
Algiers — A279   Olympics — A280

Various fountains.

1984, Mar. 22   Photo.   Perf. 11½
                Granite Paper
739 A279 50c multi   .20 .15
740 A279 80c multi   .38 .20
741 A279 2.40d multi   1.00 .60
          Nos. 739-741 (3)   1.58 .95

1984, May 19   Photo.   Perf. 11½
                Granite Paper
742 A280 1d multi   .45 .28

Brown
Stallion — A281

1984, June 14   Photo.   Perf. 11½
                Granite Paper
743 A281 80c shown   .35 .18
744 A281 2.40d White mare   1.00 .60

View Type of 1982

1984   **Litho.   Perf. 14**
745 A260 5c Mustapha Pacha   .15 .15
746 A260 20c Bab Azzoun   .15 .15
746A A260 30c Algiers   .15 .15
746B A260 40c Kolea   .15 .15
746C A260 50c Algiers   .15 .15
747 A260 70c Mostaganem   .32 .15
          Set value   .84 .40
Issue dates: Nos. 745, 746, 747, July 19. Nos.
746A-746C, Oct. 20.

Lute — A282

Native musical instruments.

1984, Sept. 22   Litho.   Perf. 15x14
748 A282 80c shown   .22 .15
749 A282 1d Drum   .28 .15
750 A282 2.40d Fiddle   .65 .35
751 A282 2.80d Bagpipe   .70 .40
          Nos. 748-751 (4)   1.85 1.05

30th Anniv. of Algerian
Revolution — A284

1984, Nov. 3   Photo.   Perf. 11½x12
757 A284 80c Partisans   .22 .15

Souvenir Sheet

758 A284 5d Algerian flags, vert.   2.00 1.00

M'Zab Valley
A285

1984, Dec. 15   Perf. 15x14, 14x15
759 A285 80c Map of valley   .22 .15
760 A285 2.40d Town of M'Zab, vert.   .65 .32

18th and 19th
Century
Metalware — A286

1985, Jan. 26   Photo.   Perf. 11½
761 A286 80c Coffee pot   .22 .15
762 A286 2d Bowl, horiz.   .50 .25
763 A286 2.40d Covered bowl   .65 .32
          Nos. 761-763 (3)   1.37 .72

Fish — A287

1985, Feb. 23   Photo.   Perf. 15x14
764 A287 50c Thunnus thynnus   .15 .15
765 A287 80c Sparus aurata   .20 .15
766 A287 2.40d Epinephelus guaza   .60 .30
767 A287 2.80d Mustelus mustelus   .65 .35
          Nos. 764-767 (4)   1.60
          Set value   .82

National
Games — A288

1985, Mar. 28   Perf. 11½x12
                Granite Paper
768 A288 80c Doves, emblem   .20 .15

Environmental
Conservation
A289

1985, Apr. 25   Perf. 13½
769 A289 80c Stylized trees   .20 .15
770 A289 1.40d Stylized waves   .38 .20

View Type of 1982 and

The   View of
Casbah — A290   Constantine — A290a

Street Scene in
Algiers — A290b

Designs: 2.50d, Djamaael Djadid Mosque,
Algiers. 2.90d, like #746. 5d, like #746A. 1.50d,
like #746B. 4.20d, like #764.

**Perf. 13½x12½, 13 (#774, 4.20d),
Perf. 13½x14 (#775)
Perf. 14½x14 (2d)**

**Photo., Litho. (2d, 6,20d, 7.50d, #775)
1985-94**
771 A290 20c dk blue & buff   .15 .15
772 A290 80c sage grn & buff   .20 .15
773 A290 1d dk olive grn   .25 .25
   a.   Bklt. pane of 5 + label   2.50
774 A290 1.50d dull red   .55 .30
775 A290b 1.50d red brown & brn   .25 .15
   a.   Booklet pane of 6   1.50
776 A290b 2d dk blue & lt blue   .15 .15
   a.   Booklet pane of 5 + label   .95
777 A290 2.40d chestnut & buff   .60 .30
   a.   Bklt. pane of 5 (20c, 3 80c,
        2.40d) + label   1.40
778 A260 2.50d bluish green   .98 .50
779 A260 2.90d slate   1.15 .58
780 A260 4.20d gray green   1.60 .85
781 A260 5d deep bister &
             black   1.95 .98
                Perf. 14
782 A260 6.20d like #731   1.05 .52
783 A260 7.50d like #745   1.30 .65
          Nos. 771-783 (13)   10.43 5.53
Nos. 771-772, 777 issued only in booklet panes.
   Issued: 20c, 80c, 2.40d, 6/1/85; 1d, 1/26/89;
2.50d, 2.90d, 5d, 2/23/89; #774, 4.20d,
3/21/91; #775, 5/20/92; 6.20d, 7.50d,
4/22/92; 2d, 10/21/93; #776a, 10/21/94.
See No. 1010.

UN, 40th   Natl. Youth
Anniv. — A291   Festival — A292

1985, June 26   Photo.   Perf. 14
784 A291 1d Dove, emblem, 40   .25 .15

1985, July 5   Litho.   Perf. 13½
785 A292 80c multicolored   .20 .15

Intl. Youth
Year — A293

1985, July 5
786 A293 80c Silhouette, globe, em-
             blem, vert.   .20 .15
787 A293 1.40d Doves, globe   .38 .20

World Map,
OPEC — A294

1985, Sept. 14   Photo.   Perf. 12½x13
788 A294 80c multicolored   .20 .15
Organization of Petroleum Exporting Countries,
25th anniv.

Family Planning   El-Meniaa
A295   Township
                                A296

1985, Oct. 3   Litho.   Perf. 14
789 A295 80c Mother and sons   .20 .15
790 A295 1.40d Weighing infant   .38 .18
791 A295 1.70d Breast-feeding   .45 .22
          Nos. 789-791 (3)   1.03 .55

1985, Oct. 24   Engr.   Perf. 13
792 A296 80c Chetaibi Bay, horiz.   .20 .15
793 A296 2d shown   .50 .25
794 A296 2.40d Bou Noura Town,
             horiz.   .65 .32
          Nos. 792-794 (3)   1.35 .72

The Palm Grove, by N. Dinet — A297

1985, Nov. 21   Photo.   Perf. 11¹/₂x12
Granite Paper
795 A297 2d multi .50 .25
796 A297 3d multi, diff. .70 .40

Tapestries A298

Various designs.

1985, Dec. 19
Granite Paper
797 A298 80c multi .20 .15
798 A298 1.40d multi .38 .20
799 A298 2.40d multi .60 .32
800 A298 2.80d multi .70 .40
   Nos. 797-800 (4) 1.88 1.07

Wildcats A299

Perf. 12x11¹/₂, 11¹/₂x12
1986, Jan. 23
Granite Paper
801 A299 80c Felis margarita .60 .15
802 A299 1d Felis caracal .80 .15
803 A299 2d Felis sylvestris 1.50 .80
804 A299 2.40d Felis serval, vert. 2.00 .95
   Nos. 801-804 (4) 4.90 2.05

UN Child Survival Campaign — A300

Algerian General Worker's Union, 30th Anniv. — A301

1986, Feb. 13   Litho.   Perf. 13¹/₂
805 A300 80c Oral vaccine .20 .15
806 A300 1.40d Mother, child, sun .40 .18
807 A300 1.70d Three children .45 .22
   Nos. 805-807 (3) 1.05 .55

1986, Feb. 24   Perf. 12¹/₂
Granite Paper
808 A301 2d multi .50 .25

National Charter — A302

Natl. Day of the Disabled — A303

1986, Mar. 6   Photo.   Perf. 11¹/₂
Granite Paper
809 A302 4d multi 1.50 .55

1986, Mar. 15   Perf. 12¹/₂x13
810 A303 80c multi .20 .15

A304   A305

1986, Apr. 17   Litho.   Perf. 14x15
811 A304 80c multi .20 .15
   Anti-Tuberculosis campaign.

1986, Apr. 24   Perf. 14
812 A305 2d Soccer ball, sombrero .50 .25
813 A305 2.40d Soccer players .65 .32
   1986 World Cup Soccer Championships, Mexico.

Inner Courtyards — A306

Blood Donation Campaign — A307

1986, May 15   Photo.   Perf. 11¹/₂
Granite Paper
814 A306 80c multi .20 .15
815 A306 2.40d multi, diff. .65 .32
816 A306 3d multi, diff. .80 .40
   Nos. 814-816 (3) 1.65 .87

1986, June 26   Litho.   Perf. 13¹/₂
817 A307 80c multi .22 .15

Southern District Radio Communication Inauguration — A308

1986, July   Perf. 13
818 A308 60c multi .16 .15

Mosque Gateways A309

1986, Sept. 27   Photo.   Perf. 12x11¹/₂
Granite Paper
819 A309 2d Door .50 .25
820 A309 2.40d Ornamental arch .65 .32

Intl. Peace Year — A310

Perf. 13¹/₂x14¹/₂
1986, Oct. 16   Photo.
821 A310 2.40d multi .65 .32

Folk Dancing A311

1986, Nov. 22   Litho.   Perf. 14x13¹/₂
822 A311 80c Woman, scarf .22 .15
823 A311 2.40d Woman, diff. .65 .32
824 A311 2.80d Man, sword .70 .40
   Nos. 822-824 (3) 1.57 .87

Flowers — A312

1986, Dec. 18   Photo.   Perf. 14
825 A312 80c Narcissus tazetta .22 .15
826 A312 1.40d Iris unguicularis .40 .20
827 A312 2.40d Capparis spinosa .65 .32
828 A312 2.80d Gladiolus segetum .70 .40
   Nos. 825-828 (4) 1.97 1.07
   See Nos. 936-938.

Abstract Paintings by Mohammed Issia Khem A313

Perf. 11¹/₂x12, 12x11¹/₂
1987, Jan. 29   Litho.
829 A313 2d Man and woman, vert. .65 .35
830 A313 5d Man and books 1.60 .80

Jewelry from Aures A314

1987, Feb. 27   Photo.   Perf. 12
Granite Paper
831 A314 1d Earrings .35 .16
832 A314 1.80d Bracelets .60 .30
833 A314 2.90d Nose rings 1.00 .50
834 A314 3.30d Necklace 1.10 .55
   Nos. 831-834 (4) 3.05 1.51
   Nos. 831-833 vert.

Petroglyphs, Atlas A315

1987, Mar. 26   Litho.   Perf. 12x11¹/₂
Granite Paper
835 A315 1d Man and woman .35 .16
836 A315 2.90d Goat 1.00 .50
837 A315 3.30d Horse, bull 1.10 .60
   Nos. 835-837 (3) 2.45 1.26

Syringe as an Umbrella — A316

1987, Apr. 7   Perf. 11¹/₂
Granite Paper
838 A316 1d multi .35 .16
   Child Immunization Campaign, World Health Day.

 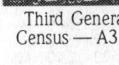

Volunteers — A317

Third General Census — A318

1987, Apr. 23   Perf. 10¹/₂
839 A317 1d multi .35 .16

1987, May 21   Perf. 13¹/₂
840 A318 1d multi .35 .16

Algerian Postage, 25th Anniv. — A319

Design: War Orphans' Fund label (1fr + 9fr) of 1962.

1987, July 5   Photo.   Perf. 11¹/₂x12
Granite Paper
841 A319 1.80d multi .60 .32

A320   A321

1987, July 5
Granite Paper
842 A320 1d multi .35 .16
Souvenir Sheet
843 A321 5d multi 1.60 1.60
   Natl. independence, 25th anniv.

Amateur Theater Festival, Mostaganem A322

1987, July 20   Perf. 12x11¹/₂
Granite Paper
844 A322 1d Actors on stage .35 .16
845 A322 1.80d Theater .60 .32
   a.   Pair, #844-845 1.00 .50
   No. 845a has continuous design.

Mediterranean
Games,
Latakia
A323

1987, Aug. 6   Perf. 13x12¹/₂, 12¹/₂x13
846 A323   1d Discus   .35   .16
847 A323 2.90d Tennis, vert.   1.00   .50
848 A323 3.30d Team handball   1.10   .55
   Nos. 846-848 (3)   2.45 1.21

Birds — A324

1987   Litho.   Perf. 13¹/₂
849 A324   1d Phoenicopterus
               ruber roseus   .55   .24
850 A324 1.80d Porphyrio porphyrio   1.00   .50
851 A324 2.50d Elanus caeruleus   1.40   .65
852 A324 2.90d Milvus milvus   1.65   .75
   Nos. 849-852 (4)   4.60 2.14

Agriculture
A325

Perf. 10¹/₂x11, 11x10¹/₂
1987, Nov. 26   Litho.
853 A325   1d Planting   .35   .16
854 A325   1d Reservoir   .35   .16
855 A325   1d Harvesting crop, vert.   .35   .16
856 A325   1d Produce, vert.   .35   .16
   Nos. 853-856 (4)   1.40   .64

African
Telecommunications
Day — A326

1987, Dec. 7   Perf. 10¹/₂
857 A326   1d multi   .35   .16

Transportation
A327

1987, Dec. 18   Litho.   Perf. 10¹/₂x11
858 A327 2.90d shown   1.00   .50
859 A327 3.30d Diesel train   1.10   .55

Algerian
Universities
A328

Various campuses.

Perf. 10¹/₂x11, 11x10¹/₂
1987, Dec. 26
860 A328   1d shown   .35   .16
861 A328 2.50d multi, diff.   .80   .40
862 A328 2.90d multi, diff.   1.00   .50
863 A328 3.30d multi, diff., vert.   1.10   .55
   Nos. 860-863 (4)   3.25 1.61

Intl. Rural
Development
Fund, 10th
Anniv.
A329

1988, Jan. 27   Perf. 10¹/₂x11
864 A329   1d multi   .50   .25

Autonomy of State-
owned
Utilities — A330

1988, Feb. 27   Litho.   Perf. 11x10¹/₂
865 A330   1d multi   .50   .25

Intl. Women's   Arab Scouts, 75th
Day — A331   Anniv. — A332

1988, Mar. 10   Litho.   Perf. 11x10¹/₂
866 A331   1d multi   .50   .25

1988, Apr. 7   Litho.   Perf. 10¹/₂
867 A332   2d multi   .95   .48

1988 Summer   Hot
Olympics,   Springs — A334
Seoul — A333

1988, July 23   Litho.   Perf. 10¹/₂
868 A333 2.90d multi   1.40   .70

1988, July 16
869 A334   1d shown   .50   .25
870 A334 2.90d Caverns, horiz.   1.40   .70
871 A334 3.30d Gazebo, fountain,
               horiz.   1.60   .80
   Nos. 869-871 (3)   3.50 1.75

World Wildlife
Fund — A335

Barbary apes, *Macaca sylvanus.*

1988, Sept. 17   Litho.   Perf. 10¹/₂
872 A335   50c Adult   .25   .15
873 A335   90c Family   .45   .22
874 A335   1d Close-up, vert.   .50   .25
875 A335 1.80d Seated on branch,
               vert.   .90   .45
   Nos. 872-875 (4)   2.10 1.07

Intl. Literacy   WHO, 40th
Day — A336   Anniv. — A337

1988, Sept. 10   Photo.   Perf. 10¹/₂
876 A336 2.90d multi   1.40   .70

1988, Oct. 15
877 A337 2.90d multi   1.40   .70

Fight Apartheid
A338

1988, Nov. 19   Litho.   Perf. 10¹/₂x11
878 A338 2.50d multi   1.20   .60

Natl. Front
Congress — A339

1988, Nov. 29   Perf. 11x10¹/₂
879 A339   1d multi   .50   .25

Agriculture
A340

1988, Dec. 24   Perf. 10¹/₂
880 A340   1d Irrigation   .50   .25
881 A340   1d Orchard, fields, live-
               stock   .50   .25

Natl.   Airports — A343
Goals — A342

1989, Mar. 9   Litho.   Perf. 11¹/₂
Granite Paper
886 A342   1d shown   .50   .25
887 A342   1d Ancient fort   .50   .25
888 A342   1d Telecommunications   .50   .25
889 A342   1d Modern buildings   .50   .25
   Nos. 886-889 (4)   2.00 1.00

Nos. 887-889 horiz.

Perf. 10¹/₂x11, 11x10¹/₂
1989, Mar. 23
890 A343 2.90d Oran Es Senia,
               horiz.   1.45   .72
891 A343 3.30d Tebessa, horiz.   1.65   .82
892 A343   5d shown   2.50 1.25
   Nos. 890-892 (3)   5.60 2.79

Development
of the South
A344

1989, Apr. 24   Litho.   Perf. 13¹/₂
893 A344   1d Irrigation   .48   .25
894 A344 1.80d Building   .88   .45
895 A344 2.50d Fossil fuel extrac-
               tion, vert.   1.20   .60
   Nos. 893-895 (3)   2.56 1.30

Eradicate
Locusts
A345

1989, May 25   Perf. 10¹/₂
896 A345   1d multi   .50   .25

National
Service — A346

1989, May 11   Litho.   Perf. 13¹/₂
897 A346   2d multicolored   .78   .40

1st Moon
Landing, 20th
Anniv.
A347

Designs: 4d, Astronaut, lunar module, Moon's
surface, vert.

1989, July 23   Litho.   Perf. 13¹/₂
898 A347 2.90d shown   1.10   .55
899 A347   4d multi   1.50   .75

Interparliamentary Union, Cent. — A348

1989, Sept. 4   Perf. 10¹/₂
900 A348 2.90d gold, brt rose lil &
               blk   1.10   .55

Produce
A349

1989, Sept. 23   Litho.   Perf. 11¹/₂
Granite Paper
901   Strip of 3   4.00
  a. A349 2d multi, diff.   .78   .40
  b. A349 3d multi, diff.   1.15   .58
  c. A349 5d shown   1.95   .98

Fish — A350

1989, Oct. 27   Litho.   Perf. 13¹/₂
902 A350   1d Sarda sarda   .40   .20
903 A350   1.80d Zeus faber   .70   .35
904 A350   2.90d Pagellus bogaraveo 1.15   .58
905 A350   3.30d Xiphias gladius   1.30   .65
        Nos. 902-905 (4)   3.55   1.78

Algerian Revolution,
35th Anniv. — A351

1989, Nov. 4   Litho.   Perf. 13¹/₂
906 A351   1d multicolored   .40   .20

African
Development Bank,
25th Anniv.
A352

Mushrooms
A353

1989, Nov. 18   Perf. 10¹/₂
907 A352   1d multicolored   .40   .20

1989, Dec. 16   Perf. 13¹/₂
908 A353   1d Boletus satanas   .40   .20
909 A353   1.80d Psalliota
                xanthoderma   .70   .35
910 A353   2.90d Lepiota procera   1.15   .58
911 A353   3.30d Lactarius deliciosus 1.30 .65
        Nos. 908-911 (4)   3.55   1.78

A354   A355

1990, Jan. 18   Litho.   Perf. 10¹/₂
912 A354   1d multicolored   .40   .20
        Pan-African Postal Union, 10th anniv.

1990, Feb. 22   Litho.   Perf. 14
913 A355   1d Energy conservation   .25   .15

A356   A357

1990, Mar. 2   Photo.   Perf. 11¹/₂
914 A356   3d multicolored   .65   .32
        African Soccer Championships.

1990, May 17   Litho.   Perf. 13¹/₂
917 A357   2.90d shown   .75   .38
918 A357   5d Trophy   1.25   .65
        World Cup Soccer Championships, Italy.

Rural
Electrification
A358

1990, June 21
919 A358   2d multicolored   .50   .25

Youth
A359

Youth Holding
Rainbow — A360

1990, July 6   Perf. 13¹/₂
920 A359   2d multicolored   .50   .25
921 A360   3d multicolored   .75   .36

Maghreb Arab
Union — A361

1990   Perf. 14x13¹/₂
922 A361   1d multicolored   .38   .20

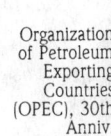

Vocations — A362

1990, Apr. 26   Litho.   Perf. 12¹/₂
923 A362   2d Craftsmen   .75   .40
924 A362   2.90d Auto mechanics   1.15   .60
925 A362   3.30d Deep sea fishing   1.25   .65
        Nos. 923-925 (3)   3.15   1.65

Organization
of Petroleum
Exporting
Countries
(OPEC), 30th
Anniv.
A363

1990   Perf. 13¹/₂
926 A363   2d multicolored   .75   .40

Savings
Promotion — A364

1990, Oct. 31   Litho.   Perf. 14
927 A364   1d multicolored   .38   .20

Namibian
Independence
A365

1990, Nov. 8
928 A365   3d multicolored   1.15   .60

A366   A367

Farm animals.

1990, Nov. 29   Perf. 13¹/₂
929 A366   1d Duck   .38   .20
930 A366   2d Rabbit, horiz.   .75   .40
931 A366   2.90d Turkey   1.10   .60
932 A366   3d Rooster, horiz.   1.15   .60
        Nos. 929-932 (4)   3.38   1.80

1990, Dec. 11
933 A367   1d multicolored   .38   .20
        Anti-French Riots, 30th anniv.

A368   A369

1990, Dec. 20   Perf. 14
934 A368   1d multicolored   .38   .20
        Fight against respiratory diseases.

1991, Feb. 24   Litho.   Perf. 13¹/₂
935 A369   1d multicolored   .36   .18
        Constitution, 2nd anniv.

Flower Type of 1986
1991, May 23   Litho.   Perf. 13¹/₂
Size: 26x36mm
936 A312   2d Jasminum fruticans   .65   .32
937 A312   4d Dianthus crinitus   1.30   .65
938 A312   5d Cyclamen africanum   1.65   .85
        Nos. 936-938 (3)   3.60   1.82

Children's
Drawings
A370

1991, June 3   Litho.   Perf. 13¹/₂
939 A370   3d shown   1.00   .50
940 A370   4d Children playing   1.30   .65

Maghreb Arab
Union
Summit — A371

1991, June 10
941 A371   1d multicolored   .32   .16

Geneva
Convention
on
Refugees,
40th Anniv.
A372

Perf. 14¹/₂x13¹/₂
1991, July 28   Litho.
942 A372   3d multicolored   1.05   .52

Postal Service
A373

1991, Oct. 12   Perf. 14
943 A373   1.50d shown   .55   .28
944 A373   4.20d Expo emblem, vert. 1.50   .75
        Telecom '91, 6th World Forum and Exposition
on Telecommunications, Geneva, Switzerland (No.
944).

Butterflies
A374

1991, Nov. 21   Litho.   Perf. 11¹/₂
Granite Paper
945 A374   2d Zerynthia rumina   .32   .16
946 A374   4d Melitaea didyma   .65   .32
947 A374   6d Vanessa atalanta   1.00   .50
948 A374   7d Nymphalis polychloros 1.15   .58
        Nos. 945-948 (4)   3.12   1.56

A375   A376

1991, Dec. 21   Perf. 12
Granite Paper
949 A375   3d Necklace   .50   .25
950 A375   4d Jewelry of Southern
                Tuaregs   .65   .32
951 A375   5d Brooch   .85   .42
952 A375   7d Rings, horiz.   1.15   .58
        Nos. 949-952 (4)   3.15   1.57

1992, Mar. 8   Litho.   Perf. 14
953 A376   1.50d Algerian Women   .22   .15

Gazelles
A377

Designs: 1.50d, Gazella dorcas. 6.20d, Gazella
cuvieri. 8.60d, Gazella dama.

1992, May 13   **Perf. 14¹/₂x13**
954 A377 1.50d multicolored   .25   .15
955 A377 6.20d multicolored   1.05   .52
956 A377 8.60d multicolored   1.45   .75
       Nos. 954-956 (3)   2.75   1.42

1992 Summer
Olympics,
Barcelona
A379

1992, June 24   Litho.   Perf. 14
958 A379 6.20d Runners   1.10   .55

A381   A382

1992, July 7   Litho.   Perf. 14
960 A381 5d multicolored   .90   .45

Independence, 30th anniv.

1992, Sept. 23   Litho.   Perf. 14
Designs: Medicinal plants.
961 A382 1.50d Ajuga iva   .20   .15
962 A382 5.10d Rhamnus alaternus   .70   .35
963 A382 6.20d Silybum marianum   .85   .42
964 A382 8.60d Lavandula stoechas 1.15   .58
       Nos. 961-964 (4)   2.90   1.50

Post Office
Modernization
A383

1992, Oct. 10   Litho.   Perf. 14
965 A383 1.50d multicolored   .22   .15

Marine
Life — A384

Designs: 1.50d, Hippocampus hippocampus.
2.70d, Caretta caretta. 6.20d, Muraena helena.
7.50d, Palinurus elephas.

1992, Dec. 23
966 A384 1.50d multicolored   .20   .15
967 A384 2.70d multicolored   .35   .18
968 A384 6.20d multicolored   .85   .42
969 A384 7.50d multicolored   1.00   .50
       Nos. 966-969 (4)   2.40   1.25

Pres.
Mohammad
Boudiaf
(1919-92)
A385

1992, Nov. 3   Litho.   Perf. 11¹/₂
Granite Paper
970 A385   2d green & multi   .28   .15
971 A385 8.60d blue & multi   1.15   .58

Coins
A386

1992, Dec. 16   Litho.   Perf. 11¹/₂
Granite Paper
972 A386 1.50d Numidia, 2nd cent.
              BC   .20   .15
973 A386   2d Dinar, 14th cent.   .28   .15
974 A386 5.10d Dinar, 11th cent.   .68   .35
975 A386 6.20d Abdelkader, 19th
              cent.   .85   .40
       Nos. 972-975 (4)   2.01   1.05

Door   Flowering
Knockers — A387   Trees — A388

1993, Feb. 17   Litho.   Perf. 14
976 A387   2d Algiers   .28   .15
977 A387 5.60d Constantine   .75   .38
978 A387 8.60d Tlemcen   1.15   .58
       Nos. 976-978 (3)   2.18   1.11

Perf. 12x11¹/₂, 11¹/₂x12
1993, Mar. 17
Granite Paper
979 A388 4.50d Neflier (medlar),
              horiz.   .60   .30
980 A388 8.60d Cognassier (quince) 1.20   .60
981 A388 11d Abricotier (apricot) 1.50   .75
       Nos. 979-981 (3)   3.30   1.65

Natl. Coast
Guard Service,
20th Anniv.
A389

1993, Apr. 3   Litho.   Perf. 14
982 A389 2d multicolored   .28   .15

Traditional Grain
Processing — A390

1993, May 19   Litho.   Perf. 14
983 A390   2d Container   .26   .15
984 A390 5.60d Millstone   .75   .38
985 A390 8.60d Press   1.15   .58
       Nos. 983-985 (3)   2.16   1.11

Royal
Mausoleums
A391

1993, June 16   Litho.   Perf. 14
986 A391 8.60d Mauretania   1.15   .58
987 A391 12d El Khroub   1.60   .80

Ports — A392

1993, Oct. 20   Litho.   Perf. 14x13¹/₂
988 A392   2d Annaba   .25   .15
989 A392 8.60d Arzew   1.10   .55

Varanus
Griseus
A393

Design: 2d, Chamaeleo vulgaris, vert.

Perf. 13¹/₂x14, 14x13¹/₂
1993, Nov. 20
990 A393   2d multicolored   .25   .15
991 A393 8.60d multicolored   1.10   .55

Tourism
A394

1993, Dec. 18   Litho.   Perf. 14x13¹/₂
992 A394   2d Tipaza   .22   .15
993 A394 8.60d Kerzaz   .80   .40

A395   Chahid Day — A396

1994, Jan. 2   Perf. 13¹/₂x14
994 A395 2d multicolored   .22   .15

SONATRACH (Natl. Society for Research, Transformation, and Commercialization of Hydrocar-
bons), 30th anniv.

1994, Feb. 18   Litho.   Perf. 13¹/₂x14
995 A396 2d multicolored   .22   .15

1994 World Cup Soccer Championships,
US — A397

1994, Mar. 16   Perf. 14x13¹/₂
996 A397 8.60d multicolored   .80   .40

A398   Ancient
                 Petroglyphs — A399

Orchids: 5.60d, Orchis simia lam. 8.60d, Ophrys
lutea cavan. 11d, Ophrys apifera huds.

1994, Apr. 20   Litho.   Perf. 11¹/₂
Granite Paper
997 A398 5.60d multicolored   .55   .28
998 A398 8.60d multicolored   .85   .42
999 A398 11d multicolored   1.10   .55
       Nos. 997-999 (3)   2.50   1.25

1994, May 21   Litho.   Perf. 13x14
1000 A399 3d Inscriptions   .35   .18
1001 A399 10d Man on horse   1.25   .60

A400   A401

1994, June 25
1002 A400 12d multicolored   1.25   .65
       Intl. Olympic Committee, cent.

1994, July 13
1003 A401 3d multicolored   .35   .18
       World Population Day.

       Views of Algiers Type of 1992
Design: 3d, like #775.

1994   Litho.   Perf. 14
1010 A290b 3d dk blue & lt blue   .35   .18

This is an expanding set. Number may change.

Jewelry from
Saharan Atlas
Region
A402

Perf. 13¹/₂x14, 14x13¹/₂
1994, Oct. 18   Litho.
1019 A402 3d Fibules, vert.   .15   .15
1020 A402 5d Belt   .25   .15
1021 A402 12d Bracelets   .55   .28
       Nos. 1019-1021 (3)   .95   .58

A403   A404

1994, Nov. 3   Litho.   Perf. 13¹/₂x14
1022 A403 3d multicolored   .38   .18
       Algerian Revolution, 40th anniv.

1994, Nov. 16   Litho.   Perf. 13¹/₂x14
1023 A404 3d Ladybugs   .15   .15
1024 A404 12d Beetles   .55   .28

Fight Against
AIDS — A405

1994, Dec. 1   Litho.   *Perf. 14x13¹/₂*
1025 A405 3d multicolored   .38 .18

Dances — A406   Minerals — A407

1994, Dec. 17   Litho.   *Perf. 13¹/₂x14*
1026 A406 3d Algeroise   .15 .15
1027 A406 10d Constantinoise   .50 .25
1028 A406 12d Alaoui   .55 .28
      Nos. 1026-1028 (3)   1.20 .68

1994, Sept. 21
1029 A407 3d Gres lite-erode   .15 .15
1030 A407 5d Cipolin   .25 .15
1031 A407 10d Marne a turitella .50 .25
      Nos. 1029-1031 (3)   .90 .55

World Tourism
Organization,
20th Anniv.
A408

1995, Jan. 28   Litho.   *Perf. 14x13¹/₂*
1032 A408 3d multicolored   .35 .20

Honey
Bees — A409   Flowers — A410

Perf. 13¹/₂x14, 14x13¹/₂
1995, Feb. 22
1033 A409 3d shown   .35 .20
1034 A409 13d On flower, horiz. 1.50 .75

1995, Mar. 29   Photo.   *Perf. 11¹/₂*
Granite Paper
1035 A410 3d Dahlias   .35 .20
1036 A410 10d Zinnias   1.10 .55
1037 A410 13d Lilacs   1.50 .75
      Nos. 1035-1037 (3)   2.95 1.50

Decorative
Stonework — A411

Various patterns.

1995, Apr. 19   *Perf. 14*
1039 A411 3d brown   .35 .20
1040 A411 4d green   .45 .25
1041 A411 5d deep claret   .55 .30
      Nos. 1039-1041 (3)   1.35 .75

This is an expanding set. Numbers may change.

End of
World
War II,
50th
Anniv.
A413

1995, May 3   *Perf. 14x13¹/₂*
1048 A413 3d multicolored   .35 .20

Souvenir Sheet

VE Day, 50th Anniv. — A414

Illustration reduced.

1995, May 10   Litho.   *Perf. 13¹/₂x14*
1049 A414 13d multicolored   1.65 .85

Volleyball,   Environmental
Cent. — A415   Protection — A416

1995, June 14
1050 A415 3d multicolored   .40 .20

1995, June 5
1051 A416 3d Air, water pollution .40 .20
1052 A416 13d Air pollution   1.65 .85

General
Electrification — A417

1995, July 5   Litho.   *Perf. 13¹/₂x14*
1053 A417 3d multicolored   .45 .20

UN, 50th
Anniv.
A418

1995, Oct. 24   *Perf. 14x13¹/₂*
1054 A418 13d multicolored   2.00 1.00

Pottery — A419

10d, Pot, Lakhdaria. 20d, Pitcher, Aokas. 21d,
Jar, Larbaa Nath Iraten. 30d, Vase, Ouadhia.

1995, Nov. 14   Litho.   *Perf. 14*
1055 A419 10d dark brown   1.50 .75
1056 A419 20d dull maroon   3.00 1.50
1057 A419 21d golden brown   3.25 1.65
1058 A419 30d dark rose brown   4.50 2.25
      Nos. 1055-1058 (4)   12.25 6.15

Aquatic
Birds — A420

1995, Dec. 20   Litho.   *Perf. 14x13¹/₂*
1059 A420 3d Tadorna tadorna   .45 .20
1060 A420 5d Gallinago gallinago .75 .35

1996 Summer
Olympics,
Atlanta
A421

1996, Jan. 24   Litho.   *Perf. 14x13¹/₂*
1061 A421 20d multicolored   3.00 1.50

Touareg
Leather
Crafts — A422

Perf. 14x13¹/₂, 13¹/₂x14
1996, Feb. 14   Litho.
1062 A422 5d shown   .75 .40
1063 A422 16d Saddle bag, vert. 2.40 1.20

Pasteur Institute of
Algeria — A423

1996, Mar. 20   Litho.   *Perf. 13¹/₂x14*
1064 A423 5d multicolored   .75 .40

Youm El
Ilm — A424

Designs: 16d, Dove, stylus, vert. 23d, Open book
showing pencil, stylus, compass, satellite in earth
orbit, vert.

Perf. 14x13¹/₂, 13¹/₂x14
1996, Apr. 16   Litho.
1065 A424 5d multicolored   .75 .40
1066 A424 16d multicolored   2.40 1.20
1067 A424 23d multicolored   3.50 3.50
      Nos. 1065-1067 (3)   6.65 5.10

Minerals
A425

Mineral, region: 10d, Iron, Djebel-Ouenza. 20d,
Gold, Tirek-Amesmessa.

1996, May 6   Litho.   *Perf. 14x13¹/₂*
1068 A425 10d multicolored   .35 .20
1069 A425 20d multicolored   .75 .35

Butterflies
A426

Designs: 5d, Pandoriana pandora. 10d, Coe-
nonympha pamphilus. 20d, Cynthia cardui. 23d,
Melanargia galathea.

1996, June 12   Litho.   *Perf. 11¹/₂*
Granite Paper
1070 A426 5d multicolored   .20 .15
1071 A426 10d multicolored   .35 .20
1072 A426 20d multicolored   .65 .35
1073 A426 23d multicolored   .85 .40
      Nos. 1070-1073 (4)   2.05 1.10

Civil Protection
A427

Designs: 5d, Giving medical aid, ambulance.
23d, Prevention of natural disasters, vert.

Perf. 14x13¹/₂, 13¹/₂x14
1996, Oct. 9   Litho.
1074 A427 5d multicolored   .20 .15
1075 A427 23d multicolored   .85 .40

World Day
Against Use of
Illegal
Drugs — A428

1996, June 26   Litho.   *Perf. 14x13¹/₂*
1076 A428 5d multicolored   .20 .15

UNICEF, 50th
Anniv. — A429

Stylized designs: 5d, Two children, wreath, pencils, flowers. 10d, Five children, pencil, key, flower,
flag, hypodermic.

1996, Nov. 20   Litho.   *Perf. 13¹/₂x14*
1077 A429 5d multicolored   .20 .15
1078 A429 10d multicolored   .35 .20

4th General
Census
A430

1997, Feb. 12   Litho.   *Perf. 14x13¹/₂*
1079 A430 5d multicolored   .20 .15

A431　　　A432

1997, Feb. 27 *Perf. 13½x14*
1080 A431 5d multicolored .20 .15
Protest at Ouargla, 35th anniv.

1996, Dec. 18 Litho. *Perf. 13½x14*
Interior Courts of Algerian Dwellings: 5d, Palace of Hassan Pasha. 10d, Khedaouj El-Amia, Algiers. 20d, Palace of Light. 30d, Abdellatif Villa.

1081 A432 5d multicolored .20 .15
1082 A432 10d multicolored .35 .20
1083 A432 20d multicolored .70 .35
1084 A432 30d multicolored 1.10 .55
Nos. 1081-1084 (4) 2.35 1.25

Paintings by Ismail Samson (1934-88)
A433

20d, Woman with Pigeons. 30d, Interrogation.

1996, Dec. 25 *Perf. 14*
1085 A433 20d multicolored .70 .35
1086 A433 30d multicolored 1.10 .55

Victory Day, 35th Anniv.
A434

1997, Mar. 19 *Perf. 14x13½*
1087 A434 5d multicolored .20 .15

Flowers — A423

Designs: 5d, Ficaria verna. 16d, Lonicera arborea. 23d, Papaver rhoeas.

1997, Apr. 23 Litho. *Perf. 13½x14*
1088 A423 5d multicolored .20 .15
1089 A423 16d multicolored .55 .30
1090 A423 23d multicolored .80 .40
Nos. 1088-1090 (3) 1.55 .85

World Day to Stop Smoking — A424　　Legislative Elections — A425

1997, May 31 Litho. *Perf. 13½x14*
1091 A424 5d multicolored .20 .15

1997, June 4
1092 A425 5d multicolored .20 .15

Scorpions
A426

Designs: 5d, Buthus occitanus tunetanus. 10d, Androctonus australis hector.

1997, June 18 *Perf. 14x13½*
1093 A426 5d multicolored .20 .15
1094 A426 10d multicolored .35 .20

Natl. Independence, 35th Anniv. — A427

Designs: 5d, Crowd celebrating, flags. 10d, Doves, broken chain, "35," flag.

1997, July 5 Litho. *Perf. 14x13½*
1095 A427 5d multicolored .20 .15
Souvenir Sheet
Perf. 14
1096 A427 10d multicolored .35 .20
No. 1096 contains one 30x40mm stamp.

A428　　　A429

Wood Carvings: 5d, Inscription, Nedroma Mosque. 23d, Door, Ketchaoua Mosque.

1997, Jan. 15 Litho. *Perf. 13½x14*
1097 A428 5d multicolored .20 .15
1098 A428 23d multicolored .80 .40

1997, Aug. 17 Litho. *Perf. 13½x14*
1099 A429 5d multicolored .20 .15
Moufdi Zakaria (1908-77), poet.

Textile Patterns
A430

1997, Sept. 17 Litho. *Perf. 14*
1100 A430 3d Dokkali .15 .15
1101 A430 5d Tellis .20 .15
1102 A430 10d Bou-Taleb .35 .20
1103 A430 20d Ddil .70 .35
Nos. 1100-1103 (4) 1.40 .85

Natl. Police Force, 25th Anniv.
A431

1997, Oct. 6 *Perf. 14x13½*
1104 A431 5d multicolored .20 .15

Express Mail Service
A432

1997, Oct. 9
1105 A432 5d multicolored .20 .15

Local Elections — A433

1997, Oct. 23 *Perf. 13½x14*
1106 A433 5d multicolored .20 .15

Lighthouses
A434

Perf. 14x13½, 13½x14
1997, Nov. 5 *Litho.*
1107 A434 5d Tenes .20 .15
1108 A434 10d Cape Caxine, vert. .35 .20

New Airpost Service, 1st Anniv.
A435

1997, Nov. 17 *Perf. 14x13½*
1109 A435 5d multicolored .20 .15

SEMI-POSTAL STAMPS

+10ᶜ

Regular Issue of 1926 Surcharged in Black or Red

1927 **Unwmk.** *Perf. 14x13½*
B1 A1 5c +5c bl grn .50 .50
B2 A1 10c +10c lilac .50 .50
B3 A2 15c +15c org brn .50 .50
B4 A2 20c +20c car rose .50 .50
B5 A2 25c +25c bl grn .50 .50
B6 A2 30c +30c lt bl .50 .50
B7 A2 35c +35c dp vio .55 .55
B8 A2 40c +40c ol grn .60 .60
B9 A3 50c +50c dp bl (R) .60 .60
a. Double surcharge 200.00 200.00
B10 A3 80c +80c red org .60 .60
B11 A4 1fr +1fr gray grn & red brn .65 .65
B12 A4 2fr +2fr Prus bl & blk brn 15.00 15.00
B13 A4 5fr +5fr red & vio 21.00 21.00
Nos. B1-B13 (13) 42.00 42.00

The surtax was for the benefit of wounded soldiers. Government officials speculated in this issue.

Railroad Terminal, Oran — SP1

Ruins at Djemila　　Mosque of Sidi
SP2　　　　　　　Abd-er-Rahman
　　　　　　　　　SP3

Designs: 10c+10c, Rummel Gorge, Constantine. 15c+15c, Admiralty Buildings, Algiers. 25c+25c, View of Algiers. 30c+30c, Trajan's Arch, Timgad. 40c+40c, Temple of the North, Djemila. 75c+75c, Mansourah Minaret, Tlemcen. 1f+1f, View of Ghardaia. 1.50f+1.50f, View of Tolga. 2f+2f, Tuareg warriors. 3f+3f, Kasbah, Algiers.

1930 **Engr.** *Perf. 12½*
B14 SP1 5c +5c orange 5.00 5.00
B15 SP1 10c +10c ol grn 5.00 5.00
B16 SP1 15c +15c dk brn 5.00 5.00
B17 SP1 25c +25c black 5.00 5.00
B18 SP1 30c +30c dk red 5.00 5.00
B19 SP1 40c +40c ap grn 5.00 5.00
B20 SP2 50c +50c ultra 5.00 5.00
B21 SP2 75c +75c red pur 5.00 5.00
B22 SP2 1fr +1fr org red 5.00 5.00
B23 SP2 1.50fr +1.50fr deep ultra 5.00 5.00
B24 SP2 2fr +2fr dk car 5.00 5.00
B25 SP2 3fr +3fr dk grn 5.00 5.00
B26 SP3 5fr +5fr grn & car 12.00 12.00
a. Center inverted 450.00
Nos. B14-B26 (13) 72.00 72.00

Centenary of the French occupation of Algeria. The surtax on the stamps was given to the funds for the celebration.
Nos. B14-B26 exist imperf. Value, set in pairs, $350.

> Catalogue values for unused stamps in this section, from this point to the end of the section, are for Never Hinged items.

No. 102 Surcharged in Red

1918-11 Nov.-1938
0.65 + 0.35

1938 *Perf. 13*
B27 A6 65c +35c on 2.25fr yel grn .50 .40
20th anniversary of Armistice.

René Caillié, Charles Lavigerie and Henri Duveyrier
SP14

1939 **Engr.**
B28 SP14 30c +20c dk bl grn 1.00 .40
B29 SP14 90c +60c car rose 1.25 .65
B30 SP14 2.25fr +75c ultra 6.75 6.25
B31 SP14 5fr +5fr brn blk 14.00 14.00
Nos. B28-B31 (4) 23.00 21.50

Pioneers of the Sahara.

French and Algerian Soldiers
SP15

1940 **Photo.** *Perf. 12*
B32 SP15 1fr +1fr bl & car .50 .40
B33 SP15 1fr +2fr brn rose & blk .50 .40
B34 SP15 1fr +4fr dp grn & red .70 .60
B35 SP15 1fr +9fr brn & car 1.00 1.00
Nos. B32-B35 (4) 2.70 2.40

The surtax was used to assist the families of mobilized men.

Type of Regular Issue, 1941 Surcharged in Carmine **+4ᶠ**

1941 **Engr.** *Perf. 13*
B36 A19 1fr +4fr black .20 .20

No. 135 Surcharged in Carmine

SECOURS
NATIONAL
+4ᶠ

B37 A19 1fr +4fr dark blue   .20 .20

The surtax was for National Relief.

No. 124 Surcharged in Black "+60c"

1942
B38 A7 90c +60c henna brn   .15 .15
   a. Double surcharge   55.00

The surtax was used for National Relief. The stamp could also be used as 1.50 francs for postage.

Mother and Child — SP16

1943, Dec. 1   Litho.   Perf. 12
B39 SP16 50c +4.50fr brt pink   .50 .25
B40 SP16 1.50fr +8.50fr lt grn   .50 .25
B41 SP16 3fr +12fr dp bl   .50 .25
B42 SP16 5fr +15fr vio brn   .50 .25
   Nos. B39-B42 (4)   2.00 1.00

The surtax was for the benefit of soldiers and prisoners of war.

Planes over Fields — SP17

1945, July 2 Unwmk. Engr. Perf. 13
B43 SP17 1.50fr +3.50fr lt ultra, red org & blk   .25 .25

The surtax was for the benefit of Algerian airmen and their families.

France No. B192 Overprinted Type "a" of 1924 in Black

1945
B44 SP146 4fr +6fr dk vio brn   .25 .20

The surtax was for war victims of the P.T.T.

Overprinted in Blue on Type of France, 1945

1945, Oct. 15
B45 SP150 2fr +3fr dk brn   .40 .40
For Stamp Day.

Overprinted in Blue on Type of France, 1946

1946, June 29
B46 SP160 3fr +2fr red   .45 .45
For Stamp Day.

Children Playing by Stream SP18

Girl — SP19

Athlete — SP20

Repatriated Prisoner and Bay of Algiers SP21

1946, Oct. 2   Engr.   Perf. 13
B47 SP18 3fr +17fr dark grn   .65 .65
B48 SP19 4fr +21fr red   .65 .65
B49 SP20 8fr +27fr rose lilac   2.75 2.75
B50 SP21 10fr +35fr dark blue   .70 .70
   Nos. B47-B50 (4)   4.75 4.75

Type of France, 1947, Overprinted type "a" of 1924 in Carmine

1947, Mar. 15
B51 SP172 4.50fr +5.50fr dp ultra   .40 .40
For Stamp Day.

Same on Type of France, 1947, Surcharged Like No. B36 in Carmine

1947, Nov. 13
B52 A173 5fr +10fr dk Prus grn   .55 .40

Type of France, 1948, Overprinted in Dark Green — f

1948, Mar. 6
B53 SP176 6fr +4fr dk grn   .45 .45
For Stamp Day.

Type of France, 1948, Overprinted type "a" of 1924 in Blue and New Value

1948, May
B54 A176 6fr +4fr red   .35 .35

Battleship Richelieu and the Admiralty, Algiers SP22

Aircraft Carrier Arromanches SP23

Unwmk.
1949, Jan. 15   Engr.   Perf. 13
B55 SP22 10fr +15fr dp blue   4.50 4.50
B56 SP23 18fr +22fr red   4.50 4.50

The surtax was for naval charities.

Type of France, 1949, Overprinted in Blue — g

1949, Mar. 26
B57 SP180 15fr +5fr lilac rose   1.10 1.10
For Stamp Day, Mar. 26-27.

Type of France, 1950, Overprinted type "f" in Green

1950, Mar. 11
B58 SP183 12fr +3fr blk brn   1.10 1.10
For Stamp Day, Mar. 11-12.

Foreign Legionary — SP24

1950, Apr. 30
B59 SP24 15fr +5fr dk grn   1.10 1.10

Charles de Foucauld and Gen. J. F. H. Laperrine SP25

1950, Aug. 21   Unwmk.   Perf. 13
B60 SP25 25fr +5fr brn ol & brn blk   3.00 3.00
50th anniversary of the presence of the French in the Sahara.

Emir Abd-el-Kader and Marshal T. R. Bugeaud SP26

1950, Aug. 21
B61 SP26 40fr +10fr dk brn & blk brn   3.00 3.00

Unveiling of a monument to Emir Abd-el-Kader at Cacheron.

Col. Colonna d'Ornano and Fine Arts Museum, Algiers SP27

1951, Jan. 11
B62 SP27 15fr +5fr blk brn, vio brn & red brn   .65 .65

Death of Col. Colonna d'Ornano, 10th anniv.

Type of France, 1951, Overprinted type "a" of 1924 in Black

1951, Mar. 10
B63 SP186 12fr +3fr brown   .85 .85
For Stamp Day.

Type of France, 1952, Overprinted type "g" in Dark Blue

1952, Mar. 8   Unwmk.   Perf. 13
B64 SP190 12fr +3fr dk bl   1.25 1.25
For Stamp Day.

French Military Medal — SP28

1952, July 5 Unwmk. Engr. Perf. 13
B65 SP28 15fr +5fr grn, yel & brn   1.25 1.25

Centenary of the creation of the French Military Medal.

Type of France 1952, Surcharged type "g" and Surtax in Black

1952, Sept. 15
B66 A222 30fr +5fr dp ultra   1.25 1.25

10th anniv. of the defense of Bir-Hakeim.

View of El Oued — SP29

Design: 12fr+3fr, View of Bou-Noura.

1952, Nov. 15   Engr.
B67 SP29 8fr +2fr ultra & red   1.10 1.10
B68 SP29 12fr +3fr red   1.90 1.90

The surtax was for the Red Cross.

Type of France, 1953, Overprinted type "a" of 1924 in Black

1953, Mar. 14   Engr.
B69 SP193 12fr +3fr purple   1.00 .90
For Stamp Day. Surtax for Red Cross.

Victory of Cythera — SP30

Unwmk.
1953, Dec. 18   Engr.   Perf. 13
B70 SP30 15fr +5fr blk brn & brn   .60 .60

The surtax was for army welfare work.

Type of France, 1954, Overprinted type "a" of 1924 in Black

1954, Mar. 20   Unwmk.   Perf. 13
B71 SP196 12fr +3fr scarlet   .65 .65
For Stamp Day.

Soldiers and Flags SP31

Foreign Legionary SP32

1954, Mar. 27
B72 SP31 15fr +5fr dk brn   .50 .50

The surtax was for old soldiers.

1954, Apr. 30
B73 SP32 15fr +5fr dk grn   1.00 1.00

The surtax was for the welfare fund of the Foreign Legion.

Nurses and Verdun Hospital, Algiers — SP33

Design: 15fr+5fr, J. H. Dunant & ruins at Djemila.

1954, Oct. 30
B74 SP33 12fr +3fr indigo & red   1.75 1.75
B75 SP33 15fr +5fr pur & red   2.00 2.00

The surtax was for the Red Cross.

Earthquake Victims and Ruins — SP34

First Aid — SP35

Design: #B80-B81, Removing wounded.

1954, Dec. 5
B76 SP34 12fr +4fr dk vio brn   1.00 1.00
B77 SP34 15fr +5fr dp bl   1.00 1.00
B78 SP35 18fr +6fr lil rose   1.75 1.75
B79 SP35 20fr +7fr violet   1.75 1.75
B80 SP35 25fr +8fr rose brn   2.00 2.00
B81 SP35 30fr +10fr brt bl grn   2.00 2.00
   Nos. B76-B81 (6)   9.50 9.50

The surtax was for victims of the Orleansville earthquake disaster of September 1954.

Type of France, 1955, Overprinted type "a" of 1924 in Black

1955, Mar. 19
B82 SP199 12fr +3fr dp ultra   1.00 1.00
For Stamp Day, Mar. 19-20.

Women and Children
SP36

Cancer Victim
SP37

1955, Nov. 5
B83 SP36 15fr +5fr blue & indigo   .60 .60
The tax was for war victims.

1956, Mar. 3   Unwmk.   Perf. 13
B84 SP37 15fr +5fr dk brn   .50 .50
The surtax was for the Algerian Cancer Society. The male figure in the design is Rodin's "Age of Bronze."

Type of France, 1956, Overprinted type "a" of 1924 in Black

1956, Mar.
B85 SP202 12fr +3fr red   .45 .45
For Stamp Day, Mar. 17-18.

Foreign Legion Rest Home — SP38

1956, Apr. 29
B86 SP38 15fr +5fr dk bl grn   1.25 1.25
Honoring the French Foreign Legion.

Type of France, 1957, Overprinted type "f" in Black

1957, Mar. 16   Engr.   Perf. 13
B87 SP204 12fr +3fr dull purple   .70 .70
For Stamp Day and to honor the Maritime Postal Service.

Fennec SP39

Design: 15fr+5fr, Stork flying over roofs.

1957, Apr. 6
B88 SP39 12fr +3fr red brn & red   3.75 3.75
B89 SP39 15fr +5fr sepia & red   3.75 3.75
The surtax was for the Red Cross.

Type of Regular Issue, 1956 Surcharged in Dark Blue

18 JUIN 1940 + 5ᶠ

1957, June 18
B90 A53 15fr +5fr scar & rose red   .95 .95
17th anniv. of General de Gaulle's appeal for a Free France.

The Giaour, by Delacroix — SP40

On the Banks of the Oued, by Fromentin SP41

Design: 35fr+10fr, Dancer, by Chasseriau.

Unwmk.
1957, Nov. 30   Engr.   Perf. 13
B91 SP40 15fr +5fr dk car   3.75 3.75
B92 SP41 20fr +5fr grn   3.75 3.75
B93 SP40 35fr +10fr dk bl   3.75 3.75
Nos. B91-B93 (3)   11.25 11.25
Surtax for army welfare organizations.

Type of France Overprinted type "f" in Blue

1958, Mar. 15   Unwmk.   Perf. 13
B94 SP206 15fr +5fr org brn   .75 .75
For Stamp Day.

Bird-of-Paradise Flower — SP42

Arms & Marshal's Baton — SP43

1958, June 14   Engr.   Perf. 13
B95 SP42 20fr +5fr grn, org & vio   2.25 2.25
The surtax was for Child Welfare.

1958, July 20
B96 SP43 20fr +5fr ultra, car & grn   1.00 1.00
Marshal de Lattre Foundation.

Independent State

Clasped Hands, Wheat, Olive Branch — SP44

Burning Books — SP45

1963, May 27   Unwmk.   Perf. 13
B97 SP44 50c +20c sl grn, brt grn & car   .80 .60
Surtax for the Natl. Solidarity Fund.

1965, June 7   Engr.   Perf. 13
B98 SP45 50c +5c ol grn, red & blk   .50 .40
Issued to commemorate the burning of the Library of Algiers, June 7, 1962.

Soldiers and Woman Comforting Wounded Soldier — SP46

1966, Aug. 20   Photo.   Perf. 11½
B99 SP46 30c +10c multi   1.25 .70
B100 SP46 95c +10c multi   1.75 1.10
Day of the Moudjahid (Moslem volunteers).

Red Crescent, Boy and Girl — SP47

1967, May 27   Litho.   Perf. 14
B101 SP47 30c +10c brt grn, brn & car .45 .35
Algerian Red Crescent Society.

Flood Victims — SP48

Design: 95c+25c, Rescuing flood victims.

1969, Nov. 15   Typo.   Perf. 10½
B102 SP48 30c +10c dl bl, sal & blk   .45 .35
Litho.
B103 SP48 95c +25c multi   1.00 .65

Red Crescent Flag — SP49

1971, May 17   Engr.   Perf. 10½
B104 SP49 30c +10c slate grn & car   .35 .28
Algerian Red Crescent Society.

Intl. Children's Day — SP50

1989, June 1   Litho.   Perf. 10½x11
B105 SP50 1d +30c multi   .65 .48
Surtax for child welfare.

Solidarity with Palestinians SP51

1990, Dec. 9   Litho.   Perf. 10½x11
B106 SP51 1d +30c multi   .50 .30

Natl. Solidarity with Education — SP52

1995, Sept. 20   Litho.   Perf. 13x14
B107 SP52 3d +50c multi   .50 .25

AIR POST STAMPS

Catalogue values for unused stamps in this section are for Never Hinged items.

Plane over Algiers Harbor — AP1

Two types of 20fr:
Type I · Monogram "F" without serifs. "POSTE" indented 3mm.
Type II · Monogram "F" with serifs. "POSTE" indented 4½mm.

Unwmk.
1946, June 20   Engr.   Perf. 13
C1   AP1   5fr red   .15 .15
C2   AP1   10fr deep blue   .15 .15
C3   AP1   15fr deep green   .40 .15
C4   AP1   20fr brown (II)   .20 .15
C4A AP1   20fr brown (I)   100.00 65.00
C5   AP1   25fr violet   .45 .15
C6   AP1   40fr gray black   .55 .15
       Set value, #C1-C4,
       C5-C6   1.65 .40
For surcharges see Nos. C7, CB1-CB2.

No. C1 Surcharged in Black   **— 10 %**

1947, Jan. 18
C7   AP1   (4.50fr) on 5fr red   .15 .15

Storks over Mosque — AP2

Plane over Village — AP3

1949-53
C8   AP2   50fr green   2.00 .25
C9   AP3   100fr brown   1.75 .25
C10   AP2   200fr bright red   4.00 3.00
C11   AP3   500fr ultra ('53)   14.00 10.00
       Nos. C8-C11 (4)   21.75 13.50

Beni Bahdel Dam — AP4

1957, July 1   Unwmk.   Perf. 13
C12   AP4   200fr dark red   3.25 .75

Caravelle over Ghardaia — AP5

Designs: 2d, Caravelle over El Oued. 5d, Caravelle over Tipasa.

1967-68   Engr.   Perf. 13
C13   AP5   1d lil, org brn & emer   1.00 .50
C14   AP5   2d brt bl, org brn & emer   2.50 1.25
C15   AP5   5d brt bl, grn & org brn ('68)   6.00 2.75
       Nos. C13-C15 (3)   9.50 4.50

Plane over Casbah, Algiers — AP6

Designs: 3d, Plane over Oran. 4d, Plane over Rhumel Gorge.

1971-72		Photo.		Perf. 12½
C16	AP6	2d grysh blk & multi	1.65	.80
C17	AP6	3d violet & blk	2.50	1.40
C18	AP6	4d blk & multi	3.25	1.75
		Nos. C16-C18 (3)	7.40	3.95

Issued: 2d, 6/12/71; 3d, 4d, 2/28/72.

Storks and Plane — AP7

1979, Mar. 24		Photo.	Perf. 11½
C19	AP7	10d multi	4.00 1.60

Plane Approaching Coastal City — AP8

1991, Apr. 26		Litho.	Perf. 13½
C20	AP8	10d shown	3.60 1.80
C21	AP8	20d Plane over city	7.20 3.60

Plane Over Djidjelli Corniche — AP9

1993, Sept. 25		Engr.	Perf. 13½x14
C22	AP9	50d blue, green & brown	6.25 3.25

AIR POST SEMI-POSTAL STAMPS

Catalogue values for unused stamps in this section are for Never Hinged items.

No. C2 Surcharged in Carmine

‡

18 Juin 1940

+10^{Fr.}

1947, June 18			Perf. 13
CB1	AP1	10fr +10fr deep blue	.70 .60

7th anniv. of Gen. Charles de Gaulle's speech in London, June 18, 1940.

No. C1 Surcharged in Blue

‡
18 JUIN 1940
+10 ^{Fr.}

1948, June 18		
CB2	AP1	5fr +10fr red	.70 .60

8th anniv. of Gen. Charles de Gaulle's speech in London, June 18, 1940.

Monument, Clock Tower and Plane — SPAP1

1949, Nov. 10		Engr.	Unwmk.
CB3	SPAP1	15fr +20fr dk brn	3.50 3.50

25th anniv. of Algeria's 1st postage stamps.

POSTAGE DUE STAMPS

D1   D2

		Perf. 14x13½		
1926-27		Typo.	Unwmk.	
J1	D1	5c light blue	.15	.15
J2	D1	10c dk brn	.15	.15
J3	D1	20c olive grn	.15	.15
J4	D1	25c car rose	.35	.35
J5	D1	30c rose red	.15	.15
J6	D1	45c blue grn	.50	.50
J7	D1	50c brn vio	.15	.15
J8	D1	60c green ('27)	1.25	.30
J9	D1	1fr red brn, straw	.15	.15
J10	D1	2fr lil rose ('27)	.15	.15
J11	D1	3fr deep blue ('27)	.15	.15
		Set value	3.00	1.90

See Nos. J25-J26, J28-J32. For surcharges, see Nos. J18-J20.

1926-27				
J12	D2	1c olive grn	.15	.15
J13	D2	10c violet	.40	.20
J14	D2	30c bister	.25	.20
J15	D2	60c dull red	.20	.20
J16	D2	1fr brt vio ('27)	11.00	1.75
J17	D2	2fr lt bl ('27)	7.50	.65
		Nos. J12-J17 (6)	19.50	3.15

See note below France No. J51.
For surcharges, see Nos. J21-J24.

Stamps of 1926 Surcharged

1927				
J18	D1	60c on 20c olive grn	.90	.25
J19	D1	2fr on 45c blue grn	1.10	.65
J20	D1	3fr on 25c car rose	.75	.25
		Nos. J18-J20 (3)	2.75	1.15

Recouvrement Stamps of 1926
Surcharged

10^c

1927-32				
J21	D2	10c on 30c bis ('32)	2.25	1.50
J22	D2	1fr on 1c olive grn	.65	.60
J23	D2	1fr on 60c dl red ('32)	11.00	.22
J24	D2	2fr on 10c violet	6.25	6.25
		Nos. J21-J24 (4)	20.15	8.57

Catalogue values for unused stamps in this section, from this point to the end of the section, are for Never Hinged items.

Type of 1926, Without "R F"

1942		Typo.	Perf. 14x13½	
J25	D1	30c dark red	.15	.15
J26	D1	2fr magenta	.18	.18
		Set value	.23	.23

Type of 1926 Surcharged in Red

T 0.50

1944			Perf. 14x13½	
J27	A2	50c on 20c yel grn	.15	.15
a.		Inverted surcharge	3.50	
b.		Double surcharge	9.50	

No. J27 was issued precanceled only. See note after No. 32.

	Type of 1926		
1944		Litho.	Perf. 12
J28	D1	1.50fr brt rose lilac	.28 .22
J29	D1	2fr greenish blue	.28 .22
J30	D1	5fr rose carmine	.28 .22
		Nos. J28-J30 (3)	.84 .66

	Type of 1926		
1947		Typo.	Perf. 14x13½
J32	D1	5fr green	.60 .45

France Nos. J80-J81 Overprinted Type "a"
of 1925 in Carmine or Black

1947			
J33	D5	10c sepia (C)	.15 .15
J34	D5	30c bright red violet	.15 .15
		Set value	.24 .20

D3

1947-55		Unwmk. Engr.	Perf. 14x13
J35	D3	20c red	.15 .15
J36	D3	60c olive	.22 .20
J37	D3	1fr dk org brn	.15 .15
J38	D3	1.50fr dull green	.40 .38
J39	D3	2fr red	.15 .15
J40	D3	3fr violet	.15 .15
J41	D3	5fr ultra ('49)	.15 .15
J42	D3	6fr black	.20 .18
J43	D3	10fr lil rose	.20 .15
J44	D3	15fr ol grn ('55)	.45 .45
J45	D3	20fr brt grn	.22 .15
J46	D3	30fr red org ('55)	.40 .38
J47	D3	50fr indigo ('51)	.95 .95
J48	D3	100fr brt bl ('53)	4.00 3.50
		Nos. J35-J48 (14)	7.79 7.09

Independent State
France Nos. J93-J97 Overprinted "EA" in
Black like Nos. 286-290

		Perf. 14x13½	
1962, July 2		Typo.	Unwmk.
		Handstamped Overprint	
J49	D6	5c bright pink	2.25 1.60
J50	D6	10c red orange	2.25 1.40
J51	D6	20c olive bister	2.25 1.40
J52	D6	50c dark green	3.00 2.75
J53	D6	1fr deep green	4.25 4.00
		Nos. J49-J53 (5)	14.00 11.15

		Typographed Overprint	
J49a	D6	5c bright pink	6.00 6.00
J50a	D6	10c red orange	6.00 6.00
J51a	D6	20c olive bister	5.50 5.50
J52a	D6	50c dark green	14.00 14.00
J53a	D6	1fr deep green	25.00 25.00
		Nos. J49a-J53a (5)	56.50 56.50

See note after No. 290.

Scales — D4   Grain — D5

1963, June 25			Perf. 14x13½
J54	D4	5c car rose & blk	.15 .15
J55	D4	10c olive & car	.15 .15
J56	D4	20c ultra & blk	.18 .15
J57	D4	50c bister brn & grn	.50 .28
J58	D4	1fr lilac & org	.85 .50
		Nos. J54-J58 (5)	1.83
		Set value	.95

#J58 Surcharged with New Value & 3 Bars

1968, Mar. 28		Typo.	Perf. 14x13½
J59	D4	60c on 1fr lilac & org	.40 .28

1972-93		Litho.	Perf. 13½x14
J60	D5	10c bister	.15 .15
J61	D5	20c deep brown	.15 .15
J62	D5	40c orange	.20 .15
J63	D5	50c dk vio blue	.22 .15
J64	D5	80c dk olive gray	.38 .15
J65	D5	1d green	.42 .15
J66	D5	2d blue	.95 .42
J67	D5	3d violet	.45 .22
J68	D5	4d lilac rose	.58 .28
		Nos. J60-J68 (9)	3.50
		Set value	1.50

Issued: 3d, 4d, 1/21/93; others, 10/21/72.

NEWSPAPER STAMPS

$\frac{1}{2}$ centime

Nos. 1 and 33
Surcharged in Red

1924-26		Unwmk.	Perf. 14x13½
P1	A16	½c on 1c dk gray	.15 .15
a.		Triple surcharge	87.50
P2	A1	½c on 1c olive ('26)	.15 .15
		Set value	.19 .19

ALLENSTEIN

'a–lən–,shtin

LOCATION — In East Prussia
AREA — 4,457 sq. mi.
POP. — 540,000 (estimated 1920)
CAPITAL — Allenstein

Allenstein, a district of East Prussia, held a plebiscite in 1920 under the Versailles Treaty, voting to join Germany rather than Poland. Later that year, Allenstein became part of the German Republic.

100 Pfennig = 1 Mark

PLÉBISCITE

Stamps of Germany, 1906-20, Overprinted **OLSZTYN ALLENSTEIN**

		Perf. 14, 14½, 14x14½, 14½x14		
1920			Wmk. 125	
1	A16	5pf green	.15	.15
2	A16	10pf carmine	.15	.15
3	A22	15pf dk vio	.15	.15
4	A22	15pf vio brn	6.50	6.50
5	A16	20pf bl vio	.15	.15
6	A16	30pf org & blk, buff	.40	.25
7	A16	40pf lake & blk	.30	.20
8	A16	50pf pur & blk, buff	.30	.20
9	A16	75pf grn & blk	.30	.20
10	A17	1m car rose	.85	.65
a.		Double overprint	375.00	600.00
11	A17	1.25m green	.70	.55
a.		Double overprint	475.00	1,000.
12	A17	1.50m yel brn	.70	.55
13	A21	2.50m lilac rose	.85	1.40
14	A19	3m blk vio	1.75	1.75
a.		Double overprint	350.00	925.00
b.		Inverted overprint	375.00	600.00
		Nos. 1-14 (14)	13.25	12.85

Overprinted

15	A16	5pf green	.15	.25
16	A16	10pf carmine	.15	.25
17	A22	15pf dark vio	.15	.15
18	A22	15pf vio brn	30.00	30.00
19	A16	20pf blue vio	.15	.15
20	A16	30pf org & blk, buff	.40	.35
21	A16	40pf lake & blk	.40	.35
22	A16	50pf pur & blk, buff	.15	.15
23	A16	75pf grn & blk	.15	.15
24	A17	1m car rose	.75	.75
a.		Inverted overprint	550.00	750.00
25	A17	1.25m green	.70	.70
26	A17	1.50m yel brn	.70	.70
27	A21	2.50m lilac rose	1.50	2.50
28	A19	3m blk vio	1.25	1.25
a.		Inverted overprint	350.00	550.00
b.		Double overprint	325.00	550.00
		Nos. 15-28 (14)	36.60	37.70

The 40pf carmine rose (Germany No. 124) exists with this oval overprint, but it is doubtful whether it was regularly issued. Value $250.

ANDORRA

an-'dôr-ə

LOCATION — On the southern slope of the Pyrenees Mountains between France and Spain.
GOVT. — Co-principality
AREA — 179 sq. mi.
POP. — 26,500 (1976)
CAPITAL — Andorre-la-Vieille

Andorra is subject to the joint control of France and the Spanish Bishop of Urgel and pays annual tribute to both. The country has no monetary unit of its own, the peseta and franc both being in general use.

100 Centimos = 1 Peseta
100 Centimes = 1 Franc

Catalogue values for unused stamps in the Spanish Administration for this country are for Never Hinged items, beginning with Scott 50 in the regular postage section and Scott C2 in the airpost section; for the French Administration of this country, Never Hinged items begin at Scott 78 for regular postage, Scott B1 for the semi-postal section, Scott C1 for the airpost section, and Scott J21 for the postage due section.

SPANISH ADMINISTRATION

:-: CORREOS :-:

Stamps of Spain, 1922-26, Overprinted in Red or Black   ANDORRA

Perf. 14, 13½x12½, 12½x11½
1928   Unwmk.
Control Numbers on Back
1	A49	2c olive green	.35	.20
2	A49	5c car rose (Bk)	.45	.25
3	A49	10c green	.45	.30
4	A49	15c slate blue	2.25	2.00
5	A49	20c violet	2.25	2.00
6	A49	25c rose red (Bk)	2.25	2.00
7	A49	30c black brown	10.00	6.75
8	A49	40c deep blue	10.00	4.75
9	A49	50c orange (Bk)	10.00	6.75
10	A49a	1p blue blk	12.00	10.00
11	A49a	4p lake (Bk)	85.00	70.00
12	A49a	10p brown (Bk)	140.00	100.00
		Nos. 1-12 (12)	275.00	205.00

Counterfeit overprints exist.

La Vall
A1

St. Julia de Loria — A3

St. Juan de Caselles A2

St. Coloma — A4

General Council — A5

1929, Nov. 25   Engr.   Perf. 14
13	A1	2c olive green	1.00	.50

Control Numbers on Back
14	A2	5c carmine lake	2.00	1.25
15	A3	10c yellow green	2.00	2.00
16	A4	15c slate green	2.00	2.00
17	A3	20c violet	2.00	2.00
18	A4	25c carmine rose	6.00	6.00
19	A1	30c olive brown	65.00	60.00
20	A2	40c dark blue	5.00	3.00

21	A3	50c deep orange	5.00	4.00
22	A5	1p slate	12.00	12.00
23	A5	4p deep rose	65.00	60.00
24	A5	10p bister brown	65.00	65.00
		Nos. 13-24 (12)	232.00	217.75

Nos. 13-24, 26, 28, 32 exist imperforate.

1931-38
Perf. 11½
13a	A1	2c	4.00	1.50
Control Numbers on Back
14a	A2	5c	7.00	6.00
15a	A3	10c	7.00	3.50
16a	A4	15c	20.00	14.00
17a	A3	20c	10.00	8.00
18a	A4	25c	6.00	4.50
19a	A1	30c ('33)	85.00	60.00
20a	A2	40c ('35)	10.00	7.50
22a	A5	1p ('38)	25.00	16.00
b.		Control number omitted		1,400.

Without Control Numbers
1936-43   Perf. 11½x11
25	A1	2c red brown ('37)	2.50	1.00
26	A2	5c dark brown	2.50	1.00
27	A3	10c blue green	10.00	4.50
a.		10c yellow green	80.00	65.00
28	A4	15c green ('37)	6.25	4.00
29	A3	20c violet	8.00	4.00
30	A4	25c deep rose ('37)	4.00	2.00
31	A1	30c carmine	4.00	2.75
31A	A2	40c dark blue	600.00	400.00
32	A1	45c rose red ('37)	4.00	2.00
33	A3	50c deep orange	8.75	4.00
34	A1	60c buff ('37)	6.00	4.00
35	A5	4p deep rose ('43)	40.00	30.00
36	A5	10p bister brn ('43)	50.00	45.00
		Nos. 25-36 (13)	746.00	504.25

Edelweiss — A6

Coat of Arms — A8

Chapel of Meritxell A10

Provost — A7

Plaza of Ordino — A9

Map A11

1948-53 Unwmk. Photo.   Perf. 12½
37	A6	2c dark olive grn ('51)	.40	.70
38	A6	5c deep orange ('53)	.40	.70
39	A6	10c deep blue ('53)	.45	.70

Engr.   Perf. 9½x10
40	A7	20c brown vio	6.50	3.00
41	A7	25c org, perf. 12½ ('53)	4.75	2.25
42	A9	30c dk slate grn	8.50	3.50
43	A9	50c deep green	10.00	5.00
44	A10	75c dark blue	15.00	5.00
45	A9	90c dp car rose	6.50	4.00
46	A10	1p brt orange ver	10.00	5.00
47	A8	1.35p dk blue vio	6.50	6.00

Perf. 10
48	A11	4p ultra ('53)	10.00	10.00
49	A11	10p dk violet brn ('51)	21.00	10.00
		Nos. 37-49 (13)	100.00	55.85

Catalogue values for unused stamps in this section, from this point to the end of the section, are for Never Hinged items.

Andorra, Spanish Administration, stamps can be mounted in the Scott annual Spain and Spanish Andorra supplement.

Bridge of St. Anthony — A12

Madonna of Meritxell, 8th Century — A13

Designs: 70c, Aynos pasture. 1p, View of Canillo. 2p, St. Coloma. 2.50p, Arms of Andorra. 3p, Old Andorra, horiz. 5p, View of Ordino, horiz.

1963-64   Unwmk.   Engr.   Perf. 13
50	A12	25c dk gray & sepia	.20	.15
51	A12	70c dk sl grn & brn blk	.20	.15
52	A12	1p slate & dull pur	.30	.15
53	A12	2p violet & dull pur	.30	.15
54	A12	2.50p rose claret	.80	.60
55	A12	3p blk & grnsh gray	1.40	.60
56	A12	5p dk brn & choc	2.00	1.10
57	A13	6p sepia & car	3.00	1.10
		Nos. 50-57 (8)	8.20	4.00

Issued: 25c-2p, 7/20/63; 2.50p-6p, 2/29/64.

Narcissus — A14

Encamp Valley — A15

1966, June 10   Engr.   Perf. 13
58	A14	50c shown	.20	.15
59	A14	1p Pinks	.20	.15
60	A14	5p Jonquils	1.10	.55
61	A14	10p Helleboe	2.50	.65
		Nos. 58-61 (4)	4.00	1.50

Common Design Types pictured following the introduction.

Europa Issue 1972
Common Design Type
1972, May 2   Photo.   Perf. 13
Size: 25½x38mm
62	CD15	8p multicolored	125.00	80.00

1972, July 4   Photo.   Perf. 13
Tourist publicity: 1.50p, Massana (village). 2p, Skiing on De La Casa Pass. 5p, Pessons Lake, horiz.
63	A15	1p multicolored	.20	.15
64	A15	1.50p multicolored	.70	.55
65	A15	2p multicolored	1.75	.55
66	A15	5p multicolored	2.25	.90
		Nos. 63-66 (4)	4.90	2.15

Butterfly Stroke — A16

Design: 2p, Volleyball, vert.
1972, Oct.   Photo.   Perf. 13
67	A16	2p lt blue & multi	.20	.15
68	A16	5p multicolored	.30	.20

20th Olympic Games, Munich, Aug. 26-Sept. 11.

St. Anthony Singers A17

1972, Dec. 5   Photo.   Perf. 13
69	A17	1p shown	.15	.15
70	A17	1.50p Les Caramelles (boys' choir)	.15	.15
71	A17	2p Nativity scene	.15	.15
72	A17	5p Man holding giant cigar, vert	.50	.15

73	A17	8p Hermit of Meritxell, vert	.70	.35
74	A17	15p Marratxa dancers	1.65	.50
		Nos. 69-74 (6)	3.30	
		Set value		1.10

Andorran customs. No. 71 is for Christmas.

Europa Issue 1973
Common Design Type and

Symbol of Unity — A18

1973, Apr. 30   Photo.   Perf. 13
75	A18	2p ultra, red & blk	.20	.15
Size: 37x25mm
76	CD16	8p tan, red & blk	.70	.30

Nativity — A19

Virgin of Ordino — A20

Christmas: 5p, Adoration of the Kings. Designs are from altar panels of Meritxell Parish Church.

1973, Dec. 14   Photo.   Perf. 13
77	A19	2p multicolored	.15	.15
78	A19	5p multicolored	.65	.40

1974, Apr. 29   Photo.   Perf. 13
Europa: 8p, Les Banyes Cross.
79	A20	2p multicolored	1.10	.40
80	A20	8p slate & brt blue	3.50	1.10

Cupboard — A21

Crowns of Virgin and Child of Roser — A22

1974, July 30   Photo.   Perf. 13
81	A21	10p multicolored	1.65	.50
82	A22	25p dark red & multi	4.00	1.65

UPU Monument, Bern — A23

1974, Oct. 9   Photo.   Perf. 13
83	A23	15p multicolored	1.25	.55
Centenary of Universal Postal Union.

Nativity A24

Christmas: 5p, Adoration of the Kings.

1974, Dec. 4   Photo.   Perf. 13
84	A24	2p multicolored	.50	.20
85	A24	5p multicolored	1.75	.45

Mail Delivery, Andorra, 19th Century — A25

12th Century Painting, Ordino Church — A26

1975, Apr. 4 Photo. Perf. 13
86 A25 3p multicolored .30 .15

Espana 75 International Philatelic Exhibition, Madrid, Apr. 4-13.

1975, Apr. 28 Photo. Perf. 13

Design: 12p, Christ in Glory, 12th century Romanesque painting, Ordino church.
87 A26 3p multicolored 1.25 .35
88 A26 12p multicolored 2.25 .60

Urgel Cathedral and Document — A27

1975, Oct. 4 Photo. Perf. 13
89 A27 7p multicolored .90 .50

Millennium of consecration of Urgel Cathedral, and Literary Festival 1975.

Nativity, Ordino A28

Christmas: 7p, Adoration of the Kings, Ordino.

1975, Dec. 3 Photo. Perf. 13
90 A28 3p multicolored .20 .15
91 A28 7p multicolored .40 .25

Caldron and CEPT Emblem — A29

Slalom and Montreal Olympic Emblem — A30

Europa: 12p, Chest and CEPT emblem, horiz.

1976, May 3 Photo. Perf. 13
92 A29 3p bister & multi .20 .15
93 A29 12p yellow & multi .60 .15

1976, July 9 Photo. Perf. 13

Design: 15p, One-man canoe and Montreal Olympic emblem, horiz.
94 A30 7p multicolored .20 .15
95 A30 15p multicolored .40 .25

21st Olympic Games, Montreal, Canada, July 17-Aug. 1.

Nativity A31

Christmas: 25p, Adoration of the Kings. Wall paintings in La Massana Church.

1976, Dec. 7 Photo. Perf. 13
96 A31 3p multicolored .15 .15
97 A31 25p multicolored .40 .25

View of Ansalonge A32

Europa: 12p, Xuclar, valley, mountains.

1977, May 2 Litho. Perf. 13
98 A32 3p multicolored .15 .15
99 A32 12p multicolored .45 .25

Cross of Terme — A33

Map of Post Offices — A34

Christmas: 12p, Church of St. Miguel d'Engolasters.

1977, Dec. 2 Photo. Perf. 13x12½
100 A33 5p multicolored .30 .25
101 A33 12p multicolored .70 .50

Souvenir Sheet

Designs: 10p, Mail delivery. 20p, Post Office, 1928. 25p, Andorran coat of arms.

1978, Mar. 31 Photo. Perf. 13x13½
102 Sheet of 4 .85 .85
a. A34 5p multicolored .15 .15
b. A34 10p multicolored .15 .15
c. A34 20p multicolored .25 .25
d. A34 25p multicolored .30 .30

Spanish postal service in Andorra, 50th anniv.

La Vall — A35

Europa: 12p, St. Juan de Caselles.

1978, May 2 Perf. 13
103 A35 5p multicolored .15 .15
104 A35 12p multicolored .25 .15
Set value .35 .20

Crown, Bishop's Mitre and Staff — A36

1978, Sept. 24 Photo. Perf. 13
105 A36 5p brown, car & yel .35 .15

700th anniversary of the signing of treaty establishing Co-Principality of Andorra.

Holy Family — A37

Young Woman — A38

Christmas: 25p, Adoration of the Kings. Both designs after frescoes in the Church of St. Mary d'Encamp.

1978, Dec. 5 Photo. Perf. 13
106 A37 5p multicolored .15 .15
107 A37 25p multicolored .35 .20
Set value .45 .25

1979, Feb. 14 Photo. Perf. 13

Designs: 5p, Young man. 12p, Bridegroom and bride riding mule.
108 A38 3p multicolored .15 .15
109 A38 5p multicolored .15 .15
110 A38 12p multicolored .20 .15
Set value .35 .25

Old Mail Truck A39

Europa: 12p, Stampless covers of 1846 & 1854.

1979, Apr. 30 Engr. Perf. 13
111 A39 5p yel grn & dk blue .15 .15
112 A39 12p dk red & violet .25 .15
Set value .35 .20

Children Holding Hands A40

1979, Oct. 18 Photo. Perf. 13
113 A40 19p multicolored .35 .20

International Year of the Child.

St. Coloma's Church — A41

Christmas: 25p, Agnus Dei roundel, St. Coloma's Church.

1979, Nov. 28 Photo. Perf. 13½
114 A41 8p multicolored .15 .15
115 A41 25p multicolored .35 .25
Set value .30

Bishop Pere d'Arg A42

Bishops of Urgel: 5p, Josep Caixal. 13p, Joan Benlloch.

1979, Dec. 27 Engr.
116 A42 1p dk blue & brown .15 .15
117 A42 5p rose lake & purple .15 .15
118 A42 13p brown & dk green .20 .15
Set value .35 .25

See Nos. 132-133, 159, 175, C4.

Antoni Fiter, Magistrate — A43

Europa: 19p, Francesc Cairat, magistrate.

1980, Apr. 28 Photo. Perf. 13x13½
119 A43 8p bister, blk & brn .15 .15
120 A43 19p lt green & blk .30 .20

Boxing, Moscow '80 Emblem A44

1980, July 23 Photo. Perf. 13½x13
121 A44 5p Downhill skiing .15 .15
122 A44 8p shown .15 .15
123 A44 50p Target shooting .70 .50
Nos. 121-123 (3) 1.00
Set value .70

12th Winter Olympic Games, Lake Placid, NY, Feb. 12-24 (5p); 22nd Summer Olympic Games, Moscow, July 19-Aug. 3.

Nativity A45

1980, Dec. 12 Litho. Perf. 13
124 A45 10p Nativity, vert. .15 .15
125 A45 22p shown .35 .20

Christmas 1980.

Children Dancing at Santa Anna Feast — A46

Europa: 30p, Going to church on Aplec de la Verge de Canolich Day.

1981, May 7 Photo. Perf. 13
126 A46 12p multicolored .15 .15
127 A46 30p multicolored .40 .25

50th Anniv. of Police Force — A47

1981, July 2 Photo. Perf. 13½x13
128 A47 30p multicolored .40 .20

Intl. Year of the Disabled A48

1981, Oct. 8 Photo. Perf. 13½
129 A48 50p multicolored .65 .30

Christmas 1981 — A49

Designs: Encamp Church retable.

1981, Dec. 3   Photo.   *Perf. 13½*
130 A49 12p Nativity   .15 .15
131 A49 30p Adoration   .40 .20

Bishops of Urgel Type of 1979

1981, Dec. 12   Engr.   *Perf. 13½*
132 A42 7p Salvador Casanas   .15 .15
133 A42 20p Josep de Boltas   .30 .15
         Set value   .20

Natl. Arms — A51

1982, Feb. 17   Photo.   *Perf. 13x13½*
134 A51 1p bright pink   .15 .15
135 A51 3p bister brown   .15 .15
136 A51 7p red orange   .15 .15
137 A51 12p lake   .15 .15
138 A51 15p ultra   .20 .15
139 A51 20p blue green   .25 .15
140 A51 30p crimson rose   .35 .15

Perf. 13½x12½
1982, Sept. 30   Engr.
Size: 25½x30½mm
141 A51 50p dark green   .80 .20
142 A51 100p dark blue   1.65 .50
         Nos. 134-142 (9)   3.85
         Set value, #134-142   .90

For type A51 without "PTA" see #192-198.

Europa
1982 — A52

1982, May 12   Photo.   *Perf. 13*
143 A52 14p New Reforms, 1866, vert. .20 .15
144 A52 33p Reform of Institutions,
         1981   .45 .25

1982 World Cup — A53

Designs: Various soccer players.

1982, June 13   Photo.   *Perf. 13x13½*
145 A53 14p multicolored   .45 .45
146 A53 33p multicolored   1.00 1.00
   a. Pair, #145-146 + label   1.50 1.50

A54   A55

Anniversaries: 9p, Permanent Spanish and
French delegations, cent. 14p, 50th anniv. of
Andorran stamps. 23p, St. Francis of Assisi (1182-
1226). 33p, Anyos Pro-Vicarial District membership
centenary (Relacio sobre la Vall de Andorra
titlepage).

1982, Sept. 7   Engr.   *Perf. 13*
147 A54 9p dk blue & brown   .15 .15
148 A54 14p black & green   .50 .20
149 A54 23p dk blue & brown   .30 .15
150 A54 33p black & olive grn   .60 .45
         Nos. 147-150 (4)   1.55
         Set value   .80

Perf. 13x13½, 13½x13
1982, Dec. 9   Photo.
Christmas: 14p, Madonna and Child, Andorra la
Vieille Church, vert. 33p, El Tio de Nadal (children
in traditional costumes striking hollow tree).
151 A55 14p multicolored   .20 .15
152 A55 33p multicolored   .45 .25

Europa
1983
A56

1983, June 7   Photo.   *Perf. 13*
153 A56 16p La Cortinada Church, ar-
         chitect, 12th cent.   .20 .15
154 A56 38p Water mill, 16th cent.   .55 .40

Local
Mushrooms — A57

1983, July 20   Photo.   *Perf. 13x12½*
155 A57 16p Lactarius sanguifluus   1.25 .50
See Nos. 165, 169, 172.

Universal
Suffrage,
50th Anniv.
A58

Photogravure and Engraved
1983, Sept. 6   *Perf. 13*
156 A58 10p multicolored   .15 .15

Visit of
Monsignor
Jacinto
Verdaguer
Bishop and
Co-Prince
A59

1983, Sept. 6
157 A59 50p multicolored   .80 .45

Christmas
1983 — A60

Saint Cerni de Nagol, Romanesque fresco,
Church of San Cerni de Nagol.

1983, Nov. 24   Photo.   *Perf. 13½*
158 A60 16p multicolored   .30 .15

Bishops of Urgel Type of 1979

1983, Dec. 7   Engr.   *Perf. 13*
159 A42 26p Joan J. Laguarda Fenollera .35 .20

1984 Winter
Olympics
A62

1984, Feb. 17   Litho.   *Perf. 13½x14*
160 A62 16p Ski jumping   .35 .15

Espana
'84 — A63

1984, Apr. 27   Photo.   *Perf. 13*
161 A63 26p Emblems   .35 .15

Europa
(1959-84)
A64

1984, May 5   Engr.
162 A64 16p brown   .25 .15
163 A64 38p blue   .60 .35

1984
Summer
Olympics
A65

1984, Aug. 9   Litho.   *Perf. 13½x14*
164 A65 40p Running   .60 .35

Mushroom Type of 1983

1984, Sept. 27   Photo.   *Perf. 13x12½*
165 A57 11p Morchella esculenta   10.00 1.50

Christmas
1984 — A66

1984, Dec. 6   Photo.   *Perf. 13½*
166 A66 17p Nativity carving   .30 .15

Europa
1985
A67

18p, Mossen Enric Arfany, composer, natl. hymn
score. 45p, Musician Playing Viol, Romanesque
fresco detail, La Cortinada Church, vert.

1985, May 3   Engr.   *Perf. 13½*
167 A67 18p dk vio, grn & choc   .25 .15
168 A67 45p green & choc   .75 .25

Mushroom Type of 1983

Perf. 13½x12½
1985, Sept. 19   Photo.
169 A57 30p Gyromitra esculenta   .50 .25

Pal Village — A68 17 PTA

1985, Nov. 7   Engr.   *Perf. 13½*
170 A68 17p brt ultra & dk blue   .30 .15

Christmas
1985 — A69

Fresco: Angels Playing Trumpet and Psaltery, St.
Bartholomew Chapel.

1985, Dec. 11   Photo.   *Perf. 13½x13*
171 A69 17p multicolored   .30 .15

Mushroom Type of 1983

Perf. 13½x12½
1986, Apr. 10   Photo.
172 A57 30p Marasmius oreades   .50 .25

Europa 1986 — A70

1986, May 5   Engr.   *Perf. 13*
173 A70 17p Water   .25 .15
174 A70 45p Soil and air   .70 .25

Bishops of Urgel Type of 1979

1986, Sept. 11   Engr.   *Perf. 13½*
175 A42 35p Justi Guitart   .50 .20

A72   A73

Santa Roma de Les Bons Church bell.

1986, Dec. 11   Litho.   *Perf. 14*
176 A72 19p multicolored   .30 .15
Christmas.

1987, Mar. 27   Photo.   *Perf. 14*
Contemporary Natl. Coat of Arms.
177 A73 48p multicolored   .70 .40
Visit of the co-princes: the Bishop of Urgel and
president of France, September 26, 1986.

Europa
1987
A74

Modern architecture: 19p, Meritxell Sanctuary
interior. 48p, Sanctuary exterior, vert.

1987, May 15   Engr.   *Perf. 14x13½*
178 A74 19p dark blue & brown   .25 .15
179 A74 48p dark blue & brown   .70 .25

Souvenir Sheet

1992
Summer
Olympics,
Barcelona
A75

20p, House of the Valleys. 50p, Bell tower,
Chapel of the Archangel Michael, and torch-bearer.

1987, July 20   Photo.   *Perf. 14*
180   Sheet of 2   4.00 4.00
   a. A75 20p multicolored   1.10 1.10
   b. A75 50p multicolored   2.75 2.75

Local Mushrooms — A76

1987, Sept. 11   *Perf. 13¹/₂x12¹/₂*
181 A76 100p Boletus edulis   1.40 .60

Christmas A77

Design: Detail from a Catalan manuscript, De Nativitat, by R. Llull.

1987, Nov. 18   Litho.   *Perf. 14*
182 A77 20p multicolored   .30 .15

Lance and Arrowhead (Bronze Age) — A78

1988, Mar. 25   Photo.   *Perf. 14*
183 A78 50p multicolored   .75 .30

Europa 1988 — A79   Pyrenean Mastiff — A80

Transport and communications: 20p, Les Bons, a medieval road. 45p, Trader and pack mules, early 20th cent.

1988, May 5   Engr.   *Perf. 14x13¹/₂*
184 A79 20p dark blue & dark red   .25 .15
185 A79 45p dark blue & dark red   .60 .25

1988, July 26   Litho.   *Perf. 14x13¹/₂*
186 A80 20p multicolored   .30 .15

Bishop of Urgel and Seigneur of Caboet Confirming Co-Principality, 700th Anniv. — A81

1988, Oct. 24   Litho.   *Perf. 14x13¹/₂*
187 A81 20p gold, blk & int blue   .30 .15

Christmas 1988 A82

1988, Nov. 30   Litho.   *Perf. 14x13¹/₂*
188 A82 20p multicolored   .30 .15

Arms Type of 1982 Without "PTA"

1988, Dec. 2   Photo.   *Perf. 13x13¹/₂*
192 A51 20p brt blue green   .30 .15

Size: 25x30¹/₂mm
Perf. 13¹/₂x12¹/₂
Engr.

194 A51   50p grnsh black   .75 .30
196 A51   100p dark blue   1.50 .50
198 A51   500p dark brown   7.75 2.50
    Nos. 192-198 (4)   10.30 3.45

This is an expanding set. Numbers will change if necessary.

Europa 1989 A83

1989, May 8   *Perf. 14x13¹/₂, 13¹/₂x14*
    Litho. & Engr.
200 A83 20p Leapfrog, vert.   .30 .15
201 A83 45p Tug of war   .60 .25

Santa Roma Church, Les Bons — A84

1989, June 20   *Perf. 13¹/₂x14*
    Litho. & Engr.
202 A84 50p blk, dp blue & grn blue   .65 .25

Anniv. Emblem — A85   Christmas — A86

1989, Oct. 26   Litho.   *Perf. 14x13¹/₂*
203 A85 20p multicolored   .30 .15

Intl. Red Cross and Red Crescent societies, 125th annivs.; Year for the Protection of Human Life.

1989, Dec. 1
204 A86 20p *The Immaculate Conception*   .30 .15

Europa 1990 A87

Post offices.

1990, May 17   *Perf. 13¹/₂x14, 14x13¹/₂*
                 Photo.
205 A87 20p shown   .30 .15
206 A87 50p Post office, vert.   .70 .30

Gomphidius Rutilus — A88

1990, June 21   Litho.   *Perf. 13x13¹/₂*
207 A88 45p multicolored   .70 .35

Plandolit House — A89   Christmas — A90

1990, Oct. 17   *Perf. 13x12¹/₂*
    Litho. & Engr.
208 A89 20p brown & org yel   .35 .15

1990, Nov. 26   Litho.   *Perf. 14x13¹/₂*
209 A90 25p lake, brn & bister   .40 .20

4th Games of the Small European States A91

1991, Apr. 29   Photo.   *Perf. 13¹/₂x14*
210 A91 25p Discus   .40 .20
211 A91 45p High jump, runner   .75 .35

Europa — A92

1991, May 10   *Perf. 14x13¹/₂, 13¹/₂x14*
                 Litho.
212 A92 25p Olympus-1 satellite   .45 .20
213 A92 55p Olympus-1, horiz.   .95 .45

A93   Christmas — A94

1991, Sept. 20   Litho.   *Perf. 13x12¹/₂*
214 A93 45p Macrolepiota Procera   .70 .35

1991, Nov. 29   Photo.   *Perf. 14x13¹/₂*
215 A94 25p multicolored   .40 .20

Woman Carrying Water Pails — A95

1992, Feb. 14   Photo.   *Perf. 13¹/₂x14*
216 A95 25p multicolored   .40 .20

Discovery of America, 500th Anniv. A96

1992, May 8   *Perf. 14x13¹/₂, 13¹/₂x14*
                 Photo.
217 A96 27p Santa Maria, vert.   .50 .20
218 A96 45p King Ferdinand   .80 .35

            Europa.

1992 Summer Olympics, Barcelona A97

1992, July 22   Photo.   *Perf. 13¹/₂x14*
219 A97 27p Kayak   .65 .30

Nativity Scene, by Fra Angelico — A98

1992, Nov. 18   Photo.   *Perf. 14*
220 A98 27p multicolored   .50 .20

Natl. Automobile Museum A99

1992, Sept. 10   *Perf. 13¹/₂x14*
    Litho. & Engr.
221 A99 27p 1894 Benz   .50 .30

Cantharellus Cibarius A100

1993, Mar. 25   Photo.   *Perf. 13¹/₂x14*
222 A100 28p multicolored   .65 .30

Contemporary Paintings — A101

Europa: 28p, Upatream, by John Alan Morrison. 45p, Rhythm, by Angel Calvente, vert.

1993, May 20   *Perf. 13¹/₂x14, 14x13¹/₂*
                 Litho.
223 A101 28p multicolored   .65 .30
224 A101 45p multicolored   1.10 .50

A102   A103

1993, Sept. 23   Litho.   *Perf. 14*
225 A102 28p multicolored   .70 .30

Art and Literature Society, 25th anniv.

Perf. 14x13¹/₂
1993, Nov. 25   Litho. & Engr.
226 A103 28p Christmas   .70 .30

Souvenir Sheet

Constitution, 1st Anniv. — A104

1994, Mar. 14   Photo.   Perf. 14
227 A104 29p multicolored   .75 .75

Sir Alexander
Fleming
(1881-1955),
Co-discoverer
of Penicillin
A105

1994, May 6   Photo.   Perf. 13¹/₂x14
228 A105 29p Portrait   .75 .75
229 A105 55p AIDS virus   1.50 1.50

Europa.

Hygrophorus
Gliocyclus
A106

1994, Sept. 27   Photo.   Perf. 14
230 A106 29p multicolored   .75 .75

Christmas — A107

1994, Nov. 29 Photo. Perf. 14x13¹/₂
231 A107 29p multicolored   .75 .75

Nature
Conservation
in Europe
A108

1995, Mar. 23   Photo.   Perf. 14
232 A108 30p Farm in valley   .80 .80
233 A108 60p Stone fence, valley   1.65 1.65

Europa
A109

1995, May 8   Photo.   Perf. 14
234 A109 60p multicolored   1.65 1.65

Christmas — A110

1995, Nov. 8   Photo.   Perf. 14
235 A110 30p Flight to Egypt   .80 .80

Entrance
Into Council
of Europe
A111

1995, Nov. 10
236 A111 30p multicolored   .80 .80

Mushrooms
A112

1996, Apr. 30   Photo.   Perf. 14
237 A112 30p Ramaria aurea   .80 .80
238 A112 60p Tuber melanosporum   1.65 1.65

Europa.

Isabelle Sandy (1884-
1975), Writer — A113

1996, May 7
239 A113 60p brown & violet   1.75 1.75

Europa.

Intl. Museum
Day — A114

Design: Antique coal-heated iron.

1996, Sept. 12   Photo.   Perf. 14
240 A114 60p multicolored   .95 .95

Christmas
A115

The Annunciation, by Andrew Martin, 1753, St.
Eulalia d'Encamp Church.

1996, Nov. 26   Photo.   Perf. 14
241 A115 30p multicolored   .45 .45

Museums of
Andorra
A116

Early bicycles designed by: 32p, Karl Drais,
1818. 65p, Pierre Michaux, 1861.

1997, Apr. 28   Photo.   Perf. 14
242 A116 32p multicolored   .45 .45
243 A116 65p multicolored   .90 .90

A117   UNESCO — A118

Europa (Stories and Legends): Hikers watching
family of bears crossing over river on fallen tree.

1997, May 6   Photo.   Perf. 14
244 A117 65p multicolored   .90 .90

1997, Sept. 30   Photo.   Perf. 14
245 A118 32p multicolored   .45 .45

Christmas — A119

1997, Nov. 25   Photo.   Perf. 14
246 A119 32p multicolored   .45 .45

AIR POST STAMPS

AP1

Unwmk.
1951, June 27   Engr.   Perf. 11
C1 AP1 1p dark violet brown   22.50 5.00

> Catalogue values for unused
> stamps in this section, from this
> point to the end of the section, are
> for Never Hinged items.

AP2   AP3

Litho. & Engr.
1983, Oct. 20   Perf. 13
C2 AP2 20p brown & bis brn   .30 .20

Jaime Sansa Nequi, Episcopal Church official.

1984, Oct. 25   Photo.   Perf. 13
C3 AP3 20p multicolored   .35 .25

Pyrenees Art Center.

Bishops of Urgel Type of 1979

1985, June 13   Engr.   Perf. 13¹/₂
C4 A42 20p Ramon Iglesias   .35 .20

SPECIAL DELIVERY STAMPS

Special Delivery Stamp of Spain, 1905
Overprinted
CORREOS

ANDORRA

1928   Unwmk.   Perf. 14
Without Control Number on Back
E1 SD1 20c red   62.50 65.00
With Control Number on Back
E2 SD1 20c pale red   45.00 50.00

Eagle over   Arms and
Mountain   Squirrel — SD3
Pass — SD2

1929   Perf. 14
With Control Number on Back
E3 SD2 20c scarlet   20.00 20.00
  a. Perf. 11¹/₂   300.00

1937   Perf. 11¹/₂x11
Without Control Number on Back
E4 SD2 20c red   7.50 6.50

1949 Unwmk. Engr. Perf. 10x9¹/₂
E5 SD3 25c red   4.00 4.00

FRENCH ADMINISTRATION

Stamps and Types of
France, 1900-1929,   **ANDORRE**
Overprinted

Perf. 14x13¹/₂
1931, June 16   Unwmk.
1 A16   1c gray   .55   .55
  a. Double overprint   950.00 950.00
2 A16   2c red brown   .60   .60
3 A16   3c orange   .60   .60
4 A16   5c green   1.00 1.00
5 A16   10c lilac   1.50 1.50
6 A22   15c red brown   3.00 3.00
7 A22   20c red violet   4.00 4.00
8 A22   25c yellow brn   4.00 4.00
9 A22   30c green   4.00 4.00
10 A22   40c ultra   6.75 6.75
11 A20   45c lt violet   7.25 7.25
12 A20   50c vermilion   6.25 6.25
13 A20   65c gray green   10.00 10.00
14 A20   75c rose lilac   13.00 13.00
15 A22   90c red   17.50 17.50
16 A20   1fr dull blue   18.00 18.00
17 A22   1.50fr light blue   25.00 25.00

Overprinted   **ANDORRE**

18 A18 2fr org & pale bl   17.00 17.00
19 A18 3fr brt vio & rose   60.00 60.00
20 A18 5fr dk bl & buff   100.00 100.00
21 A18 10fr grn & red   175.00 175.00
22 A18 20fr mag & grn   250.00 250.00
  Nos. 1-22 (22)   725.00 725.00

See No. P1 for ¹/₂c on 1c gray.
Nos. 9, 15 and 17 were not issued in France
without overprint.

Chapel of
Meritxell
A50

Bridge of St.
Anthony
A51

St. Miguel
d'Engolasters
A52

Gorge of St.
Julia
A53

Old
Andorra — A54

1932-43   Engr.   Perf. 13

23	A50	1c gray blk	.30	.25
24	A50	2c violet	.40	.40
25	A50	3c brown	.30	.30
26	A50	5c blue green	.40	.40
27	A51	10c dull lilac	.65	.60
28	A51	15c deep red	1.00	1.00
29	A51	20c lt rose	6.25	4.50
30	A51	25c brown	2.25	2.25
31	A51	25c brn car ('37)	4.50	6.50
32	A51	30c emerald	1.75	1.50
33	A51	40c ultra	5.00	4.25
34	A51	40c brn blk ('39)	.65	.60
35	A51	45c lt red	6.00	5.00
36	A51	45c bl grn ('39)	3.00	2.50
37	A52	50c lilac rose	6.50	5.00
38	A51	50c lt vio ('39)	3.00	2.50
38A	A51	50c grn ('40)	1.40	1.40
39	A51	55c lt vio ('38)	9.50	6.00
40	A51	60c yel brn ('38)	.60	.50
41	A52	65c yel grn	35.00	35.00
42	A51	65c blue ('38)	6.50	5.50
43	A51	70c red ('39)	1.30	1.00
44	A52	75c violet	3.25	2.50
45	A51	75c ultra ('39)	2.50	2.25
46	A51	80c green ('38)	13.00	9.50
46A	A53	80c bl grn ('40)	.25	.30
47	A53	90c deep rose	3.25	2.25
48	A53	90c dk grn ('39)	2.25	2.25
49	A53	1fr blue grn	9.50	6.00
50	A53	1fr scarlet ('38)	15.00	15.00
51	A53	1fr dp ultra ('39)	.25	.25
51A	A53	1.20fr brt vio ('42)	.25	.25
52	A50	1.25fr rose car ('33)	35.00	25.00
52A	A53	1.25fr rose ('38)	3.00	1.40
52B	A53	1.30fr sepia ('40)	.25	.25
53	A54	1.50fr ultra	8.25	7.50
53A	A53	1.50fr crim ('40)	.25	.25
54	A53	1.75fr violet ('33)	80.00	80.00
55	A53	1.75fr dk bl ('38)	30.00	22.50
56	A53	2fr red violet	3.75	3.50
56A	A50	2fr rose red ('40)	1.00	.65
56B	A50	2fr dk grn ('42)	.25	.20
57	A50	2.15fr dk vio ('38)	40.00	27.50
58	A50	2.25fr ultra ('39)	4.00	3.00
58A	A50	2.40fr red ('42)	.25	.20
59	A50	2.50fr gray blk ('39)	4.00	3.00
59A	A50	2.50fr dp ultra ('40)	1.30	1.25
60	A53	3fr orange brn	3.75	3.50
60A	A50	3fr red brn ('40)	.30	.25
60B	A50	4fr sl bl ('42)	.30	.25
60C	A50	4.50fr dp vio ('42)	.75	.75
61	A54	5fr brown	.40	.35
62	A54	10fr violet	.45	.40
62B	A54	15fr dp ultra ('42)	.50	.40
63	A54	20fr rose lake	.50	.40
63A	A51	50fr turq bl ('43)	1.00	.50
		Nos. 23-63A (56)	365.00	310.50

A 20c ultra exists. Value $12,500.

No. 37 Surcharged with Bars and New Value in Black

1935, Sept. 25

64	A52	20c on 50c lil rose	13.00	11.00
a.		Double surcharge	*2,000.*	

Coat of Arms
A55   A56

1936-42   Perf. 14x13

65	A55	1c black ('37)	.15	.15
66	A55	2c blue	.15	.15
67	A55	3c brown	.15	.15
68	A55	5c rose lilac	.15	.15
69	A55	10c ultra ('37)	.15	.15
70	A55	15c red violet	.55	.55
71	A55	20c emerald ('37)	.15	.15
72A	A55	30c cop red ('38)	.30	.30
72A	A55	30c blk brn ('42)	.15	.15
73	A55	35c Prus grn ('38)	30.00	30.00
74	A55	40c cop red ('42)	.15	.15
75	A55	50c Prus grn ('42)	.15	.15

76	A55	60c turq bl ('42)	.15	.15
77	A55	70c vio ('42)	.15	.15
		Nos. 65-77 (14)	32.50	32.50

> Catalogue values for unused stamps in this section, from this point to the end of the section, are for Never Hinged items.

1944

78	A56	10c violet	.15	.15
79	A56	30c deep magenta	.15	.15
80	A56	40c dull blue	.15	.15
81	A56	50c orange red	.15	.15
82	A56	60c black	.15	.15
83	A56	70c brt red violet	.15	.15
84	A56	80c blue green	.15	.15
		Set value	.60	.60

See No. 114.

St. Jean de
Caselles
A57

La Maison des
Vallees — A58

Old Andorra
A59

Provost
A60

1944-47   Perf. 13

85	A57	1fr brown violet	.30	.15
86	A57	1.20fr blue	.15	.15
87	A57	1.50fr red	.30	.15
88	A57	2fr dk blue grn	.15	.15
89	A58	2.40fr rose red	.25	.20
90	A58	2.50fr rose red ('46)	4.00	1.40
91	A58	3fr sepia	.15	.15
92	A58	4fr ultra	.30	.15
93	A59	4.50fr brown blk	.30	.15
94	A59	4.50fr dk bl grn ('47)	6.50	3.50
95	A59	5fr ultra	.25	.20
96	A59	5fr Prus grn ('46)	.50	.30
97	A59	6fr rose car ('45)	.35	.15
98	A59	10fr Prus green	.15	.15
99	A59	10fr ultra ('46)	.25	.15
100	A60	15fr rose lilac	.60	.25
101	A60	20fr deep blue	.65	.45
102	A60	25fr lt rose red ('46)	4.00	2.25
103	A60	40fr dk green ('46)	4.00	3.00
104	A60	50fr sepia	1.90	1.10
		Nos. 85-104 (20)	25.05	14.15

1948-49

105	A58	4fr lt blue grn	.70	.70
106	A59	6fr violet brn	.35	.35
107	A59	8fr indigo	1.00	1.00
108	A59	12fr bright red	.75	.75
109	A59	12fr blue grn ('49)	.85	.75
110	A59	15fr crimson ('49)	.45	.45
111	A60	18fr deep blue	2.50	1.50
112	A60	20fr dark violet	2.00	1.65
113	A60	25fr ultra ('49)	1.40	1.10
		Nos. 105-113 (9)	10.00	8.25

1949-51   Perf. 14x13, 13

114	A56	1fr deep blue	.75	.55
115	A57	3fr red ('51)	4.50	4.00
116	A57	4fr sepia	2.00	2.00
117	A58	5fr emerald	2.25	2.25
118	A58	5fr purple ('51)	4.50	4.50
119	A58	6fr blue grn ('51)	3.50	3.25
120	A58	8fr brown	1.00	.70
121	A59	15fr blk brn ('51)	5.00	4.00
122	A59	18fr rose red ('51)	13.00	7.00
123	A60	30fr ultra ('51)	20.00	7.00
		Nos. 114-123 (10)	56.50	35.25

Les Escaldres Spa — A61

St. Coloma
Belfry — A62

Designs: 15fr-25fr, Gothic cross. 30fr-75fr, Village of Les Bons.

1955-58   Unwmk.   Engr.   Perf. 13

124	A61	1fr dk gray bl	.18	.15
125	A61	2fr dp green	.18	.15
126	A61	3fr red	.18	.15
127	A61	5fr chocolate	.18	.15
128	A62	6fr dk bl grn	.45	.38
129	A62	8fr rose brown	.45	.45
130	A62	10fr brt violet	.70	.55
131	A62	12fr indigo	.75	.60
132	A61	15fr red	1.00	.85
133	A61	18fr blue grn	1.00	.85
134	A61	20fr dp purple	1.65	1.50
135	A61	25fr sepia	2.00	1.50
136	A62	30fr deep blue	24.00	16.00
137	A62	35fr Prus bl ('57)	9.00	6.75
138	A62	40fr dk green	25.00	18.00
139	A62	50fr cerise	3.00	2.25
140	A62	65fr purple ('58)	8.50	5.75
141	A62	70fr chestnut ('57)	6.00	5.75
142	A62	75fr violet blue	40.00	32.50
		Nos. 124-142 (19)	124.22	94.28

Issued: 35fr, 70fr, 8/19; 65fr, 2/10; others, 2/15.

Coat of
Arms — A63

Gothic Cross,
Meritxell — A64

Designs: 65c, 85c, 1fr, Pond of Engolasters.

1961, June 19   Typo.   Perf. 14x13

143	A63	5c brt green & blk	.15	.15
144	A63	10c red, pink & blk	.15	.15
145	A63	15c blue & black	.15	.15
146	A63	20c yellow & brown	.20	.20

		Engr. Perf. 13		
147	A64	25c violet, bl & grn	.25	.25
148	A64	30c mar, ol grn & brn	.30	.30
149	A64	45c indigo, bl & grn	13.00	6.50
150	A64	50c pur, lt brn & ol grn	1.00	1.00
151	A64	65c bl, ol & brn	17.50	14.00
152	A64	85c rose lil, vio bl & brn	17.50	14.00
153	A64	1fr grnsh bl, ind & brn	1.00	1.00
		Nos. 143-153 (11)	51.20	37.70

See Nos. 161-166A.

Imperforates

Most stamps of Andorra, French Administration, from 1961 onward exist imperforate in issued and trial colors, and also in small presentation sheets in issued colors.

Telstar and Globe Showing Andover and Pleumeur-Bodou — A65

1962, Sept. 29   Engr.

154	A65	50c ultra & purple	1.35	1.35

1st television connection of the US and Europe through the Telstar satellite, July 11-12.

"La Sardane"
A66

Charlemagne Crossing Andorra — A67

1fr, Louis le Debonnaire giving founding charter.

1963, June 22   Unwmk.   Perf. 13

155	A66	20c lil rose, cl & ol grn	3.50	3.50
156	A67	50c sl grn & dk car rose	6.00	6.00
157	A67	1fr red brn, ultra & dk grn	9.50	9.50
		Nos. 155-157 (3)	19.00	19.00

Old Andorra Church and Champs-Elysées Palace — A68

1964, Jan. 20   Engr.

158	A68	25c blk, grn & vio brn	1.20	.75

"PHILATEC," Intl. Philatelic and Postal Techniques Exhib., Paris, June 5-21, 1964.

Bishop of Urgel and Seigneur of Caboet Confirming Co-Principality, 1288 — A69

Design: 60c, Napoleon re-establishing Co-principality, 1806.

1964, Apr. 25   Engr.   Perf. 13

159	A69	60c dk brn, red brn & sl grn	12.50	12.50
160	A69	1fr brt bl, org brn & blk	12.50	12.50

Arms Type of 1961

1964, May 16   Typo.   Perf. 14x13

161	A63	1c dk blue & gray	.15	.15
162	A63	2c black & orange	.15	.15
163	A63	12c purple, emer & yel	.30	.30
164	A63	18c black, lil & pink	.30	.30
		Set value	.75	.75

Scenic Type of 1961

Designs: 40c, 45c, Gothic Cross, Meritxell. 60c, 90c, Pond of Engolasters.

1965-71   Engr.   Perf. 13

165	A64	40c dk brn, org brn & sl grn	.50	.50
165A	A64	45c vio bl, ol bis & slate	1.00	.75
166	A64	60c org brn & dk brn	.60	.60
166A	A64	90c ultra, bl grn & bister	.50	.50
		Nos. 165-166A (4)	2.60	2.35

Issued: 40c, 60c, Apr. 24, 1965. 45c, June 13, 1970. 90c, Aug. 28, 1971.

> Andorra, French Administration, stamps can be mounted in the Scott annual Monaco and French Andorra supplement.

Syncom Satellite over
Pleumeur-Bodou
Station — A70

Andorra House,
Paris — A71

1965, May 17   **Unwmk.**
167 A70 60c dp car, lil & bl   4.00 3.25
Cent. of the ITU.

1965, June 5
168 A71 25c dk bl, org brn & ol gray   .90 .75

Ski Lift — A72

Design: 25c, Chair lift, vert.

1966, Apr. 2   **Engr.**   **Perf. 13**
169 A72 25c brt bl, grn & dk brn   1.00 .80
170 A72 40c mag, brt ultra & sep   1.40 1.25
Winter sports in Andorra.

FR-1 Satellite — A73

1966, May 7   **Perf. 13**
171 A73 60c brt bl, grn & dk grn   1.50 1.50
Issued to commemorate the launching of the scientific satellite FR-1, Dec. 6, 1965.

Europa Issue, 1966
Common Design Type

1966, Sept. 24   **Engr.**   **Perf. 13**
Size: 21 1/2x35 1/2mm
172 CD9 60c brown   3.00 2.25

Folk Dancers,
Sculpture by
Josep Viladomat
A74

Telephone
Encircling the
Globe
A75

1967, Apr. 29   **Engr.**   **Perf. 13**
173 A74 30c ol grn, dp grn & slate   .60 .45
Cent. (in 1966) of the New Reform, which reaf-
firmed and strengthened political freedom in
Andorra.

Europa Issue, 1967
Common Design Type

1967, Apr. 29
Size: 22x36mm
174 CD10 30c bluish blk & lt bl   1.75 1.50
175 CD10 60c dk red & brt pink   2.75 2.00

1967, Apr. 29
176 A75 60c dk car, vio & blk   1.25 1.00
Automatic telephone service.

Injured Father
at
Home — A76

1967, Sept. 23   **Engr.**   **Perf. 13**
177 A76 2.30fr ocher, dk red brn &
    brn red   8.00 4.50
Introduction of Social Security System.

Jesus in
Garden of
Gethsemane
A77

Designs (from 16th century frescoes in La Maison des Vallees): 30c, The Kiss of Judas. 60c, The
Descent from the Cross (Pieta).

1967, Sept. 23
178 A77 25c black & red brn   .50 .40
179 A77 30c purple & red lilac   .75 .50
180 A77 60c indigo & Prus blue   1.40 .90
    Nos. 178-180 (3)   2.65 1.80
See Nos. 185-187.

Downhill Skier — A78

1968, Jan. 27   **Engr.**   **Perf. 13**
181 A78 40c org, ver & red lil   .75 .60
10th Winter Olympic Games, Grenoble, France,
Feb. 6-18.

Europa Issue, 1968
Common Design Type

1968, Apr. 27   **Engr.**   **Perf. 13**
Size: 36x22mm
182 CD11 30c gray & brt bl   5.00 3.00
183 CD11 60c brown & lilac   7.50 3.75

High
Jump — A79

1968, Oct. 12   **Engr.**   **Perf. 13**
184 A79 40c brt blue & brn   1.20 1.00
19th Olympic Games, Mexico City, Oct. 12-27.

Fresco Type of 1967

Designs (from 16th century frescoes in La Mai-
son des Vallees): 25c, The Scourging of Christ. 30c,
Christ Carrying the Cross. 60c, The Crucifixion.
(All horiz.)

1968, Oct. 12
185 A77 25c dk grn & gray grn   .60 .60
186 A77 30c dk brown & lilac   1.00 1.00
187 A77 60c dk car & vio brn   1.40 1.40
    Nos. 185-187 (3)   3.00 3.00

Europa Issue, 1969
Common Design Type

1969, Apr. 26   **Engr.**   **Perf. 13**
188 CD12 40c rose car, gray & dl bl   6.00 2.50
189 CD12 70c indigo, dl red & ol   9.00 5.00
10th anniv. of the Conf. of European Postal and
Telecommunications Administrations.

Kayak on Isère
River
A80

Drops of Water
and Diamond
A80a

1969, Aug. 2   **Engr.**   **Perf. 13**
190 A80 70c dk sl grn, ultra & ind   2.25 2.25
Intl. Canoe & Kayak Championships, Bourg-Saint-
Maurice, Savoy, July 31-Aug. 6.

1969, Sept. 27   **Engr.**   **Perf. 13**
191 A80a 70c blk, dp ultra & grnsh
    bl   4.50 4.50
European Water Charter.

St. John, the
Woman and
the
Dragon — A81

The Revelation (From the Altar of St. John, Caselles): 40c, St. John Hearing Voice from Heaven on
Patmos. 70c, St. John and the Seven Candlesticks.

1969, Oct. 18
192 A81 30c brn, dp pur & brn red   .65 .65
193 A81 40c gray, dk brn & brn ol   1.00 1.00
194 A81 70c dk red, maroon & brt
    rose lilac   1.75 1.75
    Nos. 192-194 (3)   3.40 3.40
See Nos. 199-201, 207-209, 214-216.

Field
Ball — A82

Shot Put — A83

1970, Feb. 21   **Engr.**   **Perf. 13**
195 A82 80c multi   1.75 1.25
Issued to publicize the 7th International Field
Ball Games, France, Feb. 26-Mar. 8.

Europa Issue, 1970
Common Design Type

1970, May 2   **Engr.**   **Perf. 13**
Size: 36x22mm
196 CD13 40c orange   4.00 2.00
197 CD13 80c violet blue   8.00 4.00

1970, Sept. 11   **Engr.**   **Perf. 13**
198 A83 80c bl & dk brn   1.25 1.00
1st European Junior Athletic Championships,
Colombes, France, Sept. 11-13.

Altar Type of 1969

The Revelation (from the Altar of St. John, Caselles): 30c, St. John recording angel's message. 40c,
Angel erecting column symbolizing faithful in
heaven. 80c, St. John's trial in kettle of boiling oil.

1970, Oct. 24
199 A81 30c dp car, dk brn & brt
    pur   .75 .75
200 A81 40c violet & slate grn   .90 .90
201 A81 80c ol, dk bl & car rose   1.75 1.75
    Nos. 199-201 (3)   3.40 3.40

Ice Skating
A84

1971, Feb. 20   **Engr.**   **Perf. 13**
202 A84 80c dk red, red lil & pur   2.25 1.50
World Figure Skating Championships, Lyons,
France, Feb. 23-28.

Capercaillie — A85

Nature protection: No. 204, Brown bear.

1971, Apr. 24   **Photo.**   **Perf. 13**
203 A85 80c multicolored   3.25 2.25
           Engr.
204 A85 80c blue, grn & brn   3.25 2.25

Europa Issue, 1971
Common Design Type

1971, May 8   **Engr.**   **Perf. 13**
Size: 35 1/2x22mm
205 CD14 50c rose red   5.50 3.00
206 CD14 60c lt blue green   8.50 4.00

Altar Type of 1969

The Revelation (from the Altar of St. John, Casel-
les): 30c, St. John preaching, Rev. 1:3. 50c, "The
Sign of the Beast . . ." Rev. 16:1-2. 90c, The
Woman, Rev. 17:1.

1971, Sept. 18
207 A81 30c dl grn, ol & brt grn   .75 .75
208 A81 50c rose car, org & ol brn   1.00 1.00
209 A81 90c blk, dk pur & bl   1.60 1.60
    Nos. 207-209 (3)   3.35 3.35

Europa Issue 1972
Common Design Type

1972, Apr. 29   **Photo.**   **Perf. 13**
Size: 21 1/2x37mm
210 CD15 50c brt mag & multi   5.00 3.00
211 CD15 90c multicolored   7.00 4.50

Golden
Eagle — A86

1972, May 27   **Engr.**
212 A86 60c dk grn, ol & plum   3.50 2.00
Nature protection.

Shooting
A87

1972, July 8   **Engr.**
213 A87 1fr dk purple   1.75 1.40
20th Olympic Games, Munich, Aug. 26-Sept. 11.

Altar Type of 1969

The Revelation (from the Altar of St. John, Caselles): 30c, St. John, bishop and servant. 50c, Resurrection of Lazarus. 90c, Angel with lance and nails.

1972, Sept. 16   **Engr.**   **Perf. 13**
214 A81 30c dk ol, gray & red lil   .75 .75
215 A81 50c vio blue & slate   1.10 1.10
216 A81 90c dk Prus bl & sl grn   1.75 1.75
    Nos. 214-216 (3)   3.60 3.60

De Gaulle as Coprince
of Andorra — A88

90c, De Gaulle in front of Maison des Vallées.

1972, Oct. 23   Engr.   Perf. 13
217 A88 50c violet blue   1.25 1.25
218 A88 90c dk carmine   1.75 1.75
 a. Pair, #217-218 + label   3.00 3.00
Visit of Charles de Gaulle to Andorra, 5th anniv.
See Nos. 399-400.

Europa Issue 1973
Common Design Type
1973, Apr. 28   Photo.   Perf. 13
Size: 36x22mm
219 CD16 50c violet & multi   5.50 2.75
220 CD16 90c dk red & multi   8.50 3.00

Virgin of
Canolich
A89

1973, June 16   Engr.   Perf. 13
221 A89 1fr ol, Prus bl & vio   1.65 1.65

Lily — A90   Blue Titmouse — A91

Designs: 45c, Iris. 50c, Columbine. 65c,
Tobacco. No. 226, Pinks. No. 227, Narcissuses.

1973-74   Photo.   Perf. 13
222 A90 30c car rose & multi   .40   .40
223 A90 45c yel grn & multi   .25   .25
224 A90 50c buff & multi   1.40 1.40
225 A90 65c gray & multi   .40   .40
226 A90 90c ultra & multi   .85   .85
227 A90 90c grnsh bl & multi   .75   .75
   Nos. 222-227 (6)   4.05 4.05

See Nos. 238-240.

1973-74   Photo.   Perf. 13
Nature protection: 60c, Citril finch and mistletoe. 80c, Eurasian bullfinch. 1fr, Lesser spotted
woodpecker.
228 A91 60c buff & multi   3.25 3.00
229 A91 80c gray & multi   2.25 2.00
230 A91 90c gray & multi   2.25 2.00
231 A91 1fr yel grn & multi   2.25 2.00
   Nos. 228-231 (4)   10.00 9.00

Europa Issue 1974

Virgin of Pal — A92

Design: 90c, Virgin of Santa Coloma. Statues are
polychrome 12th century carvings by rural artists.

1974, Apr. 27   Engr.   Perf. 13
232 A92 50c multicolored   5.00 3.75
233 A92 90c multicolored   10.00 5.00

Arms of Andorra   Mail Box, Chutes
and Cahors   and Globe — A94
Bridge — A93

1974, Aug. 24   Engr.   Perf. 13
234 A93 1fr blue, vio & org   1.00   .60
First anniversary of meeting of the co-princes of
Andorra: Pres. Georges Pompidou of France and
Msgr. Juan Marti Alanis, Bishop of Urgel.

1974, Oct. 5   Engr.   Perf. 13
235 A94 1.20fr multi   1.25 1.10
Centenary of Universal Postal Union.

Coronation of St. Marti, 16th
Century — A95

Europa: 80c, Crucifixion, 16th cent., vert.

Perf. 11½x13, 13x11½
1975, Apr. 26   Photo.
236 A95 80c gold & multi   4.25 3.00
237 A95 1.20fr gold & multi   5.75 3.50

Flower Type of 1973

Designs: 60c, Gentian. 80c, Anemone. 1.20fr,
Autumn crocus.

1975, May 10   Photo.   Perf. 13
238 A90 60c olive & multi   .35   .35
239 A90 80c brt rose & multi   .75   .75
240 A90 1.20fr green & multi   .80   .80
   Nos. 238-240 (3)   1.90 1.90

Abstract Design — A96

1975, June 7   Engr.   Perf. 13
241 A96 2fr bl, magenta & emer   1.75 1.75
ARPHILA 75 International Philatelic Exhibition,
Paris, June 6-16.

A97   A98

1975, Aug. 23   Engr.   Perf. 13
242 A97 80c violet bl & blk   .80   .80
Georges Pompidou (1911-74), pres. of France
and co-prince of Andorra (1969-74).

1975, Nov. 8   Engr.   Perf. 13
243 A98 1.20c Costume, IWY Em-
        blem   1.25 1.00
International Women's Year.

Skier and
Snowflake
A99

1976, Jan. 31   Engr.   Perf. 13
244 A99 1.20fr multicolored   1.25 1.00
12th Winter Olympic Games, Innsbruck, Austria,
Feb. 4-15.

Telephone and
Satellite — A100

1976, Mar. 20   Engr.   Perf. 13
245 A100 1fr multicolored   .80   .80
Centenary of first telephone call by Alexander
Graham Bell, Mar. 10, 1976.

Catalan
Forge — A101

Europa: 1.20fr, Lacemaker.

1976, May 8   Engr.   Perf. 13
246 A101 80c multi   1.50 1.10
247 A101 1.20fr multi   2.50 1.65

Thomas   Trapshooting
Jefferson   A103
A102

1976, July 3   Engr.   Perf. 13
248 A102 1.20fr multi   1.10   .90
American Bicentennial.

1976, July 17   Engr.   Perf. 13
249 A103 2fr multi   1.75 1.25
21st Olympic Games, Montreal, Canada, July 17-
Aug. 1.

Meritxell Sanctuary and Old
Chapel — A104

1976, Sept. 4   Engr.   Perf. 13
250 A104 1fr multi   1.00   .80
Dedication of rebuilt Meritxell Church, Sept. 8,
1976.

Apollo — A105   Ermine — A106

Design: 1.40fr, Morio butterfly.

1976, Oct. 16   Photo.   Perf. 13
251 A105 80c black & multi   1.75 1.25
252 A105 1.40fr salmon & multi   2.25 1.65
Nature protection.

1977, Apr. 2   Photo.   Perf. 13
253 A106 1fr vio bl, gray & blk 1.50 1.50
Nature protection.

St. Jean de   Manual Digest,
Caselles   1748, Arms of
A107   Andorra
                  A108

Europa: 1.40fr, Sant Vicens Castle.

1977, Apr. 30   Engr.   Perf. 13
254 A107 1fr multi   1.75   .90
255 A107 1.40fr multi   2.25 1.40

1977, June 11   Engr.   Perf. 13
256 A108 80c grn, bl & brn   .80   .70
Establishment of Institute of Andorran Studies.

St. Romanus
of Caesarea
A109

1977, July 23   Engr.   Perf. 12½x13
257 A109 2fr multi   1.25 1.00
Design from altarpiece in Church of St. Roma de
les Bons.

General
Council
Chamber
A110

Guillem d'Arény
Plandolit — A111

1977, Sept. 24   Engr.   Perf. 13
258 A110 1.10fr multi   2.25 1.10
259 A111 2fr car & dk brn   1.50 1.10
Andorran heritage. Guillem d'Arény Plandolit
started Andorran reform movement in 1866.

Squirrel
A112

Flag and Valira River Bridge
A113

1978, Mar. 18   Engr.   *Perf. 13*
260 A112 1fr multi   .95 .55

1978, Apr. 8
261 A113 80c multi   .60 .55

Signing of the treaty establishing the Co-Principality of Andorra, 700th anniv.

Pal Church
A114

Europa: 1.40fr, Charlemagne's Castle,
Charlemagne on horseback, vert.

1978, Apr. 29   Engr.   *Perf. 13*
262 A114   1fr multi   2.00 1.65
263 A114   1.40fr multi   3.00 2.25

Virgin of Sispony
A115

1978, May 20   Engr.   *Perf. 12x13*
264 A115 2fr multi   1.25 1.00

Visura Tribunal
A116

1978, June 24   Engr.   *Perf. 13*
265 A116 1.20fr multi   .80 .50

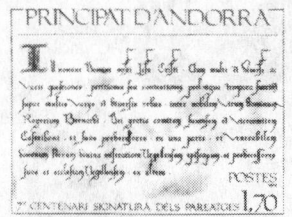

Preamble of 1278 Treaty — A117

1978, Sept. 2   Engr.   *Perf. 13x12½*
266 A117 1.70fr multi   .85 .50

700th anniversary of the signing of treaty establishing Co-Principality of Andorra.

Pyrenean Chamois
A118

White Partridges
A119

1979, Mar. 26   Engr.   *Perf. 13*
267 A118 1fr multi   .50 .35

1979, Apr. 9   Photo.   *Perf. 13*
268 A119 1.20fr multi   .75 .60

Nature protection. See Nos. 288-289.

French Mailman, 1900 — A120

Europa: 1.70fr, 1st French p.o. in Andorra.

1979, Apr. 28   Engr.   *Perf. 13*
269 A120 1.20fr multi   1.10 .90
270 A120 1.70fr multi   1.65 1.10

Falcon, Pre-Roman Painting
A121

1979, June 2   Engr.   *Perf. 12½x13*
271 A121 2fr multi   1.00 .75

A122   A123

Child with Lambs, Church, IYC emblem.

1979, July 7   Photo.   *Perf. 13*
272 A122 1.70fr multi   .80 .50

International Year of the Child.

1979, Sept. 29   Engr.   *Perf. 13*

Bas-relief, Trobada monument.

273 A123 2fr multi   1.00 .75

700th anniversary of Co-Principality of Andorra

Judo Hold — A124

Farm House, Cortinada — A125

1979, Nov. 24   Engr.   *Perf. 13*
274 A124 1.30fr multi   .80 .45

World Judo Championships, Paris, Dec. 1979.

1980, Jan. 26   Engr.   *Perf. 13*
275 A125 1.10fr multi   .50 .45

Cross-Country Skiing — A126

1980, Feb. 9
276 A126 1.80fr ultra & lil rose   1.50 .90

13th Winter Olympic Games, Lake Placid, NY, Feb. 12-24.

A128   A129

1980, Aug. 30   Engr.   *Perf. 13*
278 A128 1.20fr multi   .55 .35

World Bicycling championships.

1980, Apr. 26   Engr.   *Perf. 13*

Europa: 1.30fr, Charlemagne (742-814). 1.80fr, Napoleon I (1769-1821).

279 A129 1.30fr multi   .50 .35
280 A129 1.80fr gray grn & brn   .80 .55

Pyrenees Lily — A130

1980   Photo.
281 A130 1.10fr Dog-toothed violet   .50 .30
282 A130 1.30fr shown   .55 .35

Nature protection. Issue dates: 1.10fr, June 21, 1.30fr, May 17.

De La Vall House, 400th Anniversary of Restoration
A131

1980, Sept. 6   Engr.
283 A131 1.40fr multi   .50 .35

Angel, Church of St. Cerni de Nagol, Pre-Romanesque Fresco — A132

1980, Oct. 27   *Perf. 13x12½*
284 A132 2fr multi   1.00 .70

Bordes de Mereig Mountain Village
A133

1981, Mar. 21   Engr.   *Perf. 13*
285 A133 1.40fr bl gray & dk brn   .50 .40

Europa Issue 1981

Ball de l'Ossa, Winter Game
A134

1981, May 16   Engr.
286 A134 1.40fr shown   .65 .50
287 A134 2fr El Contrapas dance   .80 .60

Bird Type of 1979

1981, June 20   Photo.
288 A119 1.20fr Phylloscopus bonelli .60 .30
289 A119 1.40fr Tichodroma muraria   .60 .40

World Fencing Championship, Clermont-Ferrand, July 2-13 — A135

1981, July 4   Engr.
290 A135 2fr bl & blk   .70 .40

St. Martin, 12th Cent. Tapestry — A136

1981, Sept. 5   Engr.   *Perf. 12x13*
291 A136 3fr multi   1.10 .80

Intl. Drinking Water Decade
A137

Intl. Year of the Disabled
A138

1981, Oct. 17   *Perf. 13*
292 A137 1.60fr multi   .60 .40

1981, Nov. 7
293 A138 2.30fr multi   .80 .70

Europa
1982 — A139

1982, May 8 Engr. *Perf. 13*
294 A139 1.60fr Creation of Andorran
govt., 1982 .60 .40
295 A139 2.30fr Land Council, 1419 .90 .55

1982 World
Cup — A140

Designs: Various soccer players. Nos. 296-297
se-tenant with label showing natl. arms.

1982, June 12 Engr. *Perf. 13*
296 A140 1.60fr red & dk brn .60 .45
297 A140 2.60fr red & dk brn .90 .65

Souvenir Sheet

No. 52 — A141

1982, Aug. 21 Engr.
298 A141 5fr blk & rose car 1.60 1.60
1st Andorran Stamp Exhib., Aug. 21-Sept. 19.

Horse, Roman Wall Painting — A142

1982, Sept. 4 Photo. *Perf. 13x12½*
299 A142 3fr multi 1.10 .90

Wild
Cat — A143

1982, Oct. 9 Engr. *Perf. 13*
300 A143 1.80fr shown .90 .50
301 A143 2.60fr Pine trees 1.00 .65

TB Bacillus   St. Thomas Aquinas
Centenary   (1225-74)
A144   A145

1982, Nov. 13
302 A144 2.10fr Koch, lungs .75 .60

1982, Dec. 4
303 A145 2fr multi .80 .60

Manned
Flight
Bicentenary
A146

1983, Feb. 26 Engr.
304 A146 2fr multi .75 .60

Nature
Protection
A147

1983, Apr. 16 Engr. *Perf. 13*
305 A147 1fr Birch trees .40 .20
306 A147 1.50fr Trout .60 .40
See Nos. 325-326.

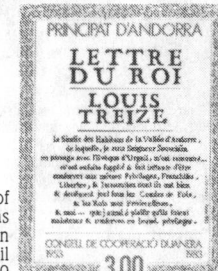

Europa
1983 — A148

Catalane Gold Works.

1983, May 7 Engr. *Perf. 13*
307 A148 1.80fr Exterior .70 .45
308 A148 2.60fr Interior .90 .60

30th Anniv. of
Customs
Cooperation
Council
A149

1983, May 14
309 A149 3fr Letter of King Louis XIII 1.25 .80

First Arms of
Valleys of
Andorra
A150

1983, Sept. 3 Engr. *Perf. 13*
310 A150 5c olive grn & red .15 .15
311 A150 10c grn & olive grn .15 .15
312 A150 20c brt pur & red .15 .15
313 A150 30c brn vio & red .15 .15
314 A150 40c dk bl & ultra .15 .15
315 A150 50c gray & red .15 .15
316 A150 1fr deep magenta .30 .20
317 A150 2fr org red & red brn .75 .35
318 A150 5fr dk brn & red 1.40 .85
Set value 2.90 1.65
See Nos. 329-335, 380-385, 464-465.

Painting,
Cortinada
Church
A151

1983, Sept. 24 *Perf. 12x13*
319 A151 4fr multi 1.50 1.00

Plandolit House — A152

1983, Oct. 15 Photo. *Perf. 13*
320 A152 1.60fr dp ultra & brn .50 .35

1984 Winter
Olympics
A153

1984, Feb. 18 Engr.
321 A153 2.80fr multicolored 1.00 .70

Pyrenees
Region Work
Community
(Labor
Org.) — A154

1984, Apr. 28 Engr. *Perf. 13*
322 A154 3fr brt blue & sepia 1.00 .65

Europa (1959-
84)
A155

1984, May 5 Engr.
323 A155 2fr brt grn 1.00 .50
324 A155 2.80fr rose car 1.25 .75

Nature Protection Type of 1983

1984, July 7 Engr. *Perf. 13*
325 A147 1.70fr Chestnut tree .65 .40
326 A147 2.10fr Walnut tree .80 .50

Pyrenees Art
Center
A155a

1984, Sept. 7 Engr.
327 A155a 3fr multi 1.10 .80

Romanesque
Fresco,
Church of St.
Cerni de
Nagol
A156

1984, Nov. 17 *Perf. 12x13*
328 A156 5fr multi 1.75 1.25

First Arms Type of 1983

1984-87 *Perf. 13*
329 A150 1.90fr emerald .65 .15
330 A150 2.20fr red orange .75 .15
a. Bklt. pane, 2 #329, 6 #330 6.25
331 A150 3fr bl grn & red brn .75 .45
332 A150 4fr brt org & brn 1.15 .85
333 A150 10fr brn org & blk 2.50 1.50
334 A150 15fr grn & dk grn 4.25 3.25
335 A150 20fr brt bl & red brn 5.25 3.00
Nos. 329-335 (7) 15.30 9.35

Nos. 329-330 issued in booklets only.
Issued: 3fr, 20fr, 12/1/84; 10fr, 2/9/85; 4fr,
15fr, 4/19/86; 1.90fr, 2.20fr, 3/28/87.

Saint Julia
Valley
A157

1985, Apr. 13 Engr.
336 A157 2fr multi .80 .45

Europa   Intl. Youth
1985 — A158   Year — A159

1985, May 4 Engr.
337 A158 2.10fr Le Val D'Andorre .95 .55
338 A158 3fr Instruments 1.40 .75

1985, June 8 Engr.
339 A159 3fr multi .90 .60

Wildlife
Conservation
A160

1985, Aug. 3 Photo.
340 A160 1.80fr Anas platyrhynchos .65 .40
341 A160 2.20fr Carduelis carduelis .85 .45

Two Saints,
Medieval
Fresco in St.
Cerni de
Nagol Church
A161

1985, Sept. 14 Engr. *Perf. 12½x13*
342 A161 5fr multi 1.50 1.10

Postal Museum
Inauguration — A162

1986, Mar. 22 Engr. *Perf. 13*
343 A162 2.20fr like No. 269 .80 .15

Europa 1986
A163

1986, May 3 Engr. *Perf. 13*
344 A163 2.20fr Ansalonga .90 .35
345 A163 3.20fr Isard 1.50 .50

1986 World Cup Soccer
Championships,
Mexico — A164

1986, June 14
346 A164 3fr multi   .85 .15

Angonella
Lake — A165

1986, June 28
347 A165 2.20fr multi   .65 .15

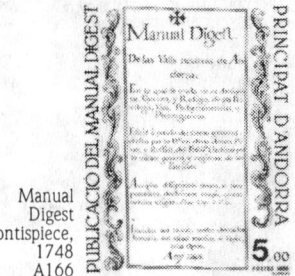

Manual
Digest
Frontispiece,
1748
A166

1986, Sept. 6   **Engr.**
348 A166 5fr chnt brn, gray ol & blk 1.65 .30

Intl. Peace
Year — A167

1986, Sept. 29
349 A167 1.90fr bl gray & grnsh bl   .65 .15

A168   A169

1986, Oct. 18   Engr.   Perf. 13¹/₂x13
350 A168 1.90fr St. Vicenc D'Enclar   .80 .15

1987, Mar. 27   Litho.   Perf. 12¹/₂x13
351 A169 2.20fr Contemporary natl.
            coat of arms   1.75 .15
Visit of the French co-prince.

Europa
1987 — A170

1987, May 2   Engr.   Perf. 13
352 A170 2.20fr Meritxell Sanctuary   1.00 .30
353 A170 3.40fr Pleta D'Ordino   1.50 .50

Ransol Village — A171

1987, June 13   Photo.
354 A171 1.90fr multicolored   1.00 .15

Nature
A172

1987, July 4
355 A172 1.90fr Cavall rogenc   1.10 .15
356 A172 2.20fr Graellsia isabellae   1.40 .15

Aryalsu,
Romanesque
Painting, La
Cortinada
Church
A173

Perf. 12¹/₂x13
1987, Sept. 5   Litho. & Engr.
357 A173 5fr multi   2.00 .35

Hiker Looking
at
Map — A174

1987, Sept. 19   Engr.   Perf. 13
358 A174 2fr olive, grn & dark brn vio .80 .15

Medieval Iron
Key, La
Cortinada
A175

1987, Oct. 17   Litho.
359 A175 3fr multi   1.10 .20

Andorran Coat of
Arms — A176

Booklet Stamp
1988, Feb. 6   Engr.   Perf. 13
360 A176 2.20fr red   .80 .20
  a. Bklt. pane of 10   8.00
See Nos. 388-389B.

Shoemaker's Last from
Roc de l'Oral — A177

1988, Feb. 13   Photo.
361 A177 3fr multi   1.25 .30

Rugby — A178

1988, Mar. 19   Engr.   Perf. 13¹/₂x13
362 A178 2.20fr emer grn, Prus grn &
             brn   .95 .20

Europa   Hot Springs,
1988 — A179   Escaldes — A180

Transport and communication: 2.20fr, Broadcast
tower. 3.60fr, Computer graphics.

1988, May 2   Engr.   Perf. 13
363 A179 2.20fr multicolored   .90 .20
364 A179 3.60fr multicolored   1.40 .35

1988, May 14   Engr.
365 A180 2.20fr Prus blue, org brn &
             emer   .85 .15

Tor
D'Ansalonga
Farmhouse,
Ansalonga
Pass — A181

1988, June 13   Engr.
366 A181 2fr multi   .75 .15

Sheepdog — A182

1988, July 2   Photo.
367 A182   2fr shown   .90 .20
368 A182 2.20fr Hare   1.10 .20

Roman Fresco, 8th Cent., St. Steven's
Church, Andorre-La-Vieille — A183

1988, Sept. 3   Engr.   Perf. 13x12¹/₂
369 A183 5fr multicolored   1.75 .40

French Revolution,
Bicent. — A184

1989, Jan. 1   Litho.   Perf. 13
370 A184 2.20fr red & vio bl   .85 .15

Poble de Pal
Village
A185

1989, Mar. 4   Engr.   Perf. 13
371 A185 2.20fr indigo & lilac   .80 .15

Europa
1989 — A186

Children's games.

1989, June 9   Engr.   Perf. 13
372 A186 2.20fr Human tower   .80 .15
373 A186 3.60fr The handkerchief   1.40 .30

Red
Cross — A187

1989, May 6
374 A187 3.60fr multi   1.25 .25

Visigothic- Merovingian
Age Cincture from a
Column, St. Vicenc
D'Anclar — A188

1989, June 3   Photo.
375 A188 3fr multi   1.00 .20

Wildlife
A189

1989, Sept. 18   Engr.   Perf. 13
376 A189 2.20fr Wild boar   .90 .20
377 A189 3.60fr Newt   1.40 .40

Scene of Salome from the Retable of St.
Michael of Mosquera, Encamp — A190

1989, Oct. 16   Perf. 13x13¹/₂
378 A190 5fr multi   1.50 .30

La Margineda
Bridge
A191

1990, Feb. 26   Engr.   Perf. 13
379 A191 2.30fr multi   .80 .15
Tourism.

Arms Types of 1983 and 1988
1990-93   Engr.   Perf. 13
380 A150 2.10fr green   .80 .15
381 A150 2.20fr vermilion   1.50 .50
382 A150 2.30fr vermilion   .85 .20
383 A150 2.40fr green   .90 .30
384 A150 2.50fr vermilion   1.75 .55
385 A150 2.80fr vermilion   1.00 .30
Nos. 380-385 (6)   6.80 2.00
Booklet Stamps
Perf. 13
386 A176 2.30fr red   .85 .20
  a.   Booklet pane of 5   4.25
387 A176 2.50fr vermilion   1.70 .55
  a.   Booklet pane of 5   8.50
388 A176 2.80fr red   1.00 .30
  c.   Booklet pane of 5   5.00
Nos. 386-388 (3)   3.55 1.05
Issued: 2.20fr, #384, 10/28/91; #387,
10/21/91; 2.40fr, 2.80fr, 8/9/93; 2.10fr, 2.30fr,
1990.

Llorts Mines
A193

1990, Apr. 21   Engr.   Perf. 12½x13
390 A193 3.20fr multicolored   1.25 .25

Europa
A194

Designs: 2.30fr, Early post office. 3.20fr, Modern
post office.
1990, May 5   Perf. 13
391 A194 2.30fr blk & scar   .95 .20
392 A194 3.20fr scar & vio   1.40 .25

Otter
A195

1990, May 25   Perf. 12x13
393 A195 2.30fr Roses, vert.   .95 .20
394 A195 3.20fr shown   1.40 .25

Censer of St.
Roma of Les
Bons
A196

1990, June 25   Perf. 12½x13
395 A196 3fr multicolored   1.10 .30

Tobacco
Drying
Sheds, Les
Bons
A197

1990, Sept. 15   Engr.   Perf. 12½x13
396 A197 2.30fr multi   .85 .20

St. Coloma
(Detail)
A198

1990, Oct. 8   Perf. 12½x13
397 A198 5fr multi   2.00 .75

Coin from
Church of St.
Eulalia
d'Encamp
A199

1990, Oct. 27   Litho.   Perf. 13
398 A199 3.20fr multi   1.10 .40

De Gaulle Type of 1972 Dated 1990
1990, Oct. 23   Engr.   Perf. 13
399 A88 2.30fr vio bl   1.00 .35
400 A88 3.20fr dk car   1.40 .55
  a.   Pair, #399-400 + label   2.40 .85
Birth centenary of De Gaulle.

4th Games of the Small
European States — A200

1991, Apr. 8   Photo.   Perf. 13
401 A200 2.50fr multicolored   .90 .30

Chapel of St.
Roma Dels
Vilars — A201

1991, Mar. 9   Engr.   Perf. 13
402 A201 2.50fr multicolored   .90 .30

Europa — A202

Perf. 13x12½, 12½x13
1991, Apr. 27
403 A202 2.50fr TV satellite   .90 .30
404 A202 3.50fr Telescope, horiz.   1.25 .45

Bottles from
Tombs of St.
Vincenc
d'Enclar
A203

1991, May 11   Photo.   Perf. 13
405 A203 3.20fr multicolored   1.25 .40

Farm Animals
A204

1991, June 22   Engr.   Perf. 13
406 A204 2.50fr Sheep   .90 .30
407 A204 3.50fr Cow   1.25 .40

Petanque World Championships — A205

1991, Sept. 14   Engr.   Perf. 13
408 A205 2.50fr multicolored   .90 .30

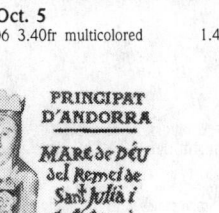

Wolfgang
Amadeus
Mozart, Death
Bicent.
A206

1991, Oct. 5
409 A206 3.40fr multicolored   1.40 .45

Virgin and
Child of St.
Julia and St.
Germa
A207

1991, Nov. 16   Engr.   Perf. 12½x13
410 A207 5fr multicolored   2.00 .65

1992 Winter Olympics,
Albertville — A208

1992, Feb. 10   Litho.   Perf. 13
411 A208 2.50fr Slalom skiing   .95 .30
412 A208 3.40fr Figure skating   1.25 .40
  a.   Pair, #411-412 + label   2.25 .70

Church of St.
Andrew of
Arinsal
A209

1992, Mar. 21   Engr.   Perf. 12x13
413 A209 2.50fr black & tan   1.10 .35

Discovery of
America,
500th Anniv.
A210

1992, Apr. 25   Perf. 13
414 A210 2.50fr Columbus' fleet   .90 .30
415 A210 3.40fr Landing in New
World   1.25 .40
Europa.

1992 Summer
Olympics,
Barcelona
A211

European
Globeflower
A212

1992, June 8   Litho.   Perf. 13
416 A211 2.50fr Kayaking   1.00 .35
417 A211 3.40fr Shooting   1.40 .45
  a.   Pair, #416-417 + label   2.40 .80

1992, July 6
Design: 3.40fr, Vulture, horiz.
418 A212 2.50fr multicolored   1.00 .35
419 A212 3.40fr multicolored   1.40 .45

Martyrdom of
St. Eulalia
A213

1992, Sept. 14   Photo.   Perf. 13
420 A213 4fr multicolored   1.65 .55

Sculpture by
Mauro
Staccioli
A214

1992, Oct. 5   Engr.   Perf. 12½x13
421 A214 5fr multicolored   2.00 .70
Ordino Arcalis '91.

Tempest in a Tea Cup, by Dennis
Oppenheim — A215

1992, Nov. 14   Engr.   Perf. 13x12½
422 A215 5fr multicolored   2.00 .70

Skiing in
Andorra — A216

Ski resorts: No. 423: a, 2.50fr, Soldeu El Tarter.
b, 3.40fr, Arinsal.
No. 424: a, 2.50fr, Pas de la Casa-Grau Roig. b,
2.50fr, Ordino Arcalis. c, 3.40fr, Pal.

1993, Mar. 13   Litho.   Perf. 13
423 A216 Pair, #a.-b. + label   2.25 .75
424 A216 Strip of 3, #a.-c.   3.25 1.00

EUROPA
SANT JULIÀ DE LÒRIA
CARLOS CRUZ-DIEZ Fisicromia per Andorra
PRINCIPAT D'ANDORRA 3.40

Sculptures — A217

Europa: 2.50fr, "Estructures Autogeneradores," by Jorge du Bon, vert. 3.40fr, Sculpture, "Fisicromia per Andorra," by Carlos Cruz-Diez.

1993, May 15　Engr.　Perf. 12¹/₂x13
425 A217 2.50fr multicolored　　1.00 .35

Litho.
Perf. 14x13¹/₂
426 A217 3.40fr multicolored　　1.40 .45

Butterflies
A218

1993, June 28　Litho.　Perf. 13
427 A218 2.50fr Polymmatus icarus　.95 .30
428 A218 4.20fr Nymphalidae　　1.50 .50

Tour de France Bicycle
Race — A219

1993, July 20　Litho.　Perf. 13
429 A219 2.50fr multicolored　　.90 .30

Andorra
School,
10th
Anniv.
A220

1993, Sept. 20　Litho.　Perf. 13
430 A220 2.80fr multicolored　　1.00 .35

Un Lloc Paga,
by Michael
Warren
A221

1993, Oct. 18　Engr.　Perf. 12¹/₂x13
431 A221 5fr blue & black　　1.75 .60

Sculpture, by
Erik Dietman
A222

1993, Nov. 8　Engr.　Perf. 12¹/₂x13
432 A222 5fr multicolored　　1.75 .60

1994 Winter
Olympics,
Lillehammer
A223

1994, Feb. 21　Litho.　Perf. 13
433 A223 3.70fr multicolored　　1.25 .45

1st Anniversary of the
Constitution — A224

Designs: 2.80fr, Monument, by Emili Armengol. 3.70fr, Stone tablet with inscription.

1994, Mar. 15　Litho.　Perf. 13
434 A224 2.80fr multicolored　　1.00 .35
435 A224 3.70fr multicolored　　1.40 .48
　a.　Pair, #434-435 + label　　2.40 .85

European
Discoveries
A225

Europa: 2.80fr, Discovery of AIDS virus. 3.70fr, Radio diffusion.

1994, May 9　Litho.　Perf. 13
436 A225 2.80fr multicolored　　1.10 .35
437 A225 3.70fr multicolored　　1.50 .50

1994 World Cup Soccer Championships,
US — A226

1994, June 20
438 A226 3.70fr multicolored　　1.50 .50

Tourist Sports — A227

#439, Mountain climbing. #440, Fishing. #441, Horseback riding. #442, Mountain biking.

1994, July 11
439 A227 2.80fr multicolored　　1.10 .35
440 A227 2.80fr multicolored　　1.10 .35
　a.　Pair, #439-440 + label　　2.20 .70

441 A227 2.80fr multicolored　　1.10 .35
442 A227 2.80fr multicolored　　1.10 .35
　a.　Pair, #441-442 + label　　2.20 .70
　　　Nos. 439-442 (4)　　4.40 1.40

Butterflies
A228

1994, Sept. 5　Litho.　Perf. 13
443 A228 2.80fr Iphiclides podalirus　1.10 .35
444 A228 4.40fr Aglais urticae　　1.75 .60

A229　　　　A230

1994, Oct. 22　Litho.　Perf. 13
445 A229 2.80fr multicolored　　1.25 .42
Meeting of the Co-Princes, 1st anniv.

1995, Feb. 27　Litho.　Perf. 13
446 A230 2.80fr multicolored　　1.25 .40
European Nature Conservation Year

1995 World Cup Rugby
Championships — A231

1995, Apr. 24　Litho.　Perf. 13
447 A231 2.80fr multicolored　　1.25 .40

Peace &
Freedom
A232

Europa: 2.80fr, Dove with olive branch. 3.70fr, Flock of doves.

1995, May 2
448 A232 2.80fr multicolored　　1.25 .40
449 A232 3.70fr multicolored　　1.65 .50

Caritas in
Andorra, 15th
Anniv.
A233

1995, May 15　Litho.　Perf. 13
450 A233 2.80fr multicolored　　1.25 1.00

Caldea Health
Spa — A234

1995, June 26　Litho.　Perf. 13
451 A234 2.80fr multicolored　　1.25 1.00

Ordino Natl.
Auditorium
A235

1995, July 10　Litho. & Engr.
452 A235 3.70fr black & buff　　1.65 1.25

Virgin of Meritxell — A236

1995, Sept. 11　Litho.　Perf. 14
453 A236 4.40fr multicolored　　1.90 1.50

Protection of
Nature
A237

Butterflies: 2.80fr, Papallona llimonera, vert. 3.70fr, Papallona melanargia galathea.

1995, Sept. 25　　　　Perf. 13
454 A237 2.80fr multicolored　　1.25 1.00
455 A237 3.70fr multicolored　　1.65 1.25

UN, 50th
Anniv. — A238

1995, Oct. 21　Litho.　Perf. 13
456 A238 2.80fr Flag, emblem　　1.25 1.00
457 A238 3.70fr Emblem, "50," flag　1.65 1.25
　a.　Pair, #456-457 + label　　3.00 3.00

Andorra's
Entrance into
Council of
Europe
A239

1995, Nov. 4
458 A239 2.80fr multicolored　　1.25 1.00

World Skiing Championships, Ordino
Arcalis — A240

1996, Jan. 29　Litho.　Perf. 13
459 A240 2.80fr multicolored　　1.25 1.25

Basketball in
Andorra — A241

1996, Jan. 29　Litho.　Perf. 13
460 A241 3.70fr multicolored　　1.65 1.65

15-Cent Minimum Value
The minimum catalogue value is 15 cents. Separating se-tenant pieces into individual stamps does not increase the value of the stamps since demand for the separated stamps may be small.

Our Lady of
Meritxell
Special
School, 25th
Anniv.
A242

1996, Feb. 17   Litho.   *Perf. 13*
461 A242 2.80fr multicolored   1.20 1.20

Songbirds
A243

1996, Mar. 25
462 A243 3fr Pit riog   1.30 1.30
463 A243 3.80fr Mallarenga
                 carbonera   1.65 1.65

First Arms Type of 1983

1996, Apr. 17   Engr.   *Perf. 13*
464 A150 2.70fr green   1.20 1.20
465 A150 3fr red   1.30 1.30

Cross of St. James
d'Engordany — A244

1996, Apr. 20   Litho.
466 A244 3fr multicolored   1.30 1.30

Censar of St.
Eulalia
d'Encamp
A245

1996, Apr. 20
467 A245 3.80fr multicolored   1.70 1.70

Europa — A246   Chess — A247

1996, May 6
468 A246 3fr Ermessenda de Cas-
              tellbo   1.30 1.30

1996, June 8   Litho.   *Perf. 13*
469 A247 4.50fr multicolored   2.00 2.00

1996 Summer
Olympic
Games,
Atlanta
A248

1996, June 29   Litho.   *Perf. 13*
470 A248 3fr multicolored   1.25 1.25

Arms of the Community of
Canillo — A249

Serpentine Die Cut 7 Vert.
1996, June 10   Litho.
Self-Adhesive
471 A249 (3fr) multicolored   1.75 1.75

Natl.
Children's
Choir, 5th
Anniv.
A250

1996, Sept. 14   *Perf. 13*
472 A250 3fr multicolored   1.30 1.30

Livestock
Fair — A251

1996, Oct. 26   Engr.   *Perf. 12x13*
473 A251 3fr multicolored   1.25 1.25

Churches
A252

#474, St. Romá de Les Bons. #475, St. Coloma.

1996, Nov. 16   Litho.   *Perf. 13*
474 A252 6.70fr multicolored   2.80 2.80
475 A252 6.70fr multicolored   2.80 2.80

A253   A254

1997, Jan. 7   Litho.   *Perf. 13*
476 A253 3fr multicolored   1.25 1.25
Pres. Francois Mitterrand (1916-96).

*Sawtooth Die Cut 7 Vert. x Straight
Die Cut*
1997, Feb. 24   Litho.
Self-Adhesive
477 A254 (3fr) Arms of Encamp   1.25 1.25
 a.   Booklet pane of 10   12.50

By its nature, No. 477a is a complete booklet.
The peelable paper backing serves as a booklet
cover.

A255   A256

1997, Mar. 22   *Perf. 13*
478 A255 3fr Volleyball   1.25 1.25

1997, May 12   Litho.   *Perf. 13*
479 A256 3fr "The White Lady"   1.25 1.25
Europa (Stories and Legends).

Oreneta
Cuablanca
A257

1997, May 31   Litho.   *Perf. 13*
480 A257 3.80fr multicolored   1.60 1.60

Paintings of
Mills — A258

1997, Sept. 15   Litho.   *Perf. 13*
481 A258 3fr Cal Pal, vert.   1.15 1.15
482 A258 4.50fr Mas d'en Sole   1.70 1.70

Religious
Artifacts
A259

Designs: 3fr, Monstrance of St. Iscle and St. Victoria. 15.50fr, Altar piece of St. Pierre d'Alxirivall.

1997, Oct. 27
483 A259 3fr multicolored   1.15 1.15
484 A259 15.50fr multicolored   5.75 5.75
 a.   Pair, #483-484 + label   6.90 6.90

Legends — A260

Designs: No. 485, Legend of Meritxell. No. 486,
The cross of seven arms. 3.80fr, The fountain of
Esmelicat.

1997, Nov. 22   Litho.   *Perf. 13*
485 A260 3fr multicolored   1.10 1.10
486 A260 3fr multicolored   1.10 1.10
487 A260 3.80fr multicolored   1.40 1.40
 a.   Strip of 3, #485-487   3.60 3.60

SEMI-POSTAL STAMP

┌─────────────────────────────────┐
│ Catalogue values for unused   │
│ stamps in this section are for   │
│ Never Hinged items.   │
└─────────────────────────────────┘

Virgin of St.
Coloma — SP1

Unwmk.
1964, July 25   Engr.   *Perf. 13*
B1 SP1 25c + 10c multi   22.00 22.00
The surtax was for the Red Cross.

AIR POST STAMPS

┌─────────────────────────────────┐
│ Catalogue values for unused   │
│ stamps in this section are for   │
│ Never Hinged items.   │
└─────────────────────────────────┘

Chamois
AP1

1950, Feb. 20   Engr.   *Perf. 13*
C1 AP1 100fr indigo   65.00 45.00

East Branch of Valira
River — AP2

1955-57
C2 AP2 100fr dark green   8.50 6.50
C3 AP2 200fr cerise   17.50 14.00
C4 AP2 500fr deep blue ('57)   90.00 65.00
  Nos. C2-C4 (3)   116.00 85.50

D'Inclès
Valley — AP3

1961-64   Unwmk.   *Perf. 13*
C5 AP3 2fr red, ol gray & claret   1.00 .65
C6 AP3 3fr bl, mar & slate grn   1.25 1.25
C7 AP3 5fr rose lil & red org   2.00 1.75
C8 AP3 10fr bl grn & slate grn   3.75 3.50
  Nos. C5-C8 (4)   8.00 7.15
  Issued: 10fr, 4/25/64; others, 6/19/61.

POSTAGE DUE STAMPS

Postage Due Stamps of France, 1893-1931,
Overprinted
ANDORRE

On Stamps of 1893-1926

1931-33   Unwmk.   *Perf. 14x13¹⁄₂*
J1 D2 5c blue   1.00 1.00
J2 D2 10c brown   1.00 1.00
J3 D2 30c rose red   .40   .40
J4 D2 50c violet brn   1.00 1.00
J5 D2 60c green   10.00 10.00
J6 D2 1fr red brn, *straw*   .50   .50
J7 D2 2fr brt violet   6.00 6.00
J8 D2 3fr magenta   1.10 1.10
  Nos. J1-J8 (8)   21.00 21.00

On Stamps of 1927-31

J9 D4 1c olive grn   1.25 1.25
J10 D4 10c rose   2.75 2.75
J11 D4 60c red   16.00 16.00
J12 D4 1fr Prus grn ('32)   65.00 65.00
J13 D4 1.20fr on 2fr bl   50.00 50.00
J14 D4 2fr ol brn ('33)   140.00 140.00
J15 D4 5fr on 1fr vio   65.00 65.00
  Nos. J9-J15 (7)   340.00 340.00

D5   D6

1935-41   Typo.
J16 D5 1c gray grn   2.25 1.25
J17 D6 5c lt bl ('37)   3.75 4.50
J18 D6 10c brn ('41)   3.00 4.50

J19	D6	2fr vio ('41)	6.00	3.25
J20	D6	5fr red org ('41)	11.00	3.25
		Nos. J16-J20 (5)	26.00	16.75

Catalogue values for unused stamps in this section, from this point to the end of the section, are for Never Hinged items.

Wheat Sheaves — D7

			Perf. 14x13½	
J21	D7	10c sepia	1.00	1.00
J22	D7	30c brt red vio	1.50	1.50
J23	D7	50c blue grn	1.75	1.75
J24	D7	1fr brt ultra	.80	.80
J25	D7	1.50fr rose red	5.75	5.75
J26	D7	2fr turq blue	1.50	1.50
J27	D7	3fr brown org	2.75	2.75
J28	D7	4fr dp vio ('45)	4.50	4.50
J29	D7	5fr brt pink	4.50	4.50
J30	D7	10fr red org ('45)	5.75	5.75
J31	D7	20fr olive brn ('46)	6.00	6.00
		Nos. J21-J31 (11)	35.80	35.80

Inscribed: "Timbre Taxe"

1946-53				
J32	D7	10c sepia ('46)	1.10	1.10
J33	D7	1fr ultra	.75	.75
J34	D7	2fr turq blue	1.00	1.00
J35	D7	3fr orange brn	2.00	2.00
J36	D7	4fr violet	2.75	2.75
J37	D7	5fr brt pink	1.75	1.75
J38	D7	10fr red orange	2.75	2.75
J39	D7	20fr olive brn	6.25	6.25
J40	D7	50fr dk green ('50)	16.50	16.50
J41	D7	100fr dp green ('53)	87.50	87.50
		Nos. J32-J41 (10)	122.35	122.35

Inscribed: "Timbre Taxe"

1961, June 19			Perf. 14x13½	
J42	D7	5c rose pink	3.00	3.00
J43	D7	10c red orange	6.00	6.00
J44	D7	20c olive	9.00	9.00
J45	D7	50c dark slate green	15.00	15.00
		Nos. J42-J45 (4)	33.00	33.00

D8   D9

1964-71		Typo.	Perf. 14x13½	
J46	D8	5c Centaury ('65)	.15	.15
J47	D8	10c Gentian ('65)	.15	.15
J48	D8	15c Corn poppy	.15	.15
J49	D8	20c Violets ('71)	.15	.15
J50	D8	30c Forget-me-not	.15	.15
J51	D8	40c Columbine ('71)	.20	.20
J52	D8	50c Clover ('65)	.30	.30
		Set value	1.00	1.00

1985, Oct. 21		Engr.	Perf. 13	
J53	D9	10c Holly	.15	.15
J54	D9	20c Blueberries	.15	.15
J55	D9	30c Raspberries	.15	.15
J56	D9	40c Bilberries	.20	.15
J57	D9	50c Blackberries	.20	.15
J58	D9	1fr Broom	.35	.30
J59	D9	2fr Rosehips	.65	.35
J60	D9	3fr Nightshade	1.00	.60
J61	D9	4fr Nabiu	1.40	.75
J62	D9	5fr Strawberries	1.75	.95
		Nos. J53-J62 (10)	6.00	3.70

NEWSPAPER STAMP

France No. P7   **ANDORRE**
Overprinted

1931		Unwmk.	Perf. 14x13½	
P1	A16	½c on 1c gray	.75	.75

ANGOLA

aŋ-'gō-lə

LOCATION — S.W. Africa between Zaire and Namibia.
GOVT. — Republic

AREA — 481,351 sq. mi.
POP. — 7,108,000 (1983 est.)
CAPITAL — Luanda

Angola was a Portuguese overseas territory until it became independent November 11, 1975, as the People's Republic of Angola.

1000 Reis = 1 Milreis
100 Centavos = 1 Escudo (1913, 1954)
100 Centavos = 1 Angolar (1932)
10 Lweys = 1 Kwanza (1977)

Catalogue values for unused stamps in this country are for Never Hinged items, beginning with Scott 328 in the regular postage section, Scott C26 in the airpost section, Scott J31 in the postage due section, and Scott RA7 in the postal tax section.

Watermark

Wmk. 232-Maltese Cross

Portuguese Crown — A1

1870-77		Typo.		Unwmk.
1	A1	5r black	3.00	1.10
a.		Perf. 13½	6.00	3.25
2	A1	10r yellow	22.50	10.00
3	A1	20r bister	3.50	2.00
a.		Perf. 13½	65.00	50.00
4	A1	25r red	10.00	3.00
		25r rose	10.00	2.00
c.		25r rose, perf. 14	225.00	75.00
d.		Perf. 13½	20.00	8.00
5	A1	40r blue ('77)	150.00	75.00
6	A1	50r green	50.00	15.00
a.		Perf. 13½	225.00	65.00
7	A1	100r lilac	3.00	2.00
a.		Perf. 12½	8.00	4.00
8	A1	200r orange ('77)	3.00	2.00
a.		Perf. 12½	4.00	1.65
9	A1	300r choc ('77)	3.00	3.00
a.		Perf. 12½	10.00	4.75

1881-85				
10	A1	10r green ('83)	4.00	1.50
a.		Perf. 13½	20.00	2.25
11	A1	20r carmine rose ('85)	9.00	5.00
12	A1	25r violet ('85)	4.00	2.00
a.		Perf. 13½	6.00	2.75
13	A1	40r buff ('82)	5.00	2.00
a.		Perf. 12½	6.00	2.00
15	A1	50r blue	14.00	1.65
a.		Perf. 13½	20.00	1.65
		Nos. 10-15 (5)	36.00	12.15

Two types of numerals are found on #2, 11, 13, 15.

The cliche of 40r in plate of 20r error, was discovered before the stamps were issued. All copies were defaced by a blue pencil mark.

In perf. 12½, Nos. 1-4, 4a and 6, as well as 7a, were printed in 1870 on thicker paper and 1875 on normal paper. Stamps of the earlier printing sell for 2 to 5 times more than those of the 1875 printing.

Some reprints of the 1870-85 issues are on a smooth white chalky paper, ungummed and perf. 13½.

Other reprints of these issues are on thin ivory paper with shiny white gum and clear-cut perf. 13½.

King Luiz — A2   King Carlos — A3

1886		Embossed	Perf. 12½	
16	A2	5r black	3.50	3.25
a.		Perf. 13½	11.50	8.50
17	A2	10r green	3.50	3.00
a.		Perf. 13½	13.00	7.25
18	A2	20r rose	10.00	6.25
a.		Perf. 13½	12.50	6.50
19	A2	25r red violet	7.50	1.50
20	A2	40r chocolate	8.00	5.00
21	A2	50r blue	10.50	2.00
22	A2	100r yellow brn	14.00	6.00
23	A2	200r gray violet	18.00	9.00
24	A2	300r orange	20.00	11.00
		Nos. 16-24 (9)	95.00	47.00

For surcharges see #61-69, 172-174, 208-210.
Reprints of 5r, 20r & 100r have cleancut perf. 13½.

1893-94		Perf. 11½, 12½, 13½	Typo.	
25	A3	5r yellow	1.00	.85
26	A3	10r redsh violet	2.00	.90
27	A3	15r chocolate	2.75	1.25
28	A3	20r lavender	2.75	1.25
29	A3	25r green	1.25	1.00
a.		Perf. 12½	4.00	2.00
30	A3	50r light blue	3.25	1.25
a.		Perf. 13½	5.00	2.75
31	A3	75r carmine	6.00	3.50
a.		Perf. 11½	8.00	6.25
32	A3	80r lt green	6.75	3.50
33	A3	100r brown, buff	6.75	3.50
a.		Perf. 11½	50.00	32.50
34	A3	150r car, rose	12.00	9.00
35	A3	200r dk blue, lt bl	14.00	11.00
36	A3	300r dk blue, sal	14.00	11.00
		Nos. 25-36 (12)	72.50	48.00

For surcharges see Nos. 70-81, 175-179, 213-216, 234.

No. P1 Surcharged in Blue

1894, Aug.				
37	N1	25r on 2½r brown	80.00	22.50

King Carlos — A5

1898-1903			Perf. 11½	
		Name and Value in Black except 500r		
38	A5	2½r gray	.15	.15
39	A5	5r orange	.15	.15
40	A5	10r yellow grn	.15	.15
41	A5	15r violet brn	1.50	.70
42	A5	15r gray green ('03)	.65	.50
43	A5	20r gray violet	.25	.20
44	A5	25r sea green	1.00	.40
45	A5	25r car ('03)	.50	.15
46	A5	50r blue	1.65	.35
47	A5	50r brown ('03)	3.00	2.00
48	A5	65r dull blue ('03)	9.00	7.00
49	A5	75r rose	4.50	1.65
50	A5	75r red violet ('03)	1.25	.90
51	A5	80r violet	5.25	1.75
52	A5	100r dk blue, blue	.90	.65
53	A5	115r org brn, pink ('03)	8.00	6.00
54	A5	130r brn, straw ('03)	8.00	6.00
55	A5	150r brn, straw	8.00	5.00
56	A5	200r red vio, pink	2.25	1.00
57	A5	300r dk blue, rose	3.25	3.25
58	A5	400r dull bl, straw ('03)	2.50	2.25
59	A5	500r blk & red, bl ('01)	2.75	2.75
60	A5	700r vio, yelsh ('01)	14.00	10.00
		Nos. 38-60 (23)	78.65	52.95

For surcharges and overprints see Nos. 83-102, 113-117, 159-171, 181-183, 217-218, 221-225.

Stamps of 1886-94 Surcharged in Black or Red

Two types of surcharge:
I - 3mm between numeral and REIS.
II - 4½mm spacing.

1902			Perf. 12½	
61	A2	65r on 40r choc	4.50	3.50
62	A2	65r on 300r org, I	4.50	3.50
a.		Type II	32.50	25.00
63	A2	115r on 10r green	3.75	3.25
a.		Inverted surcharge		
b.		Perf. 13½	18.00	17.00
64	A2	115r on 200r gray vio	3.50	2.75
65	A2	130r on 50r blue	5.75	4.75
66	A2	130r on 100r brown	4.00	3.00
67	A2	400r on 20r rose	60.00	30.00
a.		Perf. 13½	60.00	45.00
68	A2	400r on 25r violet	8.50	6.00
69	A2	400r on 5r black (R)	6.75	6.25
a.		Double surcharge		
		Nos. 61-69 (9)	101.25	63.00

For surcharges see Nos. 172-174, 208-210.

			Perf. 11½, 12½, 13½	
70	A3	65r on 5r yel, I	4.00	2.75
a.		Type II	10.00	10.00
71	A3	65r on 10r red vio, I	3.25	2.25
a.		Type II	13.00	5.25
b.		Perf. 11½, type I	8.75	5.25
c.		Perf. 11½, type II	3.50	2.50
72	A3	65r on 20r lav	4.00	2.75
a.		Type II	6.50	6.00
73	A3	65r on 25r green	3.00	2.25
a.		Perf. 11½	9.25	7.25
74	A3	115r on 80r lt grn	5.25	4.00
75	A3	115r on 100r brn, buff	5.25	3.25
a.		Perf. 13½	9.25	6.50
76	A3	115r on 150r car, rose	8.00	5.25
a.		Perf. 11½	10.00	6.00
77	A3	130r on 15r choc	2.75	2.00
78	A3	130r on 75r carmine	3.00	2.25
a.		Perf. 13½	14.00	11.50
79	A3	130r on 300r dk bl, sal	8.25	6.00
80	A3	400r on 50r lt bl	3.25	2.75
81	A3	400r on 200r bl, bl	3.25	3.25
a.		Perf. 11½	21.00	8.75
82	N1	400r on 2½r brn	1.10	1.10
a.		Type II	2.50	2.25
		Nos. 70-82 (13)	54.35	39.85

For surcharges see #175-180, 211-216, 234-235.
Reprints of Nos. 65, 67, 68 and 69 have cleancut perforation 13½.

Stamps of 1898 Overprinted — a   **PROVISORIO**

1902			Perf. 11½	
83	A5	15r brown	1.00	.60
84	A5	25r sea green	.85	.35
85	A5	50r blue	1.50	.85
86	A5	75r rose	2.75	2.00
		Nos. 83-86 (4)	6.10	3.80

For surcharge see No. 116.

No. 48 Surcharged in Black

1905				
87	A5	50r on 65r dull blue	2.75	1.25

For surcharge see No. 183.

Stamps of 1898-1903 Overprinted in Carmine or Green — b   REPUBLICA

1911				
88	A5	2½r gray	.15	.15
89	A5	5r orange yel	.15	.15
90	A5	10r light green	.22	.20
91	A5	15r gray green	.25	.20
92	A5	20r gray violet	.25	.20
93	A5	25r car (G)	.25	.15
94	A5	50r brown	1.50	.90
95	A5	75r lilac	2.50	2.50
96	A5	100r dk blue, bl	2.50	2.50
97	A5	115r org brn, pink	.90	.60
98	A5	130r brn, straw	.90	.60
99	A5	200r red lil, pnksh	.90	.60
100	A5	400r dull bl, straw	1.25	.65
101	A5	500r blk & red, bl	1.10	.65
102	A5	700r violet, yelsh	1.25	.70
		Nos. 88-102 (15)	14.07	10.75

Inverted and double overprints of Nos. 88-102 were made intentionally.

For surcharges see Nos. 217-218, 221-222, 224.

King Manuel II — A6

Ceres — A7

Overprinted in Carmine or Green

1912   *Perf. 11¹/₂x12*

103	A6	2¹/₂r violet	.22	.32
104	A6	5r black	.25	.40
105	A6	10r gray green	.35	.30
106	A6	20r carmine (G)	.35	.30
107	A6	25r violet brown	.35	.30
108	A6	50r dk blue	.60	.50
109	A6	75r bister brown	.65	.65
110	A6	100r brown, *lt green*	1.65	.70
111	A6	200r dk green, *salmon*	1.10	.70
112	A6	300r black, *azure*	1.10	.70
		Nos. 103-112 (10)	6.62	4.87

For surcharges see Nos. 219-220, 226-227.

No. 91 Surcharged
with New Values as **5**

1912, June   *Perf. 11¹/₂*

113	A5	2¹/₂r on 15r gray green	2.25	2.25
114	A5	5r on 15r gray green	1.75	1.50
115	A5	10r on 15r gray green	1.75	1.50
		Nos. 113-115 (3)	5.75	5.25

Inverted and double surcharges of Nos. 113-115 were made intentionally.

REPUBLICA

Nos. 86 and 50
Surcharged "25" in
Black and Overprinted
in Violet — c

1912

116	A5	25r on 75r rose	65.00	50.00
117	A5	25r on 75r red violet	2.75	1.50
a.		"REUPBLICA"	27.50	25.00
b.		"25" omitted	27.50	25.00
c.		"REPUBLICA" omitted	27.50	25.00

1914-26 Typo.   *Perf. 12x11¹/₂, 15x14*
Name and Value in Black

118	A7	¹/₄c olive brown	.15	.15
a.		Inscriptions inverted	6.00	
119	A7	¹/₂c black	.15	.15
120	A7	1c blue green	.15	.15
121	A7	1c yel grn ('22)	.15	.15
122	A7	1¹/₂c lilac brown	.15	.15
123	A7	2c carmine	.15	.15
124	A7	2c gray ('25)	.30	1.00
125	A7	2¹/₂c lt violet	.15	.15
126	A7	3c orange ('21)	.15	.60
127	A7	4c dull rose ('21)	.15	.15
128	A7	4¹/₂c gray ('21)	.15	.80
130	A7	5c blue	.15	.15
131	A7	6c lilac ('21)	.15	.15
132	A7	7c ultra ('21)	.15	.15
133	A7	7¹/₂c yellow brn	.15	.15
134	A7	8c slate	.15	.15
135	A7	10c orange brn	.20	.15
136	A7	12c olive brn ('21)	.35	.22
137	A7	12c dp green ('25)	.20	.15
138	A7	15c plum	.40	.15
139	A7	15c brown rose ('21)	.15	.15
140	A7	20c yel green	.25	.15
141	A7	24c ultra ('25)	1.10	.75
142	A7	25c choc ('25)	1.10	.75
143	A7	30c brown, *green*	1.25	2.00
144	A7	30c gray grn ('21)	.65	.15
145	A7	40c brown, *pink*	3.00	2.00
146	A7	40c turq blue ('21)	.60	.15
147	A7	50c orange, *sal*	6.00	4.25
148	A7	50c lt violet ('25)	1.00	.15
149	A7	60c dk blue ('22)	.55	.15
150	A7	60c dp rose ('26)	40.00	40.00
151	A7	80c pink ('22)	1.25	.15
152	A7	1e green, *blue*	3.00	2.25
153	A7	1e rose ('22)	1.50	.15
154	A7	1e dp blue ('25)	3.00	3.00
155	A7	2e dk violet ('22)	1.25	.50
156	A7	5e buff ('25)	15.00	2.25
157	A7	10e pink ('25)	22.50	10.00
158	A7	20e pale turq ('25)	50.00	35.00
		Nos. 118-158 (40)	156.85	108.97

Two kinds of paper, chalky-surfaced paper and ordinary, were used for Nos. 118-120, 122-123, 125, 130, 133-135, 138 and 140. Those on coated paper sell unused for 10 to 40 times the values listed; used for about 5 to 20 times.

All but #143, 145, 147 come perf 12x11¹/₂. All but #124, 137, 141-142, 146, 148, 151, 153-154, 156-158 come perf 15x14.

For surcharges see Nos. 228-229, 236-239.

Stamps of 1898-1903 Overprinted type "c" in Red or Green
On Stamps of 1898-1903

1914   *Perf. 11¹/₂, 12*

159	A5	10r yel green (R)	3.25	2.50
160	A5	15r gray green (R)	3.25	2.50
161	A5	20r gray violet (G)	.80	.80
163	A5	75r red violet (G)	.80	.80
164	A5	100r blue, *blue* (R)	1.25	1.25
165	A5	115r org brn, *pink* (R)	60.00	
167	A5	200r red vio, *pnksh* (G)	.90	.50
169	A5	400r dl bl, *straw* (R)	40.00	30.00
170	A5	500r blk & red, *bl* (R)	5.00	3.00
171	A5	700r vio, *yelsh* (G)	15.00	12.00

Inverted and double overprints were made intentionally. No. 165 was not regularly issued. Red overprints on the 20r, 75r, 200r were not regularly issued. The 130r was not regularly issued without surcharge (No. 225).

On Nos. 63-65, 74-76, 78-79, 82
Perf. 11¹/₂, 12¹/₂, 13¹/₂

172	A2	115r on 10r (R)	30.00	20.00
a.		Perf. 13¹/₂	30.00	20.00
173	A2	115r on 200r (R)	35.00	20.00
174	A2	130r on 50r (R)	35.00	20.00
175	A3	115r on 80r (R)	100.00	75.00
176	A3	115r on 100r (R)	250.00	150.00
177	A3	115r on 150r (G)	165.00	125.00
178	A3	130r on 75r (G)	1.75	1.65
179	A3	130r on 300r (R)	4.00	3.25
a.		Perf. 12¹/₂	7.00	4.50
180	N1	400r on 2¹/₂r (R)	.40	.40
a.		Perf. 11¹/₂	1.65	1.25
		Nos. 172-180 (9)	621.15	415.30

Overprinted   PROVISORIO

On Stamps of 1902
Perf. 11¹/₂, 12

181	A5	50r blue (R)	.90	.60
182	A5	75r rose (G)	2.75	2.00

On No. 87

183	A5	50r on 65r dull blue (R)	2.50	2.50
		Nos. 181-183 (3)	6.15	5.10

Inverted and double surcharges of Nos. 181-183 were made intentionally.

Common Design Types
pictured following the introduction.

Vasco da Gama Issue of Various Portuguese Colonies

Common Design
Types CD20-CD27
Surcharged

REPUBLICA
ANGOLA
¹/₄ C.

On Stamps of Macao

1913   *Perf. 12¹/₂ to 16*

184		¹/₄c on ¹/₂a blue grn	4.00	4.00
185		¹/₂c on 1a red	3.00	3.00
186		1c on 2a red violet	3.00	3.00
187		2¹/₂c on 4a yel green	2.00	2.00
188		5c on 8a dk blue	2.00	2.00
189		7¹/₂c on 12a vio brn	5.50	5.50
190		10c on 16a bister brn	4.00	4.00
191		15c on 24a bister	4.00	4.00
		Nos. 184-191 (8)	27.50	27.50

On Stamps of Portuguese Africa
Perf. 14 to 15

192		¹/₄c on 2¹/₂r blue grn	.75	.75
193		¹/₂c on 5r red	.75	.75
194		1c on 10r red violet	.75	.75
195		2¹/₂c on 25r yel grn	.75	.75
196		5c on 50r dk blue	.75	.75
197		7¹/₂c on 75r vio brn	2.50	2.50
198		10c on 100r bister brn	1.25	1.25
199		15c on 150r bister	1.75	1.75
		Nos. 192-199 (8)	9.25	9.25

On Stamps of Timor

200		¹/₄c on ¹/₂a blue grn	2.00	2.00
201		¹/₂c on 1a red	2.00	2.00
202		1c on 2a red vio	2.00	2.00
203		2¹/₂c on 4a yel grn	2.00	2.00
204		5c on 8a dk blue	2.00	2.00
205		7¹/₂c on 12a vio brn	3.00	3.00
206		10c on 16a bis brn	2.00	2.00
207		15c on 24a bister	2.00	2.00
		Nos. 200-207 (8)	17.00	17.00
		Nos. 184-207 (24)	53.75	53.75

REPUBLICA

Provisional Issue of
1902 Overprinted in
Carmine

1915   *Perf. 11¹/₂, 12¹/₂, 13¹/₂*

208	A2	115r on 10r green	1.00	2.00
209	A2	115r on 200r gray vio	.90	2.00
210	A2	130r on 100r brown	.90	2.00
211	A3	115r on 80r lt green	1.10	2.00
212	A3	115r on 100r brn, *buff*	.90	2.00
a.		Perf. 11¹/₂	17.00	17.00
213	A3	115r on 150r car, *rose*	1.75	2.00
214	A3	130r on 15r choc	.65	2.00
a.		Perf. 12¹/₂	7.00	7.00
215	A3	130r on 75r carmine	1.50	1.75
216	A3	130r on 300r dk bl, *sal*	1.10	1.75
		Nos. 208-216 (9)	9.60	17.50

Stamps of 1911-14 Surcharged in Black:

¹/₂ C.

¹/₂ C. ═ ═ ═
  d   e

On Stamps of 1911

1919   *Perf. 11¹/₂*

217	A5 (d)	¹/₂c on 75r red lilac	1.50	2.00
218	A5 (d)	2¹/₂c on 100r blue, *grysh*	1.75	2.00

On Stamps of 1912
Perf. 11¹/₂x12

219	A6 (e)	¹/₂c on 75r bis brn	.65	.65
220	A6 (e)	2¹/₂c on 100r brn, *lt grn*	.85	.40

On Stamps of 1914

221	A5 (d)	¹/₂c on 75r red lil	.65	.40
222	A5 (d)	2¹/₂c on 100r bl, *grysh*	.70	.60
		Nos. 217-222 (6)	6.10	6.05

Inverted and double surcharges were made for sale to collectors.

Nos. 163, 98 and Type of 1914
Surcharged with New Values and Bars in
Black

1921

223	A5 (c)	00.5c on 75r	350.00	350.00
224	A5 (b)	4c on 130r (#98)	.70	.70
225	A5 (c)	4c on 130r brn, *straw*	2.75	2.50

Nos. 109 and 108 Surcharged with New Values and Bars in Black

226	A6	00.5c on 75c	.85	.85
227	A6	1c on 50r	.75	.65

Nos. 133 and 138 Surcharged with New Values and Bars in Black

228	A7	00.5c on 7¹/₂c	.70	.60
229	A7	04c on 15c	1.10	1.10

The 04c surcharge exists on the 15c brown rose, perf 12x11¹/₂, No. 139.

República
═══
═══

Nos. 81-82 Surcharged

40 C.

1925   *Perf. 12¹/₂*

234	A3	40c on 400r on 200r bl, *bl*	.80	.65
a.		Perf. 13¹/₂	3.25	2.25
235	N1	40c on 400c on 2¹/₂r brn	.60	.60
a.		Perf. 13¹/₂	.60	.60

═ ═ ═

Nos. 150-151, 154-
155 Surcharged

70 C.

1931   *Perf. 11¹/₂*

236	A7	50c on 60c deep rose	1.10	.80
237	A7	70c on 80c pink	2.25	1.00
238	A7	70c on 1e deep blue	2.00	1.10
239	A7	1.40e on 2e dark violet	2.00	1.10
		Nos. 236-239 (4)	7.35	4.00

Ceres — A14

Perf. 12x11¹/₂

1932-46   **Typo.**   **Wmk. 232**

243	A14	1c bister brn	.15	.15
244	A14	5c dk brown	.15	.15
245	A14	10c dp violet	.15	.15
246	A14	15c black	.15	.15
247	A14	20c gray	.25	.15
248	A14	30c myrtle grn	.15	.15
249	A14	35c yel grn ('46)	4.50	2.00
250	A14	40c dp orange	.25	.15
251	A14	45c lt blue	.85	.65
252	A14	50c lt brown	.15	.15
253	A14	60c olive grn	.30	.15
254	A14	70c orange brn	.65	.15
255	A14	80c emerald	.25	.15
256	A14	85c rose	2.00	2.00
257	A14	1a claret	.65	.18
258	A14	1.40a dk blue	4.50	1.10
258A	A14	1.75a dk blue ('46)	6.00	1.10
259	A14	2a dull vio	2.25	.15
260	A14	5a pale yel grn	3.00	.50
261	A14	10a olive bis	10.00	.90
262	A14	20a orange	17.50	2.00
		Nos. 243-262 (21)	53.95	12.43

For surcharges see Nos. 263-267, 271-273, 294A-300, J31-J36.

Surcharged with New Value and Bars

5¹/₂mm between bars and new value.

1934

263	A14	10c on 45c lt bl	1.25	.70
264	A14	20c on 85c rose	1.10	.70
265	A14	30c on 1.40a dk bl	1.10	.70
266	A14	70c on 2a dl vio	1.50	1.10
267	A14	80c on 5a pale yel grn	2.25	1.00
		Nos. 263-267 (5)	7.20	4.20

See Nos. 294A-300.

CORREIOS

Nos. J26, J30
Surcharged in Black

═ **5**
CENTAVOS

═══════

1935   **Unwmk.**   *Perf. 11¹/₂*

268	D2	5c on 6c lt brown	.90	.60
269	D2	30c on 50c gray	.90	.60
270	D2	40c on 50c gray	.90	.60
		Nos. 268-270 (3)	2.70	1.80

═ ═

No. 255 Surcharged in
Black

0,15 Cent.

1938   **Wmk. 232**   *Perf. 12x11¹/₂*

271	A14	5c on 80c emerald	.40	1.00
272	A14	10c on 80c emerald	.50	1.75
273	A14	15c on 80c emerald	.65	2.50
		Nos. 271-273 (3)	1.55	5.25

Vasco da Gama Issue
Common Design Types
Engr.; Name & Value Typo. in Black
Perf. 13¹/₂x13

1938, July 26   **Unwmk.**

274	CD34	1c gray green	.15	.15
275	CD34	5c orange brn	.15	.15
276	CD34	10c dk carmine	.15	.15
277	CD34	15c dk violet brn	.15	.15
278	CD34	20c slate	.20	.15
279	CD35	30c rose violet	.25	.15
280	CD35	35c brt green	.35	.20
281	CD35	40c brown	.25	.15
282	CD35	50c brt red vio	.25	.15
283	CD36	60c gray black	.35	.15
284	CD36	70c brown vio	.30	.15
285	CD36	80c orange	.30	.15
286	CD36	1a red	.30	.15
287	CD37	1.75a blue	.85	.30
288	CD37	2a brown car	1.50	.30
289	CD37	5a olive grn	3.00	.30
290	CD38	10a blue vio	6.50	.60
291	CD38	20a red brown	15.00	1.10
		Nos. 274-291 (18)	30.00	4.60

For surcharges see Nos. 301-304.

Marble Column and
Portuguese Arms with
Cross — A20

1938, July 29   *Perf. 12¹/₂*
292	A20	80c blue green	1.00 .95
293	A20	1.75a deep blue	5.00 1.00
294	A20	20a dk red brown	14.00 11.00
		Nos. 292-294 (3)	20.00 12.95

Visit of the President of Portugal to this colony in 1938.

Stamps of 1932 Surcharged with New Value and Bars

8mm between bars and new value.

1941-45   Wmk. 232   *Perf. 12x11¹/₂*
294A	A14	5c on 80c emer ('45)	.22 .20
295	A14	10c on 45c lt blue	.65 .55
296	A14	15c on 45c lt blue	1.00 .70
297	A14	20c on 85c rose	.65 .55
298	A14	35c on 85c rose	.65 .55
299	A14	50c on 1.40a dk blue	.65 .55
300	A14	60c on 1a claret	5.75 4.00
		Nos. 294A-300 (7)	9.57 7.10

Nos. 285 to 287 Surcharged with New Values and Bars in Black or Red

1945   Unwmk.   *Perf. 13¹/₂x13*
301	CD36	5c on 80c org	.28 .20
302	CD36	50c on 1a red	.60 .20
303	CD37	50c on 1.75a bl (R)	.42 .20
304	CD37	50c on 1.75a bl	.60 .20
		Nos. 301-304 (4)	1.90 .80

Sao Miguel Fort, Luanda — A21   John IV — A22

Designs: 10c, Our Lady of Nazareth Church, Luanda. 50c, Salvador Correia de Sa e Bene vides. 1a, Surrender of Luanda. 1.75a, Diogo Cao. 2a, Manuel Cerveira Pereira. 5a, Stone Cliffs, Yelala. 10a, Paulo Dias de Novais. 20a, Massangano Fort.

     Perf. 14¹/₂

1948, May   Unwmk.   Litho.
305	A21	5c dk violet	.15 .15
306	A21	10c dk brown	.25 .20
307	A22	30c blue grn	.15 .15
308	A22	50c vio brown	.15 .15
309	A21	1a carmine	.32 .15
310	A22	1.75a slate blue	.65 .20
311	A22	2a green	.65 .20
312	A21	5a gray black	1.00 .32
313	A22	10a rose lilac	2.00 .35
314	A21	20a gray blue	5.00 1.10
a.		Sheet of 10, #305-314	40.00 40.00
		Nos. 305-314 (10)	10.32 2.97

300th anniv. of the restoration of Angola to Portugal. No. 314a sold for 42.50a.

Lady of Fatima Issue
Common Design Type

1948, Dec.
315	CD40	50c carmine	.65 .50
316	CD40	3a ultra	2.00 1.00
317	CD40	6a red orange	7.00 2.50
318	CD40	9a dp claret	17.00 3.00
		Nos. 315-318 (4)	26.65 7.00

Our Lady of the Rosary at Fatima, Portugal.

Chiumbe River — A24   Black Rocks — A25

Designs: 50c, View of Luanda. 2.50a, Sa da Bandeira. 3.50a, Mocamedes. 15a, Cubal River. 50a, Duke of Bragança Falls.

1949   Unwmk.   *Perf. 13¹/₂*
319	A24	20c dk slate blue	.15 .15
320	A25	40c black brown	.15 .15
321	A24	50c rose brown	.15 .15
322	A24	2.50a blue violet	1.10 .35
323	A24	3.50a slate gray	1.10 .25
323A	A24	15a dk green	8.25 1.50
324	A24	50a dp green	22.50 3.75
		Nos. 319-324 (7)	33.40 6.20

Sailing Vessel — A26   UPU Symbols — A27

1949, Aug.   *Perf. 14*
325	A26	1a chocolate	4.00 .32
326	A26	4a dk Prus green	10.00 .85

Centenary of founding of Mocamedes.

1949, Oct.
327	A27	4a dk grn & lt grn	3.50 1.50

75th anniv. of the UPU.

Catalogue values for unused stamps in this section, from this point to the end of the section, are for Never Hinged items.

Stamp of 1870 — A28

1950, Apr. 2   *Perf. 11¹/₂x12*
328	A28	50c yellow green	.80 .25
329	A28	1a fawn	.80 .25
330	A28	4a black	3.25 .70
a.		Sheet of 3, #328-330	7.50 7.50
		Nos. 328-330 (3)	4.85 1.20

Angola's first philatelic exhibition, marking the 80th anniversary of Angola's first stamps. No. 330a contains Nos. 328, 329 (inverted), 330, perf. 11¹/₂ and sold for 6.50a. All copies carry an oval exhibition cancellation in the margin but the stamps were valid for postage.

Holy Year Issue
Common Design Types

1950, May   *Perf. 13x13¹/₂*
331	CD41	1a dull rose vio	.32 .15
332	CD42	4a black	3.00 .32

Dark Chanting Goshawk A31   European Bee Eater A32

10c, Racquet-tailed roller. 15c, Bateleur eagle. 50c, Giant kingfisher. 1a, Yellow-fronted barbet. 1.50a, Openbill (stork). 2a, Southern ground hornbill. 2.50a, African skimmer. 3a, Shikra. 3.50a, Denham's bustard. 4a, African golden oriole. 4.50a, Long-tailed shrike. 5a, Red-shouldered glossy starling. 6a, Sharp-tailed glossy starling. 7a, Red-shouldered widow bird. 10a, Half-colored kingfisher. 12.50a, White-crowned shrike. 15a, White-winged babbling starling. 20a, Yellow-billed hornbill. 25a, Amethyst starling. 30a, Orange-breasted shrike. 40a, Secretary bird. 50a, Rosy-faced lovebird.

Photogravure and Lithographed
1951   Unwmk.   *Perf. 11¹/₂*
Birds in Natural Colors
333	A31	5c lt blue	.20 .50
334	A32	10c aqua	.20 .15
335	A32	15c salmon pink	.30 1.00
336	A32	20c pale yellow	.50 .22
337	A31	50c gray blue	.30 .15
338	A31	1a lilac	.30 .15
339	A31	1.50a gray buff	.40 .15
340	A31	2a cream	.40 .15
341	A32	2.50a gray	.40 .15
342	A32	3a lemon yel	.40 .18
343	A31	3.50a lt gray	.40 .18
344	A31	4a rose buff	1.25 .18
345	A31	4.50a rose lilac	1.25 .20
346	A31	5a green	6.25 .20
347	A31	6a blue	6.25 .55
348	A31	7a orange	6.25 .75
349	A31	10a lilac rose	40.00 1.10
350	A32	12.50a slate gray	8.50 1.75
351	A31	15a pale olive	8.50 1.75
352	A31	20a pale bis brn	45.00 4.50
353	A31	25a lilac rose	25.00 2.50
354	A32	30a pale salmon	25.00 3.00
355	A31	40a yellow	50.00 3.75
356	A31	50a turquoise	110.00 14.00
		Nos. 333-356 (24)	337.05 37.21

Holy Year Extension Issue
Common Design Type

1951, Oct.   Litho.   *Perf. 14*
357	CD43	4a orange	1.25 .50

Sheets contain alternate vertical rows of stamps and labels bearing quotations from Pope Pius XII or the Patriarch Cardinal of Lisbon.

Medical Congress Issue
Common Design Type

Design: Medical examination

1952, June   *Perf. 13¹/₂*
358	CD44	1a vio blue & brn blk	.40 .20

Head of Christ — A35

1952, Oct.   Unwmk.   *Perf. 13*
359	A35	10c dk blue & buff	.15 .15
360	A35	50c dk ol grn & ol gray	.20 .15
361	A35	2a rose vio & cream	1.25 .15
		Nos. 359-361 (3)	1.60
		Set value	.26

Issued to commemorate the Exhibition of Sacred Missionary Art held at Lisbon in 1951.

Leopard A36   Sable Antelope A37

Animals: 20c, Elephant. 30c, Eland. 40c, African crocodile. 50c, Impala. 1a, Mountain zebra. 1.50a, Sitatunga. 2a, Black rhinoceros. 2.30a, Gemsbok. 2.50a, Lion. 3a, Buffalo. 3.50a, Springbok. 4a, Brindled gnu. 5a, Hartebeest. 7a, Wart hog. 10a, Defassa waterbuck. 12.50a, Hippopotamus. 15a, Greater kudu. 20a, Giraffe.

1953, Aug. 15   *Perf. 12¹/₂*
362	A36	5c multicolored	.15 .15
363	A37	10c multicolored	.15 .15
364	A37	20c multicolored	.15 .15
365	A37	30c multicolored	.15 .15
366	A36	40c multicolored	.15 .15
367	A37	50c multicolored	.15 .15
368	A37	1a multicolored	.20 .15
369	A37	1.50a multicolored	.15 .15
370	A36	2a multicolored	.18 .15
371	A37	2.30a multicolored	.24 .15
372	A37	2.50a multicolored	.30 .15
373	A36	3a multicolored	.30 .15
374	A37	3.50a multicolored	.18 .15
375	A37	4a multicolored	6.00 .24
376	A37	5a multicolored	.32 .15
377	A37	7a multicolored	.75 .24
378	A37	10a multicolored	1.25 .20
379	A37	12.50a multicolored	4.00 1.65
380	A37	15a multicolored	4.00 1.25
381	A37	20a multicolored	5.00 .35
		Nos. 362-381 (20)	23.77 6.03

Stamp of Portugal and Arms of Colonies — A38

1953, Nov.   Photo.   *Perf. 13*
Stamp and Arms Multicolored
382	A38	50c gray & dark gray	.55 .32

Cent. of Portugal's 1st postage stamps.

Map and Plane — A39

Typographed and Lithographed
1954, May 27   *Perf. 13¹/₂*
383	A39	35c multicolored	.15 .15
384	A39	4.50e multicolored	.70 .30

Visit of Pres. Francisco H C. Lopes.

Sao Paulo Issue
Common Design Type

1954   Litho.
385	CD46	1e bister & gray	.32 .20

Map of Angola — A41   Artur de Paiva — A42

1955, Aug.   Unwmk.   *Perf. 13¹/₂*
386	A41	5c multicolored	.15 .15
387	A41	20c multicolored	.15 .15
388	A41	50c multicolored	.15 .15
389	A41	1e multicolored	.15 .15
390	A41	2.30e multicolored	.28 .15
391	A41	4e multicolored	.50 .15
392	A41	10e multicolored	.50 .15
393	A41	20e multicolored	1.00 .20
		Nos. 386-393 (8)	2.88
		Set value	.78

For overprints see Nos. 593, 598, 604.

1956, Oct. 9   *Perf. 13¹/₂x12¹/₂*
394	A42	1e blk, dk bl & ocher	.20 .15

Cent. of the birth of Col. Artur de Paiva.

Man of Malange — A43   Jose M. Antunes — A44

Various Costumes in Multicolor; Inscriptions in Black Brown

1957, Jan. 1   Photo.   *Perf. 11¹/₂*
Granite Paper
395	A43	5c gray	.15 .15
396	A43	10c orange yel	.15 .15
397	A43	15c lt blue grn	.15 .15
398	A43	20c pale rose vio	.15 .15
399	A43	30c brt rose	.15 .15
400	A43	40c blue gray	.15 .15
401	A43	50c pale olive	.15 .15
402	A43	80c lt violet	.15 .15
403	A43	1.50e buff	1.00 .15
404	A43	2.50e lt yel grn	1.00 .15
405	A43	4e salmon	.50 .15
406	A43	10e salmon pink	1.00 .25
		Nos. 395-406 (12)	4.70
		Set value	1.25

1957, Apr.   *Perf. 13¹/₂*
407	A44	1e aqua & brown	.65 .20

Birth cent. of Father Jose Maria Antunes.

Fair Emblem, Globe and Arms — A45

1958, July   Litho.   *Perf. 12x11¹/₂*
408	A45	1.50e multicolored	.25 .15

World's Fair, Brussels, Apr. 17-Oct. 19.

Tropical Medicine Congress Issue
Common Design Type

Design: Securidaca longipedunculata.

1958, Dec. 15   *Perf. 13½*
409 CD47 2.50e multicolored   1.10 .70

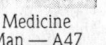

Medicine Man — A47   Welwitschia Mirabilis — A48

Designs: 1.50e, Early government doctor. 2.50e, Modern medical team.

1958, Dec. 18   *Perf. 11½x12*
410 A47 1e blue blk & brown   .20 .15
411 A47 1.50e gray, blk & brown   .50 .20
412 A47 2.50e multicolored   .75 .40
    Nos. 410-412 (3)   1.45 .75

75th anniversary of the Maria Pia Hospital, Luanda.

1959, Oct. 1   Litho.   *Perf. 14½*
Various Views of Plant and Various Frames
413 A48 1.50e lt brown, grn & blk   .55 .45
414 A48 2.50e multicolored   .85 .50
415 A48 5e multicolored   1.10 .15
416 A48 10e multicolored   2.75 1.00
    Nos. 413-416 (4)   5.25 2.70

Centenary of discovery of Welwitschia mirabilis, desert plant.

Map of West Africa, c. 1540, by Jorge Reinel — A49

1960, June 25   *Perf. 13½*
417 A49 2.50e multicolored   .20 .15

500th anniv. of the death of Prince Henry the Navigator.

Distributing Medicines — A50   Girl of Angola — A51

1960, Oct.   Litho.   *Perf. 14½*
418 A50 2.50e multicolored   .30 .15

10th anniv. of the Commission for Technical Co-operation in Africa South of the Sahara (C.C.T.A.).

1961, Nov. 30   Unwmk.   *Perf. 13*

Various portraits.

419 A51 10c multicolored   .15 .15
420 A51 15c multicolored   .15 .15
421 A51 30c multicolored   .15 .15
422 A51 40c multicolored   .15 .15
423 A51 60c multicolored   .15 .15
424 A51 1.50e multicolored   .15 .15
425 A51 2e multicolored   .60 .15
426 A51 2.50e multicolored   .85 .15
427 A51 3e multicolored   2.00 .20
428 A51 4e multicolored   .90 .20
429 A51 5e multicolored   .70 .20
430 A51 7.50e multicolored   .90 .45
431 A51 10e multicolored   .70 .15
432 A51 15e multicolored   .65 .40
432A A51 25e multicolored   1.90 .65
432B A51 50e multicolored   3.25 1.00
    Nos. 419-432B (16)   13.35 4.55

Sports Issue
Common Design Type

Sports: 50c, Flying. 1e, Rowing. 1.50e, Water polo. 2.50e, Hammer throwing. 4.50e, High jump. 15e, Weight lifting.

1962, Jan. 18   *Perf. 13½*
Multicolored Design
433 CD48 50c lt blue   .15 .15
434 CD48 1e olive bister   .70 .15
435 CD48 1.50e salmon   .32 .15
436 CD48 2.50e lt green   .40 .15
437 CD48 4.50e pale blue   .32 .25
438 CD48 15e yellow   1.50 .65
    Nos. 433-438 (6)   3.39 1.50

For overprint see No. 608.

Anti-Malaria Issue
Common Design Type

Design: Anopheles funestus.

1962, April   Litho.   *Perf. 13½*
439 CD49 2.50e multicolored   .60 .32

Gen. Norton de Matos — A54   Locusts — A56

1962, Aug. 8   Unwmk.   *Perf. 14½*
440 A54 2.50e multicolored   .30 .15

50th anniv. of the founding of Nova Lisboa.

1963, June 2   Litho.   *Perf. 14*
447 A56 2.50e multicolored   .40 .20

15th anniv. of the Intl. Anti-Locust Organ.

Arms of Luanda A57

Vila de Santo Antonio do Zaire — A58

Coats of Arms (Provinces and Cities): 10c, Massangano. 15c, Sanza-Pombo. 25c, Ambriz. 30c, Muxima. 40c, Ambrizete. 50c, Carmona. 60c, Catete. 70c, Quibaxe. No. 458, Maquelo do Zombo. 1e, Salazar. 1.20e, Bembe. No. 461, Malanje. No. 462, Caxito. 1.80e, Dondo. 2e, Henrique de Carvalho. No. 465, Moçamedes. No. 466, Damba. 3e, Novo Redondo. 3.50e, S. Salvador do Congo. 4e, Cuimba. 5e, Luso. 6.50e, Negage. 7e, Quitexe. 7.50e, S. Filipe de Benguela. 8e, Mucaba. 9e, 31 de Janeiro. 10e, Lobito. 11e, Nova Caipemba. 12.50e, Gabela. 14e, Songo. 15e Sá da Bandeira. 17e, Quimbele. 17.50e, Silva Porto. 20e, Nova Lisboa. 22.50e, Cabinda. 25e, Noqui. 30e, Serpa Pinto. 35e, Santa Cruz. 50e, General Freire.

1963   *Perf. 13½*
Arms in Original Colors; Red and Violet Blue Inscriptions
448 A57 5c tan   .15 .15
449 A57 10c lt blue   .15 .15
450 A58 15c salmon   .15 .15
451 A58 20c olive   .15 .15
452 A58 25c lt blue   .15 .15
453 A57 30c buff   .15 .15
454 A58 40c gray   .15 .15
455 A57 50c lt green   .15 .15
456 A58 60c brt yellow   .15 .15
457 A58 70c dull rose   .15 .15
458 A57 1e pale lilac   .30 .15
459 A58 1e dull yellow   .20 .15
460 A58 1.20e rose   .15 .15
461 A57 1.50e pale salmon   .60 .15
462 A58 1.50e lt green   .40 .15
463 A58 1.80e yel olive   .22 .15
464 A57 2e lt yel green   .30 .15
465 A57 2.50e lt gray   1.50 .15
466 A58 2.50e dull blue   1.25 .15
467 A57 3e olive   .42 .15
468 A57 3.50e gray   .50 .15
469 A58 4e citron   .35 .15
470 A57 5e citron   .40 .22

---

471 A58 6.50e tan   .40 .25
472 A58 7e rose lilac   .42 .25
473 A57 7.50e pale lilac   .55 .30
474 A58 8e lt aqua   .45 .30
475 A58 9e yellow   .60 .30
476 A57 10e dp salmon   .70 .35
477 A58 11e dull yel grn   .70 .55
478 A57 12.50e pale blue   .90 .45
479 A58 14e lt gray   .90 .45
480 A57 15e lt blue   1.00 .45
481 A58 17e pale blue   1.10 .70
482 A57 17.50e dull yellow   1.50 1.00
483 A57 20e lt aqua   1.50 .70
484 A57 22.50e gray   1.50 1.00
485 A58 25e citron   1.50 .70
486 A57 30e yellow   2.00 1.25
487 A58 35e grysh blue   2.00 1.50
488 A58 50e dp yellow   3.00 1.25
    Nos. 448-488 (41)   28.81 15.27

Pres. Américo Rodrigues Thomaz — A59

1963, Sept. 16   Litho.
489 A59 2.50e multicolored   .50 .30

Visit of the President of Portugal.

Airline Anniversary Issue
Common Design Type

1963, Oct. 5   Unwmk.   *Perf. 14½*
490 CD50 1e lt blue & multi   .25 .15

Cathedral of Sá da Bandeira A61   Malange Cathedral A62

Churches: 20c, Landana. 30c, Luanda Cathedral. 40c, Gabela. 50c, St. Martin's Chapel, Baia dos Tigres. 1.50e, St. Peter, Chibia. 2e, Church of Our Lady, Benguela. 2.50e, Church of Jesus, Luanda. 3e, Camabatela. 3.50e, Mission, Cabinda. 4e, Vila Folgares. 4.50e, Church of Our Lady, Lobito. 5e, Church of Cabinda. 7.50e, Cacuso Church, Malange. 10e, Lubango Mission. 12.50e, Huila Mission. 15e, Church of Our Lady, Luanda Island.

1963, Nov. 1   Litho.
Multicolored Design and Inscription
491 A61 10c gray blue   .15 .15
492 A61 20c pink   .15 .15
493 A61 30c lt blue   .15 .15
494 A61 40c tan   .15 .15
495 A61 50c lt green   .15 .15
496 A62 1e buff   .15 .15
497 A61 1.50e lt vio blue   .15 .15
498 A62 2e pale rose   .15 .15
499 A61 2.50e gray   .15 .15
500 A62 3e buff   .18 .15
501 A61 3.50e olive   .22 .15
502 A62 4e buff   .22 .20
503 A62 4.50e pale blue   .40 .22
504 A61 5e tan   .50 .22
505 A61 7.50e gray   .60 .32
506 A61 10e dull yellow   .75 .40
507 A62 12.50e bister   1.00 .80
508 A62 15e pale gray vio   2.50 .70
    Nos. 491-508 (18)   7.72
    Set value   3.65

National Overseas Bank Issue
Common Design Type

Design: Antonio Teixeira de Sousa.

1964, May 16   *Perf. 13½*
509 CD51 2.50e multicolored   .40 .22

Commerce Building and Arms of Chamber of Commerce A64

1964, Nov.   Litho.   *Perf. 12*
510 A64 1e multicolored   .15 .15

Luanda Chamber of Commerce centenary.

ITU Issue
Common Design Type

1965, May 17   Unwmk.   *Perf. 14½*
511 CD52 2.50e gray & multi   .70 .25

Plane over Luanda Airport — A65   Harquebusier, 1539 — A66

1965, Dec. 3   Litho.   *Perf. 13*
512 A65 2.50e multicolored   .22 .15

25th anniv. of DTA, Direccao dos Transportes Aereos.

1966, Feb. 25   Litho.   *Perf. 14½*

50c, Harquebusier, 1539. 1e, Harquebusier, 1640. 1.50e, Infantry officer, 1777. 2e, Standard bearer, infantry, 1777. 2.50e, Infantry soldier, 1777. 3e, Cavalry officer, 1783. 4e, Cavalry soldier, 1783. 4.50e, Infantry officer, 1807. 5e, Infantry soldier, 1807. 6e, Cavalry officer, 1807. 8e, Cavalry soldier, 1807. 9e, Infantry soldier, 1873.

513 A66 50c multicolored   .15 .15
514 A66 1e multicolored   .15 .15
515 A66 1.50e multicolored   .15 .15
516 A66 2e multicolored   .15 .15
517 A66 2.50e multicolored   .20 .15
518 A66 3e multicolored   .20 .15
519 A66 4e multicolored   .40 .25
520 A66 4.50e multicolored   .40 .25
521 A66 5e multicolored   .60 .18
522 A66 6e multicolored   .75 .50
523 A66 8e multicolored   1.25 .85
524 A66 9e multicolored   1.50 1.00
    Nos. 513-524 (12)   5.90 3.93

National Revolution Issue
Common Design Type

Design: St. Paul's Hospital and Commercial and Industrial School.

1966, May 28   Litho.   *Perf. 12*
525 CD53 1e multicolored   .20 .15

Emblem of Holy Ghost Society — A68

1966   Litho.   *Perf. 13*
526 A68 1e blue & multi   .15 .15

Centenary of the Holy Ghost Society.

Navy Club Issue
Common Design Type

Designs: 1e, Mendes Barata and cruiser Dom Carlos I. 2.50e, Capt. Augusto de Castilho and corvette Mindelo.

1967, Jan. 31   Litho.   *Perf. 13*
527 CD54 1e multicolored   .38 .15
528 CD54 2.50e multicolored   .65 .18

Fatima Basilica — A70   Angola Map, Manuel Cerveira Pereira — A71

1967, May 13   Litho.   *Perf. 12½x13*
529 A70 50c multicolored   .15 .15

50th anniv. of the apparition of the Virgin Mary to 3 shepherd children at Fatima.

1967, Aug. 15   Litho.   *Perf. 12½x13*
530 A71 50c multicolored   .15 .15

350th anniv. of the founding of Benguela.

Administration Building, Carmona — A72

1967   Litho.   Perf. 12
531 A72 1e multicolored   .15 .15
50th anniv. of the founding of Carmona.

Military Order of Valor — A73

Our Lady of Hope — A74

Designs: 50c, Ribbon of the Three Orders. 1.50e, Military Order of Avis. 2e, Military Order of Christ. 2.50e, Military Order of St. John of Espada. 3e, Order of the Empire. 4e, Order of Prince Henry. 5e, Order of Benemerencia. 10e, Order of Public Instruction. 20e, Order for Industrial and Agricultural Merit.

1967, Oct. 31   Perf. 14
532 A73 50c lt gray & multi   .15 .15
533 A73 1e lt green & multi   .15 .15
534 A73 1.50e yellow & multi   .15 .15
535 A73 2e multicolored   .15 .15
536 A73 2.50e multicolored   .15 .15
537 A73 3e lt olive & multi   .18 .15
538 A73 4e gray & multi   .20 .15
539 A73 5e multicolored   .25 .15
540 A73 10e lilac & multi   .40 .25
541 A73 20e lt blue & multi   1.00 .52
        Nos. 532-541 (10)   2.78
            Set value   1.28

1968, Apr. 22   Litho.   Perf. 14
Designs: 1e, Belmonte Castle, horiz. 1.50e, St. Jerome's Convent. 2.50e, Cabral's Armada.
542 A74 50c yellow & multi   .15 .15
543 A74 1e gray & multi   .25 .15
544 A74 1.50e lt blue & multi   .40 .15
545 A74 2.50e buff & multi   .60 .15
        Nos. 542-545 (4)   1.40
            Set value   .32
500th anniv. of the birth of Pedro Alvares Cabral, navigator who took possession of Brazil for Portugal.

Francisco Inocencio de Souza Coutinho — A75

1969, Jan. 7   Litho.   Perf. 14
546 A75 2e multicolored   .25 .20
Founding of Novo Redondo, 200th anniv.

Admiral Coutinho Issue
Common Design Type
Design: Adm. Gago Coutinho and his first ship.

1969, Feb. 17   Litho.   Perf. 14
547 CD55 2.50e multicolored   .30 .15

Compass Rose A77

Portal of St. Jeronimo's Monastery A79

1969, Aug. 29   Litho.   Perf. 14
548 A77 1e multicolored   .15 .15
500th anniv. of the birth of Vasco da Gama (1469-1524), navigator.

Administration Reform Issue
Common Design Type
1969, Sept. 25   Litho.   Perf. 14
549 CD56 1.50e multicolored   .15 .15

1969, Dec. 1   Litho.   Perf. 14
550 A79 3e multicolored   .20 .15
500th anniv. of the birth of King Manuel I.

Angolasaurus Bocagei — A80

Fossils and Minerals: 1e, Ferrometeorite. 1.50e, Dioptase crystals. 2e, Gondwanidium. 2.50e, Diamonds. 3e, Estromatolite. 3.50e, Procarcharodon megalodon. 4e, Microceratodus angolensis. 4.50e, Moscovite. 5e, Barite. 6e, Nostoceras. 10e, Rotula orbiculus angolensis.

1970, Oct. 31   Litho.   Perf. 13
551 A80 50c tan & multi   .15 .15
552 A80 1e multicolored   .15 .15
553 A80 1.50e multicolored   .15 .15
554 A80 2e multicolored   .20 .15
555 A80 2.50e lt gray & multi   .20 .15
556 A80 3e multicolored   .20 .15
557 A80 3.50e blue & multi   .30 .15
558 A80 4e lt gray & multi   .30 .15
559 A80 4.50e gray & multi   .30 .15
560 A80 5e gray & multi   .30 .15
561 A80 6e pink & multi   .60 .20
562 A80 10e lt blue & multi   .75 .32
        Nos. 551-562 (12)   3.60
            Set value   1.40

Marshal Carmona Issue
Common Design Type
1970, Nov. 15   Perf. 14
563 CD57 2.50e multicolored   .22 .15

Arms of Malanje, Cotton Boll and Field — A82

1970, Nov. 20   Perf. 13
564 A82 2.50e multicolored   .22 .15
Centenary of the municipality of Malanje.

Mail Ships and Angola No. 1 — A83

4.50e, Steam locomotive and Angola No. 4.

1970, Dec. 1   Perf. 13½
565 A83 1.50e multicolored   .30 .15
566 A83 4.50e multicolored   .65 .22
Cent. of stamps of Angola. See No. C36. For overprint see No. 616B.

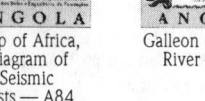

Map of Africa, Diagram of Seismic Tests — A84

Galleon on Congo River — A85

1971, Aug. 22   Litho.   Perf. 13
567 A84 2.50e multicolored   .15 .15
5th Regional Conference of Soil and Foundation Engineers, Luanda, Aug. 22-Sept. 5.

1972, May 25   Litho.   Perf. 13
568 A85 1e emerald & multi   .15 .15
4th centenary of the publication of The Lusiads by Luiz Camoens.

Olympic Games Issue
Common Design Type
1972, June 20   Perf. 14x13½
569 CD59 50c multicolored   .15 .15

Lisbon-Rio de Janeiro Flight Issue
Common Design Type
1972, Sept. 20   Litho.   Perf. 13½
570 CD60 1e multicolored   .15 .15

WMO Centenary Issue
Common Design Type
1973, Dec. 15   Litho.   Perf. 13
571 CD61 1e dk gray & multi   .15 .15

Radar Station A89

1974, June 25   Litho.   Perf. 13
572 A89 2e multicolored   .22 .15
Establishment of satellite communications network via Intelsat among Portugal, Angola and Mozambique.
For overprint see No. 616A

Harpa Doris — A90

Designs: Sea shells.

1974, Oct. 25   Litho.   Perf. 12x12½
573 A90 25c shown   .15 .15
574 A90 30c Murex me-
                lanamathos   .15 .15
575 A90 50c Venus foliaceo lamel-
                losa   .15 .15
576 A90 70c Lathyrus filosus   .15 .15
577 A90 1e Cymbium cisium   .18 .15
578 A90 1.50e Cassis tesselata   .18 .15
579 A90 2e Cypraea stercoraria   .18 .15
580 A90 2.50e Conus prometheus   .18 .18
581 A90 3e Strombus latus   .18 .18
582 A90 3.50e Tympanotonus fus-
                catus   .18 .18
583 A90 4e Cardium costatum   .25 .20
584 A90 5e Natica fulminea   .25 .20
585 A90 6e Lyropecten nodosus   .30 .20
586 A90 7e Tonna galea   .75 .25
587 A90 10e Donax rugosus   .90 .30
588 A90 25e Cymatium trigonum   1.50 .40
589 A90 30e Olivancilaria
                acuminata   2.50 .75
590 A90 35e Semifusus morio   2.50 .75
591 A90 40e Clavatula lineata   3.00 1.00
592 A90 50e Solarium granulatum   4.00 1.50
        Nos. 573-592 (20)   17.63
            Set value   4.00
For overprints see Nos. 605-607, 617-630.

No. 386 Overprinted in Blue: "1974 / FILATELIA / JUVENIL"
1974, Dec. 21   Litho.   Perf. 13½
593 A41 5c multicolored   .15 .15
Youth philately.

Republic

Star and Hand Holding Rifle — A91

1975, Nov. 11   Litho.   Perf. 13x13½
594 A91 1.50e red & multi   .15 .15
Independence in 1975.

Diquiche Mask — A92

Design: 3e, Bui ou Congolo mask.

1976, Feb. 6   Perf. 13½
595 A92 50c lt blue & multi   .15 .15
596 A92 3e multicolored   .20 .15
            Set value   .27 .15

Workers — A93

President Agostinho Neto — A94

1976, May 1   Litho.   Perf. 12
597 A93 1e red & multi   .15 .15
International Workers' Day.

No. 392 Overprinted Bar and: "DIA DO SELO / 15 Junho 1976 / REP. POPULAR / DE"
1976, June 15   Litho.   Perf. 13½
598 A41 10e multicolored   .40 .25
Stamp Day.

1976, Nov. 11   Litho.   Perf. 13
599 A94 50c yel & dk brown   .15 .15
600 A94 2e lt gray & plum   .15 .15
601 A94 3e gray & indigo   .15 .15
602 A94 5e buff & brown   .20 .15
603 A94 10e tan & sepia   .40 .15
a.   Souv. sheet of 1, imperf.   2.00 1.25
        Nos. 599-603 (5)   1.05
            Set value   .40
First anniversary of independence.

Nos. 393, 588-589, 592 Overprinted with Bar over Republica Portuguesa and: "REPUBLICA POPULAR DE"
1977, Feb. 9   Perf. 13½, 12x12½
604 A41 20e multicolored   1.25 .25
605 A90 25e multicolored   1.75 .35
606 A90 30e multicolored   2.50 .50
607 A90 50e multicolored   4.00 .75
        Nos. 604-607 (4)   9.50 1.85
Overprint in 3 lines on No. 604, in 2 lines on others.

No. 438 Overprinted with Bar over Republica Portuguesa and: "S. Silvestre / 1976 / Rep. Popular / de"
1976, Dec. 31   Perf. 13½
608 CD48 15e multicolored   3.50 .25

Angola stamps can be mounted in the Scott annual Portugal supplement.

Child and WHO
Emblem — A95

Map of Africa, Flag
of Angola — A96

1977   Litho.   Perf. 10½
609 A95 2.50k blk & lt blue   .15 .15
Campaign for vaccination against poliomyelitis.

1977   Photo.
610 A96 6k blk, red & bl   .20 .15
First congress of Popular Movement for the Liberation of Angola.

Anti-Apartheid
Emblem — A97

1979, June 20   Litho.   Perf. 13½
611 A97 1k multicolored   .15 .15
Anti-Apartheid Year.

Human Rights
Emblem — A98

Child Flowers,
Globe, IYC
Emblem — A99

1979, June 15   Litho.   Perf. 13½
612 A98 2.50k multicolored   .15 .15
Declaration of Human Rights, 30th anniv. (in 1975).

1980, May 1   Litho.   Perf. 14x14½
613 A99 3.50k multicolored   .15 .15
International Year of the Child (1979).

Running,
Moscow '80
Emblem
A100

5th Anniv. of
Independence
A101

1980, Dec. 15   Litho.   Perf. 13½
614 A100 9k shown   .32 .15
615 A100 12k Swimming, horiz.   .40 .20
22nd Summer Olympic Games, Moscow, July 19-Aug. 3.

1980, Nov. 11
616 A101 5.50k multicolored   .15 .15

Nos. 572, 566 Overprinted with Bar and:
"REPUBLICA POPULAR / DE"
1980-81   Litho.   Perf. 13½x13
616A A89 2e multi (bar only)   .50
616B A83 4.50e multicolored   1.00
Issue dates: 2e, May 17, 1981, 4.50e, June 15. See No. C37.

Nos. 577-580, 582-591 Overprinted with
Black Bar over "Republica Portuguesa"
1981, June 15   Litho.   Perf. 12x12½
617 A90 1e multicolored
618 A90 1.50e multicolored
619 A90 2e multicolored
620 A90 2.50e multicolored
621 A90 3.50e multicolored
622 A90 4e multicolored
623 A90 5e multicolored
624 A90 6e multicolored
625 A90 7e multicolored
626 A90 10e multicolored
627 A90 25e multicolored
628 A90 30e multicolored
629 A90 35e multicolored
630 A90 40e multicolored
      Nos. 617-630 (14)   15.00 8.00

Man Walking with
Canes, Tchibinda Ilunga
Statue — A102

1981, Sept. 5   Litho.   Perf. 13½
631 A102 9k multicolored   .32 .20
Turipex '81 tourism exhibition.

M.P.L.A. Workers'
Party
Congress — A103

1980, Dec. 23   Litho.   Perf. 14
632 A103 50 l Millet   .15 .15
633 A103 5k Coffee   .20 .15
634 A103 7.50k Sunflowers   .25 .15
635 A103 13.50k Cotton   .40 .20
636 A103 14k Oil   .45 .25
637 A103 16k Diamonds   .45 .25
      Nos. 632-637 (6)   1.90 1.15

People's
Power — A104

Natl. Heroes'
Day — A105

1980, Nov. 11
638 A104 40k lt blue & blk   1.25 .40

1980, Sept. 17   Perf. 14x13½
639 A105 4.50k Former Pres. Neto   .15 .15
640 A105 50k Neto, diff.   1.50 .65

Soweto
Uprising, 5th
Anniv.
A106

1981
641 A106 4.50k multicolored   .20 .15

2nd
Central
African
Games
A107

1981, Sept. 3   Litho.   Perf. 13½
642 A107 50 l Bicycling, tennis   .15 .15
643 A107 5k Judo, boxing   .20 .15
644 A107 6k Basketball, volleyball   .22 .15
645 A107 10k Handball, soccer   .40 .25
      Nos. 642-645 (4)   .97

                    Set value   .52
              Souvenir Sheet
                    Imperf
646 A107 15k multicolored   2.00

Charaxes
Kahldeni
A108

1982, Feb. 26   Litho.   Perf. 13½
647 A108 50 l shown   .15 .15
648 A108 1k Abantis zambesiaca   .15 .15
649 A108 5k Catacroptera
          cloanthe   .20 .15
650 A108 9k Myrina ficedula, vert.   .40 .15
651 A108 10k Colotis danae   .40 .15
652 A108 15k Acraea acrita   .52 .25
653 A108 100k Precis hierta   2.75 1.25
  a.   Souvenir sheet   2.00 1.00
      Nos. 647-653 (7)   4.57 2.25
  No. 653a contains Nos. 647-653, imperf., and
sold for 30k (stamps probably not valid
individually).

5th Anniv. of
UN
Membership
A109

5.50k, The Silence of the Night, by Musseque
Catambor. 7.50k, Cotton picking, Catete.
1982, Sept. 22   Litho.
654 A109 5.50k multicolored   .20 .15
655 A109 7.50k multicolored   .25 .15

20th Anniv. of
Engineering
Laboratory
A110

1982, Dec. 21   Litho.   Perf. 14
656 A110 9k Lab   .25 .15
657 A110 13k Worker, vert.   .40 .20
658 A110 100k Equipment, vert.   3.25 1.25
      Nos. 656-658 (3)   3.90 1.60

Local
Flowers
A111

1983, Feb. 18   Perf. 13½
659 A111 5k Dichrostachys glomer-
          ata   .15 .15
660 A111 12k Amblygonocarpus ob-
          tusangulus   .40 .15
661 A111 50k Albizzia versicolor   2.00 .65
      Nos. 659-661 (3)   2.55 .95

Women's Org., First
Congress — A112

Africa
Day — A113

1983   Litho.   Perf. 13½
662 A112 20k multicolored   .80 .80

1983, June 30   Perf. 13
663 A113 6.5k multi   .25 .25

World Communications Year — A114

1983, June 30   Litho.   Perf. 13½
664 A114 6.5k M'pungi   .25 .25
665 A114 12k Mondu   .40 .40

BRASILIANA
'83 Stamp
Exhibition,
Rio de
Janeiro, July
29-Aug.
7 — A115

Crop-eating insects.

1983, July 29   Litho.   Perf. 13
666 A115 4.5k Antestiopsis lineaticollis .18 .18
667 A115 6.5k Stephanoderes hampei
          ferr.   .25 .25
668 A115 10k Zonocerus variegatus   .40 .40
      Nos. 666-668 (3)   .83 .83

25th Anniv.
of Economic
Commission
for Africa
A116

1983, Aug. 2
669 A116 10k Map, emblem   .40 .40

185th Anniv.
of Post Office
A117

1983, Dec. 7   Litho.   Perf. 13½
670 A117 50 l Mail collection, vert. .15 .15
671 A117 3.5k Unloading mail
          plane   .15 .15
672 A117 5k Sorting mail   .20 .20
673 A117 15k Mailing letter, vert.   .60 .60
674 A117 30k Post office box deliv-
          ery   1.25 1.25
  a.   Min. sheet of 3, #671-672, 674   4.00 4.00
      Nos. 670-674 (5)   2.35 2.35
  No. 674a sold for 100k.

Local
Butterflies
A118

1984, Jan. 20   Litho.   Perf. 13½
675 A118 50 l Parasa karschi   .15 .15
676 A118 1k Diaphone angolensis   .15 .15
677 A118 3.5k Choeropasis jucunda .15 .15
678 A118 6.5k Hespagarista rendalli .25 .25
679 A118 15k Euchromia guineen-
          sis   .60 .60

680 A118 17.5k Mazuca roseistriga .70 .70
681 A118 20k Utetheisa callima .85 .85
Nos. 675-681 (7) 2.85 2.85

A119 A120

1984, Apr. 11 Litho. Perf. 13½
682 A119 30k multicolored 1.25 1.25
First Natl. Worker's Union Congress, Apr. 11-16 .

1984, Oct. 24 Litho. Perf. 13½
Local birds.
683 A120 10.50k Bucorvos
leadbeateri .45 .40
684 A120 14k Gyphicax angolensis .55 .50
685 A120 16k Ardea goliath .60 .50
686 A120 19.50k Pelicanus onocrotalus .80 .75
687 A120 22k Platelea alba .90 .90
688 A120 26k Balearica pavonnia 1.00 1.00
Nos. 683-688 (6) 4.30 4.05

Local Animals
A121

1984, Nov. 12
689 A121 1k Tragelephus strep-
sicerus .15 .15
690 A121 4k Antidorcos marsupialis
angolerusis .15 .15
691 A121 5k Pan troglodytes .20 .20
692 A121 10k Sycerus caffer .40 .40
693 A121 15k Hippotragus niger variani .60 .60
694 A121 20k Orycteropus afer .80 .80
695 A121 25k Crocuta crocuta 1.00 1.00
Nos. 689-695 (7) 3.30 3.30

Angolese
Monuments
A122

1985, Feb. 21 Litho. Perf. 13½
696 A122 5k San Pedro da Barra .22 .22
697 A122 12.5k Nova Oeiras .55 .55
698 A122 18k M'Banza Kongo .80 .80
699 A122 26k Massangano 1.10 1.10
700 A122 39k Escravatura Museum 1.65 1.65
Nos. 696-700 (5) 4.32 4.32

United
Workers'
Party, 25th
Anniv.
A123

1985, May Litho. Perf. 12
701 A123 77k XXV, red flags 1.50 1.50
Printed in sheets of 5.

A124 A125

1985, May
702 A124 1k Flags .15 .15
703 A124 11k Oil drilling platform,
Cabinda .22 .22
704 A124 57k Conference 1.10 1.10
a. Strip of 3, #702-704 1.40 1.40
Southern African Development Council, 5th
anniv.

Lithographed and Typographed
1985, July 5 Perf. 11
Medicinal plants.
705 A125 1k Lonchocarpus ser-
iceus .15 .15
706 A125 4k Gossypium .15 .15
707 A125 11k Cassia occidentalis .22 .22
708 A125 25.50k Gloriosa superba .50 .50
709 A125 55k Cochlospermum
angolensis 1.10 1.10
Nos. 705-709 (5) 2.12 2.12
ARGENTINA '85 exhibition.

5th Natl.
Heroes
Day — A126

Natl. flag and: 10.50k, Portrait of Agostinho
Neto, party leader. 36.50k, Neto working.

1985 Litho. Perf. 13½
710 A126 10.50k multicolored .20 .20
711 A126 36.50k multicolored .70 .70

Ministerial
Conference
of Non-
Aligned
Countries,
Luanda
A127

1985, Sept. 4 Photo. Perf. 11
712 A127 35k multicolored 1.50 1.50

UN, 40th
Anniv.
A128

1985, Oct. 29 Litho. Perf. 11
713 A128 12.50k multicolored .55 .55

Industry
and Natural
Resources
A129

1985, Nov. 11
714 A129 50 l Cement Factory .15 .15
715 A129 5k Logging .22 .22
716 A129 7k Quartz .30 .30
717 A129 10k Iron mine .42 .42
a. Souvenir sheet of 4, #714-717, imperf. 1.00 1.00
Nos. 714-717 (4) 1.09 1.09
Natl. independence, 10th anniv.

2nd Natl.
Workers'
Party
Congress
(MPLA)
A130

1985, Nov. 28 Perf. 13½
718 A130 20k multicolored .85 .85

Demostenes de Almeida Clington Races,
30th Anniv. — A131

Various runners.

1985, Dec. 13
719 A131 50 l multicolored .15 .15
720 A131 5k multicolored .22 .22
721 A131 6.50k multicolored .28 .28
722 A131 10k multicolored .42 .42
Nos. 719-722 (4) 1.07 1.07

1986 World Cup
Soccer
Championships,
Mexico — A132

Map, soccer field and various plays.

1986, May 6 Litho. Perf. 11½x11
723 A132 50 l multi .15 .15
724 A132 3.50k multi .15 .15
725 A132 5k multi .22 .22
726 A132 7k multi .30 .30
727 A132 10k multi .42 .42
728 A132 18k multi .85 .85
Nos. 723-728 (6) 2.09 2.09

Struggle
Against
Portugal, 25th
Anniv.
A133

1986, May 6 Perf. 11x11½
729 A133 15k multicolored .65 .65

First Man in
Space, 25th
Anniv.
A134

1986, Aug. 21 Litho. Perf. 11x11½
730 A134 50 l Skylab, US .15 .15
731 A134 1k Spacecraft .15 .15
732 A134 5k A. Leonov space-
walking .22 .22
733 A134 10k Lunokhod on Moon .42 .42
734 A134 13k Apollo-Soyuz link-up .60 .60
Nos. 730-734 (5) 1.54 1.54

Admission of
Angola to UN,
10th
Anniv. — A135

1986, Dec. 1 Litho. Perf. 11x11½
735 A135 22k multi .90 .90

Liberation Movement, 30th
Anniv. — A136

Angolese at work, fighting and: No. 736a,
"1956." No. 736b, Congress emblem, "1980."
No. 736c, Labor Party emblem, "1985."

1986, Dec. 3 Perf. 11½x11
736 A136 Strip of 3 .65 .65
a.-c. 5k any single .20 .20

Agostinho
Neto
University,
10th Anniv.
A137

1986, Dec. 30 Litho. Perf. 11x11½
737 A137 50 l Mathematics .15 .15
738 A137 1k Law .15 .15
739 A137 10k Medicine .45 .45
Nos. 737-739 (3) .75 .75

Tribal
Hairstyles — A138

1987, Apr. 15 Litho. Perf. 11½x11
740 A138 1k Ouioca .15 .15
741 A138 1.50k Luanda .15 .15
742 A138 5k Humbe .15 .15
743 A138 7k Muila .15 .15
744 A138 20k Muila, diff. .45 .45
745 A138 30k Dilolo .70 .70
Nos. 740-745 (6) 1.75 1.75

Landscapes — A139 Lenin — A140

Perf. 11½x12, 12x11½
1987, July 7 Litho.
746 A139 50 l Pambala Shore .15 .15
747 A139 1.50k Dala Waterfalls .15 .15
748 A139 3.50k Black Stones .15 .15
749 A139 5k Cuango River .15 .15
750 A139 10k Launda coast .22 .22
751 A139 20k Hills of Leba .50 .50
Set value 1.00 1.00
Nos. 746-747, 749 and 751 horiz.

1987, Nov. 25 Perf. 12x12½
752 A140 15k multi .58 .58
October Revolution, Russia, 70th anniv.

2nd Congress of the
Organization of
Angolan Women
(OMA) — A141

1988, May 30 Litho. Perf. 13x13½
753 A141 2k shown .15 .15
754 A141 10k Soldier, nurse, technician, student .35 .35

Victory Carnival,
10th
Anniv. — A142

Various carnival scenes.

1988, June 15 Litho. Perf. 13½x13
755 A142 5k shown .16 .16
756 A142 10k multi, diff. .32 .32

Augusto N'Gangula (1956-1968), Youth
Pioneer Killed by Portuguese Colonial
Army — A143

Agostinho Neto Pioneers' Organization
(OPA), 25th Anniv. — A144

1989, Oct. 2   Litho.   Perf. 12x11½
757 A143 12k multicolored   .40   .40
758 A144 15k multicolored   .48   .48
Pioneer Day.

10th Natl. Soccer Championships,
Benguela, May 1 — A145

1989, Oct. 16
759 A145 5k shown   .16   .16
760 A145 5k Luanda, 3 years   .16   .16
761 A145 5k Luanda, 5 years   .16   .16
Nos. 759-761 (3)   .48   .48

Intl. Fund for
Agricultural
Development, 10th
Anniv. — A146

1990, Feb. 15   Litho.   Perf. 11½x12
762 A146 10k multicolored   .70   .70

Ingombotas'
Houses
A147

Architecture: 2k, Alta Train Station. 5k, National
Museum of Anthropology. 15k, Ana Joaquina Palace. 23k, Iron Palace. 36k, Meteorological observatory, vert. 50k, People's Palace.

**   Perf. 12x11½, 11½x12**
1990, Feb. 20
763 A147 1k shown   .15   .15
764 A147 2k multicolored   .15   .15
765 A147 5k multicolored   .32   .32
766 A147 15k multicolored   .98   .98
767 A147 23k multicolored   1.50   1.50
768 A147 36k multicolored   2.30   2.30
769 A147 50k multicolored   3.25   3.25
Nos. 763-769 (7)   8.65   8.65

Luanda and
Benguela
Railways
A148

Various maps and locomotives.

1990, Mar. 1   Perf. 12x11½
770 A148 5k shown   .35   .35
771 A148 12k Garrat T (left)   .80   .80
772 A148 12k Garrat T (right)   .80   .80
  a.   Pair, #771-772   1.60   1.60
773 A148 14k Mikado   .95   .95
Nos. 770-773 (4)   2.90   2.90

Souvenir Sheet
774 A148 25k Diesel electric   2.35   2.35
No. 772a has a continuous design.

Southern
Africa
Development
Coordinating
Conf.
(SADCC),
10th Anniv.
A149

1990, Apr. 1   Litho.   Perf. 14
775 A149 5k shown   1.25   1.25
776 A149 9k Floating oil rig   2.50   2.50

Pan-African
Postal Union
(PAPU), 10th
Anniv.
A150

1990, Apr. 6
777 A150 4k shown   .75   .75
778 A150 10k Simulated stamp, map 1.50 1.50

Paintings by
Raul Indipwo
A151

1990, Apr. 24
779 A151 6k Tres Gracas   .42   .42
780 A151 9k Muxima, vert.   .65   .65
Stamp World London 90.

Hippotragus Niger Variani, Adult Male and
Female — A152

1990, May 9   Perf. 14x13½
781 A152 5k Adult male   .35   .35
782 A152 5k shown   .35   .35
783 A152 5k Adult female   .35   .35
784 A152 5k Female, calf   .35   .35
Nos. 781-784 (4)   1.40   1.40

World Wildlife Fund. Various combinations available in blocks or strips of four.

Rosa de
Porcelana — A153

1990, June 2   Litho.   Perf. 14
785 A153 5k shown   .35   .35
786 A153 8k Cravo burro   .56   .56
787 A153 10k Alamandra   .70   .70
Nos. 785-787 (3)   1.61   1.61

Souvenir Sheet
788 A153 40k Hibiscus   2.70   2.70
Belgica '90.

Miniature Sheet

Intl. Literacy Year — A154

Various animals and forest scenes.

1990, July 26   Litho.   Perf. 14
789   Sheet of 30   2.25   2.25
  a.   A154 1k any single   .15   .15
790 A154 5k Zebra   .35   .35
791 A154 5k Butterfly   .35   .35
792 A154 5k Horse   .35   .35
  a.   Block of 3, #790-792 + label 1.05 1.05

People's
Assembly, 10th
Anniv.
A155

1990, Nov. 11   Perf. 14
793 A155 10k multicolored   .70   .70

3rd Natl. Labor
Congress — A156

1990   Litho.   Perf. 13½
794 A156 14k multicolored   1.35   1.35

War of
Independence,
30th Anniv.
A157

Uniforms.

1991, Feb. 28   Litho.   Perf. 14
795 A157 6k Machete, 1961   .42   .42
  a.   Perf. 13½ vert.   .42   .42
796 A157 6k Rifle, 1962-63   .42   .42
  a.   Perf. 13½ vert.   .42   .42
797 A157 6k Rifle, 1968   .42   .42
  a.   Perf. 13½ vert.   .42   .42
798 A157 6k Automatic rifle, 1972 .42   .42
  a.   Perf. 13½ vert.   .42   .42
  b.   Bklt. pane of 4, #795a-798a 1.70
Nos. 795-798 (4)   1.68   1.68

Musical
Instruments
A158

Designs: a, Marimba. b, Mucupela. c, Ngoma la
Txina. d, Kissange.

1991, Apr. 5   Litho.   Perf. 14
799 A158 6k Block or strip of 4,
          #799a-799d   1.70   1.70

Tourism
A159

Designs: 3k, Iona National Park. 7k, Kalandula
Waterfalls. 35k, Lobito Bay. 60k, Weltwitschia
Mirabilis plant.

1991, June 25   Litho.   Perf. 14
800 A159 3k multi   .15   .15
801 A159 7k multi   .24   .24
802 A159 35k multi   1.15   1.15
803 A159 60k multi   2.00   2.00
Nos. 800-803 (4)   3.54   3.54

Dogs — A160

1991, July 5   Litho.   Perf. 14
804 A160 5k Kabir of dembos   .16   .16
805 A160 7k Ombua   .24   .24
806 A160 11k Kabir massongo   .38   .38
807 A160 12k Kawa tchowe   .40   .40
Nos. 804-807 (4)   1.18   1.18

1992 Summer
Olympics,
Barcelona
A161

1991, July 26   Perf. 13
808 A161   4k Judo   .15   .15
809 A161   6k Sailing   .20   .20
810 A161 10k Running   .35   .35
811 A161 100k Swimming   3.35   3.35
Nos. 808-811 (4)   4.05   4.05

Navigation
Aids — A162

1991, Nov. 8   Litho.   Perf. 12
812 A162 5k Quadrant   .16   .16
813 A162 15k Astrolabe   .52   .52
814 A162 20k Cross-staff   .70   .70
815 A162 50k Portolano   1.75   1.75
Nos. 812-815 (4)   3.13   3.13
Iberex '91.

Rays — A163

1992, Mar. 30   Litho.   Perf. 14
816 A163 40k Myliobatis aquila   .15   .15
817 A163 50k Aetobatus narinari .18   .18
818 A163 66k Manta birostris   .24   .24
819 A163 80k Raja miraletus   .30   .30
Nos. 816-819 (4)   .87   .87

Souvenir Sheet
Perf. 13½
820 A163 25k Manta birostris, diff. .15 .15

Quioca
Masks — A164

1992, Apr. 30   Litho.   *Perf. 13 1/2*
821 A164 60k Kalelwa   .22 .22
822 A164 100k Mukixe Wa Kino   .38 .38
823 A164 150k Cikunza   .55 .55
824 A164 250k Mukixi Wa Mbwesu .92 .92
    Nos. 821-824 (4)   2.07 2.07

See Nos. 854-857, 868-871, 883-886, 895-898.

Medicinal
Plants — A165

Designs: 200k, Ptaeroxylon obliquum. 300k,
Spondias mombin. 500k, Parinari curatellifolia.
600k, Cochlospermum angolense.

1992, May 8   *Perf. 14*
825 A165 200k brown & pale yel .75 .75
826 A165 300k brown & pale yel 1.10 1.10
827 A165 500k brown & pale yel 1.85 1.85
828 A165 600k brown & pale yel 2.20 2.20
  a.   Block or strip of 4, #825-828 5.90 5.90

Evangelization of Angola, 500th
Anniv. — A166

1992, May 10   *Perf. 13 1/2*
829 A166 150k King, missionaries .55 .55
830 A166 420k Ruins of M'banza
              Congo   1.55 1.55
831 A166 470k Maxima Church   1.75 1.75
832 A166 500k Faces of people   1.90 1.90
    Nos. 829-832 (4)   5.75 5.75

Traditional
Houses — A167

Perf. 14, 13 1/2 Vert. (#832A)
1992, May 22
832A A167 150k Dimbas   1.25 1.25
  b.   Bklt. pane of 4, #832A, 833a-835a 5.00
833 A167 330k Cokwe   1.25 1.25
  a.   Perf. 13 1/2 vert.   1.25 1.25
834 A167 360k Mbali   1.35 1.35
  a.   Perf. 13 1/2 vert.   1.35 1.35
835 A167 420k Ambwelas   1.55 1.55
  a.   Perf. 13 1/2 vert.   1.55 1.55
836 A167 500k Upper Zambezi   1.90 1.90
    Nos. 832A-836 (5)   7.30 7.30

Expo '92, Seville.

Agapornis
Roseicollis
A168

1992, June 2   *Perf. 12x11 1/2*
837 A168 150k Two birds on branch .55 .55
838 A168 200k Birds feeding   .75 .75
839 A168 250k Hand holding bird   .92 .92
840 A168 300k Bird on perch   1.10 1.10
  a.   Strip of 4, #837-840   3.35 3.35

Expo '92, Seville.

Souvenir Sheet

Visit of Pope John
Paul II to
Angola — A169

Abstract paintings: a, 340k, The Crucifixion. b,
370k, The Resurrection.

1992, June 4   Litho.   *Perf. 13 1/2*
841 A169 Sheet of 2, #a.-b. + 2 la-
              bels   1.80 1.80

1992 Summer
Olympics,
Barcelona
A170

1992, July 30   *Perf. 14*
842 A170 120k Hurdles   .32 .32
843 A170 180k Cycling   .50 .50
844 A170 240k Roller hockey   .65 .65
845 A170 360k Basketball   1.00 1.00
    Nos. 842-845 (4)   2.47 2.47

Native
Fishing — A171

1992, Aug. 5   *Perf. 11 1/2x12*
846 A171 65k Building traps   .18 .18
847 A171 90k Using nets   .25 .25
848 A171 100k Laying traps   .28 .28
849 A171 120k Fisherman in boats .32 .32
    Nos. 846-849 (4)   1.03 1.03

Souvenir Sheet

Discovery of America, 500th
Anniv. — A172

1992, Sept. 18   Litho.   *Perf. 12*
850 A172 500k multicolored   1.35 1.35

Genoa '92.

First Free Elections in
Angola — A173

Designs: 120k, People voting. 150k, Map, ballot
box, peace doves. 200k, People, dove, hand dropping ballot into ballot box.

1992, Oct. 27   Litho.   *Perf. 11 1/2x12*
851 A173 120k multicolored   .32 .32
852 A173 150k multicolored   .42 .42
853 A173 200k multicolored   .55 .55
    Nos. 851-853 (3)   1.29 1.29

Quioca Mask Type of 1992

1992, Nov. 6   *Perf. 13 1/2*
854 A164 72k Cihongo   .28 .28
855 A164 80k Mbwasu   .30 .30
856 A164 120k Cinhanga   .45 .45
857 A164 210k Kalewa   .80 .80
    Nos. 854-857 (4)   1.83 1.83

Inauguration
of Express
Mail Service
A174

1992, Dec. 14   Litho.   *Perf. 12x11 1/2*
858 A174 450k Truck   1.05 1.05
859 A174 550k Airplane   1.25 1.25

Meteorological
Instruments — A175

1993, Mar. 23   Litho.   *Perf. 11 1/2x12*
860 A175 250k Weather balloon   .58 .58
861 A175 470k Actinometer   1.10 1.10
862 A175 500k Rain gauge   1.15 1.15
    Nos. 860-862 (3)   2.83 2.83

Seashells
A176

1993, Apr. 6   *Perf. 12x11 1/2*
863 A176 210k Trochita
              trochiformis   .48 .48
864 A176 330k Strombus latus   .75 .75
865 A176 400k Aporrhais pesgal-
              linae   .95 .95
866 A176 500k Fusos aff. albinus 1.15 1.15
    Nos. 863-866 (4)   3.33 3.33

Souvenir Sheet
867 A176 1000k Pusionella nifat 2.30 2.30

Quioca Art Type of 1992

1993, June 7   Litho.   *Perf. 12*
868 A164 72k Men with vehicles .15 .15
869 A164 210k Cavalier   .45 .45
870 A164 420k Airplane   .90 .90
871 A164 600k Men carrying stretch-
              er   1.25 1.25
    Nos. 868-871 (4)   2.75 2.75

Flowering
Plants — A177

1993, June 28   *Perf. 11 1/2x12*
872 A177 360k Sansevieria cylindrica .75 .75
873 A177 400k Euphorbia tirucalli .85 .85
874 A177 500k Opuntia ficus-indica 1.05 1.05
875 A177 600k Dracaena aubryana 1.25 1.25
    Nos. 872-875 (4)   3.90 3.90

Souvenir Sheet

Africa Day — A178

1993, May 31   *Perf. 12*
876 A178 1500k Leopard   3.15 3.15

Tribal Pipes — A179

1993, Aug. 16   Litho.   *Perf. 11 1/2x12*
877 A179 72k Vimbundi   .15 .15
878 A179 200k Vimbundi, diff.   .42 .42
879 A179 420k Mutopa   .88 .88
880 A179 600k Pexi   1.25 1.25
    Nos. 877-880 (4)   2.70 2.70

Souvenir Sheet

Union of Portuguese Speaking
Capitals — A180

1993, July 30   *Perf. 12x11 1/2*
881 A180 1500k multicolored   3.15 3.15

Turtles — A181

Designs: a, 180k, Chelonia mydas (b). b, 450k,
Eretmochelys imbricata. c, 550k, Dermochelys
coriacea. d, 630k, Caretta caretta.

1993, July 9   Litho.   *Perf. 12 1/2x12*
882 A181 Block of 4, #a.-d.   3.50 3.50

Quioca Art Type of 1992

1993, Sept. 1   Litho.   *Perf. 12*
883 A164 300k Leopard   .65 .65
884 A164 600k Malhado   1.25 1.25
885 A164 800k Birds   1.65 1.65
886 A164 1000k Chickens   2.00 2.00
    Nos. 883-886 (4)   5.55 5.55

Mushrooms — A182   A183

1993 Litho. Perf. 12
887 A182 300k Tricholoma georgii .55 .55
a. Perf. 11½ vert. .55 .55
888 A182 500k Amanita phalloides .95 .95
a. Perf. 11½ vert. .95 .95
889 A182 600k Amanita vaginata 1.10 1.10
a. Perf. 11½ vert. 1.10 1.10
890 A182 1000k Macrolepiota procera 1.90 1.90
a. Perf. 11½ vert. 1.90 1.90
b. Booklet pane of 4, #887a-890a 4.50
Nos. 887-890 (4) 4.50 4.50

1994, Jan. 10 Litho. Perf. 12
Natl. Culture Day: 500k, Cinganji, wood carving of dancer. 1000k, Ohunya yo soma, staff with woman's face. 1200k, Ongende, sculpture of man on donkey. 2200k, Upi, corn pestle.

891 A183 500k multicolored .45 .45
892 A183 1000k multicolored .90 .90
893 A183 1200k multicolored 1.10 1.10
894 A183 2200k multicolored 2.00 2.00
Nos. 891-894 (4) 4.45 4.45

Hong Kong '94.

Quioca Art Type of 1992
1994, Feb. 21 Litho. Perf. 12
895 A164 1000k Bird on flower .32 .32
896 A164 2000k Plant with roots 1.30 1.30
897 A164 2500k Feto 1.65 1.65
898 A164 3000k Plant 2.00 2.00
Nos. 895-898 (4) 5.27 5.27

Social Responsibilities of AIDS — A184

Designs: 500k, Mass of people. 1000k, Witchdoctor receiving AIDS through needle, people being educated. 3000k, Stylized man, woman.

1994, May 5 Litho. Perf. 12
899 A184 500k multicolored .32 .32
900 A184 1000k multicolored .65 .65
901 A184 3000k multicolored 2.00 2.00
Nos. 899-901 (3) 2.97 2.97

1994 World Cup Soccer Championships, US — A185

1994, June 17 Perf. 14
902 A185 500k Large arrows, small ball .32 .32
903 A185 700k Small arrows, large ball .45 .45
904 A185 2200k Ball in goal 1.50 1.50
905 A185 2500k Ball, foot 1.65 1.65
Nos. 902-905 (4) 3.92 3.92

Dinosaurs A186

1994, Aug. 16 Litho. Perf. 12
906 A186 1000k Brachiosaurus .15 .15
907 A186 3000k Spinosaurus .55 .55
908 A186 5000k Ouranosaurus .90 .90
909 A186 10,000k Lesothosaurus 1.90 1.90
Nos. 906-909 (4) 3.50 3.50

Souvenir Sheet
910 A186 19,000k Lesothosaurus, map of Africa 3.50 3.50

PHILAKOREA '94, SINGPEX '94. No. 910 contains one 44x34mm stamp.

Tourism A187 TURISMO

1994, Sept. 27 Litho. Perf. 12x11½
911 A187 2000k Birds .18 .18
912 A187 4000k Wild animals .35 .35
913 A187 8000k Native women .75 .75
914 A187 10,000k Native men .90 .90
Nos. 911-914 (4) 2.18 2.18

Post Boxes — A188

Designs: 5000k, Letters, bundled mail wall box. 7500k, Wall box for letters. 10,000k, Pillar box. 21,000k, Multi-function units.

1994, Oct. 7 Perf. 14½
915 A188 5000k multicolored .45 .45
916 A188 7500k multicolored .70 .70
917 A188 10,000k multicolored .90 .90
918 A188 21,000k multicolored 1.90 1.90
Nos. 915-918 (4) 3.95 3.95

Cotton Pests — A189

Insects: 5000k, Heliothis armigera. 6000k, Bemisia tabasi. 10,000k, Dysdercus. 27,000k, Spodoptera exigua.

1994, Nov. 11 Litho. Perf. 14
919 A189 5000k multicolored .45 .45
920 A189 6000k multicolored .55 .55
921 A189 10,000k multicolored .95 .95
922 A189 27,000k multicolored 2.50 2.50
Nos. 919-922 (4) 4.45 4.45

Intl. Olympic Committee, Cent. — A190

1994, Dec. 15
923 A190 27,000k multicolored 2.75 2.75

Tribal Culture A191

Designs: 10,000k. Rubbing sticks to start fire. 15,000k, Extracting sap from tree. 20,000k, Smoking tribal pipe. 25,000k, Shooting bow & arrow. 28,000k, Mothers, children. 30,000k, Cave art.

1995, Jan. 6 Litho. Perf. 14
924 A191 10,000k multicolored .42 .42
925 A191 15,000k multicolored .65 .65
926 A191 20,000k multicolored .85 .85
927 A191 25,000k multicolored 1.00 1.00
928 A191 28,000k multicolored 1.10 1.10
929 A191 30,000k multicolored 1.25 1.25
Nos. 924-929 (6) 5.27 5.27

Traditional Ceramics A192

Designs: No. 930, Pitcher with bust of a woman as stopper. No. 931, Cone-shaped vase. No. 932, Bird-shaped vase. No. 933, Pitcher with bust of a man as stopper.

1995, Jan. 2 Litho. Perf. 14½
930 A192 (2) 2nd class natl.
931 A192 (1) 1st class natl.
932 A192 (2) 2nd class intl.
933 A192 (1) 1st class intl.
Set value 3.36 3.36

Rotary Intl., 90th Anniv. A193

: a, Immunizing boy against polio. b, Medical examination. c, Immunizing girl against polio. No. 936, Dove over map.

1995, Feb. 23 Litho. Perf. 14
934 Strip of 3 2.25 2.25
a.-c. A193 27,000k any single .75 .75
935 Strip of 3 2.25 2.25
a.-c. A193 27,000k any single .75 .75

Souvenir Sheet
936 A193 81,000k multicolored 4.00 4.00
a. English inscription 4.00 4.00

No. 934 has Portuguese inscriptions. No. 935 has English inscriptions. Both were issued in sheets of 9 stamps.
No. 936 contains Portuguese inscription in sheet margin.

Rotary Intl., 90th Anniv. — A194

Illustration reduced.

Litho. & Embossed
1995, Feb. 23 Perf. 11½x12
937 A194 81,000k gold

World Telecommunications Day — A195

Designs: No. 938, 1957 Sputnik 1. No. 939, Shuttle, Intelsat satellite.

1995 Litho. Perf. 14
938 A195 27,000k multicolored 1.50 1.50
939 A195 27,000k multicolored 1.50 1.50
a. Souvenir sheet, #938-939 3.00 3.00

Independence, 20th Anniv. — A196

1995, Nov. Litho. Perf. 14
940 A196 2900k multicolored 1.50 1.50

4th World Conference on Women, Beijing — A197

Designs: 375k, Women working in fields. 1106k, Woman teaching, girls with book. 1265k, Woman in industry, career woman. 2900k, Woman in native headdress, vert. 1500k, Native mother, children, vert.

1996, Jan. 29 Litho. Perf. 14
941 A197 375k multicolored .15 .15
942 A197 1106k multicolored .40 .40
943 A197 1265k multicolored .45 .45
944 A197 2900k multicolored 1.00 1.00
Nos. 941-944 (4) 2.00 2.00

Souvenir Sheet
945 A197 1500k multicolored .50 .50

UN Assistance Programs A198

Designs: 200k, Boy, highlift moving supplies. 1265k, Supply ship arriving. No. 948, Two high lifts. No. 949, Tractor-trailer traveling past vultures, native girl. No. 950, Man, ship.

1996 Litho. Perf. 14
946 A198 200k multicolored .15 .15
947 A198 1265k multicolored .50 .50
948 A198 2583k multicolored 1.00 1.00
949 A198 2583k multicolored 1.00 1.00
Nos. 946-949 (4) 2.65 2.65

Souvenir Sheet
950 A198 1265k multicolored .50 .50

Flora and Fauna A199

1500k, Verdant hawkmoth. 4400k, Water lily. 5100k, Panther toad. 6000k, African wild dog. 1500k: a, Western honey buzzard. b, Bateleuer. c, Common kestrel.
4400k; d, Red-crested turaco. e, Giraffe. f, Elephant.
5100k: g, Hippopotamus. h, Cattle egret. i, Lion. 6000k: j, Helmeted turtle. k, African pygmy goose. l, Egyptian plover.
12,000k, Spotted hyena.

1996, Apr. 20 Litho. Perf. 14
951-954 A199 Set of 4 1.00 1.00
955 A199 Sheet of 12, #a.-l. 4.00 4.00

Souvenir Sheet
956 A199 12,000k multicolored .80 .80

Sheets of 12

Birds — A200

Fowl: No. 957a, California quail. b, Greater prairie chicken. c, Painted quail. d, Golden pheasant. e, Roulroul partridge. f, Ceylon sourfowl. g, Himalayan snowcock. h, Temminicks tragopan. i, Lady Amherst's pheasant. j, Great curassow. k, Red-legged partridge. l, Impeyan pheasant.
Hummingbirds: No. 958a, Anna's. b, Blue-throated. c, Broad-tailed. d, Costa's. e, White-eared. f, Calliope. g, Violet-crowned. h, Rufous. i, Crimson topaz. j, Broad-billed. k, Frilled coquette. l, Ruby-throated.

No. 959, Ring-necked pheasant. No. 960, Racquet-tail hummingbird.

1996, Apr. 20
957-958 A200 5500k #a.-l., each 4.25 4.25
Souvenir Sheets
959-960 A200 12,000k each .80 .80

Lubrapex '96
A201

Wild animals: a, 180k, Lions attacking zebra. b, 450k, Zebras, lions, diff. c, 180k, Zebras grazing, lions stalking. d, 450k, Panthera leo. e, 550k, Cheetah. f, 630k, Cheetah running. g, 550k, Cheetah chasing antilope. h, 630k, Cheetah attacking antelope. i, 180k, Antilope (gnu) being attacked by wild dogs. j, 450k, Antelope, wild dogs. k, 180k, Pack of wild dogs. l, 450k, Licaon pictus. m, 550k, Panthera pardus. n, 630k, Oryx. o, 550k, Oryx, diff. p, 630k, Leopard attacking oryx.

1996, Apr. 27
961 A201 Sheet of 16, #a.-p. 6.00 6.00

Sheets of 6

Ships
A202

Designs: No. 962a, Styrbjorn, Sweden, 1789. b, Constellation, US, 1797. c, Taureau, France, 1865. d, Bomb Ketch, France, 1682. e, Sardegna, Italy, 1881. f, HMS Glasgow, England, 1867.
No. 963a, Essex, US, 1812. b, HMS Inflexible, England, 1881. c, HMS Minotaur, England, 1863. d, Napoleon, France, 1854. e, Sophia Amalia, Denmark, 1650. f, Massena, France, 1887.
No. 964, HMS Tremendous, England, 1806, vert. No. 965, Royal Prince, England, 1666.

1996, May 4
962-963 A202 6000k #a.-f., each 2.50 2.50
Souvenir Sheets
964-965 A202 12,000k each .80 .80

UN, 50th Anniv. (in 1995) A203

Designs: No. 966, Boys pumping water. No. 967, Man, woman with girl.
8000k, Unloading supplies from ship.

1996, Apr. 27 Litho. *Perf. 14*
966 A203 3500k multicolored 1.00 1.00
967 A203 3500k multicolored 1.00 1.00
Souvenir Sheet
968 A203 8000k multicolored 1.00 1.00

Sonangol, 20th Anniv. A204

Face in traditional mask, costume, native birds, and: No. 969, Oil derricks. No. 970, Oil storage tanks, ship. 2500k, Refinery equipment. 5000k, Cargo shipment, jet.

1996, May 12
969 A204 1000k multicolored .15 .15
970 A204 1000k multicolored .15 .15
971 A204 2500k multicolored .25 .25
972 A204 5000k multicolored .55 .55
Nos. 969-972 (4) 1.10 1.10

Brapex '96
A205

#973, Slaves in hold. #974, Slaves fleeing ship as it's overturned. #975, Slave boats approaching ship. #976, Slaves talking with captain.
50,000k, like #975.

1996, Oct. 19 Litho. *Perf. 14*
973 A205 20,000k multicolored 1.30 1.30
974 A205 20,000k multicolored 1.30 1.30
975 A205 30,000k multicolored 1.90 1.90
976 A205 30,000k multicolored 1.90 1.90
Nos. 973-976 (4) 6.40 6.40
Souvenir Sheet
977 A205 50,000k multicolored 3.20 3.20

Churches — A206

Designs: 5,000k, Mission, Huila. No. 979, Church of the Nazarene. No. 980, Church of Our Lady of Pó Pulo. 25,000k, St. Adrião Church.

1996, Dec. 6 Litho. *Perf. 14*
978 A206 5,000k multicolored .30 .30
979 A206 10,000k multicolored .65 .65
980 A206 10,000k multicolored .65 .65
981 A206 25,000k multicolored 1.60 1.60
Nos. 978-981 (4) 3.20 3.20

1996 Summer Olympic Games, Atlanta A207

1996, Dec. 9
982 A207 5,000k Handball, vert. .30 .30
983 A207 10,000k Swimming .65 .65
984 A207 25,000k Track & field, vert. 1.60 1.60
985 A207 35,000k Shooting 2.25 2.25
Nos. 982-985 (4) 4.80 4.80
Souvenir Sheet
986 A207 65,000k Basketball 4.00 4.00

MPLA (Liberation Movement), 40th Anniv. — A208

1996, Dec. 10 Litho. *Perf. 14*
987 A208 30,000k Dolphins, map 1.80 1.80

Trains A209

No. 988: a, AVE, Spain. b, Bullet Train, Japan. c, GM F7 Warbonnet, US. d, Deltic, Great Britain. e, Eurostar, France/Great Britain. f, ETR 450, Italy.
No. 989: a, Class E1300, Morocco. b, ICE, Germany. c, X2000, Sweden. d, TGV Duplex, France.
No. 990, Canadian Pacific 4-4-0, Canada. No. 991, Via Rail Canadian, Canada.

1997, May 29 Litho. *Perf. 14*
Sheets of 6 or 4
988 A209 100,000k #a.-f. 6.00 6.00
989 A209 140,000k #a.-d. 6.00 6.00
Souvenir Sheets
Perf. 13½
990-991 A209 110,000k each 4.00 4.00
Nos. 990-991 contain one 38x50 or 50x38mm stamp, respectively.
PACIFIC 97.

Horses A210

No. 992: a, Thoroughbred. b, Palomino, appaloosa. c, Arabians. d, Arabian colt. e, Thoroughbred colt. f, Mustang. g, Mustang, diff. h, Furioso.
No. 993: a, Thoroughbred. b, Arabian, palomino. c, Arabian, chincoteague. d, Pintos. e, Przewalski's horse. f, Thoroughbred colt. g, Arabians. h, New forest pony.
No. 994: a, Selle Francais. b, Fjord. c, Percheron. d, Italian heavy draft. e, Shagya Arab. f, Avelignese. g, Czechoslovakian warmblood. h, New forest pony.
215,000k, Thoroughbreds. 220,000k, Thoroughbreds, diff.

1997, July 5 Litho. *Perf. 14*
Sheets of 8
992 A210 100,000k #a.-h. 4.00 4.00
993 A210 120,000k #a.-h. 5.00 5.00
994 A210 140,000k #a.-h. 5.50 5.50
Souvenir Sheets
995 A210 215,000k multicolored 4.00 4.00
996 A210 220,000k multicolored 4.00 4.00
PACIFIC 97.

1998 World Cup Soccer Championships, France — A211

Winners holding World Cup trophy: No. 997: a, Uruguay, 1930. b, Germany, 1954. c, Brazil, 1970. d, Argentina, 1986. e, Brazil, 1994.
Winning team pictures: No. 998a, Germany, 1954. b, Uruguay, 1958. c, Italy, 1938. d, Brazil, 1962. e, Brazil, 1970. f, Uruguay, 1930.
220,000k, Angolan team members standing. 250,000k, 1997 Angolan team picture.

1997, July 5 Litho. *Perf. 14*
Sheets of 5 or 6
997 A211 100,000k #a.-e. + label 5.00 5.00
998 A211 100,000k #a.-f. 6.00 6.00
Souvenir Sheets
999 A211 220,000k multicolored 3.60 3.60
1000 A211 250,000k multicolored 4.00 4.00

SEMI-POSTAL STAMPS

Angolan Red Cross — SP1

1991, Sept. 19 Litho. *Perf. 14*
B1 SP1 20k +5k Mother and child .85 .85
B2 SP1 40k +5k Zebra and foal 1.50 1.50

AIR POST STAMPS

Common Design Type
Perf. 13½x13
1938, July 26 Engr. Unwmk.
Name and Value in Black
C1 CD39 10c scarlet .15 .15
C2 CD39 20c purple .25 .15
C3 CD39 50c orange .15 .15
C4 CD39 1a ultra .38 .15
C5 CD39 2a lilac brn .85 .15
C6 CD39 3a dk green 2.25 .25
C7 CD39 5a red brown 3.25 .35
C8 CD39 9a rose carmine 4.25 1.10
C9 CD39 10a magenta 5.50 1.10
Nos. C1-C9 (9) 17.03 3.55

No. C7 exists with overprint "Exposicao Internacional de Nova York, 1939-1940" and Trylon and Perisphere.

AP2   Planes Circling Globe — AP3

1947, Aug. Litho. *Perf. 10½*
C10 AP2 1a red brown 6.25 1.65
C11 AP2 2a yellow grn 6.25 1.65
C12 AP2 3a orange 8.00 1.65
C13 AP2 3.50a orange 10.00 4.00
C14 AP2 5a olive grn 90.00 15.00
C15 AP2 6a rose 90.00 17.50
C16 AP2 9a red 275.00 200.00
C17 AP2 10a green 175.00 60.00
C18 AP2 20a blue 175.00 60.00
C19 AP2 50a black 400.00 200.00
C20 AP2 100a yellow 750.00 600.00
Nos. C10-C20 (11) 1,985. 1,161.

1949, May 1 Photo. *Perf. 11½*
C21 AP3 1a henna brown .15 .15
C22 AP3 2a red brown .40 .15
C23 AP3 3a plum .65 .15
C24 AP3 6a dull green 2.00 .40
C25 AP3 9a violet brown 3.00 1.00
Nos. C21-C25 (5) 6.20 1.85

Catalogue values for unused stamps in this section, from this point to the end of the section, are for Never Hinged items.

Cambambe Dam — AP4

Designs: 1.50e, Oil refinery, vert. 3e, Salazar Dam. 4e, Capt. Teófilo Duarte Dam. 4.50e, Craveiro Lopes Dam. 5e, Cuango Dam. 6e, Quanza River Bridge. 7e, Capt. Teófilo Duarte Bridge. 8.50e, Oliveira Salazar Bridge. 12.50e, Capt. Silva Carvalho Bridge.

Perf. 11½x12, 12x11½
1965, July 12 Litho. Unwmk.
C26 AP4 1.50e multicolored 1.00 .15
C27 AP4 2.50e multicolored .60 .15
C28 AP4 3e multicolored 1.00 .15
C29 AP4 4e multicolored .40 .15
C30 AP4 4.50e multicolored .40 .15
C31 AP4 5e multicolored .65 .20
C32 AP4 6e multicolored .65 .20
C33 AP4 7e multicolored 1.25 .55
C34 AP4 8.50e multicolored 1.25 .55
C35 AP4 12.50e multicolored 1.50 .65
Nos. C26-C35 (10) 8.45 2.55

Stamp Centenary Type
Design: 2.50e, Boeing 707 jet & Angola #2.

1970, Dec. 1 Litho. *Perf. 13½*
C36 A83 2.50e multicolored .45 .15
a. Souv. sheet of 3, #565-566, C36 2.50 2.50
No. C36a sold for 15e.

No. C36 Overprinted with Bar and: "REPUBLICA POPULAR / DE"
1980, June 15 Litho. *Perf. 13½*
C37 A83 2.50e multicolored .15

POSTAGE DUE STAMPS

D1   D2

1904		Unwmk.	Typo.	*Perf. 11½x12*	
J1	D1	5r yellow grn		.25	.15
J2	D1	10r slate		.25	.15
J3	D1	20r yellow brn		.35	.32
J4	D1	30r orange		.60	.60
J5	D1	50r gray brown		.60	.60
J6	D1	60r red brown		4.00	2.50
J7	D1	100r lilac		1.75	1.65
J8	D1	130r dull blue		1.75	1.65
J9	D1	200r carmine		4.00	3.00
J10	D1	500r gray violet		4.00	3.00
		Nos. J1-J10 (10)		*17.55*	*13.62*

Postage Due Stamps
of 1904 Overprinted
in Carmine or Green

REPUBLICA

1911					
J11	D1	5r yellow grn		.20	.20
J12	D1	10r slate		.20	.20
J13	D1	20r yellow brn		.20	.20
J14	D1	30r orange		.30	.30
J15	D1	50r gray brown		.30	.30
J16	D1	60r red brown		.60	.60
J17	D1	100r lilac		.60	.60
J18	D1	130r dull blue		.60	.60
J19	D1	200r carmine (G)		.60	.60
J20	D1	500r gray violet		.70	.70
		Nos. J11-J20 (10)		*4.30*	*4.30*

1921				*Perf. 11½*	
J21	D2	½c yellow green		.15	.15
J22	D2	1c slate		.15	.15
J23	D2	2c orange brown		.15	.15
J24	D2	3c orange		.15	.15
J25	D2	5c gray brown		.15	.15
J26	D2	6c lt brown		.15	.15
J27	D2	10c red violet		.15	.15
J28	D2	13c dull blue		.20	.20
J29	D2	20c carmine		.20	.20
J30	D2	50c gray		.20	.20
		Set value		*1.15*	*1.15*

For surcharges see Nos. 268-270.

Catalogue values for unused
stamps in this section, from this
point to the end of the section, are
for Never Hinged items.

Stamps of 1932
Surcharged in Black

= =
PORTEADO
10
Centavos

1948		Wmk. 232	*Perf. 12x11½*		
J31	A14	10c on 20c gray		.20	.20
J32	A14	20c on 30c myrtle grn		.20	.20
J33	A14	30c on 50c lt brown		.45	.45
J34	A14	40c on 1a claret		.45	.45
J35	A14	50c on 2a dull vio		.90	.45
J36	A14	1a on 5a pale yel grn		1.25	1.00
		Nos. J31-J36 (6)		*3.45*	*2.75*

Common Design Type
Photogravure and Typographed

1952		Unwmk.	*Perf. 14*		

Numeral in Red, Frame Multicolored

J37	CD45	10c red brown		.15	.15
J38	CD45	30c olive green		.15	.15
J39	CD45	50c chocolate		.15	.15
J40	CD45	1a dk vio blue		.15	.15
J41	CD45	2a red brown		.20	.20
J42	CD45	5a black brown		.32	.32
		Set value		*.92*	*.92*

NEWSPAPER STAMP

N1

Perf. 11½, 12½, 13½

1893		Typo.	Unwmk.		
P1	N1	2½r brown		1.00	.70

No. P1 was also used for ordinary postage.
For surcharges see Nos. 37, 82, 180, 235.

POSTAL TAX STAMPS

Pombal Issue
Common Design Types

1925, May 8		Unwmk.	*Perf. 12½*		
RA1	CD28	15c lilac & black		.32	.25
RA2	CD29	15c lilac & black		.32	.25
RA3	CD30	15c lilac & black		.32	.25
		Nos. RA1-RA3 (3)		*.96*	*.75*

"Charity"   Coat of Arms
PT1   PT2

1929		Litho.	*Perf. 11*		

Without Gum

RA4	PT1	50c dark blue		2.00	.70

1939	Without Gum		*Perf. 10½*		
RA5	PT2	50c turq green		1.75	.15
RA6	PT2	1a red		3.25	1.50

A 1.50a, type PT2, was issued for fiscal use.

Catalogue values for unused
stamps in this section, from this
point to the end of the section, are
for Never Hinged items.

Old   Mother and
Man — PT3   Child — PT4

Designs: 1e, Boy. 1.50e, Girl.

Imprint: "Foto-Lito-E.G.A.-Luanda"

1955		Unwmk.	*Perf. 13*		

Heads in dark brow .

RA7	PT3	50c dk ocher		.15	.15
RA8	PT3	1e orange ver		.75	.40
RA9	PT3	1.50e brt yel grn		.50	.25
		Nos. RA7-RA9 (3)		*1.40*	*.80*

A 2.50e, type PT3 showing an old woman, was
issued for revenue use.
See Nos. RA16, RA19-RA21, RA25-RA27.

No. RA7 Surcharged with New Values and
two Bars in Red or Black

1957-58					

Head in dark brown

RA11	PT3	10c on 50c dk ocher (R)		.25	.25
RA12	PT3	10c on 50c dk ocher ('58)		.20	.20
RA13	PT3	30c on 50c dk ocher		.22	.22
		Nos. RA11-RA13 (3)		*.67*	*.67*

1959		Litho.	*Perf. 13*		

Design: 30c, Boy and girl.

RA14	PT4	10c orange & blk		.15	.15
RA15	PT4	30c slate & blk		.15	.15
		Set value		*.24*	*.24*

Type of 1955 Redrawn

Design: 1e, Boy.

1961, Nov.			*Perf. 13*		
RA16	PT3	1e sal pink & dk brn		.20	.20

Denomination in italics.

Yellow, White and Black Men — PT5

1962, July 1		Typo.	*Perf. 10½*		

Without Gum

RA17	PT5	50c multicolored		.65	.65
RA18	PT5	1e multicolored		.32	.32

Issued for the Provincial Settlement Committee
(Junta Provincial do Povoamento). The tax was
used to promote Portuguese settlement in Angola,
and to raise educational and living standards of
recent immigrants.
Denominations higher than 1e were used for revenue purposes.

Head Type of 1955
Without Imprint

Designs: 50c, Old man. 1e, Boy. 1.50e, Girl.

1964-65		Litho.	*Perf. 11½*		

Heads in dark brown

RA19	PT3	50c orange		.15	.15
RA20	PT3	1e dull red org ('65)		.20	.20
RA21	PT3	1.50e grn ('65)		.25	.25
		Nos. RA19-RA21 (3)		*.60*	*.60*

No. RA20 is second redrawing of 1e, with bolder
lettering and denomination in gothic. Space
between "Assistencia" and denomination on RA19-
RA21 is ½mm; on 1955 issue space is 2mm.

Map of Angola, Industrial
and Farm Workers — PT6

1965, Sept. 1		Litho.	*Perf. 13*		
RA22	PT6	50c multicolored		.35	.15
RA23	PT6	1e multicolored		.35	.25

The 2e was used for revenue purposes.

Head Type of 1955
Imprint: "I.N.A." or "INA" (1e)

Designs: 50c, Old man. 1e, Boy. 1.50e, Girl.

1966					

Heads in dark brown

RA25	PT3	50c dull orange		.15	.15
RA26	PT3	1e dull brick red		.15	.15
RA27	PT3	1e dull brick red		.32	.15
		Nos. RA25-RA27 (3)		*.62*	
		Set value			*.32*

Woman Planting
Tree — PT7

1972		Litho.	*Perf. 13*		
RA28	PT7	50c shown		.15	.15
RA29	PT7	1e Workers		.15	.15
RA30	PT7	2e Produce		.20	.20
		Set value		*.39*	*.39*

POSTAL TAX DUE STAMPS

Pombal Issue
Common Design Types

1925, May 8		Unwmk.	*Perf. 12½*		
RAJ1	CD28	30c lilac & black		.50	1.25
RAJ2	CD29	30c lilac & black		.50	1.25
RAJ3	CD30	30c lilac & black		.50	1.25
		Nos. RAJ1-RAJ3 (3)		1.50	

See note after Portugal No. RAJ4.

ANGRA

ˈaŋ-grə

LOCATION — An administrative district of
the Azores, consisting of the islands of
Terceira, Sao Jorge and Graciosa.
GOVT. — A district of Portugal
AREA — 275 sq. mi.
POP. — 70,000 (approx.)
CAPITAL — Angra do Heroismo

1000 Reis = 1 Milreis

King Carlos
A1   A2

1892-93		Typo.	Unwmk.	*Perf. 12½*	
1	A1	5r yellow		3.00	1.30
	a.	Perf. 11½		6.50	4.00
	b.	Perf. 13½		2.75	1.30
2	A1	10r redsh violet		3.00	1.30
	a.	Perf. 13½		3.75	2.00
3	A1	15r chocolate		3.50	2.00
	a.	Perf. 13½		3.75	2.00
4	A1	20r lavender		3.75	2.00
	a.	Perf. 13½		3.75	2.00
5	A1	25r green		4.00	.50
	a.	Perf. 13½		7.00	2.50
	b.	Perf. 11½		5.00	.90
7	A1	50r blue		7.75	3.00
	a.	Perf. 13½		10.00	4.50
8	A1	75r carmine		9.00	3.50
9	A1	80r yellow green		10.00	7.00
10	A1	100r brown, *yel*, perf. 13½ ('93)		35.00	10.00
	a.	Perf. 11½		140.00	95.00
11	A1	150r car, *rose* ('93)		50.00	25.00
	a.	Perf. 13½		60.00	37.50
12	A1	200r dk blue, *bl* ('93)		50.00	25.00
	a.	Perf. 13½		60.00	37.50
13	A1	300r dk blue, *sal* ('93)		50.00	25.00
	a.	Perf. 13½		60.00	37.50

Reprints of 50r, 150r, 200r and 300r, made in
1900, are perf. 11½ and ungummed. Value, each
$7.50. Reprints of all values, made in 1905, have
shiny white gum and clean-cut perf. 13½.

1897-1905				*Perf. 11½*	

**Name and Value in Black except Nos.
26 and 35**

14	A2	2½r gray		.65	.35
15	A2	5r orange		.65	.35
	a.	Diagonal half used as 2½r on cover			22.50
16	A2	10r yellow grn		.70	.40
17	A2	15r brown		8.50	3.50
18	A2	15r gray grn ('99)		.90	.45
19	A2	20r gray violet		1.50	.90
20	A2	25r sea green		2.75	.90
21	A2	25r car rose ('99)		.70	.40
22	A2	50r dark blue		5.00	1.25
23	A2	50r ultra ('05)		12.50	8.00
24	A2	65r slate bl ('98)		-1.00	.40
25	A2	75r rose		3.00	1.00
26	A2	75r gray brn & car, *straw* ('05)		16.00	19.00
27	A2	80r violet		1.50	1.00
28	A2	100r dk blue, *bl*		2.50	1.25
29	A2	115r org brn, *pink* ('98)		2.50	1.40
30	A2	130r gray brn, *straw* ('98)		2.50	1.40
31	A2	150r lt brn, *straw*		2.50	1.40
32	A2	180r sl, *pnksh* ('98)		3.00	2.00
33	A2	200r red vio, *pnksh*		5.00	2.75
34	A2	300r blue, *rose*		7.50	4.00
35	A2	500r blk & red, *bl*		16.00	10.00
	a.	Perf. 12½		21.00	12.50
		Nos. 14-35 (22)		*96.85*	*62.10*

Azores stamps were used in Angra from 1906 to
1931, when they were superseded by those of
Portugal.

ANGUILLA

aŋˌgwi-lə

LOCATION — In the West Indies southeast
of Puerto Rico
GOVT. — British territory
AREA — 60 sq. mi.
POP. — 6,500 (est. 1980)
CAPITAL — The Valley

Anguilla separated unilaterally from the
Associated State of St. Kitts-Nevis-Anguilla
in 1967, formalized in 1980 following direct

United Kingdom intervention some years before. A British Commissioner exercises executive authority.

100 Cents = 1 Dollar

Catalogue values for all unused stamps in this country are for Never Hinged items.

St. Kitts-Nevis Nos. 145-160 Overprinted

Independent Anguilla
On Type A14

Independent Anguilla
On Type A15

Wmk. 314

		1967, Sept. 4	Photo.	Perf. 14	
1	A14	½c blue & dk brn		25.00	22.50
2	A15	1c multicolored		25.00	6.50
3	A15	2c multicolored		25.00	2.00
4	A15	3c multicolored		25.00	5.00
5	A15	4c multicolored		25.00	6.00
6	A15	5c multicolored		100.00	20.00
7	A15	6c multicolored		50.00	10.00
8	A15	10c multicolored		25.00	7.50
9	A15	15c multicolored		55.00	12.00
10	A15	20c multicolored		85.00	20.00
11	A15	25c multicolored		70.00	22.50
12	A15	50c multicolored		2,000.	400.00
13	A14	60c multicolored		2,500.	900.00
14	A14	$1 multicolored		1,600.	325.00
15	A15	$2.50 multicolored		1,600.	325.00
16	A14	$5 multicolored		1,300.	300.00
		Nos. 1-16 (16)		9,510.	2,384.

Counterfeit overprints exist.

Mahogany Tree, The Quarter — A1

Designs: 2c, Sombrero Lighthouse. 3c, St. Mary's Church. 4c, Valley Police Station. 5c, Old Plantation House, Mt. Fortune. 6c, Valley Post Office. 10c, Methodist Church, West End. 15c, Wall-Blake Airport. 20c, Plane over Sandy Ground. 25c, Island Harbor. 40c, Map of Anguilla. 60c, Hermit crab and starfish. $1, Hibiscus. $2.50, Coconut harvest. $5, Spiny lobster.

Perf. 12½x13

		1967-68	Litho.	Unwmk.	
17	A1	1c orange & multi		.15	.15
18	A1	2c gray green & blk		.15	.15
19	A1	3c emerald & blk		.15	.15
20	A1	4c brt blue & blk		.15	.15
21	A1	5c lt blue & multi		.15	.15
22	A1	6c ver & black		.15	.15
23	A1	10c multicolored		.15	.15
24	A1	15c multicolored		.18	.18
25	A1	20c multicolored		.24	.24
26	A1	25c multicolored		.30	.30
27	A1	40c blue & multi		.48	.48
28	A1	60c yellow & multi		.70	.70
29	A1	$1 lt green & multi		1.40	1.40
30	A1	$2.50 multicolored		3.50	3.50
31	A1	$5 multicolored		6.50	6.50
		Nos. 17-31 (15)		14.35	14.35

Issue dates: 1c, 5c, 10c, 20c, 25c, 40c, Nov. 27, 1967; 3c, 4c, 15c, 60c, $1, $5, Feb. 10, 1968; 2c, 6c, $2.50, Mar. 21, 1968.
For overprints see Nos. 53-67, 78-82.

Sailboats A2

Designs: 15c, Boat building. 25c, Schooner Warspite. 40c, Yacht Atlantic Star.

		1968, May 11		Perf. 14	
32	A2	10c rose & multi		.32	.32
33	A2	15c olive & multi		.55	.55
34	A2	25c lilac rose & multi		.80	.80
35	A2	40c dull blue & multi		1.40	1.40
		Nos. 32-35 (4)		3.07	3.07

Purple-throated Carib — A3

Girl Guide Badge — A4

Anguillan Birds: 15c, Bananaquit. 25c, Black-necked stilt, horiz. 40c, Royal tern, horiz.

		1968, July 8			
36	A3	10c dull yel & multi		.40	.28
37	A3	15c yel green & multi		.55	.42
38	A3	25c multicolored		1.65	.95
39	A3	40c multicolored		1.90	1.65
		Nos. 36-39 (4)		4.50	3.30

Perf. 13x13½, 13½x13

1968, Oct. 14

Designs: 10c, Girl Guide badge, horiz. 25c, Badge and Headquarters, horiz. 40c, Merit Badges.

40	A4	10c lt green & multi		.20	.20
41	A4	15c lt blue & multi		.30	.30
42	A4	25c multicolored		.60	.60
43	A4	40c multicolored		.85	.85
		Nos. 40-43 (4)		1.95	1.95

Anguillan Girl Guides, 35th anniversary.

Three Kings — A5

Christmas: 10c, Three Kings seeing Star, vert. 15c, Holy Family, vert. 40c, Shepherds seeing Star. 50c, Holy Family and donkey.

		1968, Nov. 18			
44	A5	1c lilac rose & black		.15	.15
45	A5	10c blue & black		.16	.16
46	A5	15c brown & black		.35	.35
47	A5	40c brt ultra & black		.90	.90
48	A5	50c green & black		1.25	1.25
		Nos. 44-48 (5)		2.81	2.81

Bagging Salt — A6

Salt Industry: 15c, Packing salt. 40c, Salt pond. 50c, Loading salt.

		1969, Jan. 4		Perf. 13	
49	A6	10c red & multi		.15	.15
50	A6	15c lt blue & multi		.22	.22
51	A6	40c emerald & multi		.60	.60
52	A6	50c purple & multi		.70	.70
		Nos. 49-52 (4)		1.67	1.67

Nos. 17-31 Overprinted: "INDEPENDENCE/JANUARY, 1969"

		1969, Jan. 9		Perf. 12½x13	
53	A1	1c orange & multi		.15	.15
54	A1	2c gray green & blk		.15	.15
55	A1	3c emerald & blk		.15	.15
56	A1	4c brt blue & blk		.15	.15
57	A1	5c lt blue & multi		.15	.15
58	A1	6c vermilion & blk		.15	.15
59	A1	10c multicolored		.16	.16
60	A1	15c multicolored		.22	.22
61	A1	20c multicolored		.28	.28
62	A1	25c multicolored		.35	.35
63	A1	40c blue & multi		.50	.50
64	A1	60c yellow & multi		.70	.70
65	A1	$1 lt green & multi		1.25	1.25
66	A1	$2.50 multicolored		3.00	3.00
67	A1	$5 multicolored		6.25	6.25
		Nos. 53-67 (15)		13.61	13.61

Crucifixion, School of Quentin Massys — A7

Easter: 40c, The Last Supper, ascribed to Roberti.

		1969, Mar. 31	Litho.	Perf. 13½	
68	A7	25c multicolored		.40	.40
69	A7	40c multicolored		.70	.70

Amaryllis A8

		1969, June 10		Perf. 14	
70	A8	10c shown		.20	.20
71	A8	15c Bougainvillea		.35	.35
72	A8	40c Hibiscus		.80	.80
73	A8	50c Cattleya orchid		1.10	1.10
		Nos. 70-73 (4)		2.45	2.45

Turban and Star Shells — A9

Sea Shells: 15c, Spiny oysters. 40c, Scotch, royal and smooth bonnets. 50c, Triton trumpet.

		1969, Sept. 22			
74	A9	10c multicolored		.38	.38
75	A9	15c multicolored		.55	.55
76	A9	40c multicolored		1.25	1.25
77	A9	50c multicolored		1.65	1.65
		Nos. 74-77 (4)		3.83	3.83

Nos. 17, 25-28 Overprinted "CHRISTMAS 1969" and Various Christmas Designs

		1969, Oct. 27		Perf. 12½x13	
78	A1	1c orange & multi		.15	.15
79	A1	20c multicolored		.50	.35
80	A1	25c multicolored		.70	.60
81	A1	40c blue & multi		1.25	1.10
82	A1	60c yellow & multi		3.00	2.00
		Nos. 78-82 (5)		5.60	4.20

Red Goatfish A10

Designs: 15c, Blue-striped grunts. 40c, Mutton grouper. 50c, Banded butterfly-fish.

		1969, Dec. 1		Perf. 14	
83	A10	10c multicolored		.28	.28
84	A10	15c multicolored		.40	.40
85	A10	40c multicolored		1.40	1.40
86	A10	50c multicolored		1.65	1.65
		Nos. 83-86 (4)		3.73	3.73

Morning Glory — A11

		1970, Feb. 23			
87	A11	10c shown		.25	.25
88	A11	15c Blue petrea		.40	.40
89	A11	40c Hibiscus		1.40	1.40
90	A11	50c Flamboyant		1.75	1.75
		Nos. 87-90 (4)		3.80	3.80

The Way to Calvary, by Tiepolo — A12

Easter: 20c, Crucifixion, by Masaccio, vert. 40c, Descent from the Cross, by Rosso Fiorentino, vert. 60c, Jesus Carrying the Cross, by Murillo.

		1970, Mar. 26		Perf. 13½	
91	A12	10c multicolored		.15	.15
92	A12	20c multicolored		.28	.28
93	A12	40c multicolored		.60	.60
94	A12	60c multicolored		.90	.90
		Nos. 91-94 (4)		1.93	1.93

Anguilla Map, Scout Badge A13

Designs: 15c, Cub Scouts practicing first aid. 40c, Monkey bridge. 50c, Scout Headquarters, The Valley, and Lord Baden-Powell.

		1970, Aug. 10		Perf. 13	
95	A13	10c multicolored		.25	.25
96	A13	15c multicolored		.40	.40
97	A13	40c multicolored		1.00	1.00
98	A13	50c multicolored		1.25	1.25
		Nos. 95-98 (4)		2.90	2.90

Anguilla Boy Scouts, 40th anniversary.

Boat Building A14

Designs: 2c, Road construction. 3c, Blowing Point dock. 4c, Radio announcer. 5c, Cottage Hospital extension. 6c, Valley secondary school. 10c, Hotel extension. 15c, Sandy Ground. 20c, Supermarket and movie house. 25c, Bananas and mangoes. 40c, Wall-Blake airport. 60c, Sandy Ground jetty. $1, Administration building. $2.50, Cow and calf. $5, Sandy Hill Bay.

		1970, Nov. 23	Litho.	Perf. 14	
99	A14	1c multicolored		.15	.15
100	A14	2c multicolored		.15	.15
101	A14	3c multicolored		.15	.15
102	A14	4c multicolored		.15	.15
103	A14	5c multicolored		.15	.15
104	A14	6c multicolored		.15	.15
105	A14	10c multicolored		.20	.20
106	A14	15c multicolored		.28	.28
107	A14	20c multicolored		.32	.32
108	A14	25c multicolored		.38	.38
109	A14	40c multicolored		.65	.65
110	A14	60c multicolored		1.00	1.00
111	A14	$1 multicolored		1.60	1.60
112	A14	$2.50 multicolored		4.00	4.00
113	A14	$5 multicolored		8.00	8.00
		Nos. 99-113 (15)		17.33	17.33

Adoration of the Shepherds, by Guido Reni — A15

Christmas: 20c, Virgin and Child, by Benozzo Gozzoli. 25c, Nativity, by Botticelli. 40c, Santa Margherita Madonna, by Mazzola. 50c, Adoration of the Kings, by Tiepolo.

		1970, Dec. 11		Perf. 13½	
114	A15	1c multicolored		.15	.15
115	A15	20c multicolored		.35	.35
116	A15	25c multicolored		.40	.40
117	A15	40c multicolored		.60	.60
118	A15	50c multicolored		.65	.65
		Nos. 114-118 (5)		2.15	2.15

Angels Weeping over the Dead Christ, by Guercino — A16

Easter: 10c, Ecce Homo, by Correggio, vert. 15c, Christ Appearing to St. Peter, by Carracci, vert. 50c, The Supper at Emmaus, by Caravaggio.

1971, Mar. 29

119	A16	10c pink & multi	.18	.18
120	A16	15c lt blue & multi	.30	.30
121	A16	40c yel green & multi	.75	.75
122	A16	50c violet & multi	.90	.90
		Nos. 119-122 (4)	2.13	2.13

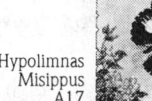

Hypolimnas Misippus A17

Butterflies: 15c, Junonia lavinia. 40c, Agraulis vanillae. 50c, Danaus plexippus.

1971, June 21   Perf. 14x14½

123	A17	10c multicolored	.70	.70
124	A17	15c multicolored	.90	.90
125	A17	40c multicolored	1.75	1.75
126	A17	50c multicolored	2.25	2.25
		Nos. 123-126 (4)	5.60	5.60

Magnanime and Aimable in Battle — A18

Ships: 15c, HMS Duke and Agamemnon against Glorieux. 25c, HMS Formidable and Namur against Ville de Paris. 40c, HMS Canada. 50c, HMS St. Albans and wreck of Hector.

1971, Aug. 30   Litho.   Perf. 14

127	A18	10c multicolored	.35	.35
128	A18	15c multicolored	.60	.60
129	A18	25c multicolored	1.25	1.25
130	A18	40c multicolored	2.00	2.00
131	A18	50c multicolored	2.75	2.75
a.		Strip of 5, #127-131	7.25	7.25

West Indies sea battles.

Ansidei Madonna, by Raphael — A19

Christmas: 25c, Mystic Nativity, by Botticelli. 40c, Virgin and Child, School of Seville, inscribed Murillo. 50c, Madonna of the Iris, ascribed to Dürer.

1971, Nov. 29   Perf. 14x13½

132	A19	20c green & multi	.40	.40
133	A19	25c blue & multi	.55	.55
134	A19	40c lilac rose & multi	.90	.90
135	A19	50c violet & multi	1.10	1.10
		Nos. 132-135 (4)	2.95	2.95

Map of Anguilla and St. Maarten, by Jefferys, 1775 — A20

Jesus Buffeted, Stained-glass Window — A21

Maps of Anguilla by: 15c, Samuel Fahlberg, 1814. 40c, Thomas Jefferys, 1775, horiz. 50c, Capt. E. Barnett, 1847, horiz.

Perf. 14x13½, 13½x14

1972, Jan. 24

136	A20	10c lt blue & multi	.22	.22
137	A20	15c lt green & multi	.35	.35
138	A20	40c lt green & multi	.90	.90
139	A20	50c lt ultra & multi	1.10	1.10
		Nos. 136-139 (4)	2.57	2.57

1972, Mar. 14   Perf. 14x13½

Easter (19th cent. Stained-glass Windows, Bray Church): 15c, Jesus Carrying the Cross. 25c, Crucifixion. 40c, Descent from the Cross. 50c, Burial.

140	A21	10c multicolored	.20	.20
141	A21	15c multicolored	.32	.32
142	A21	25c multicolored	.45	.45
143	A21	40c multicolored	.90	.90
144	A21	50c multicolored	1.00	1.00
a.		Strip of 5, #140-144	3.00	3.00

Spear Fishing A22

Sandy Ground A23

1972-75   Perf. 13½

145	A22	1c shown	.15	.15
146	A23	2c Loblolly tree, vert.	.15	.15
147	A23	3c shown	.15	.15
148	A23	4c Ferry, Blowing Point, vert.	.15	.15
149	A23	5c Agriculture	.15	.15
150	A23	6c St. Mary's Church, vert.	.15	.15
151	A23	10c St. Gerard's Church	.20	.20
152	A22	15c Cottage Hospital	.30	.30
153	A23	20c Public Library	.35	.35
154	A23	25c Sunset, Blowing Point	.50	.50
155	A22	40c Boat building	.75	.75
156	A22	60c Hibiscus	1.25	1.25
157	A23	$1 Man-o-war bird	2.50	2.50
158	A23	$2.50 Frangipani	5.75	5.75
159	A23	$5 Brown pelican	11.00	11.00
160	A22	$10 Green-back turtle	27.50	27.50
		Nos. 145-160 (16)	51.00	51.00

Issued: $10, 5/20/75; others 10/30/72.
For overprints see Nos. 229-246.

Common Design Types
pictured following the introduction.

Silver Wedding Issue, 1972
Common Design Type

Design: Queen Elizabeth II, Prince Philip, schooner and dolphin.

Perf. 14x14½

1972, Nov. 20   Photo.   Wmk. 314

161	CD324	25c olive & multi	1.75	1.75
162	CD324	40c maroon & multi	2.00	2.00

Flight into Egypt — A24

Perf. 13½

1972, Dec. 4   Litho.   Unwmk.

163	A24	1c shown	.15	.15
164	A24	20c Star of Bethlehem	.35	.35
165	A24	25c Nativity	.40	.40
166	A24	40c Three Kings	.70	.70
167	A24	50c Adoration of the Kings	1.00	1.00
a.		Vert. strip of 4, #164-167	2.75	2.75
		Nos. 163-167 (5)	2.60	2.60

Christmas.

Betrayal of Jesus — A25

1973, Mar. 26

168	A25	1c shown	.15	.15
169	A25	10c Man of Sorrow	.15	.15
170	A25	20c Jesus Carrying Cross	.28	.28
171	A25	25c Crucifixion	.32	.32
172	A25	40c Descent from Cross	.55	.55
173	A25	50c Resurrection	.75	.75
a.		Souvenir sheet of 6	2.25	2.25
b.		Vert. strip of 5, #169-173	2.25	2.25
		Nos. 168-173 (6)	2.20	2.20

Easter. #173a contains 6 stamps similar to #168-173 with bottom panel in lilac rose.

Santa Maria A26

1973, Sept. 10

174	A26	1c shown	.15	.15
175	A26	20c Old West Indies map	.55	.55
176	A26	40c Map of voyages	1.40	1.40
177	A26	70c Sighting land	2.25	2.25
178	A26	$1.20 Columbus landing	4.75	4.75
a.		Souvenir sheet of 5, #174-178	10.00	10.00
b.		Horiz. strip of 5, #175-178	9.00	9.00
		Nos. 174-178 (5)	9.10	9.10

Discovery of West Indies by Columbus.

Princess Anne's Wedding Issue
Common Design Type

1973, Nov. 14   Wmk. 314   Perf. 13½

179	CD325	60c blue grn & multi	.35	.35
180	CD325	$1.20 lilac & multi	.65	.65

Wedding of Princess Anne and Capt. Mark Phillips, Nov. 14, 1973.

Adoration of the Shepherds, by Guido Reni — A27

Paintings: 10c, Virgin and Child, by Filippino Lippi. 20c, Nativity, by Meester Van de Brunswijkse Diptiek. 25c, Madonna of the Meadow, by Bellini. 40c, Virgin and Child, by Cima. 50c, Adoration of the Kings, by Geertgen Tot Sint Jans.

1973, Dec. 2   Unwmk.

181	A27	1c multicolored	.15	.15
182	A27	10c multicolored	.18	.18
183	A27	20c multicolored	.30	.30
184	A27	25c multicolored	.35	.35
185	A27	40c multicolored	.60	.60
186	A27	50c multicolored	.80	.80
a.		Souvenir sheet of 6, #181-186	2.50	2.50
b.		Horiz. strip of 5, #182-186	2.50	2.50
		Nos. 181-186 (6)	2.38	2.38

Christmas.

Crucifixion, by Raphael — A28

Easter (Details from Crucifixion by Raphael): 15c, Virgin Mary and St. John. 20c, The Two Marys. 25c, Left Angel. 40c, Right Angel. $1, Christ on the Cross.

1974, Mar. 30

187	A28	1c lilac & multi	.15	.15
188	A28	15c gray & multi	.18	.18
189	A28	20c salmon & multi	.25	.25
190	A28	25c yel green & multi	.30	.30
191	A28	40c orange & multi	.42	.42
192	A28	$1 lt blue & multi	1.10	1.10
a.		Souvenir sheet of 6, #187-192	2.50	2.50
b.		Vert. strip of 5, #188-192	2.50	2.50
		Nos. 187-192 (6)	2.40	2.40

Churchill Making Victory Sign — A29

Designs: 20c, Roosevelt, Churchill, American and British flags. 25c, Churchill broadcasting during the war. 40c, Blenheim Palace. 60c, Churchill Statue and Parliament. $1.20, Chartwell.

1974, June 24

193	A29	1c multicolored	.15	.15
194	A29	20c multicolored	.22	.22
195	A29	25c multicolored	.28	.28
196	A29	40c multicolored	.42	.42
197	A29	60c multicolored	.65	.65
198	A29	$1.20 multicolored	1.40	1.40
a.		Souvenir sheet of 6, #193-198	3.50	3.50
b.		Horiz. strip of 5, #194-198	3.25	3.25
		Nos. 193-198 (6)	3.12	3.12

Sir Winston Spencer Churchill (1874-1965).

UPU Emblem, Map of Anguilla — A30

1974, Aug. 27

199	A30	1c black & ultra	.15	.15
200	A30	20c black & orange	.18	.18
201	A30	25c black & yellow	.20	.20
202	A30	40c black & brt lilac	.42	.42
203	A30	60c black & lt green	.60	.60
204	A30	$1.20 black & blue	1.00	1.00
a.		Souvenir sheet of 6	3.00	3.00
b.		Horiz. strip of 5, #200-204	2.50	2.50
		Nos. 199-204 (6)	2.55	2.55

UPU, centenary. No. 204a contains one each of Nos. 199-204 with second row (40c, 60c, $1.20) perf. 15 at bottom.

Fishermen Seeing Star — A31

Christmas: 20c, Nativity. 25c, King offering gift. 40c, Star over map of Anguilla. 60c, Family looking at star. $1.20, Two angels with star and "Peace."

1974, Dec. 16   Litho.   Perf. 14½

205	A31	1c brt blue & multi	.15	.15
206	A31	20c dull grn & multi	.18	.18
207	A31	25c gray & multi	.20	.20
208	A31	40c car & multi	.42	.42
209	A31	60c dp blue & multi	.60	.60
210	A31	$1.20 ultra & multi	1.00	1.00
a.	Souvenir sheet of 6, #205-210		3.00	3.00
b.	Horiz. strip of 5, #206-210		2.50	2.50
	Nos. 205-210 (6)		2.55	2.55

Virgin Mary, St.
John, Mary
Magdalene — A32

Paintings from Isenheim Altar, by Matthias Grunewald: 10c, Crucifixion. 15c, John the Baptist. 20c, St. Sebastian and Angels. $1, Burial of Christ, horiz. $1.50, St. Anthony, the Hermit.

1975, Mar. 25   Perf. 13½

211	A32	1c multicolored	.15	.15
212	A32	10c multicolored	.15	.15
213	A32	15c multicolored	.15	.15
214	A32	20c multicolored	.18	.18
215	A32	$1 multicolored	.75	.75
216	A32	$1.50 multicolored	1.25	1.25
a.	Souvenir sheet of 6		2.75	2.75
b.	Horiz. strip of 5, #212-216		2.50	2.50
	Nos. 211-216 (6)		2.63	2.63

Easter. No. 216a contains 6 stamps similar to Nos. 211-216 with simulated perforations.

Statue
of
Liberty,
N.Y.
Skyline
A33

Designs: 10c, Capitol, Washington, D.C. 15c, Congress voting independence. 20c, Washington, map and his battles. $1, Boston Tea Party. $1.50, Bicentennial emblem, historic U.S. flags.

1975, Nov. 10

217	A33	1c multicolored	.15	.15
218	A33	10c multicolored	.15	.15
219	A33	15c multicolored	.15	.15
220	A33	20c multicolored	.22	.22
221	A33	$1 multicolored	1.00	1.00
222	A33	$1.50 multicolored	1.50	1.50
a.	Souvenir sheet of 6		3.50	3.50
b.	Horiz. strip of 5, #218-222		3.25	3.25
	Nos. 217-222 (6)		3.17	3.17

American Bicentennial. No. 222a contains one each of Nos. 217-222 with second row (20c, $1, $1.50) perf. 15 at bottom.

Virgin and Child
with St. John, by
Raphael — A34

Paintings, Virgin and Child by: 10c, Cima. 15c, Dolci. 20c, Durer. $1, Bellini. $1.50, Botticelli.

1975, Dec. 8   Perf. 14x13½

223	A34	1c ultra & multi	.15	.15
224	A34	10c Prus blue & multi	.15	.15
225	A34	15c plum & multi	.15	.15
226	A34	20c car rose & multi	.20	.20
227	A34	$1 brt grn & multi	1.00	1.00
228	A34	$1.50 blue grn & multi	1.40	1.40
a.	Souvenir sheet of 6, #223-228		3.25	3.25
b.	Horiz. strip of 5, #224-228		3.25	3.25
	Nos. 223-228 (6)		3.05	3.05

Christmas.

Nos. 145-146, 148, 150-160 Overprinted "NEW CONSTITUTION 1976"

1976   Litho.   Perf. 13½

229	A22	1c #145	.15	.15
230	A22	2c on 1c #145	.15	.15
231	A23	2c #146	.85	.85
232	A22	3c on 40c #155	.15	.15
233	A23	4c #148	.15	.15
234	A22	5c on 40c #155	.15	.15
235	A23	6c #150	.15	.15
236	A23	10c on 20c #153	.15	.15
237	A23	10c #151	1.10	1.10
238	A22	15c #152	.15	.15
239	A23	20c #153	.25	.25
240	A22	30c #154	.30	.30
241	A22	40c #155	.45	.45
242	A22	60c #156	.70	.70
243	A23	$1 #157	1.10	1.10
244	A23	$2.50 #158	2.50	2.50
245	A23	$5 #159	5.00	5.00
246	A22	$10 #160	12.00	12.00
	Nos. 229-246 (18)		25.45	25.45

Flowering Trees — A35

1976, Feb. 16   Perf. 13½x14

247	A35	1c Almond	.15	.15
248	A35	10c Clusia rosea	.15	.15
249	A35	15c Calabash	.20	.20
250	A35	20c Cordia	.22	.22
251	A35	$1 Papaya	1.00	1.00
252	A35	$1.50 Flamboyant	1.40	1.40
a.	Souvenir sheet of 6, #247-252		3.25	3.25
b.	Horiz. strip of 5, #248-252		3.25	3.25
	Nos. 247-252 (6)		3.12	3.12

The Three
Marys — A36

Designs: 10c, Crucifixion. 15c, Two soldiers. 20c, Annunciation. $1, Altar tapestry, 1470, Monastery of Rheinau, Switzerland, horiz. $1.50, "Noli me Tangere" (Jesus and Mary Magdalene). Designs of vertical stamps show details from tapestry shown on $1 stamp.

1976, Apr. 5   Perf. 14x13½, 13½x14

253	A36	1c multicolored	.15	.15
254	A36	10c multicolored	.15	.15
255	A36	15c multicolored	.18	.18
256	A36	20c multicolored	.20	.20
257	A36	$1 multicolored	.90	.90
258	A36	$1.50 multicolored	1.25	1.25
a.	Souvenir sheet of 6		2.75	2.75
b.	Horiz. strip of 5, #254-258		2.75	2.75
	Nos. 253-258 (6)		2.83	2.83

Easter. No. 258a contains 6 stamps similar to Nos. 253-258 with simulated perforations.

Le Desius and La Vaillante Approaching
Anguilla — A37

Sailing Ships: 3c, Sailboat leaving Anguilla for Antigua to get help. 15c, HMS Lapwing in battle with frigate Le Desius and brig La Vaillante. 25c, La Vaillante aground off St. Maarten. $1, Lapwing. $1.50, Le Desius burning.

1976, Nov. 8   Litho.   Perf. 13½x14

259	A37	1c multicolored	.15	.15
260	A37	3c multicolored	.15	.15
261	A37	15c multicolored	.20	.20
262	A37	25c multicolored	.35	.35
263	A37	$1 multicolored	1.40	1.40

264	A37	$1.50 multicolored	2.25	2.25
a.	Souvenir sheet of 6, #259-264		6.50	6.50
b.	Strip of 6, #260-264		4.50	4.50
			4.50	4.50

Bicentenary of Battle of Anguilla between French and British ships.

Christmas Carnival — A38

Children's Paintings: 3c, 3 children dreaming of Christmas gifts. 15c, Caroling. 25c, Candlelight procession. $1, Going to Church on Christmas Eve. $1.50, Airport, coming home for Christmas.

1976, Nov. 22

265	A38	1c multicolored	.15	.15
266	A38	3c multicolored	.15	.15
267	A38	15c multicolored	.18	.15
268	A38	25c multicolored	.22	.18
269	A38	$1 multicolored	.90	.80
270	A38	$1.50 multicolored	1.25	.90
a.	Souvenir sheet of 6, #265-270		2.75	2.00
b.	Strip of 5, #266-270		2.75	2.25
	Nos. 265-270 (6)		2.85	2.33

Christmas. For overprints and surcharges, see Nos. 305-310a.

Prince Charles and HMS Minerva,
1973 — A39

Designs: 40c, Prince Philip landing at Road Bay, 1964. $1.20, Hommage to Queen at Coronation. $2.50, Coronation regalia and map of Anguilla.

1977, Feb. 9

271	A39	25c multicolored	.18	.18
272	A39	40c multicolored	.30	.30
273	A39	$1.20 multicolored	.90	.90
274	A39	$2.50 multicolored	1.75	1.75
a.	Souvenir sheet of 4, #271-274		3.50	3.50
	Nos. 271-274 (4)		3.13	3.13

25th anniv. of reign of Queen Elizabeth II.

Yellow-crowned Night Heron — A40

Designs: 2c, Great barracuda. 3c, Queen conch. 4c, Spanish bayonet (Yucca). 5c, Trunkfish. 6c, Cable and telegraph building. 10c, American sparrow hawk. 15c, Ground orchids. 20c, Parlorfish. 22c, Lobster fishing boat. 35c, Boat race. 50c Sea bean (flowers). $1, Sandy Island with palms. $2.50, Manchineel (fruit). $5, Ground lizard. $10, Red-billed tropic bird.

1977-78   Litho.   Perf. 13½x14

275	A40	1c multicolored	.15	.15
276	A40	2c multicolored	.15	.15
277	A40	3c multicolored	.15	.15
278	A40	4c multicolored	.15	.15
279	A40	5c multicolored	.15	.15
280	A40	6c multicolored	.15	.15
281	A40	10c multicolored	.15	.15
282	A40	15c multicolored	.15	.15
283	A40	20c multicolored	.25	.25
284	A40	22c multicolored	.25	.25
285	A40	35c multicolored	.45	.45
286	A40	50c multicolored	.60	.60
287	A40	$1 multicolored	1.25	1.25
288	A40	$2.50 multicolored	3.00	3.00
289	A40	$5 multicolored	6.00	6.00
290	A40	$10 multicolored	12.00	12.00
	Nos. 275-290 (16)		25.00	25.00

Issue dates: Nos. 275-280, 290 Apr. 18, 1977. Others Feb. 20, 1978.
For overprints and surcharges, see Nos. 319-324, 337-342, 387-390, 402-404, 407-415, 417-423.

Crucifixion, by Quentin Massys — A41

Easter (Paintings): 3c, Betrayal of Christ, by Ugolino. 22c, Way to Calvary, by Ugolino. 30c, The Deposition, by Ugolino. $1, Resurrection, by Ugolino. $1.50, Crucifixion, by Andrea del Castagno.

1977, Apr. 25

291	A41	1c multicolored	.15	.15
292	A41	3c multicolored	.15	.15
293	A41	22c multicolored	.18	.18
294	A41	30c multicolored	.22	.22
295	A41	$1 multicolored	.90	.90
296	A41	$1.50 multicolored	1.25	1.25
a.	Souvenir sheet of 6, #291-296		2.50	2.50
b.	Strip of 6, #292-296		2.75	2.75
	Nos. 291-296 (6)		2.85	2.85

Nos. 271-274, 274b Overprinted: "ROYAL VISIT/TO WEST INDIES"

1977, Oct. 26   Litho.   Perf. 13½x14

297	A39	25c multicolored	.15	.15
298	A39	40c multicolored	.20	.20
299	A39	$1.20 multicolored	.60	.60
300	A39	$2.50 multicolored	1.25	1.25
a.	Souvenir sheet of 4		2.50	2.50
	Nos. 297-300 (4)		2.20	2.20

Visit of Queen Elizabeth II to West Indies.

Suzanne Fourment
in Velvet Hat, by
Rubens — A42

Rubens Paintings: 40c, Helena Fourment with her Children. $1.20, Rubens with his wife. $2.50, Marchesa Brigida Spinola-Doria.

1977, Nov. 1   Perf. 14x13½

301	A42	25c black & multi	.18	.18
302	A42	40c black & multi	.25	.25
303	A42	$1.20 black & multi	.90	.90
304	A42	$2.50 black & multi	1.75	1.75
a.	Souvenir sheet of 4, #301-304		3.25	3.25
	Nos. 301-304 (4)		3.08	3.08

Peter Paul Rubens, 400th birth anniv. Nos. 301-304 printed in sheets of 5 stamps and blue label with Rubens' portrait.

Nos. 265-270b Overprinted 1977 and Surcharged

1977, Nov. 7   Perf. 13½x14

305	A38	1c multicolored	.15	.15
306	A38	5c on 3c multi	.15	.15
307	A38	12c on 15c multi	.15	.15
308	A38	18c on 25c multi	.15	.15
309	A38	$1 multicolored	.65	.65
310	A38	$2.50 on $1.50 multi	1.75	1.75
a.	Souvenir sheet of 6, #305-310		3.25	1.75
b.	Strip of 5, #306-310		3.00	3.00
	Nos. 305-310 (6)		3.00	3.00

Christmas. Stamps and souvenir sheets have "1976" and old denomination obliterated with variously shaped rectangles.

Nos. 301-304a Ovptd. in Gold: "EASTER 1978"

1978, Mar. 6   Perf. 14x13½

311	A42	25c black & multi	.18	.18
312	A42	40c black & multi	.28	.28
313	A42	$1.20 black & multi	.80	.80
314	A42	$2.50 black & multi	1.75	1.75
a.	Souvenir sheet of 4, #311-314		3.25	3.25
	Nos. 311-314 (4)		3.01	3.01

Buckingham
Palace
A43

Designs: 50c, Coronation procession. $1.50, Royal family on balcony. $2.50, Royal coat of arms.

1978, Apr. 6   *Perf. 14*

315	A43	22c multicolored	.15	.15
316	A43	50c multicolored	.20	.20
317	A43	$1.50 multicolored	.60	.60
318	A43	$2.50 multicolored	.90	.90
a.		Souvenir sheet of 4, #315-318	2.00	2.00
		Nos. 315-318 (4)	1.85	1.85

25th anniv. of coronation of Queen Elizabeth II. #315-318 each exist in a booklet pane of 2.

Nos. 284-285 and 288 Ovptd. and Surcharged: "VALLEY / SECONDARY / SCHOOL / 1953-1978"

1978, Aug. 14   Litho.   *Perf. 13¹/₂x14*

319	A40	22c multicolored	.35	.35
320	A40	35c multicolored	.50	.50
321	A40	$1.50 on $2.50 multi	2.25	2.25
		Nos. 319-321 (3)	3.10	3.10

Valley Secondary School, 25th anniv. Surcharge on No. 321 includes heavy bar over old denomination.

Nos. 286-287, 289 Ovptd. and Surcharged: "ROAD / METHODIST / CHURCH / 1878-1978"

1978, Aug. 14

322	A40	50c multicolored	.65	.65
323	A40	$1 multicolored	1.30	1.30
324	A40	$1.20 on $5 multi	1.75	1.75
		Nos. 322-324 (3)	3.70	3.70

Road Methodist Church, centenary. Surcharge on No. 324 includes heavy bar over old denomination.

Mother and Child A44

Christmas: 12c, Christmas masquerade. 18c, Christmas dinner. 22c, Serenade. $1, Star over manger. $2.50, Family going to church.

1978, Dec. 11   Litho.   *Perf. 13¹/₂*

325	A44	5c multicolored	.15	.15
326	A44	12c multicolored	.15	.15
327	A44	18c multicolored	.15	.15
328	A44	22c multicolored	.15	.15
329	A44	$1 multicolored	.75	.75
330	A44	$2.50 multicolored	1.75	1.50
a.		Souvenir sheet of 6, #325-330	3.00	2.65
		Nos. 325-330 (6)	3.10	2.65

Type A44 in Changed Colors with IYC Emblem and Inscription.

1979, Jan. 15   Litho.   *Perf. 13¹/₂*

331	A44	5c multicolored	.15	.15
332	A44	12c multicolored	.15	.15
333	A44	18c multicolored	.15	.15
334	A44	22c multicolored	.18	.18
335	A44	$1 multicolored	.85	.85
336	A44	$2.50 multicolored	1.75	1.75
a.		Souvenir sheet of 4, #331-336	3.25	3.25
		Nos. 331-336 (6)	3.23	3.23

Intl. Year of the Child. For overprint, see No. 416

Nos. 275-278, 280-281 Surcharged

1979, Feb. 8   Litho.   *Perf. 13¹/₂x14*

337	A40	12c on 2c multi	.45	.45
338	A40	14c on 4c multi	.50	.50
339	A40	18c on 3c multi	.75	.75
340	A40	25c on 6c multi	1.25	1.25
341	A40	38c on 10c multi	1.75	1.75
342	A40	40c on 1c multi	2.00	2.00
		Nos. 337-342 (6)	6.70	6.70

Valley Methodist Church A45

Church Interiors: 12c, St. Mary's Anglican Church, The Valley. 18c, St. Gerard's Roman Catholic Church, The Valley. 22c, Road Methodist Church. $1.50, St. Augustine's Anglican Church, East End. $2.50, West End Methodist Church.

1979, Mar. 30   Litho.   *Perf. 14*

343	A45	5c multicolored	.15	.15
344	A45	12c multicolored	.15	.15
345	A45	18c multicolored	.15	.15
346	A45	22c multicolored	.15	.15
347	A45	$1.50 multicolored	1.00	1.00
348	A45	$2.50 multicolored	1.60	1.60
a.		Souvenir sheet of 6	3.25	3.25
b.		Strip of 6, #343-348	3.25	3.25

Easter. No. 348a contains Nos. 343-348 in 2 horizontal rows of 3.

US No. C3a A46

Designs: No. 350, Cape of Good Hope #1. No. 351, Penny Black. No. 352, Germany #C36. No. 353, US #245. No. 354, Great Britain #93.

1979, Apr. 23   Litho.   *Perf. 14*

349	A46	1c multicolored	.15	.15
350	A46	1c multicolored	.15	.15
351	A46	22c multicolored	.15	.15
352	A46	35c multicolored	.16	.16
353	A46	$1.50 multicolored	.80	.80
354	A46	$2.50 multicolored	1.40	1.40
a.		Souvenir sheet of 6, #349-353	2.75	2.75
		Nos. 349-354 (6)	2.81	2.81

Sir Rowland Hill (1795-1879), originator of penny postage.

Wright's Flyer A — A47

History of Aviation: 12c, Louis Bleriot landing at Dover, 1909. 18c, Vickers Vimy, 1919. 22c, Spirit of St. Louis, 1927. $1.50, LZ127 Graf Zeppelin, 1928. $2.50, Concorde, 1979.

1979, May 21   Litho.   *Perf. 14*

355	A47	5c multicolored	.15	.15
356	A47	12c multicolored	.15	.15
357	A47	18c multicolored	.15	.15
358	A47	22c multicolored	.15	.15
359	A47	$1.50 multicolored	1.00	1.00
360	A47	$2.50 multicolored	1.50	1.50
a.		Souvenir sheet of 6, #355-360	3.00	3.00
		Nos. 355-360 (6)	3.10	3.10

Map of Anguilla, Map and View of Sombrero Island A48

Map of Anguilla, Map and View of: 12c, Anguillita Island. 18c, Sandy Island. 25c, Prickly Pear Cays. $1, Dog Island. $2.50, Scrub Island.

1979   Litho.   *Perf. 14*

361	A48	5c multicolored	.15	.15
362	A48	12c multicolored	.15	.15
363	A48	18c multicolored	.15	.15
364	A48	25c multicolored	.18	.18
365	A48	$1 multicolored	.65	.65
366	A48	$2.50 multicolored	1.75	1.75
a.		Souvenir sheet of 6, #361-366	3.00	3.00
		Nos. 361-366 (6)	3.03	3.03

Anguilla's Outer Islands.

Red Poinsettia — A49

1979, Oct. 22   Litho.   *Perf. 14¹/₂*

367	A49	22c shown	.15	.15
368	A49	35c Kalanchoe	.25	.25
369	A49	$1.50 Cream poinsettia	1.10	.90
370	A49	$2.50 White poinsettia	2.00	1.50
a.		Souvenir sheet of 4, #367-370	3.75	2.75
		Nos. 367-370 (4)	3.50	2.75

Christmas.

Booths and Frames A50

50c, Earls Court Exhibition Hall. $1.50, Penny Black, Great Britain #2. $2.50, Exhibition emblem.

1979, Dec. 10   Litho.   *Perf. 13, 14¹/₂*

371	A50	35c multicolored	.20	.20
372	A50	50c multicolored	.30	.30
373	A50	$1.50 multicolored	1.00	1.00
374	A50	$2.50 multicolored	1.50	1.50
a.		Souvenir sheet of 4, #371-374	3.00	3.00
		Nos. 371-374 (4)	3.00	3.00

London 1980 Intl. Stamp Exhibition, May 6-14, 1980.

Lake Placid and Olympic Rings — A51

Olympic Rings and: 18c, Ice Hockey. 35c, Figure skating. 50c, Bobsledding. $1, Ski jump. $2.50, Luge.

1980, Jan.   Litho.   *Perf. 13¹/₂, 14¹/₂*

375	A51	5c multicolored	.15	.15
376	A51	18c multicolored	.15	.15
377	A51	35c multicolored	.18	.18
378	A51	50c multicolored	.28	.28
379	A51	$1 multicolored	.55	.55
380	A51	$2.50 multicolored	1.40	1.40
a.		Souvenir sheet of 6, #375-380	3.00	3.00
		Nos. 375-380 (6)	2.71	2.71

13th Winter Olympic Games, Lake Placid, NY, Feb. 12-24.

Salt Field A52

1980, Apr. 14   Litho.   *Perf. 14*

381	A52	5c shown	.15	.15
382	A52	12c Tallying salt	.15	.15
383	A52	18c Unloading salt flats	.15	.15
384	A52	22c Storage pile	.15	.15
385	A52	$1 Bagging and grinding	.60	.60
386	A52	$2.50 Loading onto boats	1.40	1.40
a.		Souvenir sheet of 6, #381-386	2.50	2.50
		Set value	2.34	2.34

Salt industry.

Nos. 281, 288 Overprinted: "50th Anniversary / Scouting 1980"

1980, Apr. 16   *Perf. 13¹/₂x14*

387	A40	10c multicolored	.15	.15
388	A40	$2.50 multicolored	2.00	2.00

Nos. 283, 289 Overprinted: "75th Anniversary / Rotary 1980" and Rotary Emblem

1980, Apr. 16   *Perf. 13¹/₂x14*

389	A40	20c multicolored	.15	.15
390	A40	$5 multicolored	3.50	3.50

Rotary International, 75th anniversary.

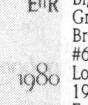

Big Ben, Great Britain #643, London 1980 Emblem A53

Designs: $1.50, Canada #756. $2.50, Statue of Liberty, US #1632.

1980, May

391	A53	50c multicolored	.25	.25
392	A53	$1.50 multicolored	.85	.85
393	A53	$2.50 multicolored	1.40	1.40
a.		Souvenir sheet of 3, #391-393	3.00	3.00
		Nos. 391-393 (3)	2.50	2.50

London 1980 International Stamp Exhibition, May 6-14.

Queen Mother Elizabeth, 80th Birthday — A54

1980, Aug. 4   Litho.   *Perf. 14*

394	A54	35c multicolored	.18	.18
395	A54	50c multicolored	.30	.30
396	A54	$1.50 multicolored	.90	.90
397	A54	$3 multicolored	1.75	1.75
a.		Souvenir sheet of 4, #394-397	3.00	3.00
		Nos. 394-397 (4)	3.13	3.13

Pelicans — A55

1980, Nov. 10   Litho.   *Perf. 14*

398	A55	5c shown	.15	.15
399	A55	22c Great gray herons	.15	.15
400	A55	$1.50 Swallows	1.00	1.00
401	A55	$3 Hummingbirds	2.00	2.00
a.		Souvenir sheet of 4, #398-401	3.25	3.25
		Nos. 398-401 (4)	3.30	3.30

Christmas. For overprints see #405-406.

Nos. 275, 278, 280-290, 334, 400-401 Overprinted: "SEPARATION 1980"

Perf. 13¹/₂x14, 14 (A55)

1980, Dec. 18   Litho.

402	A40	1c #275	.15	.15
403	A40	2c on 4c #278	.15	.15
404	A40	5c on 15c #282	.15	.15
405	A55	5c on $1.50 #400	.15	.15
406	A55	5c on $3 #401	.15	.15
407	A40	10c #281	.15	.15
408	A40	12c on $1 #287	.15	.15
409	A40	14c on $2.50 #288	.15	.15
410	A40	15c #282	.15	.15
411	A40	18c on $5 #289	.15	.15
412	A40	20c #283	.18	.18
413	A40	22c #284	.20	.20
414	A40	25c on 15c #282	.22	.22
415	A40	35c #285	.30	.30
416	A44	38c on 22c #334	.32	.32
417	A40	40c on 1c #275	.35	.35
418	A40	50c #286	.42	.42
419	A40	$1 #287	.75	.75
420	A40	$2.50 #288	1.75	1.75
421	A40	$5 #289	3.50	3.50
422	A40	$10 #290	7.25	7.25
423	A40	$10 on 6c #280	7.25	7.25
		Nos. 402-423 (22)	23.99	23.99

Petition for Separation, 1825 — A56

1980, Dec. 18   *Perf. 14*

424	A56	18c shown	.15	.15
425	A56	22c Referendum ballot, 1967	.15	.15
426	A56	35c Airport blockade, 1967	.25	.25
427	A56	50c Anguilla flag	.35	.35

428	A56	$1	Separation celebration, 1980	.65	.65
a.			Souvenir sheet of 5, #424-428	1.60	1.60
			Nos. 424-428 (5)	1.55	1.55

Separation from St. Kitts-Nevis.

Nelson's Dockyard, by R. Granger Barrett — A57

Ship Paintings: 35c, Agamemnon, Vanguard, Elephant, Captain and Victory, by Nicholas Pocock. 50c, Victory, by Monamy Swaine. $3, Battle of Trafalgar, by Clarkson Stanfield. $5, Lord Nelson, by L.F. Abbott and Nelson's arms.

1981, Mar. 2   Litho.   Perf. 14

429	A57	22c	multicolored	.15	.15
430	A57	35c	multicolored	.22	.22
431	A57	50c	multicolored	.32	.32
432	A57	$3	multicolored	1.75	1.75
			Nos. 429-432 (4)	2.44	2.44

Souvenir Sheet

| 433 | A57 | $5 | multicolored | 2.75 | 2.75 |

Lord Horatio Nelson (1758-1805), 175th death anniversary (1980).

Minnie Mouse — A58

Easter: Various Disney characters in Easter outfits.

1981, Mar. 30   Litho.   Perf. 13½

434	A58	1c	multicolored	.15	.15
435	A58	2c	multicolored	.15	.15
436	A58	3c	multicolored	.15	.15
437	A58	5c	multicolored	.15	.15
438	A58	7c	multicolored	.15	.15
439	A58	9c	multicolored	.15	.15
440	A58	10c	multicolored	.15	.15
441	A58	$2	multicolored	1.75	1.75
442	A58	$3	multicolored	2.50	2.50
			Set value	4.65	4.65

Souvenir Sheet

| 443 | A58 | $5 | multicolored | 4.75 | 4.75 |

Prince Charles, Lady Diana, St. Paul's Cathedral — A59

1981, June 15   Litho.   Perf. 14

444	A59	50c	shown	.32	.32
a.			Souvenir sheet of 2	.65	.65
445	A59	$2.50	Althorp	1.60	1.60
a.			Souvenir sheet of 2	3.25	3.25
446	A59	$3	Windsor Castle	2.00	2.00
a.			Souvenir sheet of 2	4.00	4.00
			Nos. 444-446 (3)	3.92	3.92

Souvenir Sheet

| 447 | A59 | $5 | Buckingham Palace | 2.50 | 2.50 |

Royal Wedding. Nos. 444-446a contain stamps in different colors.

Boys Climbing Tree — A60

1981   Litho.   Perf. 14

448	A60	5c	shown	.15	.15
449	A60	10c	Boys sailing boats	.15	.15
450	A60	15c	Children playing instruments	.15	.15
451	A60	$3	Children with animals	2.25	2.25
			Nos. 448-451 (4)	2.70	2.70

Souvenir Sheet

| 452 | A60 | $4 | Boys playing soccer, vert. | 3.00 | 3.00 |

UNICEF, 35th anniv.
Issued: 5c-15c, July 31; $3-$4, Sept. 30.

"The Children were Nestled all Snug in their Beds" — A61

Christmas: Scenes from Walt Disney's The Night Before Christmas.

1981, Nov. 2   Litho.   Perf. 13½

453	A61	1c	multicolored	.15	.15
454	A61	2c	multicolored	.15	.15
455	A61	3c	multicolored	.15	.15
456	A61	5c	multicolored	.15	.15
457	A61	7c	multicolored	.15	.15
458	A61	10c	multicolored	.15	.15
459	A61	12c	multicolored	.15	.15
460	A61	$2	multicolored	1.75	1.75
461	A61	$3	multicolored	2.75	2.75
			Set value	4.90	4.90

Souvenir Sheet

| 462 | A61 | $5 | multicolored | 4.75 | 4.75 |

Red Grouper — A62

1982, Jan. 1   Litho.   Perf. 14

463	A62	1c	shown	.15	.15
464	A62	5c	Ferries, Blowing Point	.15	.15
465	A62	10c	Racing boats	.15	.15
466	A62	15c	Majorettes	.15	.15
467	A62	20c	Launching boat, Sandy Hill	.20	.20
468	A62	25c	Coral	.25	.25
469	A62	30c	Little Bay cliffs	.30	.30
470	A62	35c	Fountain Cave	1.00	.50
471	A62	40c	Sandy Isld.	.40	.40
472	A62	45c	Landing, Sombrero	.45	.45
473	A62	50c	on 45c, #472	.50	.50
474	A62	50c	Seine fishing	2.00	1.00
475	A62	75c	Boat race, Sandy Ground	.75	.75
476	A62	$1	Bagging lobster, Island Harbor	2.00	1.00
477	A62	$5	Pelicans	10.00	7.50
478	A62	$7.50	Hibiscus	10.00	7.50
479	A62	$10	Queen triggerfish	13.00	10.00
			Nos. 463-479 (17)	41.45	30.95

For overprints and surcharges see Nos. 507-510, 546A-546D, 578-582, 606-608, 640-647.

Easter — A63

Princess Diana, 21st Birthday — A64

Designs: Butterflies on flowers.

1982, Apr. 5

480	A63	10c	Zebra, anthurium	.15	.15
481	A63	35c	Caribbean buckeye	.35	.35
482	A63	75c	Monarch, allamanda	.75	.75
483	A63	$3	Red rim, orchid	3.00	3.00
			Nos. 480-483 (4)	4.25	4.25

Souvenir Sheet

| 484 | A63 | $5 | Flambeau, amaryllis | 3.50 | 3.50 |

1982, May 17

Designs: Portraits, 1961-1981.

485	A64	10c	1961	.15	.15
486	A64	30c	1968	.20	.20
487	A64	40c	1970	.25	.25
488	A64	60c	1974	.40	.40
489	A64	$2	1981	1.40	1.40
490	A64	$3	1981	2.00	2.00
a.			Souvenir sheet of 6, #485-490	4.50	4.50
			Nos. 485-490 (6)	4.40	4.40

Souvenir Sheet

| 491 | A64 | $5 | 1981 | 3.75 | 3.75 |

For overprints see Nos. 639A-639G.

1982 World Cup — A65

Designs: Various Disney characters playing soccer.

1982, Aug. 3   Litho.   Perf. 11

492	A65	1c	multicolored	.15	.15
493	A65	3c	multicolored	.15	.15
494	A65	4c	multicolored	.15	.15
495	A65	5c	multicolored	.15	.15
496	A65	7c	multicolored	.15	.15
497	A65	9c	multicolored	.15	.15
498	A65	10c	multicolored	.15	.15
499	A65	$2.50	multicolored	2.25	2.25
500	A65	$3	multicolored	2.75	2.75
			Set value	5.50	5.50

Souvenir Sheet
Perf. 14

| 501 | A65 | $5 | multicolored | 5.50 | 5.50 |

Scouting Year A66

1982, July 5

502	A66	10c	Pitching tent	.15	.15
503	A66	35c	Marching band	.30	.30
504	A66	75c	Sailing	.65	.65
505	A66	$3	Flag bearers	2.50	2.50
			Nos. 502-505 (4)	3.60	3.60

Souvenir Sheet

| 506 | A66 | $5 | Camping | 4.00 | 4.00 |

Nos. 465, 474-475, 477 Overprinted: "COMMONWEALTH / GAMES 1982"

1982, Oct. 18   Litho.   Perf. 14

507	A62	10c	multicolored	.15	.15
508	A62	60c	multicolored	.45	.45
509	A62	75c	multicolored	.55	.55
510	A62	$5	multicolored	3.75	3.75
			Nos. 507-510 (4)	4.90	4.90

12th Commonwealth Games, Brisbane, Australia, Sept. 30-Oct. 9.

Christmas — A67

Scenes from Walt Disney's Winnie the Pooh.

1982, Nov. 29

511	A67	1c	multicolored	.15	.15
512	A67	2c	multicolored	.15	.15
513	A67	3c	multicolored	.15	.15
514	A67	5c	multicolored	.15	.15
515	A67	7c	multicolored	.15	.15
516	A67	10c	multicolored	.15	.15
517	A67	12c	multicolored	.15	.15
518	A67	20c	multicolored	.15	.15
519	A67	$5	multicolored	4.00	4.00

| | | Set value | 4.60 | 4.60 |

Souvenir Sheet

| 520 | A67 | $5 | multicolored | 4.50 | 4.50 |

Commonwealth Day (Mar. 14) — A68

1983, Feb. 28   Litho.   Perf. 14

521	A68	10c	Carnival procession	.15	.15
522	A68	35c	Flags	.30	.30
523	A68	75c	Economic cooperation	.65	.65
524	A68	$2.50	Salt pond	2.00	2.00
			Nos. 521-524 (4)	3.10	3.10

Souvenir Sheet

| 525 | A68 | $5 | Map showing Commonwealth | 4.00 | 4.00 |

Easter — A69

Ten Commandments.

1983, Mar. 31   Litho.   Perf. 14

526	A69	1c	multicolored	.15	.15
527	A69	2c	multicolored	.15	.15
528	A69	3c	multicolored	.15	.15
529	A69	10c	multicolored	.15	.15
530	A69	35c	multicolored	.25	.25
531	A69	60c	multicolored	.45	.45
532	A69	75c	multicolored	.55	.55
533	A69	$2	multicolored	1.50	1.50
534	A69	$2.50	multicolored	1.75	1.75
535	A69	$5	multicolored	3.75	3.75
			Nos. 526-535 (10)	8.85	8.85

Souvenir Sheet

| 536 | A69 | $5 | Moses Taking Tablets | 4.00 | 4.00 |

Local Turtles and World Wildlife Fund Emblem — A70

1983, Aug. 10   Litho.   Perf. 13½

537	A70	10c	Leatherback	.25	.25
538	A70	35c	Hawksbill	.80	.80
539	A70	75c	Green	2.00	2.00
540	A70	$1	Loggerhead	2.75	2.75
			Nos. 537-540 (4)	5.80	5.80

Souvenir Sheet

| 541 | A70 | $5 | Leatherback, diff. | 5.50 | 5.50 |

1983, Aug. 10   Litho.   Perf. 12

537a	A70	10c	Leatherback	.15	.15
538a	A70	35c	Hawksbill	.35	.35
539a	A70	75c	Green	.75	.75
540a	A70	$1	Loggerhead	1.00	1.00
			Nos. 537a-540a (4)	2.25	2.25

Manned Flight Bicentenary — A71

1983, Aug. 22   Perf. 14

542	A71	10c	Montgolfiere, 1783	.15	.15
543	A71	60c	Blanchard & Jeffries, 1785	.45	.45
544	A71	$1	Giffard's airship, 1852	.75	.75
545	A71	$2.50	Lilienthal's glider, 1890	1.75	1.75
			Nos. 542-545 (4)	3.10	3.10

Souvenir Sheet
546 A71 $5 Wright Brothers'
plane, 1909   3.75 3.75

**Nos. 465, 471, 476-477 Overprinted:
150TH ANNIVERSARY / ABOLITION OF
SLAVERY ACT**

1983, Oct. 24   **Litho.**   *Perf. 14*
546A A62 10c Racing boats   .15 .15
546B A62 40c Sandy Isld   .32 .32
546C A62 $1 Bagging lobster, Island
     Harbor   .80 .80
546D A62 $5 Pelicans   4.00 4.00
   Nos. 546A-546D (4)   5.27 5.27

Jiminy
Cricket — A72

Designs: Various Disney productions.

1983, Nov. 14   *Perf. 13½*
547 A72 1c shown   .15 .15
548 A72 2c Jiminy Cricket, kettle   .15 .15
549 A72 3c Jiminy Cricket, toys   .15 .15
550 A72 4c Mickey and Morty   .15 .15
551 A72 5c Scrooge McDuck   .15 .15
552 A72 6c Minnie and Goofy   .15 .15
553 A72 10c Goofy and Elf   .15 .15
554 A72 $2 Scrooge McDuck, diff.   1.75 1.75
555 A72 $3 Disney characters   2.75 2.75
   Set value   4.80 4.80

Souvenir Sheet
556 A72 $5 Scrooge McDuck   4.50 4.50

Boys' Brigade Centenary — A73

1983, Sept. 12   **Litho.**   *Perf. 14*
557 A73 10c Anguilla company, ban-
     ner   .15 .15
558 A73 $5 Marching with drum-
     mer   3.75 3.75
   a. Souvenir sheet of 2, #557-558   3.85 3.85

1984 Olympics, Los Angeles — A74

Mickey Mouse Competing in Decathlon.

1984, Feb. 20   **Litho.**   *Perf. 14*
559 A74 1c 100-meter run   .15 .15
560 A74 2c Long jump   .15 .15
561 A74 3c Shot put   .15 .15
562 A74 4c High jump   .15 .15
563 A74 5c 400-meter run   .15 .15
564 A74 6c Hurdles   .15 .15
565 A74 10c Discus   .15 .15
566 A74 $1 Pole vault   .95 .95
567 A74 $4 Javelin   3.75 3.75
   Set value   5.00 5.00

Souvenir Sheet
568 A74 $5 1500-meter run   5.50 5.50

1984, Apr. 24   *Perf. 12½x12*
559a A74 1c   .15 .15
560a A74 2c   .15 .15
561a A74 3c   .15 .15
562a A74 4c   .15 .15
563a A74 5c   .15 .15
564a A74 6c   .15 .15
565a A74 10c   .15 .15
566a A74 $1   .95 .95
567a A74 $4   3.75 3.75

   Set value   5.00 5.00

Souvenir Sheet
568a A74 $5 With Olympic rings emblem   5.50 5.50

Nos. 559a-567a inscribed with Olympic rings
emblem. Printed in sheets of 5 plus label.

Easter — A75

Ceiling and Wall Frescoes, La Stanze della
Segnatura, by Raphael (details).

1984, Apr. 19   **Litho.**   *Perf. 13½x14*
569 A75 10c Justice   .15 .15
570 A75 25c Poetry   .18 .18
571 A75 35c Philosophy   .25 .25
572 A75 40c Theology   .30 .30
573 A75 $1 Abraham & Paul   .75 .75
574 A75 $2 Moses & Matthew   1.50 1.50
575 A75 $3 John & David   2.25 2.25
576 A75 $4 Peter & Adam   3.00 3.00
   Nos. 569-576 (8)   8.38 8.38

Souvenir Sheet
577 A75 $5 Astronomy   3.75 3.75

Nos. 463, 469, 477-479 Surcharged

1984   **Litho.**   *Perf. 14*
578 A62 25c on $7.50 #478   .20 .20
579 A62 35c on 30c #469   .28 .28
580 A62 60c on 1c #463   .48 .48
581 A62 $2.50 on $5 #477   2.00 2.00
582 A62 $2.50 on $10 #479   2.00 2.00
   Nos. 578-582 (5)   4.96 4.96

Issue dates: 25c, May 17, others, Apr. 24.

Ausipex
'84
A76

Australian stamps.

1984, July 16   **Litho.**   *Perf. 13½*
583 A76 10c No. 2   .15 .15
584 A76 75c No. 18   .55 .55
585 A76 $1 No. 130   .80 .80
586 A76 $2.50 No. 178   2.00 2.00
   Nos. 583-586 (4)   3.50 3.50

Souvenir Sheet
587 A76 $5 Nos. 378, 379   3.75 3.75

Slavery Abolition Sesquicentennial — A77

Abolitionists and Vignettes: 10c, Thomas Fowell
Buxton, planting sugar cane. 25c, Abraham Lincoln, cotton field. 35c, Henri Christophe, armed
slave revolt. 60c, Thomas Clarkson, addressing
Anti-Slavery Society. 75c, William Wilberforce,
Slave auction. $1, Olaudah Equiano, slave raid on
Benin coast. $2.50, General Gordon, slave convoy
in Sudan. $5, Granville Sharp, restraining ship cap-
tain from boarding slave.

1984, Aug. 1   *Perf. 12*
588 A77 10c multicolored   .15 .15
589 A77 25c multicolored   .18 .18
590 A77 35c multicolored   .25 .25
591 A77 60c multicolored   .42 .42
592 A77 75c multicolored   .50 .50
593 A77 $1 multicolored   .72 .72
594 A77 $2.50 multicolored   1.75 1.75
595 A77 $5 multicolored   3.50 3.50
   a. Miniature sheet of 8, #588-595   7.75 7.75
   Nos. 588-595 (8)   7.47 7.47

For overprints see Nos. 688-695a.

   Set value   5.00 5.00

Souvenir Sheet
568a A74 $5 With Olympic rings emblem   5.50 5.50

Christmas — A78

Various Disney characters and celebrations.

Perf. 14, 12½x12 ($2)
1984, Nov. 12   **Litho.**
596 A78 1c multicolored   .15 .15
597 A78 2c multicolored   .15 .15
598 A78 3c multicolored   .15 .15
599 A78 4c multicolored   .15 .15
600 A78 10c multicolored   .15 .15
601 A78 $1 multicolored   .80 .80
602 A78 $2 multicolored   1.65 1.65
603 A78 $4 multicolored   3.25 3.25
   Set value   6.00 6.00

Souvenir Sheet
605 A78 $5 multicolored   4.25 4.25

**Nos. 464-465, 477 Overprinted or
Surcharged: "U.P.U. CONGRESS /
HAMBURG 1984"**

1984, Aug. 13
606 A62 5c #464   .15 .15
607 A62 20c on 10c #465   .16 .16
608 A62 $5 #477   4.00 4.00
   Nos. 606-608 (3)   4.31 4.31

Intl. Civil
Aviation
Org., 40th
Anniv.
A79

1984, Dec. 3   **Litho.**   *Perf. 14*
609 A79 60c Icarus, by Hans Erni   .45 .45
610 A79 75c Sun Princess, by
     Sadiou Diouf   .55 .55
611 A79 $2.50 Anniv. emblem, vert.   1.75 1.75
   Nos. 609-611 (3)   2.75 2.75

Souvenir Sheet
612 A79 $5 Map of the Caribbean   3.75 3.75

Audubon Birth
Bicent. — A80

Queen Mother 85th
Birthday — A81

Illustrations by artist and naturalist J. J. Audubon
(1785-1851).

1985, Apr. 30   **Litho.**   *Perf. 14*
613 A80 10c Hirundo rustica   .15 .15
614 A80 60c Mycteria americana   .45 .45
615 A80 75c Sterna dougallii   .55 .55
616 A80 $5 Pandion haliaetus   3.75 3.75
   Nos. 613-616 (4)   4.90 4.90

Souvenir Sheets
617 A80 $4 Vireo solitarus, horiz.   3.00 3.00
618 A80 $4 Piranga ludoviciana,
     horiz.   3.00 3.00

1985, July 2

Photographs: 10c, Visiting the children's ward at
King's College Hospital. $2, Inspecting Royal
Marine Volunteer Cadets at Deal. $3, Outside Clar-
ence House in London. $5, In an open carriage at
Ascot.

619 A81 10c multicolored   .15 .15
620 A81 $2 multicolored   1.25 1.25
621 A81 $3 multicolored   1.90 1.90
   Nos. 619-621 (3)   3.30 3.30

Souvenir Sheet
622 A81 $5 multicolored   3.75 3.75

Nos. 619-621 printed in sheetlets of 5.

Birds
A82

1985-86   **Litho.**   *Perf. 13½x14*
623 A82 5c Brown pelican   .15 .15
624 A82 10c Turtle dove   .15 .15
625 A82 15c Man-o-war   .15 .15
626 A82 20c Antillean crested
     hummingbird   .15 .15
627 A82 25c White-tailed trop-
     icbird   .35 .35
628 A82 30c Caribbean elaenia   .35 .35
629 A82 35c Black-whiskered
     vireo   .35 .35
629A A82 35c Lesser Antillean
     bullfinch ('86)   .45 .45
630 A82 40c Yellow-crowned
     night heron   .55 .55
631 A82 45c Pearly-eyed
     thrasher   .70 .70
632 A82 50c Laughing bird   .80 .80
633 A82 65c Brown booby   .80 .80
634 A82 80c Gray kingbird   1.50 1.50
635 A82 $1 Audubon's shear-
     water   2.00 2.00
636 A82 $1.35 Roseate tern   2.00 2.00
637 A82 $2.50 Bananaquit   4.00 4.00
638 A82 $5 Belted kingfisher   4.25 4.25
639 A82 $10 Green heron   8.50 8.50
   Nos. 623-639 (18)   27.20 27.20

Issue dates: 25c, 65c, $1.35, $5, July 22. 45c,
50c, 80c, $1, $10, Sept. 30. 5c-20c, 30c, No. 629,
40c, $2.50, Nov. 11. No. 629A, Mar. 10.
For overprints and surcharges see Nos. 678-682,
713-716, 723-739, 750-753, 764-767.

**Nos. 485-491 Overprinted "PRINCE
HENRY / BIRTH 15.9.84."**

1985, Oct. 31   **Litho.**   *Perf. 14*
639A A64 10c multicolored   .15 .15
639B A64 30c multicolored   .22 .22
639C A64 40c multicolored   .30 .30
639D A64 60c multicolored   .45 .45
639E A64 $2 multicolored   1.50 1.50
639F A64 $3 multicolored   2.25 2.25
   h. Souv. sheet of 6, #639A-639F   4.80 4.80
   Nos. 639A-639F (6)   4.87 4.87

Souvenir Sheet
639G A64 $5 multicolored   3.75 3.75

**Nos. 464, 469 and 477 Ovptd. with
Anniversary Emblem and "GIRL GUIDES
75th ANNIVERSARY / 1910-1985"**

1985, Oct. 14   **Litho.**   *Perf. 14*
640 A62 5c multicolored   .15 .15
641 A62 30c multicolored   .22 .22
642 A62 75c multicolored   .55 .55
643 A62 $5 multicolored   3.75 3.75
   Nos. 640-643 (4)   4.67 4.67

**Nos. 465 and 470 Overprinted or
Surcharged with Organization Emblem and
"80th ANNIVERSARY ROTARY 1985."**

1985, Nov. 18
644 A62 10c multicolored   .15 .15
645 A62 35c on 30c multi   .25 .25
   Set value   .33 .33

**Nos. 476, 469 Surcharged or Ovptd. with
Emblem, Text and "INTERNATIONAL
YOUTH YEAR"**

1985, Nov. 18
646 A62 $1 multicolored   .75 .75
647 A62 $5 on 30c multi   3.75 3.75

Brothers Grimm — A83

Christmas: Disney characters in Hansel and
Gretel.

1985, Nov. 11   **Litho.**   *Perf. 14*
648 A83 5c multicolored   .15 .15
649 A83 50c multicolored   .42 .42
650 A83 90c multicolored   .70 .70
651 A83 $4 multicolored   3.25 3.25
   Nos. 648-651 (4)   4.52 4.52

Souvenir Sheet
652 A83 $5 multicolored   4.50 4.50

Mark Twain (1835-1910), Author — A84

Disney characters in Huckleberry Finn.

1985, Nov. 11
653	A84	10c multicolored	.15	.15
654	A84	60c multicolored	.65	.65
654A	A84	$1 multicolored	1.00	1.00
655	A84	$3 multicolored	3.25	3.25
	Nos. 653-655 (4)	5.05	5.05

Souvenir Sheet
656	A84	$5 multicolored	4.50	4.50

Christmas. No. 654A printed in sheets of 8.

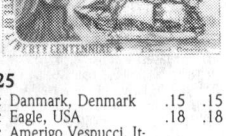

Statue of Liberty Centennial A85

1985, Nov. 25
657	A85	10c Danmark, Denmark	.15	.15
658	A85	20c Eagle, USA	.18	.18
659	A85	60c Amerigo Vespucci, Italy	.50	.50
660	A85	75c Sir Winston Churchill, G.B.	.60	.60
661	A85	$2 Nippon Maru, Japan	1.65	1.65
662	A85	$2.50 Gorch, Germany	1.90	1.90
	Nos. 657-662 (6)	4.98	4.98

Souvenir Sheet
663	A85	$5 Statue of Liberty, vert.	3.75	3.75

Easter — A86

Stained glass windows.

1986, Mar. 27   Litho.   Perf. 14
664	A86	10c multicolored	.15	.15
665	A86	25c multicolored	.20	.20
666	A86	45c multicolored	.35	.35
667	A86	$4 multicolored	3.00	3.00
	Nos. 664-667 (4)	3.70	3.70

Souvenir Sheet
668	A86	$5 multi, horiz.	4.00	4.00

A87

Halley's Comet A88

Designs: 5c, Johannes Hevelius (1611-1687), Mayan temple observatory. 10c, US Viking probe landing on Mars, 1976. 60c, Theatri Cosmicum (detail), 1668. $4, Sighting, 1835. $5, Comet over Anguilla.

1986, Mar. 24
669	A87	5c multicolored	.15	.15
670	A87	10c multicolored	.15	.15
671	A87	60c multicolored	.45	.45
672	A87	$4 multicolored	3.00	3.00
	Nos. 669-672 (4)	3.75	3.75

Souvenir Sheet
673	A88	$5 multicolored	3.75	3.75

Queen Elizabeth II, 60th Birthday
Common Design Type

1986, Apr. 21
674	CD339	20c Inspecting guards, 1946	.15	.15
675	CD339	$2 Garter Ceremony, 1985	1.50	1.50
676	CD339	$3 Trooping the color	2.25	2.25
	Nos. 674-676 (3)	3.90	3.90

Souvenir Sheet
677	CD339	$5 Christening, 1926	3.75	3.75

Nos. 623, 631, 635, 637 and 639 Ovptd. "AMERIPEX 1986"

1986, May 22   Perf. 13½x14
678	A82	5c multicolored	.15	.15
679	A82	45c multicolored	.35	.35
680	A82	$1 multicolored	.75	.75
681	A82	$2.50 multicolored	1.85	1.85
682	A82	$10 multicolored	7.50	7.50
	Nos. 678-682 (5)	10.60	10.60

Wedding of Prince Andrew and Sarah Ferguson — A89

1986, July 23   Litho.   Perf. 14, 12
683	A89	10c Couple	.15	.15
684	A89	35c Andrew	.25	.25
685	A89	$2 Sarah	1.50	1.50
686	A89	$3 Couple, diff.	2.25	2.25
	Nos. 683-686 (4)	4.15	4.15

Souvenir Sheet
687	A89	$6 Westminster Abbey	4.50	4.50

Nos. 588-595 Ovptd. "INTERNATIONAL / YEAR OF / PEACE"

1986, Sept. 29   Litho.   Perf. 12
688	A77	10c multicolored	.20	.20
689	A77	25c multicolored	.30	.30
690	A77	35c multicolored	.35	.35
691	A77	60c multicolored	.55	.55
692	A77	75c multicolored	.70	.70
693	A77	$1 multicolored	.90	.90
694	A77	$2.50 multicolored	2.00	2.00
695	A77	$5 multicolored	4.00	4.00
a.		Miniature sheet of 8, #688-695	9.00	9.00
	Nos. 688-695 (8)	9.00	9.00

Ships — A90

1986, Nov. 29   Litho.   Perf. 14
696	A90	10c Trading Sloop	.15	.15
697	A90	45c Lady Rodney	.35	.35
698	A90	80c West Derby	.65	.65
699	A90	$3 Warspite	2.40	2.40
	Nos. 696-699 (4)	3.55	3.55

Souvenir Sheet
700	A90	$6 Boat Race Day, vert.	4.50	4.50

Christmas.

Discovery of America, 500th Anniv. (in 1992) — A91   Dragon Tree — A92

Designs: 5c, Christopher Columbus, astrolabe. 10c, Aboard ship. 35c, Santa Maria. 80c, Ferdinand, Isabella, horiz. $4, Indians. No. 707, Caribbean manatee, horiz.

1986, Dec. 22
701	A91	5c multicolored	.15	.15
702	A91	10c multicolored	.15	.15
703	A91	35c multicolored	.28	.28
704	A91	80c multicolored	.65	.65
705	A91	$4 multicolored	3.20	3.20
	Nos. 701-705 (5)	4.43	4.43

Souvenir Sheets
706	A92	$5 shown	4.00	4.00
707	A92	$5 multicolored	4.00	4.00

Butterflies A93

1987, Apr. 14   Litho.   Perf. 14
708	A93	10c Monarch	.15	.15
709	A93	80c White peacock	.65	.65
710	A93	$1 Zebra	.80	.80
711	A93	$2 Caribbean buckeye	1.60	1.60
	Nos. 708-711 (4)	3.20	3.20

Souvenir Sheet
712	A93	$6 Flambeau	4.50	4.50

Easter.

Nos. 629A, 631, 634 and 639 Ovptd. with CAPEX '87 Emblem in Red

1987, May 25   Perf. 13½x14
713	A82	35c on No. 629A	.25	.25
714	A82	45c on No. 631	.35	.35
715	A82	80c on No. 634	.60	.60
716	A82	$10 on No. 639	7.50	7.50
	Nos. 713-716 (4)	8.70	8.70

Separation from St. Kitts and Nevis, 20th Anniv. — A94

Designs: 10c, Old goose iron, electric iron. 35c, Old East End School, Albena Lake-Hodge Comprehensive College. 45c, Old market place, People's Market. 80c, Old ferries and modern ferry at Blowing Point. $1, Old and new cable and wireless offices. $2, Public meeting at Burrowes Park, House of Assembly.

1987, May 25   Perf. 14
717	A94	10c multicolored	.15	.15
718	A94	35c multicolored	.25	.25
719	A94	45c multicolored	.35	.35
720	A94	80c multicolored	.60	.60
721	A94	$1 multicolored	.75	.75
722	A94	$2 multicolored	1.50	1.50
a.		Souvenir sheet of 6, #717-722	3.50	3.50
	Nos. 717-722 (6)	3.60	3.60

Nos. 623, 625-628, 629A-639 Ovptd. "20 YEARS OF PROGRESS / 1967-1987" in Red or Surcharged in Red & Black

1987, Sept. 4   Perf. 13½x14
723	A82	5c No. 623	.15	.15
724	A82	10c on 15c No. 625	.15	.15
725	A82	15c No. 625	.15	.15
726	A82	20c No. 626	.15	.15
727	A82	25c No. 627	.18	.18
728	A82	30c No. 628	.20	.20

729	A82	35c No. 629A	.22	.22
730	A82	40c No. 630	.25	.25
731	A82	45c No. 631	.30	.30
732	A82	50c No. 632	.30	.30
733	A82	65c No. 633	.45	.45
734	A82	80c No. 634	.55	.55
735	A82	$1 No. 635	.70	.70
736	A82	$1.35 No. 636	.90	.90
737	A82	$2.50 No. 637	1.75	1.75
738	A82	$5 No. 638	3.50	3.50
739	A82	$10 No. 639	6.75	6.75
	Nos. 723-739 (17)	16.65	16.65

Cricket World Cup A95

Various action scenes.

1987, Oct. 5   Perf. 14
740	A95	10c multicolored	.15	.15
741	A95	35c multicolored	.30	.30
742	A95	45c multicolored	.40	.40
743	A95	$2.50 multicolored	2.00	2.00
	Nos. 740-743 (4)	2.85	2.85

Souvenir Sheet
744	A95	$6 multicolored	4.50	4.50

Sea Shells, Crabs A96

1987, Nov. 2
745	A96	10c West Indian top shell	.15	.15
746	A96	35c Ghost crab	.30	.30
747	A96	50c Spiny Caribbean vase	.40	.40
748	A96	$2 Great land crab	1.60	1.60
	Nos. 745-748 (4)	2.45	2.45

Souvenir Sheet
749	A96	$6 Queen conch	4.75	4.75

Christmas.

Nos. 629A, 635-636 and 639 Ovptd. "40TH WEDDING ANNIVERSARY / H.M. QUEEN ELIZABETH II / H.R.H. THE DUKE OF EDINBURGH" in Scarlet

1987, Dec. 14   Litho.   Perf. 13½x14
750	A82	35c multicolored	.30	.30
751	A82	$1 multicolored	.75	.75
752	A82	$1.35 multicolored	1.00	1.00
753	A82	$10 multicolored	7.50	7.50
	Nos. 750-753 (4)	9.55	9.55

Easter (Lilies) — A97   1988 Summer Olympics, Seoul — A98

1988, Mar. 28   Litho.   Perf. 14
754	A97	30c Crinum erubescens	.30	.30
755	A97	45c Hymenocallis caribaea	.40	.40
756	A97	$1 Crinum macowanii	.90	.90
757	A97	$2.50 Hemerocallis fulva	2.25	2.25
	Nos. 754-757 (4)	3.85	3.85

Souvenir Sheet
758	A97	$6 Lilium longiflorum	5.25	5.25

1988, July 25   Litho.   Perf. 14
759	A98	35c 4x100-Meter relay	.30	.30
760	A98	45c Windsurfing	.35	.35
761	A98	50c Tennis	.40	.40
762	A98	80c Basketball	.60	.60
	Nos. 759-762 (4)	1.65	1.65

Souvenir Sheet
763	A98	$6 Women's 200 meters	4.50	4.50

Nos. 629A, 634-635 and 637 Ovptd.
"H.R.H. PRINCESS / ALEXANDRA'S /
VISIT NOVEMBER 1988"

1988, Dec. 14   Litho.   *Perf. 13½x14*
764	A82	35c multicolored	.30	.30
765	A82	80c multicolored	.60	.60
766	A82	$1 multicolored	.75	.75
767	A82	$2.50 multicolored	1.90	1.90
		Nos. 764-767 (4)	3.55	3.55

Marine Life A99

1988, Dec. 5   Litho.   *Perf. 14*
768	A99	35c Common sea fan	.30	.30
769	A99	80c Coral crab	.60	.60
770	A99	$1 Grooved brain coral	.75	.75
771	A99	$1.60 Old wife	1.20	1.20
		Nos. 768-771 (4)	2.85	2.85

Souvenir Sheet
| 772 | A99 | $6 West Indies spiny lobster | 4.50 | 4.50 |

Christmas.

Lizards A100

1989, Feb. 20   Litho.   *Perf. 13½x14*
773	A100	45c Wood slave	.35	.35
774	A100	80c Slippery back	.60	.60
775	A100	$1.75 Iguana	1.75	1.75
		Nos. 773-775 (3)	2.70	2.70

Souvenir Sheet
| 776 | A100 | $6 Tree lizard | 4.50 | 4.50 |

Easter — A101

Paintings: 35c, Christ Crowned with Thorns, by Hieronymous Bosch (c. 1450-1516). 80c, Christ Bearing the Cross, by David. $1, The Deposition, by David. $1.60, Pieta, by Rogier van der Weyden (1400-1464). $6, Crucified Christ with the Virgin Mary and Saints, by Raphael.

1989, Mar. 23   Litho.   *Perf. 14x13½*
777	A101	35c multicolored	.30	.30
778	A101	80c multicolored	.60	.60
779	A101	$1 multicolored	.75	.75
780	A101	$1.60 multicolored	1.20	1.20
		Nos. 777-780 (4)	2.85	2.85

Souvenir Sheet
| 781 | A101 | $6 multicolored | 4.50 | 4.50 |

University of the West Indies, 40th Anniv. — A102

1989, Apr. 24   Litho.   *Perf. 14x13½*
| 782 | A102 | $5 Coat of arms | 3.75 | 3.75 |

Nos. 634-636 and 638 Ovptd. "20th /
ANNIVERSARY / MOON / LANDING"

1989, July 3   Litho.   *Perf. 13½X14*
783	A82	80c multicolored	.60	.60
784	A82	$1 multicolored	.75	.75
785	A82	$1.35 multicolored	1.00	1.00
786	A82	$5 multicolored	3.75	3.75
		Nos. 783-786 (4)	6.10	6.10

Christmas — A103

Well-known and historic houses.

1989, Dec. 4   Litho.   *Perf. 13½x14*
787	A103	5c Lone Star, 1930	.15	.15
788	A103	35c Whitehouse, 1906	.30	.30
789	A103	45c Hodges House	.35	.35
790	A103	80c Warden's Place	.60	.60
		Nos. 787-790 (4)	1.40	1.40

Souvenir Sheet
| 791 | A103 | $6 Wallblake House, 1787 | 4.50 | 4.50 |

Fish A104

1990, Apr. 2   Litho.   *Perf. 13½x14*
792	A104	5c Blear eye	.15	.15
793	A104	10c Redman	.15	.15
794	A104	15c Speckletail	.15	.15
795	A104	25c Grunt	.15	.15
796	A104	30c Amber jack	.20	.20
797	A104	35c Red hind	.25	.25
798	A104	40c Goatfish	.30	.30
799	A104	45c Old wife	.35	.35
800	A104	50c Butter fish	.40	.40
801	A104	65c Shell fish	.50	.50
802	A104	80c Yellowtail snapper	.60	.60
803	A104	$1 Katy	.75	.75
804	A104	$1.35 Mutton grouper	1.00	1.00
805	A104	$2.50 Doctor fish	1.90	1.90
806	A104	$5 Angelfish	3.75	3.75
807	A104	$10 Barracuda	7.50	7.50
		Nos. 792-807 (16)	18.10	18.10

Nos. 792-793, 797 exist inscribed 1992. For overprints and surcharge see #821-824, 849.

Easter — A105

1990, Apr. 2   Litho.   *Perf. 14x13½*
811	A105	35c Last Supper	.26	.26
812	A105	45c Trial	.34	.34
813	A105	$1.35 Calvary	1.00	1.00
814	A105	$2.50 Empty tomb	1.90	1.90
		Nos. 811-814 (4)	3.50	3.50

Souvenir Sheet
| 815 | A105 | $6 The Resurrection | 4.50 | 4.50 |

See Nos. 834-838.

Cape of Good Hope #7 — A106

Stamps of Great Britain and exhibition emblem: 25c, #1, vert. 50c, #2, vert. $2.50, #93. $6, #1-2.

1990, Apr. 30   *Perf. 14*
816	A106	25c multicolored	.20	.20
817	A106	50c multicolored	.35	.35
818	A106	$1.50 shown	1.10	1.10
819	A106	$2.50 multicolored	1.90	1.90
		Nos. 816-819 (4)	3.55	3.55

Souvenir Sheet
| 820 | A106 | $6 multicolored | 4.50 | 4.50 |

Stamp World London '90, Penny Black 150th anniv.

Nos. 803-806 Overprinted:
  a. EXPO '90
  b. 1990 INTERNATIONAL / LITERACY YEAR
  c. WORLD CUP FOOTBALL / CHAMPIONSHIPS 1990
  d. 90TH BIRTHDAY / H.M. THE QUEEN MOTHER

1990, Sept. 24   Litho.   *Perf. 13½x14*
821	A104(a)	$1 Katy	.75	.75
822	A104(b)	$1.35 Mutton grouper	1.00	1.00
823	A104(c)	$2.50 Doctor fish	1.90	1.90
824	A104(d)	$5 Angelfish	3.75	3.75
		Nos. 821-824 (4)	7.40	7.40

Christmas — A107

Birds.

1990, Dec. 3   *Perf. 14*
825	A107	10c Laughing gull	.20	.20
826	A107	35c Brown booby	.35	.35
827	A107	$1.50 Bridled tern	1.40	1.40
828	A107	$3.50 Brown pelican	3.50	3.50
		Nos. 825-828 (4)	5.45	5.45

Souvenir Sheet
| 829 | A107 | $6 Least tern | 7.00 | 7.00 |

Flags A108

1991, Nov. 5   Litho.   *Perf. 13½x14*
830	A108	50c Mermaid	.40	.40
831	A108	80c New Anguilla official	.60	.60
832	A108	$1 Three dolphins	.75	.75
833	A108	$5 Governor's official	3.75	3.75
		Nos. 830-833 (4)	5.50	5.50

Nos. 811-815 Inscribed or Overprinted "1991"

1991, Apr. 30   Litho.   *Perf. 14x13½*
834	A105	35c like #811	.25	.25
835	A105	45c like #812	.35	.35
836	A105	$1.35 like #813	1.00	1.00
837	A105	$2.50 like #814	1.90	1.90
		Nos. 834-837 (4)	3.50	3.50

Souvenir Sheet
| 838 | A105 | $6 like #815 | 7.75 | 7.75 |

Easter. "1990" obliterated by black bar in souvenir sheet margin.

Christmas — A109

Perf. 14x13½, 13½x14
1991, Dec.   Litho.
839	A109	5c Angel, vert.	.15	.15
840	A109	35c Santa, vert.	.25	.25
841	A109	80c shown	.60	.60
842	A109	$1 Palm trees, poinsettias	.75	.75
		Nos. 839-842 (4)	1.75	1.75

Souvenir Sheet
| 843 | A109 | $5 Homes, holly | 3.75 | 3.75 |

Easter A110

Designs: 35c, Church, angels holding palms, vert. 45c Church, angels singing, vert. 80c, Village. $1, People going to church, vert. $5, People at beach, sailboats.

1992   Litho.   *Perf. 14*
844	A110	35c multicolored	.30	.30
845	A110	45c multicolored	.40	.40
846	A110	80c multicolored	.70	.70
847	A110	$1 multicolored	.85	.85
848	A110	$5 multicolored	4.25	4.25
		Nos. 844-848 (5)	6.50	6.50

No. 796 Surcharged   **$1.60**

1992, June 10   Litho.   *Perf. 13½x14*
| 849 | A104 | $1.60 on 30c #796 | 1.40 | 1.40 |

No. 849 inscribed "1992."

Independence, 25th Anniv. — A111

1992, Aug. 10   Litho.   *Perf. 14*
850	A111	80c Official seal, flag	.60	.60
851	A111	$1 Official seal	.70	.70
852	A111	$1.60 Flags, airport	1.25	1.25
853	A111	$2 First seal	1.40	1.40
		Nos. 850-853 (4)	3.95	3.95

Souvenir Sheet
| 854 | A111 | $10 #1, 8-11, 15-16 | 8.50 | 8.50 |

No. 854 contains one 85x85mm stamp.

Sailboat Racing A112

Designs: 20c, On course. 35c, Stylized boat poster. 45c, Start of race. No. 858, Blue Bird, 1971, vert. No. 859, Construction plans for Blue Bird, vert. $1, Stylized boat poster, diff. $6, Like Nos. 855 & 857.

Perf. 13½x14, 14x13½
1992, Oct. 12   Litho.
855	A112	20c multicolored	.15	.15
856	A112	35c multicolored	.25	.25
857	A112	45c multicolored	.35	.35
858	A112	80c multicolored	.55	.55
859	A112	80c multicolored	.55	.55
a.		Pair, #858-859	1.10	1.10
860	A112	$1 multicolored	.70	.70
		Nos. 855-860 (6)	2.55	2.55

Souvenir Sheet
| 861 | A112 | $6 multicolored | 4.55 | 4.55 |

No. 861 contains one 96x31mm stamp.

Discovery of America, 500th Anniv. A113

1992, Dec. 15   Litho.   *Perf. 14*
862	A113	80c Landfall	.70	.70
863	A113	$1 Columbus, vert.	.85	.85
864	A113	$2 Fleet	1.65	1.65
865	A113	$3 Pinta	2.50	2.50
		Nos. 862-865 (4)	5.70	5.70

Souvenir Sheet
| 866 | A113 | $6 Map of voyage, vert. | 5.00 | 5.00 |

Christmas
A114

Various Christmas trees and: 20c, Mucka Jumbie
on stilts. 70c, Masquerading house to house. $1.05,
Christmas baking, old oven style. $2.40, $5, Collecting presents.

1992, Dec. 7

867	A114	20c multicolored	.15	.15
868	A114	70c multicolored	.60	.60
869	A114	$1.05 multicolored	.90	.90
870	A114	$2.40 multicolored	2.00	2.00
		Nos. 867-870 (4)	3.65	3.65

Souvenir Sheet

871	A114	$5 Sheet of 1 + 3 labels	4.25	4.25

Labels on No. 871 are similar to Nos. 867-869,
but without denomination.

Easter — A115

Children's drawings: 20c, Kite flying. 45c, Cliff
top village service. 80c, Morning devotion on
Sombero. $1.50, Hilltop church service. $5, Good
Friday kites.

1993, Mar. 29   Litho.   Perf. 14

872	A115	20c multicolored	.15	.15
873	A115	45c multicolored	.40	.40
874	A115	80c multicolored	.65	.65
875	A115	$1.50 multicolored	1.25	1.25
		Nos. 872-875 (4)	2.45	2.45

Souvenir Sheet

876	A115	$5 multicolored	4.25	4.25

No. 876 contains one 42x56mm stamp.

Native
Industries
A116

1993, June 23   Litho.   Perf. 14

877	A116	20c Salt	.15	.15
878	A116	80c Tobacco	.65	.65
879	A116	$1 Cotton	.80	.80
880	A116	$2 Sugar cane	1.60	1.60
		Nos. 877-880 (4)	3.20	3.20

Souvenir Sheet

881	A116	$6 Fishing	4.75	4.75

Coronation of Queen
Elizabeth II, 40th
Anniv. — A117

Designs: 80c, Lord Great Chamberlain presents
the spurs of chivalry. $1, The benediction. $2,
Queen Elizabeth II, coronation photograph. $3, St.
Edward's Crown. $6, Queen, Prince Philip in Gold
State Coach.

1993, Aug. 16   Litho.   Perf. 14

882	A117	80c multicolored	.65	.65
883	A117	$1 multicolored	.80	.80
884	A117	$2 multicolored	1.60	1.60
885	A117	$3 multicolored	2.40	2.40
		Nos. 882-885 (4)	5.45	5.45

Souvenir Sheet

886	A117	$6 multicolored	4.75	4.75

Anguilla Carnival — A118

1993, Aug. 23   Litho.   Perf. 14

887	A118	20c Pan musician	.15	.15
888	A118	45c Pirates	.35	.35
889	A118	80c Stars	.65	.65
890	A118	$1 Playing mas	.80	.80
891	A118	$2 Masqueraders	1.60	1.60
892	A118	$3 Commandos	2.40	2.40
		Nos. 887-892 (6)	5.95	5.95

Souvenir Sheet

893	A118	$5 Carnival fantasy	4.00	4.00

Christmas — A119   Mail
Delivery — A120

Traditional Christmas customs: 20c, Mucka
Jumbies. 35c, Serenaders. 45c, Baking. $3, Five-
fingers Christmas tree. $4, Mucka Jumbies and
serenaders.

1993, Dec. 7   Litho.   Perf. 14x13 1/2

894	A119	20c multicolored	.20	.20
895	A119	35c multicolored	.30	.30
896	A119	45c multicolored	.40	.40
897	A119	$3 multicolored	2.50	2.50
		Nos. 894-897 (4)	3.40	3.40

Souvenir Sheet
Perf. 14

898	A119	$4 multicolored	3.50	3.50

No. 898 contains one 54x42mm stamp.

1993, Feb. 11   Litho.   Perf. 14

Designs: 20c, Traveling Branch mail van, Sandy
Ground, horiz. 45c, Mail boat, Betsy R, The Forest.
80c, Old post office, horiz. $1, Mail by jeep, Island
Harbor. $4, New post office, 1993, horiz.

899	A120	20c multicolored	.20	.20
900	A120	45c multicolored	.40	.40
901	A120	80c multicolored	.70	.70
902	A120	$1 multicolored	.85	.85
903	A120	$4 multicolored	3.50	3.50
		Nos. 899-903 (5)	5.65	5.65

Royal Visits — A121   Easter — A122

1994, Feb. 18

904	A121	45c Princess Alexandra	.35	.35
905	A121	50c Princess Alice	.45	.45
906	A121	80c Prince Philip	.70	.70
907	A121	$1 Prince Charles	.85	.85
908	A121	$2 Queen Elizabeth II	1.65	1.65
a.		Souvenir sheet of 4, #904-908	4.00	4.00
		Nos. 904-908 (5)	4.00	4.00

1994, Apr. 6   Litho.   Perf. 14x15

Stained glass windows: 20c, Crucifixion. 45c,
Empty tomb. 80c, Resurrection. $3, Risen Christ
with disciples.

909	A122	20c multicolored	.20	.20
910	A122	45c multicolored	.40	.40
911	A122	80c multicolored	.75	.75
912	A122	$3 multicolored	2.75	2.75
		Nos. 909-912 (4)	4.10	4.10

Christmas — A123

Designs: 20c, Adoration of the shepherds. 30c,
Magi, shepherds. 35c, The Annunciation. 45c,
Nativity Scene. $2.40, Flight into Egypt.

1994, Nov. 22   Litho.   Perf. 14

913	A123	20c multicolored	.20	.20
914	A123	30c multicolored	.30	.30
915	A123	35c multicolored	.35	.35
916	A123	45c multicolored	.45	.45
917	A123	$2.40 multicolored	2.50	2.50
		Nos. 913-917 (5)	3.80	3.80

1994 World Cup Soccer Championships,
US — A124

Soccer player and: 20c, Pontiac Silverdome,
Detroit. 70c, Foxboro Stadium, Boston. $1.80,
RFK Memorial Stadium, Washington. $2.40, Soldier
Field, Chicago.
$6, Two players.

1994, Oct. 3   Litho.   Perf. 13 1/2x14

918	A124	20c multicolored	.20	.20
919	A124	70c multicolored	.65	.65
920	A124	$1.80 multicolored	1.65	1.65
921	A124	$2.40 multicolored	1.90	1.90
		Nos. 918-921 (4)	4.40	4.40

Souvenir Sheet

922	A124	$6 multicolored	5.50	5.50

Easter
A125

Turtle dove: 45c, One on tree branch. 50c, One
on nest, one on branch. $5, Mother with young.

1995, Apr. 10   Litho.   Perf. 14

923	A125	20c multicolored	.20	.20
924	A125	45c multicolored	.40	.40
925	A125	50c multicolored	.45	.45
926	A125	$5 multicolored	4.75	4.75
		Nos. 923-926 (4)	5.80	5.80

UN,
50th
Anniv.
A126

Secretaries-general and: 20c, Trygve Lie (1946-
53), general assembly. 80c, UN flag, UN headquarters with "50" (no portrait). $1, Dag Hammarskjold
(1953-61), charter, U Thant (1961-71). $5, UN
complex, New York, vert. (no portrait).

Perf. 13 1/2x14, 14x13 1/2

1995, June 26   Litho.

927	A126	20c multicolored	.20	.20
928	A126	80c multicolored	.75	.75
929	A126	$1 multicolored	.95	.95
930	A126	$5 multicolored	4.75	4.75
		Nos. 927-930 (4)	6.65	6.65

Caribbean Development Bank, 25th
Anniv. — A127

Designs: 45c, Emblem, map of Anguilla. $5,
Local headquarters along waterfront.

1995, Aug. 15   Litho.   Perf. 13 1/2x14

931	A127	45c multicolored	.45	.45
932	A127	$5 multicolored	5.00	5.00
a.		Pair, #931-932	5.45	5.45

Whales
A128

Perf. 13 1/2x14, 14x13 1/2

1995, Nov. 24   Litho.

933	A128	20c Blue whale	.20	.20
934	A128	45c Right whale, vert.	.40	.40
935	A128	$1 Sperm whale	.90	.90
936	A128	$5 Humpback whale	4.25	4.25
		Nos. 933-936 (4)	5.75	5.75

Christmas
A129

1995, Dec. 12   Perf. 14 1/2

937	A129	10c Palm tree	.15	.15
938	A129	25c Fish net floats	.20	.20
939	A129	45c Sea shells	.40	.40
940	A129	$5 Fish	4.25	4.25
		Nos. 937-940 (4)	5.00	5.00

Corals — A130

1996   Litho.   Perf. 14x14 1/2

941	A130	20c Deep water gorgonia	.20	.20
942	A130	80c Common sea fan	.70	.70
943	A130	$5 Venus sea fern	4.25	4.25
		Nos. 941-943 (3)	5.15	5.15

Iguanas
A134

World Wildlife Fund: a, 20c, Baby iguanas
emerging from eggs, juvenile iguana. b, 50c, Adult
on rock. c, 75c, Two iguanas on tree limbs. d, $3,
Adult up close, adult on tree branch.

1997   Litho.   Perf. 13 1/2x14

968	A134	Strip of 4, #a.-d.	4.00	4.00

ANJOUAN

'an-jü-wän

LOCATION — One of the Comoro Islands in the Mozambique Channel between Madagascar and Mozambique.
GOVT. — Former French colony.
AREA — 89 sq. mi.
POP. — 20,000 (approx. 1912)
CAPITAL — Mossamondu
See Comoro Islands.

100 Centimes = 1 Franc

Navigation and
Commerce — A1

Perf. 14x13½

				Unwmk.	
1892-1907		**Typo.**			
Name of Colony in Blue or Carmine					
1	A1	1c black, *blue*		.85	.80
2	A1	2c brown, *buff*		1.25	1.10
3	A1	4c claret, *lav*		1.75	1.30
4	A1	5c green, *grnsh*		3.25	2.25
5	A1	10c blk, *lavender*		4.25	2.50
6	A1	10c red ('00)		17.50	12.50
7	A1	15c blue, quadrille paper		4.25	3.25
8	A1	15c gray, *lt gray* ('00)		7.50	6.00
9	A1	20c red, *green*		4.50	3.25
10	A1	25c black, *rose*		5.00	4.00
11	A1	25c blue ('00)		8.00	8.00
12	A1	30c brn, *bister*		12.50	10.00
13	A1	35c blk, *yel* ('06)		5.75	4.25
14	A1	40c red, *straw*		22.50	15.00
15	A1	45c blk, *gray grn* ('07)		80.00	70.00
16	A1	50c car, *rose*		25.00	15.00
17	A1	50c brn, *az* ('00)		17.50	9.00
18	A1	75c vio, *orange*		25.00	15.00
19	A1	1fr brnz grn, *straw*		55.00	42.50
		Nos. 1-19 (19)		301.35	225.70

Perf. 13½x14 stamps are counterfeits.

Issues of 1892-1907 Surcharged in Black or Carmine

05   10

1912					
20	A1	5c on 2c brn, *buff*		.50	.50
21	A1	5c on 4c cl, *lav* (C)		.50	.50
22	A1	5c on 15c blue (C)		.50	.50
23	A1	5c on 20c red, *green*		.50	.50
24	A1	5c on 25c blk, *rose* (C)		.50	.50
25	A1	5c on 30c brn, *bis* (C)		.50	.50
26	A1	10c on 40c red, *straw*		.70	.70
27	A1	10c on 45c black, *gray green* (C)		.85	.85
28	A1	10c on 50c car, *rose*		1.90	1.90
29	A1	10c on 75c vio, *org*		1.35	1.35
30	A1	10c on 1fr brnz grn, *straw*		1.35	1.35
		Nos. 20-30 (11)		9.15	9.15

Nos. 21-23, 30 exist in pairs, one without surcharge. Value, \$550 each.
Two spacings between the surcharged numerals are found on Nos. 20-30.
Nos. 20-30 were available for use in Madagascar and the Comoro archipelago.

The stamps of Anjouan were superseded by those of Madagascar, and in 1950 by those of Comoro Islands.

ANNAM AND TONKIN

a-'nam and 'tän-'kin

LOCATION — In French Indo-China bordering on the China Sea on the east and Siam on the west.
GOVT. — French Protectorate
AREA — 97,503 sq. mi.
POP. — 14,124,000 (approx. 1890)
CAPITAL — Annam: Hue; Tonkin: Hanoi

For administrative purposes, the Protectorates of Annam, Tonkin, Cambodia, Laos and the Colony of Cochin-China were grouped together and were known as French Indo-China.

100 Centimes = 1 Franc

Catalogue values for unused stamps are for examples without gum as most stamps were issued in that condition.

Stamps of French Colonies, 1881-86 Handstamped Surcharged in Black:

Perf. 14x13½

				Unwmk.	
1888, Jan. 21					
1	A9	1c on 2c brn, *buff*		22.50	20.00
a.		Inverted surcharge		100.00	100.00
b.		Sideways surcharge		100.00	100.00
2	A9	1c on 4c claret, *lav*		17.50	14.00
a.		Inverted surcharge		100.00	100.00
b.		Double surcharge		125.00	125.00
c.		Sideways surcharge		100.00	100.00
3	A9	5c on 10c blk, *lav*		17.50	15.00
a.		Inverted surcharge		100.00	100.00
b.		Double surcharge		125.00	125.00

Hyphen between "A" and "T"

7	A9	1c on 2c brn, *buff*		220.00	200.00
a.		Inverted surcharge		450.00	
8	A9	1c on 4c claret, *lav*		350.00	350.00
9	A9	5c on 10c blk, *lav*		160.00	160.00

A 5c on 2c was prepared but not issued. Value \$6,500.
In these surcharges there are different types of numerals and letters.
There are numerous other errors in the placing of the surcharges, including double one inverted, double both inverted, double one sideways, pair #1, 7, and pair one without surcharge. Such varieties command substantial premiums.
These stamps were superseded in 1892 by those of Indo-China.

ANTIGUA

an-'tēg-(w)ə

LOCATION — In the West Indies, southeast of Puerto Rico
GOVT. — Independent state
AREA — 171 sq. mi.
POP. — 74,000 (est. 1981)
CAPITAL — St. John's

Antigua was one of the presidencies of the former Leeward Islands colony until becoming a Crown Colony in 1956. It became an Associated State of the United Kingdom in 1967 and an independent nation on November 1, 1981, taking the name of Antigua and Barbuda.
Antigua stamps were discontinued in 1890 and resumed in 1903. In the interim, stamps of Leeward Islands were used. Between 1903-1956, stamps of Antigua and Leeward Islands were used concurrently.

12 Pence = 1 Shilling
20 Shillings = 1 Pound
100 Cents = 1 Dollar (1951)

> Catalogue values for unused stamps in this country are for Never Hinged items, beginning with Scott 96.

Values for unused stamps are for examples with original gum as defined in the catalogue introduction. Any exceptions will be noted. Very fine examples of Nos. 1-8, 11, 18-20 will have perforations touching the design on at least one frameline due to the narrow spacing of the stamps on the plates. Stamps with perfs clear of the framelines on all four sides are extremely scarce and will command higher prices.

Watermark

Wmk. 5- Star

Queen Victoria
A1   A2

Rough Perf. 14-16

				Unwmk.	
1862		**Engr.**			
1	A1	6p blue green		1,000.	650.
a.		Perf. 11-13		5,250.	
b.		Perf. 11-13x14-16		2,750.	
c.		Perf. 11-13 compound with 14-16		3,000.	

There is a question whether Nos. 1a-1c ever did postal duty.
Values for No. 1 are for stamps with perfs. cutting into the design. Values for No. 1b are for copies without gum.

1863-67				**Wmk. 5**	
2	A1	1p lilac rose		125.00	30.00
a.		Vert. pair, imperf. btwn.		15,000.	
3	A1	1p vermilion ('67)		375.00	27.50
a.		Horiz. pair, imperf. btwn.		15,500.	
4	A1	6p green		350.00	30.00
a.		6p yellow green		3,750.	70.00
c.		6p dark green		375.00	30.00

1872		**Wmk. 1**		**Perf. 12½**	
5	A1	1p lake		100.00	30.00
6	A1	1p vermilion		125.00	30.00
7	A1	6p blue green		550.00	12.00
		Nos. 5-7 (3)		775.00	72.00

1873-79				**Perf. 14**	
8	A1	1p rose		90.00	15.00
a.		Half used as ½p on cover		2,500.	
		Typo.			
9	A2	2½p red brown ('79)		600.00	175.00
10	A2	4p blue ('79)		300.00	20.00
		Engr.			
11	A1	6p blue green ('76)		300.00	15.00

1882-86		**Typo.**		**Wmk. 2**	
12	A2	½p green		3.00	10.00
13	A2	2½p red brown		125.00	45.00
14	A2	2½p ultra ('86)		12.00	12.50
15	A2	4p blue		275.00	20.00
16	A2	4p brown org ('86)		2.50	3.50
17	A2	1sh violet ('86)		175.00	125.00
		Engr.			
18	A1	1p rose ('84)		1.25	*3.00*
19	A1	6p deep green		60.00	*125.00*

No. 18 was used for a time in St. Christopher and is identified by the "A12" cancellation.

1884				**Perf. 12**	
20	A1	1p rose red		50.00	17.50

Seal of the Colony — A3

King Edward VII — A4

1903		**Typo.**	**Wmk. 1**	**Perf. 14**	
21	A3	½p blue grn & blk		2.50	3.75
22	A3	1p car & black		3.50	1.00
a.		Bluish paper ('09)		70.00	70.00
23	A3	2p org brn & vio		5.25	17.50
24	A3	2½p ultra & black		7.00	11.00
25	A3	3p ocher & gray green		8.00	12.50
26	A3	6p black & red vio		22.50	37.50
27	A3	1sh violet & ultra		25.00	37.50
28	A3	2sh pur & gray green		45.00	55.00
29	A3	2sh6p red vio & blk		21.00	35.00
30	A4	5sh pur & gray green		65.00	90.00
		Nos. 21-30 (10)		204.75	300.75

The 2½p, 1sh and 5sh exist on both ordinary and chalky paper.

1908-15				**Wmk. 3**	
31	A3	½p green		1.25	2.75
32	A3	1p carmine		2.75	1.00
a.		1p scarlet ('15)		2.50	2.25
33	A3	2p org brn & dull vio ('12)		3.25	19.00
34	A3	2½p ultra		6.00	13.00
35	A3	3p ocher & grn ('12)		6.00	15.00
36	A3	6p blk & red vio ('11)		6.50	25.00
37	A3	1sh vio & ultra		13.00	50.00
38	A3	2sh vio & green ('12)		47.50	65.00
		Nos. 31-38 (8)		86.25	190.75

Nos. 33, 35 to 38 are on chalky paper.
For overprints see Nos. MR1-MR3.

George V — A6

St. John's Harbor — A7

1913					
41	A6	5sh violet & green		70.00	*80.00*

1921-29				**Wmk. 4**	
42	A7	½p green		.50	.20
43	A7	1p rose red		.60	.20
44	A7	1p dp violet ('23)		1.00	1.10
45	A7	1½p orange ('22)		1.25	5.75
46	A7	1½p rose red ('26)		2.00	1.25
47	A7	1½p fawn ('29)		1.50	.40
48	A7	2p gray		.75	.50
49	A7	2½p ultra		2.50	5.00
50	A7	2½p orange ('23)		1.10	15.00
		Chalky Paper			
51	A7	3p violet, *yel* ('25)		3.50	7.00
52	A7	6p vio & red vio		2.25	4.00
53	A7	1sh black, *emer* ('29)		5.75	7.00
54	A7	2sh vio & ultra, *blue* ('27)		9.00	35.00
55	A7	2sh6p blk & red, *blue* ('27)		13.00	20.00
56	A7	3sh grn & vio ('22)		20.00	50.00
57	A7	4sh blk & red ('22)		42.50	50.00
		Nos. 42-57 (16)		107.20	202.40

				Wmk. 3	
		Chalky Paper			
58	A7	3p violet, *yel*		3.00	*10.00*
59	A7	4p black & red, *yel* ('22)		1.00	*4.50*
60	A7	1sh black, *emerald*		3.50	*6.00*
61	A7	2sh vio & ultra, *bl*		8.00	*17.50*
62	A7	2sh6p blk & red, *bl*		12.00	*30.00*
63	A7	5sh grn & vio, *yel* ('22)		8.00	*30.00*
64	A7	£1 vio & black, *red* ('22)		225.00	*260.00*
		Nos. 58-64 (7)		260.50	*358.00*

Old Dockyard, English Harbour — A8

Govt. House, St. John's — A9

Nelson's "Victory," 1805 — A10

Sir Thomas Warner's Ship, 1632 — A11

Perf. 12½

1932, Jan. 27		**Engr.**		**Wmk. 4**	
67	A8	½p green		1.00	1.25
68	A8	1p scarlet		1.25	1.00
69	A8	1½p lt brown		2.00	2.00
70	A9	2p gray		1.75	6.00
71	A9	2½p ultra		3.25	3.25
72	A9	3p orange		4.75	5.00
73	A10	6p violet		8.00	*11.00*
74	A10	1sh olive green		9.00	*15.00*

75	A10	2sh6p claret	37.50	47.50
76	A11	5sh red brn & black	110.00	110.00
		Nos. 67-76 (10)	178.50	202.00

Tercentenary of the colony.

Common Design Types
pictured following the introduction.

Silver Jubilee Issue
Common Design Type

1935, May 6			**Perf. 13¹/₂x14**
77	CD301	1p car & blue	1.10	1.10
78	CD301	1¹/₂p gray blk & ultra	1.25	1.50
79	CD301	2¹/₂p blue & brn	4.00	5.25
80	CD301	1sh brt vio & ind	9.50	13.50
		Nos. 77-80 (4)	15.85	21.35

Coronation Issue
Common Design Type

1937, May 12			**Perf. 11x11¹/₂**
81	CD302	1p carmine	.30	.30
82	CD302	1¹/₂p orange	.40	.40
83	CD302	2¹/₂p deep ultra	1.00	1.00
		Nos. 81-83 (3)	1.70	1.70

English
Harbour — A14

Nelson's
Dockyard — A15

Fort James — A16

St. John's
Harbor — A17

1938-48		**Engr.**	**Perf. 12¹/₂**
84	A14	¹/₂p green	.20	.20
85	A15	1p red	1.40	.50
86	A15	1¹/₂p brown violet	2.00	.35
87	A14	2p dark gray	.15	.25
88	A15	2¹/₂p deep ultra	.35	.40
89	A16	3p orange	.30	.25
90	A17	6p purple	.60	.35
91	A17	1sh red brn & blk	1.90	.60
92	A17	2sh6p deep claret	15.00	5.00
93	A17	5sh olive green	10.00	5.75
94	A15	10sh red vio ('48)	11.00	17.00
95	A16	£1 Prus blue ('48)	17.00	26.00
		Nos. 84-95 (12)	59.90	56.80

See Nos. 107-113, 115-116, 118-121, 136-142, 144-145.
For overprint see Nos. 125-126.

Catalogue values for unused stamps in this section, from this point to the end of the section, are for Never Hinged items.

Peace Issue
Common Design Type

1946, Nov. 1	**Wmk. 4**		**Perf. 13¹/₂x14**
96	CD303	1¹/₂p brown	.30	.30
97	CD303	3p deep orange	.38	.38

Silver Wedding Issue
Common Design Types

1949, Jan. 3	**Photo.**	**Perf. 14x14¹/₂**
98	CD304	2¹/₂p bright ultra	.15	.15

Engraved; Name Typographed
Perf. 11¹/₂x11

99	CD305	5sh dk brown olive	7.50	10.00

UPU Issue
Common Design Types
Perf. 13¹/₂, 11x11¹/₂

1949, Oct. 10			**Wmk. 4**
Engr.; Name Typo. on 3p and 6p			
100	CD306	2¹/₂p deep ultra	.25	.25
101	CD307	3p orange	1.10	1.10
102	CD308	6p purple	2.25	2.25
103	CD309	1sh red brown	2.50	2.50
		Nos. 100-103 (4)	6.10	6.10

University Issue
Common Design Types
Perf. 14x14¹/₂

1951, Feb. 16	**Engr.**	**Wmk. 4**
104	CD310	3c chocolate & blk	.25	.25
105	CD311	12c purple & blk	.65	.65

Coronation Issue
Common Design Type

1953, June 2		**Perf. 13¹/₂x13**
106	CD312	2c dk green & blk	.75	.75

Types of 1938 with Portrait of Queen Elizabeth II

Martello
Tower — A24

Perf. 13x13¹/₂, 13¹/₂x13

1953-56			**Wmk. 4**
107	A16	¹/₂c dk red brn ('56)	.15	.15
108	A14	1c gray	.15	.15
109	A15	2c deep green	.15	.15
110	A15	3c yellow & blk	.20	.15
111	A14	4c rose red (shades)	.90	.15
112	A15	5c dull vio & blk	1.65	.20
113	A16	6c orange	1.25	.15
114	A24	8c deep blue	1.40	.15
115	A17	12c violet	1.40	.15
116	A17	24c chocolate & blk	1.65	.15
117	A24	48c dp bl & rose lil	5.00	.60
118	A16	60c claret	5.25	.50
119	A17	$1.20 olive green	1.25	.50
120	A15	$2.40 magenta	5.50	8.50
121	A16	$4.80 greenish blue	9.00	12.50
		Nos. 107-121 (15)	34.90	24.15

See #143. For overprint see #125-126.

West Indies Federation
Common Design Type
Perf. 11¹/₂x11

1958, Apr. 22	**Engr.**	**Wmk. 314**
122	CD313	3c green	.20	.18
123	CD313	6c blue	.50	.35
124	CD313	12c carmine rose	.90	.75
		Nos. 122-124 (3)	1.60	1.28

Nos. 110 and 115 Overprinted in Red or Black: "Commemoration Antigua Constitution 1960"
Perf. 13x13¹/₂, 13¹/₂x13

1960, Jan. 1			**Wmk. 4**
125	A15	3c yellow & black	.22	.22
126	A17	12c violet (Blk)	.50	.50

Constitutional reforms effective Jan. 1, 1960.

Lord Nelson and Nelson's Dockyard A26

Perf. 11¹/₂x11

1961, Nov. 14			**Wmk. 314**
127	A26	20c brown & lilac	.50	.40
128	A26	30c dk blue & green	.80	.60

Completion of the restoration of Lord Nelson's headquarters, English Harbour.

Stamp of 1862 and Royal Mail Steam Packet in English Harbour A27

1962, Aug. 1	**Engr.**	**Perf. 13**
129	A27	3c dull green & pur	.15	.15
130	A27	10c dull green & ultra	.20	.20
131	A27	12c dull green & black	.28	.28
132	A27	50c dull grn & brn org	1.40	1.40
		Nos. 129-132 (4)	2.03	2.03

Centenary of first Antigua postage stamp.

Freedom from Hunger Issue
Common Design Type
Perf. 14x14¹/₂

1963, June 4	**Photo.**	**Wmk. 314**
133	CD314	12c green		.90	.90

Red Cross Centenary Issue
Common Design Type

1963, Sept. 2	**Litho.**	**Perf. 13**
134	CD315	3c black & red	.35	.35
135	CD315	12c ultra & red	2.25	2.25

Types of 1938-53 with Portrait of Queen Elizabeth II
Perf. 13x13¹/₂, 13¹/₂x13

1963-65		**Engr.**	**Wmk. 314**
136	A16	¹/₂c brown ('65)	.28	.28
137	A14	1c gray ('65)	.28	.28
138	A15	2c deep green	.16	.16
139	A15	3c orange yel & blk	.22	.22
140	A14	4c brown red	.35	.35
141	A15	5c dull vio & black	.35	.35
142	A16	6c orange	.38	.38
143	A24	8c deep blue	.45	.45
144	A17	12c violet	.85	.85
145	A17	24c choc & black	1.75	1.75
		Nos. 136-145 (10)	5.07	5.07

For surcharge see No. 152.

Shakespeare Issue
Common Design Type
Perf. 14x14¹/₂

1964, Apr. 23	**Photo.**	**Wmk. 314**
151	CD316	12c red brown	.75	.75

No. 144 Surcharged with New Value and Bars
Perf. 13¹/₂x13

1965, Apr. 1	**Engr.**	**Wmk. 314**
152	A17	15c on 12c violet	.50	.50

ITU Issue
Common Design Type
Perf. 11x11¹/₂

1965, May 17	**Litho.**	**Wmk. 314**
153	CD317	2c blue & ver	.15	.15
154	CD317	50c orange & vio bl	2.25	2.25

Intl. Cooperation Year Issue
Common Design Type

1965, Oct. 25		**Perf. 14¹/₂**
155	CD318	4c blue grn & claret	.15	.15
156	CD318	15c lt vio & green	.70	.70

Churchill Memorial Issue
Common Design Type

1966, Jan. 24	**Photo.**	**Perf. 14**
Design in Black, Gold and Carmine Rose			
157	CD319	¹/₂c bright blue	.15	.15
158	CD319	4c green	.25	.25
159	CD319	25c brown	1.10	.90
160	CD319	35c violet	1.75	1.50
		Nos. 157-160 (4)	3.25	2.80

Royal Visit Issue
Common Design Type

1966, Feb. 4	**Litho.**	**Perf. 11x12**
Portraits in Black			
161	CD320	6c violet blue	1.10	.90
162	CD320	15c dark car rose	1.75	1.10

World Cup Soccer Issue
Common Design Type

1966, July 1	**Wmk. 314**	**Perf. 14**
163	CD321	6c multicolored	.20	.20
164	CD321	35c multicolored	.80	.80

WHO Headquarters Issue
Common Design Type

1966, Sept. 20		**Perf. 14**
165	CD322	6c multicolored	.15	.15
166	CD322	15c multicolored	.75	.75

Nelson's
Dockyard
A35

Designs: 1c, Old post office, St. John's. 2c, Health Center. 3c, Teachers' Training College. 4c, Martello Tower, Barbuda. 5c, Ruins of officers' quarters, Shirley Heights. 6c, Government House, Barbuda. 10c, Princess Margaret School. 15c, Air terminal. 25c, General post office. 35c, Clarence

House. 50c, Government House. 75c, Administration building. $1, Court House, St. John's. $2.50, Magistrates' Court. $5, St. John's Cathedral.

Perf. 11¹/₂x11

1966, Nov. 1			**Wmk. 314**
167	A35	¹/₂c green & blue	.15	.15
168	A35	1c purple & rose	.15	.15
169	A35	2c slate & org	.15	.15
170	A35	3c rose red & blk	.15	.15
171	A35	4c dull vio & brn	.15	.15
172	A35	5c vio bl & olive	.15	.15
a.		Booklet pane of 4 ('68)	.40	
173	A35	6c dp org & pur	.15	.15
174	A35	10c brt grn & rose red	.22	.22
a.		Booklet pane of 4 ('68)	1.10	
175	A35	15c brn & blue	.30	.30
a.		Booklet pane of 4 ('68)	1.50	
176	A35	25c slate & brn	.48	.48
177	A35	35c dp rose & sep	.70	.70
178	A35	50c green & black	1.00	1.00
179	A35	75c Prus bl & vio blue	1.25	1.25
180	A35	$1 dp rose & olive	1.75	1.75
181	A35	$2.50 black & rose	4.25	4.25
182	A35	$5 ol grn & dl vio	9.00	9.00
		Nos. 167-182 (16)	20.00	20.00

For surcharge see No. 231.

1969			**Perf. 13¹/₂**
167a	A35	¹/₂c	.15	.15
168a	A35	1c	.15	.15
169a	A35	2c	.15	.15
170a	A35	3c	.15	.15
171a	A35	4c	.15	.15
172b	A35	5c	.15	.15
173a	A35	6c	.20	.20
174b	A35	10c	.30	.30
175b	A35	15c	.48	.48
176a	A35	25c	.60	.60
177a	A35	35c	.95	.95
178a	A35	50c	.25	.25
180a	A35	$1	2.50	2.50
181a	A35	$2.50	6.25	6.25
182a	A35	$5	21.00	21.00
		Nos. 167a-182a (15)	33.33	33.33

UNESCO Anniversary Issue
Common Design Type

1966, Dec. 1	**Litho.**	**Perf. 14**
183	CD323	4c "Education"	.18	.18
184	CD323	25c "Science"	.50	.50
185	CD323	$1 "Culture"	2.50	2.50
		Nos. 183-185 (3)	3.18	3.18

Independent State

Flag of Antigua, Spiny Lobster, Maps of Antigua and Barbuda A37

Designs: 15c, 35c, Flag of Antigua. 25c, Flag and Premier's Office Building.

1967, Feb. 27	**Photo.**	**Perf. 14**
186	A37	4c multicolored	.15	.15
187	A37	15c multicolored	.25	.25
188	A37	25c multicolored	.40	.40
189	A37	35c multicolored	.50	.50
		Nos. 186-189 (4)	1.30	1.30

Antigua's independence, Feb. 27, 1967.

Gilbert Memorial Church, Antigua — A38

Designs: 25c, Nathaniel Gilbert's House. 35c, Map of the Caribbean and Central America.

Perf. 14x13¹/₂

1967, May 18	**Photo.**	**Wmk. 314**
190	A38	4c brt red & black	.15	.15
191	A38	25c emerald & black	.40	.40
192	A38	35c ultra & black	.55	.55
		Nos. 190-192 (3)	1.10	1.10

Attainment of autonomy by the Methodist Church in the Caribbean and the Americas, and the opening of headquarters near St. John's, Antigua, May 1967.

Antiguan and British Royal Arms — A39

1967, July 21   Perf. 14¹/₂x14
193 A39 15c dark green & multi   .20 .20
194 A39 35c deep blue & multi   .45 .45

Granting of a new coat of arms to the State of Antigua; 300th anniv. of the Treaty of Breda.

Sailing Ship, 17th Century A40

Design: 6c, 35c, Map of Barbuda from Jan Blaeu's Atlas, 1665.

Perf. 11¹/₂x11
1967, Dec. 14   Engr.   Wmk. 314
195 A40 4c dark blue   .15 .15
196 A40 6c deep plum   .15 .15
197 A40 25c green   .30 .30
198 A40 35c black   .50 .50
     Nos. 195-198 (4)   1.10 1.10

Resettlement of Barbuda, 300th anniv.

Dow Hill Antenna — A41

Designs: 15c, Antenna and rocket blasting off. 25c, Nose cone orbiting moon. 50c, Re-entry of space capsule.

Perf. 14¹/₂x14
1968, Mar. 29   Photo.   Wmk. 314
199 A41 4c dk blue, org & black   .15 .15
200 A41 15c dk blue, org & black   .25 .25
201 A41 25c dk blue, org & black   .35 .35
202 A41 50c dk blue, org & black   .65 .65
     Nos. 199-202 (4)   1.40 1.40

Dedication of the Dow Hill tracking station in Antigua for the NASA Apollo project.

Beach and Sailfish A42

Designs: ¹/₂c, 50c, Limbo dancer, flames and dancing girls. 15c, Three girls on a beach and water skier. 35c, Woman scuba diver, corals and fish.

1968, July 1   Photo.   Perf. 14
203 A42 ¹/₂c red & multi   .15 .15
204 A42 15c sky blue & multi   .25 .25
205 A42 25c blue & multi   .35 .35
206 A42 35c brt blue & multi   .45 .45
207 A42 50c multicolored   .75 .75
     Nos. 203-207 (5)   1.95 1.95

Issued for tourist publicity.

St. John's Harbor, 1768 A43

St. John's Harbor: 15c, 1829. 25c, Map of deep-sea harbor, 1968. 35c, Dock, 1968. 2c, Like $1.

Engr. & Litho.; Engr. ($1)
1968, Oct. 31   Wmk. 314   Perf. 13
208 A43 2c dp car & lt blue   .16 .16
209 A43 15c sepia & yel grn   .25 .25
210 A43 25c dk blue & yel   .45 .45
211 A43 35c dp green & sal   .50 .50
212 A43 $1 black   1.75 1.75
     Nos. 208-212 (5)   3.11 3.11

Opening of St. John's deep-sea harbor.

Mace and Parliament A44

Mace and: 15c, Mace bearer. 25c, House of Representatives, interior. 50c, Antigua coat of arms and great seal.

1969, Feb. 3   Photo.   Perf. 12¹/₂
213 A44 4c crimson & multi   .15 .15
214 A44 15c crimson & multi   .20 .20
215 A44 25c crimson & multi   .30 .30
216 A44 50c crimson & multi   .65 .65
     Nos. 213-216 (4)   1.30 1.30

300th anniversary of Antigua Parliament.

CARIFTA Cargo — A45

Design: 4c, 15c, Ship, plane and trucks, horiz.

Perf. 13¹/₂x13, 13x13¹/₂
1969, Apr. 14   Litho.   Wmk. 314
217 A45 4c blk & brt lilac rose   .15 .15
218 A45 15c blk & brt grnsh blue   .25 .25
219 A45 25c bister & black   .30 .30
220 A45 35c tan & black   .45 .45
     Nos. 217-220 (4)   1.15 1.15

1st anniv. of CARIFTA (Caribbean Free Trade Area).

Map of Redonda Island A46

25c, View of Redonda from the sea & seagulls.

1969, Aug. 1   Photo.   Perf. 13x13¹/₂
221 A46 15c ultra & multi   .30 .30
222 A46 25c multicolored   .45 .45
223 A46 50c salmon & multi   1.25 1.25
     Nos. 221-223 (3)   2.00 2.00

Centenary of Redonda phosphate industry.

Adoration of the Kings, by Gugliemo Marcillat A47

Christmas: 10c, 50c, Holy Family, by anonymous German artist, 15th century.

1969, Oct. 15   Litho.   Perf. 13x14
224 A47 6c bister brn & multi   .15 .15
225 A47 10c fawn & multi   .20 .20
226 A47 35c gray olive & multi   .50 .50
227 A47 50c gray blue & multi   .90 .90
     Nos. 224-227 (4)   1.75 1.75

Arms of Antigua — A48

Coil Stamps
Perf. 14¹/₂x14
1970, Jan. 30   Photo.   Wmk. 314
228 A48 5c bright blue   .15 .15
229 A48 10c bright green   .20 .20
230 A48 25c deep magenta   .45 .45
     Nos. 228-230 (3)   .80 .80

No. 176 Surcharged 20¢

1970, Jan. 2   Engr.   Perf. 11¹/₂x11
231 A35 20c on 25c slate & brown   .35 .15

Sikorsky S-38 A49

Aircraft: 20c, Dornier DO-X. 35c, Hawker Siddeley 748. 50c, Douglas C-124C Globemaster II. 75c, Vickers VC 10.

1970, Feb. 16   Litho.   Perf. 14¹/₂
232 A49 5c brt green & multi   .15 .15
233 A49 20c ultra & multi   .35 .35
234 A49 35c blue grn & multi   .60 .60
235 A49 50c blue & multi   .90 .90
236 A49 75c vio blue & multi   1.50 1.50
     Nos. 232-236 (5)   3.50 3.50

40th anniversary of air service.

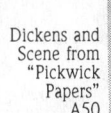

Dickens and Scene from "Pickwick Papers" A50

Charles Dickens (1812-1870), English novelist and Scene from: 5c, "Nicholas Nickleby." 35c, "Oliver Twist." $1, "David Copperfield."

Wmk. 314
1970, May 19   Litho.   Perf. 14
237 A50 5c olive & sepia   .15 .15
238 A50 20c aqua & sepia   .28 .28
239 A50 35c violet & sepia   .32 .32
240 A50 $1 scarlet & sepia   1.00 1.00
     Nos. 237-240 (4)   1.75 1.75

Carib Indian and War Canoe — A51

Ships: 1c, Columbus and "Nina." 2c, Sir Thomas Warner's arms and sailing ship. 3c, Viscount Hood and "Barfleur." 4c, Sir George Rodney and "Formidable." 5c, Capt. Horatio Nelson and "Boreas." 6c, King William IV and "Pegasus." 10c, Blackbeard (Edward Teach) and pirate ketch. 15c, Capt. Cuthbert Collingwood and "Pelican." 25c, Admiral Nelson and "Victoria." 25c, Paddle steamer "Solent" and Steam Packet Company emblem. 35c, King George V and corvette "Canada." 50c, Cruiser "Renown" and royal badge. 75c, S.S. "Federal Maple" and maple leaf. $1, Racing yacht "Sol-Quest" and Gallant 53 class emblem. $2.50, Missile destroyer "London" and her emblem. $5, Tug "Pathfinder" and arms of Antigua.

Wmk. 314 Sideways
1970, Aug. 19   Litho.   Perf. 14
241 A51 ¹/₂c ocher & multi   .15 .15
242 A51 1c Prus bl & multi   .15 .15
243 A51 2c yel grn & multi   .15 .15
244 A51 3c ol bis & multi   .15 .15
245 A51 4c bl gray & multi   .15 .15
246 A51 5c fawn & multi   .20 .15
247 A51 6c rose lil & multi   .20 .15
248 A51 10c brn org & multi   .25 .15
249 A51 15c ultra & multi   .40 .25

---

250 A51 20c ol grn & multi   .35 .20
251 A51 25c olive & multi   .40 .20
252 A51 35c dull red brn & multi   .70 .35
253 A51 50c lt brn & multi   .95 .55
254 A51 75c beige & multi   1.25 .75
255 A51 $1 Prus green & multi   1.90 1.10
256 A51 $2.50 gray & multi   5.00 2.75
257 A51 $5 yel & multi   12.50 7.00
     Nos. 241-257 (17)   25.35 14.35

1972-74   Wmk. 314 Upright
241a A51 ¹/₂c   .15 .15
242a A51 1c   .15 .15
244a A51 3c   .15 .15
245a A51 4c   .15 .15
246a A51 5c   .15 .15
247a A51 6c   .15 .15
248a A51 10c   .20 .20
249a A51 15c   1.60 .28
254a A51 75c   3.25 1.25
255a A51 $1   3.60 1.60
256a A51 $2.50   6.00 7.50
257a A51 $5   6.75 10.50
     Nos. 241a-257a (12)   22.30 22.23

For surcharge see No. 368.

1975, Jan. 21   Wmk. 373
257b A51 $5 yellow & multi   13.00 13.00

Nativity, by Albrecht Dürer — A52

Private, 4th West India Regiment, 1804 — A53

Christmas: 10c, 50c, Adoration of the Magi, by Albrecht Dürer.

Engr. & Litho.
1970, Oct. 28   Perf. 13¹/₂x14
258 A52 3c brt grnsh blue & blk   .15 .15
259 A52 10c pink & plum   .20 .20
260 A52 35c brick red & black   .50 .50
261 A52 50c lilac & violet   .90 .90
     Nos. 258-261 (4)   1.75 1.75

Perf. 14x13¹/₂
1970, Dec. 1   Litho.   Wmk. 314
Military Uniforms: ¹/₂c, Drummer Boy, 4th King's Own Regiment, 1759. 20c, Viscount Hood and "Barfleur." 3c, Grenadier Company Officer, 60th Regiment, The Royal American, 1809. 35c, Light Company Officer, 93rd Regiment, The Sutherland Highlanders, 1826-1834. 75c, Private, 3rd West India Regiment, 1851.

262 A53 ¹/₂c lake & multi   .15 .15
263 A53 10c brn org & multi   .45 .45
264 A53 20c Prus grn & multi   .75 .75
265 A53 35c dl pur & multi   1.50 1.50
266 A53 75c dk ol grn & multi   4.00 4.00
  a.   Souv. sheet of 5, #262-266 + label   10.00 10.00
     Nos. 262-266 (5)   6.85 6.85

See #274-278, 283-287, 307-311, 329-333.

Market Woman Voting — A54

Voting by: 20c, Businessman. 35c, Mother (and child). 50c, Workman.

Perf. 14¹/₂x14
1971, Feb. 1   Photo.   Wmk. 314
267 A54 5c brown   .15 .15
268 A54 20c olive black   .20 .20
269 A54 35c rose magenta   .35 .35
270 A54 50c violet blue   .60 .60
     Nos. 267-270 (4)   1.30 1.30

Adult suffrage, 20th anniversary.

5c

Last Supper, from The Small Passion, by Dürer — A55

ANTIGVA

Woodcuts by Albrecht Dürer: 35c, Crucifixion from Eichstaff Missal. 75c, Resurrection from The Great Passion.

Perf. 14x13 1/2

1971, Apr. 7   Litho.   Wmk. 314

271	A55	5c gray, red & black	.15	.15
272	A55	35c gray, violet & black	.40	.40
273	A55	75c gray, gold & black	.90	.90
		Nos. 271-273 (3)	1.45	1.45

Easter.

Military Uniform Type of 1970

Military Uniforms: 5c, Private, Suffolk Regiment, 1704. 10c, Grenadier, South Staffordshire, 1751. 20c, Fusilier, Royal Northumberland, 1778. 35c, Private, Northamptonshire. 1793, 75c, Private, East Yorkshire, 1805.

1971, July 12   Litho.   Wmk. 314

274	A53	5c gray & multi	.15	.15
275	A53	10c bluish blk & multi	.30	.30
276	A53	20c dk pur & multi	.50	.50
277	A53	35c ol & multi	1.10	1.10
278	A53	75c brown & multi	2.50	2.50
a.		Souvenir sheet of 5, #274-278 + label	7.25	7.25
		Nos. 274-278 (5)	4.55	4.55

Virgin and Child, by Veronese — A56

Christmas: 5c, 50c, Adoration of the Shepherds, by Bonifazio Veronese.

1971, Oct. 4   Perf. 14x13 1/2

279	A56	3c multicolored	.15	.15
280	A56	5c multicolored	.15	.15
281	A56	35c multicolored	.55	.55
282	A56	50c multicolored	.90	.90
		Nos. 279-282 (4)	1.75	1.75

Uniform Type of 1970

Military Uniforms: 5c, Officer, King's Own Borderers Regiment, 1815. 10c, Sergeant, Buckinghamshire Regiment, 1837. 20c, Private, South Hampshire Regiment, 1853. 35c, Officer, Royal Artillery, 1854. 75c, Private, Worcestershire Regiment, 1870.

1972, July 1

283	A53	5c ol brn & multi	.15	.15
284	A53	10c dp grn & multi	.40	.40
285	A53	20c brt vio & multi	.80	.80
286	A53	35c mar & multi	1.50	1.50
287	A53	75c dk vio bl & multi	3.25	3.25
a.		Souvenir sheet of 5, #283-287 + label	9.00	9.00
		Nos. 283-287 (5)	6.10	6.10

3 cents

Reticulated Helmet Cowrie A57

Sea Shells: 5c, Measled cowrie. 35c, West Indian fighting conch. 50c, Hawkwing conch.

1972, Aug. 1   Perf. 14 1/2x14

288	A57	3c multicolored	.15	.15
289	A57	5c ver & multi	.35	.35
290	A57	35c lt vio & multi	1.40	1.40
291	A57	50c rose red & multi	2.00	2.00
		Nos. 288-291 (4)	3.90	3.90

St. John's Cathedral, 1745-1843 A58

Christmas: 50c, Interior of St. John's. 75c, St. John's rebuilt.

1972, Nov. 6   Litho.   Perf. 14

292	A58	35c org brn & multi	.45	.45
293	A58	50c vio & multi	.85	.85
294	A58	75c multicolored	1.40	1.40
a.		Souv. sheet of 3, #292-294, perf. 15	3.50	3.50
		Nos. 292-294 (3)	2.70	2.70

Silver Wedding Issue, 1972
Common Design Type

1972, Nov. 20   Photo.   Perf. 14x14 1/2

295	CD324	20c ultra & multi	.30	.30
296	CD324	35c steel bl & multi	.50	.50

Map of Antigua, Batsman Driving Ball — A60

Designs: 35c, Batsman and wicketkeeper. $1, Emblem of Rising Sun Cricket Club.

1972, Dec. 15   Perf. 13 1/2x14

297	A60	5c multicolored	.25	.25
298	A60	35c multicolored	1.25	1.25
299	A60	$1 multicolored	3.00	3.00
a.		Souvenir sheet of 3, #297-299	5.00	5.00
		Nos. 297-299 (3)	4.50	4.50

Rising Sun Cricket Club, St. John's, 50th anniv.

Map of Antigua and Yacht — A61

1972, Dec. 29   Perf. 14 1/2

300	A61	35c shown	.35	.35
301	A61	50c Racing yachts	.40	.40
302	A61	75c St. John's G.P.O.	.70	.70
303	A61	$1 Statue of Liberty	1.10	1.10
a.		Souvenir sheet of 2, #301, 303	2.50	2.50
		Nos. 300-303 (4)	2.55	2.55

Opening of Antigua and Barbuda Information Office in New York City.

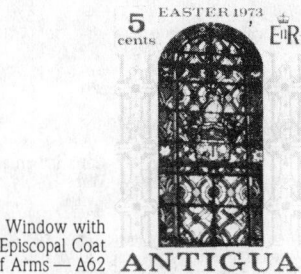

Window with Episcopal Coat of Arms — A62

Stained glass windows from Cathedral of St. John: 35c, Crucifixion. 75c, Arm of Rt. Rev. D.G. Davis, 1st bishop of Antigua.

1973, Apr. 16   Litho.   Perf. 13 1/2

304	A62	5c yellow & multi	.15	.15
305	A62	35c brt lilac & multi	.40	.40
306	A62	75c blue & multi	.80	.80
		Nos. 304-306 (3)	1.35	1.35

Easter.

Uniform Type of 1970

Military Uniforms: 5c, Private, Col. Zacharia Tiffin's Regiment, 1701. 10c, Private, 63rd Regiment, 1759. 20c, Officer, 35th Sussex Regiment, 1828. 35c, Private, 2nd West India Regiment, 1853. 75c, Sergeant, Princess of Wales Regiment, Hertfordshire, 1858.

Perf. 14x13 1/2

1973, July 1   Wmk. 314

307	A53	5c dp ultra & multi	.15	.15
308	A53	10c rose lilac & multi	.25	.25
309	A53	20c gray & multi	.45	.45
310	A53	35c multicolored	.80	.80
311	A53	75c multicolored	2.00	2.00
a.		Souvenir sheet of 5	4.00	4.00
		Nos. 307-311 (5)	3.65	3.65

No. 311a contains one each of Nos. 307-311 and label with coat of arms and date.

Butterfly Costumes — A63

Designs: 20c, Carnival revelers. 35c, Costumed group. 75c, Carnival Queen.

1973, July 30   Perf. 13 1/2x14   Unwmk.

312	A63	5c multicolored	.15	.15
313	A63	20c multicolored	.30	.30
314	A63	35c multicolored	.50	.50
315	A63	75c multicolored	1.25	1.25
a.		Souvenir sheet of 4, #312-315	2.50	2.50
		Nos. 312-315 (4)	2.20	2.20

Carnival, July 29-Aug. 7.

Virgin of the Porridge, by David — A64

Christmas: 5c, Adoration of the Kings, by Stomer. 20c, Virgin of the Grand Duke, by Raphael. 35c, Nativity with God the Father and Holy Ghost, by Tiepolo. $1, Madonna and Child, by Murillo.

1973, Oct. 15   Perf. 14 1/2   Unwmk.

316	A64	3c brt blue & multi	.15	.15
317	A64	5c emerald & multi	.15	.15
318	A64	20c gold & multi	.35	.35
319	A64	35c violet & multi	.65	.65
320	A64	$1 red & multi	1.75	1.75
a.		Souvenir sheet of 5, #316-320	3.25	3.25
		Nos. 316-320 (5)	3.05	3.05

Princess Anne and Mark Phillips A65

Design: $2, different border.

1973, Nov. 14   Litho.   Perf. 13 1/2

321	A65	35c dull ultra & multi	.20	.20
322	A65	$2 yel grn & multi	1.10	1.10
a.		Souvenir sheet of 2, #321-322	1.40	1.40

Wedding of Princess Anne and Capt. Mark Phillips.
Nos. 321-322 were issued in sheets of 5 plus label.

Nos. 321-322 and 322a Overprinted Vertically: "HONEYMOON / VISIT / DECEMBER 16th / 1973"

1973, Dec. 15   Litho.   Perf. 13 1/2

323	A65	35c multicolored	.25	.25
324	A65	$2 multicolored	1.25	1.25
a.		Souvenir sheet of 2, #323-324	1.60	1.60

Visit of Princess Anne and Mark Phillips to Antigua, Dec. 16. Same overprint in sheet margins of Nos. 323-324 and 324a.

5c

Arms of Antigua and U.W.I. A66

ANTIGUA

Designs: 20c, Dancers. 35c, Antigua campus. 75c, Chancellor Sir Hugh Wooding.

1974, Feb. 18   Wmk. 314

325	A66	5c multicolored	.15	.15
326	A66	20c multicolored	.25	.25
327	A66	35c multicolored	.40	.40
328	A66	75c multicolored	.80	.80
		Nos. 325-328 (4)	1.60	1.60

University of the West Indies, 24th anniv.

Uniform Type of 1970

Military Uniforms: 5c, Officer, 59th Foot, 1797. 10c, Gunner, Royal Artillery, 1800. 20c, Private, 1st West India Regiment, 1830. 35c, Officer, Gordon Highlanders, 1843. 75c, Private, Royal Welsh Fusiliers, 1846.

1974, May 1   Perf. 14x13 1/2

329	A53	5c dull grn & multi	.15	.15
330	A53	10c ocher & multi	.15	.15
331	A53	20c multicolored	.30	.30
332	A53	35c gray bl & multi	.50	.50
333	A53	75c dk gray & multi	1.10	1.10
a.		Souvenir sheet of 5, #329-333	2.75	2.75
		Nos. 329-333 (5)	2.20	2.20

English Mailman and Coach, Helicopter — A67

UPU, Cent.: 1c, English bellman, 1846; Orinoco mailboat, 1851; telecommunications satellite. 2c, English mailtrain guard, 1852; Swiss post passenger bus, 1906; Italian hydrofoil. 5c, Swiss messenger, 16th century; Wells Fargo coach, 1800; Concorde. 20c, German position, 1820; Japanese mailmen, 19th century; carrier pigeon. 35c, Contemporary Antiguan mailman; radar station; aquaplane. $1, Medieval French courier; American train, 1884; British Airways jet.

1974, July 15   Litho.   Perf. 14 1/2

334	A67	5c multicolored	.15	.15
335	A67	1c multicolored	.15	.15
336	A67	2c multicolored	.15	.15
337	A67	5c multicolored	.15	.15
338	A67	20c multicolored	.35	.30
339	A67	35c multicolored	.75	.50
340	A67	$1 multicolored	1.75	1.40
a.		Souvenir sheet of 7, #334-340 + label, perf. 13	3.50	3.50
		Set value	3.05	2.45

For surcharges see Nos. 365-367.

Traditional Steel Band A68

Carnival 1974 (Steel Bands): 5c, Traditional players, vert. 35c, Modern steel band. 75c, Modern players, vert.

1974, Aug. 1,   Wmk. 314   Perf. 14

341	A68	5c rose red, dk red & blk	.15	.15
342	A68	20c ocher, brn & blk	.25	.25
343	A68	35c yel grn, grn & blk	.40	.40
344	A68	75c dl bl, dk bl & blk	.75	.75
a.		Souvenir sheet of 4, #341-344	1.75	1.75
		Nos. 341-344 (4)	1.55	1.55

5c

Soccer — A69

Designs: Games' emblem and soccer.

1974, Sept. 23   Unwmk.   Perf. 14 1/2

345	A69	5c multicolored	.15	.15
346	A69	20c multicolored	.40	.40
347	A69	75c multicolored	.80	.80
348	A69	$1 multicolored	1.10	1.10
a.		Souvenir sheet of 4	2.25	2.25
		Nos. 345-348 (4)	2.45	2.45

World Cup Soccer Championship, Munich, June 13-July 7. Nos. 345-348 issued in sheets of 5 plus

label showing Soccer Cup. No. 348a contains one each of Nos. 345-348, perf. 13½, and 2 labels.
For overprints and surcharges see Nos. 361-364.

Winston Churchill (1874-1965) at Harrow — A70

Designs: 35c, St. Paul's during bombing and Churchill portrait. 75c, Churchill's coat of arms and catafalque. $1, Churchill during Boer war, warrant for arrest and map of his escape route.

1974, Oct. 20   Unwmk.   Perf. 14½

349	A70	5c multicolored	.15	.15
350	A70	35c multicolored	.30	.30
351	A70	75c multicolored	.75	.75
352	A70	$1 multicolored	.90	.90
a.		Souvenir sheet of 4, #349-352	2.10	2.10
		Nos. 349-352 (4)	2.10	2.10

Virgin and Child, by Giovanni Bellini — A71

Christmas: Paintings of the Virgin and Child.

1974, Nov. 18   Litho.   Perf. 14½

353	A71	½c shown	.15	.15
354	A71	1c Raphael	.15	.15
355	A71	2c Van der Weyden	.15	.15
356	A71	3c Giorgione	.15	.15
357	A71	5c Andrea Mantegna	.15	.15
358	A71	20c Alvise Vivarini	.25	.25
359	A71	35c Bartolommeo Montagna	.40	.40
360	A71	75c Lorenzo Costa	.85	.85
a.		Souvenir sheet of 4, #357-360, perf. 13½	1.60	1.60
		Set value	1.80	1.80

Nos. 346-348 Overprinted and No. 344 Surcharged and Overprinted: "EARTHQUAKE / RELIEF"

1974, Oct. 16   Litho.   Perf. 14½, 14

361	A69	35c multicolored	.25	.20
362	A69	75c multicolored	.70	.60
363	A69	$1 multicolored	.90	.75
364	A68	$5 on 75c multi	4.50	4.00
		Nos. 361-364 (4)	6.35	5.55

Earthquake of Oct. 8, 1974.

Nos. 338-340 and 254a Surcharged with New Value and Two Bars

1974-75   Wmk. 314   Perf. 14½

365	A67	50c on 20c	.55	.55
366	A67	$2.50 on 35c	2.75	2.75
367	A67	$5 on $1	5.25	5.25

Perf. 14

368	A51	$10 on 75c	10.50	10.50
		Nos. 365-368 (4)	19.05	19.05

Carib War Canoe, English Harbour — A72

Designs (Nelson's Dockyard): 15c, Raising ship, 1770. 35c, Lord Nelson and "Boreas." 50c, Yachts arriving for Sailing Week, 1974. $1, "Anchorage" in Old Dockyard, 1970.

1975, Mar. 17   Unwmk.   Perf. 14½

369	A72	5c multicolored	.15	.15
370	A72	15c multicolored	.32	.32
371	A72	35c multicolored	.60	.60
372	A72	50c multicolored	.90	.90
373	A72	$1 multicolored	1.75	1.75
		Nos. 369-373 (5)	3.72	3.72

Souvenir Sheet
Perf. 13½

373A	A72	Sheet of 5, #369-373	4.50	4.50

Stamps in No. 373A are 43x28mm.

Lady of the Valley Church A73

Churches of Antigua: 20c, Gilbert Memorial. 35c, Grace Hill Moravian. 50c, St. Phillip's. $1, Ebenezer Methodist.

1975, May 19   Litho.   Perf. 14½

374	A73	5c multicolored	.15	.15
375	A73	20c multicolored	.18	.18
376	A73	35c multicolored	.32	.32
377	A73	50c multicolored	.52	.52
378	A73	$1 multicolored	.90	.90
a.		Souvenir sheet of 3, #376-378, perf. 13½	2.25	2.25
		Nos. 374-378 (5)	2.07	2.07

Antigua, Senex's Atlas, 1721, and Hevelius Sextant, 1640 A74

Maps of Antigua: 20c, Jeffery's Atlas, 1775, and 18th century engraving of ship. 35c, Barbuda and Antigua, 1775 and 1975. $1, St. John's and English Harbour, 1973.

1975, July 21   Wmk. 314

379	A74	5c multicolored	.15	.15
380	A74	20c multicolored	.35	.35
381	A74	35c multicolored	.60	.60
382	A74	$1 multicolored	1.75	1.75
a.		Souvenir sheet of 4, #379-382	3.00	3.00
		Nos. 379-382 (4)	2.85	2.85

Bugler and Sunset A75

Nordjamb 75 Emblem and: 20c, Black and white Scouts, tents and flags. 35c, Lord Baden-Powell and tents. $2, Dahomey dancers.

Unwmk.

1975, Aug. 26   Litho.   Perf. 14

383	A75	15c multicolored	.30	.30
384	A75	20c multicolored	.40	.40
384	A75	35c multicolored	.60	.60
386	A75	$2 multicolored	2.75	2.75
a.		Souvenir sheet of 4, #383-386	4.50	4.50
		Nos. 383-386 (4)	4.05	4.05

Nordjamb 75, 14th Boy Scout Jamboree, Lillehammer, Norway, July 29-Aug. 7.

Eurema Elathea A76

Butterflies: 1c, Danaus plexippus. 2c, Phoebis philea. 5c, Marpesia petreus thetys. 20c, Eurema proterpia. 35c, Papilio polydamas. $2, Vanessa cardui.

1975, Oct. 30   Litho.   Perf. 14

387	A76	½c multicolored	.15	.15
388	A76	1c multicolored	.15	.15
389	A76	2c multicolored	.15	.15
390	A76	5c multicolored	.15	.15
391	A76	20c multicolored	.50	.40
392	A76	35c multicolored	.90	.75
393	A76	$2 multicolored	4.50	3.50
a.		Miniature sheet of 4, #390-393	6.75	6.75
		Nos. 387-393 (7)	6.50	5.25

Virgin and Child, by Correggio — A77

Christmas: Virgin and Child paintings.

1975, Nov. 17   Unwmk.

394	A77	½c shown	.15	.15
395	A77	1c El Greco	.15	.15
396	A77	2c Durer	.15	.15
397	A77	3c Antonello	.15	.15
398	A77	5c Bellini	.15	.15
399	A77	10c Durer	.15	.15
400	A77	35c Bellini	.45	.45
401	A77	$2 Correggio	1.90	1.90
a.		Souvenir sheet of 4, #398-401	3.25	3.25
		Set value	2.75	2.75

West Indies Team A78

Designs: 5c, Batsman I.V.A. Richards and cup, vert. 35c, Bowler A.M.E. Roberts and cup, vert.

1975, Dec. 15   Litho.   Perf. 14

402	A78	5c multicolored	.20	.15
403	A78	35c multicolored	.90	.75
404	A78	$2 multicolored	3.50	3.50
		Nos. 402-404 (3)	4.60	4.40

World Cricket Cup, victory of West Indies team.

Antillean Crested Hummingbird A79

Irrigation System, Diamond Estate — A80

Designs: 1c, Imperial parrot. 2c, Zenaida dove. 3c, Loggerhead kingbird. 4c, Red-necked pigeon. 5c, Rufous-throated solitaire. 6c, Orchid tree. 10c, Bougainvillea. 15c, Geiger tree. 20c, Flamboyant. 25c, Hibiscus. 35c, Flame of the Woods. 50c, Cannon at Fort James. 75c, Premier's Office. $1, Potworks Dam. $5, Government House. $10, Coolidge International Airport.

1976, Jan. 19   Litho.   Perf. 15

405	A79	½c multicolored	.15	.15
406	A79	1c multicolored	.15	.15
407	A79	2c multicolored	.15	.15
408	A79	3c multicolored	.15	.15
409	A79	4c multicolored	.15	.15
410	A79	5c multicolored	.15	.15
411	A79	6c multicolored	.15	.15
412	A79	10c multicolored	.15	.15
413	A79	15c multicolored	.15	.15
414	A79	20c multicolored	.15	.15
415	A79	25c multicolored	.18	.18
416	A79	35c multicolored	.26	.26
417	A79	50c multicolored	.35	.35
418	A79	75c multicolored	.52	.52
419	A79	$1 multicolored	.70	.70

Perf. 13½x14

420	A80	$2.50 multi & multi	1.50	1.50
421	A80	$5 lilac & multi	3.25	3.25
422	A80	$10 multicolored	6.75	6.75
		Nos. 405-422 (18)	15.01	15.01

In 1978 Nos. 405-422 were reissued with "1978" centered below design.
For overprints, see Nos. 607-617.

Privates, Clark's Illinois Regiment — A81

Designs: 1c, Riflemen, Pennsylvania Militia. 2c, Decorated American powder horn. 5c, Water bottle of Maryland troops. 35c, "Liberty Tree" and "Rattlesnake" flags. $1, American privateer Montgomery. $2.50, Congress Flag. $5, Continental Navy sloop Ranger.

1976, Mar. 17   Litho.   Perf. 14½

423	A81	½c multicolored	.15	.15
424	A81	1c multicolored	.15	.15
425	A81	2c multicolored	.15	.15
426	A81	5c multicolored	.15	.15
427	A81	35c multicolored	.40	.40
428	A81	$1 multicolored	1.25	1.25
429	A81	$5 multicolored	5.00	5.00
		Nos. 423-429 (7)	7.25	7.25

Souvenir Sheet
Perf. 13

430	A81	$2.50 multicolored	3.75	3.75

American Bicentennial.

High Jump, Olympic Rings — A82

Olympic Rings and: 1c, Boxing. 2c, Pole vault. 15c, Swimming. 30c, Running. $1, Bicycling. $2, Shot put.

1976, July 12   Litho.   Perf. 14½

431	A82	½c yellow & multi	.15	.15
432	A82	1c purple & multi	.15	.15
433	A82	2c emerald & multi	.15	.15
434	A82	15c brt blue & multi	.15	.15
435	A82	30c olive & multi	.40	.40
436	A82	$1 orange & multi	1.00	1.00
437	A82	$2 red & multi	2.00	2.00
a.		Souvenir sheet of 4	3.50	3.50
		Nos. 431-437 (7)	4.00	4.00

21st Olympic Games, Montreal, Canada, July 17-Aug. 1. No. 437a contains one each of Nos. 434-437, perf. 13½.

Water Skiing A83

Water Sports: 1c, Sailfish sailing. 2c, Snorkeling. 20c, Deep-sea fishing. 50c, Scuba diving. $2, Swimming.

1976, Aug. 26   Perf. 14

438	A83	½c yel grn & multi	.15	.15
439	A83	1c sepia & multi	.15	.15
440	A83	2c gray & multi	.15	.15
441	A83	20c multicolored	.15	.15
442	A83	50c brt vio & multi	.40	.40
443	A83	$2 lt gray & multi	1.25	1.25
a.		Souvenir sheet of 3, #441-443	2.50	2.50
		Nos. 438-443 (6)	2.25	2.25

French Angelfish — A84

1976, Oct. 4   Litho.   Perf. 13½x14

444	A84	15c shown	.20	.20
445	A84	30c Yellowfish grouper	.35	.35
446	A84	50c Yellowtail snappers	.65	.65
447	A84	90c Shy hamlet	1.10	1.10
		Nos. 444-447 (4)	2.30	2.30

The Annunciation
A85

Christmas: 10c, Flight into Egypt. 15c, Three Kings. 50c, Shepherds and star. $1, Kings presenting gifts to Christ Child.

1976, Nov. 15   Litho.   Perf. 14
448	A85	8c multicolored	.15	.15
449	A85	10c multicolored	.15	.15
450	A85	15c multicolored	.20	.20
451	A85	50c multicolored	.50	.50
452	A85	$1 multi	1.00	1.00
		Nos. 448-452 (5)	2.00	2.00

Mercury and UPU Emblem A86

Designs: 1c, Alfred Nobel, symbols of prize categories. 10c, Viking spacecraft. 50c, Vivi Richards (batsman) and Andy Roberts (bowler). $1, Alexander G. Bell, telephones, 1876 and 1976. $2, Schooner Freelance.

1976, Dec. 28   Litho.   Perf. 14
453	A86	½c multicolored	.15	.15
454	A86	1c multicolored	.15	.15
455	A86	10c multicolored	.15	.15
456	A86	50c multicolored	.65	.65
457	A86	$1 multicolored	1.00	1.00
458	A86	$2 multicolored	1.75	1.75
a.		Souvenir sheet of 4, #455-458	4.25	4.25
		Nos. 453-458 (6)	3.85	3.85

Special 1976 Events: UN Postal Admin., 25th anniv. (½c); Nobel Prize, 75th anniv. (1c); Viking Space Mission to Mars (10c); World Cricket Cup victory (50c); Telephone cent. ($1); Operation Sail, American Bicent. ($2).

Royal Family — A87

Designs: 30c, Elizabeth II and Prince Philip touring Antigua. 50c, Queen enthroned. 90c, Queen wearing crown. $2.50, Queen and Prince Charles. $5, Queen and Prince Philip.

1977, Feb. 7   Perf. 13½x14
459	A87	10c multicolored	.15	.15
460	A87	30c multicolored	.18	.18
461	A87	50c multicolored	.30	.30
462	A87	90c multicolored	.60	.60
463	A87	$2.50 multicolored	1.50	1.50
		Nos. 459-463 (5)	2.73	2.73

Souvenir Sheet
464	A87	$5 multicolored	4.00	4.00

25th anniv. of the reign of Queen Elizabeth II.
Nos. 459-463 were printed in sheets of 40. Sheets of 5 plus label, perf. 12, probably were not sold by the Antigua Post Office.
A booklet of self-adhesive stamps contains one pane of six rouletted and die cut 50c stamps in design of 90c, and one pane of one die cut $5. Stamps have changed colors. Panes have marginal inscriptions.
For overprints see Nos. 477-482.

Scouts
Camping
A88

Boy Scout Emblem and: 1c, Scouts on hike. 2c, Rock climbing. 10c, Cutting logs. 30c, Map and compass reading. 50c, First aid. $2, Scouts on raft.

1977, May 23   Litho.   Perf. 14
465	A88	½c multicolored	.15	.15
466	A88	1c multicolored	.15	.15
467	A88	2c multicolored	.15	.15
468	A88	10c multicolored	.15	.15
469	A88	30c multicolored	.30	.30
470	A88	50c multicolored	.50	.50
471	A88	$2 multicolored	1.90	1.90
a.		Souvenir sheet of 3, #469-471	2.50	2.50
		Set value	3.00	3.00

Caribbean Boy Scout Jamboree, Jamaica.

Carnival Queen Holding Horseshoe — A89

Designs: 30c, Carnival Queen in feather costume. 50c, Butterfly costume. 90c, Carnival Queen with ornaments. $1, Carnival King and Queen.

1977, July 18   Litho.   Perf. 14
472	A89	10c multicolored	.15	.15
473	A89	30c multicolored	.18	.18
474	A89	50c multicolored	.32	.32
475	A89	90c multicolored	.55	.55
476	A89	$1 multicolored	.60	.60
a.		Souvenir sheet of 4, #473-476	1.90	1.90
		Nos. 472-476 (5)	1.80	1.80

21st Summer Carnival.

Nos. 459-464 Overprinted: "ROYAL VISIT / 28th OCTOBER 1977"
Perf. 13½x14, 12
1977, Oct. 17   Litho.
477	A87	10c multicolored	.15	.15
478	A87	30c multicolored	.16	.16
479	A87	50c multicolored	.28	.28
480	A87	90c multicolored	.50	.50
481	A87	$2.50 multicolored	1.40	1.40
		Nos. 477-481 (5)	2.49	2.49

Souvenir Sheet
482	A87	$5 multicolored	3.00	3.00

Visit of Queen Elizabeth II, Oct. 28.

Virgin and Child, by Cosimo Tura — A90

Virgin and Child by: 1c, $2, Carlo Crivelli (different). 2c, 25c, Lorenzo Lotto (different). 8c, Jacopo da Pontormo. 10c, Tura.

1977, Nov. 15   Litho.   Perf. 14
483	A90	½c multicolored	.15	.15
484	A90	1c multicolored	.15	.15
485	A90	2c multicolored	.15	.15
486	A90	8c multicolored	.15	.15
487	A90	10c multicolored	.15	.15
488	A90	25c multicolored	.18	.18
489	A90	$2 multicolored	1.50	1.50
a.		Souvenir sheet of 4, #486-489	2.25	2.25
		Set value	2.00	2.00

Christmas.

Pineapple A91

10th anniv. of Statehood: 15c, Flag of Antigua. 50c, Police band. 90c, Prime Minister V. C. Bird. $2, Coat of Arms.

1977, Dec. 28   Litho.   Perf. 13x13½
490	A91	10c multicolored	.15	.15
491	A91	15c multicolored	.15	.15
492	A91	50c multicolored	.40	.40
493	A91	90c multicolored	.75	.75

494	A91	$2 multicolored	1.60	1.60
a.		Souv. sheet of 4, #491-494, perf. 14	2.75	2.75
		Nos. 490-494 (5)	3.05	3.05

Wright Glider III, 1902 A92

Designs: 1c, Flyer I in air, 1903. 2c, Weight and derrick launch system and Wright engine, 1903. 10c, Orville Wright, vert. 50c, Flyer III, 1905. 90c, Wilbur Wright, vert. $2, Wright Model B, 1910. $2.50, Flyer I, 1903, on ground.

1978, Mar. 28   Perf. 14
495	A92	½c multicolored	.15	.15
496	A92	1c multicolored	.15	.15
497	A92	2c multicolored	.15	.15
498	A92	10c multicolored	.15	.15
499	A92	50c multicolored	.35	.35
500	A92	90c multicolored	.60	.60
501	A92	$2 multicolored	1.40	1.40
		Set value	2.55	2.55

Souvenir Sheet
502	A92	$2.50 multicolored	2.00	2.00

1st powered flight by Wright brothers, 75th anniv.

Sunfish Regatta A93

Sailing Week 1978: 50c, Fishing and work boat race. 90c, Curtain Bluff race. $2, Powerboat rally. $2.50, Guadeloupe-Antigua race.

1978, Apr. 29   Litho.   Perf. 14½
503	A93	10c multicolored	.15	.15
504	A93	50c multicolored	.40	.40
505	A93	90c multicolored	.75	.75
506	A93	$2 multicolored	1.60	1.60
		Nos. 503-506 (4)	2.90	2.90

Souvenir Sheet
507	A93	$2.50 multicolored	2.40	2.40

Elizabeth II and Prince Philip — A94

Designs: 30c, Coronation. 50c, State coach. 90c, Elizabeth II and Archbishop. $2.50, Elizabeth II, $5, Elizabeth II, Prince Philip, Prince Charles and Princess Anne as children.

1978, June 2   Litho.   Perf. 14, 12
508	A94	10c multicolored	.15	.15
509	A94	30c multicolored	.16	.16
510	A94	50c multicolored	.30	.30
511	A94	90c multicolored	.50	.50
512	A94	$2.50 multicolored	1.50	1.50
		Nos. 508-512 (5)	2.61	2.61

Souvenir Sheet
513	A94	$5 multicolored	3.00	3.00

25th anniv. of coronation of Queen Elizabeth II.
Nos. 508-512 were printed in sheets of 50 (2 panes of 25), perf. 14, and in sheets of 3 plus label, perf. 12, with frames in changed colors.

Glass Coach A95

Royal Coaches: 50c, Irish state coach. $5, Coronation coach.

1978, June 2   Litho.   Imperf.
Self-adhesive
514		Souvenir booklet	6.75
a.	A95	Bklt. pane of 6 (3 each 25c and 50c)	2.00
b.	A95	Bklt. pane of 1 ($5)	4.50

25th anniversary of coronation of Queen Elizabeth II. No. 514 contains 2 booklet panes printed on peelable paper backing showing royal processions.

Soccer — A96   Purple Wreath — A97

Designs: Various soccer scenes. Stamps in souvenir sheet horizontal.

1978, Aug. 18   Litho.   Perf. 15
515	A96	10c multicolored	.15	.15
516	A96	15c multicolored	.15	.15
517	A96	$3 multicolored	3.00	3.00
		Nos. 515-517 (3)	3.30	3.30

Souvenir Sheet
518		Sheet of 4	3.25	3.25
a.	A96	25c multicolored	.25	.25
b.	A96	30c multicolored	.30	.30
c.	A96	50c multicolored	.50	.50
d.	A96	$2 multicolored	2.00	2.00

11th World Cup Soccer Championship, Argentina, June 1-25.

1978, Oct.   Litho.   Perf. 14
519	A97	25c shown	.22	.22
520	A97	50c Sunflowers	.45	.45
521	A97	90c Frangipani	.80	.80
522	A97	$2 Passionflower	1.75	1.75
		Nos. 519-522 (4)	3.22	3.22

Souvenir Sheet
523	A97	$2.50 Red hibiscus	2.50	2.50

St. Ildefonso Receiving Chasuble, by Rubens A98

Christmas: 25c, Flight of St. Barbara, by Rubens. $2, Holy Family, by Sebastiano del Piombo. $4, Annunciation, by Rubens.

1978, Oct. 30   Litho.   Perf. 14
524	A98	8c multicolored	.15	.15
525	A98	25c multicolored	.20	.20
526	A98	$2 multicolored	1.90	1.90
		Nos. 524-526 (3)	2.25	2.25

Souvenir Sheet
527	A98	$4 multicolored	5.00	5.00

Antigua No. 2 — A99   Crucifixion, by Durer — A100

Designs: 50c, Great Britain Penny Black, 1840. $1, Woman posting letter in pillar box, and coach. $2, Mail train, ship, plane and Concorde. $2.50, Rowland Hill.

1979, Feb. 12 — Litho. — Perf. 14

528	A99	25c multicolored	.20	.20
529	A99	50c multicolored	.40	.40
530	A99	$1 multicolored	.75	.75
531	A99	$2 multicolored	1.65	1.65
		Nos. 528-531 (4)	3.00	3.00

Souvenir Sheet

532	A99	$2.50 multicolored	2.25	2.25

Sir Rowland Hill (1795-1879), originator of penny postage.

Nos. 528-531 were printed in sheets of 50 (2 panes of 25), perf. 14, and in sheets of 5 plus label, perf. 12, with frames in changed colors.

For overprints, see Nos. 571A-571D.

1979, Mar. 15

Designs (after Dürer): 10c, Deposition. $2.50, Crucifixion. $4, Man of Sorrows.

533	A100	10c multicolored	.15	.15
534	A100	50c multicolored	.40	.40
535	A100	$4 multicolored	3.00	3.00
		Nos. 533-535 (3)	3.55	3.55

Souvenir Sheet

536	A100	$2.50 multicolored	2.25	2.25

Easter.

Child Playing with Sailboat — A101

International Year Of The Child 1979

IYC emblem, child's hand holding toy: 50c, Rocket. 90c, Automobile. $2, Train. $5, Plane.

1979, Apr. 9 — Litho. — Perf. 14

537	A101	25c multicolored	.20	.20
538	A101	50c multicolored	.40	.40
539	A101	90c multicolored	.75	.75
540	A101	$2 multicolored	1.65	1.65
		Nos. 537-540 (4)	3.00	3.00

Souvenir Sheet

541	A101	$5 multicolored	4.00	4.00

International Year of the Child.

Yellowjacks A102 30c — ANTIGUA

Sport Fish: 50c, Bluefin tunas. 90c, Sailfish. $2.50, Barracuda. $3, Wahoos.

1979, May — Litho. — Perf. 14½

542	A102	30c multicolored	.25	.25
543	A102	50c multicolored	.40	.40
544	A102	90c multicolored	.70	.70
545	A102	$3 multicolored	2.25	2.25
		Nos. 542-545 (4)	3.60	3.60

Souvenir Sheet

546	A102	$2.50 multicolored	2.00	2.00

Capt. Cook and his Birthplace at Marton — A103

Holy Family — A104

Capt. James Cook (1728-1779) and: 50c, HMS Endeavour. 90c, Marine timekeeper. $2.50, HMS Resolution. $3, Landing at Botany Bay.

1979, July 2 — Litho. — Perf. 14

547	A103	25c multicolored	.20	.20
548	A103	50c multicolored	.35	.35
549	A103	90c multicolored	.60	.60
550	A103	$3 multicolored	2.00	2.00
		Nos. 547-550 (4)	3.15	3.15

Souvenir Sheet

551	A103	$2.50 multicolored	2.25	2.25

1979, Oct. 1 — Litho. — Perf. 14

Stained-glass Windows: 25c, Flight into Egypt. 50c, Shepherd and star. $3, Angel with trumpet. $4, Three Kings offering gifts.

552	A104	8c multicolored	.15	.15
553	A104	25c multicolored	.16	.16
554	A104	50c multicolored	.32	.32
555	A104	$4 multicolored	2.50	2.50
		Nos. 552-555 (4)	3.13	3.13

Souvenir Sheet
Perf. 12x12½

556	A104	$3 multicolored	2.25	2.25

Christmas.

Javelin, Olympic Rings — A105

1980, Feb. 7 — Litho. — Perf. 14

557	A105	10c shown	.15	.15
558	A105	25c Running	.20	.20
559	A105	$1 Pole vault	.65	.65
560	A105	$2 Hurdles	1.40	1.40
		Nos. 557-560 (4)	2.40	2.40

Souvenir Sheet

561	A105	$3 Boxing, horiz.	2.00	2.00

22nd Summer Olympic Games, Moscow, July 19-Aug. 3.

Disney Characters and IYC Emblem A106

Designs: Transportation scenes. ½c, 2c, 3c, 4c, 5c, $1, $2.50, horiz.

1980, Mar. 24 — Litho. — Perf. 11

562	A106	½c Mickey, plane	.15	.15
563	A106	1c Donald, car	.15	.15
564	A106	2c Goofy driving taxi	.15	.15
565	A106	3c Mickey, Minnie in sidecar	.15	.15
566	A106	4c Huey, Dewey and Louie	.15	.15
567	A106	5c Grandma Duck	.15	.15
568	A106	10c Mickey in jeep	.15	.15
569	A106	$1 Chip and Dale sailing	1.00	1.00
570	A106	$4 Donald on train	4.00	4.00
		Set value	5.25	5.25

Souvenir Sheet

571	A106	$2.50 Goofy in glider	5.50	5.50

Nos. 528-531 in Changed Colors
Overprinted "LONDON 1980"

1980, May 6 — Litho. — Perf. 12

571A	A99	25c multicolored	.20	.20
571B	A99	50c multicolored	.35	.35
571C	A99	$1 multicolored	.60	.60
571D	A99	$2 multicolored	1.40	1.40
		Nos. 571A-571D (4)	2.55	2.55

London '80 Intl. Stamp Exhib., May 6-14.

Birth of Venus, by Botticelli A106a

ANTIGUA 30c

Designs: 10c, David, by Donatello, vert. 50c, Reclining Couple, sarcophagus, Cerveteri. 90c, The Garden of Earthly Delights, by Hieronymus Bosch. $1, Portinari Altarpiece, by Hugo van der Goes. $4, Eleanora of Toledo and her Son Giovanni de Medici, by Bronzino, vert. $5, The Holy Family, by Rembrandt.

Perf. 13½x14, 14x13½

1980, June 23 — Litho.

572	A106a	10c multicolored	.15	.15
573	A106a	30c multicolored	.15	.15
574	A106a	50c multicolored	.25	.25
575	A106a	90c multicolored	.45	.45
576	A106a	$1 multicolored	.50	.50
577	A106a	$4 multicolored	2.75	2.75
		Nos. 572-577 (6)	4.25	4.25

Souvenir Sheet
Perf. 14

578	A106a	$5 multicolored	3.75	3.75

ANTIGUA 30c

Anniversary Emblem, Intl. Headquarters, Evanston, Ill. — A107

1980, July 21 — Litho. — Perf. 14

579	A107	3c shown	.20	.20
580	A107	50c Antigua club banner	.35	.35
581	A107	90c Map of Antigua	.60	.60
582	A107	$3 Paul P. Harris, emblem	2.00	2.00
		Nos. 579-582 (4)	3.15	3.15

Souvenir Sheet

583	A107	$5 Emblems, Antigua flags	3.25	3.25

Rotary International, 75th anniv.

Queen Mother Elizabeth, 80th Birthday — A108

$2.50 ANTIGUA

1980, Sept. 15

584	A108	10c multicolored	.15	.15
585	A108	$2.50 multicolored	1.75	1.75

Souvenir Sheet
Perf. 12

586	A108	$3 multicolored	2.00	2.00

Ringed Kingfisher — A109

ANTIGUA 10c

1980, Nov. 3 — Litho. — Perf. 14

587	A109	10c shown	.15	.15
588	A109	30c Plain pigeon	.30	.30
589	A109	$1 Green-throated carib	.75	.75
590	A109	$2 Black-necked stilt	1.75	1.75
		Nos. 587-590 (4)	2.95	2.95

Souvenir Sheet

591	A109	$2.50 Roseate tern	3.50	3.50

25c

Sleeping Beauty and the Prince — A110

Christmas: Various scenes from Walt Disney's Sleeping Beauty. $4 vert.

1980, Dec. 23 — Perf. 11, 13½x14 ($4)

592	A110	½c multicolored	.15	.15
593	A110	1c multicolored	.15	.15
594	A110	2c multicolored	.15	.15
595	A110	4c multicolored	.15	.15
596	A110	8c multicolored	.15	.15
597	A110	10c multicolored	.15	.15
598	A110	25c multicolored	.22	.22
599	A110	$2 multicolored	1.75	1.75
600	A110	$2.50 multicolored	2.25	2.25
		Set value	4.50	4.50

Souvenir Sheet

601	A110	$4 multicolored	3.25	3.25

ANTIGUA 25c

Sugar-cane Railway Diesel Locomotive No. 15 A111

1981, Jan. 12 — Perf. 14

602	A111	25c shown	.16	.16
603	A111	50c Narrow-gauge steam locomotive	.40	.40
604	A111	90c Diesels #1, #10	.75	.75
605	A111	$3 Hauling sugar-cane	2.25	2.25
		Nos. 602-605 (4)	3.56	3.56

Souvenir Sheet

606	A111	$2.50 Sugar factory, train yard	1.90	1.90

Nos. 411-412, 414-422 Overprinted:
"INDEPENDENCE 1981"

1981, Mar. 31 — Litho.

607	A79	6c multicolored	.15	.15
608	A79	10c multicolored	.15	.15
609	A79	20c multicolored	.15	.15
610	A79	25c multicolored	.20	.20
611	A79	35c multicolored	.25	.25
612	A79	50c multicolored	.40	.40
613	A79	75c multicolored	.60	.60
614	A79	$1 multicolored	.75	.75
615	A80	$2.50 multicolored	1.75	1.75
616	A80	$5 multicolored	3.75	3.75
617	A80	$10 multicolored	7.50	7.50
		Nos. 607-617 (11)	15.65	15.65

Pipes of Pan, by Picasso — A112

10c Antigua

Paintings by Pablo Picasso (1881-1973): 50c, Seated Harlequin. 90c, Paulo as Harlequin. $4, Mother and Child. $5, Three Musicians.

1981, May 5 — Litho. — Perf. 14

618	A112	10c multicolored	.15	.15
619	A112	50c multicolored	.32	.32
620	A112	90c multicolored	.60	.60
621	A112	$4 multicolored	2.50	2.50
		Nos. 618-621 (4)	3.57	3.57

Souvenir Sheet
Perf. 14x14½

622	A112	$5 multicolored	3.25	3.25

Royal Wedding Issue
Common Design Type

1981, June 16 — Perf. 14

623	CD331	25c Couple	.15	.15
624	CD331	50c Glamis Castle	.35	.35
625	CD331	$4 Charles	2.75	2.75
		Nos. 623-625 (3)	3.25	3.25

Souvenir Sheet
626 CD331 $5 Glass coach   3.50 3.50
627 CD331 Booklet   9.00
  a. Pane of 6 (2x25c, 2x$1, 2x$2),
    Charles   5.00
  b. Pane of 1, $5, Couple   4.00

No. 627 contains imperf., self-adhesive stamps.
Nos. 623-625 also printed in sheets of 5 plus
label, perf. 12 in changed colors.
For surcharges see Nos. 792, 795, 802, 805.

Campfire Sing A113

1981, Oct. 28   Litho.   Perf. 15
628 A113 10c Irene Joshua   .15 .15
629 A113 50c shown   .40 .40
630 A113 90c Sailing   .70 .70
631 A113 $2.50 Milking cow   1.90 1.90
  Nos. 628-631 (4)   3.15 3.15

Souvenir Sheet
632 A113 $5 Flag raising   3.75 3.75
Girl Guides, 50th anniv.

Independence — A114   A115

1981, Nov. 1   Litho.   Perf. 15
633 A114 10c Arms   .15 .15
634 A114 50c Flag   .35 .35
635 A114 90c Prime Minister Bird .60 .60
636 A114 $2.50 St. John's Cathedral,
   horiz.   1.75 1.75
  Nos. 633-636 (4)   2.85 2.85

Souvenir Sheet
637 A114 $5 Map   3.25 3.25
No. 637 contains one 41x41mm stamp.

1981, Nov. 16
Christmas (Virgin and Child Paintings by): 8c,
Holy Night, by Jacques Stella (1596-1657). 30c
Julius Schnorr von Carolfeld (1794-1872). $1,
Alonso Cano (1601-1667). $3, Lorenzo de Credi
(1459-1537). $5, Holy Family, by Pieter von Avoni
(1600-1652).

638 A115 8c multicolored   .15 .15
639 A115 30c multicolored   .25 .25
640 A115 $1 multicolored   .75 .75
641 A115 $3 multicolored   2.25 2.25
  Nos. 638-641 (4)   3.40 3.40

Souvenir Sheet
642 A115 $5 multicolored   3.25 3.25

Intl. Year of the Disabled A116

1981, Dec. 1   Litho.   Perf. 15
643 A116 10c Swimming   .15 .15
644 A116 50c Discus   .35 .35
645 A116 90c Archery   .60 .60
646 A116 $2 Baseball   1.40 1.40
  Nos. 643-646 (4)   2.50 2.50

Souvenir Sheet
647 A116 $4 Basketball   3.00 3.00

1982 World Cup Soccer A117

Designs: Various soccer players.

1982, Apr. 15   Litho.   Perf. 14
648 A117 10c multicolored   .15 .15
649 A117 50c multicolored   .35 .35
650 A117 90c multicolored   .60 .60
651 A117 $4 multicolored   2.75 2.75
  Nos. 648-651 (4)   3.85 3.85

Souvenir Sheet
652 A117 $5 multicolored   3.75 3.75
Also issued in sheetlets of 5 + label in changed
colors, perf. 12.

A118   A119

1982, June 17   Litho.   Perf. 14½
653 A118 10c A-300 Airbus   .15 .15
654 A118 50c Hawker-Siddeley
   748   .40 .40
655 A118 90c De Havilland Twin
   Otter DCH6   .70 .70
656 A118 $2.50 Britten-Norman Is-
   lander   1.75 1.75
  Nos. 653-656 (4)   3.00 3.00

Souvenir Sheet
657 A118 $5 Jet, horiz.   3.50 3.50
Coolidge Intl. Airport opening.

1982, June 28   Litho.   Perf. 14½
658 A119 10c Cordia, vert.   .15 .15
659 A119 50c Golden spotted mongoose   .40 .40
660 A119 90c Corallita, vert.   .70 .70
661 A119 $3 Bulldog bats   2.25 2.25
  Nos. 658-661 (4)   3.50 3.50

Souvenir Sheet
662 A119 $5 Caribbean monk seals 3.75 3.75
Charles Darwin's death centenary.

Princess Diana Issue
Common Design Type
1982, July 1   Litho.   Perf. 14½x14
663 CD332 90c Greenwich Palace   .60 .60
664 CD332 $1 Wedding   .65 .65
665 CD332 $4 Diana   2.50 2.50
  Nos. 663-665 (3)   3.75 3.75

Souvenir Sheet
666 CD332 $5 Diana, diff.   3.75 3.75
For overprints and surcharges see Nos. 672-675,
797, 799, 803, 806.

Scouting Year A120

Designs: Independence Day celebration.

1982, July 15   Perf. 14
667 A120 10c Decorating buildings .15 .15
668 A120 50c Helping woman   .40 .40
669 A120 90c Princess Margaret   .70 .70
670 A120 $2.20 Cub Scout giving di-
   rections   1.75 1.75
  Nos. 667-670 (4)   3.00 3.00

Souvenir Sheet
671 A120 $5 Baden-Powell   3.75 3.75
Nos. 663-666 Overprinted: "ROYAL BABY
/ 21.6.82"

1982, Aug. 30   Litho.   Perf. 14½x14
672 CD332 90c multicolored   .70 .70
673 CD332 $1 multicolored   .75 .75
674 CD332 $4 multicolored   3.00 3.00
  Nos. 672-674 (3)   4.45 4.45

Souvenir Sheet
675 CD332 $5 multicolored   3.50 3.50
For surcharges see Nos. 798, 800, 804, 807.

Roosevelt Driving by "The Little White House" A121

1982, Sept. 20   Perf. 15
676 A121 10c shown   .15 .15
677 A121 25c Washington as blacksmith   .18 .18
678 A121 45c Churchill, Roosevelt,
   Stalin   .35 .35
679 A121 60c Washington crossing
   Delaware, vert.   .45 .45
680 A121 $1 Roosevelt on train,
   vert.   .75 .75
681 A121 $3 Roosevelt, vert.   2.25 2.25
  Nos. 676-681 (6)   4.13 4.13

Souvenir Sheets
682 A121 $4 Washington, vert.   3.00 3.00
683 A121 $4 Eleanor and Franklin 3.00 3.00
George Washington's 250th birth anniv. and
Franklin D. Roosevelt's birth centenary.

Christmas — A122

Raphael Paintings.

1982, Nov.   Litho.   Perf. 14
684 A122 10c Annunciation   .15 .15
685 A122 30c Adoration of the Magi .22 .22
686 A122 $1 Presentation at the
   Temple   .75 .75
687 A122 $4 Coronation of the Vir-
   gin   3.00 3.00
  Nos. 684-687 (4)   4.12 4.12

Souvenir Sheet
688 A122 $5 Marriage of the Virgin 3.50 3.50

500th Birth Anniv. of Raphael A123

1983, Jan. 28.   Litho.   Perf. 14½
689 A123 45c Galatea taking Reins
   of Dolphins, vert.   .35 .35
690 A123 50c Sea Nymphs carried
   by Tritons, vert.   .40 .40
691 A123 60c Winged Angel Steering
   Dolphins   .45 .45
692 A123 $4 Cupids Shooting Ar-
   rows   3.00 3.00
  Nos. 689-692 (4)   4.20 4.20

Souvenir Sheet
693 A123 $5 Galatea   3.75 3.75

A124

1983, Mar. 14   Perf. 14
694 A124 25c Pineapple crop   .20 .20
695 A124 30c Carnival   .30 .30
696 A124 60c Tourists, sailboat .40 .40
697 A124 $3 Control Tower   2.00 2.00
  Nos. 694-697 (4)   2.90 2.90
Commonwealth Day.

World Communications Year — A125

1983, Apr. 5   Litho.   Perf. 14
698 A125 15c TV screen, camera   .15 .15
699 A125 50c Police radio, car   .40 .40
700 A125 60c Long distance phone
   call   .45 .45
701 A125 $3 Dish antenna, planets 2.25 2.25
  Nos. 698-701 (4)   3.25 3.25

Souvenir Sheet
702 A125 $5 Comsat satellite   3.75 3.75

Bottlenose Dolphin A126

1983, May 9   Litho.   Perf. 15
703 A126 15c shown   .15 .15
704 A126 50c Finback whale   .35 .35
705 A126 60c Bowhead whale   .40 .40
706 A126 $3 Spectacled porpoise 2.00 2.00
  Nos. 703-706 (4)   2.90 2.90

Souvenir Sheet
707 A126 $5 Unicorn whale   3.50 3.50

Cashew Nut — A127

1983, July 11   Perf. 14
708 A127 1c shown   .15 .15
709 A127 2c Passion fruit   .15 .15
710 A127 3c Mango   .15 .15
711 A127 5c Grapefruit   .15 .15
712 A127 10c Pawpaw   .15 .15
713 A127 15c Breadfruit   .15 .15
714 A127 20c Coconut   .15 .15
715 A127 25c Oleander   .18 .18
716 A127 30c Banana   .22 .22
717 A127 40c Pineapple   .30 .30
718 A127 45c Cordcia   .35 .35
719 A127 50c Cassia   .40 .40
720 A127 60c Poui   .45 .45
721 A127 $1 Frangipani   .75 .75
722 A127 $2 Flamboyant   1.50 1.50
723 A127 $2.50 Lemon   1.75 1.75
724 A127 $5 Lignum vitae   3.75 3.75
725 A127 $10 Arms   7.50 7.50
  Nos. 708-725 (18)   18.20 18.20

1985   Perf. 12½x12
708a A127 1c   .15 .15
709a A127 2c   .15 .15
710a A127 3c   .15 .15
711a A127 5c   .15 .15
712a A127 10c   .15 .15
713a A127 15c   .15 .15
714a A127 20c   .15 .15
715a A127 25c   .15 .15
716a A127 30c   .15 .15
717a A127 40c   .18 .18
718a A127 45c   .18 .18
719a A127 50c   .20 .20
720a A127 60c   .20 .20
721a A127 $1   .40 .40
722a A127 $2   1.10 1.10
723a A127 $2.50   1.25 1.25
724a A127 $5   2.75 2.75
725a A127 $10   5.00 5.00
  Nos. 708a-725a (18)   12.61 12.61
Issue dates: $2-$5, Dec. Others Mar.

Manned Flight Bicentenary A128

1983, Aug. 15   Perf. 15
726 A128 30c Dornier DoX   .20 .20
727 A128 50c Supermarine S-6B   .35 .35
728 A128 60c Curtiss F9C, USS Akron   .40 .40
729 A128 $4 Pro Juventute balloon 2.75 2.75
  Nos. 726-729 (4)   3.70 3.70

Souvenir Sheet
730 A128 $5 Graf Zeppelin   3.25 3.25

Christmas — A129

Raphael Paintings: 10c, 30c, $1, $4, Sybils and Angels details. $5, Vision of Ezekiel.

1983, Oct. 4   Litho.   Perf. 14

731	A129	10c	Angel flying with scroll	.15	.15
732	A129	30c	Angel, diff.	.30	.30
733	A129	$1	Inscribing tablet	.30	.30
734	A129	$4	Angel showing tablet	3.25	3.25
			Nos. 731-734 (4)	4.00	4.00

Souvenir Sheet

735	A129	$5	multicolored	3.75	3.75

Methodist Church, Anniv. — A130   1984 Olympics, Los Angeles — A131

Designs: 15c, John Wesley founder of Methodism. 50c, Nathaniel Gilbert, Antiguan founder. 60c, St. John's Methodist Church Steeple. $3, Ebenezer Methodist Church.

1983, Nov.   Litho.   Perf. 14

736	A130	15c	multicolored	.15	.15
737	A130	50c	multicolored	.40	.40
738	A130	60c	multicolored	.45	.45
739	A130	$3	multicolored	2.25	2.25
			Nos. 736-739 (4)	3.25	3.25

1984, Jan.   Litho.   Perf. 15

740	A131	25c	Discus	.18	.18
741	A131	50c	Gymnastics	.40	.40
742	A131	90c	Hurdling	.70	.70
743	A131	$3	Bicycling	2.25	2.25
			Nos. 740-743 (4)	3.53	3.53

Souvenir Sheet

744	A131	$5	Volleyball, horiz.	3.75	3.75

Booker Vanguard A132

1984, June 4   Litho.   Perf. 15

745	A132	45c	shown	.35	.35
746	A132	50c	Canberra	.40	.40
747	A132	60c	Yachts	.45	.45
748	A132	$4	Fairwind	3.00	3.00
			Nos. 745-748 (4)	4.20	4.20

Souvenir Sheet

749	A132	$5	Man-of-war, vert.	3.75	3.75

Local Flowers — A133   US Presidents — A134

1984, June 25   Litho.   Perf. 15

755	A133	15c	multicolored	.15	.15
756	A133	50c	multicolored	.38	.38
757	A133	60c	multicolored	.45	.45
758	A133	$3	multicolored	2.25	2.25
			Nos. 755-758 (4)	3.23	3.23

Souvenir Sheet

759	A133	$5	multicolored	3.75	3.75

1984, July 18   Litho.   Perf. 14

760	A134	10c	Lincoln	.15	.15
761	A134	20c	Truman	.15	.15
762	A134	30c	Eisenhower	.22	.22
763	A134	40c	Reagan	.30	.30
764	A134	90c	Lincoln, diff.	.68	.68
765	A134	$1.10	Truman, diff.	.85	.85
766	A134	$1.50	Eisenhower, diff.	1.15	1.15
767	A134	$2	Reagan, diff.	1.50	1.50
			Nos. 760-767 (8)	5.00	5.00

Slavery Abolition Sesquicentennial A135

1984, Aug. 1

768	A135	40c	Moravian Mission	.30	.30
769	A135	50c	Antigua Courthouse, 1823	.38	.38
770	A135	60c	Sugar cane planting	.45	.45
771	A135	$3	Boiling House, Delaps' Estate	2.25	2.25
			Nos. 768-771 (4)	3.38	3.38

Souvenir Sheet

772	A135	$5	Willoughby Bay	3.75	3.75

Song Birds — A136

1984, Aug. 15   Perf. 15

773	A136	40c	Rufous-sided towhee	.30	.30
774	A136	50c	Parula warbler	.38	.38
775	A136	60c	House wren	.45	.45
776	A136	$2	Ruby-crowned kinglet	1.50	1.50
777	A136	$3	Yellow-shafted flicker	2.25	2.25
			Nos. 773-777 (5)	4.88	4.88

Souvenir Sheet

778	A136	$5	Yellow-breasted chat	3.75	3.75

AUSIPEX '84 — A137   The Blue Dancers, by Degas — A137a

1984, Sept. 21   Perf. 15

779	A137	$1	Grass skiing	.75	.75
780	A137	$5	Australian rules football	3.75	3.75

Souvenir Sheet

781	A137	$5	Boomerang	3.75	3.75

1984, Oct.   Litho.   Perf. 15

Paintings by Correggio: 25c, Virgin and Infant with Angels and Cherubs. 60c, The Four Saints. 90c, Saint Catherine. $3, The Campori Madonna. #790, St. John the Baptist.

Paintings by Degas: 50c, The Pink Dancers. 70c, Two Dancers. $4, Dancers at the Bar. #791, Folk Dancers.

782	A137a	15c	multicolored	.15	.15
783	A137a	25c	multicolored	.20	.20
784	A137a	50c	multicolored	.38	.38
785	A137a	60c	multicolored	.45	.45
786	A137a	70c	multicolored	.50	.50
787	A137a	90c	multicolored	.68	.68
788	A137a	$3	multicolored	2.25	2.25
789	A137a	$4	multicolored	3.00	3.00
			Nos. 782-789 (8)	7.61	7.61

Souvenir Sheets

790	A137a	$5	multicolored	3.75	3.75
791	A137a	$5	multi, horiz.	3.75	3.75

Nos. 623-626, 663-666, 672-675, 694-697 Surcharged in Black or Gold

1984, June   Perf. 14, 14½x14

792	CD331	$2 on 25c #623	1.50	1.50
793	CD331	$2 on 25c #694	1.50	1.50
794	CD334	$2 on 45c #695	1.50	1.50
795	CD331	$2 on 50c #624	1.50	1.50
796	CD334	$2 on 60c #696	1.50	1.50
797	CD332	$2 on 90c #663 (G)	1.50	1.50

798	CD332	$2 on 90c #672 (G)	1.50	1.50
799	CD332	$2 on $1 #664 (G)	1.50	1.50
800	CD332	$2 on $1 #673 (G)	1.50	1.50
801	CD334	$2 on $3 #697	1.50	1.50
802	CD331	$2 on $4 #625	1.50	1.50
803	CD332	$2 on $4 #665 (G)	1.50	1.50
804	CD332	$2 on $4 #674 (G)	1.50	1.50
		Nos. 792-804 (13)	19.50	19.50

Souvenir Sheets

805	CD331	$2 on $5 #626	1.50	1.50
806	CD332	$2 on $5 #666	1.50	1.50
807	CD332	$2 on $5 #675	1.50	1.50

Nos. 797-800, 803-804 exist with silver surcharge.

Christmas 1984 and 50th Anniv. of Donald Duck — A138

Scenes from various Donald Duck comics.

1984, Nov.   Litho.   Perf. 11

808	A138	1c	multicolored	.15	.15
809	A138	2c	multicolored	.15	.15
810	A138	3c	multicolored	.15	.15
811	A138	4c	multicolored	.15	.15
812	A138	5c	multicolored	.15	.15
813	A138	10c	multicolored	.15	.15
814	A138	$1	multicolored	1.00	1.00
815	A138	$2	multicolored	1.90	1.90
816	A138	$5	multicolored	5.00	5.00
			Nos. 808-816 (9)	8.80	8.80

Souvenir Sheets
Perf. 14

817	A138	$5	multi, horiz.	5.00	5.00
818	A138	$5	Donald on beach	5.00	5.00

20th Century Leaders A139

1984, Nov. 19   Litho.   Perf. 15

819	A139	60c	John F. Kennedy (1917-1963), vert.	.50	.50
820	A139	60c	Winston Churchill (1874-1965), vert.	.50	.50
821	A139	60c	Mahatma Gandhi (1869-1948), vert.	.50	.50
822	A139	60c	Mao Tse-Tung (1883-1976), vert.	.50	.50
823	A139	$1	Kennedy in Berlin	.80	.80
824	A139	$1	Churchill in Paris	.80	.80
825	A139	$1	Gandhi in Great Britain	.80	.80
826	A139	$1	Mao in Peking	.80	.80
			Nos. 819-826 (8)	5.20	5.20

Souvenir Sheet

827	A139	$5	Flags of Great Britain, India, China, USA	3.75	3.75

Statue of Liberty Centennial A140

1985, Jan. 7

828	A140	25c	Torch on display, 1885	.16	.16
829	A140	30c	Restoration, 1984-1986, vert.	.22	.22
830	A140	50c	Bartholdi supervising construction, 1876	.35	.35
831	A140	90c	Statue on Liberty Island	.70	.70
832	A140	$1	Dedication Ceremony, 1886, vert.	.75	.75
833	A140	$3	Operation Sail, 1976, vert.	2.25	2.25
			Nos. 828-833 (6)	4.43	4.43

Souvenir Sheet

834	A140	$5	Port of New York	3.75	3.75

Traditional Scenes A141

1985, Jan. 21

835	A141	15c	Ceramics, Arawak pot shard	.15	.15
836	A141	50c	Tatooing, body design	.38	.38
837	A141	60c	Harvesting Manioc, god Yocahu	.45	.45
838	A141	$3	Caribs in battle, war club	2.25	2.25
			Nos. 835-838 (4)	3.23	3.23

Souvenir Sheet

839	A141	$5	Tainos worshiping	3.75	3.75

Invention of the Motorcycle, Cent. A142

1985, Mar. 7   Perf. 14

840	A142	10c	Triumph 2HP Jap, 1903	.15	.15
841	A142	30c	Indian Arrow, 1949	.22	.22
842	A142	60c	BMW R100RS, 1976	.45	.45
843	A142	$4	Harley Davidson Model II, 1916	3.00	3.00
			Nos. 840-843 (4)	3.82	3.82

Souvenir Sheet

844	A142	$5	Laverda Jota, 1975	3.75	3.75

John J. Audubon, 200th Birth Anniv. A143

1985, Mar. 25   Perf. 14

845	A143	90c	Horned grebe	.68	.68
846	A143	$1	Least petrel	.75	.75
847	A143	$1.50	Great blue heron	1.15	1.15
848	A143	$3	Double-crested cormorant	2.25	2.25
			Nos. 845-848 (4)	4.83	4.83

Souvenir Sheet

849	A143	$5	White-tailed tropic bird, vert.	3.75	3.75

See Nos.910-914.

Butterflies A144

1985, Apr. 16   Perf. 14

850	A144	25c	Polygrapha cyanea	.16	.16
851	A144	60c	Leodonta dysoni	.45	.45
852	A144	95c	Junea doraete	.75	.75
853	A144	$4	Prepona xenagoras	3.00	3.00
			Nos. 850-853 (4)	4.36	4.36

Souvenir Sheet

854	A144	$5	Caerois gerdrudtus	3.75	3.75

Cessna 172 — A145

1985, Apr. 30

855	A145	30c	shown	.20	.20
856	A145	90c	Fokker DVII	.60	.60
857	A145	$1.50	Spad VII	1.00	1.00
858	A145	$3	Boeing 747	1.90	1.90
			Nos. 855-858 (4)	3.70	3.70

Souvenir Sheet

859	A145	$5	Twin Otter, Coolidge Intl. Airport	3.75	3.75

40th anniv. of the ICAO. Nos. 855, 858-859 show the ICAO and UN emblems.

Maimonides (1135-1204), Judaic Philosopher and Physician — A146

1985, June 17   Litho.   Perf. 14
860 A146 $2 yellow green   2.00 2.00

Souvenir Sheet
861 A146 $5 deep brown   4.00 4.00

Intl. Youth Year A147

1985, July 1
862 A147 25c Agriculture   .18 .18
863 A147 50c Hotel management   .35 .35
864 A147 60c Environmental studies   .50 .50
865 A147 $3 Windsurfing   2.25 2.25
       Nos. 862-865 (4)   3.28 3.28

Souvenir Sheet
866 A147 $5 Youths, national flag   3.75 3.75

Queen Mother, 85th Birthday — A148

Designs: 90c, $1, Attending a church service. No. 867A, $1.50, Touring the London Gardens, children in a sandpit. $2.50, $3, Photograph (1979). $5, With Prince Edward at the wedding of Prince Charles and Lady Diana Spencer.

Perf. 14, 12x12½ (90c, $1, $3)
1985, July 15
866A A148 90c multi ('86)   .65 .65
867   A148 $1 multi   .75 .75
867A A148 $1 multi ('86)   .75 .75
868   A148 $1.50 multi   1.10 1.10
869   A148 $2.50 multi   1.85 1.85
869A A148 $3 multi ('86)   2.25 2.25
       Nos. 866A-869A (6)   7.35 7.35

Souvenir Sheet
870 A148 $5 multicolored   3.75 3.75

Nos. 866A, 867A, 869A issued in sheets of 5 plus label on Jan. 13, 1986.

Marine Life — A149

Johann Sebastian Bach — A150

1985, Aug. 1   Perf. 14
871 A149 15c Fregata magnificens   .15 .15
872 A149 45c Diploria labyrinthiformis   .40 .40
873 A149 60c Oreaster reticulatus   .50 .50
874 A149 $3 Gymnothorax moringa   2.25 2.25
       Nos. 871-874 (4)   3.30 3.30

Souvenir Sheet
875 A149 $5 Acropora palmata   3.75 3.75

Antigua stamps can be mounted in the Scott British Leeward Islands album.

1985, Aug. 26   Litho.   Perf. 14
876 A150 25c Bass trombone   .15 .15
877 A150 50c English horn   .30 .30
878 A150 $1 Violino piccolo   .65 .65
879 A150 $3 Bass racket   1.90 1.90
       Nos. 876-879 (4)   3.00 3.00

Souvenir Sheet
880 A150 $5 Portrait   3.25 3.25

Girl Guides, 75th Anniv. A151

Public service and growth-oriented activities.

1985, Sept. 10
881 A151 15c Public service   .15 .15
882 A151 45c Guides meeting   .40 .40
883 A151 60c Lord and Lady Baden-Powell   .50 .50
884 A151 $3 Nature study   2.25 2.25
       Nos. 881-884 (4)   3.30 3.30

Souvenir Sheet
885 A151 $5 Barn swallow   3.75 3.75

State Visit of Elizabeth II, Oct. 24 A152

1985, Oct. 24   Litho.   Perf. 14½
886 A152 60c National flags   .45 .45
887 A152 $1 Elizabeth II, vert.   .75 .75
888 A152 $4 HMY Britannia   3.00 3.00
       Nos. 886-888 (3)   4.20 4.20

Souvenir Sheet
889 A152 $5 Map of Antigua   3.75 3.75

Mark Twain A153

Disney characters in Roughing It.

1985, Nov. 4   Perf. 14
890 A153 25c Cowboys and Indians   .22 .22
891 A153 50c Canoeing   .42 .42
892 A153 $1.10 Pony Express   .90 .90
893 A153 $1.50 Buffalo hunt in Missouri   1.25 1.25
894 A153 $2 Nevada silver mine   1.75 1.75
       Nos. 890-894 (5)   4.54 4.54

Souvenir Sheet
895 A153 $5 Stagecoach on Kansas plains   4.50 4.50

Jacob and Wilhelm Grimm, Fabulists and Philologists — A154

Disney characters in Spindle, Shuttle and Needle.

1985, Nov. 11
896 A154 30c multicolored   .25 .25
897 A154 60c multicolored   .55 .55
898 A154 70c multicolored   .60 .60
899 A154 $1 multicolored   .90 .90
900 A154 $3 multicolored   2.75 2.75
       Nos. 896-900 (5)   5.05 5.05

Souvenir Sheet
900A A154 $5 multicolored   4.50 4.50

UN 40th Anniv. A155

Stamps of UN and portraits: 40c, No. 18 and Benjamin Franklin. $1, No. 391 and George Washington Carver, agricultural chemist. $3, No. 299 and Charles Lindbergh. $5, Marc Chagall, artist, vert.

1985, Nov. 18   Perf. 13½x14
901 A155 40c multicolored   .30 .30
902 A155 $1 multicolored   .75 .75
903 A155 $3 multicolored   2.25 2.25
       Nos. 901-903 (3)   3.30 3.30

Souvenir Sheet
Perf. 14x13½
904 A155 $5 multicolored   3.75 3.75

Christmas — A156

Religious paintings: 10c, Madonna and Child, by De Landi. 25c, Madonna and Child, by Bonaventura Berlinghieri (d. 1244). 60c, The Nativity, by Fra Angelico (1400-1455). $4, Presentation in the Temple, by Giovanni di Paolo Grazia (c.1403-1482). $5, The Nativity, by Antoniazzo Romano.

1985, Dec. 30   Perf. 15
905 A156 10c multicolored   .15 .15
906 A156 25c multicolored   .18 .18
907 A156 60c multicolored   .45 .45
908 A156 $4 multicolored   3.00 3.00
       Nos. 905-908 (4)   3.78 3.78

Souvenir Sheet
909 A156 $5 multicolored   3.75 3.75

Audubon Type of 1985

Illustrations of North American ducks.

1986, Jan. 6   Perf. 12½x12
910 A143 60c Mallard   .45 .45
911 A143 90c Dusky duck   .65 .65
912 A143 $1.50 Common pintail   1.10 1.10
913 A143 $3 Widgeon   2.25 2.25
       Nos. 910-913 (4)   4.45 4.45

Souvenir Sheet
Perf. 14
914 A143 $5 Common eider   3.75 3.75

1986 World Cup Soccer Championships, Mexico — A157

1986, Mar. 17   Litho.   Perf. 14
915 A157 30c shown   .22 .22
916 A157 60c Heading the ball   .45 .45
917 A157 $1 Referee   .75 .75
918 A157 $4 Goal   3.00 3.00
       Nos. 915-918 (4)   4.42 4.42

Souvenir Sheet
919 A157 $5 Action   3.75 3.75

Nos. 916-917 vert.
For overprints see Nos. 963-967.

A158

Halley's Comet A159

Designs: 5c, Edmond Halley, Greenwich Observatory. 10c, Me 163B Komet. German WWII fighter plane. 60c, Montezuma sighting comet, 1517. $4, Pocahontas saving Capt. John Smith's life, 1607 sighting as sign for Powhatan Indians to raid Jamestown. $5, Comet over Antigua.

1986, Mar. 24
920 A158 5c multicolored   .15 .15
921 A158 10c multicolored   .15 .15
922 A158 60c multicolored   .45 .45
923 A158 $4 multicolored   3.00 3.00
       Nos. 920-923 (4)   3.75 3.75

Souvenir Sheet
924 A159 $5 multicolored   3.75 3.75

For overprints see Nos. 973-977.

Queen Elizabeth II, 60th Birthday
Common Design Type

1986, Apr. 21
925 CD339 60c Wedding, 1947   .45 .45
926 CD339 $1 Trooping the color   .75 .75
927 CD339 $4 Visiting Scotland   3.00 3.00
       Nos. 925-927 (3)   4.20 4.20

Souvenir Sheet
928 CD339 $5 Held by Queen Mary, 1927   3.75 3.75

Boats — A160

1986, May 15
929 A160 30c Tugboat   .22 .22
930 A160 60c Fishing boat   .45 .45
931 A160 $1 Sailboat 2056   .75 .75
932 A160 $4 Lateen-rigged sailboat   3.00 3.00
       Nos. 929-932 (4)   4.42 4.42

Souvenir Sheet
933 A160 $5 Boatbuilding   3.75 3.75

AMERIPEX '86 — A161

American trains.

1986, May 22   Perf. 15
934 A161 25c Hiawatha   .20 .20
935 A161 50c Grand Canyon   .38 .38
936 A161 $1 Powhatan Arrow   .75 .75
937 A161 $3 Empire State   2.25 2.25
       Nos. 934-937 (4)   3.58 3.58

Souvenir Sheet
938 A161 $5 Daylight   3.75 3.75

Wedding of Prince Andrew and Sarah Ferguson
Common Design Type

1986, July 23   Perf. 14
939 CD340 45c Couple   .35 .35
940 CD340 60c Prince Andrew   .45 .45
941 CD340 $4 Princes Andrew, Philip   3.00 3.00
       Nos. 939-941 (3)   3.80 3.80

Souvenir Sheet
942 CD340 $5 Couple, diff.   3.75 3.75

Conch Shells — A162

1986, Aug. 6   Litho.   Perf. 15
943 A162 15c Say fly-specked cerith   .15   .15
944 A162 45c Gmelin smooth scotch
                bonnet   .35   .35
945 A162 60c Linne West Indian
                crown conch   .45   .45
946 A162 $3 Murex ciboney   2.25 2.25
       Nos. 943-946 (4)   3.20 3.20
Souvenir Sheet
947 A162 $5 Atlantic natica   3.75 3.75

Flowers
A163

1986, Aug. 25   Litho.   Perf. 15
948 A163 10c Water lily   .15   .15
949 A163 15c Queen of the night   .15   .15
950 A163 50c Cup of gold   .38   .38
951 A163 60c Beach morning glory   .45   .45
952 A163 70c Golden trumpet   .55   .55
953 A163 $1 Air plant   .75   .75
954 A163 $3 Purple wreath   2.25 2.25
955 A163 $4 Zephyr lily   3.00 3.00
       Nos. 948-955 (8)   7.68 7.68
Souvenir Sheets
956 A163 $4 Dozakie   3.00 3.00
957 A163 $5 Four o'clock   3.75 3.75

Fungi — A164

1986, Sept. 15
958 A164 10c Hygrocybe occidentalis
                scarletina   .15   .15
959 A164 50c Trogia buccinalis   .38   .38
960 A164 $1 Collybia subpruinosa   .75   .75
961 A164 $4 Leucocoprinus brebis-
                sonii   3.00 3.00
       Nos. 958-961 (4)   4.28 4.28
Souvenir Sheet
962 A164 $5 Pyrrhoglossum pyr-
                rhum   3.75 3.75

Nos. 915-919 Ovptd. "WINNERS
Argentina 3 W. Germany 2" in Gold in 2
or 3 lines

1986, Sept. 15   Perf. 14
963 A157 30c multicolored   .22   .22
964 A157 60c multicolored   .45   .45
965 A157 $1 multicolored   .75   .75
966 A157 $4 multicolored   3.00 3.00
       Nos. 963-966 (4)   4.42 4.42
Souvenir Sheet
967 A157 $5 multicolored   3.75 3.75

Automobile,
Cent.
A165

Carl Benz and classic automobiles.

1986, Oct. 20
968 A165 10c 1933 Auburn Speed-
                ster   .15   .15
968A A165 15c 1986 Mercury Sable   .15   .15
969 A165 50c 1959 Cadillac   .38   .38
970 A165 60c 1950 Studebaker   .45   .45
970A A165 70c 1939 Lagonda V-12   .52   .52
970B A165 $1 1930 Adler Standard   .75   .75
970C A165 $3 1956 DKW   2.25 2.25

---

971 A165 $4 1936 Mercedes
                500K   3.00 3.00
       Nos. 968-971 (8)   7.65 7.65
Souvenir Sheets
972 A165 $5 1921 Mercedes
                Knight   3.75 3.75
972A A165 $5 1896 Daimler   3.75 3.75

Nos. 920-924 Ovptd. with Halley's Comet
Emblem in Black or Silver

1986, Oct. 22   Litho.   Perf. 14
973 A158 5c multicolored   .15   .15
974 A158 10c multicolored   .15   .15
975 A158 60c multicolored   .45   .45
976 A158 $4 multicolored   3.00 3.00
       Nos. 973-976 (4)   3.75 3.75
Souvenir Sheet
977 A159 $5 multicolored (S)   3.75 3.75

Christmas — A166

Disney characters as children.

1986, Nov. 4   Perf. 11
978 A166 25c Mickey   .20   .20
979 A166 30c Mickey, Minnie   .22   .22
980 A166 40c Aunt Matilda, Goofy   .30   .30
981 A166 60c Goofy, Pluto   .45   .45
982 A166 70c Pluto, Donald, Daisy   .55   .55
983 A166 $1.50 Stringing popcorn   1.15 1.15
984 A166 $3 Grandma Duck,
                Minnie   2.25 2.25
985 A166 $4 Donald, Pete   3.00 3.00
       Nos. 978-985 (8)   8.12 8.12
Souvenir Sheets
Perf. 14
986 A166 $5 Playing with
                presents   3.75 3.75
987 A166 $5 Reindeer   3.75 3.75
Nos. 985 printed in sheets of 8.

Coat of Arms — A167   Natl.
                       Flag — A168

1986, Nov. 25   Litho.   Perf. 14x14½
988 A167 10c bright blue   .15   .15
989 A168 25c orange   .20   .20
       Set value   .28   .28

Marc Chagall
(1887-1985),
Artist — A169

Designs: No. 990, The Profile, 1957. No. 991,
Portrait of the Artist's Sister, 1910. No. 992, Bride
with Fan, 1911. No. 993, David in Profile, 1914.
No. 994, Fiancee with Bouquet, 1977. No. 995,
Self-portrait with Brushes, 1909. No. 996, The
Walk, 1973. No. 997, Candles, 1938. No. 998, Fall
of Icarus, 1975. No. 999, Myth of Orpheus, 1977.

1987, Mar. 30   Litho.   Perf. 13½x14
990 A169 10c multicolored   .15   .15
991 A169 30c multicolored   .22   .22
992 A169 40c multicolored   .30   .30
993 A169 45c multicolored   .45   .45
994 A169 90c multicolored   .70   .70
995 A169 $1 multicolored   .75   .75
996 A169 $3 multicolored   2.25 2.25

---

997 A169 $4 multicolored   3.00 3.00
Size: 110x95mm
Imperf
998 A169 $5 multicolored   3.75 3.75
999 A169 $5 multicolored   3.75 3.75
       Nos. 990-999 (10)   15.32 15.32

A170

America's
Cup
A171

1987, Feb. 5   Perf. 15
1000 A170 30c Canada I, 1981   .24   .24
1001 A170 60c Gretel II, 1970   .45   .45
1002 A170 $1 Sceptre, 1958   .75   .75
1003 A170 $3 Vigilant, 1893   2.25 2.25
       Nos. 1000-1003 (4)   3.69 3.69
Souvenir Sheet
1004 A171 $5 Australia II, Liberty,
                1983   3.75 3.75

Fish, World
Wildlife
Fund
A172

Marine Birds
A173

1987, Feb. 23   Litho.   Perf. 14
1005 A172 15c Bridled burrfish   .15   .15
1006 A173 30c Brown noddy   .24   .24
1007 A172 40c Nassau grouper   .32   .32
1008 A173 50c Laughing gull   .40   .40
1009 A172 60c French angelfish   .48   .48
1010 A172 $1 Porkfish   .80   .80
1011 A173 $2 Royal tern   1.60 1.60
1012 A173 $3 Sooty tern   2.40 2.40
       Nos. 1005-1012 (8)   6.39 6.39
Souvenir Sheets
1013 A172 $5 Banded butterfly fish   4.00 4.00
1014 A173 $5 Brown booby   4.00 4.00
   The 30c, 50c, $2, $3 and Nos. 1013-1014 do
not picture the WWF emblem.
For overprints see Nos. 1137-1139A.

Statue of
Liberty,
Cent.
A174

Photographs by Peter B. Kaplan.

1987, Apr. 20   Perf. 14
1015 A174 15c Lee Iacocca   .15   .15
1016 A174 30c Statue at dusk   .24   .24
1017 A174 45c Crown, head   .35   .35
1018 A174 50c Iacocca, torch   .40   .40
1019 A174 60c Crown observatory   .48   .48
1020 A174 90c Interior restoration   .70   .70
1021 A174 $1 Head   .80   .80
1022 A174 $2 Statue at sunset   1.60 1.60
1023 A174 $3 Men on scaffold,
                flag   2.40 2.40
1024 A174 $5 Statue at night   4.00 4.00
       Nos. 1015-1024 (10)   11.12 11.12
Nos. 1015-1018, 1021-1022, 1024 vert.

A175

Transportation Innovations — A175a

1987, Apr. 19   Perf. 15
1025 A175 10c Spirit of Australia,
                1978   .15   .15
1026 A175a 15c Siemens' Electric
                locomotive,
                1879   .15   .15
1027 A175 30c USS Triton, 1960   .24   .24
1028 A175a 50c Trevithick, 1801   .38   .38
1029 A175 60c USS New Jersey,
                1942   .48   .48
1030 A175a 70c Draisine bicycle,
                1818   .52   .52
1031 A175 90c SS United States,
                1952   .68   .68
1032 A175a $1.50 Cierva C-4, 1923   1.15 1.15
1033 A175a $2 Curtiss NC-4,
                1919   1.50 1.50
1034 A175 $3 Queen Elizabeth
                II, 1969   2.25 2.25
       Nos. 1025-1034 (10)   7.50 7.50

Reptiles and
Amphibians
A176

1987, June 15   Perf. 14
1035 A176 30c Eleutherodactylus
                martinicensis   .24   .24
1036 A176 60c Thecadactylus bapi-
                cauda   .48   .48
1037 A176 $1 Anolis bimaculatus
                leachi   .75   .75
1038 A176 $3 Geochelone
                carbonaria   2.25 2.25
       Nos. 1035-1038 (4)   3.72 3.72
Souvenir Sheet
1039 A176 $5 Ameiva griswoldi   3.75 3.75

Entertainers — A177

1987, May 11
1040 A177 15c Grace Kelly   .15   .15
1041 A177 30c Marilyn Monroe   .30   .30
1042 A177 45c Orson Welles   .45   .45
1043 A177 50c Judy Garland   .50   .50
1044 A177 60c John Lennon   .60   .60
1045 A177 $1 Rock Hudson   1.00 1.00
1046 A177 $2 John Wayne   2.00 2.00
1047 A177 $3 Elvis Presley   3.00 3.00
       Nos. 1040-1047 (8)   8.00 8.00

No. 1047
Overprinted

1987, Sept. 9   Litho.   Perf. 14
1047A A177 $3 multicolored   3.00 3.00

1988
Summer
Olympics,
Seoul
A178

304

ANTIGUA

1987, Mar. 23
1048 A178 10c Basketball .15 .15
1049 A178 60c Fencing .48 .48
1050 A178 $1 Women's gymnastics .75 .75
1051 A178 $3 Soccer 2.25 2.25
Nos. 1048-1051 (4) 3.63 3.63

Souvenir Sheet
1052 A178 $5 Boxing glove 3.75 3.75

16th World
Scout
Jamboree,
Australia,
1987-88
A179

1987, Nov. 2   Litho.   Perf. 15
1053 A179 10c Campfire, red kangaroo .15 .15
1054 A179 60c Kayaking, blue-
winged kookaburra .45 .45
1055 A179 $1 Obstacle course, ring-
tailed rock wallaby .75 .75
1056 A179 $3 Field kitchen, koalas 2.25 2.25
Nos. 1053-1056 (4) 3.60 3.60

Souvenir Sheet
1057 A179 $5 Flags 3.75 3.75

US
Constitution
Bicent.
A180

Designs: 15c, Virginia House of Burgesses exercising right of freedom of speech. 45c, Connecticut
state seal. 60c, Delaware state seal. $4, Gouverneur
Morris (1752-1816), principal writer of the Constitution, vert. $5, Roger Sherman (1721-1793), jurist
and statesman, vert.

1987, Nov. 16   Litho.   Perf. 14
1058 A180 15c multicolored .15 .15
1059 A180 45c multicolored .35 .35
1060 A180 60c multicolored .48 .48
1061 A180 $4 multicolored 3.00 3.00
Nos. 1058-1061 (4) 3.98 3.98

Souvenir Sheet
1062 A180 $5 multicolored 3.80 3.80

Christmas — A181   A182

Paintings: 45c, Madonna and Child, by Bernardo
Daddi (1290-1355). 60c, Joseph, detail from The
Nativity, by Sano Di Pietro (1406-1481). $1, Mary,
detail from Di Pietro's The Nativity. $4, Music-
making Angel, by Melozzo Da Forli (1438-1494).
$5, The Flight into Egypt, by Di Pietro.

1987, Dec. 1
1063 A181 45c multicolored .32 .32
1064 A181 60c multicolored .45 .45
1065 A181 $1 multicolored .75 .75
1066 A181 $4 multicolored 2.95 2.95
Nos. 1063-1066 (4) 4.47 4.47

Souvenir Sheet
1067 A181 $5 multicolored 3.80 3.80

1988, Feb. 8   Litho.   Perf. 14
1068 A182 25c Wedding portrait .15 .15
1069 A182 60c Elizabeth II, c. 1970 .45 .45
1070 A182 $2 Christening of
Charles, 1948 1.50 1.50
1071 A182 $3 Elizabeth II, c. 1980 2.25 2.25
Nos. 1068-1071 (4) 4.35 4.35

Souvenir Sheet
1072 A182 $5 Royal family, c. 1951 3.75 3.75

40th wedding anniv. of Queen Elizabeth II and
Prince Philip.

Tropical
Birds
A183

1988, Mar. 1
1073 A183 10c Great blue heron,
vert. .15 .15
1074 A183 15c Ringed kingfisher .15 .15
1075 A183 50c Bananaquit .38 .38
1076 A183 60c Purple gallinule .45 .45
1077 A183 70c Blue-hooded
euphonia .55 .55
1078 A183 $1 Caribbean parakeet,
vert. .75 .75
1079 A183 $3 Troupial 2.30 2.30
1080 A183 $4 Hummingbird 3.00 3.00
Nos. 1073-1080 (8) 7.73 7.73

Souvenir Sheets
1081 A183 $5 Roseate flamingo,
vert. 3.75 3.75
1082 A183 $5 Brown pelicans, vert. 3.75 3.75

Salvation Army — A184

1988, Mar. 7
1083 A184 25c Day-care, Antigua .20 .20
1084 A184 30c Penicillin inoculation,
Indonesia .22 .22
1085 A184 40c Day-care Center, Bolivia .30 .30
1086 A184 45c Rehabilitation, India .35 .35
1087 A184 50c Training the blind,
Kenya .38 .38
1088 A184 60c Infant care, Ghana .45 .45
1089 A184 $1 Job training, Zambia .78 .78
1090 A184 $2 Food distribution, Sri
Lanka 1.50 1.50
Nos. 1083-1090 (8) 4.18 4.18

Souvenir Sheet
1091 A184 $5 General Eva Burrows 3.75 3.75

Discovery of
America,
500th
Anniv. (in
1992)
A186

Anniv. emblem and: 10c, Fleet. 30c, View of
fleet in harbor from Paino Indian village. 45c, Caravel anchored in harbor, Paino village. 60c, Columbus, 3 Indians in canoe. 90c, Indian, parrot, Columbus. $1, Columbus in longboat. $3, Spanish guard,
fleet in harbor. $4, Ships under full sail. No. 1100,
Stone cross given to Columbus by Queen Isabella.
No. 1101, Gold exelente.

1988, Mar. 14   Litho.   Perf. 14
1092 A185 10c multicolored .15 .15
1093 A185 30c multicolored .22 .22
1094 A185 45c multicolored .35 .35
1095 A185 60c multicolored .45 .45
1096 A185 90c multicolored .68 .68
1097 A185 $1 multicolored .75 .75
1098 A185 $3 multicolored 2.25 2.25
1099 A185 $4 multicolored 3.00 3.00
Nos. 1092-1099 (8) 7.85 7.85

Souvenir Sheets
1100 A186 $5 multicolored 3.75 3.75
1101 A186 $5 multicolored 3.75 3.75

Paintings by
Titian — A187

Details: 30c, Bust of Christ. 40c, Scourging of
Christ. 45c, Madonna in Glory with Saints. 50c,
The Averoldi Polyptych. $1, Christ Crowned with
Thorns. $2, Christ Mocked. $3, Christ and Simon
of Cyrene. $4, Crucifixion with Virgin and Saints.
No. 1110, Ecce Homo. No. 1111, Noli Me
Tangere.

1988, Apr. 11   Litho.   Perf. 13¹/₂x14
1102 A187 30c shown .22 .22
1103 A187 40c multicolored .30 .30
1104 A187 45c multicolored .35 .35
1105 A187 50c multicolored .38 .38
1106 A187 $1 multicolored .78 .78
1107 A187 $2 multicolored 1.50 1.50
1108 A187 $3 multicolored 2.25 2.25
1109 A187 $4 multicolored 3.00 3.00
Nos. 1102-1109 (8) 8.78 8.78

Souvenir Sheets
1110 A187 $5 multicolored 3.75 3.75
1111 A187 $5 multicolored 3.75 3.75

Sailing Week
A188

1988, Apr. 18   Perf. 15
1112 A188 30c Canada I, 1980 .22 .22
1113 A188 60c Gretel II, Australia,
1970 .48 .48
1114 A188 $1 Sceptre, GB, 1958 .78 .78
1115 A188 $3 Vigilant, US, 1893 2.25 2.25
Nos. 1112-1115 (4) 3.73 3.73

Souvenir Sheet
1116 A188 $5 Australia II, 1983 3.75 3.75

Walt Disney Animated Characters and
Epcot Center, Walt Disney World — A189

1988, May 3   Perf. 14x13¹/₂, 13¹/₂x14
1116A A189 1c like 25c .15 .15
1116B A189 2c like 30c .15 .15
1116C A189 3c like 40c .15 .15
1116D A189 4c like 60c .15 .15
1116E A189 5c like 70c .15 .15
1116F A189 10c like $1.50 .15 .15
1117 A189 25c The Living Seas .18 .18
1118 A189 30c World of Motion .22 .22
1119 A189 40c Spaceship Earth .30 .30
1120 A189 60c Universe of Energy .45 .45
1121 A189 70c Journey to Imagi-
nation .55 .55
1122 A189 $1.50 The Land 1.15 1.15
1123 A189 $3 Communicore 2.25 2.25
1124 A189 $4 Horizons 3.00 3.00
Nos. 1116A-1124 (14) 9.00 9.00

Souvenir Sheets
1125 A189 $5 Epcot Center 3.75 3.75
1126 A189 $5 The Contempora-
ry Resort Hotel 3.75 3.75

30c, 40c, $1.50, $3 and No. 1126 are vert.

Flowering Trees
A190   A191

1988, May 16   Perf. 14
1127 A190 10c Jacaranda .15 .15
1128 A190 30c Cordia .22 .22
1129 A190 50c Orchid tree .38 .38
1130 A190 90c Flamboyant .70 .70
1131 A190 $1 African tulip tree .75 .75
1132 A190 $2 Potato tree 1.50 1.50
1133 A190 $3 Crepe myrtle 2.25 2.25
1134 A190 $4 Pitch apple 3.00 3.00
Nos. 1127-1134 (8) 8.95 8.95

Souvenir Sheets
1135 A191 $5 Cassia 3.75 3.75
1136 A191 $5 Chinaberry 3.75 3.75

Nos. 1011-1012, 1014 and 1013 Ovptd.
in Black for Philatelic Exhibitions

a

b

c

d

1988, May 9   Litho.   Perf. 14
1137 A173 (a) $2 multicolored 1.50 1.50
1138 A173 (b) $2.25 multicolored 2.25 2.25

Souvenir Sheets
1139 A173 (c) $5 multicolored 3.75 3.75
1139A A172 (d) $5 multicolored 3.75 3.75

1988
Summer
Olympics,
Seoul
A192

1988, June 10
1140 A192 40c Gymnastic rings,
vert. .30 .30
1141 A192 60c Weight lifting, vert. .45 .45
1142 A192 $1 Water polo .75 .75
1143 A192 $3 Boxing 2.25 2.25
Nos. 1140-1143 (4) 3.75 3.75

Souvenir Sheet
1144 A192 $5 Torch-bearer, vert. 3.75 3.75

Butterflies
A193

1988-90   Litho.   Perf. 14
1145 A193 1c Monarch .15 .15
1146 A193 2c Jamaican
clearwing .15 .15
1147 A193 3c Yellow-barred
ringlet .15 .15
1148 A193 5c Cracker .15 .15
1149 A193 10c Jamaican mes-
tra .15 .15
1150 A193 15c Mimic .15 .15
1151 A193 20c Silver spot .15 .15
1152 A193 25c Zebra .18 .18
1153 A193 30c Fiery sulphur .22 .22
1154 A193 40c Androgeus
swallowtail .30 .30
1155 A193 45c Giant brim-
stone .35 .35
1156 A193 50c Orbed sulphur .38 .38

1157	A193	60c Blue-backed skipper	.45	.45
1158	A193	$1 Common white skipper	.75	.75
1159	A193	$2 Baracoa skipper	1.50	1.50
1160	A193	$2.50 Mangrove skipper	1.90	1.90
1161	A193	$5 Silver king	3.75	3.75
1161A	A193	$10 Pygmy skipper	7.50	7.50
1162	A193	$20 Parides lycimenes	15.00	15.00
		Nos. 1145-1162 (19)	33.33	33.33

Issued: $20, Feb. 19, 1990; others, Aug. 29.
This is an expanding set. Numbers will change if necessary.

John F. Kennedy
A194

1988, Nov. 22   Litho.   Perf. 14

1162A	A194	1c like 30c	.15	.15
1162B	A194	2c like $4	.15	.15
1162C	A194	3c like $1	.15	.15
1162D	A194	4c like 60c	.15	.15
1163	A194	30c First family	.22	.22
1164	A194	60c Motorcade, Mexico	.45	.45
1165	A194	$1 Funeral procession	.75	.75
1166	A194	$4 Aboard PT109	3.00	3.00
		Nos. 1162A-1166 (8)	5.02	5.02

Souvenir Sheet

1167	A194	$5 Taking Oath of Office	3.75	3.75

Miniature Sheet

Christmas, Mickey Mouse 60th Anniv. — A195

Walt Disney characters: No. 1168a, Morty and Ferdie. No. 1168b, Goofy. No. 1168c, Chip-n-Dale. No. 1168d, Huey and Dewey. No. 1168e, Minnie Mouse. No. 1168f, Pluto. No. 1168g, Mickey Mouse. No. 1168h, Donald Duck and Louie. No. 1169, Goofy driving Mickey and Minnie in a horse-drawn carriage. No. 1170, Characters on roller skates, caroling.

1988, Dec. 1   Perf. 13½x14, 14x13½

1168	A195	Sheet of 8	6.00	6.00
a.-h.		$1 any single	.75	.75

Souvenir Sheets

1169	A195	$7 multicolored	5.25	5.25
1170	A195	$7 multi, horiz.	5.25	5.25

1988, Dec. 1   Litho.   Perf. 14

1171	A195	10c like No. 1168e	.15	.15
1172	A195	25c like No. 1168f	.18	.18
1173	A195	30c like No. 1168g	.22	.22
1174	A195	70c like No. 1168h	.52	.52
		Nos. 1171-1174 (4)	1.07	1.07

Arawak Indian Whip Dance — A196

UPAE and discovery of America emblems and: a, Five adults. b, Eight adults. c, Seven adults. d, Three adults, three children.

1989, May 16   Litho.   Perf. 14

1175		Strip of 4	4.50	4.50
a.-d.	A196	$1.50 any single	1.12	1.12

Souvenir Sheet

1176	A196	$6 Arawak chief	4.50	4.50

Discovery of America 500th anniv. (in 1992), pre-Columbian societies and customs.

Jet Flight, 50th Anniv. A197

Various jet aircraft.

1989, May 29   Litho.   Perf. 14x13½

1177	A197	10c DeHavilland Comet 4	.15	.15
1178	A197	30c Messerschmitt Me262	.22	.22
1179	A197	40c Boeing 707	.30	.30
1180	A197	60c Canadair F-86 Sabre	.45	.45
1181	A197	$1 Lockheed F-104 Starfighter	.75	.75
1182	A197	$2 McDonnell Douglas DC-10	1.50	1.50
1183	A197	$3 Boeing 747	2.25	2.25
1184	A197	$4 McDonnell F-4 Phantom	3.00	3.00
		Nos. 1177-1184 (8)	8.62	8.62

Souvenir Sheets

1185	A197	$7 Grumman F-14 Tomcat	5.25	5.25
1186	A197	$7 Concorde	5.25	5.25

Caribbean Cruise Ships A198

1989, June 20   Litho.   Perf. 14

1187	A198	25c TSS Festivale	.18	.18
1188	A198	45c M.S. Southward	.32	.32
1189	A198	50c M.S. Sagafjord	.38	.38
1190	A198	60c MTS Daphne	.45	.45
1191	A198	75c M.V. Cunard Countess	.58	.58
1192	A198	90c M.S. Song of America	.68	.68
1193	A198	$3 M.S. Island Princess	2.25	2.25
1194	A198	$4 S.S. Galileo	3.00	3.00
		Nos. 1187-1194 (8)	7.84	7.84

Souvenir Sheets

1195	A198	$6 S.S. Norway	4.50	4.50
1196	A198	$6 S.S. Oceanic	4.50	4.50

Paintings by Hiroshige — A199

Designs: 25c, Fish Swimming by Duck Half-submerged in Stream. 45c, Crane and Wave. 50c, Sparrows and Morning Glories. 60c, Crested Blackbird and Flowering Cherry. $1, Great Knot Sitting among Reeds near a Bank of Water. $2, Goose on a Bank of Water. $3, Black Paradise Flycatcher and Blossoms. $4, Sleepy Owl Perched on a Pine Branch. No. 1205, Bullfinch Flying Near a Clematis Branch. No. 1206, Titmouse on a Cherry Branch.

1989, July 3   Perf. 14x13½

1197	A199	25c multicolored	.18	.18
1198	A199	45c multicolored	.35	.35
1199	A199	50c multicolored	.38	.38
1200	A199	60c multicolored	.45	.45
1201	A199	$1 multicolored	.75	.75
1202	A199	$2 multicolored	1.50	1.50
1203	A199	$3 multicolored	2.25	2.25
1204	A199	$4 multicolored	3.00	3.00
		Nos. 1197-1204 (8)	8.86	8.86

Souvenir Sheets

1205	A199	$5 multicolored	3.75	3.75
1206	A199	$5 multicolored	3.75	3.75

Hirohito (1901-1989) and enthronement of Akihito as emperor of Japan.

PHILEXFRANCE '89 — A200

Walt Disney characters, French landmarks: 1c, Helicopter over the Seine. 2c, Arc de Triomphe. 3c, Painting Notre Dame Cathedral. 4c, Entrance to the Metro. 5c, Fashion show. 10c, Follies. No. 1213, Shopping stalls on the Seine. $6, Sidewalk cafe, Left Bank. No. 1215, Hot air balloon Ear Force One. No. 1216, Dining.

1989, July 7   Perf. 14x13½

1207	A200	1c multicolored	.15	.15
1208	A200	2c multicolored	.15	.15
1209	A200	3c multicolored	.15	.15
1210	A200	4c multicolored	.15	.15
1211	A200	5c multicolored	.15	.15
1212	A200	10c multicolored	.15	.15
1213	A200	$5 multicolored	3.75	3.75
1214	A200	$6 multicolored	4.50	4.50
		Nos. 1207-1214 (8)	9.15	9.15

Souvenir Sheets

1215	A200	$5 multicolored	3.75	3.75
1216	A200	$5 multicolored	3.75	3.75

1990 World Cup Soccer Championships, Italy — A201

Natl. flag, various actions of a defending goalie.

1989, Aug. 21   Perf. 14

1217	A201	15c multicolored	.15	.15
1218	A201	25c multicolored	.18	.18
1219	A201	$1 multicolored	.75	.75
1220	A201	$4 multicolored	3.00	3.00
		Nos. 1217-1220 (4)	4.08	4.08

Souvenir Sheets

1221	A201	$5 2 players, horiz.	3.75	3.75
1222	A201	$5 3 players, horiz.	3.75	3.75

For overprints see Nos. 1344-1349.

Mushrooms A202

1989, Oct. 12   Litho.   Perf. 14

1223	A202	10c Lilac fairy helmet	.15	.15
1224	A202	25c Rough psathyrella, vert.	.18	.18
1225	A202	50c Golden tops	.38	.38
1226	A202	60c Blue cap, vert.	.45	.45
1227	A202	75c Brown cap, vert.	.58	.58
1228	A202	$1 Green gill, vert.	.75	.75
1229	A202	$3 Red pinwheel	2.25	2.25
1230	A202	$4 Red chanterelle	3.00	3.00
		Nos. 1223-1230 (8)	7.74	7.74

Souvenir Sheets

1231	A202	$6 Slender stalk	4.50	4.50
1232	A202	$6 Paddy straw mushroom	4.50	4.50

Nos. 1224, 1226-1228, 1231 vert.

Wildlife A203

1989, Oct. 19   Litho.   Perf. 14

1233	A203	25c Hutia	.20	.20
1234	A203	45c Caribbean monk seal	.35	.35
1235	A203	60c Mustache bat, vert.	.45	.45
1236	A203	$4 Manatee, vert.	3.00	3.00
		Nos. 1233-1236 (4)	4.00	4.00

Souvenir Sheet

1237	A203	$5 West Indies giant rice rat	3.75	3.75

American Philatelic Soc. Emblem, Stamps on Stamps and Walt Disney Characters Promoting Philately A204

Designs: 1c, Israel #150, printing press. 2c, Italy #1238, first day cancel. 3c, US #143L4, Pony Express recruits. 4c, Denmark #566, early radio broadcast. 5c, German Democratic Republic #702, television. 10c, Great Britain #1, stamp collector. $4, Japan #1414, integrated circuits. $6, Germany #B667, boom box. No. 1246, US #1355, C3a, and Jenny biplane over Disneyland, horiz. No. 1247, US #940, 1421 and stamps for the wounded.

1989, Nov. 2   Perf. 13½x14, 14x13½

1238	A204	1c multicolored	.15	.15
1239	A204	2c multicolored	.15	.15
1240	A204	3c multicolored	.15	.15
1241	A204	4c multicolored	.15	.15
1242	A204	5c multicolored	.15	.15
1243	A204	10c multicolored	.15	.15
1244	A204	$4 multicolored	3.00	3.00
1245	A204	$6 multicolored	4.50	4.50
		Nos. 1238-1245 (8)	8.40	8.40

Souvenir Sheets

1246	A204	$5 multicolored	3.75	3.75
1247	A204	$5 multicolored	3.75	3.75

Locomotives and Walt Disney Characters — A205

Perf. 14x13½, 13½x14

1989, Nov. 17

1248	A205	25c John Bull, 1831	.18	.18
1249	A205	45c Atlantic, 1832	.35	.35
1250	A205	50c William Crook's, 1861	.38	.38
1251	A205	60c Minnetonka, 1869	.45	.45
1252	A205	$1 Thatcher Perkins, 1863	.75	.75
1253	A205	$2 Pioneer, 1848	1.50	1.50
1254	A205	$3 Peppersass, 1869	2.25	2.25
1255	A205	$4 Gimbels Flyer	3.00	3.00
		Nos. 1248-1255 (8)	8.86	8.86

Souvenir Sheets

1256	A205	$6 #6100 Class S-1 & 1835 Thomas Jefferson	4.50	4.50
1257	A205	$6 Jupiter & #119	4.50	4.50

New York World's Fair, 50th anniv., and World Stamp Expo '89, Washington, DC.

1st Moon Landing, 20th Anniv. A206

1989, Nov. 24   Litho.   Perf. 14

1258	A206	10c Apollo 11 liftoff	.15	.15
1259	A206	45c Aldrin walking on Moon	.35	.35
1260	A206	$1 Eagle ascending from Moon	.75	.75
1261	A206	$4 Recovery after splashdown	3.00	3.00
		Nos. 1258-1261 (4)	4.25	4.25

Souvenir Sheet

1262	A206	$5 Armstrong	3.75	3.75

Nos. 1258-1259 and 1262, vert.

Souvenir Sheet

Smithsonian Institution, Washington, DC — A207

1989, Nov. 17   Litho.   Perf. 14
1263 A207 $4 multicolored   3.00 3.00
World Stamp Expo '89.

Christmas — A208

Religious paintings: 10c, *The Small Cowper Madonna.* 25c, *Madonna of the Goldfinch.* 30c, *The Alba Madonna.* 50c, *Bologna Altarpiece* (attendant). 60c, *Bologna Altarpiece* (heralding angel). 70c, *Bologna Altarpiece* (archangel). $4, *Bologna Altarpiece* (saint holding ledger). No. 1271, *Madonna of Foligno.* No. 1272, *The Marriage of the Virgin.* No. 1273, *Bologna Altarpiece* (Madonna and Child).
Bologna Altarpiece by Giotto. Other paintings by Raphael.

1989, Dec. 11   Litho.   Perf. 14
1264 A208 10c multicolored   .15   .15
1265 A208 25c multicolored   .18   .18
1266 A208 30c multicolored   .22   .22
1267 A208 50c multicolored   .38   .38
1268 A208 60c multicolored   .45   .45
1269 A208 70c multicolored   .52   .52
1270 A208 $4 multicolored   3.00 3.00
1271 A208 $5 multicolored   3.75 3.75
    Nos. 1264-1271 (8)   8.65 8.65

Souvenir Sheets
1272 A208 $5 multicolored   3.75 3.75
1273 A208 $5 multicolored   3.75 3.75

America Issue — A210

UPAE, discovery of America 500th anniv. emblems and marine life: 10c, Star-eyed hermit crab. 20c, Spiny lobster. 25c, Magnificent banded fanworm. 45c, Cannonball jellyfish. 60c, Red-spiny sea star. $2, Peppermint shrimp. $3, Coral crab. $4, Branching fire coral. No. 1283, Common sea fan. No. 1284, Portuguese man-of-war.

1990, Mar. 26   Litho.   Perf. 14
1275 A210 10c multicolored   .15   .15
1276 A210 20c multicolored   .15   .15
1277 A210 25c multicolored   .18   .18
1278 A210 45c multicolored   .35   .35
1279 A210 60c multicolored   .45   .45
1280 A210 $2 multicolored   1.50 1.50
1281 A210 $3 multicolored   2.25 2.25
1282 A210 $4 multicolored   3.00 3.00
    Nos. 1275-1282 (8)   8.03 8.03

Souvenir Sheets
1283 A210 $5 multicolored   3.75 3.75
1284 A210 $5 multicolored   3.75 3.75

1990, Apr. 17   Perf. 14
1285 A211 15c *Vanilla mexicana*   .15   .15
1286 A211 45c *Epidendrum*
            ibaguense   .35   .35
1287 A211 50c *Epidendrum*
            secundum   .38   .38
1288 A211 60c *Maxillaria conferta*   .45   .45
1289 A211 $1 *Oncidium altissimum*   .75   .75

1290 A211 $2 *Spiranthes lanceolata*   1.50 1.50
1291 A211 $3 *Tonopsis utricu-*
            larioides   2.25 2.25
1292 A211 $5 *Epidendrum noc-*
            turnum   3.75 3.75
    Nos. 1285-1292 (8)   9.58 9.58

Souvenir Sheets
1293 A211 $6 *Octomeria*
            graminifolia   4.50 4.50
1294 A211 $6 *Rodriguezia lanceo-*
            lata   4.50 4.50
EXPO '90, Osaka.

Fish A212

1990, May 21   Perf. 14
1295 A212 10c Flamefish   .15   .15
1296 A212 15c Coney   .15   .15
1297 A212 50c Squirrelfish   .38   .38
1298 A212 60c Sergeant major   .45   .45
1299 A212 $1 Yellowtail snapper   .75   .75
1300 A212 $2 Rock beauty   1.50 1.50
1301 A212 $3 Spanish hogfish   2.25 2.25
1302 A212 $4 Striped parrotfish   3.00 3.00
    Nos. 1295-1302 (8)   8.63 8.63

Souvenir sheets
1303 A212 $5 Blackbar soldierfish   3.75 3.75
1304 A212 $5 Foureye butter-
            lyfish   3.75 3.75

Victoria and Elizabeth II — A213

1990, May 3   Litho.   Perf. 15x14
1305 A213 45c green   .35   .35
1306 A213 60c bright rose   .45   .45
1307 A213 $5 bright ultra   3.75 3.75
    Nos. 1305-1307 (3)   4.55 4.55

Souvenir Sheet
1308 A213 $6 black   4.50 4.50
Penny Black, 150th anniv.

Royal Mail Transport A214

Designs: 50c, Steam packet *Britannia*, 1840. 75c, Railway mail car, 1892. $4, *Centaurus* seaplane, 1938. $6, Subway, 1927.

1990, May 3   Perf. 13½
1309 A214 50c red & deep green   .38   .38
1310 A214 75c red & vio brn   .58   .58
1311 A214 $4 red & brt ultra   3.00 3.00
    Nos. 1309-1311 (3)   3.96 3.96

Souvenir Sheet
1312 A214 $6 red & black   4.50 4.50
Stamp World London '90.

Miniature Sheet

Space Achievements — A215

Designs: a, *Voyager 2* passing Saturn. b, *Pioneer 11* photographing Saturn. c, Manned maneuvering unit. d, *Columbia* space shuttle. e, Splashdown of Apollo 10 command module. f, Skylab. g, Ed White

---

space walking, Gemini 4 mission. h, Apollo module, Apollo-Soyuz mission. i, Soyuz module, Apollo-Soyuz mission. j, *Mariner 1* passing Venus. k, Gemini 4 module. l, *Sputnik.* m, Hubble Space Telescope. n, X-15 rocket plane. o, Bell X-1 breaking sound barrier. p, Astronaut, Apollo 17 mission. q, American lunar rover. r, Lunar module, Apollo 14 mission. s, First men on the Moon, Apollo 11 mission. t, Lunokhod, Soviet lunar rover.

1990, June 11   Litho.   Perf. 14
1313 A215 Sheet of 20   6.75 6.75
a.-t. 45c any single   .32   .32

Mickey Production Studios — A216

Walt Disney characters in Hollywood: 45c, Minnie Mouse reading script. 50c, Director Mickey Mouse, take 1 of Minnie. 60c, Make-up artist Daisy Duck. $1, Clarabelle as Cleopatra. $2, Mickey, Goofy, Donald Duck. $3, Goofy destroying set. $4, Mickey, Donald editing film. No. 1322, Mickey directs surfing film. No. 1323, Minnie, Daisy, Clarabelle in musical.

1990, Sept. 3   Litho.   Perf. 14x13½
1314 A216 25c shown   .18   .18
1315 A216 45c multicolored   .34   .34
1316 A216 50c multicolored   .38   .38
1317 A216 60c multicolored   .45   .45
1318 A216 $1 multicolored   .75   .75
1319 A216 $2 multicolored   1.50 1.50
1320 A216 $3 multicolored   2.25 2.25
1321 A216 $4 multicolored   3.00 3.00
    Nos. 1314-1321 (8)   8.85 8.85

Souvenir Sheets
1322 A216 $5 multicolored   3.75 3.75
1323 A216 $5 multicolored   3.75 3.75

A217   A218

1990, Aug. 27   Litho.   Perf. 14
1324 A217 15c multicolored   .15   .15
1325 A217 35c multi, diff.   .28   .28
1326 A217 75c multi, diff.   .58   .58
1327 A217 $3 multi, diff.   2.25 2.25
    Nos. 1324-1327 (4)   3.26 3.26

Souvenir Sheet
1328 A217 $6 multi, diff.   4.50 4.50
Queen Mother, 90th birthday.

1990, Oct. 1   Litho.   Perf. 14
1329 A218 50c 20-Kilometer Walk   .38   .38
1330 A218 75c Triple jump   .55   .55
1331 A218 $1 10,000 meter run   .75   .75
1332 A218 $5 Javelin   3.75 3.75
    Nos. 1329-1332 (4)   5.43 5.43

Souvenir Sheet
1333 A218 $6 Opening ceremony,
            Los Angeles, 1984   4.50 4.50
1992 Summer Olympics, Barcelona.

Intl. Literacy Year A219

Walt Disney characters in scenes from books by Charles Dickens: 15c, Huey and Dewey, Christmas Stories. 45c, Donald Duck, Bleak House. 50c, Dewey, Bad Pete, Oliver Twist. 60c, Daisy Duck, Old Curiosity Shop. $1, Little Nell. $2, Scrooge McDuck, Pickwick Papers. $3, Mickey and Minnie Mouse, Dombey and Son. $5, Minnie, Our Mutual Friend. No. 1342, Mickey and friends, David Copperfield. No. 1343, Pinocchio, Oliver Twist.

1990, Oct. 15   Litho.   Perf. 14
1334 A219 15c multicolored   .15   .15
1335 A219 45c multicolored   .35   .35
1336 A219 50c multicolored   .38   .38
1337 A219 60c multicolored   .45   .45
1338 A219 $1 multicolored   .75   .75
1339 A219 $2 multicolored   1.50 1.50
1340 A219 $3 multicolored   2.25 2.25
1341 A219 $5 multicolored   3.75 3.75
    Nos. 1334-1341 (8)   9.58 9.58

Souvenir Sheets
1342 A219 $6 multicolored   4.50 4.50
1343 A219 $6 multicolored   4.50 4.50

Nos. 1217-1222   **Winners**
Overprinted   **West Germany 1**
                      Argentina 0

1990, Nov. 11
1344 A201 15c multicolored   .15   .15
1345 A201 25c multicolored   .18   .18
1346 A201 $1 multicolored   .75   .75
1347 A201 $4 multicolored   3.00 3.00
    Nos. 1344-1347 (4)   4.08 4.08

Souvenir Sheets
1348 A201 $5 on #1221   3.75 3.75
1349 A201 $5 on #1222   3.75 3.75
Overprint on Nos. 1348-1349 is 32x13mm.

Birds — A220

1990, Nov. 19
1350 A220 10c Pearly-eyed thrasher   .15   .15
1351 A220 25c Purple-throated carib   .18   .18
1352 A220 50c Common yellow-
            throat   .38   .38
1353 A220 60c American kestrel   .45   .45
1354 A220 $1 Yellow-bellied sap-
            sucker   .75   .75
1355 A220 $2 Purple gallinule   1.50 1.50
1356 A220 $3 Yellow-crowned night
            heron   2.25 2.25
1357 A220 $4 Blue-hooded
            euphonia   3.00 3.00
    Nos. 1350-1357 (8)   8.66 8.66

Souvenir Sheets
1358 A220 $6 Brown pelican   4.50 4.50
1359 A220 $6 Frigate bird   4.50 4.50

Christmas — A221

Paintings: 25c, Madonna and Child with Saints by del Piombo. 30c, Virgin and Child with Angels by Grunewald, vert. 40c, Holy Family and a Shepherd by Titian. 60c, Virgin and Child by Fra Filippo Lippi, vert. $1, Jesus, St. John and Two Angels by Rubens. $2, Adoration of the Shepherds by Catena. $4, Adoration of the Magi by Giorgione. $5, Virgin and Child Adored by a Warrior by Catena. No. 1368, Allegory of the Blessings of Jacob by Rubens, vert. No. 1369, Adoration of the Magi by Fra Angelico, vert.

Perf. 14x13½, 13½x14
1990, Dec. 10   Litho.
1360 A221 25c multicolored   .18   .18
1361 A221 30c multicolored   .22   .22
1362 A221 40c multicolored   .30   .30
1363 A221 60c multicolored   .45   .45
1364 A221 $1 multicolored   .75   .75
1365 A221 $2 multicolored   1.50 1.50
1366 A221 $4 multicolored   3.00 3.00
1367 A221 $5 multicolored   3.75 3.75
    Nos. 1360-1367 (8)   10.15 10.15

Miniature Sheet

Attack on Pearl Harbor, 50th Anniv. A233

Designs: No. 1488a, Bow of Nimitz class carrier, b. Ticonderoga class cruiser. b, Tourist boat to Arizona Memorial. c, USS Arizona Memorial. d, Aircraft salute to missing men. e, White tern. f, Japanese Kate torpedo bombers. g, Japanese Zero fighters. h, Battleship row in flames. i, USS Nevada breaking out. j, Zeros returning to carriers.

1991, Dec. 9   Perf. 14½x15
1488 A233 $1 Sheet of 10, #a.-j.   7.50 7.50

Inscription for No. 1488f incorrectly describes torpedo bombers as Zekes.

3rd Antigua Methodist Cub Scout Pack, 60th Anniv. A234

Designs: $2, Lord Robert Baden-Powell, scouts, vert. $3.50, Scouts around campfire. $5, Antigua & Barbuda flag, Jamboree emblem, vert.

1991, Dec. 9   Perf. 14
1489 A234 75c multicolored   .58 .58
1490 A234 $2 multicolored   1.50 1.50
1491 A234 $3.50 multicolored   2.65 2.65
   Nos. 1489-1491 (3)   4.73 4.73

Souvenir Sheet
1492 A234 $5 multicolored   3.75 3.75

17th World Scout Jamboree, Korea.

Wolfgang Amadeus Mozart, Death Bicent. A235

Portrait of Mozart and: $1.50, Scene from opera, Don Giovanni. $4, St. Peter's Cathedral, Salzburg.

1991, Dec. 9
1493 A235 $1.50 multicolored   1.15 1.15
1494 A235 $4 multicolored   3.00 3.00

Anniversaries and Events — A236

Designs: $2, Otto Lilienthal's glider No. 5. $2.50, Locomotive cab, vert.

1991, Dec. 9   Litho.   Perf. 14
1495 A236 $2 multicolored   1.50 1.50
1496 A236 $2.50 multicolored   1.90 1.90

First glider flight, cent. (No. 1495). Trans-Siberian Railway, cent. (No. 1496). Numbers have been reserved for additional values in this set.

Brandenburg Gate, Bicent. — A237

Designs: 25c, Demonstrators in autos, German flag. $2, Statue. $3, Portions of decorative frieze.

1991, Dec. 9   Litho.   Perf. 14
1499 A237 25c multicolored   .18 .18
1500 A237 $2 multicolored   1.50 1.50
1501 A237 $3 multicolored   2.25 2.25
   Nos. 1499-1501 (3)   3.93 3.93

Souvenir Sheet
1502 A237 $4 multicolored   3.00 3.00

Christmas A238

Paintings by Fra Angelico: 10c, The Annunciation. 30c, Nativity. 40c, Adoration of the Magi. 60c, Presentation in the Temple. $1, Circumcision. $3, Flight into Egypt. $4, Massacre of the Innocents. $5, Christ Teaching in the Temple. No. 1511, Adoration of the Magi, diff. No. 1512, Adoration of the Magi (Cook Tondo).

1991, Dec. 12   Perf. 12
1503 A238 10c multicolored   .15 .15
1504 A238 30c multicolored   .22 .22
1505 A238 40c multicolored   .30 .30
1506 A238 60c multicolored   .45 .45
1507 A238 $1 multicolored   .75 .75
1508 A238 $3 multicolored   2.25 2.25
1509 A238 $4 multicolored   3.00 3.00
1510 A238 $5 multicolored   3.75 3.75
   Nos. 1503-1510 (8)   10.87 10.87

Souvenir Sheets
1511 A238 $6 multicolored   4.50 4.50
1512 A238 $6 multicolored   4.50 4.50

Queen Elizabeth II's Accession to the Throne, 40th Anniv.
Common Design Type
Queen Elizabeth II and various island scenes.

1992, Feb. 6   Litho.   Perf. 14
1513 CD348 10c multicolored   .15 .15
1514 CD348 30c multicolored   .22 .22
1515 CD348 $1 multicolored   .75 .75
1516 CD348 $5 multicolored   3.75 3.75
   Nos. 1513-1516 (4)   4.87 4.87

Souvenir Sheets
1517 CD348 $6 Beach   4.50 4.50
1518 CD348 $6 Flora   4.50 4.50

Mushrooms — A239

1992   Litho.   Perf. 14
1519 A239 10c Amanita caesarea   .15 .15
1520 A239 15c Collybia fusipes   .15 .15
1521 A239 30c Boletus aereus   .22 .22
1522 A239 40c Laccaria amethystina   .30 .30
1523 A239 $1 Russula virescens   .75 .75
1524 A239 $2 Tricholoma auratum   1.50 1.50
1525 A239 $4 Calocybe gambosa   3.00 3.00
1526 A239 $5 Panus tigrinus   3.75 3.75
   Nos. 1519-1526 (8)   9.82 9.82

Souvenir Sheet
1527 A239 $6 Auricularia auricula   4.50 4.50
1528 A239 $6 Clavariadelphus truncatus   4.50 4.50

Issued: 10c, 30c, $1, $5, #1528, May 18; others, Mar.

Disney Characters at Summer Olympics, Barcelona A240

Designs: 10c, Mickey presenting gold medal to mermaid for swimming. 15c, Dewey and Huey watching Louie in kayak. 30c, Uncle McScrooge, Donald yachting. 50c, Donald, horse trying water polo. $1, Big Pete weight lifting. $2, Donald, Goofy fencing. $4, Mickey, Donald playing volleyball. $5, Goofy vaulting over horse. No. 1537, Mickey playing basketball, horiz. No. 1538, Minnie Mouse on uneven parallel bars, horiz. No. 1539, Mickey, Goofy, and Donald judging Minnie's floor exercise, horiz. No. 1540, Mickey running after soccer ball.

1992, Mar. 16   Perf. 13
1529 A240 10c multicolored   .15 .15
1530 A240 15c multicolored   .15 .15
1531 A240 30c multicolored   .22 .22
1532 A240 50c multicolored   .38 .38
1533 A240 $1 multicolored   .75 .75
1534 A240 $2 multicolored   1.50 1.50
1535 A240 $4 multicolored   3.00 3.00
1536 A240 $5 multicolored   3.75 3.75
   Nos. 1529-1536 (8)   9.90 9.90

Souvenir Sheets
1537-1540 A240 $6 each   4.50 4.50

Dinosaurs A241

1992, Apr. 6   Perf. 14
1541 A241 10c Pteranodon   .15 .15
1542 A241 15c Brachiosaurus   .15 .15
1543 A241 30c Tyrannosaurus rex   .22 .22
1544 A241 50c Parasaurolophus   .38 .38
1545 A241 $1 Deinonychus   .75 .75
1546 A241 $2 Triceratops   1.50 1.50
1547 A241 $4 Protoceratops   3.00 3.00
1548 A241 $5 Stegosaurus   3.75 3.75
   Nos. 1541-1548 (8)   9.90 9.90

Souvenir Sheets
1549 A241 $6 Apatosaurus   4.50 4.50
1550 A241 $6 Allosaurus   4.50 4.50

Nos. 1541-1544 are vert.

Easter A242

Paintings: 10c, Supper at Emmaus, by Caravaggio. 15c, The Vision of St. Peter, by Francisco de Zurbaran. 30c, $1, Christ Driving the Money Changers from the Temple, by Tiepolo (detail on $1). 40c, Martyrdom of St. Bartholomew (detail), by Jusepe de Ribera. $2, Crucifixion (detail), by Albrecht Altdorfer. $4, $5, The Deposition (diff. detail), by Fra Angelico. No. 1559, Crucifixion, by Albrecht Altdorfer, vert. No. 1560, The Last Supper, by Vicente Juan Masip.

1992   Perf. 14x13½
1551 A242 10c multicolored   .15 .15
1552 A242 15c multicolored   .15 .15
1553 A242 30c multicolored   .22 .22
1554 A242 40c multicolored   .30 .30
1555 A242 $1 multicolored   .75 .75
1556 A242 $2 multicolored   1.50 1.50
1557 A242 $4 multicolored   3.00 3.00
1558 A242 $5 multicolored   3.75 3.75
   Nos. 1551-1558 (8)   9.82 9.82

Souvenir Sheet
Perf. 13½x14
1559 A242 $6 multicolored   4.50 4.50
1560 A242 $6 multicolored   4.50 4.50

Spanish Art — A243

Designs: 10c, The Miracle at the Well, by Alonso Cano. 15c, The Poet Luis de Gongora y Argote, by Velazquez. 30c, The Painter Francisco Goya, by Vincente Lopez Portana. 40c, Maria de Las Nieves Michaela Fourdiniere, by Luis Paret y Alcazar. $1, Charles III Eating before His Court, by Paret y Alcazar, horiz. $2, A Rain Shower in Granada, by Antonio Munoz Degrain, horiz. $4, Sarah Bernhardt, by Santiago Rusinol y Prats. $5, The Hermitage Garden, by Joaquin Mir Trinxet. No. 1569, Olympus: Battle with the Giants, by Francisco Bayeu y Subias. No. 1570, The Ascent of Monsieur Boucle's Montgolfier Balloon in the Gardens of Aranjuez, by Antonio Carnicero.

1992, May 11
1561 A243 10c multicolored   .15 .15
1562 A243 15c multicolored   .15 .15
1563 A243 30c multicolored   .22 .22
1564 A243 40c multicolored   .30 .30
1565 A243 $1 multicolored   .75 .75
1566 A243 $2 multicolored   1.50 1.50
1567 A243 $4 multicolored   3.00 3.00
1568 A243 $5 multicolored   3.75 3.75

Size: 120x95mm
Imperf
1569 A243 $6 multicolored   4.50 4.50
1570 A243 $6 multicolored   4.50 4.50
   Nos. 1561-1570 (10)   18.82 18.82

Granada '92.

Discovery of America, 500th Anniv. — A244

Designs: 15c, San Salvador Island. 30c, Martin Alonzo Pinzon, captain of Pinta. 40c, Columbus, signature, coat of arms. $1, Pinta. $2, Nina. $4, Santa Maria. No. 1577, Sea monster. No. 1578, Map, sailing ship.

1992, May 25   Litho.   Perf. 14
1571 A244 15c multicolored   .15 .15
1572 A244 30c multicolored   .22 .22
1573 A244 40c multicolored   .30 .30
1574 A244 $1 multicolored   .75 .75
1575 A244 $2 multicolored   1.50 1.50
1576 A244 $4 multicolored   3.00 3.00
   Nos. 1571-1576 (6)   5.92 5.92

Souvenir Sheets
1577 A244 $6 multicolored   4.50 4.50
1578 A244 $6 multicolored   4.50 4.50

World Columbian Stamp Expo '92, Chicago.

Hummel Figurines — A245

Wanderers: 15c, No. 1587a, Boy sitting on rock pointing to flower in cap. 30c, No. 1587b, Girl sitting on fence. 40c, No. 1587c, Boy holding binoculars. 50c, No. 1587d, Boy carrying umbrella. $1, No. 1588a, Two boys looking up at direction marker. $2, No. 1588b, Boy carrying basket on back, walking with stick. $4, No. 1588c, Two girls, goat. $5, No. 1588d, Boy carrying walking stick.

1993, Jan. 6   Litho.   Perf. 14
1579 A245 15c multicolored   .15 .15
1580 A245 30c multicolored   .22 .22
1581 A245 40c multicolored   .30 .30
1582 A245 50c multicolored   .38 .38

1583	A245	$1 multicolored	.75	.75
1584	A245	$2 multicolored	1.50	1.50
1585	A245	$4 multicolored	3.00	3.00
1586	A245	$5 multicolored	3.75	3.75
		Nos. 1579-1586 (8)	10.05	10.05

Souvenir Sheet

1587	A245	$1.50 Sheet of 4, #a.-d.	4.50	4.50
1588	A245	$1.50 Sheet of 4, #a.-d.	4.50	4.50

Hummingbirds and Flowers — A246

Designs: 10c, Antillean crested, wild plantain. 25c, Green mango, parrot's plantain. 45c, Purple-throated carib, lobster claws. 60c, Antillean mango, coral plant. $1, Vervain, cardinal's guard. $2, Rufous breasted hermit, heliconia. $4, Blue-headed, red ginger. $5, Green-throated carib, ornamental banana. No. 1597, Bee, jungle flame. No. 1598, Western streamertails, bignonia.

1992, Aug. 10   Litho.   Perf. 14

1589	A246	10c multicolored	.15	.15
1590	A246	25c multicolored	.18	.18
1591	A246	45c multicolored	.35	.35
1592	A246	60c multicolored	.45	.45
1593	A246	$1 multicolored	.75	.75
1594	A246	$2 multicolored	1.50	1.50
1595	A246	$4 multicolored	3.00	3.00
1596	A246	$5 multicolored	3.75	3.75
		Nos. 1589-1596 (8)	10.13	10.13

Souvenir Sheets

1597	A246	$6 multicolored	6.75	6.75
1598	A246	$6 multicolored	6.75	6.75

Genoa '92.

Discovery of America, 500th Anniv. — A247

1992   Litho.   Perf. 14½

1599	A247	$1 Coming ashore	.75	.75
1600	A247	$2 Natives, ships	1.50	1.50

Organization of East Caribbean States.

Souvenir Sheet

Madison Square Garden, NYC — A248

1992   Litho.   Perf. 14

1601	A248	$6 multicolored	5.00	5.00

Postage Stamp Mega-Event, Jacob Javits Center, New York City.

Elvis Presley (1935-1977) A249

Various pictures of Elvis Presley.

1992   Perf. 13½x14

1602	A249	$1 Sheet of 9, #a.-i.	7.00	7.00

Inventors and Pioneers A250

Designs: 10c, Ts'ai Lun, paper. 25c, Igor I. Sikorsky, 4-engine airplane. 30c, Alexander Graham Bell, telephone. 40c, Johannes Gutenberg, printing press. 60c, James Watt, steam engine. $1, Anton van Leeuwenhoek, microscope. $4, Louis Braille, Braille printing. $5, Galileo, telescope. No. 1607, Phonograph. No. 1608, Steamboat.

1992, Oct. 19   Litho.   Perf. 14

1603	A250	10c multicolored	.15	.15
1604	A250	25c multicolored	.18	.18
1605	A250	30c multicolored	.22	.22
1605A	A250	40c multicolored	.40	.40
1605B	A250	60c multicolored	.45	.45
1605C	A250	$1 multicolored	.75	.75
1605D	A250	$4 multicolored	3.00	3.00
1606	A250	$5 multicolored	3.75	3.75
		Nos. 1603-1606 (8)	8.90	8.90

Souvenir Sheet

1607	A250	$6 multicolored	4.50	4.50
1608	A250	$6 multicolored	4.50	4.50

Christmas A251

Details from Paintings: 10c, Virgin and Child with Angels, by School of Piero Della Francesca. 25c, Madonna Degli Alberelli, by Giovanni Bellini. 30c, Madonna and Child with St. Anthony Abbot and St. Sigismund, by Neroccio di Landi. 40c, Madonna and the Grand Duke, by Raphael. 60c, The Nativity, by George de la Tour. $1, Holy Family, by Jacob Jordaens. $4, Madonna and Child Enthroned, by Margaritone. $5, Madonna and Child on a Curved Throne, by Byzantine artist. No. 1617, Madonna and Child, by Domenico Ghirlandaio (both names misspelled). No. 1618, The Holy Family, by Pontormo.

1992   Perf. 13½x14

1609	A251	10c multicolored	.15	.15
1610	A251	25c multicolored	.18	.18
1611	A251	30c multicolored	.22	.22
1612	A251	40c multicolored	.30	.30
1613	A251	60c multicolored	.45	.45
1614	A251	$1 multicolored	.75	.75
1615	A251	$4 multicolored	3.00	3.00
1616	A251	$5 multicolored	3.75	3.75
		Nos. 1609-1616 (8)	8.80	8.80

Souvenir Sheet

1617	A251	$6 multicolored	4.50	4.50
1618	A251	$6 multicolored	4.50	4.50

A252

A253

Anniversaries and Events: 10c, Cosmonauts. 40c, Graf Zeppelin, Goodyear blimp. 45c, Right Rev. Daniel C. Davis, St. John's Cathedral. 75c, Konrad Adenauer. $1, Bus Mosbacher, Weatherly. $1.50, Rain forest. No. 1625, Felis tigris. No. 1626, Flag, emblems, plant. No. 1627, Women acting on stage. $2.25, Women carrying baskets of food on their heads. $3, Lions Club emblem, club member.

No. 1630, West German, NATO flags. No. 1631, China's Long March Booster Rocket. No. 1632, Dr. Hugo Eckener. No. 1633, The Hindenburg. No. 1634, Brandenburg Gate, German flag. No. 1635, Monarch butterfly. No. 1636, Columbus Space Station.

1992   Litho.   Perf. 14

1619	A252	10c multicolored	.15	.15
1620	A252	40c multicolored	.30	.30
1621	A253	45c multicolored	.35	.35
1622	A252	75c multicolored	.58	.58
1623	A252	$1 multicolored	.75	.75
1624	A252	$1.50 multicolored	1.15	1.15
1625	A252	$2 multicolored	1.50	1.50
1626	A253	$2 multicolored	1.50	1.50
1627	A253	$2 multicolored	1.50	1.50
1628	A252	$2.25 multicolored	1.70	1.70
1629	A252	$3 multicolored	2.25	2.25
1630	A252	$4 multicolored	3.00	3.00
1631	A252	$4 multicolored	3.00	3.00
1632	A252	$6 multicolored	4.50	4.50
		Nos. 1619-1632 (14)	22.23	22.23

Souvenir Sheets

1633-1636	A252	$6 each	4.50	4.50

Intl. Space Year (#1619, 1631, 1636). Count Zeppelin, 75th anniv. of death (#1620, 1632-1633). Diocese of Northeast Caribbean and Aruba District, 150th anniv. (#1621). Konrad Adenauer, 25th anniv. of death (#1622, 1630, 1634). 1962 winner of America's Cup (#1623). Earth Summit, Rio (#1624-1625, 1635). Inter-American Institute for Cooperation on Agriculture, 50th anniv. (#1626). Cultural Development, 40th anniv. (#1627). WHO Intl. Conf. on Nutrition, Rome (#1628). Lions Club, 75th anniv. (#1629).

Issued: #1619, 1621-1623, 1626-1631, 1634, 1636, Nov.; #1624-1625, 1635, Dec. 14.

Euro Disney, Paris — A254

Disney characters: 10c, Golf course. 25c, Davy Crockett Campground. 30c, Cheyenne Hotel. 40c, Santa Fe Hotel. $1, New York Hotel. $2, In car, map showing location. $4, Pirates of the Caribbean. $5, Adventureland. No. 1645, Mickey Mouse on map with star, vert. No. 1646, Roof turret at entrance, Mickey Mouse in uniform. No. 1646A, Mickey Mouse, colored spots on poster, vert. No. 1646B, Mickey on poster, vert., diff.

1992-93   Litho.   Perf. 14x13½

1637	A254	10c multicolored	.15	.15
1638	A254	25c multicolored	.18	.15
1639	A254	30c multicolored	.22	.22
1640	A254	40c multicolored	.30	.30
1641	A254	$1 multicolored	.75	.75
1642	A254	$2 multicolored	1.50	1.50
1643	A254	$4 multicolored	3.00	3.00
1644	A254	$5 multicolored	3.75	3.75
		Nos. 1637-1644 (8)	9.85	9.82

Souvenir Sheets
Perf. 13½x14

1645-1646B	A254	$6 each	4.50	4.50

Issue dates: Nos. 1638-1639, 1642-1643, 1646-1646B, Feb. 22, 1993. Others, Dec. 1992.

Miniature Sheets

Louvre Museum, Bicent. A255

Details or entire paintings, by Peter Paul Rubens: No. 1647a, Destiny of Marie de' Medici. b, Birth of Marie de'Medici. c, Marie's Education. d, Destiny of Marie de'Medici, diff. e, Henry IV Receives the Portrait. f, The Meeting at Lyons. g, The Marriage. h, The Birth of Louis XIII.

No. 1648a, The Capture of Juliers. b, The Exchange of Princesses. c, The Happiness of the Regency. d, The Majority of Louis XIII. e, The Flight from Blois. f, The Treaty of Angouleme. g, The Peace of Angers. h, The Queen's Reconciliation with Her Son.

$6, Helene Fourment Au Carosse.

1993, Mar. 22   Litho.   Perf. 12

1647	A255	$1 Sheet of 8, #a.-h. + label	6.00	6.00
1648	A255	$1 Sheet of 8, #a.-h. + label	6.00	6.00

Souvenir Sheet
Perf. 14½

1649	A255	$6 multicolored	4.50	4.50

No. 1649 contains one 55x88mm stamp.

Flowers — A256

1993, Mar. 15   Litho.   Perf. 14

1650	A256	15c Cardinal's guard	.15	.15
1651	A256	25c Giant granadilla	.18	.18
1652	A256	30c Spider flower	.22	.22
1653	A256	40c Gold vine	.30	.30
1654	A256	$1 Frangipani	.75	.75
1655	A256	$2 Bougainvillea	1.50	1.50
1656	A256	$4 Yellow oleander	3.00	3.00
1657	A256	$5 Spicy jatropha	3.75	3.75
		Nos. 1650-1657 (8)	9.85	9.85

Souvenir Sheets

1658	A256	$6 Bird lime tree	4.50	4.50
1659	A256	$6 Fairy lily	4.50	4.50

Endangered Species — A257

Designs: No. 1660a, St. Lucia parrot. b, Cahow. c, Swallow-tailed kite. d, Everglades kite. e, Imperial parrot. f, Humpback whale. g, Puerto Rican plain pigeon. h, St. Vincent parrot. i, Puerto Rican parrot. j, Leatherback turtle. k, American crocodile. l, Hawksbill turtle.
No. 1662, West Indian manatee.

1993, Apr. 5

1660	A257	$1 Sheet of 12, #a.-l.	9.00	9.00

Souvenir Sheets

1661	A257	$6 like #1660f	4.50	4.50
1662	A257	$6 multicolored	4.50	4.50

Philatelic Publishing Personalities — A258

Portrait, stamp: No. 1663, J. Walter Scott (1842-1919), US "#C3a," Antigua #1. No. 1664, Theodore Champion, France #8, Antigua #1. No. 1665, E. Stanley Gibbons (1856-1913), cover of his first price list and catalogue, Antigua #1. No. 1666, Hugo Michel (1866-1944), Bavaria #1, Antigua #1. No. 1667, Alberto (1877-1944) and Giulio (1902-1987) Bolaffi, Sardinia #1, Great Britain #3. No. 1668, Richard Borek (1874-1947), Brunswick #24, Bavaria #1.
Front pages, Mekeel's Weekly Stamp News: No. 1669a, Jan. 7, 1890. b, Feb. 12, 1993.

1993, June 14

1663	A258	$1.50 multicolored	1.10	1.10
1664	A258	$1.50 multicolored	1.10	1.10
1665	A258	$1.50 multicolored	1.10	1.10
1666	A258	$1.50 multicolored	1.10	1.10
1667	A258	$1.50 multicolored	1.10	1.10
1668	A258	$1.50 multicolored	1.10	1.10
		Nos. 1663-1668 (6)	6.60	6.60

Souvenir Sheet

1669	A258	$3 Sheet of 2, #a.-b.	4.50	4.50

Mekeel's Weekly Stamp News, cent. (in 1891; #1669).

Miniature Sheets

ANTIGUA & BARBUDA 30c

Coronation Anniversary
1953-1993

Coronation of Queen Elizabeth II, 40th Anniv. — A259

Coronation: 1670a, 30c, Official photograph. b, 40c, Crown of Queen Elizabeth, the Queen Mother. c, $2, Dignataries attending ceremony. d, $4, Queen, Prince Edward.
$6, Portrait, by Denis Fildes.
First decade, 1953-1963: No. 1671a, Wedding photograph of Princess Margaret and Antony Armstrong-Jones. b, Queen opening Parliament, Prince Philip. c, Queen holding infant. d, Royal family. e, Queen Elizabeth II, formal portrait. f, Queen, Charles de Gaulle. g, Queen, Pope John XXIII. h, Queen inspecting troops.
Second decade, 1963-1973: No. 1672a, Investiture of Charles as Prince of Wales. b, Queen opening Parliament, Prince Philip, diff. c, Queen holding infant, diff. d, Queen, Prince Philip, children. e, Wearing blue robe, diadem. f, Prince Philip, Queen seated. g, Prince Charles, Queen at microphone. h, Queen conversing, model airplane.
Third decade, 1973-1983: No. 1673a, Wedding photograph of Prince Charles and Princess Diana. b, Queen opening Parliament, Prince Philip, diff. c, Princess Diana with infant. d, Princess Anne with infant. e, Portrait of Queen. f, Queen waving, Prince Philip. g, Queen, Pope John Paul II. h, Wedding portrait of Mark Phillips and Princess Anne.
Fourth decade, 1983-1993: No. 1674a, Wedding photograph of Sarah Ferguson and Prince Andrew. b, Queen opening Parliament, Prince Philip, diff. c, Princess Diana holding infant, diff. d, Sarah Ferguson, infant. e, Queen wearing blue dress. f, Queen waving from carriage, Prince Philip. g, Queen wearing military uniform. h, Queen Mother.

1993, June 2   Litho.   Perf. 13¹/₂x14
1670 A259   Sheet, 2 each #a.-d.   10.00 10.00
Sheets of 8
1671 A259 $1 #a.-h. + label   6.00 6.00
1672 A259 $1 #a.-h. + label   6.00 6.00
1673 A259 $1 #a.-h. + label   6.00 6.00
1674 A259 $1 #a.-h. + label   6.00 6.00
Souvenir Sheet
Perf. 14
1675 A259 $6 multicolored   4.50 4.50
No. 1675 contains one 28x42mm stamp.

Antigua & Barbuda
40c

Wedding of Japan's Crown Prince Naruhito and Masako Owada
A260

Cameo photos of couple and: 40c, Crown Prince. $3, Princess.
$6, Princess wearing white coat, vert.

1993, Aug. 16   Litho.   Perf. 14
1676 A260 40c multicolored   .30 .30
1677 A260 $3 multicolored   2.25 2.25
Souvenir Sheet
1678 A260 $6 multicolored   4.50 4.50

1881 Picasso 1973

ANTIGUA & BARBUDA 30¢

Picasso (1881-1973) — A261

Paintings: 30c, Cat and Bird, 1939. 40c, Fish on a Newspaper, 1957. $5, Dying Bull, 1934. $6, Woman with a Dog, 1953.

1993, Aug. 16   Litho.   Perf. 14
1679 A261 30c multicolored   .25 .25
1680 A261 40c multicolored   .32 .32
1681 A261 $5 multicolored   4.00 4.00
    Nos. 1679-1681 (3)   4.57 4.57
Souvenir Sheet
1682 A261 $6 multicolored   4.50 4.50

40c

Copernicus (1473-1543) — A262

Designs: 40c, Astronomical devices. $4, Photograph of supernova. $5, Copernicus.

1993, Aug. 16
1683 A262 40c multicolored   .32 .32
1684 A262 $4 multicolored   3.25 3.25
Souvenir Sheet
1685 A262 $5 multicolored   3.75 3.75

ANTIGUA & BARBUDA

30c   Willy Brandt

Willy Brandt (1913-1992), German Chancellor — A263

Designs: 30c, Helmut Schmidt, George Leber, Brandt. $4, Brandt, newspaper headlines. $6, Brandt at Warsaw Ghetto Memorial, 1970.

1993, Aug. 16
1686 A263 30c multicolored   .25 .25
1687 A263 $4 multicolored   3.25 3.25
Souvenir Sheet
1688 A263 $6 multicolored   4.50 4.50

Antigua & Barbuda

Polska '93 — A264 $1

Paintings: $1, Study of a Woman Combing Her Hair, by Wladyslaw Slewinski, 1897. $3, Artist's Wife with Cat, by Konrad Kryzanowski, 1912. $6, General Confusion, by S. I. Witkiewicz, 1930, vert.

1993, Aug. 16
1689 A264 $1 multicolored   .80 .80
1690 A264 $3 multicolored   2.50 2.50
Souvenir Sheet
1691 A264 $6 multicolored   4.50 4.50

Antigua & Barbuda

$5

Inauguration of Pres. William J. Clinton — A265

Designs: $5, Pres. Clinton driving car. $6, Pres. Clinton, inauguration ceremony, vert.

1993, Aug. 16
1692 A265 $5 multicolored   4.00 4.00
Souvenir Sheet
1693 A265 $6 multicolored   4.50 4.50
No. 1693 contains one 43x57mm stamp.

ANTIGUA & BARBUDA 15c

1994 Winter Olympics, Lillehammer, Norway — A266

Designs: 15c, Irina Rodnina, Alexei Ulanov, gold medalists, pairs figure skating, 1972. $5, Alberto Tomba, gold medal, giant slalom, 1988, 1992. $6, Yvonne van Gennip, Andrea Ehrig, gold, bronze medalists, speedskating, 1988.

1993, Aug. 16
1694 A266 15c multicolored   .15 .15
1695 A266 $5 multicolored   4.00 4.00
Souvenir Sheet
1696 A266 $6 multicolored   4.50 4.50

$2   ANTIGUA & BARBUDA

WORLD CUP '94

1994 World Cup Soccer Championships, US — A267

English soccer players: No. 1697, Gordon Banks. No. 1698, 1709, Bobby Moore. No. 1699, Peter Shilton. No. 1700, Nobby Stiles. No. 1701, Bryan Robson. No. 1702, Geoff Hurst. No. 1703, Gary Lineker. No. 1704, Bobby Charlton. No. 1705, Martin Peters. No. 1706, John Barnes. No. 1707, David Platt. No. 1708, Paul Gascoigne. No. 1710, Player holding 1990 Fair Play Winners Trophy.

1993, July 30   Litho.   Perf. 14
1697-1708 A267 $2 Set of 12   18.00 18.00
Souvenir Sheets
1709 A267 $6 multicolored   4.50 4.50
1710 A267 $6 multicolored   4.50 4.50
Nos. 1697-1708 issued in sheets of five plus label identifying player.

1969 - DR. HUGO ECKENER, AIRSHIP PIONEER - 1993

Aviation Anniversaries — A268

Designs: 30c, Dr. Hugo Eckener, Dr. Wm. Beckers, zeppelin over Lake George, NY. No. 1712, Chicago Century of Progress Exhibition seen from zeppelin. No. 1713, George Washington, Blanchard's balloon, vert. No. 1714, Gloster E.28/39, first British jet plane. $4, Pres. Wilson watching take-off of first scheduled air mail plane. No. 1716, Hindenburg over Ebbets Field, Brooklyn, NY, 1937. No. 1717, Gloster Meteor in combat. No. 1718, Eckener, vert. No. 1719, Alexander Hamilton, Pres. Washington, John Jay, gondola of Blanchard's balloon. No. 1720, PBY-5.

1993, Oct. 11
1711 A268 30c multicolored   .22 .22
1712 A268 40c multicolored   .30 .30
1713 A268 40c multicolored   .30 .30
1714 A268 40c multicolored   .30 .30
1715 A268 $4 multicolored   3.00 3.00
1716 A268 $5 multicolored   3.75 3.75
1717 A268 $5 multicolored   3.75 3.75
    Nos. 1711-1717 (7)   11.62 11.62
Souvenir Sheets
1718 A268 $6 multicolored   4.50 4.50
1719 A268 $6 multicolored   4.50 4.50
1720 A268 $6 multicolored   4.50 4.50
Dr. Hugo Eckener, 125th anniv. of birth (#1711-1712, 1716, 1718). First US balloon flight, bicent. (#1713, 1715, 1719). Royal Air Force, 75th anniv. (#1714, 1717, 1720).
No. 1720 contains one 57x43mm stamp.

MICKEY MOUSE MOVIE POSTERS
The Musical Farmer, 1932

ANTIGUA BARBUDA 40c

MICKEY MOUSE THE MUSICAL FARMER

Mickey Mouse Movie Posters A269

Nos. 1721-1729: 10c, The Musical Farmer, 1932. 15c, Little Whirlwind, 1941. 30c, Pluto's Dream House, 1940. 40c, Gulliver Mickey, 1934. 50c, Alpine Climbers, 1936. $1, Mr. Mouse Takes a Trip, 1940. $2, The Nifty Nineties, 1941. $4, Mickey Down Under, 1948. $5, The Pointer, 1939.
Souvenir Sheets: No. 1730, $6, The Simple Things, 1953. No. 1731, $6, The Prince and the Pauper, 1990.

1993, Oct. 25   Litho.   Perf. 13¹/₂x14
1721-1731 A269 Set of 11   21.00 21.00

30c   Antigua & Barbuda

St. John's Lodge #492, 150th Anniv. A270

Designs: 10c, W.K. Heath, Grand Inspector 1961-82, vert. 30c, Present Masonic Hall. 40c, 1st Masonic Hall. 60c, J.L.E. Jeffery, Grand Inspector 1953-61, vert.

1993, Aug. 16   Litho.   Perf. 14
1732-1735 A270 Set of 4   1.10 1.10

Antigua & Barbuda

First Ford Engine and Benz's First 4-Wheel Car, Cent. A271

Designs: 30c, Lincoln Continental. 40c, 1914 Mercedes racing car. $4, 1966 Ford GT40. $5, 1954 Mercedes Benz gull wing coupe, street version. No. 1740, Mustang emblem. No. 1741, US #1286A, Germany #471.

1993, Oct. 11   Litho.   Perf. 14
1736-1739 A271 Set of 4   7.00 7.00
Souvenir Sheets
1740-1741 A271 $6 each   4.50 4.50

Antigua & Barbuda

Christmas — A272

Nos. 1742-1750, Disney characters in The Nutcracker: 10c, 15c, 20c, 30c, 40c, 50c, 60c, $3, $6. 1751, Minnie and Mickey. No. 1752, Mickey, vert.

1993, Nov. 8   Perf. 14x13¹/₂, 13¹/₂x14
1742-1750 A272 Set of 9   8.50 8.50
Souvenir Sheets
1751-1752 A272 $6 each   4.50 4.50

Antigua & Barbuda — Fine Art — A273

Paintings by Rembrandt: No. 1753, 15c, Hannah and Samuel. 30c, Isaac & Rebecca (The Jewish Bride). 40c, Jacob Wrestling with the Angel. $5, Moses with the Tablets of the Law.
Paintings by Matisse: No. 1754, 15c, Guitarist. 60c, Interior with a Goldfish Bowl. $1, Portrait of Mlle. Yvonne Landsberg. $4, The Toboggan, Plate XX from Jazz. No. 1761, The Blinding of Samson by the Philistines, by Rembrandt. No. 1762, The Three Sisters, by Matisse.

1993, Nov. 22 — Perf. 13½x14
1753-1760 A273 Set of 8 ... 9.00 9.00
Souvenir Sheets
1761-1762 A273 $6 each ... 4.50 4.50

A274

Hong Kong '94
Antigua & Barbuda 40c A275

Stamps, fishing boats at Shau Kei Wan: No. 1763, Hong Kong #370, bow of boat. No. 1764, Stern of boat, #1300.
Museum of Qin figures, Shaanxi Province, Tomb of Qin First Emperor: No. 1765a, Inside museum. b, Cavalryman, horse. c, Warriors in battle formation. d, Painted bronze horses, chariot. e, Pekingese dog (not antiquity). f, Chin warrior figures, horses.

1994, Feb. 18 Litho. Perf. 14
1763 A274 40c multicolored ... .30 .30
1764 A274 40c multicolored ... .30 .30
 a. Pair, #1763-1764 ... .60 .60
Miniature Sheet
1765 A275 40c Sheet of 6, #a.-f. ... 1.75 1.75

Nos. 1763-1764 issued in sheets of 5 pairs. No. 1764a is a continuous design.
New Year 1994 (Year of the Dog) (#1765e).

Hong Kong '94 — A276

Disney characters: 10c, Mickey's "Pleasure Junk." 15c, Mandarin Minnie. 30c, Donald, Daisy journey by house boat. 50c, Mickey, Birdman of Mongkok. $1, Pluto encounters a good-luck dog. $2, Minnie, Daisy celebrate Bun Festival. $4, Goofy, the noodle maker. $5, Goofy pulls Mickey in a rickshaw.
No. 1774, Mickey celebrating New Year with Dragon Dance, horiz. No. 1775, View of Hong Kong Harbor, horiz.

1994, Feb. 18 Litho. Perf. 13½x14
1766-1773 A276 Set of 8 ... 10.00 10.00
Souvenir Sheets
Perf. 14x13½
1774-1775 A276 $5 each ... 3.75 3.75

Miniature Sheets of 8

Sierra Club, Cent. — A277

No. 1776: a, Bactrian camel, emblem UR. b, Bactrian camel, emblem UL. c, African elephant, emblem UL. d, African elephant, emblem UR. e, Leopard, blue background. f, Leopard, emblem UR. g, Leopard, emblem UL. h, Club emblem.
No. 1777: a, Sumatran rhinoceros, lying on ground. b, Sumatran rhinoceros, looking straight ahead. c, Ring-tailed lemur standing. d, Ring-tailed lemur sitting on branch. e, Red-fronted brown lemur on branch. f, Red-fronted brown lemur, diff. g, Red-fronted brown lemur, diff.
No. 1778, Sumatran rhinoceros, horiz. No. 1779, Ring-tailed lemur, horiz. No. 1780, Bactrian camel, horiz. No. 1781, African elephant, horiz.

1994, Mar. 1 Litho. Perf. 14
1776 A277 $1.50 #a.-h. ... 9.00 9.00
1777 A277 $1.50 #a.-g, #1776h ... 9.00 9.00
Souvenir Sheets
1778-1781 A277 $1.50 each ... 1.10 1.10

Miniature Sheets

New Year 1994 (Year of the Dog) A278

Small breeds of dogs: No. 1782a, West highland white terrier. b, Beagle. c, Scottish terrier. d, Pekingese. e, Dachshund. f, Yorkshire terrier. g, Pomeranian. h, Poodle. i, Shetland sheepdog. j, Pug. k, Shih tzu. l, Chihuahua.
Large breeds of dogs: No. 1783a, Mastiff. b, Border collie. c, Samoyed. d, Airedale terrier. e, English setter. f, Rough collie. g, Newfoundland. h, Weimaraner. i, English springer spaniel. j, Dalmatian. k, Boxer. l, Old English sheepdog.
No. 1784, Welsh corgi. No. 1785, Labrador retriever.

1994, Apr. 5 Perf. 14
1782 A278 50c Sheet of 12, #a.-l. ... 4.50 4.50
1783 A278 75c Sheet of 12, #a.-l. ... 6.75 6.75
Souvenir Sheets
1784-1785 A278 $6 each ... 4.50 4.50

Orchids — A279

Butterflies — A280

Designs: 10c, Spiranthes lanceolata. 20c, Ionopsis utricularioides. 30c, Tetramicra canaliculata. 50c, Oncidium picturatum. $1, Epidendrum difforme. $2, Epidendrum ciliare. $4, Epidendrum ibaguense. $5, Epidendrum nocturnum.
No. 1794, Encyclia cochleata. No. 1795, Rodriguezia lanceolata.

1994, Apr. 11 Perf. 14
1786-1793 A279 Set of 8 ... 10.00 10.00
Souvenir Sheets
1794-1795 A279 $6 each ... 4.50 4.50

1994, June 27 Perf. 14
Designs: 10c, Monarch. 15c, Florida white. 30c, Little sulphur. 40c, Troglodyte. $1, Common long-tail skipper. $2, Caribbean buckeye. $4, Polydamas swallowtail. $5, Zebra.
#1804, Cloudless sulphur. #1805, Hanno blue.
1796-1803 A280 Set of 8 ... 10.00 10.00
Souvenir Sheets
1804-1805 A280 $6 each ... 4.50 4.50

Miniature Sheet of 9

Marine Life — A281

Designs: No. 1806a, Bottlenose dolphin. b, Killer whale (a). c, Spinner dolphin (b). d, Ocean sunfish (a). e, Caribbean reef shark, short fin pilot whale (d, f). f, Butterfly fish. g, Moray eel. h, Trigger fish. i, Red lobster (h).
#1807, Blue marlin, horiz. #1808, Sea horse.

1994, July 21 Litho. Perf. 14
1806 A281 50c a.-i. ... 3.50 3.50
Souvenir Sheets
1807-1808 A281 $6 each ... 4.50 4.50

Intl. Year of the Family A282

1994, Aug. 4
1809 A282 90c multicolored ... .70 .70

D-Day, 50th Anniv. A283

Designs: 40c, Short Sunderland attacks U-boat. $2, Lockheed P-38 Lightning attacks train. $3, B-26 Marauders of 9th Air Force.
$6, Hawker Typhoon Fighter Bombers.

1994, Aug. 4
1810-1812 A283 Set of 3 ... 4.25 4.25
Souvenir Sheet
1813 A283 $6 multicolored ... 4.50 4.50

A284

Intl. Olympic Committee, Cent. — A285

Designs: 50c, Edwin Moses, US, hurdles, 1984. $1.50, Steffi Graf, Germany, tennis, 1988. $6, Johann Olav Koss, Norway, speed skating, 1994.

1994, Aug. 4
1814 A284 50c multicolored ... .38 .38
1815 A284 $1.50 multicolored ... 1.10 1.10
Souvenir Sheet
1816 A285 $6 multicolored ... 4.50 4.50

English Touring Cricket, Cent. A286

35c, M.A. Atherton, England, Wisden Trophy. 75c, I.V.A. Richards, Leeward Islands, vert. $1.20, R.B. Richardson, Leeward Islands, Wisden Trophy.

$3, First English team, 1895.

1994, Aug. 4 Set of 3
1817-1819 A286 ... 1.75 1.75
Souvenir Sheet
1820 A286 $3 multicolored ... 2.25 2.25

Miniature Sheets of 6

First Manned Moon Landing, 25th Anniv. A287

No. 1821: a, Edwin E. Aldrin, Jr. b, First footprint on Moon. c, Neil A. Armstrong. d, Aldrin descending to lunar surface. e, Aldrin deploys ALSET. f, Aldrin, US flag, Tranquility Base.
No. 1822: a, Scientific research, Tranquility Base. b, Plaque on Moon. c, Eagle ascending to docking. d, Command module in lunar orbit. e, US No. C76 made from die carried to Moon. f, Pres. Nixon, Apollo 11 crew.
$6, Armstrong, Aldrin, Postmaster General Blount.

1994, Aug. 4
1821-1822 A287 $1.50 #a.-f. ... 6.75 6.75
Souvenir Sheet
1823 A287 $6 multicolored ... 4.50 4.50

A288

PHILAKOREA '94 — A289

Designs: 40c, Entrance bridge, Songgwangsa Temple. 90c, Song-op Folk Village, Cheju. $3, Panoramic view, Port Sogwip'o.
Ceramics, Koryo & Choson Dynasties: No. 1827a, Long-necked bottle. b, Jar. c, Jar, diff. d, Ewer in form of bamboo shoot. e, Jar, diff. f, Pear-shaped bottle. g, Porcelain jar with dragon design. h, Porcelain jar with bonsai design.
$4, Ox, ox herder, vert.

1994, Aug. 4 Perf. 14, 13½ (#1827)
1824-1826 A288 Set of 3 ... 3.50 3.50
Miniature Sheet of 8
1827 A289 75c #a.-h. ... 6.00 6.00
Souvenir Sheet
1828 A288 $4 multicolored ... 3.00 3.00

Miniature Sheets of 8

Stars of Country & Western Music — A290

No. 1829: a, Patsy Cline. b, Tanya Tucker. c, Dolly Parton. d, Anne Murray. e, Tammy Wynette. f, Loretta Lynn. g, Reba McEntire. h, Skeeter Davis.
No. 1830a, Travis Tritt. b, Dwight Yoakam. c, Billy Ray Cyrus. d, Alan Jackson. e, Garth Brooks. f, Vince Gill. g, Clint Black. h, Eddie Rabbit.
No. 1831: a, Hank Snow. b, Gene Autry. c, Jimmie Rogers. d, Ernest Tubb. e, Eddy Arnold. f, Willie Nelson. g, Johnny Cash. h, George Jones.
No. 1832, Kitty Wells, horiz. No. 1833, Hank Williams, Sr. No. 1834, Hank Williams, Jr.

1994, Aug. 18   Litho.   Perf. 14
1829-1831 A290 75c #a.-h., each   4.50 4.50
Souvenir Sheets
1832-1834 A290 $6 each   4.50 4.50

1994 World Cup Soccer Championships, US — A291

Designs: 15c, Hugo Sanchez, Mexico. 35c, Juergen Klinsman, Germany. 65c, Antigua player. $1.20, Cobi Jones, US. $4, Roberto Baggio, Italy. $5, Bwalya Kalusha, Zambia.
No. 1841, FIFA World Cup Trophy, vert. No. 1842, Maldive Islands player, vert.

1994, Sept. 19
1835-1840 A291 Set of 6   8.50 8.50
Souvenir Sheets
1841-1842 A291 $6 each   4.50 4.50

Order of the Caribbean Community — A292

First award recipients: 65c, Sir Shridath Ramphal, statesman, Guyana. 90c, William Demas, economist, Trinidad & Tobago. $1.20, Derek Walcott, writer, St. Lucia.

1994
1843-1845 A292 Set of 3   2.00 2.00

Herman E. Sieger (1902-54) A293

Design: Germany #C35, Graf Zeppelin, Sieger.

1994   Litho.   Perf. 14
1846 A293 $1.50 multicolored   1.25 1.25

Birds A294

Designs: 10c, Magnificent frigate birds. 15c, Bridled quail dove. 30c, Magnificent frigate bird hatchling. 40c, Purple-throated carib, vert. No. 1851, $1, Antigua broad-wing hawk, vert. No. 1852, $1, Magnificent frigate bird, vert. $3, Magnificent frigate bird, white head. $4, Yellow warbler.
No. 1855, West Indian Whistling duck. No. 1856, Magnificent frigate bird, diff., vert.

1994, Dec. 12   Litho.   Perf. 14
1847-1854 A294 Set of 8   7.50 7.50
Souvenir Sheets
1855-1856 A294 $6 each   4.50 4.50
World Wildlife Fund (#1847, 1849, 1852-1853).

Christmas A295

Paintings of Madonnas: 15c, The Virgin and Child by the Fireside, by Robert Campin. 35c, The Reading Madonna, by Giorgione. 40c, Madonna and Child, by Giovanni Bellini. 45c, The Litta Madonna, by da Vinci. 65c, The Virgin and Child Under the Apple Tree, by Lucas Cranach the Elder. 75c, Madonna and Child, by Master of the Female Half-Lengths. $1.20, An Allegory of the Church, by Alessandro Allori. $5, Madonna and Child Wreathed with Flowers, by Jacob Jordaens.
No. 1865, The Virgin Enthroned with Child, by Bohemian Master. No. 1866, Madonna and Child with (painting's) Commissioners, by Palma Vecchio.

1994, Dec. 12   Perf. 13½x14
1857-1864 A295 Set of 8   6.75 6.75
Souvenir Sheets
1865-1866 A295 $6 each   4.50 4.50

Birds — A296

Designs: 15c, Magnificent frigate bird. 25c, Blue-hooded euphonia. 35c, Meadowlark. 40c, Red-billed tropic bird. 45c, Greater flamingo. 60c, Yellow-faced grassquit. 65c, Yellow-billed cuckoo. 70c, Purple-throated carib. 75c, Bananaquit. 90c, Painted bunting. $1.20, Red-legged honeycreeper. $2, Jacana. $5, Greater antillean bullfinch. $10, Caribbean elaenia. $20, Trembler.

1994   Perf. 14½x14
1867 A296 15c multicolored   .15 .15
1868 A296 25c multicolored   .18 .18
1869 A296 35c multicolored   .28 .28
1870 A296 40c multicolored   .60 .60
1871 A296 45c multicolored   .35 .35
1872 A296 60c multicolored   .45 .45
1873 A296 65c multicolored   .48 .48
1874 A296 70c multicolored   .52 .52
1875 A296 75c multicolored   .55 .55
1876 A296 90c multicolored   .70 .70
1877 A296 $1.20 multicolored   .90 .90
1878 A296 $2 multicolored   1.50 1.50
1879 A296 $5 multicolored   4.50 4.50
1880 A296 $10 multicolored   7.50 7.50
1881 A296 $20 multicolored   15.00 15.00
Nos. 1867-1881 (15)   33.66 33.66

Prehistoric Animals — A297

Designs, vert: 15c, Pachycephalosaurus. 20c, Afrovenator. 65c, Centrosaurus. 90c, Pentaceratops. $1.20, Tarbosaurus. $5, Styracosaur.
No. 1888a, Kronosaur. b, Ichthyosaur. c, Plesiosaur. d, Archelon. e, Two tyrannosaurs. f, One tyrannosaur. g, One parasaurolophus. h, Two parasaurolophuses. i, Oviraptor. j, Protoceratops with eggs. k, Pteranodon, protoceratops. l, Protoceratops.
#1889, Carnotaurus. #1890, Corythosaurus.

1995, May 15   Litho.   Perf. 14
1882-1887 A297 Set of 6   6.25 6.25
Miniature Sheet of 12
1888 A297 75c #a.-l.   6.75 6.75
Souvenir Sheets
1889-1890 A297 $6 each   4.50 4.50

1996 Summer Olympics, Atlanta — A298

Gold medalists: 15c, Al Oerter, US, discus. 20c, Greg Louganis, US, diving. 65c, Naim Suleymanoglu, Turkey, weight lifting. 90c, Louise Ritter, US, high jump. $1.20, Nadia Comaneci, Romania, gymnastics. $5, Olga Boldarenko, USSR, 10,000-meter run.
No. 1897, Lutz Hessilch, Germany, 1000-meter sprint cycling, vert. No. 1898, US team, eight-oared shell, 800-, 1500-meters.

1995, June 6   Litho.   Perf. 14
1891-1896 A298 Set of 6   6.00 6.00
Souvenir Sheets
1897-1898 A298 $6 each   4.50 4.50

Miniature Sheets of 6 or 8

End of World War II, 50th Anniv. A299

No. 1899: a, Chiang Kai-Shek. b, Gen. MacArthur. c, Gen. Chennault. d, Brigadier Orde C. Wingate. e, Gen. Stillwell. f, Field Marshall William Slim.
No. 1900: a, Map of Germany showing battle plan. b, Tanks, infantry advance. c, Red Army at gates of Berlin. d, German defenses smashed. e, Airstrikes on Berlin. f. German soldiers give up. g, Berlin falls to Russians. h, Germany surrenders.
$3, Plane, ship, Adm. Chester Nimitz. $6, Gen. Konev at command post outside Berlin, vert.

1995, July 20
1899 A299 $1.20 #a.-f. + label   5.50 5.50
1900 A299 $1.20 #a.-h. + label   7.25 7.25
Souvenir Sheets
1901 A299 $3 multicolored   2.25 2.25
1902 A299 $6 multicolored   4.50 4.50

Antigua & Barbuda
UN, 50th Anniv. — A300

Antigua & Barbuda
FAO, 50th Anniv. — A301

No. 1903: a, 75c, Earl of Halifax, signatures. b, 90c, Virginia Gildersleeve. c, $1.20, Harold Stassen. $6, Franklin D. Roosevelt.

1995, July 20   Litho.   Perf. 14
1903 A300 Strip of 3, #a.-c.   2.25 2.25
Souvenir Sheet
1904 A300 $6 multicolored   4.50 4.50
No. 1903 is a continuous design.

1995, July 20
Street market scene: No. 1905a, 75c, Two women, bananas. b, 90c, Women, crates, produce. c, $1.20, Women talking, one with box of food on head.
$6, Tractor.
1905 A301 Strip of 3, #a.-c.   2.25 2.25
Souvenir Sheet
1906 A301 $6 multicolored   4.50 4.50
No. 1905 is a continuous design.

Rotary Intl., 90th Anniv. — A302

1995, July 20
1907 A302 $5 shown   3.75 3.75
Souvenir Sheet
1908 A302 $6 Natl. flag, Rotary emblem   4.50 4.50

Queen Mother, 95th Birthday A303

No. 1909: a, Drawing. b, White & dark pink hat. c, Formal portrait. d, Blue green hat, dress.
No. 1910, Light blue dress, pearls.

1995, July 20   Perf. 13½x14
1909 A303 $1.50 Strip or block of 4, #a.-d.   4.50 4.50
Souvenir Sheet
1910 A303 $6 multicolored   4.50 4.50
No. 1909 was issued in sheets of 2 each.

Miniature Sheet of 12

Ducks — A304

No. 1911: a, Ring-necked duck. b, Ruddy duck. c, Green-winged teal (d). d, Wood duck. e, Hooded merganser (f). f, Lesser scaup (g). g, West Indian tree duck (h, k, l). h, Fulvous whistling duck (l). i, Bahama pintail. j, Shoveler (i). k, Masked duck (l). l, American widgeon.
$6, Blue-winged teal.

1995, Aug. 31   Litho.   Perf. 14
1911 A304 75c #a.-l.   6.75 6.75
Souvenir Sheet
1912 A304 $6 multicolored   4.50 4.50

Bees A305

Designs: 90c, Mining bee. $1.20, Solitary bee. $1.65, Leaf-cutter. $1.75, Honey bee.
$6, Solitary mining bee.

1995, Sept. 7
1913-1916 A305 Set of 4   4.25 4.25
Souvenir Sheet
1917 A305 $6 multicolored   4.50 4.50

Miniature Sheet of 12

Domestic Cats A306

Designs: a, Somali. b, Persian. c, Devon rex. d, Turkish angora. e, Himalayan. f, Maine coon. g, Nonpedigree. h, American wirehair. i, British shorthair. j, American curl. k, Black nonpedigree. l, Birman.
$6, Siberian, vert.

1995, Sept. 7
1918 A306 45c #a.-l.   4.00 4.00
Souvenir Sheet
1919 A306 $6 multicolored   4.50 4.50

Miniature Sheet

Tourism
A307 $2

Stylized paintings depicting: a, Caring. b, Marketing. c, Working. d, Enjoying life.

1995, July 31   Litho.   *Perf. 14*
1920 A307 $2 Sheet of 4, #a.-d.   6.00 6.00

Greenbay Moravian
Church, 150th
Anniv. — A308

Designs: 20c, First structure, wood & stone. 60c, First stone, concrete building, Mar. 1967. 75c, $2, Present structure. 90c, John A. Buckley, first minister of African descent. $1.20, John Ephraim Knight, longest serving minister. $6, Front of present structure.

1995, Sept. 4
1921-1926 A308   Set of 6   4.25 4.25
Souvenir Sheet
1927 A308 $6 multicolored   4.50 4.50

Miniature Sheet of 12

Flowers — A309

No. 1928: a, Narcissus. b, Camellia. c, Iris. d, Tulip. e, Poppy. f, Peony. g, Magnolia. h, Oriental lily. i, Rose. j, Pansy. k, Hydrangea. l, Azaleas. $6, Bird of paradise, calla lily.

1995, Sept. 7
1928 A309 75c #a.-l.   6.75 6.75
Souvenir Sheet
1929 A309 $6 multicolored   4.50 4.50

1995 Boy
Scout
Jamboree,
Holland
A310

Tents: No. 1930a, Explorer. b, Camper. c, Wall. No. 1931a, Trail tarp. b, Miner's. c, Voyager. No. 1932, Scout with camping equipment, vert. No. 1933, Scout making camp fire.

1995, Oct. 5
1930-1931 A310 $1.20 Strip of 3,
#a.-c., each   2.75 2.75
Souvenir Sheets
1932-1933 A310 $6 each   4.50 4.50
For overprints see Nos. 1963-1966.

Trains
A311

Designs: 35c, Gabon. 65c, Canadian. 75c, US. 90c, British high-speed. $1.20, French high-speed. No. 1939, American high-speed (Amtrak).
No. 1940: a, Australian diesel. b, Italian high-speed. c, Thai diesel. d, US steam. e, South African steam. f, Natal steam. g, US war train. h, British steam. i, British steam, diff.
No. 1941, Australian diesel, vert. No. 1942, Asian steam, vert.

1995, Oct. 23   Litho.   *Perf. 14*
1934-1939 A311   Set of 6   7.50 7.50
Miniature Sheet
1940 A311 $1.20 Sheet of 9, #a.-i.   8.25 8.25
Souvenir Sheets
1941-1942 A311 $6 each   4.50 4.50

Miniature Sheet

Birds — A312

No. 1943: a, Purple-thoated carib. b, Antillean crested hummingbird. c, Bananaquit (d). d, Mangrove cuckoo. e, Troupial. f, Green-throated carib (e, g). g, Yellow warbler (h). h, Blue-hooded Euphonia. i, Scally-breasted thrasher. j, Burrowing owl (i). k, Caribbean crackle (k). l, Adelaide's warbler.
$6, Purple gallinule.

1995
1943 A312 75c Sheet of 12, #a.-l.   6.75 6.75
Souvenir Sheet
1944 A312 $6 multicolored   4.50 4.50

Miniature Sheets of 9

Nobel Prize Fund Established,
Cent. — A313

Recipients: No. 1945a, S.Y. Agnon, literature, 1966. b, Kipling, literature, 1907. c, Aleksandr Solzhenitsyn, literature, 1970. d, Jack Steinberger, physics, 1988. e, Andrei Sakharov, peace, 1975. f, Otto Stern, physics, 1943. g, Steinbeck, literature, 1962. h, Nadine Gordimer, literature, 1991. i, Faulkner, literature, 1949.
No. 1946: a, Hammarskjold, peace, 1961. b, Georg Wittig, chemistry, 1979. c, Wilhelm Ostwald, chemistry, 1909. d, Koch, physiology or medicine, 1945. e, Karl Ziegler, chemistry, 1963. f, Fleming, physiology or medicine, 1945. g, Hermann Staudinger, chemistry, 1953. h, Manfred Eigen, chemistry, 1967. i, Arno Penzias, physics, 1978.
No. 1947, Elie Wiesel, peace, 1986, vert. No. 1948, Dalai Lama, peace, 1989, vert.

1995, Nov. 8
1945-1946 A313 $1 #a.-i. + label,
each   6.75 6.75
Souvenir Sheets
1947-1948 A313 $6 each   4.50 4.50

Christmas
A314

Details or entire paintings: 15c, Rest on the Flight into Egypt, by Veronese. 35c, Madonna with The Child, by Van Dyck. 65c, Sacred Conversation Piece, by Veronese. 75c, Vision of Saint Anthony, by Van Dyck. 90c, The Virgin and the Infant, by Van Eyck. No. 1954, The Immaculate Conception, by Tiepolo.
$5, Christ Appearing to His Mother, by Van Der Weyden. No. 1956, Infant Jesus and the Young St. John, by Murillo.

1995   Litho.   *Perf. 13¹/₂x14*
1949-1954 A314   Set of 6   6.75 6.75
Souvenir Sheets
1955 A314 $5 multicolored   3.75 3.75
1956 A314 $6 multicolored   4.50 4.50

Miniature Sheet

Elvis Presley
(1935-77)
A315

Nos. 1957-1958, Various portraits depicting Presley's life.

1995, Dec. 8   *Perf. 14*
1957 A315 $1 Sheet of 9, #a.-i.   6.75 6.75
Souvenir Sheet
1958 A315 $6 multicolored   4.50 4.50

John Lennon (1940-
80),
Entertainer — A316

45c, 50c, 65c, 75c, Various portraits of Lennon.

1995, Dec. 8
1959-1962 A316   Set of 4   1.75 1.75
Souvenir Sheet
1962A   A316 $6 like 75c   4.50 4.50
Nos. 1959-1962 were each issued in miniature sheets of 16.
No. 1962A has a continuous design.

Nos. 1930-1933 Ovptd.

1995, Dec. 14
1963-1964 A310 $1.20 Strip of 3,
#a.-c., each   2.75 2.75
Souvenir Sheets
1965-1966 A310 $6 each   4.50 4.50
Size and location of overprint varies.

Mushrooms
A317

Designs: No. 1967a, Hygrophoropsis aurantiaca. b, Hygrophorus bakerensis. c, Hygrophorus conicus. d, Hygrophorus miniatus.
No. 1968a, Suillus brevipes. b, Suillus luteus. c, Suillus granulatus. d, Suillus caerulescens.
No. 1969, Conocybe filaris. No. 1970, Hygrocybe flavescens.

1996, Apr. 22   Litho.   *Perf. 14*
1967-1968 A317 75c Strip of 4, #a.-
d., each   2.25 2.25
Souvenir Sheets
1969-1970 A317 $6 each   4.50 4.50
#1967-1968 were each issued in sheets of 12 stamps.

Sailing Ships
A318

Designs: 15c, Resolution. 25c, Mayflower. 45c, Santa Maria. No. 1970D, 75c, Aemilia, Holland, 1630. No. 1970E, 75c, Sovereign of the Seas, England, 1637. 90c, HMS Victory, England, 1765.
Battleships: No. 1971: a, Aemila, Holland, 1630. b, Sovereign of the Seas, England, 1637. c, Royal Louis, France, 1692. d, HMS Royal George, England, 1715. e, Le Protecteur, France, 1761. f, HMS Victory, England, 1765.
Ships of exploration: No. 1972: a, Santa Maria. b, Victoria. c, Golden Hinde. d, Mayflower. e, Griffin. f, Resolution.
No. 1973, Grande Hermine. No. 1974, USS Constitution, 1797.

1996, Apr. 25
1970A-1970F A318   Set of 6   2.50 2.50
Sheets of 6
1971 A318 $1.20 #a.-f.   5.50 5.50
1972 A318 $1.50 #a.-f.   6.75 6.75
Souvenir Sheets
1973-1974 A318 $6 each   4.50 4.50

1996 Summer Olympics, Atlanta — A319

Designs: 65c, Florence Griffith Joyner, women's track, vert. 75c, Olympic Stadium, Seoul, 1988. 90c, Allison Jolly, yachting. $1.20, 2000m Tandem cyclying.
Medalists: No. 1979a, Wolfgang Nordwig, pole vault. b, Shirley Strong, women's 100m hurdles. c, Sergei Bubka, pole vault. d, Filbert Bayi, 3000m steeplechase. e, Victor Saneyev, triple jump. f, Silke Renk, women's javelin. g, Daley Thompson, decathlon. h, Bob Richards, pole vault. i, Parry O'Brien, shot put.
Diving medalists: No. 1980a, Ingrid Kramer, women's platform. b, Kelly McCormick, women's springboard. c, Gary Tobian, men's springboard. d, Greg Louganis, men's diving. e, Michelle Mitchell, women's platform. f, Zhou Jihong, women's platform. g, Wendy Wyland, women's platform. h, Xu Yanmei, women's platform. i, Fu Mingxia, women's platform.
$5, Bill Toomey, decathlon. $6, Mark Lenzi, men's springboard.

1996, May 6
1975-1978 A319   Set of 4   2.60 2.60
Sheets of 9
1979-1980 A319 90c #a.-i., each   6.25 6.25
Souvenir Sheets
1981 A319 $5 multicolored   3.75 3.75
1982 A319 $6 multicolored   4.50 4.50

Sea Birds
A320

Designs: No. 1983a, Black skimmer. b, Black-capped petrel. c, Sooty tern. d, Royal tern.
No. 1984a, Pomarina jaegger. b, White-tailed tropicbird. c, Northern gannet. d, Laughing gull.
$5, Great frigatebird. $6, Brown pelican.

1996, May 13
1983-1984 A320 75c Vert. strip of 4,
#a.-d., each   2.25 2.25

Souvenir Sheets

1985 A320 $5 multicolored 3.75 3.75
1986 A320 $6 multicolored 4.50 4.50

Nos. 1983-1984 were each issued in sheets of 12 stamps with each strip in sheet having a different order.

Disney Characters In Scenes from Jules Verne's Science Fiction Novels — A321

Designs: 1c, Around the World in Eighty Days. 2c, Journey to the Center of the Earth. 5c, Michel Strogoff. 10c, From the Earth to the Moon. 15c, Five Weeks in a Balloon. 20c, Around the World in Eighty Days, diff. $1, The Mysterious Island. $2, From the Earth to the Moon, diff. $3, Captain Grant's Children. $5, Twenty Thousand Leagues Under the Sea.
No. 1997, Twenty Thousand Leagues Under the Sea, diff. No. 1998, Journey to the Center of the Earth, diff.

1996, June 6   Litho.   Perf. 14x13¹/₂
1987-1996 A321   Set of 10 .... 8.75 8.75
Souvenir Sheets
1997-1998 A321 $6 each 4.50 4.50

Bruce Lee (1940-73), Martial Arts Expert — A322

Various portraits.

1996, June 13   Perf. 14
1999 A322 75c Sheet of 9, #a.-i. .. 5.25 5.25
Souvenir Sheet
2000 A322 $5 multicolored 3.75 3.75
China '96 (#1999).

Queen Elizabeth II, 70th Birthday A323

Designs: a, In blue dress, pearls. b, Carrying bouquet of flowers. c, In uniform.
$6, Painting as younger woman.

1996, July 17   Perf. 13¹/₂x14
2001 A323 $2 Strip of 3, #a.-c. ... 4.50 4.50
Souvenir Sheet
2002 A323 $6 multicolored 4.50 4.50
No. 2001 was issued in sheets of 9 stamps.

Traditional Cavalry — A324

---

a, Ancient Egyptian. b, 13th cent. English. c, 16th cent. Spanish. d, 18th cent. Chinese.
$6, 19th cent. French.

1996, July 24   Litho.   Perf. 14
2003 A324 60c Block of 4, #a.-d. .. 1.80 1.80
Souvenir Sheet
2004 A324 $6 multicolored 4.50 4.50
No. 2003 was issued in sheets of 16 stamps.

A325   A326

UNICEF, 50th Anniv.: 75c, Girl. 90c, Children. $1.20, Woman holding baby. $6, Girl, diff.

1996, July 30
2005-2007 A325   Set of 3 .... 2.10 2.10
Souvenir Sheet
2008 A325 $6 multicolored 4.50 4.50

1996, July 30
Site, flower: 75c, Tomb of Zachariah, verbascum sinuatum. 90c, Pool of Siloam, hyacinthus orientalis. $1.20, Hurva Synagogue, ranunculus asiaticus.
$6, Model of Herod's Temple.
2009-2011 A326   Set of 3 .... 2.15 2.15
Souvenir Sheet
2012 A326 $6 multicolored 4.50 4.50
Jerusalem, 3000th anniv.

Radio, Cent. — A327

Entertainers: 65c, Kate Smith. 75c, Dinah Shore. 90c, Rudy Vallee. $1.20, Bing Crosby.
$6, Jo Stafford.

1996, July 30
2013-2016 A327   Set of 4 .... 2.75 2.75
Souvenir Sheet
2017 A327 $6 multicolored 4.50 4.50

Christmas A328

Details or entire paintings, by Filippo Lippi: 60c, Madonna Enthroned. 90c, Adoration of the Child and Saints. $1, Annunciation. $1.20, Birth of the Virgin. $1.60, Adoration of the Child. $1.75, Madonna and Child.
No. 2024, Madonna and Child, diff. No. 2025, Circumcision.

1996, Nov. 25   Perf. 13¹/₂x14
2018-2023 A328   Set of 6 .... 5.25 5.25
Souvenir Sheets
2024-2025 A328 $6 each 4.50 4.50

Disney Pals A329

Designs: 1c, Goofy, Wilbur. 2c, Donald, Goofy. 5c, Donald, Panchito, Jose Carioca. 10c, Mickey, Goofy. 15c, Dale, Chip. 20c, Pluto, Mickey. $1, Daisy, Minnie at ice cream shop. $2, Daisy, Minnie. $3, Gus Goose, Donald.
No. 2035, Donald, vert. No. 2036, Goofy.

1997, Feb. 17   Litho.   Perf. 14x13¹/₂
2026-2034 A329   Set of 9 .... 5.00 5.00
Souvenir Sheets
Perf. 13¹/₂x14, 14x13¹/₂
2035-2036 A329 $6 each 4.50 4.50

Salute to Broadway A330

Stars, show: No. 2037: a, Robert Preston, The Music Man. b, Michael Crawford, Phantom of the Opera. c, Zero Mostel, Fiddler on the Roof. d, Patti Lupone, Evita. e, Raul Julia, Threepenny Opera. f, Mary Martin, South Pacific. g, Carol Channing, Hello Dolly. h, Yul Brynner, The King and I. i, Julie Andrews, My Fair Lady.
$6, Mickey Rooney, Sugar Babies.

1997   Perf. 14
2037 A330 $1 Sheet of 9, #a.-i. .. 6.80 6.80
Souvenir Sheet
2038 A330 $6 multicolored 4.50 4.50

Butterflies — A331

Designs: 90c, Charaxes porthos. $1.20, Aethiopana honorius. $1.60, Charaxes hadrianus. $1.75, Precis westermanni.
No. 2043: a, Charaxes protoclea. b, Byblia ilithyia. c, Black-headed tchagra (bird). d, Charaxes nobilis. e, Pseudacraea boisduvali. f, Charaxes smaragdalis. g, Charaxes lasti. h, Pseudacraea poggei. i, Graphium colonna.
No. 2044a, Carmine bee-eater (bird). b, Pseudacraea eurytus. c, Hypolimnas monteironis. d, Charaxes anticlea. e, Graphium leonidas. f, Graphium illyris. g, Nepheronia argia. h, Graphium policenes. i, Papilio dardanus.
No. 2045, Euxanthe tiberius, horiz. No. 2046, Charaxes lactitinctus, horiz. No. 2047, Euphaedra neophron.

1997, Mar. 10
2039-2042 A331   Set of 4 .... 4.00 4.00
Sheets of 9
2043-2044 A331 $1.10 #a.-i., each .. 7.50 7.50
Souvenir Sheets
2045-2047 A331 $6 each 4.50 4.50

UNESCO, 50th Anniv. — A332

World Heritage Sites: 60c, Convent of the Companions of Jesus, Morelia, Mexico. 90c, Fortress, San Lorenzo, Panama, vert. $1, Canaima Natl. Park, Venezuela, vert. $1.20, Huascarán Natl. Park, Peru, vert. $1.60, Church of San Francisco, Guatemala, vert. $1.75, Santo Domingo, Dominican Republic, vert.
No. 2054, vert: a-c, Guanajuato, Mexico. d, Jesuit missions of the Chiquitos, Bolivia. e, Huascarán Natl. Park, Peru. f, Jesuit missions, La Santisima, Paraguay. g, Cartagena, Colombia. h, Old Havana fortification, Cuba.
No. 2055: a, Tikal Natl. Park, Guatemala. b, Rio Platano Reserve, Honduras. c, Ruins of Copán, Honduras. d, Capuchin Monastery, Antigua, Guatemala. e, Teotihuacán, Mexico.
No. 2056, Teotihuacán, Mexico, diff. No. 2057, Tikal Natl. Park, Guatemala, diff.

1997, Apr. 10   Litho.   Perf. 14
2048-2053 A332   Set of 6 .... 5.25 5.25
Sheets of 8 or 5
2054 A332 $1.10 #a.-h. + label ... 6.75 6.75
2055 A332 $1.65 #a.-e. + label ... 6.25 6.25
Souvenir Sheets
2056-2057 A332 $6 each 4.50 4.50

Fauna — A333

No. 2058: a, Red bishop. b, Yellow baboon. c, Superb starling. d, Ratel. e, Hunting dog. f, Serval.
No. 2059: a, Okapi. b, Giant forest squirrel. c, Masked weaver. d, Common genet. e, Yellow-billed stork. f, Red-headed agama.
No. 2060, Malachite kingfisher. No. 2061, Gray crowned crane. No. 2062, Bat-eared fox.

1997, Apr. 24
2058 A333 $1.20 Sheet of 6, #a.-f. .. 5.50 5.50
2059 A333 $1.65 Sheet of 6, #a.-f. .. 7.50 7.50
Souvenir Sheets
2060-2062 A333 $6 each 4.50 4.50

Charlie Chaplin (1889-1977), Comedian, Actor A334

Various portraits.

1997   Litho.   Perf. 14
2063 A334 $1 Sheet of 9, #a.-i. .. 6.75 6.75
Souvenir Sheet
2064 A334 $6 multicolored 4.50 4.50

Paul P. Harris (1868-1947), Founder of Rotary, Intl. — A335

Designs: $1.75, Service above self, James Grant, Ivory Coast, 1994, portrait of Harris.
$6, Group study exchange, New Zealand.

1997, June 12		*Litho.*	*Perf. 14*
2065	A335	$1.75 multicolored	1.30 1.30
Souvenir Sheet			
2066	A335	$6 multicolored	4.50 4.50

Heinrich von Stephan (1831-97) A336

Portrait of Von Stephan and: No. 2067: a, Kaiser Wilhelm I. b, UPU emblem. c, Pigeon Post.
$6, Von Stephan, Basel messenger, 1400's.

1997, June 12			
2067	A336	$1.75 Sheet of 3, #a.-c.	4.00 4.00
Souvenir Sheet			
2068	A336	$6 multicolored	4.50 4.50
PACIFIC 97.			

Queen Elizabeth II, Prince Philip, 50th Wedding Anniv. A337

No. 2069: a, Queen. b, Royal arms. c, Queen, Prince in royal attire. d, Queen, King riding in open carriage. e, Balmoral Castle. f, Prince Philip.
$6, Early portrait of Queen, King in royal attire.

1997, June 12			
2069	A337	$1 Sheet of 6, #a.-f.	4.50 4.50
Souvenir Sheet			
2070	A337	$6 multicolored	4.50 4.50

Grimm's Fairy Tales A338

Scenes from "Cinderella:" No. 2071: a, Mother, stepsisters. b, Cinderella, fairy godmother. c, Cinderella, Prince Charming.
$6, Prince trying shoe on Cinderella.

1997, June 13			*Perf. 13¹/₂x14*
2071	A338	$1.75 Sheet of 3, #a.-c.	4.00 4.00
Souvenir Sheet			
2072	A338	$6 multicolored	4.50 4.50

Chernobyl Disaster, 10th Anniv. — A339

Designs: $1.65, UNESCO. $2, Chabad's Children of Chernobyl.

1997, June 12			
2073	A339	$1.65 multicolored	1.25 1.25
2074	A339	$2 multicolored	1.50 1.50

Mushrooms A340

Designs: 45c, Marasmius rotula. 65c, Cantharellus cibarius. 70c, Lepiota cristata. 90c, Auricularia mesenterica. $1, Pholiota alnicola. $1.65, Leccinum aurantiacum.
No. 2081: a, Entoloma serrulatum. b, Panaeolus sphinctrinus. c, Volvariella bombycina. d, Conocybe percincta. e, Pluteus cervinus. f, Russula foetens.
No. 2082, Panellus serotinus. No. 2083, Amanita cothurnata.

1997, Aug. 12		*Litho.*	*Perf. 14*
2075-2080 A340		Set of 6	4.00 4.00
Sheets of 6			
2081 A340		$1.75 #a.-f.	8.00 8.00
Souvenir Sheets			
2082-2083 A340		$6 each	4.50 4.50

Orchids — A341 45¢

Designs: 45c, Odontoglossum cervantesii. 65c, Medford star. 75c, Motes resplendent. 90c, Debutante. $1, Apple blossom. $2, Dendrobium.
No. 2090: a, Angel lace. b, Precious stones. c, Orange theope butterfly. d, Promenaea xanthina. e, Lycaste macrobulbon. f, Amesiella philippinensis. g, Machu Picchu. h, Zuma urchin.
No. 2091: a, Sophia Martin. b, Dogface butterfly. c, Mini purple. d, Showgirl. e, Mem. Dorothy Bertsch. f, Black II. g, Leeanum. h, Paphiopedilum macranthum.
No. 2092, Seine. No. 2093, Paphiopedilum gratrixianum.

1997, Aug. 19		*Litho.*	*Perf. 14*
2084-2089 A341		Set of 6	4.25 4.25
Sheets of 8			
2090-2091 A341		$1.65 #a.-h., each	5.00 5.00
Souvenir Sheets			
2092-2093 A341		$6 each	4.50 4.50

1998 World Cup Soccer Championships, France — A342

Designs: 60c, Maradona, Argentina, 1986. 75c, Fritzwalter, W. Germany, 1954. 90c, Zoff, Italy, 1982. $1.20, Moore, England, 1966. $1.65, Alberto, Brazil, 1970. $1.75, Matthäus, W. Germany.
No. 2100, vert: a, Ademir, Brazil, 1950. b, Eusebio, Portugal, 1966. c, Fontaine, France, 1958. d, Schillaci, Italy, 1990. e, Leonidas, Brazil, 1938. f, Stabile, Argentina, 1930. g, Nejedly, Czechoslovakia, 1934. h, Muller, W. Germany, 1970.
No. 2101, Players, W. Germany, 1990. No. 2102, Bebeto, Brazil, vert.

1997, Oct. 6		*Litho.*	*Perf. 14*
2094-2099 A342		Set of 6	6.00 6.00
Sheet of 8 + Label			
2100 A342		$1 #a.-h.	6.00 6.00
Souvenir Sheets			
2101-2102 A342		$6 each	4.50 4.50

Domestic Animals A343

Dogs: No. 2103: a, Dachshund. b, Staffordshire terrier. c, Sharpei. d, Beagle. e, Norfolk terrier. f, Golden retriever.
Cats: No. 2104: a, Scottish fold. b, Japanese bobtail. c, Tabby manx. d, Bicolor American shorthair. e, Sorrel abyssinian. f, Himalayan blue point.
No. 2105, Siberian husky, vert. No. 2106, Red tabby American shorthair kitten, vert.

1997, Oct. 27		*Litho.*	*Perf. 14*
Sheets of 6			
2103-2104 A343		$1.65 #a.-f., each	7.50 7.50
Souvenir Sheets			
2105-2106 A343		$6 each	4.50 4.50

ANTIGUA & BARBUDA $1.65

Early Trains A344

No. 2107: a, Original Trevithick drawing, 1804. b, "Puffing Billy," William Hedley, 1860. c, Crampton locomotive, Northern Railway, France, 1858. d, Twenty-five ton locomotive, Lawrence Machine Shop, 1860's. e, First locomotive, "Mississippi," built in England. f, "Coppernob," locomotive by Edward Bury, Furness Railway.
No. 2108: a, "Jenny Lind," by David Joy for E.B. Wilson. b, "Atlantic" type locomotive, by Schenectady Locomotive Works, 1899. c, British built tank engine, Japan, by Kisons of Leeds, 1881. d, Express freight locomotive, 4-8-2 type, Pennsylvania Railroad. e, Four-cylinder locomotive, by Karl Golsdorf, Austria. f, "E" series 0-10-0 locomotive, produced by Lugansk Works, Russia, 1930.
No. 2109, "Patente" George Stephenson, 1843. No. 2110, Brunel's Trestle, Lynher River.

1997, Nov. 10			
Sheets of 6			
2107-2108 A344		$1.65 #a.-f., each	7.50 7.50
Souvenir Sheets			
2109-2110 A344		$6 each	4.50 4.50

Christmas A345　15c

Entire paintings or details: 15c, The Angel Leaving Tobias and His Family, by Rembrandt. 25c, The Resurrection, by Martin Knoller. 60c, Astronomy, by Raphael. 75c, Music-making Angel, by Melozzo da Forli. 90c, Amor, by Parmigianino. $1.20, Madonna and Child with Saints John the Baptist, Anthony, Stephen and Jerome, by Rosso Fiorentino.
No. 2117, The Portinari Altarpiece, by Hugo Van Der Goes. No. 2118, The Wedding of Tobias, by Gianantonio and Francesco Guardi.

1997, Dec. 2		*Litho.*	*Perf. 14*
2111-2116 A345		Set of 6	5.25 5.25
Souvenir Sheets			
2117-2118 A345		$6 each	4.50 4.50

WAR TAX STAMPS

No. 31 and Type A3 Overprinted in Black or Red **WAR STAMP**

1916-18		Wmk. 3	*Perf. 14*
MR1	A3	½p green	.30 .30
MR2	A3	½p green (R) ('17)	.35 .35
MR3	A3	1½p orange ('18)	.40 .40
		Nos. MR1-MR3 (3)	1.05 1.05

ARGENTINA

ˌär-jən-'tē-nə

LOCATION — In South America
GOVT. — Republic
AREA — 1,084,120 sq. mi.
POP. — 27,949,480 (1980)
CAPITAL — Buenos Aires

100 Centavos = 1 Peso
100 Centavos = 1 Austral (1985)

Catalogue values for unused stamps in this country are for Never Hinged items, beginning with Scott 587 in the regular postage section, Scott B12 in the semi-postal section, Scott C59 in the airpost section, Scott CB1 in the airpost semi-postal section and Scott O79 in the officials section.

Watermarks

Wmk. 84- Italic RA

Wmk. 85- Small Sun, 4¹/₂mm

Wmk. 86- Large Sun, 6mm

Wmk. 87- Honeycomb

Wmk. 88- Multiple Suns

Wmk. 89- Large Sun

In this watermark the face of the sun is 7mm in diameter, the rays are heavier than in the large sun watermark of 1896-1911 and the watermarks are placed close together, so that parts of several frequently appear on one stamp. This paper was intended to be used for fiscal stamps and is usually referred to as "fiscal sun paper."

Wmk. 90- RA in Sun

In 1928 watermark 90 was slightly modified, making the diameter of the Sun 9mm instead of 10mm. Several types of this watermark exist.

Wmk. 205- AP in Oval

The letters "AP" are the initials of "AHORRO POSTAL." This paper was formerly used exclusively for Postal Savings stamps.

Wmk. 287- Double Circle and Letters in Sheet

Wmk. 288- RA in Sun with Straight Rays

Wmk. 365- Argentine Arms, "Casa de Moneda de la Nacion" & "RA" Multiple

Values for Unused
Unused values for Nos. 5-17 are for examples without gum. Examples with original gum command higher prices. Unused values of Nos. 1-4B and stamps after No. 17 are for examples with original gum as defined in the catalogue introduction.

Argentine Confederation

Symbolical of the Argentine Confederation

A1   A2

1858, May 1 Unwmk. Litho. *Imperf.*

1	A1 5c red		1.50	24.00
a.	Colon after "5"		1.75	32.50
b.	Colon after "V"		1.75	32.50
2	A1 10c green		2.50	55.00
a.	Half used as 5c on cover			500.00
3	A1 15c blue		16.00	150.00
a.	One-third used as 5c on cover			3,500.
	Nos. 1-3 (3)		20.00	229.00

There are nine varieties of Nos. 1, 2 and 3. Counterfeits and forged cancellations of Nos. 1-3 are plentiful.

1860, Jan.

4	A2 5c red	3.25	70.00
4A	A2 10c green	7.00	
4B	A2 15c blue	25.00	
	Nos. 4-4B (3)	35.25	

Nos. 4A and 4B were never placed in use. Some compositions of Nos. 4-4B contain 8 different types across the sheet. Other settings exist with minor variations. Counterfeits and forged cancellations of Nos. 4-4B are plentiful.

Argentine Republic

Seal of the Republic — A3

Broad "C" in "CENTAVOS," Accent on "U" of "REPUBLICA"

1862, Jan. 11

5	A3 5c rose		40.00	37.50
a.	5c rose lilac		87.50	35.00
6	A3 10c green		140.00	65.00
b.	Diagonal half used as 5c on cover			4,250.
7	A3 15c blue		275.00	225.00
a.	Without accent on "U"		5,500.	2,400.
b.	Tete beche pair		45,000.	27,500.
i.	15c ultramarine		425.00	325.00
j.	Diagonal third used as 5c on cover			5,000.

Broad "C" in "CENTAVOS," No Accent on "U"

1863

7C	A3 5c rose	18.00	21.00
d.	5c rose lilac	100.00	110.00
e.	Worn plate (rose)	200.00	52.50
7F	A3 10c yellow green	350.00	140.00
g.	10c olive green	500.00	250.00
k.	10c green, ribbed paper	425.00	200.00
l.	Worn plate (green)	325.00	150.00
m.	Worn plate (olive green)	425.00	165.00

Narrow "C" in "CENTAVOS," No Accent on "U"

1864

7H	A3 5c rose red	160.00	32.50

The so-called reprints of 10c and 15c are counterfeits. They have narrow "C" and straight lines in shield. Nos. 7C and 7H have been extensively counterfeited.

Rivadavia Issue

Bernardino Rivadavia
A4   A5

Rivadavia — A6

1864-67 Engr. Wmk. 84 Imperf.

Clear Impressions

8	A4 5c brown rose	1,300.	160.
a.	5c orange red ('67)	1,500.	160.
9	A5 10c green	2,000.	1,200.
10	A6 15c blue	7,250.	4,000.

Perf. 11½

Dull to Worn Impressions

11	A4 5c brown rose ('65)	30.00	12.00
11B	A4 5c lake	77.50	17.50
12	A5 10c green	80.00	30.00
a.	Half used as 5c on cover		750.00
b.	Horiz. pair, imperf vert.		1,750.
13	A6 15c blue	275.00	110.00

1867-72 Unwmk. Imperf.

Clear Impressions

14	A4 5c carmine ('72)	250.	65.
15	A4 5c rose	200.	100.
15A	A5 10c green	4,000.	4,000.
16	A6 15c blue	2,000.	1,750.

Nos. 15A-16 issued without gum.

1867 Perf. 11½

17	A4 5c carmine	350.00	150.00

Nos. 14, 15 and 17 exist with part of papermaker's wmk. "LACROIX FRERES."

Rivadavia   Manuel
A7   Belgrano
                A8

Jose de San Martin — A9

Groundwork of Horizontal Lines

1867-68 Perf. 12

18	A7 5c vermilion	200.00	10.00
18A	A8 10c green	30.00	4.50
b.	Diag. half used as 5c on cover		750.00
19	A9 15c blue	65.00	15.00

Groundwork of Crossed Lines

20	A7 5c vermilion	10.50	.65
21	A9 15c blue	92.50	12.00

See Nos. 27, 33-34, 39 and types A19, A33, A34, A37. For surcharges and overprints see Nos. 30-32, 41-42, 47-51, O6-O7, O26.

Gen. Antonio   Mariano
G. Balcarce   Moreno
A10   A11

Carlos Maria   Gervasio Antonio
de   Posadas — A13
Alvear — A12

Cornelio Saavedra — A14

1873

22	A10 1c purple	5.00	2.00
a.	1c gray violet	6.25	2.00
23	A11 4c brown	4.75	.40
a.	4c red brown	17.00	2.00
24	A12 30c orange	100.00	15.00
a.	Vert. pair, imperf horiz.	4,000.	
25	A13 60c black	100.00	4.75
26	A14 90c blue	25.00	2.25
	Nos. 22-26 (5)	234.75	24.40

For overprints see Nos. O5, O12-O14, O19-O21, O25, O29.

1873 Laid Paper

27	A8 10c green	200.00	20.00

Nos.18, 18A Surcharged in Black

Nos. 30-31   No. 32

1877, Feb. Wove Paper

30	A7 1c on 5c vermilion	47.50	15.00
a.	Inverted surcharge	350.00	200.00
31	A7 2c on 5c vermilion	92.50	60.00
a.	Inverted surcharge	700.00	500.00
32	A8 8c on 10c green	125.00	30.00
b.	Inverted surcharge	500.00	425.00
	Nos. 30-32 (3)	265.00	105.00

Varieties also exist with double and triple surcharges, surcharge on reverse, 8c on No. 27, all made clandestinely from the original cliches of the surcharges.

Forgeries of these surcharges include the inverted and double varieties.

1876-77 Rouletted

33	A7 5c vermilion	150.00	60.00
34	A7 8c lake ('77)	25.00	.35

Belgrano
A17

Dalmacio Vélez Sarsfield
A18

San Martín — A19

1878   *Rouletted*
35	A17	16c green	8.00	1.10
36	A18	20c blue	10.00	3.00
37	A19	24c blue	17.00	3.00
		Nos. 35-37 (3)	35.00	7.10

See No. 56. For overprints see Nos. O9-O10, O15-O17, O22, O28.

Vicente Lopez — A20

Alvear — A21

1877-80   *Perf. 12*
38	A20	2c yellow green	4.25	.90
39	A7	8c lake ('80)	4.25	.35
a.		8c brown lake	27.50	.35
40	A21	25c lake ('78)	22.50	6.00
		Nos. 38-40 (3)	31.00	7.25

For overprints see Nos. O4, O11, O18, O24.

No. 18 Surcharged in Black

½   ½
(PROVISORIO) (PROVISORIO)
Large "P"   Small "P"

1882
41	A7	½c on 5c ver	1.50	1.50
a.		Double surcharge	80.00	80.00
b.		Inverted surcharge	20.00	20.00
c.		"PROVISORIO" omitted	80.00	80.00
d.		Fraction omitted	50.00	
e.		"PROVISOBIO"	30.00	30.00
f.		Pair, one without surcharge	200.00	
g.		Small "P" in "PROVISORIO"	2.50	2.50
h.		As "a," small "P" in "PROVISORIO"	32.50	32.50
i.		As "b," small "P" in "PROVISORIO"	40.00	40.00
j.		As "d," small "P" in "PROVISORIO"	15.00	15.00

Perforated across Middle of Stamp
42	A7	½c on 5c ver	3.00	3.00
a.		"PROVISORIO"	40.00	40.00
b.		Large "P" in "PROVISORIO"	30.00	22.50

The surcharge on #41-42 is found in two types: Small "P" and narrow "V." Large "P" and wider "V."

A23

1882   *Typo.*   *Perf. 12*
43	A23	½c brown	1.40	.80
a.		Imperf., pair	40.00	40.00
44	A23	1c red, perf. 14	3.50	1.00
a.		Perf. 12	9.00	4.25
45	A23	12c ultra	55.00	8.75
a.		Perf. 14	45.00	8.75
46	A23	12c grnsh blue, perf. 14	125.00	11.00
		Nos. 43-46 (4)	184.90	21.55

See type A29. For overprints see Nos. O2, O8, O23, O27.

No. 21 Surcharged in Red:

a   b   c

1884   *Engr.*   *Perf. 12*
47	A9 (a)	½c on 15c blue	2.00	1.50
a.		Groundwork of horiz. lines	100.00	80.00
b.		Inverted surcharge	27.50	20.00
48	A9 (b)	1c on 15c blue	16.00	13.00
a.		Groundwork of horiz. lines	10.00	6.00
b.		Inverted surcharge	80.00	55.00
c.		Double surcharge	40.00	32.50
d.		Triple surcharge	350.00	

Nos. 20-21 Surcharged in Black
49	A7 (a)	½c on 5c ver	4.00	3.00
a.		Inverted surcharge	150.00	110.00
b.		Date omitted	150.00	
c.		Pair, one without surcharge	375.00	
d.		Double surcharge	550.00	
50	A9	½c on 15c blue	10.00	8.00
a.		Groundwork of horiz. lines	30.00	25.00
b.		Inverted surcharge	70.00	55.00
c.		Pair, one without surcharge	325.00	
51	A7 (c)	4c on 5c ver	10.00	6.00
a.		Inverted surcharge	25.00	20.00
b.		Double surcharge	325.00	200.00
c.		Pair, one without surcharge but with "4" in manuscript	550.00	350.00
d.		Pair, one without surcharge	250.00	
		Nos. 47-51 (5)	42.00	31.50

A29

1884-85   *Engr.*   *Perf. 12*
52	A29	½c red brown	.90	.45
a.		Horiz. pair, imperf vert.	300.00	250.00
53	A29	1c rose red	5.25	.45
a.		Horiz. pair, imperf vert.	300.00	250.00
54	A29	12c grnsh blue ('85)	30.00	1.25
a.		12c deep blue	25.00	1.25
b.		Horiz. pair, imperf vert.	300.00	250.00
		Nos. 52-54 (3)	36.15	2.15

For overprints see Nos. O1, O3, O9.

San Martin Type of 1878

1887   *Engr.*
56	A19	24c blue	17.50	1.40

Justo Jose de Urquiza
A30

Lopez
A31

Miguel Juarez Celman — A32

Rivadavia (Large head) — A33

Rivadavia (Small head)
A34

Domingo F. Sarmiento
A35

Nicolas Avellaneda
A36

San Martin
A37

Julio A. Roca
A37a

Belgrano
A37b

Manuel Dorrego — A38

Moreno — A39

Bartolome Mitre — A40

CINCO CENTAVOS.
A33 - Shows collar on left side only.
A34 - Shows collar on both sides. Lozenges in background larger and clearer than in A33.

1888-90   *Litho.*   *Perf. 11½*
57	A30	½c blue	.50	.45
b.		Vert. pair, imperf. horiz.	120.00	65.00
c.		Horiz. pair, imperf. vert.	120.00	65.00
58	A31	2c yellow green	9.25	6.00
b.		Vert. pair, imperf. horiz.	80.00	
c.		Horiz. pair, imperf. vert.	200.00	
59	A32	3c blue green	1.75	.60
b.		Horiz. pair, imperf. horiz.	80.00	
c.		Horiz. pair, imperf. vert.	100.00	
d.		Vert. pair, imperf. btwn.	25.00	
60	A33	5c carmine	8.00	.75
b.		Horiz. pair, imperf. horiz.	100.00	
61	A34	5c carmine	11.00	1.25
b.		Vert. pair, imperf. btwn.		
c.		Horiz. pair, imperf. horiz.		400.00
62	A35	6c red	25.00	15.00
b.		Vert. pair, imperf. btwn.	80.00	
c.		Perf. 12	52.50	42.50
63	A36	10c brown	15.00	1.10
64	A37	15c orange	15.00	1.65
d.		Vert. pair, imperf. between		600.00
64A	A37a	20c green	12.00	1.25
64B	A37b	25c purple	15.00	1.65
65	A38	30c chocolate	21.00	2.50
b.		30c reddish chocolate brown	400.00	80.00
c.		Horiz. pair, imperf. btwn.	400.00	325.00
66	A39	40c slate, perf. 12	25.00	3.00
b.		Perf. 11½	80.00	16.00
b.		Horiz. pair, imperf. btwn. (#66)		600.00
67	A40	50c blue	100.00	8.25
		Nos. 57-67 (13)	258.50	43.45

In this issue there are several varieties of each value, the difference between them being in the relative position of the head to the frame.

Imperf., Pairs
57a	A30	½c	75.00	60.00
58a	A31	2c	55.00	
59a	A32	3c	35.00	25.00
61a	A34	5c		100.00
62a	A35	6c	55.00	
63a	A36	10c	55.00	
64c	A37	15c		200.00
65a	A38	30c	275.00	200.00

Urquiza
A41

Velez Sarsfield
A42

Miguel Juarez Celman
A43

Rivadavia (Large head)
A44

Sarmiento
A45

Juan Bautista Alberdi
A46

1888-89   *Engr.*   *Perf. 11½, 11½x12*
68	A41	½c ultra	.30	.15
a.		Vert. pair, imperf. horiz.		
b.		Imperf., pair	30.00	
69	A42	1c brown	.85	.15
a.		Vert. pair, imperf. horiz.	65.00	
b.		Vert. pair, imperf. btwn.		
c.		Imperf., pair	30.00	
d.		Horiz. pair, imperf. btwn.	100.00	
70	A43	3c blue green	2.50	.70
71	A44	5c rose	2.75	.15
a.		Imperf., pair	40.00	
72	A45	6c blue black	1.40	.55
b.		Perf. 11½x12	12.50	3.00
73	A46	12c blue	5.50	1.75
a.		Imperf., pair	30.00	
b.		bluish paper	8.00	2.00
c.		Perf. 11½	8.25	3.25
		Nos. 68-73 (6)	13.30	3.45

#69-70 exist with papermakers' watermarks.
See No. 77, types A50, A61. For surcharges see Nos. 83-84.

Jose Maria Paz
A48

Santiago Derqui
A49

Rivadavia (Small head)
A50

Avellaneda
A51

Moreno
A53

Mitre
A54

Posadas — A55

1890   *Engr.*   *Perf. 11½*
75	A48	¼c green	.15	.15
76	A49	2c violet	.85	.15
a.		2c purple	.85	.16
b.		2c slate	1.25	.28
c.		Horiz. pair, imperf. btwn.	25.00	
d.		Imperf., pair	35.00	
e.		Perf. 11½x12	5.00	.25
77	A50	5c carmine	1.90	.15
a.		Imperf., pair	50.00	25.00
b.		Perf. 11½x12	5.00	.30
c.		Vert. pair, imperf. btwn.	75.00	60.00
d.		Horiz. pair, imperf. btwn.	75.00	60.00
78	A51	10c brown	1.65	.25
b.		Imperf., pair	150.00	
c.		Vert. pair, imperf. btwn.	225.00	
80	A53	40c olive green	5.00	.80
a.		Imperf., pair	40.00	
b.		Horiz. pair, imperf. btwn.		250.00
81	A54	50c orange	4.00	.80
a.		Imperf., pair	60.00	
b.		Perf. 11½x12	4.25	1.10
82	A55	60c black	15.00	2.75
a.		Imperf., pair		
b.		Vert. pair, imperf. btwn.	125.00	100.00
		Nos. 75-82 (7)	28.55	5.05

Type A50 differs from type A44 in having the head smaller, the letters of "Cinco Centavos" not as tall, and the curved ornaments at sides close to the first and last letters of "Republica Argentina."

Lithographed Surcharge on No. 73 in Black or Red

1890   *Perf. 11½x12*

83	A46	¼c on 12c blue	.40	.40
a.		Perf. 11½	35.00	25.00
b.		Double surcharge	75.00	35.00
c.		Inverted surcharge	80.00	
84	A46	¼c on 12c blue (R)	.40	.40
a.		Double surcharge	52.50	52.50
b.		Perf. 11½	7.00	2.00

Surcharge is different on #83 and 84.
Nos. 83-84 exist as pairs, one without surcharge. These were privately produced.

Rivadavia
A57

Jose de San Martin
A58

Gregorio Araoz de
Lamadrid — A59

Admiral Guillermo
Brown — A60

1891   Engr.   *Perf. 11½*

85	A57	8c carmine rose	1.25	.20
a.		Imperf., pair	75.00	
86	A58	1p deep blue	40.00	5.75
87	A59	5p ultra	200.00	16.00
88	A60	20p green	300.00	45.00
		Nos. 85-88 (4)	541.25	66.95

A 10p brown and a 50p red were prepared but not issued. Values: 10p $1,500 for fine, 50p $1,000 with rough or somewhat damaged perfs.

Velez
Sarsfield — A61

"Santa Maria,"
"Nina" and
"Pinta" — A62

1890   *Perf. 11½*

89	A61	1c brown	.80	.40
b.		Horiz. pair, imperf. btwn.		550.00

Type A61 is a re-engraving of A42. The figure "1" in each upper corner has a short horizontal serif instead of a long one pointing downward. In type A61 the first and last letters of "Correos y Telegrafos" are closer to the curved ornaments below than in type A42. Background is of horizontal lines (crosshatching on No. 69).

1892, Oct. 12   Wmk. 85   *Perf. 11½*

90	A62	2c light blue	6.00	3.00
a.		Double impression	190.00	
91	A62	5c dark blue	8.50	5.00

Discovery of America, 400th anniv. Counterfeits of Nos. 90-91 are litho.

Rivadavia
A63

Belgrano
A64

San Martin — A65

Perf. 11½, 12 and Compound
1892-95   Wmk. 85

92	A63	½c dull blue	.30	.15
a.		½c bright ultra	50.00	25.00
93	A63	1c brown	.35	.15
94	A63	2c green	.35	.15
95	A63	3c orange ('95)	1.00	.15
96	A63	5c carmine	1.50	.15
b.		5c green (error)	350.00	350.00

98	A64	10c carmine rose	10.00	.40
99	A64	12c deep blue ('93)	7.00	.40
100	A64	16c gray	12.50	.55
101	A64	24c gray brown	12.50	.55
b.		Perf. 12	25.00	7.00
102	A64	50c blue green	18.00	.55
b.		Perf. 12	25.00	2.75
103	A65	1p lake ('93)	10.00	.70
a.		1p red brown	17.50	5.00
104	A65	2p dark green	21.00	2.25
b.		Perf. 12	77.50	27.50
105	A65	5p dark blue	38.00	2.75
		Nos. 92-105 (13)	132.50	8.90

The high values of this and succeeding issues are frequently punched with the word "INUTILIZADO," parts of the letters showing on each stamp. These punched stamps sell for only a small fraction of the catalogue values.

Reprints of No. 96b have white gum. The original stamp has yellowish gum. Value $125.

Imperf., Pairs

92b	A63	½c	30.00
93a	A63	1c	55.00
94a	A63	2c	55.00
96a	A63	5c	25.00
98a	A64	10c	55.00
99a	A64	12c	55.00
100a	A64	16c	55.00
101a	A64	24c	55.00
102a	A64	50c	55.00
103b	A65	1p	60.00
105a	A65	5p	140.00

Nos. 102a, 103b and 105a exist only without gum; the other imperfs are found with or without gum, and values are the same for either condition.

Vertical Pairs, Imperf. Between

92c	A63	½c	125.00	
93b	A63	1c	100.00	
94b	A63	2c	50.00	
95a	A63	3c	250.00	
96c	A63	5c	45.00	50.00
98b	A64	10c	100.00	
99b	A64	12c	100.00	

Horizontal Pairs, Imperf. Between

93c	A63	1c	110.00	
94c	A63	2c	55.00	
96d	A63	5c	55.00	45.00
98c	A64	10c	110.00	

1896-97   Wmk. 86

106	A63	½c slate	.50	.15
a.		½c gray blue	.50	.15
b.		½c indigo	.50	.15
107	A63	1c brown	.50	.15
108	A63	2c yellow green	.60	.15
109	A63	3c orange	.60	.15
110	A63	5c carmine	.60	.15
a.		Imperf., pair	100.00	
111	A64	10c carmine rose	8.00	.15
112	A64	12c deep blue	4.00	.15
a.		Imperf., pair	—	
113	A64	16c gray	10.00	.80
114	A64	24c gray brown	10.50	1.25
a.		Imperf., pair	100.00	
115	A64	30c orange ('97)	10.00	.60
116	A64	50c blue green	10.00	.60
117	A64	80c dull violet	18.00	.80
118	A65	1p lake	25.00	.75
119	A65	1p20c black ('97)	10.00	3.50
120	A65	2p dark green	15.00	7.00
121	A65	5p dark blue	90.00	10.00
a.		Perf. 12	325.00	90.00
		Nos. 106-121 (16)	213.30	26.35

Vertical Pairs, Imperf. Between

106c	A63	½c	200.00	
107a	A63	1c	125.00	
108a	A63	2c	125.00	
109a	A63	3c	200.00	
110b	A63	5c	125.00	125.00
112b	A64	12c	125.00	100.00

Horizontal Pairs, Imperf. Between

107b	A63	1c	125.00	
108b	A63	2c	125.00	
110c	A63	5c	125.00	80.00
111a	A64	10c	125.00	
112c	A64	12c	125.00	

Allegory, Liberty Seated
A66   A67

Perf. 11½, 12 and Compound
1899-1903

122	A66	½c yellow brown	.15	.15
123	A66	1c green	.20	.15
124	A66	2c slate	.20	.15
125	A66	3c orange ('01)	.85	.15
126	A66	4c yellow ('03)	1.50	.20
127	A66	5c carmine rose	.20	.15
128	A66	6c black ('03)	1.00	.15
129	A66	10c dark green	1.50	.30
130	A66	12c dull blue	1.00	.50
131	A66	12c olive grn ('01)	1.00	.50
132	A66	15c sea green ('01)	2.75	.50
132B	A66	15c dull blue ('01)	3.00	.50
133	A66	16c orange	7.50	3.75
134	A66	20c claret	2.00	.15
135	A66	24c violet	3.50	.70
136	A66	30c rose	7.50	.40

137	A66	30c vermilion ('01)	3.75	.40
a.		30c scarlet	50.00	2.50
138	A66	50c brt blue	4.75	.40
139	A67	1p bl & blk, perf. 11½	14.00	.65
a.		Center inverted	1,500.	525.00
b.		Perf. 12	250.00	125.00
140	A67	5p orange & blk	57.50	7.00
		Punch cancellation		1.50
141	A67	10p green & blk	50.00	9.25
		Center inverted	2,750.	
		Punch cancellation		1.75
142	A67	20p red & black	200.00	21.00
		Center inverted	3,500.	
		Punch cancellation		1.75
a.		Center invtd.(punch cancel)		2,000.
		Nos. 122-142 (22)	363.85	47.35

Imperf., Pairs

122a	A66	½c	30.00
123a	A66	1c	45.00
124a	A66	2c	15.00
125a	A66	3c	250.00
127a	A66	5c	15.00
128a	A66	6c	45.00
129a	A66	10c	45.00
132a	A66	15c	45.00

Vertical Pairs, Imperf. Between

122b	A66	½c	10.00	10.00
123b	A66	1c	10.00	10.00
124b	A66	2c	5.00	5.00
125b	A66	3c	200.00	150.00
126a	A66	4c	250.00	200.00
127b	A66	5c	5.00	3.00
128b	A66	6c	12.00	10.00
129b	A66	10c	75.00	
132c	A66	15c	12.00	10.00

Horizontal Pairs, Imperf. Between

122c	A66	½c	30.00	20.00
123c	A66	1c	50.00	20.00
124c	A66	2c	10.00	5.00
125c	A66	3c	220.00	150.00
126b	A66	4c	275.00	
127c	A66	5c	10.00	5.00
128c	A66	6c	17.50	10.00
129c	A66	10c	17.50	10.00
132d	A66	15c	35.00	20.00
138a	A66	50c	165.00	

River Port of
Rosario
A68

1902, Oct. 26   *Perf. 11½, 11½x12*

143	A68	5c deep blue	4.50	2.50
a.		Imperf., pair	95.00	
b.		Vert. pair, imperf. btwn.	95.00	
c.		Horiz. pair, imperf. btwn.	75.00	

Completion of port facilities at Rosario.

 San Martin
A69   A70

Perf. 13½, 13½x12½

1908-09   Typo.

144	A69	½c violet	.15	.15
145	A69	1c brnsh buff	.20	.15
146	A69	2c chocolate	.55	.15
147	A69	3c green	.70	.30
148	A69	4c redsh violet	1.40	.30
149	A69	5c carmine	.30	.15
150	A69	6c olive bister	.80	.25
151	A69	10c gray green	1.50	.15
152	A69	12c yellow buff	.40	.40
153	A69	12c dk blue ('09)	1.25	.15
154	A69	15c apple green	1.75	.85
155	A69	20c ultra	1.25	.15
156	A69	24c red brown	3.25	.60
157	A69	30c dull rose	5.00	.60
158	A69	50c black	4.75	.40
159	A70	1p sl bl & pink	11.00	1.75
		Nos. 144-159 (16)	34.25	6.50

The 1c blue was not issued. Value $250.
Wmk. 86 appears on ½, 1, 6, 20, 24 and 50c. Other values have similar wmk. with wavy rays. Stamps lacking wmk. are from outer rows printed on sheet margin.

Pyramid of
May — A71

Nicolas Rodriguez
Pena and Hipolito
Vieytes — A72

Meeting at Pena's
Home — A73

Designs: 3c, Miguel de Azcuenaga (1754-1833) and Father Manuel M. Alberti (1763-1811). 4c, Viceroy's house and Fort Buenos Aires. 5c, Cornelio Saavedra (1759-1829). 10c, Antonio Luis Beruti (1772-1842) and French distributing badges. 12c, Congress building. 20c, Juan Jose Castelli (1764-1812) and Domingo Matheu (1765-1831). 24c, First council. 30c, Manuel Belgrano (1770-1820) and Juan Larrea (1782-1847). 50c, First meeting of republican government, May 25, 1810. 1p, Mariano Moreno (1778-1811) and Juan Jose Paso (1758-1833). 5p, Oath of the Junta. 10p, Centenary Monument. 20p, Jose Francisco de San Martin (1778-1850).

Inscribed "1810 1910"
Various Frames

1910, May 1   Engr.   *Perf. 11½*

160	A71	½c bl & gray bl	.30	.15
161	A72	1c blue grn & blk	.30	.15
b.		Horiz. pair, imperf. btwn.	65.00	
162	A73	2c olive & gray	.20	.15
163	A72	3c green	.70	.15
164	A73	4c dk blue & grn	.70	.25
165	A71	5c carmine	.40	.15
166	A73	10c yel brn & blk	1.75	.20
167	A73	12c brt blue	1.40	.25
168	A72	20c gray brn & blk	3.25	.35
169	A73	24c org brn & bl	1.75	.90
170	A72	30c lilac & blk	1.75	.65
171	A71	50c carmine & blk	4.50	.90
172	A72	1p brt blue	10.00	3.50
173	A73	5p orange & vio	70.00	30.00
		Punch cancel		2.50
174	A71	10p orange & blk	90.00	65.00
		Punch cancel		3.00
175	A71	20p dp blue & ind	150.00	90.00
		Punch cancel		4.50
		Nos. 160-175 (16)	337.00	192.75

Centenary of the republic.

Center Inverted

160a	A71	½c	650.00
161a	A72	1c	650.00
163a	A72	3c	800.00
164a	A73	4c	375.00
167a	A73	12c	650.00
171a	A71	50c	650.00
173a	A73	5p	650.00

Domingo F.
Sarmiento
A87

Agriculture
A88

1911, May 15   Typo.   *Perf. 13½*

176	A87	5c gray brn & blk	.75	.50

Domingo Faustino Sarmiento (1811-88), pres. of Argentina, 1868-74.

Wmk. 86, without Face
1911   Engr.   *Perf. 12*
Size: 19x25mm

177	A88	5c vermilion	.40	.15
178	A88	12c deep blue	5.00	.20
		Set value		.25

Wmk. 86, with Face
1911   Typo.   *Perf. 13½x12½*
Size: 18x23mm

179	A88	½c violet	.15	.15
180	A88	1c brown ocher	.15	.15
181	A88	2c chocolate	.20	.15
a.		Perf. 13½	4.25	1.75
b.		Imperf., pair	26.00	
182	A88	3c green	.40	.15
183	A88	4c brown violet	.35	.25
184	A88	10c gray green	.50	.15
185	A88	20c ultra	4.25	1.00
186	A88	24c red brown	5.25	3.50
187	A88	30c claret	1.75	.50
188	A88	50c black	8.00	.85
		Nos. 179-188 (10)	21.00	6.85

The 5c dull red is a proof. In this issue Wmk. 86 comes: straight rays (4c, 20c, 24c) and wavy rays (2c). All other values exist with both forms.

Wmk. 87 (Horiz. or Vert.)
1912-14   *Perf. 13½x12½*

189	A88	½c violet	.15	.15
190	A88	1c ocher	.15	.15
191	A88	2c chocolate	.30	.15
192	A88	3c green	.60	.15
193	A88	4c brown violet	.60	.15
194	A88	5c red	.15	.15

195	A88	10c deep green	1.40 .15
196	A88	12c deep blue	1.40 .15
197	A88	20c ultra	8.00 .70
198	A88	24c red brown	3.25 1.65
199	A88	30c claret	8.00 .60
200	A88	50c black	5.00 .60
		Nos. 189-200 (12)	29.00 4.75

See Nos. 208-212. For overprints see Nos. OD1-OD8, OD47-OD54, OD102-OD108, OD146-OD152, OD183-OD190, OD235-OD241, OD281-OD284, OD318-OD323.

Perf. 13½

189a	A88	½c	.80 .25
190a	A88	1c	.80 .25
191a	A88	2c	.80 .15
192a	A88	3c	35.00 16.00
193a	A88	4c	1.65 .70
194a	A88	5c	.30 .15
196a	A88	12c	3.25 .80
197a	A88	20c	5.00 .70
		Nos. 189a-197a (8)	47.60 19.00

A89

1912-13   Perf. 13½

201	A89	1p dull bl & rose	6.00 1.00
		Punch cancel	.30
202	A89	5p slate & ol grn	19.00 6.00
			.60
203	A89	10p violet & blue	75.00 9.00
			1.40
204	A89	20p blue & claret	175.00 60.00
		Punch cancel	.60
		Nos. 201-204 (4)	275.00 76.00

1915   Unwmk.   Perf. 13½x12½

208	A88	1c ocher	.50 .15
209	A88	2c chocolate	.50 .15
212	A88	5c red	.50 .15
		Nos. 208-212 (3)	1.50
		Set value	.20

Only these denominations were printed on paper without watermark.

Other stamps of the series are known unwatermarked but they are from the outer rows of sheets the other parts of which are watermarked.

Francisco Narciso de Laprida
A90

Declaration of Independence
A91

1916, July 9   Litho.   Wmk. 87

215	A90	½c violet	.20 .15
216	A90	1c buff	.25 .15

Perf. 13½x12½

217	A90	2c chocolate	.20 .15
218	A90	3c green	.45 .15
219	A90	4c red violet	.65 .15

Perf. 13½

220	A91	5c red	.30 .15
a.		Imperf., pair	40.00
221	A91	10c gray green	1.50 .15
222	A92	12c blue	.65 .15
223	A92	20c ultra	1.00 .25
224	A92	24c red brown	1.65 .75
225	A92	30c claret	1.65 .35
226	A92	50c gray black	3.25 .45
227	A92a	1p slate bl & red	9.25 4.00
		Punch cancel	.50
a.		Imperf., pair	325.00
228	A92a	5p black & gray grn	110.00 40.00
229	A92a	10p violet & blue	110.00 75.00
		Punch cancel	2.50
230	A92a	20p dull blue & cl	165.00 67.50
		Punch cancel	1.00
a.		Imperf., pair	650.00
		Nos. 215-230 (16)	406.00 189.50

Jose de San Martin
A92   A92a

Perf. 13½, 13½x12½

Cent. of Argentina's declaration of independence of Spain, July 9, 1816.

The watermark is either vert. or horiz. on Nos. 215-220, 222; only vert. on No. 221, and only horiz. on Nos. 223-230.

For overprints see #OD9, OD55-OD56, OD109, OD153, OD191-OD192, OD285, OD324.

A93

A94

A94a

Juan Gregorio Pujol — A95

1917   Perf. 13½, 13½x12½

231	A93	½c violet	.20 .15
232	A93	1c buff	.25 .15
233	A93	2c brown	.25 .15
234	A93	3c lt green	.75 .15
235	A93	4c red violet	.80 .40
236	A93	5c red	.25 .15
a.		Imperf., pair	14.00
237	A93	10c gray green	1.50 .15

Perf. 13½

238	A94	12c blue	1.00 .15
239	A94	20c ultra	1.50 .18
240	A94	24c red brown	4.50 2.00
241	A94	30c claret	4.50 .60
242	A94	50c gray black	4.00 .60
243	A94a	1p slate bl & red	4.00 .35
244	A94a	5p black & gray grn	20.00 3.00
			1.50
245	A94a	10p violet & blue	47.50 9.25
		Punch cancel	1.00
246	A94a	20p dull blue & cl	77.50 15.00
		Punch cancel	.80
a.		Center inverted	1,200. 875.00
		Nos. 231-246 (16)	168.50 32.43

The watermark is either vert. or horiz. on Nos. 231-236, 238; only vert. on No. 237, and only horiz. on Nos. 239-246.

1918, June 15   Litho.   Perf. 13½

247	A95	5c bister & gray	.70 .25

Cent. of the birth of Juan G. Pujol (1817-61), lawyer and legislator.

Perf. 13½, 13½x12½

1918-19   Unwmk.

248	A93	½c violet	.15 .15
249	A93	1c buff	.15 .15
a.		Imperf., pair	14.00
250	A93	2c brown	.15 .15
251	A93	3c lt green	.25 .15
252	A93	4c red violet	.25 .15
253	A93	5c red	.15 .15
254	A93	10c gray green	1.10 .15

Perf. 13½

255	A94	12c blue	1.25 .15
256	A94	20c ultra	1.65 .15
257	A94	24c red brown	2.00 .50
258	A94	30c claret	2.50 .30
259	A94	50c gray black	5.50 .26
		Nos. 248-259 (12)	15.10
		Set value	1.50

The stamps of this issue sometimes show letters of papermakers' watermarks.

There were two printings, in 1918 and 1923, using different ink and paper.

Perf. 13½, 13½x12½

1920   Wmk. 88

264	A93	½c violet	.20 .15
265	A93	1c buff	.26 .15
266	A93	2c brown	.26 .15
267	A93	3c green	1.50 .32
268	A93	4c red violet	2.00 1.25
269	A93	5c red	.40 .15
270	A93	10c gray green	3.25 .15

Perf. 13½

271	A94	12c blue	1.75 .15
272	A94	20c ultra	2.50 .15
274	A94	30c claret	8.25 .70
275	A94	50c gray black	5.00 .90
		Nos. 264-275 (11)	25.37
		Set value	3.50

See #292-300, 304-307A, 310-314, 318, 322. For overprints see Nos. OD10-OD20, OD57-OD71, OD74, OD110-OD121, OD154-OD159, OD161-OD162, OD193-OD207, OD209-OD211, OD242-OD252, OD254-OD255, OD286-OD290, OD325-OD328, OD330.

Belgrano's Mausoleum
A96

Creation of Argentine Flag
A97

Gen. Manuel Belgrano — A98

1920, June 18   Perf. 13½

280	A96	2c red	.38 .20
a.		Perf. 13½x12½	.38 .20
281	A97	5c rose & blue	.38 .15
282	A98	12c green & blue	.75 .75
		Nos. 280-282 (3)	1.51 1.10

Belgrano (1770-1820), Argentine general, patriot and diplomat.

Gen. Justo Jose de Urquiza — A99

Bartolome Mitre — A100

1920, Nov. 11

283	A99	5c gray blue	.25 .15

Gen. Justo Jose de Urquiza (1801-70), pres. of Argentina, 1854-60. See No. 303.

1921, June 26   Unwmk.

284	A100	2c violet brown	.25 .20
285	A100	5c light blue	.25 .15
		Set value	.30

Bartolome Mitre (1821-1906), pres. of Argentina, 1862-65.

Allegory, Pan-America — A101

1921, Aug. 25   Perf. 13½

286	A101	3c violet	.55 .20
287	A101	5c blue	.80 .15
288	A101	10c vio brown	1.40 .35
289	A101	12c rose	2.00 .75
		Nos. 286-289 (4)	4.75 1.55

Inscribed "Buenos Aires-Agosto de 1921"
A102

Inscribed "Republica Argentina"
A103

1921, Oct.   Perf. 13½x12½

290	A102	5c rose	.28 .15
a.		Perf. 13½	1.25 .15
291	A102	5c rose	1.50 .15
a.		Perf. 13½	2.50 .15
		Set value	.15

1st Pan-American Postal Cong., Buenos Aires, Aug., 1921.

See Nos. 308-309, 319. For overprints see Nos. OD72, OD160, OD208, OD253, OD329.

Perf. 13½, 13½x12½

1920   Wmk. 89

292	A93	½c violet	2.00 .75
293	A93	1c buff	5.00 .75
294	A93	2c brown	3.00 .75
297	A93	5c red	4.00 .50

298	A93	10c gray green	4.00 .40

Perf. 13½

299	A94	12c blue	3,000. 125.00
300	A94	20c ultra	12.00 .75
		Nos. 292-298,300 (6)	30.00 3.90

1920

303	A99	5c gray blue	275.00 190.00

Perf. 13½, 13½x12½

1922-23   Wmk. 90

304	A93	½c violet	.15 .15
305	A93	1c buff	.15 .15
306	A93	2c brown	.15 .15
307	A93	3c green	.45 .28
307A	A93	4c red violet	3.75 1.00
308	A102	5c rose	2.25 .15
309	A103	5c red	1.50 .15
310	A93	10c gray green	4.75 .28

Perf. 13½

311	A94	12c blue	.85 .15
312	A94	20c ultra	1.25 .15
313	A94	24c red brown	9.25 4.50
314	A94	30c claret	5.50 .50
		Nos. 304-314 (12)	30.00 7.61

Paper with Gray Overprint RA in Sun

Perf. 13½, 13½x12½

1922-23   Unwmk.

318	A93	2c brown	3.00 1.00
319	A103	5c red	2.00 .30

Perf. 13½

322	A94	20c ultra	15.00 1.50
		Nos. 318-322 (3)	20.00 2.80

San Martín
A104   A105

With Period after Value

1923, May   Litho.   Wmk. 90

323	A104	½c red violet	.20 .18
324	A104	1c buff	.32 .15
325	A104	2c dark brown	.32 .15
326	A104	3c lt green	.32 .22
327	A104	4c red brown	.32 .18
328	A104	5c red	.32 .15
329	A104	10c dull green	2.50 .15
330	A104	12c deep blue	.40 .15
331	A104	20c ultra	1.00 .15
332	A104	24c lt brown	2.50 1.50
333	A104	30c claret	7.75 .60
334	A104	50c black	4.00 .35

Without Period after Value

Wmk. 87   Perf. 13½

335	A105	1p blue & red	4.00 .15
336	A105	5p gray lilac & grn	16.00 1.75
		Punch cancel	.60
337	A105	10p claret & blue	55.00 10.50
		Punch cancel	1.00
338	A105	20p slate & brn lake	90.00 30.00
		Punch cancel	.60
a.		Center inverted	
		Nos. 323-338 (16)	184.95 46.33

Nos. 335-338 and 353-356 canceled with round or oval killers in purple (revenue cancellations) sell for one-fifth to one-half as much as postally used copies.

For overprints see Nos. 399-404.

Design of 1923
Without Period after Value
Perf. 13½, 13½x12½

1923-24   Litho.   Wmk. 90

340	A104	½c red violet	.15 .15
341	A104	1c buff	.15 .15
342	A104	2c dk brown	.15 .15
343	A104	3c green	.15 .15
a.		Imperf., pair	8.00
344	A104	4c red brown	.40 .15
345	A104	5c red	.15 .15
346	A104	10c dull green	.28 .15
347	A104	12c deep blue	.48 .15
348	A104	20c ultra	.70 .15
349	A104	24c lt brown	1.65 .70
350	A104	25c purple	.80 .15
351	A104	30c claret	1.65 .15
352	A104	50c black	1.65 .15
353	A105	1p blue & red	.60 .15
354	A105	5p dk violet & grn	15.00 .75
		Punch cancel	.22
355	A105	10p claret & blue	32.50 3.25
		Punch cancel	.22
356	A105	20p slate & lake	47.50 7.50
		Punch cancel	.22
		Nos. 340-356 (17)	105.31 14.15

1931-33
Typographed

343b	A104	3c	1.40	.25
345a	A104	5c	2.50	.15
346a	A104	10c	4.00	.20
347a	A104	12c	8.50	1.50
348a	A104	20c	32.50	1.65
350a	A104	25c	20.00	.75
351a	A104	30c	15.00	.40
	Nos. 343b-351a (7)		83.90	4.90

The typographed stamps were issued only in coils and have a rough impression with heavy shading about the eyes and nose. Nos. 343 and 346 are known without watermark.

Nos. 341-345, 347-349, 351a may be found in pairs, one with period.

See note after No. 338. See Nos. 362-368. For overprints see Nos. OD21-OD33, OD75-OD87, OD122-OD133, OD163-OD175, OD212-OD226, OD256-OD268, OD291-OD304, OD331-OD345.

Rivadavia — A106

1926, Feb. 8   *Perf. 13¹/₂*
357 A106 5c rose   .42 .15

Presidency of Bernardino Rivadavia, cent.

Rivadavia
A108

San Martin
A109

General Post Office,
1926 — A110

General Post
Office,
1826 — A111

1926, July 1   *Perf. 13¹/₂x12¹/₂*
358 A108 3c gray green   .15 .15
359 A109 5c red   .15 .15

Perf. 13¹/₂

360	A110	12c deep blue	.90	.20
361	A111	25c chocolate	1.65	.15
a.		"1326" for "1826"	6.00	.75
	Nos. 358-361 (4)		2.85	
		Set value		.40

Centenary of the Post Office.
For overprints see Nos. OD34, OD88, OD134, OD227-OD228, OD269, OD305, OD346.

Type of 1923-31 Issue
Without Period after Value

1927   Wmk. 205   *Perf. 13¹/₂x12¹/₂*

362	A104	¹/₂c red violet	.25	.25
a.		Pelure paper	1.75	1.50
363	A104	1c buff	.25	.25
364	A104	2c dark brown	.25	.15
a.		Pelure paper	.35	.15
365	A104	5c red	.30	.15
a.		Period after value	3.50	1.90
b.		Pelure paper	.40	.25
366	A104	10c dull green	4.50	2.25
367	A104	20c ultra	18.00	2.25

Perf. 13¹/₂

368	A105	1p blue & red	35.00	7.00
	Nos. 362-368 (7)		58.55	12.30

Arms of
Argentina and
Brazil — A112

Wmk. RA in Sun (90)
1928, Aug. 27   *Perf. 12¹/₂x13*
369 A112 5c rose red   1.00 .25
370 A112 12c deep blue   1.50 .50

Cent. of peace between the Empire of Brazil and the United Provinces of the Rio de la Plata.

Allegory, Discovery
of the New World
A113

"Spain" and
"Argentina"
A114

"America" Offering
Laurels to
Columbus — A115

1929, Oct. 12   Litho.   *Perf. 13¹/₂*
371 A113 2c lilac brown   .85 .25
372 A114 5c light red   .85 .15
373 A115 12c dull blue   2.00 .75
   Nos. 371-373 (3)   3.70 1.15

Discovery of America by Columbus, 437th anniv.

Spirit of
Victory
Attending
Insurgents
A116

March of the Victorious
Insurgents
A117

Perf. 13¹/₂x12¹/₂ (A116), 12¹/₂x13 (A117)

1930

374	A116	¹/₂c violet gray	.15	.15
375	A116	1c myrtle green	.20	.20
376	A116	2c dull violet	.25	.15
377	A116	3c green	.30	.25
378	A116	4c violet	.25	.25
379	A116	5c rose red	.15	.15
380	A116	10c gray black	.70	.35
381	A117	12c dull blue	.50	.25
382	A117	20c ocher	.50	.25
383	A117	24c red brown	2.25	1.50
384	A117	25c green	2.50	1.50
385	A117	30c deep violet	4.50	2.00
386	A117	50c black	6.25	2.50
387	A117	1p sl bl & red	11.00	10.00
388	A117	2p black & org	22.50	10.00
389	A117	5p dull grn & blk	65.00	40.00
390	A117	10p dp red brn & dull blue	90.00	42.50
391	A117	20p yel grn & dl bl	225.00	100.00
392	A117	50p dk grn & vio	600.00	450.00
	Nos. 374-390 (17)		207.00	112.00

Revolution of 1930.
Nos. 387-392 with oval (parcel post) cancellation sell for less.
For overprint see No. 405.

1931   *Perf. 12¹/₂x13*

393	A117	¹/₂c red violet	.15	.15
394	A117	1c gray black	1.25	.50
395	A117	3c green	.60	.30
396	A117	4c red brown	.35	.25
397	A117	5c red	.15	.15
a.		Plane omitted, top left corner	3.00	1.65
398	A117	10c dull green	1.25	.30
	Nos. 393-398 (6)		3.75	1.65

Revolution of 1930.

Stamps of 1924-25 Overprinted in Red or Green

- 6 -
Septiembre
1930 - 1931

1931, Sept. 6   *Perf. 13¹/₂, 13¹/₂x12¹/₂*

399	A104	3c green	.20	.20
400	A104	10c dull green	.60	.60
401	A104	30c claret (G)	3.25	3.25
402	A104	50c black	3.25	3.25

Overprinted in Blue

1930
Septiembre
6
1931

403 A105 1p blue & red   3.75 3.25
404 A105 5p dk violet & grn   70.00 20.00

No. 388 Overprinted in Blue
6 Septiembre 1931

Perf. 12¹/₂x13
405 A117 2p black & orange   13.00 9.00
   Nos. 399-405 (7)   94.05 39.55

1st anniv. of the Revolution of 1930.
See Nos. C30-C34.

Refrigeration
Compressor — A118

Perf. 13¹/₂x12¹/₂
1932, Aug. 29   Litho.
406 A118 3c green   .40 .25
407 A118 10c scarlet   1.25 .15
408 A118 12c gray blue   3.25 1.25
   Nos. 406-408 (3)   4.90 1.65

6th Intl. Refrigeration Congress.

Port of La Plata — A119

Pres. Julio A.
Roca — A120

Municipal
Palace — A121

Cathedral of La
Plata — A122

Dardo
Rocha — A123

Perf. 13¹/₂x13, 13x13¹/₂ (10c)
1933, Jan.

409	A119	3c green & dk brn	.35	.30
410	A120	10c orange & dk vio	.50	.20
411	A121	15c dk blue & dp blue	3.50	1.75
412	A122	20c violet & yel brn	1.65	1.00
413	A123	30c dk grn & vio brn	14.00	5.50
	Nos. 409-413 (5)		20.00	8.75

50th anniv. of the founding of the city of La Plata, Nov. 19th, 1882.

Christ of the
Andes — A124

Buenos Aires
Cathedral
A125

1934, Oct. 1   *Perf. 13x13¹/₂, 13¹/₂x13*
414 A124 10c rose & brown   .70 .20
415 A125 15c dark blue   1.40 .45

32nd Intl. Eucharistic Cong., Oct. 10-14.

"Liberty" with
Arms of Brazil
and Argentina
A126

Symbolical of
"Peace" and
"Friendship"
A127

1935, May 15   *Perf. 13x13¹/₂*
416 A126 10c red   .85 .25
417 A127 15c blue   1.65 .50

Visit of Pres. Getulio Vargas of Brazil.

Belgrano
A128

Sarmiento
A129

Urquiza
A130

Louis Braille
A131

San Martin
A132

Brown
A133

Moreno
A134

Alberdi
A135

Nicolas
Avellaneda
A136

Rivadavia
A137

Mitre
A138

Bull (Cattle
Breeding)
A139

Martin Güemes
A140

Agriculture
A141

Merino Sheep
(Wool) — A142

Sugar Cane
A143

Oil Well
(Petroleum)
A144

Map of South America
A145   A146

Fruit
A147

Iguacu Falls
(Scenic
Wonders)
A148

Grapes
(Vineyards)
A149

Cotton
A150

Two types of A140:
Type I - Inscribed Juan Martin Guemes.
Type II - Inscribed Martin Güemes.

Perf. 13, 13¹/₂x13, 13x13¹/₂

1935-51		**Litho.**	**Wmk. 90**	
418	A128	¹/₂c red violet	.15	.15
419	A129	1c buff	.15	.15
a.		Typo.	.15	.15
420	A130	2c dark brown	.15	.15
421	A131	2¹/₂c black ('39)	.15	.15
422	A132	3c green	.15	.15
423	A132	3c lt gray ('39)	.15	.15
424	A134	3c lt gray ('46)	.15	.15
425	A133	4c lt gray	.15	.15
426	A133	4c sage green ('39)	.15	.15
427	A134	5c yel brn, typo.	.15	.15
a.		Tete beche pair, typo.	4.50	2.25
b.		Booklet pane of 8, typo.		
c.		Booklet pane of 4, typo.		
d.		Litho.	1.40	.15
428	A135	6c olive green	.22	.15
429	A136	8c orange ('39)	.15	.15
430	A137	10c car, typo.	.28	.15
431	A137	10c brown ('42)	.15	.15
a.			.42	.15
432	A138	12c brown	.20	.15
433	A138	12c red ('39)	.15	.15
434	A139	15c slate bl ('36)	.85	.15
435	A139	15c pale ultra ('39)	.52	.15
436	A140	15c lt gray bl (II) ('42)	37.50	1.75
437	A140	20c lt ultra (I)	.60	.15
438	A140	20c lt ultra (II) ('36)	.35	.15
439	A140	20c bl gray (II) ('39)	.35	.15
439A	A139	20c dk bl & pale bl, ('42) 22x33mm	.85	.15
440	A139	20c blue ('51)	.15	.15
a.		Typo.	.15	.15

441	A141	25c carmine ('36)	.22	.15
442	A142	30c org brn ('36)	.52	.15
443	A143	40c dk violet ('36)	.42	.15
444	A144	50c red & org ('36)	.35	.15
445	A145	1p brn blk & lt bl ('36)	17.00	.70
446	A146	1p brn blk & lt bl ('37)	7.00	.16
a.		Chalky paper	42.50	.85
447	A147	2p brn lake & dk ultra ('36)	.85	.15
448	A148	5p ind & ol grn ('36)	6.00	.28
449	A149	10p brn lake & blk ('36)	35.00	1.95
450	A150	20p bl grn & brn ('36)	47.50	7.50
		Nos. 418-450 (34)	158.68	
		Set value		12.00

See Nos. 485-500, 523-540, 659, 668. For overprints see Nos. O37-O41, O43-O51, O53-O56, O58-O78, O108, O112, OD35-OD46, OD89-OD101, OD135-OD145, OD176-OD182C, OD229-OD234F, OD270-OD280, OD306-OD317, OD347-OD357.

No. 439A exists with attached label showing medallion. Value $42.50 unused, $22.50 used.

Souvenir Sheet

A151

Without Period after Value

1935, Oct. 17		**Litho.**	**Imperf.**	
452	A151	Sheet of 4	52.50	30.00
a.		10c dull green	7.00	4.00

Phil. Exhib. at Buenos Aires, Oct. 17-24, 1935. The stamps were on sale during the 8 days of the exhibition only. Sheets measure 83x101mm.

Plaque — A152

1936, Dec. 1			**Perf. 13x13¹/₂**	
453	A152	10c rose	.52	.25

Inter-American Conference for Peace.

Domingo
Faustino
Sarmiento
A153

"Presidente
Sarmiento"
A154

1938, Sept. 5				
454	A153	3c sage green	.18	.15
455	A153	5c red	.18	.15
456	A153	15c deep blue	.60	.15
457	A153	50c orange	1.75	1.00
		Nos. 454-457 (4)	2.71	
		Set value		1.20

50th anniv. of the death of Domingo Faustino Sarmiento, pres., educator and author.

1939, Mar. 16

458	A154	5c greenish blue	.35	.15

Final voyage of the training ship "Presidente Sarmiento."

Allegory of the
UPU — A155

Coat of
Arms — A157

Post Office,
Buenos
Aires — A156

Iguacu
Falls — A158

Bonete Hill,
Nahuel Huapi
Park — A159

Allegory of Modern
Communications
A160

Argentina, Land
of Promise
A161

Lake Frias,
Nahuel Huapi
Park — A162

Perf. 13x13¹/₂, 13¹/₂x13

1939, Apr. 1			**Photo.**	
459	A155	5c rose carmine	.16	.15
460	A156	15c grnsh black	.42	.26
461	A157	20c brt blue	.42	.15
462	A158	25c dp blue grn	.85	.40
463	A159	50c brown	1.65	.65
464	A160	1p brown violet	1.90	.80
465	A161	2p magenta	8.75	5.25
466	A162	5p purple	35.00	16.00
		Nos. 459-466 (8)	49.15	23.66

Universal Postal Union, 11th Congress.

Souvenir Sheets

A163

A164

1939, May 12		**Wmk. 90**	**Imperf.**	
467	A163	Sheet of 4	6.00	4.25
a.		5c rose carmine (A155)	1.25	.75
b.		20c bright blue (A157)	1.25	.75
c.		25c deep blue green (A158)	1.25	.75
d.		50c brown (A159)	1.25	.75
468	A164	Sheet of 4	6.00	4.28

Issued in four forms:

a.	Unsevered horizontal pair of sheets, type A163 at left, A164 at right	15.00	15.00
b.	Unsevered vertical pair of sheets, type A163 at top, A164 at bottom	15.00	15.00
c.	Unsevered block of 4 sheets, type A163 at left, A164 at right	52.50	52.50
d.	Unsevered block of 4 sheets, type A163 at top, A164 at bottom	52.50	52.50

11th Cong. of the UPU and the Argentina Intl. Phil. Exposition (C.Y.T.R.A.).
No. 468 contains Nos. 467a-467d.

Family and New
House — A165

Perf. 13¹/₂x13

1939, Oct. 2		**Litho.**	**Wmk. 90**	
469	A165	5c bluish green	.25	.15

1st Pan-American Housing Congress.

Bird Carrying
Record — A166

Head of Liberty and
Arms of
Argentina — A167

Record and
Winged
Letter — A168

1939, Dec. 11		**Photo.**	**Perf. 13**	
470	A166	1.18p indigo	15.00	7.00
471	A167	1.32p bright blue	15.00	7.00
472	A168	1.50p dark brown	50.00	27.50
		Nos. 470-472 (3)	80.00	41.50

These stamps were issued for the recording and mailing of flexible phonograph records.

Map of the
Americas — A169

1940, Apr. 14			**Perf. 13x13¹/₂**	
473	A169	15c ultramarine	.42	.15

50th anniv. of the Pan American Union.

Souvenir Sheet

Reproductions of Early Argentine
Stamps — A170

Wmk. RA in Sun (90)

1940, May 25		**Litho.**	**Imperf.**	
474	A170	Sheet of 5	9.50	5.50
a.		5c dark blue (Corrientes A2)	1.10	.70
b.		5c red (Argentina A1)	1.10	.70

c. 5c dark blue (Cordoba #1)   1.10   .70
d. 5c red (Argentina A3)   1.10   .70
e. 10c dark blue (Buenos Aires A1)   1.10   .70

100th anniv. of the first postage stamp.

General Domingo French and Colonel Antonio Beruti — A171

1941, Feb. 20   *Perf. 13¹/₂x13*
475 A171 5c dk gray blue & lt blue   .32   .15

Issued in honor of General French and Colonel Beruti, patriots.

Marco M. de Avellaneda A172

Statue of Gen. Julio Roca A173

1941, Oct. 3   *Perf. 13x13¹/₂*
476 A172 5c dull slate blue   .32   .15

Marco M. de Avellaneda, (1814-41), Army leader and martyr.

1941, Oct. 19   Photo.   Wmk. 90
477 A173 5c dark olive green   .32   .15

Dedication of a monument to Lt. Gen. Julio Argentino Roca (1843-1914).

Carlos Pellegrini and Bank of the Nation — A174

1941, Oct. 26   *Perf. 13¹/₂x13*
478 A174 5c brown carmine   .32   .15

Founding of the Bank of the Nation, 50th anniv.

Gen. Juan Lavalle — A175

1941, Dec. 5   *Perf. 13x13¹/₂*
479 A175 5c bright blue   .32   .15

Gen. Juan Galo de Lavalle (1797-1841).

National Postal Savings Bank — A176

1942, Apr. 5   Litho.   *Perf. 13¹/₂x13*
480 A176 1c pale olive   .20   .15

Jose Manuel Estrada — A177

1942, July 13   *Perf. 13x13¹/₂*
481 A177 5c brown violet   .32   .15

Jose Estrada (1842-1894), writer and diplomat. No. 481 exists with label, showing medallion, attached. Value, pair $10.

Types of 1935-51
Perf. 13, 13x13¹/₂, 13¹/₂x13

1942-50   Litho.   Wmk. 288
485 A128 ¹/₂c brown violet   4.75 1.00
486 A129 1c buff ('50)   .15   .15
487 A130 2c dk brown ('50)   .15   .15
488 A132 3c lt gray   16.00 1.25
489 A134 3c lt gray ('49)   .16   .15
490 A137 10c red brown ('49)   .20   .15
491 A138 12c red   .20   .15
492 A140 15c lt gray blue (II)   .28   .15
493 A139 20c dk sl bl & pale bl   1.25 .15
494 A141 25c dull rose ('49)   .60   .15
495 A142 30c orange brn ('49)   1.25 .15
496 A143 40c violet ('49)   8.00 .15
497 A142 50c red & org ('49)   8.00 .18
498 A146 1p brn blk & lt bl   6.50 .18
499 A147 2p brn lake & bl
          ('49)   13.00 .75
500 A148 5p ind & ol grn
          ('49)   50.00 4.50
   Nos. 485-500 (16)   110.49 9.36

No. 493 measures 22x33mm.

Post Office, Buenos Aires — A178

Proposed Columbus Lighthouse — A179

Inscribed: "Correos y Telegrafos."

1942, Oct. 5   Litho.   Perf. 13
503 A178 35c lt ultra   2.75 .15

See Nos. 541-543.

1942, Oct. 12   Wmk. 288
504 A179 15c dull blue   3.00 .15

Wmk. 90
505 A179 15c dull blue   60.00 5.00

450th anniv. of the discovery of America by Columbus.

Jose C. Paz — A180

Books and Argentine Flag — A181

1942, Dec. 15   Wmk. 288
506 A180 5c dark gray   .35   .15

Cent. of the birth of Jose C. Paz, stateman and founder of the newspaper La Prensa.

1943, Apr. 1   Litho.   Perf. 13
507 A181 5c dull blue   .18   .15

1st Book Fair of Argentina.

Arms of Argentina Inscribed "Honesty, Justice, Duty" — A182

1943-50   Wmk. 288   Perf. 13
Size: 20x26mm
508 A182 5c red ('50)   2.50 .15
Wmk. 90
509 A182 5c red   .22   .15
a. 5c dull red, unsurfaced paper   3.00 .15
510 A182 15c green   .70   .15
Perf. 13x13¹/₂
Size: 22x33mm
511 A182 20c dark blue   1.10 .15
   Nos. 508-511 (4)   4.52
         Set value   .30

Change of political organization, June 4, 1943.

Independence House, Tucuman A183

Liberty Head and Savings Bank A184

1943-51   Wmk. 90   Perf. 13
512 A183 5c blue green   .90   .15
Wmk. 288
513 A183 5c blue green ('51)   .35   .15
         Set value   .15

Restoration of Independence House.

1943, Oct. 25   Wmk. 90
514 A184 5c violet brown   .15   .15
Wmk. 288
515 A184 5c violet brown   37.50 3.00

1st conference of National Postal Savings.

Port of Buenos Aires in 1800 — A185

1943, Dec. 11   Wmk. 90
516 A185 5c gray black   .15   .15

Day of Exports.

Warship, Merchant Ship and Sailboat A186

Arms of Argentine Republic A187

1944, Jan. 31   Perf. 13
517 A186 5c blue   .18   .15

Issued to commemorate Sea Week.

1944, June 4
518 A187 5c dull blue   .15   .15

1st anniv. of the change of political organization in Argentina.

St. Gabriel A188

Cross at Palermo A189

1944, Oct. 11
519 A188 3c yellow green   .15   .15
520 A189 5c deep rose   .15   .15
         Set value   .15

Fourth national Eucharistic Congress.

Allegory of Savings A190

Reservists A191

1944, Oct. 24
521 A190 5c gray   .15   .15

20th anniv. of the National Savings Bank.

1944, Dec. 1
522 A191 5c blue   .15   .15

Day of the Reservists.

Types of 1935-51
Perf. 13x13¹/₂, 13¹/₂x13

1945-47   Litho.   Unwmk.
523 A128 ¹/₂c brown vio ('46)   .15   .15
524 A129 1c yellow brown   .15   .15
525 A130 2c sepia   .15   .15
526 A132 3c lt gray (San Mar-
          tin)   .42   .15
527 A134 3c lt gray (Moreno)
          ('46)   .15   .15
528 A135 6c olive grn ('47)   .18   .15
529 A137 10c brown ('46)   1.25 .15
530 A140 15c lt gray bl (II)   .75   .15
531 A139 20c dk sl bl & pale bl   1.25 .15
532 A141 25c dull rose   .45   .15
533 A142 30c orange brown   .35   .15
534 A143 40c violet   1.25 .15
535 A146 50c red & orange   1.25 .15
536 A146 1p brown blk & lt bl   1.65 .15
537 A147 2p brown lake & bl   8.00 .22
538 A148 5p ind & ol grn ('46)   45.00 2.50
539 A149 10p dp cl & int blk   5.50 .15
540 A150 20p bl grn & brn ('46)   5.75 .90
   Nos. 523-540 (18)   73.65
         Set value   5.25

No. 531 measures 22x33mm.

Post Office Type Inscribed: "Correos y Telecommunicaciones"

1945   Unwmk.   *Perf. 13x13¹/₂*
541 A178 35c lt ultra   1.25 .15
Wmk. 90
542 A178 35c lt ultra   1.25 .15
Wmk. 288
543 A178 35c lt ultra   .35   .15
   Nos. 541-543 (3)   2.85
         Set value   .15

Bernardino Rivadavia
A192   A193

Mausoleum of Rivadavia A194

Perf. 13¹/₂x13
1945, Sept. 1   Litho.   Unwmk.
544 A192 3c blue green   .15   .15
545 A193 5c rose   .15   .15
546 A194 20c blue   .28   .15
   Nos. 544-546 (3)   .58
         Set value   .15

Cent. of the death of Bernardino Rivadavia, Argentina's first president.
No. 546 exists with mute label attached. The pair sells for four times the price of the single stamp.

San Martin A195

Monument to Army of the Andes, Mendoza A196

Argentina stamps can be mounted in the Scott annual Argentina supplement.

1945-46   Wmk. 90   Typo. or Litho.
547 A195 5c carmine   .15   .15
  a. Litho. ('46)   .15   .15
Wmk. 288
548 A195 5c carmine, litho.   120.00 20.00
Unwmk.
549 A195 5c carmine ('46)   .52   .15
  a. Litho. ('46)   .20   .15
For overprints see Nos. O42, O57.

1946, Jan. 14   Litho.   Perf. 13½x13
550 A196 5c violet brown   .15   .15
Issued to honor the Unknown Soldier of the War for Independence.

A197   A198

1946, Apr. 12
551 A197 5c Franklin D. Roosevelt   .15   .15

1946, June 4   Perf. 13x13½
Liberty Administering Presidential Oath.
552 A198 5c blue   .15   .15
Inauguration of Pres. Juan D. Perón, 6/4/46.

Argentina Receiving Popular Acclaim — A199

1946, Oct. 17   Perf. 13½x13
553 A199 5c rose violet   .16   .15
554 A199 10c blue green   .24   .15
555 A199 15c dark blue   .48   .18
556 A199 50c red brown   .70   .30
557 A199 1p carmine rose   1.40   .70
  Nos. 553-557 (5)   2.98
  Set value   1.25
First anniversary of the political organization change of Oct. 17, 1945.

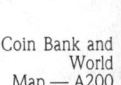

Coin Bank and World Map — A200

1946, Oct. 31   Unwmk.
558 A200 30c dk rose car & pink   .60   .15
Universal Day of Savings, October 31, 1946.

Argentine Industry A201

International Bridge Connecting Argentina and Brazil A202

1946, Dec. 6   Perf. 13x13½
559 A201 5c violet brown   .15   .15
Day of Argentine Industry, Dec. 6.

1947, May 21   Litho.   Perf. 13½x13
560 A202 5c green   .15   .15
Opening of the Argentina-Brazil International Bridge, May 21, 1947.

Map of Argentine Antarctic Claims — A203

Justice — A204

1947-49   Unwmk.   Perf. 13x13½
561 A203 5c violet & lilac   .35   .15
562 A203 20c dk car rose & rose   .70   .15
Wmk. 90
563 A203 20c dk car rose & rose   2.00   .20
Wmk. 288
564 A203 20c dk car rose & rose ('49)   2.00   .15
  Nos. 561-564 (4)   5.05
  Set value   .35
1st Argentine Antarctic mail, 43rd anniv.

1947, June 4   Unwmk.
565 A204 5c brn vio & pale yel   .15   .15
1st anniversary of the Peron government.

Icarus Falling — A205

1947, Sept. 25   Perf. 13½x13
566 A205 15c red violet   .15   .15
Aviation Week.

Training Ship Presidente Sarmiento — A206

1947, Oct. 5   Perf. 13x13½
567 A206 5c blue   .18   .15
50th anniv. of the launching of the Argentine training frigate "Presidente Sarmiento."

Cervantes and Characters from Don Quixote — A207

Perf. 13½x13
1947, Oct. 12   Photo.   Wmk. 90
568 A207 5c olive green   .15   .15
400th anniv. of the birth of Miguel de Cervantes Saavedra, playwright and poet.

Gen. Jose de San Martin — A208

Perf. 13½x13
1947-49   Unwmk.   Litho.
569 A208 5c dull green   .15   .15
Wmk. 288
570 A208 5c dull green ('49)   .15   .15
  Set value   .15
Transfer of the remains of Gen. Jose de San Martin's parents.

School Children — A209

Statue of Araucanian Indian — A210

1947-49   Unwmk.   Perf. 13x13½
571 A209 5c green   .15   .15
Wmk. 90
574 A209 20c brown   .35   .15
Wmk. 288
575 A209 5c green ('49)   .35   .15
  Nos. 571-575 (3)   .85
  Set value   .22
Argentine School Crusade for World Peace.

1948, May 21   Wmk. 90
576 A210 25c yellow brown   .30   .15
American Indian Day, Apr. 19.

Cap of Liberty — A211

Manual Stop Signal — A212

1948, July 16
577 A211 5c ultra   .15   .15
Revolution of June 4, 1943, 5th anniv.

1948, July 22
578 A212 5c chocolate & yellow   .15   .15
Traffic Safety Day, June 10.

Post Horn and Oak Leaves — A213

Argentine Farmers — A214

1948, July 22   Unwmk.
579 A213 5c lilac rose   .15   .15
200th anniversary of the establishment of postal service on the Plata River.

Perf. 13x13½
1948, Sept. 20   Wmk. 288
580 A214 10c red brown   .15   .15
Agriculture Day, Sept. 8, 1948.

Liberty and Symbols of Progress — A215

Perf. 13x13½
1948, Nov. 23   Photo.   Wmk. 287
581 A215 25c red brown   .18   .15
3rd anniversary of President Juan D. Peron's return to power, October 17, 1945.

Souvenir Sheets

A216

15c, Mail coach. 45c, Buenos Aires in 18th cent. 55c, 1st train, 1857. 85c, Sailing ship, 1767.

1948, Dec. 21   Unwmk.   Imperf.
582 A216 Sheet of 4   3.00   3.00
  a. 15c dark green   .45   .45
  b. 45c orange brown   .45   .45
  c. 55c lilac brown   .45   .45
  d. 85c ultramarine   .45   .45

A217

Designs: 85c, Domingo de Basavilibaso (1709-75). 1.05p, Postrider. 1.20p, Sailing ship, 1798. 1.90p, Courier in the Andes, 1772.

583 A217 Sheet of 4   14.00 11.00
  a. 85c brown   3.00   2.50
  b. 1.05p dark green   3.00   2.50
  c. 1.20p dark blue   3.00   2.50
  d. 1.90p red brown   3.00   2.50
200th anniversary of the establishment of regular postal service on the Plata River.

Winged Wheel — A218

Perf. 13½x13
1949, Mar. 1   Wmk. 288
584 A218 10c blue   .22   .15
Railroad nationalization, 1st anniv.

Liberty A219

1949, June 20   Engr.   Wmk. 90
585 A219 1p red & red violet   .42   .15
Ratification of the Constitution of 1949.

Allegory of the UPU A220

1949, Nov. 19
586 A220 25c dk grn & yel grn   .22   .15
75th anniv. of the UPU.

Catalogue values for unused stamps in this section, from this point to the end of the section, are for Never Hinged items.

Gen. Jose de San Martin — A221

San Martin at Boulogne sur Mer A222

Mausoleum of San Martin — A223

Designs: 20c, 50c, 75c, Different Portraits of San Martin. 1p, House where San Martin died.

Engr., Photo. (25c, 1p, 2p)
1950, Aug. 17   Wmk. 90   Perf. 13½
587	A221	10c indigo & dk pur	.15 .15
588	A221	20c red brn & dk brn	.15 .15
589	A222	25c brown	.15 .15
590	A221	50c dk green & ind	.42 .15
591	A221	75c choc & dk grn	.42 .15
a.	Souv. sheet of 4, #587, 588, 590, 591, imperf.	1.25 .80
592	A222	1p dark green	.85 .25
593	A223	2p dp red lilac	.70 .35
	Nos. 587-593 (7)	2.84
	Set value	.90

Death cent. of General Jose de San Martin.

Map Showing Antarctic Claims — A224

1951, May 21   Litho.   Perf. 13x13½
594 A224 1p choc & lt blue   .70 .15
For overprint see No. O52.

Pegasus and Train A225

Communications Symbols — A226

Design: 25c, Ship and dolphin.

1951, Oct. 17   Photo.   Perf. 13½
595 A225 5c dark brown   .15 .15
596 A225 25c Prus green   .24 .15
597 A226 40c rose brown   .28 .15
Nos. 595-597 (3)   .67
Set value   .32
Close of Argentine Five Year Plan.

Woman Voter and "Argentina" A227

1951, Dec. 14   Perf. 13½x13
598 A227 10c brown violet   .15 .15
Granting of women's suffrage.

Eva Peron
A228   A229

Litho. or Engraved (#605)
1952, Aug. 26   Wmk. 90   Perf. 13
599	A228	1c orange brown	.15 .15
600	A228	5c gray	.15 .15
601	A228	10c rose lilac	.15 .15
602	A228	20c rose pink	.15 .15
603	A228	25c dull green	.15 .15
604	A228	40c dull violet	.15 .15
605	A228	45c deep blue	.15 .15
606	A228	50c dull brown	.15 .15

Photo.
607	A229	1p dark brown	.26 .15
608	A229	1.50p deep green	1.50 .15
609	A229	2p brt carmine	.45 .15
610	A229	3p indigo	.75 .15
	Nos. 599-610 (12)	4.16
	Set value	.75
For overprints see Nos. O79-O85.

Inscribed: "Eva Peron"
1952-53   Perf. 13x13½
611	A229	1p dark brown	.30 .15
612	A229	1.50p deep green	1.10 .15
613	A229	2p brt car ('53)	1.10 .15
614	A229	3p indigo	2.75 .15

Engr.
Perf. 13½x13
Size: 30x40mm
615	A229	5p red brown	2.75 .35
616	A229	10p red	7.00 1.40
617	A229	20p green	11.00 4.00
618	A228	50p ultra	20.00 10.00
	Nos. 611-618 (8)	46.00 16.35
For overprints see Nos. O86-O93.

Indian Funeral Urn — A230

1953, Aug. 28   Photo.   Perf. 13x13½
619 A230 50c blue green   .18 .15
Founding of Santiago del Estero, 400th anniv.

Rescue Ship "Uruguay" A231

1953, Oct. 8   Perf. 13½
620 A231 50c ultra   .85 .15
50th anniv. of the rescue of the Antarctic expedition of Otto C. Nordenskjold.

Planting Argentine Flag in the Antarctic — A232

1954, Jan. 20   Engr.   Perf. 13½x13
621 A232 1.45p blue   1.25 .15
50th anniv. of Argentina's 1st antarctic p.o. and the establishing of the La Hoy radio p.o. in the South Orkneys.

Wired Communications A233

Television A234

Perf. 13x13½, 13½x13
1954, Apr.   Photo.   Wmk. 90
622	A233	1.50p shown	.35 .25
623	A233	3p Radio	1.10 .28
624	A234	5p shown	1.40 .55
	Nos. 622-624 (3)	2.85 1.08
Intl. Plenipotentary Conf. of Telecommunications, Buenos Aires, 1952.

Pediment, Buenos Aires Stock Exchange A235

1954, July 13   Perf. 13½x13
625 A235 1p dark green   .28 .15
Cent. of the establishment of the Buenos Aires Stock Exchange.

Eva Peron — A236

1954   Wmk. 90
626 A236 3p dp car rose   1.25 .25
Wmk. 288
627 A236 3p dp car rose   175.00 32.50
2nd anniv. of the death of Eva Peron.

Jose de San Martin A237

Wheat A238

Industry A238a

Eva Peron Foundation Building A239

Cliffs of Humahuaca A240

Gen. Jose de San Martin — A241

Designs: 50c, Buenos Aires harbor. 1p, Cattle ranch (Ganaderia). 3p, Nihuil Dam. 5p, Iguacu Falls, vert. 20p, Mt. Fitz Roy, vert.

Perf. 13½, 13x13½ (80c), 13½x13 (#639, 641-642)
Engraved (#632, 638-642), Photogravure (#634-637)
1954-59   Wmk. 90
628	A237	20c brt red, typo.	.15 .15
629	A237	20c red, litho. ('55)	.60 .15
630	A237	40c red, litho. ('56)	.16 .15
631	A237	40c brt red, typo. ('55)	.25 .15
632	A239	50c blue ('56)	.15 .15
633	A239	50c bl, litho. ('59)	.16 .15
634	A238	80c brown	.22 .15
635	A239	1p brown ('58)	.26 .15
636	A238a	1.50p ultra ('58)	.20 .15
637	A239	2p dk rose lake	.32 .15
638	A239	3p violet brn ('56)	.32 .15
639	A240	5p gray grn ('55)	5.25 .15
a.	Perf. 13½	6.50 .15
640	A240	10p yel grn ('55)	3.75 .15
641	A240	20p dull vio ('55)	7.75 .15
a.	Perf. 13½	9.50 .15
642	A241	50p ultra & ind ('55)	7.75 .15
a.	Perf. 13½	7.75 .15
	Nos. 628-642 (15)	27.29
	Set value	.80

See Nos. 699-700. For similar designs inscribed "Republica Argentina" see Nos. 823-827, 890, 935, 937, 940, 990, 995, 1039, 1044, 1048.
For overprints see Nos. O94-O106, O142, O153-O157.

Allegory — A242

1954, Aug. 26   Typo.   Perf. 13½
643 A242 1.50p slate black   .65 .15
Cent. of the establishment of the Buenos Aires Grain Exchange.

Clasped Hands and Congress Medal — A243

1955, Mar. 21   Photo.   Perf. 13¹/₂x13
644 A243 3p red brown   .80 .15
Issued to publicize the National Productivity and Social Welfare Congress.

Allegory of Aviation — A244

Argentina Breaking Chains — A245

1955, June 18   Wmk. 90   Perf. 13¹/₂
645 A244 1.50p olive gray   .65 .15
Commercial aviation in Argentina, 25th anniv.

1955, Oct. 16   Litho.
647 A245 1.50p olive green   .32 .15
Liberation Revolution of Sept. 16, 1955.

Army Navy and Air Force Emblems A246

Perf. 13¹/₂x13
1955, Dec. 31   Photo.   Wmk. 90
648 A246 3p blue   .42 .15
"Brotherhood of the Armed Forces."

A247   A248

1956, Feb. 3   Perf. 13¹/₂
649 A247 1.50p Justo Jose de Urquiza .28 .15
Battle of Caseros, 104th anniversary.

1956, July 28   Engr.   Perf. 13¹/₂x13
650 A248 2p Coin and die   .28 .15
75th anniversary of the Argentine Mint.

1856 Stamp of Corrientes
A249

Juan G. Pujol — A250

Design: 2.40p, Stamp of 1860-78.

1956, Aug. 21
651 A249 40c dk grn & blue   .15 .15
652 A249 2.40p brn & lil rose   .30 .15
Photo.
653 A250 4.40p brt blue   .65 .18
  a. Souv. sheet of 3, #651-653, imperf. 2.25 2.00
    Nos. 651-653 (3)   1.10 .48
Centenary of Argentine postage stamps.
No. 653a for the Argentine stamp cent. and Philatelic Exhib. for the Cent. of Corrientes Stamps, Oct. 12-21. The 4.40p is photo., the other two stamps and border litho. Colors of 40c and 2.40p differ slightly from engraved stamps.

Felling Trees, La Pampa
A251

Maté Herb and Gourd, Misiones
A252

Design: 1p, Cotton plant and harvest, Chaco.

1956, Sept. 1   Perf. 13¹/₂
654 A251 50c ultra   .15 .15
655 A251 1p magenta   .18 .15
656 A252 1.50p green   .22 .15
    Nos. 654-656 (3)   .55
    Set value   .15
Elevation of the territories of La Pampa, Chaco and Misiones to provinces.

"Liberty"
A253

Florentino Ameghino
A254

Perf. 13¹/₂
1956, Sept. 15   Wmk. 90   Photo.
657 A253 2.40p lilac rose   .30 .15
1st anniv. of the Revolution of Liberation.

1956, Nov. 30
658 A254 2.40p brown   .30 .15
Issued to honor Florentino Ameghino (1854-1911), anthropologist.
For overprint see No. O110.

Adm. Brown Type of 1935-51
1956   Litho.   Perf. 13
Two types:
I. Bust touches upper frame line of name panel at bottom.
II. White line separates bust from frame line.
Size: 19¹/₂-20¹/₂x26-27mm
659 A133 20c dull purple (I)   .18 .15
  a. Type II   .18 .15
  b. Size 19¹/₂x25¹/₄mm (I)   .15 .15
For overprint see No. O108.

Benjamin Franklin
A255

1956, Dec. 22   Photo.   Perf. 13¹/₂
660 A255 40c intense blue   .30 .15
250th anniv. of the birth of Benjamin Franklin.

Frigate "Hercules"
A256

Guillermo Brown
A257

1957, Mar. 2
661 A256 40c brt blue   .15 .15
662 A257 2.40p gray black   .35 .15
    Nos. 661-662,C63-C65 (5)   1.05
    Set value   .42
Admiral Guillermo (William) Brown (1777-1857), founder of the Argentine navy.

Roque Saenz Pena (1851-1914)
A258

Church of Santo Domingo, 1807
A259

1957, Apr. 1
663 A258 4.40p grnsh gray   .45 .15
Roque Saenz Pena, pres. 1910-14.
For overprint see No. O111.

1957, July 6   Wmk. 90
664 A259 40c brt blue green   .15 .15
150th anniv. of the defense of Buenos Aires.

"La Portena" — A260

1957, Aug. 31   Wmk. 90   Perf. 13¹/₂
665 A260 40c pale brown   .18 .15
Centenary of Argentine railroads.

Esteban Echeverria
A261

"Liberty"
A262

1957, Sept. 2   Perf. 13x13¹/₂
666 A261 2p claret   .22 .15
Esteban Echeverria (1805-1851), poet.
For overprint see No. O109.

1957, Sept. 28   Perf. 13¹/₂
667 A262 40c carmine rose   .15 .15
Constitutional reform convention.

Portrait Type of 1935-51
1957, Oct. 28   Litho.   Perf. 13¹/₂
Size: 16¹/₂x22mm
668 A128 5c Jose Hernandez   .15 .15
For overprint see No. O112.

Oil Derrick and Hands Holding Oil — A263

Perf. 13¹/₂
1957, Dec. 21   Wmk. 90   Photo.
669 A263 40c bright blue   .18 .15
50th anniv. of the national oil industry.

Museum, La Plata — A264

1958, Jan. 11
670 A264 40c dark gray   .15 .15
City of La Plata, 75th anniversary.

A265   A266

40c, Locomotive & arms of Argentina & Bolivia.
1p, Map of Argentine-Bolivian boundary & plane.

1958, Apr. 19   Wmk. 90   Perf. 13¹/₂
671 A265 40c slate & dp car   .28 .15
672 A266 1p dark brown   .28 .15
    Set value   .25
Argentine-Bolivian friendship. No. 671 for the opening of the Jacuiba-Santa Cruz railroad; No. 672, the exchange of presidential visits.

Symbols of the Republic
A267

Flag Monument
A268

1958, Apr. 30   Photo. & Engr.
673 A267 40c multicolored   .15 .15
674 A267 1p multicolored   .16 .15
675 A267 2p multicolored   .25 .15
    Nos. 673-675 (3)   .56
    Set value   .25
Transmission of Presidential power.

1958, June 21   Litho.   Wmk. 90
676 A268 40c blue & violet bl   .15 .15
1st anniv. of the Flag Monument of Rosario.

Map of Antarctica A269

Stamp of Cordoba and Mail Coach A270

1958, July 12   *Perf. 13¹/₂*
677 A269 40c car rose & blk   .48 .18
International Geophysical Year, 1957-58.

1958, Oct. 18
678 A270 40c pale blue & slate   .15 .15
   Nos. 678,C72-C73 (3)   .60
     Set value   .25
Contenary of Cordoba postage stamps.

"Slave" by Michelangelo and UN Emblem — A271

Engraved and Lithographed
1959, Mar. 14   **Wmk. 90**   *Perf. 13¹/₂*
679 A271 40c violet brn & gray   .15 .15
10th anniv. (in 1958) of the signing of the Universal Declaration of Human Rights.

Orchids and Globe — A272

1959, May 23   **Photo.**   *Perf. 13¹/₂*
680 A272 1p dull claret   .22 .15
1st International Horticulture Exposition.

Pope Pius XII — A273

William Harvey — A274

1959, June 20   **Engr.**   *Perf. 13¹/₂*
681 A273 1p yellow & black   .18 .15
Pope Pius XII, 1876-1958.

1959, Aug. 8   **Litho.**   **Wmk. 90**
1p, Claude Bernard. 1.50p, Ivan P. Pavlov.

682 A274 50c green   .15 .15
683 A274 1p dark red   .15 .15
684 A274 1.50p brown   .22 .15
   Nos. 682-684 (3)   .52
     Set value   .18
21st International Congress of Physiological Sciences, Buenos Aires.

Type of 1958 and

Domestic Horse A275

Jose de San Martin A276

Tierra del Fuego — A277

Inca Bridge, Mendoza A278

Ski Jumper A279

Mar del Plata A280

Designs: 10c, Cayman. 20c, Llama. 50c, Puma. No. 690, Sunflower. 3p, Zapata Slope, Catamarca. 12p, 23p, 25p, Red Quebracho tree. 20p, Nahuel Huapi Lake. 22p, "Industry" (cogwheel and factory).
Two overall paper sizes for 1p, 5p:
  I -   27x37¹/₂mm or 37¹/₂x27mm.
  II -   27x39mm or 39x27mm.

Perf. 13x13¹/₂
1959-70   **Litho.**   **Wmk. 90**
685 A275 10c slate green   .15 .15
686 A275 20c dl red brn ('61)   .15 .15
687 A275 50c bister ('60)   .15 .15
688 A275 50c bis, typo. ('60)   .18 .15
689 A275 1p rose red   .15 .15

Perf. 13¹/₂
690 A278 1p brn, photo., I ('61)   .15 .15
  a.   Paper II ('69)   .18
690B A278 1p brown, I   .65 .15
691 A276 2p rose red ('61)   .25 .15
692 A276 2p red, typo. (19¹/₂ x
          26mm) ('61)   .32 .15
  a.   Redrawn (19¹/₂ x 25mm)   4.75 .15
693 A277 3p dk bl, photo. ('60)   .16 .15
694 A276 4p red, typo ('62)   .18 .15
694A A276 4p red ('62)   .38 .15
695 A277 5p gray brn, photo., I   .38 .15
  e.   5p dark brown, paper II ('70)   6.25 .15
695A A276 8p ver ('65)   1.25 .15
695B A276 8p ver, typo. ('65)   .32 .15
695C A276 10p ver ('65)   .65 .15
695D A276 10p red, typo. ('66)   .48 .15

Photo.
696 A278 10p lt red brn ('60)   .48 .15
697 A278 12p dk brn vio ('62)   .80 .15
697A A278 12p dk brn, litho.
          ('64)   8.00 .15
698 A278 20p Prus grn ('60)   2.75 .15
698A A276 20p red, typo. ('67)   .25 .15
699 A238a 22p ultra ('62)   1.50 .15
700 A238a 22p ultra, litho. ('62)   24.00 .15
701 A278 23p green ('65)   4.75 .15
702 A278 25p dp vio ('66)   1.25 .15
703 A278 25p pur, litho. ('66)   6.25 .15
704 A279 100p blue ('61)   5.00 .15
705 A280 300p dp vio ('62)   2.75 .15
   Nos. 685-705 (29)   63.73
     Set value   1.50

See Nos. 882-887, 889, 892, 923-925, 928-930, 938, 987-989, 991.
For overprints and surcharges see Nos. 1076, C82-C83, O113-O118, O122-O124, O126-O141, O143-O145, O163.
The 300p remained on sale as a 3p stamp after the 1970 currency exchange.

Symbolic Sailboat — A281

Child Playing with Doll — A282

1959, Oct. 3   **Litho.**   *Perf. 13¹/₂*
706 A281 1p blk, red & bl   .15 .15
Red Cross sanitary education campaign.

1959, Oct. 17
707 A282 1p red & blk   .15 .15
Issued for Mother's Day, 1959.

Buenos Aires 1p Stamp of 1859 — A283

1959, Nov. 21   **Wmk. 90**   *Perf. 13¹/₂*
708 A283 1p gray & dk bl   .15 .15
Issued for the Day of Philately.

Bartolomé Mitre and Justo José de Urquiza A284

1959, Dec. 12   **Photo.**   *Perf. 13¹/₂*
709 A284 1p purple   .15 .15
Treaty of San Jose de Flores, centenary.

WRY Emblem A285

Abraham Lincoln A286

1960, Apr. 7   **Litho.**   **Wmk. 90**
710 A285 1p bister & car   .15 .15
711 A285 4.20p apple grn & dp claret   .32 .20
     Set value   .27
World Refugee Year, July 1, 1959-June 30, 1960. See No. B25.

1960, Apr. 14   **Photo.**   *Perf. 13¹/₂*
712 A286 5p ultra   .42 .18
Sesquicentennial (in 1959) of the birth of Abraham Lincoln.

Cornelio Saavedra and Cabildo, Buenos Aires — A287

"Cabildo" and: 2p, Juan José Paso. 4.20p, Manuel Alberti and Miguel Azcuénaga. 10.70p, Juan Larrea and Domingo Matheu.

Perf. 13¹/₂
1960, May 28   **Wmk. 90**   **Photo.**
713 A287 1p rose lilac   .15 .15
714 A287 2p bluish grn   .15 .15
715 A287 4.20p gray & grn   .24 .15
716 A287 10.70p gray & ultra   .45 .20
   Nos. 713-716,C75-C76 (6)   1.49
     Set value   .55
150th anniversary of the May Revolution. Souvenir sheets are Nos. C75a and C76a.

Luis Maria Drago — A288

Juan Bautista Alberdi — A289

1960, July 8
717 A288 4.20p brown   .22 .15
Ccentenary of the birth of Dr. Luis Maria Drago, statesman and jurist.

1960, Sept. 10   **Wmk. 90**   *Perf. 13¹/₂*
718 A289 1p green   .15 .15
150th anniversary of the birth of Juan Bautista Alberdi, statesman and philosopher.

Map of Argentina and Antarctic Sector — A290

Caravel and Emblem — A291

1960, Sept. 24   **Litho.**   *Perf. 13¹/₂*
719 A290 5p violet   .85 .22
National census of 1960.

1960, Oct. 1   **Photo.**
720 A291 1p dk olive grn   .15 .15
721 A291 5p brown   .45 .15
   Nos. 720-721,C78-C79 (4)   1.15
     Set value   .15
8th Congress of the Postal Union of the Americas and Spain.

Virgin of Luján, Patroness of Argentina A292

Argentine Boy Scout Emblem A293

1960, Nov. 12   **Wmk. 90**   *Perf. 13¹/₂*
722 A292 1p dark blue   .15 .15
First Inter-American Marian Congress.

1961, Jan. 17   **Litho.**
723 A293 1p car rose & blk   .28 .15
International Patrol Encampment of the Boy Scouts, Buenos Aires.

"Shipment of Cereals," by Quinquela Martin A294

1961, Feb. 11   **Photo.**   *Perf. 13¹/₂*
724 A294 1p red brown   .28 .15
Export drive: "To export is to advance."

Naval Battle of San Nicolás — A295

Mariano Moreno by Juan de Dios Rivera — A296

1961, Mar. 2   *Perf. 13¹/₂*
725 A295 2p gray   .28 .15
Naval battle of San Nicolas, 150th anniv.

1961, Mar. 25   *Perf. 13¹/₂*
726 A296 2p blue   .15 .15
Mariano Moreno (1778-1811), writer, politician, member of the 1810 Junta.

Emperor Trajan Statue — A297

Rabindranath Tagore — A298

1961, Apr. 11
727 A297 2p slate green   .15 .15
Visit of Pres. Giovanni Gronchi of Italy to Argentina, April 1961.

1961, May 13   Photo.   *Perf. 13¹/₂*
728 A298 2p purple, *grysh*   .15 .15
Centenary of the birth of Rabindranath Tagore, Indian poet.

San Martin Statue, Madrid — A299

1961, May 24   Wmk. 90
729 A299 1p olive gray   .15 .15
Unveiling of a statue of General José de San Martin in Madrid.

Manuel Belgrano — A300

1961, June 17   *Perf. 13¹/₂*
730 A300 2p violet blue   .15 .15
Erection of a monument by Hector Rocha, to General Manuel Belgrano in Buenos Aires.

Explorers, Sledge and Dog Team — A301

1961, Aug. 19   Photo.   Wmk. 90
731 A301 2p black   .70 .22
10th anniversary of the General San Martin Base, Argentine Antarctic.

Spanish Conquistador and Sword — A302

Sarmiento Statue by Rodin, Buenos Aires — A303

1961, Aug. 19   Litho.
732 A302 2p red & blk   .15 .15
First city of Jujuy, 400th anniversary.

1961, Sept. 9   Photo.
733 A303 2p violet   .15 .15
Domingo Faustino Sarmiento (1811-88), political leader and writer.

Symbol of World Town Planning A304

1961, Nov. 25   Litho.   *Perf. 13¹/₂*
734 A304 2p ultra & yel   .15 .15
World Town Planning Day, Nov. 8.

Manuel Belgrano Statue, Buenos Aires A305

Grenadier, Flag and Regimental Emblem A306

1962, Feb. 24   Photo.
735 A305 2p Prus blue   .15 .15
150th anniversary of the Argentine flag.

1962, Mar. 31   Wmk. 90   *Perf. 13¹/₂*
736 A306 2p carmine rose   .15 .15
150th anniversary of the San Martin Grenadier Guards regiment.

Mosquito and Malaria Eradication Emblem — A307

1962, Apr. 7   Litho.
737 A307 2p vermilion & blk   .15 .15
WHO drive to eradicate malaria.

Church of the Virgin of Lujàn — A308

Bust of Juan Jufrè — A309

1962, May 12   *Perf. 13¹/₂*
738 A308 2p org brn & blk   .15 .15
75th anniversary of the pontifical coronation of the Virgin of Lujan.

1962, June 23   Photo.
739 A309 2p Prus blue   .15 .15
Founding of San Juan, 4th cent.

"Soaring into Space" A310

Juan Vucetich A311

1962, Aug. 18   Litho.   *Perf. 13¹/₂*
740 A310 2p maroon, blk & bl   .15 .15
Argentine Air Force, 50th anniversary.

1962, Oct. 6   Photo.   Wmk. 90
741 A311 2p green   .15 .15
Juan Vucetich (1864-1925), inventor of the Argentine system of fingerprinting.

Domingo F. Sarmiento A312

February 20th Monument, Salta A313

Design: 4p, Jose Hernadez.

1962-66   Photo.   *Perf. 13¹/₂*
742   A312 2p deep green   .65 .15
     Litho.
742A A312 2p lt green ('64)   .55 .15
     Photo.
742B A312 4p dull red ('65)   .45 .15
     Litho.
742C A312 4p rose red ('66)   .60 .15
     Nos. 742-742C (4)   2.25
     Set value   .20
See No. 817-819. For overprints see Nos. O119-O121, O125, O149.

1963, Feb. 23   Photo.   Wmk. 90
743 A313 2p dark green   .15 .15
150th anniversary of the Battle of Salta, War of Independence.

Gear Wheels — A314

1963, Mar. 16   Litho.   *Perf. 13¹/₂*
744 A314 4p gray, blk & brt rose   .15 .15
Argentine Industrial Union, 75th anniv.

National College, Buenos Aires — A315

Child Draining Cup — A316

1963, Mar. 16   Wmk. 90
745 A315 4p dull org & blk   .18 .15
National College of Buenos Aires, cent.

1963, Apr. 6
746 A316 4p multicolored   .15 .15
FAO "Freedom from Hunger" campaign.

Frigate "La Argentina," 1817, by Emilio Biggeri — A317

1963, May 18   Photo.
747 A317 4p bluish green   .28 .15
Issued for Navy Day, May 17.

Seat of 1813 Assembly and Official Seal — A318

1963, July 13   Litho.   *Perf. 13¹/₂*
748 A318 4p lt blue & blk   .15 .15
150th anniversary of the 1813 Assembly.

Battle of San Lorenzo, 1813 A319

1963, Aug. 24
749 A319 4p grn & blk, *grnsh*   .20 .15
Sesquicentennial of the Battle of San Lorenzo.

Queen Nefertari Offering Papyrus Flowers, Abu Simbel — A320

1963, Sept. 14   *Perf. 13¹/₂*
750 A320 4p ocher, blk & bl grn   .28 .15
Campaign to save the historic monuments in Nubia.

Government House, Buenos Aires A321

1963, Oct. 12   Wmk. 90   *Perf. 13¹/₂*
751 A321 5p rose & brown   .16 .15
Inauguration of President Arturo Illia.

"Science" A322

Francisco de las Carreras, Supreme Court Justice A323

1963, Oct. 16   Litho.
752 A322 4p org brn, bl & blk   .15 .15
10th Latin-American Neurosurgery Congress.

1963, Nov. 23   Photo.   *Perf. 13¹/₂*
753 A323 5p bluish green   .15 .15
Centenary of judicial power.

Blackboards
A324

1963, Nov. 23   **Litho.**
754 A324 5p red, blk & bl   .15 .15
Issued to publicize "Teachers for America"
through the Alliance for Progress program.

Kemal Atatürk   "Payador" by
A325   Juan Carlos
                             Castagnino
                             A326

1963, Dec. 28   Photo.   Perf. 13½
755 A325 12p dark gray   .28 .15
25th anniversary of the death of Kemal Atatürk,
president of Turkey.

1964, Jan. 25   **Litho.**
756 A326 4p ultra, blk & lt bl   .32 .15
Fourth National Folklore Festival.

Maps of South
Georgia, South
Orkney and
South Sandwich
Islands — A327

4p, Map of Argentina & Antarctic claims, vert.

1964, Feb. 22   Wmk. 90   Perf. 13½
Size: 33x22mm
757 A327 2p lt & dk bl & bister   1.25   .24
Size: 30x40mm
758 A327 4p lt & dk bl & ol grn   1.75   .30
    Nos. 757-758,C92 (3)   4.75 1.24
60th anniversary of Argentina's claim to
Antarctic territories.

Jorge Newbery
in
Cockpit — A328

1964, Feb. 23   **Photo.**
759 A328 4p deep green   .16 .15
Newbery, aviator, 50th death anniv.

John F.   José Brochero by
Kennedy — A329   José
                             Cuello — A330

1964, Apr. 14   Engr.   Wmk. 90
760 A329 4p claret & dk bl   .35 .15
President John F. Kennedy (1917-63).

1964, May 9   Photo.   Perf. 13½
761 A330 4p light sepia   .16 .15
50th anniversary of the death of Father Jose
Gabriel Brochero.

Soldier of Patricios
Regiment — A331

1964, May 29   Litho.   Wmk. 90
762 A331 4p blk, ultra & red   .38 .20
Issued for Army Day. Later Army Day stamps,
inscribed "Republica Argentina," are of type A340a.

Pope John
XXIII — A332

1964, June 27   **Engr.**
763 A332 4p orange & blk   .22 .15
Issued in memory of Pope John XXIII.

University of   Pigeons and UN
Cordoba   Building,
Arms — A333   NYC — A334

1964, Aug. 22   Litho.   Wmk. 90
764 A333 4p blk, ultra & yel   .15 .15
350th anniv. of the University of Cordoba.

1964, Oct. 24   **Perf. 13½**
765 A334 4p dk blue & lt blue   .15 .15
Issued for United Nations Day.

Joaquin V.   Julio Argentino
Gonzalez — A335   Roca — A336

1964, Nov. 14   **Photo.**
766 A335 4p dk rose carmine   .15 .15
Centenary (in 1963) of the birth of Joaquin V.
Gonzalez, writer.

1964, Dec. 12   **Perf. 13½**
767 A336 4p violet blue   .15 .15
General Julio A. Roca, (1843-1914), president of
Argentina, (1880-86, 1898-1904).

Market at
Montserrat Square,
by Carlos
Morel — A337

1964, Dec. 19   **Photo.**
768 A337 4p sepia   .30 .18
19th century Argentine painter Carlos Morel.

Icebreaker General San   Girl with Piggy
Martin — A338   Bank — A339

Design: 2p, General Belgrano Base, Antarctica.

1965   **Perf. 13½**
769 A338 2p dull purple   .42 .15
770 A338 4p ultra   .48 .15
Issued to publicize the national territory of Tierra
del Fuego, Antarctic and South Atlantic Isles.
Issue dates: 4p, Feb. 27; 2p, June 5.

1965, Apr. 3   **Litho.**
771 A339 4p red org & blk   .15 .15
National Postal Savings Bank, 50th anniv.

Sun and
Globe — A340

1965, May 29
772 A340 4p blk, org & dl bl   .24 .15
    Nos. 772,C98-C99 (3)   1.66   .85
International Quiet Sun Year, 1964-65.

Hussar of Pueyrredon   Ricardo Rojas
Regiment   (1882-1957)
A340a   A341

1965, June 5   Wmk. 90   Perf. 13½
773 A340a 8p dp ultra, blk & red   .48 .18
Issued for Army Day. See Nos. 796, 838, 857,
893, 944, 958, 974, 1145.

1965, June 26   **Photo.**
Portraits: No. 775, Ricardo Guiraldes (1886-
1927). No. 776, Enrique Larreta (1873-1961). No.
777, Leopoldo Lugones (1874-1938). No. 778,
Roberto J. Payro (1867-1928).

774 A341 8p brown   .35 .16
775 A341 8p brown   .35 .16
776 A341 8p brown   .35 .16
777 A341 8p brown   .35 .16
778 A341 8p brown   .35 .16
    Nos. 774-778 (5)   1.75   .80
Issued to honor Argentine writers. Printed se-
tenant in sheets of 100 (10x10); 2 horizontal rows
of each design with Guiraldes in top rows and Rojas
in bottom rows.

Hipolito
Yrigoyen — A342

1965, July 3   **Litho.**
779 A342 8p pink & black   .20 .15
Hipolito Yrigoyen (1852-1933), president of
Argentina 1916-22, 1928-30.

Children
Looking
Through
Window
A343

1965, July 24   **Photo.**
780 A343 8p salmon & blk   .24 .15
International Seminar on Mental Health.

Child's
Funerary
Urn and
16th
Century
Map
A344

1965, Aug. 7   **Litho.**
781 A344 8p lt grn, dk red, brn &
            ocher   .32 .15
City of San Miguel de Tucuman, 400th anniv.

Cardinal Cagliero   Dante Alighieri
A345   A346

1965, Aug. 21   **Photo.**
782 A345 8p violet   .20 .15
Juan Cardinal Cagliero (1839-1926), missionary
to Argentina and Bishop of Magida.

1965, Sept. 16   Wmk. 90   Perf. 13½
783 A346 8p light ultra   .28 .15
Dante Alighieri (1265-1321), Italian poet.

Clipper "Mimosa"
and Map of
Patagonia
A347

1965, Sept. 25   **Litho.**
784 A347 8p red & black   .28 .15
Centenary of Welsh colonization of Chubut, and
the founding of the city of Rawson.

Map of Buenos
Aires, Cock and
Compass Emblem
of Federal
Police — A348

1965, Oct. 30   Photo.   Perf. 13½
785 A348 8p carmine rose   .32 .15
Issued for Federal Police Day.

Child's Drawing of Children — A349

1965, Nov. 6   Litho.   Wmk. 90
786 A349 8p lt yel grn & blk   .28 .15
Public education law, 81st anniversary.

Church of St. Francis, Catamarca A350

Ruben Dario A351

1965, Dec. 8
787 A350 8p org yel & red brn   .20 .15
Brother Mamerto de la Asuncion Esquiu, preacher, teacher and official of 1885 Provincial Constitutional Convention.

Litho. and Photo.
1965, Dec. 22   Perf. 13½
788 A351 15p bl vio, gray   .20 .15
Ruben Dario (pen name of Felix Ruben Garcia Sarmiento, 1867-1916), Nicaraguan poet, newspaper correspondent and diplomat.

"The Orange Seller" A352

Pueyrredon Paintings: No. 790, "Stop at the Grocery Store." No. 791, "Landscape at San Fernando" (sailboats). No. 792, "Bathing Horses at River Plata."

1966, Jan. 29   Photo.   Perf. 13½
789 A352 8p bluish green   .70 .40
790 A352 8p bluish green   .70 .40
791 A352 8p bluish green   .70 .40
792 A352 8p bluish green   .70 .40
 a.   Block of 4, #789-792 + 2 labels   2.80 1.60
Prilidiano Pueyrredon (1823-1870), painter.

Sun Yat-sen, Flags of Argentina and China — A353

1966, Mar. 12   Wmk. 90   Perf. 13½
793 A353 8p dk red brown   .70 .22
Dr. Sun Yat-sen (1866-1925), founder of the Republic of China.

Souvenir Sheet

Rivadavia Issue of 1864 — A354

Wmk. 90
1966, Apr. 20   Litho.   Imperf.
794 A354   Sheet of 3   .95 .95
 a.   4p gray & red brown   .15 .15
 b.   5p gray & green   .15 .15
 c.   8p gray & dark blue   .16 .16
2nd Rio de la Plata Stamp Show, Buenos Aires, Mar. 16-24.

People of Various Races and WHO Emblem A355

1966, Apr. 23   Perf. 13½
795 A355 8p brown & blk   .28 .15
Opening of the WHO Headquarters, Geneva.

Soldier Type of 1965
Army Day: 8p, Cavalryman, Guemes Infernal Regiment.

1966, May 28   Litho.
796 A340a 8p multicolored   .55 .30

Coat of Arms — A356

Arms: a, Buenos Aires. b, Federal Capital. c, Catamarca. d, Cordoba. e, Corrientes. f, Chaco. g, Chubut. h, Entre Rios. i, Formosa. j, Jujuy. k, La Pampa. l, La Rioja. m, Mendoza. n, Misiones. o, Neuquen. p, Salta. q, San Juan. r, San Luis. s, Santa Cruz. t, Santa Fe. u, Santiago del Estero. v, Tucuman. w, map of Rio Negro. x, map of Tierra del Fuego, Antarctica. y, South Atlantic Islands.

1966, July 30   Wmk. 90   Perf. 13½
797   Sheet of 25   40.00
 a.-y.   A356 10p black & multi   1.00 .65
150th anniv. of Argentina's Declaration of Independence.

Three Crosses, Caritas Emblem — A357

1966, Sept. 10   Litho.   Perf. 13½
798 A357 10p ol grn, blk & lt bl   .22 .15
Caritas, charity organization.

Hilario Ascasubi (1807-75) — A358

Portraits: #800, Estanislao del Campo (1834-80). #801, Miguel Cane (1851-1905). #802, Lucio V. Lopez (1848-94). #803, Rafael Obligado (1851-1920). #804, Luis Agote (1868-1954), M.D. #805, Juan B. Ambrosetti (1865-1917), naturalist and archaeologist. #806, Miguel Lillo (1862-1931), botanist and chemist. #807, Francisco P. Moreno (1852-1919), naturalist and paleontologist. #808, Francisco J. Muñiz (1795-1871), physician.

1966   Photo.   Wmk. 90
799 A358 10p dk blue green   .42 .35
800 A358 10p dk blue green   .42 .35
801 A358 10p dk blue green   .42 .35
802 A358 10p dk blue green   .42 .35
803 A358 10p dk blue green   .42 .35
804 A358 10p deep violet   .42 .35
805 A358 10p deep violet   .42 .35
806 A358 10p deep violet   .42 .35

807 A358 10p deep violet   .42 .35
808 A358 10p deep violet   .42 .35
 Nos. 799-808 (10)   4.20 3.50
Nos. 799-803 issued Sept. 17 to honor Argentine writers. Printed se-tenant in sheets of 100 (10x10); 2 horizontal rows of each portrait. Nos. 804-808 issued Oct. 22 to honor Argentine scientists; 2 horizontal rows of each portrait. Scientists set has value at upper left, frame line with rounded corners.

Anchor — A359

1966, Oct. 8   Litho.
809 A359 4p multicolored   .22 .15
Argentine merchant marine.

Flags and Map of the Americas — A360

Argentine National Bank — A361

1966, Oct. 29   Perf. 13½
810 A360 10p gray & multi   .24 .15
7th Conference of American Armies.

1966, Nov. 5   Photo.
811 A361 10p brt blue green   .20 .15
75th anniv. of the Argentine National Bank.

La Salle Monument and College, Buenos Aires — A362

1966, Nov. 26   Litho.   Perf. 13½
812 A362 10p brown org & blk   .20 .15
75th anniv. of the Colegio de la Salle, Buenos Aires, and to honor Saint Jean Baptiste de la Salle (1651-1719), educator.

Map of Argentine Antarctica and Expedition Route — A363

1966, Dec. 10   Wmk. 90
813 A363 10p multicolored   .70 .45
1965 Argentine Antarctic expedition, which planted the Argentine flag on the South Pole. See No. 851.

Juan Martin de Pueyrredon A364

Gen. Juan de Las Heras A365

1966, Dec. 17   Photo.   Perf. 13½
814 A364 10p dull red brn   .18 .15
Issued to honor Juan Martin de Pueyrredon (1777-1850), Governor of Cordoba and of the United Provinces of the River Plata.

1966, Dec. 17   Engr.
815 A365 10p black   .18 .15
Issued to honor Gen. Juan Gregorio de Las Heras (1780-1866), Peruvian field marshal and aide-de-camp to San Martin.

Inscribed "Republica Argentina" Types of 1955-61 and

Guillermo Brown — A366

Trout Leaping in National Park — A366a

Designs: 6p, Jose Hernandez. 50p, Gen. Jose de San Martin. 500p, Red deer in forest.

Two overall paper sizes for 6p, 50p (No. 827) and 90p:
I - 27x37½mm
II - 27x39mm

1965-68   Wmk. 90   Photo.   Perf. 13½
817 A366   6p rose red, litho, I ('67)   1.25 .15
818 A366   6p rose red ('67)   2.25 .15
819 A366   6p brn, 15x22mm ('68)   .15 .15
823 A238a 43p dk car rose   6.25 .15
824 A238a 45p brn ('66)   4.25 .15
825 A238a 45p brn, litho ('67)   7.00 .15
826 A241 50p dk bl, 29x40mm   7.00 .15
827 A241 50p dk bl, 22x31½mm, I ('67)   4.75 .15
 a.   Paper II   2.75 .15
828 A366 90p ol bis, I ('67)   3.00 .15
 a.   Paper II   12.00 .15

Engr.
829   A495   500p yellow grn ('66)   1.40 .28
829A A366a 1,000p vio bl ('68)   5.50 1.25
 Nos. 817-829A (11)   42.80
  Set value   2.25
The 500p and 1,000p remained on sale as 5p and 10p stamps after the 1970 currency exchange. See Nos. 888, 891, 939, 941, 992, 1031, 1040, 1045-1047. For surcharge and overprints see Nos. 1077, O153-O158, O162.

Pre-Columbian Pottery — A367

1967, Feb. 18   Litho.   Perf. 13½
830 A367 10p multicolored   .28 .15
20th anniv. of UNESCO.

"The Meal" by Fernando Fader A368

1967, Feb. 25   Photo.   Wmk. 90
831 A368 10p red brown   .28 .15

Issued in memory of the Argentine painter Fernando Fader (1882-1935).

Col. Juana Azurduy de Padilla (1781-1862), Soldier — A369

Schooner "Invincible," 1811 — A370

Famous Argentine Women: #833, Juana Manuela Gorriti, writer. #834, Cecilia Grierson (1858-1934), physician. #835, Juana Paula Manso (1819-75), writer and educator. #836, Alfonsina Storni (1892-1938), writer and educator.

1967, May 13   Photo.   Perf. 13½
832 A369 6p dark brown   .32 .20
833 A369 6p dark brown   .32 .20
834 A369 6p dark brown   .32 .20
835 A369 6p dark brown   .32 .20
836 A369 6p dark brown   .32 .20
    Nos. 832-836 (5)   1.60 1.00

Printed se-tenant in sheets of 100 (10x10); 2 horizontal rows of each portrait.

1967, May 20   Litho.
837 A370 20p multicolored   .85 .35

Issued for Navy Day.

Soldier Type of 1965

Army Day: 20p, Highlander (Arribeños Corps).

1967, May 27
838 A340a 20p multicolored   .70 .28

Souvenir Sheet

Manuel Belgrano and José Artigas — A371

1967, June 22   Imperf.
839 A371   Sheet of 2   .40 .40
 a.   6p gray & brown   .15 .15
 b.   22p brown & gray   .24 .24

Third Rio de la Plata Stamp Show, Montevideo, Uruguay, June 18-25.

Peace Dove and Valise A372

PADELAI Emblem A373

1967, Aug. 5   Litho.   Perf. 13½
840 A372 20p multicolored   .22 .15

Issued for International Tourist Year 1967.

1967, Aug. 12   Litho.
841 A373 20p multicolored   .22 .15

75th anniv. of the Children's Welfare Association (Patronato de la Infancia-PADELAI).

Stagecoach and Modern City — A374

1967, Sept. 23   Wmk. 90   Perf. 13½
842 A374 20p rose, yel & blk   .26 .15

Centenary of Villa Maria, Cordoba.

San Martin by Ibarra — A375

"Battle of Chacabuco" by P. Subercaseaux — A376

1967, Sept. 30   Litho.
843 A375 20p blk brn & pale yel .55 .15
         Engr.
844 A376 40p blue black   .85 .20
         Set value   .27

Battle of Chacabuco, 150th anniversary.

Exhibition Rooms — A377

1967, Oct. 11   Photo.
845 A377 20p blue gray   .20 .15

Government House Museum, 10th anniv.

Pedro L. Zanni, Fokker and 1924 Flight Route — A378

1967, Oct. 21   Litho.   Perf. 13½
846 A378 20p multicolored   .28 .15

Issued for Aviation Week and to commemorate the 1924 flight of the Fokker seaplane "Province of Buenos Aires" from Amsterdam, Netherlands, to Osaka, Japan.

Training Ship General Brown, by Emilio Biggeri A379

1967, Oct. 28   Wmk. 90
847 A379 20p multicolored   .85 .35

Issued to honor the Military Naval School.

Ovidio Lagos and Front Page — A380

St. Barbara — A381

1967, Nov. 11   Photo.
848 A380 20p sepia   .15 .15

Centenary of La Capital, Rosario newspaper.

1967, Dec. 2   Perf. 13½
849 A381 20p rose red   .28 .15

St. Barbara, patron saint of artillerymen.

Portrait of his Wife, by Eduardo Sivori — A382

1968, Jan. 27   Photo.   Perf. 13½
850 A382 20p blue green   .28 .15

Eduardo Sivori (1847-1918), painter.

Antarctic Type of 1966 and

Admiral Brown Scientific Station A383

Planes over Map of Antarctica A384

6p, Map showing radio-postal stations 1966-67.

1968, Feb. 17   Litho.   Wmk. 90
851 A363 6p multicolored   .45 .18
852 A383 20p multicolored   .60 .24
853 A384 40p multicolored   1.00 .30
    Nos. 851-853 (3)   2.05 .72

Issued to publicize Argentine research projects in Argentine Antarctica.

The Annunciation, by Leonardo da Vinci — A385

Man in Wheelchair and Factory — A386

1968, Mar. 23   Photo.   Perf. 13½
854 A385 20p lilac rose   .20 .15

Issued for the Day of the Army Communications System and its patron saint, Gabriel.

1968, Mar. 23   Litho.
855 A386 20p green & black   .20 .15

Day of Rehabilitation of the Handicapped.

Children and WHO Emblem — A387

1968, May 11   Wmk. 90   Perf. 13½
856 A387 20p dk vio bl & ver   .20 .15

20th anniv. of WHO.

Soldier Type of 1965

Army Day: 20p, Uniform of First Artillery Regiment "General Iriarte."

1968, June 8   Litho.
857 A340a 20p multicolored   .75 .24

Frigate "Libertad," Painting by Emilio Biggeri A388

1968, June 15   Wmk. 90
858 A388 20p multicolored   .75 .24

Issued for Navy Day.

Guillermo Rawson and Old Hospital — A389

1968, July 20   Photo.   Perf. 13½
859 A389 6p olive bister   .16 .15

Cent. of Rawson Hospital, Buenos Aires.

Student Directing Traffic for Schoolmates A390

1968, Aug. 10   Litho.   Perf. 13½
860 A390 20p lt bl, blk, buff & car .15 .15

Traffic safety and education.

O'Higgins Joining San Martin at Battle of
Maipu, by P. Subercaseaux — A391

1968, Aug. 15   **Engr.**
861 A391 40p bluish black   .65 .30
    Sesquicentennial of the Battle of Maipu.

Osvaldo Magnasco
(1864-1920), Lawyer,
Professor of Law and
Minister of
Justice — A392

1968, Sept. 7   **Photo.**   *Perf. 13¹/₂*
862 A392 20p brown   .22 .15

Grandmother's
Birthday, by
Patricia
Lynch — A393

The Sea, by Edgardo
Gomez — A394

1968, Sept. 21   **Litho.**
863 A393 20p multicolored   .24 .15
864 A394 20p multicolored   .24 .15
     Set value   .16

   The designs were chosen in a competition among
kindergarten and elementary school children.

Mar del Plata at
Night — A395

1968, Oct. 19   **Litho.**   *Perf. 13¹/₂*
865 A395 20p black, ocher & bl   .22 .15
   Nos. 865,C113-C114 (3)   1.27 .61

   4th Plenary Assembly of the Intl. Telegraph and
Telephone Consultative Committee, Mar del Plata,
Sept. 23-Oct. 25.

Frontier
Gendarme
A396

Patrol Boat
A397

1968, Oct. 26
866 A396 20p multicolored   .30 .15
867 A397 20p blue, vio bl & blk   .30 .15

   No. 866 honors the Gendarmery; No. 867 the
Coast Guard.

Aaron de
Anchorena and
Pampero
Balloon — A398

1968, Nov. 2   **Photo.**
868 A398 20p blue & multi   .32 .15
   22nd Aeronautics and Space Week.

St. Martin of Tours, by
Alfredo Guido — A399

1968, Nov. 9   **Litho.**
869 A399 20p lilac & dk brn   .20 .15
   St. Martin of Tours, patron saint of Buenos Aires.

Municipal Bank
Emblem — A400

1968, Nov. 16
870 A400 20p multicolored   .20 .15
   90th anniv. of the Buenos Aires Municipal Bank.

Anniversary
Emblem
A401

1968, Dec. 14   **Wmk. 90**   *Perf. 13¹/₂*
871 A401 20p car rose & dk grn   .20 .15
   25th anniversary of ALPI (Fight Against Polio
Association).

Shovel and
State Coal
Fields Emblem
A402

Pouring Ladle
and Army
Manufacturing
Emblem
A403

1968, Dec. 21   **Litho.**
872 A402 20p orange, bl & blk   .26 .15
873 A403 20p dl vio, dl yel & blk   .26 .15
     Set value   .18

   Issued to publicize the National Coal and Steel
industry at the Rio Turbio coal fields and the Zapla
blast furnaces.

Woman Potter, by
Ramon Gomez
Cornet — A404

1968, Dec. 21   **Photo.**   *Perf. 13¹/₂*
874 A404 20p carmine rose   .48 .40
   Centenary of the Witcomb Gallery.

View of
Buenos
Aires and
Rio de la
Plata by
Ulrico
Schmidl
A405

1969, Feb. 8   **Litho.**   **Wmk. 90**
875 A405 20p yellow, blk & ver   .48 .35
   Ulrico Schmidl (c. 1462-1554) who wrote "Journey to the Rio de la Plata and Paraguay."

Types of 1955-67

   Designs: 50c, Puma. 1p, Sunflower. 3p, Zapata
Slope, Catamarca. 5p, Tierra del Fuego. 6p, José
Hernandez. 10p, Inca Bridge, Mendoza. 50p, José
de San Martin. 90p, Guillermo Brown. 100p, Ski
jumper.

Photo.; Litho. (50c, 3p, 10p)

1969-70		**Wmk. 365**	*Perf. 13¹/₂*
882 A275	50c bister ('70)	.70	.15
883 A277	5p brown	1.25	.15
884 A279	100p blue	26.00	.70

Unwmk.

885 A278	1p brown ('70)	.65	.15
886 A277	3p dk blue ('70)	.65	.15
a.	Wmk. 90	5.25	.35
887 A277	5p brown ('70)	.75	.15
888 A366	6p red brn,		
	15x22mm ('70)	1.25	.15
889 A278	10p dull red ('70)	.52	.15
a.	Wmk. 90	425.00	32.50
890 A241	50p dk bl,		
	22x31¹/₂mm		
	('70)	1.75	.15
891 A366	90p ol brn,		
	22x32mm ('70)	3.50	.18
892 A279	100p blue ('70)	9.00	.30
	Nos. 882-892 (11)	46.02	
	Set value		1.78

   For surcharges see Nos. 1076-1077.

Soldier Type of 1965

   Army Day: 20p, Sapper (gastador) of Buenos
Aires Province, 1856.

Perf. 13¹/₂

1969, May 31   **Wmk. 365**   **Litho.**
893 A340a 20p multicolored   .85 .35

Frigate Hercules,
by Emilio
Biggeri — A406

1969, May 31
894 A406 20p multicolored   1.00 .28
   Issued for Navy Day.

"All Men are
Equal"
A407

ILO Emblem
A408

1969, June 28   **Wmk. 90**
895 A407 20p black & ocher   .20 .15
   International Human Rights Year.

1969, June 28   **Litho.**   **Wmk. 365**
896 A408 20p lt green & multi   .20 .15
   50th anniv. of the ILO.

Pedro N. Arata
(1849-1922),
Chemist — A409

Radar Antenna,
Balcarce Station
and
Satellite — A410

   Portraits: No. 898, Miguel Fernandez (1883-
1950), zoologist. No. 899, Angel P. Gallardo (1867-
1934), biologist. No. 900, Cristobal M. Hicken
(1875-1933), botanist. No. 901, Eduardo Ladislao
Holmberg, M.D. (1852-1937), natural scientist.

1969, Aug. 9   **Wmk. 365**   *Perf. 13¹/₂*
897 A409 6p Arata   .42 .15
898 A409 6p Fernandez   .42 .15
899 A409 6p Gallardo   .42 .15
900 A409 6p Hicken   .42 .15
901 A409 6p Holmberg   .42 .15
   Nos. 897-901 (5)   2.10
     Set value   .50

   Argentine scientists. See No. 778 note.

1969, Aug. 23   **Wmk. 99**
902 A410 20p yellow & blk   .28 .15
   Communications by satellite through Intl. Telecommunications Satellite Consortium (INTELSAT).
See No. C115.

Nieuport 28,
Flight Route and
Map of Buenos
Aires Province
A411

1969, Sept. 13   **Litho.**   **Wmk. 90**
903 A411 20p multicolored   .28 .15
   50th anniv. of the first Argentine airmail service
from El Palomar to Mar del Plata, flown Feb. 23-24,
1919, by Capt. Pedro L. Zanni.

Military
College
Gate and
Emblem
A412

1969, Oct. 4   **Wmk. 365**   *Perf. 13¹/₂*
904 A412 20p multicolored   .28 .15
   Cent. of the National Military College, El Palomar (Greater Buenos Aires).

Gen. Angel
Pacheco
A413

La Farola, Logotype
of La Prensa
A414

1969, Nov. 8   **Photo.**   **Wmk. 365**
905 A413 20p deep green   .22 .15
   Gen. Angel Pacheco (1795-1869).

1969, Nov. 8   **Litho.**   *Perf. 13¹/₂*
#907, Bartolomé Mitre & La Nacion logotype.

906 A414 20p orange, yel & blk   .70 .22
907 A414 20p brt green & blk   .70 .22
   Cent. of newspapers La Prensa and La Nacion.

Julian Aguirre — A415

Musicians: No. 909, Felipe Boero. No. 910, Constantino Gaito. No. 911, Carlos Lopez Buchardo. No. 912, Alberto Williams.

Perf. 13½

1969, Dec. 6   Wmk. 365   Photo.

908	A415	6p Aguirre	.55	.30
909	A415	6p Boero	.55	.30
910	A415	6p Gaito	.55	.30
911	A415	6p Buchardo	.55	.30
912	A415	6p Williams	.55	.30
		Nos. 908-912 (5)	2.75	1.50

Argentine musicians. See No. 778 note.

Lt. Benjamin Matienzo and Nieuport Plane A416

1969, Dec. 13   Litho.

913 A416 20p multicolored   .55 .35

23rd Aeronautics and Space Week.

High Power Lines and Map A417

Design: 20p, Map of Santa Fe Province and schematic view of tunnel.

1969, Dec. 13

914	A417	6p multicolored	.50	.15
915	A417	20p multicolored	1.00	.15
		Set value		.18

Completion of development projects: 6p for the hydroelectric dams on the Limay and Neuquen Rivers, the 20p the tunnel under Rio Grande from Sante Fe to Parana.

Lions Emblem A418

1969, Dec. 20   Wmk. 365   Perf. 13½

916 A418 20p black, emer & org   .60 .24

Argentine Lions Intl. Club, 50th anniv.

Madonna and Child, by Raul Soldi — A419

1969, Dec. 27   Litho.

917 A419 20p multicolored   .70 .28

Christmas 1969.

Manuel Belgrano, by Jean Gericault — A420

The Creation of the Flag, Bas-relief by Jose Fioravanti — A421

Perf. 13½

1970, July 4   Unwmk.   Photo.

918 A420 20c deep brown   .35 .15

Litho.   Perf. 12½

919 A421 50c bister, blk & bl   .85 .50

Gen. Manuel Belgrano (1770-1820), Argentine patriot.

San Jose Palace A422

1970, Aug. 9   Litho.   Perf. 13½

920 A422 20c yellow grn & multi   .22 .15

Cent. of the death of Gen. Justo Jose de Urquiza (1801-70), pres. of Argentina, 1854-60.

Schooner "Juliet" A423

1970, Aug. 8   Unwmk.

921 A423 20c multicolored   1.00 .40

Issued for Navy Day.

Receiver of 1920 and Waves A424

1970, Aug. 29

922 A424 20c lt blue & multi   .30 .15

50th anniv. of Argentine broadcasting.

Types of 1955-67 Inscribed "Republica Argentina" and Types A425, A426

Belgrano A425

Lujan Basilica A426

Designs: 1c, Sunflower. 3c, Zapata Slope, Catamarca. 5c, Tierra del Fuego. 8c, No. 931, Belgrano. 10c, Inca Bridge, Mendoza. 25c, 50c, 70c, Jose de San Martin. 65c, 90c, 1.20p, San Martin. 1p, Ski jumper. 1.15p, 1.80p, Adm. Brown.

1970-73   Photo.   Unwmk.   Perf. 13½

923	A278	1c dk green ('71)	.15	.15
924	A277	3c car rose ('71)	.15	.15
925	A277	5c blue ('71)	.15	.15
926	A425	6c deep blue	.15	.15

927	A425	8c green ('72)	.15	.15
928	A278	10c dull red ('71)	.38	.15
929	A278	10c brn, litho. ('71)	.52	.15
930	A278	10c orange brn ('72)	.45	.15
931	A425	10c brown ('73)	.20	.15
932	A426	18c yel & dk brn, litho ('73)	.20	.15
933	A425	25c brown ('71)	.32	.15
934	A425	50c scarlet ('72)	1.25	.15
935	A241	65c brn, 22x31½mm, paper II ('71)	.65	.15
936	A425	70c dk blue ('73)	.32	.15
937	A241	90c emer, 22x31½mm ('72)	3.25	.15
938	A279	1p brn, 22½x29½mm ('71)	1.90	.15
939	A366	1.15p dk bl, 22½x32mm ('71)	1.10	.15
940	A241	1.20p org, 22x31½mm ('73)	1.10	.15
941	A366	1.80p brown ('73)	1.10	.15
		Nos. 923-941 (19)	13.49	
		Set value		1.00

The imprint "Casa de Moneda de la Nacion" (in capitals) appears on 3c, 5c, Nos. 928-929; 65c, 90c, 1p, 1.20p.

On type A425 only the 6c is inscribed "Ley 18.188" below denomination.

Fluorescent paper was used in printing the 25c, 50c, and 70c. The 3c, 5c, 8c, No. 931 and 65c were issued on both ordinary and fluorescent paper.

See Nos. 987-996, 1032-1038, 1042-1043, 1089-1107. For overprint and surcharge see Nos. 1010, 1078.

Soldier Type of 1965

20c, Galloping messenger of Field Army, 1879.

1970, Oct. 17   Litho.   Perf. 13½

944 A340a 20c multicolored   .80 .26

Dome of Cathedral of Cordoba — A430

1970, Nov. 7   Unwmk.

945 A430 50c gray & blk   .80 .15

Bishopric of Tucuman, 400th anniv. See #C131.

People Around UN Emblem — A431

1970, Nov. 7

946 A431 20c tan & multi   .20 .15

25th anniversary of the United Nations.

State Mint and Medal A432

1970, Nov. 28   Unwmk.   Perf. 13½

947 A432 20c gold, grn & blk   .20 .15

Inauguration of the State Mint Building, 25th anniversary.

St. John Bosco and Dean Funes College A433

1970, Dec. 19   Litho.

948 A433 20c olive & blk   .20 .15

Honoring the work of the Salesian Order in Patagonia.

Nativity, by Horacio Gramajo Gutierrez — A434

1970, Dec. 19

949 A434 20c multicolored   .55 .35

Christmas 1970.

Argentine Flag, Map of Argentine Antarctica — A435

1971, Feb. 20   Litho.   Perf. 13½

950 A435 20c multicolored   1.25 .50

Argentine South Pole Expedition, 5th anniv.

Phosphorescent Sorting Code and Albert Einstein — A436

1971, Apr. 30   Unwmk.   Perf. 13½

951 A436 25c multicolored   .48 .30

Electronics in postal development.

Symbolic Road Crossing A437

1971, May 29   Litho.

952 A437 25c blue & blk   .25 .18

Inter-American Regional Meeting of the Intl. Federation of Roads, Buenos Aires, Mar. 28-31.

Elias Alippi — A438

Actors: No. 954, Juan Aurelio Casacuberta. No. 955, Angelina Pagano. No. 956, Roberto Casaux. No. 957, Florencio Parravicini. See No. 778 note.

1971, May 29   Litho.

953	A438	15c Alippi	.35	.20
954	A438	15c Casacuberta	.35	.20
955	A438	15c Pagano	.35	.20

956	A438	15c Casaux	.35	.20
957	A438	15c Parravicini	.35	.20
		Nos. 953-957 (5)	1.75	1.00

Soldier Type of 1965
Army Day, May 29: Artilleryman, 1826.

1971, July 3   **Unwmk.**   *Perf. 13½*
958 A340a 25c multicolored   1.25 .50

Bilander "Carmen," by Emilio Biggeri A439

1971, July 3
959 A439 25c multicolored   1.25 .25

Navy Day

Peruvian Order of the Sun A440

1971, Aug. 28
960 A440 31c multicolored   .32 .15

Sesquicentennial of Peru's independence.

Güemes in Battle, by Lorenzo Gigli A441

No. 962, Death of Güemes, by Antonio Alice.

1971, Aug. 28
   Size: 39x29mm
961 A441 25c multicolored   .48 .30
   Size: 84x29mm
962 A441 25c multicolored   .48 .30

Sesquicentennial of the death of Martin Miguel de Güemes, leader in Gaucho War, Governor and Captain General of Salta Province.

Stylized Tulip — A442

1971, Sept. 18
963 A442 25c tan & multi   .26 .15

3rd Intl. and 8th Natl. Horticultural Exhib.

Father Antonio Saenz, by Juan Gut — A443

1971, Sept. 18
964 A433 25c gray & multi   .26 .15

Sesquicentennial of University of Buenos Aires, and to honor Father Antonio Saenz, first Chancellor and Rector.

Fabricaciones Militares Emblem — A444

1971, Oct. 16   **Unwmk.**   *Perf. 13½*
965 A444 25c brn, gold, bl & blk   .26 .15

30th anniv. of military armament works.

Cars and Trucks A445

Design: 65c, Tree converted into paper.

1971, Oct. 16
966 A445 25c dull bl & multi   .52 .20
967 A445 65c green & multi   1.25 .50
   Nos. 966-967,C134 (3)   2.37 .94

Nationalized industries.

Luis C. Candelaria and his Plane, 1918 A446

1971, Nov. 27
968 A446 25c multicolored   .25 .18

25th Aeronautics and Space Week.

Observatory and Nebula of Magellan A447

1971, Nov. 27
969 A447 25c multicolored   .25 .15

Cordoba Astronomical Observatory, cent.

Christ in Majesty — A448

1971, Dec. 18   **Litho.**
970 A448 25c blk & multi   .25 .15

Christmas 1971. Design is from a tapestry by Horacio Butler in Basilica of St. Francis, Buenos Aires.

Mother and Child, by J. C. Castagnino — A449

1972, May 6   **Unwmk.**   *Perf. 13½*
971 A449 25c fawn & black   .25 .18

25th anniv. (in 1971) of UNICEF.

Mailman's Bag A450

1972, Sept. 2   **Litho.**   *Perf. 13½*
972 A450 25c lemon & multi   .16 .15

Bicentenary of appointment of first Argentine mailman.

Adm. Brown Station, Map of Antarctica A451

1972, Sept. 2
973 A451 25c blue & multi   .70 .35

10th anniv. (in 1971) of Antarctic Treaty.

Soldier Type of 1965
Army Day: 25c, Sergeant, Negro and Mulatto Corps, 1806-1807.

1972, Sept. 23
974 A340a 25c multicolored   .75 .35

Brigantine "Santisima Trinidad" A452

1972, Sept. 23
975 A452 25c multicolored   .75 .35

Navy Day. See No. 1006.

A453   A454

1972, Sept. 30   **Litho.**   *Perf. 13½*
976 A453 45c Oil pump   .90 .20

50th anniv. of the organ. of the state oil fields (Yacimientos Petroliferos Fiscales).

1972, Sept. 30
977 A454 25c Sounding balloon   .25 .15

Cent. of Natl. Meteorological Service.

Trees and Globe — A455

1972, Oct. 14   *Perf. 13x13½*
978 A455 25c bl, blk & lt bl   .70 .20

7th World Forestry Congress, Buenos Aires, Oct. 4-18.

Arms of Naval School, Frigate "Presidente Sarmiento" — A456

1972, Oct. 14
979 A456 25c gold & multi   .65 .35

Centenary of Military Naval School.

Early Balloon and Plane, Antonio de Marchi — A457   Bartolomé Mitre — A458

1972, Nov. 4   *Perf. 13½*
980 A457 25c multicolored   .26 .20

Aeronautics and Space Week, and in honor of Baron Antonio de Marchi (1875-1934), aviation pioneer.

1972, Nov. 4   **Engr.**
981 A458 25c dark blue   .16 .15

Pres. Bartolome Mitre (1821-1906), writer, historian, soldier.

Flower and Heart — A459

1972, Dec. 2   **Litho.**   *Perf. 13½*
982 A459 90c lt bl, ultra & blk   .60 .35

"Your heart is your health," World Health Day.

"Martin Fierro," by Juan C. Castignano — A460   "Spirit of the Gaucho," by Vicente Forte — A461

1972, Dec. 2   **Litho.**   *Perf. 13½*
983 A460 50c multicolored   .32 .20
984 A461 90c multicolored   .65 .35

Intl. Book Year 1972, and cent. of publication of the poem, Martin Fierro, by Jose Hernandez (1834-86).

Iguacu Falls and Tourist Year Emblem — A462

1972, Dec. 16   *Perf. 13x13½*
985 A462 45c multicolored   .28 .15

Tourism Year of the Americas.

King, Wood Carving, 18th Century — A463

1972, Dec. 16   *Perf. 13½*
986 A463 50c multicolored   .50 .25
Christmas 1972.

Types of 1955-73 Inscribed "Republica Argentina" and

Moon Valley, San Juan Province — A463a

Designs: 1c, Sunflower. 5c, Tierra del Fuego. 10c, Inca Bridge, Mendoza. 50c, Lujan Basilica. 65c, 22.50p, San Martin. 1p, Ski jumper. 1.15p, 4.50p, Guillermo Brown. 1.80p, Manuel Belgrano.

Litho.; Photo. (1c, 65c, 1p)
Perf. 13½, 12½ (1.80p)
1972-75   **Wmk. 365**
987 A278   1c dk green   .16 .15
988 A277   5c dark blue   .16 .15
989 A278   10c bister brn   .16 .15
989A A426   50c dull pur ('75)   .16 .15
990 A241   65c gray brown   3.25 .15
991 A279   1p brown   1.40 .15
992 A366   1.15p dk gray bl   1.40 .15
993 A425   1.80p blue ('75)   .16 .15
994 A366   4.50p green ('75)   .65 .15
995 A241   22.50p vio bl ('75)   1.40 .15
996 A463a   50p multi ('75)   2.75 .32
          Nos. 987-996 (11)   11.65
          Set value   1.05
Paper size of 1c is 27½x39mm; others of 1972, 37x27, 27x37mm.
Size of 22.50p, 50p: 26½x38½mm.
See Nos. 1050, 1108.

Cock (Symbolic of Police) — A464   First Coin of Bank of Buenos Aires — A465

1973, Feb. 3   **Litho.**   **Unwmk.**
997 A464 50c lt green & multi   .30 .15
Sesqui. of Federal Police of Argentina.

1973, Feb. 3   *Perf. 13½*
998 A465 50c purple, yel & brn   .15 .15
Sesquicentennial of the Bank of Buenos Aires Province.

DC-3 Planes Over Antarctica A466

1973, Apr. 28   **Litho.**   *Perf. 13½*
999 A466 50c lt blue & multi   1.50 .60
10th anniversary of Argentina's first flight to the South Pole.

Rivadavia's Chair, Argentine Arms and Colors — A467

1973, May 19   **Litho.**   *Perf. 13½*
1000 A467 50c multicolored   .25 .15
Inauguration of Pres. Hector J. Campora, May 25, 1973.

San Martin, by Gil de Castro — A468

San Martin and Bolivar A469

1973, July 7   **Litho.**   *Perf. 13½*
1001 A468 50c lt green & multi   .35 .15
1002 A469 50c yellow & multi   .35 .15
Gen. San Martin's farewell to the people of Peru and his meeting with Simon Bolivar at Guayaquil July 26-27, 1822.

Eva Peron A470

1973, July 26   **Litho.**   *Perf. 13½*
1003 A470 70c black, org & bl   .20 .15
Maria Eva Duarte de Peron (1919-1952), political leader.

House of Viceroy Sobremonte, by Hortensia de Virgilion — A471

1973, July 28   *Perf. 13x13½*
1004 A471 50c blue & multi   .20 .15
400th anniversary of the city of Cordoba.

Woman, by Lino Spilimbergo A472   New and Old Telephones A473

1973, Aug. 28   **Litho.**   *Perf. 13½*
1005 A472 70c multicolored   .70 .15
Philatelists' Day. See Nos. B60-B61.

Ship Type of 1972
Navy Day: 70c, Frigate "La Argentina."

1973, Oct. 27   **Litho.**   *Perf. 13½*
1006 A452 70c multicolored   .60 .35

1973, Oct. 27
1007 A473 70c brt blue & multi   .40 .20
25th anniv. of natl. telecommunications system.

Plume Made of Flags of Participants A474

1973, Nov. 3   *Perf. 13½*
1008 A474 70c yellow bis & multi   .25 .15
12th Cong. of Latin Notaries, Buenos Aires.

No. 940 Overprinted TRANSMISION DEL MANDO PRESIDENCIAL 12 OCTUBRE 1973

1973, Nov. 30   **Photo.**
1010 A241 1.20p orange   .85 .20
Assumption of presidency by Juan Peron, Oct. 12.

Virgin and Child, Window, La Plata Cathedral — A476

Christmas: 1.20p, Nativity, by Bruno Venier, b. 1914.

1973, Dec. 15   **Litho.**   *Perf. 13½*
1011 A476   70c gray & multi   .35 .18
1012 A476   1.20p black & multi   .70 .35

The Lama, by Juan Batlle Planas — A477

Paintings: 50c, Houses in Boca District, by Eugenio Daneri, horiz. 90c, The Blue Grotto, by Emilio Pettoruti, horiz.

1974, Feb. 9   **Litho.**   *Perf. 13½*
1013 A477   50c multicolored   .28 .15
1014 A477   70c multicolored   .35 .20
1015 A477   90c multicolored   .60 .28
          Nos. 1013-1015,B64 (4)   1.51 .85
Argentine painters.

Mar del Plata A478

1974, Feb. 9
1016 A478 70c multicolored   .28 .15
Centenary of Mar del Plata.

Weather Symbols A479   Justo Santa Maria de Oro A480

1974, Mar. 23   **Litho.**   *Perf. 13½*
1017 A479 1.20p multicolored   .35 .20
Cent. of intl. meteorological cooperation.

1974, Mar. 23
1018 A480 70c multicolored   .20 .15
Bicentenary of the birth of Brother Justo Maria de Oro (1772-1836), theologian, patriot, first Argentine bishop.

Belisario Roldan (1873-1922), Writer — A481

1974, June 29   **Photo.**   **Unwmk.**
1019 A481 70c bl & brn   .20 .15

Poster with Names of OAS Members A482

1974, June 29   **Litho.**
1020 A482 1.38p multicolored   .18 .15
Organization of American States, 25th anniv.

ENCOTEL Emblem — A483

1974, Aug. 10   **Litho.**   *Perf. 13*
1021 A483 1.20p blue, gold & blk   .42 .15
ENCOTEL, Natl. Post and Telegraph Press.

Flags of Argentina, Bolivia, Brazil, Paraguay, Uruguay — A484

1974, Aug. 16   *Perf. 13½*
1022 A484 1.38p multicolored   .22 .15
6th Meeting of Foreign Ministers of Rio de la Plata Basin Countries.

El Chocon Hydroelectric Complex, Limay River — A485

Somisa Steel Mill, San Nicolas — A486

Gen. Belgrano Bridge, Chaco-Corrientes — A487

Perf. 13¹/₂, 13x13¹/₂ (4.50p)
1974, Sept. 14

1023	A485	70c multicolored	.40	.18
1024	A486	1.20p multicolored	.60	.35
1025	A487	4.50p multicolored	2.00	.52
	Nos. 1023-1025 (3)		3.00	1.05

Development projects.

Brigantine Belgrano, by Emilio Biggeri A488

1974, Oct. 26   Litho.   Perf. 13¹/₂

1026	A488	1.20p multicolored	.60	.30

Departure into exile in Chile of General San Martin, Sept. 22, 1822.

Alberto R. Mascias and Bleriot Plane — A489

1974, Oct. 26   Unwmk.

1027	A489	1.20p multicolored	.50	.25

Air Force Day, Aug. 10, and to honor Alberto Roque Garcias (1878-1951), aviation pioneer. Exists with wmk. 365.

Hussar, 1812, by Eleodoro Marenco — A490

1974, Oct. 26   Unwmk.

1028	A490	1.20p multicolored	.50	.25

Army Day.

Post Horn and Flags A491

1974, Nov. 23   Unwmk.   Perf. 13¹/₂

1029	A491	2.65p multicolored	.85	.20

Centenary of Universal Postal Union. Exists with wmk. 365.

Franciscan Monastery A492

1974, Nov. 23   Litho.

1030	A492	1.20p multicolored	.40	.15

400th anniversary, city of Santa Fe.

Trout Type of 1968

1974   Engr.   Unwmk.

1031	A366a	1000p vio bl	3.25	.80

Due to a shortage of 10p stamps a quantity of this 1,000p was released for use as 10p.

Types of 1954-73 Inscribed "Republica Argentina" and

Red Deer in Forest — A495

Congress Building A497

Designs: 30c, 60c, 1.80p, Manuel Belgrano. 50c, Lujan Basilica. No. 1036, 2p, 6p, San Martin (16x22¹/₂mm). 2.70p, 7.50p, 22.50p, San Martin (22x31¹/₂mm). 4.50p, 13.50p, Guillermo Brown. 10p, Leaping trout.

1974-76   Unwmk.   Photo.   Perf. 13¹/₂

1032	A425	30c brown vio	.15	.15
1033	A426	50c blk & brn red	.15	.15
1034	A426	50c bister & bl	.15	.15
1035	A425	60c ocher	.15	.15
1036	A425	1.20p red	.30	.15
1037	A425	1.80p deep blue	.15	.15
1038	A425	2p dark purple	.20	.15
1039	A241	2.70p dk bl, 22x31¹/₂mm	.24	.15
1040	A366	4.50p green	.85	.15
1041	A495	5p yellow green	.40	.15
1042	A425	6p red orange	.20	.15
1043	A425	6p emerald	.20	.15
1044	A425	7.50p grn, 22x31¹/₂mm	.85	.15
1045	A366a	10p violet blue	1.00	.15
1046	A366	13.50p scar, 16x22¹/₂mm	.85	.15
1047	A366	13.50p scar, 22x31¹/₂mm	.85	.15
1048	A241	22.50p dp bl, 22x31¹/₂mm	.75	.15
1049	A497	30p yel & dk red brn	1.10	.15
1050	A463a	50p multicolored	1.50	.15
	Nos. 1032-1050 (19)		10.04	
	Set value			1.50

Nos. 1033-1035, 1037-1038, 1042-1044, 1046-1048 issued in 1976, No. 1050 in 1976.
Fluorescent paper was used in printing No. 1036, 2p, Nos. 1044 and 1047. The 30p was issued on both ordinary and fluorescent paper.
See No. 829. For type of A495 overprinted see No. 1144.

Miniature Sheet

A498

1974, Dec. 7   Litho.   Perf. 13¹/₂

1052	A498	Sheet of 6	3.50	2.75
a.		1p Mariano Necochea	.25	
b.		1.20p Jose de San Martin	.25	
c.		1.70p Manuel Isidoro Suarez	.35	
d.		1.90p Juan Pascual Pringles	.42	
e.		2.70p Latin American flags	.65	
f.		4.50p Jose Felix Bogado	1.10	

Sesqui. of Battles of Junin and Ayacucho.

Dove, by Vito Campanella A499

St. Anne, by Raul Soldi — A500

1974, Dec. 21   Litho.   Perf. 13¹/₂

1053	A499	1.20p multicolored	.48	.15
1054	A500	2.65p multicolored	.75	.30

Christmas 1974.

Boy Looking at Stamp — A501

1974, Dec. 21

1055	A501	1.70p black & yel	.38	.15

World Youth Philately Year.

Space Monsters, by Raquel Forner A502

Argentine modern art: 4.50p, Dream, by Emilio Centurion.

1975, Feb. 22   Litho.   Perf. 13¹/₂

1056	A502	2.70p multi	.90	.26
1057	A502	4.50p multi	1.75	.40

Indian Woman and Cathedral, Catamarca — A503

Tourist Publicity: #1059, Carved chancel and street scene. #1060, Grazing cattleand monastery yard. #1061, Painted pottery and power station. #1062, Farm cart and colonial mansion. #1063, Perito Moreno glacier and spinning mill. #1064, Lake Lapataia and scientific surveyor. #1065, Los Alerces National Park and oil derrick.

1975   Litho.   Unwmk.   Perf. 13¹/₂

1058	A503	1.20p shown	.25	.15
1059	A503	1.20p Jujuy	.25	.15
1060	A503	1.20p Salta	.25	.15
1061	A503	1.20p Santiago del Estero	.25	.15
1062	A503	1.20p Tucuman	.25	.15
1063	A503	6p Santa Cruz	.50	.15
1064	A503	6p Tierra del Fuego	.50	.15
1065	A503	6p Chubut	.50	.15
	Nos. 1058-1065 (8)		2.75	1.20

Issue dates: 1.20p, Mar. 8; 6p, Dec. 20.

"We Have Been Inoculated" A504

1975, Apr. 26   Unwmk.   Perf. 13¹/₂

1066	A504	2p multi	.45	.22

Children's inoculation campaign (child's painting).

Hugo A. Acuña and South Orkney Station — A505

Designs: No. 1068, Francisco P. Moreno and Lake Nahuel Huapi. No. 1069, Lt. Col. Luis Piedra Buena and cutter, Luisito. No. 1070, Ensign José M. Sobral and Snow Hill House. No. 1071, Capt. Carlos M. Moyano and Cerro del Toro (mountain).

1975, June 28   Litho.   Perf. 13

1067	A505	2p grnsh bl & multi	.26	.15
1068	A505	2p yel grn & multi	.26	.15
1069	A505	2p lt vio & multi	.26	.15
1070	A505	2p gray bl & multi	.26	.15
1071	A505	2p pale grn & multi	.26	.15
	Nos. 1067-1071 (5)		1.30	.75

Pioneers of Antarctica.

Frigate "25 de Mayo" A506

1975, Sept. 27   Unwmk.   Perf. 13¹/₂

1072	A506	6p multi	.42	.22

Navy Day 1975.

Eduardo Bradley and Balloon — A507

1975, Sept. 27   Wmk. 365

1073	A507	6p multi	.42	.22

Air Force Day.

Declaration of Independence, by Juan M.
Blanes — A508

1975, Oct. 25
1074 A508 6p multi   .32 .15
    Sesquicentennial of Uruguay's declaration of
independence.

Flame
A509

1975, Oct. 17   Unwmk.
1075 A509 6p gray & multi   .32 .15
    Loyalty Day, 30th anniversary of Pres. Peron's
accession to power.

Nos. 886, 891 and 932 Surcharged

30 c

REVALORIZADO
6 c.

REVALORIZADO
5 pesos

1975   Lithographed, Photogravure
1076 A277 6c on 3p   .15 .15
1077 A366 30c on 90p   .15 .15
1078 A426 5p on 18c   .35 .18
    Nos. 1076-1078 (3)   .65
        Set value   .38
    Issue dates: 6c, Oct. 30; 30c, Nov. 20; 5p, Oct.
24. The 6c also exists on No. 886a.

International
Bridge, Flags
of Argentina
and Uruguay
A510

1975, Oct. 25   Litho.   Wmk. 365
1081 A510 6p multi   .35 .18
    Opening of bridge connecting Colon, Argentina,
and Paysandu, Uruguay.

Post Horn,
Surcharged
A511

1975, Nov. 8
1082 A511 10p on 20c multi   .45 .15
    Introduction of postal code. Not issued without
surcharge.

Nurse
Holding
Infant
A512

1975, Dec. 13   Litho.   Perf. 13½
1083 A512 6p multi   .45 .15
    Children's Hospital, centenary.

Nativity, Nueva
Pompeya
Church — A513

1975, Dec. 13   Litho.   Unwmk.
1084 A513 6p multi   .30 .18
    Christmas 1975.

Types of 1970-75 and

Church of St.
Francis,
Salta — A515

    Designs: 3p, No. 1099, 60p, 90p, Manuel Bel-
grano. 12p, 15p, 20p, 30p, No. 1100, 100p, 110p,
120p, 130p, San Martin. 15p, 70p, Guillermo
Brown. 300p, Moon Valley (lower inscriptions
italic). 500p, Adm. Brown Station, Antarctica.

1976-78 Photo. Unwmk. Perf. 13½
1089 A425   3p slate   .15 .15
1090 A425 12p rose red   .25 .15

Perf. 12½x13
Litho.   Wmk. 365
1091 A425 12p rose red   .20 .15
1092 A425 12p emerald   .20 .15

Perf. 13½
Photo.   Unwmk.
1093 A425 12p emer ('77)   .20 .15
1094 A425 15p rose red   .20 .15
1095 A425 15p vio bl ('77)   .20 .15
1097 A425 20p rose red ('77)   .35 .15
1098 A425 30p rose red ('77)   .35 .15
1099 A425 40p dp grn   .52 .15
1100 A425 40p rose red ('77)   .35 .15
1101 A425 60p dk bl ('77)   .70 .20
1102 A425 70p dk bl ('77)   .85 .20
1103 A425 90p emer ('77)   1.00 .28
1104 A425 100p red   .75 .24
1105 A425 110p rose red ('78)   .52 .18
1106 A425 120p rose red ('78)   .60 .20
1107 A425 130p rose red ('78)   .70 .24

Litho.
1108 A463a 300p multi   3.50 1.50
1109 A515 500p multi ('77)   8.25 1.40
1110 A515 1000p multi ('77)   10.00 2.00
    Nos. 1089-1110 (21)   29.84 8.09
    Fluorescent paper was used in printing both 12p
rose red, 15p rose red, 20p, 30p, 40p rose red,
100p, 110p, 120p, 130p. No. 1099 and the 300p
were issued on both ordinary and fluorescent paper.
300p and 500p exist with wmk. 365.
See Nos. B73-B74.

A516

1976 Photo. Unwmk. Perf. 13½
1112 A516 12c gray & blk   .15 .15
1113 A516 50c gray & grn   .15 .15
1114 A516   1p red & blk   .15 .15
1115 A516   4p bl & blk   .15 .15
1116 A516   5p org & blk   .15 .15
1117 A516   5p dp brn & blk   .15 .15
1118 A516 10p gray & vio bl   .22 .15

1119 A516 27p lt grn & blk   .52 .15
1120 A516 30p lt bl & blk   .90 .15
1121 A516 45p yel & blk   .90 .15
1122 A516 50p dl grn & blk   1.25 .15
1123 A516 100p brt grn & red   1.65 .25

Perf. 13x12½
1976   Litho.   Wmk. 365
1124 A516   5p org & blk   .20 .15
1125 A516 27p lt grn & blk   .52 .15
1126 A516 45p yel & blk   1.25 .15
    Nos. 1112-1126 (15)   8.31
        Set value   1.35
    The 1p, 6p, 10p, 50p and No. 1116 were issued
on both ordinary and fluorescent paper.

Jet and Airlines Emblem — A517

Perf. 13x13½
1976, Apr. 24   Litho.   Unwmk.
1130 A517 30p bl, lt bl & dk bl   1.00 .20
    Argentine Airlines, 25th anniversary.

Frigate Heroina and Map of Falkland
Islands — A518

1976, Apr. 26
1131 A518 6p multi   1.00 .40
    Argentina's claim to Falkland Islands.

Louis
Braille — A519

Perf. 13½
1976, May 22   Engr.   Wmk. 365
1132 A519 19.70 dp bl   .28 .15
    Sesquicentennial of the invention of the Braille
system of writing for the blind by Louis Braille
(1809-1852).

Private, 7th
Infantry
Regiment — A520

1976, May 29   Litho.   Unwmk.
1133 A520 12p multi   .38 .18
    Army Day.

Schooner
Rio de la
Plata, by
Emilio
Biggeri
A521

1976, June 19
1134 A521 12p multi   .38 .18
    Navy Day.

Dr.
Bernardo
Houssay
A522

    Argentine Nobel Prize Winners: 15p, Luis F.
Leloir, chemistry, 1970. 20p, Carlos Saavedra
Lamas, peace, 1936. Bernardo Houssay, medicine
and physiology, 1947.

1976, Aug. 14   Litho.   Perf. 13½
1135 A522 10p org & blk   .22 .15
1136 A522 15p yel & blk   .32 .16
1137 A522 20p ocher & blk   .45 .22
    Nos. 1135-1137 (3)   .99 .53

Rio de la
Plata
International
Bridge
A523

1976, Sept. 18   Litho.   Perf. 13½
1138 A523 12p multi   .28 .15
    Inauguration of International Bridge connecting
Puerte Unzue, Argentina, and Fray Bentos,
Uruguay.

Pipelines
and Cooling
Tower, Gen.
Mosconi
Plant
A524

1976, Nov. 20   Litho.   Perf. 13½
1139 A524 28p multi   .42 .20

Pablo
Teodoro
Fels and
Bleriot
Monoplane,
1910
A525

1976, Nov. 20
1140 A525 15p multi   .32 .15
    Air Force Day.

Nativity
A526

1976, Dec. 18   Litho.   Perf. 13½
1141 A526 20p multi   .65 .28
    Christmas. Painting by Edith Chiapetto.

Water Conference
Emblem — A527

1977, Mar. 19   Litho.   Perf. 13½
1142 A527 70p multi   .70 .25
    UN Water Conf., Mar del Plata, Mar. 14-25.

Dalmacio Velez Sarsfield A528

1977, Mar. 19   **Engr.**
1143 A528 50p blk & red brn   .70 .28
Dalmacio Velez Sarsfield (1800-1875), author of Argentine civil code.

Red Deer Type of 1974 Surcharged

1977, July 30   **Photo.**   **Perf. 13½**
1144 A495 100p on 5p brn   1.40 .35
Sesquicentennial of Uruguayan postal service. Not issued without surcharge.

Soldier, 16th Lancers — A529

1977, July 30
1145 A529 30p multi   .40 .20
Army Day.

Schooner Sarandi, by Emilio Biggeri A530

1977, July 30
1146 A530 30p multi   .42 .22
Navy Day.

Soccer Games' Emblem — A531

70p, Argentina '78 emblem, flags & soccer field.

1977, May 14
1147 A531 30p multi   .40 .18
1148 A531 70p multi   .85 .42
11th World Cup Soccer Championship, Argentina, June 1-25, 1978.

The Visit, by Horacio Butler A532

Consecration, by Miguel P. Caride — A533

1977, Mar. 26   **Litho.**
1149 A532 50p multi   .52 .25
1150 A533 70p multi   .65 .38
Argentine artists.

Sierra de la Ventana — A534

Views: No. 1152, Civic Center, Santa Rosa. No. 1153, Skiers, San Martin de los Andes. No. 1154, Boat on Lake Fonck, Rio Negro.

1977, Oct. 8   **Litho.**   **Perf. 13x13½**
1151 A534 30p multi   .32 .16
1152 A534 30p multi   .32 .16
1153 A534 30p multi   .32 .16
1154 A534 30p multi   .32 .16
    Nos. 1151-1154 (4)   1.28 .64

Guillermo Brown, by R. del Villar — A535

1977, Oct. 8   **Perf. 13½**
1155 A535 30p multi   .38 .22
Adm. Guillermo Brown (1777-1857), leader in fight for independence, bicentenary of birth.

Jet — A536

Double-decker, 1926 — A537

1977   **Litho.**   **Perf. 13½**
1156 A536 30p multi   .24 .15
1157 A537 40p multi   .32 .20
50th anniversary of military plane production (30p); Air Force Day (40p).
Issue dates: 30p, Dec. 3; 40p, Nov. 26.

Adoration of the Kings — A538

1977, Dec. 17
1158 A538 100p multi   1.00 .28
Christmas 1977.

Historic City Hall, Buenos Aires — A539   Chapel of Rio Grande Museum, Tierra del Fuego — A540

Designs: 5p, 20p, La Plata Museum. 10p, Independence Hall, Tucuman. 40p, City Hall, Salta, vert. No. 1165, City Hall, Buenos Aires. 100p, Columbus Theater, Buenos Aires. 200p, flag Monument, Rosario. 280p, 300p, Chapel of Rio Grande Museum, Tierra del Fuego. 480p, 520p, 800, Ruins of Jesuit Mission Church of San Ignacio, Misiones. 500p, Candonga Chapel, Cordoba. 1000p, G.P.O., Buenos Aires. 2000p, Civic Center, Bariloche, Rio Negro.

Three types of 10p: I. Nine vertical window bars; small imprint "E. MILIAVACA Dib." II. Nine bars; large imprint "E. MILIAVACA DIB." III. Redrawn; 5 bars; large imprint.

1977-81 Photo. Unwmk. Perf. 13½
     Size: 32x21mm, 21x32mm
1159 A540 5p gray & blk   .15 .15
1160 A540 10p lt ultra & blk, I   .15 .15
a.   Type II   .15 .15
1161 A540 10p lt bl & blk, III   .15 .15
1162 A540 20p citron & blk, litho.   .15 .15
1163 A540 40p gray bl & blk   .15 .15
1164 A539 50p yel & blk   .24 .15
1165 A540 50p citron & blk   .28 .15
1166 A540 100p org & blk, litho.   .16 .15
a.   Wmk. 365   .35 .15
1167 A540 100p red org & blk   92.50 24.00
1168 A540 100p turq & blk   .15 .15
1169 A539 200p lt bl & blk   .15 .15
1170 A540 280p rose & blk   .48 .24
1171 A540 300p lemon & blk   14.00 .20
1172 A540 480p org & blk   .95 .15
1173 A540 500p yel grn & blk   1.75 .24
1174 A540 520p org & blk   1.75 .20
1175 A540 800p rose lil & blk   1.75 .30
1176 A540 1000p lem bis & blk   2.25 .32
1177 A540 1000p gold & blk, 40x29mm   2.50 .38
1178 A540 2000p multi   3.75 .38
    Nos. 1159-1178 (20)   2.25 .38
     Set value   33.36
       3.35

#1161, 1163, 1165, 1167, 1169, 1171, 1173, 1176, 1177 were issued on both ordinary and fluorescent paper. No. 1174 was issued only on fluorescent paper. All others were issued only on ordinary paper.
Issued: #1164, 5/30/77; 280p, 12/15/77; #1160, 3/14/78; 480p, 5/22/78; 5p, 7/25/78; 20p, 500p, 9/8/78; #1166, 9/20/78; #1177, 9/28/78; 520p, 9/30/78; 300p, 10/5/78; 40p, 12/1/78; #1161/79; #1165, 1/8/79; 800p, 3/20/79; #1167, 4/25/79; 200p, 6/23/79; #1176, 12/15/79; 2000p, 6/25/80; #1168, 5/26/81.
For overprints see Nos. 1253, 1315.

Soccer Games' Emblem A544

1978, Feb. 10   **Photo.**   **Perf. 13½**
1179 A544 200p yel grn & bl   .85 .28
11th World Cup Soccer Championship, Argentina, June 1-25. Exists with wmk. 365.

View of El Rio, Rosario — A545

Designs (Argentina '78 Emblem and): 100p, Rio Tercero Dam, Cordoba. 150p, Cordillera Mountains, Mendoza. 200p, City Center, Mar del Plata. 300p, View of Buenos Aires.

1978, May 6   **Litho.**   **Perf. 13**
1180 A545 50p multi   .16 .15
1181 A545 100p multi   .32 .15
1182 A545 150p multi   .50 .16
1183 A545 200p multi   .50 .24
1184 A545 300p multi   1.10 .32
    Nos. 1180-1184 (5)   2.58 1.02
Sites of 11th World Cup Soccer Championship, June 1-25.

Children — A546

1978, May 20
1185 A546 100p multi   .35 .15
50th anniversary of Children's Institute.

Labor Day, by B. Quinquela Martin — A547

Design: No. 1187, Woman's torso, sculpture by Orlando Pierri.

1978, May 20   **Perf. 13½**
1186 A547 100p multi   .35 .15
1187 A547 100p multi   .35 .15

Argentina, Hungary, France, Italy and Emblem — A548

Stadium A549

Teams and Argentina '78 Emblem: 200p, Poland, Fed. Rep. of Germany, Tunisia, Mexico. 300p, Austria, Spain, Sweden, Brazil. 400p, Netherlands, Iran, Peru, Scotland.

1978   **Litho.**   **Perf. 13**
1188 A548 100p multi   .32 .15
1189 A548 200p multi   .65 .15
1190 A548 300p multi   .95 .25
1191 A548 400p multi   1.25 .30
    Nos. 1188-1191 (4)   3.17 .85

     Souvenir Sheet
Lithographed and Engraved
     Perf. 13½
1192 A549 700p buff & blk   2.50 1.40
11th World Cup Soccer Championship, Argentina, June 1-25. Issued: Nos. 1188-1191, June 6, No. 1192, June 3.

Stadium Type of 1978 Inscribed in Red:
"ARGENTINA / CAMPEON"
Lithographed and Engraved
1978, Sept. 2   *Perf. 13¹/₂*
1193 A549 1000p bulf, blk & red   3.25 1.40

Argentina's victory in 1978 Soccer Championship. No. 1193 has margin similar to No. 1192 with Rimet Cup emblem added in red.

Young Tree
Nourished
by Old
Trunk, UN
Emblem
A550

1978 Sept. 2   **Litho.**
1194 A550 100p multi   .35 .22

Technical Cooperation among Developing Countries Conf., Buenos Aires, Sept. 1978.

Emblems
of Buenos
Aires and
Bank
A551

1978, Sept. 16
1195 A551 100p multi   .35 .22

Bank of City of Buenos Aires, centenary.

General
Savio and
Steel
Production
A552

1978, Sept. 16
1196 A552 100p multi   .35 .22

Gen. Manuel N. Savio (1892-1948), general manager of military heavy industry.

San
Martin — A553

1978, Oct.   **Engr.**
1197 A553 2000p grnsh blk   6.25 1.10

1979   **Wmk. 365**
1198 A553 2000p grnsh blk   4.75 .35

Gen Jose de San Martin (1778-1850), soldier and statesman. See No. 1292.

Globe and Argentine
Flag — A554

1978, Oct. 7   Litho.   *Perf. 13¹/₂*
1199 A554 200p multi   .70 .28

12th International Cancer Congress, Buenos Aires, Oct. 5-11.

Chessboard, Queen
and Pawn — A555

1978, Oct. 7
1200 A555 200p multi   2.00 .65

23rd National Chess Olympics, Buenos Aires, Oct. 25-Nov. 12.

Correct
Positioning of
Stamps — A557

Design: 50p, Use correct postal code number.

1978   Photo.   *Perf. 13¹/₂*
1201 A557 20p ultra   .15 .15
1203 A557 50p carmine   .22 .15
        Set value   .15

No. 1201 issued on both ordinary and fluorescent paper.

A558   A559

1978-82   Photo.   *Perf. 13¹/₂*
1204 A558 150p bl & ultra   .35 .15
1205 A558 180p bl & ultra   .45 .15
1206 A558 200p bl & ultra   .32 .15
1207 A559 240p ol bis & bl ('79) .38 .15
1208 A559 260p blk & lt bl ('79) .42 .15
1209 A559 290p blk & lt bl ('79) .45 .15
1210 A559 310p mag & bl ('79)   .50 .18
1211 A559 350p ver & bl ('79)   .65 .20
1212 A559 450p ultra & bl   .52 .18
1213 A559 600p grn & bl ('80)   .70 .24
1214 A559 700p blk & bl ('80)   .70 .24
1215 A559 800p red & bl ('81)   .65 .15
1216 A559 1100p gray & bl ('81)   .90 .15
1217 A559 1500p blk & bl ('81)   .35 .15
1218 A559 1700p grn & bl ('82)   .45 .15
        Nos. 1204-1218 (15)   7.79
        Set value   2.00

No. 1204 issued on fluorescent and ordinary paper. No. 1206 issued only on fluorescent paper. For overprint see No. 1338.

Balsa "24"
A561

Ships: 200p, Tug Legador. 300p, River Parana tug No. 34. 400p, Passenger ship Ciudad de Parana.

1978, Nov. 4   Litho.   *Perf. 13¹/₂*
1220 A561 100p multi   .24 .15
1221 A561 200p multi   .48 .20
1222 A561 300p multi   .70 .30
  a. Pair, #1221-1222   1.20
1223 A561 400p multi   .95 .40
  a. Pair, #1220. 1223   1.20
        Nos. 1220-1223 (4)   2.37 1.05

20th anniversary of national river fleet. Issued on fluorescent paper.

View and
Arms of
Bahia
Blanca
A562

1978, Nov. 25   Litho.   *Perf. 13¹/₂*
1224 A562 20p multi   .48 .15

Sesquicentennial of Bahia Blanca.

"Spain,"
(Queen
Isabella
and
Columbus)
by Arturo
Dresco
A563

1978, Nov. 25
1225 A563 300p multi   2.75 .30

Visit of King Juan Carlos and Queen Sofia of Spain to Argentina, Nov. 26.

Virgin and Child,
San Isidro
Cathedral — A564

1978, Dec. 16
1226 A564 200p gold & multi   .55 .28

Christmas 1978.

Slope at Chacabuco, by Pedro
Subercaseaux — A565

Painting: 1000p, The Embrace of Maipu (San Martin and O'Higgins), by Pedro Subercaseaux, vert.

1978, Dec. 16   Litho.   *Perf. 13¹/₂*
1227 A565 500p multi   1.00 .26
1228 A565 1000p multi   2.00 .40

José de San Martin, 200th birth anniversary.

Adolfo
Alsina
A566

Design: No. 1230, Mariano Moreno.

1979, Jan. 20
1229 A566 200p lt bl & blk   .30 .15
1230 A566 200p yel red & blk   .30 .15
        Set value   .16

Adolfo Alsina (1828-1877), political leader, vice-president; Mariano Moreno (1778-1811), lawyer, educator, political leader.

Argentina
No. 37 and
UPU
Emblem
A567

1979, Jan. 20
1231 A567 200p multi   .22 .15

Centenary of Argentina's UPU membership.

Still-life, by
Carcova
A568

Painting: 300p, The Laundresses, by Faustino Brughetti.

1979, Mar. 3
1232 A568 200p multi   .45 .15
1233 A568 300p multi   .60 .20

Ernesto de la Carcova (1866-1927) and Faustino Brughetti (1877-1956), Argentine painters.

A569   A570

1979, Mar. 3
1234 A569 200p Balcarce Earth station   .55 .25

Third Inter-American Telecommunications Conference, Buenos Aires, March 5-9.

1979
1235 A570 30p Stamp collecting   .15 .15

Printed on ordinary and fluorescent paper.

European
Olive — A571

Laurel and
Regimental
Emblem — A572

1979, June 2   Litho.   *Perf. 13¹/₂*
1236 A571 100p shown   .26 .15
1237 A571 200p Tea   .55 .26
1238 A571 300p Sorghum   .85 .46
1239 A571 400p Common flax   1.10 .55
        Nos. 1236-1239 (4)   2.76 1.36

1979, June 9
1240 A572 200p gold & multi   .42 .22

Founding of Subteniente Berdina Village in memory of Sub-lieutenant Rodolfo Hernan Berdina, killed by terrorists in 1975.

"75" and Automobile Club Emblem A573

1979, June 9
1241 A573 200p gold & multi .40 .20
Argentine Automobile Club, 75th anniv.

Exchange Building and Emblem A574

1979, June 9
1242 A574 200p bl, blk & gold .40 .20
Grain Exchange, 125th anniversary.

Cavalry Officer, 1817 — A575

1979, July 7 Litho. Perf. 13½
1243 A575 200p multi 1.00 .30
Army Day.

Corvette Uruguay and Navy Emblem — A576

#1245, Hydrographic service ship & emblem.

1979 Perf. 13
1244 A576 250p multi .85 .35
1245 A576 250p multi .85 .35
Navy Day; Cent. of Naval Hydrographic Service. Issued: #1244, July 28; #1245, July 7.

Tree and Man — A577

1979, July 28 Perf. 13½
1246 A577 250p multi .60 .22
Protection of the Environment Day, June 5.

"Spad" Flying over Andes, and Vicente Almandos Almonacid A578

1979, Aug. 4
1247 A578 250p multi .70 .22
Air Force Day.

Gen. Julio A. Roca Occupying Rio Negro, by Juan M. Blanes A579

1979, Aug. 4
1248 A579 250p multi .70 .22
Conquest of Rio Negro Desert, centenary.

Rowland Hill — A580

1979, Sept. 29 Litho. Perf. 13½
1249 A580 300p gray red & blk .55 .22
Sir Rowland Hill (1795-1879), originator of penny postage.

Viedma Navarez Monument A581

1979, Sept. 29
1250 A581 300p multi .60 .22
Viedma and Carmen de Patagones towns, bicentenary.

Pope Paul VI — A582

Design: No. 1252, Pope John Paul I.

1979, Oct. 27 Engr. Perf. 13½
1251 A582 500p black 1.00 .28
1252 A582 500p sepia 1.00 .28

No. 1169 Overprinted in Red: "75 ANIV. / SOCIEDAD/ FILATELICA / DE ROSARIO"

1979, Nov. 10 Photo. Perf. 13½
1253 A539 200p lt bl & blk .60 .20
Rosario Philatelic Society, 75th anniversary.

A583   A584

1979, Nov. 10 Litho.
1254 A583 300p multi .70 .28
Frontier resettlement.

1979, Dec. 1 Litho. Perf. 13½
1255 A584 300p multi .70 .28
Military Geographic Institute centenary.

Christmas 1979 A585

1979, Dec. 1
1256 A585 300p multi .55 .22

General Mosconi Birth Centenary — A586

1979, Dec. 15 Engr. Perf. 13½
1257 A586 1000p blk & bl 1.50 .24

Rotary Emblem and Globe A587

1979, Dec. 29 Litho.
1258 A587 300p multi 1.75 .35
Rotary International, 75th anniversary.

Child and IYC Emblem — A588

Family, by Pablo Menicucci A589

1979, Dec. 29
1259 A588 500p lt bl & sepia .75 .15
1260 A589 1000p multi 1.50 .22
International Year of the Child.

Microphone, Waves, ITU Emblem — A590

1980, Mar. 22 Litho. Perf. 13x13½
1261 A590 500p multi .95 .26
Regional Administrative Conference on Broadcasting by Hectometric Waves for Area 2, Buenos Aires, Mar. 10-29.

Guillermo Brown — A591

1980 Engr. Perf. 13½
1262 A591 5000p black 4.50 .15
See No. 1372.

Argentine Red Cross Centenary A592

1980, Apr. 19 Litho. Perf. 13½
1263 A592 500p multi .52 .20

OAS Emblem — A593

1980, Apr. 19
1264 A593 500p multi .55 .22
Day of the Americas, Apr. 14.

Dish Antennae, Balcarce A594

1980, Apr. 26 Litho. & Engr.
1265 A594 300p shown .38 .20
1266 A594 300p Hydroelectric Station, Salto Grande .38 .20
1267 A594 300p Bridge, Zarate-Brazo Largo .38 .20
Nos. 1265-1267 (3) 1.14 .60

Capt. Hipolito Bouchard, Frigate "Argentina" — A595

1980, May 31 Litho. Perf. 13x13½
1268 A595 500p multicolored .70 .28
Navy Day.

"Villarino," San Martin, by Theodore Gericault — A596

1980, May 31
1269 A596 500p multicolored .70 .28
Return of the remains of Gen. Jose de San Martin to Argentina, centenary.

Buenos Aires Gazette, 1810, Signature A597

1980, June 7 *Perf. 13½*
1270 A597 500p multicolored .55 .22
Journalism Day.

Miniature Sheet

Coaches in Victoria Square — A598

1980 June 14
1271 Sheet of 14 9.00 9.00
a. A598 500p any single .60 .60
Buenos Aires, 400th anniv. No. 1271 shows ceramic mural of Victoria Square by Rodolfo Franco in continuous design. See No. 1285.

Gen. Pedro Aramburu — A599

1980, July 12 *Litho.* *Perf. 13½*
1272 A599 500p yel & blk .55 .22
Gen. Pedro Eugenio Aramburu (1903-1970), provisional president, 1955.

Army Day A600

1980, July 12
1273 A600 500p multicolored .85 .28

Gen. Juan Gregorio de Las Heras (1780-1866), Hero of 1817 War of Independence — A601

Grandees of Argentina Bicentenary: No. 1275, Rivadavia. No. 1276, Brig. Gen Jose Matias Zapiola (1780-1874), naval commander and statesman.

1980, Aug. 2 *Litho.* *Perf. 13½*
1274 A601 500p tan & blk .55 .22
1275 A601 500p multicolored .55 .22
1276 A601 500p lt lilac & blk .55 .22
Nos. 1274-1276 (3) 1.65 .66

Avro "Gosport" Biplane, Maj. Francisco de Artega — A602

1980, Aug. 16 *Perf. 13*
1277 A602 500p multicolored .70 .22
Air Force Day. Artega (1882-1930) was first director of Military Aircraft Factory where Avro "Gosport" was built (1927).

University of La Plata, 75th Anniversary A603

1980, Aug. 16 *Perf. 13½*
1278 A603 500p multi .55 .22

Souvenir Sheets

Emperor Penguin — A604

South Orkneys Argentine Base
A605 A606

No. 1279 (A604): a, shown. b, Bearded penguin. c, Adelie penguins. d, Papua penguins. e, Sea elephants. f, A605 shown. g, A606 shown. h, Fur seals. i, Giant petrels. j, Blue-eyed cororants. k, Stormy petrels. m, Anarctic doves.

1980, Sept. 27 *Litho.* *Perf. 13½*
1279 Sheet of 12 11.00 11.00
a.-m. A604 500p, any single .75 .60
1280 Sheet of 12 11.00 11.00
a. A605 500p Puerto Soledad .75 .60
b. A606 500p Different view .75 .60
75th anniv. of Argentina's presence in the South Orkneys and 150th anniv. of political and military command in the Falkland Islands. Nos. 1279-1280 each contain 12 stamps (4x3) with landscape designs in center of sheets. Silhouettes of Argentine exploration ships in margins. #1280 contains #1279a-1279e, 1279h-1279m, 1280a-1280b.

Anti-smoking Campaign — A608

1980, Oct. 11
1282 A608 700p multi .90 .22

National Census — A609

1980, Sept.
1283 A609 500p blk & bl 1.00 .20

Madonna and Child (Congress Emblem) A610

1980, Oct. 1 *Litho.*
1284 A610 700p multi .85 .15
National Marian Cong., Mendoza, Oct. 8-12

Mural Type of 1980
Miniature Sheet
1285 Sheet of 14 9.00 9.00
a. A598 500p, any single .60 .50
Buenos Aires, 400th anniv./Buenos Aires '80 Stamp Exhib., Oct. 24-Nov. 2. No. 1285 shows ceramic mural Arte bajo la Ciudad by Alfredo Guido in continuous design.

Technical Military Academy, 50th Anniversary A611 | Amateur Radio Operation A612

1980, Nov. 1
1286 A611 700p multi .75 .15

1980, Nov. 1
1287 A612 700p multi .75 .15

Medal — A613 | Lujan Cathedral Floor Plan — A614

1980, Nov. 29 *Litho.* *Perf. 13½*
1288 A613 700p multi .75 .25
1289 A614 700p olive & brn .75 .25
Christmas 1980. 150th anniv. of apparition of Holy Virgin to St. Catherine Laboure, Paris (No. 1288), 350th anniv. of apparition at Lujan.

150th Death Anniversary of Simon Bolivar — A615

1980, Dec. 13
1290 A615 700p multi .75 .25

Soccer Gold Cup Championship, Montevideo, 1980 — A616

1981, Jan. 3 *Litho.*
1291 A616 1000p multi 1.10 .25

San Martin Type of 1978
1981, Jan. 20 *Engr.* *Perf. 13½*
1292 A553 10,000p dark blue 7.25 .16

Landscape in Lujan, by Marcos Tiglio A617

Paintings: No. 1304, Expansion of Light along a Straight Line, by Miguel Angel Vidal, vert.

1981, Apr. 11 *Litho.*
1303 A617 1000p multi .85 .30
1304 A617 1000p multi .85 .30

Intl. Sports Medicine Congress, June 7-12 — A618

1981, June 6 *Litho.* *Perf. 13½*
1305 A618 1000p bl & dk brn .75 .20

Esperanza Base, Antarctica A619

Cargo Plane, Map of Vice-Commodore Marambio Island — A620

Perf. 13½, 13x13½ (No. 1308)
1981, June 13
1306 A619 1000p shown 1.40 .42
1307 A619 2000p Almirante Irizar 2.50 .55
1308 A620 2000p shown 2.50 .85
Nos. 1306-1308 (3) 6.40 1.82
Antarctic Treaty 20th anniv.

Antique Pistols (Military Club Centenary) A621

1981, June 27 *Perf. 13½*
1309 A621 1000p Club building .80 .15
1310 A621 2000p shown .80 .15

Gen. Juan A. Alvarez de Arenales (1770-1831) A622

Famous Men: No. 1312, Felix G. Frias (1816-1881), writer. No. 1313, Jose E. Uriburu (1831-1914), statesman.

1981, Aug. 8   Litho.   Perf. 13½
1311	A622	1000p multi	.70 .15
1312	A622	1000p multi	.70 .15
1313	A622	1000p multi	.70 .15
	Nos. 1311-1313 (3)		2.10 .45

Naval Observatory Centenary — A623

1981, Aug. 15   Litho.   Perf. 13x13½
1314 A623 1000p multi   .75 .24

No. 1176 Overprinted in Red: "50 ANIV. DE LA ASOCIACION / FILATELICA Y NUMISMATICA / DE BAHIA BLANCA"

1981, Aug. 15   Photo.   Perf. 13½
1315 A540 1000p lem & blk   1.90 .25

50th anniv. of Bahia Blanca Philatelic and Numismatic Society.

St. Cayetano, Stained-glass Window, Buenos Aires — A624

1981, Sept. 5   Litho.   Perf. 13½
1316 A624 1000p multi   .70 .15

St. Cayetano, founder of Teatino Order, 500th birth anniv.

Pablo Castaibert (1883-1909) and his Monoplane (Air Force Day) — A625

1981, Sept. 5   Perf. 13x13½
1317 A625 1000p multi   .65 .15

Intl. Year of the Disabled A626

1981, Sept. 10   Perf. 13½
1318 A626 1000p multi   .65 .15

22nd Latin-American Steelmakers' Congress, Buenos Aires, Sept. 21-23 — A627

1981, Sept. 19
1319 A627 1000p multi   .65 .15

Army Regiment No. 1 (Patricios), 175th Anniv. — A628

1981, Oct. 10   Litho.   Perf. 13½
1320 A628 1500p Natl. arms   .45 .15
1321 A628 1500p shown   .45 .15
a. Pair, #1320-1321   .90 .30

A629   A630

San Martin as artillery Captain in Battle of Bailen, 1808.

1981, Oct. 5
1322 Sheet of 8 + 4 labels   4.75 1.75
a. A629 1000p multi   .35 .18
b. A629 1500p multi   .52 .18

Espamer '81 Intl. Stamp Exhib. (Americas, Spain, Portugal), Buenos Aires, Nov. 13-22.
No. 1322 contains 2 each se-tenant pairs with label between.

1981, Oct. 5
1323 A630 1000p multi   2.25 .32

Anti-indiscriminate whaling.

Espamer '81 Emblem and Ship — A631

1981
1324 A631 1300p multi   .55 .16

No. 1324 Overprinted in Blue: "CURSO SUPERIOR DE ORGANIZACIONES DE FILATELICOS-UPAE-BUENOS AIRES-1981"

1981, Nov. 7   Photo.   Perf. 13½
1325 A631 1300p multi   1.25 .18

Postal Administration philatelic training course.

Soccer Players — A632

Designs: Soccer players.

1981, Nov. 13   Litho.
1326 Sheet of 4 + 2 labels   7.25 7.25
a. A632 1000p multi   .25 .25
b. A632 3000p multi   .65 .65
c. A632 5000p multi   1.10 1.10
d. A632 15,000p multi   3.25 3.25

Espamer '81.

"Peso" Coin Centenary A633

1981, Nov. 21
1327 A633 2000p Patacon, 1881   .38 .15
1328 A633 3000p Argentine Oro, 1881 .60 .15
Set value   .20

Christmas 1981 — A634

1981, Dec. 12
1329 A634 1500p multi   .85 .24

Traffic Safety A635

1981, Dec. 19   Litho.
1330 A635 1000p Observe traffic lights, vert. .75 .38
1331 A635 2000p Drive carefully, vert. .75 .38
1332 A635 3000p Cross at white lines .75 .38
1333 A635 4000p Don't shine headlights 1.50 .38
Nos. 1330-1333 (4)   3.75 1.52

Francisco Luis Bernardez, Ciuda Laura — A636

Writers and title pages from their works: 2000p, Lucio V. Mansilla, Excursion a los indios ranqueles. 3000p, Conrado Nale Roxlo, El Grillo. 4000p, Victoria Ocampo, Sur.

1982, Mar. 20   Litho.
1334 A636 2000p shown   .60 .20
1335 A636 2000p multi   .85 .20
1336 A636 3000p multi   1.25 .28
1337 A636 4000p multi   1.75 .28
Nos. 1334-1337 (4)   4.45 .96

No. 1218 Overprinted: "LAS / MALVINAS / SON/ ARGENTINAS"

1982, Apr. 17   Photo.   Perf. 13½
1338 A559 1700p green & blue   .48 .20

Argentina's claim on Falkland Islds.

Robert Koch — A637

American Airforces Commanders' 22nd Conf. — A638

1982, Apr. 17   Litho.   Wmk. 365
1339 A637 2000p multi   .48 .25

TB bacillus centenary and 25th Intl. Tuberculosis Conference.

1982, Apr. 17
1340 A638 2000p multi   .70 .28

Stone Carving, City Founder's Signature (Don Hernando de Lerma) A639

1982, Apr. 17
1341 A639 2000p multi   .70 .28

Souvenir Sheet
1342 A639 5000p multi   2.00 2.00

City of Salta, 400th anniv. No. 1342 contains one 43x30mm stamp.

Naval Center Centenary — A640

1982, Apr. 24   Perf. 13x13½
1343 A640 2000p multi   .70 .28

Chorisia Speciosa — A641

1982   Unwmk.   Photo.   Perf. 13½
1344	A641	200p	Zinnia peruviana	.15 .15
1345	A641	300p	Ipomoea purpurea	.15 .15
1346	A641	400p	Tillandsia aeranthos	.15 .15
1347	A641	500p	shown	.15 .15
1348	A641	800p	Oncidium bifolium	.15 .15
1349	A641	1000p	Erythrina crista-galli	.15 .15
1350	A641	2000p	Jacaranda mimosi-folia	.22 .15
1351	A641	3000p	Bauhinia candicans	.32 .15
1352	A641	5000p	Tecoma stans	.52 .15
1353	A641	10,000p	Tabebuia ipe	1.10 .22
1354	A641	20,000p	Passiflora coerulea	2.25 .35
1355	A641	30,000p	Aristolochia littoralis	3.25 .52
1356	A641	50,000p	Oxalis enneaphylla	5.25 .70
	Nos. 1344-1356 (13)			13.81
	Set value			2.35

Nos. 1344-1346, 1348-1350 issued on fluorescent paper. Nos. 1353-1356 issued on ordinary paper. Others issued on both fluorescent and ordinary paper.
Issue dates: 500p, 2000p, 5000p, 10,000p, May 22. 200p, 300p, 1000p, 20,000p, Sept. 25. 400p, 800p, 30,000p, 50,000p, Dec. 4. 3000p, Dec. 18.
See Nos. 1429-1443A, 1515-1527, 1683-1691. For overprint see No. 1382.

10th Death Anniv. of Gen. Juan C. Sanchez A641a

1982, May 29   Litho.   Wmk. 365
1364 A641a 5000p grn & blk   .90 .28

Luis Venet, First Commander — A641b

1982, June 12
1365 A641b 5000p org & blk   1.10 .45
Size: 83x28mm
1366 A641b 5000p Map   .75 .30
  a.   Pair, Nos. 1365-1366   2.00 2.00
153rd Anniv. of Malvinas Political and Military Command District.

Visit of Pope John Paul II — A641c

1982, June 12
1367 A641c 5000p multi   1.75 .55

Organ Grinder, by Aldo Severi (b. 1928) — A641d

3000p, Still Life, by Santiago Cogorno (b. 1915).

1982, July 3   Wmk. 365
1368 A641d 2000p shown   .26 .20
1369 A641d 3000p multi   .40 .20

Guillermo Brown Type of 1980 and:

Jose de San Martin — A641e

Litho. and Engr.
1982   Unwmk.   Perf. 13½
1372 A591 30,000p blk & bl   3.25 .65
1376 A641e 50,000p sepia & car   6.50 .85

Issue dates: 30,000p, June; 50,000p, July.

Scouting Year A641f

Perf. 13½
1982, Aug. 7   Litho.   Wmk. 365
1380 A641f 5000p multi   1.25 .15

Alconafta Fuel Campaign A641g

1982, Aug. 7   Wmk. 365
1381 A641g 2000p multi   .32 .15

No. 1352 Overprinted: "50 ANIVERSARIO SOCIEDAD FILATELICA DE TUCUMAN"
1982, Aug. 7   Photo.   Unwmk.
1382 A641 5000p multi   1.50 1.25

Rio III Central Nuclear Power Plant, Cordoba A642

Perf. 13½
1982, Sept. 4   Litho.   Wmk. 365
1383 A642 2000p shown   .30 .15
1384 A642 2000p Control room   .30 .15
      Set value   .15

Namibia Day — A643

1982, Sept. 4
1385 A643 5000p Map   .75 .15

Formosa Cathedral A644

Churches and Cathedrals of the Northeast: 2000p, Our Lady of Itati, Corrientes, vert. 3000p, Resistencia Cathedral, Chaco, vert. 10,000p, St. Ignatius Church ruins, Misiones.

1982, Sept. 18   Litho. & Engr.
1386 A644   2000p dk grn & blk   .24 .15
1387 A644   3000p dk brn & brn   .35 .15
1388 A644   5000p dk bl & brn   .60 .20
1389 A644 10,000p dp org & blk   1.10 .35
      Nos. 1386-1389 (4)   2.29 .85

Tension Sideral, by Mario Alberto Agatiello — A645

Sculpture (Espamer '81 and Juvenex '82 Exhibitions): 3000p, Sugerencia II, by Eduardo Mac Entyre. 5000p, Storm, by Carlos Silva.

1982, Oct. 2   Litho.   Perf. 13½
1390 A645 2000p multi   .24 .15
1391 A645 3000p multi   .45 .15
1392 A645 5000p multi   .60 .18
      Nos. 1390-1392 (3)   1.29
      Set value   .39

Sante Fe Bridge A646

1982, Oct. 16   Litho. & Engr.
1393 A646 2000p bl & blk   .38 .15
2nd Southern Cross Games, Santa Fe and Rosario, Nov. 26-Dec. 5.

10th World Men's Volleyball Championship — A647

1982, Oct. 16   Litho.   Wmk. 365
1394 A647 2000p multi   .24 .15
1395 A647 5000p multi   .48 .18

Los Andes Newspaper Centenary A648

Design: Army of the Andes Monument, Hill of Glory, Mendoza.

1982, Oct. 30
1396 A648 5000p multi   .50 .18

A649   A650

1982, Oct. 30   Wmk. 365
1397 A649 5000p Signs   .55 .22
50th Anniv. of Natl. Roads, Administration.

1982, Nov. 20   Litho.
La Plata City Cent.: No. 1400: a, Cathedral, diff. b, Head, top. c, Observatory. d, City Hall, diff. e, Head, bottom. f, University.

1398 A650 5000p Cathedral   .75 .15
1399 A650 5000p City Hall   .75 .15
1400   Sheet of 6   2.25 1.00
a.-f.   A650 2500p any single   .28 .15

Well, Natl. Hydrocarbon Congress Emblem — A651

1982, Nov. 20
1401 A651 5000p multi   .50 .20
Oil Discovery, Comodoro Rivadavia, 75th anniv.

Jockey Club of Buenos Aires Centenary — A652   Christmas 1982 — A653

#1403, Carlos Pellegrini, first president.

1982, Dec. 4   Litho.
1402 A652 5000p Emblem   .52 .15
1403 A652 5000p multi   .52 .15
      Set value   .20

1982, Dec. 18   Perf. 13½
1404 A653 3000p St. Vincent de Paul 1.50 .15
Size: 29x38mm
1405 A653 5000p St. Francis of Assisi 1.25 .15
      Set value   .15

Pedro B. Palacios (1854-1917), Writer — A654

Writers: 2000p, Leopoldo Marechal (1900-1970). 3000p, Delfina Bunge de Galvez (1881-1952). 4000p, Manuel Galvez (1882-1962). 5000p, Evaristo Carriego (1883-1912).

1983, Mar. 26   Litho.   Perf. 13½
1406 A654 1000p multi   .15 .15
1407 A654 2000p multi   .22 .15
1408 A654 3000p multi   .32 .15
1409 A654 4000p multi   .42 .15
1410 A654 5000p multi   .55 .18
  a.   Strip of 5, #1406-1410   1.75 1.00
      Set value   .57

Recovery of the Malvinas (Falkland Islands) — A655

1983, Apr. 9   Litho.   Perf. 13½
1411 A655 20,000p Map, flag   .60 .30

Telecommunications Systems — A656

1983, Apr. 16   **Wmk. 365**
1412 A656 5000p SITRAM .75 .15
1413 A656 5000p RED ARPAC .75 .15
Set value .15

Naval League
Emblem — A657

1983, May 14   **Litho.**   **Perf. 13½**
1414 A657 5000p multi .35 .15
Navy Day and 50th anniv. of Naval League.

Allegory, by Victor
Rebuffo — A658

1983, May 14
1415 A658 5000p multi .35 .15
Natl. Arts Fund, 25th Anniv.

75th Anniv. of
Colon Opera
House, Buenos
Aires — A659

1983, May 28   **Wmk. 365**
1416 A659 5000p Main hall .70 .15
1417 A659 10000p Stage 1.00 .15
Set value .17

Protected
Species
A660

1983, July 2   **Litho.**   **Perf. 13½**
1418 A660 1p Chrysocyon brachy-
urus .32 .15
1419 A660 1.50p Ozotoceros bezoar-
ticus .48 .15
1420 A660 2p Myrmecophaga
tridactyla .55 .15
1421 A660 2.50p Leo onca .65 .16
Nos. 1418-1421 (4) 2.00
Set value .42

City of Catamarca,
300th
Anniv. — A661

Foundation of the City of Catamarca, by Luis
Varela Lezana (1900-1982).

1983, July 16   **Litho.**   **Perf. 13½**
1422 A661 1p multi .32 .15

Mamerto Esquiu
(1826-1883)
A662

1983, July 16
1423 A662 1p multi .32 .15

Bolivar, by
Herrera
Toro — A663

Bolivar, Engraving by
Kepper — A664

Perf. 13 (A663), 13½ (A664)
1983   **Unwmk.**
1424 A663 1p multi .30 .15
1425 A664 2p black .60 .15
1426 A664 10p San Martin 3.00 1.50
Nos. 1424-1426 (3) 3.90 1.80
Issue dates: 1p, 2p, July 23. 10p, Aug. 20.
See Nos. 1457-1462B.

Gen. Toribio de
Luzuriaga (1782-
1842)
A665

1983, Aug. 20   **Litho.**   **Perf. 13½**
1427 A665 1p multi .30 .15

50th Anniv.
of San
Martin
National
Institute
A666

1983, Aug. 20   **Engr.**   **Unwmk.**
1428 A666 2p sepia .60 .16

Flower Type of 1982 in New Currency
1983-85   **Photo.**   **Perf. 13½**
1429 A641 5c like #1347 .15 .15
1430 A641 10c like #1349 .15 .15
1431 A641 20c like #1350 .15 .15
1432 A641 30c like #1351 .15 .15
1433 A641 40c Eichhornia crassipes .15 .15
1434 A641 50c like #1352 .15 .15
1435 A641 1p like #1353 .15 .15
1435A A641 1.80p Mutisia retusa .15 .15
1436 A641 2p like #1354 .22 .15
1437 A641 3p like #1355 .32 .15
1438 A641 5p like #1356 .55 .20
1439 A641 10p Alstroemeria
aurantiaca 1.10 .80
1440 A641 20p like #1345 .55 .16
1441 A641 30p Embothrium
coccineum 3.50 2.50
1442 A641 50p like #1346 1.10 .40

1443 A641 100p like #1348 1.65 .48
1443A A641 300p Cassia carnaval .80 .24
Nos. 1429-1443A (17) 10.99
Set value 5.25
Issue Dates: 20p, Aug. 27, 1984. 50p, Oct. 19,
1984. 100p, Dec. 1984. 300p, June 15, 1985.
Nos. 1429, 1433, 1435A issued on fluorescent
paper. Nos. 1443, 1443A issued on ordinary paper.
Others issued on both ordinary and fluorescent
paper.
For overprint and surcharge see #1489, 1530.

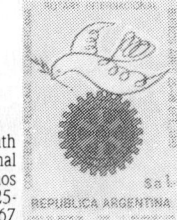

Intl. Rotary South
American Regional
Conference, Buenos
Aires, Sept. 25-
28 — A667

1983, Sept. 24   **Litho.**
1444 A667 1p multi .55 .24

9th Pan
American
Games,
Caracas,
Aug. 13-28
A668

1983, Sept. 24
1445 A668 1p Track .32 .15
1446 A668 2p Emblem .65 .28

World
Communications
Year — A669

1983, Oct. 8   **Perf. 13½**
1447 A669 2p multi .60 .24

Squash Peddler by
Antonio Berni
(1905-1981)
A670

2p, Figure in Yellow by Luis Seoane (1910-79).

1983, Oct. 15   **Perf. 13½**
1448 A670 1p multi .32 .15
1449 A670 2p multi .52 .22

World Communications Year — A671

Designs: 1p, Wagon, 18th cent. 2p, Post chaise,
19th cent. 4p, Steam locomotive, 1857. 5p, Tramway, 1910.

1983, Nov. 19   **Litho.**   **Perf. 13½**
1450 A671 1p multi .15 .15
1451 A671 2p multi .24 .15
1452 A671 4p multi .50 .20
1453 A671 5p multi .65 .26
Nos. 1450-1453 (4) 1.54 .76

A672   A673

1983, Nov. 26   **Litho.**   **Perf. 12½x12**
1454 A672 2p General Post Office .42 .18
World Communications Year.

1983, Dec. 10   **Photo.**   **Perf. 13½**
1455 A673 2p Coin, 1813 .30 .18
Return to elected government.

Eudyptes
Crestatus
A674

Designs: b, Diomedea exulans. c, Diomedea
melanophris. d, Eudyptes chrysolophus. e, Luis
Piedra Buena. f, Carlos Maria Moyano. g, Luis Py.
h, Augusto Lasserre. i, Phoebetria palpebrata. j,
Hydrurga leptonyx. k, Lobodon carcinophagus. l,
Leptonychotes weddelli.

1983, Dec. 10   **Litho.**
1456 Sheet of 12 4.50 2.25
a.-l. A674 2p any single .35 .15
Southern pioneers and fauna. Margin depicts
various airplanes and emblems.

Bolivar Type of 1983
Famous men: 10p, Angel J. Carranza (1834-99),
historian. No. 1458, 500p, Guillermo Brown. No.
1459, Estanislao del Campo (1834-80), poet. 30p,
Jose Hernandez (1834-86), author. 40p, Vicente
Lopez y Planes (1784-1856), poet and patriot. 50p,
San Martin. 200p, Belgrano.

1983-85   **Litho. & Engr.**   **Perf. 13½**
1457 A664 10p pale bl & dk bl .15 .15
1458 A664 20p dk bl & blk 2.75 1.40
1459 A664 20p dl brn ol & ol
blk .15 .15
1460 A664 30p pale bl & bluish
blk .15 .15
1461 A664 40p lt bl grn & blk .18 .15
1462 A664 50p Prus & choc 1.10 .24
1462A A664 200p int bl & blk 3.00 .95
1462B A664 500p brn & int bl 1.50 .32
Nos. 1457-1462B (8) 8.98 3.51
Issue dates: #1458, Oct. 6, 1983. 10p #1459,
30p, 40p, Mar. 23, 1985. 50p, Apr. 23, 1985.
200p, Nov. 2, 1985. 500p, May 2, 1985.

Christmas
1983
A675

Nativity Scenes: 2p, Tapestry, by Silke. 3p,
Stained-glass window, San Carlos de Bariloche's
Wayn Church, vert.

1983, Dec. 17   **Litho.**   **Perf. 13½**
1463 A675 2p multi .30 .15
1464 A675 3p multi .55 .28

Centenary of El Dia
Newspaper — A676

1984, Mar. 24   **Litho.**
1465 A676 4p Masthead, printing roll .38 .20

Alejandro
Carbo
Teachers'
College
Centenary
A677

1984, June 2   Litho.   Perf. 13¹/₂
1466 A677 10p Building   .42 .22

1984
Olympics
A678

#1468, Weightlifting, discus, shot put. #1469,
Javelin, fencing. #1470, Bicycling, swimming.

1984, July 28   Litho.   Perf. 13¹/₂
1467 A678 5p shown   .22 .15
1468 A678 5p multicolored   .22 .15
1469 A678 10p multicolored   .45 .22
1470 A678 10p multicolored   .45 .22
      Nos. 1467-1470 (4)   1.34 .74

Rosario Stock
Exchange
Centenary
A679

1984, Aug. 11
1471 A679 10p multicolored   .45 .22

Wheat
A680

1984, Aug. 11
1472 A680 10p shown   .48 .24
1473 A680 10p Corn   .48 .24
1474 A680 10p Sunflower   .48 .24
      Nos. 1472-1474 (3)   1.44 .72

18th FAO Regional Conference for Latin America
and Caribbean (No. 1472); 3rd Natl. Corn Congress (No. 1473); World Food Day (No. 1474).

Wildlife
Protection
A681

1984, Sept. 22   Litho.   Perf. 13¹/₂
1475 A681 20p Hippocamelus bisulcus   .40 .15
1476 A681 20p Vicugna vicugna   .40 .15
1477 A681 20p Aburria jacutinga   .40 .15

1478 A681 20p Mergus octosetaceus   .40 .15
1479 A681 20p Podiceps gallardoi   .40 .15
      Nos. 1475-1479 (5)   2.00 .75

First Latin
American Theater
Festival, Cordoba,
Oct. — A682

1984, Oct. 13   Litho.   Perf. 13¹/₂
1480 A682 20p Mask   .25 .15

Intl.
Eucharistic
Congress,
50th Anniv.
A683

Design: Apostles' Communion, by Fra Angelico.

1984, Oct. 13
1481 A683 20p multicolored   .30 .15

Glaciares
Natl. Park
(UNESCO
World
Heritage
List)
A684

1984, Nov. 17   **Litho.**
1482 A684 20p Sea   .25 .15
1483 A684 30p Glacier   .42 .15
      Set value   .25

City of
Puerto
Deseado
Centenary
A685

1984, Nov. 17   Perf. 13¹/₂
1484 A685 20p shown   .30 .15
1485 A685 20p Ushuaia centenary   .30 .15
      Set value   .15

Childrens'
Paintings,
Christmas
1984
A686

1984, Dec. 1   Litho.   Perf. 13¹/₂
1486 A686 20p Diego Aguero   .32 .15
1487 A686 30p Leandro Ruiz   .60 .15
1488 A686 50p Maria Castillo, vert.   .60 .15
      Nos. 1486-1488 (3)   1.52 .45

No. 1439 Overprinted

1984, Dec. 1   Photo.   Perf. 13¹/₂
1489 A641 10p multicolored   .26 .22
Buenos Aires Philatelic Center, 50th anniv.

Vista Del Jardin
Zoologico, by
Fermin
Eguia — A687

Paintings: No. 1491, El Congreso Iluminado, by
Francisco Travieso. No. 1492, Galpones (La Boca),
by Marcos Borio.

1984, Dec. 15   Perf. 13¹/₂
1490 A687 20p multi   .28 .15
1491 A687 20p multi, vert.   .28 .15
1492 A687 20p multi, vert.   .28 .15
      Nos. 1490-1492 (3)   .84 .45

Gen. Martin Miguel de Guemes (1785-
1821) — A688

1985, Mar. 23   Litho.   Perf. 13¹/₂
1493 A688 30p multicolored   .26 .15

ARGENTINA '85 Exhibition — A689

First airmail service from: 20p, Buenos Aires to
Montevideo, 1917. 40p, Cordoba to Villa Dolores,
1925. 60p, Bahia Blanca to Comodoro Rivadavia,
1929. 80p, Argentina to Germany, 1934. 100p,
naval service to the Antarctic, 1952.

1985, Apr. 27
1494 A689 20p Bleriot Gnome   .16 .15
1495 A689 40p Junker F-13L   .32 .15
1496 A689 60p Latte 25   .50 .20
1497 A689 80p L.Z. 127 Graf
                  Zeppelin   .65 .30
1498 A689 100p Consolidated PBY
                  Catalina   .85 .40
      Nos. 1494-1498 (5)   2.48 1.20

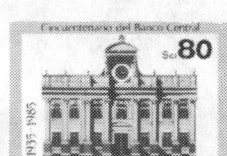

Central
Bank, 50th
Anniv.
A690

1985, June 1
1499 A690 80p Bank Bldg., Buenos
                  Aires   .55 .18

Jose A.
Ferreyra
(1889-1943),
Director of
Munequitas
Portenas
A691

Famous directors and their films: No. 1501, Leopoldo Torre Nilsson (1924-1978), scene from Martin Fierro.

1985, June 1
1500 A691 100p shown   .60 .18
1501 A691 100p multi   .60 .18

Carlos Gardel
(1890-1935),
Entertainer — A692

Paintings: No. 1502, Gardel playing the guitar on
stage, by Carlos Alonso (b. 1929). No. 1503, Gardel in a wide-brimmed hat, by Hermegildo Sabat (b.
1933). No. 1504, Portrait of Gardel in an ornamental frame, by Aldo Severi (b. 1928) and Martiniano Arce (b. 1939).

1985, June 15
1502 A692 200p multi   .95 .45
1503 A692 200p multi   .95 .45
1504 A692 200p multi   .95 .45
      Nos. 1502-1504 (3)   2.85 1.35

The
Arrival, by
Pedro
Figari
A693

A Halt on the Plains, by Prilidiano
Pueyrredon — A693a

Oil paintings (details): 30c, The Wagon Square,
by C. B. de Quiros. Ilustration A693a is reduced.

1985, July 6   Litho.   Perf. 13¹/₂
1505 A693 20c multi   1.00 .24
1506 A693 30c multi   1.25 .24

Souvenir Sheet
Perf. 12
1507 A693a   Sheet of 2   2.50 2.50
  a.   20c Pilgrims, vert.   .30 .30
  b.   30c Wagon   .40 .40

ARGENTINA '85. No. 1507 contains 2
30x40mm stamps. See No. 1542.

Buenos Aires
to
Montevideo,
1917 Teodoro
Fels Flight
A694

Historic flight covers: No. 1508, Shown. No.
1509, Villa Dolores to Cordoba, 1925. No. 1510,
Buenos Aires to France, 1929 St. Exupery flight.
No. 1511, Buenos Aires to Bremerhaven, 1934
Graf Zeppelin flight. No. 1512, First Antarctic flight,
1952.

1985, July 13   Perf. 12x12¹/₂
1508 A694 10c emer & multi   .40 .15
1509 A694 10c ultra & multi   .40 .15
1510 A694 10c lt choc & multi   .40 .15
1511 A694 10c chnt & multi   .40 .15
1512 A694 10c ap grn & multi   .40 .15
      Nos. 1508-1512 (5)   2.00
      Set value   .60

ARGENTINA '85.

Illuminated Fruit, by Fortunato Lacamera
(1887-1951) — A695

Paintings: 20c, Woman with Bird, by Juan del
Prete, vert.

1985, Sept. 7   *Perf. 13¹/₂*
1513 A695 20c multi   .85 .30
1514 A695 30c multi   1.00 .30

Flower Types of 1982-85

Designs: 1a, Begonia micranthera var. hieronymi. 5a, Gymnocaylcium bruchii.

1985-88   **Photo.**   *Perf. 13¹/₂*
1515 A641 ¹/₂c like #1356   .15 .15
1516 A641 1c like #1439   .15 .15
1517 A641 2c like #1345   .15 .15
1518 A641 3c like #1441   .15 .15
1519 A641 5c like #1346   .22 .15
1520 A641 10c like #1348   .35 .15
1521 A641 20c like #1347   .70 .16
1522 A641 30c like #1443A   1.10 .25
1523 A641 50c like #1344   1.75 .35
1524 A641 1a multi   3.50 .65
1525 A641 2a like #1351   .38 .15
1526 A641 5a multi   6.75 3.00

Size: 15x23mm

1527 A641 8¹/₂c like #1349   .32 .15
   Nos. 1515-1527 (13)   15.67 5.61

Issue dates: ¹/₂c, 1c, Dec. 16. 2c, 8¹/₂c, 30c, Sept. 18. 3c, 5c, 10c, 50c, 1a, Sept. 7. 20c, Oct. 17. 5a, Mar. 21, 1987. 2a, Dec. 5, 1988.

No. 1435 Surcharged

1986, Nov. 4   **Photo.**   *Perf. 13¹/₂*
1530 A641 10c on 1p No. 1435   .15 .15

Folk Musical Instruments
A699

1985, Sept. 14   **Litho.**   *Perf. 13¹/₂*
1531 A699 20c Frame drum   .55 .22
1532 A699 20c Long flute   .55 .22
1533 A699 20c Jew's harp   .55 .22
1534 A699 20c Pan flutes   .55 .22
1535 A699 20c Musical bow   .55 .22
   Nos. 1531-1535 (5)   2.75 1.10

Juan Bautista Alberdi (1810-1884), Historian, Politician
A700

Famous men: Nicolas Avellaneda (1836-1885), President in 1874. 30c, Fr. Luis Beltran (1784-1827), military and naval engineer. 40c, Ricardo Levene (1885-1959), historian, author.

1985, Oct. 5
1536 A700 10c multi   .22 .15
1537 A700 20c multi   .45 .22
1538 A700 30c multi   .65 .32
1539 A700 40c multi   1.10 .45
   Nos. 1536-1539 (4)   2.42 1.14

Type of 1985 and

Skaters
A701

Deception, by J. H. Rivoira
A702

1985, Oct. 19   **Litho.**   *Perf. 13¹/₂*
1540 A701 20c multi   .35 .32

1541 A702 30c multi   .50 .48

Size: 147x75mm
Imperf

1542 A693a 1a multi   1.90

IYY. No. 1542 is inscribed in silver with the UN 40th anniversary and IYY emblems.

Provincial Views — A703

Designs: No. 1543, Rock Window, Buenos Aires. No. 1544, Forclaz Windmill, Entre Rios. No. 1545, Lake Potrero de los Funes, San Luis. No. 1546, Mission church, north-east province. No. 1547, Penguin colony, Punta Tombo, Chubut. No. 1548, Water Mirrors, Cordoba.

1985, Nov. 23   *Perf. 13¹/₂*
1543 A703 10c multi   .26 .25
1544 A703 10c multi   .26 .25
1545 A703 10c multi   .26 .25
1546 A703 10c multi   .26 .25
1547 A703 10c multi   .26 .25
1548 A703 10c multi   .26 .25
   Nos. 1543-1548 (6)   1.56 1.50

Christmas 1985 — A704

Designs: 10c, Birth of Our Lord, by Carlos Cortes. 20c, Christmas, by Hector Viola.

1985, Dec. 7
1549 A704 10c multi   .24 .18
1550 A704 20c multi   .48 .45

Natl. Campaign for the Prevention of Blindness
A705

1985, Dec. 7
1551 A705 10c multi   .24 .18

Rio Gallegos City, Cent. — A716

1985, Dec. 21   **Litho.**   *Perf. 13¹/₂*
1552 A716 10c Church   .24 .18

Natl. Grape Harvest Festival, 50th Anniv.
A717

1986, Mar. 15
1553 A717 10c multi   .24 .18

Historical Architecture in Buenos Aires — A718

Designs: No. 1554, Valentin Alsina House, Italian Period, 1860-70. No. 1555, House on Cerrito Street, French influence, 1880-1900. No. 1556, House on the Avenida de Mayo y Santiago del Estero, Art Nouveau, 1900-10. No. 1557, Customs Building, academic architecture, 1900-15. No. 1558, Isaac Fernandez Blanco Museum, house of architect Martin Noel, natl. restoration, 1910-30. Nos. 1554-1556 vert.

1986, Apr. 19
1554 A718 20c multi   .40 .30
1555 A718 20c multi   .40 .30
1556 A718 20c multi   .40 .30
1557 A718 20c multi   .40 .30
1558 A718 20c multi   .40 .30
   Nos. 1554-1558 (5)   2.00 1.50

Antarctic Bases, Pioneers and Fauna — A719

Designs: a, Base, Jubany. b, Arctocephalus gazella. c, Otaria byronia. d, Gen. Belgrano Base. e, Daption capensis. f, Diomedia melanophris. g, Apterodytes patagonica. h, Macronectes giganteus. i, Hugo Alberto Acuna (1885-1953). j, Spheniscus magellanicus. k, Gallinago gallinage. l, Capt. Agustin del Castillo (1855-89).

1986, May 31
1559   Sheet of 12   9.00 9.00
  a.-l. A719 10c any single   .75 .75

Famous People — A720   Statuary, Buenos Aires — A721

#1560, Dr. Alicia Moreau de Justo, human rights activist. #1561, Dr. Emilio Ravignani (1886-1954), historian. #1562, Indira Gandhi.

1986, July 5   **Litho.**   *Perf. 13¹/₂*
1560 A720 10c multi   .40 .22
1561 A720 10c multi   .40 .22
1562 A720 30c multi   1.25 .65
   Nos. 1560-1562 (3)   2.05 1.09

1986, July 5

Designs: 20c, Fountain of the Nereids, by Dolores Lola Mora (1866-1936). 30c, Lamenting at Work, by Rogelio Yrurtia (1879-1950), horiz.

1563 A721 20c multi   .52 .45
1564 A721 30c multi   .80 .65

Famous Men — A722

Designs: No. 1565, Francisco N. Laprida (1786-1829), politician. No. 1566, Estanislao Lopez

---

(1786-1838), brigadier general. No. 1567, Francisco Ramirez (1786-1821), general.

1986, Aug. 9   **Litho.**   *Perf. 13*
1565 A722 20c dl yel, brn & blk   .42 .38
1566 A722 20c dl yel, brn & blk   .42 .38
1567 A722 20c dl yel, brn & blk   .42 .38
   Nos. 1565-1567 (3)   1.26 1.14

Fr. Ceferino Namuncura (1886-1905)
A723

1986, Aug. 30   *Perf. 13¹/₂*
1568 A723 20c multi   .60 .40

Miniature Sheets

Natl. Team Victory, 1986 World Cup Soccer Championships, Mexico — A724

Designs: No. 1569a-1569d, Team. Nos. 1569e-1569h, Shot on goal. Nos. 1570a-1570d, Action close-up. Nos. 1570e-1570h, Diego Maradona holding soccer cup.

1986, Nov. 8   **Litho.**   *Perf. 13¹/₂*
1569 A724   Sheet of 8   9.25 12.00
  a.-h.   75c any single   1.15 1.50
1570 A724   Sheet of 8   9.25 12.00
  a.-h.   75c any single   1.15 1.50

San Francisco (Cordoba), Cent.
A725

1986, Nov. 8
1571 A725 20c Municipal Building   .50 .45

Trelew City (Chubut), Cent.
A726

1986, Nov. 22   **Litho.**   *Perf. 13¹/₂*
1572 A726 20c Old railroad station, 1865   .50 .45

Mutualism Day
A727

1986, Nov. 22
1573 A727 20c multi   .60 .45

Christmas
A728

Designs: 20c, Naif retable, by Aniko Szabo (b. 1945). 30c, Everyone's Tree, by Franca Delacqua (b. 1947).

1986, Dec. 13   Litho.   Perf. 13½
1574 A728 20c multicolored   .50 .35
1575 A728 30c multicolored   .60 .35

Santa Rosa de Lima,
400th Birth
Anniv. — A729

Rio Cuarto
Municipal
Building — A730

1986, Dec. 13
1576 A729 50c multicolored   1.75 .75

1986, Dec. 20
1577 A730 20c shown   .40 .25
1578 A730 20c Court Building, Cordoba   .40 .25
Rio Cuarto City, bicent. Court Building, Cordoba, 50th anniv.

Antarctic Treaty,
25th
Anniv. — A731

1987, Mar. 7   Litho.   Perf. 13½
1579 A731 20c Marine biologist   .35 .20
1580 A731 30c Ornithologist   .60 .25

Souvenir Sheet
Perf. 12
1581   Sheet of 2   1.00 .50
a.   A731 20c like No. 1579   .40 .20
b.   A731 30c like No. 1580   .55 .25
No. 1581 contains 2 stamps, size: 40x50mm.

Natl.
Mortgage
Bank, Cent.
A732

1987, Mar. 21   Perf. 13½
1582 A732 20c multicolored   .65 .45

Natl. Cooperative Associations
Movement — A733

1987, Mar. 21
1583 A733 20c multicolored   .65 .45

Second State Visit of
Pope John
Paul II — A734

Engr., Litho. (No. 1585)
1987, Apr. 4   Perf. 13½
1584 A734 20c shown   .35 .25
1585 A734 80c Papal blessing   1.40 .70

Souvenir Sheet
Perf. 12
1586 A734 1a like 20c   2.25 2.25
No. 1586 contains one 40x50mm stamp.

Intl.
Peace
Year
A735

30c, Pigeon, abstract sculpture by Victor Kaniuka.

1987, Apr. 11   Litho.
1587 A735 20c multicolored   .35 .20
1588 A735 30c multicolored   .55 .35

Low Handicap
World Polo
Championships
A736

Design: Polo Players, painting by Alejandro Moy.

1987, Apr. 11
1589 A736 20c multicolored   .75 .20

Miniature Sheet

ICOM '86 — A737

Designs: a, Emblem. b, Family crest, National History Museum, Buenos Aires. c, St. Bartholomew, Enrique Larreta Museum of Spanish Art, Buenos Aires. d, Zoomorphic club, Patagonian Museum, San Carlos de Bariloche. e, Supplication, anthropomorphic sculpture, Natural Sciences Museum, La Plata. f, Wrought iron lattice from the house of J. Urquiza, president of the Confederation of Argentina, Entre Rios History Museum, Parana. g, St. Joseph, 18th cent. wood figurine, Northern History Museum, Salta. h, Funerary urn, Provincial Archaeological Museum, Santiago del Estero.

1987, May 30
1590   Sheet of 8   3.50 3.50
a.-h.   A737 25c any single   .40 .30
Intl. Council of Museums, 14th general conf.

Natl. College of Monserrat, Cordoba,
300th Anniv. — A738

1987, July 4   Imperf.
1591 A738 1a multicolored   1.40 1.40
Monserrat '87 Philatelic Exposition.

Fight Drug
Abuse
A739

Design: The Proportions of Man, by da Vinci.

1987, Aug. 15   Perf. 13½
1592 A739 30c multicolored   .45 .20

Famous
Men
A740

Portraits and quotations: 20c, Jorge Luis Borges (1899-1986), writer. 30c, Armando Discepolo (1887-1971), playwright. 50c, Carlos A. Pueyrredon (1887-1962), professor, Legion of Honor laureate.

1987, Aug. 15
1593 A740 20c multicolored   .30 .15
1594 A740 30c multicolored   .50 .25
1595 A740 50c multicolored   .75 .35
Nos. 1593-1595 (3)   1.55 .75

Pillar Boxes
A741   A742

1987   Photo.   Perf. 13½
1596 A741 (30c) yel, blk & dark red   .80 .30
1597 A742 (33c) lt blue grn, blk & yel   .85 .35
Issue dates: (30c), June 8; (33c), July 13.

The Sower,
by Julio
Vanzo
A743

1987, Sept. 12
1598 A743 30c multicolored   .35 .15
Argentine Agrarian Federation, 75th anniv.

10th Pan
American Games,
Indianapolis, Aug.
7-25 — A744

1987, Sept. 26
1599 A744 20c Basketball   .25 .20
1600 A744 30c Rowing   .35 .20
1601 A744 50c Yachting   .55 .20
Nos. 1599-1601 (3)   1.15 .60

Children
Playing
Doctor,
WHO
Emblem
A745

1987, Oct. 7
1602 A745 30c multi   .35
Vaccinate every child campaign.

Heroes of the
Revolution
A746

Signing of
the San
Nicolas
Accord,
1852, by
Rafael del
Villar
A747

Independence anniversaries and historic events: No. 1603, Maj.-Col. Ignacio Alvarez Thomas (1787-1857). No. 1604, Col. Manuel Crispulo Bernabe Dorrego (1787-1829). No. 1606, 18th cent. Spanish map of the Falkland Isls., administered by Jacinto de Altolaguirre.

1987, Oct. 17
1603 A746 25c shown   .30 .20
1604 A746 25c multi   .30 .20
1605 A747 50c shown   .55 .30
1606 A747 50c multi   .55 .30
Nos. 1603-1606 (4)   1.70 1.00
Museum established in the House of the San Nicholas Accord, 50th anniv. (#1605); Jacinto de Altolaguirre (1754-1787), governor the Malvinas Isls. for the King of Spain (#1606).

Celedonio
Galvan
Moreno, 1st
Director
A748

1987, Nov. 21
1607 A748 50c multicolored   .55 .40
Postas Argentinas magazine, 50th anniv.

LRA National Radio, Buenos Aires, 50th Anniv. — A749

1987, Nov. 21
1608 A749 50c multicolored .55 .40

Natl. Philatelic Society, Cent. A750

1987, Nov. 21
1609 A750 1a Jose Marco del Pont 1.10 .55

Christmas A751

Tapestries: 50c, *Navidad*, by Alisia Frega. 1a, *Vitral*, by Silvina Trigos.

1987, Dec. 5
1610 A751 50c multicolored .55 .20
1611 A751 1a multicolored 1.10 .55

Natl. Parks — A752

1987, Dec. 19   *Perf. 13x13¹/₂*
1612 A752 50c Baritu .55 .35
1613 A752 50c Nahuel Huapi .55 .35
1614 A752 50c Rio Pilcomayo .55 .35
1615 A752 50c Tierra del Fuego .55 .35
1616 A752 50c Iguacu .55 .35
　　Nos. 1612-1616 (5) 2.75 1.75
See Nos. 1647-1651, 1715-1719, 1742-1746.

Landscapes in Buenos Aires Painted by Jose Cannella A753

1988-89   *Litho.*   *Perf. 13¹/₂*
1617 A753 5a Caminito 2.00 1.10
1618 A753 10a Viejo Almacen 4.00 2.25
1618A A753 10a like No. 1618 1.05 .50
1618B A753 50a like No. 1617 1.05 .50
　c.　Wmk 365 120.00
　　Nos. 1617-1618B (4) 8.10 4.35
No. 1618 inscribed "Viejo Almacen"; No. 1618A inscribed "El Viejo Almacen."
Issue dates: 5a, #1618, 3/15; #1618A, 10/20; 50a, 5/30/89.
For overprint see No. 1635.

Minstrel in a Tavern, by Carlos Morel A754

Paintings: No. 1620, Interior of Curuzu, by Candido Lopez.

1988, Mar. 19   *Litho.*   *Perf. 13¹/₂*
1619 A754 1a shown .60 .30
1620 A754 1a multicolored .60 .30
　　See Nos. 1640-1641.

Argentine-Brazilian Economic Cooperation and Integration Program for Mutual Growth — A755

1988, Mar. 19
1621 A755 1a multicolored .50 .25

Cities of Alta Gracia and Corrientes, 400th Annivs. A756

1988, Apr. 9   *Litho.*   *Perf. 13¹/₂*
1622 A756 1a Alta Gracia Church .75 .40
1623 A756 1a Chapel of St. Anne, Corrientes .75 .40

Labor Day — A757

Grain Carriers, a tile mosaic by Alfredo Guido, Line D of Nueve de Julio station, Buenos Aires subway: a, (UL). b, (UR). c, (LL). d, (LR).

1988, May 21
1624 A757 Block of 4 2.00 2.00
　a.-d.　50c any single .50 .50

1988 Summer Olympics, Seoul — A758

1988, July 16   *Litho.*   *Perf. 13¹/₂*
1625 A758 1a Running .30 .15
1626 A758 2a Soccer .75 .30
1627 A758 3a Field hockey 1.10 .50
1628 A758 4a Tennis 1.40 .65
　　Nos. 1625-1628 (4) 3.55 1.60

Mendoza Bank, Cent. A759

Natl. Gendarmerie, Cent. — A760

1988, Aug. 13
1629 A759 2a multicolored .65 .45
1630 A760 2a multicolored .65 .45

Sarmiento and Cathedral School to the North, Buenos Aires A761

1988, Sept. 10   *Litho.*   *Perf. 13¹/₂*
1631 A761 3a multicolored .65 .45
Domingo Faustino Sarmiento (1811-1888), educator, politician.

St. Cayetano, Patron of Workers — A762

El Amor, by Antonio Berni, Pacific Gallery, Buenos Aires — A763

1988, Sept. 10   *Litho.*
1632 A762 2a multicolored .45 .45
1633 A762 3a Our Lady of Carmen, Cuyo .70 .70

Souvenir Sheet
Perf. 12
1634 A763 5a multicolored 1.00 1.00
Liniers Philatelic Circle and the Argentine Western Philatelic Institution (IFADO), 50th annivs.
No. 1634 contains one 40x30mm stamp.

No. 1617 Ovptd. with Congress Emblem and:

**"XXI CONGRESO
DE LA SOCIEDAD
INTERNACIONAL
DE UROLOGIA"**

1988, Oct. 29   *Litho.*   *Perf. 13¹/₂*
1635 A753 5a multicolored 3.50 .40
21st Congress of the Intl. Urology Soc.

Tourism A763a

1988, Nov. 1   *Litho.*   *Perf. 13¹/₂*
1635A A763a 3a Purmamarca, Jujuy .50 .25
Size: 28¹/₂x38mm
1635B A763a 20a Ushuaia 3.35 1.65

Buenos Aires Subway, 75th Anniv. A764

1988, Dec. 17   *Litho.*   *Perf. 13¹/₂*
1636 A764 5a Train, c. 1913 1.10 .55

Christmas A765

Frescoes in Ucrania Cathedral, Buenos Aires: No. 1637, *Virgin Patron.* No. 1638, *Virgin of Tenderness.*

1988, Dec. 17
1637 A765 5a multicolored 1.25 .50
1638 A765 5a multicolored 1.25 .50

St. John Bosco (1815-1888), Educator, and Church in Ushuaia — A766

1989, Apr. 8   *Litho.*   *Perf. 13¹/₂*
1639 A766 5a multicolored .30 .20
　　Dated 1988.

Art Type of 1988
Paintings: No. 1640, *Blancos*, by Fernando Fader (1882-1935). No. 1641, *Rincon de los Areneros*, by Justo Lynch (1870-1953).

1989, Apr. 8
1640 A754 5a multicolored .50 .15
1641 A754 5a multicolored .50 .15

Holy Week A767

Sculpture and churches: No. 1642, *The Crown of Thorns*, Calvary of Tandil, and Church of Our Lady Carmelite, Tandil. No. 1643, *Jesus the Nazarene* and Metropolitan Cathedral, Buenos Aires. No. 1644, *Jesus Encounters His Mother* (scene of the crucifixion), La Quebrada Village, San Luis. No. 1645, *Our Lady of Sorrow* and Church of Humahuaca, Jujuy.

1989, Apr. 22   *Litho.*   *Perf. 13¹/₂*
1642 A767 2a multicolored .20 .15
1643 A767 2a multicolored .20 .15
1644 A767 3a multicolored .30 .20
1645 A767 3a multicolored .30 .20
　　Nos. 1642-1645 (4) 1.00 .70
Printed in sheets of 16+4 labels containing blocks of 4 of each design. Labels picture Jesus's arrival in Jerusalem (Palm Sunday).

Prevent
Alcoholism
A768

1989, Apr. 22
1646 A768 5a multicolored   .30   .20

Natl. Park Type of 1987

1989, May 6   *Perf. 13x13¹/₂*
1647 A752 5a Lihue Calel   .70   .15
1648 A752 5a El Palmar   .70   .15
1649 A752 5a Calilegua   .70   .15
1650 A752 5a Chaco   .70   .15
1651 A752 5a Los Glaciares   .70   .15
    Nos. 1647-1651 (5)   3.50   .75

Admission
of
Argentina
to the ITU,
Cent.
A769

1989, May 6   *Perf. 13¹/₂*
1652 A769 10a multicolored   .45   .20

World Model Aircraft
Championships — A770

1989, May 27   *Litho.*   *Perf. 13¹/₂*
1653 A770 5a F1A glider   .20   .15
1654 A770 5a F1B rubber band mo-
    tor   .20   .15
1655 A770 10a F1C gas motor   .35   .20
    Nos. 1653-1655 (3)   .75   .50

French Revolution, Bicent. — A771

Designs: 10a, "All men are born free and equal."
15a, French flag and *La Marianne*, by Gandon. 25a,
Liberty Guiding the People, by Delacroix.

1989, July 1   *Litho.*   *Perf. 13¹/₂*
1656 A771 10a shown   .15   .15
1657 A771 15a multicolored   .15   .15
    Set value   .20   .15

Souvenir Sheet
Perf. 12
1658 A771 25a multicolored   .25   .15

No. 1658 contains one 40x30mm stamp.

The Republic, a
Bronze Bust in
the Congreso de
la Nacion, Buenos
Aires — A772

1989, Aug. 12   *Litho.*   *Perf. 13¹/₂*
1659 A772 300a on 50a multi   .75   .50

Peaceful transition of power (presidential office).
Not issued without surcharge.

Immigration to Argentina — A773

1989, Aug. 19   *Perf. 13¹/₂*
1660 A773 150a S.S. *Weser*, 1889   .65   .35
1661 A773 200a Immigrant hotel,
    1889   .75   .45

Souvenir Sheet
Perf. 12
1662   1.65 1.65
  a.   A773 150a like No. 1660   .65   .35
  b.   A773 200a like No. 1661   .75   .45

No. 1662 contains 40c30mm stamps.

Famous
Men
A774

Designs: No. 1663, Fr. Guillermo Furlong (1889-
1974), historian, and title page of *The Jesuits*. No.
1664, Dr. Gregorio Alvarez (1889-1986), physician, and title page of *Canto a Chos Malal*. 200a,
Brig.-Gen. Enrique Martinez (1789-1870) and lithograph *La Batalla de Maipu*, by Teodoro Gericault.

1989, Oct. 7   *Litho.*   *Perf. 13¹/₂*
1663 A774 150a multicolored   .35   .20
1664 A774 150a multicolored   .35   .20
1665 A774 200a multicolored   .35   .20
    Nos. 1663-1665 (3)   1.05   .60

America
Issue — A775

Emblem of the Postal Union of the Americas and
Spain (PUAS) and pre-Columbian art from Cata-
marca Province: 200a, Wooden mask from Atajo,
Loma Morada. 300a, Urn of the Santa Maria Cul-
ture (Phase 3) from Punta de Balastro, Santa Maria
Department.

1989, Oct. 14
1666 A775 200a multicolored   .50   .35
1667 A775 300a multicolored   .75   .50

Federal Police
Week — A776

Children's drawings: No. 1668, Diego Molinari,
age 13. No. 1669, Carlos Alberto Sarago, age 8. No.
1670, Roxana Andrea Osuna, age 7. No. 1671,
Pablo Javier Quaglia, age 9.

1989, Oct. 28   *Litho.*   *Perf. 13¹/₂*
1668 A776 100a multi   .25   .15
1669 A776 100a multi   .25   .15
1670 A776 150a multi   .40   .20
1671 A776 150a multi   .40   .20
    Nos. 1668-1671 (4)   1.30   .70

Battle of Vuelta de Obligado,
1845 — A777

(Illustration reduced.)

1989, Dec. 2   *Litho.*   *Perf. 13x13¹/₂*
1672 A777 300a multicolored   .40   .20

Paintings
A778

Cristo de los
Cerros, Sculpture
by Chipo
Cespedes — A779

1989, Dec. 2   *Perf. 13¹/₂*
1673 A778 200a Gato Frias   .35   .20
1674 A778 200a Maria Carballido   .35   .20
1675 A779 300a shown   .35   .20
    Nos. 1673-1675 (3)   1.05   .60
    Christmas.

Buenos Aires Port, Cent. — A780

(Illustration reduced.)

1990, Mar. 3   *Litho.*   *Perf. 13¹/₂*
1676 A780 200a Strip of 4   7.50 2.50
  a.-d.   200a any single   1.25   .65

Aconcagua Intl. Fair, Mendoza — A781

Design: Aconcagua mountain, Los Horcones
Lagoon and fair emblem.
(Illustration reduced.)

1990, Mar. 3
1677 A781 Pair   2.00 1.00
  a.-b.   500a any single   1.00   .50

Natl.
Savings
and
Insurance
Fund, 75th
Anniv.
A782

1990, May 5   *Litho.*   *Perf. 13¹/₂*
1678 A782 1000a multicolored   .35   .20

Miniature Sheet

1990 World Cup Soccer Championships,
Italy — A783

Designs: a, Athlete's torso (striped jersey). b, Athlete's torso (solid jersey). c, Players' feet, soccer
ball. d, Player (knee to waist).

1990, May 5
1679   Sheet of 4   5.00 5.00
  a.-d. A783 2500a multicolored   1.00 1.00

Carlos Pellegrini, Commercial High School
Founder, Cent. — A784

1990, June 2   *Litho.*   *Perf. 13¹/₂*
1680 A784 2000a multicolored   .30   .20

Youth
Against
Drugs
A785

1990, June 2
1681 A785 2000a multicolored   .30   .20

Intl.
Literacy
Year
A786

1990, July 14   *Litho.*   *Perf. 13¹/₂*
1682 A786 2000a multicolored   .30   .20

Flower Type of 1982 in New Currency
1989-90   *Photo.*   *Perf. 13¹/₂*
1683 A641 10a like #1433   .15   .15
1684 A641 20a like #1435A   .15   .15
1685 A641 50a like #1354   .15   .15
1686 A641 100a like #1439   .20   .15
1687 A641 300a like #1345   .40   .20
1688 A641 500a like #1441   .65   .35
1689 A641 1000a like #1355   .15   .15
1690 A641 5000a like #1349   1.00   .70
1691 A641 10,000a like #1350   1.50 1.00
    Nos. 1683-1691 (9)   4.35 3.00

Issued: 20a, 100a, 300a, 500a, 8/1/89; 10a,
8/24/89; 50a, 8/30/89; 1000, 3/8/90; 5000a,
4/6/90; 10,000a, 7/2/90.

World Basketball
Championships
A787

1990, Aug. 11   Litho.   Perf. 13½
1703 A787 2000a multicolored   2.00 1.50

Souvenir Sheet
Perf. 12
1704 A787 5000a Jump ball   3.75 2.75

Postal
Union of
the
Americas
and Spain,
14th
Congress
A788

1990, Sept. 15   Litho.   Perf. 13½
1705 A788 3000a Arms, seal   1.50 .75
1706 A788 3000a Sailing ships   1.50 .75
1707 A788 3000a Modern freighter   1.50 .75
1708 A788 3000a Van, cargo plane   1.50 .75
    Nos. 1705-1708 (4)   6.00 3.00

America
Issue
A789

1990, Oct. 13
1709 A789 3000a Iguacu Falls,
        hamelia erecta   1.50 .60
1710 A789 3000a Puerto Deseado,
        elephant seal   1.50 .60

Natl. Parks Type of 1987
1990, Oct. 27   Perf. 13x13½
1715 A752 3000a Lanin   1.50 .65
1716 A752 3000a Laguna Blanca   1.50 .65
1717 A752 3000a Perito Moreno   1.50 .65
1718 A752 3000a Puelo   1.50 .65
1719 A752 3000a El Rey   1.50 .65
    Nos. 1715-1719 (5)   7.50 3.25

Stamp Day
A790

1990, Oct. 27   Perf. 13½
1720 A790 3000a multicolored   1.50 .60

Salvation
Army,
Cent.
A793

Designs: No. 1722, Natl. University of the Littoral, Santa Fe, cent.

1990, Dec. 1   Litho.   Perf. 13½
1721 A793 3000a multicolored   1.75 1.00
1722 A793 3000a multicolored   1.75 1.00
    a.   Pair, #1721-1722 + label   3.75 2.25

Miniature Sheets

Christmas — A794

Stained glass windows: No. 1723, The Immaculate Conception. No. 1724, The Nativity. No. 1725, Presentation of Jesus at the Temple.

1990, Dec. 1   Perf. 13½x13
Sheets of 4
1723 A794 3000a #a.-d.   6.00 6.00
1724 A794 3000a #a.-d.   6.00 6.00
1725 A794 3000a #a.-d.   6.00 6.00

Landscapes
A795

Paintings: No. 1726, Los Sauces, by Atilio Malinverno. No. 1727, Paisaje, by Pio Collivadino, vert.

1991, May 4   Litho.   Perf. 13½
1726 A795 4000a multicolored   1.00 .85
1727 A795 4000a multicolored   1.00 .85

Return of Remains
of Juan Manuel de
Rosas (1793-1877)
A796

1991, June 1   Litho.   Perf. 13½
1728 A796 4000a multicolored   1.00 .85

Swiss Confederation, 700th
Anniv. — A797

1991, Aug. 3   Litho.   Perf. 13½
1729 A797 4000a multicolored   .95 .80

Miniature Sheet

Cartoons — A798

Designs: a, Hernan, the Corsair by Jose Luis Salinas. b, Don Fulgencio by Lino Palacio. c, Medical Rules of Salerno by Oscar Esteban Conti. d, Buenos Aires Undershirt by Alejandro del Prado. e, Girls! by Jose A.G. Divito. f, Langostino by Eduardo Carlos Ferro. g, Mafalda by Joaquin Salvador Lavoro. h, Mort Cinder by Alberto Breccia.

1991, Aug. 3
1730 A798 4000a Sheet of 8, #a.-h.   7.75 7.50

City of La Rioja,
400th
Anniv. — A799

1991, Sept. 14   Litho.   Perf. 13½
1731 A799 4000a multicolored   1.00 .85

First Balloon Flight over the Andes, 75th
Anniv. — A800

Illustration reduced.

1991, Sept. 14
1732 A800 4000a multicolored   1.00 .85

America
Issue
A801

Designs: No. 1733, Magellan's caravel, Our Lady of Victory. No. 1734, Ships of Juan Diaz de Solis.

1991, Nov. 9   Litho.   Perf. 13½
1733 A801 4000a multicolored   1.00 .80
1734 A801 4000a multicolored   1.00 .80

Anniversaries — A802

Designs: a, J. Enrique Pestalozzi, founder of newspaper, Daily Argentinian. b, Leandro N. Alem, founder of Radical People's Party. c, Man with rifle, emblem of Argentine Federal Shooting Club. d, Dr. Nicasio Etchepareborda, emblem of College of Odontology. e, Dalmiro Huergo, emblem of Graduate School of Economics.

1991, Nov. 30
1735 A802 4000a Strip of 5, #a.-e.   5.00 4.00

Christmas — A803

Stained glass windows from Our Lady of Lourdes Basilica, Buenos Aires: Nos. 1736a-1736b, Top and bottom portions of Virgin of the Valley, Catamarca. Nos. 1736c-1736d, Top and bottom portions of Virgin of the Rosary of the Miracle, Cordoba.

1991, Nov. 30
1736 A803 4000a Block of 4, #a.-b.   5.00 3.50

Famous
Men
A804

Designs: a, Gen. Juan de Lavalle (1797-1841), Peruvian medal of honor. b, Brig. Gen. Jose Maria del Rosario Siriaco Paz (1791-1854), medal. c, Marco Manuel de Avellaneda (1813-1841), lawyer. d, Guillermo Enrique Hudson (1841-1922), author.

1991, Dec. 14   Litho.   Perf. 13½
1737 A804 4000a Block of 4, #a.-d.   5.00 3.50

Birds — A805

1991, Dec. 28
1738 A805 4000a Pterocnemia pennata   1.25 .85
1739 A805 4000a Morphnu guianensis   1.25 .85
1740 A805 4000a Ara chloroptera   1.25 .85
    Nos. 1738-1740 (3)   3.75 2.55

Miniature Sheet

Arbrafex '92,
Argentina-Brazil
Philatelic
Exhibition — A806

Traditional costumes: a, Gaucho, woman. b, Gaucho, horse. c, Gaucho in store. d, Gaucho holding lariat.

1992   Litho.   Perf. 13½
1741 A806 38c Sheet of 4, #a.-d.   3.00 3.00

Natl. Parks Type of 1987
1992, Apr. 4   Litho.   Perf. 13x13½
1742 A752 38c Alerces   .75 .55
1743 A752 38c Formosa Nature Reserve   .75 .55
1744 A752 38c Petrified Forest   .75 .55
1745 A752 38c Arrayanes   .75 .55
1746 A752 38c Laguna de los Pozuelos   .75 .55
    Nos. 1742-1746 (5)   3.75 2.75

Mushrooms — A807

1992-94   Photo.   *Perf. 13½*
1748	A807	10c Psilocybe cubensis	.20	.15
1749	A807	25c Coprinus atramentarius	.50	.35
a.		Wmk. 365	30.00	30.00
1750	A807	38c like #1748	.75	.55
1751	A807	48c like #1749	.95	.65
1752	A807	50c Suillus granulatus	1.00	.70
1753	A807	51c Morchella esculenta	1.00	.70
1754	A807	61c Amanita muscaria	1.25	.85
1755	A807	68c Coprinus comatus	1.25	.85
1756	A807	1p like #1754	2.00	1.40
1757	A807	1.25p like #1752	2.50	1.75
1758	A807	1.77p Stropharia oeruginosa	3.50	2.50
1759	A807	2p like #1753	4.00	2.75
		Nos. 1748-1759 (12)	18.90	13.20

No. 1758 not issued without overprint "Centro Filatelico de Neuquen y Rio Negro 50th Aniversario."
Issued: 38c, 4/4/92; 48c, 51c, 61c, 8/1/92; 1.77p, 11/7/92; 25c, 50c, 8/17/93; 1p, 2p, 8/26/93; 10c, 1/11/94; 1.25p, 10/10/92; #1749a, 1997.
See design A838.

Falkland Islands War, 10th Anniv. A808

1992, May 2   Litho.   *Perf. 13½*
1767	A808	38c Pucara 1A-58	.75	.55
1768	A808	38c Cruiser Gen. Belgrano	.75	.55
1769	A808	38c Soldier and truck	.75	.55
		Nos. 1767-1769 (3)	2.25	1.65

Miniature Sheet

Preserve the Environment A809

a, Deer. b, Geese. c, Butterflies. d, Whale.

1992, June 6   Litho.   *Perf. 12*
1770	A809	38c Sheet of 4, #a.-d.	3.00	3.00

Paintings by Florencio Molina Campos A810

1992, June 6   *Perf. 13½*
1771	A810	38c A La Sombra	.75	.55
1772	A810	38c Tileforo Areco, vert.	.75	.55

Famous Men A811

Designs: No. 1773, Gen. Lucio N. Mansilla (1792-1871). No. 1774, Jose Manuel Estrada (1842-1894), writer. No. 1775, Brig. Gen. Jose I. Garmendia (1842-1915).

1992, July 4   Litho.   *Perf. 13½*
1773	A811	38c multicolored	.75	.55
1774	A811	38c multicolored	.75	.55
1775	A811	38c multicolored	.75	.55
		Nos. 1773-1775 (3)	2.25	1.65

Fight Against Drugs — A812

1992, Aug. 1   *Perf. 13½x13*
1776	A812	38c multicolored	.75	.55

Col. Jose M. Calaza, 140th Birth Anniv. A813

1992, Sept. 5   Litho.   *Perf. 13½*
1777	A813	38c multicolored	.75	.55

Discovery of America, 500th Anniv. — A814

Designs: a, Columbus, castle, ship. b, Native drawings, Columbus.

1992, Oct. 10   Litho.   *Perf. 13½*
1778	A814	38c Pair, #a.-b.	1.50	1.50

Argentine Film Posters — A815

1992, Nov. 7   Litho.   *Perf. 13½*
1779	A815	38c Dios Se Lo Pague, 1948	.75	.55
1780	A815	38c Las Aguas Bajan Turbias, 1952	.75	.55
1781	A815	38c Un Guapo Del 900, 1960	.75	.55
1782	A815	38c La Tregua, 1974	.75	.55
1783	A815	38c La Historia Oficial, 1984	.75	.55
		Nos. 1779-1783 (5)	3.75	2.75

Christmas — A816

1992, Nov. 28
1784	A816	38c multicolored	.75	.55

Miniature Sheet

Iberoprenfil '92 — A817

Lighthouses: a, Punta Mogotes. b, Rio Negro. c, San Antonio. d, Cabo Blanco.

1992, Dec. 5
1785	A817	38c Sheet of 4, #a.-d.	3.00	3.00

Fight Against AIDS
A818   A819

1992, Dec. 12   Litho.   *Perf. 13½*
1786	A818	10c multicolored	.20	.15
1787	A819	26c multicolored	.55	.40

Intl. Space Year A820

1992, Dec. 19
1788	A820	38c multicolored	.75	.55

Souvenir Sheet

Miraculous Lord Crucifix, 400th Anniv. of Arrival in America — A821

1992, Dec. 26   *Perf. 12*
1789	A821	76c multicolored	1.50	1.50

Jujuy City, 400th Anniv. — A822

1993, Apr. 24   Litho.   *Perf. 13½*
1790	A822	38c multicolored	.75	.55

Argentina Soccer Assoc., Cent. A823

1993, Mar. 27
1791	A823	38c multicolored	.75	.55

Souvenir Sheet

Intl. Philatelic Exhibitions — A824

Designs: a, 38c, City Hall, Poznan, Poland. b, 48c, Statue of Christ the Redeemer, Rio de Janeiro, Brazil. c, 76c, Royal Palace, Bangkok, Thailand.

1993, May 8   Litho.   *Perf. 12*
1792	A824	Sheet of 3, #a.-c.	3.25	3.25

Polska '93 (#1792a), Brasiliana '93 (#1792b), Bangkok '92 (#1792c).

Luis C. Candelaria's Flight Over Andes Mountains, 75th Anniv. — A825

1993, June 26   Litho.   *Perf. 13x13½*
1793	A825	38c multicolored	.75	.55

Illustration reduced.

Order of San Martin, 50th Anniv. — A826

National History Academy, Cent. — A827

1993, May 29   *Perf. 13½*
1794	A826	38c multicolored	.75	.55
1795	A827	38c multicolored	.75	.55

c 38 Armed Forces Memorial Day — A828

1993, June 12
1796 A828 38c National Gendarmerie .75 .55
1797 A828 38c Coast Guard .75 .55

Paintings A829

Norberto Russo "Vieja Casona" 38c

#1798, Old House, by Norberto Russo. #1799, Pa'las Casas, by Adriana Zaefferer.

1993, Aug. 14 Litho. Perf. 13½
1798 A829 38c multicolored .75 .55
1799 A829 38c multicolored .75 .55

Pato — A830

1993, Aug. 28 Litho. Perf. 12
1800 A830 1p multicolored 2.00 1.40

Nut-Bearing Trees — A831

#1801, Enterolobium contortisiliquum. #1802, Prosopis alba. #1803, Magnolia grandiflora. #1804, Erythrina falcata. Illustration reduced.

1993, Sept. 25 Litho. Perf. 13x13½
1801 A831 75c multicolored 1.50 1.00
1802 A831 75c multicolored 1.50 1.00
1803 A831 1.50p multicolored 3.00 2.00
1804 A831 1.50p multicolored 3.00 2.00
Nos. 1801-1804 (4) 9.00 6.00

America Issue A832

Whales: 50c, Eubalaena australis. 75c, Cephalorhynchus commersonii.

1993, Oct. 9 Perf. 13½
1805 A832 50c multicolored 1.00 .70
1806 A832 75c multicolored 1.50 1.10

Miniature Sheet

Christmas, New Year — A833

Denomination at: a, UL. b, UR. c, LL. d, LR.

1993, Dec. 4 Litho. Perf. 13½
1807 A833 75c Sheet of 4, #a.-d. 6.00 6.00

Cave of the Hands, Santa Cruz — A834

1993, Dec. 18
1808 A834 1p multicolored 2.00 1.40

New Emblem, Argentine Postal Service — A835

Illustration reduced.

1994, Jan. 8 Perf. 11½
1809 A835 75c multicolored 1.50 1.00

A836

1994 World Cup Soccer Championships, US — A837

Players from: 25c, Germany, 1990. 50c, Brazil, 1970. 75c, 1.50p, Argentina, 1986. 1p, Italy, 1982.

1994, June 11 Litho. Perf. 13½
1810 A836 25c multicolored .50 .15
1811 A836 50c multicolored 1.00 .70
1812 A836 75c multicolored 1.50 1.00
1813 A836 1p multicolored 2.00 1.40
Nos. 1810-1813 (4) 5.00 3.25

Souvenir Sheet
Perf. 12
1814 A836 1.50p multicolored 3.00 3.00

No. 1814 contains one 40x50mm stamp with continuous design.
Nos. 1810-1813 issued in sheets containing a block of 4 of each stamp + 4 labels.

1994, July 23 Perf. 13½
Drawings of championships by: No. 1815, Julian Lisenberg. No. 1816, Matias Taylor, vert. No.

1817, Torcuato S. Gonzalez Agote, vert. No. 1818, Maria Paula Palma.

1815 A837 75c multicolored 1.50 1.00
1816 A837 75c multicolored 1.50 1.00
1817 A837 75c multicolored 1.50 1.00
1818 A837 75c multicolored 1.50 1.00
Nos. 1815-1818 (4) 6.00 4.00

A838

Molothrus Badius — A838a

1994-95 Litho. Perf. 13½
1819 A838 10c like #1748 .20 .15
1820 A838 25c like #1749 .50 .35
1823 A838 50c like #1752 1.00 .70
1828 A838 1p like #1754 2.00 1.40
1832 A838 2p like #1753 4.00 2.75
1835 A838a 9.40p multicolored 19.00 13.00
Nos. 1819-1835 (6) 26.70 18.35

Issued: 10c, 25c, 50c, 1p, 2p, 6/14/94; 9.40p, 4/12/95.
This is an expanding set. Numbers may change.

Wildlife of Falkland Islands A839

Designs: 25c, Melanodera melanodera. 50c, Pygoscelis papua. 75c, Tachyeres brachypterus. 1p, Mirounga leonina.

1994, Aug 6
1839 A839 25c multicolored .50 .35
1840 A839 50c multicolored 1.00 .70
1841 A839 75c multicolored 1.50 1.00
1842 A839 1p multicolored 2.00 1.40
Nos. 1839-1842 (4) 5.00 3.45

City of San Luis, 400th Anniv. — A840

1994, Aug. 20
1843 A840 75c multicolored 1.50 1.00

Province of Tierra del Fuego, Antarctica and South Atlantic Islands — A841

1994, Aug. 20
1844 A841 75c multicolored 1.50 1.00

Argentine Inventors — A842

Designs: No. 1845, Ladislao Jose Biro (1899-1985), ball point pen. No. 1846, Raul Pateras de Pescara (1890-1966), helicopter. No. 1847, Quirino Cristiani (1896-1984), animated drawings. No. 1848, Enrique Finochietto (1881-1948), surgical instruments.

1994, Oct. 1
1845 A842 75c multicolored 1.50 1.00
1846 A842 75c multicolored 1.50 1.00
1847 A842 75c multicolored 1.50 1.00
1848 A842 75c multicolored 1.50 1.00
a. Block of 4, #1845-1848 6.00 6.00

Issued in sheets containing 4 #1848a + 4 labels.

UNICEF Christmas A843

1994, Nov. 26 Litho. Perf. 11½
1849 A843 50c shown 1.00 .70
1850 A843 75c Bell, bulb, star, diff. 1.50 1.00

Take Care of Our Planet A844

Children's paintings: No. 1851, Boy, girl holding earth, vert. No. 1852, Children outdoors, vert. No. 1853, World as house. No. 1854, People around "world" table.

1994, Dec. 3 Perf. 13½
1851 A844 25c multicolored .50 .35
1852 A844 25c multicolored .50 .35
1853 A844 50c multicolored 1.00 .70
1854 A844 50c multicolored 1.00 .70
Nos. 1851-1854 (4) 3.00 2.10

Christmas — A845

1994, Dec. 10
1855 A845 50c Annunciation 1.00 .70
1856 A845 75c Madonna & Child 1.50 1.00

Nos. 1855-1856 each issued in sheets of 20 + 5 labels.

12th Pan American Games, Mar del Plata A846

1995 Litho. Perf. 13½
1857 A846 75c Running 1.50 1.00
1858 A846 75c Cycling 1.50 1.00
1859 A846 75c Diving 1.50 1.00
1860 A846 1.25p Gymnastics, vert. 2.50 1.75
1861 A846 1.25p Soccer, vert. 2.50 1.75
Nos. 1857-1861 (5) 9.50 6.50

Issued: No. 1857, 2/18; others, 3/11.

Natl. Constitution — A847

Design: 75c, Natl. Congress Dome, woman from statue The Republic Triumphant.

1995, Apr. 8
1862 A847 75c multicolored   1.50 1.00

21st Intl. Book Fair — A848

Illustration reduced.

1995, Apr. 8
1863 A848 75c multicolored   1.50 1.00

Birds
A849

1995   Litho.   Perf. 13½
1876 A849 5p Carduelis magel-
            lanica   10.00 7.00
1880 A849 10p Zonotrichia capen-
            sis   20.00 14.00

Issued: 5p, 10p, 5/23/95. This is an expanding set. Numbers may change.

A850

1995, Mar. 25   Litho.   Die Cut
Self-Adhesive
1883A A850 25c multicolored   .50 .35
1884 A850 75c multicolored   1.50 1.00
a.   Booklet pane, 2 #1883A, 6
     #1884   12.50
     Complete booklet, #1884a   12.50
b.   Booklet pane, 4 #1883A, 12
     #1884   25.00
     Complete booklet, #1884b   25.00

Argentine
Engineers'
Center,
Cent.
A851

1995, June 3   Perf. 13½
1885 A851 75c multicolored   1.50 1.00

Jose Marti (1853-95) — A852

#1887, Antonio Jose de Sucre (1795-1830).

1995, Aug. 12   Litho.   Perf. 13½
1886 A852 1p multicolored   2.00 1.40
1887 A852 1p multicolored   2.00 1.40

Fauna — A853

1995, Sept. 1   Litho.   Perf. 13½
1888 A853 5c Ostrich   .15 .15
1889 A853 25c Penguin   .50 .35
1890 A853 50c Toucan   1.00 1.00
1891 A853 75c Condor   1.50 1.00
1892 A853 1p Owl   2.00 1.40
1893 A853 2p Bigua   4.00 2.75
1894 A853 2.75p Tero   5.50 3.75
Booklet Stamps
1895 A853 25c Alligator   .50 .35
1896 A853 50c Fox   1.00 .70
1897 A853 75c Anteater   1.50 1.00
1898 A853 75c Deer   1.50 1.00
1899 A853 75c Whale   1.50 1.00
a.   Booklet pane, 1 each Nos. 1889-
     1891, 1895-1899   9.00 —
     Complete booklet, #1899a   9.00
     Nos. 1888-1899 (12)   20.65 14.15

See No. 1958.

Native
Heritage — A854

a, Cave drawings, shifting sands. b, Stone mask. c, Anthropomorphous vessel. d, Woven textile.

1995, Sept. 9
1900 A854 75c Block of 4, #a.-d.   6.00 6.00

Sunflower, Postal Service Emblem — A855

1995, Oct. 7
1901 A855 75c multicolored   1.50 1.00

Juan D. Peron (1895-1974) — A856

1995, Oct. 7
1902 A856 75c lt ol bis & dk bl   1.50 1.00

Miniature Sheet

Anniversaries — A857

Annivs: a, UN, 50th. b, ICAO, 50th (in 1994). c, FAO, 50th. d, ILO, 75th (in 1994).

1995, Oct. 14   Perf. 12
1903 A857 75c Sheet of 4, #a.-d.   6.00 6.00

Christmas and New Year — A858

Designs: Nos. 1904, 1908, Christmas tree, presents. No. 1905, "1996." No. 1906, Champagne glasses. No. 1907, Present.

1995, Nov. 25   Litho.   Perf. 13½
1904 A858 75c multicolored   1.50 1.00
Booklet Stamps
Perf. 13½ on 1 or 2 Sides
1905 A858 75c multicolored   1.50 1.00
1906 A858 75c multicolored   1.50 1.00
1907 A858 75c multicolored   1.50 1.00
1908 A858 75c multicolored   1.50 1.00
a.   Booklet pane, #1905-1908 + label 6.00 —
     Complete booklet, #1908a   6.00
     Nos. 1904-1908 (5)   7.50 5.00

No. 1908a is a continuous design. Ribbon extends from edge to edge on #1908 and stops at edge of package on #1905.

Miniature Sheet

Motion Pictures, Cent. — A859

Black and white film clips, director: a, The Battleship Potemkin, Sergei Eisenstein (Soviet Union). b, Casablanca, Michael Curtiz (US). c, Bicycle Thief, Vittorio De Sica (Italy). d, Limelights, Charles Chaplin (England). e, The 400 Blows, Francois Truffaut (France). f, Chronicle of the Lonely Child, Leonardo Favio (Argentina).

1995, Dec. 2   Perf. 13½
1909 A859 75c Sheet of 6, #a.-f.   9.00 9.00

The Sky — A860

1995, Dec. 16   Perf. 13½ on 3 Sides
Booklet Stamps
1910 A860 25c Dirigible   .50 .35
1911 A860 25c Kite   .50 .35
1912 A860 25c Hot air balloon   .50 .35
1913 A860 50c Balloons   1.00 .70
1914 A860 50c Paper airplane   1.00 .70
1915 A860 75c Airplane   1.50 1.00
1916 A860 75c Helicopter   1.50 1.00
1917 A860 75c Parachute   1.50 1.00
a.   Booklet pane, #1910-1917 + label 8.00
     Complete booklet, No. 1917a   8.00

Nos. 1910-1917 do not appear in Scott number order in No. 1917a, which has a continuous design.

America
Issue
A861

Postal vehicles from Postal and Telegraph Museum: No. 1918, Horse and carriage. No. 1919, Truck.

1995, Dec. 16   Perf. 13½
1918 A861 75c multicolored   1.50 1.00
1919 A861 75c multicolored   1.50 1.00

Olympic
Games,
Cent.
A862

1996, Mar. 30   Litho.   Perf. 13½
1920 A862 75c Running   1.50 1.00
1921 A862 1p Discus   2.00 1.40

Physicians
A863

Designs: a, Francisco J. Muniz (1795-1871). b, Ricardo Gutierrez (1838-96). c, Ignacio Pirovano (1844-95). d, Esteban L. Maradona (1895-1995).

1996, Apr. 20   Litho.   Perf. 12
1922 A863 50c Sheet of 4, #a.-d.   4.00 4.00

Jerusalem, 3000th Anniv. — A864

7th cent. mosaic maps of city, denomination at: No. 1923, LL. No. 1924, LR.

1996, May 18   Litho.   Perf. 13½
1923 A864 75c multicolored   1.50 1.00
1924 A864 75c multicolored   1.50 1.00
a.   Pair, #1923-1924   3.00 3.00

No. 1924a is a continuous design and was issued in sheets of 8 + 4 labels.

Endangered Fauna — A865

1996, June 15   Litho.   Perf. 13½
1925 A865 75c Capybara   1.50 1.00
1926 A865 75c Guanaco   1.50 1.00
a.   Pair, #1925-1926   3.00 3.00

America Issue.

Summer Olympic
Games — A866

Designs: 75c, Torch bearer, Buenos Aires, candidate for 2004 Games. 1p, Men's eight with coxswain, Atlanta, 1996.

1996, July 6
1927 A866 75c multicolored   1.50 1.00
1928 A866 1p multicolored   2.00 1.40

National Parks — A867

Wildlife, national park: No. 1929, Mountain turkey, Diamante. No. 1930, Parrot, San Antonio Nature Reserve. No. 1931, Deer, Otamendi Natl. Reserve. No. 1932, Rabbit, El Leoncito Nature Reserve.
Illustration reduced.

1996, Aug. 24   Litho.   Perf. 13x13 1/2
1929	A867	75c multicolored	1.50 1.00
1930	A867	75c multicolored	1.50 1.00
1931	A867	75c multicolored	1.50 1.00
1932	A867	75c multicolored	1.50 1.00
	Nos. 1929-1932 (4)		6.00 4.00

Central Post Office,
Buenos Aires — A868

1996, Oct. 5   Litho.   Die Cut
Self-Adhesive
Size: 25x35mm
1933	A868	75c multicolored	1.50 1.50

Vignette of No. 1933 is broken by circular and rectangular die cut areas to guard against reuse.
See Nos. 1983-1984.

Carousel Figures — A869

#1934, Hand-carved decorative ornaments. #1935, Child on carousel horse. #1936, Carousel. #1937, Heads of horses. #1938, Child in airplane. #1939, Carousel pig. #1940, Boy in car.

1996, Oct. 5   Perf. 13 1/2 Horiz.
Booklet Stamps
1934	A869	25c multicolored	.50 .50
1935	A869	25c multicolored	.50 .50
1936	A869	25c multicolored	.50 .50
1937	A869	50c multicolored	1.00 1.00
1938	A869	50c multicolored	1.00 1.00
1939	A869	50c multicolored	1.00 1.00
1940	A869	75c multicolored	1.50 1.50
a.	Booklet pane, #1934-1940		6.00
	Complete booklet, #1940a		6.00

Sequence of stamps in No. 1940a: No. 1940, 1934, 1937, 1935, 1938, 1936, 1939.

Port Belgrano Naval Base, Cent. — A870

Designs: 25c, LST "San Antonio." 50c, Corvette *Rosales*. 75c, Destroyer *Hercules*. 1p, Aircraft carrier, "25th of May."

1996-97   Litho.   Perf. 13 1/2
1941	A870	25c multicolored	.50 .50
1942	A870	50c multicolored	1.00 1.00
1943	A870	75c multicolored	1.50 1.50
1944	A870	1p multicolored	2.00 2.00
	Nos. 1941-1944 (4)		5.00 5.00

Issued: 25c, 1p, 10/5/96; 50c, 75c, 2/1/97.

Christmas
A871

Tapestries: 75c, Nativity, by Gladys Angelica Rinaldi, vert. 1p, Candles, by Norma Bonet de Maekawa.

1996, Nov. 30   Litho.   Perf. 13 1/2
1945	A871	75c multicolored	1.50 1.50
1946	A871	1p multicolored	2.00 2.00

Exploration of Antarctica — A872

Designs: 75c, Melchior Base. 1.25p, Icebreaker ARA Alte. Irizar.

1996, Nov. 30
1947	A872	75c multicolored	1.50 1.50
1948	A872	1.25p multicolored	2.50 2.50

National Gallery, Cent. — A873

Paintings of women by: 75c, Paul Gauguin, vert. No. 1950, Edouard Monet, vert. No. 1951, Amedeo Modigliani, vert. 1.25p, Pablo Picasso.

1996, Dec. 14
1949	A873	75c multicolored	1.50 1.50
1950	A873	1p multicolored	2.00 2.00
1951	A873	1p multicolored	2.00 2.00
1952	A873	1.25p multicolored	2.50 2.50
	Nos. 1949-1952 (4)		8.00 8.00

Mining Industry — A874

1997, Feb. 1   Litho.   Perf. 13 1/2
1953	A874	75c Granite	1.50 1.50
1954	A874	1.25p Borax	2.50 2.50

Traditional Costumes — A875

1997, Feb. 22   Litho.   Perf. 13 1/2
1955	A875	75c multicolored	1.50 1.50

America issue.

Repatriation of the Curved Sword of Gen.
San Martin, Cent. — A876

1997, Mar. 15   Litho.   Perf. 13 1/2
1956	A876	75c multicolored	1.50 1.50

29th Youth Rugby World
Championships — A877

1997, Mar. 22
1957	A877	75c multicolored	1.50 1.50

Fauna Type of 1995
1997, Feb. 22   Litho.   Perf. 13 1/2
1958	A853	10c Reddish sandpiper	.20 .20

Buenos Aires-Rio de
Janeiro Regatta,
50th
Anniv. — A879

1997, Apr. 5   Litho.   Perf. 13 1/2
1960	A879	75c Fortuna II	1.50 1.50

Natl.
History
Museum,
Cent.
A880

1997, May 17
1961	A880	75c multicolored	1.50 1.50

La Plata Natl.
University,
Cent. — A881

1997, May 17
1962	A881	75c multicolored	1.50 1.50

Lighthouses
A882

Designs: a, Cabo Virgenes. b, Isla Pingüino. c, San Juan de Salvamento. d, Punta Delgada.

1997, May 31
1963	A882	75c Sheet of 4, #a.-d.	6.00 6.00

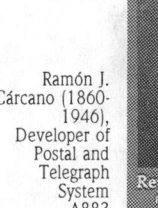
Ramón J.
Cárcano (1860-
1946),
Developer of
Postal and
Telegraph
System
A883

1997, May 31
1964	A883	75c multicolored	1.50 1.50

Buenos Aires, Candidate for 2004 Summer
Olympics — A884

1997, June 21
1965	A884	75c multicolored	1.50 1.50

Cia. Lacroze Serv. Suburbano «1912» 75c

First Electric Tram in Buenos Aires, Cent. — A885

Designs: a, Lacroze Suburban Service Tram Co., 1912. b, Lacroze Urban Service Tram Co., 1907. c, Anglo Argentina Tram Co., 1930. d, Buenos Aires City Transportation Corp., 1942. e, Military Manufacture Tram, 1956. f, South Electric Tram, 1908.

1997, July 12
Sheet of 6

1966 A885 75c #a.-f. + 2 labels   9.00 9.00

Monument to Joaquín V. González (1863-1923), La Rioja — A886

1997, Aug. 9

1967 A886 75c multicolored   1.50 1.50

75C   Ginastera   CARLOS NINE

Musicians and Composers — A887

Paintings: No. 1968, Alberto Ginastera (1916-83), by Carlos Nine. No. 1969, Astor Piazzolla (1921-92), by Carlos Alonso. No. 1970, Anibal Troilo (1914-75), by Hermenegildo Sabat. No. 1971, Atahualpa Yupanqui (b. 1908), by Luis Scafati.

1997, Aug. 9

1968 A887 75c multicolored   1.50 1.50
1969 A887 75c multicolored   1.50 1.50
1970 A887 75c multicolored   1.50 1.50
1971 A887 75c multicolored   1.50 1.50
    Nos. 1968-1971 (4)   6.00 6.00

Argentine Authors — A888

Designs: No. 1972, Jorge Luis Borges (1899-1986), maze. No. 1973, Julio Cortázar (1914-84), hop scotch game.

1997, Aug. 30   **Litho.**   *Perf. 13*

1972 A888 1p multicolored   2.00 2.00
1973 A888 1p multicolored   2.00 2.00

75c

Women's Political Rights Law, 50th Anniv. — A889

1997, Sept. 6   **Litho.**   *Perf. 13½*

1974 A889 75c Eva Perón   1.50 1.50

Mercosur (Common Market of Latin America) — A890

1997, Sept. 27   **Litho.**   *Perf. 13½*

1975 A890 75c multicolored   1.50 1.50

Launching of Frigate President Sarmiento, Cent. — A891

No. 1976, Painting of ship by Hugo Leban.
No. 1977: a, Ship. b, Ship's figurehead, vert.

1997, Oct. 4

1976 A891 75c multicolored   1.50 1.50

Souvenir Sheet
Perf. 12

1977 A891 75c Sheet of 2, #a.-b.   3.00 3.00

No. 1977 contains two 40x30mm stamps.

Ernesto "Che" Guevara (1928-67) — A892

1997, Oct. 18

1978 A892 75c multicolored   1.50 1.50

Ecology on Stamps — A893

Children's drawings: No. 1979, Animal, by J. Chiapparo, vert. No. 1980, Vicuna, by L.L. Portal, vert. No. 1981, Seal, by A. Lloren. No. 1982, Bird in flight, by J. Saccone.

1997, Nov. 8   **Litho.**   *Perf. 13½*

1979 A893 50c multicolored   1.00 1.00
1980 A893 50c multicolored   1.00 1.00
1981 A893 75c multicolored   1.50 1.50
1982 A893 75c multicolored   1.50 1.50
    Nos. 1979-1982 (4)   5.00 5.00

Central Post Office, Buenos Aires, Type of 1996

1997   **Litho.**   *Die Cut*
Self-Adhesive
Size: 23x35mm

1983 A868 25c multicolored   .50 .50
1984 A868 75c multicolored   1.50 1.50
   a. Booklet pane, 2 #1983, 6 #1984   10.00
     Complete booklet, #1984a   10.00

Nos. 1983-1984 are broken at both the top and bottom of each stamp by three lines of wavy die cutting.

SEMI-POSTAL STAMPS

Samuel F. B. Morse — SP1

Globe — SP2

Landing of Columbus — SP5

Map of Argentina — SP6

Designs: 10c+5c, Alexander Graham Bell. 25c+15c, Rowland Hill.

Wmk. RA in Sun (90)

1944, Jan. 5		**Litho.**		**Perf. 13**
B1	SP1	3c +2c lt vio & sl bl	.35	.25
B2	SP2	5c +5c dl red & sl bl	.65	.20
B3	SP1	10c +5c org & slate	1.25	.70
B4	SP1	25c +15c red brn & sl bl	1.75	1.10
B5	SP5	1p +50c lt grn & sl bl	8.00	7.25
		Nos. B1-B5 (5)	12.00	9.50

The surtax was for the Postal Employees Benefit Association.

1944, Feb. 17		**Wmk. 90**		**Perf. 13**
B6	SP6	5c +10c ol yel & slate	.75	.50
B7	SP6	5c +50c vio brn & slate	3.25	2.00
B8	SP6	5c +1p dl org & slate	9.00	6.50
B9	SP6	5c +20p dp bl & slate	22.50	15.00
		Nos. B6-B9 (4)	35.50	24.00

The surtax was for the victims of the San Juan earthquake.

Souvenir Sheets

National Anthem and Flag — SP7

Illustration reduced.

1944, July 17   *Imperf.*

B10 SP7 5c +1p vio brn & lt bl   1.90 1.90
B11 SP7 5c +50p bl blk & lt bl   350.00 250.00

Surtax for the needy in the provinces of La Rioja and Catamarca.

Catalogue values for unused stamps in this section, from this point to the end of the section, are for Never Hinged items.

Stamp Designing — SP8

1950, Aug. 26   **Photo.**   *Perf. 13½*

B12 SP8 10c +10c violet   .24 .24
   Nos. B12,CB1-CB5 (6)   20.42 15.61

Argentine Intl. Philatelic Exhibition, 1950.

Poliomyelitis Victim — SP9

1956, Apr. 14   *Perf. 13½x13*

B13 SP9 20c +30c slate   .30 .15

The surtax was for the poliomyelitis fund. Head in design is from Correggio's "Antiope," Louvre.

Stamp of 1858 and Mail Coach on Raft — SP10

Designs: 2.40p+1.20p, Album, magnifying glass and stamp of 1858. 4.40p+2.20p, Government seat of Confederation, Parana.

1958, Mar. 29   **Litho.**   *Perf. 13½*

B14 SP10 40c +20c brt grn & dl pur   .32 .24
B15 SP10 2.40p +1.20p ol gray & bl .40 .26
B16 SP10 4.40p +2.20p lt bl & dp claret   .60 .40
   Nos. B14-B16,CB8-CB12 (8) 5.84 4.66

Surtax for Intl. Centennial Philatelic Exhibition, Paraná, Entre Rios, Apr. 19-27.

View of Flooded Land — SP11

1958, Oct. 4   **Photo.**   *Perf. 13½*

B17 SP11 40c +20c brown   .15 .15
   Nos. B17,CB13-CB14 (3)   1.20 1.10

The surtax was for flood victims in the Buenos Aires district.

Child Receiving
Blood — SP12　　Runner — SP13

1958, Dec. 20　Litho.　Wmk. 90
B18 SP12　1p +50c blk & rose red　.20 .15
　　The surtax went to the Anti-Leukemia
Foundation.

1959, Sept. 5　　　Perf. 13½
　　Designs: 50c+20c, Basketball players, vert.
1p+50c, Boxers, vert.
B19 SP13　20c +10c emer & blk　.20 .16
B20 SP13　50c +20c yel & blk　.15 .15
B21 SP13　1p +50c mar & blk　.20 .16
　　Nos. B19-B21,CB15-CB16 (5)　1.55 1.21
　　3rd Pan American Games, Chicago, Aug. 27-
Sept. 7, 1959.

Condor — SP14

　　Birds: 50c+20c, Fork-tailed flycatchers. 1p+50c,
Magellanic woodpecker.

1960, Feb. 6
B22 SP14　20c +10c dk bl　.15 .15
B23 SP14　50c +20c dp vio bl　.15 .15
B24 SP14　1p +50c brn & buff　.20 .15
　　Nos. B22-B24,CB17-CB18 (5)　1.25
　　　Set value　　　　.72
　　The surtax was for child welfare work.
See Nos. B30, CB29.

Souvenir Sheet

Uprooted Oak Emblem — SP15

1960, Apr. 7　Wmk. 90　Imperf.
B25 SP15　Sheet of 2　1.25 1.25
　a.　1p + 50c bister & carmine　.55 .55
　b.　4.20p + 2.10p apple grn & dp claret　.55 .55
　　WRY, July 1, 1959-June 30, 1960.
　　The surtax was for aid to refugees.

Jacaranda — SP16

　　Flowers: 1p+1p, Passionflower. 3p+3p, Orchid.
5p+5p, Tabebuia.

1960, Dec. 3　Photo.　Perf. 13½
B26 SP16　50c +50c deep blue　.15 .15
B27 SP16　1p +1p bluish grn　.15 .15
B28 SP16　3p +3p henna brn　.32 .22
B29 SP16　5p +5p dark brn　.52 .35
　　Nos. B26-B29 (4)　1.14
　　　Set value　　　.70
　　"TEMEX 61" (Intl. Thematic Exposition).
For overprints see Nos. B31-B34.

Type of 1960
Bird: 4.20p+2.10p, Blue-eyed shag.

1961, Feb. 25　Wmk. 90　Perf. 13½
B30 SP14　4.20p +2.10p chestnut brn　.48 .32
　　Surtax for child welfare work. See #CB29.

　　Nos. B26-B29 Overprinted in Black,
Brown, Blue or Red: "14 DE ABRIL DIA
DE LAS AMERICAS"

1961, Apr. 15
B31 SP16　50c +50c deep blue　.15 .15
B32 SP16　1p +1p bluish grn (Brn)　.15 .15
B33 SP16　3p +3p henna brn (Bl)　.32 .25
B34 SP16　5p +5p dk brn (R)　.52 .42
　　Nos. B31-B34 (4)　1.14 .97
　　Day of the Americas, Apr. 14.

Cathedral,　　　Stamp of
Cordoba — SP17　1862 — SP18

Flight into Egypt, by Ana
Maria Moncalvo — SP19

　　Design: 10p+10p, Cathedral, Buenos Aires.

Perf. 13½
1961, Oct. 21　Wmk. 90　Photo.
B35 SP17　2p +2p rose claret　.22 .15
B36 SP18　3p +3p green　.32 .18
B37 SP17　10p +10p brt blue　.90 .52
　a.　Souvenir sheet of 3　1.75 1.10
　　Nos. B35-B37 (3)　1.44 .85
　　1962 International Stamp Exhibition.
No. B37a contains three imperf. stamps similar to
Nos. B35-B37 in dark blue.

1961, Dec. 16　　　Litho.
B38 SP19　2p +1p lilac & blk brn　.15 .15
B39 SP19　10p +5p light & deep claret　.52 .15
　　　Set value　　　.22
　　The surtax was for child welfare.

Chalk-browed　　Soccer — SP21
Mockingbird — SP20

　　Design: 12p+6p, Rufous-collared sparrow.

1962, Dec. 29　　　Perf. 13½
B40 SP20　4p +2p bis, brn & bl grn　.90 .60
B41 SP20　12p +6p gray, yel, grn &　
　　　brn　1.50 1.10
　　The surtax was for child welfare. See Nos. B44,
B47, B48-B50, CB32, CB35-CB36.

1963, May 18　　　Perf. 13½
B42 SP21　4p +2p multi　.22 .15
B43 SP21　12p +6p Horsemanship　.45 .35
　a.　Dark carmine (jacket) omitted　
　　Nos. B42-B43,CB31 (3)　1.22 1.00
　　4th Pan American Games, Sao Paulo.

Bird Type of 1962
Design: Vermilion flycatcher.

1963, Dec. 21　　　Litho.
B44 SP20　4p +2p blk, red, org & grn　.60 .28
　　The surtax was for child welfare. See No. CB32.

Fencers — SP22

　　Design: 4p+2p, National Stadium, Tokyo, horiz.

1964, July 18　Wmk. 90　Perf. 13½
B45 SP22　4p +2p red, ocher & brn　.16 .15
B46 SP22　12p +6p bl grn & blk　.40 .32
　　Nos. B45-B46,CB33 (3)　1.06 .97
　　18th Olympic Games, Tokyo, Oct. 10-25, 1964.
See No. CB33.

Bird Type of 1962
Design: Red-crested cardinal.

1964, Dec. 23　　　Litho.
B47 SP20　4p +2p dk bl, red & grn　.60 .30
　　The surtax was for child welfare. See #CB35.

Bird Type of 1962
Inscribed "R. ARGENTINA"
　　Designs: 8p+4p, Lapwing. 10p+5p, Scarlet-
headed marshbird, horiz. 20p+10p, Amazon
kingfisher.

1966-67　　　Perf. 13½
B48 SP20　8p +4p blk, ol, brt grn &　
　　　red　.80 .35
B49 SP20　10p +5p blk, bl, org & grn　.80 .55
B50 SP20　20p +10p blk, yel, bl &　
　　　pink　.40 .35
　　Nos. B48-B50,CB36,CB38-CB39 (6)　4.30 3.25
　　The surtax was for child welfare.
　　Issue dates: 8p+4p, Mar. 26, 1966. 10p+5p, Jan.
14, 1967. 20p+10p, Dec. 23, 1967.

Grandmother's Birthday, by Patricia Lynch;
Lions Emblem — SP23

Perf. 12½x13½
1968, Dec. 14　Litho.　Wmk. 90
B51 SP23　40p + 20p multi　.45 .38
　　1st Lions Intl. Benevolent Phil. Exhib. Surtax for
the Children's Hospital Benevolent Fund.

White-faced Tree
Duck — SP24

1969, Sept. 20　Wmk. 365　Perf. 13½
B52 SP24　20p + 10p multi　.48 .35
　　Surtax for child welfare. See No. CB40.

Slender-tailed
Woodstar
(Hummingbird)
SP25

1970, May 9　Wmk. 365　Perf. 13½
B53 SP25　20c + 10c multi　.45 .40
　　The surtax was for child welfare. See Nos. CB41,
B56-B59, B62-B63.

Dolphinfish — SP26

1971, Feb. 20　Unwmk.　Perf. 12½
　　　Size: 75x15mm
B54 SP26　20c + 10c multi　.52 .45
　　Surtax for child welfare. See No. CB42.

Children with
Stamps, by
Mariette
Lydis — SP27

1971, Dec. 18　Litho.　Perf. 13½
B55 SP27　1p + 50p multi　.48 .32
　　2nd Lions Intl. Solidarity Stamp Exhib.

Bird Type of 1970
Birds: 25c+10c, Saffron finch. 65c+30c, Rufous-
bellied thrush, horiz.

1972, May 6　Unwmk.　Perf. 13½
B56 SP25　25c + 10c multi　.32 .20
B57 SP25　65c + 30c multi　.45 .32
　　Surtax was for child welfare.

Bird Type of 1970
Birds: 50c+25c, Southern screamer (chaja).
90c+45c, Saffron-cowled blackbird, horiz.

1973, Apr. 28
B58 SP25　50c + 25c multi　.48 .32
B59 SP25　90c + 45c multi　.70 .48
　　Surtax was for child welfare.

Painting Type of Regular Issue
　　Designs: 15c+15c, Still Life, by Alfredo Guttero,
horiz. 90c+90c, Nude, by Miguel C. Victorica,
horiz.

1973, Aug. 28　Litho.　Perf. 13½
B60 A472　15c + 15c multi　.28 .18
B61 A472　90c + 90c multi　1.00 .70

Bird Type of 1970
Birds: 70c+30c, Blue seed-eater. 1.20p+60c,
Hooded siskin.

1974, May 11　Litho.　Perf. 13½
B62 SP25　70c + 30c multi　.50 .35
B63 SP25　1.20p + 60c multi　.75 .42
　　Surtax was for child welfare.

Painting Type of 1974
Design: 70c+30c, The Lama, by Juan Batlle
Planas.

1974, May 11　Litho.　Perf. 13½
B64 A477　70c + 30c multi　.28 .22
　　PRENFIL-74 UPU, Intl. Exhib. of Phil. Periodi-
cals, Buenos Aires, Oct. 1-12.

Plushcrested
Jay — SP28

　　Designs: 13p+6.50p, Golden-collared macaw.
20p+10p, Begonia. 40p+20p, Teasel.

1976, June 12　Litho.　Perf. 13½
B65 SP28　7p + 3.50p multi　.20 .15
B66 SP28　13p + 6.50p multi　.32 .20
B67 SP28　20p + 10p multi　.48 .32
B68 SP28　40p + 20p multi　.95 .48
　　Nos. B65-B68 (4)　1.95 1.15
　　Argentine philately.

Telegraph, Communications
Satellite — SP29

Designs: 20p+10p, Old and new mail trucks.
60p+30p, Old, new packet boats. 70p+35p,
Biplane and jet.

1977, July 16   Litho.   Perf. 13½
B69 SP29 10p + 5p multi .... .30 .20
B70 SP29 20p + 10p multi .... .50 .60
B71 SP29 60p + 30p multi .... 1.00 .85
B72 SP29 70p + 35p multi .... 1.25 .85
　　Nos. B69-B72 (4) 3.05 2.50
　　Surtax was for Argentine philately.
No. B70 exists with wmk. 365.

Church of St. Francis Type, 1977,
Inscribed: "EXPOSICION ARGENTINA
'77"

1977, Aug. 27
B73 A515 160p + 80p multi 2.50 2.00
　　Surtax was for Argentina '77 Philatelic Exhibi-
tion. Issued in sheets of 4.

No. B73 Overprinted with Soccer Cup
Emblem

1978, Feb. 4   Litho.   Perf. 13½
B74 A515 160p + 80p multi 4.50 4.25
　a.   Souvenir sheet of 4 .... 20.00 19.00
　　11th World Cup Soccer Championship, Argentina, June 1-25.

Spinus
Magellanicus
SP30

Birds: #B75, Variable seedeater. #B76, Yellow
thrush. #B77, Pyrocephalus rubineus. #B78, Great
kiskadee.

1978, Aug. 5   Litho.   Perf. 13½
B75 SP30 50p + 50p multi .... .90 .60
B76 SP30 100p + 100p multi .... 1.10 .90
B77 SP30 150p + 150p multi 1.40 1.25
B78 SP30 200p + 200p multi 1.75 1.75
B79 SP30 500p + 500p multi 8.50 7.25
　　Nos. B75-B79 (5) 13.65 11.75
　　ARGENTINA '78, Inter-American Philatelic Ex-
hibition, Buenos Aires, Oct. 27-Nov. 5. Nos. B75-B79
issued in sheets of 4 with marginal inscriptions
commemorating Exhibition and 1978 Soccer
Championship.

Caravel "Magdalena," 16th
Century — SP31

Sailing Ships: 500+500p, 3 master "Rio de la
Plata," 17th cent. 600+600p, Corvette
"Descubierta," 18th cent. 1500+1500p, Naval
Academy yacht "A.R.A. Fortuna," 1979.

1979, Sept. 8   Litho.   Perf. 13½
B80 SP31 400p +400p multi 4.00 2.25
B81 SP31 500p +500p multi 4.75 2.50
B82 SP31 600p +600p multi 6.00 3.25
B83 SP31 1500p +1500p multi 15.00 8.00
　　Nos. B80-B83 (4) 29.75 16.00
　　Buenos Aires '80, International Philatelic Exhibi-
tion, Oct. 24-Nov. 2, 1980. Issued in sheets of 4.

Purmamarca
Church — SP32

Churches: 200p + 100p, Molinos. 300p + 150p,
Animana. 400p + 200p, San Jose de Lules.

1979, Nov. 3   Litho.   Perf. 13½
B84 SP32 100p + 50p multi .... .25 .15
B85 SP32 200p + 100p multi .... .45 .15
B86 SP32 300p + 150p multi .... .60 .18
B87 SP32 400p + 200p multi .... .90 .24
　　Nos. B84-B87 (4) 2.20
　　Set value .... .62

Buenos Aires No. 3, Exhibition and Society
Emblems — SP33

Argentine Stamps: 750p+750p, type A580.
1000p+1000p, No. 91. 2000p+2000p, type A588.

1979, Dec. 15   Litho.   Perf. 13½
B88 SP33 250p + 250p multi ...... .90 .70
B89 SP33 750p + 750p multi 2.25 1.75
B90 SP33 1000p + 1000p multi 3.00 2.50
B91 SP33 2000p + 2000p multi 6.00 5.00
　　Nos. B88-B91 (4) 12.15 9.95
　　PRENFIL '80, Intl. Philatelic Literature and Publi-
cations Exhib., Buenos Aires, Nov. 7-16, 1980.

Minuet, by
Carlos E.
Pellegrini
SP34

Paintings: 700p+350p, Media Cana, by Carlos
Morel. 800p+400p, Cielito, by Pellegrini.
1000p+500p, El Gato, by Juan Leon Palliere.

1981, July 11   Litho.   Perf. 13½
B92 SP34 500p + 250p multi ...... .70 .35
B93 SP34 700p + 350p multi ..... 1.00 .70
B94 SP34 800p + 400p multi ..... 1.10 .90
B95 SP34 1000p + 500p multi 1.40 1.25
　　Nos. B92-B95 (4) 4.20 3.20
　　Espamer '81 Intl. Stamp Exhib. (Americas, Spain,
Portugal), Buenos Aires, Nov. 13-22.

Canal, by
Beatrix
Bongliani
(b. 1933)
SP35

Tapestries: 1000p+500p, Shadows, by Silvia
Sieburger, vert. 2000p+1000p, Interpretation of a
Rectangle, by Silke R. de Haupt, vert.
4000p+2000p, Tilcara, by Tana Sachs.

1982, July 31   Litho.   Perf. 13½
B96 SP35 1000p + 500p multi ..... .20 .20
B97 SP35 2000p + 1000p multi .... .40 .40
B98 SP35 3000p + 1500p multi .... .60 .60
B99 SP35 4000p + 2000p multi .... .80 .80
　　Nos. B96-B99 (4) 2.00 2.00

Boy Playing
Marbles — SP36

1983, July 2   Litho.   Perf. 13½
B100 SP36 20c + 10c shown .... .20 .15
B101 SP36 30c + 15c Jumping rope . .45 .16
B102 SP36 50c + 25c Hopscotch ... .85 .20
B103 SP36 1p + 50c Flying kites . 1.10 .48
B104 SP36 2p + 1p Spinning top . 1.65 .65
　　Nos. B100-B104 (5) 4.25 1.64
　　Surtax was for natl. philatelic associations.
See Nos. B106-B110.

Compass,
15th
Cent.
SP37

ARGENTINA '85 Intl. Stamp Show: b, Arms of
Spain, Argentina. c, Columbus' arms. d-f, Colum-
bus' arrival at San Salvador Island. Nos. B105d-
B105f in continuous design; ships shown on singles
range in size, left to right, from small to large.
Surtax was for exhibition.

1984, Apr. 28   Litho.   Perf. 13½
B105   Block of 6 .... 3.75 3.75
　a.-f.   SP37 5p + 2.50p, any single .52 .26

Children's Game Type of 1983

1984, July 7   Litho.   Perf. 13½
B106 SP36 2p + 1p Blind Man's Buff . .15 .15
B107 SP36 3p + 1.50p The Loop ... .30 .24
B108 SP36 4p + 2p Leap Frog ..... .35 .30
B109 SP36 5p + 2.50p Rolling the
　　　　　　　loop .... .45 .35
B110 SP36 6p + 3p Ball Mold ..... .55 .45
　　Nos. B106-B110 (5) 1.80 1.49

Butterflies
SP38

1985, Nov. 9   Litho.   Perf. 13½
B111 SP38 5c + 2c Rothschildia
　　　　　　　jacobaeae .... .20 .15
B112 SP38 10c + 5c Heliconius era-
　　　　　　　to phyllis .... .45 .30
B113 SP38 20c + 10c Precis evarete
　　　　　　　hilaris .... .85 .60
B114 SP38 25c + 12c Cyanopepla
　　　　　　　pretiosa .... 1.10 .75
B115 SP38 40c + 20c Papilio andro-
　　　　　　　geus 1.65 1.10
　　Nos. B111-B115 (5) 4.25 2.90

Children's
Drawings
SP39

1986, Aug. 30   Litho.
B116 SP39 5c + 2c N. Pastor .... .15 .15
B117 SP39 10c + 5c T. Valleistein . .30 .30
B118 SP39 20c + 10c J.M. Flores .. .60 .60
B119 SP39 25c + 13c M.E. Pezzuto . .75 .75
B120 SP39 40c + 20c E. Diehl 1.10 1.10
　　Nos. B116-B120 (5) 2.90 2.90
　　Surtax for natl. philatelic associations.

Miniature Sheets

Fresh-water
Fish — SP40

No. B121: a, Metynnis maculatus. b, Cynolebias
nigripinnis. c, Leporinus solarii. d, Aphyocharax
rathbuni. e, Corydoras aeneus. f, Thoracocharax
securis. g, Cynolebias melanotaenia. h, Cichlasoma
facetum.
No. B122: a, Tetragonopterus argenteus. b,
Hemigrammus caudovittatus. c, Astyanax bimacu-
latus. d, Gymnocorymbus ternetzi. e, Hoplias
malabaricus. f, Aphyocharax rubripinnis. g, Apis-
togramma agassizi. h, Pyrrhulina rachoviana.

1987, June 27
B121   Sheet of 8 .... 2.00 1.75
　a.-h. SP40 10c +5c, any single . .25 .20
B122   Sheet of 8 .... 4.00 3.50
　a.-h. SP40 20c +10c, any single . .50 .40

PRENFIL '88, Intl. Philatelic Literature and
Media Exhibition, Buenos Aires, Nov. 25-
Dec. 2 — SP41

Locomotives and railroad car: No. B123, Yatay
locomotive, 1888. No. B124, FCCA electric passenger car, 1914. No. B125, B-15 locomotive, 1942.
No. B126, GT-22 No. 200 locomotive, 1988.

1988, June 4   Litho.   Perf. 13½
B123 SP41 1a +50c multi .... .65 .50
B124 SP41 1a +50c multi .... .65 .50
B125 SP41 1a +50c multi .... .65 .50
B126 SP41 1a +50c multi .... .65 .50
　　Nos. B123-B126 (4) 2.60 2.00
　　Nos. B123-B125 each issued in sheets of 4.

Horses
SP42

Paintings: No. B127, The Waiting, by Gustavo
Solari. No. B128, Mare and Foal, by E. Castro. No.
B129, Saint Isidor, by Castro. No. B130, At
Lagoon's Edge, by F. Romero Carranza. No. B131,
Under the Tail, by Castro.

1988, Oct. 29   Litho.   Perf. 13½
B127 SP42 2a +1a multi .... .70 .50
B128 SP42 2a +1a multi .... .70 .50
B129 SP42 2a +1a multi .... .70 .50
B130 SP42 2a +1a multi .... .70 .50
B131 SP42 2a +1a multi .... .70 .50
　　Nos. B127-B131 (5) 3.50 2.50

PRENFIL
'88 — SP43

Covers of philatelic magazines.

1988, Nov. 26   Litho.   Perf. 13½
B132 SP43 1a +1a Cronaca Filateli-
　　　　　　　ca, Italy .... .40 .30
B133 SP43 1a +1a CO-FI, Brazil .. .40 .30
B134 SP43 1a +1a References de la
　　　　　　　Poste, France .... .40 .30
B135 SP43 2a +2a Postas Argentinas . .65 .50
　　Nos. B132-B135 (4) 1.85 1.40

Souvenir Sheet

ARBRAPEX '88 — SP44

Designs: No. B136a, *Candel Delivery at San Ignacio*, by Leonie Matthis, Cornelio Saavedra Museum, Buenos Aires. No. B136b, *Immaculate Conception*, a statue in the Isaac Fernandez Blanco Museum, Buenos Aires.

1988, Nov. 26		**Perf. 12**	
B136 SP44 Sheet of 2		1.60	1.25
a. 2a +2a multi		.65	.50
b. 3a +3a multi		.95	.70

Fish SP45

Designs: No. B137, *Diplomystes viedmensis*. No. B138, *Haplochiton taeniatus*. No. B139, *Percichthys trucha*. No. B140, *Galaxias platei*. No. B141, *Salmo fario*.

1989, June 24	**Litho.**	**Perf. 13½**	
B137 SP45 10a +5a multi		.15	.15
B138 SP45 10a +5a multi		.15	.15
B139 SP45 10a +5a multi		.15	.15
B140 SP45 10a +5a multi		.15	.15
B141 SP45 10a +5a multi		.15	.15
Set value		.50	.40

Printed in sheets of 4.

Discovery of America 500th Anniv. (in 1992) and ESPAMER '90 — SP46

Documents and chronicles: No. B142, Columbus's coat of arms, *Book of Privileges* title page. No. B143, Illustration from *New Chronicle and Good Government*, by Guaman Poma de Ayala. No. B144, Illustration from *Discovery and Conquest of Peru*, by Pedro de Cieza de Leon. No. B145, Illustration from *Travel to the River Plate*, by Ulrico Schmidl.

1989, Sept. 16	**Litho.**	**Perf. 13½**	
Yellow, Rose Violet & Black			
B142 SP46 100a +50a		.90	.80
B143 SP46 150a +50a		.90	.80
B144 SP46 200a +100a		.90	.80
B145 SP46 250a +100a		.90	.80
Nos. B142-B145 (4)		3.60	3.20

Insects — SP47

Designs: No. B146, *Podisus nigrispinus*. No. B147, *Adalia bipunctata*. No. B148, *Nabis punctipennis*. No. B149, *Hippodamia convergens*. No. B150, *Calleida suturalis*.

1990, June 30	**Litho.**	**Perf. 13½**	
B146 SP47 1000a +500a multi		1.00	.85
B147 SP47 1000a +500a multi		1.00	.85
B148 SP47 1000a +500a multi		1.00	.85
B149 SP47 1000a +500a multi		1.00	.85
B150 SP47 1000a +500a multi		1.00	.85
Nos. B146-B150 (5)		5.00	4.25

Souvenir Sheet

First Natl. Exposition of Aerophilately — SP48

Designs: a, Lieut. Marcos A. Zar, Macchi seaplane. b, Capt. Antonio Parodi, Ansaldo SVA biplane. (Illustration reduced.)

1990, July 14	**Litho.**	**Perf. 12**	
B151 Sheet of 2		6.00	5.00
a. SP48 2000a +2000a multi		3.00	2.50
b. SP48 3000a +3000a multi		3.00	2.50

Souvenir Sheet

1992 Summer Olympics, Barcelona SP49

Designs: a, Shot put. b, High jump. c, Hurdles. d, Pole vault.

1990, Dec. 15	**Litho.**	**Perf. 13½**	
B152 Sheet of 4		9.00	9.00
a.-d. SP49 2000a +2000a multi		2.25	2.25

Espamer '91 Philatelic Exhibition. See No. B155.

Souvenir Sheet

Discovery of America, 500th Anniv. (in 1992) — SP50

Voyage of Alesandro Malaspina, 1789-1794: a, Sailing ship. b, Malaspina. c, Indian, hut. d, Indian, horse, artist drawing.

1990, Oct. 13	**Litho.**	**Perf. 13½**	
B153 Sheet of 4		6.00	6.00
a.-d. SP50 2000a +1000a, any single		1.50	1.50

Espamer '91, Buenos Aires.

Souvenir Sheet

Race Cars and Drivers — SP51

Designs: a, Juan Manuel Fangio. b, Juan Manuel Bordeu. c, Carlos Alberto Reutemann. d, Oscar and Juan Galvez.

1991	**Litho.**	**Perf. 13½**	
B154 SP51 Sheet of 4		4.75	4.75
a.-d. 2500a +2500a, any single		1.25	1.25

Espamer '91.

Souvenir Sheet
1992 Summer Olympics Type of 1990

Women's gymnastics routines: a, Floor exercise. b, Uneven parallel bars. c, Balance beam. d, Rhythmic gymnastics.

1991, June 29	**Litho.**	**Perf. 13½**	
B155 Sheet of 4		4.75	4.75
a.-d. SP49 2500a +2500a, any single		1.25	1.25

Espamer '91.

Iberoprenfil '92 SP52

Designs: No. B156, Castor missile. No. B157, Satellite LUSAT 1.

1991, Dec. 28	**Litho.**	**Perf. 13½**	
B156 SP52 4000a +4000a multi		2.00	1.75
B157 SP52 4000a +4000a multi		2.00	1.75

Dinosaurs — SP53

1992, May 2	**Litho.**	**Perf. 13½**	
B158 SP53 38c +38c Carnotaurus		1.50	1.50
B159 SP53 38c +38c Amargasaurus		1.50	1.50

Iberoprenfil '92, Buenos Aires SP54

Paintings by Raul Soldi (b. 1905): No. B160, The Fiesta. No. B161, Church of St. Anne of Glew.

1992, Sept. 5	**Litho.**	**Perf. 13½**	
B160 SP54 76c +76c multi		3.00	3.00
B161 SP54 76c +76c multi		3.00	3.00

Parafil '92 — SP55

1992, Nov. 21	**Litho.**	**Perf. 13½**	
B162 SP55 76c +76c multi		3.00	3.00

2nd Argentine-Paraguayan Philatelic Exhibition, Buenos Aires.

Souvenir Sheet

Birds — SP56

a, Egretta thula. b, Amblyramphus holosericeus. c, Paroaria coronata. d, Chloroceryle amazona.

1993, July 17	**Litho.**	**Perf. 13½**	
B163 SP56 38c +38c Sheet of 4		6.00	6.00

Souvenir Sheet

Latin American Air Post Philatelic Exhibition — SP57

Designs: a, 25c+25c, Antoine de Saint-Exupery (1940-44), pilot, author. b, 75c+75c, "The Little Prince," vert. Illustration reduced.

1995, June 3	**Litho.**	**Perf. 12**	
B164 SP57 Sheet of 2, #a.-b.		4.00	4.00

Souvenir Sheet

Exploration of Antarctica SP58

75c+25c, Transport ship ARA Bahia Aguirre. 1.25p+75c, Argentine Air Force Hercules C-130.

1995, July 8			
B165 SP58 Sheet of 2, #a.-b.		6.00	6.00

Aerofila '96 SP59

Historic airplanes, pilots: No. B166, "Plus ultra," Ramón Franco Bahamonde (1896-1938). No. B167, 14 Bis, Alberto Santos-Dumont (1873-1932). No. B168, Spirit of St. Louis, Charles A. Lindbergh (1902-1974). No. B169, Buenos Aires, Eduardo A. Olivero (1896-1966).

1996, July 13	**Litho.**	**Perf. 13½**	
B166 SP59 25c +25c multi		1.00	1.00
B167 SP59 25c +25c multi		1.00	1.00
B168 SP59 50c +50c multi		2.00	2.00
B169 SP59 50c +50c multi		2.00	2.00
Nos. B166-B169 (4)		6.00	6.00

Ceramic Murals from Buenos Aires Subway — SP60

1996, Sept. 21	**Litho.**	**Perf. 13½**	
B170 SP60 1p +50c Dragon		3.00	
B171 SP60 1.50p +1p Bird		5.00	

MEVIFIL '97, 1st Intl. Exhibition of Audio-Visual and Philatelic Information Media — SP61

Designs: No. B172, France Type A1. No. B173, Spain Type A3. No. B174, Argentina Type A4. No. B175, Buenos Aires Type A1.

1997, May 10   Litho.   *Perf. 13½*

B172	SP61	50c +50c multi	2.00	2.00
B173	SP61	50c +50c multi	2.00	2.00
B174	SP61	50c +50c multi	2.00	2.00
B175	SP61	50c +50c multi	2.00	2.00
a.		Block of 4, #B172-B175	8.00	8.00

Issued in sheets of 16 stamps + 4 labels.

Trains — SP62

Designs: No. B176, Las Nubes (Train to the Clouds), Salta. No. B177, Historical train, Buenos Aires. No. B178, Old Patagonian Express, Rio Negro-Chubut. No. B179, Southern Fueguino Railway, Tierra Del Fuego.
Illustration reduced.

1997, Sept. 6   Litho.   *Perf. 13*

B176	SP62	50c +50c multi	2.00	2.00
B177	SP62	50c +50c multi	2.00	2.00
B178	SP62	50c +50c multi	2.00	2.00
B179	SP62	50c +50c multi	2.00	2.00
		Nos. B176-B179 (4)	8.00	8.00

No. B164 Ovptd. in Red Violet in Sheet Margin

1997, Sept. 27   Litho.   *Perf. 12*

B180	SP57	Sheet of 2	4.00	4.00

Argentine Air Post, 70th anniv.

AIR POST STAMPS

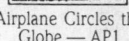

Airplane Circles the Globe — AP1

Eagle — AP2

Wings Cross the Sea — AP3

Condor on Mountain Crag — AP4

Perforations of Nos. C1-C37 vary from clean-cut to rough and uneven, with many skipped perfs.

Perf. 13x13½, 13x13½

1928, Mar. 1   Litho.   Wmk. 90

C1	AP1	5c lt red	1.25	.50
C2	AP1	10c Prus blue	2.25	1.00
C3	AP2	15c lt brown	2.25	.80
C4	AP1	18c lilac gray	3.00	2.75
a.		18c brown lilac	3.25	2.75
b.		Double impression	375.00	
C5	AP2	20c ultra	2.25	.80
C6	AP2	24c deep blue	3.50	2.75
C7	AP3	25c brt violet	3.50	1.50
C8	AP3	30c rose red	5.25	1.00
C9	AP4	35c rose	3.50	1.00
C10	AP1	36c bister brn	2.50	1.50
C11	AP4	50c gray black	4.00	.50
C12	AP2	54c chocolate	3.50	1.00

C13	AP2	72c yellow grn	4.75	2.00
a.		Double impression	300.00	
C14	AP3	90c dk brown	9.00	1.75
C15	AP3	1p slate bl & red	11.00	.65
C16	AP3	1.08p rose & dk bl	16.00	4.50
C17	AP4	1.26p dull vio & grn	20.00	8.00
C18	AP4	1.80p blue & lil rose	20.00	8.00
C19	AP4	3.60p gray & blue	42.50	19.00
		Nos. C1-C19 (19)	160.00	60.00

The watermark on No. C4a is larger than on the other stamps of this set, measuring 10mm across Sun.

Zeppelin First Flight

Air Post Stamps of 1928 Overprinted in Blue

1930, May

C20	AP2	20c ultra	10.00	5.00
C21	AP4	50c gray black	20.00	10.00
a.		Inverted overprint	475.00	
C22	AP4	1p slate bl & red	21.00	10.00
a.		Inverted overprint	650.00	
C23	AP4	1.80p blue & lil rose	55.00	25.00
C24	AP4	3.60p gray & blue	150.00	70.00
		Nos. C20-C24 (5)	256.00	120.00

Overprinted in Green

C25	AP2	20c ultra	10.00	6.00
C26	AP4	50c gray black	12.50	9.00
C27	AP3	90c dark brown	10.00	6.00
C28	AP3	1p slate bl & red	20.00	12.50
C29	AP4	1.80p blue & lil rose	600.00	400.00
a.		Thick paper	850.00	
		Nos. C25-C29 (5)	652.50	433.50

Air Post Stamps of 1928 Overprinted in Red or Blue

1930

6

Septiembre
-1931-

6 de Septiembre

1930 — 1931

On AP1-AP2   On AP3-AP4

1931

C30	AP1	18c lilac gray	2.00	1.50
C31	AP2	72c yellow green	14.00	10.50
C32	AP3	90c dark brown	14.00	10.50
C33	AP4	1.80p bl & lil rose (Bl)	30.00	22.50
C34	AP4	3.60p gray & blue	57.50	40.00
		Nos. C30-C34 (5)	117.50	85.00

1st anniv. of the Revolution of 1930.

Zeppelin Issue

Nos. C1, C4, C4a, C14 Overprinted in Blue or Red

GRAF ZEPPELIN 1932
On AP1

GRAF ZEPPELIN 1932
On AP3

1932, Aug. 4

C35	AP1	5c lt red (Bl)	3.00	2.00
C36	AP1	18c lilac gray (R)	12.50	8.00
a.		18c brown lilac (R)	100.00	60.00
C37	AP3	90c dark brown (R)	32.50	26.00
		Nos. C35-C37 (3)	48.00	37.00

Plane and Letter — AP5

Mercury — AP6

Plane in Flight — AP7

Perf. 13½x13, 13x13½

1940, Oct. 23   Photo.   Wmk. 90

C38	AP5	30c deep orange	5.00	.15
C39	AP6	50c dark brown	7.50	.20
C40	AP5	1p carmine	1.75	.15
C41	AP7	1.25p deep green	.50	.15
C42	AP5	2.50p bright blue	1.25	.20
		Nos. C38-C42 (5)	16.00	
		Set value		.70

Plane and Letter — AP8

Mercury and Plane — AP9

Perf. 13½x13, 13x13½

1942, Oct. 6   Litho.   Wmk. 90

C43	AP8	30c orange	.15	.15
C44	AP9	50c dull brn & buff	.40	.15
		Set value		.15

See Nos. C49-C52, C57, C61.

Plane over Iguaçu Falls — AP10

Plane over the Andes — AP11

Perf. 13½x13

1946, June 10   Unwmk.

C45	AP10	15c dull red brn	.25	.15
C46	AP11	25c gray green	.15	.15
		Set value		.15

See Nos. C53-C54.

Allegory of Flight — AP12

Astrolabe — AP13

Perf. 13½x13, 13x13½

1946, Sept. 25   Litho.   Unwmk.
Surface-Tinted Paper

C47	AP12	15c sl grn, *pale grn*	.55	.15
C48	AP13	60c vio brn, *ocher*	.55	.35

Types of 1942

1946-48   Unwmk.   *Perf. 13½x13*

C49	AP8	30c orange	1.40	.15
C50	AP9	50c dull brn & buff	2.50	.15
C51	AP8	1p carmine ('47)	1.25	.15
C52	AP8	2.50p brt blue ('48)	5.50	.75
		Nos. C49-C52 (4)	10.65	1.20

Types of 1946

1948   Wmk. 90

C53	AP10	15c dull red brn	.15	.15
C54	AP11	25c gray green	.25	.15
		Set value		.15

Atlas (National Museum, Naples) — AP14

Map of Argentine Republic, Globe and Caliper AP15

Perf. 13½x13, 13x13½

1948-49   Photo.   Wmk. 288

C55	AP14	45c dk brown ('49)	.35	.20
C56	AP15	70c dark green	.50	.25

4th Pan-American Reunion of Cartographers, Buenos Aires, Oct.-Nov., 1948.

Mercury Type of 1942

1949   Litho.   *Perf. 13x13½*

C57	AP9	50c dull brn & buff	.40	.15

Marksmanship Trophy — AP16

1949, Nov. 4   Photo.

C58	AP16	75c brown	.75	.20

World Rifle Championship, 1949.

> Catalogue values for unused stamps in this section, from this point to the end of the section, are for Never Hinged items.

Douglas DC-3 and Condor AP17

Perf. 13x13½

1951, June 20   Wmk. 90

C59	AP17	20c dk olive grn	.20	.15

10th anniversary of the State air lines.

Douglas DC-6 and Condor — AP18

1951, Oct. 17   *Perf. 13½*

C60	AP18	20c blue	.20	.15

End of Argentine 5-year Plan.

Plane-Letter Type of 1942

1951   Litho.   *Perf. 13½x13*

C61	AP8	1p carmine	.40	.15

Jesus by Leonardo da Vinci (detail, "Virgin of the Rocks") — AP19

Perf. 13½x13
1956, Sept. 29   Photo.   Wmk. 90
C62 AP19 1p dull purple .35 .15

Issued to express the gratitude of the children of Argentina to the people of the world for their help against poliomyelitis.

Battle of Montevideo AP20

Leonardo Rosales and Tomas Espora — AP21

Guillermo Brown — AP22

AP23

1957, Mar. 2   Perf. 13½
C63 AP20 60c blue gray .15 .15
C64 AP21 1p brt pink .15 .15
C65 AP22 2p brown .25 .15
 Set value .45 .25

Cent. of the death of Admiral Guillermo Brown, founder of the Argentine navy.

1957, Aug. 16

Map of Americas and Arms of Buenos Aires.
C66 AP23 2p rose violet .42 .20

Issued to publicize the Inter-American Economic Conference in Buenos Aires.

AP24   AP25

1957, Aug. 31   Wmk. 90   Perf. 13½
C67 AP24 60c Modern jlcomotive .15 .15

Centenary of Argentine railroads.

1957, Sept. 14
C68 AP25 1p Globe, Flag,Compass Rose .20 .15
C69 AP25 2p Key .30 .15
 Set value .15

1957 International Congress for Tourism.

Birds Carrying Letters — AP26

1957, Nov. 6
C70 AP26 1p bright blue .15 .15

Issued for Letter Writing Week, Oct. 6-12.

Early Plane — AP27

1958, May 31   Perf. 13½
C71 AP27 2p maroon .20 .15

50th anniversary of the Argentine Aviation Club.

Stamp Anniv. Type
Designs: 80c, Stamp of Buenos Aires and view of the Plaza de la Aduana. 1p, Stamp of 1858 and "The Post of Santa Fe."

1958   Litho.   Perf. 13½
C72 A270 80c pale bis & sl bl .20 .15
C73 A270 1p red org & dk bl .25 .15

Centenary of the first postage stamps of Buenos Aires and the Argentine Confederation. Issue dates: 80c, Oct. 18; 1p, Aug. 23.

Comet Jet over World Map AP29

1959, May 16   Perf. 13½
C74 AP29 5p black & olive .35 .15

Inauguration of jet flights by Argentine Airlines.

Type of Regular Issue, 1960.
"Cabildo" and: 1.80p, Mariano Moreno. 5p, Manuel Belgrano and Juan Jose Castelli.

Perf. 13½
1960, May 28   Wmk. 90   Photo.
C75 A287 1.80p red brown .15 .15
 a. Souvenir sheet of 3 .65 .40
C76 A287 5p buff & purple .35 .15
 a. Souvenir sheet of 3 1.25 .80
 Set value .20

Souvenir sheets are imperf. No. C75a contains one No. C75 and 1p and 2p resembling Nos. 713-714; stamps in reddish brown. No. C76a contains one No. C76 and 4.20p and 10.70p resembling Nos. 715-716; stamps are in green.

Symbolic of New Provinces — AP30

1960, July 8   Litho.
C77 AP30 1.80p dp car & blue .15 .15

Elevation of the territories of Chubut, Formosa, Neuquen, Rio Negro and Santa Cruz to provinces.

Type of Regular Issue, 1960
1960, Oct. 1   Photo.   Perf. 13½
C78 A291 1.80p rose lilac .15 .15
C79 A291 10.70p brt grnsh blue .40 .15

UNESCO Emblem AP31

1962, July 14   Litho.
C80 AP31 13p ocher & brown .40 .25

15th anniv. of UNESCO.

Mail Coach — AP32

1962, Oct. 6   Wmk. 90   Perf. 13½
C81 AP32 5.60p gray brn & blk .20 .15

Mailman's Day, Sept. 14, 1962.

No. 695 and Type of 1959 Surcharged in Green
AEREO 5 60 PESOS

1962, Oct. 31   Photo.
C82 A277 5.60p on 5p brown .30 .15
C83 A277 18p on 5p brn, grnsh 1.00 .20

UPAE Emblem AP33   Skylark AP34

1962, Nov. 24   Photo.   Perf. 13½
C84 AP33 5.60p dark blue .20 .15

50th anniv. of the founding of the Postal Union of the Americas and Spain, UPAE.

1963, Feb. 9   Litho.

Design: 11p, Super Albatros.
C85 AP34 5.60p blue & black .20 .15
C86 AP34 11p blue, blk & red .30 .15

9th World Gliding Championships.

Symbolic Plane — AP35

1963-65   Wmk. 90   Perf. 13½
C87 AP35 5.60p dk pur, car & brt grn .40 .15
C88 AP35 7p black & bis ('64) .55 .15
C88A AP35 7p black & bis ('65) 4.00 .55
C89 AP35 11p blk, dk pur & grn .55 .25
C90 AP35 18p dk pur, red & vio bl 1.10 .35
C91 AP35 21p brown, red & gray 1.40 .55
 Nos. C87-C91 (6) 8.00 2.00

"Argentina" reads down on No. C88, up on No. C88A. See Nos. C101-C104, C108-C111, C123-C126, C135-C141. For overprint and surcharges see Nos. C96, C146-C150.

Type of Regular Issue, 1964
18p, Map of Falkland Islands (Islas Malvinas).

1964, Feb. 22   Perf. 13½
Size: 33x22mm
C92 A327 18p lt & dk bl & ol grn 1.75 .70

UPU Monument, Bern, and UN Emblem — AP36

1964, May 23   Engr.   Perf. 13½
C93 AP36 18p red & dk brown .52 .25

15th UPU Cong., Vienna, Austria, May-June 1964.

Discovery of America, Florentine Woodcut — AP37

1964, Oct. 10   Litho.
C94 AP37 13p tan & black .35 .30

Day of the Race, Columbus Day.

Lt. Matienzo Base, Antarctica AP38

1965, Feb. 27   Photo.   Perf. 13½
C95 AP38 11p salmon pink .52 .15

Issued to publicize the national territory of Tierra del Fuego, Antarctic and South Atlantic Isles.

No. C88A Overprinted in Silver: "PRIMERS / JORNADAS FILATELICAS / RIOPLATENSES"
1965, Mar. 17   Litho.
C96 AP35 7p black & bister .24 .15

1st Rio de la Plata Stamp Show, sponsored jointly by the Argentine and Uruguayan Philatelic Associations, Montevideo, Mar. 19-28.

ITU Emblem — AP39   Ascending Rocket — AP40

1965, May 11   Wmk. 90   Perf. 13½
C97 AP39 18p slate, blk & red .42 .22

Centenary of the ITU.

1965, May 29   Photo.   Perf. 13½

Design: 50p, Earth with trajectories and magnetic field, horiz.
C98 AP40 18p vermilion .42 .20
C99 AP40 .50p dp violet blue 1.00 .50

6th Symposium on Space Research, held in Buenos Aires, and to honor the Natl. Commission of Space Research.

Type of 1963-65 Inscribed "Republica Argentina" Reading Down
1965, Oct. 13   Litho.   Wmk. 90
C101 AP35 12p dk car rose & brn 1.40 .20
C102 AP35 15p vio blue & dk red .85 .26
C103 AP35 27.50p dk bl grn & gray 1.40 .40
C104 AP35 30.50p dk brown & dk bl 2.00 .60
 Nos. C101-C104 (4) 5.65 1.46

Argentine Antarctica Map and Centaur Rocket — AP41

1966, Feb. 19   Perf. 13½
C105 AP41 27.50p blue, blk & dp org 1.00 .75

Launchings of sounding balloons and of a Gamma Centaur rocket in Antarctica during February, 1965.

Sea Gull and Southern Cross AP42

1966, May 14   Perf. 13½
C106 AP42 12p Prus blue, blk & red .32 .15

50th anniv. of the Naval Aviation School.

Blériot Plane
Flown by Fels,
1917 — AP43

1967, Sept. 2   Litho.   Perf. 13½
C107 AP43 26p olive, bl & blk   .26   .15
Flight by Theodore Fels from Buenos Aires to
Montevideo, Sept. 2, 1917, allegedly the 1st intl.
airmail flight.

Type of 1963-65 Inscribed "Republica
Argentina" Reading Down

1967, Dec. 20   Perf. 13½
C108 AP35 26p brown   .60   .22
C109 AP35 40p violet   4.50   .30
C110 AP35 68p blue green   3.00   .45
C111 AP35 78p ultra   1.25   .60
     Nos. C108-C111 (4)   9.35 1.57

Vito Dumas
and Ketch
"Legh II"
AP44

1968, July 27   Litho.   Wmk. 90
C112 AP44 68p bl, blk, red & vio bl   .65   .40
Issued to commemorate Vito Dumas's one-man
voyage around the world in 1943.

Type of Regular Issue and

Assembly
Emblem
AP45

Design: 40p, Globe and map of South America.

1968, Oct. 19   Litho.   Perf. 13½
C113 A395 40p brt pink, lt bl & blk   .40   .16
C114 AP45 68p bl, lt bl, gold & blk   .65   .30
4th Plenary Assembly of the Intl. Telegraph and
Telephone Consultative Committee, Mar del Plata,
Sept. 23-Oct. 25.

Radar Antenna,
Balcarce
Station — AP46

**   Perf. 13½**
1969, Aug. 23   Wmk. 90   Photo.
C115 AP46 40p blue gray   .70   .22
Communications by satellite through Intl. Telecommunications Consortium (INTELSAT).

Atucha
Nuclear
Center
AP47

1969, Dec. 13   Litho.   Wmk. 365
C116 AP47 26p blue & multi   1.40   .80
Completion of Atucha Nuclear Center.

Type of 1963-65 Inscribed "Republica
Argentina" Reading Down

1969-71   Perf. 13½
C123 AP35 40p violet   5.00   .32
C124 AP35 68p dk blue grn ('70)   2.00   .60
**   Unwmk.**
C125 AP35 26p yellow brn ('71)   .32   .20
C126 AP35 40p violet ('71)   2.75   .40
     Nos. C123-C126 (4)   10.07 1.52

Old Fire
Engine and
Fire Brigade
Emblem
AP48

1970, Aug. 8   Litho.   Unwmk.
C128 AP48 40c green & multi   .55   .28
Centenary of the Fire Brigade.

Education Year
Emblem — AP49

1970, Aug. 29   Perf. 13½
C129 AP49 68c blue & blk   .42   .25
Issued for International Education Year.

Fleet Leaving
Valparaiso, by
Antonio Abel
AP50

1970, Oct. 17   Litho.   Perf. 13½
C130 AP50 26c multicolored   1.00   .35
150th anniv. of the departure for Peru of the
liberation fleet from Valparaiso, Chile.

Sumampa
Chapel
AP51

1970, Nov. 7   Photo.
C131 AP51 40c multicolored   .95   .35
Bishopric of Tucuman, 400th anniversary.

Buenos
Aires
Planetarium
AP52

1970, Nov. 28   Litho.   Perf. 13½
C132 AP52 40c multicolored   .60   .26

Jorge
Newbery
and
Morane
Saulnier
Plane
AP53

1970, Dec. 19
C133 AP53 26c bl, blk, yel & grn .38   .25
24th Aeronautics and Space Week.

Industries Type of Regular Issue
Design: 31c, Refinery.

1971, Oct. 16   Litho.   Perf. 13½
C134 A445 31c red, blk & yel   .60   .24

Type of 1963-65 Inscribed "Republica
Argentina" Reading Down
1971-74   Unwmk.
C135 AP35 45c brown   3.25   .15
C136 AP35 68c red   .48   .15
C137 AP35 70c vio blue ('73)   .80   .15
C138 AP35 90c emerald ('73)   1.90   .15
C139 AP35 1.70p blue ('74)   .48   .25
C140 AP35 1.95p emerald ('74)   .48   .30
C141 AP35 2.65p dp claret ('74)   .48   .40
     Nos. C135-C141 (7)   7.87
     Set value   1.30
Fluorescent paper was used for Nos. C135-C136,
C138-C141. The 70c was issued on both papers.

Don Quixote,
Drawing by Ignacio
Zuloaga — AP54

1975, Apr. 26   Photo.   Perf. 13½
C145 AP54 2.75p yellow, blk & red   .60   .35
Day of the Race and for Espana 75 Intl. Philatelic
Exhibition, Madrid, Apr. 4-13.

No. C87
Surcharged   **100** ● **PESOS**

1975, Sept. 15   Litho.   Wmk. 90
C146 AP35 9.20p on 5.60p   .90   .18
C147 AP35 19.70p on 5.60p   1.25   .45
C148 AP35 100p on 5.60p   5.50 2.25
     Nos. C146-C148 (3)   7.65 2.88

REVALORIZADO
No. C87
Surcharged   **920** PESOS

1975, Oct. 15
C149 AP35 9.20p on 5.60p   .70   .30
C150 AP35 19.70p on 5.60p   1.25   .60

Argentine
State
Airline,
50th
Anniv.
AP55

1990, Sept. 15   Litho.   Perf. 13½
C151 AP55 2500a Junkers JU52-3M   1.25   .90
C152 AP55 2500a Grumman SA-16   1.25   .90
C153 AP55 2500a Fokker F-27   1.25   .90
C154 AP55 2500a Fokker F-28   1.25   .90
     Nos. C151-C154 (4)   5.00 3.60

AIR POST SEMI-POSTAL STAMPS

Catalogue values for unused
stamps in this section are for Never
Hinged items.

Philatelic Exhibition Type

Designs: 45c+45c, Stamp engraving. 70c+70c,
Proofing stamp die. 1p+1p, Sheet of stamps.
2.50p+2.50p, The letter. 5p+5p, Gen. San Martin.

**   Perf. 13½**
1950, Aug. 26   Wmk. 90   Photo.
CB1 SP8 45c + 45c violet bl   .38   .24
CB2 SP8 70c + 70c dark
            brown   .55   .38
  a. Souv. sheet of 3, #B12, CB1,
      CB2, imperf.   3.00 3.00

CB3 SP8 1p + 1p cerise   1.50 1.50
CB4 SP8 2.50p + 2.50p ol gray   8.50 6.00
CB5 SP8 5p + 5p dull green   9.25 7.25
     Nos. CB1-CB5 (5)   20.18 15.37
Argentine Intl. Philatelic Exhib., 1950.

Pieta by
Michelangelo
SPAP2

1951, Dec. 22   Perf. 13½x13
CB6 SPAP2 2.45p +7.55p grnsh
            blk   21.00 14.00
Surtax as for the Eva Peron Foundation.

Flower and Child's   Stamp of
Head — SPAP3   1858 — SPAP4

1958, Mar. 15   Perf. 13½
CB7 SPAP3 1p +50c deep claret   .28   .25
Surtax for National Council for Children.

1958, Mar. 29   Litho.   Wmk. 90
CB8 SPAP4 1p + 50c gray ol & bl   .40   .32
CB9 SPAP4 2p + 1p rose lilac &
            vio   .52   .42
CB10 SPAP4 3p + 1.50p green &
            brown   .60   .52
CB11 SPAP4 5p + 2.50p gray ol &
            car rose   1.00   .85
CB12 SPAP4 10p + 5p gray ol & brn 2.00 1.65
     Nos. CB8-CB12 (5)   4.52 3.76
The surtax was for the Intl. Centennial Philatelic
Exhibition, Buenos Aires, Apr. 19-27.

Type of Semi-Postal Issue, 1958
Designs: 1p+50c, Flooded area. 5p+2.50p,
House and truck under water.

1958, Oct. 4   Photo.   Perf. 13½
CB13 SP11 1p + 50c dull purple   .25   .20
CB14 SP11 5p + 2.50p grnsh blue   .80   .50
The surtax was for victims of a flood in the
Buenos Aires district.

Type of Semi-Postal Issue, 1959
1959, Sept. 5   Litho.   Perf. 13½
CB15 SP13 2p + 1p Rowing   .40   .26
CB16 SP13 3p + 1.50p Woman diver .60   .48

Type of Semi-Postal Issue, 1960
Birds: 2p+1p, Rufous tinamou. 3p+1.50p, Rhea.

1960, Feb. 6   Perf. 13½
CB17 SP14 2p + 1p rose car & sal .30   .20
CB18 SP14 3p + 1.50p slate green .45   .35
The surtax was for child welfare work.
See No. CB29.

Buenos Aires Market   Seibo, National
Place, 1810 — SPAP5   Flower — SPAP6

6p+3p, Oxcart water carrier. 10.70p+5.30p, Settlers landing. 20p+10p, The Fort.

1960, Aug. 20   Photo.   Wmk. 90

CB19	SPAP5	2 + 1p rose brown	.16	.15
CB20	SPAP5	6 + 3p gray	.35	.24
CB21	SPAP5	10.70 + 5.30p blue	.60	.35
CB22	SPAP5	20 + 10p bluish grn	1.00	.85
		Nos. CB19-CB22 (4)	2.11	1.59

Inter-American Philatelic Exhibition EFIMAYO 1960, Buenos Aires, Oct. 12-24, held to for the sesquicentennial of the May Revolution of 1910. For overprints see Nos. CB25-CB28.

1960, Sept. 10   Perf. 13 1/2

10.70p+5.30p, Copihue, Chile's national flower.

CB23	SPAP6	6 + 3p lilac rose	.35	.28
CB24	SPAP6	10.70 + 5.30p vermilion	.52	.42

The surtax was for earthquake victims in Chile.

Nos. CB19-CB22 Overprinted: "DIA DE LAS NACIONES UNIDAS 24 DE OCTUBRE"

1960, Oct. 8

CB25	SPAP5	2 + 1p rose brown	.20	.15
CB26	SPAP5	6 + 3p gray	.32	.28
CB27	SPAP5	10.70 + 5.30p blue	.48	.42
CB28	SPAP5	20 + 10p bluish green	.85	.75
		Nos. CB25-CB28 (4)	1.85	1.60

United Nations Day, Oct. 24, 1960.

Type of Semi-Postal Issue, 1960

Design: Emperor penguins.

1961, Feb. 25   Photo.   Wmk. 90

CB29	SP14	1.80p + 90c gray	.32	.20

The surtax was for child welfare work.

Stamp of 1862 — SPAP7

Crutch, Olympic Torch and Rings — SPAP8

1962, May 19   Litho.

CB30	SPAP7	6.50p + 6.50p Prus bl & grnsh bl	.70	.65

Opening of the "Argentina 62" Philatelic Exhibition, Buenos Aires, May 19-29.

Type of Semi-Postal Issue, 1963

1963, May 18   Wmk. 90   Perf. 13 1/2

CB31	SP21	11p + 5p Bicycling	.55	.50

Type of Semi-Postal Issue, 1962

1963, Dec. 21   Perf. 13 1/2

CB32	SP20	11p + 5p Great kiskadee	.70	.60

The surtax was for child welfare.

Type of Semi-Postal Issue, 1964

1964, July 18   Litho.

CB33	SP22	11p + 5p Sailboat	.50	.50

1964, Sept. 19   Litho.   Perf. 13 1/2

CB34	SPAP8	18p + 9p bluish grn, blk, red & yel	.60	.60

13th "Olympic" games for the handicapped, Tokyo, 1964.

Bird Type of Semi-Postal Issue, 1962

1964, Dec. 23   Litho.   Wmk. 90

CB35	SP20	18p + 9p Chilean swallow	.90	.75

The surtax was for child welfare.

Bird Type of Semi-Postal Issue, 1962, Inscribed "R. ARGENTINA"

Design: Rufous ovenbird.

1966, Mar. 26   Perf. 13 1/2

CB36	SP20	27.50p + 12.50p bl, ocher, yel & grn	.80	.70

The surtax was for child welfare.

Coat of Arms — SPAP9

1966, June 25   Litho.   Perf. 13 1/2

CB37	SPAP9	10p + 10p yellow & multi	1.75	1.40

ARGENTINA '66 Philatelic Exhibition held in connection with the sesquicentennial celebration of the Declaration of Independence, Buenos Aires, July 16-23. The surtax was for the Exhibition. Issued in sheets of 4.

Bird Type of Semi-Postal Issue, 1962, Inscribed "R. ARGENTINA"

Designs: 15p+7p, Blue and yellow tanager. 26p+13p, Toco toucan.

1967   Litho.   Wmk. 90

CB38	SP20	15p + 7p blk, bl, grn & yel	1.00	.90
CB39	SP20	26p + 13p blk, org, yel & bl	.50	.40

The surtax was for child welfare. Issue dates: 15p+7p, Jan. 14. 26p+13p, Dec. 23.

Bird Type of Semi-Postal Issue, 1969

Design: 26p+13p, Lineated woodpecker.

1969, Sept. 20   Wmk. 365   Perf. 13 1/2

CB40	SP24	26p + 13p multi	.48	.40

The surtax was for child welfare.

Bird Type of Semi-Postal Issue, 1970

Design: 40c+20c, Chilean flamingo.

1970, May 9   Litho.   Wmk. 365

CB41	SP25	40c + 20c multi	.45	.40

The surtax was for child welfare.

Fish Type of Semi-Postal Issue, 1971

Design: Pejerrey (atherinidae family).

1971, Feb. 20   Unwmk.   Perf. 12 1/2   Size: 75x15mm

CB42	SP26	40c + 20c lt blue & multi	.40	.40

The surtax was for child welfare.

OFFICIAL STAMPS

Regular Issues Overprinted in Black

OFICIAL

1884-87   Unwmk.   Perf. 12, 14

O1	A29	1/2c brown	12.00	10.00
O2	A23	1c red	8.00	6.00
b.		Perf. 12	40.00	30.00
O3	A29	1c red	.50	.35
b.		Double overprint	35.00	35.00
O4	A20	2c green	.50	.35
b.		Double overprint	35.00	35.00
O5	A11	4c brown	.50	.35
O6	A7	8c lake	.50	.35
O7	A8	10c green	40.00	25.00
O8	A23	12c ultra (#45)	6.50	4.00
a.		Perf. 14	325.00	125.00
O9	A29	12c grnsh blue	.80	.60
O10	A19	24c blue	1.00	.85
O11	A21	25c lake	16.00	12.50
O12	A12	30c orange	32.50	20.00
O13	A13	60c black	20.00	12.50
O14	A14	90c blue	20.00	15.00
b.		Double overprint		
		Nos. O1-O14 (14)	158.80	107.85

Inverted Overprint

O1a	A29	1/2c	16.00	12.50
O2a	A23	1c Perf. 14	50.00	40.00
c.		Perf. 12	32.50	30.00
O3a	A29	1c	1.50	1.00
O4a	A20	2c	65.00	40.00
O5a	A11	4c	40.00	32.50
O6a	A7	8c	60.00	60.00
O8b	A23	12c Perf. 12	12.50	
O9a	A29	12c	125.00	65.00
O10a	A19	24c	2.75	1.65
O13a	A13	60c	90.00	50.00
O14a	A14	90c	50.00	40.00

1884   *Rouletted*

O15	A17	16c green	1.75	1.00
a.		Double overprint	15.00	
b.		Inverted overprint	125.00	
O16	A18	20c blue	8.00	7.00
a.		Inverted overprint	60.00	40.00
O17	A19	24c blue	1.25	1.00
a.		Inverted overprint	4.00	2.50
b.		Double ovpt., one inverted	250.00	
		Nos. O15-O17 (3)	11.00	9.00

Overprinted Diagonally in Red

1885   *Perf. 12*

O18	A20	2c green	2.00	1.50
a.		Inverted overprint	40.00	32.50
O19	A11	4c brown	2.00	1.25
a.		Inverted overprint	40.00	30.00
b.		Double overprint	50.00	—
O20	A13	60c black	20.00	16.00
O21	A14	90c blue	200.00	150.00

1885   *Rouletted*

O22	A19	24c blue	17.50	12.50

On all of these stamps, the overprint is found reading both upwards and downwards. Counterfeits exist of No. O21 overprint and others.

Regular Issues Handstamped Horizontally in Black   **OFICIAL**

1884   *Perf. 12, 14*

O23	A23	1c red	50.00	17.00
a.		Perf. 12	150.00	100.00
O24	A20	2c green, diagonal overprint	25.00	15.00
a.		Horizontal overprint	150.00	125.00
O25	A11	4c brown	10.00	7.50
O26	A7	8c lake	10.00	10.00
O27	A23	12c ultra	27.50	20.00

Overprinted Diagonally

O28	A19	24c bl, rouletted	20.00	14.00
O29	A13	60c black	15.00	10.00

Counterfeit overprints exist.

Liberty Head — O1

Perf. 11 1/2, 12 and Compound

1901, Dec. 1   Engr.

O31	O1	1c gray	.20	.15
b.		Vert. pair, imperf. horiz.	50.00	
c.		Horiz. pair, imperf. vert.	50.00	
O32	O1	2c orange brown	.30	.20
O33	O1	5c red	.40	.20
b.		Vert. pair, imperf. horiz.	50.00	
O34	O1	10c dark green	.45	.20
O35	O1	30c dark blue	4.00	1.00
O36	O1	50c orange	1.65	1.00
		Nos. O31-O36 (6)	7.00	2.75

Imperf, Pairs

O31a	O1	1c	40.00	
O32a	O1	2c	40.00	
O33a	O1	5c	50.00	
O34a	O1	10c	40.00	
O35a	O1	30c	65.00	
O36a	O1	50c	50.00	

Regular Stamps of 1935-51 Overprinted in Black

SERVICIO OFICIAL
c

Perf. 13x13 1/2, 13 1/2x13, 13

1938-54   Wmk. RA in Sun (90)

O37	A129	1c buff ('40)	.15	.15
O38	A130	2c dk brn ('40)	.15	.15
O39	A132	3c grn ('39)	.15	.15
O40	A132	3c lt gray ('39)	.15	.15
O41	A134	5c yel brn	.15	.15
O42	A195	5c car ('53)	.15	.15
O43	A137	10c carmine	.15	.15
O44	A137	10c brn ('39)	.15	.15
O45	A140	15c lt gray bl, type II ('47)	.15	.15
O46	A139	15c slate blue	.50	.15
O47	A139	15c pale ultra ('39)	.15	.15
O48	A139	20c blue ('53)	.30	.15
O49	A141	25c carmine	.15	.15
a.		Overprint 11mm	.20	.15
O49B	A143	40c dk violet	.90	.15
O50	A144	50c red & org	.15	.15
a.		Overprint 11mm		
O51	A146	1p brn blk & lt bl ('40)	.20	.15
a.		Overprint 11mm		
O52	A224	1p choc & lt bl ('51)	.20	.15
a.		Overprint 11mm		
O53	A147	2p brn lake & dk ultra (ovpt. 11mm) ('54)	.70	.15
		Nos. O37-O53 (18)	4.60	
		Set value		1.05

Overprinted in Black on Stamps and Types of 1945-47

Perf. 13x13 1/2, 13 1/2x13

1945-46   Unwmk.

O54	A130	2c sepia	2.75	.40
O55	A134	3c lt gray	2.25	.30
O56	A134	5c yel brn	.65	.15
O57	A195	5c dp car	.15	.15
O58	A137	10c brown	.15	.15
a.		Double overprint		
O59	A140	15c lt gray bl, type II	.15	.15
O61	A141	25c dull rose	.15	.15
O62	A144	50c red & org	.55	.15
O63	A146	1p brn blk & lt bl	.15	.15
O64	A147	2p brn lake & bl	.40	.15
O65	A148	5p ind & ol grn	.15	.15
O66	A149	10p dp cl & int blk	.45	.15
O67	A150	20p bl grn & brn	1.00	.15
		Nos. O54-O67 (13)	8.95	
		Set value		1.50

Overprinted in Black on Stamps and Types of 1942-50

Perf. 13, 13x13 1/2

1944-51   Wmk. 288

O73	A134	3c lt gray	1.10	.50
O74	A134	5c yellow brown	.25	.15
O75	A137	10c red brown	.15	.15
O76	A140	15c lt gray bl, type II	.25	.15
O77	A144	50c red & org (overprint 11 mm)	1.50	.50
O78	A146	1p brn blk & lt bl (overprint 11mm)	1.75	.35
		Nos. O73-O78 (6)	5.00	
		Set value		1.50

> Catalogue values for unused stamps in this section, from this point to the end of the section, are for Never Hinged items.

Nos. 600-606 Overprinted in Black

SERVICIO OFICIAL
d

1953   Wmk. 90   Perf. 13

O79	A228	5c gray	.15	.15
O80	A228	10c rose lilac	.15	.15
O81	A228	20c rose pink	.15	.15
O82	A228	25c dull green	.15	.15
O83	A228	40c dull violet	.15	.15
O84	A228	45c deep blue	.20	.15
O85	A228	50c dull broen	.15	.15

SERVICIO OFICIAL
e

SERVICIO OFICIAL
f

Nos. 611-617 Overprinted Type "e" in Blue

Perf. 13x13 1/2, 13 1/2x13

O86	A229	1p dk brown	.15	.15
O87	A229	1.50p dp green	.30	.15
O88	A229	2p brt carmine	.20	.15
O89	A229	3p indigo	.55	.25

Size: 30x40mm

O90	A229	5p red brown	.55	.45
O91	A228	10p red	2.75	1.75
O92	A229	20p green	30.00	20.00
		Nos. O79-O92 (14)	35.60	23.95

No. 612 Overprinted Type "f" in Blue

O93	A229	1.50p dp grn	1.00	.30

Regular Issues of 1954-59 Variously Overprinted in Black or Blue

S. OFICIAL
g

SERVICIO OFICIAL
h

Perf. 13 1/2, 13x13 1/2, 13 1/2x13

1955-61   Litho.   Wmk. 90

O94	A237(c)	20c red (#629)	.15	.15
O95	A237(d)	20c red (#629)	.15	.15
O96	A237(d)	40c red, ovpt. 15mm (#630)	.15	.15

Engr.

O97	A239(g)	50c bl (#632)	.15	.15

Photo.

O98	A239(h)	1p brn (#635)	.15	.15
O99	A239(h)	1p brn (Bl, #635)	.15	.15
O100	A239(h)	1p brn (Bk, #635)	.15	.15

Engr.

O101	A239(h)	3p vio brn (#638)	.15	.15
O102	A240(h)	5p gray grn (#639)	.30	.15
O103	A240(e)	10p yel grn (#640)	.45	.15

O104 A240(f) 20p dl vio (#641) .75 .30
O105 A240(h) 20p dl vio (#641) .75 .25
O106 A241(e) 50p ultra & ind (#642) 1.10 .20
Nos. O94-O106 (13) 4.55
Set value 1.30

The overprints on Nos. O99-O100 and O103-O104 are horizontal; that on No. O109 is vertical. On No. O106 overprint measures 23mm.

Issue dates: No. O102, 1957. Nos. O97, O101, O103, O105, 1958. Nos. O98-O99, O104, 1959. No. O100, 1960. No. O106, 1961.

No. 659 Overprinted Type "d"
1957   Wmk. 90   Litho.   Perf. 13
O108 A133 20c dl pur (ovpt. 15mm) .15 .15

Nos. 666, 658 and 663 Variously Overprinted
1957   Photo.   Perf. 13x13½, 13½
O109 A261(g) 2p claret .20 .15
O110 A254(e) 2.40p brown .20 .15
O111 A258(c) 4.40p grnsh gray .25 .15
Nos. O109-O111 (3) .65
Set value .20

Nos. 668, 685-687, 690-691, 693-705, 742, 742C and Types of 1959-65 Overprinted in black, Blue or Red Types "e," "g,"

S. OFICIAL   S. OFICIAL
i   j

S. OFICIAL   S. OFICIAL   S.
k   m   n

Lithographed; Photogravure
1960-68   Perf. 13x13½, 13½
O112 A128(g) 5c buff (vert. ovpt.) .15 .15
O113 A275(j) 10c sl grn .15 .15
O114 A275(i) 20c dl red brn .15 .15
O115 A275(i) 50c bister .15 .15
O116 A278(k) 1p brn (vert. ovpt.) .15 .15
O117 A278(j) 1p brn, photo. (vert. ovpt.) .20 .15
O117A A278(j) 1p brn, litho. (down) .20 .15
O118 A276(j) 2p rose red .15 .15
O119 A312(m) 2p dp grn (down) .25 .15
O120 A312(j) 2p brt grn (up) .15 .15
O121 A312(j) 2p grn litho. (down) .25 .15
O122 A277(e) 3p dk bl (horiz.) .20 .15
O123 A277(j) 3p dk blue .20 .15
O124 A276(j) 4p red, litho. .20 .15
O125 A312(j) 4p rose red, litho. (down) .20 .15
O126 A277(e) 5p brn (Bl) (horiz.) .25 .15
O127 A277(e) 5p brn (Bk) (horiz.) .25 .15
O128 A277(j) 5p sepia .15 .15
O129 A277(e) 5p sepia (horiz. ovpt.) .15 .15
O130 A276(j) 8p red .20 .15
O131 A278(i) 10p lt red brn .45 .15
O132 A276(j) 10p vermilion .20 .15
O133 A278(j) 10p brn car (up) .20 .15
O134 A278(m) 12p dk brn vio .35 .15
O135 A278(k) 20p Prus grn .50 .15
O136 A278(j) 20p Prus grn (up) .40 .15
O137 A278(j) 20p red, litho. .35 .15
O138 A278(m) 20p red, litho. .25 .15
O139 A278(j) 23p grn (vert. ovpt.) .50 .15
O140 A278(j) 25p dp vio, photo. (R) (up) .50 .15
O141 A278(j) 25p pur, litho. (R) (down) .50 .15
O142 A241(n) 50p dk blue 1.10 .15
O143 A279(m) 100p bl (horiz. ovpt.) 1.10 .35
O144 A279(m) 100p blue (up) 1.10 .35
O145 A280(m) 300p dp violet 2.25 .60
Nos. O112-O145 (35) 13.50
Set value 3.20

The "m" overprint measures 15½mm on 2p; 14½mm on 12p, 100p and 300p; 13mm on 20p. Issue dates: Nos. O122, O127, O135, 1961. Nos. O122-O114, O116, O118, 1962. No. O124, 1963. Nos. O119, O134, O143, 1964. No. O117, O125, O130, O139, O144, 1965. Nos. O120, O128, O132-O133, O136, O140, O142, O145, 1966. Nos. O121, O129, O137-O138, O141, 1967. No. O117A, 1968.

Nos. 699, 823-825, 827-829, and Type of 1962 Overprinted in Black or Red Types "j," "m," or "o"

o   SERVICIO OFICIAL

Inscribed: "Republica Argentina"
Litho., Photo., Engr.
1964-67   Wmk. 90   Perf. 13½
O149 A312(j) 6p rose red (down) .25 .15
O153 A238a(m) 22p ultra .50 .15
O154 A238a(j) 43p dk car rose (down) .75 .15
O155 A238a(j) 45p brn, photo. (up) .75 .15
O156 A238a(j) 45p brn, litho. (up) 1.10 .20
O157 A241(j) 50p dk bl (up) (R) 2.25 .15
O158 A366(j) 90p ol bis (up) 2.75 .20
O162 A495(o) 500p yel grn 3.50 .80
Nos. O149-O162 (8) 11.85
Set value 1.50

Issued: No. O153, 1964; No. O155, 1966; Nos. O149, O156-O162, 1967.

Type of 1959-67 Ovptd. Type "j"
1969   Litho.   Wmk. 365   Perf. 13½
O163 A276 20p vermilion .20 .15

OFFICIAL DEPARTMENT STAMPS

Regular Issues of 1911-37 Overprinted in Black

M. A.   M. A.
Type I   Type II

Ministry of Agriculture (M. A.)
Type I
1913-37
On Stamp of 1911
OD1 A88 2c #181 .15 .15
On Stamps of 1912-14
OD2 A88 1c #190 .15 .15
OD3 A88 2c #191 .15 .15
OD4 A88 5c #194 .30 .15
OD5 A88 12c #196 .15 .15
Set value .65 .25
On Stamps of 1915-16
OD6 A88 1c #208 .15 .15
OD7 A88 2c #209 .15 .15
OD8 A88 5c #212 .15 .15
OD9 A91 5c #220 .15 .15
Set value .45 .32
On Stamp of 1917
OD10 A94 12c #238 .30 .15
On Stamps of 1918-19
OD11 A93 1c #249 .15 .15
OD12 A93 2c #250 .15 .15
OD13 A93 5c #253 .15 .15
OD14 A94 5c #255 .15 .15
OD15 A94 20c #256 .15 .15
Set value .55 .35
On Stamps of 1920
OD16 A93 1c #265 .30 .25
OD17 A93 2c #266 .50 .25
OD18 A93 5c #269 .20 .15
Nos. OD16-OD18 (3) 1.00
Set value .55
On Stamps of 1922-23
OD19 A94 12c #311 1.00 .40
OD20 A94 20c #312 25.00
On Stamps of 1923
OD21 A104 1c #324 .15 .15
OD22 A104 2c #325 .25 .15
OD23 A104 5c #328 .15 .15
OD24 A104 12c #330 .15 .15
OD25 A104 20c #331 .15 .15
Set value .45 .30
On Stamps of 1923-31
OD26 A104 1c #341 .15 .15
OD27 A104 2c #342, I .15 .15
  a. Type II 1.50 .75
OD28 A104 3c #343 .15 .15
OD29 A104 5c #345, II .15 .15
  a. Type I .20 .15
OD30 A104 10c #346, II .15 .15
  a. Type I .60 .15
OD31 A104 12c #347 .15 .15
OD32 A104 20c #348, I .15 .15
  a. Type II .40 .15
OD33 A104 30c #351 .15 .15
Set value .70 .40
On Stamp of 1926
OD34 A110 12c #360 .15 .15

Type II
On Stamps of 1935-37
OD35 A129 1c #419 .15 .15
OD36 A130 2c #420 .15 .15
OD37 A132 3c #422 .15 .15
OD38 A134 5c #427 .15 .15
OD39 A137 10c #430 .15 .15
OD40 A139 15c #434 .50 .15
OD41 A140 20c #437 .30 .15
OD42 A140 30c #438 .20 .15
OD43 A141 25c #441 .25 .15
OD44 A142 30c #442 .15 .15
OD45 A145 1p #445 2.50 1.50
OD46 A146 1p #446 .50 .25
Nos. OD35-OD46 (12) 5.15
Set value 2.00

Ministry of War (M. G.)
Type I
On Stamp of 1911
OD47 A88 2c #181 .15 .15
On Stamps of 1912-14
OD48 A88 1c #190 .15 .15
OD49 A88 2c #191 .75 .15
OD50 A88 5c #194 .15 .15
OD51 A88 12c #196 .15 .15
Set value 1.05 .20
On Stamps of 1915-16
OD52 A88 1c #208 6.00 .75
OD53 A88 2c #209 .60 .15
OD54 A88 5c #212 .75 .15
OD55 A91 5c #220 1.00 .25
OD56 A92 12c #222 1.00 .35
Nos. OD52-OD56 (5) 9.35 1.65
On Stamps of 1917
OD57 A93 1c #232 .30 .15
OD58 A93 2c #233 .40 .15
OD59 A93 5c #236 .30 .15
OD60 A94 12c #238 .60 .15
Nos. OD57-OD60 (4) 1.60
Set value .20
On Stamps of 1918-19
OD61 A93 1c #249 .15 .15
OD62 A93 2c #250 .15 .15
OD63 A93 5c #253 .15 .15
OD64 A94 5c #255 .40 .15
OD65 A94 20c #256 1.25 .15
Nos. OD61-OD65 (5) 2.10
Set value .25
On Stamps of 1920
OD66 A93 2c #266 .40 .15
OD67 A93 5c #269 .40 .15
OD68 A94 12c #271 .35 .15
Nos. OD66-OD68 (3) 1.15
On Stamp of 1920
OD69 A94 12c #299 2.00 .25
On Stamps of 1922-23
OD70 A93 1c #305 .75 .15
OD71 A93 2c #306 1.50 .45
OD72 A103 5c #309 .75 .15
OD73 A94 20c #312 .30 .15
Nos. OD70-OD73 (4) 3.30
Set value .70
On Stamp of 1922-23
OD74 A93 2c #318 5.00 .50
On Stamps of 1923
OD75 A104 1c #324 .15 .15
OD76 A104 2c #325 .15 .15
OD77 A104 5c #328 .15 .15
OD78 A104 12c #330 .15 .15
OD79 A104 20c #331 1.00 .15
Nos. OD75-OD79 (5) 1.60
Set value .25
On Stamps of 1923-31
OD80 A104 1c #341 1.25 .45
OD81 A104 2c #342 .20 .15
OD82 A104 3c #343, I .15 .15
  a. Type II .40 .15
OD83 A104 5c #345, I .15 .15
  a. Type II .20 .15
OD84 A104 10c #346, II .15 .15
  a. Type I .60 .15
OD85 A104 20c #348, I .15 .15
  a. Type II .40 .15
OD86 A104 30c #351, II .20 .15
  a. Type I 1.00 .15
OD87 A105 1p #353 2.00 .30
Nos. OD80-OD87 (8) 4.25
Set value .75
On Stamp of 1926
OD88 A109 5c #359 .60 .15

Type II
On Stamps of 1935-37
OD89 A129 1c #419 .15 .15
OD90 A130 2c #420 .15 .15
OD91 A132 3c #422 .15 .15
OD92 A134 5c #427 .15 .15
OD93 A137 10c #430 .15 .15
OD94 A139 15c #434 .25 .15
OD95 A140 20c #437 1.00 .15
OD96 A140 30c #438 .25 .15
OD97 A141 25c #441 .15 .15
OD98 A142 30c #442 .15 .15
OD99 A144 50c #444 .25 .15

OD100 A145 1p #445 1.25 .50
OD101 A146 1p #446 .50 .25
Set value 4.00 1.30

Ministry of Finance (M. H.)
Type I
On Stamp of 1911
OD102 A88 2c #181 .15 .15
On Stamps of 1912-14
OD103 A88 1c #190 .15 .15
OD104 A88 1c #191 .15 .15
OD105 A88 5c #194 .20 .15
OD106 A88 12c #196 .15 .15
Set value .40 .20
On Stamps of 1915-16
OD107 A88 2c #209 .15 .15
OD108 A88 5c #212 .15 .15
OD109 A91 5c #220 .15 .15
Set value .30 .16
On Stamps of 1917
OD110 A93 2c #233 .15 .15
OD111 A93 5c #236 1.25 .15
OD112 A94 12c #238 .15 .15
Nos. OD110-OD112 (3) 1.55
Set value .25
On Stamps of 1918-19
OD113 A93 2c #250 25.00
OD114 A93 5c #253 .20 .15
OD115 A94 5c #255 .45 .15
OD116 A94 20c #256 .45 .15
On Stamps of 1920
OD117 A93 1c #265 .75 .45
OD118 A93 5c #266 1.25 .45
OD119 A93 5c #269 .30 .15
OD120 A94 12c #271 .60 .20
Nos. OD117-OD120 (4) 2.90 1.25
On Stamp of 1922-23
OD121 A94 20c #312 12.50 2.50
On Stamps of 1923
OD122 A104 1c #324 .75 .40
OD123 A104 2c #325 .15 .15
OD124 A104 5c #328 .15 .15
OD125 A104 12c #330 .15 .15
OD126 A104 20c #331 .15 .15
Set value .90 .60
On Stamps of 1923-31
OD127 A104 3c #343 7.00 1.50
OD128 A104 5c #345 .15 .15
OD129 A104 10c #346 .15 .15
OD130 A104 12c #347 7.00 3.75
OD131 A104 20c #348, I .15 .15
  a. Type II .35 .15
OD132 A104 30c #351 .25 .15
OD133 A105 1p #353 .40 .15
Nos. OD127-OD133 (7) 15.10 6.00
On Stamp of 1926
OD134 A110 12c #360 12.50 12.50

Type II
On Stamps of 1935-37
OD135 A129 1c #419 .15 .15
OD136 A130 2c #420 .15 .15
OD137 A132 3c #422 .15 .15
OD138 A134 5c #427 .15 .15
OD139 A137 10c #430 .15 .15
OD140 A139 15c #434 .45 .15
OD141 A140 20c #437 .15 .15
OD142 A140 30c #438 .15 .15
OD143 A142 30c #442 .15 .15
OD144 A145 1p #445 2.00 1.00
OD145 A146 1p #446 .50 .20
Set value 3.50 1.70

Ministry of the Interior (M. I.)
Type I
On Stamp of 1911
OD146 A88 2c #181 .25 .15
On Stamps of 1912-14
OD147 A88 1c #190 .15 .15
OD148 A88 2c #191 .15 .15
OD149 A88 5c #194 .15 .15
OD150 A88 12c #196 .15 .15
Set value .40 .30
On Stamps of 1915-17
OD151 A88 2c #209 .80 .30
OD152 A88 5c #212 .75 .15
OD153 A91 5c #220 .60 .15
OD154 A93 12c #236 1.50 .15
Nos. OD151-OD154 (4) 3.65
Set value .65
On Stamps of 1918-19
OD155 A93 2c #250 .15 .15
OD156 A93 5c #253 .15 .15
Set value .20 .15
On Stamps of 1920
OD157 A93 1c #265 3.75 1.25
OD158 A93 5c #269 .75 .35

On Stamps of 1922-23
OD159 A93 2c #306 12.50 12.50
OD160 A103 5c #309 3.50 1.25
OD161 A94 12c #311 1.25 .40
OD162 A94 20c #312 1.25 .40
Nos. OD159-OD162 (4) 18.50 14.55

On Stamps of 1923
OD163 A104 1c #324 .15 .15
OD164 A104 2c #325 .15 .15
OD165 A104 5c #328 .15 .15
OD166 A104 12c #330 2.00 2.00
OD167 A104 20c #331 .75 .15
Nos. OD163-OD167 (5) 3.20
Set value 2.10

On Stamps of 1923-31
OD168 A104 1c #341 .15 .15
OD169 A104 2c #342 .15 .15
OD170 A104 3c #343, II .15 .15
  a. Type I 1.25 .30
OD171 A104 5c #345, I .15 .15
  a. Type II .15 .15
OD172 A104 10c #346, II .15 .15
OD173 A104 12c #347 .30 .15
OD174 A104 20c #348, II .15 .15
  a. Type I .75 .15
OD175 A104 30c #351 .15 .15
Set value .60 .45

Type II
On Stamps of 1935-37
OD176 A129 1c #419 .15 .15
OD177 A130 2c #420 .15 .15
OD178 A132 3c #422 .15 .15
OD178A A134 5c #427 .15 .15
OD179 A137 10c #430 .30 .15
OD180 A139 15c #434 .30 .15
OD181 A140 20c #437 .75 .15
OD182 A140 20c #438 .20 .15
OD182A A142 30c #442 .15 .15
OD182B A145 1p #445 2.00 1.00
OD182C A146 1p #446 .50 .25
Set value 4.00 1.65

Ministry of Justice and Instruction (M. J. I.)
Type I
On Stamp of 1911
OD183 A88 2c #181 1.25 .15

On Stamps of 1912-14
OD184 A88 1c #190 1.50 .15
OD185 A88 2c #191 1.00 .15
OD186 A88 5c #194 .45 .15
OD187 A88 12c #196 .45 .15
Nos. OD184-OD187 (4) 3.40
Set value .30

On Stamps of 1915-17
OD188 A88 1c #208 .30 .15
OD189 A88 2c #209 .30 .15
OD190 A91 5c #212 1.00 .15
OD191 A91 5c #220 .25 .15
OD192 A92 12c #222 .75 .15
Nos. OD188-OD192 (5) 2.60
Set value .45

On Stamps of 1917
OD193 A93 1c #232 .25 .15
OD194 A93 2c #233 .75 .15
OD195 A93 5c #236 .25 .15
OD196 A94 12c #238 17.50 5.00
Nos. OD193-OD196 (4) 18.75 5.45

On Stamps of 1918-19
OD197 A93 1c #249 .15 .15
OD198 A93 2c #250 .15 .15
OD199 A93 5c #253 .15 .15
OD200 A94 12c #255 .20 .15
OD201 A94 20c #256 .50 .15
Set value 1.00 .35

On Stamps of 1920
OD202 A93 1c #265 .25 .15
OD203 A93 2c #266 .20 .15
OD204 A93 5c #269 .20 .15
OD205 A94 20c #271 .40 .15
Nos. OD202-OD205 (4) 1.05
Set value .30

On Stamps of 1922-23
OD206 A93 1c #305 .25 .15
OD207 A93 2c #306 1.50 .50
OD208 A103 5c #309 .25 .15
OD209 A94 12c #311 10.00 1.75
OD210 A94 20c #312 1.50 .30
Nos. OD206-OD210 (5) 13.50 2.85

On Stamp of 1922-23
OD211 A93 2c #318 2.50 2.50

On Stamps of 1923
OD212 A104 1c #324 .15 .15
OD213 A104 2c #325 .15 .15
OD214 A104 5c #328 .15 .15
OD215 A104 12c #330 .15 .15
OD216 A104 20c #331 .50 .15
Set value 1.00 .30

On Stamps of 1923-31
OD217 A104 ½c #340 2.00 .75
OD218 A104 1c #341, I .15 .15
  a. Type II .15 .15
OD219 A104 2c #342 .15 .15
OD220 A104 3c #343, I .15 .15
  a. Type II .15 .15
OD221 A104 5c #345, I .15 .15
  a. Type II .15 .15

OD222 A104 10c #346, II .15 .15
  a. Type I .30 .15
OD223 A104 12c #347, I .15 .15
  a. Type II .30 .15
OD224 A104 20c #348, I .15 .15
  a. Type II .15 .15
OD225 A104 30c #351 .15 .15
OD226 A105 1p #353 .40 .50
Set value 2.10 1.30

On Stamps of 1926
OD227 A109 5c #359 .15 .15
OD228 A110 12c #360 .20 .15
Set value .30 .15

Type II
On Stamps of 1935-37
OD229 A129 1c #419 .15 .15
OD230 A130 2c #420 .15 .15
OD231 A132 3c #422 .15 .15
OD232 A134 5c #427 .15 .15
OD233 A137 10c #430 .15 .15
OD234 A139 15c #434 .45 .15
OD234A A140 20c #437 .15 .15
OD234B A140 20c #438 .20 .15
OD234C A141 25c #441 .15 .15
OD234D A142 30c #442 .15 .15
OD234E A145 1p #445 1.00 .60
OD234F A146 1p #446 .30 .20
Set value 2.60 1.20

Ministry of Marine (M. M.)
Type I
On Stamp of 1911
OD235 A88 2c #181 .20 .15

On Stamps of 1912-14
OD236 A88 1c #190 .15 .15
OD237 A88 2c #191 .15 .15
OD238 A88 5c #194 2.00 .15
OD239 A88 12c #196 .15 .15
Nos. OD236-OD239 (4) 2.45
Set value .25

On Stamps of 1915-16
OD240 A88 2c #209 .60 .15
OD241 A88 5c #212 .40 .15
Set value .15

On Stamps of 1917
OD242 A93 1c #232 .15 .15
OD243 A93 2c #233 .15 .15
OD244 A93 5c #236 .15 .15
Nos. OD242-OD244 (3) .45
Set value .15

On Stamps of 1918-19
OD245 A93 1c #249 .15 .15
OD246 A93 2c #250 .15 .15
OD247 A93 5c #253 .25 .15
OD248 A94 12c #255 .15 .15
OD249 A94 20c #256 3.00 .35
Nos. OD245-OD249 (5) 3.80
Set value .60

On Stamps of 1920
OD250 A93 1c #265 .15 .15
OD251 A93 2c #266 .20 .15
OD252 A93 5c #269 .25 .15
Nos. OD250-OD252 (3) .60
Set value .20

On Stamps of 1922-23
OD253 A103 5c #309 1.00 .15
OD254 A94 12c #311 7.00 7.00
OD255 A94 20c #312 7.00 1.50
Nos. OD253-OD254 (2) 8.00 7.15

On Stamps of 1923
OD256 A104 1c #324 .15 .15
OD257 A104 2c #325 .15 .15
OD258 A104 5c #328 .35 .15
OD259 A104 12c #330 .65 .15
OD260 A104 20c #331 .65 .15
Nos. OD256-OD260 (5) 1.95
Set value .35

On Stamps of 1923-31
OD261 A104 1c #341 .75 .25
OD262 A104 2c #342 .15 .15
OD263 A104 3c #343 .60 .20
OD264 A104 5c #345, I .15 .15
  a. Type II .60 .15
OD265 A104 10c #346 .60 .15
OD266 A104 20c #348, II .60 .15
  a. Type I .75 .15
OD267 A104 30c #351 .15 .15
OD268 A105 1p #353 11.00 3.00
Nos. OD261-OD268 (8) 14.85
Set value 3.60

On Stamp of 1926
OD269 A109 5c #359 .50 .15

Type II
On Stamps of 1935-37
OD270 A129 1c #419 .15 .15
OD271 A130 2c #420 .15 .15
OD272 A132 3c #422 .15 .15
OD273 A134 5c #427 .15 .15
OD274 A137 10c #430 .25 .15
OD275 A139 15c #434 .30 .15
OD276 A140 20c #437 .40 .15
OD277 A140 20c #438 .30 .15
OD278 A142 30c #442 .25 .15
OD279 A145 1p #445 3.25 1.00
OD280 A146 1p #446 .75 .25
Nos. OD270-OD280 (11) 6.10
Set value 1.65

Ministry of Public Works (M. O. P.)
Type I
On Stamp of 1911
OD281 A88 2c #181 .30 .15

On Stamps of 1912-14
OD282 A88 1c #190 .30 .15
OD283 A88 5c #194 .15 .15
OD284 A88 12c #196 1.50 .35
Nos. OD282-OD284 (3) 1.95
Set value .45

On Stamps of 1916-19
OD285 A91 5c #220 10.00 1.00
OD286 A94 12c #238 25.00
OD287 A94 20c #256 25.00

On Stamps of 1920
OD288 A93 2c #266 6.00 2.50
OD289 A93 5c #269 2.00 .15
OD290 A94 20c #271 20.00 6.00
Nos. OD288-OD290 (3) 28.00 8.65

On Stamps of 1923
OD291 A104 1c #324 .40 .15
OD292 A104 2c #325 .30 .15
OD293 A104 5c #328 .40 .15
OD294 A104 12c #330 .60 .15
OD295 A104 20c #331 1.00 .15
Nos. OD291-OD295 (5) 2.70
Set value .50

On Stamps of 1923-31
OD296 A104 1c #341 .15 .15
OD297 A104 2c #342 .15 .15
OD298 A104 3c #343 .15 .15
OD299 A104 5c #345, I .15 .15
  a. Type II .15 .15
OD300 A104 10c #346 .15 .15
OD301 A104 12c #347 9.00 1.25
OD302 A104 20c #348, I .15 .15
  a. Type II 2.50 .50
OD303 A104 30c #351 .40 .15
OD304 A105 1p #353 .40 .15
Nos. OD296-OD304 (9) 30.30 8.30

On Stamp of 1926
OD305 A109 5c #359 .60 .15

Type II
On Stamps of 1935-37
OD306 A129 1c #419 .15 .15
OD307 A130 2c #420 .15 .15
OD308 A132 3c #422 .15 .15
OD309 A134 5c #427 .15 .15
OD310 A137 10c #430 .30 .15
OD311 A139 15c #434 .60 .15
OD312 A140 20c #437 .75 .15
OD313 A140 20c #438 .15 .15
OD314 A142 30c #442 .15 .15
OD315 A144 50c #444 .15 .15
OD316 A145 1p #445 2.00 1.00
OD317 A146 1p #446 .50 .25
Set value 4.75 1.70

Ministry of Foreign Affairs and Religion (M. R. C.)
Type I
On Stamp of 1911
OD318 A88 2c #181 5.00 1.25

On Stamps of 1912-14
OD319 A88 1c #190 .15 .15
OD320 A88 2c #191 .15 .15
OD321 A88 5c #194 .40 .15
OD322 A88 12c #196 1.50 .25
Nos. OD319-OD322 (4) 2.20
Set value .40

On Stamps of 1915-19
OD323 A88 5c #212 .40 .15
OD324 A91 5c #220 .15 .15
OD325 A94 20c #256 2.00 .75
Nos. OD323-OD325 (3) 2.55
Set value .90

On Stamps of 1920
OD326 A93 1c #265 .40 .15
OD327 A93 5c #269 .15 .15
Set value .15

On Stamps of 1922-23
OD328 A93 2c #306 9.00 3.50
OD329 A103 5c #309 27.50
OD330 A93 10c #311 22.50
Nos. OD328-OD330 (3) 59.00

On Stamps of 1923
OD331 A104 1c #324 .15 .15
OD332 A104 2c #325 .15 .15
OD333 A104 5c #328 .15 .15
OD334 A104 12c #330 .15 .15
OD335 A104 20c #331 .40 .15
Set value .40 .30

On Stamps of 1923-31
OD336 A104 ½c #340 1.00 .50
OD337 A104 1c #341 .15 .15
OD338 A104 2c #342 .15 .15
OD339 A104 3c #343 .15 .15
OD340 A104 5c #345 .15 .15
OD341 A104 10c #346, II .15 .15
  a. Type I 1.50 .15
OD342 A104 12c #347 .15 .15
OD343 A104 20c #348, I .15 .15
  a. Type II .15 .15
OD344 A104 30c #351, II .15 .15
  a. Type I .15 .15
OD345 A105 1p #353 .40 .50
Set value 2.00 1.10

On Stamp of 1926
OD346 A110 12c #360 .15 .15

Type II
On Stamps of 1935-37
OD347 A129 1c #419 .15 .15
OD348 A130 2c #420 .15 .15
OD349 A132 3c #422 .15 .15
OD350 A134 5c #427 .15 .15
OD351 A137 10c #430 .15 .15
OD352 A139 15c #434 .15 .15
OD353 A140 20c #437 .15 .15
OD354 A140 20c #438 .15 .15
OD355 A142 30c #442 .15 .15
OD356 A145 1p #445 2.50 1.25
OD357 A146 1p #446 1.00 .50
Set value 4.25 2.25

BUENOS AIRES

The central point of the Argentine struggle for independence. At intervals Buenos Aires maintained an independent government but after 1862 became a province of the Argentine Republic.

8 Reales = 1 Peso

Values of Buenos Aires Nos. 1-8 vary according to condition. Quotations are for fine copies. Very fine to superb specimens sell at much higher prices, and inferior or poor copies sell at reduced values, depending on the condition of the individual specimen.

Steamship — A1

1858 Unwmk. Typo. Imperf.
1 A1 1 (in) pesos lt brn 350. 250.
2 A1 2 (dos) pesos blue 175. 140.
  b. Diagonal half used as 1p on cover 7,500.
3 A1 3 (tres) pesos grn 1,400. 750.
  a. 3p dark green 1,700. 825.
4 A1 4 (cuatro) pesos ver 4,750. 1,500.
  a. Half used as 2p on cover 15,000.
5 A1 5 (cinco) pesos org 4,250. 1,400.
  a. 5p ocher 4,250. 1,400.
  b. 5p olive yellow 4,250. 1,400.
Issued: #2-5, Apr. 29; #1, Oct. 26.

1858, Oct. 26
6 A1 4 (cuatro) reales brown 250. 200.
  a. 4r gray brown 250. 200.
  b. 4r yellow brown 250. 200.

1859, Jan. 1
7 A1 1 (in) pesos blue 165. 225.
  a. 1p indigo 200. 250.
  b. Impression on reverse of stamp in blue 3,000.
  c. Double impression 250. 300.
  d. Tete beche pair 65,000.
  e. Half used as 4r on cover 7,500.
8 A1 1 (to) pesos blue 350. 225.

Nos. 1, 2, 3 and 7 have been reprinted on very thick, hand-made paper. The same four stamps and No. 8 have been reprinted on thin, hard, white wove paper.
Counterfeits of Nos. 1-8 are plentiful.

Liberty Head — A2

1859, Sept. 3
9 A2 4r green, *bluish* 250.00 160.00
10 A2 1p blue 35.00 17.50
11 A2 2p vermilion 350.00 150.00
  a. 2p red 300.00 125.00

Both clear and rough impressions of these stamps may be found. They have generally been called Paris and Local prints, respectively, but the opinion now obtains that the differences are due to the impression and that they do not represent separate issues. Values are for fine impressions. Rough or blurred impressions sell for less.

Many shades exist of Nos. 1-11.

1862, Oct. 4

12	A2	1p rose	200.00	100.00
13	A2	2p blue	350.00	75.00

All three values have been reprinted in black, brownish black, blue and red brown on thin hard white paper. The 4r has also been reprinted in green on bluish paper.

Values are for fine impressions. Rough or blurred impressions sell for less.

CORDOBA

A province in the central part of the Argentine Republic.

100 Centavos = 1 Peso

Arms of Cordoba — A1

Unwmk.
1858, Oct. 28   Litho.   Imperf.
Laid Paper

1	A1	5c blue	125.
2	A1	10c black	2,500.

Cordoba stamps were printed on laid paper, but stamps from edges of the sheets sometimes do not show any laid lines and appear to be on wove paper. Counterfeits are plentiful.

CORRIENTES

The northeast province of the Argentine Republic.

1 Real M(oneda) C(orriente) =
12½ Centavos M.C. = 50 Centavos
100 Centavos Fuertes = 1 Peso Fuerte

Ceres

A1   A2

1856, Aug. 21   Unwmk.   Imperf.

1	A1	1r black, *blue*	85.00	115.00

No. 1 used is valued with pen cancellation.

Pen Stroke Through "Un Real"
1860, Feb. 8

2	A1	(3c) black, *blue*	350.00	175.00

No. 2 used is valued with pen cancellation.

1860-78

3	A2	(3c) black, *blue*	9.50	30.00
4	A2	(2c) blk, *yel grn* ('64)	37.50	37.50
a.		(2c) black, *blue green*	92.50	110.00
5	A2	(2c) blk, *yel* ('67)	7.50	19.00
6	A2	(3c) blk, *dk bl* ('71)	3.00	19.00
7	A2	(3c) blk, *rose red* ('76)	100.00	50.00
a.		(3c) black, *lil rose* ('75)	135.00	80.00
8	A2	(3c) blk, *dk rose* ('79)	8.00	32.50
a.		(3c) black, *red vio* ('77)	60.00	35.00
		Nos. 3-8 (6)	165.50	188.00

Pen canceled examples of Nos. 3-8 sell for much less.

Printed from settings of 8 varieties, 3 or 4 impressions constituting a sheet. Some impressions were printed inverted and tete beche pairs may be cut from adjacent impressions.

From Jan. 1 to Feb. 24, 1864, No. 4 was used as a 5 centavos stamp but copies so used can only be distinguished when they bear dated cancellations.

The reprints show numerous spots and small defects which are not found on the originals. They are printed on gray blue, dull blue, gray green, dull orange and light magenta papers.

ARMENIA

är-'mē-nē-ə

LOCATION — South of Russia bounded by Georgia, Azerbaijan, Iran and Turkey

GOVT. — Republic
AREA — 11,306 sq. mi.
POP. — 3,300,000 (1989)
CAPITAL — Yerevan

With Azerbaijan and Georgia, Armenia made up the Transcaucasian Federation of Soviet Republics.

Stamps of Armenia were replaced in 1923 by those of Transcaucasian Federated Republics.

With the breakup of the Soviet Union on Dec. 26, 1991, Armenia and ten former Soviet republics established the Commonwealth of Independent States.

100 Kopecks = 1 Ruble
100 Luma = 1 Dram (1993)

> Catalogue values for unused stamps in this country are for Never Hinged items, beginning with Scott 430 in the regular postage section.

Counterfeits abound of all overprinted and surcharged stamps.

Watermark

Diamonds — Wmk. 171

> Perforations
> Perforations are the same as the basic Russian stamps.

National Republic
Russian Stamps of 1902-19 Handstamped

Thirteen types exist of both framed and unframed overprints. The device is the Armenian "H," initial of Hayasdan (Armenia). Inverted and double overprints are found.

Surcharged   К 60 к

Type I - Without periods.
Type II - Periods after 1st "K" and "60."

Black Surcharge

1919   Unwmk.   Perf. 14x14½

1	A14	60k on 1k orange (II)	2.50	.40
a.		Imperf. (I)	1.00	.24
b.		Imperf. (II)	1.00	.24

Violet Surcharge

2	A14	60k on 1k orange (II)	.50	.50

Handstamped in Violet — a

				Perf.	
6	A15	4k carmine		2.00	2.00
7	A15	5k claret, imperf.		7.50	7.50
a.		Perf.		5.00	5.00
9	A14	10k on 7k lt blue		5.00	1.25
11	A8	15k red brn & bl		3.00	.25
11	A8	20k blue & car		2.00	1.00
13	A11	35k red brn & grn		3.50	3.50
14	A8	50k violet & green		3.50	3.50
15	A14	60k on 1k orange (II)		2.00	2.00
a.		Imperf. (I)		1.90	2.00
b.		Imperf. (II)		8.50	9.00
18	A13	5r dk bl, grn & pale bl		3.50	4.25
19	A12	7r dk grn & pink		1.75	2.00
20	A13	10r on scarlet, yel & gray		1.75	2.00

Handstamped in Black

31	A14	2k green, imperf.	1.00	.15
a.		Perf.	5.00	.40
32	A14	3k red, imperf.	1.00	.20
a.		Perf.	5.00	.40
33	A15	4k carmine	.15	.15
34	A14	5k claret	1.00	.20
a.		Imperf.	5.00	
36	A15	10k dark blue	2.00	.65
37	A14	10k on 7k lt blue	.50	.15
38	A11	15k red brn & bl	.50	.15
a.		Imperf.	3.00	3.00
39	A8	20k blue & car	1.00	.20
40	A11	25k grn & gray vio	1.00	.20
41	A11	35k red brn & grn	1.00	.15
42	A8	50k violet & green	1.00	.15

43	A14	60k on 1k orange (II)	2.50	2.50
43A	A11	70k brown & org	1.00	.30
b.		Imperf.	.50	.30
44	A9	1r pale brn, dk brn & org	1.50	.30
a.		Imperf.	.50	.50
45	A12	3½r mar & lt grn, imperf.	5.00	.65
a.		Perf.	5.00	.85
46	A13	5r dk bl, grn & pale bl	.60	.65
a.		Imperf.	6.00	1.00
47	A12	7r dk green & pink	.60	1.10
48	A13	10r scar, yel & gray	50.00	

Handstamped in Violet — c

Unwmk.   Perf.
Wove Paper

62	A14	2k green, imperf.	.40	.40
a.		Perf.	4.50	4.50
63	A14	3k red, imperf.	.25	.25
a.		Perf.	3.00	2.75
64	A15	4k carmine	.50	.50
65	A14	5k claret	3.00	.40
a.		Imperf.	3.00	.60
67	A15	10k dark blue	1.00	.85
68	A14	10k on 7k lt bl	1.00	.65
69	A11	15k red brn & bl	2.50	2.50
70	A8	20k blue & car	.40	.40
71	A11	25k grn & gray vio	1.00	1.00
72	A11	35k red brn & grn	1.50	1.50
73	A8	50k violet & grn	.50	.50
74	A14	60k on 1k org (II)	2.50	2.00
a.		Imperf. (I)	1.65	1.65
b.		Imperf. (II)	2.00	2.00
75	A9	1r pale brn, dk brn & org	.60	.60
a.		Imperf.	1.50	1.50
76	A12	3½r mar & lt grn, imperf.	.75	.75
a.		Perf.	1.00	1.00
77	A13	5r dk bl, grn & pale bl, imperf.	5.00	5.00
a.		Perf.	4.00	4.00
78	A12	7r dk green & pink	7.50	7.50
79	A13	10r scar, yel & gray	2.25	1.90

Imperf

85	A11	70k brown & org	5.00	2.00

Handstamped in Black
Perf.

90	A14	1k orange	10.00	4.50
a.		Imperf.	10.00	6.00
91	A14	2k green, imperf.	1.00	.15
a.		Perf.	7.50	2.50
92	A14	3k red, imperf.	1.00	.20
a.		Perf.	10.00	2.75
93	A15	4k carmine	.50	.50
94	A14	5k claret	1.00	.15
a.		Imperf.	3.00	.60
95	A14	7k light blue	15.00	15.00
96	A15	10k dark blue	12.00	12.00
97	A14	10k on 7k lt bl	.15	.15
98	A11	15k red brn & bl	.20	.15
99	A8	20k blue & car	.15	.15
100	A11	25k grn & gray vio	.50	.20
101	A11	35k red brn & grn	.20	.15
102	A8	50k violet & grn	.20	.15
102A	A14	60k on 1k org, imperf. (I)	.30	.30
b.		Imperf. (II)	.50	.50
c.		Perf. (II)	2.50	1.25
103	A9	1r pale brn, dk brn & org	1.00	1.00
a.		Imperf.	.75	.75
104	A12	3½r maroon & lt grn	4.00	.50
a.		Imperf.	.50	.30
105	A13	5r dk bl, grn & pale bl	2.50	2.50
a.		Imperf.	2.50	2.50
106	A12	7r dk green & pink	3.00	2.50
107	A13	10r scar, yel & gray	7.00	3.50

Imperf

113	A11	70k brown & org	1.00	.25

Handstamped in Violet or Black:

f   g

5r   10r

Violet Surcharge, Type f

1920   Perf.

120	A14	3r on 3k red, imperf.	.85	.85
a.		Perf.	2.50	2.50
121	A14	5r on 3k red	3.75	3.25
122	A15	5r on 4k car	10.00	8.00
123	A14	5r on 5k claret, imperf.	10.00	10.00
a.		Perf.	10.00	8.00
124	A14	5r on 10k dk blue	10.00	8.00
125	A14	5r on 10k on 7k lt bl	10.00	8.00
126	A8	5r on 20k bl & car		

Imperf

127	A14	5r on 2k green	7.00	7.00
128	A11	5r on 35k red brn & grn	7.00	7.00

Black Surcharge, Type f or Type g
(#130)
Perf.

130	A14	1r on 1k orange	.50	.50
a.		Imperf.	.75	.75
131	A14	3r on 3k red	.15	.15
a.		Imperf.	.15	.15
132	A15	3r on 4k carmine	3.00	3.00
133	A14	5r on 2k green, imperf.	.15	.15
a.		Perf.	2.00	2.00
134	A14	5r on 3k red	5.00	5.00
a.		Imperf.	2.50	2.50
135	A15	5r on 4k carmine	.40	.40
a.		Imperf.	4.75	4.75
136	A14	5r on 5k claret	.50	.50
a.		Imperf.	.50	.50
137	A14	5r on 7k lt blue	2.00	2.00
138	A15	5r on 10k dk blue	.50	.50
139	A14	5r on 10k on 7k lt bl	.50	.50
140	A11	5r on 15k red brn & blue	2.00	2.00
141	A11	5r on 15k red brn & blue	.50	.50
a.		Imperf.	2.00	2.00
142	A8	5r on 20k bl & car	.50	.50
a.		Imperf.	10.00	10.00
143	A11	5r on 20k on 14k bl & rose	12.00	12.00
144	A11	5r on 25k grn & gray vio	12.00	12.00

Black Surcharge, Type g or Type f
(#148A, 151)

145	A14	10r on 1k org, imperf.	.90	.90
a.		Perf.	225.00	225.00
146	A14	10r on 3k red	175.00	175.00
147	A14	10r on 5k claret	15.00	15.00
a.		Imperf.	6.00	
148	A8	10r on 20k bl & car	15.00	15.00
148A	A11	10r on 25k grn & gray vio	8.00	8.00
149	A11	10r on 25k grn & gray vio	5.00	5.00
a.		Imperf.	8.00	8.00
150	A11	10r on 35k red brn & grn	.50	.50
151	A8	10r on 50k brn vio & grn	1.75	1.75
152	A8	10r on 50k brn vio & grn	.45	.45
152A	A11	10r on 70k brn & org, imperf.	3.00	3.00
b.		Perf.	200.00	200.00
152C	A8	25r on 20k bl & car	4.00	4.00
153	A11	25r on 25k grn & gray vio	2.00	2.00
154	A11	25r on 35k red brn & grn	2.00	2.00
a.		Imperf.	3.50	3.50
155	A8	25r on 50k vio & grn	4.00	4.00
a.		Imperf.	5.00	5.00
156	A11	25r on 70k brn & org	8.00	8.00
a.		Imperf.	5.00	5.00
157	A9	50r on 1r pale brn, dk brn & org, imperf.	1.00	1.00
a.		Perf.	5.00	5.00
158	A13	50r on 5r dk bl, grn & lt bl	10.00	10.00
159	A12	100r on 3½r mar & lt grn	7.00	7.00
a.		Imperf.	7.00	7.00
160	A13	100r on 5r dk bl, grn & pale bl	10.00	10.00
161	A12	100r on 7r dk grn & pink	10.00	10.00
a.		Imperf.	35.00	35.00
162	A13	100r on 10r scar, yel & gray	10.00	10.00

Wmk. Wavy Lines (168)
Perf. 11½
Vertically Laid Paper

163	A12	100r on 3½r blk & gray	50.00	50.00
164	A12	100r on 7r blk & yel	35.00	35.00

1920   Unwmk.   Imperf.
Wove Paper

166	A14	(g)	1r on 60k on 1k org (I)	12.00	12.00
168	A14	(f)	5r on 1k orange	9.00	9.00
173	A11	(f)	5r on 35k red brn & grn	2.50	2.50
177	A11	(g)	50r on 70k brn & org	5.00	5.00
179	A12	(g)	50r on 3½r mar & lt grn	2.00	2.00
181	A9	(g)	100r on 1r pale brn, dk brn & org	4.00	4.00

Romanov Issues Surcharged Type g or Type f (#185-187, 190)
On Stamps of 1913

1920   Perf. 13½

184	A16	1r on 1k brn org	10.00	10.00
185	A18	3r on 3k rose red	15.00	15.00
186	A19	5r on 4k dull red	10.00	10.00
187	A22	5r on 14k blue grn	60.00	60.00
187A	A19	10r on 4k dull red	30.00	
187B	A26	10r on 35k gray blk & dk grn		
187C	A19	25r on 4k dull red	10.00	10.00

188	A26	25r on 35k gray vio & dk grn	2.75	2.75
189	A28	25r on 70k yel grn & brn	2.75	2.75
190	A31	50r on 3r dk violet	2.00	2.00
190A	A16	100r on 1k brn org	100.00	100.00
190B	A17	100r on 2k green	100.00	100.00
191	A30	100r on 2r brown	10.50	10.50
192	A31	100r on 3r dk vio	10.50	10.50

On Stamps of 1915, Type g
Thin Cardboard
Inscriptions on Back
Perf. 12

193	A21	100r on 10k blue	3.00	
194	A23	100r on 15k brown	3.00	
195	A24	100r on 20k ol grn	3.00	

On Stamps of 1916, Type f
Perf. 13½

196	A20	5r on 10k on 7k brown	5.00	5.00
197	A22	5r on 20k on 14k bl grn	8.00	8.00

Surch. Type f or Type g (#204-205A, 207-207C, 210-211) over Type c
Type c in Violet
Perf.

200	A15	5r on 4k carmine	1.00	1.00
201	A15	5r on 10k dk blue	1.00	1.00
202	A11	5r on 15k red brn & bl	2.00	2.00
203	A8	5r on 20k blue & car	1.75	1.75
204	A11	10r on 25k grn & gray vio	1.50	1.50
205	A11	10r on 35k red brn & grn	3.00	3.00
205A	A8	10r on 50k brn vio & grn	3.50	3.50
206	A8	25r on 50k brn vio & grn	150.00	150.00
207	A9	50r on 1r pale brn, dk brn & org, imperf.	3.50	3.50
a.		Perf.	25.00	25.00
207B	A12	100r on 3½r mar & lt grn	30.00	
207C	A12	100r on 7r dk grn & pink	9.00	

Imperf

208	A14	5r on 2k green	25.00	25.00
209	A13	5r on 5k claret	25.00	25.00
210	A11	25r on 70k brn & org	5.50	5.50
211	A13	100r on 5r dk bl, grn & pale bl	1.00	1.00

Surcharged Type g or Type f (212-213, 215, 219-219A, 221-222) over Type c
Type c in Black
Perf.

212	A14	5r on 7k lt bl	150.00	150.00
213	A14	5r on 10k on 7k lt bl	5.00	5.00
214	A11	5r on 15k red brn & bl	.50	.50
215	A8	5r on 20k blue & car	3.00	3.00
215A	A11	10r on 5r on 25k grn & gray vio	5.00	5.00
216	A11	10r on 35k red brn & grn	.50	.50
217	A8	10r on 50k brn vio & grn	1.00	1.00
217A	A9	50r on 1r pale brn, dk brn & org	1.00	1.00
b.		Imperf.	1.10	1.10
217C	A12	100r on 3½r mar & lt grn	1.50	1.50
218	A13	100r on 5r dk bl, grn & pale bl	10.00	10.00
a.		Imperf.	1.75	1.75
219	A12	100r on 7r dk grn & pink	15.00	15.00
219A	A13	100r on 10r scar, yel & gray	10.00	10.00

Imperf

220	A14	1r on 60k on 1k org (I)	20.00	20.00
221	A14	5r on 2k green	.80	.80
222	A14	5r on 5k claret	3.00	3.00
223	A11	10r on 70k brn & org	2.00	2.00
224	A11	25r on 70k brn & org	2.00	2.00

Surcharged Type g or Type f (#233) over Type a
Type a in Violet
Imperf

231	A9	50r on 1r pale brn, dk brn & org	140.00	140.00
232	A13	100r on 5r dk bl, grn & pale bl	10.50	

Type a in Black
Perf.

233	A8	5r on 20k blue & car	.80	.80
233A	A11	10r on 25k grn & gray vio	55.00	55.00
234	A11	10r on 35k red brn & grn	.90	.90
235	A12	100r on 3½r mar & lt grn	1.25	1.25
a.		Imperf.	1.50	1.50

Imperf

237	A14	5r on 2k green	125.00	125.00
237A	A11	10r on 70k brn & org		

Surcharged Type a and New Value
Type a in Violet
Perf.

238	A11	10r on 15k red brn & blue	.80	.80

Type a in Black

239	A8	5r on 20k blue & car	3.00	3.00
239A	A8	10r on 20k blue & car	3.00	3.00
239B	A8	10r on 50k brn red & grn	7.50	

Imperf

240	A12	100r on 3½r mar & lt grn	1.90	1.90

Surcharged Type c and New Value
Type c in Black

1920			Perf.	
241	A15	5r on 4k red	1.75	1.75
242	A11	5r on 15k red brn & bl	1.00	1.00
243	A8	10r on 20k blue & car	1.75	1.75
243A	A11	10r on 25k grn & gray vio	1.00	1.00
244	A11	10r on 35k red brn & grn	1.00	1.00
a.		With additional surch. "5r"	1.50	1.50
245	A12	100r on 3½r mar & lt grn	1.50	1.50

Imperf

247	A14	3r on 3k red	4.75	4.75
248	A14	5r on 2k green	.30	.30
249	A9	50r on 1r pale brn, dk brn & org	.90	.90

Type c in Violet

249A	A14	5r on 2k green	6.50	

Postal Savings Stamps Surcharged

| A1 | A2 | A3 |

Perf. 14½x15
Wmk. 171

250	A1	60k on 1k red & buff	50.00	50.00
251	A2	1r on 1k red & buff	5.00	5.00
252	A3	5r on 5k green & buff	7.25	7.25
253	A3	5r on 10k brown & buff	30.00	3.00

Russian Semi-Postal Stamps of 1914-18 Surcharged with Armenian Monogram and New Values like Regular Issues
On Stamps of 1914
Unwmk.   Perf.

255	SP5	25r on 1k red brn & dk grn, straw	60.00	60.00
256	SP6	25r on 3k mar & gray grn, pink	60.00	60.00
257	SP7	50r on 7k dk brn & dk grn, buff	20.00	20.00
258	SP5	100r on 1k red brn & dk grn, straw	25.00	25.00
259	SP6	100r on 3k mar & gray grn, pink	25.00	25.00
260	SP7	100r on 7k dk brn & dk grn, buff	25.00	25.00

On Stamps of 1915-19

261	SP5	25r on 1k org brn & gray	75.00	75.00
262	SP6	25r on 3k car & gray	30.00	30.00
263	SP8	50r on 10k dk bl & brn	25.00	25.00
264	SP5	100r on 1k org brn & gray	3.25	3.50
265	SP8	100r on 10k dk bl & brn	3.25	3.50

These surcharged semi-postal stamps were used for ordinary postage.

A set of 10 stamps in the above designs, and in a third design showing a woman quilling, was prepared in 1920, but not issued. Value of set, $4. Exist with "SPECIMEN" overprint and imperf. Reprints exist.

Soviet Socialist Republic

Hammer and Sickle — A7

Mythological Monster — A8

Symbols of Soviet Republics on Designs from old Armenian Manuscripts — A9

Ruined City of Ani — A10

Mythological Monster — A11

Armenian Soldier — A12

Soviet Symbols, Armenian Designs — A14

Mythological Monster — A13

Mt. Alagöz and Plain of Shirak A15

Fisherman on River Aras — A16

Post Office in Erevan and Mt. Ararat A17

Ruin in City of Ani — A18

Street in Erevan — A19

Lake Sevan and Sevan Monastery A20

Mythological Subject from old Armenian Monument — A21

Mt. Ararat A22

1921	Unwmk.	Perf. 11½, Imperf.		
278	A7	1r gray green	.30	
279	A8	2r slate gray	.30	
280	A9	3r carmine	.30	
281	A10	5r dark brown	.30	
282	A11	25r gray	.30	.20
283	A12	50r red	.15	
284	A13	100r orange	.15	
285	A14	250r dark blue	.15	
286	A15	500r brown vio	.15	
287	A16	1000r sea green	.25	
288	A17	2000r bister	.30	
289	A18	5000r dark brown	.30	
290	A19	10,000r dull red	.30	
291	A20	15,000r slate gray	.30	
292	A21	20,000r lake	.30	
293	A22	25,000r gray blue	.65	
294	A22	25,000r brown olive	5.50	
		Nos. 278-294 (17)	10.00	

Except the 25r, Nos. 278-294 were not regularly issued and used. Counterfeits exist.

For surcharges see Nos. 347-390.

Russian Stamps of 1909-17 Surcharged

Wove Paper
Lozenges of Varnish on Face

1921, Aug.			Perf. 13½
295	A9	5000r on 1r	6.00
296	A12	5000r on 3½r	6.00
297	A13	5000r on 5r	6.00

298 A12 5000r on 7r   *6.00*
299 A13 5000r on 10r   *6.00*
    Nos. 295-299 (5)   *30.00*

Nos. 295-299 were not officially issued. Counterfeits abound.

Mt. Ararat and Soviet Star
A23   A24

Soviet
Symbols — A25   Crane — A26

Peasant — A27   Harpy — A28

Peasant
Sowing — A29   Soviet
Symbols — A30

Forging — A31

Plowing
A32

1922   *Perf. 11½*
300 A23   50r green & red   .35
301 A24   300r slate bl & buff   .40
302 A25   400r blue & pink   .40
303 A26   500r vio & pale lil   .40
304 A27   1000r dull bl & pale bl   .40
305 A28   2000r black & gray   .65
306 A29   3000r black & grn   .65
307 A30   4000r black & lt brn   .65
308 A31   5000r black & dull red   .55
309 A32   10,000r black & pale rose   .55
   a.   Tête bêche pair   11.00
    Nos. 300-309 (10)   5.00

Nos. 300 to 309 were not placed in use without surcharge.
Stamps of types A23 to A32, printed in other colors than Nos. 300 to 309, are essays.

Nos. 300-309 with Handstamped
Surcharge of New Values in Rose, Violet or
Black

1922
310   10,000 on 50r (R)   8.50   11.00
311   10,000 on 50r (V)   8.50   11.00
312   10,000 on 50r   8.50   11.00

313   15,000 on 300r (R)   8.50   14.00
314   15,000 on 300r (V)   8.50   14.00
315   15,000 on 300r   8.50   14.00
316   25,000 on 400r (V)   8.50   14.00
317   25,000 on 400r   8.50   14.00
318   30,000 on 500r (R)   10.00   17.00
319   30,000 on 500r (V)   10.00   17.00
320   30,000 on 500r   10.00   17.00
321   50,000 on 1000r (R)   8.50   14.00
322   50,000 on 1000r (V)   8.50   14.00
323   50,000 on 1000r   8.50   14.00
324   75,000 on 3000r   11.00   20.00
325   100,000 on 2000r (R)   20.00   20.00
326   100,000 on 2000r (V)   20.00   20.00
327   100,000 on 2000r   20.00   20.00
328   200,000 on 4000r (V)   22.50   22.50
329   200,000 on 4000r   22.50   22.50
330   300,000 on 5000r (V)   30.00   45.00
331   300,000 on 5000r   30.00   45.00
332   500,000 on 10,000r (V)   30.00   30.00
333   500,000 on 10,000r   30.00   30.00
    Nos. 310-333 (24)   359.50   471.00

Goose — A33   Armenian Woman
at Well — A35

Armenian
Village
Scene — A34

Mt.
Ararat — A36

Mt. Ararat
A37

New Values in Gold Kopecks,
Handstamped Surcharge in Black
1922   *Imperf.*
334 A33   1(k) on 250r rose   8.00   8.00
335 A33   1(k) on 250r gray   14.00   14.00
336 A34   2(k) on 500r rose   5.50   5.50
337 A34   2(k) on 500r gray   5.50   5.50
338 A35   4(k) on 1000r rose   5.50   5.50
339 A35   4(k) on 1000r gray   10.00   10.00
340 A36   5(k) on 2000r rose   5.50   5.50
341 A36   10(k) on 2000r rose   5.50   5.50
342 A37   15(k) on 5000r rose   35.00   35.00
343 A37   20(k) on 5000r gray   5.50   5.50
    Nos. 334-343 (10)   100.00   100.00

Nos. 334-343 were issued for postal tax purposes. Nos. 334-343 exist without surcharge but are not known to have been issued in that condition. Counterfeits exist of both sets.

Regular Issue of 1921 Handstamped with
New Values in Black or Red
Short, Thick Numerals
1922   *Imperf.*
347 A8   2(k) on 2r (R)   25.00   25.00
350 A11   4(k) on 25r (R)   10.00   10.00
353 A13   10(k) on 100r (R)   7.50   7.50
354 A14   15(k) on 250r   3.00   3.00
355 A15   20(k) on 500r   15.00   15.00
   a.   With "k" written in red   10.00   10.00
357 A22   50(k) on 25,000r bl (R)   12.00   12.00
358 A22   50(k) on 25,000r brn ol (R)   9.00   9.00
359 A22   50(k) on 25,000r brn ol
    Nos. 347-358 (7)   81.50   81.50

         Perf. 11½
360 A7   1(k) on 1r, imperf.   25.00   25.00
   a.   Perf.   15.00   15.00
361 A7   1(k) on 1r (R)   35.00   35.00
   a.   Imperf.   40.00   40.00
362 A8   2(k) on 2r, imperf.   40.00   40.00
   a.   Perf.   40.00   40.00
363 A15   2(k) on 500r   35.00   35.00
   a.   Imperf.   50.00

364 A15   2(k) on 500r (R)   9.00   9.00
365 A11   4(k) on 25r, imperf.   25.00   25.00
   a.   Perf.   25.00   25.00
366 A12   5(k) on 50r, imperf.   1.75   1.75
   a.   Perf.   2.50   2.50
367 A13   10(k) on 100r   20.00   20.00
   a.   Imperf.   20.00   20.00
368 A21   35(k) on 20,000r, imperf.   50.00   50.00
   a.   With "k" written in violet   50.00   50.00
   b.   Perf.   65.00   65.00
   c.   As "a," perf.   65.00   65.00
   d.   With "kop" written in violet, imperf.
    Nos. 360-368 (9)   240.75   240.75

Manuscript Surcharge in Red
         Perf. 11½
371 A14   1k on 250r dk bl   40.00   40.00

Handstamped in Black or Red
Tall, Thin Numerals
         Imperf
377 A11   4(k) on 25r (R)   4.25   4.25
379 A13   10(k) on 100r   10.00   10.00
380 A15   20(k) on 500r   6.00   6.00
381 A22   50k on 25,000r bl   75.00   75.00
   a.   Surcharged "50" only   50.00   50.00
382 A22   50k on 25,000r bl (R)   12.00   12.00
382A A22   50k on 25,000r brn ol   24.00   24.00
    Nos. 377-382A (6)   131.25   131.25

On Nos. 381, 382 and 382A the letter "k" forms part of the surcharge.

         Perf. 11½
383 A7   1(k) on 1r (R)   3.00   3.00
   a.   Imperf.
384 A14   1(k) on 250r   1.75   1.75
385 A15   2(k) on 500r   8.00   8.00
   a.   Imperf.   12.00   12.00
386 A15   2(k) on 500r (R)   4.75   4.75
387 A9   3(k) on 3r   20.00   20.00
   a.   Imperf.   20.00   20.00
388 A21   3(k) on 20,000r, imperf.   10.00   10.00
   a.   Perf.   50.00   50.00
389 A11   4(k) on 25r   2.50   2.50
   a.   Imperf.   4.25   4.25
390 A12   5(k) on 50r, imperf.   10.00   10.00
   a.   Perf.   15.00   15.00
    Nos. 383-390 (8)   60.00   60.00

> Catalogue values for unused stamps in this section, from this point to the end of the section, are for Never Hinged items.

Mt. Ararat — A45

a, 20k. b, 2r. c, 5r.

1992, May 28   Litho.   *Perf. 14*
430 A45   Strip of 3, #a.-c.   2.50
Souvenir Sheet
431 A45   7r Eagle & Mt. Ararat   27.50

AT & T Communications System in
Armenia — A45a

1992, July 1   Litho.   *Perf. 13x13½*
431A A45a 50k multicolored   3.00

A46   A47

1992 Summer Olympics, Barcelona: a, 40k, Ancient Greek wrestlers. b, 3.60r, Boxing. c, 5r, Weight lifting. d, 12r, Gymnastics.

1992, July 25   Litho.   *Perf. 14*
432 A46   Strip of 4, #a.-d.   4.00

1992-93   Litho.   *Perf. 14½, 15x14½*
20k, Natl. flag. 1r, Goddess Waroubini, Orgov radio telescope. 2r, Yerevan Airport. No. 436, Goddess Anahit. No. 437, Runic message, 7th cent B.C. 5r, UPU emblem. 20r, Silver cup.

433 A47   20k multicolored   .15
434 A47   1r gray green   .15
435 A47   2r blue   .55
436 A47   3r brown   .90
437 A47   3r bronze   .15
438 A47   5r brown black   1.50
439 A47   20r gray   .15
    Nos. 433-439 (7)   3.55

No. 435 is airmail. See Nos. 464-471, 521-524.
Issued: #436, 20k, 2r, 5r, 8/25/92; others, 5/12/93.

David of Sassoun, by Hakop
Kojoian — A50a

Religious
Artifacts — A50   Yerevan
'93 — A52

Scenic Views — A51

1993, May 23   Litho.   *Perf. 14*
448 A50   40k Marker   .15   .15
449 A50   80k Gospel page   .25   .25
450 A50   3.60r Bas-relief, 13th cent.   1.00   1.00
451 A50   5r Icon of the Madonna   1.65   1.65
    Nos. 448-451 (4)   3.05   3.05

Souvenir Sheet
       Perf. 14x13½
451A A50a 12r multicolored   4.50   4.50

1993, May 24   *Perf. 14*
Designs (illustration reduced): 40k, Garni Canyon, vert. 80k, Shaki Waterfall, Zangezur, vert. 3.60r, Arpa River Canyon, vert. 5r, Lake Sevan. 12r, Mount Aragats.

452 A51   40k multicolored   .15   .15
453 A51   80k multicolored   .15   .15
454 A51   3.60r multicolored   .50   .50
455 A51   5r multicolored   .65   .65
456 A51   12r multicolored   1.65   1.65
    Nos. 452-456 (5)   3.10   3.10

1993, May 25   *Perf. 14½*
457 A52   10r multicolored   .50   .50
   a.   Min. sheet of 6 + 2 labels   4.25

For surcharges see Nos. 485-486.

Souvenir Sheet

Noah's Descent from Mt. Ararat, by Hovhannes Aivazovsky — A52

1993, May 24 Litho. **Perf. 14½**
458 A52 7r multicolored 2.50 2.50

Religious Relics, Echmiadzin — A53

Designs: 3r, Wooden panel, descent from cross, 9th cent. 5r, Gilded silver reliquary for Holy Cross of Khotakerats. 12r, Cross depicting right hand of St. Karapet, 14th cent. 30r, Reliquary for arm of St. Thaddeus the Apostle, 17th cent. 50r, Gilded silver vessel for consecrated ointment, 1815.

1994, Aug. 4 Litho. **Perf. 14x14½**
459 A53 3d multicolored .15 .15
460 A53 5d multicolored .15 .15
461 A53 12d multicolored .30 .30
462 A53 30d multicolored .80 .80
463 A53 50d multicolored 1.25 1.25
Nos. 459-463 (5) 2.65 2.65

Artifacts and Landmarks Type of 1993

Gods of Van (Urartu): 10 l, Shivini, god of the sun. 50 l, Tayshaba, god of elements. 10d, Khaldi, supreme god.
25d, Natl. arms.

1994 **Perf. 14½**
464 A47 10 l black & brown .15 .15
465 A47 50 l black & red brown .15 .15
469 A47 10d black & gray .50 .50
471 A47 25d red & bister 1.25 1.25
Nos. 464-471 (4) 2.05 2.05

Issued: 10 l, 50 l, 10d, 25d, 8/4/94.
This is an expanding set. Numbers may change.

A54

1994, Dec. 31 Litho. **Perf. 14½x14**
479 A54 16d No. 1a .45 .45

First Armenian postage stamp, 75th anniv.

A54a   A54b

1994, Dec. 30 Litho. **Perf. 14x14½**
480 A54a 30d Early printing press .75 .75

First Armenian periodical, 170th anniv.

1994, Dec. 30 Litho. **Perf. 14x14½**
481 A54b 30d Natl. arms, stadium .55 .55

Natl. Olympic Committee.

A54c   A54d

1994, Dec. 30 Litho. **Perf. 14x14½**
482 A54c 40d Olympic rings .75 .75

Intl. Olympic Committee, Cent.

1994, Dec. 31 Litho. **Perf. 14x14½**
483 A54d 50d multi + label 1.00 1.00

Ervand Otian (1869-1926)

50 A54e

1994, Dec. 31 Litho. **Perf. 14½x14**
484 A54e 50d multi + label 1.00 1.00

Levon Shant (1869-1951).

No. 457 Surcharged in Blue or Red Brown

40 **40**
a   b

1994, Sept. 10 Litho. **Perf. 14**
485 A52(a) 40d on 10r (Bl) 1.65 1.65
486 A52(b) 40d on 10r (RB) 1.65 1.65

Yerevan '94.

A55   A56

Christianity in Armenia: 60d, Cross, 10th-11th cent. No. 488, Kings Abgar & Trdat, 1836. No. 489, St. Bartholomew, St. Thaddeus. 80d, St. Gregory, the Illuminator. 90d, Baptism of the Armenian people, 1892. 400d, Plan of Echmiadzin, c. 1660, engr. by Jakob Peeters.

1995, Apr. 3 Litho. **Perf. 14x15**
487 A55 60d multicolored 1.10 1.10
488 A55 70d multicolored 1.25 1.25
489 A55 70d multicolored 1.25 1.25
490 A55 80d multicolored 1.40 1.40
491 A55 90d multicolored 1.65 1.65
Nos. 487-491 (5) 6.65 6.65

Souvenir Sheet
492 A55 400d multicolored 7.00 7.00

Nos. 488-489 are 45x44mm.

1995, Apr. 3
493 A56 150d gray & black 1.75 1.75

Vazgen I (1908-94), Catholikos of All Armenians.

Armenia Fund — A57

1995, Apr. 27 **Perf. 15x14**
494 A57 90d multicolored 1.00 1.00

UN, 50th Anniv. A58

1995, Apr. 28
495 A58 90d multicolored 1.00 1.00

Cultural Artifacts — A59

Designs: 30d, Black polished pottery, 14th-13th cent. B.C. 60d, Silver cup, 5th cent. B.C. 130d, Gohar carpet, 1700 A.D.

1995, Apr. 27 **Perf. 15x14**
496 A59 30d multicolored .35 .35
497 A59 60d multicolored .65 .65
498 A59 130d multicolored 1.50 1.50
Nos. 496-498 (3) 2.50 2.50

Birds — A60

1995, Apr. 27 **Perf. 14**
499 A60 40d Milvus milvus .80 .80
500 A60 60d Aquila chrysaetos 1.25 1.25

End of World War II, 50th Anniv. A61

Designs: No. 501, P. Kitsook, 408th Armenian Rifle Division. No. 502, A. Sargissin, N. Safarian, 89th Taman Armenian Triple Order-Bearer Division. No. 503, B. Chernikov, N. Tavartkeladze, V. Penkovsky, 76th Armenian Alpine Rifle Red Banner (51st Guards) Division. No. 504, S. Zakian, H. Babayan, I. Lyudnikov, 390th Armenian Rifle Division. No. 505, A. Vasillian, M. Dobrovolsky, Y. Grechany, G. Sorokin, 409th Armenian Rifle Division.
No. 506, vert.: a, Marshal Hovhannes Baghramian. b, Adm. Hovhannes Issakov. c, Marshal Hamazasp Babajanian. d, Marshal Sergey Khoudyakov.
No. 507: Return of the Hero, by Mariam Aslamazian.

1995, Sept. 30 Litho. **Perf. 15x14**
501 A61 60d multicolored .50 .50
502 A61 60d multicolored .50 .50
503 A61 60d multicolored .50 .50
504 A61 60d multicolored .50 .50
505 A61 60d multicolored .50 .50
Nos. 501-505 (5) 2.50 2.50

Miniature Sheet
Perf. 15x14½
506 A61 60d Sheet of 4, #a.-d. 2.25 2.25

Souvenir Sheet
Perf. 15x14
507 A61 300d multicolored 2.75 2.75

Authors A62

Designs: No. 508, Ghevond Alishan (1820-1901). No. 509, Gregor Artsruni (1845-92), vert. No. 510, Franz Werfel (1890-1945).

1995, Oct. 5 Litho. **Perf. 15x14**
508 A62 90d blue & black .75 .75
509 A62 90d multicolored .75 .75
510 A62 90d blue & maroon .75 .75
Nos. 508-510 (3) 2.25 2.25

Nos. 508-510 issued with se-tenant label.

A64

Prehistoric artifacts: 40d, Four-wheeled carriages, 15th cent. BC, horiz. 60d, Bronze model of geocentric solar system, 11-10th cent. BC. 90d, Tombstone, Red Tufa, 7-6th cent. BC.

1995, Dec. 5 **Perf. 14½x15, 15x14½**
512 A64 40d multicolored .50 .50
513 A64 60d multicolored .80 .80
514 A64 90d multicolored 1.25 1.25
Nos. 512-514 (3) 2.55 2.55

A65

Christianity in Armenia — A66

Views of Yerevan: 60d, Brandy distillery, wine cellars. 80d, Abovian Street. 90d, Sports and concert complex. 100d, Baghramian Avenue. 120d, Republic Square.
400d, Panoramic photograph of Yerevan.

1995, Dec. 5 **Perf. 15x14**
515 A65 60d salmon & black .65 .65
516 A65 80d pale orange & black .85 .85
517 A65 90d buff & black .95 .95

Size: 61x24mm
518 A65 100d pale yellow bis & blk 1.10 1.10
519 A65 120d dull orange & black 1.25 1.25
Nos. 515-519 (5) 4.80 4.80

Souvenir Sheet
520 A66 400d multicolored 4.25 4.25

 40

No. 464 Surcharged in Green, Red, Blue Violet, or Red Brown

1996, Mar. 30 Litho. **Perf. 14½**
521 A47 40d on 10l (G) .50 .50
522 A47 100d on 10l (R) 1.25 1.25
523 A47 150d on 10l (BV) 1.75 1.75
524 A47 200d on 10l (RB) 2.50 2.50
Nos. 521-524 (4) 6.00 6.00

Alexsandre Griboyedov
(1795-1829),
Writer — A67

1996, Apr. 24   Litho.   Perf. 14x14¹/₂
525 A67 90d multicolored   .70   .70
No. 525 is printed se-tenant with label.

Khrimian
Hayrik (1820-
1907),
Catholicos of
All Armenians
A68

1996, Apr. 30   Perf. 14¹/₂x14
526 A68 90d brown & blue   .70   .70
No. 526 is printed se-tenant with label.

Admiral
Lazar
Serbryakov
(1795-1862)
A69

1996, Apr. 30
527 A69 90d multicolored   .70   .70
No. 527 is printed se-tenant with label.

Armenian Red Cross,
75th Anniv. — A70

1996, May 3   Perf. 14x14¹/₂
528 A70 60d multicolored   .45   .45

Motion
Pictures,
Cent.
A71

1996, May 3   Perf. 14¹/₂x14
529 A71 60d multicolored   .45   .45

Endangered
Fauna — A72

1996, May 3   Perf. 14
530 A72 40d Carpa aegagrus   .30   .30
531 A72 60d Panthera pardus   .45   .45

1996 Summer   Modern Olympic
Olympics,   Games,
Atlanta — A73   Cent. — A74

Designs: a, 40d, Cyclist. b, 60d, Athletic event.
c, 90d, Wrestling.

1996, June 25
532 A73 Strip of 3, #a.-c.   1.40 1.40

1996, June 25   Perf. 14x14¹/₂
533 A74 60d multicolored   .45   .45

Fridtjof Nansen (1861-1930), Arctic
Explorer — A75

1996, May 20 Litho.   Perf. 14x14¹/₂
534 A75 90d multicolored   .60   .60

32nd Chess
Olympiad,
Yerevan — A76

#535, Petrosian-Botvinnik, World Championship
match, Moscow, 1963. #536, Kasparov-Karpov,
World Championship Match, Leningrad, 1986.
#537, G. Kasparian, first prize winner, Contest of
the Shakhmati v SSSR magazine, 1939. #538, 32nd
Chess Olympiad, Yerevan.

1996, Sept. 15 Litho.   Perf. 14
535 A76 40d multicolored   .25   .25
536 A76 40d multicolored   .25   .25
537 A76 40d multicolored   .25   .25
538 A76 40d multicolored   .25   .25
 a.   Booklet pane, #535-538   1.00
        Complete booklet, 2 #538a   2.00
        Nos. 535-538 (4)   1.00 1.00
No. 538a issued 9/24.

Tigran Petrosian, World
Chess Champion, Chess
House, Yerevan — A77

1996, Sept. 20   Perf. 14x15
539 A77 90d multicolored   .60   .60

Capra
Aegagrus
A78

World Wildlife Fund: 70d, Two running. 100d,
One standing. 130d, One holding head down.
350d, Two facing forward.

1996, Oct. 20   Litho.   Perf. 14¹/₂x14
540 A78 70d multicolored   .45   .45
541 A78 100d multicolored   .65   .65
542 A78 130d multicolored   .80   .80
543 A78 350d multicolored   2.20 2.20
 a.   Block of 4, #540-543   4.10 4.10
 b.   Booklet pane, 2 #543a   8.20
        Complete booklet, #543b   8.20
        Issued in sheets of 16 stamps.

Christianity in Armenia,
1700th Anniv. — A79

Armenian churches: No. 544, St. Catherine
Church, St. Petersburg, 1780. No. 545, Church of
the Holy Mother, Kishinev, 1803. No. 546, Church
of the Holy Mother, Samarkand, 1903. No. 547,
Armenian Church, Lvov, 1370. No. 548, St. Hrip-
sime Church, Yalta, 1913.
500d, Church of St. Gevorg of Etchmiadzin, Tbi-
lisi, 1805.

1996   Litho.   Perf. 14x15
544 A79 100d multicolored   .50   .50
545 A79 100d multicolored   .50   .50
546 A79 100d multicolored   .50   .50
547 A79 100d multicolored   .50   .50
548 A79 100d multicolored   .50   .50
        Nos. 544-548 (5)   2.50 2.50

Souvenir Sheet
549 A79 500d multicolored   2.50 2.50

First Armenian Printing Press,
Etchmiadzin, 225th Anniv. — A80

1997, Mar. 26   Litho.   Perf. 15x14
550 A80 70d multicolored   .35   .35

Armenian
Entertainers
A81

#551, Folk singer, Jivani (1846-1909). #552,
Arno Babajanian (1921-83), composer, vert.

1997, Mar. 26   Perf. 15x14, 14x15
551 A81 90d multicolored   .45   .45
552 A81 90d multicolored   .45   .45

 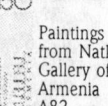

Paintings
from Natl.
Gallery of
Armenia
A82

Designs: No. 553, "One of my Dreams," by Egh-
ishe Tadevossian. No. 554, "Countryside," by
Gevorg Bashinjaghian. No. 555, "Portrait of Natalia
Tehumian," by Hakob Hovnatanian, vert. No. 556,
"Salomé," by Vardges Surenianls, vert.

1997, May 28   Litho.   Perf. 15x14
553 A82 150d multicolored   .70   .70
554 A82 150d multicolored   .70   .70
555 A82 150d multicolored   .70   .70
556 A82 150d multicolored   .70   .70
        Nos. 553-556 (4)   2.80 2.80

Rouben Mamulian (1897-1987), Motion
Picture Director — A83

1997, Oct. 8   Litho.   Perf. 15x14
557 A83 150d multicolored   .70   .70

Moscow '97, World
Philatelic
Exhibition — A84

1997, Oct. 17   Perf. 14x15
558 A84 170d multicolored   .80   .80

Eghishe Charents (1897-1937),
Poet — A85

1997, Oct. 19   Perf. 15x14
559 A85 150d multicolored   .70   .70

Stories and
Legends — A86

Europa: 170d, Hayk, the Progenitor of the
Armenians. 250d, Vahagn, the Dragon Slayer.

1997, Oct. 18   Perf. 14x15
560 A86 170d multicolored   .80   .80
561 A86 250d multicolored   1.15 1.15

AIR POST STAMPS

AP1   AP2

Design: 90d, Artiom Katsian (1886-1943), world
record holding pilot on range and altitude in 1909.

1995, Dec. 5   Litho.   Perf. 14x15
C1 AP1 90d multicolored   1.50 1.50

1996, Apr. 30 Litho.   Perf. 14x14¹/₂
C2 AP2 90d multicolored   .70   .70
Nelson Stepanian (1913-44), World War II fighter
ace.

ARUBA

ə-'rü-bə

LOCATION — West Indies, north of Venezuela
AREA — 78 sq. mi.
POP. — 67,014

On Jan. 1, 1986 Aruba, formerly part of Netherlands Antilles, achieved a separate status within the Kingdom of the Netherlands.

100 Cents = 1 Gulden

Catalogue values for all unused stamps in this country are for Never Hinged items.

Traditional House — A1

1986-87 Litho. Unwmk. Perf. 14x13
1	A1	5c shown	.15	.15
2	A1	15c King William III Tower	.15	.15
3	A1	20c Loading crane	.15	.15
4	A1	25c Lighthouse	.20	.20
5	A1	30c Snake	.25	.25
6	A1	35c Owl	.30	.30
7	A1	45c Shell	.40	.40
8	A1	55c Frog	.50	.50
9	A1	60c Water skier	.55	.55
10	A1	65c Net fishing	.60	.60
11	A1	75c Music box	.70	.70
12	A1	85c Pre-Columbian bisque pot	.75	.75
13	A1	90c Bulb cactus	.80	.80
14	A1	100c Grain	.85	.85
15	A1	150c Watapana tree	1.40	1.40
16	A1	250c Aloe plant	2.25	2.25
		Nos. 1-16 (16)	10.00	10.00

Issue dates: 5c, 30c, 60c, 150c, Jan. 1. 15c, 35c, 65c, 250c, Feb. 5. 20c, 45c, 75c, 100c, Apr. 7, 1987. 25c, 55c, 85c, 90c, July 17, 1987.

Independence A2

1986, Jan. 1 Perf. 14x13, 13x14
18	A2	25c Map	.20	.20
19	A2	45c Coat of arms, vert.	.35	.35
20	A2	55c Natl. anthem, vert.	.45	.45
21	A2	100c Flag	.75	.75
		Nos. 18-21 (4)	1.75	1.75

Intl. Peace Year — A3

1986, Aug. 29 Litho. Perf. 14x13
22	A3	60c shown	.45	.45
23	A3	100c Barbed wire	.75	.75

Princess Juliana and Prince Bernhard, 50th Wedding Anniv. — A4

1987, Jan. 7 Photo. Perf. 13x14
24	A4	135c multicolored	1.25	1.25

State Visit of Queen Beatrix and Prince Claus of the Netherlands A5

1987, Feb. 16 Litho. Perf. 14x13
25	A5	55c shown	.50	.50
26	A5	60c Prince William-Alexander	.50	.50

Tourism — A6

1987, June 5 Litho.
27	A6	60c Beach and sea	.90	.90
28	A6	100c Rock and cacti	1.50	1.50

Aloe Vera Plant — A7   Coins — A8

1988, Jan. 27 Litho. Perf. 13x14
29	A7	45c Field	.50	.50
30	A7	60c Plant	.65	.65
31	A7	100c Harvest	1.10	1.10
		Nos. 29-31 (3)	2.25	2.25

1988, Mar. 16 Litho. Perf. 13x14
32	A8	25c 25-cent	.35	.35
33	A8	55c 50-cent	.70	.70
34	A8	65c 5 and 10-cent	.85	.85
35	A8	150c 1-florin	2.00	2.00
		Nos. 32-35 (4)	3.90	3.90

Love Issue — A9   A10

1988, May 4
36	A9	70c shown	.75	.75
37	A9	135c Seashells, coastal scenery	1.45	1.45

1988, Aug. 24
38	A10	35c shown	.40	.40
39	A10	100c Emblems	1.10	1.10

Aruba, the 162nd member of the Intl. Olympic Committee (35c), 1988 Summer Olympics, Seoul (100c).

Carnival — A11

1989, Jan. 5 Perf. 14x13
40	A11	45c Two children	.45	.45
41	A11	60c Girl	.60	.60
42	A11	100c Entertainer	1.00	1.00
		Nos. 40-42 (3)	2.05	2.05

Maripampun, Omphalophalmum Rubrum — A12

1989, Mar. 16 Litho. Perf. 14x13
43	A12	35c Leaves	.35	.35
44	A12	55c Pods	.55	.55
45	A12	200c Blossom	1.95	1.95
		Nos. 43-45 (3)	2.85	2.85

New Year 1990 — A13   UPU — A14

Dande band members playing instruments or singing: 25c, Violin, tambor, cuatro, marimba. 70c, Lead singer, guitar. 150c, Accordion, urri, guitar.

1989, Nov. 16 Litho. Perf. 13x14
46	A13	25c multicolored	.25	.25
47	A13	70c multicolored	.70	.70
48	A13	150c multicolored	1.50	1.50
		Nos. 46-48 (3)	2.45	2.45

1989, June 8 Litho. Perf. 13x14
49	A14	250c multicolored	2.50	2.50

Crotalus durissus unicolor — A15

1989, Aug. 24 Perf. 14x13
50	A15	45c shown	.50	.50
51	A15	55c multi, diff.	.60	.60
52	A15	60c multi, diff.	.70	.70
		Nos. 50-52 (3)	1.80	1.80

Species in danger of extinction.

Man Living in Harmony with Nature — A16

1990, Feb. 7 Perf. 13x14, 14x13
53	A16	45c The land	.50	.50
54	A16	55c shown	.60	.60
55	A16	100c The sea	1.15	1.15
		Nos. 53-55 (3)	2.25	2.25

Environmental protection. #53, 55 horiz.

Marine Life — A17

Designs: 60c, Giant caribbean anemone, Pederson's cleaning shrimp. 70c, Queen angelfish, red and orange coral. 100c, Banded coral shrimp, fire sponge, yellow boring sponge.

1990, Apr. 4 Litho. Perf. 14x13
56	A17	60c multicolored	.70	.70
57	A17	70c multicolored	.80	.80
58	A17	100c multicolored	1.15	1.15
		Nos. 56-58 (3)	2.65	2.65

A18   A19

1990, May 30 Litho. Perf. 13x14
59	A18	35c multicolored	.30	.30
60	A18	200c Character trademark	1.75	1.75

World Cup Soccer Championships, Italy.

1990, Sept. 12
61	A19	45c Tools	.50	.50
62	A19	60c Stone figure	.65	.65
63	A19	100c Jar	1.05	1.05
		Nos. 61-63 (3)	2.20	2.20

Archeological discoveries.

Landscapes A20

1991, Jan. 31 Litho. Perf. 14x13
64	A20	55c Seashore	.60	.60
65	A20	65c Desert	.70	.70
66	A20	100c Cactus, ocean view	1.10	1.10
		Nos. 64-66 (3)	2.40	2.40

Working Women — A21   Medicinal Plants — A22

Designs: 35c, Taking care of others. 70c, Housewife. 100c, Women in society.

1991, Mar. 28 Litho. Perf. 13x14
67	A21	35c multicolored	.40	.40
68	A21	70c multicolored	.85	.85
69	A21	100c multicolored	1.25	1.25
		Nos. 67-69 (3)	2.50	2.50

Style of inscriptions varies.

1991, May 29
70	A22	65c Ocimum sanctum	.70	.70
71	A22	75c Jatropha gossypifolia	.80	.80
72	A22	95c Croton flavens	1.05	1.05
		Nos. 70-72 (3)	2.55	2.55

A23   A24

Aruban Handicrafts: 35c, Fish net, wood float, wooden needle. 250c, Straw hat, hat block.

1991, July 31 Litho. Perf. 13x14
73	A23	35c lt bl, dk bl & blk	.40	.40
74	A23	250c pink, lil rose & blk	2.75	2.75

1991, Nov. 29 Litho. Perf. 13x14
75	A24	35c Toucan	.40	.40
76	A24	70c People shaking hands	.75	.75
77	A24	100c Windmill	1.10	1.10
		Nos. 75-77 (3)	2.25	2.25

Welcome to Aruba.

 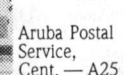
Aruba Postal Service, Cent. — A25

Designs: 60c, Government decree, 1892, vert. 75c, First post office. 80c, Current post office.

Perf. 13x14, 14x13
1992, Jan. 31 Litho.
78	A25	60c multicolored	.65	.65
79	A25	75c multicolored	.85	.85
80	A25	80c multicolored	.90	.90
		Nos. 78-80 (3)	2.40	2.40

Equality
Day — A26

1992, Mar. 25   Litho.   Perf. 14x13
81 A26 100c People of five races   1.00 1.00
82 A26 100c Woman, man, scales   1.00 1.00

Discovery of America,
500th Anniv. — A27

1992, July 30   Litho.   Perf. 13x14
83 A27 30c Columbus   .35 .35
84 A27 40c Sailing ship   .45 .45
85 A27 50c Natives, map   .55 .55
    Nos. 83-85 (3)   1.35 1.35

Natural Bridges
in Aruba — A28

Designs: 70c, Seroe Colorado Bridge, south
coast. 80c, Natural Bridge, north coast.

1992, Nov. 30   Litho.   Perf. 14x13
86 A28 70c multicolored   .85 .85
87 A28 80c multicolored   .90 .90

A29   A30

1993, Jan. 29   Litho.   Perf. 13x14
88 A29 200c multicolored   2.50 2.50
Express mail service.

1993, Mar. 31   Litho.   Perf. 13x14
Various rock formations found in Districts of Ayo
and Casibari.
89 A30 50c multicolored   .65 .65
90 A30 60c multicolored   .75 .75
91 A30 100c multicolored   1.25 1.25
    Nos. 89-91 (3)   2.65 2.65

Folklore — A31   Sailing
    Sports — A32

40c, String instruments, drum. 70c, Traditional
music & games. 80c, Dera Gai song lyrics.

1993, May 28   Litho.   Perf. 13x14
92 A31 40c multicolored   .50 .50
93 A31 70c multicolored   .85 .85
94 A31 80c multicolored   1.00 1.00
    Nos. 92-94 (3)   2.35 2.35

1993, July 30   Litho.   Perf. 13x14
95 A32 50c Sailboating   .60 .60
96 A32 65c Land sailing   .80 .80
97 A32 75c Wind surfing   .95 .95
    Nos. 95-97 (3)   2.35 2.35

Iguana
Iguana — A33

Perf. 14x13, 13x14
1993, Sept. 1   Litho.
98 A33 35c Young   .45 .45
99 A33 60c Almost grown   .75 .75
100 A33 100c Mature, vert.   1.25 1.25
    Nos. 98-100 (3)   2.45 2.45

Burrowing
Owl — A34

Perf. 14x13, 13x14
1994, Jan. 28   Litho.
101 A34 5c Two adults   .15 .15
102 A34 10c Two adults, young   .15 .15
103 A34 35c Adult with prey, vert.   .45 .45
104 A34 40c Adult, vert.   .50 .50
    Nos. 101-104 (4)   1.25 1.25

World Wildlife Fund.

A35   A36

Intl. Olympic Committee, Cent.: 90c, Baron
Pierre de Coubertin (1863-1937), founder of modern Olympics.

1994, Mar. 29   Litho.   Perf. 13x14
105 A35 50c multicolored   .65 .65
106 A35 90c multicolored   1.10 1.10

1994, July 7   Litho.   Perf. 13x14
107 A36 65c shown   .80 .80
108 A36 150c Mascot, soccer ball   1.90 1.90
1994 World Cup Soccer Championships, US.

Wild Fruit — A37

Designs: 40c, Malpighia punicifolia. 70c, Cordia
sebestena. 85c, Pithecellobium unguis-cati. 150c,
Coccoloba uvifera.

1994, Sept. 28   Litho.   Perf. 13x14
109 A37 40c multicolored   .50 .50
110 A37 70c multicolored   .90 .90
111 A37 85c multicolored   1.10 1.10
112 A37 150c multicolored   1.90 1.90
    Nos. 109-112 (4)   4.40 4.40

Architectural
Landmarks
A38

Designs: 35c, Government building, 1888. 60c,
Ecury residence, 1929, vert. 100c, Protestant
Church, 1846, vert.

1995, Jan. 27   Litho.   Perf. 14x13
113 A38 35c multicolored   .45 .45
Perf. 13x14
114 A38 60c multicolored   .75 .75
115 A38 100c multicolored   1.25 1.25
    Nos. 113-115 (3)   2.45 2.45

UN, 50th   Interpaso
Anniv. — A39   Horses — A40

Designs: 30c, Flags, sea, UN emblem, dove, text
from UN charter. 200c, World with flags, doves,
UN emblem.

1995, Mar. 29   Litho.   Perf. 13x14
116 A39 30c multicolored   .35 .35
117 A39 200c multicolored   2.25 2.25

1995, May 26   Perf. 14x13, 13x14
Designs: 25c, 10-time champion Casanova II, ribbons, horiz. 75c, Paso Fino, horiz. 80c, Horse doing
figure 8. 90c, Girl on horse.
118 A40 25c multicolored   .28 .28
119 A40 75c multicolored   .85 .85
120 A40 80c multicolored   .90 .90
121 A40 90c multicolored   1.00 1.00
    Nos. 118-121 (4)   3.03 3.03

Vegetables — A41

1995, July 28   Litho.   Perf. 13x14
122 A41 25c Vigna sinensis   .30 .30
123 A41 50c Cucumis anguria   .55 .55
124 A41 70c Hibiscus esculentus   .80 .80
125 A41 85c Cucurbita moschata   .95 .95
    Nos. 122-125 (4)   2.60 2.60

Turtles — A42

1995, Sept. 27   Litho.   Perf. 14x13
126 A42 15c Hawksbill   .15 .15
127 A42 50c Green   .55 .55
128 A42 95c Loggerhead   1.00 1.00
129 A42 100c Leatherback   1.10 1.10
    Nos. 126-129 (4)   2.80 2.80

Separate Status, 10th
Anniv. — A43

Statesmen and politicians: No. 130, Jan Hendrik
Albert Eman (1887-1957). No. 131, Juan Enrique
Irausquin (1904-62). No. 132, Cornelis Albert
Eman (1916-67). No. 133, Gilberto Francois Croes
(1938-85).

1996, Jan. 1   Litho.   Perf. 13x14
130 A43 100c multicolored   1.10 1.10
131 A43 100c multicolored   1.10 1.10
132 A43 100c multicolored   1.10 1.10
133 A43 100c multicolored   1.10 1.10
    Nos. 130-133 (4)   4.40 4.40

The 1986 date on No. 133 is in error.

America
Issue — A44

National dresswear: 65c, Woman wearing long,
full dress, apron, vert. 70c, Man wearing hat, bow
tie, white shirt, black pants, vert. 100c, Couple
dancing.

Perf. 13x14, 14x13
1996, Mar. 25   Litho.
134 A44 65c multicolored   .75 .75
135 A44 70c multicolored   .80 .80
136 A44 100c multicolored   1.10 1.10
    Nos. 134-136 (3)   2.65 2.65

1996 Summer
Olympic
Games,
Atlanta
A45

1996, May 28   Litho.   Perf. 14x13
137 A45 85c Runners   1.10 1.10
138 A45 130c Cyclist   1.65 1.65

A46   A47

Famous Women: No. 139, Livia (Mimi) Ecury
(1920-91), nurse. No. 140, Lolita Euson (1914-94),
poet. No. 141, Laura Wernet-Paskel (1911-62),
teacher.

1996, Sept. 27   Litho.   Perf. 13x14
139 A46 60c multicolored   .70 .70
140 A46 60c multicolored   .70 .70
141 A46 60c multicolored   .70 .70
    Nos. 139-141 (3)   2.10 2.10

1997, Jan. 23   Litho.   Perf. 13x14
Year of Papiamento 1997: 50c, Sign promoting
use of Papiamento language, children playing on
beach, people in water, boat. 140c, "Papiamento,"
sunrise.
142 A47 50c multicolored   .55 .55
143 A47 140c multicolored   1.65 1.65

Mailman on
Bicycle, 1936-
57 — A48

America issue: 70c, Mailman handing mail to
woman, jeep, 1957-88. 80c, Mailman on motor
scooter placing mail in mailbox, 1995.

1997, Mar. 27   Litho.   Perf. 14x13
144 A48 60c multicolored   .70 .70
145 A48 70c multicolored   .80 .80
146 A48 80c multicolored   .90 .90
    Nos. 144-146 (3)   2.40 2.40

Aruban
Architectrue
A49

Designs: 30c, Decorated cunucu house. 64c,
Steps with "popchi's." 100c, Arends's Building,
vert.

1997, Mar. 27   Litho.   Perf. 14x13
147 A49 30c multicolored   .40 .40
148 A49 65c multicolored   .80 .80
149 A49 100c multicolored   1.25 1.25
    Nos. 147-149 (3)   2.45 2.45

Marine Life — A50

Designs: a, Marlin jumping out of water, lighthouse. b, Dolphin jumping out of water, trees, plants on beach. c, Iguana on rock, beach. d, Dolphin, fish. e, Two dolphins, fish. f, Fish, turtles, owl on beach. g, Various fish among coral. h, Diver, shipwreck, fish, coral. i, Various fish.

1997, May   Litho.   Perf. 12¹/₂x13
150 A50 90c Sheet of 9, #a.-i.   10.00 10.00
PACIFIC 97.

Cruise Tourism — A51

Designs: 35c, Ship at pier, tourists walking toward ship. 50c, Ship with gangway lowered, tourists. 150c, Ship out to sea, small boat.

1997, July 24   Litho.   Perf. 14x13
151 A51 35c multicolored   .40 .40
152 A51 50c multicolored   .55 .55
153 A51 150c multicolored   1.70 1.70
    Nos. 151-153 (3)   2.65 2.65

Aruban Wild Flowers — A52

50c, Erythrina velutina. 60c, Cordia dentata. 70c, Tabebuia billbergii. 130c, Guaiacum officinale.

1997, Sept. 25
154 A52 50c multicolored   .55 .55
155 A52 60c multicolored   .70 .70
156 A52 70c multicolored   .80 .80
157 A52 130c multicolored   1.45 1.45
    Nos. 154-157 (4)   3.50 3.50

SEMI-POSTAL STAMPS

> Surtax for child welfare organizations unless otherwise stated.

Solidarity SP1

1986, May 7   Litho.   Perf. 14x13
B1 SP1 30c + 10c shown   .30 .30
B2 SP1 35c + 15c Three ropes   .40 .40
B3 SP1 60c + 25c One rope   .60 .60
    Nos. B1-B3 (3)   1.30 1.30
Surtax for social and cultural projects.

Child Welfare — SP2

1986, Oct. 29   Litho.   Perf. 14x13
B4 SP2 45c + 20c Boy, caterpillar   .70 .70
B5 SP2 70c + 25c Boy, cocoon   1.00 1.00
B6 SP2 100c + 40c Girl, butterfly   1.50 1.50
    Nos. B4-B6 (3)   3.20 3.20

Christmas SP3

1987, Oct. 27   Litho.   Perf. 14x13
B7 SP3 25c +10c Boy on beach   .35 .35
B8 SP3 45c +20c Drawing Christmas tree   .70 .70
B9 SP3 70c +30c Child, creche figures   1.10 1.10
    Nos. B7-B9 (3)   2.15 2.15

Solidarity SP4

YMCA emblem in various geometric designs.

1988, Aug. 3   Litho.   Perf. 14x13
B10 SP4 45c +20c shown   .70 .70
B11 SP4 60c +25c multi, diff.   .90 .90
B12 SP4 100c +50c multi, diff.   1.60 1.60
    Nos. B10-B12 (3)   3.20 3.20
11th YMCA world council.
Surtax for social and cultural projects.

Children's Toys — SP5

1988, Oct. 26   Perf. 13x14
B13 SP5 45c +20c Jacks   .70 .70
B14 SP5 70c +30c Top   1.10 1.10
B15 SP5 100c +50c Kite   1.60 1.60
    Nos. B13-B15 (3)   3.40 3.40

Children — SP6

1989, Oct. 26   Perf. 14x13
B16 SP6 45c +20c Baby spoon   .65 .65
B17 SP6 60c +30c Chasing a ball   .85 .85
B18 SP6 100c +50c Adult & child holding hands   1.50 1.50
    Nos. B16-B18 (3)   3.00 3.00

Solidarity — SP7

1990, July 25
B19 SP7 55c +25c shown   1.10 1.10
B20 SP7 100c +50c Family, house   2.00 2.00
Surtax for social and cultural projects.

SP8

SP9

Christmas song.

1990, Oct. 24   Litho.   Perf. 13x14
B21 SP8 45c +20c Wind surfboards   .75 .75
B22 SP8 60c +30c shown   1.05 1.05
B23 SP8 100c +50c Kites, lizard   1.70 1.70
    Nos. B21-B23 (3)   3.50 3.50

1991, Oct. 25   Litho.   Perf. 13x14
Literacy: 45c+25c, Discovery of reading. 60c+35c, Pointing to letter. 100c+50c, Child reading.
B24 SP9 45c +25c multi   .75 .75
B25 SP9 60c +35c multi   1.00 1.00
B26 SP9 100c +50c multi   1.65 1.65
    Nos. B24-B26 (3)   3.40 3.40

1995, Oct. 26   Litho.   Perf. 13x14
B40 SP15 50c +25c multi   .85 .85
B41 SP15 70c +35c multi   1.25 1.25
B42 SP15 100c +50c multi   1.65 1.65
    Nos. B40-B42 (3)   3.75 3.75

Solidarity SP10

55c+30c, Girl scouts, flag & emblem. 100c+50c, Hand holding cancer fund emblem, people.

1992, May 27   Litho.   Perf. 14x13
B27 SP10 55c +30c multi   .90 .90
B28 SP10 100c +50c multi   1.65 1.65
Surtax for social and cultural projects.

Postal Services of Aruba, Cent. — SP11

Designs: 50c+30c, Heart. 70c+35c, Airplane, letters. 100c+55c, Pigeon with letter in beak, vert.

1992, Oct. 30   Litho.   Perf. 14x13
B29 SP11 50c +30c multi   1.00 1.00
B30 SP11 70c +35c multi   1.40 1.40
    Perf. 13x14
B31 SP11 100c +50c multi   2.00 2.00
    Nos. B29-B31 (3)   4.40 4.40

Youth Foreign Study Programs SP12

Abstract designs of: 50c+30c, Landscapes. 75c+40c, Young man, scenes of other countries, vert. 100c+50c, Integrating cultures.

1993, Oct. 27   Perf. 14x13, 13x14
B32 SP12 50c +30c multi   1.00 1.00
B33 SP12 75c +40c multi   1.40 1.40
B34 SP12 100c +50c multi   1.90 1.90
    Nos. B32-B34 (3)   4.30 4.30

Intl. Year of the Family — SP13

Designs: 50c+35c, Family seated, reading, studying. 100c+50c, Family playing in front of house.

1994, May 30   Litho.   Perf. 14x13
B35 SP13 50c +35c multi   1.10 1.10
B36 SP13 100c +50c multi   1.90 1.90
Surtax for social and cultural projects.

SP14

Designs: 50c+30c, Children on anchor with umbrella. 80c+35c, Children inside Sun. 100c+50c, Child riding owl.

1994, Oct. 27   Litho.   Perf. 14x13
B37 SP14 50c +30c multi   1.00 1.00
B38 SP14 80c +35c multi   1.40 1.40
B39 SP14 100c +50c multi   1.90 1.90
    Nos. B37-B39 (3)   4.30 4.30

SP15

SP16

Children's drawings: 50c+25c, Children with balloons, house. 70c+35c, Three people with picnic basket on sunny day. 100c+50c, People gardening on sunny day.

1996, July 26   Litho.   Perf. 13x14
El Sol Naciente Lodge, 75th Anniv.: 60c+30c, Masonic emblems. 100c+ 50c, Columns, terrestrial and celestial globes.
B43 SP16 60c +30c multi   1.15 1.15
B44 SP16 100c +50c multi   1.90 1.90

SP17

Cartoons: 50c+25c, Mother, baby rabbit waiting at school bus stop. 70c+35c, Mother, baby owl, outside school. 100c+50c, Children flying kite.

1996, Oct. 24   Litho.   Perf. 14x13
B45 SP17 50c +25c multi   .95 .95
B46 SP17 70c +35c multi   1.30 1.30
B47 SP17 100c +50c multi   1.90 1.90
    Nos. B45-B47 (3)   4.15 4.15

SP18

Designs: 50c+25c, Girl sitting among aloe plants. 70c+35c, Boy, butterfly, cactus, vert. 100c+50c, Girl swimming under water, fish, coral.

Perf. 14x13, 13x14
1997, Oct. 23   Litho.
B48 SP18 50c +25c multi   .85 .85
B49 SP18 70c +35c multi   1.20 1.20
B50 SP18 100c +50c multi   1.70 1.70
    Nos. B48-B50 (3)   3.75 3.75

ASCENSION

ə-'sen(t)-shən

LOCATION — An island in the South Atlantic Ocean, 900 miles from Liberia
GOVT. — A part of the British Crown Colony of St. Helena
AREA — 34 sq. mi.
POP. — 1,625 (1982)

In 1922 Ascension was placed under the administration of the Colonial Office and annexed to the British Crown Colony of St. Helena. The only post office is at Georgetown.

12 Pence = 1 Shilling
20 Shillings = 1 Pound
100 Pence = 1 Pound (1971)

> Catalogue values for unused stamps in this country are for Never Hinged items, beginning with Scott 50.

Stamps and Types of St. Helena, 1912-22
Overprinted in Black or Red

ASCENSION

1922   Wmk. 4   Perf. 14
1 A9 ½p green & blk   3.00 7.50
2 A10 1p green   4.00 7.50
3 A10 1½p rose red   13.00 32.50
4 A9 2p gray & blk   10.00 10.00
5 A9 3p ultra   10.00 12.50
6 A10 8p dl vio & blk   20.00 32.00
7 A10 2sh ultra & blk, blue   62.50 85.00
8 A10 3sh vio & blk   110.00 120.00
    Wmk. 3
9 A9 1sh blk, gray grn (R)   22.50 32.50
    Nos. 1-9 (9)   255.00 339.50

Seal of Colony — A3

1924-27   Typo.   Wmk. 4   Perf. 14
Chalky Paper

10	A3	½p black & gray	2.25	7.00
11	A3	1p green & blk	3.50	4.50
12	A3	1½p rose red	5.00	16.00
13	A3	2p bluish gray & gray	6.50	3.50
14	A3	3p ultra	4.25	8.00
15	A3	4p blk & gray, yel	35.00	60.00
16	A3	5p ol & lil ('27)	9.00	12.00
17	A3	6p rose lil & gray	40.00	45.00
18	A3	8p violet & gray	9.50	13.00
19	A3	1sh brown & gray	15.00	17.00
20	A3	2sh ultra & gray, blue	50.00	57.50
21	A3	3sh blk & gray, blue	70.00	85.00
		Nos. 10-21 (12)	250.00	328.50

View of Georgetown
A4

Map of Ascension — A5

Sooty Tern Breeding Colony A9

Designs: 1½p, Pier at Georgetown. 3p, Long Beach. 5p, Three Sisters. 5sh, Green Mountain.

1934, July 2   Engr.

23	A4	½p violet & blk	.20	.55
24	A5	1p lt grn & blk	.65	.65
25	A4	1½p red & black	.80	.80
26	A5	2p org & black	1.65	1.65
27	A4	3p ultra & blk	.95	.95
28	A4	5p blue & black	1.00	1.40
29	A3	8p dk brn & blk	3.25	8.00
30	A9	1sh carmine & blk	5.75	11.00
31	A5	2sh6p violet & blk	32.50	50.00
32	A4	5sh brown & blk	62.50	65.00
		Nos. 23-32 (10)	109.25	140.00

Silver Jubilee Issue
Common Design Type

1935, May 6   Perf. 11x12

33	CD301	1½p car & dk blue	1.75	4.00
34	CD301	2p blk & ultra	3.50	5.00
35	CD301	5p ind & grn	10.00	16.00
36	CD301	1sh brn vio & indigo	20.00	30.00
		Nos. 33-36 (4)	35.25	55.00

25th anniv. of the reign of King George V.

Coronation Issue
Common Design Type

1937, May 19   Perf. 13½x14

37	CD302	1p deep green	.20	.20
38	CD302	2p deep orange	.80	.80
39	CD302	3p bright ultra	1.00	1.00
		Nos. 37-39 (3)	2.00	2.00
		Set, never hinged	3.00	

Georgetown
A11

Designs: 1p, 2p, 4p, Green Mountain. 1½p, 2sh6p, Pier at Georgetown. 3p, 5sh, Long Beach. 6p, 10sh, Three Sisters.

1938-49   Perf. 13½
Center in Black

40	A11	½p violet	.20	.20
a.		Perf. 13 ('44)	.15	.15
41	A11	1p green	16.00	7.50
41A	A11	1p org yellow, perf. 13 ('42)	.15	.15
b.		Perf. 14 ('49)	.30	.30
c.		Perf. 13½	2.25	2.25
42	A11	2p orange	.50	.50
a.		Perf. 14 ('49)	1.40	1.50
b.		Perf. 13 ('44)	.30	.30
43	A11	2p orange	.35	.35
a.		Perf. 14 ('49)	2.00	13.00
b.		Perf. 13 ('44)	.30	.30

44	A11	3p ultra	45.00	22.50
44A	A11	3p black ('40)	2.50	.75
c.		Perf. 13 ('44)	.20	.20
44B	A11	4p ultra, perf. 13 ('44)	1.00	.75
d.		Perf. 13½	.45	.45
45	A11	6p gray blue	.55	.55
a.		Perf. 13 ('44)	1.40	1.40
		Perf. 13		
46	A11	1sh dk brown ('44)	3.25	1.25
a.		Perf. 13½	1.00	1.00
47	A11	2sh6p car ('44)	10.00	5.00
a.		Perf. 13½	8.50	5.00
48	A11	5sh yel brn ('44)	25.00	6.50
a.		Perf. 13½	16.00	10.00
49	A11	10sh red vio ('44)	45.00	22.50
a.		Perf. 13½	35.00	25.00
		Nos. 40-49 (13)	149.50	68.50
		Set, never hinged	260.00	

See Nos. 54-56.

> Catalogue values for unused stamps in this section, from this point to the end of the section, are for Never Hinged items.

Peace Issue
Common Design Type
Perf. 13½x14

1946, Oct. 21   Engr.   Wmk. 4

50	CD303	2p deep orange	.25	.25
51	CD303	4p deep blue	.30	.30

Silver Wedding Issue
Common Design Types

1948, Oct. 20   Photo.   Perf. 14x14½

52	CD304	3p black	.50	.50

Engraved; Name Typographed
Perf. 11½x11

53	CD305	10sh slate violet	40.00	40.00

Type of 1938

Designs: 1p, Three Sisters. 1½p, Georgetown Pier. 2p, Green Mountain.

1949, June 1   Engr.   Wmk. 4   Perf. 13

54	A11	1p green & black	.30	.30
		Perf. 14		
55	A11	1½p lilac rose & blk	.35	.35
a.		Perf. 13	.50	.50
56	A11	2p red & black	.50	.50
		Nos. 54-56 (3)	1.15	1.15

Issue date: No. 55a, Feb. 25, 1953.

UPU Issue
Common Design Types
Engr.; Name Typo. on Nos. 58, 59

1949, Oct. 10   Perf. 13½, 11x11½

57	CD306	3p rose carmine	1.25	1.25
58	CD307	4p indigo	2.75	2.75
59	CD308	6p olive	3.25	3.25
60	CD309	1sh slate	6.75	6.75
		Nos. 57-60 (4)	14.00	14.00

Coronation Issue
Common Design Type

1953, June 2   Engr.   Perf. 13½x13

61	CD312	3p gray & black	1.50	1.50

Reservoir
A16

Designs: 1p, Map of Ascension. 1½p, Georgetown. 2p, Map showing Ascension between South America and Africa and cable lines. 2½p, Mountain road. 3p, Yellow-billed tropic bird. 4p, Longfinned tuna. 6p, Waves. 7p, Young green turtles. 1sh, Land crab. 2sh6p, Sooty tern (wide-awake). 5sh, Perfect Crater. 10sh, View from Northwest.

1956, Nov. 19   Wmk. 4   Perf. 13
Center in Black

62	A16	½p brown	.15	.15
63	A16	1p lilac rose	.35	.30
64	A16	1½p orange	.35	.25
65	A16	2p carmine	.55	.35
66	A16	2½p orange brown	.65	.55
67	A16	3p blue	.90	.50
68	A16	4p turq blue	.85	.85
69	A16	6p dark blue	1.10	1.10
70	A16	7p violet	1.40	1.40
71	A16	1sh scarlet	1.90	1.50
72	A16	2sh6p brown violet	19.00	11.00
73	A16	5sh bright green	25.00	16.00
74	A16	10sh purple	50.00	30.00
		Nos. 62-74 (13)	102.20	63.95

Brown Booby — A17

Birds: 1½p, Black tern. 2p, Fairy tern. 3p, Red-billed tropic bird in flight. 4½p, Brown noddy. 6p, Sooty tern. 7p, Frigate bird. 10p, Blue-faced booby. 1sh, Yellow-billed tropic bird. 1sh6p, Red-billed tropic bird. 2sh6p, Madeiran storm petrel. 5sh, Red-footed booby (brown phase). 10sh, Frigate birds. £1, Red-footed booby (white phase).

Perf. 14x14½

1963, May 23   Photo.   Wmk. 314

75	A17	1p multicolored	.15	.15
a.		Booklet pane of 4	.15	
76	A17	1½p multicolored	.15	.15
a.		Booklet pane of 4	.50	
b.		Blue omitted	70.00	
77	A17	2p multicolored	.15	.15
a.		Booklet pane of 4	1.10	
78	A17	3p multicolored	.20	.15
a.		Booklet pane of 4	1.25	
79	A17	4½p multicolored	.25	.20
80	A17	6p multicolored	.35	.25
a.		Booklet pane of 4	3.25	
81	A17	7p multicolored	.35	.30
82	A17	10p multicolored	.50	.40
83	A17	1sh multicolored	.55	.50
84	A17	1sh6p multicolored	1.10	1.00
a.		Booklet pane of 4	6.25	
85	A17	2sh6p multicolored	2.75	2.50
86	A17	5sh multicolored	5.50	5.00
87	A17	10sh multicolored	12.50	10.00
88	A17	£1 multicolored	22.50	20.00
		Nos. 75-88 (14)	47.00	40.75

Freedom from Hunger Issue
Common Design Type

1963, June 4   Wmk. 314

89	CD314	1sh6p car rose	3.50	2.50

Red Cross Centenary Issue
Common Design Type

1963, Sept. 2   Litho.   Perf. 13

90	CD315	3p black & red	.90	.90
91	CD315	1sh6p ultra & red	6.00	6.00

ITU Issue
Common Design Type
Perf. 11x11½

1965, May 17   Litho.   Wmk. 314

92	CD317	3p mag & violet	.70	.70
93	CD317	6p grnsh bl & brn org	1.65	1.65

Intl. Cooperation Year Issue
Common Design Type

1965, Oct. 25   Wmk. 314   Perf. 14½

94	CD318	1p bl grn & claret	.45	.30
95	CD318	6p lt vio & green	1.75	1.65

Churchill Memorial Issue
Common Design Type

1966, Jan. 24   Photo.   Perf. 14
Design in Black, Gold and Carmine Rose

96	CD319	1p bright blue	.45	.25
97	CD319	3p green	1.50	.85
98	CD319	6p brown	2.00	1.65
99	CD319	1sh6p violet	6.25	4.75
		Nos. 96-99 (4)	10.20	7.50

World Cup Soccer Issue
Common Design Type

1966, July 1   Litho.   Perf. 14

100	CD321	3p multicolored	.70	.55
101	CD321	6p multicolored	1.40	2.25

WHO Headquarters Issue
Common Design Type

1966, Sept. 20   Litho.   Perf. 14

102	CD322	3p multicolored	1.25	1.00
103	CD322	1sh6p multicolored	3.25	3.00

Apollo Satellite Station, Ascension — A18

Wmk. 314

1966, Nov. 7   Photo.   Perf. 14

104	A18	4p purple & black	.15	.15
105	A18	8p blue grn & blk	.15	.15
106	A18	1sh3p brn ol & blk	.30	.20
107	A18	2sh6p brt grnsh blue & black	.60	.40
		Nos. 104-107 (4)	1.20	.90

Opening of the Apollo communications satellite-earth station, part of the US Apollo program.

UNESCO Anniversary Issue
Common Design Type

1967, Jan. 3   Litho.   Perf. 14

108	CD323	3p "Education"	.70	.65
109	CD323	6p "Science"	2.00	1.75
110	CD323	1sh6p "Culture"	5.00	5.00
		Nos. 108-110 (3)	7.70	7.40

BBC Emblem
A19

Photo.; Gold Impressed

1967, Dec. 1   Wmk. 314   Perf. 14½

111	A19	1p ultra & gold	.15	.15
112	A19	3p dk green & gold	.15	.15
113	A19	6p brt purple & gold	.25	.20
114	A19	1sh6p brt red & gold	.60	.50
		Nos. 111-114 (4)	1.15	1.00

Opening of the British Broadcasting Company's South Atlantic Relay Station on Ascension Island.

Human Rights Flame and Chain — A20

Perf. 14½x14

1968, July 8   Litho.   Wmk. 314

115	A20	6p org, car & blk	.20	.15
116	A20	1sh6p gray, mag & blk	.30	.25
117	A20	2sh6p brt grn, plum & blk	.60	.50
		Nos. 115-117 (3)	1.10	.90

International Human Rights Year.

Blackfish
A21

Fish: No. 119, Sailfish. 6p, Oldwife. 8p, Leather jacks. 1sh6p, Yellowtails. 1sh9p, Tuna. 2sh3p, Mako sharks. 2sh11p, Rock hind (jack).

Perf. 13x12½

1968-69   Wmk. 314   Litho.

118	A21	4p brt grnsh bl & blk	.30	.20
119	A21	4p red & multi	.35	.25
120	A21	6p yel olive & multi	.45	.35
121	A21	8p brt rose lil & multi	.60	.40
122	A21	1sh6p brown & multi	2.00	1.50
123	A21	1sh9p emer & multi	1.10	.95
124	A21	2sh3p ocher & multi	1.75	1.25
125	A21	2sh11p dp org & multi	3.50	2.25
		Nos. 118-125 (8)	10.05	7.15

Issue dates: No. 119, 6p, 1sh6p, 2sh11p, Mar. 3, 1969. Others, Oct. 23, 1968.
See Nos. 130-133.

Arms of R.N.S. Rattlesnake — A22

Coats of Arms of Royal Naval Ships: 9p, Weston. 1sh9p, Undaunted. 2sh3p, Eagle.

Perf. 14x14¹/₂
1969, Oct. 1 Photo. Wmk. 314
126	A22	4p multicolored	.25	.25
127	A22	9p multicolored	.50	.50
128	A22	1sh9p multicolored	1.25	1.25
129	A22	2sh3p multicolored	1.75	1.75
a.		Min. sheet of 4, #126-129	6.75	5.75
		Nos. 126-129 (4)	3.75	3.75

See Nos. 134-137, 152-159, 166-169.

Fish Type of 1968

Deep-sea fish: 4p, Wahoo. 9p, Coalfish. 1sh9p, Dolphinfishes. 2sh3p, Soldierfish.

1970, Apr. 6 Litho. Perf. 14
130	A21	4p bluish grn & multi	.55	.35
131	A21	9p org & multi	.90	.60
132	A21	1sh9p ultra & multi	1.75	1.40
133	A21	2sh3p gray & multi	3.25	2.00
		Nos. 130-133 (4)	6.45	4.35

Naval Arms Type of 1969

4p, Penelope. 9p, Carlisle. 1sh6p, Amphion. 2sh6p, Magpie.

Perf. 12¹/₂x12
1970, Sept. 7 Photo. Wmk. 314
134	A22	4p ultra, gold & blk	.25	.25
135	A22	9p lt blk, blk, gold & red	.50	.50
136	A22	1sh6p grnsh bl, gold & blk	1.25	1.25
137	A22	2sh6p lt grnsh bl, gold & blk	2.00	2.00
a.		Miniature sheet of 4, #134-137	7.50	6.00
		Nos. 134-137 (4)	4.00	4.00

Decimal Currency Issue

Tycho Brahe's Observatory, Quadrant and Supernova, 1572 — A23

Man into Space: ¹/₂p, Chinese rocket, 1232, vert. 1p, Medieval Arab astronomers, vert. 2p, Galileo, his telescope and drawing of moon, 1609. 2¹/₂p, Isaac Newton, telescope and apple. 3¹/₂p, Harrison's chronometer and ship, 1735. 4¹/₂p, First American manned orbital flight (Project Mercury, 1962, vert.). 5p, Reflector of Palomar telescope and ring nebula in Lyra, Messier 57. 7¹/₂p, Jodrell Bank telescope. 10p, Mariner 7, 1969, and telescopic view of Mars. 12¹/₂p, Sputnik 2 and dog Laika, 1957. 25p, Astronaut walking in space, 1965 (Gemini 4; vert.). 50p, US astronauts and moon landing module, 1969. £1, Future space research station.

1971, Feb. 15 Litho. Perf. 14¹/₂
138	A23	¹/₂p multicolored	.15	.15
a.		Booklet pane of 4	.50	
139	A23	1p multicolored	.15	.15
a.		Booklet pane of 4	.75	
140	A23	1¹/₂p multicolored	.20	.20
a.		Booklet pane of 4	1.00	
141	A23	2p multicolored	.20	.20
a.		Booklet pane of 4	1.90	
142	A23	2¹/₂p multicolored	.35	.35
a.		Booklet pane of 4	2.50	
143	A23	3¹/₂p multicolored	.45	.45
a.		Booklet pane of 4	3.50	
144	A23	4¹/₂p multicolored	.60	.60
145	A23	5p multicolored	.65	.65
146	A23	7¹/₂p multicolored	.75	.75
147	A23	10p multicolored	1.00	1.00
148	A23	12¹/₂p multicolored	1.40	1.40
149	A23	25p multicolored	2.50	2.50
150	A23	50p multicolored	5.25	5.25
151	A23	£1 multicolored	10.00	10.00
		Nos. 138-151 (14)	23.65	23.65

For overprints see Nos. 189-191.

Ascension
Arms of H.M.S.
Phoenix — A24

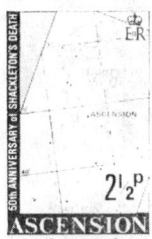

ASCENSION
Course of
Quest — A25

Coats of Arms of Royal Naval Ships: 4p, Milford. 9p, Pelican. 15p, Oberon.

1971, Nov. 15 Photo. Perf. 13¹/₂x13
152	A24	2p gold & multi	.25	.25
153	A24	4p gold & multi	.55	.55
154	A24	9p gold & multi	1.65	1.65

155	A24	15p gold & multi	3.25	3.25
a.		Souvenir sheet of 4, #152-155	8.00	10.00
		Nos. 152-155 (4)	5.70	5.70

Naval Arms Type of 1969

1¹/₂p, Lowestoft. 3p, Auckland. 6p, Nigeria. 17¹/₂p, Bermuda.

1972, May 22 Litho. Perf. 14x14¹/₂
156	A22	1¹/₂p bl, gold & blk	.20	.20
157	A22	3p grnsh bl, gold & blk	.45	.45
158	A22	6p grn, gold, blk & bl	.90	.90
159	A22	17¹/₂p lil, gold, blk & red	2.75	2.75
a.		Miniature sheet of 4, #156-159	5.00	5.50
		Nos. 156-159 (4)	4.30	4.30

1972, Aug. 2 Perf. 14

Designs: 4p, Shackleton and "Quest", horiz. 7¹/₂p, Shackleton's cabin and Quest in pack ice, horiz. 11p, Shackleton statue, London, and memorial cairn, South Georgia.

160	A25	2¹/₂p multicolored	.30	.30
161	A25	4p multicolored	.50	.50
162	A25	7¹/₂p multicolored	1.00	1.00
163	A25	11p multicolored	1.65	1.65
a.		Souvenir sheet of 4, #160-163	4.50	4.50
		Nos. 160-163 (4)	3.45	3.45

Sir Ernest Henry Shackleton (1874-1922), explorer of Antarctica.

Silver Wedding Issue, 1972
Common Design Type

Design: Queen Elizabeth II, Prince Philip, land crab and shark.

1972, Nov. 20 Photo. Perf. 14x14¹/₂
164	CD324	2p violet & multi	.15	.15
165	CD324	16p car rose & multi	.80	.80

Naval Arms Type of 1969

2p, Birmingham. 4p, Cardiff. 9p, Penzance. 13p, Rochester.

1973, May 28 Litho. Wmk. 314
166	A22	2p blue & multi	.60	.42
167	A22	4p yel grn & multi	1.50	1.10
168	A22	9p lt blue & multi	3.00	2.25
169	A22	13p violet & multi	4.25	3.75
a.		Min. sheet of 4, #166-169	21.00	24.00
		Nos. 166-169 (4)	9.35	7.52

Turtles — A26

1973, Aug. 28 Perf. 13¹/₂
170	A26	4p Green	1.65	1.10
171	A26	9p Loggerhead	3.25	2.25
172	A26	12p Hawksbill	5.25	3.50
		Nos. 170-172 (3)	10.15	6.85

Light Infantry Marine
Sergeant, 1900 — A27

Uniforms (Royal Marines): 6p, Private, 1816. 12p, Officer, Light Infantry, 1880. 20p, Color Sergeant, Artillery, 1910.

1973, Oct. 31 Perf. 14¹/₂
173	A27	2p multicolored	.50	.50
174	A27	6p lt green & multi	1.75	1.75
175	A27	12p lt blue & multi	3.50	3.50
176	A27	20p lt lilac & multi	6.00	6.00
		Nos. 173-176 (4)	11.75	11.75

Departure of the Royal Marines from Ascension, 50th anniv.

Princess Anne's Wedding Issue
Common Design Type

1973, Nov. 14 Perf. 14
177	CD325	2p ocher & multi	.15	.15
178	CD325	18p multicolored	.65	.65

Letter and
UPU
Emblem
A29

UPU Cent.: 9p, Emblem and Mercury.

Perf. 14¹/₂
1974, Mar. 27 Litho. Wmk. 314
179	A29	2p multicolored	.20	.20
180	A29	9p vio blue & multi	.70	.70

Young
Churchill
and
Blenheim
Palace
A30

25p, Churchill and UN Headquarters, NYC.

1974, Nov. 30 Litho. Unwmk.
181	A30	5p slate grn & multi	.20	.20
182	A30	25p purple & multi	.85	.85
a.		Souvenir sheet of 2, #181-182	2.00	1.75

Sir Winston Churchill (1874-1965).

Skylab over
Photograph
of
Ascension
Taken by
Skylab
3 — A31

Skylab Space Station: 18p, Command module and photo of Ascension from Skylab 4.

1975, Mar. 20 Wmk. 314 Perf. 14¹/₂
183	A31	2p multicolored	.15	.15
184	A31	18p multicolored	1.00	1.00

US Air Force C-141A Starlifter — A32

Aircraft: 5p, Royal Air Force C-130 Hercules. 9p, Vickers VC-10. 24p, U.S. Air Force C-5A Galaxy.

Perf. 13¹/₂x14
1975, June 19 Litho. Wmk. 314
185	A32	2p multicolored	.25	.25
186	A32	5p multicolored	.60	.60
187	A32	9p multicolored	1.10	1.10
188	A32	24p multicolored	3.00	3.00
a.		Souvenir sheet of 4, #185-188	8.00	10.00
		Nos. 185-188 (4)	4.95	4.95

Wideawake Airfield, Ascension Island.

APOLLO-SOYUZ
Nos. 144, 148-149   LINK
Overprinted   1975

1975, Aug. Litho. Perf. 14¹/₂
189	A23	4¹/₂p multicolored	.20	.20
190	A23	12¹/₂p multicolored	.40	.40
191	A23	25p multicolored	.95	.95
		Nos. 189-191 (3)	1.55	1.55

Apollo Soyuz space test project (Russo-American cooperation), launching July 15; link-up, July 17.

HMS Peruvian and Zenobia Arriving Oct. 22, 1815
A33

Designs: 5p, Water Supply, Dampiers Drip. 9p, First Landing, Oct. 1815. 15p, The Garden on Green Mountain. All designs after paintings by Isobel McManus.

1975, Oct. 22 Wmk. 373 Perf. 14¹/₂
192	A33	2p lt blue & multi	.15	.15
193	A33	5p lt blue & multi	.30	.20
194	A33	9p red & multi	.45	.40
195	A33	15p red & multi	.90	.75
		Nos. 192-195 (4)	1.80	1.50

British occupation, 160th anniv.

Canaries
A34

Designs: 2p, Fairy tern, vert. 3p, Waxbills. 4p, Black noddy, vert. 5p, Brown noddy. 6p, Common mynah. 7p, Madeira storm petrels, vert. 8p, Sooty terns. 9p, White booby, vert. 10p, Red-footed booby. 15p, Red-throated francolin, vert. 18p, Brown booby, vert. 25p, Red-billed bo'sun bird. 50p, Yellow-billed bo'sun bird. £1, Ascension frigatebird, vert. £2, Boatswain Island Bird Sanctuary and birds.

Perf. 14x14¹/₂, 14¹/₂x14
1976, Apr. 26 Litho. Wmk. 373
Size: 35x27mm, 27x35mm
196	A34	1p multicolored	.15	.15
197	A34	2p multicolored	.15	.15
198	A34	3p multicolored	.15	.15
199	A34	4p multicolored	.15	.15
200	A34	5p multicolored	.20	.15
201	A34	6p multicolored	.22	.15
202	A34	7p multicolored	.25	.20
203	A34	8p multicolored	.30	.20
204	A34	9p multicolored	.40	.25
205	A34	10p multicolored	.45	.25
206	A34	15p multicolored	.65	.40
207	A34	18p multicolored	.85	.50
208	A34	25p multicolored	1.25	.65
209	A34	50p multicolored	2.25	1.25
210	A34	£1 multicolored	3.25	2.75

Perf. 13¹/₂
Size: 46x33mm
211	A34	£2 multicolored	6.50	5.25
		Nos. 196-211 (16)	17.17	12.60

Great Britain Type A1 with Ascension Cancel — A35

9p, Ascension No. 1, vert. 25p, Freighter Southampton Castle.

1976, May 4 Perf. 13¹/₂x14, 14x13¹/₂
212	A35	5p lt brn, car & blk	.15	.15
213	A35	9p gray grn, grn & blk	.30	.30
214	A35	25p blue & multi	.95	.95
		Souvenir sheet of 3	2.25	2.25
		Nos. 212-214 (3)	1.40	1.40

Festival of Stamps 1976. #214a contains one each of Ascension #214, St. Helena #297 and Tristan da Cunha #208.

US Base
A36

Designs: 9p, NASA Station, Devil's Ashpit. 25p, Viking satellite landing on Mars.

Perf. 13¹/₂
1976, July 4 Litho. Wmk. 373
215	A36	8p black & multi	.55	.55
216	A36	9p black & multi	.65	.65
217	A36	25p black & multi	1.50	1.50
		Nos. 215-217 (3)	2.70	2.70

American Bicentennial. No. 215 also for the 20th anniv. of Bahamas Long Range Proving Ground (extension) Agreement.

Queen in Coronation Coach — A37

Designs: 8p, Prince Philip on Ascension Island, 1957, vert. 12p, Queen leaving Buckingham Palace in coronation coach.

Perf. 14x13½, 13½x14
1977, Feb. 7   Litho.   Wmk. 373

218	A37	8p multicolored	.20	.20
219	A37	12p multicolored	.25	.25
220	A37	25p multicolored	.55	.55
		Nos. 218-220 (3)	1.00	1.00

Reign of Queen Elizabeth II, 25th anniv.

Water Pipe in Tunnel — A38

5p, Breakneck Valley wells. 12p, Break tank in pipe line, horiz. 25p, Dam & reservoir, horiz.

1977, June 27   Litho.   Perf. 14½

221	A38	3p multicolored	.15	.15
222	A38	5p multicolored	.20	.20
223	A38	12p multicolored	.50	.50
224	A38	25p multicolored	1.00	1.00
		Nos. 221-224 (4)	1.85	1.85

Water supplies constructed by Royal Marines, 1832 and 1881.

Mars Bay Site, 1877 — A39

Designs: 8p, Mars Bay and instrument sites. 12p, Prof. and Mrs. Gill before their tent. 25p, Map of Ascension.

Perf. 13½x14
1977, Oct. 3   Litho.   Wmk. 373

225	A39	3p multicolored	.15	.15
226	A39	8p multicolored	.30	.25
227	A39	12p multicolored	.50	.45
228	A39	25p multicolored	1.10	.85
		Nos. 225-228 (4)	2.05	1.70

Centenary of visit of Prof. David Gill (1843-1914), astronomer, to Ascension.

Elizabeth II Coronation Anniversary Issue
Souvenir Sheet
Common Design Types
Unwmk.

1978, May 21   Litho.   Perf. 15

229		Sheet of 6	2.50	2.50
a.	CD326	25p Lion of England	.40	.40
b.	CD327	25p Elizabeth II	.40	.40
c.	CD328	25p Green turtle	.40	.40

No. 229 contains 2 se-tenant strips of Nos. 229a-229c, separated by horizontal gutter with commemorative and descriptive inscriptions and showing central part of coronation procession with coach.

East Crater (Broken Tooth) — A40

Volcanoes: 5p, Hollands Crater (Hollow Tooth). 12p, Bears Back. 15p, Green Mountain. 25p, Two Boats village.

1978, Sept. 4   Litho.   Perf. 14½

230	A40	3p multicolored	.15	.15
231	A40	5p multicolored	.15	.15
232	A40	12p multicolored	.40	.40
233	A40	15p multicolored	.50	.50
234	A40	15p multicolored	.85	.85
a.		Souvenir sheet, 2 each #230-234	4.50	4.50
b.		Strip of 5, #230-234	2.00	2.00

No. 234b shows panoramic view of volcanic terrain.

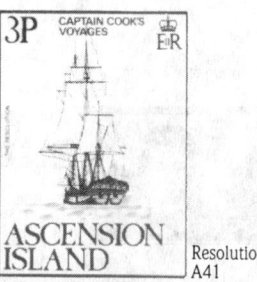

Resolution A41

Capt. Cook's voyages: 8p, Cook's chronometer. 12p, Green turtle. 25p, Cook after Flaxman/Wedgwood medallion.

Litho.; Litho. & Engr. (25p)
1979, Jan. 8   Perf. 11

235	A41	3p multicolored	.15	.15
236	A41	8p multicolored	.30	.25
237	A41	12p multicolored	.55	.40
238	A41	25p multicolored	1.10	.85
		Nos. 235-238 (4)	2.10	1.65

St. Mary's Church, Georgetown — A42

Designs: 12p, Old map of Ascension Island. 50p, Ascension, by Rembrandt.

Perf. 14½
1979, May 24   Litho.   Wmk. 373

239	A42	8p multicolored	.15	.15
240	A42	12p multicolored	.25	.25
241	A42	50p multicolored	.95	.95
		Nos. 239-241 (3)	1.35	1.35

Ascension Day.

Landing Cable at Comfortless Cove — A43

Eastern Telegraph Co., 80th anniv.: 8p, Cable Ship Anglia. 12p, Map showing cables across the Atlantic, vert. 15p, Cable-laying ship. 25p, Cable and earth station.

1979, Sept. 15

242	A43	3p rose car & black	.15	.15
243	A43	8p dk yel grn & black	.20	.20
244	A43	12p yel bister & black	.35	.35
245	A43	15p violet & black	.45	.45
246	A43	25p deep org & black	.70	.70
		Nos. 242-246 (5)	1.85	1.85

Ascension No. 45 — A44

1979, Dec. 17   Wmk. 373   Perf. 14

247	A44	3p shown	.15	.15
248	A44	8p No. 73	.15	.15
249	A44	12p No. 14	.20	.20
250	A44	50p Hill portrait, vert.	.85	.85
		Nos. 247-250 (4)	1.35	1.35

Sir Rowland Hill (1795-1879), originator of penny postage.

Anogramma Ascensionis A45

1980, Feb. 18   Litho.   Perf. 14½

251	A45	3p shown	.15	.15
252	A45	6p Xiphopteris ascension-ense	.15	.15
253	A45	8p Sporobolus caespitosus	.20	.20
254	A45	12p Sporobolus durus, vert.	.25	.25
255	A45	18p Dryopteris ascensionis, vert.	.40	.40
256	A45	24p Marattia purpurascens, vert.	.50	.50
		Nos. 251-256 (6)	1.65	1.65

17th Century Bottle Post, London 1980 Emblem — A46

1980, May 1   Wmk. 373   Perf. 14

257	A46	8p shown	.15	.15
258	A46	12p 36-gun frigate, 19th century	.25	.25
259	A46	15p "Garth Castle," 1863	.30	.30
260	A46	50p "St. Helena," Lockheed C141	.85	.85
a.		Souvenir sheet of 4, #257-260	2.25	2.50
		Nos. 257-260 (4)	1.55	1.55

London 1980 Intl. Stamp Exhib., May 6-14.

Queen Mother Elizabeth Birthday
Common Design Type

1980, Aug. 11   Litho.   Perf. 14

261	CD330	15p multicolored	.40	.40

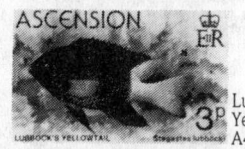

Lubbock's Yellowtail A47

1980, Sept. 15   Litho.   Perf. 13½x14

262	A47	3p shown	.15	.15
263	A47	10p Resplendent angelfish	.30	.30
264	A47	25p Hedgehog butterflyfish	.70	.70
265	A47	40p Marmalade razorfish	1.10	1.10
		Nos. 262-265 (4)	2.25	2.25

Tortoisen, by Thomas Maxon A48

Map of South Atlantic Ridge and Contintental Drift — A49

15p, Wideawake Fair, by Linton Palmer, 1866.

1980, Nov. 17   Perf. 13½, 14 (60p)

266	A48	10p multicolored	.20	.20
267	A48	15p multicolored	.35	.35
268	A49	60p multicolored	1.25	1.25
		Nos. 266-268 (3)	1.80	1.80

Royal Geographical Soc., 50th anniv.

Green Mountain Farm, 1881 — A50

Designs: 15p, Two Boats, 1881. 20p, Green Mountain and Two Boats farms, 1981. 30p, Green Mountain Farm, 1981.

1981, Feb. 15   Litho.   Perf. 14

269	A50	12p multicolored	.20	.20
270	A50	15p multicolored	.30	.30
271	A50	20p multicolored	.35	.35
272	A50	30p multicolored	.65	.65
		Nos. 269-272 (4)	1.50	1.50

Cable and Wireless Earth Station A51

1981, Apr. 27   Litho.   Perf. 14

273		Sheet of 10	3.75	3.75
a.	A51	15p multicolored	.35	.35

Flight of Columbia space shuttle. Gutter contains story of Ascension and space shuttle; margin shows craft and dish antenna.

Poinsettia A52

1981, May 11   Wmk. 373   Perf. 13½

274	A52	1p shown	.15	.15
275	A52	2p Clustererd wax flower	.15	.15
276	A52	3p Kolanchoe, vert.	.15	.15
277	A52	4p Yellow pops	.15	.15
278	A52	5p Camel's foot creeper	.15	.15
279	A52	8p White oleander	.20	.20
280	A52	10p Ascension lily, vert.	.25	.25
281	A52	12p Coral plant, vert.	.30	.30
282	A52	15p Yellow allamanda	.40	.40
283	A52	20p Ascension euphorbia	.50	.50
284	A52	30p Flame of the forest, vert.	.85	.85
285	A52	40p Bougainvillea	1.00	1.00

Size: 42x53mm

286	A52	50p Solanum	1.25	1.25
287	A52	£1 Ladies petticoat	2.75	2.75
288	A52	£2 Red hibiscus	5.25	5.25
		Nos. 274-288 (15)	13.50	13.50

Nos. 275-276, 280, 282-283 and 287 also issued inscribed 1982.
For overprints see Nos. 321-322.

Linschoten's Map of Ascension, 1599 (Illustration reduced) — A53

Maxwell's Map of Ascension, 1793 — A54

Designs: Old maps of Ascension.

1981, May 22   Perf. 14½

289	A53	Sheet of 4	.60	.60
a.-d.		5p any single	.15	.15
290	A54	10p shown	.25	.25
291	A54	12p Maxwell, 1793, diff.	.35	.35

292 A54 15p Eckberg & Chapman,
1811 .40 .40
293 A54 40p Campbell, 1819 1.10 1.10
Nos. 289-293 (5) 2.70 2.70

Royal Wedding Issue
Common Design Type

1981, July 22 Wmk. 373 Perf. 14
294 CD331 10p Bouquet .20 .20
295 CD331 15p Charles .30 .30
296 CD331 50p Couple 1.00 1.00
Nos. 294-296 (3) 1.50 1.50

Nos. 294-296 each se-tenant with label.

Man Shining
Cannon — A55

1981, Sept. 14 Litho. Perf. 14
297 A55 5p shown .15 .15
298 A55 10p Mountain climbing .20 .20
299 A55 15p First aid treatment .35 .35
300 A55 40p Duke of Edinburgh .90 .90
Nos. 297-300 (4) 1.60 1.60

Duke of Edinburgh's Awards, 25th anniv.

Scouting
Year — A56

1982, Feb. 22 Litho. Perf. 14
301 A56 10p Parallel rope walking .25 .25
302 A56 15p 1st Ascension scout flag .40 .40
303 A56 20p Radio operators .55 .55
304 A56 40p Baden-Powell .75 .75
a. Souvenir sheet of 4 2.25 2.25
Nos. 301-304 (4) 1.95 1.95

No. 304a contains stamps in designs of Nos. 301-304 (30x30mm, perf. 14½, diamond-shape).

Sesquicentennial of Charles Darwin's
Visit — A57

1982, Apr. 19
305 A57 10p Portrait .25 .25
306 A57 12p Pistols .35 .35
307 A57 15p Rock crab .40 .40
308 A57 40p Beagle 1.10 1.10
Nos. 305-308 (4) 2.10 2.10

40th Anniv.
of
Wideawake
Airfield
A58

1982, June 15 Litho. Perf. 14
309 A58 5p Fairey Swordfish .60 .60
310 A58 10p North American B25C
Mitchell .80 .80
311 A58 15p Boeing EC-135N Aria 1.10 1.10
312 A58 50p Lockheed Hercules 1.65 1.65
Nos. 309-312 (4) 4.15 4.15

Princess Diana Issue
Common Design Type

Perf. 14½x14
1982, July 1 Wmk. 373
313 CD333 12p Arms .30 .30
314 CD333 15p Diana .40 .40
315 CD333 25p Wedding .60 .60
316 CD333 50p Portrait 1.25 1.25
Nos. 313-316 (4) 2.55 2.55

Christmas and 50th Anniv. of BBC
Overseas Broadcasting — A59

Anniv. Emblem and: 5p, Bush House (London headquarters). 10p, Atlantic relay station. 25p, Lord Reith, first director general. 40p, King George V delivering Christmas address, 1932.

1982, Dec. 20 Litho. Perf. 14
317 A59 5p multicolored .15 .15
318 A59 10p multicolored .30 .30
319 A59 25p multicolored .70 .70
320 A59 40p multicolored 1.10 1.10
Nos. 317-320 (4) 2.25 2.25

Nos. 282-283 Overprinted: "1st
PARTICIPATION / COMMONWEALTH
GAMES 1982"

1982 Litho. Perf. 13½
321 A52 15p multicolored .40 .40
322 A52 20p multicolored .50 .50

12th Commonwealth Games, Brisbane, Australia, Sept. 30-Oct. 9.

A60 7p

1983, Mar. 1 Perf. 14
323 A60 7p Marasmius echi-
nosphaerus .25 .25
324 A60 12p Chlorophyllum
molybdites .45 .45
325 A60 15p Leucocoprinus cepaes-
tipes .55 .55
326 A60 20p Lycoperdon marginatum .75 .75
327 A60 50p Marasmiellus distan-
tifolius 1.75 1.75
Nos. 323-327 (5) 3.75 3.75

View of
Georgetown
A61

1983, May 12 Litho. Perf. 14
328 A61 12p shown .30 .30
329 A61 15p Farm, Green Mountain .30 .30
330 A61 20p Boatswain Bird Isld. .45 .45
331 A61 60p Telemetry Hill 1.10 1.10
Nos. 328-331 (4) 2.15 2.15

See Nos. 359-362.

Manned Flight Bicentenary — A62

Military Aircraft.

1983, Aug. 1 Wmk. 373 Perf. 14
332 A62 12p Wessex Five helicopter .75 .75
333 A62 15p Vulcan B2 .85 .85
334 A62 20p Nimrod MR2P 1.00 1.00
335 A62 60p Victor K2 1.75 1.75
Nos. 332-335 (4) 4.35 4.35

Introduced
Species
A63

1983, Sept. Litho. Wmk. 373
336 A63 12p Iguanid .30 .30
337 A63 15p Rabbit .40 .40
338 A63 20p Cat .50 .50
339 A63 60p Donkey 1.50 1.50
Nos. 336-339 (4) 2.70 2.70

Tellina Antonii
Philippi
A64

1983, Nov. 28 Litho. Perf. 14½
340 A64 7p shown .20 .20
341 A64 12p Nodipecten nodosus .35 .35
342 A64 15p Cypraea lurida oceanica .45 .45
343 A64 20p Nerita ascensionis gmelin .60 .60
344 A64 50p Micromelo undatus 1.50 1.50
Nos. 340-344 (5) 3.10 3.10

St. Helena Colony,
150th Anniv. — A65

Designs: First issue inscribed Ascension instead of overprinted.

1984, Jan. 10 Litho. Perf. 14
345 A65 12p No. 3 .30 .30
346 A65 15p No. 4 .40 .40
347 A65 20p No. 6 .50 .50
348 A65 60p No. 9 1.50 1.50
Nos. 345-348 (4) 2.70 2.70

Souvenir Sheet

Visit of Prince
Andrew — A66

1984, Apr. 10 Perf. 14½x14
349 Sheet of 2 2.25 2.25
a. A66 12p Andrew .25 .25
b. A66 70p In naval uniform 1.75 1.75

Lloyd's List Issue
Common Design Type

1984, May 28
351 CD335 12p Naval semaphore .25 .25
352 CD335 15p "Southampton Castle" .35 .35
353 CD335 20p Pier Head .45 .45
354 CD335 70p Dane 1.50 1.50
Nos. 351-354 (4) 2.55 2.55

1984 Coins
and Wildlife
A67

1984, June Perf. 14
355 A67 12p One penny, yellowfin
tuna .45 .45
356 A67 15p Two pence, donkeys .60 .60
357 A67 20p Fifty pence, green turtle .70 .70
358 A67 70p One pound, sooty terns 1.75 1.75
Nos. 355-358 (4) 3.50 3.50

View Type of 1983

1984, Oct. Litho. Wmk. 373
359 A61 12p Devil's Riding School .25 .25
360 A61 15p St. Mary's Church .35 .35
361 A61 20p Two Boats Village .50 .50
362 A61 70p Ascension Isld. 1.65 1.65
Nos. 359-362 (4) 2.75 2.75

Trees — A68

1985, Mar. 8 Litho. Perf. 14½x14
363 A68 7p Bermuda cypress .50 .50
364 A68 12p Norfolk Island pine .55 .55
365 A68 15p Screwpine .65 .65
366 A68 20p Eucalyptus .80 .80
367 A68 50p Spore tree 2.00 2.00
Nos. 363-367 (5) 4.50 4.50

Military
Firearms
A69

Large guns and insignia: 12p, Thirty-two pounder small bore muzzle loader, c. 1820; Royal Marines hat plate, c. 1816. 15p, Seven-inch rifled muzzle loader, c. 1866; royal cipher. 20p, Seven-pounder rifled muzzle loader, c. 1877; Royal Artillery badge. 70p, HMS Hood 5.5-inch gun; ship crest.

1985, July 21 Wmk. 373 Perf. 14½
368 A69 12p multicolored .65 .65
369 A69 15p multicolored .75 .75
370 A69 20p multicolored .80 .80
371 A69 70p multicolored 2.25 2.25
Nos. 368-371 (4) 4.45 4.45

Queen Mother 85th Birthday
Common Design Type

Designs: 12p, With Duke of York, Balmoral, 1924. 15p, With Princes Andrew and Edward. 20p, At Ascot. 70p, Christening of Prince Henry, Windsor Castle. 75p, Leaving the QEII, 1968.

Perf. 14½x14
1985, June 7 Wmk. 384
372 CD336 12p multicolored .25 .25
373 CD336 15p multicolored .30 .30
374 CD336 20p multicolored .40 .40
375 CD336 70p multicolored 1.40 1.40
Nos. 372-375 (4) 2.35 2.35

Souvenir Sheet
376 CD336 75p multicolored 1.65 1.50

Intl. Youth Year, Girl
Guides 75th
Anniv. — A70

1985, Oct. 4 Wmk. 373
377 A70 12p Guides' banner .65 .65
378 A70 15p First aid .75 .75
379 A70 20p Camping .85 .85
380 A70 70p Lady Baden-Powell 2.50 2.50
Nos. 377-380 (4) 4.75 4.75

Wildflowers
A71

Halley's Comet
A72

Wmk. 384

1985, Dec. 6   Litho.   Perf. 14

381	A71	12p Clerodendrum fragrans	.40	.40
382	A71	15p Shell ginger	.45	.45
383	A71	20p Cape daisy	.60	.60
384	A71	70p Ginger lily	1.75	1.75
		Nos. 381-384 (4)	3.20	3.20

1986, Mar. 7

Designs: 12p, Newton's reflector telescope. 15p, Edmond Halley, Old Greenwich Observatory. 20p, Short's Gregorian telescope, comet, 1759. 70p, ICE space probe, Ascension satellite tracking station.

385	A72	12p multicolored	.55	.55
386	A72	15p multicolored	.65	.65
387	A72	20p multicolored	.70	.70
388	A72	70p multicolored	2.00	2.00
		Nos. 385-388 (4)	3.90	3.90

Queen Elizabeth II 60th Birthday
Common Design Type

Designs: 7p, Infant photograph, 1926. 15p, 1st worldwide Christmas broadcast, 1952. 20p, Garter Ceremony, Windsor Castle, 1983. 35p, Royal Tour, New Zealand, 1981. £1, Visiting Crown Agents' offices, 1983.

1986, Apr. 21   Perf. 14x14½

389	CD337	7p scarlet, blk & sil	.15	.15
390	CD337	15p ultra, blk & sil	.25	.25
391	CD337	20p green & multi	.35	.35
392	CD337	35p violet & multi	.65	.65
393	CD337	£1 rose vio & multi	1.75	1.75
		Nos. 389-393 (5)	3.15	3.15

For overprints see Nos. 431-435.

AMERIPEX
'86 — A73

1986, May 22   Perf. 14½

394	A73	12p No. 183	.35	.35
395	A73	15p No. 260	.45	.45
396	A73	20p No. 215	.55	.55
397	A73	70p No. 310	2.00	2.00
		Nos. 394-397 (4)	3.35	3.35

Souvenir Sheet

398	A73	75p Statue of Liberty, New York Harbor	2.25	2.25

Statue of Liberty, cent.

Royal Wedding Issue, 1986
Common Design Type

Designs: 15p, Couple kissing. 35p, Andrew in navy uniform, helicopter.

Wmk. 384

1986, July 23   Litho.   Perf. 14

399	CD338	15p multicolored	.45	.45
400	CD338	35p multicolored	1.00	1.00

Ships
A74

1986, Oct. 14   Wmk. 384   Perf. 14½

401	A74	1p Ganymede, c. 1811	.15	.15
402	A74	2p Kangaroo, c. 1811	.15	.15
403	A74	4p Trinculo, c. 1811	.15	.15
404	A74	5p Daring, c. 1811	.15	.15
405	A74	9p Thais, c. 1811	.25	.25
406	A74	10p Pheasant, 1819	.30	.30
407	A74	15p Myrmidon, 1819	.40	.40
408	A74	18p Atholl, 1825	.50	.50
409	A74	20p Medina, 1830	.55	.55
410	A74	25p Saracen, 1840	.70	.70
411	A74	30p Hydra, c. 1845	.80	.80
412	A74	50p Sealark, 1840	1.25	1.25
413	A74	70p Rattlesnake, 1868	1.75	1.75
414	A74	£1 Penelope, 1889	2.75	2.75
415	A74	£2 Monarch, 1897	5.50	5.50
		Nos. 401-415 (15)	15.35	15.35

For surcharges see Nos. 502-504.

Edible
Bush Fruits
A75

1987, Jan. 29   Perf. 14

416	A75	12p Cape gooseberry	.35	.35
417	A75	15p Prickly pear	.45	.45
418	A75	20p Guava	.60	.60
419	A75	70p Loquat	2.00	2.00
		Nos. 416-419 (4)	3.40	3.40

1st Manned Space   Military Uniforms,
Flight, 25th   1815-20 — A77
Anniv. — A76

1987, Mar. 30

420	A76	15p Ignition	.45	.45
421	A76	18p Lift-off	.55	.55
422	A76	25p Reentry	.70	.70
423	A76	£1 Splashdown	3.00	3.00
		Nos. 420-423 (4)	4.70	4.70

Souvenir Sheet

424	A76	70p Friendship 7 capsule	2.25	2.25

1987, June 29

Designs: a, Captains in full dress, 1st landing on Ascension. b, Surgeon and sailors at campsite. c, Seaman returning from Dampier's Drip with water supply. d, Midshipman at lookout post. e, Commander and surveyor.

425		Strip of 5	4.00	4.00
a.-e.	A77	25p multicolored	.80	.80

See Nos. 458, 474, 482, 507.

Butterflies
A78

1987, Aug. 10   Perf. 14½

426	A78	15p Painted lady	.60	.60
427	A78	18p Monarch	.75	.75
428	A78	25p Diadem	1.00	1.00
429	A78	£1 Long-tailed blue	3.75	3.75
		Nos. 426-429 (4)	6.10	6.10

See Nos. 436-439, 459-462.

Birds — A79

Designs: a, Ascension frigatebirds (males). b, Brown booby, frigatebird, white boobies. c, Frigatebird, white booby. d, Ascension frigatebirds (females). e, Adult frigatebird feeding young.

1987, Oct. 8   Wmk. 373   Perf. 14

430		Strip of 5	6.00	6.00
a.-e.	A79	25p any single	1.25	1.25

No. 430 has continuous design.
See No. 453.

Nos. 389-393 Ovptd. "40TH WEDDING ANNIVERSARY" in Silver

Perf. 14x14½

1987, Dec. 9   Litho.   Wmk. 384

431	CD337	7p scar, blk & sil	.20	.20
432	CD337	15p ultra, blk & sil	.40	.40
433	CD337	20p green & multi	.60	.60
434	CD337	35p violet & multi	1.00	1.00
435	CD337	£1 rose vio & multi	3.00	3.00
		Nos. 431-435 (5)	5.20	5.20

40th wedding anniv. of Queen Elizabeth II and Prince Philip.

Insects Type of 1987

1988, Jan. 18   Perf. 14½

436	A78	15p Field cricket	.60	.60
437	A78	18p Bush cricket	.75	.75
438	A78	25p Ladybug	1.00	1.00
439	A78	£1 Burnished brass moth	4.00	4.00
		Nos. 436-439 (4)	6.35	6.35

Capt. William Bate (d. 1838), 1st Garrison Commander and Colonial Founder of Ascension
A80

Designs: 9p, Bate's Memorial, St. Mary's Church. 15p, Commodore's Cottage, Cross Hill. 18p, North East or Bate's Cottage, 1833. 25p, Landmarks on map. 70p, Bate and 3 soldiers.

1988, Apr. 14   Perf. 14

440	A80	9p multicolored	.35	.35
441	A80	15p multicolored	.55	.55
442	A80	18p multicolored	.65	.65
443	A80	25p multicolored	.90	.90
444	A80	70p multicolored	2.50	2.50
		Nos. 440-444 (5)	4.95	4.95

Australia Bicentennial Emblem and Ships Named HMS Resolution — A81

1988, June 23   Litho.   Perf. 14

445	A81	9p 3-Masted squarerigger, 1667	.35	.35
446	A81	18p 3-Masted squarerigger, 1772	.65	.65
447	A81	25p Navy cruiser, 1892	.90	.90
448	A81	65p Battleship, 1916	2.25	2.25
		Nos. 445-448 (4)	4.15	4.15

Australia bicentennial.

Nos. 445-448 Overprinted

SYDPEX
88
30.7.88 – 7.8.88

Wmk. 384

1988, July 30   Perf. 14

449	A81	9p multicolored	.35	.35
450	A81	18p multicolored	.65	.65
451	A81	25p multicolored	.90	.90
452	A81	65p multicolored	2.25	2.25
		Nos. 449-452 (4)	4.15	4.15

SYDPEX '88, July 30-Aug. 7.

Bird Type of 1987

Behaviors of the wideawake tern, Sterna fuscata: a, Two adults, flock overhead. b, Nesting (two birds). c, Nesting (three birds). d, Adult and young. e, Tern flapping its wings.

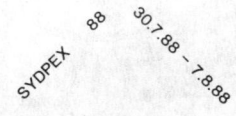

1988, Aug. 15   Perf. 14

453		Strip of 5	6.00	6.00
a.-e.	A79	25p any single	1.25	1.25

No. 453 has continuous design.

Lloyds of London, 300th Anniv.
Common Design Type

Designs: 8p, Lloyd's Coffee House, Tower Street, 1688. 18p, Cable ship Alert, horiz. 25p, Satellite recovery in space, horiz. 65p, Ship Good Hope Castle on fire off Ascension, 1973.

Wmk. 373

1988, Oct. 17   Litho.   Perf. 14

454	CD341	8p multicolored	.30	.30
455	CD341	18p multicolored	.60	.60
456	CD341	25p multicolored	.85	.85
457	CD341	65p multicolored	2.25	2.25
		Nos. 454-457 (4)	4.00	4.00

Military Uniforms Type of 1987

Uniforms of the Royal Marines: a, Marines arrive in Ascension (marines), 1821. b, Semaphore station (officer, marine), 1829. c, Octagonal tank (sergeant), 1831. d, Water pipe tunnel (officers), 1833. e, Constructing barracks (officer), 1834.

1988, Nov. 21

458		Strip of 5	5.00	5.00
a.-e.	A77	25p multicolored	1.00	1.00

Insect Type of 1987
Perf. 14½

1989, Jan. 16   Litho.   Wmk. 384

459	A78	15p Plume moth	.60	.60
460	A78	18p Green bottle	.70	.70
461	A78	25p Weevil	.95	.95
462	A78	£1 Paper wasp	3.75	3.75
		Nos. 459-462 (4)	6.00	6.00

Land Crabs, Gecarcinus Lagostoma — A82

1989, Apr. 17

463	A82	15p multi	.50	.50
464	A82	18p multi, diff.	.65	.65
465	A82	25p multi, diff.	.90	.90
466	A82	£1 multi, diff.	3.50	3.50
		Nos. 463-466 (4)	5.55	5.55

Miniature Sheet

467		Sheet of 4	5.50	5.50
a.	A82	15p like No. 463	.50	.50
b.	A82	18p like No. 464	.65	.65
c.	A82	25p like No. 465	.85	.85
d.	A82	£1 like No. 466	3.50	3.50

Vignettes of Nos. 467a-467d do not have frame.

Moon Landing, 20th Anniv.
Common Design Type

Apollo 7: 15p, Tracking Station, Ascension Is. 18p, Launch, Cape Kennedy. 25p, Mission emblem. 70p, Expended Saturn IVB stage. £1, Lunar landing profile for the Apollo 11 mission.

1989, July 20   Perf. 14x13½
Size of Nos. 469-470: 29x29mm

468	CD342	15p multicolored	.40	.40
469	CD342	18p multicolored	.50	.50
470	CD342	25p multicolored	.70	.70
471	CD342	70p multicolored	1.90	1.90
		Nos. 468-471 (4)	3.50	3.50

Souvenir Sheet

472	CD342	£1 multicolored	3.00	3.00

Souvenir Sheet

PHILEXFRANCE
89
A83

1989, July 7   Perf. 14x13½

473	A83	75p Emblems, No. 60	2.50	2.50

Miniature Sheet

World Stamp Expo '89, Washington, DC, and PHILEXFRANCE '89, Paris — A84

The Statue of Liberty and scenes from the centenary celebrations, 1986: a, Operation Sail. b, Face. c, Upper body. d, Three crown points. e, Ships in harbor, view of lower Manhattan. f, Ship in port, New York City.

1989, Aug. 21   **Wmk. 373**
474   Sheet of 6   2.75   2.75
a.-f. A84 15p any single   .45   .45

Devil's Ashpit Tracking Station A85

1989, Sept. 30   **Wmk. 384**   *Perf. 14*
475   Sheet, 5 each #a.-b.   6.75   6.75
a.   A85 18p shown   .55   .55
b.   A85 25p US space shuttle launch   .80   .80

Termination of NASA tracking operations, begun in 1965, at the station.

Shells and Mollusks A86

       Wmk. 384
1989, Nov. 6   **Litho.**   *Perf. 14*
476 A86   8p   *Strombus latus*   .30   .30
477 A86 18p   *Tonna galea*   .65   .65
478 A86 25p   *Harpa doris*   .85   .85
479 A86 £1   *Charonia variegata*   3.25   3.25
     Nos. 476-479 (4)   5.05   5.05

Donkeys — A87

Perf. 14 on 3 Sides
1989, Nov. 17   **Litho.**   **Wmk. 384**
Booklet Stamps
480 A87 18p shown   .50   .50
a.   Booklet pane of 6   3.00
481 A87 25p Green turtle   .75   .75
a.   Booklet pane of 4   3.00

No. 480a sold for £1.

Military Type of 1987

Royal Navy equipment, c. 1815-1820: a, Seaman's pistol, hat, cutlass. b, Midshipman's belt buckle, button, sword, hat. c, Surgeon's hat, sword, instrument chest. d, Captain's hat, telescope, sword. e, Admiral's epaulet, megaphone, hat, pocket.

1990, Feb. 12   **Litho.**   *Perf. 14*
482   Strip of 5   4.25   4.25
a.-e. A77 25p any single   .85   .85

World Wildlife Fund — A88

Frigate birds *(Fregata aquila)*: 9p, Family group. 10p, Chick. 11p, Male in flight. 15p, Female and immature in flight.

Perf. 14¹⁄₂x14
1990, Mar. 5   **Litho.**   **Wmk. 373**
483 A88   9p multicolored   .60   .60
484 A88 10p multicolored   .65   .65
485 A88 11p multicolored   .70   .70
486 A88 15p multicolored   .95   .95
     Nos. 483-486 (4)   2.90   2.90

Great Britain Nos. 1-2 — A89

Exhibition emblem and: 18p, Early Ascension cancellations. 25p, Unloading mail at Wideawake Airfield. £1, Main P.O., Royal Mail van.

1990, May 3   **Litho.**   *Perf. 14*
487 A89   9p shown   .30   .30
488 A89 18p multicolored   .60   .60
489 A89 25p multicolored   .85   .85
490 A89 £1 multicolored   3.25   3.25
     Nos. 487-490 (4)   5.00   5.00

Penny Black 150th anniv., Stamp World London '90.

Queen Mother, 90th Birthday
Common Design Types
1990, Aug. 4   **Wmk. 384**   *Perf. 14x15*
491 CD343 25p Portrait, 1940   .85   .85

Perf. 14¹⁄₂
492 CD344 £1 King, Queen with soldiers   3.25   3.25

Garth Castle, 1910 — A90

Designs: 18p, RMS St. Helena, 1982. 25p, Launching new RMS St. Helena, 1989. 70p, Duke of York launching new RMS St. Helena. £1, New RMS St. Helena.

Perf. 14¹⁄₂
1990, Sept. 13   **Litho.**   **Wmk. 373**
493 A90   9p multicolored   .35   .35
494 A90 18p multicolored   .65   .65
495 A90 25p multicolored   .90   .90
496 A90 70p multicolored   2.50   2.50
     Nos. 493-496 (4)   4.40   4.40

Souvenir Sheet
497 A90 £1 multicolored   3.50   3.50

See St. Helena Nos. 535-539, Tristan da Cunha Nos. 482-486.

Christmas — A91

Sculpture (8p) and paintings of Madonna and Child by: 8p, Felici. 18p, Unknown artist. 25p, Gebhard. 65p, Gritti.

1990, Oct. 24   *Perf. 14*
498 A91   8p multicolored   .30   .30
499 A91 18p multicolored   .65   .65
500 A91 25p multicolored   .90   .90
501 A91 65p multicolored   3.25   3.25
     Nos. 498-501 (4)   5.10   5.10

Nos. 410, 412 &   **BRITISH FOR 175 YEARS**
414 Ovptd. in Silver

1991, Feb. 5   **Wmk. 384**   *Perf. 14¹⁄₂*
502 A74 25p on #410   1.00   1.00
503 A74 50p on #412   2.00   2.00
504 A74 £1   on #414   4.00   4.00
     Nos. 502-504 (3)   7.00   7.00

Elizabeth & Philip, Birthdays
Common Design Types
1991, June 18
505 CD345 25p multicolored   .80   .80
506 CD346 25p multicolored   .80   .80
a.   Pair, #505-506 + label   1.60

Military Uniforms Type of 1987

Royal Marines Equipment 1821-1844: a, Officer's shako, epaulettes, belt plate, button. b, Officer's cap, sword, epaulettes, belt plate. c, Drum Major's shako with cords, staff. d, Sergeant's shako, chevrons, belt plate, canteen. e, Drummer's drum, sticks, shako.

1991, Aug. 1   **Wmk. 373**   *Perf. 14*
507 A77 25p Strip of 5, #a.-e.   4.00   4.00

Atlantic Relay Station, 25th Anniv. A92

Designs: 15p, BBC Atlantic relay station. 18p, English Bay transmitters. 25p, Satellite receiving station, vert. 70p, Antenna support tower, vert.

1991, Sept. 17   **Wmk. 384**   *Perf. 14¹⁄₂*
508 A92 15p multicolored   .50   .50
509 A92 18p multicolored   .60   .60
510 A92 25p multicolored   .85   .85
511 A92 70p multicolored   2.50   2.50
     Nos. 508-511 (4)   4.45   4.45

Christmas — A93

Designs: 8p, St. Mary's Church, exterior. 18p, St. Mary's Church, interior. 25p, Grotto of Our Lady of Ascension, exterior. 65p, Grotto of Our Lady of Ascension, interior.

1991, Oct. 1   *Perf. 14*
512 A93   8p multicolored   .30   .30
513 A93 18p multicolored   .60   .60
514 A93 25p multicolored   .85   .85
515 A93 65p multicolored   2.25   2.25
     Nos. 512-515 (4)   4.00   4.00

Fish A94

       Wmk. 373
1991, Dec. 10   **Litho.**   *Perf. 14*
516 A94   1p Blackfish   .15   .15
517 A94   2p Five finger   .15   .15
518 A94   4p Resplendent angelfish   .15   .15
519 A94   5p Silver fish   .15   .15
520 A94   9p Gurnard   .30   .30
521 A94 10p Blue dad   .35   .35
522 A94 15p Cunning fish   .50   .50
523 A94 18p Grouper   .60   .60
524 A94 20p Moray eel   .65   .65
525 A94 25p Hardback soldierfish   .85   .85
526 A94 30p Blue marlin   1.00   1.00
527 A94 50p Wahoo   1.65   1.65
528 A94 70p Yellowfin tuna   2.25   2.25
529 A94 £1 Blue shark   3.25   3.25
530 A94 £2.50 Bottlenose dolphin   8.50   8.50
     Nos. 516-530 (15)   20.50   20.50

Queen Elizabeth II's Accession to the Throne, 40th Anniv.
Common Design Type
       Wmk. 373
1992, Feb. 6   **Litho.**   *Perf. 14*
531 CD349   9p multicolored   .30   .30
532 CD349 15p multicolored   .50   .50
533 CD349 18p multicolored   .60   .60
534 CD349 25p multicolored   .85   .85
535 CD349 70p multicolored   2.25   2.25
     Nos. 531-535 (5)   4.50   4.50

Discovery of America, 500th Anniv. — A95

       Wmk. 373
1992, Feb. 18   **Litho.**   *Perf. 14*
536 A95   9p STV Eye of the Wind   .30   .30
537 A95 18p STV Soren Larsen   .60   .60
538 A95 25p Pinta, Santa Maria, & Nina   .85   .85
539 A95 70p Columbus, Santa Maria   2.25   2.25
     Nos. 536-539 (4)   4.00   4.00

World Columbian Stamp Expo '92, Chicago and Genoa '92 Intl. Philatelic Exhibitions.

Wideawake Airfield, 50th Anniv. — A96

       Wmk. 373
1992, May 5   **Litho.**   *Perf. 14*
540 A96 15p Control tower   .50   .50
541 A96 18p Nose hangar   .60   .60
542 A96 25p Construction work   .85   .85
543 A96 70p Laying fuel pipeline   2.25   2.25
     Nos. 540-543 (4)   4.20   4.20

Ascension's Participation in Falkland Islands' Liberation, 10th Anniv. — A97

#548a, 15p + 3p like #544. b, 18p + 4p like #545. c, 25p + 5p like #546. d, 65p + 13p like #547.

       Wmk. 373
1992, June 12   **Litho.**   *Perf. 14*
544 A97 15p Nimrod Mk.2   .50   .50
545 A97 18p VC10   .60   .60
546 A97 25p Wessex HU Mk.5 helicopter   .85   .85
547 A97 65p Vulcan B2   2.25   2.25
     Nos. 544-547 (4)   4.20   4.20

Souvenir Sheet
548 A97   Sheet of 4, #a.-d.   5.00   5.00

Surtax for Soldiers', Sailors' and Airmen's Families Association.

Christmas A98

Children's drawings: 8p, Snowman, rocks, candle. 18p, Underwater Santa, Christmas tree. 25p, Hello, bells. 65p, Nativity Scene, angel.

       Wmk. 384
1992, Oct. 13   **Litho.**   *Perf. 14*
549 A98   8p multicolored   .30   .30
550 A98 18p multicolored   .70   .70
551 A98 25p multicolored   .95   .95
552 A98 65p multicolored   2.50   2.50
     Nos. 549-552 (4)   4.45   4.45

Yellow Canary — A99

Perf. 14¹⁄₂
1993, Jan. 12   **Litho.**   **Wmk. 373**
553 A99 15p Singing male   .45   .45
554 A99 18p Adult male, female   .55   .55
555 A99 25p Young calling for food   .80   .80
556 A99 70p Mixed flock   2.25   2.25
     Nos. 553-556 (4)   4.05   4.05

Royal Air Force, 75th Anniv.
Common Design Type

Designs: 20p, Sopwith Snipe. No. 558, Supermarine Southampton. 30p, Avro Anson. 70p, Vickers Wellington 1C.

No. 561a, Westland Lysander. b, Gloster Meteor. c, DeHavilland Comet. d, British Aerospace Nimrod.

Wmk. 373

1993, Apr. 1	**Litho.**		**Perf. 14**
557	CD350	20p multicolored	.60 .60
558	CD350	25p multicolored	.70 .70
559	CD350	30p multicolored	.85 .85
560	CD350	70p multicolored	2.25 2.25
	Nos. 557-560 (4)		4.40 4.40

Souvenir Sheet

561	CD350	25p Sheet of 4, #a.-d.	3.00 3.00

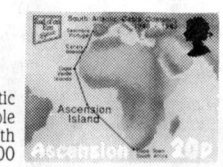

South Atlantic Cable Company, 25th Anniv. — A100

Designs: 20p, Map showing cable route. 25p, Cable ship laying cable. 30p, Map of Ascension. 70p, Cable ship off Ascension.

Perf. 14x14½

1993, June 8	**Litho.**		**Wmk. 384**
562	A100	20p multicolored	.60 .60
563	A100	25p multicolored	.75 .75
564	A100	30p multicolored	.90 .90
565	A100	70p multicolored	2.00 2.00
	Nos. 562-565 (4)		4.25 4.25

Flowers A101

Perf. 14x14½

1993, Aug. 3	**Litho.**		**Wmk. 384**
566	A101	20p Lantana camara	.60 .60
567	A101	25p Moonflower	.75 .75
568	A101	30p Hibiscus	.90 .90
569	A101	70p Frangipani	2.00 2.00
	Nos. 566-569 (4)		4.25 4.25

Christmas — A102

Designs: 12p, Child mailing Christmas card. 20p, Mail loaded onto Tristar. 25p, Plane in flight. 30p, Mail unloaded at Wideawake Airfield. 65p, Child reading card, Georgetown.

Perf. 14½x14

1993, Oct. 19	**Litho.**		**Wmk. 373**
570	A102	12p multicolored	.35 .35
571	A102	20p multicolored	.60 .60
572	A102	25p multicolored	.75 .75
573	A102	30p multicolored	.90 .90
574	A102	65p multicolored	2.00 2.00
a.	Souvenir sheet of 5, #570-574		4.50 4.50
	Nos. 570-574 (5)		4.60 4.60

Stamps from No. 574a show a continuous design, while Nos. 570-574 have white borders on sides.

Prehistoric Aquatic Reptiles — A103

1994, Jan. 25	**Wmk. 373**		**Perf. 14**
575	A103	12p Ichthyosaurus	.35 .35
576	A103	20p Metriorhynchus	.60 .60
577	A103	25p Mosasaurus	.75 .75
578	A103	30p Elasmosaurus	.90 .90
579	A103	65p Plesiosaurus	1.90 1.90
	Nos. 575-579 (5)		4.50 4.50

Ovptd. with Hong Kong '94 Emblem

1994, Feb. 18			
580	A103	12p on #575	.35 .35
581	A103	20p on #576	.60 .60
582	A103	25p on #577	.75 .75
583	A103	30p on #578	.90 .90
584	A103	65p on #579	1.90 1.90
	Nos. 580-584 (5)		4.50 4.50

Green Turtle A104

Designs: 20p, Four on beach. 25p, Crawling in sand. No. 587, Crawling from sea. 65p, Swimming. No. 589a, Side view, crawling from sea. b, Digging nest. c, Hatchlings heading to sea. d, Digging nest, diff.

1994, Mar. 22			
585	A104	20p multicolored	.60 .60
586	A104	25p multicolored	.75 .75
587	A104	30p multicolored	.90 .90
588	A104	65p multicolored	1.90 1.90
	Nos. 585-588 (4)		4.15 4.15

Souvenir Sheet

589	A104	30p Sheet of 4, #a.-d.	3.50 3.50

Civilian Ships A105

Ships serving during Falkland Islands War, 1982: 20p, Tug Yorkshireman. 25p, Minesweeper support ship RMS St. Helena. 30p, Oil tanker British ESK. 65p, Cruise liner Uganda, hospital ship.

1994, June 14			
590	A105	20p multicolored	.60 .60
591	A105	25p multicolored	.75 .75
592	A105	30p multicolored	.90 .90
593	A105	65p multicolored	1.90 1.90
	Nos. 590-593 (4)		4.15 4.15

Sooty Tern A106

1994, Aug. 16			
594	A106	20p Chick	.60 .60
595	A106	25p Juvenile	.75 .75
596	A106	30p Brooding adult	.90 .90
597	A106	65p Displaying male	1.90 1.90
	Nos. 594-597 (4)		4.15 4.15

Souvenir Sheet

598	A106	£1 Dread	3.00 3.00

Christmas A107

Donkeys: 12p, Mare with foal. 20p, Young adult. 25p, Foal. 30p, Adult, egrets. 65p, Adult.

1994, Oct. 11			**Perf. 14x14½**
599	A107	12p multicolored	.40 .40
600	A107	20p multicolored	.60 .60
601	A107	25p multicolored	.75 .75
602	A107	30p multicolored	.95 .95
603	A107	65p multicolored	2.00 2.00
	Nos. 599-603 (5)		4.70 4.70

Flowers A108

Designs: 20p, Leonurus japonicus, vert. 25p, Periwinkle. 30p, Four o'clock, vert. 65p, Blood flower.

1995, Jan. 10			**Perf. 14**
604	A108	20p multicolored	.60 .60
605	A108	25p multicolored	.75 .75
606	A108	30p multicolored	.95 .95
607	A108	65p multicolored	2.00 2.00
	Nos. 604-607 (4)		4.30 4.30

Island Scenes, c. 1895 A109

Designs: 12p, Horse-drawn wagon, Two Boats, Green Mountain. 20p, Island stewards' store. 25p, Royal Navy headquarters, barracks. 30p, Police office. 65p, Pier head.

1995, Mar. 7	**Wmk. 384**		**Perf. 14½**
608	A109	12p sepia	.35 .35
609	A109	20p sepia	.60 .60
610	A109	25p sepia	.75 .75
611	A109	30p sepia	.90 .90
612	A109	65p sepia	2.00 2.00
	Nos. 608-612 (5)		4.60 4.60

End of World War II, 50th Anniv.
Common Design Types

Designs: 20p, 5.5-inch guns taken from HMS Hood, 1941. 25p, Fairey Swordfish, first aircraft to land at Ascension. 30p, HMS Dorsetshire patrolling South Atlantic. 65p, HMS Devonshire patrolling South Atlantic.
£1, Reverse of War Medal, 1939-45.

1995, May 8	**Wmk. 373**		**Perf. 14**
613	CD351	20p multicolored	.60 .60
614	CD351	25p multicolored	.75 .75
615	CD351	30p multicolored	.90 .90
616	CD351	65p multicolored	2.00 2.00
	Nos. 613-616 (4)		4.25 4.25

Souvenir Sheet

617	CD352	£1 multicolored	3.00 3.00

Butterflies — A110

1995, Sept. 1			**Wmk. 384**
618	A110	20p Long-tailed blue	.60 .60
619	A110	25p Painted lady	.75 .75
620	A110	30p Diadem	.90 .90
621	A110	65p African monarch	2.00 2.00
	Nos. 618-621 (4)		4.25 4.25

Souvenir Sheet

622	A110	£1 Red admiral	3.00 3.00

Singapore '95 (#622).

Christmas A111

Designs based on children's drawings: 12p, Santa on boat. 20p, Santa on wall. 25p, Santa in chimney. 30p, Santa on dolphin. 65p, South Atlantic run.

1995, Oct. 10			**Wmk. 373**
623	A111	12p multicolored	.35 .35
624	A111	20p multicolored	.60 .60
625	A111	25p multicolored	.75 .75
626	A111	30p multicolored	.90 .90
627	A111	65p multicolored	2.00 2.00
	Nos. 623-627 (5)		4.60 4.60

Mollusks A112

12p, Cypraea lurida. 25p, Cypraea spurca. 30p, Harpa doris. 65p, Umbraculum umbraculum.

Wmk. 384

1996, Jan. 10	**Litho.**		**Perf. 14**
628	A112	12p multicolored	.35 .35
629	A112	25p multicolored	.75 .75
630	A112	30p multicolored	.90 .90
631	A112	65p multicolored	2.00 2.00
a.	Strip of 4, #628-631		4.00 4.00

Queen Elizabeth II, 70th Birthday
Common Design Type

Various portraits of Queen, scenes of Ascension: 20p, St. Marys Church. 25p, The Residency. 30p, Roman Catholic Grotto. 65p, The Exiles Club.

Perf. 13½

1996, Apr. 22	**Litho.**		**Wmk. 384**
632	CD354	20p multicolored	.65 .65
633	CD354	25p multicolored	.80 .80
634	CD354	30p multicolored	1.00 1.00
635	CD354	65p multicolored	2.00 2.00
	Nos. 632-635 (4)		4.45 4.45

CAPEX '96 A113

Island transport: 20p, US Army Jeep. 25p, 1924 Citroen 7.5HP two seater. 30p, 1930 Austin Ten-four Tourer. 65p, Series 1 Land Rover.

Wmk. 384

1996, June 8	**Litho.**		**Perf. 14**
636	A113	20p multicolored	.65 .65
637	A113	25p multicolored	.80 .80
638	A113	30p multicolored	1.00 1.00
639	A113	65p multicolored	2.00 2.00
	Nos. 636-639 (4)		4.45 4.45

Birds and Their Young — A114

Designs: 1p, Madeiran storm petrel. 2p, Red-billed tropicbird. 4p, Indian mynah. 5p, House sparrow. 7p, Common waxbill. 10p, White tern. 12p, Francolin. 15p, Brown noddy. 20p, Yellow canary. 25p, Black noddy. 30p, Red-footed booby. 40p, Yellow-billed tropicbird. 65p, Brown booby. £1, Masked booby. £2, Sooty tern. £3, Ascension frigate bird.

Wmk. 373

1996, Aug. 12	**Litho.**		**Perf. 13**
640	A114	1p multicolored	.15 .15
641	A114	2p multicolored	.15 .15
642	A114	4p multicolored	.15 .15
643	A114	5p multicolored	.15 .15
644	A114	7p multicolored	.20 .20
645	A114	10p multicolored	.35 .35
646	A114	12p multicolored	.40 .40
647	A114	15p multicolored	.50 .50
648	A114	20p multicolored	.65 .65
649	A114	25p multicolored	.80 .80
650	A114	30p multicolored	1.00 1.00
651	A114	40p multicolored	1.25 1.25
652	A114	65p multicolored	2.00 2.00
a.	Sheet of 1, perf. 14		2.10 2.10
653	A114	£1 multicolored	3.25 3.25
a.	Souvenir sheet of 1		3.25 3.25
654	A114	£2 multicolored	6.50 6.50
655	A114	£3 multicolored	10.00 10.00
	Nos. 640-655 (16)		27.50 27.50

No. 652a for Hong Kong '97. Issued 2/3/97.
No. 653a for return of Hong Kong to China. Issued 7/1/97.

BBC Atlantic Relay Station, 30th Anniv. A115

Various views of relay station: 20p, 25p, Towers. 30p, Towers, buildings. 65p, Satellite dish, towers, beach.

1996, Sept. 9   Wmk. 384   Perf. 14

656	A115	20p multicolored	.65	.65
657	A115	25p multicolored	.80	.80
658	A115	30p multicolored	1.00	1.00
659	A115	65p multicolored	2.00	2.00
		Nos. 656-659 (4)	4.45	4.45

Christmas
A116

Santa Claus: 12p, On satellite dish. 20p, Playing golf. 25p, By beach. 30p, On RAF Tristar. 65p, Aboard RMS St. Helena.

Perf. 14x14½

1996, Sept. 23   Litho.   Wmk. 373

660	A116	12p multicolored	.40	.40
661	A116	20p multicolored	.65	.65
662	A116	25p multicolored	.80	.80
663	A116	30p multicolored	1.00	1.00
664	A116	65p multicolored	2.00	2.00
		Nos. 660-664 (5)	4.85	4.85

UNICEF, 50th anniv.

20p   Trees — A117

Perf. 14½

1997, Jan. 7   Litho.   Wmk. 373

665	A117	20p Date palm	.65	.65
666	A117	25p Mauritius hemp	.80	.80
667	A117	30p Norfolk Island pine	1.00	1.00
668	A117	65p Dwarf palm	2.00	2.00
		Nos. 665-668 (4)	4.45	4.45

Hong Kong '97.

Ascension Island
Flags — A118

Flag, ship or aircraft: 12p, Great Britain Red Ensign, tanker Maserk Ascension. 25p, RAF Ensign, Tristar. 30p, NASA emblem, Space Shuttle Atlantis. 65p, Royal Navy White Ensign, HMS Northumberland.

Perf. 14½

1997, Apr. 1   Litho.   Wmk. 373

669	A118	12p multicolored	.40	.40
670	A118	25p multicolored	.80	.80
671	A118	30p multicolored	.95	.95
672	A118	65p multicolored	2.00	2.00
		Nos. 669-672 (4)	4.15	4.15

Herbs
A119

Designs: a, Solanum sodomaeum. b, Ageratum conyzoides. c, Leonurus sibricus. d, Cerastium vulgatum. e, Commelina diffusa.

Perf. 14x14½

1997, June 7   Litho.   Wmk. 373

673	A119	30p Strip of 5, #a.-e.	5.00	5.00

Ascension stamps can be mounted in the Scott British Africa album.

A120   Birds — A121

Queen Elizabeth II and Prince Philip, 50th Wedding Anniv.: No. 674, Queen Elizabeth II. No. 675, Prince Philip playing polo. No. 676, Queen petting horse. No. 677, Prince Philip. No. 678, Prince Philip, Queen Elizabeth II. No. 679, Prince Harry, Prince William riding horses.
£1.50, Queen Elizabeth, Prince Philip riding in open carriage.

1997   Litho.   Wmk. 384   Perf. 13½

674	A120	20p multicolored	.65	.65
675	A120	20p multicolored	.65	.65
a.		Pair, #674-675	1.30	1.30
676	A120	25p multicolored	.85	.85
677	A120	25p multicolored	.85	.85
a.		Pair, #676-677	1.70	1.70
678	A120	30p multicolored	1.00	1.00
679	A120	30p multicolored	1.00	1.00
a.		Pair, #678-679	2.00	2.00
		Nos. 674-679 (6)	5.00	5.00

Souvenir Sheet

680	A120	£1.50 multicolored	4.75	4.75

Perf. 14 on 3 Sides

1997   Litho.   Wmk. 373

Booklet Stamps

681	A121	15p like #644	.50	.50
682	A121	35p like #648	1.10	1.10
a.		Booklet pane, 2 ea #681-682	3.25	
		Complete booklet, #682a	3.25	

Game
Fish — A122

Perf. 14x14½

1997   Litho.   Wmk. 373

683	A122	12p Black marlin	.40	.40
684	A122	20p Atlantic sailfish	.65	.65
685	A122	25p Swordfish	.80	.80
686	A122	30p Wahoo	.95	.95
687	A122	£1 Yellowfin tuna	3.25	3.25
		Nos. 683-687 (5)	6.05	6.05

Christmas — A123

St. Mary's Church: 15p, Interior view. 35p, Stained glass window, Madonna and Child. 40p, Stained glass window, Falklands, 1982. 50p, Stained glass window.

1997   Litho.   Wmk. 384   Perf. 14

688	A123	15p multicolored	.50	.50
689	A123	35p multicolored	1.15	1.15
690	A123	40p multicolored	1.30	1.30
691	A123	50p multicolored	1.70	1.70
		Nos. 688-691 (4)	4.65	4.65

POSTAGE DUE STAMPS

Outline Map of
Ascension — D1

1986   Litho.   Perf. 15x14

J1	D1	1p beige & brown	.15	.15
J2	D1	2p orange & brown	.15	.15
J3	D1	5p org ver & brn	.15	.15
J4	D1	7p violet & black	.20	.20

J5	D1	10p ultra & black	.25	.25
J6	D1	25p pale green & blk	.60	.60
		Set value	1.25	1.25

AUSTRALIAN STATES

NEW SOUTH WALES

'nü saúth ,wā(ə)lz

LOCATION — Southeast coast of Australia in the South Pacific Ocean
GOVT. — British Crown Colony
AREA — 309,432 sq. mi.
POP. — 1,500,000 (estimated, 1900)
CAPITAL — Sydney

In 1901 New South Wales united with five other British colonies to form the Commonwealth of Australia. Stamps of Australia are now used.

12 Pence = 1 Shilling
20 Shillings = 1 Pound

Watermarks

Wmk. 12- Crown   Wmk. 13- Large
and Single-lined A   Crown and Double-
lined A

Wmk. 49-   Wmk. 50- Single-
Double-lined   lined Numeral
Numerals
Corresponding
with the Value

Wmk. 51- Single-   Wmk. 52- Single-
lined Numeral   lined Numeral

Wmk. 53- 5/-

Wmk. 54- Small   Wmk. 55- Large
Crown and NSW   Crown and NSW

Right Column (far right)

Wmk. 56-
NSW

Wmk. 57- 5/-
NSW in
Diamond

Wmk. 58- 20/-
NSW in Circle

Wmk. 70- V and
Crown

Wmk. 199-
Crown and A
in Circle

Values for unused stamps are for examples with original gum as defined in the catalogue introduction except for Nos. 1-20 which are rarely found with gum and are valued without gum. Very fine examples of Nos. 35-100, F3-F5, J1-J10 and O1-O40 will have perforations touching the framelines or design on one or more sides due to the narrow spacing of the stamps on the plates and imperfect perforation methods. Stamps with perfs clear of the design on all four sides are scarce and will command higher prices.

Seal of the Colony
A1   A2

A1 has no clouds. A2 has clouds added to the design, except in pos. 15.

1850   Unwmk.   Engr.   Imperf.

1	A1	1p red, yelsh wove	4,000.	400.
b.		1p red, bluish wove	4,000.	350.
2	A2	1p red, yelsh wove	2,500.	275.
b.		1p red, yellowish laid	4,000.	450.
c.		1p red, bluish wove	2,500.	275.
d.		1p red, bluish laid		
e.		Hill unshaded	4,250.	450.
g.		No clouds	4,250.	450.
h.		No trees	4,250.	450.

Twenty-five varieties.
Stamps from early impressions of the plate sell at considerably higher prices.

No. 1 was reproduced by the collotype process in a souvenir sheet distributed at the London International Stamp Exhibition 1950. The paper is white.

Plate I — A3   Plate II — A4

Plate I: Vertically lined background.

Plate I re-touched: Lines above and below "POSTAGE" and "TWO PENCE" deepened. Outlines of circular band around picture also deepened.

Plate II (First re-engraving of Plate I): Horizontally lined background; the bale on the left side is dated and there is a dot in the star in each corner.

Plate II retouched: Dots and dashes added in lower spandrels.

Plate I
Late (worn plate) Impressions

3	A3 2p blue, *yelsh wove*	1,600.	150.
a.	Early impressions	4,500.	350.

Twenty-four varieties.

Plate I, Retouched

4	A3 2p blue, *yelsh wove*	2,750.	250.

Twelve varieties.

Plate II
Late (worn plate) Impressions

5	A4 2p blue, *yelsh wove*	1,750.	175.
a.	2p blue, *bluish wove*	1,750.	175.
b.	2p blue, *grayish wove*	1,750.	175.
c.	"CREVIT" omitted	—	350.
d.	Pick and shovel omitted	—	275.
f.	No whip	3,250.	225.
h.	Early impressions	4,000.	225.

Plate II, Retouched

5F	A4 2p blue, *bluish wove*	2,250.	200.
g.	No whip	—	275.
i.	"CREVIT" omitted	—	375.

Twelve varieties.

Plate III — A5   Plate IV — A6

Plate III (Second re-engraving of Plate I): The bale is not dated and, with the exception of Nos. 7, 10 and 12, it is single-lined. There are no dots in the stars.

Plate IV (Third re-engraving of Plate I): The bale is double-lined and there is a circle in the center of each star.

1850-51

6	A5 2p blue, *grayish wove*	2,100.	175.
a.	Fan with 6 segments	—	350.
b.	Double-lined bale	—	225.
c.	No whip	—	250.
7	A6 2p blue, *bluish wove* ('51)	2,250.	150.
a.	2p blue, *white laid*	2,750.	150.
b.	2p blue, *grayish wove*	2,250.	150.
c.	Fan with 6 segments	—	200.
d.	No clouds	—	200.

Twenty-four varieties.

Plate V — A7   A8

Plate V (Fourth re-engraving of Plate I): There is a pearl in the fan-shaped ornament below the central design.

1850-51

8	A7 2p blue, *grayish wove* ('51)	2,250.	165.
a.	2p ultra, *white laid*	3,250.	275.
b.	Fan with 6 segments	—	250.
c.	Pick and shovel omitted	—	250.
9	A8 3p green, *bluish wove*	2,250.	200.
a.	3p green, *yellowish wove*	3,750.	225.
b.	3p green, *yellowish laid*	4,500.	400.
c.	3p green, *bluish laid*	4,500.	400.
d.	No whip	2,500.	300.

Twenty-four varieties.

Queen Victoria
A9   A10

TWO PENCE
Plate I - Background of wavy lines.
Plate II - Stars in corners.
Plate III (Plate I re-engraved) - Background of crossed lines.

SIX PENCE
Plate I - Background of fine lines.
Plate II (Plate I re-engraved) - Background of coarse lines.

1851   **Yellowish Wove Paper**

10	A9 1p carmine	1,650.	250.
b.	No leaves to right of "SOUTH"	3,250.	365.00
c.	Two leaves to right of "SOUTH"	3,250.	425.00
d.	"WALE"	3,250.	425.00
11	A9 2p ultra, Plate I	750.00	90.00

1852   **Bluish Laid Paper**

12	A9 1p carmine	3,000.	400.
a.	No leaves to right of "SOUTH"		500.
b.	Two leaves to right of "SOUTH"		600.
c.	"WALE"		600.

1852-55
Bluish or Grayish Wove Paper

13	A9 1p red	750.00	125.00
a.	1p carmine	1,000.	140.00
b.	No leaves to right of "SOUTH"		200.00
c.	Two leaves to right of "SOUTH"		250.00
d.	"WALE"		200.00
14	A9 2p blue, Plate I	300.00	27.50
a.	2p ultramarine	325.00	27.50
b.	2p slate	425.00	27.50
15	A10 2p blue, Plate II ('53)	900.00	87.50
a.	"WAEES"	2,300.	450.00
16	A9 2p blue, Plate III ('55)	425.00	55.00
17	A9 3p green	900.00	140.00
a.	3p emerald	1,300.	100.00
b.	"WACES"	2,300.	325.00
18	A9 6p brown, Plate I	2,000.	250.00
a.	6p black brown	2,000.	250.00
b.	"WALLS"	4,250.	425.00
19	A9 6p brown, Plate II	2,000.	250.00
a.	6p bister brown	2,000.	225.00
20	A9 8p yellow ('53)	3,600.	550.00
a.	8p orange	3,600.	550.00
b.	No leaves to right of "SOUTH"		900.00

The plates of the 1, 2, 3 and 8p each contained 50 varieties and those of the 6p 25 varieties.

The 2p, plate II, 6p, plate II, and 8p have been reprinted on grayish blue wove paper. The reprints of the 2p have the spandrels and background much worn. Most of the reprints of the 6p have no floreate ornaments to the right and left of "South". On all the values the wreath has been retouched.

Type of 1851 and:

A11   A12

A13   A14

1854-55   **Wmk. 49**

23	A9 1p orange	125.00	13.00
a.	No leaves to right of "SOUTH"	275.00	60.00
b.	Two leaves to right of "SOUTH"	400.00	100.00
c.	"WALE"	400.00	125.00
24	A9 2p blue	100.00	10.00
a.	2p ultramarine	100.00	10.00
25	A9 3p green	150.00	25.00
a.	"WACES"		80.00
b.	Watermarked "2"		50.00

Value for No. 25b is for copy with the design cut into.

26	A11 5p green	800.00	375.00
27	A11 6p sage green	425.00	32.50
28	A12 6p brown	450.00	30.00
a.	Watermarked "8"	1,650.	85.00
29	A12 6p gray	325.00	30.00
a.	Watermarked "8"	1,650.	80.00
30	A13 8p orange ('55)	4,750.	1,000.
a.	8p yellow	4,750.	1,000.
31	A14 1sh pale red brown	650.00	75.00
a.	1sh red	650.00	75.00
b.	Watermarked "8"	2,000.	150.00

See Nos. 38-42, 56, 58, 65, 67.

Nos. 38-42 exist with wide margins. Copies with perforations trimmed are often offered as Nos. 26, 30, and 30a.

A15   A16

1856

32	A15 1p red	90.00	16.00
a.	1p orange	90.00	16.00
b.	Printed on both sides		2,250.
33	A15 2p blue	110.00	5.00
a.	Watermarked "1"		5,000.
b.	Watermarked "5"	550.00	25.00
c.	Watermarked "8"		125.00
34	A15 3p green	750.00	80.00
a.	3p yellow green	725.00	75.00
b.	Watermarked "2"		4,000.
	Nos. 32-34 (3)	950.00	101.00

The 1p has been reprinted in orange on paper watermarked Small Crown and NSW, and the 2p in deep blue on paper watermarked single lined "2." These reprints are usually overprinted "SPECIMEN."

See Nos. 34C-37, 54, 63, 90.

1859   **Litho.**

34C	A15 2p light blue		625.00

1860-63   **Engr.**   **Wmk. 49**   **Perf. 13**

35	A15 1p red	55.00	8.00
a.	1p orange	100.00	8.00
b.	Perf. 12x13		2,000.
c.	Perf. 12	90.00	15.00
36	A15 2p blue, perf. 12	100.00	9.00
a.	Watermarked "1"		3,500.
c.	Perf. 12x13	2,600.	250.00
37	A15 3p blue green	50.00	8.00
a.	3p yellow green	50.00	8.00
b.	3p deep green	45.00	10.00
c.	Watermarked "6"	60.00	10.50
d.	Perf. 12	600.00	45.00
38	A11 5p dark green	40.00	12.50
a.	5p yellow green	50.00	21.00
b.	Perf. 12	165.00	42.50
39	A12 6p brown, perf. 12	275.00	45.00
a.	6p gray, perf. 12	275.00	45.00
40	A12 6p violet	55.00	3.00
a.	6p aniline lilac	950.00	150.00
b.	Watermarked "5"	360.00	30.00
c.	Watermarked "12"	240.00	20.00
d.	Perf. 12	275.00	25.00
41	A13 8p yellow	140.00	40.00
a.	8p orange	150.00	35.00
b.	Perf. 12	2,100.	550.00
42	A14 1sh rose	65.00	8.00
a.	1sh carmine	55.00	5.75
b.	Perf. 12	400.00	50.00
	Nos. 35-42 (8)	780.00	133.50

1864   **Wmk. 50**   **Perf. 13**

43	A15 1p red	45.00	15.00

1861-80   **Wmk. 53**   **Perf. 13**

44	A16 5sh dull violet	250.00	40.00
a.	5sh purple	225.00	30.00
b.	5sh dull violet, perf. 12	1,650.	400.00
c.	5sh purple, perf. 12	250.00	50.00
d.	5sh purple, perf. 10	250.00	42.50
e.	5sh purple, perf. 12x10	450.00	65.00

See No. 101. For overprint see No. O11.
Reprints are perf. 10 and overprinted "REPRINT" in black.

A17   A18

1862-65   **Typo.**   **Unwmk.**   **Perf. 13**

45	A17 1p red ('65)	72.50	20.00
a.	Perf. 14	72.50	55.00
46	A18 2p blue	30.00	2.50
a.	Perf. 14	60.00	17.50

1863-64   **Wmk. 50**   **Perf. 13**

47	A17 1p red	21.00	.90
a.	Watermarked "2"	95.00	10.50
48	A18 2p blue	10.00	.35
a.	Watermarked "1"	135.00	5.00

1862   **Wmk. 49**   **Perf. 13**

49	A18 2p blue	50.00	8.50
a.	Watermarked "5"	135.00	18.00
b.	Perf. 12x13	600.00	
c.	Perf. 12	165.00	16.00

See Nos. 52-53, 61-62, 70-76.

A19   A20

1867, Sept.   **Wmk. 51, 52**   **Perf. 13**

50	A19 4p red brown	30.00	3.25
a.	Imperf.		
51	A20 10p lilac	11.00	3.50
a.	Imperf.		
b.	Horiz. pair, imperf. between	600.00	

See Nos. 55, 64, 91, 97, 117, 129.

A21   A22

A23

Typo.; Engr. (3p, 5p, 8p)
1871-84   **Wmk. 54**   **Perf. 13**

52	A17 1p red	4.50	.15
a.	Perf. 10	400.00	15.00
b.	Perf. 13x10	15.00	
c.	Horiz. pair imperf. between		
53	A18 2p blue	7.00	.20
a.	Imperf.		
b.	Horiz. pair, imperf. vert.		800.00
c.	Perf. 10	400.00	21.00
d.	Perf. 13x10	4.50	
e.	Perf. 12x13		
f.	Perf. 11x12		30.00
54	A15 3p green ('74)	21.00	1.75
a.	Perf. 11	225.00	150.00
b.	Perf. 12	500.00	250.00
c.	Perf. 10x12	175.00	35.00
d.	Perf. 12x11	135.00	50.00
e.	Perf. 10	70.00	4.50
f.	Perf. 13x10	135.00	13.00
55	A19 4p red brown ('77)	40.00	5.00
a.	Perf. 10	300.00	50.00
b.	Perf. 13x10	75.00	2.50
56	A11 5p dk grn, perf. 10 ('84)	15.00	7.50
a.	Imperf.		
b.	Perf. 12	325.00	135.00
c.	Perf. 10x12	24.00	9.00
d.	Perf. 13x10		
57	A21 6p lilac ('72)	35.00	.75
a.	Imperf.		
b.	Perf. 13x10	50.00	1.75
c.	Perf. 10x12	325.00	9.00
58	A13 8p yellow ('77)	90.00	16.00
a.	Imperf.		
b.	Perf. 10	325.00	21.00
c.	Perf. 13x10	225.00	18.00
59	A22 9p on 10p red brown, perf. 12 (Bk)	14.00	3.00
a.	Double surcharge, blk & bl	195.00	
b.	Perf. 10x12	375.00	300.00
c.	Perf. 10	12.00	3.25
d.	Perf. 12x11	18.00	5.75
e.	Perf. 13	18.00	5.75
f.	Perf. 13	24.00	2.75
g.	Perf. 11	40.00	7.25
h.	Perf. 10x11	50.00	12.00
60	A23 1sh black ('76)	75.00	1.50
a.	Imperf.		
b.	Perf. 13x10	275.00	3.25
c.	Perf. 10	550.00	12.00
d.	Perf. 11		
	Nos. 52-60 (9)	301.50	35.85

The surcharge on #59 measures 15mm.
See #66, 68. For overprints see #O1-O10.

Typo.; Engr. (3p, 5p, 8p)
1882-91   **Wmk. 55**   **Perf. 11x12**

61	A17 1p red	5.00	.15
a.	Perf. 10	9.00	.20
b.	Perf. 10x13	120.00	5.00
c.	Perf. 10x12	325.00	85.00
d.	Perf. 12x11		150.00
e.	Perf. 10x11	600.00	150.00
f.	Perf. 11		200.00
g.	Perf. 13		135.00
62	A18 2p blue	5.00	.20
a.	Perf. 10	12.00	.20
b.	Perf. 13	90.00	2.50
c.	Perf. 10x13	600.00	135.00
d.	Perf. 12x10	325.00	70.00
e.	Perf. 11		135.00
f.	Perf. 12x11		135.00
g.	Perf. 11x10	600.00	135.00
h.	Perf. 12		275.00
63	A15 3p green	4.75	.35
a.	Imperf., pair	200.00	
b.	Vert. pair, imperf. btwn.	225.00	
c.	Imperf., vert., pair		
d.	Double impression		
e.	Perf. 10	7.25	.35
f.	Perf. 12	7.25	.35
g.	Perf. 11	8.00	.35
h.	Perf. 12x11	8.00	.40
i.	Perf. 10x12	210.00	12.50
m.	Perf. 10x11	20.00	1.25
n.	Perf. 12x10	100.00	12.00

64	A19	4p red brown	27.50	1.40
a.		Perf. 10	27.50	1.65
b.		Perf. 10x12		150.00
c.		Perf. 12		40.00
65	A11	5p dk blue green	7.25	.70
a.		Imperf., pair	225.00	
b.		Perf. 11	13.00	.75
c.		Perf. 10	13.00	.80
d.		Perf. 12	13.00	.80
e.		Perf. 10x12		
f.		5p green, perf. 12x11	7.50	.75
g.		5p green, perf. 11x10	42.50	2.00
h.		5p green, perf. 12x10	75.00	3.75
i.		5p green, perf. 10x11	35.00	3.75
j.		5p green, perf. 11		3.75
66	A21	6p lilac, perf. 10	30.00	.75
a.		Horiz. pair, imperf. between		825.00
b.		Perf. 10x12	30.00	.75
c.		Perf. 11x12	32.50	1.25
d.		Perf. 12	95.00	2.75
e.		Perf. 11x10	60.00	.75
f.		Perf. 11	95.00	.75
g.		Perf. 10x13		325.00
67	A13	8p yellow, perf. 10	100.00	15.00
a.		Perf. 11	90.00	13.00
b.		Perf. 12	120.00	18.00
c.		Perf. 10x12	100.00	20.00
68	A23	1sh black	60.00	.75
a.		Perf. 10		12.00
b.		Perf. 11	55.00	.75
c.		Perf. 12	225.00	12.00
d.		Perf. 10x12		
		Nos. 61-68 (8)	239.50	19.30

Nos. 63 and 65 exist with two types of watermark 55 - spacings of 1mm or 2mm between crown and NSW.

See No. 90. For surcharges and overprints see Nos. 92-94, O12-O19.

The 1, 2, 4, 6, 8p and 1sh have been reprinted on paper watermarked Large Crown and NSW. The 1, 2, 4p and 1sh are perforated 11x12, the 6p is perforated 10 and the 8p 11. All are overprinted "REPRINT," the 1sh in red and the others in black.

1886-87 Typo. Wmk. 56 *Perf. 11x12*
Bluish Revenue Stamp Paper

70	A17	1p scarlet	11.00	2.50
a.		Perf. 10	18.00	4.50
71	A18	2p dark blue	15.00	4.50
a.		Perf. 10	65.00	9.00

For overprint, see No. O20.

A24

Perf. 12 (#73-75), 12x10 (#72, 75A) and Compound

1885-86
"POSTAGE" in Black

72	A24	5sh green & vio	450.00	65.00
a.		Perf. 10		
73	A24	10sh rose & vio	1,250.	240.00
74	A24	£1 rose & vio	2,750.	1,000.
a.		Perf. 13		2,100.

"POSTAGE" in Blue
Bluish Paper

75	A24	10sh rose & vio	175.00	35.00
b.		Perf. 10	750.00	165.00
c.		Perf. 12x11	375.00	150.00

White Paper

75A	A24	£1 rose & vio	3,750.	1,750.

For overprints, see Nos. O21-O23.
The 5sh with black overprint and the £1 with blue overprint have been reprinted on paper watermarked NSW. They are perforated 12x10 and are overprinted "REPRINT" in black.

1894 White Paper
"POSTAGE" in Blue

76	A24	10sh rose & violet	175.00	30.00
a.		Double overprint		

See No. 108B.

View of Sydney — A25   Emu — A26

Captain Cook — A27   Victoria and Coat of Arms — A28

Lyrebird A29   Kangaroo A30

1888-89 Wmk. 55 *Perf. 11x12*

77	A25	1p violet	3.50	.15
a.		Perf. 12	4.50	.15
b.		Perf. 12x11½	16.00	.15
78	A26	2p blue	3.00	.15
a.		Imperf., pair	125.00	
b.		Perf. 12	7.50	.15
c.		Perf. 12x11½	13.00	.15
79	A27	4p brown	9.00	.75
a.		Perf. 12x11½	15.00	.75
b.		Perf. 12	15.00	.75
c.		Perf. 11	450.00	135.00
d.		Imperf.		
80	A28	6p carmine rose	22.50	1.25
a.		Perf. 12	15.00	1.25
b.		Perf. 12x11½	35.00	1.75
81	A29	8p red violet	11.00	.75
a.		Perf. 12	9.00	1.50
b.		Perf. 12x11½	12.00	1.50
82	A30	1sh vio brown ('89)	14.00	.75
a.		Imperf., pair	725.00	
b.		Perf. 11	16.00	.75
c.		Perf. 12	24.00	.75
		Nos. 77-82 (6)	63.00	3.80

First British settlement in Australia, cent. For overprints see Nos. O24-O29.

1888 Wmk. 56 *Perf. 11x12*

83	A25	1p violet	11.00	1.40
84	A26	2p blue	65.00	6.75

See #104B-106C, 113-115, 118, 125-127, 130.

Map of Australia — A31   Governors Capt. Arthur Phillip (above) and Lord Carrington — A32

1888-89 Wmk. 53 *Perf. 10*

85	A31	5sh violet ('89)	240.00	55.00
86	A32	20sh ultra	375.00	175.00

See #88, 120. For overprints see #O30-O31.

1890 Wmk. 57 *Perf. 10*

87	A31	5sh violet	200.00	17.50
a.		Perf. 11	200.00	22.50
b.		Perf. 10x11	225.00	17.50
c.		Perf. 12	360.00	25.00

Perf. 11x12
Wmk. 58

88	A32	20sh ultra	225.00	75.00
a.		Perf. 11	250.00	57.50
b.		Perf. 10	250.00	77.50
c.		Perf. 12	350.00	135.00

For overprints see Nos. O32-O33.

"Australia" A33   Victoria A37

1890, Dec. 22 Wmk. 55 *Perf. 11x12*

89	A33	2½p ultra	2.00	.38
a.		Perf. 12	11.50	.38
b.		Perf. 12x11½	67.50	50.00

For overprint see No. O35.

Type of 1856

1891 Engr. Wmk. 52 *Perf. 10*

90	A15	3p green	10.00	15.00
a.		Double impression		

Type of 1867

1893 Typo. *Perf. 11*

91	A20	10p lilac	15.00	6.00
a.		Perf. 10	16.00	7.50
b.		Perf. 11x10 or 10x11	24.00	12.00
c.		Perf. 12x11	175.00	24.00

Types of 1862-84 Surcharged in Black:
SEVEN-PENCE

Halfpenny a	HALFPENNY b

1891, Jan. 5 Wmk. 55 *Perf. 11x12*

92	A17(a)	½p on 1p gray	1.25	1.25
a.		Imperf.		
b.		Surcharge omitted		
c.		Double surcharge		
93	A21(b)	7½p on 6p brown	3.50	1.65
a.		Perf. 10	3.50	1.25
b.		Perf. 11	3.50	1.25
c.		Perf. 12	4.25	1.75
d.		Perf. 10x12	4.25	1.75
94	A23(b)	12½p on 1sh red	7.00	4.00
a.		Perf. 12x11½	4.75	4.00
b.		Perf. 10	7.00	4.00
c.		Perf. 11	4.75	4.00
d.		Perf. 12	5.50	4.00
		Nos. 92-94 (3)	11.75	6.90

For overprints see Nos. O34, O36-O37.

1892

95	A37	½p slate	1.25	.15
a.		Perf. 12x11½	1.25	.15
b.		Perf. 12	1.25	.15
c.		Perf. 10	27.50	.90
d.		Perf. 10x12	150.00	10.50
e.		Perf. 11	165.00	9.00

See #102, 109, 121. For overprint see #O38.

Types of 1867-71

1897 *Perf. 11x12*

96	A22	9p on 10p red brn (Bk)	8.00	3.25
a.		9p on 10p org brn (Bk)	8.00	3.25
b.		Surcharge omitted	125.00	
c.		Double surcharge	125.00	100.00
d.		Perf. 11	11.00	7.50
e.		Perf. 12	9.00	7.50
97	A20	10p violet	12.00	5.50
a.		Perf. 12x11½	12.00	5.50
b.		Perf. 11	13.00	6.00
c.		Perf. 12	13.00	6.00

The surcharge on No. 96 measures 13½mm. For overprints see Nos. O39-O40.

Seal A38   Victoria A39

A40

ONE PENNY:
Die I - The first pearl in the crown at the left is merged into the arch, the shading under the fleur-de-lis is indistinct, and the "s" of "WALES" is open.
Die II - The first pearl is circular, the vertical shading under the fleur-de-lis is clear, and the "s" of "WALES" not so open.

2½ PENCE:
Die I - There are 12 radiating lines in the star on the Queen's breast.
Die II - There are 16 radiating lines in the star. The eye is nearly full of color.

1897 *Perf. 12*

98	A38	1p rose red (II)	2.50	.15
a.		Die I, perf. 11x12	3.00	.15
b.		Imperf., pair	75.00	
c.		Imperf. horiz., pair	600.00	
d.		Die I, perf. 12x11½	4.50	.15
e.		Die I, perf. 12	7.50	.60
f.		Die II, perf. 12x11½	2.00	.15
g.		Die II, perf. 11x12	3.00	.15
99	A39	2p deep blue	2.25	.15
a.		Perf. 11x12	2.75	.15
b.		Perf. 12x11½	2.75	.15
100	A40	2½p dp purple (II)	4.25	1.10
a.		Die I, perf. 12x11	6.50	1.10
b.		Die I, perf. 11	7.50	1.90
c.		Die I, perf. 11½x12	10.50	1.10
d.		Die I, perf. 11x12	4.25	1.10
e.		Die II, perf. 11½x12	8.00	1.10
		Nos. 98-100 (3)	9.00	1.40

Sixtieth year of Queen Victoria's reign.
See Nos. 103-104, 110-112, 122-124.

Type of 1861

1897 Engr. Wmk. 53 *Perf. 11*

101	A16	5sh red violet	75.00	15.00
a.		Imperf., pair	3,000.	
b.		Perf. 11x12 or 12x11	75.00	17.00
c.		Perf. 12	90.00	15.00

Perf. 12x11½, 11½x12

1899, Oct. Typo. Wmk. 55

HALF PENNY:
Die I - Narrow "H" in "HALF."

102	A37	½p blue green (I)	1.00	.15
a.		Imperf., pair	60.00	45.00
103	A39	2p ultra	1.25	.15
a.		Imperf., pair	55.00	
104	A40	2½p dk blue (II)	2.50	.38
a.		Imperf., pair	90.00	
104B	A27	4p org brown	9.00	.50
c.		Imperf., pair	300.00	
105	A28	6p emerald	37.50	3.25
a.		Imperf., pair	235.00	
106	A28	6p orange	11.00	.75
a.		6p yellow	14.00	.75
b.		Imperf., pair	195.00	
106C	A29	8p magenta	9.00	2.00
		Nos. 102-106C (7)	71.25	7.18

Lyrebird A41   "Australia" A42

1903 *Perf. 12x11½*

107	A41	2sh6p blue green	42.50	14.00

See Nos. 119, 131.

1903 Wmk. 70 *Perf. 12½*

108	A42	9p org brn & ultra	10.00	2.75
a.		Perf. 11	750.00	425.00

See No. 128.

Type of 1885-86
1904   Wmk. 56   Perf. 11
Chalky Paper
"POSTAGE" in Blue

108B	A24	10sh brt rose & violet	175.00 25.00
c.		Perf. 12x11	140.00 25.00
d.		Perf. 12	140.00 25.00

The watermark (NSW) of No. 108B is 20x7mm, with rounded angles in "N" and "W." On No. 75, the watermark is 21x7mm, with sharp angles in the "N" and "W."

HALF PENNY:
Die II - Wide "H" in "HALF."

Perf. 11, 11x12½, 12x11½ and Compound

1905-06			**Wmk. 12**
109	A37	½p blue grn (II)	1.25 .40
a.		½p blue green (I)	2.75 .40
b.		Booklet pane of 12	
110	A38	1p car rose (II)	1.25 .15
a.		Booklet pane of 6	
b.		Booklet pane of 12	
111	A39	2p deep ultra	1.50 .15
112	A40	2½p dk blue (II)	2.50 .40
113	A27	4p org brown	8.25 .75
114	A28	6p orange	10.00 .75
a.		6p yellow	8.50 .75
b.		Perf. 11	250.00
115	A29	8p magenta	11.00 1.50
117	A20	10p violet	12.50 2.25
118	A30	1sh vio brown	11.00 .75
119	A41	2sh6p blue green	27.50 12.00
		Wmk. 199	
120	A32	20sh ultra	200.00 75.00
		Nos. 109-115,117-120 (11)	286.75 94.10
1906-07			**Wmk. 13**
121	A37	½p green (I)	5.00 .50
122	A38	1p rose (II)	3.50 .32
123	A39	2p ultra	3.50 .32
124	A40	2½p blue (II)	70.00
125	A27	4p org brown	8.75 3.25
126	A28	6p orange	22.50 8.25
127	A29	8p red violet	27.50 9.25
128	A42	9p org brn & ultra, perf. 12x12½	8.00 1.65
a.		Perf. 11	65.00 55.00
		('06)	
129	A20	10p violet	52.50
130	A30	1sh vio brown	27.50 6.50
131	A41	2sh6p blue green	50.00 32.50
		Nos. 121-131 (11)	278.75
		Nos. 121-123,125-128,130-131 (9)	62.54

Portions of some of the sheets on which the above are printed show the watermark "COMMONWEALTH OF AUSTRALIA." Stamps may also be found from portions of the sheet without watermark.

SEMI-POSTAL STAMPS

Allegory of Charity
SP1   SP2

1897, June		**Wmk. 55**	**Perf. 11**
B1	SP1	1p (1sh) green & brown	35.00 25.00
B2	SP2	2½p (2sh6p) rose, bl & gold	225.00 250.00

Diamond Jubilee of Queen Victoria.
The difference between the postal and face values of these stamps was donated to a fund for a home for consumptives.

REGISTRATION STAMPS

Queen Victoria — R1

1856, Jan. 1		**Unwmk. Engr.**	*Imperf.*
F1	R1	(6p) orange & blue	600.00 75.00
F2	R1	(6p) red & blue	575.00 75.00
a.		Frame printed on back	2,750. 1,350.

1860		**Perf. 12, 13**	
F3	R1	(6p) orange & blue	280.00 30.00
F4	R1	(6p) red & blue	265.00 30.00

Nos. F1 to F4 exist also on paper with papermaker's watermark in sheet.

1863			**Wmk. 49**
F5	R1	(6p) red & blue	75.00 15.00

Fifty varieties.
Nos. F1-F2 were reprinted on thin white wove unwatermarked paper and on thick yellowish wove unwatermarked paper; the former are usually overprinted "SPECIMEN." No. F4 was reprinted on thin white wove unwatermarked paper; perf. 10 and overprinted "REPRINT" in black.

POSTAGE DUE STAMPS

D1

Perf. 10, 11, 11½, 12 and Compound

1891-92		**Typo.**	**Wmk. 55**
J1	D1	½p green, perf 10	3.25 1.50
J2	D1	1p green	4.00 .75
a.		Perf. 12	20.00 3.75
J3	D1	2p green	5.00 .75
a.		Perf. 10x12	17.00 4.00
J4	D1	3p green	10.00 2.50
J5	D1	4p green	10.00 .75
J6	D1	6p green, perf 10	15.00 2.25
J7	D1	8p green, perf 10	70.00 10.00
a.		Perf. 10	85.00
J8	D1	5sh green, perf 10	165.00 25.00
J9	D1	10sh green, perf 12x10	225.00 50.00
J10	D1	20sh green, perf 12x10	300.00
a.		Perf. 10	350.00 70.00
b.		Perf. 12	350.00
		Nos. J1-J10 (10)	807.25 93.50

Nos. J1-J5 exist on both ordinary and chalky paper.
Used values for Nos. J8-J10 are for c-t-o copies.

OFFICIAL STAMPS

Regular Issues Overprinted in Black or Red

Perf. 10, 11, 12, 13 and Compound

1879-80			**Wmk. 54**
O1	A17	1p red	9.25 1.50
a.		Perf. 10	325.00 40.00
b.		Perf. 10x13	22.50 4.50
O2	A18	2p blue	15.00 3.50
a.		Perf. 11x12	250.00
b.		Perf. 10	250.00 40.00
O3	A15	3p green (R)	300.00
O4	A15	3p green	225.00 65.00
a.		Watermarked "6"	500.00
b.		Double overprint	
O5	A19	4p red brown	225.00 11.50
a.		Perf. 10x13	300.00 14.00
O6	A11	5p dark green	24.00 13.00
O7	A21	6p lilac	300.00 10.00
a.		Perf. 10	
b.		Perf. 10x13	65.00
O8	A13	8p yellow (R)	1,000. 200.00
O9	A13	8p yellow	22.50
O10	A23	1sh black (R)	300.00 11.00
a.		Perf. 10	16.00
b.		Perf. 10x13	30.00
1880			**Wmk. 53**
O11	A16	5sh lilac, perf. 11	265.00 75.00
a.		Double overprint	
b.		Perf. 10	375.00 150.00
c.		Perf. 12x10	325.00 130.00
d.		Perf. 13	465.00 82.50
e.		Perf. 10x12	
1881			**Wmk. 55**
O12	A17	1p red	6.00 .75
a.		Perf. 10x13	225.00
O13	A18	2p blue	6.50 1.00
a.		Perf. 10x13	360.00 100.00
O14	A15	3p green	6.00 1.65
a.		Double overprint	
b.		Perf. 12	240.00 130.00
c.		Perf. 11	
O15	A19	4p red brown	11.00 2.25
a.		Perf. 10x12	90.00
b.		Perf. 12	360.00 225.00
O16	A11	5p dark green	12.00 5.00
a.		Perf. 10	100.00
b.		Perf. 10x13	400.00 130.00
O17	A21	6p lilac	22.50 4.00
a.		Perf. 10	60.00
b.		Perf. 11x12	72.50 16.00
O18	A13	8p yellow	27.50 9.50
a.		Double overprint	
b.		Perf. 12	240.00 50.00

O19	A23	1sh black (R)	27.50 3.25
a.		Double overprint	70.00
b.		Perf. 11	
		Nos. O12-O19 (8)	119.00 27.40

Beware of other red overprints on watermark 55 stamps.

1881			**Wmk. 56**
O20	A17	1p red	32.50 10.00
1887-90			
O21	A24	10sh on #75	350.00
O22	A24	£1 on #75A	3,250. 3,250.

No. 75 Overprinted

1889			
O23	A24	10sh rose & vio	1,950. 600.00
a.		Perf. 10	3,500. 2,250.

Overprinted

1888-89			**Wmk. 55**
O24	A25	1p violet	1.50 .15
a.		Overprinted "O" only	
O25	A26	2p blue	1.50 .15
O26	A27	4p red brown	6.00 1.50
O27	A28	6p carmine	8.00 2.00
O28	A29	8p red lilac	14.00 4.00
O29	A30	1sh vio brown	14.00 2.00
a.		Double overprint	
		Nos. O24-O29 (6)	45.00 9.80
		Wmk. 53	
O30	A31	5sh violet (R)	700.00 450.00
O31	A32	20sh ultra	1,250.
1890			**Wmk. 57**
O32	A31	5sh violet	150.00 60.00
a.		Perf. 12	625.00
		Wmk. 58	
O33	A32	20sh ultra	2,000.

Centenary of the founding of the Colony (Nos. O24-O33).

1891			**Wmk. 55**
O34	A17(a)	½p on 1p gray & black	47.50 14.00
a.		Double overprint	
O35	A33	2½p ultra	7.00 3.25
O36	A21(b)	7½p on 6p brn & black	35.00 12.00
O37	A23(b)	12½p on 1sh red & black	60.00 32.50
		Nos. O34-O37 (4)	149.50 61.75
1892			
O38	A37	½p gray	5.50 4.00
1894			**Wmk. 54**
O39	A22	9p on 10p red brn	300.00 350.00
		Wmk. 52	
O40	A20	10p lilac, perf. 10	225.00 200.00
a.		Perf. 11x10	350.00 325.00

The official stamps became obsolete on Dec. 31, 1894. In Aug., 1895, sets of 32 varieties of "O.S." stamps, together with some envelopes and postal cards, were placed on sale at the Sydney post office at £2 per set. These sets contained most of the varieties listed above and a few which are not known in the original issues. An obliteration consisting of the letters G.P.O. or N.S.W. in three concentric ovals was lightly applied to the center of each block of four stamps. It is understood that the earlier stamps and many of the overprints were reprinted to make up these sets.

QUEENSLAND

'kwēnz-ˌland

LOCATION — Northeastern part of Australia
GOVT. — British Crown Colony
AREA — 670,500 sq. mi.
POP. — 498,129 (1901)
CAPITAL — Brisbane

Originally a part of New South Wales, Queensland was constituted a separate colony in 1859. It was one of the six British Colonies that united in 1901 to form the Commonwealth of Australia.

12 Pence = 1 Shilling
20 Shillings = 1 Pound

Values for unused stamps are for examples with original gum as defined in the catalogue introduction. Very fine examples of Nos. 4-73, 84-125, 128-140, and F1-F3b will have perforations touching the design on at least one or more sides due to the narrow spacing of the stamps on the plates. Stamps with perfs clear of the design on all four sides are scarce and will command higher prices.

Watermarks

Wmk. 5- Small Star   Wmk. 6- Large Star

Wmk. 12- Crown and Single-lined A   Wmk. 13- Crown and Double-lined A

Wmk. 65- "Queensland Postage Stamps" in Sheet in Script Capitals

Wmks. 66 & 67- "Queensland" in Large Single-lined Roman Capitals in the Sheet and Short-pointed Star to Each Stamp (Stars Vary Slightly in Size and Shape)

Wmk. 68- Crown and Q   Wmk. 69- Large Crown and Q

There are two varieties of the watermark 68, differing slightly in the position and shape of the crown and the tongue of the "Q."

Wmk. 70- V and Crown

Queen
Victoria — A1

1860, Nov. 1 Engr. Wmk. 6 Imperf.
1	A1	1p deep rose	3,000.	750.
2	A1	2p deep blue	6,250.	2,250.
3	A1	6p deep green	4,250.	750.

Clean-Cut Perf. 14 to 16
4	A1	1p deep rose	1,750.	225.
5	A1	2p deep blue	475.	100.
6	A1	6p deep green	475.	60.

Clean-Cut Perf. 14 to 16
1860-61 Wmk. 5
6A	A1	2p blue	525.00	100.00
b.		Horiz. pair, imperf. vert.		875.00
6D	A1	3p brown ('61)	275.00	50.00
6E	A1	6p deep green	550.00	50.00
6F	A1	1sh gray violet	475.00	65.00

Regular Perf. 14
6H	A1	1p rose	125.00	35.00
6I	A1	2p deep blue	325.00	50.00

Rough Perf. 14 to 16
7	A1	1p deep rose	80.00	35.00
8	A1	2p blue	90.00	35.00
9	A1	3p brown ('61)	55.00	30.00
a.		Horiz. pair, imperf. vert.	2,000.	
10	A1	6p deep green	150.00	25.00
a.		6p yellow green	200.00	25.00
11	A1	1sh dull violet	400.00	85.00

Thick Yellowish Paper
Square Perf. 12½ to 13
1862-67 Unwmk.
12	A1	1p Indian red	325.00	70.00
13	A1	1p orange ('63)	60.00	15.00
a.		Perf. 13, round holes ('67)	60.00	15.00
b.		Horiz. pair, imperf. between	—	525.00
c.		Imperf., pair		
14	A1	2p deep blue	40.00	17.00
a.		2p pale blue	90.00	30.00
b.		Perf. 13, round holes ('67)	90.00	30.00
c.		Imperf., pair	—	500.00
d.		Imperf. between	—	900.00
f.		Vert. pair, imperf. between	1,200	
15	A1	3p brown ('63)	55.00	30.00
a.		Imperf.		
b.		Perf. 13, round holes ('67)		
16	A1	6p yellow grn ('63)	80.00	15.00
a.		6p green	125.00	25.00
b.		Perf. 13, round holes ('67)	125.00	25.00
c.		Imperf., pair	—	500.00
d.		Horiz. pair, imperf. between	—	950.00
17	A1	1sh gray ('63)	125.00	25.00
c.		Imperf. horizontally		
c.		Horiz. pair, imperf. between	—	950.00
d.		Perf. 13, round holes ('67)		

White Wove Paper
1865 Wmk. 5 Rough Perf. 13
18	A1	1p orange	55.00	20.00
a.		Horiz. pair, imperf. vert.	425.00	
19	A1	2p light blue	50.00	16.00
a.		Vert. pair, imperf. horiz.	900.00	
b.		Half used as 1p on cover		2,000.
20	A1	6p yellow green	135.00	24.00
		Nos. 18-20 (3)	240.00	60.00

Perf. 13, Round Holes
1866 Wmk. 65
21	A1	1p orange vermilion	160.00	25.00
22	A1	2p blue	55.00	18.00
b.		Diagonal half used as 1p on cover		—

1866 Unwmk. Litho. Perf. 13
23	A1	4p lilac	90.00	18.00
a.		4p slate	140.00	20.00
24	A1	5sh pink	225.00	50.00
b.		Vert. pair, imperf between	—	725.00

Wmk. 66, 67
1868-74 Engr. Perf. 13
25	A1	1p orange ('71)	45.00	5.00
26	A1	2p blue	45.00	1.90
27	A1	3p grnsh brn ('71)	85.00	2.50
a.		3p brown	87.50	3.50
b.		3p olive brown	87.50	3.50
28	A1	6p yel green ('71)	125.00	8.50
a.		6p deep green	175.00	11.00
30	A1	1sh grnsh gray ('72)	375.00	40.00
31	A1	1sh violet ('74)	200.00	20.00

Perf. 12
32	A1	1p orange	275.00	30.00
33	A1	2p blue		37.50
34	A1	3p brown	275.00	110.00
35	A1	6p deep green	900.00	42.50
36	A1	1sh violet	—	37.50

Perf. 13x12
36A	A1	1p orange		250.00
37	A1	2p blue	1,500.	100.00
37A	A1	3p brown		1,250.

The reprints are perforated 13 and the colors differ slightly from those of the originals.

1868-75 Wmk. 68 Perf. 13
38	A1	1p orange	45.00	5.00
39	A1	1p rose ('74)	50.00	9.00
40	A1	2p blue	35.00	2.50
b.		Imperf., pair	315.00	
41	A1	3p brown ('75)	65.00	14.00
42	A1	6p yel green ('69)	100.00	7.50
a.		6p apple green	135.00	10.00
b.		6p deep green	125.00	10.00
43	A1	1sh violet ('75)	150.00	26.00
		Nos. 38-43 (6)	445.00	64.00

No. 40 exists in vert. pair, imperf. btwn.

1876-78 Perf. 12
44	A1	1p orange	35.00	3.00
a.		Imperf.	300.00	
45	A1	1p rose	45.00	11.00
46	A1	2p blue	22.50	1.50
a.		Imperf.		
47	A1	3p brown	60.00	10.00
48	A1	6p yellow green	125.00	5.00
a.		6p apple green	135.00	4.75
b.		6p deep green	135.00	4.75
49	A1	1sh violet	42.50	5.00
		Nos. 44-49 (6)	330.00	35.50

#44, 49 exist in vertical pairs, imperf. between.

Perf. 13x12
49B	A1	1p orange		165.00
49C	A1	2p blue	1,800.	200.00
49D	A1	4p yellow		
49E	A1	6p deep green		200.00

The reprints are perforated 12 and are in paler colors than the originals.

1879 Unwmk. Perf. 12
50	A1	6p pale emerald	200.00	25.00
a.		Horiz. pair, imperf. vert.		650.00

A2

A3

1875-81 Litho. Wmk. 68 Perf. 13
50B	A1	4p yellow ('75)	800.00	42.50

Perf. 12
51	A1	4p buff ('76)	600.00	22.50
a.		4p yellow	600.00	22.50
52	A1	2sh pale blue ('81)	55.00	12.00
a.		2sh deep blue	67.50	12.00
b.		Imperf.		
53	A2	2sh6p lt red ('81)	110.00	30.00
54	A1	5sh orange brn ('81)	150.00	27.50
a.		5sh fawn	150.00	27.50
55	A1	10sh brown ('81)	325.00	110.00
a.		Imperf., pair	550.00	
56	A1	20sh rose ('81)	650.00	90.00
		Nos. 50B-56 (7)	2,690.	334.50

Nos. 53-56, 62-64, 74-83 with pen (revenue) cancellations removed are often offered as unused.

1879-81 Typo. Wmk. 68 Perf. 12
57	A3	1p rose red	9.50	1.50
a.		1p red orange	9.50	1.75
b.		1p brown orange	30.00	5.50
c.		"QOEENSLAND"	110.00	32.50
d.		Imperf.		
e.		Vert. pair, imperf. horiz.		90.00
58	A3	2p gray blue	22.50	.70
a.		2p deep ultra	27.50	.80
b.		Imperf.		
c.		"PENGE"		70.00
d.		"TW" joined	25.00	1.10
e.		Vert. pair, imperf. horiz.	450.00	
59	A3	4p orange yellow	100.00	10.00
a.		Imperf.		
60	A3	6p yellow green	55.00	5.00
a.		Imperf.		
61	A3	1sh pale violet ('81)	50.00	5.00
a.		1sh deep violet	45.00	3.75
		Nos. 57-61 (5)	237.00	22.20

The stamps of type A3 were electrotyped from plates made up of groups of four types, differing in minor details. Two dies were used for the 1p and 2p, giving eight varieties for each of those values. Nos. 59-60 exist imperf. vertically.
For surcharge see No. 65.

Moiré on Back
1878-79 Unwmk.
62	A3	1p brown org ('79)	400.00	60.00
a.		"QOEENSLAND"		2,000.
63	A3	2p deep ultra ('79)	500.00	30.00
a.		"PENGE"	4,750.	725.00
64	A1	1sh red violet	100.00	47.50
		Nos. 62-64 (3)	1,000.	137.50

No. 57b
Surcharged
Vertically in Black **Half-penny**

1881 Wmk. 68
65	A3	½p on 1p brn org	175.00	95.00
a.		"QOEENSLAND"	1,000.	825.00

A4

A5

1882-83 Typo. Perf. 12
66	A4	1p pale red	5.75	.20
a.		1p rose	5.75	.20
b.		Imperf. pair	30.00	30.00
67	A4	2p gray blue	9.00	.20
a.		2p deep ultra	9.00	.20
68	A4	4p yellow ('83)	20.00	1.00
a.		"PENGE"	125.00	45.00
b.		Imperf., pair		150.00
69	A4	6p yellow green	10.00	.70
70	A4	1sh violet ('83)	12.00	1.00
		Nos. 66-70 (5)	56.75	3.10

There are eight minor varieties of the 1p, twelve of the 2p and four each of the other values. On the 1p there is a period after "PENNY." On all values the lines of shading on the neck extend from side to side.
Compare design A4 with A6, A10, A11, A15, A16.

1883 Perf. 9½x12
71	A4	1p rose	160.00	25.00
72	A4	2p gray blue	350.00	55.00
73	A4	1sh pale violet	225.00	30.00
		Nos. 71-73 (3)	735.00	110.00

Beware of faked perfs.
See Nos. 94, 95, 100.

Wmk. 68 Twice Sideways
1882-85 Engr. Perf. 12
Thin Paper
74	A5	2sh ultra	60.00	18.00
75	A5	2sh6p vermilion	50.00	22.50
76	A5	5sh car rose ('85)	50.00	25.00
77	A5	10sh brown	95.00	42.50
78	A5	£1 dark green ('83)	165.00	55.00
		Nos. 74-78 (5)	420.00	163.00

The 2sh, 5sh and £1 exist imperf.
There are two varieties of the watermark on Nos. 74-78, as in the 1879-81 issue.
Copies with revenue cancels sell for $3.25-6.50.

1886 Thick Paper Wmk. 69 Perf. 12
79	A5	2sh ultra	100.00	35.00
80	A5	2sh6p vermilion	40.00	22.50
81	A5	5sh car rose	37.50	30.00
82	A5	10sh dark brown	100.00	40.00
83	A5	£1 dark green	175.00	60.00
		Nos. 79-83 (5)	452.50	187.50

High value stamps with cancellations removed are offered as unused.
Copies with revenue cancels sell for $3.25-6.50.
See Nos. 126-127, 141-144.

A6

Redrawn
1887-89 Typo. Wmk. 68 Perf. 12
84	A6	1p orange	4.50	.20
a.		Imperf., pair	40.00	60.00
85	A6	2p gray blue	9.00	.20
a.		2p deep ultra	11.50	.24
86	A6	2sh red brown ('89)	65.00	20.00

Perf. 9½x12
88	A6	2p deep ultra	250.00	110.00
		Nos. 84-88 (4)	328.50	130.40

The 1p has no period after the value.
In the redrawn stamps the shading lines on the neck are not completed at the left, leaving an irregular white line along that side.

Variety "LA" joined exists on Nos. 84-86, 88, 90, 91, 93, 97, 98, 102.
On No. 88 beware of faked perfs.

A7

A8

1890-92 Perf. 12½, 13
89	A7	½p green	4.50	.32
90	A6	1p orange red	3.00	.15
91	A6	2p gray blue	5.00	.15
92	A8	2½p rose carmine	11.00	.35
93	A6	3p brown ('92)	9.00	2.00
94	A4	4p orange	15.00	1.25
a.		4p yellow	16.00	1.25
b.		"PENGE"	65.00	27.50
95	A4	6p green	11.00	2.00
96	A6	2sh red brown	40.00	8.25
		Nos. 89-96 (8)	98.50	14.47

The ½p and 3p exist imperf.

1895 Wmk. 69 Perf. 12½, 13
Thick Paper
98	A6	1p orange	3.50	.50
99	A6	2p gray blue	3.50	.50

Perf. 12
100	A4	1sh pale violet	17.00	3.75
		Nos. 98-100 (3)	24.00	4.75

A9

A10

Moiré on Back
1895 Unwmk. Perf. 12½, 13
101	A9	½p green	1.90	1.90
a.		Without moire	55.00	
102	A6	1p orange	2.25	2.25
a.		"PE" missing		

Wmk. 68
103	A9	½p green	2.25	.35
a.		½p deep green	1.65	.35
b.		Printed on both sides	60.00	
104	A10	1p orange	2.50	.15
105	A10	2p gray blue	3.25	.25

Wmk. 69
Thick Paper
106	A9	½p green	1.90	1.90

1895-96 Unwmk. Thin Paper
Crown and Q Faintly Impressed
107	A9	½p green	2.75	.80
108	A10	1p orange	4.00	1.10
108A	A6	2p gray blue	11.00	

A11

A12

A13

1895-96 Wmk. 68
109	A11	1p red	8.50	.16
110	A12	2½p rose	9.00	1.75
111	A13	5p violet brown	11.00	1.75
111A	A11	6p yellow green		

A14

A15

A16

A17

A18

A19

TWO PENCE:
Type I - Point of bust does not touch frame.
Type II - First redrawing. The top of the crown, the chignon and the point of the bust touch the frame. The forehead is completely shaded.
Type III - Second redrawing. The top of crown does not touch the frame, though the chignon and the point of the bust do. The forehead and the bridge of the nose are not shaded.

1897-1900   *Perf. 12½, 13*
112	A14	½p deep green	3.50	2.00
a.		Perf. 12		150.00
113	A15	1p red	1.50	.15
a.		Perf. 12	1.75	.20
114	A16	2p gray blue (I)	2.00	.15
a.		Perf. 12		6.00
115	A17	2½p rose	17.00	6.25
116	A17	2½p violet, *blue*	8.50	.70
117	A15	3p brown	8.00	.70
118	A15	4p bright yellow	8.00	.70
119	A18	5p violet brown	7.50	1.25
120	A15	6p yellow green	9.00	.70
121	A19	1sh lilac	13.00	1.65
a.		1sh light violet	16.00	1.65
122	A19	2sh turq blue	32.50	6.00
		Nos. 112-122 (11)	110.50	20.25

1898   *Serrated Roulette 13*
123	A15	1p scarlet	5.00	2.00
a.		Serrated and perf. 13	6.00	3.00
b.		Serrated in black	10.00	10.00
c.		Serrated without color and in black	9.00	9.00
d.		Same as "b," and perf. 13	85.00	
e.		Same as "c," and perf. 13	110.00	

Queen Victoria — A20

1899   **Typo.**   *Perf. 12, 12½, 13*
124	A20	½p blue green	1.00	.25

Unwatermarked stamps are proofs.

"Australia" — A21

NINE PENCE:
Type I- "QUEENSLAND" 18x1½mm.
Type II- "QUEENSLAND" 17½x1¼mm.

1903   **Wmk. 70**   *Perf. 12½*
125	A21	9p org brn & ultra, type I	13.00	3.50
a.		9p org brn & ultra, type II	12.00	3.00

See No. 128.

Type of 1882
Perf. 12, 12½, 13
1906   **Litho.**   **Wmk. 68**
126	A5	5sh rose	150.00	82.50
127	A5	£1 dark green	500.00	150.00

1907   **Typo.**   **Wmk. 13**   *Perf. 12½*
128	A21	9p yel brn & ultra, type I	15.00	3.00
a.		9p yel brn & ultra, type II	27.50	4.25
b.		Perf. 11, type II		240.00

1907   **Wmk. 68**   *Perf. 12½, 13*
129	A16	2p ultra, type II	9.00	1.25
129A	A18	5p dark brown	9.00	1.90
b.		5p olive brown	9.00	1.90

1907-09   **Wmk. 12**
130	A20	½p deep green	1.25	.30
131	A15	1p red	1.25	.15
a.		Imperf., pair	200.00	
132	A16	2p ultra, type II	7.50	.15
133	A16	2p ultra, type III	2.25	.15

134	A15	3p pale brown	10.00	1.00
135	A15	4p bright yellow	12.00	2.75
136	A15	4p gray black ('09)	12.00	1.65
137	A18	5p brown	8.50	1.65
a.		5p olive brown	10.50	3.25
138	A19	6p yellow green	12.00	2.50
139	A19	1sh violet	15.00	3.75
140	A19	2sh turquoise bl	35.00	9.00

Wmk. 12 Sideways
Litho.
141	A5	2sh6p deep orange	50.00	37.50
142	A5	5sh rose	55.00	37.50
143	A5	10sh dark brown	100.00	50.00
144	A5	£1 blue green	225.00	135.00
		Nos. 130-144 (15)	546.75	268.05

SEMI-POSTAL STAMPS

Queen Victoria, Colors and Bearers — SP1

SP2

Perf. 12, 12½
1900, June 19   **Wmk. 68**
B1	SP1	1p red lilac	80.00	90.00
B2	SP2	2p deep violet	200.00	210.00

These stamps were sold at 1sh and 2sh respectively. The difference was applied to a patriotic fund in connection with the Boer War.

REGISTRATION STAMPS

R1

Clean-Cut Perf. 14 to 16
1861   **Wmk. 5**   **Engr.**
F1	R1	(6p) olive yellow	400.00	75.00
a.		Horiz. pair, imperf. vert.	4,500.	

Rough Perf. 14 to 16
F2	R1	(6p) dull yellow	50.00	35.00

1864   *Perf. 12½ to 13*
F3	R1	(6p) golden yellow	80.00	40.00
a.		Imperf.		
b.		Double impression	900.00	

The reprints are watermarked with a small truncated star and perforated 12.

SOUTH AUSTRALIA
ˈsaüth ȯ-ˈstrāl-yə

LOCATION — Central part of southern Australia
GOVT. — British Colony
AREA — 380,070 sq. mi.
POP. — 358,346 (1901)
CAPITAL — Adelaide

South Australia was one of the six British colonies that united in 1901 to form the Commonwealth of Australia.

12 Pence = 1 Shilling
20 Shillings = 1 Pound

Values for unused stamps are for examples with original gum as defined in the catalogue introduction. Very fine examples of Nos. 10-60 and O1-O60 will have perforations slightly cutting into the framelines or design on one or more sides due to the narrow spacing of the stamps on the plates. Stamps with perfs clear on all sides are scarce to rare and will command higher to substantially higher prices.

Watermarks

Wmk. 6- Star with Long Narrow Points

Wmk. 7- Star with Short Broad Points

Wmk. 70- Crown and V

Wmk. 72- Crown and SA

Wmk. 73- Crown and SA, Letters Close

Wmk. 74- Crown and Single-lined A

Queen Victoria — A1

1855-56   **Engr.**   **Wmk. 6**   *Imperf.*
London Print
1	A1	1p dark green	2,750.	375.
2	A1	2p dull carmine	600.	80.
3	A1	6p deep blue	2,500.	150.
4	A1	1sh violet ('56)	4,500.	

No. 4 was never put in use. Nos. 1 and 3 without watermark are proofs.

1856-59   **Local Print**
5	A1	1p deep yel grn ('58)	6,000.	550.00
a.		1p deep green ('58)		550.00
6	A1	2p blood red	1,500.	80.00
a.		2p orange red ('56)		90.00
7	A1	2p pale red ('57)	700.00	60.00
a.		Printed on both sides		650.00
8	A1	6p slate blue ('57)	2,500.	175.00
9	A1	1sh orange ('57)	4,750.	350.00
a.		Printed on both sides		
		1sh red orange		375.00

1858-59   *Rouletted*
10	A1	1p yellow grn ('59)	475.00	45.00
a.		Horiz. pair, imperf. between		
b.		1p pale yellow green	500.00	50.00

11	A1	2p pale red ('59)	125.00	22.50
a.		Printed on both sides		
12	A1	6p slate blue	375.00	27.50
13	A1	1sh orange ('59)	1,250.	35.00
c.		Printed on both sides		1,400.

See Nos. 14-16, 19-20, 25-26, 28-29, 32, 35-36, 41-43, 47, 51-52, 69-70, 73, 113, 118. For overprints see Nos. O1-O2, O5, O7, O9, O11-O13, O17, O20, O27, O30, O32, O39-O40, O42, O52, O76, O85.

A2

A3

Surcharge on #22-24, 34, 49-50

TEN PENCE

1860-69   *Rouletted*
14	A1	1p dull blue green	45.00	22.50
a.		1p deep green	250.00	65.00
b.		1p bright green	250.00	65.00
15	A1	1p sage green	72.50	27.50
16	A1	2p vermilion ('62)	50.00	4.00
a.		Horiz. pair, imperf. btwn.	700.00	350.00
b.		Rouletted and perf. all around		700.00
c.		Printed on both sides		500.00
18	A2	4p dull violet ('67)	75.00	17.00
19	A1	6p grnsh blue ('63)	65.00	3.75
20	A1	6p dull blue	85.00	3.75
a.		6p sky blue	125.00	6.50
b.		6p Prussian blue	750.00	50.00
c.		Horiz. pair, imperf. between		850.00
d.		6p ultramarine	60.00	3.75
e.		Horiz. pair, imperf. btwn. (#20f)		425.00
f.		6p indigo blue	—	60.00
g.		Rouletted and perf. all around (#20f)	—	350.00
21	A3	9p gray lilac ('69)	55.00	9.00
a.		Double impression		
c.		Rouletted and perf. all around	1,750.	275.00
22	A3	10p on 9p red orange (Bl) ('66)	125.00	25.00
23	A3	10p on 9p yel (Bl) ('67)	165.00	21.00
24	A3	10p on 9p yel (Blk) ('69)	1,300.	32.50
a.		Inverted surcharge		2,750.
c.		Printed on both sides	—	1,100.
d.		Rouletted x perf. 10		
24E	A1	1sh red brown	135.00	13.00
f.		Vert. pair, imperf. btwn.		1,250.
25	A1	1sh lake brown ('65)	135.00	13.00
a.		Horiz. pair, imperf. btwn.		425.00
26	A1	1sh brown ('63)	140.00	16.00
		1sh chestnut ('64)	150.00	11.00
27	A2	2sh carmine ('67)	165.00	27.50
a.		Horiz. pair, imperf. btwn.		

There are six varieties of the surcharge "TEN PENCE" in this and subsequent issues.
Nos. 16b, 20g, 21c, 28a, 32c, 33a are rouletted remainders that were later perforated.
See Nos. 31, 33, 46, 48, 53, 63, 68, 72, 74, 112, 113B, 119-120. For overprints see Nos. O4, O6, O8, O10, O16, O18, O21, O26, O29, O31, O33, O37-O38, O41B, O43, O53. For surcharges see Nos. 34, 44-45, 49-50, 59, 67, 71, O19, O28, O36, O41. Compare with design A6a.

1867-72   *Perf. 11½ to 12½xRoulette*
28	A1	1p blue green	225.00	32.50
a.		Rouletted and perf. all around		650.00
29	A1	1p yellow green	140.00	20.00
31	A2	4p dull violet ('68)	1,500.	110.00
a.		4p purple ('69)		110.00
32	A1	6p Prus blue	450.00	21.00
a.		6p sky blue	500.00	17.50
b.		Printed on both sides		
c.		Rouletted and perf. all around		300.00
d.		6p indigo blue ('69)	475.00	25.00
33	A3	9p gray lilac ('72)		275.00
34	A3	10p on 9p yel (Bl) ('68)	800.00	35.00
a.		Printed on both sides	—	500.00
35	A1	1sh chestnut ('68)	275.00	30.00
36	A1	1sh lake brown ('69)	275.00	25.00

#44-45   **3-PENCE**

Perf. 10, 11½, 12½ and Compound
1867-74
41	A1	1p yellow green	45.00	17.50
42	A1	1p blue green	60.00	12.50
a.		Printed on both sides		
43	A1	1sh violet		1,250.
44	A2	3p on 4p dp bl (Blk) ('70)	60.00	5.50
a.		3p on 4p ultra, black surcharge	125.00	5.50
b.		Surcharge omitted	20,000.	5,000.
c.		Double surcharge		4,500.
d.		Surcharged on both sides		3,250.
45	A2	3p on 4p sl bl (Red) ('70)	425.00	32.50
46	A2	4p dull violet	60.00	9.00

47	A1	6p dark blue	90.00	8.00
a.		6p sky blue	350.00	9.25
b.		Imperf. vert., pair		
48	A1	9p red lilac ('72)	47.50	5.00
a.		9p violet	115.00	5.50
b.		9p red violet	115.00	5.50
c.		Printed on both sides		350.00
49	A3	10p on 9p yel (Bl) ('68)	1,500.	26.00
50	A3	10p on 9p yel (Blk) ('69)	150.00	21.00
51	A1	1sh deep brown	150.00	12.00
52	A1	1sh red brown	100.00	12.00
a.		1sh chestnut	125.00	12.50
53	A2	2sh carmine	60.00	7.50
a.		Printed on both sides		400.00
b.		Horiz. pair, imperf. vert.		

See Nos. 67, O14, O28, O36.

A6   A6a

1868   **Typo.**   **Wmk. 72**   *Rouletted*

54	A6a	2p orange red	65.00	4.00
a.		Imperf.		
b.		Printed on both sides		275.00
c.		Horiz. pair, imperf. btwn.		275.00

1869   *Perf. 11½ to 12½xRoulette*

55	A6a	2p orange red	150.00

1870   *Perf. 10xRoulette*

56	A6a	2p orange red	350.00	30.00

Perf. 10, 11½, 12½ and Compound
1868-75

57	A6	1p blue green ('75)	24.00	4.50
58	A6a	2p orange red	13.00	1.00
a.		Printed on both sides		200.00
b.		Horiz. pair, imperf. vert.		

Engr.

59	A3	10p on 9p yellow (Bl)	1,500.

1869   **Typo.**   **Wmk. 6**   *Rouletted*

60	A6a	2p orange red	65.00	11.50
a.		Imperf.		
b.		Printed on both sides		

Perf. 11½ to 12½xRoulette

61	A6a	2p orange red	125.00

Perf. 11½ to 12½

61B	A6a	2p orange red	

See Nos. 62, 64-66, 97-98, 105-106, 115-116, 133-134, 145-146. For overprints see Nos. O3, O22-O25, O34-O35, O44-O47, O55-O56, O62-O63, O68-O69, O74, O78-O79. For surcharges see Nos. 75, O49.

1871   **Wmk. 70**   *Perf. 10*

62	A6a	2p orange red	75.00	16.00

Engr.

63	A2	4p dull violet	2,250.	350.00
a.		Printed on both sides		

Copies of the 4p from edge of sheet sometimes lack watermark.

Perf. 10, 11½, 12½ and Compound
1876-80   **Typo.**   **Wmk. 73**

64	A6	1p green	6.00	.50
65	A6a	2p orange	4.25	.50
66	A6a	2p blood red ('80)	225.00	7.50
		Nos. 64-66 (3)	235.25	8.50

See #97-98, 105-106, 115-116, 133-134, 145-146.

HALF-

8 PENCE   PENNY
No. 71   No. 75

1876-84   **Engr.**   **Wmk. 7**

67	A2	3p on 4p ultra (Blk)	65.00	17.50
a.		3p on 4p deep blue		15.00
b.		Double surcharge		1,500.
68	A2	4p reddish violet	50.00	1.50
a.		4p dull violet	60.00	9.00
69	A1	6p deep blue	65.00	4.50
a.		Horiz. pair, imperf. vert.		
70	A1	6p pale ultra ('84)	40.00	2.25
71	A1	8p on 9p bister brn	65.00	5.50
a.		8p on 9p yellow brown	57.50	2.50
b.		8p on 9p gray brown ('80)	52.50	4.00
d.		Double surcharge		380.00
72	A3	9p rose lilac	10.00	5.50
a.		Printed on both sides		300.00

73	A1	1sh red brown	37.50	3.25
a.		1sh brown	40.00	2.50
b.		Horiz. pair, imperf. btwn.		300.00
74	A2	2sh carmine	35.00	4.50
a.		Horiz. pair, imperf. vert.		
b.		Imperf., pair		400.00

For overprint see No. O41.

1882   **Wmk. 73**   *Perf. 10*
Black Surcharge

75	A6	½p on 1p green	10.50	4.00

A9

A10

A11   A12

Perf. 10, 11½, 12½ and Compound
1883-90   **Typo.**

76	A9	½p chocolate brown	2.25	.25
a.		½p red brown ('89)	2.25	.25
b.		½p bister brown	3.50	.25
78	A10	3p deep green ('86)	6.50	.75
a.		3p olive green ('90)	11.00	1.50
79	A11	4p violet ('90)	7.75	1.75
80	A12	6p blue ('87)	7.75	1.00
		Nos. 76-80 (4)	24.25	3.75

See Nos. 96, 100-101, 104, 108-109, 111. For overprints see Nos. O50-O51, O54, O58, O60-O61, O64, O66-O67, O71, O73, O75, O81-O82. For surcharges see Nos. 94-95, 99, O48, O57, O59.

A13

1886-96   *Perf. 10, 11½ to 12½*

81	A13	2sh6p violet	27.50	6.50
82	A13	5sh rose	40.00	16.00
83	A13	10sh green	100.00	25.00
84	A13	15sh buff	200.00	140.00
85	A13	£1 blue	165.00	60.00
86	A13	£2 red brown	475.00	150.00
87	A13	50sh rose red	600.00	200.00
88	A13	£3 olive green	825.00	
89	A13	£4 lemon	1,000.	
90	A13	£5 gray	2,700.	
90A	A13	£5 brown ('96)	2,600.	
91	A13	£10 bronze	3,000.	700.00
92	A13	£15 silver	6,500.	
93	A13	£20 lilac	8,250.	

For overprints see Nos. O83-O84.

2½d.   **5D.**
#94, 99   #95

Perf. 10, 11½x12½ and Compound
1891
Brown Surcharge

94	A11	2½p on 4p green	8.00	1.40
a.		"½" nearer the "2"	30.00	20.00
b.		Pair, imperf. between		375.00
c.		Fraction bar omitted	90.00	80.00

Carmine Surcharge

95	A12	5p on 6p red brown	17.00	6.00
a.		No period after "D"	165.00	

See #99. For overprints see Nos. O48, O57, O59.

Many stamps of the issues of 1855-91 have been reprinted; they are all on paper watermarked Crown and SA, letters wide apart, and are overprinted "REPRINT."

1893   **Typo.**   *Perf. 15*

96	A9	½p brown	3.00	.18
a.		Horiz. pair, imperf. between	125.00	
b.		Pair, perf. 12 between and perf. 15 around	195.00	50.00

97	A6	1p green	3.50	.20
98	A6a	2p orange	6.50	.15
a.		Horiz. pair, imperf. between	225.00	
99	A11	2½p on 4p green	12.00	1.65
a.		"½" nearer the "2"	40.00	35.00
b.		Fraction bar omitted		
100	A11	4p gray violet	13.00	2.00
101	A12	6p blue	32.50	4.25
		Nos. 96-101 (6)	70.50	8.43

Kangaroo,   Coat of
Palm — A16   Arms — A17

1894, Mar. 1

102	A16	2½p blue violet	13.00	1.50
103	A17	5p dull violet	15.00	2.00

See Nos. 107, 110, 117, 135-136, 147, 151. For overprints see Nos. O65, O70, O72, O80.

1895-97   *Perf. 13*

104	A9	½p pale brown	3.00	.25
105	A6	1p green	5.25	.50
a.		Vert. pair, imperf. between		
106	A6a	2p orange	4.25	.15
107	A16	2½p blue violet	7.50	.32
108	A10	3p olive green ('97)	5.00	.30
109	A11	4p bright violet	6.50	.32
110	A17	5p dull violet	7.00	.32
111	A12	6p blue	8.00	.38
		Nos. 104-111 (8)	46.50	2.54

Some authorities regard the so-called redrawn 1p stamps with thicker lettering (said to have been issued in 1897) as impressions from a new or cleaned plate.

Perf. 11½, 12½, Clean-Cut, Compound
1896   **Engr.**   **Wmk. 7**

112	A3	9p lilac rose	12.50	6.50
113	A1	1sh dark brown	26.00	5.50
a.		Horiz. pair, imperf. btwn.		
c.		Vert. pair, imperf. btwn.	180.00	
113B	A2	2sh carmine	32.50	8.00
		Nos. 112-113B (3)	71.00	20.00

Adelaide Post Office — A18

1899   **Typo.**   **Wmk. 73**   *Perf. 13*

114	A18	½p yellow green	1.75	.25
115	A6	1p carmine	3.00	.20
a.		1p scarlet	2.75	.50
116	A6a	2p purple	2.25	.25
117	A16	2½p dark blue	7.00	.75
		Nos. 114-117 (4)	14.00	1.45

See #132, 144. For overprint see #O77.

Perf. 11½, 12½

1901   **Engr.**   **Wmk. 72**

118	A1	1sh dark brown	24.00	16.00
a.		1sh red brown	27.50	15.00
b.		Horiz. pair, imperf. vert.		
119	A2	2sh carmine	27.50	15.00

1902

120	A3	9p magenta	20.00	20.00

A19   A20

Perf. 11½, 12½ and Compound
1902-03   **Typo.**   **Wmk. 73**

121	A19	3p olive green	4.75	.75
122	A19	4p red orange	7.50	1.50
123	A19	6p blue green	6.50	1.50
124	A19	8p ultra (value 19mm long)	8.50	2.25
124A	A19	8p ultra (value 16½mm long) ('03)	13.00	3.00
b.		"EIGNT"	900.00	3,000.

125	A19	9p claret	8.50	2.25
a.		Pair, imperf. between	300.00	
126	A19	10p org buff	11.00	3.50
127	A19	1sh brown ('03)	12.00	3.00
a.		Horiz. or vert. pair, imperf. btwn.	700.00	
128	A19	2sh6p purple	32.50	9.00
129	A19	5sh rose	75.00	52.50
130	A19	10sh green ('03)	110.00	65.00
131	A19	£1 blue	275.00	150.00
		Nos. 121-131 (12)	564.25	294.25

1904   *Perf. 12x11½*

132	A18	½p yellow green	3.00	.60
133	A6	1p rose	6.50	.60
134	A6a	2p purple	6.50	.60
135	A16	2½p dark blue	14.00	1.50
136	A17	5p dull violet	11.00	1.75
		Nos. 132-136 (5)	41.00	5.05

1904-08   *Perf. 12 and 12x11½*

137	A20	6p blue green	8.25	1.75
138	A20	8p ultra ('06)	11.50	2.25
139	A20	9p claret	8.00	1.65
139A	A20	10p org buff ('07)	20.00	5.25
b.		Pair, imperf. between	325.00	225.00
140	A20	1sh brown	12.00	2.00
a.		Pair, imperf. between	250.00	
141	A20	2sh6p purple ('05)	55.00	8.25
142	A20	5sh scarlet	55.00	32.50
142B	A20	10sh green ('08)	165.00	125.00
143	A20	£1 deep blue	200.00	140.00
		Nos. 137-143 (9)	534.75	318.65

See Nos. 148-150, 152-157.

1906-12   **Wmk. 74**

144	A18	½p green	1.50	.15
145	A6	1p carmine	1.50	.15
146	A6a	2p purple	2.50	.15
a.		Horiz. pair, imperf. between		
147	A16	2½p dk blue ('11)	10.50	1.50
148	A20	3p ol grn (value 19mm long)	6.50	1.25
a.		Horiz. pair, imperf. between		
149	A20	3p ol grn (value 17mm long) ('09)	8.50	1.50
150	A20	4p red orange	9.75	1.75
151	A17	5p dull vio ('08)	8.50	2.00
152	A20	6p blue grn ('07)	7.50	1.10
a.		Vert. pair, imperf. between	240.00	
153	A20	8p ultra ('09)	15.00	5.50
154	A20	9p claret	15.00	4.00
a.		Vert. pair, imperf. between	195.00	
b.		Horiz. pair, imperf. between	225.00	
155	A20	1sh brown	11.00	3.00
a.		Pair, imperf. between	175.00	
156	A20	2sh6p purple ('09)	32.50	10.50
157	A20	5sh lt red ('12)	82.50	
		Nos. 144-157 (14)	212.75	31.55

OFFICIAL STAMPS

For Departments
Regular Issues Overprinted in Red,
Black or Blue:

A. (Architect), A. G. (Attorney General), A. O. (Audit Office), B. D. (Barracks Department), B. G. (Botanical Gardens), B. M. (Bench of Magistrates), C. (Customs), C. D. (Convict Department), C. L. (Crown Lands), C. O. (Commissariat Officer), C. S. (Chief Secretary), C. Sgn. (Colonial Surgeon), C. P. (Commissioner of Police), C. T. (Commissioner of Titles), D. B. (Destitute Board), D. R. (Deed Registry), E. (Engineer), E. B. (Education Board), G. P. (Government Printer), G. S. (Government Storekeeper), G. T. (Goolwa Tramway), G. F. (Gold Fields), H. (Hospital), H. A. (House of Assembly), I. A. (Immigration Agent), I. E. (Intestate Estates), I. S. (Inspector of Sheep), L. A. (Lunatic Asylum), L. C. (Legislative Council), L. L. (Legislative Library), L. T. (Land Titles), M. (Military), M. B. (Marine Board), M. R. (Manager of Railways), M. R. G. (Main Roads Gambierton), N. T. (Northern Territory), O. A. (Official Assignee), P. (Police), P. A. (Protector of Aborigines), P. O. (Post Office), P. S. (Private Secretary), P. W. (Public Works), R. B. (Road Board), R. G. (Registrar General of Births, &c.), S. (Sheriff), S. C. (Supreme Court), S.G. (Surveyor General), S. M. (Stipendiary Magistrate), S. T. (Superintendent of Telegraph), T. (Treasurer), T. R. (Titles Registry), V. (Volunteers), V. A. (Valuator), V. N. (Vaccination), W. (Waterworks).

1868-74   **Wmk. 6**   *Rouletted*

O1	A1	1p green	
O2	A1	2p pale red	
O3	A6a	2p vermilion	
O4	A2	4p dull violet	
O5	A1	6p slate blue	
O6	A3	9p gray lilac	
O7	A1	1sh brown	
O8	A2	2sh carmine	

Perf. 11½ to 12½ x Roulette

O9	A1	1p green	
O10	A2	4p dull violet	
O11	A1	6p blue	
O12	A1	1sh brown	

Perf. 10, 11½, 12½ and Compound

O13	A1	1p green		
O14	A2	3p on 4p slate blue (Red)		
O16	A2	4p dull violet		
O17	A1	6p deep blue		
O18	A3	9p violet		
O19	A3	10p on 9p yellow (Blk)		
O20	A1	1sh brown		
O21	A2	2sh carmine		

Rouletted
Wmk. 72

O22	A6a	2p orange	

Perf. 10 x Roulette

O23	A6a	2p orange	

Perf. 10, 11½, 12½ and Compound

O24	A6a	2p orange	

Wmk. 70
Perf. 10

O25	A6a	2p orange	
O26	A2	4p dull violet	

For General Use

Overprinted in Black **O.S.**

Perf. 10, 11½, 12½ and Compound
1874　　　　　　　　　　**Wmk. 6**

O27	A1	1p green	—	450.00
a.		Printed on both sides		
O28	A2	3p on 4p ultra	150.00	
a.		No period after "S"		375.00
O29	A2	4p dull violet	27.50	9.50
a.		Inverted overprint		25.00
b.		No period after "S"		
c.		Perf. 10	1,650.	400.00
O30	A1	6p deep blue	55.00	9.50
a.		No period after "S"		22.50
O31	A3	9p violet	250.00	60.00
a.		No period after "S"	300.00	
O32	A1	1sh red brown	55.00	16.00
a.		Double overprint		27.50
b.		No period after "S"	110.00	40.00
O33	A2	2sh carmine	67.50	14.00
a.		Double overprint		
b.		No period after "S"		32.50

1874-75　　　　　　　　**Wmk. 72**

O34	A6	1p blue green	100.00	27.50
a.		Inverted overprint		
O35	A6a	2p orange	14.00	1.40

1876-86　　　　　　　　**Wmk. 7**

O36	A2	3p on 4p ultra		
O37	A2	4p dull violet	100.00	17.00
O38	A2	4p reddish vio	37.50	3.00
a.		Double overprint		
b.		Inverted overprint		
c.		Dbl. ovpt., one inverted		
O39	A1	6p dark blue	62.50	5.00
a.		Double overprint		37.50
b.		Inverted overprint		
O40	A1	6p ultramarine	57.50	4.50
a.		Double overprint		
b.		Inverted overprint		
O41	A3	8p on 9p yel brn	425.00	125.00
a.		Double overprint	750.00	
O41B	A3	9p violet	4,000.	
O42	A1	1sh red brown	45.00	5.00
a.		Inverted overprint	150.00	75.00
b.		Double overprint		
O43	A2	2sh carmine	110.00	8.00
a.		Double overprint		70.00
b.		Inverted overprint		75.00

1880-91　　　　　　　　**Wmk. 73**

O44	A6	1p blue green	11.00	.50
a.		Inverted overprint		22.50
b.		Double overprint	35.00	20.00
c.		Dbl. ovpt., one inverted		
O45	A6	1p yellow green	12.00	.50
O46	A6a	2p orange	11.00	.50
a.		Inverted overprint		10.00
b.		Double overprint	70.00	25.00
c.		Overprinted sideways		
d.		Dbl. ovpt., one inverted		
e.		Dbl. ovpt., both inverted		57.50
O47	A6a	2p blood red	52.50	5.00
O48	A11	2½p on 4p green	35.00	9.50
a.		"½" nearer the "2"		75.00
b.		Double overprint		
c.		Pair, one without ovpt.		
		Nos. O44-O48 (5)	121.50	15.75

1882-90　　　　　　　　*Perf. 10*

O49	A6	½p on 1p green	25.00	8.00
a.		Inverted overprint		
O50	A11	4p violet	21.00	1.90
O51	A12	6p blue	12.00	1.25
a.		Double overprint		
		Nos. O49-O51 (3)	58.00	11.15

Overprinted in Black **O.S.**

Perf. 10, 11½, 12½ and Compound
1891　　　　　　　　　　**Wmk. 7**

O52	A1	1sh red brown	42.50	3.50
O53	A2	2sh carmine	100.00	10.00
a.		Double overprint		

1891-95　　　　　　　　**Wmk. 73**

O54	A9	½p brown	12.00	2.50
O55	A6	1p blue green	12.00	.30
a.		Double overprint	80.00	
O56	A6a	2p orange	12.00	.30
O57	A11	2½p on 4p green	45.00	2.75
a.		"½" nearer the "2"	52.50	18.00
b.		Inverted overprint	100.00	
O58	A11	4p violet	17.50	1.25
a.		Double overprint		
O59	A12	5p on 6p red brn	55.00	2.50
O60	A12	6p blue	9.75	.75
		Nos. O54-O60 (7)	163.25	10.35

1893　　　　　　　　　　*Perf. 15*

O61	A9	½p brown	15.00	1.75
O62	A6	1p green	11.00	.30
O63	A6a	2p orange	12.00	.15
a.		Inverted overprint		18.00
b.		Double overprint		32.50
O64	A11	4p gray violet	65.00	1.75
a.		Double overprint		21.00
O65	A17	5p dull violet	80.00	4.50
O66	A12	6p blue	20.00	.70
		Nos. O61-O66 (6)	203.00	9.15

1896　　　　　　　　　　*Perf. 13*

O67	A9	½p brown	12.50	1.75
a.		Triple overprint		
O68	A6	1p green	16.00	.15
O69	A6a	2p orange	11.00	.15
O70	A16	2½p blue violet	60.00	1.40
O71	A11	4p brt violet	65.00	1.75
a.		Double overprint	30.00	40.00
O72	A17	5p dull violet	60.00	4.25
O73	A12	6p blue	25.00	.90
		Nos. O67-O73 (7)	249.50	10.35

On No. O67a, one overprint is upright, two sideways.

Same Overprint in Dark Blue
1891-95　　　　　　　　*Perf. 10*

O74	A6	1p green	150.00 15.00
O75	A12	6p blue	

Black Overprint
Perf. 11½, 12½, Clean-Cut
1897　　　　　　　　　　**Wmk. 7**

O76	A1	1sh brown	40.00	4.50
a.		Double overprint		

Overprinted in Black **O. S.**

1900　　**Wmk. 73**　　*Perf. 13*

O77	A18	½p yellow green	10.00	1.75
O78	A6	1p carmine rose	11.50	.15
a.		Inverted overprint		
b.		Double overprint		
O79	A6a	2p purple	11.50	.15
a.		Inverted ovpt.	40.00	
O80	A16	2½p dark blue	82.50	1.40
a.		Inverted overprint		30.00
O81	A11	4p violet	65.00	.70
a.		Inverted overprint	125.00	
O82	A12	6p blue	20.00	.70
		Nos. O77-O82 (6)	200.50	4.85

1901　　　　　　　　　　*Perf. 10*

O83	A13	2sh6p violet	2,000. 2,000.
O84	A13	5sh rose	2,250. 2,250.

On Nos. O77-O82 the letters "O.S." are 11½mm apart; on Nos. O83-O84, 14½mm apart.

Overprinted in Black **O.S.**

1903　**Wmk. 72**　*Perf. 11½, 12½*

O85	A1	1sh red brown	40.00	25.00

Many of the official stamps are found with one or both of the periods after "O.S." missing. This occurs more often in the later than in the earlier issues.

TASMANIA

taz-'mā-nē-ə

LOCATION — An island off the southeastern coast of Australia
GOVT. — British Colony
AREA — 26,215 sq. ml.
POP. — 172,475 (1901)
CAPITAL — Hobart

　Tasmania was one of the six British colonies that united in 1901 to form the Commonwealth of Australia. The island was originally named Van Diemen's Land by its discoverer, Abel Tasman, the present name

having been adopted in 1853. Stamps of Australia are now used.

12 Pence = 1 Shilling
20 Shillings = 1 Pound

Watermarks

Wmk. 6- Large Star

Wmk. 49-
Double-lined
Numeral

Wmk. 75-
Double-lined
Numeral

Wmk. 50- Single-
lined "2"

Wmk. 51- Single-
lined "4"

Wmk. 52- Single-
lined "10"

Wmk. 70- V and
Crown

Wmk. 13- Crown
& Double-lined A

Wmk. 76- TAS

Wmk. 77- TAS

Wmk. 78- Multiple TAS

Values for unused stamps are for examples with original gum as defined in the catalogue introduction except for Nos. 1-2a and 10 which are valued without gum as few examples exist with any remaining original gum. Very fine examples of Nos. 17-75a will have perforations touching the design on one or more sides due to the narrow spacing of the stamps on the plates. Stamps with perfs clear of the design on all four sides are scarce and command higher prices.

Queen Victoria
A1　　　　　　A2
1853, Nov. 1 Unwmk. Engr. *Imperf.*

1	A1	1p blue	3,250.	750.00
2	A2	4p red orange	2,000.	300.00
		4p yellow orange	2,250.	300.00
		Cut to shape		15.00

Twenty-four varieties of each.

　The reprints are made from defaced plates and show marks across the face of each stamp. They are on thin and thick, unwatermarked paper and thin cardboard; only the first are perforated. Nearly all the reprints of Tasmania may be found with and without the overprint "REPRINT."

Nos. 1-47A with pen or revenue cancellations sell for a small fraction of the price of postally used specimens. Copies are found with pen cancellation removed.

 Queen Victoria — A3

1855　　**Wmk. 6**　　**Wove Paper**

4	A3	1p dark carmine	6,000.	825.00
5	A3	2p deep green	1,800.	500.00
6	A3	4p deep blue	1,250.	80.00

1856-57　　　　　　　　**Unwmk.**

7	A3	1p pale red	6,000.	500.00
8	A3	2p emerald ('57)	7,250.	700.00
9	A3	4p blue ('57)	650.00	85.00

1856　　　　　　　　**Pelure Paper**

10	A3	1p brown red	3,000.	600.00

1857　　　　　　　**Wmk. 49, 75**

11	A3	1p carmine	80.00	15.00
a.		1p orange red	85.00	15.00
b.		1p brown red	400.00	22.50
		Double impression	165.00	
12	A3	2p sage green	130.00	42.50
a.		2p yellow green	250.00	50.00
b.		2p green	—	35.00
13	A3	4p blue	100.00	13.00
b.		Printed on both sides		
		Nos. 11-13 (3)	310.00	

See #17-19, 23-25, 29-31, 35-37, 39-41, 45-47A.

A4　　　　　　　　A4a

1858

14	A4	6p gray lilac	125.00	50.00
a.		6p red violet	600.00	150.00
b.		Double impression		200.00
15	A4	6p blue gray	325.00	70.00
16	A4a	1sh vermilion	550.00	52.50
		Nos. 14-16 (3)	1,000.	172.50

No. 15 watermarked large star was not regularly issued.

1864　　　　　　　　*Rouletted*

17	A3	1p carmine	375.00	125.00
		1p brick red		180.00
18	A3	2p yellow grn		375.00
19	A3	4p blue		180.00
21	A4	6p gray lilac		225.00
22	A4a	1sh vermilion		625.00

1864-69　　　　　　　　*Perf. 10*

23	A3	1p brick red	50.00	19.00
		1p carmine	50.00	19.00
		1p orange red	50.00	19.00
24	A3	2p yellow green	275.00	65.00
a.		2p sage green	375.00	150.00

TASMANIA (continued)

25	A3	4p blue	125.00	9.00
a.		Double impression		100.00
26	A4	6p lilac	140.00	12.50
a.		6p red lilac	375.00	55.00
27	A4	6p slate blue	190.00	20.00
28	A4a	1sh vermilion	100.00	17.50
a.		Horiz. pair, imperf. vert.		
		Nos. 23-28 (6)	880.00	143.00

1864-69 *Perf. 11½, 12, 12½, 13*

29	A3	1p carmine	24.00	6.00
a.		1p orange red	40.00	16.00
b.		1p brick red	42.50	22.50
c.		Double impression		
d.		Wmkd. "2"		950.00
		As "d," pen cancel		125.00
30	A3	2p yellow green	130.00	35.00
a.		2p dark green	200.00	35.00
b.		2p sage green	250.00	100.00
31	A3	4p blue	65.00	11.00
32	A4	6p red lilac	25.00	11.00
a.		6p purple	75.00	21.00
b.		6p violet	110.00	17.50
d.		Horiz. pair, imperf. vert.		
e.		Double impression		100.00
33	A4	6p slate blue	250.00	65.00
34	A4a	1sh vermilion	90.00	27.50
a.		Double impression		165.00
b.		Horiz. pair, imperf. vert.		
		Nos. 29-34 (6)	584.00	155.50

The reprints are on unwatermarked paper, perforated 11½, and on thin cardboard, imperforate and perforated.

Pin-perf. 5½ to 9½, 13½ to 14½
1867

35	A3	1p carmine	350.00	77.50
36	A3	2p yellow green		275.00
37	A3	4p blue		165.00
38	A4	6p gray		150.00
38A	A4	6p red lilac		450.00
38B	A4a	1sh vermilion		

Oblique Roulette

39	A3	1p carmine	675.00	275.00
40	A3	2p yellow green		400.00
41	A3	4p blue		325.00
42	A4	6p gray		550.00
43	A4	6p red lilac		575.00
44	A4a	1sh vermilion		750.00

1868 *Serrate Perf. 19*

45	A3	1p carmine	225.00	100.00
46	A3	2p yellow green		175.00
47	A3	4p blue	650.00	110.00
47A	A3	6p purple		500.00

Queen Victoria — A5

1870-71 *Typo.* *Wmk. 50* *Perf. 12*

48	A5	2p green	45.00	5.00
a.		Imperf.		
b.		Perf. 11½	35.00	3.25
c.		Double impression		

See Nos. 49-75, 98, 108-109.

Wmk. 51

49	A5	1p rose ('71)	60.00	20.00
a.		Imperf., pair	600.00	215.00
50	A5	4p blue	725.00	300.00

Wmk. 52

51	A5	1p rose	40.00	9.00
a.		Imperf., pair	265.00	250.00
c.		Perf. 11½	1.000.	
52	A5	10p black	20.00	6.00
a.		Imperf., pair	120.00	
b.		Perf. 11½	25.00	20.00

The reprints are on unwatermarked paper. The 4p has also been reprinted on thin cardboard, imperf and perf.

1871-76 *Wmk. 76* *Perf. 11½*

53	A5	1p rose	4.50	.60
a.		Imperf.		
c.		Perf. 12	65.00	9.00
53B	A5	1p vermilion ('73)	250.00	95.00
54	A5	2p deep green ('72)	12.00	.60
a.		2p yellow green	120.00	1.25
b.		2p blue green	45.00	.60
c.		Imperf., pair		120.00
d.		2p green, perf. 12	450.00	135.00
e.		Double impression		
55	A5	3p brown	37.50	4.50
a.		3p purple brown	37.50	4.50
b.		As "a," imperf. pair		325.00
56	A5	3p red brown ('71)	37.50	4.50
a.		3p indian red	35.00	4.50
b.		Imperf., pair		120.00
c.		Vert. pair, imperf. horiz.		
57	A5	4p dull yellow ('76)	40.00	7.50
a.		Perf. 12	225.00	15.00
58	A5	9p blue	20.00	7.50
a.		Imperf., pair		120.00
b.		Perf. 12	40.00	40.00
59	A5	5sh bright violet	125.00	25.00
a.		Imperf.		
b.		Horiz. pair, imperf. vert.		

---

c.		Perf. 12	175.00	150.00
		Pen cancel		.30
		Nos. 53-59 (8)	526.50	145.20

The reprints are on unwatermarked paper, the 5sh has also been reprinted on thin cardboard; all are perforated.

1878 *Wmk. 77* *Perf. 14*

60	A5	1p rose	4.50	.60
61	A5	2p deep green	4.50	.60
62	A5	8p violet brown	15.00	4.50
		Nos. 60-62 (3)	24.00	5.70

The 8p has been reprinted on thin unwatermarked paper, perforated 11½.

1880-83 *Perf. 12, 11½*

63	A5	3p indian red, perf. 12	9.00	2.00
a.		Imperf. pair	85.00	
b.		Horiz. pair, imperf. between	600.00	
c.		Perf. 11½	10.50	3.00
64	A5	4p lem, perf. 11½ ('83)	40.00	7.50
a.		4p olive yellow, perf. 11½	100.00	21.00
b.		Printed on both sides	210.00	
c.		Imperf.		
d.		4p deep yellow, perf. 12	75.00	22.50

Type of 1871
Surcharged in Black **Halfpenny**

1889 *Perf. 14*

65	A5	½p on 1p carmine	9.00	1.75
a.		"al" sideways in surcharge	825.00	500.00

No. 65 has been reprinted on thin cardboard, perforated 12, with the surcharge "Halfpenny" 19mm long.

1889-96 *Perf. 11½*

66	A5	½p red orange	2.25	.70
a.		½p yellow orange	2.25	.70
b.		Perf. 12	2.00	.85
67	A5	1p dull red	8.25	2.00
a.		1p vermilion	5.00	2.00
68	A5	1p car, perf. 12	8.25	3.25
a.		1p pink, perf. 12	27.50	5.00
b.		1p salmon rose, perf. 12	8.25	3.25
c.		Imperf. pair	92.50	92.50

Perf. 12

69	A5	4p bister ('96)	18.00	8.25
70	A5	9p chalky bl ('96)	10.00	3.25
		Nos. 66-70 (5)	46.75	17.45

1891 *Wmk. 76* *Perf. 11½*

71	A5	½p orange	16.00	8.25
a.		½p brown orange	16.00	8.25
b.		Imperf. pair	82.50	
c.		Perf. 12	35.00	9.25
72	A5	1p salmon rose	21.00	11.50
a.		1p carmine, perf. 12	40.00	20.00
73	A5	4p ol bis, perf. 12	15.00	6.50
		Nos. 71-73 (3)	52.00	26.25

See Nos. 98, 108-109.

d.
Surcharged in Black **2½**

1891 *Wmk. 77* *Perf. 11½*
Surcharge 14mm High

74	A5	2½p on 9p lt blue	6.00	6.50
a.		Dbl. surcharge, one invtd.	210.00	200.00
b.		Imperf. pair	135.00	

Perf. 12
Surcharge 15mm High

75	A5	2½p on 9p lt blue	5.50	5.00
a.		Surcharged in blue		

No. 74 has been reprinted on thin unwatermarked paper, imperforate. There is also a reprint on thin cardboard, in deep ultramarine, with surcharge 16½mm high, and perforated 12.

A8

A9

1892-99 *Typo.* *Perf. 14*

76	A8	½p orange & vio	.85	.35
77	A9	2½p magenta	2.50	.65
78	A8	5p pale bl & brn	3.50	1.40
79	A8	6p blue vio & blk	3.50	1.50
80	A8	10p red brn & grn ('99)	6.75	5.50
81	A8	1sh rose & green	4.50	1.50
82	A8	2sh6p brown & blue	25.00	8.00
83	A8	5sh brn vio & red	37.50	17.00

84	A8	10sh brt vio & brn	75.00	45.00
85	A8	£1 green & yel	525.00	225.00
		Nos. 76-85 (10)	684.10	305.90

No. 80 shows the numeral on white tablet. See Nos. 99, 110-111.

Lake Marion
A10

Mt. Wellington
A11

View of Hobart — A12

Tasman's Arch — A13

Spring River, Port Davey — A14

Russell Falls — A15

Mt. Gould and Lake St. Clair — A16

Dilston Falls — A17

1899-1900 *Engr.* *Wmk. 78* *Perf. 14*

86	A10	½p dark green	5.00	1.75
87	A11	1p carmine	5.00	.60
88	A12	2p violet	5.50	.45
89	A13	2½p dark blue	11.00	5.00
90	A14	3p dark brown	8.50	1.75
91	A15	4p ocher	16.00	2.25
92	A16	5p ultramarine	16.00	7.50
93	A17	6p lake	20.00	6.50
		Nos. 86-93 (8)	87.00	25.80

See Nos. 94-97, 102-107, 114-117.

Perf. 11, 12½, 11x12½
1902-03 *Litho., Typo.* *Wmk. 70*

94	A10	½p green	2.25	.30
95	A11	1p carmine	5.50	.15
96	A11	1p dull red	5.00	.20
97	A12	2p violet	3.25	.15
98	A5	9p blue	9.00	3.00
a.		9p ultramarine	225.00	
b.		9p indigo	90.00	
c.		Perf. 11	7.25	3.50
99	A8	1sh rose & green	12.00	3.75
a.		Perf. 11	27.50	27.50
		Nos. 94-99 (6)	37.00	7.55

Nos. 94, 97 are litho., Nos. 96, 98-99 typo. No. 95 was printed both ways.

No. 78 Surcharged in Black **1 1d. ½**

1904 *Wmk. 77* *Perf. 14*

100	A8	1½p on 5p blue & brn	1.75	1.25

Perf. 11, 12, 12½ and Compound
1905-08 *Typo.* *Wmk. 13*

102	A10	½p dull green	2.00	.15
a.		Booklet pane of 12		
103	A11	1p carmine	2.00	.15
a.		Booklet pane of 18		

104	A12	2p violet	3.50	.15
105	A14	3p dark brown	7.00	2.00
106	A15	4p ocher	13.00	2.25
107	A17	6p lake	40.00	5.00
108	A5	8p violet brown	19.00	5.00
109	A5	9p blue	8.00	3.00
110	A8	1sh rose & green	13.00	2.50
111	A8	10sh brt vio & brn	100.00	62.50
a.		Perf. 11	175.00	
		Nos. 102-111 (10)	207.50	82.70

Nos. 104-107 also printed litho.

1911 *Redrawn*

114	A12	2p bright violet	3.50	.30
115	A15	4p dull yellow	16.00	8.00
116	A17	6p lake	17.00	8.00
		Nos. 114-116 (3)	36.50	16.30

The redrawn 2p measures 33½x25mm instead of 32½x24½mm. There are many slight changes in the clouds and other parts of the design.

The 4p is much lighter, especially the waterfall and trees above it. This appears to be a new or cleaned plate rather than a redrawn one.

In the redrawn 6p there are more colored lines in the waterfall and the river and more white dots in the trees.

No. 114
Surcharged in Red **ONE PENNY**

1912

117	A12	1p on 2p bright violet	.85	.50

VICTORIA

vik-'tōr-ē-ə

LOCATION — In the extreme southeastern part of Australia
GOVT. — British Colony
AREA — 87,884 sq. mi.
POP. — 1,201,341 (1901)
CAPITAL — Melbourne

Victoria was one of the six former British colonies which united on Jan. 1, 1901, to form the Commonwealth of Australia.

12 Pence = 1 Shilling
20 Shillings = 1 Pound

Unused values for Nos. 1-16 are for stamps without gum as these stamps are seldom found with original gum. Otherwise, unused values are for stamps with original gum as defined in the catalogue introduction.

Very fine examples of all rouletted, perforated and serrate perforated stamps from Nos. 9-109 and F2 will have roulettes, perforations or serrate perforations touching the design. Examples clear on four sides range from scarce to rare and will command higher prices.

Watermarks

Wmk. 6- Large Star

Wmk. 80

Wmk. 50

Wmk. 80a

Wmk. 81

Wmk. 139

Wmk. 49

Wmk. 75

Wmk. 70- V and Crown

Wmk. 13- Crown & Double-lined A

Queen Victoria A1

Victoria on Throne A2

1850 Litho. Unwmk. Imperf.

1	A1	1p dull red	875.00	90.00
a.		1p vermilion	600.00	125.00
2	A1	1p rose	375.00	75.00
a.		1p pink	410.00	85.00
3	A1	3p blue	600.00	50.00
a.		3p light blue	550.00	50.00
4	A1	3p indigo	625.00	50.00
		Nos. 1-4 (4)	2,475.	265.00

Nos. 1-4 exist with and without frame line.

THREE TYPES OF 2p:

Type I - Border, two sets of nine wavy lines crisscrossing. Background, 22 groups of wavy triple lines below "VICTORIA."

Type II - Border, same. Background, 15 groups of wavy triple lines below "VICTORIA."

Type III - Border, two sets of five wavy lines crisscrossing. Background, same as type II.

5	A1	2p lilac, I	3,000.	300.00
a.		2p brn lilac, I	3,750.	325.00
6	A1	2p brn lilac, II	1,000.	90.00
a.		2p gray lilac, II	1,000.	90.00
7	A1	2p brn lilac, III	875.00	80.00
a.		2p gray lilac, III	875.00	90.00
b.		Value omitted, III		2,500.
8	A1	2p yel brn, III	650.00	55.00

Rouletted 7

9	A1	1p vermilion		2,250.
10	A1	3p blue		140.00
a.		3p deep blue	1,600.	190.00

Perf. 12

12	A1	3p blue	2,000.	125.00
a.		3p deep blue	2,000.	125.00

1852 Engr. Imperf.

14	A2	2p reddish brown	160.00	35.00

#14 was reprinted on paper with watermark 70, imperf. & perf. 12½, overprinted "REPRINT."

1854 Litho.

15	A2	2p gray brown	220.00	35.00
16	A2	2p brown lilac	200.00	30.00
a.		2p red lilac	250.00	35.00

Fifty varieties.

A3

A4

1854-58 Typo.

17	A3	6p orange	150.00	27.50
a.		6p red orange	180.00	25.00

See Nos. 19-20, 22-24A, 26-28.

Lithographed

18	A4	1sh blue	450.00	20.00

See Nos. 21, 25.

Typographed

19	A3	2sh green	1,100.	125.00

1857-58 Rouletted 7, 9½

20	A3	6p orange	525.00	60.00

Lithographed

21	A4	1sh blue	1,500.	90.00

Typographed

22	A3	2sh green ('58)	4,000.	225.00

Small Serrate Perf. 19

23	A3	6p orange	1,200.	100.00

Large Serpentine Perf. 10½

24	A3	6p orange	800.00	55.00

Serrate x Serpentine Perf.

24A	A3	6p orange		125.00

1859 Litho. Perf. 12

25	A4	1sh blue	180.00	14.00

Typographed

26	A3	2sh green	260.00	37.50

1861 Wmk. "SIX PENCE" (80)

27	A3	6p black	260.00	50.00

Wmk. Single-lined "2" (50)

1864 Perf. 12, 13

28	A3	2sh blue, green	250.00	8.50

A5

1856, Oct. Wmk. Large Star (6)

Engr. Imperf.

29	A5	1p green	125.00	30.00

1858 Rouletted 5½-6½

30	A5	6p blue	175.00	7.00

Nos. 29 and 30 have been reprinted on paper watermarked V and Crown. They are imperforate and overprinted "REPRINT."

A6

A7

1857-61 Typo. Imperf.

31	A6	1p yellow green	100.00	15.00
a.		Printed on both sides		900.00
32	A6	4p vermilion	275.00	15.00
a.		Printed on both sides		900.00
33	A6	4p rose	200.00	11.50

Rouletted 7 to 9½

34	A6	1p yellow green	325.00	125.00
35	A6	4p rose	525.00	40.00

Perf. 12

36	A6	1p yellow green	600.00	325.00

Unwmk. Imperf.

37	A6	1p blue green	300.00	18.00
38	A6	2p lilac	240.00	15.00
39	A6	4p rose	500.00	30.00

Copies of No. 39 printed in dull carmine on thin paper are regarded as printer's waste and of little value. They are also found printed on both sides.

Rouletted 7 to 9½

40	A6	1p blue green	300.00	10.00
a.		1p yellow green	400.00	32.50
b.		Horiz. pair, imperf. btwn.		1,000.
41	A6	2p lilac	1,200.	32.50
42	A6	4p rose	300.00	8.00
a.		Horiz. pair, imperf. btwn.		1,000.

Perf. 12

43	A6	1p blue green	160.00	10.00
a.		1p yellow green	200.00	15.00
b.		Horiz. pair, imperf. btwn.		650.00
44	A6	2p lilac		90.00
45	A6	4p rose	180.00	5.00
b.		Vert. pair, imperf. btwn.		

Serrate Perf. 19

45A	A6	2p lilac	600.00	250.00

Laid Paper
Imperf

46	A6	4p rose	600.00	25.00

Rouletted 5 to 7

47	A6	2p dark lilac		8.00
a.		2p brown lilac	225.00	8.00
b.		2p violet	150.00	5.00
48	A6	4p rose	160.00	5.50

Perf. 12

49	A6	1p green	240.00	14.00
50	A6	4p rose	150.00	11.00

Wove Paper

1860 Wmk. Value in Words (80)

51	A6	1p yellow green	60.00	8.00
a.		Wmk. "FOUR PENCE" (error)		2,000.
52	A6	2p gray lilac	140.00	7.50
a.		2p brown lilac	400.00	24.00

Wmk. "THREE PENCE" (80)

53	A6	2p gray lilac	240.00	10.00

Single-lined "2" (50)

54	A6	2p lilac	160.00	16.00
a.		2p gray lilac	160.00	16.00
b.		2p brown lilac	160.00	16.00
c.		As "b," wmkd. single-lined "6"		4,500.

1860 Unwmk. Laid Paper

56	A7	3p deep blue	360.00	45.00

Wmk. Value in Words (80)
Perf. 11½ to 12

1860-62 Wove Paper

57	A7	3p blue	175.00	10.00
58	A7	3p claret	175.00	35.00
a.		Perf. 13	190.00	40.00
59	A7	4p rose	175.00	4.50
60	A7	6p orange	3,000.	325.00
61	A7	6p black	250.00	8.00

Wmk. "FIVE SHILLINGS" (80)

62	A7	4p rose	1,500.	20.00

Wmk. Single-lined "4" (80a)

1863 Imperf.

63	A7	4p rose	—	135.00

Rouletted

64	A7	4p rose	2,400.	200.00

Perf. 11½ to 12

65	A7	4p rose	100.00	8.00

1863 Unwmk. Perf. 12

66	A7	4p rose	450.00	10.50

A8

A9

1861-63 Wmk. 80 Perf. 11½ to 12

67	A8	1p green	90.00	9.00
68	A9	6p black	175.00	7.50

Wmk. Double-lined "1" (139)

69	A8	1p green	200.00	13.00

Wmk. Single-lined Figures (50)

70	A8	1p green	45.00	6.50
71	A9	6p black	175.00	6.50

The 1p and 6p of 1861-63 are known on paper without watermark but were probably impressions on the margins of watermarked sheets.

A10

A11

A12

A13

Wmk. Single-lined Figures (50, 80a, 81)

1863-67 Perf. 11½ to 13

74	A10	1p green	70.00	4.00
a.		Double impression		900.00
75	A10	2p gray lilac	75.00	4.00
a.		2p violet	50.00	2.75
76	A10	4p rose	110.00	3.00
a.		Double impression		900.00
77	A11	6p blue	87.50	3.00
78	A10	8p orange	300.00	50.00
79	A12	10p brn, rose	150.00	4.50
80	A13	1sh blue, blue	150.00	3.00
		Nos. 74-80 (7)	942.50	71.50

See Nos. 81-82, 84-96, 99-101, 108-112, 115-119, 124-126, 144, 188. Compare type A11 with type A54.

A14

Wmk. Double-lined "1" (139)

81	A10	1p green	95.00	5.00
82	A10	2p gray lilac	250.00	8.00
83	A14	3p lilac	200.00	35.00
84	A11	6p blue	65.00	6.00
		Nos. 81-84 (4)	610.00	54.00

See Nos. 97, 113, 155, 186. Compare type A14 with type A51.

Wmk. Double-lined "2" (49)

85	A11	6p blue		3,250.

Wmk. Single-lined "4" (80a)

86	A10	1p green	150.00	11.00
87	A10	2p gray lilac	200.00	7.00
88	A11	6p blue		1,500.

Wmk. Double-lined "4" (75)

89	A10	1p green	1,300.	145.00
90	A10	2p gray lilac	200.00	6.00
91	A10	4p rose	225.00	7.00
92	A11	6p blue	325.00	18.00

Wmk. Single-lined "6" (50)

93	A10	1p green	250.00	10.00
94	A10	2p gray lilac	225.00	5.75

Wmk. Single-lined "8" (50)

95	A10	1p green	200.00	15.00
96	A10	2p gray lilac	250.00	6.50
97	A14	3p lilac	200.00	30.00
99	A12	10p slate	400.00	120.00

Wmk. "SIX PENCE" (80)

100	A10	1p green	750.00	21.00
101	A11	6p blue	350.00	15.00

All values of the 1864-67 series except the 3p and 8p are known on unwatermarked paper. They are probably varieties from watermarked sheets which have been so placed on the printing press that some of the stamps escaped the watermark.

One copy of the 2p gray lilac, type A10, is reported to exist with only "PENCE" of watermark 80 showing. Some believe this is part of the "SIX PENCE" watermark.

1870   Wmk. "THREE PENCE" (80)

108	A11	6p blue	225.00	6.25

Wmk. "FOUR PENCE" (80)

109	A11	6p blue	500.00	40.00

A15

1867-78   Wmk. (70)   Perf. 11½ to 13

110	A10	1p green	60.00	2.00
111	A10	2p lilac	85.00	3.25
a.		2p gray lilac	62.50	2.00
112	A10	2p lilac, *lilac*	90.00	4.00
113	A14	3p red lilac	300.00	18.00
a.		3p lilac	350.00	20.00
114	A14	3p orange	22.50	2.00
a.		3p yellow	62.50	2.00
115	A10	4p rose	90.00	3.50
116	A11	6p blue	25.00	2.50
117	A11	6p ultra	27.50	2.50
a.		6p lilac blue	62.50	2.25
118	A10	8p brn, *rose*	125.00	5.00
119	A13	1sh bl, *blue*	250.00	10.00
120	A15	5sh bl, *yel*	1,700.	450.00
121	A15	5sh bl & rose	125.00	15.00
a.		Without blue line under crown	140.00	17.00
122	A15	5sh ultra & rose	175.00	20.00

See #126, 144, 188. For surcharge see #124.
For additional stamps of type A15, see No. 191. Compare type A15 with type A58.

A16   A19

1870   Perf. 13

123	A16	2p lilac	40.00	2.00
a.		Perf. 12	40.00	1.25

No. 110 Surcharged in
Red

½   ½
HALF

1873, July 19   Perf. 13, 12

124	A10	½p on 1p green	35.00	10.00

9   9

No. 79 Surcharged in
Blue

NINEPENCE

1871   Wmk. Single-lined "10" (81)

125	A12	9p on 10p brn, *rose*	350.00	11.00
a.		Double surcharge		1,200.

1873-78   Typo.

126	A10	8p brown, *rose* ('78)	125.00	6.50
127	A19	9p brown, *rose*	125.00	6.50

For additional stamps of type A19, see Nos. 128-129, 174-175. Compare type A19 with type A55.

1875   Wmk. V and Crown (70)

128	A19	9p brown, *rose*	140.00	11.00

8d   8d

No. 128 Surcharged
in Black

EIGHTPENCE

1876

129	A19	8p on 9p brn, *rose*	175.00	14.00

A21   A22   A23

A24   A25

1873-81   Perf. 13, 12

130	A21	½p rose ('74)	5.50	.35
131	A21	½p rose, *rose* ('78)	20.00	8.00
132	A21	1p grn ('75)	15.00	1.00
133	A22	1p grn, *gray* ('78)	90.00	60.00
134	A22	1p grn, *yel* ('78)	60.00	15.00
135	A23	2p violet	15.00	.25
136	A23	2p vio, *grnsh* ('78)	125.00	15.00
137	A23	2p vio, *buff* ('78)	125.00	15.00
137A	A23	2p vio, *lil* ('78)		340.00
138	A24	1sh bl, *bl* ('76)	55.00	4.00
139	A25	2sh bl, *grn* ('81)	175.00	20.00

See Nos. 140, 156A-159, 184, 189-190. Compare type A21 with type A46, A24 with type A56, A25 with A57.

1878
Double-lined Outer Oval

140	A23	2p violet	20.00	.25
a.		Imperf., pair		400.00
b.		Pair, imperf. btwn.		

A26   A27

A28

1881-83   Perf. 12½

141	A26	1p green ('83)	14.00	.90
142	A27	2p brown	27.50	.25
143	A27	2p lilac	12.00	.15
144	A10	4p car rose	200.00	2.75
145	A28	4p car rose	30.00	1.50
		Nos. 141-145 (5)	283.50	5.55

See Nos. 156, 185, 187. Compare type A26 with type A47, A27 with A49, A28 with A52.

A29   A30

A31   A32

A33   A34

1884-86

146	A29	½p rose	6.00	.40
147	A30	1p green	6.00	.20
148	A31	2p violet	4.75	.15
a.		2p lilac rose	10.50	.16
149	A30	3p bister	8.00	.50
a.		3p ocher	6.50	.50

150	A32	4p magenta	32.50	2.25
a.		4p violet (error)	4,000.	400.00
151	A30	6p gray blue	42.50	1.40
a.		6p ultramarine	35.00	1.40
152	A33	8p rose, *rose*	22.50	4.50
153	A34	1sh blue, *yel*	47.50	3.25
154	A33	2sh olive, *grn*	22.50	2.00
		Nos. 146-154 (9)	192.25	14.65

See Nos. 177-178, 192A. Compare types A31-A32 with types A37-A38.

Nos. 114, 145, 138-139 Overprinted
"STAMP / DUTY"
Vertically in Blue or Black

1885

155	A14	3p orange (Bl)	60.00	21.00
156	A28	4p car rose (Bl)	50.00	12.50
156A	A24	1sh bl, *bl* (Bl)		1,250.
157	A24	1sh bl, *bl* (Bk)	95.00	22.50
158	A25	2sh bl, *grn* (Bk)	75.00	20.00
		Nos. 155-156,157-158 (4)	280.00	76.00

Reprints of 4p and 1sh have brighter colors than originals. They lack the overprint "REPRINT."

A35   A36

A37   A38

A39   A40

1886-87   Perf. 12½

159	A35	½p lilac	16.00	3.00
160	A35	½p rose	4.50	.15
160A	A35	½p scarlet	5.00	.15
161	A36	1p green	5.00	.15
162	A37	2p violet	3.00	.15
a.		2p red lilac	2.00	.15
b.		Imperf.		
163	A38	4p red	6.00	.60
164	A39	6p blue	7.50	.40
165	A39	6p ultra	7.50	.15
166	A40	1sh lilac brown	22.50	1.50
		Nos. 159-166 (9)	77.00	6.25

See No. 180.

A41   A42

1889

167	A41	1sh6p blue	110.00	62.50
168	A41	1sh6p orange	15.00	4.00

Southern Cross   Queen Victoria
A43   A44

1890-95   Perf. 12½

169	A42	1p org brn	2.25	.15
a.		1p chocolate brown	2.75	
170	A42	1p yel brn	2.00	.15
171	A42	1p brn org, *pink* ('91)	1.65	.50
172	A43	2½p brn red, *yel*	6.00	.50
173	A44	5p choc ('91)	7.00	.50
174	A19	9p green ('92)	20.00	5.00
175	A19	9p rose red	13.00	1.50
a.		9p rose ('95)	13.00	1.50

176	A40	1sh deep claret	15.00	.50
a.		1sh red brown	13.00	.38
b.		1sh maroon	20.00	1.00
177	A33	2sh yel grn	25.00	10.00
178	A33	2sh emerald	20.00	10.00
		Nos. 169-178 (10)	111.90	24.80

In 1891 many stamps of the early issues were reprinted. They are on paper watermarked V and Crown, perforated 12, 12½, and overprinted "REPRINT."

See Nos. 181, 183, 192. Compare type A43 with type A50, A44 with A53.

A45

1897

179	A45	1½p yellow green	4.00	1.75

See No. 182. Compare type A45 with type A48.

1899

180	A35	½p emerald	5.00	.20
181	A42	1p brt rose	4.00	.15
182	A45	1½p red, *yel*	2.75	1.50
183	A43	2½p dark blue	6.50	1.25
		Nos. 180-183 (4)	18.25	3.10

1901

184	A21	½p blue green	1.90	.50
a.		"VICTORIA"	65.00	25.00
185	A27	2p violet	4.50	.15
186	A14	3p brown org	14.00	1.50
187	A28	4p bister	25.00	5.00
188	A11	6p emerald	9.00	2.75
189	A24	1sh orange yel	30.00	10.00
190	A25	2sh blue, *rose*	40.00	11.00
191	A15	5sh rose red & bl	60.00	20.00
		Nos. 184-191 (8)	184.40	50.90

1901

192	A42	1p olive green	6.50	5.00
192A	A30	3p sage green	21.00	12.00

Nos. 192-192A were available for postal use until June 30, 1901, and thereafter restricted to revenue use.

A46   A47   A48

A49   A50

A51   A52

A53   A54

A55   A56

A57

A58

1901   *Perf. 11, 12½ and Compound*

193	A46	½p blue green	1.50	.15
194	A47	1p rose red	1.25	.15
a.		1p rose	1.25	.15
195	A48	1½p red, *yellow*	2.25	.50
a.		Perf. 11	50.00	32.50
196	A49	2p violet	2.75	.15
197	A50	2½p blue	3.25	.15
198	A51	3p brown org	6.00	.30
199	A52	4p bister	6.00	.35
200	A53	5p chocolate	5.25	.25
201	A54	6p emerald	8.00	.50
202	A55	9p rose	10.00	.75
203	A56	1sh org yel	11.50	.75
204	A57	2sh blue, *rose*	21.00	2.25
205	A58	5sh rose red & bl	65.00	12.50
a.		5sh carmine & blue	65.00	9.00
		Nos. 193-205 (13)	143.75	18.75

See Nos. 209-229, 232.

King Edward VII
A59   A60

1901-05

206	A59	£1 deep rose	300.00	125.00
a.		Perf. 11 ('05)	325.00	140.00
208	A60	£2 dk blue ('02)	750.00	200.00
a.		Perf. 11 ('05)	850.00	600.00

See Nos. 230-231.

1903   **Redrawn**

209	A56	1sh yellow	15.00	1.40
a.		1sh orange	13.00	1.40

No. 209 has the network lighter than No. 203. In the latter the "P" and "E" of "POSTAGE" are in a position more nearly horizontal than on No. 209.

Perf. 11, 12x12½, 12½, 12½x11

1905-10   **Wmk. 13**

218	A46	½p blue green	1.25	.60
219	A47	1p rose red	1.00	.15
a.		1p carmine rose	2.00	.15
220	A49	2p violet	3.25	.15
a.		2p purple	3.25	.15
221	A50	2½p blue	3.50	.25
222	A51	3p brown org	4.50	.30
a.		3p dull yellow	5.25	.25
223	A52	4p bister	6.50	.40
224	A53	5p chocolate	6.00	.32
225	A54	6p emerald	8.25	.48
226	A55	9p orange brown	10.00	1.10
a.		9p brown rose	13.00	1.10
227	A55	9p car rose	10.00	1.10
228	A56	1sh yellow ('08)	10.00	1.00
229	A58	5sh orange red & ultra	62.50	12.50
a.		5sh rose red & ultra	70.00	12.50
230	A59	£1 pale red ('07)	325.00	110.00
a.		£1 rose ('10)	325.00	100.00
231	A60	£2 dull blue	750.00	300.00
		Nos. 218-229 (12)	126.75	18.35

No. 220 Surcharged in **ONE PENNY**
Red

1912, July 1

232	A49	1p on 2p violet	.32	.20

POSTAL-FISCAL STAMPS

On Jan. 1, 1884, all postage and fiscal stamps were made available for either purpose. Therefore all stamps inscribed "Stamp Duty" on hand at that date or issued thereafter can be considered as postage stamps.

Values for used are for postally canceled.

Victoria stamps can be mounted in the Scott Australia album.

PF5

PF6

PF7   PF8

PF9

PF10

Coat of Arms — PF11

Wmk. V and Crown (70)

1884-96   **Typo.**   *Perf. 12½*

AR1	PF5	1sh6p rose	150.00	15.00
AR2	PF6	2sh bl, *grn*	150.00	12.00
AR3	PF7	2sh6p orange	150.00	30.00
AR4	PF8	3sh bister	87.50	15.00

Lithographed

AR5	PF8	3sh vio, *bl*	275.00	30.00
AR6	PF9	4sh orange	85.00	5.75
a.		4sh vermilion	85.00	5.75

Typographed

AR7	PF10	5sh claret, *yel*	70.00	10.00
AR8	PF10	5sh car rose ('96)	130.00	6.75
AR9	PF11	6sh yel grn	275.00	22.50
		Nos. AR1-AR9 (9)	1,372.	147.00

PF12

PF13

PF14

PF15

PF16

PF17

PF18

PF19

AR10	PF12	10sh brown	250.00	100.00
AR11	PF12	10sh gray grn	240.00	17.50

Lithographed

AR12	PF13	15sh lilac		250.00

Typographed

AR13	PF13	15sh pale brn	500.00	150.00

Lithographed

AR14	PF14	£1 org, *yel*	500.00	47.50
AR15	PF15	£1 5sh pink	1,350.	90.00
AR16	PF16	£1 10sh ol grn	1,000.	22.50
AR17	PF17	35sh violet		
		Revenue cancellation		250.00

Typographed

AR18	PF18	£2 blue	1,200.	65.00
AR19	PF19	45sh gray lilac	2,000.	250.00

PF20

PF21

Litho.

AR20	PF20	£5 rose		200.00

Typographed

AR21	PF21	£5 claret & ultra	1,200.	60.00

SEMI-POSTAL STAMPS

SP1

Queen Victoria and Figure of Charity — SP2

Wmk. V and Crown (70)

1897, Oct.   **Typo.**   *Perf. 12½*

B1	SP1	1p deep blue	8.50	18.00
B2	SP2	2½p red brown	110.00	110.00

These stamps were sold at 1sh and 2sh6p respectively. The premium was given to a charitable institution.

Victoria Cross — SP3

Scout Reporting — SP4

1900

B3	SP3	1p brown olive	70.00	70.00
B4	SP4	2p emerald	140.00	140.00

These stamps were sold at 1sh and 2sh respectively. The premium was given to a patriotic fund in connection with the South African War.

REGISTRATION STAMPS

R1

1854, Dec. 1   **Typo.**   **Unwmk.**   *Imperf.*

F1	R1	1sh rose & blue	1,000.	100.00

1857   **Rouletted 7**

F2	R1	1sh rose & blue	5,000.	150.00

LATE FEE STAMP

LF1

1855, Jan. 1   **Typo.**   **Unwmk.**   *Imperf.*

I1	LF1	6p lilac & green	650.00	150.00

POSTAGE DUE STAMPS

D1

Wmk. V and Crown (70)

1890   **Typo.**   *Perf. 12½*

J1	D1	½p claret & blue	2.00	1.65
J2	D1	1p claret & blue	3.25	1.25
J3	D1	2p claret & blue	5.00	1.50
J4	D1	4p claret & blue	6.00	1.75
J5	D1	5p claret & blue	5.50	1.65
J6	D1	6p claret & blue	6.25	1.50
J7	D1	10p claret & blue	60.00	32.50
J8	D1	1sh claret & blue	35.00	5.00
J9	D1	2sh claret & blue	92.50	42.50
J10	D1	5sh claret & blue	140.00	90.00
		Nos. J1-J10 (10)	355.50	179.30

1891

J11	D1	½p lake & blue	2.50	1.25
J12	D1	1p brown red & blue	4.25	1.25
J13	D1	2p brown red & blue	4.25	.90
J14	D1	4p lake & blue	6.50	4.50
		Nos. J11-J14 (4)	17.50	8.65

1894

J15	D1	½p bl grn & rose	1.65	1.40
J16	D1	1p bl grn & rose	.70	.35
J17	D1	2p bl grn & rose	1.50	.30
J18	D1	4p bl grn & rose	3.50	1.25
J19	D1	5p bl grn & rose	4.00	2.25
J20	D1	6p bl grn & rose	4.00	2.50
J21	D1	10p bl grn & rose	10.00	8.50
J22	D1	1sh bl grn & rose	5.00	2.75
J23	D1	2sh green & rose	60.00	20.00
J24	D1	5sh green & rose	100.00	35.00
		Nos. J15-J24 (10)	190.35	74.30

1906   **Wmk. 13**

J25	D1	½p yel grn & rose	1.65 1.65
J26	D1	1p yel grn & rose	3.00 .65
J27	D1	2p yel grn & rose	6.50 1.50
J28	D1	4p yel grn & rose	13.00 10.00
		Nos. J25-J28 (4)	24.15 13.80

A 5p with wmk. 13 exists but was not issued.

WESTERN AUSTRALIA

ˈwes–tərn o–ˈstrāl–yə

LOCATION — Western part of Australia, occupying about a third of that continent
GOVT. — British Colony
AREA — 975,920 sq. mi.
POP. — 184,124 (1901)
CAPITAL — Perth

Western Australia was one of the six British colonies that united on January 1, 1901, to form the Commonwealth of Australia.

12 Pence = 1 Shilling
20 Shillings = 1 Pound

Unused values for Nos. 1-10 are for stamps without gum as these stamps are seldom found with original gum. Otherwise, unused values are for stamps with original gum as defined in the catalogue introduction.

Very fine examples of all rouletted and perforated stamps from Nos. 6-34 have roulettes or perforations touching the design. Examples clear on all four sides range from scarce to rare and will command higher prices.

Watermarks

Wmk. 82- Swan

Wmk. 83- Crown and W A

Wmk. 70- V and Crown

Wmk. 13- Crown & Double-lined A

Wmk. 74- Crown and Single-lined A

Swan

A1   A2

1854-57   **Engr.**   **Wmk. 82**   *Imperf.*

1	A1	1p black	750. 190.

Litho.

2	A2	2p brown, *red* ('57)	1,300. 425.
a.		2p brown, *deep red* ('57)	1,500. 475.
b.		Printed on both sides	1,500. 750.

See Nos. 4, 6-7, 9, 14-39, 44-52, 54, 59-61. For surcharges see Nos. 41, 55-56.

A3   A4

3	A3	4p blue	275. 150.
a.		Frame inverted	60,000.
		As "a," cut to shape	16,000.
b.		4p slate blue	1,000. 575.
4	A2	6p bronze ('57)	3,000. 600.
5	A4	1sh pale brown	400. 225.
a.		1sh dark brown	500. 375.
b.		1sh dark red brown	800. 400.
c.		1sh pale red brown	1,800.

Engraved
Rouletted

6	A1	1p black	1,750. 500.

Lithographed

7	A2	2p brown, *red* ('57)	3,250. 1,200.
a.		Printed on both sides	
8	A3	4p blue	1,400. 600.
9	A2	6p bronze ('57)	3,500. 1,000.
10	A4	1sh brown	2,000. 700.

The 2p, 4p and 6p are known with pin-perforation but this is believed to be unofficial.

1860   **Engr.**   *Imperf.*

14	A1	2p vermilion	100.00 87.50
a.		2p pale orange	95.00 60.00
15	A1	4p blue	185.00 800.00
16	A1	6p dull green	1,100. 600.00

Rouletted

17	A1	2p vermilion	600.00 200.00
a.		2p pale orange	600.00 200.00
18	A1	4p deep blue	2,500. —
19	A1	6p dull green	— 400.00

1861   *Clean-Cut Perf. 14 to 16*

20	A1	1p rose	330.00 80.00
a.		Imperf.	
21	A1	2p blue	70.00 25.00
a.		Imperf., pair	
b.		Horiz. pair, imperf. vert.	
22	A1	4p vermilion	265.00 150.00
a.		Imperf.	
23	A1	6p purple brn	175.00 35.00
a.		Imperf.	
24	A1	1sh green	300.00 45.00
a.		Imperf.	

Rough Perf. 14 to 16

24B	A1	1p rose	200.00 27.50
24C	A1	6p pur brn, *bluish*	750.00 50.00
24D	A1	1sh deep green	1,200. 350.00

Perf. 14

25	A1	1p rose	140.00 45.00
25A	A1	2p blue	70.00 30.00
25B	A1	4p vermilion	200.00 85.00

Unwmk.   **Perf. 13**

26	A1	1p lake	40.00 5.50
28	A1	6p violet	90.00 32.50

1865-79   **Wmk. 1**   *Perf. 12½*

29	A1	1p bister	40.00 2.00
30	A1	1p yel ocher	60.00 5.50
31	A1	2p yellow	45.00 .60
a.		2p lilac (error) ('79)	7,500. 3,750.
32	A1	4p carmine	50.00 5.50
a.		Double impression	6,000.
33	A1	6p violet	62.50 6.00
a.		6p lilac	130.00 6.00
b.		6p red lilac	120.00 6.00
c.		Double impression	
34	A1	1sh bright green	85.00 10.50
a.		1sh sage green	140.00 18.00
		Nos. 29-34 (6)	342.50 30.10

1872-78   *Perf. 14*

35	A1	1p bister	50.00 2.00
36	A1	1p yellow ocher	40.00 .48
37	A1	2p yellow	40.00 .40
38	A1	4p carmine	200.00 65.00
39	A1	6p lilac	80.00 4.00
		Nos. 35-39 (5)	410.00 71.88

A5   A8

1872   **Typo.**

40	A5	3p red brown	26.00 3.75
a.		3p brown	26.00 3.75

See #53, 92. For surcharges see #57, 69-72A.

No. 31 Surcharged **ONE PENNY** in Green

1875   **Engr.**   *Perf. 12½*

41	A1	1p on 2p yellow	200.00 45.00
a.		Pair, one without surcharge	
b.		"O" of "ONE" omitted	
c.		Triple surcharge	

Forged surcharges exist.

1882   **Wmk. 2**   *Perf. 12*

44	A1	1p ocher yellow	85.00 1.65
46	A1	2p yellow	110.00 1.10
47	A1	4p carmine	160.00 27.50
48	A1	6p pale violet	275.00 27.50
		Nos. 44-48 (4)	630.00 57.75

1882   *Perf. 14*

49	A1	1p ocher yellow	14.00 .20
50	A1	2p yellow	18.00 .20
51	A1	4p carmine	72.50 11.50
52	A1	6p pale violet	80.00 2.50
a.		6p violet	47.50 2.50

Typographed

53	A5	3p red brown	8.50 .70
a.		3p brown	12.50 .45
		Nos. 49-53 (5)	193.00 15.10

1883   **Engr.**   *Perf. 12x14*

54	A1	1p ocher yellow	1,650. 300.00

Nos. 44 and 49 Surcharged in Red $\frac{1}{2}$

1884   *Perf. 12*

55	A1	½p on 1p ocher yel	9.00 12.00

Perf. 14

56	A1	½p on 1p ocher yel	13.00 15.00

No. 40 Surcharged in Green **1d.**

1885   **Typo.**   **Wmk. 1**

57	A5	1p on 3p red brown	27.50 8.50
a.		1p on 3p brown	12.00 6.00
b.		"1" with straight top	27.50 11.00

Wmk. Crown and C A (2)

1885   **Typo.**   *Perf. 14*

58	A8	½p green	2.00 .15

See No. 89.

1888   **Engr.**

59	A1	1p rose	12.00 .70
60	A1	2p slate	30.00 2.00
61	A1	4p deep brown	82.50 18.00
		Nos. 59-61 (3)	124.50 20.70

A9   A10

A11   A12

1890-93   **Typo.**

62	A9	1p carmine rose	6.50 .15
63	A10	2p slate	10.00 .15
64	A11	2½p blue	6.00 .80
65	A12	4p orange brown	6.00 .80
66	A12	5p bister	8.25 1.00
67	A12	6p violet	14.00 .80
68	A12	1sh olive green	16.00 2.25
		Nos. 62-68 (7)	66.75 5.95

See Nos. 73-74, 76, 80, 90, 94.

Nos. 40 and 53a Surcharged in Green **ONE PENNY**

1893   **Wmk. Crown and C C (1)**

69	A5	1p on 3p red brown	9.50 5.00
a.		1p on 3p brown	8.00 3.25
b.		Double surcharge	725.00

Wmkd. Crown and C A (2)

70	A5	1p on 3p brown	40.00 9.00

Nos. 40a and 53a Surcharged in Green **Half-penny**

1895   **Wmk. Crown and C C (1)**

71	A5	½p on 3p brown	7.00 3.00
a.		Double surcharge	700.00

Green and Red Surcharge

72	A5	½p on 3p brown	125.00

Wmk. Crown and C A (2)

72A	A5	½p on 3p brown	75.00

After the supply of paper watermarked Crown and C C was exhausted, No. 72A was printed. Ostensibly this was to provide samples for Postal Union distribution, but a supply for philatelic demands was also made.

Types of 1890-93 and

A15

1899-1901   **Typo.**   **Wmk. 83**

73	A9	1p carmine rose	3.50 .15
74	A10	2p yellow	9.00 .15
75	A15	2½p blue ('01)	6.00 .20
		Nos. 73-75 (3)	18.50 .50

A16   A17

A18   A19

A20   A21

A22   Southern Cross — A23

A24   A25

Queen Victoria

Perf. 12½, 12x12½

1902-05   **Wmk. 70**

76	A9	1p carmine rose	6.50 .15
a.		1p salmon	
b.		Perf. 11	100.00 5.00
c.		Perf. 12½x11	180.00
77	A16	2p yellow	3.25 .20
b.		Perf. 11	125.00 5.50
c.		Perf. 12½x11	220.00
79	A17	4p orange brn	6.00 .80
a.		Perf. 11	375.00 110.00
80	A12	5p olive bis ('05)	72.50 40.00
a.		Perf. 11	45.00 21.00
81	A18	8p pale yel grn	20.00 2.75
82	A19	9p orange	27.50 4.00
a.		Perf. 11	60.00 40.00
83	A20	10p red	27.50 5.50
84	A21	2sh red, *yel*	42.50 8.25
a.		Perf. 11	125.00 55.00

85	A22	2sh6p dk bl, *rose*	40.00	7.75
86	A23	5sh blue green	70.00	19.00
87	A24	10sh violet	175.00	60.00
88	A25	£1 brown org	475.00	225.00
		Nos. 76-88 (12)	965.75	373.40

Perf. 12½, 12x12½

1905-12   **Wmk. 13**

89	A8	½p dp green ('10)	2.25	.35
90	A9	1p rose	3.00	.20
e.		Perf. 11	13.00	.50
f.		Perf. 12½x11	200.00	82.50
91	A16	2p yellow	3.00	.15
a.		Perf. 11	11.00	4.50
b.		Perf. 12½x11	230.00	95.00
92	A5	3p brown	6.50	.40
a.		Perf. 11	12.00	2.75
b.		Perf. 12½x11	265.00	82.50
93	A17	4p orange brn	8.00	1.50
a.		4p bister brown	8.00	1.50
b.		Perf. 11	465.00	90.00
94	A12	5p olive bis	10.00	.70
a.		Perf. 11	25.00	8.50
95	A18	8p pale yel grn ('12)	16.00	17.00
96	A19	9p orange	21.00	3.00
b.		Perf. 11	65.00	55.00
97	A20	10p red orange	21.00	10.00
98	A23	5s blue green	140.00	40.00
		Nos. 89-98 (10)	230.75	73.30

For surcharge see No. 103.

A26   A27

1906-07   **Wmk. 83**   **Perf. 14**

99	A26	6p bright violet	18.00	.70
100	A27	1sh olive green	25.00	6.00

1912   **Wmk. 74**   **Perf. 11½x12**

101	A26	6p bright violet	11.00	3.00
102	A27	1sh gray green	22.50	4.00
a.		Perf. 12½		

No. 91 Surcharged **ONE PENNY**

1912   **Wmk. 13**   **Perf. 12½**

103	A16	1p on 2p yellow	.75	.40

Stamps of Western Australia were replaced by those of Australia.

AUSTRALIA

ȯ-'strāl-yə

LOCATION — Oceania, south of Indonesia, bounded on the west by the Indian Ocean
GOVT. — Self-governing dominion of the British Commonwealth
AREA — 2,967,909 sq. mi.
POP. — 15,276,100 (est. 1982)
CAPITAL — Canberra

Australia includes the former British colonies of New South Wales, Victoria, Queensland, South Australia, Western Australia and Tasmania.

12 Pence = 1 Shilling
20 Shillings = 1 Pound
100 Cents = 1 Dollar (1966)

Catalogue values for unused stamps in this country are for Never Hinged items, beginning with Scott 197 in the regular postage section, Scott C6 in the air post section, Scott J71 in the postage due section, and all of the Australian Antarctic Territory.

Watermarks

Wmk. 8- Wide
Crown and Wide A

Wmk. 9- Wide
Crown and
Narrow A

Wmk. 10- Narrow
Crown and
Narrow A

Wmk. 11-
Multiple Crown
and A

Wmk. 12- Crown   Wmk. 13- Large
and Single-lined A   Crown and Double-
                          lined A

Wmk. 55- Large
Crown and NSW

Wmk. 203- Small
Crown and A
Multiple

Wmk. 228- Small
Crown and C of A
Multiple

Kangaroo and
Map—A1

1913 Typo. **Wmk. 8**   Perf. 11½, 12

1	A1	½p yellow green	5.00	1.75
2	A1	1p carmine	6.75	.50
d.		Wmkd. sideways	800.00	210.00

3	A1	2p gray	22.50	4.00
4	A1	2½p dark blue	25.00	8.50
5	A1	3p olive bister	40.00	4.50
6	A1	4p orange	45.00	18.00
7	A1	5p orange brown	40.00	25.00
8	A1	6p ultra	45.00	13.00
9	A1	9p purple	40.00	20.00
10	A1	1sh blue green	45.00	12.50
11	A1	2sh brown	150.00	75.00
12	A1	5sh yellow & gray	250.00	140.00
13	A1	10sh pink & gray	600.00	425.00
		Never hinged	725.00	
14	A1	£1 ultra & brown	1,300.	1,000.
		Never hinged	1,500.	
15	A1	£2 dp rose & blk	2,250.	1,400.
		Nos. 1-12 (12)	714.25	322.75
		Set, never hinged	1,300.	

On No. 4 "2½d" is colorless in solid blue background.
See Nos. 38-59, 96-102, 121-129, 206.

King George V   Kookaburra
A2   (Kingfisher)
                         A3

1913-14 Unwmk. Engr.   Perf. 11

17	A2	1p carmine	4.25	4.25
		Never hinged	5.75	
a.		Vert. pair, imperf. between	5.75	
18	A3	6p lake brown ('14)	70.00	35.00
		Never hinged	150.00	

See No. 95.

A4

ONE PENNY
Die I - Normal die, having outside the oval band with "AUSTRALIA" a white line and a heavy colored line.
Die Ia - As die I with a small white spur below the right serif at foot of the "1" in left tablet.
Die II - A heavy colored line between two white lines back of the emu's neck. A white scratch crossing the vertical shading lines at the lowest point of the bust.
TWO PENCE
Die I - The numeral "2" is thin. The upper curve is 1mm. across and a very thin line connects it with the foot of the figure.
Die II - The "2" is thicker than in die I. The top curve is 1½mm across and a strong white line connects it with the foot of the figure. There are thin vertical lines across the ends of the groups of short horizontal lines at each side of "TWO PENCE."
THREE PENCE
Die I - The ends of the thin horizontal lines in the background run into the solid color of the various parts of the design. The numerals are thin and the letters of "THREE PENCE" are thin and irregular.
Die II - The oval about the portrait, the shields with the numerals, etc., are outlined by thin white lines which separate them from the horizontal background lines. The numerals are thick and the letters of "THREE PENCE" are heavy and regular.
FIVE PENCE
Die I - The top of the flag of the "5" is slightly curved.
Die II - The top of the flag of the "5" is flat. There are thin white vertical lines across the ends of the short horizontal lines at each side of "FIVE PENCE."

1914-24 Typo. Wmk. 9   Perf. 14

19	A4	½p emerald ('15)	2.50	.40
a.		Thin "½" at right	1,400.	700.00
20	A4	½p orange ('23)	2.50	1.25
21	A4	1p red (I)	4.25	.15
a.		1p carmine rose (I)	8.25	.80
b.		1p red (Ia)	375.00	4.75
c.		1p carmine (II) ('18)	60.00	30.00
		Never hinged	95.00	
22	A4	1p vio (I) ('22)	3.50	.60
a.		1p red violet	5.50	1.50
		Never hinged	8.00	
23	A4	1p green (I) ('24)	3.50	.20
24	A4	1½p choc ('18)	5.00	.20
a.		1½p red brown	5.50	.20
		Never hinged	12.00	
b.		1½p black brown	4.50	.25
		Never hinged	6.75	
25	A4	1½p emerald ('23)	2.75	.15
26	A4	1½p scarlet ('24)	2.00	.15
27	A4	2p brn org (I) ('20)	5.00	.25
a.		2p orange (I) ('20)	6.50	.30
		Never hinged	19.00	
b.		Booklet pane of 6		
28	A4	2p red (I) ('22)	5.00	.15
29	A4	2p red brn (I) ('24)	15.00	3.75
30	A4	3p ultra (I) ('24)	25.00	2.25

31	A4	4p orange ('15)	17.00	2.25
a.		4p yellow	110.00	16.00
32	A4	4p violet ('21)	17.50	13.00
33	A4	4p lt ultra ('22)	37.50	4.50
34	A4	4p ol bis ('24)	27.50	4.00
35	A4	4½p violet ('24)	22.50	4.00
36	A4	5p org brn (I) ('15)	18.00	5.00
37	A4	1sh4p lt blue ('20)	65.00	19.00
		Nos. 19-37 (19)	281.00	59.25
		Set, never hinged	675.00	

See Nos. 60-76, 113-120, 124.

1915   **Perf. 11½, 12**

38	A1	2p gray	42.50	11.00
		Never hinged	95.00	
39	A1	2½p dark blue	42.50	15.00
		Never hinged	140.00	
40	A1	6p ultra	125.00	19.00
		Never hinged	275.00	
41	A1	9p violet	125.00	32.50
		Never hinged	275.00	
42	A1	1sh blue green	125.00	20.00
		Never hinged	325.00	
43	A1	2sh brown	375.00	87.50
		Never hinged	900.00	
44	A1	5sh yellow & gray	700.00	165.00
		Never hinged	1,500.	
		Nos. 38-44 (7)	1,535.	350.00

1915-24   **Wmk. 10**

45	A1	2p gray	20.00	5.00
46	A1	2½p dark blue	20.00	7.50
a.		"1" of fraction omitted	10,000.	3,500.
47	A1	3p olive bister	17.00	3.00
48	A1	6p ultra	45.00	7.00
a.		6p chalky blue	65.00	7.00
49	A1	6p yel brn ('23)	20.00	1.75
50	A1	9p violet	35.00	4.50
a.		9p lilac	30.00	4.50
51	A1	1sh blue grn ('16)	35.00	2.50
a.		Wmkd. sideways ('20)	72.50	72.50
52	A1	2sh brown ('16)	150.00	15.00
53	A1	2sh vio brn ('24)	50.00	20.00
54	A1	5sh yel & gray ('18)	180.00	80.00
a.		Wmkd. sideways	3,000.	2,500.
55	A1	10sh brt pink & gray ('17)	400.00	150.00
		Never hinged	750.00	
a.		Wmkd. sideways	5,000.	3,000.
56	A1	£1 ultra & brn ('16)	1,250.	700.00
a.		£1 ultra & brn org ('16)	1,300.	700.00
b.		Wmkd. sideways	5,000.	2,000.
57	A1	£1 gray ('24)	450.00	275.00
		Never hinged	825.00	
58	A1	£2 dp rose & blk ('19)	2,250.	1,250.
59	A1	£2 rose & vio brn ('24)	1,750.	1,200.
		Nos. 45-54 (10)	572.00	146.25
		Set, never hinged	1,300.	

Perf. 14, 14½, 14½x14

1918-23   **Wmk. 11**

60	A4	½p emerald	3.00	1.00
		Never hinged	4.25	
a.		Thin "½" at right	110.00	45.00
61	A4	1p rose (I)	20.00	9.00
		Never hinged	27.50	
62	A4	1p dl grn (I) ('24)	4.75	4.75
		Never hinged	7.00	
63	A4	1½p choc ('19)	5.00	1.00
		Never hinged	11.00	
a.		1½p red brown ('19)	8.00	1.00
		Never hinged	12.50	
		Nos. 60-63 (4)	32.75	15.75

1924   **Unwmk.**   **Perf. 14**

64	A4	1p green (I)	4.25	3.75
		Never hinged	5.50	
65	A4	1½p carmine	4.25	3.00
		Never hinged	6.75	

Perf. 14, 13½x12½

1926-30   **Wmk. 203**

66	A4	½p orange	1.40	1.00
a.		Perf. 14 ('27)	5.25	5.25
		Never hinged	6.75	
67	A4	1p green (I)	1.50	.40
a.		1p green (Ia)	47.50	60.00
		Never hinged	65.00	
b.		Perf. 14	2.75	.45
		Never hinged	4.50	
68	A4	1½p rose red ('27)	2.75	.15
c.		Perf. 14 ('26)	6.00	.65
		Never hinged	12.00	
69	A4	1½p red brn ('30)	4.00	2.00
70	A4	2p red brn (I) ('28)	7.00	4.00
a.		Perf. 14 ('27)	24.00	16.00
		Never hinged	40.00	
71	A4	2p red (II) ('30)	4.00	.20
a.		2p red (I) ('30)	5.00	1.65
		Never hinged	12.00	
c.		Unwmkd. (II) ('31)	1,500.	1,000.
72	A4	3p ultra (I)	22.50	2.25
a.		3p ultra (II) ('29)	14.00	1.00
		Never hinged	30.00	
b.		Perf. 14	17.50	4.50
		Never hinged	37.50	
73	A4	4p ol bis ('29)	16.00	.80
a.		Perf. 14 ('28)	42.50	22.50
		Never hinged	85.00	
74	A4	4½p dk vio ('27)	17.00	3.75
a.		Perf. 13½x12½ ('28)	37.50	13.00
		Never hinged	67.50	
75	A4	5p brn buff (II) ('30)	16.00	.95
76	A4	1sh4p pale turq bl ('28)	85.00	20.00
a.		Perf. 14 ('27)	125.00	67.50
		Never hinged	300.00	
		Nos. 66-76 (11)	177.15	35.50
		Set, never hinged	275.00	

For surcharges & overprints see #106-107, O3-O4.

Parliament House, Canberra — A5

Unwmk.

				Engr.	Perf. 11
1927, May 9					

94	A5	1½p brown red		.45	.20
		Never hinged		.85	
a.		Vert. pair, imperf. btwn.		2,750.	2,500.

Opening of Parliament House at Canberra.

Melbourne Exhibition Issue
Kookaburra Type of 1914

1928, Oct. 29

95	A3	3p deep blue	3.75	3.00
		Never hinged	5.25	
a.		Pane of 4	110.00	135.00
		Never hinged	175.00	

No. 95a was issued at the Melbourne Intl. Phil. Exhib. No marginal inscription. Printed in sheets of 60 stamps (15 panes). No. 95 was printed in sheets of 120 and issued Nov. 2 throughout Australia.

Kangaroo-Map Type of 1913
Perf. 11½, 12

1929-30   **Wmk. 203**   **Typo.**

96	A1	6p brown	21.00	3.00
		Never hinged	27.50	
97	A1	9p violet	30.00	4.00
		Never hinged	70.00	
98	A1	1sh blue green	27.50	2.25
		Never hinged	65.00	
99	A1	2sh red brown	60.00	9.00
		Never hinged	140.00	
100	A1	5sh yel & gray	190.00	60.00
		Never hinged	325.00	
101	A1	10sh pink & gray	325.00	250.00
		Never hinged	575.00	
102	A1	£2 dl red & blk ('30)	1,800.	425.00
		Never hinged	2,453.	753.25
		Nos. 96-102 (7)		

For overprint see No. O5.

Black Swan — A6   Capt. Charles Sturt — A7

Unwmk.

			Engr.	Perf. 11
1929, Sept. 28				

| 103 | A6 | 1½p dull red | .75 | .75 |
| | | Never hinged | 1.40 | |

Centenary of Western Australia.

1930, June 2

104	A7	1½p dark red	.40	.15
		Never hinged	.45	
105	A7	3p dark blue	3.50	3.00
		Never hinged	6.00	

Capt. Charles Sturt's exploration of the Murray River, cent.

FIVE

Nos. 68 and 74a surcharged

PENCE

1930   **Wmk. 203**   **Perf. 13½x12½**

106	A4	2p on 1½p rose red	.75	.25
		Never hinged	1.50	
107	A4	5p on 4½p dark violet	5.00	5.00
		Never hinged	10.00	

"Southern Cross" over Hemispheres A8

Perf. 11, 11½

1931, Mar. 19   **Unwmk.**

111	A8	2p dull red	.75	.15
		Never hinged	1.10	
112	A8	3p blue	4.75	3.25
		Never hinged	8.00	
		Nos. 111-112,C2 (3)	13.00	10.90

Trans-oceanic flights (1928-1930) of Sir Charles Edward Kingsford-Smith (1897-1935).
See #C3 for similar design. For overprints see #CO1, O1-O2.

Types of 1913-23 Issues
Perf. 13½x12½

1931-36   **Typo.**   **Wmk. 228**

113	A4	½p orange ('32)	2.50	1.65
		Never hinged	3.00	
114	A4	1p green (I)	1.00	.15
		Never hinged	1.90	
115	A4	1½p red brn ('36)	6.00	4.50
		Never hinged	7.25	
116	A4	2p red (II)	1.75	.15
		Never hinged	2.50	
117	A4	3p ultra (II) ('32)	17.50	.30
		Never hinged	21.00	
118	A4	4p ol bis ('33)	16.00	.45
		Never hinged	26.00	
120	A4	5p brn buff (II) ('32)	12.00	1.00
		Never hinged	20.00	

Perf. 11½, 12; 13½x12½ (1sh4p)

121	A1	6p yel brn ('36)	16.00	11.00
		Never hinged	20.00	
122	A1	9p violet ('32)	11.00	1.75
		Never hinged	35.00	
124	A4	1sh4p lt blue ('32)	47.50	6.00
		Never hinged	135.00	
125	A1	2sh red brn ('35)	4.00	.90
		Never hinged	6.00	
126	A1	5sh yel & gray ('32)	125.00	18.00
127	A1	10sh pink & gray ('32)	325.00	100.00
128	A1	£1 gray ('35)	450.00	165.00
129	A1	£2 dl rose & blk ('34)	2,000.	350.00
		Nos. 113-129 (15)	3,035.	660.15

For redrawn 2sh see No. 206. For overprints see Nos. O6-O11.

Sydney Harbor Bridge — A9

Unwmk.

			Engr.	Perf. 11
1932, Mar. 14				

130	A9	2p red	1.90	.50
		Never hinged	2.25	
131	A9	3p blue	4.00	3.00
		Never hinged	6.75	
132	A9	5sh gray green	350.00	200.00
		Never hinged	575.00	

Wmk. 228
Perf. 10½
Typo.

| 133 | A9 | 2p red | 1.65 | .80 |
| | | Never hinged | 2.75 | |

Opening of the Sydney Harbor Bridge on Mar. 19, 1932.
Value for 5sh, used, is for CTO copies.
For overprints see Nos. O12-O13.

Kookaburra A14   Male Lyrebird A16

1932, June 1   *Perf. 13½x12½*

| 139 | A14 | 6p light brown | 15.00 | .50 |
| | | Never hinged | 25.00 | |

1932, Feb. 15   **Unwmk.**   *Perf. 11*
Size: 21½x25mm

| 141 | A16 | 1sh green | 37.50 | .75 |
| | | Never hinged | 75.00 | |

See #175, 300. For overprint see #O14.

Yarra Yarra Tribesman, Yarra River and View of Melbourne A17

Perf. 10½

1934, July 2   **Engr.**   **Wmk. 228**

142	A17	2p vermilion	1.10	.40
		Never hinged	1.75	
a.		Perf. 11½	3.75	1.00
		Never hinged	6.50	
143	A17	3p blue	2.75	2.25
		Never hinged	5.25	
a.		Perf. 11½	4.25	2.50
		Never hinged	6.50	
144	A17	1sh black	40.00	20.00
		Never hinged	67.50	
a.		Perf. 11½	40.00	16.00
		Never hinged	72.50	
		Nos. 142-144 (3)	43.85	22.65

Centenary of Victoria.

Merino Sheep — A18

1934, Nov. 1   *Perf. 11½*

147	A18	2p copper red	2.50	.20
		Never hinged	3.50	
148	A18	3p dark blue	8.50	4.50
		Never hinged	12.00	
149	A18	9p dark violet	35.00	25.00
		Never hinged	67.50	
		Nos. 147-149 (3)	46.00	29.70

Capt. John Macarthur (1767-1834), "father of the New South Wales woolen industry."
There are two types of the 2p.

Cenotaph in Whitehall, London — A19   George V on His Charger "Anzac" — A20

1935, Mar. 18   *Perf. 13½x12½*

| 150 | A19 | 2p red | .65 | .15 |
| | | Never hinged | .90 | |

Perf. 11

| 151 | A19 | 1sh black | 40.00 | 30.00 |
| | | Never hinged | 70.00 | |

Anzacs' landing at Gallipoli, 20th anniv.

1935, May 2   *Perf. 11½*

152	A20	2p red	.40	.15
		Never hinged	.70	
153	A20	3p blue	3.00	2.50
		Never hinged	7.50	

154	A20	2sh violet	37.50	32.50
		Never hinged	70.00	
		Nos. 152-154 (3)	40.90	35.15

25th anniv. of the reign of King George V.

Amphitrite Joining Cables between Australia and Tasmania — A21

1936, Apr. 1

157	A21	2p red	.35	.15
		Never hinged	.45	
158	A21	3p dark blue	3.25	2.00
		Never hinged	4.75	

Australia/Tasmania telephone link.

Proclamation Tree and View of Adelaide, 1936 — A22

1936, Aug. 3

159	A22	2p red	.40	.15
		Never hinged	1.10	
160	A22	3p dark blue	3.25	2.75
		Never hinged	5.00	
161	A22	1sh green	12.00	8.00
		Never hinged	20.00	
		Nos. 159-161 (3)	15.65	10.90

Centenary of South Australia.

Gov. Arthur Phillip at Sydney Cove — A23

1937, Oct. 1   *Perf. 13x13½*

163	A23	2p red	.90	.15
		Never hinged	1.90	
164	A23	3p ultra	2.75	1.65
		Never hinged	4.50	

165 A23 9p violet   16.00 11.00
    Never hinged   25.00
    Nos. 163-165 (3)   19.65 12.80
150th anniversary of New South Wales.

Kangaroo
A24

Queen
Elizabeth
A25

King George VI
A26   A27

Koala — A28

Merino
Sheep — A29

Kookaburra
(Kingfisher)
A30

Platypus
A31

Queen Elizabeth and King George VI
in Coronation Robes
A32   A33

King George VI
and Queen
Elizabeth — A34

Two Types of A25 and A26:
  Type I - Highlighted background. Lines around
letters of Australia Postage and numerals of value.
  Type II - Background of heavy diagonal lines
without the highlighted effect. No lines around letters and numerals.

Perf. 13¹/₂x14, 14x13¹/₂

1937-46		Engr.	Wmk. 228	
166	A24	¹/₂p org, perf. 15x14 ('42)	.15	.15
a.		Perf. 13¹/₂x14 ('38)	.70	.25
a.		Never hinged	1.25	
167	A25	1p emerald (I)	.20	.15
168	A26	1¹/₂p dull red brn (II)	3.00	2.00
a.		Perf. 15x14 ('41)	4.25	3.50
a.		Never hinged	6.25	
169	A26	2p scarlet (I)	.30	.15
170	A27	3p dp ultra, thin paper ('38)	12.00	1.00
a.		3p ultramarine	12.00	.50
a.		Never hinged	30.00	
171	A28	4p grn, perf. 15x14 ('42)	.85	.20
a.		Perf. 13¹/₂x14 ('38)	2.50	.90
a.		Never hinged	5.00	

172	A29	5p pale rose vio, perf. 14x15 ('46)	1.25	.50
a.		Perf. 14x13¹/₂ ('38)	2.50	.55
a.		Never hinged	4.00	
173	A30	6p vio brn, perf. 15x14 ('42)	.60	.15
a.		Perf. 13¹/₂x14	5.25	.85
a.		Never hinged	15.00	
b.		6p chocolate, perf. 15x14	1.00	.15
b.		Never hinged	1.50	
174	A31	9p sep, perf. 14x15 ('43)	1.75	.15
a.		Perf. 14x13¹/₂ ('38)	3.75	.90
a.		Never hinged	7.25	
175	A16	1sh gray grn, perf. 15x14 ('41)	1.10	.15
a.		Perf. 13¹/₂x14	17.00	2.00
a.		Never hinged	47.50	
176	A27	1sh4p magenta ('38)	1.50	.80

Perf. 13¹/₂

177	A32	5sh dl red brn ('38)	5.00	2.50
178	A33	10sh dl gray vio ('38)	30.00	12.00
179	A34	£1 bl gray ('38)	60.00	27.50
		Nos. 166-179 (14)	117.70	47.40
		Set, never hinged	200.00	

No. 175 measures 17¹/₂x21¹/₂mm.
See #223A, 293, 295, 298, 300. For surcharge &
overprints see #190, M1, M4-M5, M7.

1938-42			**Perf. 15x14**	
180	A25	1p emerald (II)	.55	.25
181	A25	1p dl red brn (II) ('41)	.50	.15
181B	A26	1¹/₂p bl grn (II) ('41)	.60	.15
182	A26	2p scarlet (II)	.60	.15
182B	A26	2p red vio (II) ('41)	.20	.15
183	A27	3p dk ultra ('40)	12.00	.70
183A	A27	3p dk vio brn ('42)	.20	.15
		Nos. 180-183A (7)	14.65	
		Set value		1.20
		Set, never hinged	35.00	

No. 183 differs from Nos. 170-170a in the shading
lines on the king's left eyebrow which go downward, left to right, instead of the reverse. Also,
more of the left epaulette shows.
For surcharges & overprint see #188-189, M3.

Coil Perforation
A special perforation was applied to
stamps intended for use in coils to make
separation easier. It consists of small
and large holes (2 small, 10 large, 2
small) on the stamps' narrow side. Some
of the stamps so perforated were sold in
sheets.
This coil perforation may be found on
Nos. 166, 181, 182, 182B, 193, 215,
223A, 231, 257, 315-316, 319, 319a
and others.

Nurse, Sailor, Soldier
and Aviator — A35

Perf. 13¹/₂x13

1940, July 15		Engr.	Wmk. 228	
184	A35	1p green	1.00	.15
		Never hinged	2.00	
185	A35	2p red	1.00	.15
		Never hinged	2.00	
186	A35	3p ultra	4.00	3.00
		Never hinged	7.00	
187	A35	6p chocolate	12.50	10.00
		Never hinged	21.00	
		Nos. 184-187 (4)	18.50	13.30

Australia's participation in WWII.

No. 182 Surcharged in Blue 2²/₂d

1941, Dec. 10			**Perf. 15x14**	
188	A26	2¹/₂p on 2p red	.20	.15
		Never hinged	.25	

No. 183 Surcharged in
Blue and Yellow 3¹/₂d

189	A27	3¹/₂p on 3p dk ultra	.40	.35
		Never hinged	.50	

No. 172a
Surcharged in
Purple 5¹/₂d

Perf. 14x13¹/₂

190	A29	5¹/₂p on 5p pale rose violet	3.25	3.50
		Never hinged	4.00	
		Nos. 188-190 (3)	3.85	4.00

Queen Elizabeth
A36   A37

King George VI
A38   A39

George VI and Blue
Wrens — A40   Emu — A41

1942-44		Engr.	**Perf. 14¹/₂x14**	
191	A36	1p brown vio ('43)	.15	.15
192	A37	1¹/₂p green	.20	.15
193	A38	2p lt rose vio ('44)	.15	.15
194	A39	2¹/₂p red	.20	.15
195	A40	3¹/₂p ultramarine	.20	.15
196	A41	5¹/₂p indigo	.35	.15
		Nos. 191-196 (6)	1.25	
		Set value		.35
		Set, never hinged	1.75	

See #224-225. For overprint see #M2.

Catalogue values for unused
stamps in this section, from this
point to the end of the section, are
for Never Hinged items.

Duke and Duchess
of Gloucester — A42

1945, Feb. 19		Engr.	**Perf. 14¹/₂**	
197	A42	2¹/₂p brown red	.15	.15
198	A42	3¹/₂p bright ultra	.25	.35
199	A42	5¹/₂p indigo	.25	.45
		Nos. 197-199 (3)	.65	.90

Inauguration of the Duke of Gloucester as Governor General.

Official Crest and
Inscriptions — A43

Dove and Australian
Flag
A44

Angel of Peace;
"Motherhood"
and "Industry"
A45

1946, Feb. 18		Wmk. 228	**Perf. 14¹/₂**	
200	A43	2¹/₂p carmine	.20	.15
201	A44	3¹/₂p deep ultra	.20	.25
202	A45	5¹/₂p deep yellow green	.40	.35
		Nos. 200-202 (3)	.80	.75

End of WWII. See #1456-1458.

Sir Thomas Mitchell
and Map of
Queensland — A46

1946, Oct. 14
203 A46 2½p dark carmine .15 .15
204 A46 3½p deep ultra .20 .25
205 A46 1sh olive green .80 .38
    Nos. 203-205 (3) 1.15 .78

Sir Thomas Mitchell's exploration of central Queensland, cent.

Kangaroo-Map Type of 1913 Redrawn
1945, Dec. Typo. Perf. 11½
206 A1 2sh dk red brown 4.50 1.65

The R and A of AUSTRALIA are separated at the base and there is a single line between the value tablet and "Two Shillings." On No. 125 the tail of the R touches the A, while two lines appear between value tablet and "Two Shillings." There are many other minor differences in the design.
For overprint see No. M6.

John Shortland — A47

Pouring Steel — A48

Loading Coal — A49

1947, Sept. Engr. Perf. 14½x14
207 A47 2½p brown red .28 .15

Perf. 14½
208 A48 3½p deep blue .22 .30
209 A49 5½p deep green .38 .30
    Nos. 207-209 (3) .88 .75

150th anniv. of the discovery of the Hunter River estuary, site of Newcastle by Lieut. John Shortland. By error the 2½p shows his father, Capt. John Shortland.

Princess Elizabeth — A50

Perf. 14x14½
1947, Nov. 20 Wmk. 228
210 A50 1p brown violet .18 .15

See No. 215.

Hereford Bull A51

Crocodile A52

1948, Feb. 16 Perf. 14½
211 A51 1sh3p violet brown 1.90 .70
212 A52 2sh chocolate 2.50 .15

See No. 302.

William J. Farrer — A53

Design: No. 214, Ferdinand von Mueller.

1948 Perf. 14½x14
213 A53 2½p red .18 .15
214 A53 2½p dark red .24 .15
    Set value .15

William J. Farrer (1845-1906), wheat researcher, and Ferdinand von Mueller (1825-1896), German-born botanist.
Issue dates: #213, July 12. #214, Sept. 13.

Elizabeth Type of 1947
1948, Aug. Unwmk. Perf. 14x14½
215 A50 1p brown violet .15 .15

Scout in Uniform — A55

Arms of Australia — A56

1948, Nov. 15 Engr. Wmk. 228
216 A55 2½p brown red .18 .15

Pan-Pacific Scout Jamboree, Victoria, Dec. 29, 1948 to Jan. 9, 1949. See No. 249.

1949-50 Wmk. 228 Perf. 14x13½
218 A56 5sh dark red 4.00 .15
219 A56 10sh red violet 21.00 .30
220 A56 £1 deep blue 35.00 3.50
221 A56 £2 deep green ('50) 140.00 15.00
    Nos. 218-221 (4) 200.00 18.95

Henry Lawson A57

Outback Mail Carrier and Plane A58

Perf. 14½x14
1949, June 17 Unwmk.
222 A57 2½p rose brown .15 .15

Henry Hertzberg Lawson (1867-1922), author and poet.

1949, Oct. 10
223 A58 3½p violet blue .25 .16

UPU, 75th anniv.

Types of 1938, 1942-44 & A59

Aborigine A59

John Forrest A60

1948-50 Unwmk. Perf. 14½x14
223A A24 ½p orange ('49) .15 .15
224 A37 1½p green ('49) .28 .15
225 A38 2p lt rose violet .30 .15

Wmk. 228
226 A59 8½p dark brown ('50) .50 .32
    Nos. 223A-226 (4) 1.23
    Set value .47

Issue dates: 2p, Dec., ½p, Sept., 1½p, Aug. 29, 8½p, Aug. 14.
See Nos. 248, 303.

1949, Nov. 28 Wmk. 228
227 A60 2½p brown red .15 .15

Forrest (1847-1918), explorer & statesman.

New South Wales A61

Victoria A62

First stamp designs.

Perf. 14½x14
1950, Sept. 27 Unwmk.
228 A61 2½p rose brown .25 .15
229 A62 2½p rose brown .25 .15
    a. Pair, #228-229 .65 .40
    Set value .20

Cent. of Australian adhesive postage stamps. Issued in sheets of 160 stamps containing alternate copies of Nos. 228 and 229.

Elizabeth A63

A65

George VI A64

A66

1950-51 Engr. Unwmk.
230 A63 1½p deep green .30 .15
231 A63 2p yellow grn ('51) .20 .15
232 A64 2½p violet brn ('51) .20 .15
233 A64 3p dull green ('51) .30 .15
    Nos. 230-233 (4) 1.00
    Set value .20

Issue dates: 1½p, June 19, 2p, Mar. 28, 2½p, May 23, 3p, Nov. 14.

1950-52 Wmk. 228
234 A64 2½p red .15 .15
235 A64 3p red ('51) .15 .15
236 A65 3½p red brown ('51) .28 .15
237 A65 4½p scarlet ('52) .42 .35
238 A65 6½p choc ('52) .30 .35
238A A65 6½p blue green ('52) .40 .15
239 A66 7½p deep blue ('51) .45 .30
    Nos. 234-239 (7) 2.15
    Set value 1.20

Issued: 2½p, Apr. 12; 3p, Feb. 28; 7½p, Oct. 31; 3½p, Nov. 28; 4½p, #238, Feb. 20; #238A, Apr. 9.

Sir Edmund Barton A67

Duke of York Opening First Federal Parliament A68

Designs: No. 241, Sir Henry Parkes. 1sh6p, Parliament House, Canberra.

Perf. 14½x14
1951, May 1 Engr. Unwmk.
240 A67 3p carmine .40 .15
241 A67 3p carmine .40 .15
    a. Pair, #240, 241 .80 .65
242 A68 5½p deep blue .40 .65
243 A68 1sh6p red brown 1.25 .90
    Nos. 240-243 (4) 2.45
    Set value 1.65

Founding of the Commonwealth of Australia, 50th anniv.

Edward Hammond Hargraves A69

King George VI A70

Design: No. 245, Charles Joseph Latrobe (1801-1875), first governor of Victoria.

1951, July 2
244 A69 3p rose brown .25 .15
245 A69 3p rose brown .25 .15
    a. Pair, #244, 245 .65 .65
    Set value .15

Discovery of gold in Australia, cent. (No. 244); Establishment of representative government in Victoria, cent. (No. 245). Sheets contain alternate rows of Nos. 244 and 245.

1952, Mar. 19 Wmk. 228 Perf. 14½
247 A70 1sh½p slate blue 1.65 .22

Aborigine Type of 1950 Redrawn
Size: 20½x25mm
248 A59 2sh6p dark brown 3.25 .25

Portrait as on A59; lettering altered and value repeated at lower left. See No. 303.

Scout Type of 1948
Dated "1952-53"
Perf. 14x14½
1952, Nov. 19 Wmk. 228
249 A55 3½p red brown .18 .15

Pan-Pacific Scout Jamboree, Greystanes, Dec. 30, 1952, to Jan. 9, 1953.

Modern Dairy, Butter Production — A71

Perf. 14½
1953, Feb. 11 Unwmk. Typo.
250 A71 3p shown .75 .15
251 A71 3p Wheat .75 .15
252 A71 3p Beef .75 .15
    a. Strip of 3, #250-252 6.50 6.50
253 A71 3½p shown .75 .15
254 A71 3½p Wheat .75 .15
255 A71 3½p Beef .75 .15
    a. Strip of 3, #253-255 4.50 5.50
    Nos. 250-255 (6) 4.50
    Set value .60

Both the 3p and 3½p were printed in panes of 50 stamps: 17 Butter, 17 Wheat and 16 Beef. The stamps were issued to encourage food production.

Queen Elizabeth II — A72

Perf. 14½x14

1953-54		Unwmk.	Engr.
256	A72	1p purple	.16 .15
256A	A72	2½p deep blue ('54)	.28 .15
257	A72	3p dark green	.28 .15

Wmk. 228

258	A72	3½p dark red	.28 .15
258B	A72	6½p orange ('54)	.90 .15
		Nos. 256-258B (5)	1.90
		Set value	.30

Issue dates: 3½p, Apr. 21. 3p, June 17. 1p, Aug. 19. 2½p, 6½p, June 23.
See Nos. 292 and 296.

Coronation Issue

Queen Elizabeth II A73

1953, May 25			Unwmk.
259	A73	3½p rose red	.28 .15
260	A73	7½p violet	.70 .45
261	A73	2sh dull green	2.25 1.10
		Nos. 259-261 (3)	3.23 1.70

Boy and Girl with Calf — A74

1953, Sept. 3			Perf. 14½
262	A74	3½p dp green & red brn	.25 .15

Official establishment of Young Farmers' Clubs, 25th anniv.

Lieut. Gov. David Collins A75

Tasmania Stamp of 1853 A77

Sullivan Cove, Hobart A76

#264, Lieut. Gov. William Paterson (facing left).

1953, Sept. 23			Perf. 14½x14
263	A75	3½p red brown	.35 .15
264	A75	3½p red brown	.35 .15
a.		Pair, #263-264	1.25 1.10
265	A76	2sh green	4.25 4.00
		Nos. 263-265 (3)	4.95 4.30

Settlement in Tasmania, 150th anniv. Sheets contain alternate rows of Nos. 263 and 264.

1953, Nov. 11			Perf. 14½
266	A77	3p red	.18 .15

Tasmania's first postage stamps, cent.

Elizabeth II and Duke of Edinburgh — A78

Elizabeth II — A79

Telegraph Pole and Key — A80

1954, Feb. 2		Perf. 14½x14, 14x14½	
267	A78	3½p rose red	.18 .15
268	A79	7½p purple	.35 .75
269	A78	2sh green	1.50 1.00
		Nos. 267-269 (3)	2.03 1.90

Visit of Queen Elizabeth II and the Duke of Edinburgh, 1954.

1954, Apr. 7		Engr.	Perf. 14
270	A80	3½p dark red	.25 .15

Inauguration of the telegraph in Australia, cent.

Red Cross and Globe — A81

Swan — A82

1954, June 9			Perf. 14½x14
271	A81	3½p deep blue & red	.18 .15

Australian Red Cross Society.

1954, Aug. 2		Unwmk.	Perf. 14½
274	A82	3½p black	.20 .15

Western Australia's first postage stamp, cent.

Diesel and Early Steam Locomotives A83

1954, Sept. 13			Perf. 14x14½
275	A83	3½p red brown	.20 .15

Centenary of Australian railroads.

Antarctic Flora and Fauna and Map A84

Olympic Circles and Arms of Melbourne A85

1954, Nov. 17			Perf. 14
276	A84	3½p black	.18 .15

Australia's interest in the Antarctic continent.

1954, Dec. 1

| 277 | A85 | 2sh dark blue | 2.00 1.50 |

16th Olympic Games to be held in Melbourne Nov.-Dec. 1956. See No. 286.

Globe, Flags and Rotary Emblem — A86

1955, Feb. 23			Perf. 14x14½
278	A86	3½p carmine	.18 .15

Rotary International, 50th anniv.

Elizabeth II — A87

Top of US Monument, Canberra — A88

1955, Mar. 9		Wmk. 228	Perf. 14½
279	A87	1sh½p dk gray blue	3.50 .25

See No. 301.

1955, May 4		Unwmk.	Perf. 14x14½
280	A88	3½p deep ultra	.18 .15

Friendship between Australia and the US.

Cobb and Company Mail Coach — A89

1955, July 6			Perf. 14½x14
281	A89	3½p dark brown	.20 .15
282	A89	2sh brown	2.50 2.00

Pioneers of Australia's coaching era.

World Map, YMCA Emblem A90

Engr. and Typo.

1955, Aug. 10			Perf. 14
283	A90	3½p Prus green & red	.20 .15

Centenary of YMCA.

Florence Nightingale and Modern Nurse — A91

Queen Victoria — A92

1955, Sept. 21		Engr.	Perf. 14x14½
284	A91	3½p red violet	.18 .15

Centenary of Florence Nightingale's work in the Crimea and of the founding of modern nursing.

1955, Oct. 17			Perf. 14½
285	A92	3½p green	.18 .15

South Australia's first postage stamps, cent.

Olympic Type of 1954

1955, Nov. 30		Unwmk.	Perf. 14
286	A85	2sh deep green	2.25 1.65

16th Olympic Games at Melbourne, Nov. 22-Dec. 8, 1956.

Queen Victoria, Queen Elizabeth II and Badges of Victoria, New South Wales and Tasmania A93

1956, Sept. 26			Perf. 14½x14
287	A93	3½p brown carmine	.25 .15

Centenary of responsible government in Victoria, New South Wales and Tasmania.

Melbourne Coat of Arms — A94

Southern Cross, Olympic Torch — A95

Collins Street, Melbourne A96

Design: 2sh, Melbourne across Yarra River.

1956, Oct. 31		Engr.	Perf. 14½, 14
288	A94	4p dark carmine	.22 .15
289	A95	7½p ultramarine	.55 .42

Photo.
Perf. 14x14½

| 290 | A96 | 1sh multicolored | .75 .38 |

Perf. 12x11½
Granite Paper

| 291 | A96 | 2sh multicolored | 1.40 .60 |
| | | Nos. 288-291 (4) | 2.92 1.55 |

16th Olympic Games, Melbourne, 11/22-12/8.
A lithographed souvenir sheet incorporating reproductions of Nos. 288-291 in reduced size was of private origin and not postally valid.

Types of 1938-55 and

Queen Elizabeth II — A97

Perf. 14½x14, 14x15, 15x14, 14½

1956-57		Engr.	Unwmk.
292	A72	3½p dark red	1.00 .15
293	A28	4p green	1.65 .16
294	A97	4p claret ('57)	.30 .15
a.		Booklet pane of 6 ('57)	7.50
295	A30	6p brown violet	2.75 .16
296	A72	6½p orange	1.75 .15
297	A97	7½p violet ('57)	3.00 .15
298	A31	9p sepia	9.00 .52
299	A97	10p gray blue ('57)	2.75 .15
300	A16	1sh gray green	6.00 .35
301	A87	1sh7p redsh brn ('57)	4.50 .35
302	A52	2sh chocolate	12.00 .28
303	A59	2sh6p brown ('57)	9.00 .30
		Nos. 292-303 (12)	53.70 3.07

No. 300 measures 17½x21½mm. No. 303 measures 20½x25mm and is the redrawn type of 1952.
Issued: 3½p, 7/2; 2sh, 7/21; #293, 6p, 8/18; 6½p, Sept. 9p, 1sh, 12/13; 2sh6p, 1/30; 10p, 3/6; #294, 1sh7p, 3/13; 7½p, 11/13.

South Australia Coat of Arms — A99

1957, Apr. 17		Unwmk.	Perf. 14½
304	A99	4p brown red	.18 .15

Centenary of responsible government in South Australia.

Caduceus and Map of Australia A100

1957, Aug. 21			Perf. 14½x14
305	A100	7p violet blue	.60 .15

Royal Flying Doctor Service of Australia.

Star of Bethlehem and Praying Child — A101

1957, Nov. 6   **Engr.**
306 A101 3½p dull rose   .22 .15
307 A101 4p pale purple   .22 .15
     Christmas.

Canberra War Memorial, Sailor and Airman A102

Design: No. 309, As No. 308 with soldier and service woman. Printed in alternate rows in sheet.

1958, Feb. 10   **Unwmk.**
308 A102 5½p brown carmine   1.25 .75
309 A102 5½p brown carmine   1.25 .75
  a.   Pair, #308-309   3.50 3.50

Sir Charles Kingsford-Smith and "Southern Cross" — A103

1958, Aug. 27   **Perf. 14x14½**
310 A103 8p brt violet blue   1.00 .90
   1st air crossing of the Tasman Sea, 30th anniv. See New Zealand No. 321.

Broken Hill Mine A104   Nativity A105

1958, Sept. 10   **Perf. 14½x14**
311 A104 4p brown   .25 .15
   Broken Hill mining field, 75th anniv.

1958, Nov. 5   **Perf. 14½x15**
312 A105 3½p dark red   .15 .15
313 A105 4p dark purple   .22 .15
     Set value   .15
     Christmas.

A106   A107   A109

A108   A110

Platypus A111   Tasmanian Tiger A112

Flannel Flower A113   Aboriginal Stockman Cutting Out a Steer A114

Designs: 3p, Queen Elizabeth II facing right. 6p, Banded anteater. 8p, Tiger cat. 9p, Kangaroos. 11p, Rabbit bandicoot. 1sh6p, Christmas bells (flower). 2sh3p, Wattle (flower). 2sh5p, Banksia (flower). 3sh, Waratah (flower).

FIVE PENCE
Die I - Four short lines inside "5" at right of ball; six short lines left of ball; full length line above ball is seventh from bottom. Odd numbered horizontal rows in each sheet are in Die I.
Die II - Five short lines inside "5" at right of ball; seven at left; full length line above ball is eighth from bottom. Even numbered horizontal rows in each sheet are in Die II.

Perf. 14½x14, 14x14½, 14½
1959-64   **Engr.**   **Unwmk.**
314 A106 1p dull violet   .25 .15
315 A107 2p red brown   .35 .15
316 A108 3p bluish green   .35 .15
317 A108 3½p dark green   .45 .15
318 A109 4p carmine   .35 .15
  a.   Booklet pane of 6   25.00
319 A110 5p dark blue (I)   .65 .15
  a.   5p dark blue (II)   .65 .15
  b.   Booklet pane of 6 ('60)   12.00
320 A111 6p chocolate   .65 .15
321 A111 8p red brown   .60 .15
322 A111 9p brown black   2.50 .20
323 A111 11p dark blue   .95 .15
324 A111 1sh slate green   3.75 .15
325 A112 1sh2p dk purple   1.50 .20
326 A113 1sh6p red, *yellow*   2.50 .60
327 A113 2sh dark blue   2.50 .15
328 A113 2sh3p green, *yel*   2.50 .20
328A A113 2sh3p yellow grn   7.50 1.00
329 A113 2sh5p brown, *yellow*   8.75 .40
330 A113 3sh crimson   3.50 .35

Wmk. 228
331 A114 5sh red brown   25.00 1.00
   Nos. 314-331 (19)   64.50
     Set value   4.60

Issued: 1p, 4p, 2/2; 3½p, 3/18; 2sh, 4/8; 3p, 5/20; 3sh, 7/15; 1sh, #328, 9/9; 5p, 10/1; 9p, 10/21; 1sh6p, 2/3/60; 2sh5p, 3/16/60; 8p, 5/11/60; 6p, 9/30/60; 11p, 5/3/61; 5sh, 7/26/61; 2p, 1sh2p, 3/21/62; #328A, 10/28/64.

Luminescent Printings
Paper with an orange red phosphorescence (surface coating), was used for some printings of the Colombo Plan 1sh, No. 340, the Churchill 5p, No. 389, and several regular postage stamps. These include 2p, 3p, 6p, 8p, 9p, 11p, 1sh2p, 1sh6p and 2sh3p (Nos. 315, 316, 365, 367, 321, 368, 323, 325, 369, 328A).
Stamps printed only on phosphorescent paper include the Monash 5p, Hargrave 5p, ICY 2sh3p and Christmas 5p (Nos. 388, 390-393) and succeeding commemoratives; the 2sh, 2sh6p and 3sh regular birds (Nos. 370, 372, 373); and most of the regular series in decimal currency.
Ink with a phosphorescent content was used in printing most of the 5p red, No. 366, almost all of the 5p red booklets, No. 366a, most of the decimal 4c regular, No. 397, and its booklet pane, No. 397a, and all of No. 398.

Postmaster Isaac Nichols Boarding Vessel to Receive Mail — A115

1959, Apr. 22   **Perf. 14½x14**
332 A115 4p dark gray blue   .25 .15
   First post office, Sydney, 150th anniv.

Parliament House, Brisbane, and Queensland Arms — A116

1959, June 5   **Perf. 14x14½**
333 A116 4p dk green & violet   .25 .15
   Cent. of Queensland self-government.

Approach of the Magi — A117

1959, Nov. 4   **Perf. 15x14½**
334 A117 5p purple   .25 .15
     Christmas.

Girl Guide and Lord Baden-Powell A118

1960, Aug. 18   **Perf. 14½x14**
335 A118 5p dark blue   .32 .15
   50th anniversary of the Girl Guides.

The Overlanders by Sir Daryl Lindsay — A119   Melbourne Cup and Archer, 1861 Winner — A120

1960, Sept. 21   **Perf. 14½**
336 A119 5p lilac rose   .35 .15
Exploration of Australia's Northern Territory, cent.

1960, Oct. 12   **Unwmk.**
337 A120 5p sepia   .35 .15
   Centenary of the Melbourne Cup.

Queen Victoria A121   Open Bible and Candle A122

1960 Nov. 2   **Engr.**   **Perf. 14½**
338 A121 5p dark green   .22 .15
   Centenary of the first Queensland stamps.

1960, Nov. 9   **Unwmk.**
339 A122 5p maroon   .20 .15
   Christmas; beginning of 350th anniv. year of the publication of the King James translation of the Bible.

Colombo Plan Emblem — A123

1961, June 30   **Perf. 14x14½**
340 A123 1sh red brown   .80 .15
   Colombo Plan for the peaceful development of South East Asia countries, 10th anniv.

Dame Nellie Melba, by Sir Bertram Mackennal — A124

1961, Sept. 20   **Perf. 14½**
341 A124 5p deep blue   .35 .15
   Dame Nellie Melba, singer, birth cent.

Page from Book of Hours, 15th Century — A125   John McDouall Stuart — A126

1961, Nov. 8   **Perf. 14½x14**
342 A125 5p reddish brown   .38 .15
   Christmas; end of the 350th anniv. year of the publication of the King James translation of the Bible.

1962, July 25   **Unwmk.**   **Perf. 14½**
345 A126 5p carmine   .35 .15
   First south-north crossing of Australia by John McDouall Stuart, cent.

Nurse and Rev. Flynn's Grave — A127

1962, Sept. 5   **Photo.**   **Perf. 13½**
346 A127 5p multicolored   .35 .15
  a.   Red omitted   275.00
   Australian Inland Mission founded by Rev. John Flynn, 50th anniv.

Woman and Globe — A128   Madonna and Child — A129

1962, Sept. 26   **Engr.**   **Perf. 14x14½**
347 A128 5p dark green   .35 .15
   World Conf. of the Associated Country Women of the World, Melbourne, Oct. 2-12.

1962, Oct. 17   **Perf. 14½**
348 A129 5p deep violet   .38 .15
     Christmas.

View of Perth and Kangaroo Paw — A130

Arms of Perth — A131

1962, Nov. 1   **Photo.**   **Perf. 14**
349 A130 5p multicolored   .38 .15
  a.   Red omitted   450.00

Perf. 14½x14
350 A131 2sh3p emer, blk, red & ultra   5.00 5.00
   British Empire and Commonwealth Games, Perth, Nov. 22-Dec. 1.

Elizabeth
II — A132

Elizabeth II and
Prince
Philip — A133

1963, Feb. 18　　Engr.　　Perf. 14½
351	A132	5p dark green	.30	.15
352	A133	2sh3 red brown	5.75	5.00

Visit of Elizabeth II and Prince Philip.

Walter Burley Griffin and
Arms of Canberra
A134

Red Cross
Centenary
Emblem
A135

1963, Mar. 8　Unwmk.　Perf. 14½x14
353　A134　5p dark green　　　　.35　.15

50th anniv. of Canberra; Walter Burley Griffin, American architect, who laid out plan for Canberra.

1963, May 8　Photo.　Perf. 13½x13
354　A135　5p dk blue, red & gray　.35　.15

Centenary of the International Red Cross.

Explorers Blaxland, Lawson and
Wentworth Looking West from Mt.
York — A136

1963, May 28　Engr.　Perf. 14½x14
355　A136　5p dark blue　　　　　.30　.15

1st crossing of the Blue Mts., 150th anniv.

Globe, Ship,
Plane and Map
of Australia
A137

1963, Aug. 28　　　　　Unwmk.
356　A137　5p red　　　　　　　　.35　.15

Importance of exports to Australian economy.

Elizabeth
II — A138

Black-backed Magpie
and Eucalyptus — A139

Abel Tasman and Ship
A144

George Bass,
Whaleboat
A145

Designs: 6p, Yellow-tailed thornbill, horiz. 1sh6p, Galah on tree stump. 2sh, Golden whistler. 2sh5p, Blue wren and bracken fern. 2sh6p, Scarlet robin, horiz. 3sh, Straw-necked ibis. 5sh, William Dampier and "Roebuck" sailing ship. 7sh6p, Capt. James Cook. 10sh, Matthew Flinders and three-master "Investigator." £2, Admiral Philip Parker King.

1963-65　Unwmk.　Engr.　Perf. 15x14
365	A138	5p green	.25	.15
a.		Booklet pane of 6 ('64)	20.00	
b.		Pair, imperf. btwn.	3.75	3.75
366	A138	5p red	.25	.15
a.		Booklet pane of 6	25.00	

Photo.
Perf. 13½
367	A139	6p multicolored	.45	.15
a.		Vert. pair, imperf. btwn.		
368	A139	9p multicolored	2.50	1.90
369	A139	1sh6p multicolored	1.25	1.10
370	A139	2sh multicolored	2.50	.38
371	A139	2sh5p multicolored	8.25	2.25
372	A139	2sh6p multicolored	3.75	1.50
a.		Red omitted	1,000.	
373	A139	3sh multicolored	2.50	1.25

Engr.
Perf. 14½x14, 14½x15
374	A144	4sh violet blue	3.75	.55

Wmk. 228
375	A145	5sh red brown	5.25	1.25
376	A144	7sh6p olive green	24.00	15.00
377	A144	10sh deep claret	30.00	7.25
378	A145	£1 purple	50.00	22.50
379	A145	£2 brown black	100.00	90.00
		Nos. 365-379 (15)	234.70	145.38

No. 365a was printed in sheets of 288 which were sold intact by the Philatelic Bureau. These sheets have been broken to obtain pairs and blocks which are imperf. between (see No. 365b).
Issued: #365, 4sh, 10/9/63; 10sh, £1, 2/26/64; 9p, 1sh6p, 2sh5p, 3/11/64; 6p, 8/19/64; 7sh6p, £2, 8/26/64; 5sh, 11/25/64; 2sh, 2sh6p, 3sh, 4/21/65; #366, 6/30/65.
See Nos. 400-401, 406-417.

Star of Bethlehem — A146

1963, Oct. 25　Unwmk.　Perf. 14½
380　A146　5p blue　　　　　　　.20　.15

Christmas.

Cable Around
World and
Under
Sea — A147

1963, Dec. 3　Photo.　Perf. 13½
381　A147　2sh3p gray, ver, blk &
　　　　　　blue　　　　　　　6.00　5.00

Opening of the Commonwealth Pacific (telephone) cable service (COMPAC).
See New Zealand No. 364.

Bleriot 60 Plane,
1914 — A148

1964, July 1　Engr.　Perf. 14½x14
382	A148	5p olive green	.20	.15
383	A148	2sh3p red	5.25	4.75

50th anniv. of the first air mail flight in Australia; Maurice Guillaux, aviator.

Child Looking at
Nativity
Scene — A149

1964, Oct. 21　Photo.　Perf. 13½
384	A149	5p bl, blk, red & buff	.20	.15
a.		Red omitted	375.00	
b.		Black omitted	375.00	

Christmas.

"Simpson and His
Donkey" by Wallace
Anderson — A150

1965, Apr. 14　Engr.　Perf. 14x14½
385	A150	5p olive bister	.20	.15
386	A150	8p dark blue	1.25	.90
387	A150	2sh3p rose claret	4.50	4.00
		Nos. 385-387 (3)	5.95	5.05

50th anniv. of the landing of the Australian and New Zealand Army Corps (ANZAC) at Gallipoli, Turkey, Apr. 25, 1915. Private John Simpson Kirkpatrick saved the lives of many wounded soldiers. The statue erected in his honor stands in front of Melbourne's Shrine of Remembrance.

Radio Mast and
Satellite Orbiting
Earth
A151

Winston
Churchill
A152

1965, May 10　Photo.　Perf. 13½
388	A151	5p multicolored	.20	.15
a.		Black ("5d" and pylon) omitted	650.00	

ITU, cent.

1965, May 24
389　A152　5p lt blue, gray & blk　　.25　.15

Sir Winston Spencer Churchill (1874-1965), statesman and WWII leader.
See New Zealand No. 371.

John Monash
and
Transmission
Tower — A153

Lawrence Hargrave and
Sketch for 1902
Seaplane — A154

1965, June 23　Photo.　Perf. 13½
390　A153　5p red, yel, blk & lt brn　.25　.15

Birth cent. of General Sir John Monash (1865-1931), soldier, Vice-Chancellor of University of Melbourne and chairman of the Victoria state electricity commission.

1965, Aug. 4　Unwmk.　Perf. 13½
391	A154	5p multicolored	.25	.15
a.		Purple (5d) omitted	190.00	

50th anniv. of the death of Lawrence Hargrave (1850-1915), aviation pioneer.

ICY Emblem
A155

Nativity
A156

1965, Sept. 1　Photo.　Perf. 13½
392　A155　2sh3p lt blue & green　2.75　2.50

International Cooperation Year.

1965, Oct. 20　Unwmk.　Perf. 13½
393	A156	5p multicolored	.30	.15
a.		Gold omitted	300.00	
b.		Ultramarine omitted	325.00	

Christmas.

Types of 1963-65 and

Elizabeth
II — A157

Humbug
Fish — A158

Designs: No. 400, Yellow-tailed thornbill, horiz. 6c, blue-faced honeyeater, horiz. 8c, Coral fish. 9c, Hermit crab. 10c Anemone fish. 13c, Red-necked avocet. 15c, Galah on tree stump. 20c, Golden whistler. 24c Azure kingfisher, horiz. 25c, Scarlet robin, horiz. 30c, Straw-necked ibis. 40c Abel Tasman and ship. 50c, William Dampier and "Roebuck" sailing ship. 75c, Capt. James Cook. $1, Matthew Flinders and three-master "Investigator." $2, George Bass and whaleboat. $4, Admiral Philip Parker King.

Perf. 14½x14 (A157); 13½ (A158, A139)
Engr. (A157), Photo. (A158, A139)
1966-71
394	A157	1c red brown	.25	.15
395	A157	2c olive green	.50	.15
396	A157	3c Prus green	.65	.15
397	A157	4c red	.15	.15
a.		Booklet pane of 5 + label	30.00	
398	A157	5c on 4c red ('67)	.75	.15
a.		Booklet pane of 5 + label ('67)	5.50	
399	A157	5c dk blue ('67)	1.00	.15
a.		Booklet pane of 5 + label	11.00	
b.		Booklet pane of 10	55.00	
400	A139	5c lt grn, blk, brn & yel	.20	.15
a.		Booklet pane of 10	45.00	
401	A139	6c gray, blk, lem & bl	.55	.15
401A	A157	6c orange ('70)	.15	.15
402	A158	7c brn, ver, blk & gray	1.00	.15
402A	A157	7c dp rose lilac ('71)	.20	.15
403	A158	8c multicolored	1.10	.15
404	A158	9c multicolored	1.50	.15
405	A158	10c lt brn, blk, org & bl	1.10	.25
406	A139	13c lt bl grn, blk, gray & red	2.00	.50
a.		Red omitted	400.00	
407	A139	15c lt grn, blk, gray & rose	3.50	.40
a.		Gray omitted	1,500.	
408	A139	20c pink, blk, yel & gray	5.75	.15
a.		Yellow omitted	350.00	
409	A139	24c tan, blk, vio bl & org	1.10	.75
410	A139	25c gray, grn, blk & red	3.75	.15
a.		Red omitted	750.00	
411	A139	30c lt grn, buff, blk & red	19.00	.50
a.		Red omitted	575.00	

Engr.
Perf. 14½x14, 14½x15
412	A144	40c violet blue	13.50	.30
413	A145	50c brown red	17.00	.15
414	A144	75c olive green	.85	1.10
415	A144	$1 deep claret	2.50	.30
		Perf 15x14	75.00	15.00
416	A145	$2 purple	7.50	1.10
417	A145	$4 sepia	5.50	4.50
		Nos. 394-417 (26)	91.05	12.10

No. 398 issued in booklets only.
Booklet panes Nos. 399b and 400a were issued for the use of "Australian Defence Forces," as the covers read, in Viet Nam.
Issued: #398, 399, 9/29/67; #401A, 9/28/70; #402A, 10/1/71; #415a, 1973; others, 2/14/66.

Coil Stamps
1966-67　Photo.　Perf. 15 Horiz.
418	A157	3c emerald, blk & buff	.40	.35
419	A157	4c org red, blk & buff	.60	.15
420	A157	5c blue, black & buff	.75	.15
		Nos. 418-420 (3)	1.75	
		Set value		.55

Issued: 5c, Sept. 29, 1967; others, Feb. 14, 1966.

Rescue — A159

1966 July 6　Photo.　Perf. 13½
421　A159　4c blue, ultra & black　　.25　.15

Royal Life Saving Society, 75th anniv.

Adoration of the Shepherds A160

1966, Oct. 19   Photo.   Perf. 13½
422 A160 4c olive & black .25 .15
Christmas.

Dutch Sailing Ship, 17th Century A161

Hands Reaching for Bible A162

1966, Oct. 24   Photo.   Perf. 13½
423 A161 4c bl, blk, dp org & gold .25 .15
350th anniv. of Dirk Hartog's discovery of the Australian west coast, and his landing on the island named after him.

1967, Mar. 7   Photo.   Perf. 13½
424 A162 4c multicolored .25 .15
British and Foreign Bible Soc., 150th anniv.

Combination Lock and Antique Keys — A163

1967, Apr. 5   Photo.   Perf. 13½
425 A163 4c emerald, blk & lt blue .25 .15
150th anniv. of banking in Australia (Bank of New South Wales).

Lions Intl., 50th Anniv. — A164

1967, June 7   Photo.   Perf. 13½
426 A164 4c ultra, black & gold .25 .15

YWCA Emblems and Flags — A165

1967, Aug. 21   Photo.   Perf. 13½
427 A165 4c dk blue, lt bl & lilac .25 .15
World Council Meeting of the YWCA, Monash University, Victoria, Aug. 14-Sept. 1.

Seated Women Symbolizing Obstetrics and Gynecology, Female Symbol A166

1967, Sept. 20   Photo.   Perf. 13½
428 A166 4c lilac, dk blue & blk .25 .15
5th World Congress of Gynecology and Obstetrics, Sydney, Sept. 23-30.

Gothic Arches and Christmas Bell Flower — A167

Cross, Stars of David and Yin Yang Forming Mandala — A168

1967   Photo.   Perf. 13½
429 A167 5c multicolored .25 .15
430 A168 25c multicolored 2.25 2.25
Christmas.
Issue dates: 5c, Oct. 18; 25c, Nov. 27.

Satellite Orbiting Earth — A169

Satellite and Antenna, Moree, N.S.W. — A170

Design: 20c, World weather map connecting Washington, Moscow and Melbourne, and computer and teleprinter tape spools.

1968, Mar. 20   Photo.   Perf. 13½
431 A169 5c dull yel, red, bl & dk blue .25 .15
432 A169 20c blue, blk & red 3.00 3.00
433 A170 25c Prus blue, blk & lt green 3.50 3.50
Nos. 431-433 (3) 6.75 6.65
Use of satellites for weather observations and communications.

Kangaroo Paw, Western Australia A171

Sturt's Desert Rose, Northern Territory A171a

State Flowers: 13c, Pink heath, Victoria. 15c, Tasmanian blue gum, Tasmania. 20c, Sturt's desert pea, South Australia. 25c, Cooktown orchid, Queensland. 30c, Waratah, New South Wales.

1968, July 10   Photo.   Perf. 13½
Flowers in Natural Colors
434 A171 6c bister & dk brn .30 .20
435 A171 13c lt grnsh blue .40 .15
436 A171 15c dk brn & yel 1.50 .25
437 A171 20c lemon & black 5.25 .15
438 A171 25c light ultra 3.75 .15
439 A171 30c chocolate 1.10 .15
Nos. 434-439 (6) 12.30 1.05

Coil Stamps

1970-75   Perf. 14½ Horiz.
Designs: 5c, Golden wattle, national flower. 7c, 10c, Sturt's desert pea.
439A A171a 2c dk grn & multi .20 .15
  i. Lettering and value bolder .20 .15
439B A171a 4c gray & multi .50 .40
439C A171a 5c gray & multi .20 .15
439D A171a 6c gray & multi 1.10 .50
  h. Green omitted 300.00
439E A171a 7c blk, red & grn .35 .15
  f. Green omitted 150.00
439G A171a 10c blk, red & grn .30 .15
Nos. 439A-439G (6) 2.65 1.50
Issued: 4c, 5c, 4/27; 6c, 10/28; 2c, 7c, 10/1/71; 10c, 1/15/75; #439Ai, 11/73.

Soil Testing Through Chemistry and by Computer A172

Hippocrates and Hands Holding Hypodermic A173

1968, Aug. 6   Photo.   Perf. 13½
440 A172 5c multicolored .25 .15
441 A173 5c multicolored .25 .15
9th Intl. Congress of Soil Science, University of Adelaide, Aug. 6-16 (No. 440); General Assembly of World Medical Associations, Sydney, Aug. 6-9 (No. 441). Nos. 440-441 printed in sheets of 100 in two separate panes of 50 connected by a gutter. Each sheet contains 10 gutter pairs.

Runner and Aztec Calendar Stone A174

Symbolic House and Money A175

Design: 25c, Aztec calendar stone and Mexican flag, horiz.

1968, Oct. 2
442 A174 5c multicolored .20 .15
443 A174 25c multicolored 2.25 2.00
19th Olympic Games, Mexico City, Oct. 12-27. Nos. 442-443 printed in sheets of 100 in two separate panes of 50 connected by a gutter. Each sheet contains 10 gutter pairs.

1968, Oct. 16
444 A175 5c multicolored .25 .15
11th Triennial Congress of the Intl. Union of Building Societies and Savings Associations, Sydney, Oct. 20-27.

View of Bethlehem and Church Window — A176

1968, Oct. 23   Photo.   Perf. 13½
445 A176 5c lt bl, red, grn & gold .20 .15
  a. Red omitted 350.00
Christmas.

Edgeworth David (1858-1934), Geologist A177

Sir Edmund Barton (1849-1920) A178

Reginald C. and John R. Duigan, Aviators — A179

Famous Australians: No. 447, Caroline Chisholm (1808-1877), social worker and reformer. No. 448, Albert Namatjira (1902-1959), aborigine, artist. No. 449, Andrew Barton (Banjo) Paterson (1864-1941), poet and writer.

1968, Nov. 6   Engr.   Perf. 15x14
446 A177 5c green, greenish 1.25 .15
  a. Booklet pane of 5 + label 6.25
447 A177 5c purple, pink 1.25 .15
  a. Booklet pane of 5 + label 6.25
448 A177 5c dark brown, buff 1.25 .15
  a. Booklet pane of 5 + label 6.25
449 A177 5c indigo, lt blue 1.25 .15
  a. Booklet pane of 5 + label 6.25
Nos. 446-449 (4) 5.00
Set value .48

1969, Oct. 22   Engr.   Perf. 15x14
Prime Ministers: No. 451, Alfred Deakin (1856-1919). No. 452, John C. Watson (1867-1941). No.453, Sir George H. Reid (1845-1918).
450 A178 5c indigo, greenish 1.25 .15
  a. Booklet pane of 5 + label 6.25
451 A178 5c indigo, greenish 1.25 .15
  a. Booklet pane of 5 + label 6.25
452 A178 5c indigo, greenish 1.25 .15
  a. Booklet pane of 5 + label 6.25
453 A178 5c indigo, greenish 1.25 .15
  a. Booklet pane of 5 + label 6.25
Nos. 450-453 (4) 5.00
Set value .48

1970, Nov. 16   Engr.   Perf. 15x14
Famous Australians: No. 455, Lachlan Macquarie (1761-1824), Governor of New South Wales. No. 456, Adam Lindsay Gordon (1833-1870), poet. No. 457, Edward John Eyre (1815-1901), explorer.
454 A179 6c dark blue 1.25 .15
  a. Booklet pane of 5 + label 6.25
455 A179 6c dark brown, salmon 1.25 .15
  a. Booklet pane of 5 + label 6.25
456 A179 6c magenta, brt pink 1.25 .15
  a. Booklet pane of 5 + label 6.25
457 A179 6c brown red, salmon 1.25 .15
  a. Booklet pane of 5 + label 6.25
Nos. 454-457 (4) 5.00
Set value .48
Nos. 446-457 were issued in booklet panes only; all stamps have 1 or 2 straight edges.

Macquarie Lighthouse — A180

Perf. 14½x13½
1968, Nov. 27   Engr.
458 A180 5c indigo, buff .35 .15
Macquarie Lighthouse, Outer South Head, Sydney, 150th anniv.

Surveyor George W. Goyder and Assistants, 1869; Building in Darwin, 1969 — A181

1969, Feb. 5   Photo.   Perf. 13½
459 A181 5c black brn & dull yel .20 .15
First permanent settlement of the Northern Territory of Australia, cent.

Melbourne Harbor Scene — A182

1969, Feb. 26   Photo.   Perf. 13½
460 A182 5c dull blue & multi .20 .15
6th Biennial Conference of the Intl. Assoc. of Ports and Harbors, Melbourne, March 3-8.

Overlapping Circles — A183

1969, June 5   Photo.   Perf. 13½
461 A183 5c gray, vio bl, bl & gold .20 .15
ILO, 50th anniv.

Sugar Cane — A184

Designs (Primary industries): 15c, Eucalyptus (timber). 20c, Wheat. 25c, Ram, ewe and lamb (wool).

1969, Sept. 17   *Perf. 13¹/₂x13*
462 A184 7c blue & multi   .75 .75
463 A184 15c emerald & multi   3.75 3.25
464 A184 20c org brn & multi   1.40 .40
465 A184 25c gray, black & yel   1.25 .50
   Nos. 462-465 (4)   7.15 4.90

Nativity — A185   Tree of Life — A186

Perf. 13¹/₂x13, 13x13¹/₂
1969, Oct. 15   **Photo.**
466 A185 5c multicolored   .20 .15
467 A186 25c multicolored   2.75 2.75
   Christmas.

Vickers Vimy Flown by Ross Smith, England to Australia A187

Designs: No. 469, B.E. 2E plane, automobile and spectators. No. 470, Ford truck and surveyors Lieuts. Hudson Fysh and P.J. McGinness.

1969, Nov. 12   *Perf. 13x13¹/₂*
468 A187 5c bl, blk, cop red & ol .60 .35
469 A187 5c bl, blk, cop red & ol .60 .35
470 A187 5c cop red, black & ol   .60 .35
   a. Strip of 3, #468-470   1.80 3.00
   Nos. 468-470 (3)   1.80 1.05

50th anniv. of the first England to Australia flight by Capt. Ross Smith and Lieut. Keith Smith.

Nos. 468-470 are printed se-tenant with various combinations possible.

Diesel Locomotive and New Track Linking Melbourne, Sydney and Brisbane with Perth — A188

1970, Feb. 11 **Photo.** *Perf. 13x13¹/₂*
471 A188 5c multicolored   .25 .15
   Completion of the standard gauge railroad between Sydney and Perth.

EXPO '70 Australian Pavilion — A189

Design: 20c, Southern Cross and Japanese inscription: "From the country of the south with warm feeling."

1970, Mar. 16 **Photo.** *Perf. 13x13¹/₂*
472 A189 5c bl, blk, red & brnz   .25 .15
473 A189 20c red & black   1.00 .45
   EXPO '70 Intl. Exhib., Osaka, Japan, Mar. 15-Sept. 13.

Queen Elizabeth II and Prince Philip — A190

Australian Flag — A191

1970, Mar. 31
474 A190 5c yel bister & black   .25 .15
475 A191 30c vio blue & multi   2.25 2.75
   Visit of Queen Elizabeth II, Prince Philip and Princess Anne to Australia.

Steer, Alfalfa and Native Spear Grass — A192

1970, Apr. 13 Photo. *Perf. 13x13¹/₂*
476 A192 5c emerald & multi   .25 .22
   11th Intl. Grasslands Congress, Surfers Paradise, Queensland, Apr. 13-23.

Capt. James Cook and "Endeavour" — A193

Designs: No. 478, Sextant and "Endeavour." No. 479, "Endeavour," landing party and kangaroo. No. 480, Daniel Charles Solander, Sir Joseph Banks, Cook, map and botanical drawing. No. 481, Cook taking possession with Union Jack; "Endeavour" and coral. 30c, Cook, "Endeavour," sextant, kangaroo and aborigines.

1970, Apr. 20   *Perf. 13¹/₂x13*
   Size: 24x35¹/₂mm
477 A193 5c org brn & multi   .50 .15
478 A193 5c org brn & multi   .50 .15
479 A193 5c org brn & multi   .50 .15
480 A193 5c org brn & multi   .50 .15
481 A193 5c org brn & multi   .50 .15
   a. Strip of 5, #477-481   2.50 2.50
   Size: 62x29mm
482 A193 30c org brn & multi   3.50 3.50
   a. Souv. sheet of 6, #477-482, imperf. 11.00 11.00
   Nos. 477-482 (6)   6.00 4.25

Cook's discovery and exploration of the eastern coast of Australia, 200th anniv.
No. 481a has continuous design.
No. 482a with brown marginal overprint "Souvenir Sheet ANPEX 1970..." is of private origin.

Snowy Mountains Hydroelectric Project — A194

Designs: 8c, Ord River hydroelectric project (dam, cotton plant and boll). 9c, Bauxite and aluminum production (mine, conveyor belt and aluminum window frame). 10c, Oil and natural gas (offshore drilling rig and pipelines).

1970, Aug. 31 Photo. *Perf. 13x13¹/₂*
483 A194 7c multicolored   1.65 .38
484 A194 8c multicolored   .25 .15
485 A194 9c multicolored   .25 .15
486 A194 10c multicolored   1.10 .15
   Nos. 483-486 (4)   3.25 .83

Australian economic development.

Flame Symbolizing Democracy and Freedom of Speech — A195

1970, Oct. 2 Photo. *Perf. 13¹/₂x13*
487 A195 6c green & multi   .25 .15
   16th Commonwealth Parliamentary Assoc. Conference, Canberra, Oct. 2-9.

Herd of Illawarra Shorthorns and Laboratory A196

1970, Oct. 7   *Perf. 13x13¹/₂*
488 A196 6c multicolored   .25 .15
   18th Intl. Dairy Cong., Sydney, Oct. 12-16.

Madonna and Child, by William Beasley A197

UN Emblem, Dove and Symbols A198

1970, Oct. 14   *Perf. 13¹/₂x13*
489 A197 6c multicolored   .25 .15
   Christmas.

1970, Oct. 19
490 A198 6c blue & multi   .25 .15
   25th anniversary of the United Nations.

Qantas Boeing 707, and Avro 504 — A199

Design: 30c, Sunbeam Dyak powered Avro 504 on ground and Qantas Boeing 707 in the air.

1970, Nov. 2   *Perf. 13x13¹/₂*
491 A199 6c multicolored   .24 .15
492 A199 30c multicolored   1.40 1.40
   Qantas, Australian overseas airlines, 50th anniv.

Japanese Noh Actor, Australian Dancer and Chinese Opera Character — A200

Designs: 15c, Chinese pipe and trumpet, Australian aboriginal didgeridoo, Thai fiddle, Indian double oboe and Tibetan drums. 20c, Red Sea dhow, Chinese junk, Australian lifeguard's surfboat, Malaysian and South Indian river boats.

1971, Jan. 6 Photo. *Perf. 13¹/₂x13*
493 A200 7c multicolored   .60 .15
494 A200 15c multicolored   1.50 1.10
495 A200 20c multicolored   1.50 .80
   Nos. 493-495 (3)   3.60 2.05

Link between Australia and Asia; 28th Intl. Congress of Orientalists, Canberra, Jan. 6-12.

Southern Cross — A201

1971, Apr. 21 Photo. *Perf. 13¹/₂x13*
496 A201 6c multicolored   .25 .15
   Australian Natives Assoc., cent.

Symbolic Market Graphs — A202   Rotary Emblem — A203

1971, May 5   *Perf. 13¹/₂x13*
497 A202 6c silver & multi   .25 .15
   Centenary of Sydney Stock Exchange.

1971, May 17   *Perf. 13x13¹/₂*
498 A203 6c multicolored   .25 .15
   First Intl. Rotary Convention held in Australia, Sydney, May 16-20.

DH-9A, Australian Mirage Jet Fighters A204

RSPCA Centenary A205

1971, June 9   *Perf. 13¹/₂x13*
499 A204 6c multicolored   .35 .15
   Royal Australian Air Force, 50th anniv.

1971, July 5 Photo. *Perf. 13¹/₂x13*
Designs: 12c, Man and lamb (animal science). 18c, Kangaroo (fauna conservation). 24c, Seeing eye dog (animals' aid to man).
500 A205 6c blk, brown & org   .28 .15
501 A205 12c blk, dk grn & yel   .75 .18
502 A205 18c brown & multi   .95 .30
503 A205 24c blue & multi   1.25 .50
   Nos. 500-503 (4)   3.23 1.13

Royal Society for Prevention of Cruelty to Animals in Australia, cent.

Longnecked Tortoise, Painted on Bark — A206

Aboriginal Art: 25c, Mourners' body paintings, Warramunga tribe. 30c, Cave painting, Western Arnhem Land, vert. 35c, Graveposts, Bathurst and Melville Islands, vert.

Perf. 13x13¹/₂, 13¹/₂x13
1971, Sept. 29
504 A206 6c multicolored   .65 .25
505 A206 25c multicolored   .65 .45
506 A206 30c multicolored   .90 .35
507 A206 35c multicolored   .65 .40
   Nos. 504-507 (4)   2.85 1.45

Three Kings and Star — A207

1971, Oct. 13 Photo. *Perf. 13¹/₂x13*
508   Block of 7   50.00
   a. A207 7c brt grn, dk bl (Kings) & lil 9.00 .30
   b. A207 7c lil, red brn, grn & dk bl   6.25 .15
   c. A207 7c red brown & lilac   1.75 .15
   d. A207 7c lilac, red brn & brt grn   2.75 .15
   e. A207 7c red brown & dark blue   3.00 .15
   f. A207 7c lilac, green & dk blue   20.00 1.40
   g. A207 7c brt grn, dk bl & lilac (Kings) 3.50 .15

Christmas. Nos. 508a-508g printed se-tenant in sheets of 50. Each sheet contains 2 green crosses formed by 4 No. 508g and three No. 508a.

7c Australia
Andrew Fisher (1862-1928) — A208

Cameo Brooch — A209

Prime Ministers: No. 515, Joseph Cook (1860-1947). No. 516, William Morris Hughes (1864-1952). No. 517, Stanley Melbourne Bruce (1883-1967).

1972, Mar. 8   Engr.   Perf. 15x14

514	A208	7c dark blue	.75	.15
	a.	Booklet pane of 5 + label	4.00	
515	A208	7c dark red	.75	.15
	a.	Booklet pane of 5 + label	4.00	
516	A208	7c dark blue	.75	.15
	a.	Booklet pane of 5 + label	4.00	
517	A208	7c dark red	.75	.15
	a.	Booklet pane of 5 + label	4.00	
		Nos. 514-517 (4)	3.00	
		Set value		.40

Nos. 514-517 were issued in booklets only; all stamps have one or two straight edges.

1972, Apr. 18   Photo.   Perf. 13½

518	A209	7c multicolored	.25	.15

Country Women's Assoc., 50th anniv.

Apple and Banana — A210

1972, June 14

519	A210	20c shown	1.50	1.50
520	A210	25c Rice	2.25	2.25
521	A210	30c Fish	2.25	2.25
522	A210	35c Cattle	5.25	5.25
		Nos. 519-522 (4)	11.25	11.25

Worker in Sheltered Workshop — A211

18c, Amputee assembling electrical circuit, horiz. 24c, Boy wearing Toronto splint, playing ball.

1972, Aug. 2   Perf. 13½x13

523	A211	12c green & brown	.25	.15
524	A211	18c orange & olive	1.25	.22
525	A211	24c brown & ultra	.50	.22
		Nos. 523-525 (3)	2.00	.59

Rehabilitation of the handicapped.

Overland Telegraph Line — A212

1972, Aug. 22   Photo.   Perf. 13x13½

526	A212	7c dk red, blk & lemon	.25	.15

Centenary of overland telegraph line.

Athlete, Olympic Rings — A213

1972, Aug. 28   Perf. 13½x13

527	A213	7c shown	.15	.15
528	A213	7c Swimming	.15	.15
529	A213	7c Rowing	.15	.15
530	A213	35c Equestrian	4.50	4.25
		Nos. 527-530 (4)	4.95	4.70

20th Olympic Games, Munich, Aug. 26-Sept. 11.

Abacus, Numerals, Computer Circuits A214

1972, Oct. 16   Photo.   Perf. 13x13½

531	A214	7c multicolored	.20	.15

10th Intl. Congress of Accountants.

19th Cent. Combine Harvester A215

Perf. 13½x13, 13x13½

1972, Nov. 15   Photo.

532	A215	5c Pioneer family, vert.	.16	.15
533	A215	10c Water pump, vert.	.48	.15
534	A215	15c shown	.30	.15
535	A215	40c Pioneer house	.65	.28
536	A215	50c Cobb & Co. coach	1.10	.32
537	A215	60c Early Morse key, vert.	1.00	.55
538	A215	80c Paddle-wheel steamer	1.10	.45
		Nos. 532-538 (7)	4.79	2.05

Australian pioneer life.

Jesus and Children — A216

Dove, Cross and "Darkness into Light" — A217

Metric Conversion, Mass — A218

Perf. 14½x14, 13½x13

1972, Nov. 29

539	A216	7c tan & multi	.35	.15
540	A217	35c blue & multi	9.00	9.00

Christmas.

1973, Mar. 7   Photo.   Perf. 14x14½

Metric conversion: No. 542, Temperature, horiz. No. 543, Length. No. 544, Volume.

541	A218	7c pale vio & multi	.80	.20
542	A218	7c yellow & multi	.80	.20
543	A218	7c yel green & multi	.80	.20
544	A218	7c brt rose & multi	.80	.20
		Nos. 541-544 (4)	3.20	.80

Conversion to metric system.

Stylized Caduceus and Laurel — A219

1973, Apr. 4   Photo.   Perf. 14½x14

545	A219	7c dk bl, emer & lil rose	.25	.15

WHO, 25th anniv.

Dame Mary Gilmore, Writer A220

Shipping Industry A221

Famous Australians: No. 547, William Charles Wentworth, explorer. No. 548, Sir Isaac Isaacs, lawyer, first Australian-born Governor-General. No. 549, Marcus Clarke, writer.

Engr. & Litho.

1973, May 16   Perf. 15x14

546	A220	7c bister & black	1.25	.15
547	A220	7c bister & black	1.25	.15
548	A220	7c black & violet	1.25	.15
549	A220	7c black & violet	1.25	.15
	a.	Block of 4, #546-549	5.00	
		Set value		.48

1973, June 6   Photo.   Perf. 13½x13

Designs: 25c, Iron ore and steel. 30c, Truck convoy (beef road). 35c, Aerial mapping.

550	A221	20c ultra & multi	2.25	2.25
551	A221	25c red & multi	1.90	1.90
552	A221	30c ol brn & multi	2.50	2.50
553	A221	35c olive & multi	3.50	3.50
		Nos. 550-553 (4)	10.15	10.15

Australian economic development.

Banded Coral Shrimp A222

Chrysoprase A223

Helichrysum Thomsonii A223a

Wombat A224

Radio Astronomy A225

Red Gums of the Far North, by Hans Heysen — A226

Coming South (Immigrants), by Tom Roberts — A226a

Paintings: $1, Sergeant of Light Horse, by George Lambert. No. 575, On the Wallaby Track. $4, Shearing the Rams, by Tom Roberts. No. 577, McMahon's Point, by Arthur Streeton. No. 578, Mentone.

Perf. 14x15, 15x14 (A222, A223, A223a); Perf. 14x14½ (A224); Perf. 13x13½ (A225, A226, $1)

1973-84   Photo.

554	A222	1c shown	.15	.15
555	A222	2c Fiddler crab	.15	.15
556	A222	3c Coral crab	.15	.15
557	A222	4c Mauve stinger	.15	.15
558	A223	6c shown	.15	.15
559	A223	7c Agate	.15	.15
560	A223	8c Opal	.15	.15
561	A223	9c Rhodonite	.15	.15
562	A223	10c Star sapphire ('74)	.15	.15
563	A225	11c Atomic absorption spectrophotometry ('75)	.55	.25
564	A223a	18c shown ('75)	.50	.15
565	A224	20c shown ('74)	.40	.15
566	A225	24c shown ('75)	1.00	.40
567	A224	25c Spiny anteater ('74)	1.25	.35
568	A224	30c Brushtail possum ('74)	.70	.20
569	A225	33c Immunology ('75)	1.00	1.00
570	A223a	45c Callistemon teretifolius, horiz. ('75)	.65	.25
571	A225	48c Oceanography ('75)	1.75	1.10
572	A224	75c Feather-tailed glider ('74)	1.25	.75
573	A226a	$1 multi ('74)	1.50	.25
574	A226	$2 shown ('74)	2.75	.30
575	A226	$2 multi ('81)	2.50	.30
576	A226	$4 multi ('74)	5.00	2.25

Litho.

Perf. 14½

577	A226a	$5 multi ('79)	7.00	2.00
578	A226	$5 multi ('84)	6.00	1.25
579	A226a	$10 shown ('77)	12.00	3.25
		Nos. 554-579 (26)	47.15	15.55

Issued: 1c-9c, 7/11; 20c, 25c, 30c, 75c, 2/13; $1, #574, 4/24; 10c, 10/16; 11c, 24c, 33c, 48c, 5/14; 18c, 45c, 8/27; $10, 10/19; #577, 3/14; #575, 6/17; #578, 4/4.

No. 560 Surcharged in Red

9c

Perf. 15x14

580	A223	9c on 8c multi ('74)	.20	.15

Hand Protecting Playing Children A227

1973, Sept. 5   Photo.   Perf. 13x13½

581	A227	7c bis brn, grn & plum	.25	.15

50th anniv. of Legacy, an ex-servicemen's organization concerned with the welfare of widows and children of servicemen.

Baptism of Christ A228

The Good Shepherd A229

1973, Oct. 3   Perf. 14x14½

582	A228	7c gold & multi	.30	.15
	a.	Perf 14x15	4.00	.60

Perf. 13½

583	A229	30c gold & multi	3.75	4.25

Christmas.

Buchanan's Hotel, Townsville — A230

St. James' Church, Sydney — A231

Designs: 7c, Opera House, Sydney. 40c, Como House, Melbourne.

1973, Oct. 17   Photo.   *Perf. 14¹/₂x14*
584 A230 7c lt blue & ultra   .40   .15
 a. Perf. 15x14   4.00   .80
585 A230 10c bister & black   .60   .35

Perf. 13x13¹/₂, 13¹/₂x13
586 A230 40c dl pink, gray & blk   .75 1.00
587 A231 50c gray & multi   2.00 2.00
        Nos. 584-587 (4)   3.75 3.50

Australian architecture; opening of the Sydney Opera House, Oct. 14, 1973 (No. 584).

Radio and Gramophone Speaker
A232

1973, Nov. 21   Photo.   *Perf. 13¹/₂x13*
588 A232 7c dull blue, blk & brn   .25   .15

Broadcasting in Australia, 50th anniv.

Supreme Court Judge on Bench
A233

Australian Football
A234

1974, May 15   Photo.   *Perf. 14x14¹/₂*
589 A233 7c multicolored   .25   .15

150th anniv. of the proclamation of the Charter of Justice in New South Wales and Van Diemen's Land (Australia's Third Charter).

1974, July 24   Photo.   *Perf. 14x14¹/₂*
590 A234 7c shown   .35   .15
591 A234 7c Cricket   .35   .15
592 A234 7c Golf   .35   .15
593 A234 7c Surfing   .35   .15
594 A234 7c Tennis   .35   .15
595 A234 7c Bowls, horiz.   .35   .15
596 A234 7c Rugby, horiz.   .35   .15
        Nos. 590-596 (7)   2.45 1.05

Carrier Pigeon — A235

Designs: 30c, Carrier pigeons, vert.

1974, Oct. 9   Photo.   *Perf. 14¹/₂x14*
597 A235 7c multicolored   .25   .15
 a. Perf 15x14   .75   .15

Perf. 13¹/₂x13
598 A235 30c multicolored   1.00 1.00

UPU, cent. A booklet containing a strip of 5 each of Nos. 597-598 was produced and sold for $4 Australian by the National Stamp Week Promotion Council with government approval.

William Charles Wentworth
A236

Adoration of the Kings, by Dürer
A237

Typo. & Litho.

1974, Oct. 9   *Perf. 14x15*
599 A236 7c bister & black   .35   .15
 a. Perf 14x14¹/₂   .90   .25

Sesquicentennial of 1st Australian independent newspaper. W. C. Wentworth and Dr. Robert Wardell were the editors and the "A" is type from masthead of "The Australian."

1974, Nov. 13   Engr.   *Perf. 14x14¹/₂*
Christmas: 35c, Flight into Egypt, by Albrecht Dürer.

600 A237 10c buff & black   .22   .15
601 A237 35c buff & black   .90   .90

Pre-school Education
A238

Correspondence Schools
A239

Science Education
A240

Advanced Education — A241

Perf. 13x13¹/₂, 13¹/₂x13

1974, Nov. 20   Photo.
602 A238 5c multicolored   .25   .15
603 A239 11c multicolored   .38   .28
604 A240 40c multicolored   .40   .30
605 A241 60c multicolored   1.00   .95
        Nos. 602-605 (4)   2.03 1.68

"Avoid Pollution"
A242

"Road Safety"
A243

Design: No. 607, "Avoid bush fires."

1975, Jan. 29   Photo.   *Perf. 14¹/₂x14*
606 A242 10c multicolored   .30   .15
 a. Perf. 15x14   7.50 3.75
607 A242 10c multicolored   .30   .15
 a. Perf. 15x14   1.50 1.00

Perf. 14x14¹/₂
608 A243 10c multicolored   .30   .15
        Nos. 606-608 (3)   .90   .45

Environmental dangers.

Symbols of Womanhood, Sun, Moon
A244

Joseph B. Chifley (1885-1951)
A245

1975, Mar. 12   Photo.   *Perf. 14x14¹/₂*
609 A244 10c dk vio blue & grn   .25   .15

International Women's Year.

1975, Mar. 26
610 A245 10c shown   .20   .15
611 A245 10c John Curtin, 1885-
            1945   .20   .15
612 A245 10c Arthur W. Fadden,
            1895-1973   .20   .15

---

613 A245 10c Joseph A. Lyons,
            1879-1939   .20   .15
614 A245 10c Earle Page, 1880-1963   .20   .15
615 A245 10c John H. Scullin, 1876-
            1953   .20   .15
        Nos. 610-615 (6)   1.20
        Set value   .60

Australian Prime Ministers.

Australia Post
Australian Postal Commission
A246

Design: No. 617, Australian Telecommunications Commission.

1975, July 1   Photo.   *Perf. 14¹/₂x14*
616 A246 10c red, black & gray   .40   .20
 a. Perf. 15x14   .50   .25
617 A246 10c yel, black & gray   .40   .20
 a. Pair, #616-617   .95   .75
 b. Perf. 15x14   .50   .25
 c. Pair, #616a, 617b   1.25 1.00

Formation of Australian Postal and Telecommunications Commissions. Printed checkerwise.

Edith Cowan, Judge and Legislator
A247

Truganini, Last Tasmanian Aborigine
A248

Portraits: No. 619, Louisa Lawson (1848-1920), journalist. No. 620, Ethel Florence (Henry Handel) Richardson (1870-1946), novelist. No. 621, Catherine Spence (1825-1910), teacher, journalist, voting reformer. No. 622, Emma Constance Stone (1856-1902), first Australian woman physician.

1975, Aug. 6   Photo.   *Perf. 14x14¹/₂*
618 A247 10c olive grn & multi   .32   .32
 a. Perf 14x15   .35   .35
619 A247 10c yel bister & multi   .32   .32
 a. Perf 14x15   .35   .35
620 A248 10c olive & multi   .32   .32
 a. Perf 14x15   .35   .35
621 A248 10c gray & multi   .32   .32
 a. Perf 14x15   .35   .35
622 A247 10c violet & multi   .32   .32
 a. Perf 14x15   .35   .35
623 A248 10c brown & multi   .32   .32
 a. Perf 14x15   .35   .35
        Nos. 618-623 (6)   1.92 1.92

Famous Australian women.

Spirit House (PNG) and Sydney Opera House — A249

Bird in Flight and Southern Cross — A250

1975, Sept. 16   Photo.   *Perf. 13¹/₂*
624 A249 18c multicolored   .40   .15
625 A250 25c multicolored   .75   .55

Papua New Guinea independence, Sept. 16, 1975.

Adoration of the Kings — A251

"The Light Shineth in the Darkness" — A252

1975, Oct. 29   Photo.   *Perf. 14¹/₂x14*
626 A251 15c multicolored   .30   .15
627 A252 45c silver & multi   1.50 1.50

Christmas.

Australian Coat of Arms — A253

Two Types of A253:
Type I - Kangaroo: eye is dot, right paw has 1 toe, left foot has 1 toe. Emu: feet have 1 toe.
Type II - Kangaroo: eye is line, right paw has 3 toes, left foot has 2 toes. Emu: feet have 2 toes. Other differences exist.

1976, Jan. 5   Photo.   *Perf. 14¹/₂x14*
628 A253 18c multicolored, type I   .40   .15
 a. Type II   .75   .25

"Williams' Coffin" Telephone, 1878 — A254

1976, Mar. 10   Photo.   *Perf. 13¹/₂*
629 A254 18c buff & multi   .35   .18

Centenary of first telephone call by Alexander Graham Bell, Mar. 10, 1876.

John Oxley — A255

Designs: Australian explorers.

1976, June 9   Photo.   *Perf. 13¹/₂*
630 A255 18c shown   .25   .16
631 A255 18c Hamilton Hume and
            William Hovell   .25   .16
632 A255 18c John Forrest   .25   .16
633 A255 18c Ernest Giles   .25   .16
634 A255 18c Peter Warburton   .25   .16
635 A255 18c William Gosse   .25   .16
        Nos. 630-635 (6)   1.50   .96

Survey Rule, Graph, Punched Tape — A256

1976, June 15   *Perf. 15x14*
636 A256 18c multicolored   .30   .18

Commonwealth Scientific and Industrial Research Organization, 50th anniv.

Soccer Goalkeeper
A257

Olympic Rings and: No. 638, Woman gymnast, vert. 25c, Woman diver, vert. 40c, Bicycling.

Perf. 13x13¹/₂, 13¹/₂x13
1976, July 14   Photo.
637 A257 18c multicolored   .30   .15
638 A257 18c multicolored   .30   .15
639 A257 25c multicolored   .45   .40
640 A257 40c multicolored   .65   .50
        Nos. 637-640 (4)   1.70 1.20

21st Olympic Games, Montreal, Canada, July 17-Aug. 1.

"AT HOME" AUCTIONS
Every Week!
The WORLD'S LARGEST
MAIL-BID
AUCTION COMPANY

If you need it we have it!

From delightful topical stamp collections to serious specialist studies. From multi-volume world collections to cigarette cards. From huge boxes with hidden gems to silk flags dropped over Java during World War II!

Why buy from Postal Auctions?

Even the richest and most enthusiastic collector would find it impossible to attend a mere fraction of the stamp auctions that take place throughout the world.

Thousands of overseas buyers choose us *(in fact most of our clients live outside the UK)* because we offer the widest choice of material from all over the world at the most competetive estimates.

Buy in comfort from your Home, Office, Aircraft or Train

Snatch a minute to buy from the World's largest weekly source of interesting and unusual lots - it just couldn't be easier, safer or more enjoyable.

The Ultimate Source of World Stamps

Our weekly auction catalogue has been designed to fit into your pocket, ensure you carry it with you wherever you go. You never quite know when you may decide to participate in one of the greatest stamp auctions, in the World!

Sandafayre Limited
Knutsford
Cheshire
WA16 8XN
UK

AFFIX
POSTAGE
HERE

Richmond Bridge,
Tasmania
A258

Mt. Buffalo,
Victoria
A259

Designs: 25c, Broken Bay, New South Wales. 35c, Wittenoom Gorge, Western Australia. 70c, Barrier Reef, Queensland. 85c, Ayers Rock, Northern Territory.

Perf. 14¹/₂x14, 14x14¹/₂

1976, Aug. 25			**Photo.**		
641	A258	5c multicolored		.25	.15
642	A258	25c multicolored		.45	.20
643	A258	35c multicolored		.42	.30
644	A259	50c multicolored		.65	.25
645	A258	70c multicolored		.80	.35
646	A258	85c multicolored		1.25	1.00
		Nos. 641-646 (6)		3.82	2.25

Blamire Young and
Australia No. 59 — A260

1976, Sept. 27		**Photo.**	**Perf. 13¹/₂**	
647	A260	18c apple green & multi	.35	.15
Miniature Sheet				
648		Sheet of 4	1.65	1.50
a.		A260 18c yellow & dark brown	.38	.35
b.		A260 18c rose, dk brown & yel	.38	.35
c.		A260 18c blue, dk brn, rose & yel	.38	.35

Natl. Stamp Week, Sept. 27-Oct. 3. Blamire Young (1862-1935), designer of Australia's 1st issue. No. 648 shows different stages of 4-color printing. The 4th stamp in sheet is identical with No. 647.

Virgin and
Child, after
Simone
Cantarini
A261

Holly, Toy
Koala,
Christmas Tree
and Decoration,
Partridge
A262

1976, Nov. 1		**Photo.**	**Perf. 14¹/₂x14**	
649	A261	15c brt car & lt blue	.32	.20
		Perf. 13¹/₂		
650	A262	45c multicolored	.80	.75
		Christmas.		

John Gould (1804-
1881) Ornithologist
A263

Violinists
A264

Famous Australians: No. 652, Thomas Laby (1880-1946), nuclear scientist. No. 653, Sir Baldwin Spencer (1860-1929), anthropologist (aborigines). No. 654, Griffith Taylor (1880-1963), geographer and arctic explorer.

1976, Nov. 10		**Perf. 15x14**		
651	A263	18c shown	.30	.18
652	A263	18c Laby	.30	.18
653	A263	18c Spencer	.30	.18
654	A263	18c Taylor	.30	.18
		Nos. 651-654 (4)	1.20	.72

1977, Jan. 19		**Photo.**	**Perf. 14x14¹/₂**	
655	A264	20c shown	.35	.20
656	A264	30c Dramatic scene	.42	.20
657	A264	40c Dancer	.70	.40
658	A264	60c Opera singer	.90	.20
		Nos. 655-658 (4)	2.37	1.00

Performing arts in Australia.

Elizabeth II
A265

Wicket Keeper, Slip
Fieldsman
A266

Design: 45c, Elizabeth II and Prince Philip.

1977, Feb. 2				
659	A265	18c multicolored	.30	.15
660	A265	45c multicolored	.75	.75

Reign of Queen Elizabeth II, 25th anniv.

1977, Mar. 9		**Photo.**	**Perf. 13¹/₂**	

Cricket match, 19th century: No. 662, Umpire and batsman. No. 663, Two fieldsmen. No. 664, Batsman and umpire. No. 665, Bowler and fieldsman. 45c, Batsman facing bowler.

661	A266	18c gray & multi	.35	.25
662	A266	18c gray & multi	.35	.25
663	A266	18c gray & multi	.35	.25
664	A266	18c gray & multi	.35	.25
665	A266	18c gray & multi	.35	.25
a.		Strip of 5, #661-665	2.00	2.00
666	A266	45c gray & multi	.90	.90
		Nos. 661-666 (6)	2.65	2.15

Parliament
House, Canberra
A267

1977, Apr. 13		**Perf. 14¹/₂x14**		
667	A267	18c multicolored	.40	.15

Parliament House, Canberra, 50th anniv.

Trade Union
Workers
A268

1977, May 9		**Photo.**	**Perf. 13**	
668	A268	18c multicolored	.35	.15

Australian Council of Trade Unions (ACTU), 50th anniv.

Surfing
Santa — A269

Virgin and
Child — A270

1977, Oct. 31		**Photo.**	**Perf. 14x14¹/₂**	
669	A269	15c multicolored	.35	.15
		Perf. 13¹/₂x13		
670	A270	45c multicolored	.75	.75
		Christmas.		

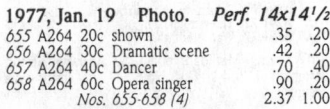

Australian
Flag — A271

1978, Jan. 26		**Photo.**	**Perf. 13x13¹/₂**	
671	A271	18c multicolored	.35	.15

Australia Day, 190th anniversary of first permanent settlement in New South Wales.

Harry Hawker
and Sopwith
"Camel"
A272

Australian Aviators and their Planes: No. 673, Bert Hinkler and Avro Avian. No. 674, Charles Kingsford-Smith and Fokker "Southern Cross." No. 675, Charles Ulm and "Southern Cross."

1978, Apr. 19		**Litho.**	**Perf. 15¹/₂**	
672	A272	18c ultra & multi	.30	.15
673	A272	18c blue & multi	.30	.15
674	A272	18c orange & multi	.30	.15
675	A272	18c yellow & multi	.30	.15
a.		Souv. sheet, 2 each #674-675, imperf.	1.65	1.65
		Nos. 672-675 (4)	1.20	.60

No. 675a for 50th anniv. of first Trans-Pacific flight from Oakland, Cal., to Brisbane.

Beechcraft
Baron Landing
A273

1978, May 15		**Photo.**	**Perf. 13¹/₂**	
676	A273	18c multicolored	.30	.20

Royal Flying Doctor Service, 50th anniv.

Illawarra Flame
Tree — A274

Sturt's Desert
Rose, Map of
Australia — A275

Australian trees: 25c, Ghost gum. 40c, Grass tree. 45c, Cootamundra wattle.

1978, June 1				
677	A274	18c multicolored	.18	.15
678	A274	25c multicolored	.60	.60
679	A274	40c multicolored	.70	1.10
680	A274	45c multicolored	.65	1.00
		Nos. 677-680 (4)	2.13	2.85

1978, June 19		**Litho.**	**Perf. 15¹/₂**	
681	A275	18c multicolored	.35	.18

Establishment of Government of the Northern Territory.

Hooded
Dotterel — A276

Australian birds: 20c, Little grebe. 25c, Spurwing Plover. 30c, Pied oystercatcher. 55c, Lotus bird.

1978		**Photo.**	**Perf. 13¹/₂**	
682	A276	5c multicolored	.15	.15
683	A276	20c multicolored	.25	.15
684	A276	25c multicolored	.35	.15
685	A276	30c multicolored	.40	.30
686	A276	55c multicolored	.70	.50
		Nos. 682-686 (5)	1.85	
		Set value		1.10

Issued: Nos. 683, 686, July 3; others, July 17. See Nos. 713-718, 732-739, 768.

Australia No. 95
on Album
Page — A277

Virgin and Child, by
Simon
Marmion — A278

1978, Sept. 25		**Litho.**	**Perf. 15¹/₂**	
687	A277	20c multicolored	.38	.15
a.		Miniature sheet of 4	1.65	1.65

National Stamp Week; 50th anniv. of Melbourne Intl. Phil. Exhib., Oct. 1928.

1978		**Perf. 15**	

Paintings from National Gallery, Victoria: 15c, Virgin and Child, after Van Eyck. 55c, Holy Family, by Perino del Vaga.

688	A278	15c multicolored	.22	.15
689	A278	25c multicolored	.50	.52
690	A278	55c multicolored	.80	.80
		Nos. 688-690 (3)	1.52	1.47

Christmas. Issued: 25c, Oct. 3, others, Nov. 1.

Tulloch
A279

Race horses: 35c, Bernborough, vert. 50c, Phar Lap, vert. 55c, Peter Pan.

Perf. 15x14, 14x15

1978, Oct. 18			**Photo.**	
691	A279	20c multicolored	.28	.15
692	A279	35c multicolored	.52	.55
693	A279	50c multicolored	.75	.80
694	A279	55c multicolored	.75	.90
		Nos. 691-694 (4)	2.30	2.40

Australian horse racing.

Flag Raising at Sydney
Cove — A280

1979, Jan. 26		**Litho.**	**Perf. 15¹/₂**	
695	A280	20c multicolored	.35	.18

Australia Day, Jan. 26.

Passenger
Steamer
Canberra
A281

Ferries and Murray River Steamers: 35c, M.V. Lady Denman. 50c, P.S. Murray River Queen. 55c, Hydrofoil Curl Curl.

1979, Feb. 14		**Photo.**	**Perf. 13¹/₂**	
696	A281	20c multicolored	.32	.15
697	A281	35c multicolored	.52	.40
698	A281	50c multicolored	.75	.65
699	A281	55c multicolored	.80	.85
		Nos. 696-699 (4)	2.39	2.05

Port Campbell
Australia 20c A282

Designs: Australian National Parks.

1979, Apr. 9   Litho.   Perf. 15½
700	A282	20c shown	.30	.15
701	A282	20c Uluru	.30	.15
702	A282	20c Royal	.30	.15
703	A282	20c Flinders Ranges	.30	.15
704	A282	20c Namburg	.30	.15
a.		Strip of 5, #700-704	1.50	
705	A282	20c Girraween, vert.	.30	.15
706	A282	20c Mount Field, vert.	.30	.15
a.		Pair, #705-706	.60	
		Nos. 700-706 (7)	2.10	
		Set value		.70

Double
Fairlie — A283

Australian steam locomotives: 35c, Puffing Billy.
50c, Pichi Richi. 55c, Zig Zag.

Perf. 13½, 15x14 (20c)
1979, May 16   Photo.
707	A283	20c multicolored	.35	.15
708	A283	35c multicolored	.65	.40
709	A283	50c multicolored	.90	.75
710	A283	55c multicolored	.95	1.00
		Nos. 707-710 (4)	2.85	2.30

"Black
Swan" — A284

1979, June 6   Photo.   Perf. 13½
711	A284	20c multicolored	.38	.20

150th anniversary of Western Australia.

Children
Playing, IYC
Emblem
A285

1979, Aug. 13   Litho.   Perf. 13½x13
712	A285	20c multicolored	.30	.20

International Year of the Child.

Bird Type of 1978

Australian birds: 1c, Zebra finch. 2c, Crimson
finch. 15c, Forest kingfisher, vert. 20c, Eastern yellow robin. 40c, Lovely wren, vert. 50c, Flame
robin, vert.

1979, Sept. 17   Photo.   Perf. 13½
713	A276	1c multicolored	.15	.15
714	A276	2c multicolored	.15	.15
715	A276	15c multicolored	.30	.15
716	A276	20c multicolored	.30	.15
717	A276	40c multicolored	.50	.20
718	A276	50c multicolored	.70	.20
		Nos. 713-718 (6)	2.10	
		Set value		.65

Christmas 1979
AUSTRALIA   **25c**
Christmas Letters,
Flag-wrapped
Parcels
A286

Trout Fishing
A287

Christmas: 15c, Nativity, icon. 55c, Madonna
and Child, by Buglioni.

1979   Litho.   Perf. 13
719	A286	15c multicolored	.15	.15
720	A286	25c multicolored	.30	.30
721	A286	55c multicolored	.90	.90
		Nos. 719-721 (3)	1.35	1.35

Issue dates: 25c, Sept. 24. Others, Nov. 1.

1979, Oct. 24   Photo.   Perf. 14x14½

Sport fishing: 35c, Angler. 50c, Black marlin fishing. 55c, Surf fishing.

722	A287	20c multicolored	.28	.15
723	A287	35c multicolored	.48	.48
724	A287	50c multicolored	.70	.48
725	A287	55c multicolored	.75	.70
		Nos. 722-725 (4)	2.21	1.81

Matthew
Flinders, Map of
Australia
A288

1980, Jan. 23   Litho.   Perf. 13½
726	A288	20c multicolored	.30	.15

Australia Day, Jan. 28.

Dingo — A289

1980, Feb. 20   Litho.   Perf. 13½x13
727	A289	20c shown	.30	.20
728	A289	25c Border collie	.32	.35
729	A289	35c Australian terrier	.60	.40
730	A289	50c Australian cattle dog	.80	.70
731	A289	55c Australian kelpie	.65	.70
		Nos. 727-731 (5)	2.67	2.35

Bird Type of 1978
Perf. 13½, 14x15 (22c), 13x12½
(28c, 60c)
1980   Litho., Photo. (22c)
732	A276	10c Golden-shoulder par-rot, vert.	.15	.15
a.		Perf. 14½x14	1.25	.50
733	A276	22c White-tailed kingfisher, vert.	.30	.15
734	A276	28c Rainbow bird, vert.	.45	.15
735	A276	35c Regent bower bird, vert.	.45	.20
736	A276	45c Masked woodswallow	.95	.20
a.		Perf. 14x14½	4.00	2.00
737	A276	60c King parrot, vert.	.75	.25
738	A276	80c Rainbow pitta	1.00	.40
739	A276	$1 Western magpie, vert.	1.25	.30
		Nos. 732-739 (8)	5.30	1.80

Issued: #733, 734, 737, Mar. 31; others, July 1.

Queen Elizabeth II, 54th
Australia   **22c**   Birthday — A290

1980, Apr. 21   Litho.   Perf. 13x13½
740	A290	22c multicolored	.35	.15

Wanderer
A291

High Court
Building, Canberra
A292

1980, May 7   Litho.   Perf. 13x13½
741		Strip of 5	1.75	1.50
a.	A291	22c shown	.32	.15
b.	A291	22c Stealing sheep	.32	.15

---

c.	A291	22c Squatter on horseback	.32	.15
d.	A291	22c Three troopers	.32	.15
e.	A291	22c Wanderer's ghost	.32	.15

"Waltzing Matilda", poem by Andrew Barton
Patterson (1864-1941). No. 741 in continuous
design.

1980, May 19
742	A292	22c multicolored	.38	.15

Opening of High Court of Australia Building,
Canberra, May 26.

Salvation Army
Officers — A294

Perf. 13x13½, 13½x13
1980, Aug. 11
747	A294	22c shown	.32	.15
748	A294	22c St. Vincent de Paul So-ciety, vert.	.32	.15
749	A294	22c Meals on Wheels, vert.	.32	.15
750	A294	22c "Life. Be in it." (Jog-gers, bicyclists)	.32	.15
		Nos. 747-750 (4)	1.28	
		Set value		.48

Mailman c.
1900 — A295

Holy Family, by
Prospero
Fontana — A296

1980, Sept. 29   Litho.   Perf. 13x13½
751	A295	22c Mailbox	.35	.16
752	A295	22c shown	.35	.16
753	A295	22c Mail truck	.35	.16
754	A295	22c Mailman, mailbox	.35	.16
755	A295	22c Mailman, diff.	.35	.16
a.		Souvenir sheet of 3	1.25	1.00
b.		Strip of 5, #751-755	1.75	1.00

Natl. Stamp Week, Sept. 29-Oct. 5. #755a contains stamps similar to #751, 753, 755.

1980   Perf. 13x13½

Christmas: 15c, Virgin Enthroned, by Justin
O'Brien. 60c, Virgin and Child, by Michael Zuern
the Younger, 1680.

756	A296	15c multicolored	.22	.15
757	A296	28c multicolored	.45	.45
758	A296	60c multicolored	.90	.65
		Nos. 756-758 (3)	1.57	1.25

Issued: 15c, 60c, Nov. 3; 28c, Oct. 1.

CA-6 Wackett
Trainer,
1941 — A297

Designs: Australian military training planes.

1980, Nov. 19   Perf. 13½x14
759	A297	22c shown	.32	.32
760	A297	40c Winjeel, 1955	.60	.60
761	A297	45c Boomerang, 1944	.65	.52
762	A297	60c Nomad, 1975	1.00	.60
		Nos. 759-762 (4)	2.57	2.04

Bird Type of 1978
1980, Nov. 17   Litho.   Perf. 13½
768	A276	18c Spotted catbird, vert.	.35	.15

Flag on Map
of Australia
A298   **22c**

1981, Jan. 21
771	A298	22c multicolored	.35	.15

Australia Day, Jan. 21.

Jockey Darby Munro
(1913-1966), by Tony
Rafty — A299

Australian sportsmen (Cariacutres by Tony Rafty):
35c, Victor Trumper (1877-1915), cricket batsman.
55c, Norman Brookes (1877-1968), tennis player.
60c, Walter Lindrum (1898-1960), billiards player.

1981, Feb. 18   Perf. 14x14½
772	A299	22c multicolored	.25	.15
773	A299	35c multicolored	.45	.45
774	A299	55c multicolored	.65	.65
775	A299	60c multicolored	.75	.75
		Nos. 772-775 (4)	2.10	2.00

Australia
No. C2 and
Cover — A300

Perf. 13x13½, 13½x13
1981, Mar. 25   Litho.
776	A300	22c Australia No. C2, vert.	.30	.25
777	A300	60c shown	.90	.80

Australia-United Kingdom official airmail service,
50th anniv.

Map of
Australia, APEX
Emblem
A301

1981, Apr. 6   Photo.   Perf. 13x13½
778	A301	22c multicolored	.30	.15

50th anniv. of APEX (young men's service club).

Queen
Elizabeth's
Personal Flag of
Australia
A302

1981, Apr. 21   Perf. 13
779	A302	22c multicolored	.35	.15

Queen Elizabeth II, 55th birthday.

License Inspected,
Forrest Creek, by S.T.
Gill — A303

Gold Rush Era (Sketches by S.T. Gill): No. 781,
Puddling. No. 782, Quality of Washing Stuff. No.
783, Diggers on Route to Deposit Gold.

1981, May 20   Photo.   Perf. 13x13½
780	A303	22c multicolored	.30	.15
781	A303	22c multicolored	.30	.15
782	A303	22c multicolored	.30	.15
783	A303	22c multicolored	.30	.15
		Nos. 780-783 (4)	1.20	.60

Lace
Monitor — A303a

Tasmanian
Tiger — A304

Two Types of A304:
Type I - Indistinct line at right of ear, stripes even
with base of tail.
Type II - Heavy line at right of ear, stripes longer.

1981-83   **Litho.**

784	A303a	1c shown	.15	.15
785	A303a	3c Corroboree frog	.15	.15
786	A304	5c Queensland hairy-nosed wombat, vert.	.15	.15
787	A303a	15c Eastern snake-necked tortoise	.20	.15
788	A304	24c shown, type I	.35	.18
a.		Type II		
789	A304	25c Greater bilby, vert.	.35	.18
790	A303a	27c Blue Mountains tree frog	.40	.20
791	A304	30c Bridled nail-tailed wallaby, vert.	.42	.22
792	A303a	40c Smooth knob-tailed gecko	.55	.28
793	A304	50c Leadbeater's opossum	.85	.40
794	A304	55c Stick-nest rat, vert.	.85	.42
795	A303a	65c Yellow-faced whip snake	1.00	.48
796	A303a	70c Crucifix toad	1.10	.55
797	A303a	75c Eastern water dragon	1.10	.55
798	A303a	85c Centralian blue-tongued lizard	1.25	.65
799	A303a	90c Freshwater crocodile	1.40	.70
800	A303a	95c Thorny devil	1.50	.75
		Nos. 784-800 (17)	11.77	6.16

Perfs: 1c, 70c, 85c, 95c, 13½; 3c, 15c, 27c, 40c, 50c, 65c, 75c, 90c, 12½x13; 5c, 25c, 30c, 55c, 13x12½; 24c, 13x13½.

Issued: 24c, 7/1/81; 5c, 25c, 30c, 50c, 55c, 7/15/81; 3c, 27c, 65c, 75c, 4/19/82; 15c, 40c, 90c, 6/16/82. 1c, 70c, 85c, 95c, 2/2/83.

1982-84   **Perf. 14x14½, 14½x14**

785a	A303a	3c ('84)	.32	.15
786a	A304	5c ('84)	.90	.15
787a	A303a	15c ('84)	.70	.25
789a	A304	25c ('83)	1.10	.20
790a	A303a	27c	.75	.24
792a	A303a	40c ('84)	2.00	.28
793a	A304	50c ('84)	1.25	.40
795a	A303a	65c ('84)	1.40	.60
797a	A303a	75c ('84)	1.50	.80
		Nos. 785a-797a (9)	9.92	3.07

Prince Charles and Lady Diana — A305

1981, July 29   **Litho.**   **Perf. 13**

804	A305	24c multicolored	.42	.15
805	A305	60c multicolored	1.15	.75

Royal Wedding.

Cortinarius Cinnabarinus A306

Intl. Year of the Disabled A307

Designs: Fungi.

1981, Aug. 19   **Litho.**   **Perf. 13**

806	A306	24c shown	.35	.15
807	A306	35c Coprinus comatus	.52	.52
808	A306	55c Armillaria luteobubalina	.95	.80
809	A306	60c Cortinarius austrovenetus	1.10	1.00
		Nos. 806-809 (4)	2.92	2.47

1981, Sept. 16   **Perf. 14x13½**

810	A307	24c multicolored	.40	.15

Christmas Bush for His Adorning A308

Globe A309

Christmas (Carols by William James and John Wheeler): 30c, The Silver Stars are in the Sky. 60c, Noeltime.

1981   **Litho.**   **Perf. 13x13½**

811	A308	18c multicolored	.35	.15
812	A308	30c multicolored	.50	.35
813	A308	60c multicolored	1.25	1.00
		Nos. 811-813 (3)	2.10	1.50

Issue dates: 30c, Sept. 28; others, Nov. 2.

1981, Sept. 30

814	A309	24c multicolored	.38	.15
815	A309	60c multicolored	1.00	.90

Commonwealth Heads of Government Meeting, Melbourne, Sept. 30-Oct. 7.

Yacht — A310

1981, Oct. 14   **Litho.**   **Perf. 13x13½**

816	A310	24c Ocean racer	.45	.15
817	A310	35c Lightweight sharpie	.60	.60
818	A310	55c 12-Meter	.90	.60
819	A310	60c Sabot	1.10	1.00
		Nos. 816-819 (4)	3.05	2.35

Australia Day, Jan. 26 — A311

1982, Jan. 20   **Litho.**   **Perf. 13x13½**

820	A311	24c multicolored	.40	.15

Sperm Whale — A312

Perf. 13x13½, 13½x13

1982, Feb. 17

821	A312	24c shown	.38	.15
822	A312	35c Southern right whale, vert.	.60	.60
823	A312	55c Blue whale, vert.	.90	.75
824	A312	60c Humpback whale	1.00	1.00
		Nos. 821-824 (4)	2.88	2.50

Elizabeth II, 56th Birthday — A313   Roses — A314

1982, Apr. 21   **Perf. 13½**

825	A313	27c multicolored	.42	.18

1982, May 19   **Perf. 13x13½**

826	A314	27c Marjorie Atherton	.40	.32
827	A314	40c Imp	.65	.60
828	A314	65c Minnie Watson	1.00	1.00
829	A314	75c Satellite	1.10	.95
		Nos. 826-829 (4)	3.15	2.87

50th Anniv. of Australian Broadcasting Commission A315

1982, June 16   **Perf. 13½x13**

830	A315	27c Announcer, microphone	.45	.25
831	A315	27c Emblem	.45	.25
a.		Pair, #830-831		.90

#830-831 se-tenant in continuous design.

Alice Springs Post Office, 1872 — A316

1982, Aug. 4   **Perf. 13½x14, 14x13½**

832	A316	27c shown	.38	.16
833	A316	27c Kingston, 1869	.38	.16
834	A316	27c York, 1893	.38	.16
835	A316	27c Flemington, 1890, vert.	.38	.16
836	A316	27c Forbes, 1881, vert.	.38	.16
837	A316	27c Launceston, 1889, vert.	.38	.16
838	A316	27c Rockhampton, 1892, vert.	.38	.16
		Nos. 832-838 (7)	2.66	1.12

Christmas — A317

1st Australian Christmas cards, 1881. 21c, horiz.

1982   **Litho.**   **Perf. 14½**

839	A317	21c multicolored	.35	.15
840	A317	35c multicolored	.60	.30
841	A317	75c multicolored	1.25	1.10
		Nos. 839-841 (3)	2.20	1.55

Issue dates: 35c, Sept. 15; others, Nov. 1.

12th Commonwealth Games, Brisbane, Sept. 30-Oct. 9 — A318

1982, Sept. 22   **Litho.**   **Perf. 14x14½**

842	A318	27c Archery	.45	.15
843	A318	27c Boxing	.45	.15
844	A318	27c Weightlifting	.45	.15
a.		Souvenir sheet of 3, #842-844	1.50	1.40
845	A318	75c Pole vault	.90	.90
		Nos. 842-845 (4)	2.25	1.35

Natl. Stamp Week — A319

1982, Sept. 27   **Perf. 13x13½**

846	A319	27c No. 132	.40	.15

A320

A321

Design: Gurgurr (Moon Spirit), Bark Painting by Yirawala Gunwinggu Tribe.

1982, Oct. 12   **Perf. 14½**

847	A320	27c multicolored	.40	.15

Opening of Natl. Gallery, Canberra.

Perf. 12½x13½

1982, Nov. 17   **Photo.**

Designs: Various eucalypts (gum trees).

848	A321	1c Pink-flowered marri	.15	.15
849	A321	2c Gungurru	.15	.15
850	A321	3c Red-flowering gum	1.00	.16
851	A321	10c Tasmanian blue gum	1.00	.25

852	A321	27c Forrest's marlock	.75	.50
a.		Bklt. pane of 9 + label (#850-851, 2 #848-849, 3 #852)	5.00	
b.		Bklt. pane (2 each #848-849, 852)	2.10	
		Nos. 848-852 (5)	3.05	1.21

Nos. 848-852 issued in booklets only.

Mimi Spirits Singing and Dancing, by David Milaybuma A322

Aboriginal Bark Paintings: Music and dance of the Mimi Spirits, Gunwinggu Tribe.

1982, Nov. 17   **Litho.**   **Perf. 13½x14**

853	A322	27c shown	.40	.25
854	A322	40c Lofty Nabardayal	.65	.65
855	A322	65c Jimmy Galareya	1.00	.75
856	A322	75c Dick Nguleingulei Murrumuru	1.10	1.00
		Nos. 853-856 (4)	3.15	2.65

Historic Fire Engines A323

1983, Jan. 12   **Perf. 13½x14**

857	A323	27c Shand Mason Steam, 1891	.40	.25
858	A323	40c Hotchkiss, 1914	.65	.65
859	A323	65c Ahrens-Fox PS2, 1929	1.00	1.00
860	A323	75c Merryweather Manual, 1851	1.10	1.00
		Nos. 857-860 (4)	3.15	2.90

Australia Day — A324

1983, Jan. 26   **Litho.**   **Perf. 14½**

861	A324	27c Sirius	.45	.25
862	A324	27c Supply	.45	.25
a.		Pair, #861-862	.90	.75

Australia 27c
A325

A326

1983, Feb. 2   **Perf. 14x13½**

863	A325	27c multicolored	.40	.15

Australia-New Zealand Closer Economic Relationship agreement (ANZCER).

1983, Mar. 9   **Litho.**   **Perf. 14½**

864	A326	27c Equality, dignity	.45	.20
865	A326	27c Social justice, cooperation	.45	.20
866	A326	27c Liberty, freedom	.45	.20
867	A326	75c Peace, harmony	1.25	1.25
		Nos. 864-867 (4)	2.60	1.85

Commonwealth day.

Queen Elizabeth II, 57th Birthday A327

1983, Apr. 20   **Perf. 14½**

868	A327	27c Britannia	.40	.15

World Communications Year — A328

1983, May 18   Litho.   Perf. 13¹/₂x14
869 A328 27c multicolored   .42 .15

50th Anniv. of Australian Jaycees Youth Organization A329

1983, June 8
870 A329 27c multicolored   .38 .15

St. John Ambulance Cent. — A330   Regent Skipper — A331

1983, June 8   Perf. 13¹/₂x14
871 A330 27c multicolored   .38 .15

1983   Perf. 13¹/₂, 14¹/₂x14 (30c)
872 A331   4c shown   .15 .15
873 A331 10c Cairn's birdwing   .15 .15
874 A331 20c Macleay's swallow-
                tail   .28 .15
875 A331 27c Ulysses   .42 .15
875A A331 30c Chlorinda hairstreak   .50 .16
876 A331 35c Blue tiger   .52 .20
877 A331 45c Big greasy   .60 .28
878 A331 60c Wood white   .85 .35
879 A331 80c Amaryllis azure   1.00 .40
880 A331 $1 Sword grass brown   1.25 .15
        Nos. 872-880 (10)   5.72 2.16

Issue dates: 30c, Oct. 24; others, June 15.

The Sentimental Bloke, by C.J. Dennis, 1909 — A332

Folktale scenes: a, The bloke. b, Doreen - the intro. c, The stror at coot. d, Hitched. e, The mooch of life.

1983, Aug. 3   Perf. 14¹/₂
881   Strip of 5   2.25 1.50
a.-e. A332 27c multi, any single   .45 .30

Kookaburra Bird Wearing Santa Hat — A333

1983   Litho.   Perf. 13¹/₂x14
882 A333 24c Nativity   .35 .35
883 A333 35c multicolored   .52 .35
884 A333 85c Holiday beach scene   1.25 .60
        Nos. 882-884 (3)   2.12 1.30

Christmas. Issued: #883, 9/14; #882, 884, 11/2.

Australia stamps can be mounted in the Scott Australia album.

Inland Explorers — A334

Clay sculptures by Dianne Quinn: No. 885, Ludwig Leichhardt (1813-48). No. 886, William John Wills (1834-61), Robert O'Hara Burke (1821-61). No. 887, Paul Edmund de Strzelecki (1797-1873). No. 888, Alexander Forrest (1849-1901).

1983, Sept. 26   Perf. 14¹/₂
885 A334 30c multicolored   .40 .16
886 A334 30c multicolored   .40 .16
887 A334 30c multicolored   .40 .16
888 A334 30c multicolored   .40 .16
        Nos. 885-888 (4)   1.60 .64

Australia Day — A335

1984, Jan. 26   Litho.   Perf. 13¹/₂x14
889 A335 30c Cooks' Cottage   .40 .18

50th Anniv. of Official Air Mail Service — A336

Designs: Pilot Charles Ulm (1898-1934); his plane, "Faith in Australia," and different flight covers.

1984, Feb. 22   Litho.   Perf. 13¹/₂
890 A336 45c Australia-New Zealand   1.00 .60
891 A336 45c Australia-Papua New
                Guinea   1.00 .60
a.   Pair, #890-891   2.00 1.50

Thomson, 1898 — A337

Australian-made vintage cars: b, Tarrant, 1906. c, Australian Six, 1919. d, Summit, 1923. e, Chic, 1924.

1984, Mar. 14   Perf. 14¹/₂
892   Strip of 5   2.25 1.50
a.-e. A337 30c any single   .45 .25

Queen Elizabeth II, 58th Birthday — A338

1984, Apr. 18   Perf. 14¹/₂
893 A338 30c multicolored   .42 .18

Clipper Ships — A339

Perf. 14x13¹/₂, 13¹/₂x14
1984, May 23
894 A339 30c Cutty Sark, 1869,
                vert.   .35 .30
895 A339 45c Orient, 1853   .55 .55
896 A339 75c Sobraon, 1866   .90 .90
897 A339 85c Thermopylae, 1868,
                vert.   1.10 1.10
        Nos. 894-897 (4)   2.90 2.85

Freestyle Skiing — A340   Coral Hopper — A341

1984, June 6   Litho.   Perf. 14¹/₂
898 A340 30c shown   .50 .20
899 A340 30c Slalom, horiz.   .50 .20
900 A340 30c Cross-country, horiz.   .50 .20
901 A340 30c Downhill   .50 .20
        Nos. 898-901 (4)   2.00 .80

Perf. 13¹/₂, 14x14¹/₂ (30c, 33c)
1984-86   Litho.
902 A341   2c shown   .15 .15
903 A341   3c Jimble   .15 .15
904 A341   5c Tasseled anglerfish   .15 .15
905 A341 10c Stonefish   .15 .15
906 A341 20c Red handfish   .25 .15
907 A341 25c Orange-tipped cowrie   .45 .25
908 A341 30c Choat's wrasse   .55 .20
909 A341 33c Leafy sea dragon   .45 .20
910 A341 40c Red velvet fish   .55 .20
911 A341 45c Textile cone shell   .65 .30
912 A341 50c Blue-lined surge-
                onfish   .90 .50
913 A341 55c Bennett's nudibranch   1.00 .50
914 A341 60c Lionfish   .85 .40
915 A341 65c Stingray   .95 .40
916 A341 70c Blue-ringed octopus   1.00 .50
917 A341 80c Pineapple fish   1.15 .55
918 A341 85c Regal angelfish   1.50 .95
919 A341 90c Crab-eyed goby   1.20 .55
920 A341 $1 Crown of thorns star-
                fish   1.50 .60
        Nos. 902-920 (19)   13.55 6.95

Issued: 2c, 25c, 30c, 50c, 55c, 85c, June 18; 5c, 20c, 40c, 80c, 90c, June 12, 1985; 3c, 10c, 45c, 60c, 65c, 70c, $1, June 11, 1986.

1984 Summer Olympics A342

Event stages.

Perf. 13¹/₂x14, 14x13¹/₂
1984, July 25   Litho.
922 A342 30c Start (facing down)   .45 .20
923 A342 30c Competing (facing
                right)   .45 .20
924 A342 30c Finish, vert.   .45 .20
        Nos. 922-924 (3)   1.35 .60

Ausipex '84 — A343   Christmas — A344

Designs: No. 926a, Victoria #3. b, New South Wales #1. c, Tasmania #1. d, South Australia #1. e, Western Australia #1. f, Queensland #3.

1984   Litho.   Perf. 14¹/₂
925 A343 30c No. 2   .45 .16
Souvenir Sheet
926   Sheet of 7   3.50 3.00
a.-f. A343 30c any single   .50 .20

#926 contains #925, 926a-926f. Issue dates: #925, Aug. 22; #926, Sept. 21.

1984   Litho.   Perf. 14x13¹/₂
927 A344 24c Angel and Child   .30 .25
928 A344 30c Veiled Virgin and
                Child   .35 .25
929 A344 40c Angel   .50 .40
930 A344 50c Three Kings   .65 .45
931 A344 85c Madonna and Child   1.10 1.00
        Nos. 927-931 (5)   2.90 2.35

Stained-glass windows. Issue dates: 40c, Sept. 17; others, Oct. 30.

European Settlement Bicentenary A345   Settlement of Victoria Sesquicentenary A346

Design: No. 932, Bicentennial Emblem.
Rock paintings: No. 933, Stick figures, Cobar Region, New South Wales. No. 934, Bunjil's Cave, Grampians, Western Victoria. No. 935, Quinkan Gallery, Cape York, Queensland. No. 936, Wandjina Spirit and Snake Babies, Gibb River, Western Australia. No. 937, Rock Python, Western Australia. No. 938, Silver Barramundi, Kakadu Natl. Park, Northern Territory. 85c, Rock Possum, Kakadu Natl. Park.

1984, Nov. 7   Litho.   Perf. 14¹/₂
932 A345 30c multicolored   .45 .25
933 A345 30c multicolored   .45 .25
934 A345 30c multicolored   .45 .25
935 A345 30c multicolored   .45 .25
936 A345 30c multicolored   .45 .25
937 A345 30c multicolored   .45 .25
938 A345 30c multicolored   .45 .25
939 A345 85c multicolored   1.25 .60
        Nos. 932-939 (8)   4.40 2.35

1984, Nov. 19
940 A346 30c Helmeted honeyeater   .45 .20
941 A346 30c Leadbeater's possum   .45 .20
a.   Pair, #940-941   .90

Australia Day — A347

1985, Jan. 25   Litho.
942 A347 30c Musgrave Ranges, by
                Sidney Nolan   .45 .20
943 A347 30c The Walls of China, by
                Russell Drysdale   .45 .20
a.   Pair, #942-943   .90

Intl. Youth Year — A348

1985, Feb. 13   Litho.   Perf. 14x13¹/₂
944 A348 30c multicolored   .40 .15

Royal Victorian Volunteer Artillery — A349   District Nursing Service Centenary — A350

Colonial military uniforms: b, Western Australian Pinjarrah Cavalry. c, New South Wales Lancers. d, New South Wales Contingent to the Sudan. e, Victorian Mounted Rifles.

1985, Feb. 25   Perf. 14¹/₂
945   Strip of 5   2.25 2.00
a.-e. A349 33c any single   .45 .16

1985, Mar. 13
946 A350 33c multicolored   .40 .16

Australian
Cockatoo
A351

1c

Perf. 14 Horiz. on 1 or 2 sides
1985, Mar. 13
947 A351 1c apple grn, yel & buff   .50 .50
948 A351 33c apple grn, yel, & lt
          grnsh blue   .45 .20
  a.   Bklt. pane, 1 #947, 3 #948   2.75

Issued in booklets only.

A352   **33c**   A353   **33c**

1985, Apr. 10   **Perf. 13**
949 A352 33c Abel Tasman, explorer   .55 .32
950 A352 33c The Eendracht   .55 .32
951 A352 33c William Dampier   .55 .32
952 A352 90c Globe and hand   1.50 .90
  a.   Souvenir sheet of 4, #949-952 3.50 2.00
      Nos. 949-952 (4)   3.15 1.86

1985, Apr. 22   **Perf. 14x13¹/₂**
953 A353 33c Queen's Badge, Order of
              Australia   .45 .16

Queen Elizabeth II, 59th birthday.

A354   A356   **33c**

1985, May 15   Litho.   Perf. 14x13
954 A354 33c Soil   .45 .30
955 A354 50c Air   .65 .32
956 A354 80c Water   1.00 .70
957 A354 90c Energy   1.10 .90
      Nos. 954-957 (4)   3.20 2.40

Environmental conservation.

1985, July 17   Litho.   Perf. 14¹/₂
Illustrations from classic children's books: a,
Elves & Fairies, by Annie Rentoul. b, The Magic
Pudding, text and illustrations by Norman Lindsay.
c, Ginger Meggs, by James Charles Bancks. d,
Blinky Bill, by Dorothy Wall. e, Snugglepot and
Cuddleple, by May Gibbs.
960   Strip of 5   2.25 1.25
  a.-e. A356 33c any single   .40 .18

33c   AUSTRALIA

Electronic
Mail — A357

1985, Sept. 18   Litho.
961 A357 33c multicolored   .42 .16

45c   AUSTRALIA   Christmas
A358

Angel in a ship, detail from a drawing by
Albrecht Durer (1471-1528).

1985, Sept. 18   Litho.
962 A358 45c multicolored   .45 .18

See Nos. 967-970.

Australia   **33c**

Coastal
Shipwrecks
A359

Salvaged antiquities: 33c, Astrolabe from Batavia, 1629. 50c, German beardman (Bellarmine) jug
from Vergulde Draeck, 1656. 90c, Wooden bobbins
from Batavia, and scissors from Zeewijk, 1727. $1,
Silver buckle from Zeewijk.

1985, Oct. 2   Litho.   Perf. 13
963 A359 33c multicolored   .50 .20
964 A359 50c multicolored   .75 .75
965 A359 90c multicolored 1.40 1.25
966 A359 $1 multicolored   1.50 1.00
      Nos. 963-966 (4)   4.15 3.20

Christmas Type of 1985
Illustrations by Scott Hartshorne.

1985, Nov. 1   Litho.   Perf. 14
967 A358 27c Angel with trumpet   .32 .18
968 A358 33c Angel with bells   .40 .24
969 A358 55c Angel with star   .70 .65
970 A358 90c Angel with ornament 1.10 1.10
      Nos. 967-970 (4)   2.52 2.17

Australia   **33c**   AUSTRALIA   **33c**
Day — A360   AUSSAT — A361

1986, Jan. 24   Litho.   Perf. 14¹/₂
971 A360 33c Aboriginal painting   .42 .16

1986, Jan. 24
Various communications satellites.
972 A361 33c multicolored   .35 .16
973 A361 80c multicolored 1.15 .75

Australia

South Australia,
Sesquicent.
33c A362

1986, Feb. 12   Perf. 13¹/₂x14
974 A362 33c Sailing ship Buffalo   .52 .16
975 A362 33c City Sign, sculpture by
              O.H. Hajek   .52 .16
  a.   Pair, #974-975   1.05

AUSTRALIA   **33c**

Cook's New
Holland
Expedition
A363

1986, Mar. 12   Perf. 13
976 A363 33c Hibiscus merankensis   .45 .30
977 A363 33c Banksia serrata   .45 .30
978 A363 50c Dillenia alata   .68 .68
979 A363 80c Corria reflexa   1.10 .85
980 A363 90c Parkinson   1.25 1.10
981 A363 90c Banks   1.25 1.25
      Nos. 976-981 (6)   5.18 4.48

Australian bicentennial. Sydney Parkinson (d.
1775), artist. Sir Joseph Banks (1743-1820),
naturalist.

33c AUSTRALIA   **33c** AUSTRALIA

Halley's Comet   Elizabeth II,
A364   60th Birthday
                      A365

1986, Apr. 9   Perf. 14x13¹/₂
982 A364 33c Radio telescope, trajecto-
              ry diagram   .42 .18

1986, Apr. 21   Perf. 14¹/₂
983 A365 33c multicolored   .42 .18

Australia   **33c**

Horses — A366

1986, May 21
984 A366 33c Brumbies   .50 .28
985 A366 80c Stock horse mustering 1.20 .65
986 A366 90c Show-jumping   1.35 .95
987 A366 $1 Australian pony   1.50 .95
      Nos. 984-987 (4)   4.55 2.83

33c AUSTRALIA

Click Go the Shears,
Folk Song — A366a

Lines from the song: b, Old shearer stands. c,
Ringer looks around. d, Boss of the board. e, Tar-
boy is there. f, Shearing is all over.

1986, July 21   Litho.   Perf. 14¹/₂
987A   Strip of 5   2.75 1.50
  b.-f.   A366a 33c, any single   .55 .18
Amalgamated Shearers' Union, predecessor of
the Australian Workers' Union, cent.

AUSTRALIA **33c**   Australia
Bicentennial
A367

Settling of Botany Bay penal colony: No. 988,
King George III, c. 1767, by A. Ramsay. No. 989,
Lord Sydney, secretary of state, 1783-1789, by Gilbert Stuart. No. 990, Capt. Arthur Phillip, 1st penal
colony governor, by F. Wheatley, 1786. $1, Capt.
John Hunter, governor, 1795-1800, by W. B. Bennett, 1815.

1986, Aug. 6   Litho.   Perf. 13
988 A367 33c multicolored   .50 .30
989 A367 33c multicolored   .50 .30
990 A367 33c multicolored   .50 .30
991 A367 $1 multicolored   1.50 1.00
      Nos. 988-991 (4)   3.00 1.90

Australia **36c**

Wildlife — A368   Alpine
                  Wildflowers — A369

Designs: a, Red kangaroo. b, Emu. c, Koala. d,
Kookaburra. e, Platypus.

1986, Aug. 13   Perf. 14¹/₂x14
992   Strip of 5   2.00 1.25
  a.-e. A368 36c any single   .40 .15

Rouletted 9¹/₂ Vert. on 1 or 2 sides
1986, Aug. 25   Booklet Stamps
993 A369 3c Royal bluebell   .45 .30
994 A369 5c Alpine marsh marigold 1.00 .50
995 A369 25c Mount Buffalo sunray 1.00 .75
996 A369 36c Silver snow daisy   .90 .20
  a.   Bklt. pane, #993, #994, 2 #996 3.25
  b.   Bklt. pane, #993, #995, 2 #996 3.25
      Nos. 993-996 (4)   3.35 1.75

AUSTRALIA **36c**   Triumph '83

Orchids — A370   America's Cup
                 Triumph
                 '83 — A371

1986, Sept. 18   Perf. 14¹/₂
997 A370 36c Elythranthera
              emarginata   .60 .15
998 A370 55c Dendrobium nindii   1.00 .60
999 A370 90c Caleana major   1.65 1.00
1000 A370 $1 Thelymitra variegata 1.75 1.10
      Nos. 997-1000 (4)   5.00 2.85

1986, Sept. 26   Perf. 14x13¹/₂
1001 A371 36c Australia II crossing
              finish line   .60 .25
1002 A371 36c Trophy   .60 .25
1003 A371 36c Boxing kangaroo   .60 .25
      Nos. 1001-1003 (3)   1.80 .75

Intl. Peace
Year — A372

1986, Oct. 22   Litho.   Perf. 14x13¹/₂
1004 A372 36c multicolored   .48 .16

AUSTRALIA **60c**   Christmas
A373

Kindergarten nativity play: No. 1005, Holy Fam-
ily, vert. No. 1006, Three Kings, vert. No. 1007,
No. 1008a, Angels, peasants. No. 1008b,
Holy Family, angels, vert. No. 1008c, Shepherd,
angels, vert. No. 1008d, Three Kings. No. 1008e,
Shepherds.

1986, Nov. 3   Litho.
1005 A373 30c multicolored   .50 .18
  a.   Perf 14x13¹/₂   1.00 .50
1006 A373 36c multicolored   .60 .24
1007 A373 60c multicolored   1.00 .65
      Nos. 1005-1007 (3)   2.10 1.07

Souvenir Sheet
1008   Sheet of 5   2.50 2.50
  a.-e. A373 30c any single   .50 .50

Perfs: Nos. 1005-1006, 1008c, 15x14¹/₂; Nos.
1007, 1008a, 1008e, 14¹/₂x15; No. 1008b,
15x14¹/₂x15x15; 1008d, 14¹/₂x15x14¹/₂x14¹/₂.

Australia   **36c**
Day — A374   Australia

1987, Jan. 23   Litho.   Perf. 13¹/₂x14
1009 A374 36c Flag, circuit board   .42 .16
1010 A374 36c Made in Australia cam-
              paign emblem   .42 .16

America's Cup — A375

Fruits — A376

Views of yachts racing.

1987, Jan. 28   *Perf. 15x14¹/₂*
1011	A375	36c multicolored	.52	.28
1012	A375	55c multicolored	.80	.55
1013	A375	90c multicolored	1.40	.90
1014	A375	$1 multicolored	1.65	.95
		Nos. 1011-1014 (4)	4.37	2.68

1987, Feb. 11   *Perf. 14x13¹/₂*
1015	A376	36c Melons, grapes	.55	.32
1016	A376	65c Tropical fruit	1.00	.60
1017	A376	90c Pears, apples, oranges	1.40	.90
1018	A376	$1 Berries, peaches	1.50	.95
		Nos. 1015-1018 (4)	4.45	2.77

Agricultural Shows — A377

1987, Apr. 10   *Litho.*   *Perf. 14x13¹/₂*
1019	A377	36c Livestock	.55	.15
1020	A377	65c Produce	1.00	.60
1021	A377	90c Carnival	1.40	.90
1022	A377	$1 Farmers	1.50	.95
		Nos. 1019-1022 (4)	4.45	2.60

Queen Elizabeth II, 61st Birthday A378

1987, Apr. 21   *Perf. 13¹/₂x14*
1023	A378	36c multicolored	.45	.15

First Fleet Leaving England — A379

Continuous design: No. 1024a, Convicts awaiting transportation. b, Capt. Arthur Phillip, Mrs. Phillip, longboat on shore. c, Sailors relaxing and working. d, Longboats heading from and to fleet. 4e, Fleet in harbor.

No. 1025a, Longboat approaching Tenerife, The Canary Isls. b, Fishing in Tenerife Harbor. $1, Fleet, dolphins.

1987   *Perf. 13*
1024		Strip of 5	4.00	4.00
a.-e.		A379 36c any single	.80	.20
1025		Pair	1.05	1.00
a.-b.		A379 36c any single	.52	.20
1026	A379	$1 multicolored	1.50	1.50
		Nos. 1024-1026 (3)	6.55	6.50

Australia bicent.; departure of the First Fleet, May 13, 1787; arrival at Tenerife, June 1787. Issued: #1024, May 13; #1025-1026, June 3.

1987, Aug. 6

First Fleet arrives at Rio de Janeiro, Aug. 1787: a, Whale, storm in the Atlantic. b, Citrus grove. c, Market. d, Religious procession. e, Fireworks over harbor.

1027		Strip of 5	2.25	2.25
a.-e.		A379 37c any single	.45	.15

No. 1027 has a continuous design.

1987, Oct. 13

First Fleet arrives at Cape of Good Hope, Oct. 1787: No. 1028a, British officer surveys livestock and supplies, Table Mountain. No. 1028b, Ships anchored in Table Bay. No. 1029, Fishermen pull in nets as the Fleet approaches the Cape.

1028		Pair	.90	.90
a.-b.		A379 37c any single	.45	.20
1029	A379	$1 multicolored	1.25	.50

No. 1028 has a continuous design.

1988, Jan. 26

Arrival of the First Fleet, Sydney Cove, Jan. 1788: a, Five aborigines on shore. b, Four aborigines on shore. c, Kangaroos. d, White cranes. e, Flag raising.

1030		Strip of 5	2.75	2.75
a.-e.		A379 37c any single	.55	.20

Printed se-tenant in a continuous design.

The Early Years: Sydney Cove and Parramatta Colonies — A380

Details from panorama "View of Sydney from the East Side of the Cove," 1808, painted by convict artist John Eyre to illustrate The Present Picture of New South Wales, published in London in 1811, and paintings in British and Australian museums: a, Government House, 1790, Sydney, by midshipman George Raper. b, Government Farm, Parramatta, 1791, attributed to the Port Jackson Painter. c, Parramatta Road, 1796, attributed to convict artist Thomas Watling. d, The Rocks and Sydney Cove, 1800, an aquatint engraving by Edward Dayes. e, Sydney Hospital, 1803, by George William Evans, an explorer and surveyor-general of New South Wales. Printed se-tenant in a continuous design.

1988, Apr. 13   *Litho.*   *Perf. 13*
1031		Strip of 5	3.00	3.00
a.-e.		A380 37c any single	.60	.20

Australia Bicentennial.

The Man from Snowy River, 1890, Ballad by A.B. Paterson — A381

Fauna — A382

Excerpts: a, At the station. b, Mountain bred. c, Terrible descent. d, At their heels. e, Brought them back.

1987, June 24   *Perf. 14x13¹/₂*
1034		Strip of 5	2.75	2.75
a.-e.		A381 36c any single	.55	.30

Printed se-tenant in a continuous design.

1987, July 1   *Perf. 14¹/₂x14*

Designs: a, Possum. b, Cockatoo. c, Wombat. d, Rosella. e, Echidna.

1035		Strip of 5	2.25	2.25
a.-e.		A382 37c any single	.45	.15

Printed se-tenant in a continuous design.

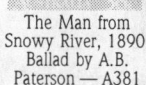

Technology — A383

1987, Aug. 19   *Perf. 14¹/₂*
1036	A383	37c Bionic ear	.38	.18
1037	A383	53c Microchips	.55	.28
1038	A383	63c Robotics	.70	.32
1039	A383	68c Zirconia ceramics	.75	.35
		Nos. 1036-1039 (4)	2.38	1.13

Children A384 37c

1987, Sept. 16
1040	A384	37c Crayfishing	.45	.18
1041	A384	55c Cat's cradle	.65	.28
1042	A384	90c Eating meat pies	1.00	.45
1043	A384	$1 Playing with a joey	1.25	.50
		Nos. 1040-1043 (4)	3.35	1.41

Christmas A385

Carolers: a, Woman, two girls. b, Man, two girls. c, Four children. d, Man, two women, boy. e, Six youths. 37c, three women, two men. Nos. 1044a-1044e are vert.

1987, Nov. 2   *Litho.*   *Perf. 14¹/₂*
1044		Strip of 5	2.00	2.00
a.-e.		A385 30c any single	.40	.15

    Perf. 13¹/₂x14
1045	A385	37c multicolored	.45	.20
1046	A385	63c shown	.80	.30
		Nos. 1044-1046 (3)	3.25	2.50

Carols by Candlelight, Christmas Eve, Sidney Myer Bowl, Melbourne.

Aboriginal Crafts — A386

Designs: 3c, Spearthrower, Western Australia. 15c, Shield, New South Wales. No. 1049, Basket, Queensland. No. 1050, Bowl, Central Australia. No. 1051, Belt, Northern Territory.

    Perf. 15¹/₂ Horiz.
			Photo.	
1047	A386	3c multicolored	1.25	1.25
1048	A386	15c multicolored	1.90	1.25
1049	A386	37c multicolored	1.10	.35
a.		Bklt. pane, 2 each #1047, #1049	4.50	
1050	A386	37c multicolored	1.25	.35
1051	A386	37c multicolored	1.25	.35
a.		Bklt. pane, 1 #1048, 3 #1050, 2 #1051	9.00	
		Nos. 1047-1051 (5)	6.75	3.55

Issued only in booklets.

Caricature of Australian Koala and American Bald Eagle — A387

1988, Jan. 26   *Perf. 13*
1052	A387	37c multicolored	.55	.18

Australia bicentennial. See No. 1086 and US No. 2370.

Living Together — A388

Cartoons.

1988   *Perf. 14*
1053	A388	1c Religion	.15	.15
1054	A388	2c Industry	.15	.15
1055	A388	3c Local government	.15	.15
1056	A388	4c Trade unions	.15	.15
1057	A388	5c Parliament	.15	.15
1058	A388	10c Transportation	.18	.15
1059	A388	15c Sports	.25	.15
1060	A388	20c Commerce	.35	.15
1061	A388	25c Housing	.42	.15
1062	A388	30c Welfare	.52	.16
1063	A388	37c Postal services	.62	.22
a.		Booklet pane of 10	6.25	
1063B	A388	39c Tourism	.65	.22
c.		Booklet pane of 10	6.50	
1064	A388	40c Recreation	.68	.22
1065	A388	45c Health	.78	.25
1066	A388	50c Mining	.85	.28
1067	A388	53c Primary industry	.90	.30
1068	A388	55c Education	.95	.32
1069	A388	60c Armed Forces	1.05	.45
1070	A388	63c Police	1.10	.38
1071	A388	65c Telecommunications	1.15	.38
1072	A388	68c The media	1.20	.40
1073	A388	70c Science and technology	1.20	.40
1074	A388	75c Visual arts	1.30	.45
1075	A388	80c Performing arts	1.40	.48
1076	A388	90c Banking	1.55	.50
1077	A388	95c Law	1.65	.55
1078	A388	$1 Rescue and emergency services	1.70	.58
		Nos. 1053-1078 (27)	21.20	7.79

Issued: 1c, 2c, 3c, 5c, 30c, 40c, 55c, 60c, 63c, 65c, 68c, 75c, 95c, 3/16; 39c, 9/28; others, 2/17.

Queen Elizabeth II, 62nd Birthday A389

1988, Apr. 21   *Perf. 14¹/₂*
1079	A389	37c multicolored	.58	.20

EXPO '88, Brisbane, Apr. 30-Oct. 30 — A390

1988, Apr. 29   *Perf. 13*
1080	A390	37c multicolored	.58	.20

Opening of Parliament House, Canberra A391

1988, May 9   *Perf. 14¹/₂*
1081	A391	37c multicolored	.58	.20

Australia Bicentennial A392

Designs: No. 1082, Colonist, clipper ship. No. 1083, British and Australian parliaments, Queen Elizabeth II. No. 1084, Cricketer W.G. Grace. No. 1085, John Lennon (1940-1980), William Shakespeare (1564-1616) and Sydney Opera House. #1083a, 1085a have continuous design picturing flag of Australia.

1988, June 21   *Litho.*   *Perf. 13*
1082	A392	37c multicolored	.80	.20
1083	A392	37c multicolored	.80	.20
a.		Pair, #1082-1083	1.75	.2

1084	A392	$1 multicolored	2.25	.55
1085	A392	$1 multicolored	2.25	.55
a.		Pair, #1084-1085	4.75	2.50
		Nos. 1082-1085 (4)	6.10	1.50

See Great Britain Nos. 1222-1225.

Caricature Type of 1988

Design: Caricature of an Australian koala and New Zealand kiwi.

1988, June 21   Litho.   Perf. 13½

1086	A387	37c multicolored	.60	.20

Australia bicentennial. See New Zealand No. 907.

"Dream" Lore on Art of the Desert — A393

Aboriginal paintings from Papunya Settlement in the Flinders University Art Museum: 37c, Bush Potato Country, by Turkey Tolsen Tjupurrula with by David Corby Tjapaltjarri. 55c, Courtship Rejected, by Limpi Puntungka Tjapangati. 90c, Medicine Story, anonymous. $1, Ancestor Dreaming, by Tim Leura Tjapaltjarri.

1988, Aug. 1   Litho.   Perf. 13

1087	A393	37c multicolored	.62	.20
1088	A393	55c multicolored	.90	.50
1089	A393	90c multicolored	1.50	.50
1090	A393	$1 multicolored	1.65	.55
		Nos. 1087-1090 (4)	4.67	2.00

1988 Summer Olympics, Seoul — A394

1988, Sept. 14   Perf. 14½

1091	A394	37c Basketball	.62	.20
1092	A394	65c Running	1.10	.90
1093	A394	$1 Rhythmic gymnastics	1.65	.55
		Nos. 1091-1093 (3)	3.37	1.65

34th Commonwealth Parliamentary Conference, Canberra A395

1988, Sept. 19

1094	A395	37c Scepter and mace	.62	.20

Works in the Contemporary Decorative Arts Collection at the Natl. Gallery — A396

Roulette 9 Horiz.

1988, Sept. 28   Litho.

1095	A396	2c "Australian Fetish," by Peter Tully	2.50	1.75
1096	A396	5c Vase by Colin Levy	2.50	1.75
1097	A396	37c Teapot by Frank Bauer	.75	.35
a.		Bklt. pane of 3 (2c, 2 39c)	4.50	
b.		Bklt. pane of 6 (5c, 5 39c)	6.25	
		Nos. 1095-1097 (3)	5.75	3.85

Nos. 1095-1097 issued in booklets only.

Views — A397

1988, Oct. 17   Photo.   Perf. 13

1098	A397	39c The Desert	.65	.22
1099	A397	55c The Top End	.90	.30
1100	A397	65c The Coast	1.10	.38
1101	A397	70c The Bush	1.15	.40
		Nos. 1098-1101 (4)	3.80	1.30

Christmas A398

Children's design contest winning drawings: 32c, Nativity scene, by Danielle Hush, age 7. 39c, Koala wearing a Santa hat, by Kylie Courtney, age 6. 63c, Cockatoo wearing a Santa hat, by Benjamin Stevenson, age 10.

1988, Oct. 31   Perf. 13½x13

1102	A398	32c multicolored	.55	.18
1103	A398	39c multicolored	.65	.22
1104	A398	63c multicolored	1.05	.35
		Nos. 1102-1104 (3)	2.25	.75

Sir Henry Parkes (1815-1896), Advocate of the Federation of the Six Colonies — A399

1989, Jan. 25   Litho.   Perf. 14x13½

1105	A399	39c multicolored	.70	.22

Australia Day.

Sports — A400

1989, Feb. 13   Perf. 14x14½

1106	A400	1c Bowls	.15	.15
a.		Perf. 13½x14 ('90)	.15	.15
1107	A400	2c Bowling	.15	.15
a.		Perf. 13x13½ ('91)	.15	.15
1108	A400	3c Football	.15	.15
1109	A400	39c Fishing	.70	.22
a.		Booklet pane of 10	7.00	
d.		Perf. 13x13½ on 3 sides ('90)	.70	.22
e.		Booklet pane of 10, #1109d	7.00	
1109B	A400	41c Cycling	.62	.20
c.		Booklet pane of 10	6.25	
1110	A400	55c Kite-flying	.98	.32
1111	A400	70c Cricket	1.25	.42
1112	A400	$1.10 Golf	1.95	.65

1990-94

1114	A400	5c Kayaking, canoeing	.15	.15
a.		Perf. 13x13½	.15	.15
1115	A400	10c Windsurfing	.16	.15
a.		Perf. 13x13½	.15	.15
1116	A400	20c Tennis	.32	.15
a.		Perf. 13x13½	.30	.30
1117	A400	65c Rock climbing	1.00	.32
a.		Perf. 13x13½	1.00	1.00
1118	A400	$1 Running	1.55	.52
a.		Perf. 13x13½	3.75	2.00

Issued: #1114a, 1115a, 1116a, 1117a, 1118, 1/17/90; #1118a, 1/91; #1115, 1117, 2/92; #1116, 7/93; #1114, 3/94.

1990, Aug. 27

1119	A400	43c Skateboarding	.68	.18
a.		Booklet pane of 10	6.80	

Perf. 13½

1120	A400	$1.20 Hang-gliding	1.90	.48

1991, Aug. 22   Perf. 14x14½

1121	A400	75c Netball	1.15	.38
1122	A400	80c Squash	1.25	.40
1123	A400	85c Diving	1.30	.42
1124	A400	90c Soccer	1.40	.45
		Nos. 1106-1124 (19)	16.81	5.86

For self-adhesive stamps see #1185-1186. This is an expanding set. Numbers will change when completed.

Botanical Gardens — A401

Designs: $2, Nooroo, New South Wales. $5, Mawarra, Victoria. $10, Palm House, Adelaide Botanical Garden. $20, A View of the Artist's House and Garden in Mills Plains, Van Diemen's Land by John Glover.

1989   Litho. & Engr.   Perf. 14

1132	A401	$2 multicolored	3.00	1.00
a.		Perf. 14x13½ ('91)	3.00	1.00
1133	A401	$5 multicolored	7.75	2.50
a.		Perf. 14x13½	8.50	2.50
1134	A401	$10 multicolored	15.00	4.25

Perf. 14½x14

1135	A401	$20 multicolored	27.50	8.00
		Nos. 1132-1135 (4)	53.25	15.75

Issued: $10, 4/12; $2, $5, 9/13; $20, 8/15.

Sheep — A402

1989, Feb. 27   Perf. 13½x14

1136	A402	39c Merino	.70	.22
1137	A402	39c Poll Dorset	.70	.22
1138	A402	85c Polwarth	1.50	.50
1139	A402	$1 Corriedale	1.75	.58
		Nos. 1136-1139 (4)	4.65	1.52

World Sheep and Wool Congress, Tasmania, Feb. 27-Mar. 6.

Queen Elizabeth II, 63rd Birthday — A403

1989, Apr. 21   Litho.   Perf. 14½

1140	A403	39c Statue by John Dowie	.65	.22

Colonial Australia A404

Pastoral Era: a, Immigrant ship in port, c. 1835. b, Pioneer's hut, wool bales in dray. c, Squatter's homestead. d, Shepherds. e, Explorers.

1989, May 10

1141		Strip of 5	3.25	1.10
a.-e.	A404	39c any single	.65	.22

Stars of Stage and Screen — A405

Performers and directors: 39c, Gladys Moncrieff and Roy Rene, the stage, 1920's. 85c, Charles Chauvel and Chips Rafferty, talking films. $1, Nellie Stewart and James Cassius Williamson, the stage, 1890's. $1.10, Lottie Lyell and Raymond Longford, silent films.

1989, July 12   Litho.   Perf. 14½

1142	A405	39c multicolored	.58	.20
a.		Perf. 14x13½ ('90)	6.50	6.50
1143	A405	85c multicolored	1.25	.82
1144	A405	$1 multicolored	1.50	.50
1145	A405	$1.10 multicolored	1.65	.55
		Nos. 1142-1145 (4)	4.98	2.07

Impressionist Paintings A406

Paintings by Australian artists: No. 1146, Impression for Golden Summer, by Sir Arthur Streeton. No. 1147, All on a Summer's Day, by Charles Conder, vert. No. 1148, Petit Dejeuner, by Frederick McCubbin. No. 1149, Impression, by Tom Roberts.

Perf. 13½x14, 14x13½

1989, Aug. 23   Litho.

1146	A406	41c shown	.62	.20
1147	A406	41c multicolored	.62	.20
1148	A406	41c multicolored	.62	.20
1149	A406	41c multicolored	.62	.20
		Nos. 1146-1149 (4)	2.48	.80

The Urban Environment — A407

1989, Sept. 1   Litho.   Perf. 15½

Booklet Stamps

1150	A407	41c Freeways	.70	.25
1151	A407	41c Architecture	.70	.25
1152	A407	41c Commuter train	.70	.25
a.		Bklt. pane of 7, 2 each #1150, 1152 and 3 #1151	5.00	
		Nos. 1150-1152 (3)	2.10	.75

No. 1152a sold for $3.

Australian Youth Hostels, 50th Anniv. A408

1989, Sept. 13   Perf. 14½

1153	A408	41c multicolored	.65	.22

Street Cars — A409

Designs: No. 1154, Horse-drawn tram, Adelaide, 1878. No. 1155, Steam tram, Sydney, 1884. No. 1156, Cable car, Melbourne, 1886. No. 1157, Double-deck electric tram, Hobart, 1893. No. 1158, Combination electric tram, Brisbane, 1901.

1989, Oct. 11   Litho.   Perf. 13½x14

1154	A409	41c multicolored	.65	.22
1155	A409	41c multicolored	.65	.22
1156	A409	41c multicolored	.65	.22
a.		Perf. 14½ on 3 sides	1.30	1.30
b.		Booklet pane of 10, #1156a	13.00	
1157	A409	41c multicolored	.65	.22
1158	A409	41c multicolored	.65	.22
		Nos. 1154-1158 (5)	3.25	1.10

Purchase of booklet containing No. 1156b included STAMPSHOW '89 admission ticket and a Melbourne one-day transit pass. Sold for $8.

Australia 36c

Christmas — A410

Radio Australia, 50th Anniv. — A411

Illuminations: 36c, Annunciation, from the Nicholai Joseph Foucault Book of Hours, c. 1510-20. 41c, Annunciation to the Shepherds, from the Wharncliffe Hours, c. 1475. 80c, Adoration of the Magi, from Parisian Book of Hours, c. 1490-1500.

1989, Nov. 1   Perf. 14x13½
| 1159 | A410 | 36c multicolored | .55 | .18 |
| a. | | Booklet pane of 10 | 5.50 | |

Perf. 15x14½
1160	A410	41c multicolored	.65	.22
1161	A410	80c multicolored	1.25	.42
		Nos. 1159-1161 (3)	2.45	.82

1989, Nov. 1   Perf. 14x13½
| 1162 | A411 | 41c multicolored | .65 | .22 |

Australia Day — A412

Special Occasions — A413

1990, Jan. 17   Litho.   Perf. 15x14½
| 1163 | A412 | 41c Golden wattle | .65 | .22 |

1990, Feb. 7   Perf. 14x13½
1164	A413	41c Thinking of You	.65	.22
a.		Booklet pane of 10	6.50	
b.		Perf. 14½ on 3 sides	.65	.16
c.		Booklet pane of 10, #1164b	6.50	

See No. 1193.

Women Practicing Medicine in Australia, Cent. A414

1990, Feb. 7   Perf. 14½x15
| 1165 | A414 | 41c Constance Stone | .65 | .22 |

Dr. Constance Stone, Australia's first woman doctor.

A415   A416

Fauna of the High Country.

1990, Feb. 21   Perf. 14x13½
1166	A415	41c Greater glider	.65	.22
1167	A415	65c Spotted-tailed quoll	1.00	.32
1168	A415	70c Mountain pygmy-possum	1.10	.35
1169	A415	80c Brush-tailed rock-wallaby	1.25	.42
		Nos. 1166-1169 (4)	4.00	1.31

1990, Mar. 14
1170	A416	41c Quit smoking	.65	.22
1171	A416	41c Don't drink and drive	.65	.22
1172	A416	41c Eat right	.65	.22
1173	A416	41c Medical check-ups	.65	.22
		Nos. 1170-1173 (4)	2.60	.88

Community health.

A417   A418

Scenes from WW II, 1940-41: #1174, Anzacs at the front. #1175, Women working in factories, aircraft at the ready. 65c, Veterans and memorial parade. $1, Helicopters picking up wounded, cemetery. $1.10, Anzacs reading mail from home, 5 women watching departure of 2 ships.

1990, Apr. 12   Litho.   Perf. 14½
1174	A417	41c shown	.65	.22
1175	A417	41c multicolored	.65	.22
1176	A417	65c multicolored	1.00	.35
1177	A417	$1 multicolored	1.55	.50
1178	A417	$1.10 multicolored	1.75	.58
		Nos. 1174-1178 (5)	5.60	1.87

Australia and New Zealand Army Corps (ANZAC).

Penny Black, 150th Anniv. A419

Stamps on stamps: a, New South Wales No. 44. b, South Australia No. 4. c, Tasmania No. 2. d, Victoria No. 120. e, Queensland No. 111A. f, Western Australia No. 3a.

1990, May 1   Perf. 13½x14
1180		Block of 6	3.60	1.20
a.-f.	A419	41c any single	.60	.20
g.		Souvenir sheet of 6	3.60	1.20

The Gold Rush — A420

a, Off to the diggings. b, The diggings. c, Panning for gold. d, Commissioner's tent. e, Gold escort.

1990, May 16   Perf. 13
| 1181 | | Strip of 5 | 3.00 | 1.00 |
| a.-e. | A420 | 41c any single | .60 | .20 |

Cooperation in Antarctic Research A421

1990, June 13   Litho.   Perf. 14½x14
1182	A421	41c Glaciology	.62	.20
1183	A421	$1.10 Krill (marine biology)	1.65	.55
a.		Min. sheet of 2, #1182-1183	2.30	.75

See Russia Nos. 5902-5903. For overprint see No. 1198.

Colonial Australia A422

Boom Time: a, Land boom. b, Building boom. c, Investment boom. d, Retail boom. e, Factory boom.

1990, July 12   Litho.   Perf. 13
| 1184 | | Strip of 5 | 3.25 | 1.10 |
| a.-e. | A422 | 41c any single | .65 | .22 |

Sports Type of 1989

1990-91   Typo.   Die Cut Perf. 11½
Self-Adhesive
1185	A400	41c Cycling	.75	.20
1186	A400	43c Skateboarding	.68	.18
a.		Litho.	.70	.18

Blue background has large dots on No. 1186 and smaller dots on No. 1186a. No. 1186 is on waxed paper backing printed with 0 to 4 koalas. No. 1186a is on plain paper backing printed with one kangaroo.
Issued: 41c, 5/16; #1186, 8/27; #1186a, 1991. This is an expanding set. Numbers will change if necessary.

Salmon Gums by Robert Juniper — A423

Design: 43c, The Blue Dress by Brian Dunlop.

1990, Sept. 3   Litho.   Perf. 15½ Vert.
Booklet Stamps
1191	A423	28c multicolored	.45	.15
a.		Perf. 14½ vert.	.45	.15
1192	A423	43c multicolored	.68	.18
a.		Bklt. pane, #1191, 4 #1192	3.17	
b.		Perf. 14½ vert.	.68	.18
c.		Booklet pane, #1191a, 4 #1192b	3.25	

Thinking Of You Type

1990, Sept. 3   Perf. 14½
| 1193 | A413 | 43c multicolored | .68 | .18 |
| a. | | Booklet pane of 10 | 6.80 | |

Christmas A424

1990, Oct. 31   Litho.   Perf. 14½
1194	A424	38c Kookaburras	.62	.20
a.		Booklet pane of 10	6.20	
1195	A424	43c Nativity, vert.	.70	.22
1196	A424	80c Opossum	1.35	.45
		Nos. 1194-1196 (3)	2.67	.87

Local Government in Australia, 150th Anniv. — A425

1990, Oct. 31
| 1197 | A425 | 43c Town Hall, Adelaide | .70 | .22 |

No. 1183a Ovptd. in Gold

WORLD STAMP EXHIBITION
24 AUG - 2 SEPT 1990

1990   Litho.   Perf. 14½x14
| 1198 | A421 | Miniature sheet of 2 | 2.40 | 2.40 |

Overprint applied to sheet margin only.

Flags — A426

1991, Jan. 10   Litho.   Perf. 14½
1199	A426	43c National flag	.70	.22
1200	A426	90c White ensign	1.40	.45
1201	A426	$1 Air Force ensign	1.55	.52
1202	A426	$1.20 Red ensign	1.85	.62
		Nos. 1199-1202 (4)	5.50	1.81

Australia Day.

Water Birds A427

1991, Feb. 14
1203	A427	43c Black swan	.70	.22
1204	A427	43c Black-necked stork, vert.	.70	.22
1205	A427	85c Cape Barren goose, vert.	1.30	1.00
1206	A427	$1 Chestnut teal	1.55	.52
		Nos. 1203-1206 (4)	4.25	1.96

Women's Wartime Services, 50th Anniv. A428

50th Anniversaries: No. 1208, Siege of Tobruk. $1.20, Australian War Memorial, Canberra.

1991, Mar. 14   Litho.   Perf. 14½
1207	A428	43c shown	.70	.22
1208	A428	43c multicolored	.70	.22
1209	A428	$1.20 multicolored	1.85	.58
		Nos. 1207-1209 (3)	3.25	1.02

Queen Elizabeth II's 65th Birthday — A429

1991, Apr. 11   Litho.   Perf. 14½
| 1210 | A429 | 43c multicolored | .70 | .22 |

Insects A430

1991, Apr. 11
1211	A430	43c Hawk moth	.70	.22
1212	A430	43c Cotton harlequin bug	.70	.22
1213	A430	80c Leichhardt's grasshopper	1.25	.40
1214	A430	$1 Jewel beetle	1.55	.50
		Nos. 1211-1214 (4)	4.20	1.34

Australian Photography, 150th Anniv. — A431

Designs: No. 1215a, Bondi, by Max Dupain, 1939. No. 1215b, Gears for the Mining Industry, Vickers Ruwolt Melbourne, by Wolfgang Sievers, 1967. 70c, Wheel of Youth, by Harold Cazneaux, 1929. $1.20, Teacup Ballet, by Olive Cotton, 1935.

1991, May 13   Litho.   Perf. 14½
1215		Pair	1.35	.44
a.-b.	A431 43c any single		.68	.22
1216	A431	70c blk, olive & claret	1.10	.36
1217	A431	$1.20 blk, gray & Prus bl	1.85	.62
	Nos. 1215-1217 (3)		4.30	1.42

Golden Days of Radio — A432

Pets — A433

1991, June 13   Litho.   Perf. 14½
1218	A432	43c Music & variety shows	.68	.22
1219	A432	43c Soap operas	.68	.22
1220	A432	85c Quiz shows	1.30	1.25
1221	A432	$1 Children's stories	1.55	.52
	Nos. 1218-1221 (4)		4.21	2.21

1991, July 25   Litho.   Perf. 14½
1222	A433	43c Puppy	.68	.22
1223	A433	43c Kitten	.68	.22
1224	A433	70c Pony	1.10	.36
1225	A433	$1 Cockatoo	1.50	.50
	Nos. 1222-1225 (4)		3.96	1.30

George Vancouver (1757-1798) and Edward John Eyre (1815-1901), Explorers — A434

1991, Sept. 26   Litho.   Perf. 14½
1226	A434	$1.05 multicolored	1.70	.55
a.	Souvenir sheet of 1		1.70	.55
b.	As "a," overprinted in gold		1.50	1.50

Vancouver's visit to Western Australia, 200th anniv. and Eyre's journey to Albany, Western Australia, 150th anniv.
No. 1226b overprinted in sheet margin with show emblem and: "PHILANIPPON / WORLD STAMP / EXHIBITION / TOKYO / 16-24 NOV 1991" followed by Japanese inscription.
Issue date: #1226b, Nov. 16.

Australian Literature of the 1890's A435

Designs: 43c, Seven Little Australians by Ethel Turner. 75c, On Our Selection by Steele Rudd. $1, Clancy of the Overflow by A.B. "Banjo" Paterson, vert. $1.20, The Drover's Wife by Henry Lawson, vert.

1991, Oct. 10
1227	A435	43c multicolored	.68	.22
1228	A435	75c multicolored	1.20	.40
1229	A435	$1 multicolored	1.60	.52
1230	A435	$1.20 multicolored	1.90	.62
	Nos. 1227-1230 (4)		5.38	1.76

Christmas A436

1991, Nov. 1
1231	A436	38c Shepherd	.60	.20
a.	Booklet pane of 20		12.00	
1232	A436	43c Baby Jesus	.68	.22
1233	A436	90c Wise man, camel	1.40	.45
	Nos. 1231-1233 (3)		2.68	.87

Thinking of You — A437

1992, Jan. 2   Litho.   Perf. 14½x15
1234	A437	45c Wildflowers	.70	.25
a.	Booklet pane of 10		7.00	

Threatened Species — A438

Designs: No. 1235a, Parma wallaby. b, Ghost bat. c, Long-tailed dunnart. d, Little pygmy possum. e, Dusky hopping mouse. f, Squirrel glider.

1992, Jan. 2   Litho.   Perf. 14x14½
1235		Block of 6	4.00	1.50
a.-f.	A438 45c any single		.65	.25

Die Cut
Perf. 11½
Self-Adhesive
1241	A438	45c like #1235a	.65	.25
a.	Typo.		.65	.25
1242	A438	45c like #1235b	.65	.25
a.	Typo.		.65	.25
1243	A438	45c like #1235c	.65	.25
a.	Typo.		.65	.25
1244	A438	45c like #1235d	.65	.25
a.	Typo.		.65	.25
1245	A438	45c like #1235e	.65	.25
a.	Typo.		.65	.25
1246	A438	45c like #1235f	.65	.25
a.	Typo.		.65	.25
b.	Bklt. pane, 2 each #1241-1244, 1 each #1245-1246		6.20	
c.	Pane of 5, #1242-1246		3.10	
d.	Strip of 6, #1241-1246		3.75	
e.	Strip of 6, #1241a-1246a		3.75	
f.	#1246c overprinted		3.10	

Litho. stamps are sharper in appearance than typo. stamps, most notably on the black lettering. Nos. 1246b and 1246c have tagging bars which make the right portion of the stamps appear toned.
No. 1246f - overprinted in Gold on sheet margin of No. 1246c with emblem of "WORLD COLUMBIAN / STAMP EXPO '92 / MAY 22-31, 1992 - CHICAGO." Issued in May.
See Nos. 1277-1295D, 1406-1417.

Wetlands — A439

Perf. 14½ Horiz.
1992, Jan. 2   Photo.
Booklet Stamps
1247	A439	20c Noosa River, Queensland	.55	.25
a.	Perf. 14 horiz.			
1248	A439	45c Lake Eildon, Victoria	.55	.25
a.	Bklt. pane, 1 #1247, 4 #1248		2.75	
b.	Perf. 14 horiz.			
c.	Bklt. pane, 1 #1247a, 4 #1248b Complete booklet, #1248c			

Sailing Ships A440

Perf. 14½x15, 15x14½
1992, Jan. 15   Litho.
1249	A440	45c Young Endeavour	.70	.24
1250	A440	45c Britannia, vert.	.70	.24
1251	A440	$1.05 Akarana, vert.	1.60	.52
1252	A440	$1.20 John Louis	1.80	.60
a.	Sheet of 4, #1249-1252		4.80	4.80
b.	As "a," overprinted		4.80	4.80
c.	As "a," overprinted		4.80	4.80
	Nos. 1249-1252 (4)		4.80	1.60

Australia Day. Discovery of America, 500th anniv. (No. 1252a).
Overprint in gold on sheet margin of No. 1252b contains emblem and "WORLD COLUMBIAN / STAMP EXPO '92 / MAY 22-31, 1992-CHICAGO." No. 1252b issued in May.
Overprint in gold on sheet margin of No. 1252c contains emblem and "GENOVA '92 / 18-27 SEPTEMBER." No. 1252c issued in Sept.

Australian Battles, 1942 — A441

1992, Feb. 19   Litho.   Perf. 14½
1253	A441	45c Bombing of Darwin	.65	.22
1254	A441	75c Milne Bay	1.05	.38
1255	A441	75c Kokoda Trail	1.05	.38
1256	A441	$1.05 Coral Sea	1.50	.52
1257	A441	$1.20 El Alamein	1.70	.60
	Nos. 1253-1257 (5)		5.95	2.10

Intl. Space Year — A442

1992, Mar. 19
1258	A442	45c Helix Nebula	.65	.22
1259	A442	$1.05 The Pleiades	1.50	.52
1260	A442	$1.20 Spiral Galaxy NGC 2997	1.70	.60
a.	Sheet of 3, #1258-1260		3.85	3.85
b.	As "a," overprinted		3.85	3.85
	Nos. 1258-1260 (3)		3.85	1.34

Overprint on sheet margin of No. 1260b contains emblem of "WORLD COLUMBIAN / STAMP EXPO '92 / MAY 22-31, 1992-CHICAGO." No. 1260b issued in May.

Queen Elizabeth II, 66th Birthday A443

1992, Apr. 9   Perf. 14x14½
1261	A443	45c Wmk. 228 & #258	.65	.22

Vineyard Regions A444

Designs: No. 1262, Hunter Valley New South Wales. No. 1263, North Eastern Victoria. No. 1264, Barossa Valley South Australia. No. 1265, Coonawarra South Australia. No. 1266, Margaret River Western Australia.

1992, Apr. 9
1262	A444	45c multicolored	.65	.22
1263	A444	45c multicolored	.65	.22
1264	A444	45c multicolored	.65	.22
1265	A444	45c multicolored	.65	.22
1266	A444	45c multicolored	.65	.22
	Nos. 1262-1266 (5)		3.25	1.10

Land Care — A445

Designs: a, Salt action. b, Farm planning. c, Erosion control. d, Tree planting. e, Dune care.

1992, June 11   Litho.   Perf. 14½x14
1267		Strip of 5	3.25	1.10
a.-e.	A445 45c Any single		.62	.22

1992 Summer Olympics and Paralympics, Barcelona A446

1992, July 2   Perf. 14½
1268	A446	45c Cycling	.62	.22
1269	A446	$1.20 Weight lifting	1.75	.60
1270	A446	$1.20 High jump	1.75	.60
	Nos. 1268-1270 (3)		4.12	1.42

Threatened Species Type of 1992

1992-96   Litho.   Perf. 14x14½
1277	A438	30c Saltwater crocodile	.42	.15
1278	A438	35c Echidna	.50	.18
1279	A438	40c Platypus	.55	.18
1280	A438	45c Kangaroo	.65	.22
1281	A438	45c Adult kangaroo with joey	.65	.22
1282	A438	45c Two adult kangaroos	.65	.22
f.	Sheet of 3, #1280-1282		2.10	1.00
1282A	A438	45c Four koalas	.65	.22
1282B	A438	45c Koala walking	.65	.22
1282C	A438	45c Koala in tree	.65	.22
d.	Block of 6, #1280-1282C		4.00	4.00
e.	Souvenir sheet of 6, #1280-1282C		4.00	4.00
1283	A438	50c Koala	.70	.25
1286	A438	60c Common brushtail possum	.85	.30
1287	A438	70c Kookaburra	.95	.35
1288	A438	85c Pelican	1.25	.40
1289	A438	90c Eastern gray kangeroo	1.25	.40
1290	A438	95c Common wombat	1.35	.45
1292	A438	$1.20 Pink cockatoo	1.65	.55
1293	A438	$1.35 Emu	2.00	.65
	Nos. 1277-1293 (17)		15.37	5.18

PHILAKOREA '94 (#1282e).
No. 1282f inscribed in sheet margin with "CHINA '96 - 9th Asian International Exhibition" in Chinese and English and exhibition emblems.
Issued: 35c, 50c, 60c, 95c, 8/13; 40c, 70c, 90c, $1.20, 8/12/93; 30c, 85c, $1.35, 3/10/94; 45c, 5/12/94; #1282e, 8/94; #1282f, 5/18/96.
This is an expanding set. Numbers may change.

1994   Litho.   Die Cut Perf. 11
Self-Adhesive
1294	A438	45c like #1280	.65	.22
1295	A438	45c like #1281	.65	.22
1295A	A438	45c like #1282	.65	.22
1295B	A438	45c like #1282A	.65	.22
1295C	A438	45c like #1282B	.65	.22
1295D	A438	45c like #1282C	.65	.22
e.	Bklt. pane, #1295A, 1295D, 2 each #1294-1295, 1295B-1295C		6.50	
f.	Strip of 6, #1294-1295D		4.00	

Issued: Nos. 1294-1295D, 5/12/94. This is an expanding set. Numbers may change.

Opening of Sydney Harbor Tunnel, August 29 — A447

Sydney Harbor Bridge and Tunnel: a, Left side. b, Right side.

1992, Aug. 28   Litho.   Perf. 14½
1296	A447	45c Pair, #a.-b.	1.30	.45
c.	Pair, #d.-e., perf 15½		1.30	.45

Buildings in Western Australia Goldfield Towns — A448

Designs: No. 1297, Warden's Courthouse, Coolgardie. No. 1298, Post Office, Kalgoorlie. $1.05, York Hotel, Kalgoorlie. $1.20, Town Hall, Kalgoorlie.

1992, Sept. 17   Litho.   Perf. 14x14½
1297	A448	45c multicolored	.62	.22
1298	A448	45c multicolored	.62	.22
1299	A448	$1.05 multicolored	1.45	.50
1300	A448	$1.20 multicolored	1.65	.58
	Nos. 1297-1300 (4)		4.34	1.52

Sheffield Shield Cricket Competition, Cent. — A449

Cricket match, 1890s: 45c, Bowler. $1.20, Batsman, wicket keeper.

1992, Oct. 15   Litho.   Perf. 14½
1301 A449 45c multicolored   .60   .20
1302 A449 $1.20 multicolored   1.60   .55

Christmas A450

Designs: 40c, Children dressed as Mary and Joseph with baby carriage. 45c, Boy jumping from bed Christmas morning. $1, Boy and girl singing Christmas carol.

1992, Oct. 30   Litho.   Perf. 14x14½
1303 A450 40c multicolored   .55   .55
a.   Booklet pane of 20   11.00
1304 A450 45c multicolored   .60   .20
1305 A450 $1 multicolored   1.30   .42
       Nos. 1303-1305 (3)   2.45 1.17

Watercolor Paintings by Albert Namatjira A451

Designs: No. 1306a, Ghost Gum, Central Australia. b, Across the Plain to Mount Giles.

1993, Jan. 14   Litho.   Perf. 14x15
1306 A451 45c Pair, #a.-b.   1.20   .40

Australia Day.

Dreamings A452

Aboriginal paintings: 45c, Wild Onion Dreaming, by Pauline Nakamarra Woods. 75c, Yam Plants, by Jack Wunuwun, vert. 85c, Goose Egg Hunt, by George Milpurrurru, vert. $1, Kalumpiwarra-Ngulalintji, by Rover Thomas.

Perf. 14x14½, 14½x14
1993, Feb. 4   Litho.
1307 A452 45c red & multi   .60   .20
1308 A452 75c org yel & multi   1.00   .30
1309 A452 85c buff & multi   1.10   .35
1310 A452 $1 salmon & multi   1.30   .45
       Nos. 1307-1310 (4)   4.00 1.30

World Heritage Sites in Australia — A453

1993, Mar. 4   Litho.   Perf. 14½x14
1311 A453 45c Uluru (Ayers Rock)   .60   .20
1312 A453 85c Fraser Island   1.10   .38
1313 A453 95c Shark Bay   1.25   .40
1314 A453 $2 Kakadu   2.60   .85
       Nos. 1311-1314 (4)   5.55 1.83
       See Nos. 1485-1488.

World War II Ships A454

Designs: 45c, Cruiser HMAS Sydney II. 85c, Corvette HMAS Bathurst. $1.05, Destroyer HMAS Arunta. $1.20, Hospital Ship Centaur.

1993, Apr. 7   Litho.   Perf. 14x14½
1315 A454 45c multicolored   .60   .20
1316 A454 85c multicolored   1.15   .28
1317 A454 $1.05 multicolored   1.40   .48
1318 A454 $1.20 multicolored   1.60   .52
       Nos. 1315-1318 (4)   4.75 1.48

A455   A456

1993, Apr. 7   Perf. 14½x14
1319 A455 45c multicolored   .62   .20
       Queen Elizabeth II, 67th birthday.

1993, May 7   Litho.   Perf. 14½x14
Designs based on 19th century trade union banners: No. 1320, Baker, shoe maker. No. 1321, Stevedore, seamstresses. $1, Blacksmith, telephone operator, cook. $1.20, Carpenters.
1320 A456 45c multicolored   .60   .20
1321 A456 45c multicolored   .60   .20
1322 A456 $1 multicolored   1.30   .45
1323 A456 $1.20 multicolored   1.55   .52
       Nos. 1320-1323 (4)   4.05 1.37
       Working life in the 1890s.

Trains — A457

Designs: No. 1324, Centenary Special, Tasmania. No. 1325, Spirit of Progress. No. 1326, Western Endeavour. No. 1327, Silver City Comet. No. 1328, Kuranda Tourist Train. No. 1329, The Ghan.

1993, June 1   Perf. 14x14½
1324 A457 45c multicolored   .60   .20
1325 A457 45c multicolored   .60   .20
1326 A457 45c multicolored   .60   .20
1327 A457 45c multicolored   .60   .20
1328 A457 45c multicolored   .60   .20
1329 A457 45c multicolored   .60   .20
a.   Block of 6, #1324-1329   3.60 1.20

Die Cut Perf. 12x11½
Self-Adhesive
1330 A457 45c like No. 1324   .60   .20
1331 A457 45c like No. 1325   .60   .20
1332 A457 45c like No. 1326   .60   .20
1333 A457 45c like No. 1327   .60   .20
1334 A457 45c like No. 1328   .60   .20
1335 A457 45c like No. 1329   .60   .20
a.   Strip of 6, #1330-1335   3.60
b.   Bklt. pane of 10, #1332, 1335, 2
      each #1330-1331, 1333-1334   6.00

Aboriginal Art — A458

Aboriginal paintings: 45c, Black Cockatoo Feather, by Fiona Foley, vert. 75c, Ngarrgooroon Country, by Hector Jandany. $1, Ngak Ngak, by Ginger Riley. $1.05, Untitled work, by Robert Cole, vert.

Perf. 14½x14, 14x14½
1993, July 1   Litho.
1336 A458 45c henna brown & multi .60   .20
1337 A458 75c brown & multi   1.00   .30
1338 A458 $1 gray & multi   1.30   .42
1339 A458 $1.05 olive & multi   1.35   .45
       Nos. 1336-1339 (4)   4.25 1.37

Dame Enid Lyons, MP, and Sen. Dorothy Tangney A459

Design: No. 1340, Stylized globe, natl. arms, Inter-Parliamentary Conference emblem.

1993, Sept. 2   Litho.   Perf. 14½
1340 A459 45c multicolored   .60   .20
1341 A459 45c multicolored   .60   .20
a.   Pair, #1340-1341   1.20   .40

90th Inter-Parliamentary Union Conference (#1340). First women in Australian Federal Parliament, 50th anniv. (#1341). Nos. 1340-1341 printed in panes of 25 with 16 #1340 and 9 #1341. Panes with 16 #1341 and 9 #1340 were issued Nov. 19, but were available only through Philatelic Agency.

A460   A461

Dinosaurs: No. 1342, 1348, Ornithocheirus, horiz. No. 1343, 1349, Leaellynasaura. No. 1344, Allosaurus. No. 1345, Timimus. No. 1346, Muttaburrasaurus. No. 1347, Minmi, horiz.

1993, Oct. 1   Perf. 14x14½, 14½x14
1342 A460 45c multicolored   .60   .20
1343 A460 45c multicolored   .60   .20
1344 A461 45c multicolored   .60   .20
1345 A461 45c multicolored   .60   .20
Size: 29x50mm
1346 A461 75c multicolored   1.00   .35
1347 A461 $1.05 multicolored   1.40   .48
a.   Souvenir sheet of 6, #1342-1347   4.80 4.80
b.   As "a," overprinted   4.80 4.80
c.   As "a," overprinted   4.80 4.80
       Nos. 1342-1347 (6)   4.80 1.63

Self-Adhesive
Die Cut Perf. 11½
1348 A460 45c multicolored   .60   .20
1349 A460 45c multicolored   .60   .20
a.   Bklt. pane, 5 each #1348-1349   6.00

Overprint in gold on sheet margin of No. 1347b contains "BANGKOK 1993" show emblem and "WORLD PHILATELIC / EXHIBITION / BANGKOK 1-10 OCTOBER 1993."
Overprint in gold on sheet margin of No. 1347c contains dinosaur and "Sydney / STAMP & COIN / SHOW / 15-17 October 1993."

Christmas — A462

1993, Nov. 1   Litho.   Perf. 14½x14
1354 A462 40c Goodwill   .52   .18
a.   Booklet pane of 20   10.50
1355 A462 45c Joy   .60   .20
1356 A462 $1 Peace   1.25   .45
       Nos. 1354-1356 (3)   2.37   .83

Australia Day — A463

Landscape paintings: 45c, Shoalhaven River Bank-Dawn, by Arthur Boyd. 85c, Wimmera (from Mt. Arapiles), by Sir Sidney Nolan. $1.05, Lagoon, Wimmera, by Nolan. $2, White Cockatoos in Paddock with Flame Trees, by Boyd, vert.

Perf. 14½x14, 14x14½
1994, Jan. 13   Litho.
1357 A463 45c multicolored   .65   .22
1358 A463 85c multicolored   1.25   .42
1359 A463 $1.05 multicolored   1.50   .50
1360 A463 $2 multicolored   3.00 1.00
       Nos. 1357-1360 (4)   6.40 2.14
       See Nos. 1418-1421, 1476-1479, 1572-1574.

Royal Life Saving Society, Cent. A464

1994, Jan. 20   Litho.   Perf. 14½x14
1361 A464 45c Vigilance   .65   .22
1362 A464 45c Education   .65   .22
1363 A464 95c Drill   1.40   .45
1364 A464 $1.20 Fitness   1.75   .55
       Nos. 1361-1364 (4)   4.45 1.44

Die Cut Perf. 11½
Self-Adhesive
1365 A464 45c like #1361   .60   .20
1366 A464 45c like #1362   .60   .20
a.   Pair, #1365-1366   1.25
b.   Booklet pane, 5 #1366a   6.25

Thinking of You — A465

1994, Feb. 3   Litho.   Perf. 14½x14
1367 A465 45c Rose   .60   .20
1368 A465 45c Tulips   .60   .20
1369 A465 45c Poppies   .60   .20
a.   Pair, #1368-1369   1.25   .40
b.   Booklet pane, 5 #1369a   6.25
       Nos. 1367-1369 (3)   1.80   .60

A466   A467

1994, Apr. 8   Litho.   Perf. 14½
1370 A466 45c multicolored   .65   .22
       Queen Elizabeth II, 68th birthday.

1994, Apr. 8   Perf. 14½x14
1371 A467 95c multicolored   1.25   .45
       Opening of Friendship Bridge, Thailand-Laos.

Intl. Year of the Family — A468

Children's paintings of their families: 45c, Bobbie Lea Blackmore. 75c, Kathryn Teoh. $1, Maree McCarthy.

1994, Apr. 14   Litho.   Perf. 14x14½
1372 A468 45c multicolored   .65   .22
1373 A468 75c multicolored   1.10   .35
1374 A468 $1 multicolored   1.50   .50
       Nos. 1372-1374 (3)   3.25 1.07

Australian
Women's Right
to Vote,
Cent. — A469

1994, June 9   Litho.   Perf. 14x14¹/₂
1375 A469 45c multicolored   .65 .22

Bunyips Folklore
Creatures
A470

Types of Bunyips: No. 1376, Aboriginal legend.
No. 1377, Nature Spirit. 90c, Berkeley's Creek.
$1.35, Natural history.

1994, July 14   Litho.   Perf. 14x14¹/₂
1376 A470 45c multicolored   .65 .22
1377 A470 45c multicolored   .65 .22
  a. Pair, #1376-1377   1.25 .42
1378 A470 90c multicolored   1.25 .42
1379 A470 $1.35 multicolored   2.00 .65
  Nos. 1376-1379 (4)   4.55 1.51

World War II
Prime
Ministers
A471

Designs: a, Robert Menzies. b, Arthur Fadden. c,
John Curtin. d, Francis (Frank) Forde. e, Joseph
Benedict (Ben) Chifley.

1994, Aug. 11
1380 Strip of 5   3.25 1.10
  a.-e. A471 45c any single   .65 .22

Aviation
Pioneers — A472

Designs: No. 1381, Lawrence Hargrave, box
kites. No. 1382, Ross and Keith Smith, Vickers
Vimy. $1.35, Ivor McIntyre, Stanley Globe, Fairey
IIID A10-3 seaplane. $1.80, Freda Thompson,
DeHavilland Moth Major.

1994, Aug. 29   Engr.   Perf. 12
1381 A472 45c multicolored   .65 .22
1382 A472 45c multicolored   .65 .22
1383 A472 $1.35 multicolored   2.00 .65
1384 A472 $1.80 multicolored   2.50 .82
  Nos. 1381-1384 (4)   5.80 1.91

First England-Australia flight within 30-day time
span (#1382). First aerial circumnavigation of Australia (#1383). First woman to fly solo from
England-Australia (#1384).

Australian Zoo Animals
A473   A474

Perf. 14x14¹/₂, 14¹/₂x14
1994, Sept. 28   Litho.
1385 A473 45c Scarlet macaw   .65 .22
1386 A473 45c Cheetah, vert.   .65 .22
1387 A474 45c Fijian crested iguana .65 .22
1388 A474 45c Orang-utan   .65 .22

Size: 50x30mm
Perf. 14¹/₂x14
1389 A473 $1 Asian elephant   1.50 1.50
  Souv. sheet of 5, #1385-1389, perf.
  14¹/₂   4.25 4.25

  b. As "a," ovptd.   4.25 4.25
  c. As "a," ovptd.   4.25 4.25
  d. As "a," ovptd.   4.25 4.25
  e. As "a," ovptd.   4.25 4.25
  Nos. 1385-1389 (5)   4.10 2.38

Self-Adhesive
Die Cut Perf. 11¹/₂
1390 A473 45c like #1385   .65 .22
1391 A473 45c like #1386   .65 .22
  a. Booklet pane, 6 #1390, 4 #1391   6.50

Overprint in gold on sheet margin:
No. 1389b, show emblem and "Brisbane Stamp
Show Zoos / October 21-23, 1994."
No. 1389c, show emblem and "SYDNEY /
STAMP / AND / COIN / SHOW / 30/9/94 TO
2/10/94."
No. 1389d, show emblem and "Stampshow '94
Melbourne October 27-30 / National/State
Centennial Exhibition 1894-1994."
No. 1389e, show emblem and "STAMP SHOW
94 / Fremantle Convention Centre / 5-6 Novem-
ber 1994."

Christmas
A475

Details from Adoration of the Magi, by Giovanni
Toscani: 40c, Madonna and Child, vert. 45c, One
of Magi, horse and groom. $1, Joseph receiving
frankincense from Magi. $1.80, Entire painting.

1994, Oct. 31   Litho.   Perf. 14¹/₂x14
1392 A475 40c multicolored   .60 .20
  a. Booklet pane of 20   12.00
  Complete booklet, #1392a   12.00

Perf. 14x14¹/₂
1393 A475 45c multicolored   .70 .25
1394 A475 $1 multicolored   1.60 .40

Size: 50x30mm
1395 A475 $1.80 multicolored   2.75 .80
  Nos. 1392-1395 (4)   5.65 1.65

50th Sydney-
Hobart Yacht
Race — A476

Designs: a, Yachts bow-on, Sydney Opera House,
Harbor Bridge. b, Two yachts abeam.

1994, Oct. 31   Perf. 14¹/₂
1396 Pair   1.40 .50
  a.-b. A476 45c any single   .70 .25

Self-Adhesive
Die Cut Perf. 11¹/₂
1397   A476 45c like #1396a   .70 .25
1397A A476 45c like #1396b   .70 .25

A477

1994, Nov. 2   Litho.   Die Cut Perf. 17
Self-Adhesive
Booklet Stamps
Background Color
1398 A477 45c bluish green   .70 .25
1399 A477 45c blue   .70 .25
1400 A477 45c purple   .70 .25
1401 A477 45c yellow green   .70 .25
1402 A477 45c pale yellow green .70 .25
1403 A477 45c pale red brown   .70 .25
1404 A477 45c rose   .70 .25
1405 A477 45c orange yellow   .70 .25
  a. Booklet pane of 20   14.00
  Nos. 1398-1405 (8)   5.60 2.00

No. 1405a contains 3 each #1399, 1401, 1403,
1405 and 2 each #1398, 1400, 1402, 1404. No.
1405a was sold in ATM machines, at the Natl.
Philatelic Center, and Australian Philatelic Bureau.

Threatened Species Type of 1992
1994, Aug.   Litho.   Die Cut Perf. 11¹/₂
Self-Adhesive
Size: 53x31mm
1406 A438 45c like #1235a   .70 .25
1407 A438 45c like #1235b   .70 .25
1408 A438 45c like #1235c   .70 .25
1409 A438 45c like #1235d   .70 .25
1410 A438 45c like #1235e   .70 .25

1411 A438 45c like #1235f   .70 .25
  a. Strip of 6, #1406-1411   4.25
  Nos. 1406-1411 (6)   4.20 1.50

Nos. 1406-1411 have computer-generated
denomination and inscription "NPC" at bottom.
Inscriptions "AUSTRALIA," animal name and
"THREATENED SPECIES" appear beside design
instead of above and below it as on No. 1235.

Die Cut Perf. 11
1994, Nov. 17   Litho.
Self-Adhesive
Size: 40x27mm
1412 A438 45c like #1280   .70 .25
1413 A438 45c like #1282B   .70 .25
1414 A438 45c like #1282   .70 .25
1415 A438 45c like #1282A   .70 .25
1416 A438 45c like #1281   .70 .25
1417 A438 45c like #1282C   .70 .25
  Nos. 1412-1417 (6)   4.20 1.50

Nos. 1412-1417 have computer-generated
denominations and location codes printed at bottom of each stamp. They differ from Nos. 1280-
1282c in size and location of inscriptions.
Nos. 1412-1417 can be printed with denominations from 45c-$100. We have listed the 45c value
with the NPC (National Philatelic Center) code
which is available through the Australian Philatelic
Bureau.
Nos. 1412-1417 were issued with "SINGAPORE
'95" code on Sept. 1, 1995.

Australia Day Type of 1994
Paintings: No. 1418, Back Verandah, by Russell
Drysdale. No. 1419, Skull Springs Country, by Guy
Grey-Smith. $1.05, Outcamp, by Robert Juniper.
$1.20, Kite Flying, by Ian Fairweather.

1995, Jan. 12   Litho.   Perf. 15x14¹/₂
1418 A463 45c multicolored   .70 .25
1419 A463 45c multicolored   .70 .25
1420 A463 $1.05 multicolored   1.60 .40
1421 A463 $1.20 multicolored   1.75 .45
  Nos. 1418-1421 (4)   4.75 1.35

St. Valentine's
Day — A478

Various designs: a, Red heart. b, Red & gold
heart. c, Gold heart.

1995, Feb. 6   Litho.   Perf. 14¹/₂x14
1422 Strip of 3   2.10 .75
  a.-c. A478 45c any single   .70 .25

See No. 1480.

Endeavour
A479

#1423: a, Captain Cook's Endeavour. b, Replica.

1995, Feb. 9   Litho.   Perf. 14x14¹/₂
1423 Pair   1.40 .50
  a.-b. A479 45c any single   .70 .25

Booklet Stamps
Size: 44x26mm
Perf. 14 Horiz.
1424 A479 20c like #1423a   .30 .15
1425 A479 45c like #1423b   .70 .25
  a. Booklet pane, 1 #1424, 4 #1425   3.25
  Complete booklet, #1425a   3.25

Natl. Trust, 50th
Anniv. — A480

Designs: No. 1426a, Coalport plate. Regency
style bracket clock. No. 1426b, 15th-16th cent. x-
frame Italian style chair, 19th cent. Steiner doll. $1,
Advance Australia teapot, neo-classical parian-ware
statuette. $2, China urn, silver bowl.

1995, Mar. 16   Engr.   Perf. 14x14¹/₂
1426 Pair   1.40 .50
  a.-b. A480 45c any single   .70 .25
1427 A480 $1 red brown & blue 1.50 .50
1428 A480 $2 blue & green   3.00 1.00
  Nos. 1426-1428 (3)   5.90 2.00

Opals — A481

1995, Apr. 5   Litho.   Perf. 14¹/₂x14
1429 A481 $1.20 Light opal   1.75 .90
1430 A481 $2.50 Black opal   3.75 1.90

Nos. 1429-1430 each contain a holographic
image. Soaking in water may affect the hologram.
See Nos. 1554-1555.

Australia 45c
A482   A483

1995, Apr. 20   Litho.   Perf. 14¹/₂
1431 A482 45c multicolored   .65 .22

Queen Elizabeth II, 69th birthday.

1995, Apr. 20   Litho.   Perf. 14¹/₂x14
Famous Australians from World War II.
1432 A483 45c Sir Edward Dunlop   .65 .22
1433 A483 45c Mrs. Jessie Vasey   .65 .22
1434 A483 45c Tom Derrick   .65 .22
1435 A483 45c Rawdon Hume Mid-
            dleton   .65 .22
  a. Block of 4, #1432-1435   2.60 .85

Self-Adhesive
Die Cut Perf. 11¹/₂
1436 A483 45c like #1432   .65 .22
1437 A483 45c like #1433   .65 .22
1438 A483 45c like #1434   .65 .22
1439 A483 45c like #1435   .65 .22
  a. Booklet pane, 6 #1436, 2 each
    #1437-1439   6.50
  b. Strip of 4, #1436-1439   2.60
  Nos. 1432-1439 (8)   5.20 1.76

See Nos. 1452-1455.

UN, 50th
Anniv.
A484

1995, May 11   Litho.   Perf. 14x14¹/₂
1440 A484 45c + label, multi   .65 .22
  a. Block of 4 + 4 labels   2.75

No. 1440 was issued se-tenant with label in
blocks of 4 + 4 labels in four designs. In alternating
rows, labels appear on left or right side of stamp.

A485   A486

Poster, scene from: No. 1441, The Story of the
Kelly Gang, 1906. No. 1442, On Our Selection,
1932. No. 1443, Jedda, 1955. No. 1444, Picnic at
Hanging Rock, 1970s. No. 1445, Strictly Ballroom,
1992.

1995, June 8   Litho.   Perf. 14x14¹/₂
1441 A485 45c multicolored   .65 .22
1442 A485 45c multicolored   .65 .22
1443 A485 45c multicolored   .65 .22

1444 A485 45c multicolored   .65   .22
1445 A485 45c multicolored   .65   .22
   a. Strip of 5, #1441-1445   3.25 1.10

Self-Adhesive
Die Cut Perf. 11¹/₂

1446 A485 45c like #1441   .65   .22
1447 A485 45c like #1442   .65   .22
1448 A485 45c like #1443   .65   .22
1449 A485 45c like #1444   .65   .22
1450 A485 45c like #1445   .65   .22
   a. Strip of 5, #1446-1450   3.25
   b. Booklet pane, 2 each #1446-1450   6.50

Motion Pictures, cent.

By its nature No. 1450b constitutes a complete
booklet. The peelable backing serves as a booklet
cover.

1995, July 13   Litho.   Perf. 14¹/₂x14
People with Disabilities: No. 1451a, Person flying kite from wheelchair. b, Blind person playing
violin, guide dog.

1451   Pair   1.25   .42
   a.-b. A486 45c any single   .60   .20

Famous Australians from World War II
Type of 1995

1995, Aug. 10   Litho.   Perf. 14¹/₂x14
1452 A483 45c Leon Goldsworthy   .65   .22
1453 A483 45c Len Waters   .65   .22
1454 A483 45c Ellen Savage   .65   .22
1455 A483 45c Percy Collins   .65   .22
   a. Block of 4, #1452-1455   2.60   .90

Peace Types of 1946
Perf. 14x14¹/₂, 14¹/₂x14

1995, Aug. 10   Engr.
1456 A43   45c red brown   .65   .22
1457 A45   45c dark green   .65   .22
1458 A44 $1.50 dark blue   2.25   .75
   Nos. 1456-1458 (3)   3.55 1.19

End of World War II, 50th anniv.

Wildlife
A487

Designs: a, Koalas. b, Pandas.

1995, Sept. 1   Litho.   Perf. 14
1459   Pair   1.30   .40
   a.-b. A487 45c any single   .65   .20
   c. Souv. sheet #1459a, perf. 11x11¹/₂ .65   .65
   d. Souv. sheet #1459b, perf. 11x11¹/₂ .65   .65
   e. #1459c Ovptd. in sheet margin   .65   .65
   f. #1459d Ovptd. in sheet margin   .65   .65

Overprints read: No. 1459e: "AUSTRALIAN
STAMP EXHIBITION." No. 1459f: "INTERNA-
TIONAL STAMP & COIN EXPO. / BEIJING '95."
Issued: No. 1459f, 9/14/95.
See People's Republic of China Nos. 2597-2598.

Australian
Medical
Discoveries
A488

Designs: No. 1461a, Joseph Slattery, Thomas
Lyle, Walter Filmer, x-ray pioneers. No. 1461b, Jean
Macnamara, Macfarlane Burnet, viruses and immu-
nology. No. 1461C, Fred Hollows, eye care, vert.
$2.50, Howard Florey, co-discoverer of penicillin,
vert.

Perf. 14x14¹/₂, 14¹/₂x14
1995, Sept. 7
1461   Pair   1.30   .40
   a.-b. A488 45c any single   .65   .20
1461C A488 45c multicolored   .65   .20
1461D A488 $2.50 multicolored   3.75 1.25
   Nos. 1461-1461D (3)   5.70 1.85

No. 1461D exists in sheetlets of 10.

The World
Down Under
A489

Designs: Nos. 1462a, 1465a, Flatback turtle.
Nos. 1462b, 1465b, Flame angelfish, nudibranch.
Nos. 1463a, 1465c, Potato cod, giant maori wrasse.

Nos. 1463b, 1465d, Giant trevally. Nos. 1464a,
1465e, Black marlin. Nos. 1464b, 1465f, Mako &
tiger sharks.

1995, Oct. 3   Litho.   Perf. 14x14¹/₂
1462   Pair   1.30   .40
   a.-b. A489 45c any single   .65   .20
1463   Pair   1.30   .40
   a.-b. A489 45c any single   .65   .20
1464   Pair   1.30   .40
   a.-b. A489 45c any single   .65   .20
   Nos. 1462-1464 (3)   3.90 1.20

Miniature Sheet of 6
1465 A489 45c #a.-f.   4.00 1.30
   h. Ovptd. in sheet margin   4.00
   i. Ovptd. in sheet margin   4.00
   i. Ovptd. in sheet margin   4.00
   j. Ovptd. in sheet margin   4.00
   k. Ovptd. in sheet margin   4.00

Nos. 1462-1464 have pale blue border on three
sides. No. 1465 is a continuous design and does not
have the pale border. Fish on No. 1465 are printed
with additional phosphor ink producing a glow-in-
the-dark effect under ultraviolet light.
Overprints in gold in sheet margin of No. 1465
include show emblems and text:
No. 1465g: "ADELAIDE / STAMP AND / COL-
LECTIBLES / FAIR / 14/10/95 - 15/10/95."
No. 1465h: "SYDNEY / CENTREPOINT 95 /
STAMPSHOW."
No. 1465i: "Brisbane Stamp Show / 20-22 October 1995."
No. 1465j: "Melbourne Stamp & Coin Fair / 27-
29 October 1995."
No. 1465k: "Swanpex WA / 28-29 October
1995."

Booklet Stamps
Self-Adhesive
Die Cut Perf. 11¹/₂

1466 A489 45c like #1462a   .65   .20
1467 A489 45c like #1462b   .65   .20
1468 A489 45c like #1463a   .65   .20
1469 A489 45c like #1463b   .65   .20
1470 A489 45c like #1464a   .65   .20
1471 A489 45c like #1464b   .65   .20
   a. Booklet pane, #1470-1471, 2 each   6.50
     #1466-1469
   b. Strip of 6, #1466-1471   4.00

By its nature, No. 1471a constitutes a complete
booklet. The peelable backing serves as a booklet
cover.

Christmas — A490

Stained glass windows, Our Lady Help of Chris-
tians Church, Melbourne: 40c, Madonna and
Child. 45c, Angel carrying banner. $1, Three rejoic-
ing angels.

1995, Nov. 1   Litho.   Perf. 14¹/₂x14
1472 A490 40c multicolored   .60   .30
1473 A490 45c multicolored   .65   .30
1474 A490 $1 multicolored   1.50   .75
   Nos. 1472-1474 (3)   2.75 1.35

Booklet Stamp
Self-Adhesive
Die Cut Perf. 11¹/₂

1475 A490 40c multicolored   .60   .20
   a. Booklet pane of 20   12.00

Madonna and Child on No. 1475 are printed
with additional phosphor ink giving parts of the
stamp a rough texture.
By its nature, No. 1475a constitutes a complete
booklet. The peelable backing serves as a booklet
cover, which also contains 20 labels. The complete
booklet is available with backing showing two different advertisements.

Australia Day Type of 1994
Paintings by Australian women: 45c, West Aus-
tralian Banksia, by Margaret Preston, vert. 85c, The
Babe is Wise, by Lina Bryans, vert. $1, The Bridge
in Curve, by Grace Cossington Smith. $1.20, Beach
Umbrellas, by Vida Lahey.

Perf. 14x14¹/₂, 14¹/₂x14
1996, Jan. 16   Litho.
1476 A463 45c multicolored   .65   .20
1477 A463 85c multicolored   1.25   .40
1478 A463 $1 multicolored   1.50   .50
1479 A463 $1.20 multicolored   1.75   .60
   Nos. 1476-1479 (4)   5.15 1.70

Heart and
Roses
A491

1996, Jan. 30   Perf. 14x14¹/₂
1480 A491 45c gold & multi   .65   .20
   See No. 1422.

Military
Aviation
A492

#1481, Firefly, Sea Fury. #1482, Beaufighter, Kit-
tyhawk. #1483, Hornet. #1484, Kiowa.

1996, Feb. 26   Litho.   Perf. 14x14¹/₂
1481 A492 45c multicolored   .70   .20
1482 A492 45c multicolored   .70   .20
1483 A492 45c multicolored   .70   .20
1484 A492 45c multicolored   .70   .20
   a. Block of 4, #1481-1484   2.80   .80

Australian World Heritage Sites Type of 1993
Designs: 45c, Tasmanian Wilderness. 75c, Wil-
landra Lakes. 95c, Fossil Cave, Naracoorte. $1,
Lord Howe Island.

1996, Mar. 14   Litho.   Perf. 14¹/₂x14
1485 A453 45c multicolored   .70   .20
1486 A453 75c multicolored   1.20   .40
1487 A453 95c multicolored   1.45   .45
1488 A453 $1 multicolored   1.50   .50
   Nos. 1485-1488 (4)   4.85 1.55

Indonesian Bear
Cuscus — A493

Design: No. 1489, Australian Spotted Cuscus.

1996, Mar. 22
1489 A493 45c multicolored   .70   .20
1490 A493 45c multicolored   .70   .20
   a. Pair, Nos. 1489-1490   1.40   .40
   b. Souvenir sheet, No. 1490a   1.40   .40

No. 1490a has continuous design. See Indonesia
Nos. 1640-1642.

Queen
Elizabeth II,
70th Birthday
A494

Perf. 14x14¹/₂
1996, Apr. 11   Litho. & Engr.
1491 A494 45c multicolored   .70   .20

North Melbourne
Kangaroos
A495

Brisbane Bears
A496

Sydney
Swans — A497

Carlton
Blues — A498

Adelaide
Crows — A499

Fitzroy
Lions — A500

Richmond
Tigers — A501

St. Kilda
Saints — A502

Melbourne
Demons — A503

Collingwood
Magpies — A504

Fremantle
Dockers — A505

Footscray
Bulldogs — A506

West Coast
Eagles — A507

Essendon
Bombers — A508

Geelong
Cats — A509

Hawthorn
Hawks — A510

1996, Apr. 23   Litho.   *Perf. 14¹/₂x14*

1492	A495	45c multicolored	.70	.20
1493	A496	45c multicolored	.70	.20
1494	A497	45c multicolored	.70	.20
1495	A498	45c multicolored	.70	.20
1496	A499	45c multicolored	.70	.20
1497	A500	45c multicolored	.70	.20
1498	A501	45c multicolored	.70	.20
1499	A502	45c multicolored	.70	.20
1500	A503	45c multicolored	.70	.20
1501	A504	45c multicolored	.70	.20
1502	A505	45c multicolored	.70	.20
1503	A506	45c multicolored	.70	.20
1504	A507	45c multicolored	.70	.20
1505	A508	45c multicolored	.70	.20
1506	A509	45c multicolored	.70	.20
1507	A510	45c multicolored	.70	.20
a.		Min. sheet of 16, #1492-1507		11.25

Booklet Stamps
Self-Adhesive
Serpentine Die Cut 11¹/₂

1508	A495	45c multicolored	.70	.20
a.		Booklet pane of 10	7.00	
1509	A496	45c multicolored	.70	.20
a.		Booklet pane of 10	7.00	
1510	A497	45c multicolored	.70	.20
a.		Booklet pane of 10	7.00	
1511	A498	45c multicolored	.70	.20
a.		Booklet pane of 10	7.00	
1512	A499	45c multicolored	.70	.20
a.		Booklet pane of 10	7.00	
1513	A500	45c multicolored	.70	.20
a.		Booklet pane of 10	7.00	
1514	A501	45c multicolored	.70	.20
a.		Booklet pane of 10	7.00	
1515	A502	45c multicolored	.70	.20
a.		Booklet pane of 10	7.00	
1516	A503	45c multicolored	.70	.20
a.		Booklet pane of 10	7.00	
1517	A504	45c multicolored	.70	.20
a.		Booklet pane of 10	7.00	
1518	A505	45c multicolored	.70	.20
a.		Booklet pane of 10	7.00	
1519	A506	45c multicolored	.70	.20
a.		Booklet pane of 10	7.00	
1520	A507	45c multicolored	.70	.20
a.		Booklet pane of 10	7.00	
1521	A508	45c multicolored	.70	.20
a.		Booklet pane of 10	7.00	
1522	A509	45c multicolored	.70	.20
a.		Booklet pane of 10	7.00	
1523	A510	45c multicolored	.70	.20
a.		Booklet pane of 10	7.00	

By their nature, Nos. 1508a-1523a are complete booklets. The peelable paper backing serves as a booklet cover.

Australian Football League, cent.

Flora and Fauna — A511

Designs: 5c, Leadbeater's possum. 10c, Powerful owl. 20c, Saltwater crocodile, Kangkong flower. 25c, Northern dwarf tree frog, red lily. No. 1528, Little kingfisher. No. 1529, Jacana. No. 1530, Jabiru. No. 1531, Brolga. $1, Big greasy butterfly, water lily. $2, Blackwood wattle. $5, Mountain ash, fern. $10, Kakadu Wetlands during lightning storm, great egret, red lily.

1996-97   Litho.   *Perf. 14x14¹/₂*

1524	A511	5c multicolored	.15	.15
1525	A511	10c multicolored	.15	.15
1526	A511	20c multicolored	.30	.15
1527	A511	25c multicolored	.40	.15
1528	A511	45c multicolored	.70	.20
1529	A511	45c multicolored	.70	.20
1530	A511	45c multicolored	.70	.20
1531	A511	45c multicolored	.70	.20
a.		Block of 4, #1528-1531	2.80	.80
1532	A511	$1 multicolored	1.60	.40
1533	A511	$2 multicolored	3.25	1.00

Size: 30x50mm

1534	A511	$5 multicolored	8.00	2.60
1535	A511	$10 multicolored	15.00	4.00
a.		Souvenir sheet of 1	15.00	4.00
b.		As "a", ovptd. in sheet margin	15.00	4.00
		Nos. 1524-1535 (12)	31.65	9.40

Booklet Stamps
Self-Adhesive
Serpentine Die Cut 11¹/₂

1536	A511	45c like #1529	.70	.20
1537	A511	45c like #1528	.70	.20
1538	A511	45c like #1531	.70	.20
1539	A511	45c like #1530	.70	.20
a.		Booklet pane, 3 ea #1536, #1538, 2 ea #1537, #1539	7.00	
b.		Strip of 4, #1536-1539	2.80	

No. 1538b overprinted in silver in sheet margin with PACIFIC 97 emblem and "Australia Post Exhibition Sheet No. 4."

By its nature No. 1539a is a complete booklet. The peelable backing serves as a booklet cover.

Issued: 5c, 10c, $2, $5, 5/9/96; 20c, 25c, $1, $10, #1538a, 4/10/97; #1528-1531, 1536-1539, 6/2/97.

Modern Olympic Games, Cent. A512

#1540, Edwin Flack, 1st Australian gold medalist, runners. #1541, Fanny Durack, 1st Australian woman gold medalist, swimmers. $1.05, Paralympics, Atlanta.

Perf. 14x14¹/₂

1996, June 6   Litho. & Engr.

1540	A512	45c multicolored	.70	.20
1541	A512	45c multicolored	.70	.20
a.		Pair, #1540-1541	1.40	.40
1542	A512	$1.05 multicolored	1.60	.45
		Nos. 1540-1542 (3)	3.00	.85

Transfer of Olympic Flag from Atlanta to Sydney A513

1996, July 22   Litho.

1543	A513	45c multicolored	.70	.20

Issued in sheets of 10.

Children's Book Council, 50th Anniv. — A514

Covers from "Book of the Year" books: No. 1544, "Animalia." No. 1545, "Greetings from Sandy Beach." No. 1546, "Who Sank the Boat?" No. 1547, "John Brown, Rose and the Midnight Cat."

1996, July 4   Litho.   *Perf. 14x14¹/₂*

1544	A514	45c multicolored	.70	.70
1545	A514	45c multicolored	.70	.70
1546	A514	45c multicolored	.70	.70
1547	A514	45c multicolored	.70	.70
a.		Block of 4, #1544-1547	2.80	2.80

Serpentine Die Cut 11¹/₂
Self-Adhesive

1548	A514	45c like #1544	.70	.20
1549	A514	45c like #1546	.70	.20
1550	A514	45c like #1547	.70	.20
1551	A514	45c like #1545	.70	.20
a.		Booklet pane, 4 #1548, 2 each #1549-1551	7.00	
b.		Strip of 4, #1548-1551	2.80	

By its nature, No. 1551a is a complete booklet. The peelable paper backing serves as a booklet cover.

National Council of Women, Cent. — A515

Designs: 45c, Margaret Windeyer (1866-1939), honorary life president. $1, Rose Scott (1847-1925), founding executive member.

1996, Aug. 8   Litho.   *Perf. 14¹/₂x14*

1552	A515	45c claret & yellow	.70	.70
1553	A515	$1 blue & yellow	1.50	1.50

Gems Type of 1995

1996, Sept. 5   Litho.   *Perf. 14¹/₂x14*

1554	A481	45c Pearl	.70	.70
1555	A481	$1.20 Diamond	1.90	1.90

No. 1555 contains a holographic image. Soaking in water may affect the hologram.

Arts Councils in Regional Australia A516

Silhouettes of performing artists, outdoor scene: 20c, Ballet dancer, violinist, field, bales, trees. 45c, Violinist, hand holding flower, dancer, tree in field.

1996, Sept. 12   Litho.   *Perf. 14 Horiz.*
Booklet Stamps

1556	A516	20c multicolored	.30	.15
1557	A516	45c multicolored	.70	.20
a.		Booklet pane, 1 #1556, 4 #1557	3.25	
		Complete booklet, #1557a	3.25	

Pets
A517   A518

1996-97   *Perf. 14x14¹/₂, 14¹/₂x14*

1558	A517	45c Cockatoo	.70	.20
1559	A517	45c Ducks, vert.	.70	.20
1560	A517	45c Dog, cat, vert.	.70	.20
a.		Pair, #1559-1560	1.40	.40
1561	A518	45c Dog, puppy	.70	.20
1562	A518	45c Kittens	.70	.20
a.		Pair, #1561-1562	1.40	.40

Size: 29x49mm

1563	A518	45c Pony, horse	.70	.20
a.		Souvenir sheet #1558-1563	4.25	1.25
b.		As "a", ovptd.	4.25	1.25
c.		As "a", ovptd.	4.25	1.25
d.		As "a", ovptd.	4.25	1.25
e.		As "a", ovptd.	4.25	1.25
f.		As "a", ovptd.	4.25	1.25
g.		As "a", ovptd.	4.25	1.25
h.		As "a", ovptd.	4.25	1.25
		Nos. 1558-1563 (6)	4.20	1.20

Self-Adhesive
Serpentine Die Cut 11¹/₂

1564	A518	45c like #1561	.70	.20
1565	A518	45c like #1562	.70	.20
a.		Bklt. pane, 6 #1564, 4 #1565	7.00	

No. 1563a is a continuous design.

Overprints in gold on sheet margin: No. 1563b, show emblem and "10TH ASIAN INTERNATIONAL PHILATELIC EXHIBITION 1996" in Chinese and English. No. 1563c, pets emblem and, "ASDA CENTREPOINT '96 STAMP AND COIN SHOW / 5-7 October 1996." No. 1563d, pets emblem and "ST PETERS STAMP & COLLECTIBLE FAIR / 12-13 OCTOBER 1996." No. 1563e, pets emblem and "MELBOURNE '96 NATIONAL PHILATELIC EXHIBITION / 17-20 OCTOBER 1996." No. 1563f, pets emblem and "QUEENSLAND SPRING STAMP AND COIN SHOW / 25-27 OCTOBER 1996." No. 1563g, pets emblem and "SWANPEX '96 / 26-27 OCTOBER 1996." No. 1563h: Hong Kong '97 emblem and "11TH ASIAN INTERNATIONAL STAMP EXHIBITION / 12-16 FEBRUARY 1997."

By its nature, No. 1565a is a complete booklet. The peelable paper backing serves as a booklet cover.

Issued: Nos. 1558-1563, 1563a, 1564-1465, 10/1/96; Nos. 1563b-1563g, 10/3/96; No. 1563h, 2/12/97.

Baron Ferdinand von Mueller (1825-96), Botanist — A519

1996, Oct. 9   *Perf. 14*

1566	A519	$1.20 multicolored	1.90	.55

See Germany No. 1949.

Christmas — A520

1996, Nov. 1   *Perf. 14¹/₂x14*

1567	A520	40c Madonna and Child	.65	.20
1568	A520	45c Wise man	.70	.20
1569	A520	$1 Shepherd boy, lamb	1.50	.30
		Nos. 1567-1569 (3)	2.85	.70

Self-Adhesive
Serpentine Die Cut 12

1570	A520	40c like #1567	.65	.20
a.		Booklet pane of 20	13.00	

By its nature, No. 1570a is a complete booklet. The peelable paper backing serves as a booklet cover.

Exploration of Australian Coast & Christmas Island by Willem de Vlamingh, 300th Anniv. — A521

Portrait of a Dutch Navigator, by Jan Verkolje.

1996, Nov. 1   *Perf. 14x14¹/₂*

1571	A521	45c multicolored	.70	.20
a.		Pair, #1571 & Christmas Island #404	1.40	.40

Australia Day Type of 1994

Paintings: 85c, Landscape '74, by Fred Williams. 90c, The Balcony 2, by Brett Whiteley. $1.20, Fire Haze at Gerringong, by Lloyd Rees.

1997, Jan. 16   Litho.   *Perf. 14¹/₂x14*

1572	A463	85c multicolored	1.30	.40
1573	A463	90c multicolored	1.40	.45
1574	A463	$1.20 multicolored	1.90	.60
		Nos. 1572-1574 (3)	4.60	1.45

Sir Donald Bradman, Cricketer — A522

1997, Jan. 23   Litho.   *Perf. 14¹/₂*

1575	A522	45c Portrait	.70	.20
1576	A522	45c At bat	.70	.20
a.		Pair, #1575-1576	1.40	.40

Greetings — A523

1997, Jan. 29   *Perf. 14¹/₂x14*

1577	A523	45c Rose	.70	.20

Serpentine Die Cut 11¹/₂
Booklet Stamp
Self-Adhesive

1578	A523	45c like #1577	.70	.20
a.		Booklet pane of 10	7.00	

By its nature, No. 1578a is a complete booklet. The peelable paper backing, which also contains 12 labels, serves as a booklet cover.

Classic Cars — A524

#1579, 1934 Ford Coupe Utility. #1580, 1948 GMH Holden 48-215 (FX). #1581, 1958 Austin Lancer. #1582, 1962 Chrysler Valiant R Series.

1997, Feb. 27   Litho.   *Perf. 14x14¹/₂*

1579	A524	45c multicolored	.70	.20
a.		Booklet pane of 4	2.80	
1580	A524	45c multicolored	.70	.20
a.		Booklet pane of 4	2.80	
1581	A524	45c multicolored	.70	.20
a.		Booklet pane of 4	2.80	

1582 A524 45c multicolored   .70   .20
  a. Booklet pane of 4   2.80
  b. Block of 4, #1579-1582   2.80   .80
    Complete booklet, #1579a, 1580a,
    1581a, 1582a   16.00

Complete booklet contains 2 postal cards and 16
self-adhesive labels.

Serpentine Die Cut 12
Booklet Stamps
Self-Adhesive

1583 A524 45s like #1579   .70   .20
1584 A524 45c like #1580   .70   .20
1585 A524 45c like #1581   .70   .20
1586 A524 45c like #1582   .70   .20
  a. Booklet pane of 10, 2 ea #1583,
    1585, 3 ea #1584, 1586   7.00
  b. Strip of 4, #1583-1586   2.80

By its nature, No. 1586a is a complete booklet.
The peelable backing serves as a booklet cover. The
backing for No. 1586b is inscribed with a 3x8mm
black vertical box and "SNP CAMBEC."

Circuses in Australia,
150th
Anniv. — A525

#1591, Queen of the Arena, May Wirth (1894-
1978). #1592, Wizard of the Wire, Con Colleano
(1899-1973). #1593, Clowns. #1594, Tumblers.

1997, Mar. 13   Litho.   Perf. 14¹/₂x14
1591 A525 45c multicolored   .70   .20
1592 A525 45c multicolored   .70   .20
1593 A525 45c multicolored   .70   .20
1594 A525 45c multicolored   .70   .20
  a. Block of 4, #1591-1594   2.80   .80

Queen Elizabeth
II, 71st
Birthday, 50th
Wedding
Anniv. — A526

1997, Apr. 17   Engr.   Perf. 14x14¹/₂
1595 A526 45c Design A50   .70   .20

A527   A528

1997, Apr. 17   Perf. 14¹/₂x14
1596 A527 45c multicolored   .70   .20
Lions Clubs of Australia, 50th anniv.

1997, May 8   Litho.   Perf. 14¹/₂x14
Dolls and Teddy Bears: No. 1597, Doll wearing
red hat. No. 1598, Bear standing. No. 1599, Doll
wearing white dress holding teddy bear. No. 1600,
Doll in brown outfit. No. 1601, Teddy bear seated.

1597 A528 45c multicolored   .70   .20
1598 A528 45c multicolored   .70   .20
1599 A528 45c multicolored   .70   .20
1600 A528 45c multicolored   .70   .20
1601 A528 45c multicolored   .70   .20
  a. Strip of 5, #1597-1601   3.50   1.00

Emergency
Services
A529

#1602, Disaster victim evacuated. #1603, Police
rescue hiker. $1.05, Rapid response saves home.
$1.20, Ambulance dash saves life.

1997, July 10   Litho.   Perf. 14x14¹/₂
1602 A529   45c multicolored   .70   .20
1603 A529   45c multicolored   .70   .20
  a. Pair, #1602-1603   1.40   .40
1604 A529 $1.05 multicolored   1.60   .50
1605 A529 $1.20 multicolored   1.80   .55
    Nos. 1602-1605 (4)   4.80   1.45

Arrival of
Merino
Sheep in
Australia,
Bicent.
A530

Designs: No. 1606, George Peppin, Junior (1827-
76), breeder, Merino sheep. No. 1607, "Pepe"
chair, uses of wool.

1997, Aug. 7   Litho.   Perf. 14x14¹/₂
1606 A530 45c multicolored   .70   .20
1607 A530 45c multicolored   .70   .20
  a. Pair, #1606-1607   1.40   .40

Scenes from
"The
Dreaming,"
Animated
Stories for
Children
A531

Designs: 45c, Dumbi the Owl. $1, The Two
Willy-Willies. $1.20, How Brolga Became a Bird.
$1.80, Tuggan-Tuggan.

1997, Aug. 21   Perf. 14¹/₂
1608 A531   45c multicolored   .70   .20
1609 A531 $1 multicolored   1.50   .40
1610 A531 $1.20 multicolored   1.80   .45
1611 A531 $1.80 multicolored   2.70   .70
    Nos. 1608-1611 (4)   6.70   1.75

Prehistoric
Animals — A532

Designs: No. 1612, Rhoetosaurus brownei. No.
1613, Mcnamaraspis kaprios. No. 1614, Ninjemys
oweni. No. 1615, Paracyclotosaurus davidi. No.
1616, Woolungasaurus glendowerensis.

1997, Sept. 4   Litho.   Perf. 14¹/₂x14
1612 A532 45c multicolored   .65   .20
1613 A532 45c multicolored   .65   .20
1614 A532 45c multicolored   .65   .20
1615 A532 45c multicolored   .65   .20
1616 A532 45c multicolored   .65   .20
  a. Strip of 5, #1612-1616   3.25   1.00
Printed in sheets of 10 stamps.

Nocturnal Animals
A533   A534

Perf. 14¹/₂x14, 14x14¹/₂
1997, Oct. 1   Litho.
1617 A533 45c Barking owl   .65   .20
1618 A533 45c Spotted-tailed quoll   .65   .20
  a. Pair, #1617-1618   1.30   .40
1619 A534 45c Platypus   .65   .20
1620 A534 45c Brown antechinus   .65   .20
1621 A534 45c Dingo   .65   .20
  a. Strip of 3, #1619-1621   2.00   .60

Size: 49x29mm
1622 A534 45c Yellow-bellied glider   .65   .20
  a. Souvenir sheet, #1617-1622   4.00   1.50
    Nos. 1617-1622 (6)   3.90   1.20

No. 1622a is printed with additional phosphor
ink revealing a glow-in-the-dark spider and web
under ultraviolet light.

Size: 21x32mm
Serpentine Die Cut Perf. 11¹/₂
Self-Adhesive
1623 A533 45c like #1617   .65   .20
1624 A533 45c like #1618   .65   .20
  a. Booklet pane, 5 each #1623-1624   6.50
  b. Pair, #1623-1624   1.30

By its nature No. 1624a is a complete booklet.
The peelable paper backing serves as a booklet
cover.

Breast
Cancer
Awareness
A535

1997, Oct. 27   Litho.   Perf. 14x14¹/₂
1625 A535 45c multicolored   .65   .20

Christmas
A536

Children in Christmas Nativity pageant: 40c,
Angels. 45c, Mary holding Baby Jesus. $1, Three
Wise Men.

1997, Nov. 3
1626 A536 40c multicolored   .60   .20
1627 A536 45c multicolored   .65   .20
1628 A536 $1 multicolored   1.40   .45
    Nos. 1626-1628 (3)   2.65   .85

Booklet Stamps
Serpentine Die Cut Perf. 11¹/₂
Self-Adhesive

1629 A536 40c multicolored   .60   .20
  a. Booklet pane of 20   12.00

By its nature No. 1629a is a complete booklet.
The peelable paper backing serves as a booklet
cover, which also contains 20 labels.

AIR POST STAMPS

Airplane over
Bush
Lands — AP1

Unwmk.
1929, May 20   Engr.   Perf. 11
C1 AP1 3p deep green   7.50   3.00
    Never hinged   12.50
  a. Booklet pane of 4 ('30)   125.00

Kingsford-Smith Type of 1931

1931, Mar. 19
C2 A8 6p gray violet   7.50   7.50
    Never hinged   12.50

AP3

1931, Nov. 4
C3 AP3 6p olive brown   15.00   9.00
    Never hinged   22.50
    For overprint see No. CO1.

Mercury and
Hemispheres
AP4

1934, Dec. 1   Perf. 11
C4 AP4 1sh6p violet brown   30.00   1.75
    Never hinged   75.00

Perf. 13x13¹/₂
1937, Oct. 22   Wmk. 228
C5 AP4 1sh6p violet brown   7.50   .25
    Never hinged   12.50

> Catalogue values for unused
> stamps in this section, from this
> point to the end of the section, are
> for Never Hinged items.

Mercury and
Globe — AP5

1949, Sept. 1   Perf. 14¹/₂
C6 AP5 1sh6p sepia   1.75   .15

1956, Dec. 6   Unwmk.
C7 AP5 1sh6p sepia   16.00   .85

Super-Constellation over Globe — AP6

1958, Jan. 6   Perf. 14¹/₂x14
C8 AP6 2sh dark violet blue   2.50   1.75

Inauguration of Australian "Round the World" air
service.

AIR POST OFFICIAL STAMP

No. C3 Overprinted

Perf. 11, 11½

1931, Nov. 17 **Unwmk.**
CO1 AP3 6p olive brown 25.00 30.00
   Never hinged 40.00

Issued primarily for official use, but to prevent speculation, a quantity was issued for public distribution.

POSTAGE DUE STAMPS

Very fine examples of Nos. J1-J38 will have perforations touching the design on one or more sides due to the narrow spacing of the stamps on the plates. Stamps with perfs clear of the design on all four sides are scarce and will command higher prices.

D1   D2

1902 Typo. Wmk. 55 Perf. 11½, 12
J1	D1	½p emerald	8.25	9.50
J2	D1	1p emerald	16.00	6.50
a.		Perf. 11	600.00	250.00
J3	D1	2p emerald	20.00	7.75
J4	D1	3p emerald	30.00	10.00
J5	D1	4p emerald	35.00	10.00
J6	D1	6p emerald	45.00	19.00
J7	D1	8p emerald	125.00	110.00
J8	D1	5sh emerald	250.00	82.50
		Nos. J1-J8 (8)	529.25	255.25

The 1p, 2p and 4p, type D1, exist also in perforations compounding 11 with 11½ & 12.

Perf. 11½, 12, 11 and 11 Compound with 11½, 12

1902-04
J9	D2	½p emerald	7.25	8.25
a.		Perf. 11	82.50	65.00
J10	D2	1p emerald	4.50	2.75
a.		Perf. 11	110.00	37.50
J11	D2	2p emerald	15.00	3.50
J12	D2	3p emerald	55.00	8.75
J13	D2	4p emerald	50.00	6.00
J14	D2	5p emerald	50.00	16.00
a.		Perf. 11	125.00	32.50
J15	D2	6p emerald	72.50	18.00
J16	D2	8p emerald	125.00	40.00
J17	D2	10p emerald	87.50	15.00
J18	D2	1sh emerald	57.50	14.00
a.		Perf. 11	175.00	45.00
J19	D2	2sh emerald	110.00	25.00
J20	D2	5sh emerald	225.00	22.50
a.		Perf. 11	375.00	150.00
J21	D2	10sh emerald	2,750.	1,050.
J22	D2	20sh emerald	4,000.	1,900.
		Nos. J9-J20 (12)	859.25	179.75

Perf. 11½, 12 Compound with 11
1906 **Wmk. 12**
J23	D2	½p emerald	14.00	10.00
J24	D2	1p emerald	30.00	5.50
a.		Perf. 11	650.00	250.00
J25	D2	2p emerald	50.00	10.00
J26	D2	3p emerald	375.00	300.00
J27	D2	4p emerald	77.50	25.00
a.		Perf. 11	900.00	400.00
J28	D2	6p emerald	140.00	22.50
		Nos. J23-J28 (6)	686.50	375.50

1907 **Wmk. 13** **Perf. 11½x11**
J29	D2	½p emerald	45.00	45.00
J30	D2	1p emerald	72.50	45.00
J31	D2	2p emerald	165.00	100.00
J32	D2	4p emerald	225.00	125.00
J33	D2	6p emerald	325.00	140.00
		Nos. J29-J33 (5)	832.50	455.00

D3   D4

Perf. 11, 11½x11 (1sh, 5sh)
1908-09 **Wmk. 12**
J34	D3	1sh emer ('09)	125.00	16.00
J35	D3	2sh emerald	1,100.	500.00
J36	D3	5sh emerald	225.00	52.50
J37	D3	10sh emerald	1,900.	1,750.
J38	D3	20sh emerald	5,250.	5,000.

Perf. 11, 12x12½, 12½, 14
1909 **Wmk. 13**
J39	D4	½p green & car	8.75	3.50
J40	D4	1p green & car	11.00	1.65
J41	D4	2p green & car	14.00	1.90
J42	D4	3p green & car	22.50	6.50
J43	D4	4p green & car	25.00	3.75
J44	D4	6p green & car	22.50	3.50
J45	D4	1sh green & car	22.50	2.75
J46	D4	2sh green & car	82.50	14.00
J47	D4	5sh green & car	82.50	14.00
J48	D4	10sh green & car	350.00	300.00
J49	D4	£1 green & car	550.00	325.00
		Nos. J39-J49 (11)	1,191.	676.55

1922-25 **Wmk. 10** **Perf. 14, 11**
J50	D4	½p grn & car ('23)	6.50	1.75
J51	D4	1p green & car	6.50	1.90
J52	D4	1½p yellow green & rose ('25)	3.75	3.25
J53	D4	2p green & car	8.00	3.75
J54	D4	3p green & car	15.00	2.75
J55	D4	4p green & car	19.00	2.25
J56	D4	6p green & car	22.50	13.00
		Nos. J50-J56 (7)	81.25	28.65

1931-37 **Wmk. 228** **Perf. 11, 14**
J57	D4	½p yel green & rose ('34)	10.00	9.00
J58	D4	1p yel grn & rose	4.00	.75
J59	D4	2p yel grn & rose	4.00	.75
J60	D4	3p yel grn & rose ('37)	125.00	42.50
J61	D4	4p yel green & rose ('34)	20.00	2.00
J62	D4	6p yel grn & rose ('36)	350.00	300.00
J63	D4	1sh yel green & rose ('34)	50.00	17.50
		Nos. J57-J63 (7)	563.00	372.50

D5

Engraved; Value Typo.
1938 **Perf. 14½x14**
J64	D5	½p green & car	.75	1.25
J65	D5	1p green & car	5.00	.50
J66	D5	2p green & car	4.50	.50
J67	D5	3p green & car	15.00	3.50
J68	D5	4p green & car	4.50	.25
J69	D5	6p green & car	45.00	17.50
J70	D5	1sh green & car	20.00	7.50
		Nos. J64-J70 (7)	94.75	31.00

> Catalogue values for unused stamps in this section, from this point to the end of the section, are for Never Hinged items.

Type of 1938
Value Tablet Redrawn

Original   Redrawn

Pence denominations: "D" has melon-shaped center in redrawn tablet. The redrawn 3p differs slightly, having semi-melon-shaped "D" center, with vertical white stroke half filling it.

1sh. 1938: Numeral "1" narrow, with six background lines above.

1sh. 1947: Numeral broader, showing more white space around dotted central ornament. Three lines above.

1946-57 **Wmk. 228**
J71	D5	½p grn & car ('56)	2.50	1.40
J72	D5	1p grn & car ('47)	1.25	.25
J73	D5	2p green & car	.75	1.00
J74	D5	3p green & car	4.00	.35
J75	D5	4p grn & car ('52)	5.00	.50
J76	D5	5p grn & car ('48)	7.50	1.25
J77	D5	6p grn & car ('47)	7.50	.65
J78	D5	7p grn & car ('53)	5.00	3.00
J79	D5	8p grn & car ('57)	12.50	11.50
J80	D5	1sh grn & car ('47)	12.50	1.25
		Nos. J71-J80 (10)	58.50	21.15

1953-54
White Tablet, Carmine Numeral
J81	D5	1sh grn & car ('54)	9.00	5.00
J82	D5	2sh green & car	12.50	10.00
J83	D5	5sh green & car	17.50	2.50
		Nos. J81-J83 (3)	39.00	17.50

Issued: 2sh, 5sh, Aug. 26; 1sh, Feb. 17.

Redrawn Type of 1947-57

Two Types of Some Pence Values:
Type I - Background lines touch numeral, "D" and period.
Type II - Lines do not touch numeral, etc.
Second engraving of 1sh has sharper and thicker lines.
The ½p type II has 7 dots under the "2."
The 8p type II has distinct lines in centers of "8" and between "8" and "D."

Engr.; Value Typo.
1958-60 **Unwmk.** **Perf. 14½x14**
J86	D5	½p grn & car (II)	2.50	1.10
a.		Six dots under the "2"	3.75	.95
J87	D5	1p grn & car (II)	2.50	.40
a.		Type I	3.25	.40
J88	D5	3p grn & car (I)	2.50	.75
J89	D5	4p grn & car (I)	5.00	4.00
a.		Type II ('59)	12.00	3.00
J90	D5	5p grn & car (I)	11.00	6.00
a.		Type II ('59)	70.00	22.50
J91	D5	6p grn & car (II)	6.50	1.75
J92	D5	8p grn & car (II)	10.00	15.00
a.		Indistinct lines	15.00	15.00
J93	D5	10p grn & car (II)	7.50	3.25

White Tablet, Carmine Numeral
J94	D5	1sh green & car	8.50	2.50
a.		2nd redrawing ('60)	9.00	.60
J95	D5	2sh grn & car	26.00	5.50
		Nos. J86-J95 (10)	82.00	40.25

Issued: 1sh, 9/8/58; 10p, 12/9/59; 2sh, 3/8/60; 3p, 6p, 5/25/60; others, 2/27/58.

MILITARY STAMPS

Nos. 166, 191, 183A, 173, 175, 206 and 177 Overprinted in Black:

B.C.O.F.
JAPAN
1946
a

B.C.O.F.
JAPAN
1946
b

B.C.O.F.
JAPAN
1946
c

Perf. 14½x14, 15x14, 11½, 13½x13
1946-47 **Wmk. 228**
M1	A24(a)	½p orange	2.75	2.75
M2	A36(b)	1p brown vio	2.25	2.25
a.		Blue overprint	100.00	67.50
M3	A27(b)	3p dk vio brn	2.00	.75
M4	A30(a)	6p brn violet	5.00	5.00
M5	A16(a)	1sh gray green	7.50	7.50
M6	A1 (c)	2sh dk red brn	22.50	22.50
M7	A32(c)	5sh dl red brn	110.00	100.00
		Nos. M1-M7 (7)	152.00	140.75

"B.C.O.F." stands for "British Commonwealth Occupation Force."
Forged overprints of Nos. M6-M7 exist.
Issued: #M1-M3, 10/11/46; #M4-M7, 5/8/47.

OFFICIAL STAMPS

Perforated Initials
In 1913-31, postage stamps were perforated "OS" for federal official use. This catalogue does not list varieties with perforated initials.

Overprinted Official stamps are comparatively more difficult to find well centered than the basic issues on which they are printed. This is because poorly centered sheets were purposely chosen to be overprinted.

Overprinted

On Regular Issue of 1931
1931, May 4 Unwmk. **Perf. 11, 11½**
O1	A8	2p dull red	60.00	22.50
O2	A8	3p blue	175.00	35.00

These stamps were issued primarily for official use but to prevent speculation a quantity was issued for public distribution.
Used values are for cto copies.
Counterfeit overprints exist.

On Regular Issues of 1928-32
1932 **Wmk. 203** **Perf. 13½x12½**
O3	A4	2p red (II)	10.00	.90
O4	A4	4p olive bister	30.00	6.00

Perf. 11½, 12
O5	A1	6p brown	67.50	35.00

1932-33 **Wmk. 228** **Perf. 13½x12½**
O6	A4	½p orange	6.00	1.25
a.		Inverted overprint	3,000.	1,500.
O7	A4	1p green (I)	2.00	.75
O8	A4	2p red (II)	5.00	.60
a.		Inverted overprint		2,250.
O9	A4	3p ultra (II) ('33)	14.00	7.50
O10	A4	5p brown buff	42.50	21.00

Perf. 11½, 12
O11	A1	6p yellow brown	35.00	25.00
		Nos. O6-O11 (6)	104.50	56.10

1932 **Unwmk.** **Perf. 11, 11½**
O12	A9	2p red	5.50	4.50
O13	A9	3p blue	18.00	18.00
O14	A16	1sh gray green	55.00	32.50
		Nos. O12-O14 (3)	78.50	55.00

AUSTRALIAN ANTARCTIC TERRITORY

> Catalogue values for all unused stamps in this section are for Never Hinged items.

All stamps are also valid for postage in Australia.

Edgeworth David, Douglas Mawson and A.F. McKay (1908-09 South Pole Expedition) — A1

Australian Explorers and Map of Antarctica — A2

Designs: 8p, Loading weasel (snow truck). 1sh, Dog team and iceberg, vert. 2sh3p, Emperor penguins and map, vert.

Perf. 14½, 14½x14, 14x14½
1957-59 **Engr.** **Unwmk.**
L1	A1	5p brown	.50	.15
L2	A2	8p dark blue	2.25	1.25
L3	A2	1sh dark green	4.00	2.10
L4	A2	2sh ultra ('57)	3.50	.32
L5	A2	2sh3p green	12.00	6.00
		Nos. L1-L5 (5)	22.25	9.82

Nos. L1 and L2 were printed as 4p and 7p stamps and surcharged typographically in black and dark blue before issuance.
Sizes of stamps: No. L2, 34x21mm; Nos. L3, L5, 21x34mm; No. L4, 43½x25½mm.

1961, July 5 **Perf. 14½**
L6	A1	5p dark blue	1.10	.18

The denomination on No. L6 is not within a typographed circle, but is part of the engraved design.

Sir Douglas Mawson   Lookout and Iceberg
A3   A4

1961, Oct. 18
L7	A3	5p dark green	.70	.18

50th anniv. of the 1911-14 Australian Antarctic Expedition.

Perf. 13½x13, 13x13½

1966-68   Photo.   Unwmk.

Designs: 1c, Aurora australis and camera dome. 2c, Banding penguins. 5c, Branding of elephant seals. 7c, Measuring snow strata. 10c, Wind gauges. 15c, Weather balloon. 20c, Helicopter. 25c, Radio operator. 50c, Ice compression tests. $1, "Mock sun" (parahelion) and dogs. 20c, 25c, 50c and $1 horizontal.

L8	A4	1c multicolored	.55	.30
L9	A4	2c multicolored	1.00	.45
L10	A4	4c multicolored	1.10	.45
L11	A4	5c multicolored	1.75	1.25
L12	A4	7c multicolored	.55	.35
L13	A4	10c multicolored	2.50	.90
L14	A4	15c multicolored	3.25	3.25
L15	A4	20c multicolored	7.00	4.00
L16	A4	25c multicolored	4.00	4.25
L17	A4	50c multicolored	21.00	8.00
L18	A4	$1 multicolored	27.50	18.00
		Nos. L8-L18 (11)	70.20	41.20

Issued: 5c, 9/25/68; others, 9/28/66.
Nos. L8-L18 are on phosphorescent helecon paper. Fluorescent orange is one of the colors used in printing the 10c, 15c, 20c and 50c.

Sastrugi Snow Formation — A5

1971, June 23   Photo.   Perf. 13x13½

L19	A5	6c shown	.55	.55
L20	A5	30c Pancake ice	6.00	6.00

10th anniv. of the Antarctic Treaty pledging peaceful uses of and scientific cooperation in Antarctica.

Capt. Cook, Sextant, Azimuth Compass — A6

Design: 35c, Chart of Cook's circumnavigation of Antarctica, and "Resolution."

1972, Sept. 13   Photo.   Perf. 13x13½

L21	A6	7c bister & multi	2.00	.95
L22	A6	35c buff & multi	5.50	6.00

Bicentenary of Capt. James Cook's circumnavigation of Antarctica.

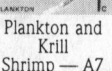

Plankton and Krill Shrimp — A7

Mawson's D.H. Gipsy Moth, 1931 — A8

Food Chain (Essential for Survival): 7c, Adelie penguin feeding on krill shrimp. 9c, Leopard seal pursuing fish, horiz. 10c, Killer whale hunting seals, horiz. 20c, Wandering albatross, horiz. $1, Sperm whale attacking giant squid.

Explorers' Aircraft: 8c, Rymill's DH Fox Moth returning to Barry Island. 25c, Hubert Wilkins Lockheed Vega, horiz. 30c, Lincoln Ellsworth's Northrop Gamma. 35c, Lars Christensen's Avro Avian and Framnes Mountains, horiz. 50c, Richard Byrd's Ford Tri-Motor dropping US flag over South Pole.

Perf. 13½x13, 13x13½

1973, Aug. 15

L23	A7	1c multicolored	.15	.15
L24	A8	5c multicolored	.15	.16
L25	A7	7c multicolored	1.40	.60
L26	A8	8c multicolored	.28	.28
L27	A7	9c multicolored	.25	.25
L28	A7	10c multicolored	3.00	1.25
L29	A7	20c multicolored	.35	.35
L30	A8	25c multicolored	.35	.35
L31	A8	30c multicolored	.35	.35
L32	A8	35c multicolored	.32	.45
L33	A8	50c multicolored	1.25	.85
L34	A7	$1 multicolored	2.25	.85
		Nos. L23-L34 (12)	10.10	5.89

Adm. Byrd, Plane, Mountains A9

Design: 20c, Adm. Byrd, Floyd Bennett tri-motored plane, map of Antarctica.

1979, June 20   Litho.   Perf. 15½

L35	A9	20c multicolored	.48	.48
L36	A9	55c multicolored	1.00	.95

50th anniv. of first flight over South Pole by Richard Byrd (1888-1957).

"S.Y. Nimrod" A10

2c, 5c, 22c, 25c, 40c, 55c, $1 are vertical. No. L41 actually pictures the S.S. Morning.

Perf. 13½x13, 13x13½

1974-81   Litho.

L37	A10	1c S.Y. Aurora	.15	.15
L38	A10	2c R.Y. Penola	.15	.15
L39	A10	5c M.V. Thala Dan	.15	.15
L40	A10	10c H.M.S. Challenger	.15	.15
L41	A10	15c shown	.95	.95
L42	A10	15c S.Y. Nimrod, stern view	.25	.22
L43	A10	20c R.R.S. Discovery II	.32	.30
L44	A10	22c R.Y.S. Terra Nova	.28	.28
L45	A10	25c S.S. Endurance	.40	.35
L46	A10	30c S.S. Fram	.50	.50
L47	A10	35c M.S. Nella Dan	.45	.45
L48	A10	40c M.S. Kista Dan	.50	.50
L49	A10	45c L'Astrolabe	.55	.55
L50	A10	50c S.S. Norvegia	.70	.70
L51	A10	55c S.Y. Discovery	.80	.85
L52	A10	$1 H.M.S. Resolution	1.25	.65
		Nos. L37-L52 (16)	7.55	6.85

A11

A12

1982, May 5   Litho.   Perf. 14x13½

L53	A11	27c Mawson, landscape	.35	.35
L54	A11	75c Mawson, map	1.25	1.25

Sir Douglas Mawson (1882-1958), explorer.

1983, Apr. 6   Litho.   Perf. 14½

Local Wildlife: a, Light-mantled sooty albatross. b, Macquarie Isld. shags. c, Elephant seals. d, Royal penguins. e, Antarctic prions.

L55		Strip of 5, multi	2.25	2.25
a.-e.		A12 27c, any single	.45	.45

12th Antarctic Treaty Consultative Meeting, Canberra, Sept. 13-27 — A13

1983, Sept. 7   Litho.   Perf. 14½

L56	A13	27c multicolored	.42	.42

South Magnetic Pole Expedition, 75th Anniv. — A14

1984, Jan. 16

L57	A14	30c Prismatic compass	.40	.40
L58	A14	85c Aneroid barometer	1.25	1.25

Dog Team, Mawson Station — A15

1984-87   Litho.   Perf. 14½x15

L60	A15	2c Summer afternoon	.15	.15
L61	A15	5c shown	.15	.15
L62	A15	10c Evening	.15	.15
L63	A15	15c Prince Charles Mts.	.22	.22
L64	A15	20c Morning	.28	.28
L65	A15	25c Sea ice, iceberg	.40	.40
L66	A15	30c Mt. Coates	.48	.48
L67	A15	33c Iceberg Alley, Mawson	.48	.48
L68	A15	36c Winter evening	.50	.50
L69	A15	45c Brash ice, vert.	.65	.65
L70	A15	60c Midwinter shadows	.85	.85
L71	A15	75c Coastline	1.20	1.20
L72	A15	85c Landing field	1.35	1.35
L73	A15	90c Pancake ice, vert.	1.30	1.30
L74	A15	$1 Emperor penguins, Auster Rookery	1.45	1.45
		Nos. L60-L74 (15)	9.61	9.61

Issue dates: 5c, 25c, 30c, 75c, 85c, July 18, 1984. 15c, 33c, 45c, 90c, $1, Aug. 7, 1985. 2c, 10c, 20c, 36c, 60c, Mar. 11, 1987.

A16

A17

1986, Sept. 17   Litho.   Perf. 14x13½

L75	A16	36c multicolored	.55	.55

Antarctic Treaty, 25th anniv.

1988, July 20   Litho.   Perf. 13

Environment, Conservation and Technology: a, Hour-glass dolphins and the Nella Dan. b, Emperor penguins and Davis Station. c, Crabeater seal and helicopters. d, Adelie penguins and snow-ice transport vehicle. e, Gray-headed albatross and photographer.

L76		Strip of 5	3.10	1.20
a.-e.		A17 37c any single	.62	.20

Paintings by Sir Sidney Nolan (b. 1917) — A18

1989, June 14   Litho.   Perf. 14x13½

L77	A18	39c Antarctica	.65	.65
L78	A18	39c Iceberg Alley	.65	.65
L79	A18	60c Glacial Flow	1.00	1.00
L80	A18	80c Frozen Sea	1.35	1.35
		Nos. L77-L80 (4)	3.65	3.65

Aurora Australis A19

Design: $1.20, Research ship Aurora Australis.

1991, June 20   Litho.   Perf. 14½

L81	A19	43c multicolored	.65	.20
L82	A19	$1.20 multicolored	1.90	.65

Antarctic Treaty, 30th anniv. (No. L81).

Regional Wildlife A20

Perf. 14x14½, 14½x14

1992-93   Litho.

L83	A20	45c Adelie penguin	.60	.25
L84	A20	75c Elephant seal	.95	.35
L85	A20	85c Northern giant petrel	1.10	.40
L86	A20	95c Weddell seal	1.25	.45
L86A	A20	$1 Royal penguins	1.25	.50
L87	A20	$1.20 Emperor penguin, vert.	1.50	.60
L88	A20	$1.40 Fur seals	1.65	.70
L89	A20	$1.50 King penguins, vert.	1.90	.75
		Nos. L83-L89 (8)	10.20	4.00

Issued: $1, $1.40, $1.50, 1/14/93; others, 5/14/92.

The Last Huskies A21

1994, Jan. 13   Litho.   Perf. 14½

L90	A21	45c Dog up close, vert.	.70	.20
L91	A21	75c Sled team	1.10	.35
L92	A21	85c Dog seated, vert.	1.25	.40
L93	A21	$1.05 Three dogs	1.50	.50
		Nos. L90-L93 (4)	4.50	1.45

Whales & Dolphins A22

1995, June 15   Litho.   Perf. 14½

L94	A22	45c Humpback whale	.65	.20
L95	A22	45c Hourglass dolphin, vert.	.65	.20
L96	A22	45c Minke whale, vert.	.65	.20
a.		Pair, #L95-L96	1.30	.45
L97	A22	$1 Killer whale	1.40	.50
a.		Souvenir sheet of 4, #L94-L97	3.50	3.50
b.		As "a," overprinted	3.50	3.50
c.		As "a," overprinted	3.50	3.50
		Nos. L94-L97 (4)	3.35	1.10

No. L97b is overprinted in gold in sheet margin with Singapore '95 emblem and: "Australia Post Exhibition Sheet No. 2," and, in both Chinese and English, with "Singapore 95 World Stamp Exhibition."

No. L97c is overprinted in gold in sheet margin with exhibition emblem, "Australian Post Exhibition Sheet No. 3" and "CAPEX '96 WORLD PHILATELIC EXHIBITION / EXPOSITION PHILATELIQUE MONDIALE"

Issued: #L97b, 9/1/95; #L97c, 6/15/96.

Landscapes, by Christian Clare Robertson — A23

#L98, Rafting sea ice. #L99, Shadow on the Plateau. $1, Ice cave. $1.20, Twelve Lake.

1996, May 16   Litho.   Perf. 14½x14

L98	A23	45c multicolored	.70	.25
L99	A23	45c multicolored	.70	.25
a.		Pair, #L98-L99	1.40	.50
L100	A23	$1 multicolored	1.60	.50
L101	A23	$1.20 multicolored	1.90	.60
		Nos. L98-L101 (4)	4.90	1.60

Australian Natl. Antarctic Research Expeditions, 50th Anniv. A24

Designs: No. L102, Apple field huts. No. L103, Inside an apple hut. 95c, Summer surveying. $1.05, Sea ice research. $1.20, Remote field camp.

1997, May 15   Litho.   Perf. 14x14½

L102	A24	45c multicolored	.70	.20
L103	A24	45c multicolored	.70	.20
a.		Pair, #L102-L103	1.40	.40

L104	A24	95c multicolored	1.50 .45
L105	A24	$1.05 multicolored	1.65 .50
L106	A24	$1.20 multicolored	1.90 .55
		Nos. L102-L106 (5)	6.45 1.90

AUSTRIA

'òs-trē-ə

LOCATION — Central Europe
GOVT. — Republic
AREA — 32,376 sq. mi.
POP. — 7,555,338 (1981)
CAPITAL — Vienna

Before 1867 Austria was an absolute monarchy, which included Hungary and Lombardy-Venetia. In 1867 the Austro-Hungarian Monarchy was established, with Austria and Hungary as equal partners. After World War I, in 1918, the different nationalities established their own states and only the German-speaking parts remained, forming a republic under the name "Deutschosterreich" (German Austria), which name was shortly again changed to "Austria." In 1938 German forces occupied Austria, which became part of the German Reich. After the liberation by Allied troops in 1945, an independent republic was re-established.

60 Kreuzer = 1 Gulden
100 Neu-Kreuzer = 1 Gulden (1858)
100 Heller = 1 Krone (1899)
100 Groschen = 1 Schilling (1925)

Catalogue values for unused stamps in this country are for Never Hinged items, beginning with Scott 432 in the regular postage section, Scott B165 in the semi-postal section, Scott C47 in the airpost section, Scott J175 in the postage due section, and Scott 4N1 in the AMG section.

Unused stamps without gum sell for about one-third or less of the values quoted.

Watermarks

Wmk. 91 - "BRIEF-MARKEN" In Double-lined Capitals Across the Middle of the Sheet

Wmk. 140 - Crown

Issues of the Austrian Monarchy (including Hungary)

Coat of Arms — A1

NINE KREUZER
Type I. One heavy line around coat of arms center. On the 9kr the top of "9" is about on a level with "Kreuzer" and not near the top of the label. Each cliche has the "9" in a different position.
Type IA. As type I, but with 1¼mm between "9" and "K."
Type II. One heavy line around coat of arms center. On the 9kr the top of "9" is much higher than the top of the word "Kreuzer" and nearly touches the top of the label.

Type III. As type II, but with two, thinner, lines around the center.

Wmk. K.K.H.M. in Sheet or Unwmk.
1850 Typo. Imperf.

The stamps of this issue were at first printed on a rough hand-made paper, varying in thickness and having a watermark in script letters K.K.H.M., the initials of Kaiserlich Königliches Handels-Ministerium (Imperial and Royal Ministry of Commerce), vertically in the gutter between the panes. Parts of these letters show on margin stamps in the sheet. From 1854 a thick, smooth machine-made paper without watermark was used.

Thin to Thick Paper

1	A1	1kr yellow	900.00	70.00
a.		Printed on both sides	1,900.	130.00
b.		1kr orange	1,100.	100.00
c.		1kr brown orange	1,900.	350.00
2	A1	2kr black	775.00	60.00
a.		Ribbed paper	1,350.	
b.		2kr gray black	1,100.	70.00
d.		Half used as 1kr on cover		23,500.
3	A1	3kr red	300.00	3.00
a.		Ribbed paper	1,600.	72.50
b.		Laid paper	8,000.	
c.		Printed on both sides	7,500.	
4	A1	6kr brown	475.00	4.00
a.		Ribbed paper	1,150.	
c.		Diagonal half used as 3kr on cover		10,000.
5	A1	9kr blue, type II	650.00	3.00
a.		9kr blue, type I	1,150.	7.50
b.		9kr blue, type IA	13,500.	1,000.
c.		Laid paper, type III	6,750.	
d.		Printed on both sides, type II	7,500.	

1854 Machine-made Paper, Type III

1d	A1	1kr yellow	800.00	67.50
2c	A1	2kr black	675.00	47.50
3e	A1	3kr red	250.00	2.00
f.		3kr red, type I	2,100.	25.00
4b	A1	6kr brown	375.00	3.25
5e	A1	9kr blue	500.00	2.00

In 1852-54, Nos. 1 to 5, rouletted 14, were used in Tokay and Homonna. A 12kr blue exists, but was not issued.
The reprints are type III in brighter colors, some on paper watermarked "Briefmarken" in the sheet.
For similar design see Lombardy-Venetia A1.

Emperor Franz Josef
A2   A3   A4

A5   A6

1858-59 Embossed Perf. 14½

Two Types of Each Value.
Type I. Loops of the bow at the back of the head broken, except the 2kr. In the 2kr, the "2" has a flat foot, thinning to the right. The frame line in the UR corner is thicker than the line below. In the 5kr the top frame line is unbroken.
Type II. Loops complete. Wreath projects further at top of head. In the 2kr, the "2" has a more curved foot of uniform thickness, with a shading line in the upper and lower curves. The frame line UR is thicker than the line below. In the 5kr the top frame line is broken.

6	A2	2kr yellow, type II	675.00	42.50
a.		2kr yellow, type I	1,600.	350.00
b.		2kr orange, type II	1,800.	250.00
c.		Half used as 1kr on cover		25,000.
7	A3	3kr black, type II	1,900.	175.00
a.		3kr black, type I	1,100.	250.00
8	A3	3kr green, type II ('59)	925.00	125.00
9	A4	5kr red, type II	250.00	.85
a.		5kr red, type I	350.00	11.00
b.		5kr red, type II with type I frame	425.00	22.50
10	A5	10kr brown, type II	550.00	2.50
a.		10kr brown, type I	625.00	5.00
b.		Half used as 5kr on cover		10,000.
11	A6	15kr blue, type II	550.00	2.00
a.		Type I	1,050.	12.50

The reprints are of type II and are perforated 10½, 11, 12, 12½ and 13. There are also imperforate reprints of Nos. 6 to 8.
For similar designs see Lombardy-Venetia A2-A6.

Franz Josef — A7   Coat of Arms — A8

1860-61 Embossed Perf. 14

12	A7	2kr yellow	300.00	25.00
a.		Half used as 1kr on cover		12,500.
13	A7	3kr green	275.00	22.50
14	A7	5kr red	175.00	.75
15	A7	10kr brown	250.00	1.75
a.		Half used as 5kr on cover		5,500.
16	A7	15kr blue	225.00	1.00

The reprints are perforated 9, 9½, 10, 10½, 11, 11½, 12, 12½, 13 and 13½. There are also imperforate reprints of the 2 and 3kr.
For similar design see Lombardy-Venetia A7. For overprints see Poland Nos. J11-J12.

1863

17	A8	2kr yellow	425.00	80.00
a.		Half used as 1kr on cover		12,500.
18	A8	3kr green	350.00	75.00
19	A8	5kr rose	275.00	6.50
20	A8	10kr blue	750.00	8.00
21	A8	15kr yellow brown	950.00	10.00

For similar design see Lombardy-Venetia A1.

Wmk. 91, or, before July 1864, Unwmkd.
1863-64 Perf. 9½

22	A8	2kr yellow ('64)	125.00	10.00
a.		Half used as 1kr on cover		12,500.
23	A8	3kr green ('64)	125.00	10.00
24	A8	5kr rose	45.00	.40
25	A8	10kr blue	125.00	2.00
a.		Half used as 5kr on cover		10,500.
26	A8	15kr yellow brown	125.00	1.50
		Nos. 22-26 (5)	545.00	24.40

The reprints are perforated 10½, 11½, 13 and 13½. There are also imperforate reprints of the 2 and 3kr.

Issues of Austro-Hungarian Monarchy

From 1867 to 1871 the independent postal administrations of Austria and Hungary used the same stamps.

A9   A10

5 kr:
Type I. In arabesques in lower left corner, the small ornament at left of the curve nearest the figure "5" is short and has three points at bottom.
Type II. The ornament is prolonged within the curve and has two points at bottom. The corresponding ornament at top of the lower left corner does not touch the curve (1872).
Type III. Similar to type II but the top ornament is joined to the curve (1881). Two different printing methods were used for the 1867-74 issues. The first produced stamps on which the hair and whiskers were coarse and thick, from the second they were fine and clear.

1867-72 Wmk. 91 Typo. Perf. 9½
Coarse Print

27	A9	2kr yellow	85.00	1.75
a.		Half used as 1kr on cover		12,500.
28	A9	3kr green	80.00	2.00
29	A9	5kr rose, type I	55.00	.15
a.		5kr rose, type II	50.00	.15
b.		Perf. 10½, type II	125.00	
c.		Cliché of 3kr in plate of 5kr		52,500.
30	A9	10kr blue	165.00	1.50
a.		Half used as 5kr on cover		15,000.
31	A9	15kr brown	140.00	4.00
32	A9	25kr lilac	20.00	12.50
a.		25kr gray lilac	20.00	15.00
b.		25kr brown violet	125.00	30.00

Perf. 12

33	A10	50kr light brown	27.50	80.00
a.		50kr pale red brown	250.00	95.00
b.		50kr brownish rose	325.00	175.00
c.		Pair, imperf. btwn., vert. or horizontal	700.00	1,000.

Issues for Austria only
1874-80 Perf. 9½
Fine Print

34	A9	2kr yellow ('76)	7.50	.75
35	A9	3kr green ('76)	24.00	.50
36	A9	5kr rose, type III	12.50	.20
37	A9	10kr blue ('75)	65.00	.40
38	A9	15kr brown ('77)	5.00	3.50
39	A9	25kr gray lil ('78)	1.25	100.00

Perf. 9

34a	A9	2kr	140.00	40.00
35a	A9	3kr	125.00	20.00
36a	A9	5kr	50.00	2.00
37a	A9	10kr	250.00	22.50
38a	A9	15kr	325.00	67.50

Perf. 10½

34b	A9	2kr	35.00	2.75
35b	A9	3kr	55.00	1.75
36b	A9	5kr	8.00	.50
37b	A9	10kr	110.00	1.75
38b	A9	15kr	150.00	16.00

Perf. 12

34c	A9	2kr	165.00	87.50
35c	A9	3kr	140.00	12.50
36c	A9	5kr	35.00	3.25
37c	A9	10kr	300.00	90.00
38c	A9	15kr	425.00	110.00
40	A10	50kr brown ('80)	10.00	100.00
b.		Perf. 10½x12	250.00	—

Perf. 13

34d	A9	2kr	200.00	200.00
35d	A9	3kr	125.00	20.00
36d	A9	5kr	70.00	12.50
37d	A9	10kr	165.00	55.00
38d	A9	15kr	375.00	275.00
40a	A10	50kr	20.00	110.00

Various compound perforations exist.
For similar designs see Offices in the Turkish Empire A1-A2.

A11

Perf. 9, 9½, 10, 10½, 11½, 12, 12½
1883
Inscriptions in Black

41	A11	2kr brown	5.50	.50
42	A11	3kr green	4.75	.30
43	A11	5kr rose	10.00	.25
a.		Vert. pair, imperf. btwn.	250.00	350.00
44	A11	10kr blue	4.75	.35
45	A11	20kr gray	55.00	3.25
46	A11	50kr red lilac	50.00	50.00

The last printings of Nos. 41 to 46 are watermarked "ZEITUNGS-MARKEN" instead of "BRIEF-MARKEN."
The 5kr has been reprinted in a dull red rose, perforated 10½.
For similar design see Offices in the Turkish Empire A3.
For surcharges see Offices in the Turkish Empire Nos. 15-19.

A12   A13

Perf. 9 to 13½, also Compound
1890-96   Unwmk.
Granite Paper
Numerals in black, Nos. 51 to 61

51	A12	1kr dark gray	1.10	.20
a.	Pair, imperf. between		190.00	350.00
52	A12	2kr light brown	.25	.20
53	A12	3kr gray green	.40	.25
a.	Pair, imperf. between		200.00	425.00
54	A12	5kr rose	.40	.25
a.	Pair, imperf. between		180.00	325.00
55	A12	10kr ultramarine	.60	.20
a.	Pair, imperf. between		225.00	425.00
56	A12	12kr claret	2.00	.35
a.	Pair, imperf. between		—	—
57	A12	15kr lilac	1.00	.25
a.	Pair, imperf. between		225.00	425.00
58	A12	20kr olive green	30.00	2.00
59	A12	24kr gray blue	2.00	1.25
a.	Pair, imperf. between		240.00	425.00
60	A12	30kr dark brown	2.50	.60
61	A12	50kr violet	5.00	7.00

Engr.

62	A13	1gld dark blue	1.25	2.00
63	A13	1gld pale lilac ('96)	35.00	3.50
64	A13	2gld carmine	3.50	10.00
65	A13	2gld green ('96)	15.00	25.00
		Nos. 51-65 (15)	100.00	53.05

Nearly all values of the 1890-1907 issues are found with numerals missing in one or more corners, some with numerals printed on the back.
For surcharges see Offices in the Turkish Empire Nos. 20-25, 28-31.

A14

Perf. 9 to 13½, also Compound
1891   Typo.
Numerals in black

66	A14	20kr olive green	2.25	.25
67	A14	24kr gray blue	5.00	.75
68	A14	30kr brown	2.25	.25
a.	Pair, imperf. between		250.00	350.00
b.	Perf. 9		100.00	32.50
69	A14	50kr violet	3.00	.35
		Nos. 66-69 (4)	12.50	1.60

For surcharges see Offices in the Turkish Empire Nos. 26-27.

A15   A16

A17   A18

Perf. 10½ to 13½ and Compound
1899
Without Varnish Bars
Numerals in black, Nos. 70-82

70	A15	1h lilac	.55	.15
b.	Imperf.		55.00	110.00
c.	Perf. 10½		15.00	4.50
d.	Numerals inverted		375.00	950.00
71	A15	2h dark gray	2.50	.50
72	A15	3h bister brown	5.00	.15
b.	"3" in lower right corner sideways			1,100.
73	A15	5h blue green	8.00	.15
b.			10.50	3.00
74	A15	6h orange	.40	.15
75	A15	10h rose	8.00	.15
b.	Perf. 10½		275.00	125.00
76	A16	20h brown	.55	.20
77	A16	25h ultramarine	50.00	.30
78	A16	30h red violet	16.00	2.25
b.	Horiz. pair, imperf. btwn.		275.00	
80	A17	40h green	27.50	2.50
81	A17	50h gray blue	17.50	3.50
b.	All four "50's" parallel			1,600.
82	A17	60h brown	35.00	.90
b.	Horiz. pair, imperf. btwn.		275.00	
c.	Perf. 10½		50.00	1.50

Engr.

83	A18	1k carmine rose	2.00	.20
a.	1k carmine		5.00	.20
b.	Vert. pair, imperf. btwn.		275.00	300.00
84	A18	2k gray lilac	45.00	.40
a.	Vert. pair, imperf. btwn.		300.00	500.00
85	A18	4k gray green	4.00	8.00
		Nos. 70-85 (15)	222.00	19.50

For surcharges see Offices in Crete Nos. 1-7, Offices in the Turkish Empire Nos. 32-45.

1901   **With Varnish Bars**

70a	A15	1h lilac	1.75	.40
71a	A15	2h dark gray	1.75	.35
72a	A15	3h bister brown	.35	.15
73a	A15	5h blue green	.20	.15
74a	A15	6h orange	.20	.15
75a	A16	10h rose	.25	.15
76a	A16	20h brown	.80	.15
77a	A16	25h ultra	.90	.20
78a	A16	30h red violet	1.75	.85
79	A17	35h green	.90	.35
80a	A17	40h green	1.65	3.25
81a	A17	50h gray blue	4.00	6.75
82a	A17	60h brown	8.00	
		Nos. 70a-78a,79,80a-82a (13)	16.50	13.50

The diagonal yellow bars of varnish were printed across the face to prevent cleaning.

A19   A20

A21

Perf. 12½ to 13½ and Compound
1905-07   Typo.
Colored Numerals
Without Varnish Bars

86	A19	1h lilac	.20	.15
87	A19	2h dark gray	.20	.15
88	A19	3h bister brown	.20	.15
89	A19	5h dk blue green	8.50	.15
90	A19	5h yellow grn ('06)	.40	.15
91	A19	6h deep orange	.40	.15
92	A20	10h carmine ('06)	.55	.15
93	A20	12h violet ('07)	1.10	.30
94	A20	20h brown ('06)	2.00	.15
95	A20	25h ultra ('06)	3.50	.20
96	A20	30h red violet ('06)	6.00	.15

Black Numerals

97	A20	10h carmine	7.50	.15
98	A20	20h brown	35.00	.75
99	A20	25h ultra	35.00	1.75
100	A20	30h red violet	35.00	1.75

White Numerals

101	A21	35h green	2.25	.20
102	A21	40h deep violet	2.25	.55
103	A21	50h dull blue	3.00	2.50
104	A21	60h yellow brown	3.00	.30
105	A21	72h rose	3.00	.95
		Nos. 86-105 (20)	149.05	10.75

For surcharges see Offices in Crete #8-14.

1904

With Varnish Bars

86a	A19	1h lilac	.50	.20
87a	A19	2h dark gray	1.75	.30
88a	A19	3h bister brown	1.75	.15
89a	A19	5h dk blue green	4.00	.15
91a	A19	6h deep orange	6.00	.20
97a	A20	10h carmine	2.50	.15
98a	A20	20h brown	32.50	.40
99a	A20	25h ultra	37.50	.40
100a	A20	30h red violet	40.00	.75
101a	A21	35h green	35.00	.30
102a	A21	40h deep violet	32.50	2.75
103a	A21	50h dull blue	32.50	.40
104a	A21	60h yellow brown	32.50	.65
105a	A21	72h rose	1.00	.50
		Nos. 86a-105a (14)	260.00	11.00

Stamps of the 1901, 1904 and 1905 issues perf. 9 or 10½, also compound with 12½, were not sold at any post office, but were supplied only to some high-ranking officials. This applies also to the contemporary issues of Austrian Offices Abroad.

Karl VI — A22   Franz Josef — A23

Schönbrunn Castle — A24

Franz Josef — A25

Designs: 2h, Maria Theresa. 3h, Joseph II. 5h, 10h, 25h, Franz Josef. 6h, Leopold II. 12h, Franz I. 20h, Ferdinand I. 30h, Franz Josef as youth. 35h, Franz Josef in middle age. 60h, Franz Josef on horseback. 1k, Franz Josef in royal robes. 5k, Hofburg, Vienna.

1908-13			Typo.	Perf. 12½
110	A22	1h gray black	.35	.20
111	A22	2h blue violet ('13)	.25	.20
a.	2h violet		.30	.15
112	A22	3h magenta	.20	.20
113	A22	5h yellow green	.20	.20
a.	Booklet pane of 6		20.00	
114	A22	6h buff	.60	.45
b.	6h orange brown ('13)		1.00	1.00
115	A22	10h rose	.20	.20
a.	Booklet pane of 6		70.00	
116	A22	12h scarlet	1.25	.30
117	A22	20h chocolate	1.75	.20
118	A22	25h ultra ('13)	1.10	.20
a.	25h deep blue		1.75	.20
119	A20	30h olive green	3.75	.25
120	A22	35h slate	3.00	.25

Engr.

121	A23	50h dark green	.70	.25
a.	Pair, imperf. btwn., vert. or horiz.		210.00	225.00
122	A23	60h deep carmine	.40	.25
a.	Pair, imperf. btwn., vert. or horiz.		300.00	325.00
123	A23	72h dk brown ('13)	1.75	.25
124	A23	1k purple	12.00	.25
a.	Pair, imperf. btwn., vert. or horiz.		210.00	225.00
125	A24	2k lake & olive grn	20.00	.40
126	A24	5k bister & dk vio	37.50	3.50
127	A25	10k blue, bis & dp brn	165.00	42.50
		Nos. 110-127 (18)	250.00	50.00
		Set, never hinged	475.00	

Definitive set issued for the 60th year of the reign of Emperor Franz Josef.
The 1h-35h exist on both ordinary (1913) and chalk-surfaced (1908) paper.
All values exist imperforate. They were not sold at any post office, but presented to a number of high government officials. This applies also to all imperforate stamps of later issues, including semi-postals, etc., and those of the Austrian Offices Abroad.
Litho. forgeries of No. 127 exist.
For overprint and surcharge see #J47-J48.
For similar designs see Offices in Crete A5-A6, Offices in the Turkish Empire A16-A17.

Birthday Jubilee Issue
Similar to 1908 Issue, but designs enlarged by labels at top and bottom bearing dates "1830" and "1910"

1910			Typo.
128	A22	1h gray black	3.75	4.00
129	A22	2h violet	5.00	5.75
130	A22	3h magenta	5.00	5.75
131	A22	5h yellow green	.20	.25
132	A22	6h buff	2.25	2.00
133	A22	10h rose	.20	.25
134	A22	12h scarlet	3.00	3.00
135	A22	20h chocolate	3.75	4.50
136	A22	25h deep blue	.85	1.00
137	A22	30h olive green	3.75	4.50
138	A22	35h slate	3.75	4.50

Engr.

139	A23	50h dark green	4.50	5.75
140	A23	60h deep carmine	4.50	5.75
141	A23	1k purple	4.50	8.00
142	A24	2k lake & ol grn	112.50	140.00
143	A24	5k bister & dk vio	92.50	160.00
144	A25	10k blue, bis & dp brn	175.00	225.00
		Nos. 128-144 (17)	425.00	580.00
		Set, never hinged	800.00	

80th birthday of Emperor Franz Josef.
All values exist imperforate.
Litho. forgeries of Nos. 142-144 exist.

Austrian Crown — A37   Franz Josef — A38

Coat of Arms
A39   A40

1916-18			Typo.
145	A37	3h brt violet	.15	.15
146	A37	5h lt green	.15	.15
a.	Booklet pane of 6		14.00	
b.	Booklet pane of 4 + 2 labels		27.50	
147	A37	6h deep orange	.20	.40
148	A37	10h magenta	.15	.15
a.	Booklet pane of 6		27.50	
149	A37	12h light blue	.35	1.00
150	A38	15h rose red	.45	.15
a.	Booklet pane of 6		15.00	
151	A38	20h chocolate	3.75	.15
152	A38	25h blue	5.50	.40
153	A38	30h slate	5.00	.65
154	A39	40h olive green	.15	.15
155	A39	50h blue green	.25	.15
156	A39	60h deep blue	.20	.15
157	A39	80h orange brown	.20	.15
158	A39	90h red violet	.20	.15
159	A39	1k car, yel ('18)	.35	.20

Engr.

160	A40	2k dark blue	.45	.20
161	A40	3k claret	5.00	.90
162	A40	4k deep green	1.00	1.75
163	A40	10k deep violet	17.50	30.00
		Nos. 145-163 (19)	41.00	37.00
		Set, never hinged	100.00	

Stamps of type A38 have two varieties of the frame. Stamps of type A40 have various decorations about the shield.

Nos. 145-163 exist imperf. Value, set $400.

1917 — Ordinary Paper

164	A40	2k light blue	.75	.50
165	A40	3k carmine rose	10.00	.75
166	A40	4k yellow green	1.25	1.25
167	A40	10k violet	100.00	60.00
		Nos. 164-167 (4)	112.00	62.50
		Set, never hinged	215.00	

Nos. 164-167 exist imperf. Value, set $250.

See Nos. 172-175 (granite paper). For overprints and surcharges see Nos. 181-199, C1-C3, J60-J63, N1-N5, N10-N19, N33-N37, N42-N51. Western Ukraine 2-7, 11-15, 19-28, 57-58, 85-89, 94-103, N3-N14, NJ13.

Emperor Karl I — A42

1917-18 — Typo.

168	A42	15h dull red	.15	.15
a.		Booklet pane of 6	14.00	
169	A42	20h dk green ('18)	.15	.15
a.		20h green ('17)	.40	.15
170	A42	25h dull green	.40	.15
171	A42	30h dull violet	.40	.15
		Set value	1.00	.20
		Set, never hinged	4.00	

Nos. 168-171 exist imperf. Value, set $40.

For overprints and surcharges see Nos. N6-N9, N20, N38-N41, N52, N64. Western Ukraine 1, 8, 16-18, 90-93, N15-N18.

1918-19 — Engr. Granite Paper

172	A40	2k light blue	.25	.50
a.		Perf. 11½	425.00	350.00
173	A40	3k carmine rose	.25	1.25
174	A40	4k yellow green ('19)	3.50	9.25
175	A40	10k lt violet ('19)	4.25	8.00
		Nos. 172-175 (4)	8.25	19.00
		Set, never hinged	17.00	

Issues of the Republic

Austrian Stamps of 1916-18 Overprinted

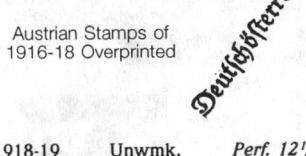
Deutschösterreich

1918-19 — Unwmk. Perf. 12½

181	A37	3h bright violet	.15	.15
182	A37	5h light green	.15	.15
183	A37	6h deep orange	.15	.20
184	A37	10h magenta	.15	.20
185	A37	12h light blue	.15	.35
186	A42	15h dull red	.15	.35
187	A42	20h deep green	.15	.15
188	A42	25h blue	.15	.15
189	A42	30h dull violet	.15	.15
190	A39	40h olive green	.15	.15
191	A39	50h deep green	.35	.35
192	A39	60h deep blue	.25	.40
193	A39	80h orange brown	.15	.15
a.		Inverted overprint	175.00	175.00
194	A39	90h red violet	.15	.15
195	A39	1k carmine, *yel*	.20	.15

Granite Paper

196	A40	2k light blue	.20	.15
b.		Pair, imperf. between	175.00	175.00
b.		Perf. 11½	10.00	5.00
197	A40	3k carmine rose	.20	.40
198	A40	4k yellow green	1.00	1.25
a.		Perf. 11½	17.50	10.00
199	A40	10k deep violet	8.00	12.50
		Nos. 181-199 (19)	12.00	17.50
		Set, never hinged	22.50	

Nos. 181, 182, 184, 187-191, 194, 197 and 199 exist imperforate.

Post Horn — A43

Coat of Arms — A44

Allegory of New Republic — A45

1919-20 — Typo. Perf. 12½ Ordinary Paper

200	A43	3h gray	.15	.15
201	A44	5h yellow green	.15	.15
202	A44	5h gray ('20)	.15	.15
203	A44	6h orange	.15	.30
204	A44	10h deep rose	.15	.15
205	A44	10h red ('20)	.15	.15
a.		Thick grayish paper ('20)	.15	.15
206	A43	12h grnsh blue	.15	.40
207	A43	15h bister ('20)	.20	.65
a.		Thick grayish paper ('20)	.15	.15
208	A44	20h dark green	.15	.15
a.		20h yellow green	.15	.15
b.		As "a." thick grysh paper ('20)	.45	1.25
209	A44	25h blue	.15	.15
210	A43	25h violet ('20)	.15	.15
211	A45	30h dark brown	.15	.15
212	A45	40h violet	.15	.15
213	A45	40h lake ('20)	.15	.15
214	A45	45h olive green	.20	.45
215	A45	50h dark blue	.15	.15
a.		Thick grayish paper ('20)	.15	.15
216	A43	60h olive green ('20)	.15	.15
217	A44	1k carmine, *yel*	.15	.15
218	A44	1k light blue ('20)	.15	.15
		Set value	1.25	2.50
		Set, never hinged	2.50	

All values exist imperf. (For regularly issued imperfs, see Nos. 227-235).

For overprints and surcharge see Nos. B11-B19, B30-B38, J102, N21, N27, N53, N58, N65, N71.

Parliament Building — A46

1919-20 — Engr. Perf. 12½, 11½ Granite Paper

219	A46	2k vermilion & blk	.25	.45
a.		Center inverted	3,250.	
220	A46	2½k olive bis ('20)	.15	.20
221	A46	3k blue & blk ('20)	.15	.15
222	A46	4k carmine & blk	.15	.15
a.		Center inverted	1,600.	1,200.
223	A46	5k black ('20)	.15	.15
a.		Perf. 11½x12½	45.00	60.00
224	A46	7½k plum	.15	.35
a.		Perf. 11½	75.00	100.00
b.		Perf. 11½x12½	75.00	125.00
225	A46	10k olive grn & blk brn	.20	.45
a.		Perf. 11½x12½	100.00	110.00
b.		Perf. 11½	16.00	20.00
226	A46	20k lilac & red ('20)	.15	.55
a.		Center inverted	6,500.	5,750.
b.		Perf. 11½	40.00	70.00
		Set value	1.00	
		Set, never hinged	2.50	

A number of values exist imperforate between. Values, $300 to $400 a pair.

See No. 248. For overprints and surcharge see Nos. B23-B29, B43-B49, N30, N60, N74.

1920 — Typo. Imperf. Ordinary Paper

227	A44	5h yellow green	.15	.30
228	A44	5h gray	.15	.15
229	A44	10h deep rose	.15	.15
230	A44	10h red	.15	.15
231	A43	15h bister	.15	.15
232	A43	25h violet	.15	.15
233	A45	30h dark brown	.15	.15
234	A45	40h violet	.15	.15
235	A43	60h olive green	.15	.15
		Set value	.60	.90
		Set, never hinged	1.25	

Arms

A47   A48

1920-21 — Typo. Perf. 12½ Ordinary Paper

238	A47	80h rose	.15	.15
239	A47	1k black brown	.15	.15
241	A47	1½k green ('21)	.15	.15
242	A47	2k blue	.15	.15
243	A48	3k yel grn & dk grn ('21)	.15	.15
244	A48	4k red & claret ('21)	.15	.15
245	A48	5k vio & claret ('21)	.15	.15
246	A47	7½k yellow & brown ('21)	.15	.15
247	A48	10k ultra & blue ('21)	.15	.15
		Set value	.70	.70
		Set, never hinged	1.25	

Nos. 238-245, 247 exist on white paper of good quality and on thick grayish paper of inferior quality; No. 246 only on white paper.

For overprints and surcharges see Nos. B20-B22, B39-B42, N22-N23, N31, N54-N55, N61-N62, N66-N67.

1921 — Engr.

248	A46	50k dk violet, *yel*	.35	.80
		Never hinged	.65	
a.		Perf. 11½	30.00	47.50

Symbols of Agriculture A49

Symbols of Labor and Industry A50

Numeral A52

Fields Crossed by Telegraph Wires A53

White-Shouldered Eagle — A54

Church of Minorite Friars — A55

1922-24 — Typo. — Perf. 12½

250	A49	½k olive bister	.15	.35
251	A50	1k brown	.15	.15
252	A50	2k cobalt blue	.15	.15
253	A49	2½k orange brown	.15	.15
254	A50	4k dull violet	.15	.45
255	A50	5k gray green	.15	.15
256	A49	7½k gray violet	.15	.15
257	A50	10k claret	.15	.15
258	A49	12½k gray green	.15	.15
259	A49	15k bluish green	.15	.15
260	A49	20k dark blue	.15	.15
261	A49	25k claret	.15	.15
262	A49	30k pale gray	.15	.15
263	A49	45k pale red	.15	.15
264	A50	50k orange brown	.15	.15
265	A50	60k yellow green	.15	.15
266	A50	75k ultramarine	.15	.15
267	A50	80k yellow	.15	.15
268	A49	100k gray	.15	.15
269	A49	120k brown	.15	.15
270	A49	150k orange	.15	.15
271	A49	160k light green	.15	.15
272	A49	180k red	.15	.15
273	A49	200k pink	.15	.15
274	A49	240k dark violet	.15	.15
275	A49	300k light blue	.20	.15
276	A49	400k deep green	.85	.15
a.		400k gray green	.85	
277	A49	500k yellow	.20	.15
278	A49	600k slate	.20	.15
279	A49	700k brown ('24)	.45	.15
280	A49	800k violet ('24)	.90	2.00
281	A50	1000k violet ('23)	.45	.15
282	A50	1200k car rose ('23)	.25	.30
283	A50	1500k orange ('24)	1.50	.15
284	A50	1600k slate ('23)	2.00	1.75
285	A50	2000k deep blue ('23)	4.00	.30
286	A50	3000k lt blue ('23)	12.50	.65
287	A50	4000k dk bl, bl ('24)	5.25	1.75
		Nos. 250-287 (38)	32.50	
		Set value		10.00
		Set, never hinged	75.00	

Nos. 250-287 exist imperf. Value, set $500.
For overprints & surcharges see #N24-N26, N28-N29, N32, N56, N59, N63, N68-N70, N72-N73.

Symbols of Art and Science — A51

1922-24 — Engr. — Perf. 12½

288	A51	20k dark brown	.15	.15
a.		Perf. 11½	1.10	1.25
a.		Never hinged	1.65	
289	A51	25k blue	.15	.15
a.		Perf. 11½	1.10	1.25
a.		Never hinged	1.65	
290	A51	50k brown red	.15	.15
a.		Perf. 11½	2.50	3.50
a.		Never hinged	4.25	
291	A51	100k deep green	.15	.15
a.		Perf. 11½	6.00	7.00
a.		Never hinged	9.00	
292	A51	200k dark violet	.15	.15
a.		Perf. 11½	9.00	15.00
a.		Never hinged	12.00	
293	A51	500k dp orange	.15	1.00
294	A51	1000k blk vio, yel	.15	.15
a.		Perf. 11½	175.00	250.00
a.		Never hinged	450.00	
295	A51	2000k olive grn, yel	.15	.15
296	A51	3000k claret brn ('23)	8.00	.35
297	A51	5000k gray black ('23)	2.00	.95

Granite Paper

298	A51	10,000k red brown ('24)	3.00	2.50
		Nos. 288-298 (11)	14.20	5.85
		Set, never hinged	32.50	

On Nos. 281-287, 291-298 "kronen" is abbreviated to "k" and transposed with the numerals. Nos. 288-298 exist imperf. Value, set $300.

Güssing — A56

National Library, Vienna — A57

Designs: 15g, Hochosterwitz. 16g, 20g, Dunstein. 18g, Traunsee. 24g, Salzburg. 30g, Seewiesen. 40g, Innsbruck. 50g, Worthersee. 60g, Hohenems. 2s, St. Stephen's Cathedral, Vienna.

1929-30 — Typo. — Perf. 12½
Size: 25½x21½mm

326	A56	10g brown orange	.75	.15
327	A56	10g bister ('30)	.75	.15
328	A56	15g violet brown	.55	.90
329	A56	16g dark gray	.15	.15
330	A56	18g blue green	.40	.30
331	A56	20g dark gray ('30)	.40	.15
332	A56	24g maroon	4.25	4.00
333	A56	24g lake ('30)	7.25	.30
334	A56	30g dark violet	4.25	.15
335	A56	40g dark blue	8.00	.15
336	A56	50g gray violet ('30)	30.00	.20
337	A56	60g olive green	22.50	.20

Engr.
Size: 21x26mm

338	A57	1s black brown	5.00	.20
339	A57	2s dark green	9.25	4.50
		Nos. 326-339 (14)	93.50	11.50
		Set, never hinged	300.00	

Type of 1929-30 Issue
Designs: 12g, Traunsee. 64g, Hohenems.

1932 — Perf. 12
Size: 21x16½mm

340	A56	10g olive brown	.90	.15
341	A56	12g blue green	1.50	.15
342	A56	18g blue green	.85	1.90
343	A56	20g dark gray	1.25	.15
344	A56	24g carmine rose	5.00	.15
345	A56	24g dull violet	4.00	.15
346	A56	30g dark violet	16.00	.15
347	A56	30g carmine rose	3.75	.15
348	A56	40g dark blue	19.00	.60
349	A56	40g dark violet	5.50	.20

Numeral (White-Shouldered Eagle) — A52 / A54
1925-27 Typo. — Perf. 12

303	A52	1g dark gray	.15	.15
304	A52	2g claret	.20	.15
305	A52	3g scarlet	.25	.15
306	A52	4g grnsh blue ('27)	.70	.15
307	A52	5g brown orange	1.40	.15
308	A52	6g ultramarine	.85	.15
309	A52	7g chocolate	1.50	.15
310	A52	8g yellow green	6.25	.15
311	A53	10g orange	.15	.15
313	A53	15g red lilac	.15	.15
314	A53	16g dark blue	.15	.15
315	A53	18g olive green	.90	.20
316	A54	20g dark violet	.30	.15
317	A54	24g carmine	.40	.15
318	A54	30g dark brown	.35	.15
319	A54	40g ultramarine	.50	.15
320	A54	45g yellow brown	.70	.15
321	A54	50g gray	.85	.15
322	A54	80g turquoise blue	3.00	2.00

Perf. 12½
Engr.

323	A55	1s deep green	15.00	.20
a.		1s light green	125.00	1.25
324	A55	2s brown rose	6.25	5.00
		Nos. 303-324 (21)	40.00	
		Set value		8.50
		Set, never hinged	145.00	

#303-305, 307-324 exist imperf. Value, set $275.
For type A52 surcharged see Nos. B118.

350	A56	50g gray violet	21.00	.20
351	A56	50g dull blue	6.25	.20
352	A56	60g gray green	47.50	1.50
353	A56	64g gray green	7.50	.15
		Nos. 340-353 (14)	140.00	
		Set value		5.00
		Set, never hinged	500.00	

For overprints and surcharges see Nos. B87-B92, B119-B121.

Burgenland A67

Tyrol A68

Costumes of various districts: 3g, Burgenland. 4g, 5g, Carinthia. 6g, 8g, Lower Austria. 12g, 20g, Upper Austria. 24g, 25g, Salzburg. 30g, 35g, Styria. 45g, Tyrol. 60g, Vorarlberg bridal couple. 64g, Vorarlberg. 1s, Viennese family. 2s, Military.

1934-35 — Typo. — Perf. 12

354	A67	1g dark violet	.15	.15
355	A67	3g scarlet	.15	.15
356	A67	4g olive green	.15	.15
357	A67	5g red violet	.15	.15
358	A67	6g ultramarine	.20	.15
359	A67	8g green	.15	.15
360	A67	12g dark brown	.15	.15
361	A67	20g yellow brown	.15	.15
362	A67	24g grnsh blue	.15	.15
363	A67	25g violet	.20	.15
364	A67	30g maroon	.15	.15
365	A67	35g rose carmine	.35	.25

Perf. 12½

366	A68	40g slate gray	.40	.15
367	A68	45g brown red	.35	.15
368	A68	60g ultramarine	.60	.15
369	A68	64g brown	.75	.15
370	A68	1s deep violet	.65	.35
371	A68	2s dull green	37.50	45.00

Designs Redrawn
Perf. 12 (6g), 12½ (2s)

372	A67	6g ultra ('35)	.15	.15
373	A68	2s emerald ('35)	2.50	4.50
		Nos. 354-373 (20)	45.00	52.50
		Set, never hinged	90.00	

The design of No. 358 looks as though the man's ears were on backwards, while No. 372 appears correctly.
On No. 373 there are seven feathers on each side of the eagle instead of five.
Nos. 354-373 exist imperf. Value, set $375.
For surcharges see Nos. B128-B131.

Dollfuss Mourning Issue

Engelbert Dollfuss — A85

1934-35 — Engr. — Perf. 12½

374	A85	24g greenish black	.45	.20
		Never hinged	.80	
375	A85	24g indigo ('35)	.75	.55
		Never hinged	1.40	

"Mother and Child," by Joseph Danhauser — A86

"Madonna and Child," after Painting by Dürer — A87

1935, May 1

376	A86	24g dark blue	.40	.20
		Never hinged	.80	

Mother's Day. Nos. 376-377 exist imperf. Value, each $165.

1936, May 5 — Photo.

377	A87	24g violet blue	.15	.20
		Never hinged	.30	

Mother's Day.

Farm Workers — A88

Design: 5s, Factory workers.

1936, June — Engr. — Perf. 12½

378	A88	3s red orange	12.50	15.00
		Never hinged	24.00	
379	A88	5s brown black	25.00	40.00
		Never hinged	45.00	

Nos. 378-379 exist imperf. Value, set $250.

Engelbert Dollfuss — A90 / Mother and Child — A91

1936, July 25

380	A90	10s dark blue	675.00	800.00
			900.00	

Second anniv. of death of Engelbert Dollfuss, chancellor. Exists imperf. Value, $1,750.

1937, May 5 — Photo. — Perf. 12

381	A91	24g henna brown	.20	.15
		Never hinged		.40

Mother's Day. Exists imperf. Value, $175.

S.S. Maria Anna — A92

Steamships: 24g, Uranus. 64g, Oesterreich.

1937, June 9

382	A92	12g red brown	.55	.25
383	A92	24g deep blue	.55	.25
384	A92	64g dark green	.55	.65
		Nos. 382-384 (3)	1.65	1.15
		Set, never hinged	3.50	

Cent. of steamship service on Danube River. Exist imperf. Value, set $135.

First Locomotive, "Austria" — A95

Designs: 25g, Modern steam locomotive. 35g, Modern electric train.

1937, Nov. 22

385	A95	12g black brown	.25	.15
386	A95	25g dark violet	.50	.65
387	A95	35g brown red	1.00	1.00
		Nos. 385-387 (3)	1.75	1.80
		Set, never hinged	3.75	

Centenary of Austrian railways. Exist imperf. Value, set $135.

Rose and Zodiac Signs — A98

1937 — Engr. — Perf. 13x12½

388	A98	12g dark green	.15	.15
389	A98	24g dark carmine	.15	.15
		Set value	.25	.25
		Set, never hinged	.35	

For Use in Vienna, Lower Austria and
Burgenland
Germany Nos. 509-511 and 511B
Overprinted in Black

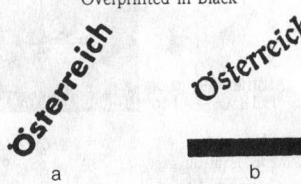

a   b

1945		Unwmk.	Perf. 14	
390	A115(a)	5pf dp yellow green	.15	.20
391	A115(b)	6pf purple	.15	.20
392	A115(a)	8pf red	.15	.20
393	A115(b)	12pf carmine	.15	.20
		Nos. 390-393 (4)		.80
		Set value		.25
		Set, never hinged		.40

Nos. 390-393 exist with overprint inverted or
double.
Germany No. 507, the 3pf, with overprint "a"
was prepared, not issued, but sold to collectors after
the definitive Republic issue had been placed in use.
Value $30, hinged, $60, never hinged.

German Semi-Postal Stamps, #B207, B209,
B210, B283 Surcharged in Black

c

d

1945		Perf. 14, 14x13½, 13½x14		
394	SP181(c)	5pf on 12pf + 88pf	.50	1.50
395	SP184(d)	6pf on 6pf + 14pf	2.50	11.00
396	SP242(d)	8pf on 42pf + 108pf	.50	1.50
397	SP183(d)	12pf on 3pf + 7pf	.50	1.50
		Nos. 394-397 (4)	4.00	15.50
		Set, never hinged		10.00

The surcharges are spaced to fit the stamps.

Stamps of Germany, Nos. 509 to 511,
511B, 519 and 529 Overprinted

e   f

1945		Typo.	Perf. 14	
		Size: 18½x22½mm		
398	A115(e)	5pf dp yellow green	.25	.45
399	A115(f)	5pf dp yellow green	4.00	7.75
400	A115(e)	6pf purple	.15	.35
401	A115(e)	8pf red	.15	.35
402	A115(e)	12pf carmine	.20	.35
		Engr.		
		Size: 21½x26mm		
403	A115(e)	30pf olive green	6.25	10.00
a.		Thin bar at bottom	15.00	17.50
a.		Never hinged	25.00	
404	A118(e)	42pf brt green	15.00	32.50
a.		Thin bar at bottom	15.00	27.50
a.		Never hinged	25.00	
		Nos. 398-404 (7)	26.00	51.75
		Set, never hinged	55.00	

On Nos. 403a and 404a, the bottom bar of the
overprint is 2½mm wide, and, as the overprint
was applied in two operations, "Österreich" is usually not exactly centered in its diagonal slot. On
Nos. 403 and 404, the bottom bar is 3mm wide,
and "Österreich" is always well centered.
Germany Nos. 524-527 (the 1m, 2m, 3m and
5m), overprinted with vertical bars and "Österreich" similar to "e" and "f," were prepared, not
issued, but sold to collectors after the definitive
Republic issue had been placed in use. Value for set,
$70 hinged, $150 ever hinged.

Counterfeits exist of Nos. 403-404, 403a-404a
and 1m-5m overprints.

For Use in Styria

Stamps of Germany Nos.
506 to 511, 511A, 511B,
514 to 523 and 529
Overprinted in Black

1945		Unwmk. Typo.	Perf. 14	
		Size: 18½x22½mm		
405	A115	1pf gray black	1.50	3.00
406	A115	3pf lt brown	1.50	3.00
407	A115	4pf slate	5.00	10.00
408	A115	5pf dp yellow grn	1.00	2.00
409	A115	6pf purple	.20	.30
410	A115	8pf red	.75	1.65
411	A115	10pf dark brown	1.50	3.25
412	A115	12pf carmine	.15	.30
		Engr.		
413	A115	15pf brown lake	.75	1.75
414	A115	16pf pck green	14.00	18.00
415	A115	20pf blue	2.75	5.25
416	A115	24pf orange brown	10.00	18.00
		Size: 22½x26mm		
417	A115	25pf brt ultra	1.00	2.75
418	A115	30pf olive green	1.00	2.00
419	A115	40pf brt red violet	1.25	2.25
420	A118	42pf brt green	2.00	3.50
421	A115	50pf myrtle green	1.40	3.50
422	A115	60pf dk red brown	2.25	4.75
423	A115	80pf indigo	2.00	3.75
		Nos. 405-423 (19)	50.00	89.00
		Set, never hinged	89.00	
		Overprinted on Nos. 524-527		
		Perf. 12½, 14		
424	A116	1m dk slate grn	7.50	20.00
a.		Perf. 12½	100.00	
425	A116	2m violet	7.50	25.00
a.		Perf. 14	12.00	45.00
426	A116	3m copper red	25.00	55.00
a.		Perf. 14	125.00	
427	A116	5m dark blue	225.00	525.00
a.		Perf. 14	575.00	
		Nos. 424-427 (4)	265.00	
		Set, never hinged	450.00	

On the preceding four stamps the innermost vertical lines are 10½mm apart; on the pfennig values
6½mm apart.
Counterfeits exist of Nos. 405-427 overprints.

Germany Nos. 524 to
527 Overprinted in Black

1945			Perf. 14	
428	A116	1m dk slate grn	10.50	22.50
429	A116	2m violet	10.50	27.50
		Perf. 12½		
430	A116	3m copper red	21.00	60.00
431	A116	5m dark blue	140.00	450.00
a.		Perf. 14	600.00	
		Nos. 428-431 (4)	182.00	
		Set, never hinged	375.00	

On the preceding four stamps, "Österreich" is
thinner, measuring 16mm. On the previous set of
23 values it measures 18mm.
Counterfeits exist of Nos. 428-431 overprints.

Catalogue values for unused
stamps in this section, from this
point to the end of the section, are
for Never Hinged items.

For Use in Vienna, Lower Austria and
Burgenland

A99   A100
Coat of Arms

Typographed or Lithographed
1945, July 3 Unwmk. Perf. 14x13½
Size: 21x25mm

432	A99	3pf brown	.15	.15
433	A99	4pf slate	.15	.15
434	A99	5pf dark green	.15	.15
435	A99	6pf deep violet	.15	.15
436	A99	8pf orange brown	.15	.15
437	A99	10pf deep brown	.15	.15
438	A99	12pf rose carmine	.15	.15
439	A99	15pf orange red	.15	.15
440	A99	16pf dull blue green	.15	.35
		Perf. 14		
		Size: 24x28½mm		
441	A99	20pf light blue	.15	.15
442	A99	24pf orange	.15	.20
443	A99	25pf dark blue	.15	.15
444	A99	30pf deep gray grn	.15	.15
445	A99	38pf ultramarine	.15	.15
446	A99	40pf brt red vio	.15	.15
447	A99	42pf sage green	.15	.15
448	A99	50pf blue green	.15	.60
449	A99	60pf maroon	.15	.60
450	A99	80pf dull lilac	.15	.60
		Engr. Perf. 14x13½		
451	A100	1m dark green	.15	.60
452	A100	2m dark purple	.15	.60
453	A100	3m dark violet	.15	.60
454	A100	5m brown red	.15	.60
		Set value	1.75	6.00

Nos. 432, 433, 437, 439, 440, 443, 446, 448,
449 are typographed. Nos. 434, 435, 441, 442 are
lithographed; the other values exist both ways.
For overprint see No. 604.

For General Use

Lermoos, Winter
Scene — A101

The Prater Woods,
Vienna — A105

Hochosterwitz,
Carinthia
A106

Lake Constance
A110

Dürnstein,
Lower Austria
A124

Designs: 4g, Eisenerz surface mine. 5g, Leopold-
sberg, near Vienna. 6g, Hohensalzburg, Salzburg
Province. 12g, Wolfgang See, near Salzburg. 15g,
Forchtenstein Castle, Burgenland. 16g, Gesäuse
Valley. 24g, Höldrichs Mill, Lower Austria. 25g,
Oetz Valley Outlet, Tyrol. 30g, Neusiedler Lake,
Burgenland. 35g, Belvedere Palace, Vienna. 38g,
Langbath Lake. 40g, Mariazell, Styria. 42g,
Traunkirchen. 45g, Hartenstein Castle. 50g, Sil-
vretta Mountains, Vorarlberg. 60g, Railroad via-
ducts near Semmering. 70g, Waterfall of Bad-Gas-
tein, Salzburg. 80g, Kaiser Mountains, Tyrol. 90g,
Wayside Shrine, Tragöss, Styria. 2s, St. Christof am
Arlberg, Tyrol. 3s, Heiligenblut, Carinthia. 5s,
Schönbrunn, Vienna.

1945-46		Perf. 14x13½ Photo.	Unwmk.	
455	A101	3g sapphire	.15	.15
456	A101	4g dp orange ('46)	.15	.15
457	A101	5g dk carmine rose	.15	.15
458	A101	6g dk slate green	.15	.15
459	A105	8g golden brown	.15	.15
460	A106	10g dark green	.15	.15
461	A106	12g dark brown	.15	.15
462	A106	15g dk slate bl ('46)	.15	.15
463	A106	16g chnt brn ('46)	.15	.15
		Perf. 13½x14		
464	A110	20g dp ultra ('46)	.15	.15
465	A110	24g dp yellow grn ('46)	.15	.15
466	A110	25g gray black ('46)	.15	.15
467	A110	30g dark red	.15	.15
468	A110	35g brown red ('46)	.15	.15
469	A110	38g brown olive ('46)	.15	.15
470	A110	40g gray	.15	.15
471	A110	42g brown orange ('46)	.15	.15
472	A110	45g dark blue ('46)	.15	.25
473	A110	50g dark blue	.15	.15
474	A110	60g dark violet	.15	.15
a.		Imperf., pair	50.00	60.00
475	A110	70g Prus blue ('46)	.15	.25
476	A110	80g brown	.15	.40
477	A110	90g Prussian green	1.10	1.10
478	A124	1s dk red brn ('46)	.75	.75
479	A124	2s blue gray ('46)	2.75	2.75
480	A124	3s dk slate grn ('46)	.75	.80
481	A124	5s dark red ('46)	1.50	1.75
		Set value	8.00	7.00

See Nos. 486-488, 496-515. For overprints and
surcharges see Nos. 492-493, B166, B280, B287.

No. 461 Overprinted in
Carmine

1946, Sept. 26				
482	A106	12g dark brown	.15	.20

Meeting of the Soc. for Cultural and Economic
Relations with the USSR, Vienna, Sept. 26-29.

City Hall Park,
Vienna
A128

Hochosterwitz,
Carinthia
A129

1946-47		Perf. 14x13½ Photo.	Unwmk.	
483	A128	8g deep plum	.15	.15
484	A128	8g olive brown	.15	.15
a.		8g dark olive green	.15	.15
485	A129	10g dk brn vio ('47)	.15	.15
		Perf. 13½x14		
486	A110	30g blue gray ('47)	.15	.15
487	A110	50g brown violet ('47)	.25	.25
488	A110	60g violet blue ('47)	2.00	1.10
		Set value	2.50	1.60

See No. 502.

Franz
Grillparzer — A130

Franz
Schubert — A131

1947		Engr. Perf. 14x13½		
489	A130	18g chocolate	.15	.15
		Photo.		
490	A130	18g dk violet brn	.15	.15
		Set value	.15	.20

Death of Grillparzer, dramatic poet, 75th anniv.
A second printing of No. 490 on thicker paper
has a darker frame and clearer delineation of the
portrait.
Issue dates: #489, Feb. 10; #490, Mar. 31.

1947, Mar. 31			Engr.	
491	A131	12g dark green	.15	.15

150th birth anniv. of Franz Schubert, musician
and composer.

Nos. 469 and 463 Surcharged in Brown

1947, Sept. 1   Photo.   Perf. 14
492 A110   75g on 38g brown ol   .20 .80
493 A106   1.40s on 16g chnt brn   .15 .15
The surcharge on No. 493 varies from brown to black brown.

Symbols of Global Telegraphic Communication A132

1947, Nov. 5   Engr.   Perf. 14x13½
495 A132   40g dark violet   .15 .15
Centenary of the telegraph in Austria.

Scenic Type of 1946

1946, Aug.   Photo.   Perf. 13½x14
496 A124   1s dark brown   1.25 .50
497 A124   2s dark blue   7.00 2.75
498 A124   3s dark slate green   2.25 .75
499 A124   5s dark red   32.50 8.00
    Nos. 496-499 (4)   43.00 12.00

On Nos. 478 to 481 the upper and lower panels show a screen effect. On Nos. 496 to 499 the panels appear to be solid color.

Scenic Types of 1945-46

1947-48   Photo.   Perf. 14x13½
500 A101   3g bright red   .15 .15
501 A101   5g bright red   .15 .15
502 A129   10g bright red   .15 .15
503 A106   15g brt red ('48)   1.40 1.25

Perf. 13½x14
504 A110   20g bright red   .50 .15
505 A110   30g bright red   .75 .15
506 A110   40g bright red   .75 .15
507 A110   50g bright red   1.00 .15
508 A110   60g brt red ('48)   6.50 1.25
509 A110   70g brt red ('48)   3.50 .15
510 A110   80g brt red ('48)   3.50 .15
511 A110   90g brt red ('48)   3.75 .25
512 A124   1s dark violet   .80 .15
513 A124   2s dark violet   1.10 .20
514 A124   3s dk violet ('48)   9.00 1.00
515 A124   5s dk violet ('48)   11.00 1.50
    Nos. 500-515 (16)   44.00
    Set value   6.00

Carl Michael Ziehrer (1843-1922), Composer — A133

#517, Adalbert Stifter (1805-68), novelist. #518, Anton Bruckner (1824-96), composer. 60g, Friedrich von Amerling (1803-87), painter.

1948-49   Engr.
516 A133   20g dull green   .35 .20
517 A133   40g chocolate   5.00 2.50
518 A133   40g dark green   5.00 4.00
519 A133   60g rose brown   .65 .30
    Nos. 516-519 (4)   11.00 7.00
Issue dates: 20g, Jan. 21, No. 517, Sept. 6, No. 518, Sept. 3, 1949, 60g, Jan. 26.

Vorarlberg, Montafon Valley — A134

Costume of Vienna, 1850 — A135

Designs (Austrian Costumes): 3g, Tyrol, Inn Valley. 5g, Salzburg, Pinzgau. 10g, Styria, Salzkammergut. 15g, Burgenland, Lutzmannsburg. 25g, Vienna, 1850. 30g, Salzburg, Pongau. 40g, Vienna, 1840. 45g, Carinthia, Lesach Valley. 50g, Vorarlberg, Bregenzer Forest. 60g, Carinthia, Lavant Valley. 70g, Lower Austria, Wachau. 75g, Styria, Salzkammergut. 80g, Styria, Enns Valley. 90g, Central Styria. 1s, Tyrol, Puster Valley. 1.20s, Lower Austria, Vienna Woods. 1.40s, Upper Austria, Inn District. 1.45s, Wilten. 1.50s, Vienna, 1853. 1.60s, Vienna, 1830. 1.70s, East Tyrol, Kals. 2s, Upper Austria. 2.20s, Ischl, 1820. 2.40s, Kitzbuhel. 2.50s, Upper Steiermark, 1850. 2.70s, Little Walser Valley. 3s, Burgenland. 3.50s, Lower Austria, 1850. 4.50s, Gail Valley. 5s, Ziller Valley. 7s, Steiermark, Sulm Valley.

Perf. 14x13½
1948-52   Unwmk.   Photo.
520 A134   3g gray ('50)   .60 .50
521 A134   5g dark green ('49)   .25 .15
522 A134   10g deep blue   .25 .15
523 A134   15g brown   .60 .15
524 A134   20g yellow green   .20 .15
525 A134   25g brown ('49)   .20 .15
526 A134   30g dk car rose   2.50 .15
527 A134   30g dk violet ('50)   .60 .15
528 A134   40g violet   2.50 .15
529 A134   40g green ('49)   .20 .15
530 A134   45g violet blue   2.25 .40
531 A134   50g orange brn ('49)   .60 .15
532 A134   60g scarlet   .20 .15
533 A134   70g brt blue grn ('49)   .20 .15
534 A134   75g blue   3.75 .40
535 A134   80g carmine rose ('49)   .35 .15
536 A134   90g brown vio ('49)   22.50 .30
537 A134   1s ultramarine   4.00 .15
538 A134   1s rose red ('50)   62.50 .15
539 A134   1s dk green ('51)   .20 .15
540 A134   1.20s violet ('49)   .40 .15
541 A134   1.40s brown   2.50 .15
542 A134   1.45s dk carmine ('51)   1.00 .15
543 A134   1.50s ultra ('51)   .60 .15
544 A134   1.60s orange red ('49)   .20 .15
545 A134   1.70s violet blue ('50)   2.50 .55
546 A134   2s blue green   .40 .15
547 A134   2.20s slate ('52)   4.75 .15
548 A134   2.40s blue ('51)   1.00 .15
549 A134   2.50s brown ('52)   4.50 .15
550 A134   2.70s dk brown ('51)   .45 .45
551 A134   3s brown car ('49)   1.90 .15
552 A134   3.50s dull grn ('51)   9.75 .15
553 A134   4.50s brown vio ('51)   .60 .40
554 A134   5s dark red vio   1.00 .15
555 A134   7s olive ('52)   1.50 .15

Engr.
556 A135   10s gray ('50)   27.50 5.00
    Nos. 520-556 (37)   165.00
    Set value   9.00

In 1958-59, 21 denominations of this set were printed on white paper, differing from the previous grayish paper with yellowish gum.

Pres. Karl Renner — A136

1948, Nov. 12   Perf. 14x13½
557 A136   1s deep blue   1.90 1.10
Founding of the Austrian Republic, 30th anniv. See Nos. 573, 636.

Franz Gruber and Josef Mohr — A137

1948, Dec. 18   Perf. 13½x14
558 A137   60g red brown   4.25 4.00
130th anniv. of the hymn "Silent Night, Holy Night".

Symbolical of Child Welfare — A138

Johann Strauss, the Younger — A139

1949, May 14   Photo.   Perf. 14x13½
559 A138   1s bright blue   11.50 1.25
1st year of activity of UNICEF in Austria.

1949   Engr.
30g, Johann Strauss, the elder. #561, Johann Strauss, the younger. #562, Karl Millöcker.
560 A139   30g violet brown   2.25 1.65
561 A139   1s dark blue   2.75 1.10
562 A139   1s dark blue   12.00 6.25
    Nos. 560-562 (3)   17.00 9.00
Johann Strauss, the elder (1804-49), Johann Strauss, the younger (1825-99), and Karl Millöcker (1842-1899), composers. See #574.

Esperanto Star, Olive Branches — A140

St. Gebhard — A141

1949, June 25   Photo.
563 A140   20g blue green   1.00 .50
Austrian Esperanto Congress at Graz.

1949, Aug. 6   Engr.
564 A141   30g dark violet   1.50 1.25
St. Gebhard (949-995), Bishop of Vorarlberg.

Letter, Roses and Post Horn — A142

UPU, 75th Anniv.: 60g, Plaque. 1s, "Austria," wings and monogram.

1949, Oct. 8   Perf. 13½x14
565 A142   40g dark green   3.75 1.65
566 A142   60g dk carmine   3.75 1.65
567 A142   1s dk violet blue   6.50 4.75
    Nos. 565-567 (3)   14.00 8.05

Moritz Michael Daffinger — A143

Andreas Hofer — A144

30g, Alexander Girardi. #569, Daffinger. #570, Hofer. #571, Josef Madersperger.

1950   Unwmk.   Perf. 14x13½
568 A144   30g dark blue   1.50 .75
569 A143   60g red brown   6.00 3.25
570 A144   60g dark violet   10.50 6.50
571 A144   60g purple   4.50 2.25
    Nos. 568-571 (4)   22.50 12.75

Alexander Girardi (1850-1918), actor; Moritz Michael Daffinger (1790-1849), painter; Andreas Hofer (1767-1810), patriot; Josef Madersperger (1768-1850), inventor.
Issue dates: 30g, Dec. 5; No. 569, Jan. 25; No. 570, Feb. 20; No. 571, Oct. 2.

Austrian Stamp of 1850 — A146

1950, May 20   Perf. 14½
572 A146   1s black, straw   1.65 .90
Centenary of Austrian postage stamps.

Renner Type of 1948, Frame and Inscriptions Altered

1951, Mar. 3
573 A136   1s black, straw   1.40 .20
In memory of Pres. Karl Renner, 1870-1950.

Strauss Type of 1949

Portrait: 60g, Joseph Lanner.

1951, Apr. 12
574 A139   60g dk blue green   3.50 1.10
150th birth anniv. of Joseph Lanner, composer.

Martin Johann Schmidt — A147

Boy Scout Emblem — A148

1951, June 28   Engr.   Perf. 14x13½
575 A147   1sh brown red   4.50 2.00
150th death anniv. of Martin Johann Schmidt, painter.

1951, Aug. 3   Engr. and Litho.
576 A148   1sh dk grn, ocher & pink   3.50 2.75
7th World Scout Jamboree, Bad Ischl-St. Wolfgang, Aug. 3-13, 1951.

Wilhelm Kienzl A149

Josef Schrammel A150

Design: 1s, Karl von Ghega.

1951-52   Engr.   Unwmk.
577 A149   1s deep green ('52)   6.50 1.10
578 A149   1.50s indigo   3.00 .90
579 A150   1.50s violet blue ('52)   6.50 1.10
    Nos. 577-579 (3)   16.00 3.10
Ghega (1802-60), civil engineer; Kienzl (1857-1941), composer; Schrammel (1852-95), composer. See #582.
Issued: 1s, Mar. 2; #578, Oct. 3; #579, Mar. 3.

Breakfast Pavilion, Schönbrunn A151

1952, May 24   Perf. 13½x14
580 A151   1.50s dark green   5.75 1.00
Vienna Zoological Gardens, 200th anniv.

Globe as Dot Over "i" — A152

School Girl — A153

1952, July 1   *Perf. 14x13¹/₂*
581 A152 1.50s dark blue   5.00 .65

Formation of the Intl. Union of Socialist Youth Camp, Vienna, July 1-10, 1952.

Type Similar to A150

Portrait: 1s, Nikolaus Lenau.

1952, Aug. 13
582 A150 1s deep green   6.00 1.10

Nikolaus Lenau, pseudonym of Nikolaus Franz Niembsch von Strehlenau (1802-50), poet.

1952, Sept. 6
583 A153 2.40s dp violet blue   9.00 1.75

Issued to stimulate letter-writing between Austrian and foreign school children.

Hugo Wolf — A154

Pres. Theodor Körner — A155

1953, Feb. 21   Engr.   *Perf. 14x13¹/₂*
587 A154 1.50s dark blue   6.00 .70

Hugo Wolf, composer, 50th death anniv.

1953, Apr. 24
588 A155 1.50s dk violet blue   6.00 .70

80th birthday of Pres. Theodor Körner. See Nos. 591, 614.

State Theater, Linz, and Masks — A156

1953, Oct. 17   *Perf. 13¹/₂x14*
589 A156 1.50s dark gray   14.00 1.50

State Theater at Linz, 150th anniv.

Child and Christmas Tree — A157

Karl von Rokitansky — A158

1953, Nov. 30   *Perf. 14x13¹/₂*
590 A157 1s dark green   1.40 .20

See No. 597.

Type Similar to A155

Portrait: 1.50s, Moritz von Schwind.

1954, Jan. 21   *Perf. 14x13¹/₂*
591 A155 1.50s purple   12.00 1.10

Moritz von Schwind, painter, 150th birth anniv.

1954, Feb. 19
592 A158 1.50s purple   14.00 1.40

Karl von Rokitansky, physician, 150th birth anniv. See No. 595.

Esperanto Star and Wreath A159

Engr. and Photo.
1954, June 5   *Perf. 13¹/₂x14*
593 A159 1s dk brown & emer   4.50 .20

Esperanto movement in Austria, 50th anniv.

A160   A161

1954, Aug. 4   Engr.   *Perf. 14x13¹/₂*
594 A160 1s dark blue green   10.00 1.65

300th birth anniv. of Johann Michael Rottmayr von Rosenbrunn, painter.

Type Similar to A158

Portrait: 1.50s, Carl Auer von Welsbach.

1954, Aug. 4
595 A158 1.50s violet blue   30.00 1.50

25th death anniv. of Carl Auer von Welsbach (1858-1929), chemist.

1954, Oct. 2   Unwmk.

Organ, St. Florian Monastery and Cherub.

596 A161 1s brown   2.25 .18

2nd Intl. Congress for Catholic Church Music, Vienna, Oct. 4-10, 1954.

Christmas Type of 1953
1954, Nov. 30
597 A157 1s dark blue   2.75 .25

Arms of Austria and Official Publication A162

1954, Dec. 18   Engr.
598 A162 1s salmon & black   2.25 .20

Austria's State Printing Plant, 150th anniv., and Wiener Zeitung, government newspaper, 250th year of publication.

Parliament Building A163

Designs: 1s, Western railroad station, Vienna. 1.45s, Letters forming flag. 1.50s, Public housing, Vienna. 2.40s, Limberg dam.

1955, Apr. 27   *Perf. 13¹/₂x14*
599 A163 70g rose violet   1.50 .20
600 A163 1s deep ultra   5.50 .20
601 A163 1.45s scarlet   8.25 1.65

---

602 A163 1.50s brown   17.50 .20
603 A163 2.40s dk blue green   8.25 3.00
    Nos. 599-603 (5)   41.00 5.25

10th anniv. of Austria's liberation.

Type of 1945 Overprinted in Blue

STAATSVERTRAG 1955

1955, May 15   *Perf. 14x13¹/₂*
604 A100 2s blue gray   2.00 .20

Signing of the state treaty with the US, France, Great Britain and Russia, May 15, 1955.

Workers of Three Races Climbing Globe — A164

1955, May 20   *Perf. 13¹/₂x14*
605 A164 1s indigo   2.00 1.65

4th congress of the Intl. Confederation of Free Trade Unions, Vienna, May.

Burgtheater, Vienna — A165

Design: 2.40s, Opera House, Vienna.

1955, July 25
606 A165 1.50s light sepia   3.00 .20
607 A165 2.40s dark blue   4.00 1.25

Re-opening of the Burgtheater and Opera House in Vienna.

Symbolic of Austria's Desire to Join the UN — A166

1955, Oct. 24   Unwmk.
608 A166 2.40s green   14.00 1.40

Tenth anniversary of UN.

Wolfgang Amadeus Mozart — A167   Symbolic of Austria's Joining the UN — A168

1956, Jan. 21   *Perf. 14x13¹/₂*
609 A167 2.40s slate blue   3.75 .50

200th birth anniv. of Wolfgang Amadeus Mozart, composer.

1956, Feb. 20
610 A168 2.40s chocolate   11.00 1.10

Austria's admission to the UN.

Globe Showing Energy of the Earth — A169

1956, May 8   *Perf. 13¹/₂x14*
611 A169 2.40s deep blue   10.00 1.40

Fifth Intl. Power Conf., Vienna, June 17-23.

Map of Europe and City Maps — A170

J.B. Fischer von Erlach — A171

Photo. and Typo.
1956, June 8   *Perf. 14x13¹/₂*
612 A170 1.45s lt grn blk & red   2.50 .50

23rd Intl. Housing and Town Planning Congress, Vienna, July 22-28.

1956, July 20   Engr.
613 A171 1.50s brown   1.25 1.10

300th birth anniv. of Johann Bernhard Fischer von Erlach, architect.

Körner Type of 1953
1957, Jan. 11
614 A155 1.50s gray black   1.50 1.25

Death of Pres. Theodor Körner.

Dr. Julius Wagner-Jauregg A172

Anton Wildgans A173

1957, Mar. 7   *Perf. 14x13¹/₂*
615 A172 2.40s brn violet   3.25 1.25

Birth cent. of Dr. Julius Wagner-Jauregg, psychiatrist.

1957, May 3   Unwmk.
616 A173 1s violet blue   .30 .15

Anton Wildgans, poet, 25th death anniv.

Old and New Postal Motor Coach — A174

1957, June 14   *Perf. 13¹/₂x14*
617 A174 1s black, *yellow*   .30 .15

Austrian Postal Motor Coach Service, 50th anniv.

Gasherbrum II and Glacier A175

1957, July 27
618 A175 1.50s gray blue   .35 .15

Austrian Karakorum Expedition, which climbed Mount Gasherbrum II on July 7, 1956.

A176   A177

Designs: 20g, Farmhouse at Mörbisch. 50g, Heiligenstadt, Vienna. 1s, Mariazell. 1.40s, County seat, Klagenfurt. 1.50s, Rabenhof Building, Erdberg, Vienna. 1.80s, The Mint, Hall, Tyrol. 2s, Christkindl Church. 3.40s, Steiner Gate, Krems. 4s, Vienna Gate, Hainburg. 4.50s, Schwechat Airport,

426 AUSTRIA

Vienna. 5.50s, Chur Gate, Feldkirch. 6s, County seat, Graz. 6.40s, "Golden Roof," Innsbruck. 10s, Heidenreichstein Castle.

1957-61 Litho. Perf. 14x13½
Size: 20x25mm
618A	A176	20g violet blk ('61)	.15	.15
619	A176	50g bluish black ('59)	.15	.15

Engr.
|620|A176|1s chocolate|1.25|.15|

Typo.
|621|A176|1s chocolate|1.75|.15|

Litho.
622	A176	1s choc ('59)	.90	.15
622A	A176	1.40s brt greenish bl ('60)	.30	.15
623	A176	1.50s rose lake ('58)	.50	.15
624	A176	1.80s brt ultra ('60)	.30	.15
625	A176	2s dull blue ('58)	6.00	.15
626	A176	3.40s yel grn ('60)	.90	.80
627	A176	4s brt red lil ('60)	.75	.15
627A	A176	4.50s dl green ('60)	1.00	.50
628	A176	5.50s grnsh gray ('60)	.55	.20
629	A176	6s brt vio ('60)	1.00	.15
629A	A176	6.40s brt blue ('60)	1.00	.90

Engr.
Size: 22x28mm
630	A177	10s dk bl grn	3.00	.45
	Nos. 618A-630 (16)	19.50		
	Set value		3.50	

Of the three 1s stamps above, Nos. 620 and 621 have two names in imprint (designer H. Strohofer, engraver G. Wimmer). No. 622 has only Strohofer's name.
Values for Nos. 618A-624, 626-630 are for stamps on white paper. Most denominations also come on grayish paper with yellowish gum.
See Nos. 688-702.

1960-65 Photo. Perf. 14½x14
Size: 17x21mm
|630A|A176|50g slate ('64)|.15|.15|
Size: 18x21½mm
|630B|A176|1s chocolate|.15|.15|
Size: 17x21mm
|630C|A176|1.50s dk car ('65)|.20|.15|
| |Set value| |.35|.25|

Nos. 630A-630C issued in sheets and coils.

Graukogel, Badgastein — A180

1958, Feb. 1 Engr. Perf. 14x13½
|631|A180|1.50s dark blue|.25|.15|
Intl. Ski Federation Alpine championships, Badgastein, Feb. 2-7.

Plane over Map of Austria — A181

1958, Mar. 27 Perf. 13½x14
|632|A181|4s red|.45|.15|
Re-opening of Austrian Airlines.

Austria stamps can be mounted in the Scott annually supplemented Austria album.

Mother and Daughter A182

Walther von der Vogelweide A183

1958, May 8 Unwmk. Perf. 14x13½
|633|A182|1.50s dark blue|.25|.15|
Issued for Mother's Day.

1958, July 17 Litho. and Engr.
|634|A183|1.50s multicolored|.25|.15|
3rd Austrian Song Festival, Vienna, July 17-20.

Oswald Redlich — A184

Giant "E" on Map — A185

1958, Sept. 17 Engr.
|635|A184|2.40s ultramarine|.45|.15|
Prof. Oswald Redlich (1858-1944), historian, birth cent.

Renner Type of 1948
1958, Nov. 12
|636|A136|1.50s deep green|.45|.25|
Austrian Republic, 40th anniv.

1959, Mar. 9
|637|A185|2.40s emerald|.35|.20|
Idea of a United Europe.

Cigarette Machine and Trademark of Tobacco Monopoly — A186

Archduke Johann — A187

1959, May 8 Unwmk. Perf. 13½
|638|A186|2.40s dark olive bister|.30|.15|
Austrian tobacco monopoly, 175th anniv.

1959, May 11 Perf. 14x13½
|639|A187|1.50s deep green|.25|.20|
Archduke Johann of Austria, military leader and humanitarian, death cent.

Capercaillie A188

Joseph Haydn A189

Animals: 1.50s, Roe buck. 2.40s, Wild boar. 3.50s, Red deer, doe and fawn.

1959, May 20 Engr.
640	A188	1s rose violet	.30	.15
641	A188	1.50s blue violet	.65	.15
642	A188	2.40s dk bl green	.45	.35
643	A188	3.50s dark brown	.35	.20
	Nos. 640-643 (4)	1.75	.85
Congress of the Intl. Hunting Council, Vienna, May 20-24.

1959, May 30 Unwmk.
|644|A189|1.50s violet brown|.45|.20|
Joseph Haydn, composer, 150th death anniv.

Coat of Arms, Tyrol A190

Antenna, Zugspitze A191

1959, June 13 Perf. 14x13½
|645|A190|1.50s rose red|.25|.15|
Fight for liberation of Tyrol, 150th anniv.

1959, June 19 Perf. 13½
|646|A191|2.40s dk bl grn|.30|.15|
Inauguration of Austria's relay system.

Field Ball Player A192

Orchestral Instruments A193

1s, Runner. 1.80s, Gymnast on vaulting horse. 2s, Woman hurdler. 2.20s, Hammer thrower.

1959-70 Engr. Perf. 14x13½
647	A192	1s lilac	.20	.15
648	A192	1.50s blue green	.50	.20
648A	A192	1.80s carmine ('62)	.45	.35
648B	A192	2s rose lake ('70)	.25	.15
648C	A192	2.20s bluish blk ('67)	.25	.15
	Nos. 647-648C (5)	1.65	1.00

Litho. and Engr.
1959, Aug. 19 Perf. 14x13½
|649|A193|2.40s dull bl & blk|.30|.15|
World tour of the Vienna Philharmonic Orchestra.

Family Fleeing over Mountains A194

1960, Apr. 7 Engr. Perf. 13½x14
|650|A194|3s Prussian green|.65|.25|
WRY, July 1, 1959-June 30, 1960.

President Adolf Schärf — A195

1960, Apr. 20 Perf. 14x13½
|651|A195|1.50s gray olive|.65|.15|
Pres. Adolf Scharf, 70th birthday.

Young Hikers and Hostel — A196

1960, May 20 Perf. 13½x14
|652|A196|1s carmine rose|.25|.15|
Youth hiking; youth hostel movement.

Anton Eiselsberg — A197

Gustav Mahler — A198

Litho. and Engr.
1960, June 20 Perf. 14x13½
|653|A197|1.50s buff & dk brn|.70|.15|
Dr. Anton Eiselsberg, surgeon, birth cent.

1960, July 7 Engr.
|654|A198|1.50s chocolate|.70|.15|
Gustav Mahler, composer, birth cent.

Jakob Prandtauer, Melk Abbey — A199

Gross Glockner Mountain Road — A200

1960, July 16 Unwmk.
|655|A199|1.50s red brown|.70|.15|
Jakob Prandtauer, architect, 300th birth anniv.

1960, Aug. 3
|656|A200|1.80s dark blue|.70|.50|
Gross Glockner Mountain Road, 25th anniv.

Ionic Capital — A201

1960, Aug. 29 Perf. 14x13½
|657|A201|3s black|1.40|.75|
Europa: Idea of a United Europe.

Griffen, Carinthia A202

1960, Oct. 10 Engr. Perf. 13½x14
|658|A202|1.50s slate green|.30|.15|
40th anniv. of the plebiscite which kept Carinthia with Austria.

Flame and Broken
Chain — A203

1961, May 8 Unwmk. *Perf. 14x13¹/₂*
659 A203 1.50s scarlet .30 .15
Victims in Austria's fight for freedom.

First Austrian
Mail Plane,
1918 — A204

1961, May 15 *Perf. 13¹/₂x14*
660 A204 5s violet blue .70 .30
Airmail Phil. Exhib., LUPOSTA 1961, Vienna,
May.

Transportation by
Road, Rail and
Waterway — A205

Mountain Mower,
by Albin Egger-
Lienz — A206

Engraved and Typographed
1961, May 29 *Perf. 13¹/₂*
661 A205 3s rose red & olive .45 .30
13th European Conference of Transportation
ministers, Vienna, May 29-31.

1961, June 12 Engr. *Perf. 13¹/₂x14*
Designs: 1.50s, The Kiss, by August von Pet-
tenkofen. 3s, Girl, by Anton Romako. 5s, Ariadne's
Triumph, by Hans Makart.

Inscriptions in Red Brown
662 A206 1s rose lake .15 .15
663 A206 1.50s dull violet .25 .25
664 A206 3s olive green .75 .70
665 A206 5s blue violet .45 .40
Nos. 662-665 (4) 1.60 1.50
Society of Creative Artists, Künstlerhaus, Vienna,
cent.

Sonnblick
Mountain and
Observatory
A207

Mercury and Globe
A208

1961, Sept. 1 *Perf. 14x13¹/₂*
666 A207 1.80s violet blue .40 .30
Sonnblick meteorological observatory, 75th anniv.

1961, Sept. 18
667 A208 3s black .70 .40
Intl. Banking Congress, Vienna, Sept. 1961.
English inscription listing UN financial groups.

Coal Mine
Shaft — A209

Designs: 1.50s, Generator. 1.80s, Iron blast furnace. 3s, Pouring steel. 5s, Oil refinery.

1961, Sept. 15 Engr. *Perf. 14x13¹/₂*
668 A209 1s black .20 .15
669 A209 1.50s green .25 .20
670 A209 1.80s dark car rose .55 .40
671 A209 3s bright lilac .70 .55
672 A209 5s blue .90 .70
Nos. 668-672 (5) 2.60 2.00
15th anniversary of nationalized industry.

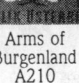

Arms of
Burgenland
A210

Franz Liszt
A211

1961, Oct. 9 Engr. and Litho.
673 A210 1.50s blk, yel & dk red .35 .15
Burgenland as part of the Austrian Republic, 40th
anniv.

1961, Oct. 20 Engr.
674 A211 3s dark brown .55 .40
Franz Liszt, composer, 150th birth anniv.

Parliament
A212

1961, Dec. 18 *Perf. 13¹/₂x14*
675 A212 1s brown .20 .15
Austrian Bureau of Budget, 200th anniv.

Kaprun-Mooserboden Reservoir — A213

Hydroelectric Power Plants: 1.50s, Ybbs-Per-
senbeug dam and locks. 1.80s, Lünersee dam and
reservoir. 3s, Grossraming dam. 4s, Bisamberg
transformer plant. 6.40s, St. Andrä power plant.

1962, Mar. 26 Unwmk.
676 A213 1s violet blue .15 .15
677 A213 1.50s red lilac .25 .20
678 A213 1.80s green .40 .35
679 A213 3s brown .40 .35
680 A213 4s rose red .40 .35
681 A213 6.40s gray 1.25 1.10
Nos. 676-681 (6) 2.85 2.50
Nationalization of the electric power industry,
15th anniv.

Johann Nestroy
A214

Friedrich
Gauermann
A215

1962, May 25 *Perf. 14x13¹/₂*
682 A214 1s violet .20 .15
Johann Nepomuk Nestroy, Viennese playwright,
author and actor, death cent.

1962, July 6 Engr.
683 A215 1.50s intense blue .20 .15
Friedrich Gauermann (1807-1862), landscape
painter, death cent.

Scout Emblem and
Handshake — A216

1962, Oct. 5
684 A216 1.50s dark green .35 .20
Austria's Boy Scouts, 50th anniv.

Lowlands
Forest
A217

1.50s, Deciduous forest. 3s, Fir & larch forest.

1962, Oct. 12 *Perf. 13¹/₂x14*
685 A217 1s greenish gray .20 .15
686 A217 1.50s reddish brown .25 .25
687 A217 3s dk slate green .90 .70
Nos. 685-687 (3) 1.35 1.10

Buildings Types of 1957-61
Designs: 30g, City Hall, Vienna. 40g, Porcia Castle, Spittal on the Drau. 60g, Tanners' Tower, Wels.
70g, Residenz Fountain, Salzburg. 80g, Old farmhouse, Pinzgau. 1s, Romanesque columns, Millstatt
Abbey. 1.20s, Kornmesser House, Bruck on the
Mur. 1.30s, Schatten Castle, Feldkirch, Vorarlberg.
2s, Dragon Fountain, Klagenfurt. 2.20s, Beethoven
House, Vienna. 2.50s, Danube Bridge, Linz. 3s,
Swiss Gate, Vienna. 3.50s, Esterhazy Palace, Eisenstadt. 8s, City Hall, Steyr. 20s, Melk Abbey.

1962-70 Litho. *Perf. 14x13¹/₂*
Size: 20x25mm
688 A176 30g greenish gray .50 .15
689 A176 40g rose red .15 .15
690 A176 60g violet brown .35 .15
691 A176 70g dark brown .25 .15
692 A176 80g yellow brown .35 .15
693 A176 1s brown ('70) .20 .15
694 A176 1.20s red lilac .40 .15
695 A176 1.30s green ('67) .15 .15
696 A176 2s dk blue ('68) .25 .15
697 A176 2.20s green 1.40 .15
698 A176 2.50s violet .80 .15
699 A176 3s bright blue .65 .15
700 A176 3.50s rose carmine .80 .15
701 A176 8s claret ('65) 1.00 .15
Perf. 13¹/₂
Engr.
Size: 28x36¹/₂mm
702 A177 20s rose claret ('63) 2.50 .35
Nos. 688-702 (15) 9.75
Set value 1.15
Values for Nos. 688-702 are for stamps on white
paper. Some denominations also come on grayish
paper with yellowish gum.

Electric
Locomotive
and Train of
1837
A218

Lithographed and Engraved
1962, Nov. 9 *Perf. 13¹/₂x14*
703 A218 3s buff & black .90 .40
125th anniversary of Austrian railroads.

Postilions and
Postal Clerk,
1863 — A219

Hermann
Bahr — A220

1963, May 7 Photo. *Perf. 14x13¹/₂*
704 A219 3s dk brn & citron .70 .40
First Intl. Postal Conference, Paris, cent.

Lithographed and Engraved
1963, July 19 *Perf. 14x13¹/₂*
705 A220 1.50s blue & black .25 .15
Centenary of birth of Hermann Bahr, poet.

St. Florian Statue,
Kefermarkt,
Contemporary and Old
Fire Engines — A221

1963, Aug. 30 Unwmk.
706 A221 1.50s brt rose & blk .25 .15
Austrian volunteer fire brigades, cent.

Factory, Flag
and "ÖGB" on
Map of Austria
A222

1963, Sept. 23 Litho. *Perf. 13¹/₂x14*
707 A222 1.50s gray, red & dk brn .25 .15
5th Congress of the Austrian Trade Union Federation (ÖGB), Sept. 23-28.

Arms of
Austria and
Tyrol — A223

1963, Sept. 27 Unwmk.
708 A223 1.50s tan, blk, red & yel .25 .15
Tyrol's union with Austria, 600th anniv.

Prince Eugene of Savoy — A224

Centenary Emblem — A225

1963, Oct. 18   **Engr.**   *Perf. 14x13¹/₂*
709 A224 1.50s violet   .25 .15

Prince Eugene of Savoy (1663-1736), Austrian general, 300th birth anniv.

1963, Oct. 25   **Engr. and Photo.**
710 A225 3s blk, sil & red   .50 .20

Intl. Red Cross, cent.

Slalom A226

Sports: 1.20s, Biathlon (skier with rifle). 1.50s, Ski jump. 1.80s, Women's figure skating. 2.20s, Ice hockey. 3s, Tobogganing. 4s, Bobsledding.

Photo. and Engr.
1963, Nov. 11   *Perf. 13¹/₂x14*
711 A226 1s multi   .15 .15
712 A226 1.20s multi   .15 .15
713 A226 1.50s multi   .20 .15
714 A226 1.80s multi   .25 .15
715 A226 2.20s multi   .40 .25
716 A226 3s multi   .30 .20
717 A226 4s multi   .55 .35
     Nos. 711-717 (7)   2.00 1.40

9th Winter Olympic Games, Innsbruck, Jan. 29-Feb. 9, 1964.

Baroque Creche by Josef Thaddäus Stammel — A227

1963, Nov. 29   **Engr.**   *Perf. 14x13¹/₂*
718 A227 2s dark Prus green   .25 .15

Flowers A228

1964, Apr. 17   **Litho.**   *Perf. 14*
719 A228 1s Nasturtium   .15 .15
720 A228 1.50s Peony   .20 .15
721 A228 1.80s Clematis   .25 .15
722 A228 2.20s Dahlia   .35 .20
723 A228 3s Morning glory   .40 .25
724 A228 4s Hollyhock   .50 .35
     Nos. 719-724 (6)   1.85 1.25

Vienna Intl. Garden Show, Apr. 16-Oct. 11.

St. Mary Magdalene and Apostle — A229

Pallas Athena and National Council Chamber — A230

1964, May 21   **Engr.**   *Perf. 13¹/₂*
725 A229 1.50s bluish black   .25 .15

Romanesque art in Austria. The 12th century stained-glass window is from the Weitensfeld Church, the bust of the Apostle from the portal of St. Stephen's Cathedral, Vienna.

Engr. and Litho.
1964, May 25   *Perf. 14x13¹/₂*
726 A230 1.80s black & emer   .30 .15

2nd Parliamentary and Scientific Conf., Vienna.

The Kiss, by Gustav Klimt A231

1964, June 5   **Litho.**   *Perf. 13¹/₂*
727 A231 3s multicolored   .35 .25

Re-opening of the Vienna Secession, a museum devoted to early 20th century art (art nouveau).

Brother of Mercy and Patient — A232

1964, June 11   **Engr.**   *Perf. 14x13¹/₂*
728 A232 1.50s dark blue   .25 .15

Brothers of Mercy in Austria, 350th anniv.

"Bringing the News of Victory at Kunersdorf" by Bernardo Bellotto A233

"The Post in Art": 1.20s, Changing Horses at Relay Station, by Julius Hörmann. 1.50s, The Honeymoon Trip, by Moritz von Schwind. 1.80s, After the Rain, by Ignaz Raffalt. 2.20s, Mailcoach in the Mountains, by Adam Klein. 3s, Changing Horses at Bavarian Border, by Friedrich Gauermann. 4s, Postal Sleigh (Truck) in the Mountains, by Adalbert Pilch. 6.40s, Saalbach Post Office, by Adalbert Pilch.

1964, June 15   *Perf. 13¹/₂x14*
729 A233 1s rose claret   .15 .15
730 A233 1.20s sepia   .15 .15
731 A233 1.50s violet blue   .15 .15
732 A233 1.80s brt violet   .15 .15
733 A233 2.20s black   .20 .15
734 A233 3s dl car rose   .30 .20
735 A233 4s slate green   .35 .20
736 A233 6.40s dull claret   .80 .45
     Nos. 729-736 (8)   2.25
     Set value   1.25

15th UPU Cong., Vienna, May-June 1964.

Workers — A234

1964, Sept. 4   *Perf. 14x13¹/₂*
737 A234 1s black   .15 .15

Centenary of Austrian Labor Movement.

Europa Issue, 1964
Common Design Type

1964, Sept. 14   **Litho.**   *Perf. 12*
Size: 21x36mm
738 CD7 3s dark blue   .50 .15

Emblem of Radio Austria and Transistor Radio Panel A235

1964, Oct. 1   **Photo.**   *Perf. 13¹/₂*
739 A235 1s black brn & red   .15 .15

Forty years of Radio Austria.

A236   A237

Litho. and Engr.
1964, Oct. 12   *Perf. 14x13¹/₂*
740 A236 1.50s Old printing press   .15 .15

6th Congress of the Intl. Graphic Federation, Vienna, Oct. 12-17.

Typo. and Engr.
1965, Apr. 20   *Perf. 12*
Pres. Adolf Schärf and Scharf Student Center.
741 A237 1.50s bluish black   .20 .15

Dr. Adolf Schärf (1890-1965), Pres. of Austria (1957-65).

Ruins and New Buildings — A238

1965, Apr. 27   **Engr.**   *Perf. 14x13¹/₂*
742 A238 1.80s carmine lake   .20 .15

Twenty years of reconstruction.

Oldest Seal of Vienna University — A239

St. George, 16th Century Wood Sculpture — A240

Photo. and Engr.
1965, May 10   *Perf. 14x13¹/₂*
743 A239 3s gold & red   .35 .20

University of Vienna, 600th anniv.

1965, May 17   **Engr.**
744 A240 1.80s bluish black   .25 .15

Art of the Danube Art School, 1490-1540, exhibition, May-Oct. 1965. The stamp background shows an engraving by Albrecht Altdorfer.

ITU Emblem, Telegraph Key and TV Antenna — A241

Ferdinand Raimund — A242

1965, May 17   **Unwmk.**
745 A241 3s violet blue   .35 .20

ITU, cent.

1965   **Engr.**   *Perf. 14x13¹/₂*
Portraits: No. 746, Dr. Ignaz Philipp Semmelweis. No. 747, Bertha von Suttner. No. 749, Ferdinand Georg Waldmüller.
746 A242 1.50s violet   .30 .15
747 A242 1.50s bluish black   .30 .15
748 A242 3s dark brown   .55 .15
749 A242 3s greenish blk   .55 .20
     Nos. 746-749 (4)   1.70
     Set value   .50

Semmelweis (1818-65), who discovered the cause of puerperal fever and introduced antisepsis into obstetrics (#746). 60th anniv. of the awarding of the Nobel Prize for Peace to von Suttner (1843-1914), pacifist and author (#747). Raimund (1790-1836), actor and playwright (#748). Waldmüller (1793-1865), painter (#749).

Issue dates: No. 746, Aug. 13; No. 747, Dec. 1; No. 748, June 1; No. 749, Aug. 23.

Dancers with Tambourines A243

Red Cross and Strip of Gauze A244

Design: 1.50s, Male gymnasts with practice bars.

1965, July 20   **Photo. and Engr.**
750 A243 1.50s gray & black   .20 .15
751 A243 3s bister & blk   .35 .25

4th Gymnaestrada, intl. athletic meet, Vienna, July 20-24.

1965, Oct. 1   **Litho.**   *Perf. 14x13¹/₂*
752 A244 3s black & red   .35 .15

20th Intl. Red Cross Conference, Vienna.

Austrian Flag and Eagle with Mural Crown — A245

Austrian Flag, UN Headquarters and Emblem — A246

1965, Oct. 7   **Photo. and Engr.**
753 A245 1.50s gold, red & blk   .15 .15

50th anniv. of the Union of Austrian Towns.

Lithographed and Engraved
1965, Oct. 25   Unwmk.   *Perf. 12*
754 A246 3s blk, brt bl & red   .45   .15

Austria's admission to the UN, 10th anniv.

University of
Technology,
Vienna — A247

1965, Nov. 8   Engr.   *Perf. 13¹/₂x14*
755 A247 1.50s violet   .15   .15

Vienna University of Technology, 150th anniv.

Map of Austria with Postal Zone
Numbers — A248

1966, Jan. 14   Photo.   *Perf. 12*
756 A248 1.50s yel, red & blk   .15   .15

Introduction of postal zone numbers, Jan. 1,
1966.

PTT Building,
Emblem and
Churches of Sts.
Maria Rotunda and
Barbara
A249

Maria von Ebner
Eschenbach
A250

Lithographed and Engraved
1966, Mar. 4   *Perf. 14x13¹/₂*
757 A249 1.50s blk, *dull yellow*   .15   .15

Headquarters of the Post and Telegraph Administration, cent.

1966, Mar. 11   Engr.
758 A250 3s plum   .35   .15

50th death anniv. of Maria von Ebner
Eschenbach (1830-1916), novelist and poet.

Ferris Wheel,
Prater — A251

1966, Apr. 19   Engr.   *Perf. 14x13¹/₂*
759 A251 1.50s slate green   .15   .15

Opening of the Prater (park), Vienna, to the public by Emperor Joseph II, 200th anniv.

A252   A253

1966, May 6   Unwmk.   *Perf. 12*
760 A252 3s dark brown   .35   .15

Josef Hoffmann (1870-1956), architect, 10th
death anniv.

Photo. and Engr.
1966, May 27   *Perf. 14*
761 A253 1.50s Wiener Neustadt
Arms   .15   .15

Wiener Neustadt Art Exhib., centered around the
time and person of Frederick III (1440-93).

Austrian
Eagle and
Emblem of
National
Bank
A254

1966, May 27   *Perf. 14*
762 A254 3s gray grn, dk brn & dk
green   .35   .15

Austrian National Bank, 150th anniv.

Puppy — A255   A256

Litho. and Engr.
1966, June 16   *Perf. 12*
763 A255 1.80s yellow & black   .25   .15

120th anniv. of the Vienna Humane Society.

1966, Aug. 17   Litho.   *Perf. 13¹/₂*

Alpine Flowers: 1.50s, Columbine. 1.80s, Turk's
cap. 2.20s, Wulfenia carinthiaca. 3s, Globeflowers.
4s, Fire lily. 5s, Pasqueflower.

Flowers in Natural Colors
764 A256	1.50s dark blue	.15	.15
765 A256	1.80s dark blue	.25	.15
766 A256	2.20s dark blue	.35	.20
767 A256	3s dark blue	.50	.30
768 A256	4s dark blue	.50	.35
769 A256	5s dark blue	.50	.35
	Nos. 764-769 (6)	2.25	1.50

Fair Building
A257

1966, Aug. 26   Engr.   *Perf. 13¹/₂x13*
770 A257 3s violet blue   .35   .15

First International Fair at Wels.

Peter Anich, Map,
Globe and
Books — A258

Sick Worker and
Health
Emblem — A259

1966, Sept. 1   *Perf. 14x13¹/₂*
771 A258 1.80s black   .20   .15

Peter Anich (1723-1766), Tirolean cartographer
and farmer, 200th death anniv.

1966, Sept. 19   Engr. and Litho.
772 A259 3s black & vermilion   .35   .15

15th Occupational Medicine Congress, Vienna,
Sept. 19-24.

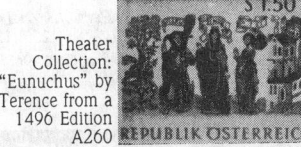

Theater
Collection:
"Eunuchus" by
Terence from a
1496 Edition
A260

Designs: 1.80s, Map Collection: Title page of
Geographia Blavania (Cronus, Hercules and celestial sphere). 2.20s, Picture Archive and Portrait Collection: View of Old Vienna after a watercolor by
Anton Stutzinger. 3s, Manuscript Collection: Illustration from the 15th century "Livre du Cuer
d'Amours Espris" of the Duke René d'Anjou.

Photogravure and Engraved
1966, Sept. 28   *Perf. 13¹/₂x14*
773 A260	1.50s multicolored	.15	.15
774 A260	1.80s multicolored	.20	.15
775 A260	2.20s multicolored	.25	.20
776 A260	3s multicolored	.30	.20
	Nos. 773-776 (4)	.90	.70

Austrian National Library.

Young Girl
A261

Strawberries
A262

Litho. and Engr.
1966, Oct. 3   *Perf. 14x13¹/₂*
777 A261 3s light blue & black   .35   .15

"Save the Child" society, 10th anniv.

1966, Nov. 25   Photo.   *Perf. 13¹/₂x13*
778 A262	50g shown	.20	.15
779 A262	1s Grapes	.20	.15
780 A262	1.50s Apple	.20	.15
781 A262	1.80s Blackberries	.25	.20
782 A262	2.20s Apricots	.25	.20
783 A262	3s Cherries	.35	.25
	Nos. 778-783 (6)	1.45	1.10

Coat of Arms of
University of
Linz — A263

Ice Skater,
1866 — A264

Photo. and Engr.
1966, Dec. 9   *Perf. 14x13¹/₂*
784 A263 3s multi   .35   .15

Inauguration of the Universary of Linz, Oct. 8,
1966.

Photo. and Engr.
1967, Feb. 3   *Perf. 14x13¹/₂*
785 A264 3s pale bl & dk bl   .35   .15

Centenary of Vienna Ice Skating Club.

Ballet
Dancer — A265

Karl
Schönherr — A266

1967, Feb. 15   Engr.   *Perf. 11¹/₂x12*
786 A265 3s deep claret   .35   .15
  a.   Perf. 12   1.25   1.10

"Blue Danube" waltz by Johann Strauss, cent.

1967, Feb. 24   Engr.   *Perf. 14x13¹/₂*
787 A266 3s gray brown   .35   .15

Dr. Karl Schönherr (1867-1943), poet, playwright and physician.

Ice Hockey
Goalkeeper
A267

Photogravure and Engraved
1967, Mar. 17   *Perf. 13¹/₂x14*
788 A267 3s pale grn & dk bl   .35   .15

Ice Hockey Championships, Vienna, Mar. 18-29.

Violin, Organ and
Laurel — A268

1967, Mar. 28   Engr.   *Perf. 13¹/₂*
789 A268 3.50s indigo   .40   .15

Vienna Philharmonic Orchestra, 125th anniv.

Motherhood,
Watercolor by
Peter Fendi
A269

1967, Apr. 28   Litho.   *Perf. 14*
790 A269 2s multicolored   .25   .15

Mother's Day.

Gothic Mantle
Madonna — A270

1967, May 19   Engr.   *Perf. 13¹/₂x14*
791 A270 3s slate   .35   .15

"Austrian Gothic," art exhibition, Krems, 1967.
The Gothic wood carving is from Frauenstein in
Upper Austria.

Medieval Gold Cross — A271

Swan, Tapestry by Oscar Kokoschka — A272

Litho. and Engr.

1967, June 9 **Perf. 13½**
792 A271 3.50s Prus grn & multi .40 .15

Salzburg Treasure Chamber; exhibition at Salzburg Cathedral, June 12-Sept. 15.

1967, June 9 **Photo.**
793 A272 2s multicolored .25 .15

Nibelungen District Art Exhibition, Pöchlarn, celebrating the 700th anniversary of Pöchlarn as a city. The design is from the border of the Amor and Psyche tapestry at the Salzburg Festival Theater.

View and Arms of Vienna A273

Engraved and Photogravure

1967, June 12 **Perf. 13x13½**
794 A273 3s black & red .35 .15

10th Europa Talks, "Science and Society in Europe," Vienna, June 13-17.

Prize Bull "Mucki" A274

1967, Aug. 28 **Engr.** **Perf. 13½**
795 A274 2s deep claret .35 .15

Centenary of the Ried Festival and the Agricultural Fair.

Potato Beetle — A275

Engraved and Photogravure

1967, Aug. 29 **Perf. 13½x14**
796 A275 3s black & multi .35 .15

6th Intl. Congress for Plant Protection, Vienna.

First Locomotive Used on Brenner Pass — A276

1967, Sept. 23 **Photo.** **Perf. 12**
797 A276 3.50s tan & slate grn .45 .15

Centenary of railroad over Brenner Pass.

Christ in Glory — A277

1967, Oct. 9 **Perf. 13½**
798 A277 2s multicolored .25 .15

Restoration of the Romanesque (11th century) frescoes in the Lambach monastery church.

Main Gate to Fair, Prater, Vienna — A278

1967, Oct. 24 Photo. Perf. 13½x14
799 A278 2s choc & buff .25 .15

Congress of Intl. Trade Fairs, Vienna, Oct., 1967.

Medal Showing Minerva and Art Symbols A279

Frankfurt Medal for Reformation, 1717 A280

Litho. & Engr.

1967, Oct. 25 **Perf. 13½**
800 A279 2s dk brn, dk bl & yel .25 .15

Vienna Academy of Fine Arts, 275th anniv. The medal was designed by Georg Raphael Donner (1693-1741) and is awarded as an artist's prize.

1967, Oct. 31 **Engr.** **Perf. 14x13½**
801 A280 3.50s blue black .40 .15

450th anniversary of the Reformation.

Mountain Range and Stone Pines A281

1967, Nov. 7 **Perf. 13½**
802 A281 3.50s green .40 .15

Centenary of academic study of forestry.

Land Survey Monument, 1770 — A282

St. Leopold, Window, Heiligenkreuz Abbey — A283

1967, Nov. 7 **Photo.**
803 A282 2s olive black .25 .15

150th anniversary of official land records.

1967, Nov. 15 **Engr. & Photo.**
804 A283 1.80s multicolored .25 .15

Margrave Leopold III (1075-1136), patron saint of Austria.

Tragic Mask and Violin — A284

Nativity from 15th Century Altar — A285

1967, Nov. 17 **Perf. 13½**
805 A284 3.50s bluish lil & blk .40 .15

Academy of Music and Dramatic Art, 150th anniv.

1967, Nov. 27 **Engr.** **Perf. 14x13½**
806 A285 2s green .25 .15

Christmas.
The design shows the late Gothic carved center panel of the altar in St. John's Chapel in Nonnberg Convent, Salzburg.

Innsbruck Stadium, Alps and FISU Emblem — A286

Camillo Sitte — A287

1968, Jan. 22 **Engr.** **Perf. 13½**
807 A286 2s dark blue .25 .15

Winter University Games under the auspices of FISU (Fédération Internationale du Sport Universitaire), Innsbruck, Jan. 21-28.

1968, Apr. 17 **Perf. 13½**
808 A287 2s black brown .25 .15

125th birth anniv. of Camillo Sitte (1843-1903), architect and city planner.

Mother and Child — A288

1968, May 7
809 A288 2s slate green .25 .15

Mother's Day.

Cup and Serpent Emblem — A289

1968, May 7 **Photo.**
810 A289 3.50s dp plum, gray & gold .40 .15

Bicentenary of the Veterinary College.

Bride with Lace Veil — A290

1968, May 24 **Engr.** **Perf. 12**
811 A290 3.50s blue black .40 .15

Embroidery industry of Vorarlberg, cent.

Horse Race A291

1968, June 4 **Perf. 13½**
812 A291 3.50s sepia .40 .20

Centenary of horse racing at Freudenau, Vienna.

Dr. Karl Landsteiner A292

Peter Rosegger A293

1968, June 14 **Perf. 14x13½**
813 A292 3.50s dark blue .40 .20

Birth cent. of Dr. Karl Landsteiner (1868-1943), pathologist, discoverer of the four main human blood types.

1968, June 26
814 A293 2s slate green .25 .15

50th death anniv. of Peter Rosegger (1843-1918), poet and writer.

Angelica Kauffmann, Self-portrait A294

Bronze Statue of Young Man, 1st Century B.C. A295

1968, July 15 **Engr.** **Perf. 14x13½**
815 A294 2s intense black .25 .15

"Angelica Kauffmann and her Contemporaries," art exhibitions, Bregenz, July 28-Oct. 13, and Vienna, Oct. 22, 1968-Jan. 6, 1969.

1968, July 15 **Litho. & Engr.**
816 A295 2s grnsh gray & blk .25 .15

20 years of excavations on Magdalene Mountain, Carinthia.

Bishop, Romanesque
Bas-relief — A296

1968, Sept. 20   Engr.   *Perf. 14x13½*
817 A296 2s blue gray   .25 .15
Graz-Seckau Bishopric, 750th anniv.

Koloman
Moser — A297

Human Rights
Flame — A298

Engr. & Photo.
1968, Oct. 18   *Perf. 12*
818 A297 2s black brn & ver   .25 .15
50th death anniv. of Koloman Moser (1868-1918), stamp designer and painter.

1968, Oct. 18   Photo.   *Perf. 14x13½*
819 A298 1.50s gray, dp car & dk
green   .30 .15
International Human Rights Year.

A299   A300

Designs: No. 820, Pres. Karl Renner and States' arms. No. 821, Coats of arms of Austria and Austrian states. No. 822, Article I of Austrian Constitution and States' coats of arms.

Engr. & Photo.
1968, Nov. 11   *Perf. 13½*
820 A299 2s black & multi   .35 .30
821 A299 2s black & multi   .35 .30
822 A299 2s black & multi   .35 .30
   Nos. 820-822 (3)   1.05 .90
50th anniversary of Republic of Austria.

1968, Nov. 29   Engr.   *Perf. 14x13½*
Crèche, Memorial Chapel, Oberndorf-Salzburg.
823 A300 2s slate green   .25 .15
Christmas; 150th anniv. of "Silent Night, Holy Night" hymn.

Angels, from Last Judgment by Troger
(Röhrenbach-Greillenstein Chapel) — A301

Baroque Frescoes: No. 825, Vanquished Demons, by Paul Troger, Altenburg Abbey. No. 826, Sts. Peter and Paul, by Troger, Melk Abbey. No. 827, The Glorification of Mary, by Franz Anton Maulpertsch, Maria Treu Church, Vienna. No. 828, St. Leopold Carried into Heaven, by Maulpertsch, Ebenfurth Castle Chapel. No. 829, Symbolic figures

from The Triumph of Apollo, by Maulpertsch, Halbthurn Castle.

Engr. & Photo.
1968, Dec. 11   *Perf. 13½x14*
824 A301 2s multicolored   .30 .30
825 A301 2s multicolored   .30 .30
826 A301 2s multicolored   .30 .30
827 A301 2s multicolored   .30 .30
828 A301 2s multicolored   .30 .30
829 A301 2s multicolored   .30 .30
   Nos. 824-829 (6)   1.80 1.80

St. Stephen — A302

Statues in St. Stephen's Cathedral, Vienna: No. 831, St. Paul. No. 832, Mantle Madonna. No. 833, St. Christopher. No. 834, St. George and the Dragon. No. 835, St. Sebastian.

1969, Jan. 28   Engr.   *Perf. 13½*
830 A302 2s black   .30 .30
831 A302 2s rose claret   .30 .30
832 A302 2s gray violet   .30 .30
833 A302 2s slate blue   .30 .30
834 A302 2s slate green   .30 .30
835 A302 2s dk red brn   .30 .30
   Nos. 830-835 (6)   1.80 1.80
500th anniversary of Diocese of Vienna.

Parliament
and Pallas
Athena
Fountain,
Vienna
A303

1969, Apr. 8   Engr.   *Perf. 13½*
836 A303 2s greenish black   .25 .15
Interparliamentary Union Conf., Vienna, 4/7-13.

Europa Issue, 1969
Common Design Type
1969, Apr. 28   Photo.   *Perf. 12*
837 CD12 2s gray grn, brick red &
blue   .25 .15

Council of Europe
Emblem — A304

1969, May 5
838 A304 3.50s gray, ultra, blk & yel   .45 .25
20th anniversary of Council of Europe.

Frontier
Guards — A305

Engr. & Photo.
1969, May 14   *Perf. 12*
839 A305 2s sepia & red   .25 .15
Austrian Federal Army.

Don Giovanni, by
Mozart — A306

Cent. of Vienna Opera House: a, Don Giovanni, Mozart. b, Magic Flute, Mozart. c, Fidelio, Beethoven. d, Lohengrin, Wagner. e, Don Carlos, Verdi. f, Carmen, Bizet. g, Rosencavalier, Richard Strauss. h, Swan Lake, Ballet by Tchaikovsky.

1969, May 23   *Perf. 13½*
840 A306 Sheet of 8   4.00 4.00
a.-h.   2s, any single   .35 .35
Centenary of Vienna Opera House.
No. 840 contains 8 stamps arranged around gold and red center label showing Opera House. Printed in sheets containing 4 Nos. 840 with wide gutters between.

A307   A308

Gothic armor of Maximilian I.

1969, June 4   Engr.
841 A307 2s bluish black   .25 .15
Emperor Maximilian I Exhibition, Innsbruck, May 30-Oct. 5.

1969, June 16   Photo.   *Perf. 13½*
Oldest Municipal Seal of Vienna.
842 A308 2s tan, red & black   .25 .15
19th Cong. of the Intl. Org. of Municipalities, Vienna, June 1969.

A309   A310

Girl's head and village house.

Engraved and Photogravure
1969, June 16   *Perf. 13½x14*
843 A309 2s yel grn & sepia   .25 .15
20th anniv. of the Children's Village Movement in Austria (SOS Villages).

1969, Aug. 22   Photo.   *Perf. 13x13½*
Hands holding wrench, and UN emblem.
844 A310 2s deep green   .25 .15
ILO, 50th anniv.

A311   A312

Austria's flag and shield circling the world.

Engraved and Lithographed
1969, Aug. 22   *Perf. 14x13½*
845 A311 3.50s slate & red   .40 .20
Year of Austrians Living Abroad, 1969.

Engraved and Photogravure
1969, Sept. 26   *Perf. 13½*
Etchings: No. 846, Young Hare, by Dürer. No. 847, El Cid Killing a Bull, by Francisco de Goya. No. 848, Madonna with the Pomegranate, by Raphael. No. 849, The Painter, by Peter Brueghel. No. 850, Rubens' Son Nicolas, by Rubens. No. 851,

Self-portrait, by Rembrandt. No. 852, Lady Reading, by Francois Guerin. No. 853, Wife of the Artist, by Egon Schiele.

Gray Frame, Buff Background
846 A312 2s black & brown   .30 .30
847 A312 2s black   .30 .30
848 A312 2s black   .30 .30
849 A312 2s black   .30 .30
850 A312 2s black & salmon   .30 .30
851 A312 2s black   .30 .30
852 A312 2s black & salmon   .30 .30
853 A312 2s black   .30 .30
   Nos. 846-853 (8)   2.40 2.40
Etching collection in the Albertina, Vienna, 200th anniv.

President Franz
Jonas — A313

1969, Oct. 3
854 A313 2s gray & vio blue   .25 .15
70th birthday of Franz Jonas, Austrian Pres.

Post Horn,
Globe and
Lightning
A314

1969, Oct. 17   *Perf. 13½x14*
855 A314 2s multicolored   .25 .15
Union of Postal and Telegraph employees, 50th anniv.

Savings Box,
about 1450
A315

Madonna, by
Albin Egger-Lienz
A316

1969, Oct. 31   Photo.   *Perf. 13x13½*
856 A315 2s silver & slate green   .25 .15
The importance of savings.

Engr. & Photo.
1969, Nov. 24   *Perf. 12*
857 A316 2s dp claret & pale yel   .25 .15
Christmas.

Josef
Schöffel — A317

St. Klemens M.
Hofbauer — A318

1970, Feb. 6   Engr.   *Perf. 14x13½*
858 A317 2s dull purple   .25 .15
60th death anniv. of Josef Schöffel, (1832-1910), who saved the Vienna Woods.

Engraved and Photogravure
1970, Mar. 13   *Perf. 14x13½*
859 A318 2s dk brn & lt tan   .25 .15
150th death anniv. St. Klemens Maria Hofbauer (1751-1820); Redemptorist preacher in Poland and Austria, canonized in 1909.

Chancellor Leopold Figl
A319

Belvedere Palace, Vienna
A320

1970, Apr. 27   Engr.   Perf. 13½
860 A319 2s dark olive gray   .25 .15
861 A320 2s dark rose brown   .25 .15
        Set value   .20
25th anniversary of Second Republic.

A321

A322

1970, May 19   Engr.   Perf. 13½
862 A321 2s Krimml waterfalls   .30 .15
European Nature Conservation Year, 1970.

Litho. & Engr.
1970, June 5   Perf. 13½
St. Leopold on oldest seal of Innsbruck University.
863 A322 2s red & black   .30 .15
Leopold Franzens University, Innsbruck, 300th anniv.

Organ, Great Hall, Music Academy — A323

Photo. & Engr.
1970, June 5   Perf. 14
864 A323 2s gold & deep claret   .25 .15
Vienna Music Academy Building, cent.

Tower Clock, 1450-1550
A324

The Beggar Student, by Carl Millöcker
A325

Old Clocks from Vienna Horological Museum: #866, Lyre clock, 1790-1815. #867, Pendant clock 1600-50. #868, Pendant watch, 1800-30. #869, Bracket clock, 1720-60. #870, French column clock, 1820-50.

1970
865 A324 1.50s buff & sepia   .25 .25
866 A324 1.50s greenish & grn   .25 .25
867 A324 2s pale bl & dk bl   .30 .30
868 A324 2s pale rose & lake   .30 .30

869 A324 3.50s buff & brown   .50 .50
870 A324 3.50s pale lil & brn vio   .50 .50
        Nos. 865-870 (6)   2.10 2.10
Issued: #865, 867, 869, 6/22; others, 10/23.

1970   Photo & Engr.   Perf. 13½
Operettas: No. 872, Fledermaus, by Johann Strauss. No. 873, The Dream Waltz, by Oscar Strauss. No. 874, The Bird Seller, by Carl Zeller. No. 875, The Merry Widow, by Franz Lehar. No. 876, Two Hearts in Three-quarter Time, by Robert Stolz.
871 A325 1.50s pale grn & grn   .25 .25
872 A325 1.50s yel & vio blue   .25 .25
873 A325 2s pale rose & vio brn   .30 .30
874 A325 2s pale grn & sep   .30 .30
875 A325 3.50s pale bl & ind   .50 .50
876 A325 3.50s beige & slate   .50 .50
        Nos. 871-876 (6)   2.10 2.10
Issued: #871, 873, 875, 7/3; others 9/11.

Bregenz Festival Stage — A326

1970, July 23   Photo.
877 A326 3.50s dark blue & buff   .40 .20
25th anniversary of Bregenz Festival.

Salzburg Festival Emblem — A327

1970, July 27   Perf. 14
878 A327 3.50s blk, red, gold & gray .40 .20
50th anniversary of Salzburg Festival.

A328

A329

1970, Aug. 31   Engr.
879 A328 3.50s dark gray   .45 .20
13th General Assembly of the World Veterans Federation, Aug. 28-Sept. 4. The head of St. John is from a sculpture showing the Agony in the Garden in the chapel of the Parish Church in Ried. It is attributed to Thomas Schwanthaler (1634-1702).

1970, Sept. 16   Perf. 14x13½
880 A329 2s chocolate   .25 .15
Thomas Koschat (1845-1914), Carinthian composer of songs.

Mountain Scene
A330

1970, Sept. 16   Photo.   Perf. 14x13½
881 A330 2s vio bl & pink   .25 .15
Hiking and mountaineering in Austria.

Alfred Cossmann
A331

Arms of Carinthia
A332

1970, Oct. 2   Engr.   Perf. 14x13½
882 A331 2s dark brown   .25 .15
Alfred Cossmann (1870-1951), engraver.

1970, Oct. 2   Photo. & Engr.   Perf. 14
883 A332 2s ol, red, gold, blk & sil .25 .15
Carinthian plebiscite, 50th anniversary.

UN Emblem — A333

1970, Oct. 23   Litho.   Perf. 14x13½
884 A333 3.50s lt blue & blk   .50 .20
25th anniversary of the United Nations.

Adoration of the Shepherds, Carving from Garsten Vicarage
A334

1970, Nov. 27   Engr.   Perf. 13½x14
885 A334 2s dk violet blue   .25 .15
Christmas.

Karl Renner — A335

Beethoven, by Georg Waldmüller — A336

1970, Dec. 14   Engr.   Perf. 14x13½
886 A335 2s deep claret   .25 .15
Karl Renner (1870-1950), Austrian Pres., birth cent.

Photo. & Engr.
1970, Dec. 16   Perf. 13½
887 A336 3.50s black & buff   .50 .20
Ludwig van Beethoven (1770-1827), composer, birth bicentenary.

Enrica Handel-Mazzetti
A337

1971, Jan. 11   Engr.   Perf. 14x13½
888 A337 2s sepia   .25 .15
Birth cent. of Enrica von Handel-Mazzetti (1871-1955), novelist and poet.

"Watch Out for Children!"
A338

1971, Feb. 18   Photo.   Perf. 13½
889 A338 2s blk, red brn & brt grn   .25 .15
Traffic safety.

Saltcellar, by Benvenuto Cellini
A339

Art Treasures: 1.50s, Covered vessel, made of prase, gold and precious stones, Florentine, 1580. 2s, Emperor Joseph I, ivory statue by Matthias Steinle, 1693.

Photo. & Engr.
1971, Mar. 22   Perf. 14
890 A339 1.50s gray & slate grn   .20 .15
891 A339 2s gray & deep plum   .25 .20
892 A339 3.50s gray, blk & bister   .55 .35
        Nos. 890-892 (3)   1.00 .70

Emblem of Austrian Wholesalers' Organization
A340

1971, Apr. 16   Photo.   Perf. 13½
893 A340 3.50s multicolored   .45 .20
Intl. Chamber of Commerce, 23rd Congress, Vienna, Apr. 17-23.

Jacopo de Strada, by Titian — A341

Paintings in Vienna Museum: 2s, Village Feast, by Peter Brueghel, the Elder. 3.50s, Young Venetian Woman, by Albrecht Dürer.

1971, May 6   Engr.   Perf. 13½
894 A341 1.50s rose lake   .25 .15
895 A341 2s greenish black   .25 .20
896 A341 3.50s deep brown   .50 .35
        Nos. 894-896 (3)   1.00 .70

Seal of Paulus of Franchenfordia, 1380 — A342

Photo. & Engr.
1971, May 6   Perf. 13½x14
897 A342 3.50s dk brn & bister   .40 .20
Congress commemorating the centenary of the Austrian Notaries' Statute, May 5-8.

St. Matthew
A343

August Neilreich
A344

1971, May 27   *Perf. 12¹/₂x13¹/₂*
898 A343 2s brt rose lil & brn   .25 .15

Exhibition of "1000 Years of Art in Krems." The statue of St. Matthew is from the Lentl Altar, created about 1520 by the Master of the Pulkau Altar.

1971, June 1   Engr.   *Perf. 14x13¹/₂*
899 A344 2s brown   .25 .15

August Neilreich (1803-71), botanist.

Singer with Lyre — A345

Photo. & Engr.
1971, July 1   *Perf. 13¹/₂x14*
900 A345 4s lt bl, vio bl & gold   .50 .30

Intl. Choir Festival, Vienna, July 1-4.

Coat of Arms of
Kitzbuhel — A346

1971, Aug. 23   *Perf. 14*
901 A346 2.50s gold & multi   .35 .15

700th anniversary of the town of Kitzbuhel.

Vienna Stock Exchange — A347

1971, Sept. 1   Engr.   *Perf. 13¹/₂x14*
902 A347 4s reddish brown   .55 .20

Bicentenary of the Vienna Stock Exchange.

First and Latest Exhibition Halls — A348

1971, Sept. 6   Photo.   *Perf. 13¹/₂x13*
903 A348 2.50s dp rose lilac   .35 .15

Vienna Intl. Fair, 50th anniv.

Trade Union
Emblem
A349

Arms of
Burgenland
A350

1971, Sept. 20   *Perf. 14x13¹/₂*
904 A349 2s gray, buff & red   .25 .15

Austrian Trade Union Assoc., 25th anniv.

1971, Oct. 1
905 A350 2s dk bl, gold, red & blk   .25 .15

50th anniv. of Burgenland joining Austria.

Marcus
Car — A351

1971, Oct. 1   Photo. & Engr.   *Perf. 14*
906 A351 4s pale green & blk   .50 .25

Austrian Automobile, Motorcycle and Touring Club, 75th anniv.

Europa Bridge — A352

1971, Oct. 8   Engr.   *Perf. 14x13¹/₂*
907 A352 4s violet blue   .50 .25

Opening of highway over Brenner Pass.

Styria's Iron
Mountain
A353

Designs: 2s, Austrian Nitrogen Products, Ltd., Linz. 4s, United Austrian Iron and Steel Works, Ltd. (VOEST), Linz Harbor.

1971, Oct. 15   *Perf. 13¹/₂*
908 A353 1.50s reddish brown   .25 .15
909 A353   2s bluish black   .30 .20
910 A353   4s dk slate grn   .45 .35
    Nos. 908-910 (3)   1.00 .70

25 years of nationalized industry.

High-speed Train
on Semmering
A354

Trout Fisherman
A355

1971, Oct. 21   *Perf. 14*
911 A354 2s claret   .25 .15

Inter-city rapid train service.

1971, Nov. 15   *Perf. 13¹/₂*
912 A355 2s dark red brn   .25 .15

Erich Tschermak-
Seysenegg
A356

Infant Jesus as
Savior, by Dürer
A357

Photo. & Engr.
1971, Nov. 15   *Perf. 14x13¹/₂*
913 A356 2s pale ol & dk pur   .25 .15

Birth cent. of Dr. Erich Tschermak-Seysenegg (1871-1962), botanist.

1971, Nov. 26   *Perf. 13¹/₂*
914 A357 2s gold & multi   .25 .15

Christmas.

Franz Grillparzer,
by Moritz
Daffinger — A358

Fountain, Main
Square,
Friesach — A359

    Perf. 14x13¹/₂
1972, Jan. 21   Litho. & Engr.
915 A358 2s buff, gold & blk   .30 .15

Death cent. of Franz Grillparzer (1791-1872), dramatic poet.

1972, Feb. 23   Engr.   *Perf. 14x13¹/₂*

Designs: 2s, Fountain, Heiligenkreuz Abbey. 2.50s, Leopold Fountain, Innsbruck.

916 A359 1.50s rose lilac   .25 .15
917 A359   2s brown   .25 .20
918 A359 2.50s olive   .30 .25
    Nos. 916-918 (3)   .80 .60

Cardiac Patient
and Monitor
A360

1972, Apr. 11   *Perf. 13¹/₂x14*
919 A360 4s violet brown   .55 .25

World Health Day.

A361   A362

Design: St. Michael's Gate, Royal Palace, Vienna.

1972, Apr. 11   *Perf. 14x13¹/₂*
920 A361 4s violet blue   .55 .25

Conference of European Post and Telecommunications Ministers, Vienna, Apr. 11-14.

1972, May 5   Photo. & Engr.   *Perf. 14*
921 A362 2s Sculpture, Gurk Cathedral   .30 .15

900th anniv. of Gurk (Carinthia) Diocese. The design is after the central column supporting the sarcophagus of St. Hemma in Gurk Cathedral.

City Hall,
Congress
Emblem — A363

1972, May 23   Litho. & Engr.
922 A363 4s red, blk & yel   .55 .20

9th Intl. Congress of Public and Cooperative Economy, Vienna, May 23-25.

Power Line in
Carnic
Alps — A364

Designs: 2.50s, Power Station, Semmering. 4s, Zemm Power Station (lake in Zillertaler Alps).

1972, June 28   *Perf. 13¹/₂x14*
923 A364   70g gray & violet   .15 .15
924 A364 2.50s gray & red brn   .30 .30
925 A364   4s gray & slate   .45 .45
    Nos. 923-925 (3)   .90 .90

Nationalization of the power industry, 25th anniv.

Runner with
Olympic
Torch — A365

St. Hermes, by
Conrad
Laib — A366

Engr. & Photo.
1972, Aug. 21   *Perf. 14x13¹/₂*
926 A365 2s sepia & red   .25 .15

Olympic torch relay from Olympia, Greece, to Munich, Germany, passing through Austria.

1972, Aug. 21   Engr.
927 A366 2s violet brown   .25 .15

Exhibition of Late Gothic Art, Salzburg.

Pears — A367

1972, Sept.   *Perf. 14*
928 A367 2.50s dk blue & multi   .30 .15

World Congress of small plot Gardeners, Vienna, Sept. 7-10.

Souvenir Sheet

Spanish
Walk — A368

1972, Sept. 12   *Perf. 13¹/₂*
929 A368   Sheet of 6   2.75 2.75
  a.   2s Spanish walk   .25 .25
  b.   2s Piaffe   .25 .25
  c.   2.50s Levade   .32 .32
  d.   2.50s On long rein   .32 .32
  e.   4s Capriole   .52 .52
  f.   4s Courbette   .52 .52

400th anniv. of the Spanish Riding School in Vienna.

Arms of University of Agriculture A369 — Church and Old University A370

Photo. & Engr.
1972, Oct. 17 — Perf. 14x13½
930 A369 2s black & multi .25 .15
University of Agriculture, Vienna, cent.

1972, Nov. 7 — Engr.
931 A370 4s red brown .55 .20
Paris Lodron University, Salzburg, 350th anniv.

Carl Michael Ziehrer — A371

1972, Nov. 14
932 A371 2s rose claret .25 .15
50th death anniv. of Carl Michael Ziehrer (1843-1922), composer.

Virgin and Child, Wood, 1420-30 A372

Photo. & Engr.
1972, Dec. 1 — Perf. 13½
933 A372 2s olive & chocolate .25 .15
Christmas.

Racing Sleigh, 1750 A373

Designs: 2s, Coronation landau, 1824. 2.50s, Imperial state coach, 1763.

1972, Dec. 12
934 A373 1.50s pale gray & brn .20 .15
935 A373 2s pale gray & sl grn .30 .15
936 A373 2.50s pale gray & plum .35 .25
Nos. 934-936 (3) .85 .55
Collection of historic state coaches and carriages in Schönbrunn Palace.

Map of Austrian Telephone System — A374

1972, Dec. 14 — Photo. — Perf. 14
937 A374 2s yellow & blk .25 .15
Completion of automation of Austrian telephone system.

"Drugs are Death" — A375

1973, Jan. 26 — Photo. — Perf. 13½x14
938 A375 2s scarlet & multi 1.50 .45
Fight against drug abuse.

Alfons Petzold — A376 — Theodor Körner — A377

1973, Jan. 26 — Engr. — Perf. 14x13½
939 A376 2s reddish brn .25 .15
50th death anniv. of Alfons Petzold (1882-1923), poet.

Photo. & Engr.
1973, Apr. 24 — Perf. 14x13½
940 A377 2s gray & deep claret .25 .15
Theodor Körner (1873-1957), Austrian Pres., birth cent.

Douglas DC-9 — A378

1973, May 14 — Perf. 13½x14
941 A378 2s vio bl & rose red .30 .15
First intl. airmail service, Vienna to Kiev, Mar. 31, 1918, 55th anniv.; Austrian Aviation Corporation, 50th anniv.; Austrian Airlines, 15th anniv.

Otto Loewi — A379 — "Support" — A380

1973, June 4 — Engr. — Perf. 14x13½
942 A379 4s deep violet .55 .20
Birth cent. of Otto Loewi (1873-1961), pharmacologist, winner of 1936 Nobel prize.

1973, June 25
943 A380 2s dark blue .25 .15
Federation of Austrian Social Insurance Institutes, 25th anniv.

Europa Issue 1973

Post Horn and Telephone — A381

1973, July 9 — Photo. — Perf. 14
944 A381 2.50s ocher, blk & yel .30 .15

Dornbirn Fair Emblem A382

1973, July 27 — Perf. 13½x14
945 A382 2s multicolored .30 .15
Dornbirn Trade Fair, 25th anniversary.

Hurdles — A383 — Leo Slezak — A384

1973, Aug. 13 — Engr. — Perf. 14x13½
946 A383 4s gray olive .50 .20
23rd Intl. Military Pentathlon Championships, Wiener Neustadt, Aug. 13-18.

1973, Aug. 17 — Perf. 14
947 A384 4s dark brown .50 .20
Leo Slezak (1873-1946), operatic tenor.

Gate, Vienna Hofburg, and ISI Emblem — A385

Photogravure and Engraved
1973, Aug. 20 — Perf. 14x13½
948 A385 2s gray, dk brn & ver .25 .15
39th Congress of Intl. Statistical Institute, Vienna, Aug. 20-30.

Tegetthoff off Franz Josef Land, by Julius Prayer — A386

1973, Aug. 30 — Engr. — Perf. 13½x14
949 A386 2.50s Prussian grn .30 .15
Discovery of Franz Josef Land by an Austrian North Pole expedition, cent.

Academy of Science, by Canaletto A387

1973, Sept. 4
950 A387 2.50s violet .30 .15
Intl. meteorological cooperation, cent.

Arms of Viennese Tanners A388 — Max Reinhardt A389

Photo. & Engr.
1973, Sept. 4 — Perf. 14
951 A388 4s red & multi .55 .20
13th Congress of the Intl. Union of Leather Chemists' Societies, Vienna, Sept. 1-7.

1973, Sept. 7 — Engr. — Perf. 13x13½
952 A389 2s rose magenta .25 .15
Max Reinhardt (1873-1943), theatrical director and stage manager.

Trotter A390

1973, Sept. 28 — Perf. 13½
953 A390 2s green .30 .15
Centenary of Vienna Trotting Association.

Ferdinand Hanusch — A391

1973, Sept. 28 — Perf. 14x13½
954 A391 2s rose brown .25 .15
50th death anniv. of Ferdinand Hanusch (1866-1923), secretary of state.

Police Radio Operator A392

1973, Oct. 2 — Perf. 13½x14
955 A392 4s violet blue .50 .20
50th anniv. of Intl. Criminal Police Org. (INTERPOL).

Josef Petzval's Photographic Lens — A393

1973, Oct. 8 — Litho. & Engr. — Perf. 14
956 A393 2.50s blue & multi .30 .15
EUROPHOT Photographic Cong., Vienna.

Emperor's Spring, Hell Valley — A394

Photo. & Engr.
1973, Oct. 23 — Perf. 13½x14
957 A394 2s sepia, blue & red .25 .15
Vienna's first mountain spring water supply system, cent.

Almsee, Upper Austria — A395

Hofburg and Prince Eugene Statue, Vienna — A395a

Designs: 50g, Farmhouses, Zillertal, Tirol. 1s, Kahlenbergerdorf. 1.50s, Bludenz, Vorarlberg. 2s, Inn Bridge, Alt Finstermunz. 2.50s, Murau, Styria. 3s, Bischofsmütze, Salzburg. 3.50s, Easter Church, Oberwart. 4.50s, Windmill, Retz. 5s, Aggstein Castle, Lower Austria. 6s, Lindauer Hut, Vorarlberg. 6.50s, Holy Cross Church, Villach, Carinthia. 7s, Falkenstein Castle, Carinthia. 7.50s, Hohensalzburg. 8s, Votive column, Reiteregg, Styria. 10s, Lake Neusiedl, Burgenland. 11s, Old Town, Enns. 16s, Openair Museum, Bad Tatzmannsdorf. 20s, Myra waterfalls.

Photo. & Engr.

1973-78   *Perf. 13¹/₂x14*

Size: 23x29mm

Type A395

958	50g gray & slate green	.15	.15
959	1s brn & dk brown	.15	.15
960	1.50s rose & brown	.25	.15
961	2s gray bl & dk blue	.30	.15
962	2.50s vio & dp violet	.35	.15
963	3s lt ultra & vio blue	.45	.15
963A	3.50s dl org & brown	.50	.15
964	4s brt lil & pur	.55	.15
965	4.50s brt grn & bl green	.60	.15
966	5s lilac & vio	.65	.15
967	6s dp rose & dk violet	.80	.15
968	6.50s bl grn & indigo	.90	.15
969	7s sage grn & sl green	.95	.15
970	7.50s lil rose & claret	1.00	.25
971	8s dl red & dp brown	1.10	.20
972	10s gray grn & dk green	1.40	.20
973	11s ver & dk carmine	1.65	.15
974	16s ocher & black	2.25	.60
975	20s ol bis & ol grn	2.75	1.25

Type A395a

976	50s gray vio & vio bl	6.75	2.50
	Nos. 958-976 (20)	23.50	
	Set value		5.75

Issue dates: 1974, Nos. 960-963. 1975, Nos. 958-959, 967, 976. 1976, Nos. 965, 971, 973. 1977, Nos. 968, 970, 974-975. 1978, No. 963A. See Nos. 1100-1109.

Nativity — A396

Pregl — A397

1973, Nov. 30   *Perf. 14*
977 A396 2s multicolored   .30 .15
Christmas. Design from 14th century stained-glass window.

1973, Dec. 12   **Engr.**   *Perf. 14x13¹/₂*
978 A397 4s deep blue   .50 .20
50th anniv. of the awarding of the Nobel prize for chemistry to Fritz Pregl (1869-1930).

Telex Machine A398

Hofmannsthal A399

1974, Jan. 14   **Photo.**   *Perf. 14x13¹/₂*
979 A398 2.50s ultramarine   .30 .15
50th anniversary of Radio Austria.

1974, Feb. 1   **Engr.**   *Perf. 14*
980 A399 4s violet blue   .50 .20
Birth cent. of Hugo Hofmannsthal (1874-1929), poet and playwright.

Anton Bruckner and Bruckner House A400

1974, Mar. 22   **Engr.**   *Perf. 14*
981 A400 4s brown   .50 .20
Founding of Anton Bruckner House (concert hall), Linz, and birth of Anton Bruckner (1824-1896), composer, 150th anniv.

Vegetables A401

Photo. & Engr.
1974, Apr. 18   *Perf. 14*
982 A401 2s shown   .30 .20
983 A401 2.50s Fruits   .35 .30
984 A401 4s Flowers   .50 .50
     Nos. 982-984 (3)   1.15 1.00
Intl. Garden Show, Vienna, Apr. 18-Oct. 14.

Seal of Judenburg A402

Karl Kraus A403

1974, Apr. 24   **Photo.**   *Perf. 14x13¹/₂*
985 A402 2s plum & multi   .30 .15
750th anniversary of Judenburg.

1974, Apr. 6   **Engr.**
986 A403 4s dark red   .50 .20
Karl Kraus (1874-1936), poet and satirist, birth cent.

St. Michael, by Thomas Schwanthaler — A404

1974, May 3
987 A404 2.50s slate green   .30 .15
Exhibition of the works by the Schwanthaler Family of sculptors, (1633-1848), Reichersberg am Inn, May 3-Oct. 13.

A405

A406

Europa: King Arthur, from tomb of Maximilian I

1974, May 8   *Perf. 13¹/₂*
988 A405 2.50s ocher & slate blue   .30 .15

Photo. & Engr.
1974, May 17   *Perf. 14x13¹/₂*
989 A406 2s gray & vio brn   .30 .15
Austrian Automobile Assoc., 75th anniv.

De Dion Bouton motor tricycle.

Satyr's Head, Terracotta A407

1974, May 22   *Perf. 13¹/₂x14*
990 A407 2s org brn, gold & blk   .30 .15
Exhibition, "Renaissance in Austria," Schallaburg Castle, May 22-Nov. 14.

Road Transport Union Emblem A408

Maulbertsch, Self-portrait A409

1974, May 24   **Photo.**   *Perf. 14x13¹/₂*
991 A408 4s deep orange & blk   .50 .20
14th Congress of the Intl. Road Transport Union, Innsbruck.

1974, June 7   **Engr.**   *Perf. 14x13¹/₂*
992 A409 2s violet brown   .25 .15
Franz Anton Maulbertsch (1724-96), painter, 250th birth anniv.

Gendarmes, 1824 and 1974 — A410

1974, June 7   **Photo.**   *Perf. 13¹/₂x14*
993 A410 2s red & multi   .25 .15
125th anniversary of Austrian gendarmery.

Fencing A411

Photo. & Engr.
1974, June 14   *Perf. 13¹/₂*
994 A411 2.50s red org & blk   .30 .15

Transportation Symbols — A412

St. Virgil, Sculpture from Nonntal Church — A413

1974, June 18   **Photo.**   *Perf. 14x13¹/₂*
995 A412 4s lt ultra & multi   .50 .20
European Conference of Transportation Ministers, Vienna, June 18-21.

1974, June 28   **Engr.**   *Perf. 13¹/₂x14*
996 A413 2s violet blue   .25 .15
Consecration of the Cathedral of Salzburg by Scotch-Irish Bishop Feirgil (St. Virgil), 1200th anniv. Salzburg was a center of Christianization in the 8th century.

Franz Jonas and Austrian Eagle — A414

1974, June 28
997 A414 2s black   .25 .15
Jonas (1899-1974), Austrian Pres., 1965-1974.

Franz Stelzhamer A415

Diver — A416

1974, July 12   **Engr.**   *Perf. 14x13¹/₂*
998 A415 2s indigo   .25 .15
Franz Stelzhamer (1802-1874), poet who wrote in Upper Austrian vernacular, death cent.

Photo. & Engr.
1974, Aug. 16   *Perf. 13x13¹/₂*
999 A416 4s blue & sepia   .50 .20
13th European Swimming, Diving and Water Polo Championships, Vienna, Aug. 18-25.

Ferdinand Ritter von Hebra — A417

1974, Sept. 10   **Engr.**   *Perf. 14x13¹/₂*
1000 A417 4s brown   .50 .20
30th Meeting of the Assoc. of German-speaking Dermatologists, Graz, Sept. 10-14. Dr. von Hebra (1816-1880) was a founder of modern dermatology.

Arnold
Schonberg
A418

1974, Sept. 13   *Perf. 13¹/₂x14*
1001 A418 2.50s purple   .30 .15
Schönberg (1874-1951), composer.

Radio Station,
Salzburg
A419

1974, Oct. 1   **Photo.**   *Perf. 13¹/₂x14*
1002 A419 2s multicolored   .25 .15
50th anniversary of Austrian broadcasting.

Edmund Eysler (1874-
1949),
Composer — A420

1974, Oct. 4   **Engr.**   *Perf. 14x13¹/₂*
1003 A420 2s dark olive   .25 .15

Mailman, Mail
Coach and
Train, UPU
Emblem
A421

4s, Mailman, jet, truck, 1974, & UPU emblem.

1974, Oct. 9   **Photo.**   *Perf. 13¹/₂*
1004 A421 2s deep claret & lil   .25 .15
1005 A421 4s dark blue & gray   .50 .20
Centenary of Universal Postal Union.

Gauntlet
Protecting
Rose — A422

1974, Oct. 23   **Photo.**   *Perf. 13¹/₂x14*
1006 A422 2s multicolored   .25 .15
Environment protection.

Austrian Sports
Pool Emblem
A423

1974, Oct. 23   **Photo.**   *Perf. 13¹/₂x14*
1007 A423 70g multicolored   .15 .15
Austrian Sports Pool (lottery), 25th anniv.

Carl Ditters von
Dittersdorf
A424

Virgin and Child,
Wood, c. 1600
A425

1974, Oct. 24   **Engr.**   *Perf. 14x13¹/₂*
1008 A424 2s Prussian green   .25 .15
Von Dittersdorf (1739-1799), composer.

1974, Nov. 29   **Photo. & Engr.**
1009 A425 2s brown & gold   .35 .15
Christmas.

A426   A427

1974, Dec. 18
1010 A426 4s gray & black   .55 .20
Franz Schmidt (1874-1939), composer.

Photo. & Engr.
1975, Jan. 24   *Perf. 13¹/₂*
1011 A427 2.50s St. Christopher   .40 .15
European Architectural Heritage Year. The design
shows part of a wooden figure from central panel of
the retable in the Kefermarkt Church, 1490-1497.

Safety Belt and
Skeleton
Arms — A428

Stained Glass
Window, Vienna
City Hall — A429

1975, Apr. 1   **Photo.**   *Perf. 14x13¹/₂*
1012 A428 70g violet & multi   .15 .15
Introduction of obligatory use of automobile
safety belts.

1975, Apr. 2   *Perf. 14*
1013 A429 2.50s multicolored   .30 .15
11th meeting of the Council of European Municipalities, Vienna, Apr. 2-5.

Austria as
Mediator — A430

Forest — A431

1975, May 2   **Litho.**   *Perf. 14*
1014 A430 2s blk & bister   .30 .15
2nd Republic of Austria, 30th anniv.

1975, May 6   **Engr.**
1015 A431 2s green   .35 .15
National forests, 50th anniversary.

High Priest, by
Michael
Pacher — A432

Gosaukamm
Funicular — A433

Europa Issue 1975
Photo. & Engr.
1975, May 27   *Perf. 14x13¹/₂*
1016 A432 2.50s black & multi   .40 .15
Design is detail from painting "The Marriage of
Joseph and Mary," by Michael Pacher (c. 1450-
1500).

1975, June 23   *Perf. 14x13¹/₂*
1017 A433 2s slate & red   .30 .15
4th Intl. Funicular Cong., Vienna, June 23-27.

Josef Misson
and Mühlbach
am
Manhartsberg
A434

1975, June 27   *Perf. 13¹/₂x14*
1018 A434 2s choc & redsh brn   .25 .15
Josef Misson (1803-1875), poet who wrote in
Lower Austrian vernacular, death cent.

Setting Sun and
"P" — A435

1975, Aug. 27   **Litho.**   *Perf. 14x13¹/₂*
1019 A435 1.50s org, blk & bl   .20 .15
Austrian Assoc. of Pensioners 25th anniv. meeting, Vienna, Aug. 1975.

Ferdinand
Porsche
A436

Photo. & Engr.
1975, Sept. 3   *Perf. 13¹/₂x14*
1020 A436 1.50s gray & purple   .25 .15
Ferdinand Porsche (1875-1951), engineer, developer of Porsche and Volkswagen cars, birth cent.

Leo Fall (1873-1925),
Composer — A437

1975, Sept. 16   **Engr.**   *Perf. 14x13¹/₂*
1021 A437 2s violet   .25 .15

Judo
Throw — A438

Heinrich
Angeli — A439

1975, Oct. 20   **Photo.**   *Perf. 14x13¹/₂*
1022 A438 2.50s gold & multi   .30 .15
10th World Judo Championships, Vienna, Oct.
20-26.

1975, Oct. 21   **Engr.**   *Perf. 14x13¹/₂*
1023 A439 2s rose lake   .30 .15
Heinrich Angeli (1840-1925), painter, 50th
death anniv.

Johann Strauss
and Dancers
A440

Photo. & Engr.
1975, Oct. 24   *Perf. 13¹/₂x14*
1024 A440 4s ocher & sepia   .55 .20
Johann Strauss (1825-1899), composer.

Stylized Musician
Playing a
Viol — A441

Symbolic
House — A442

1975, Oct. 30   *Perf. 14x13¹/₂*
1025 A441 2.50s silver & vio bl   .35 .15
Vienna Symphony Orchestra, 75th anniv.

1975, Oct. 31   **Photo.**
1026 A442 2s multicolored   .25 .15
Austrian building savings societies, 50th anniv.

Fan with
"Hanswurst"
Scene, 18th
Century
A443

1975, Nov. 14   **Photo.**   *Perf. 13¹/₂x14*
1027 A443 1.50s green & multi   .20 .15
Salzburg Theater bicentenary.

Virgin and Child,
from 15th
Century Altar
A444

"The Spiral Tree," by
Hundertwasser
A445

Photo. & Engr.
1975, Nov. 28   *Perf. 13x13½*
1028 A444 2s gold & dull purple   .25 .15
Christmas.

Photo., Engr. & Typo.
1975, Dec. 11   *Perf. 13½x14*
1029 A445 4s multicolored   .65 .25
Austrian modern art. Friedensreich Hundertwasser is the pseudonym of Friedrich Stowasser (b. 1928).

Old Burgtheater
A446

No. 1030b, Grand staircase, new Burgtheater.

Perf. 14 (pane), 13½x14 (stamps)
1976, Apr. 8   **Engr.**
1030   Pane of 2 + label   1.10 1.10
  a.   A446 3s violet blue   .30 .30
  b.   A446 3s deep brown   .30 .30
Bicentenary of Vienna Burgtheater. Label (head of Pan) and inscription in vermilion.

Dr. Robert Barany (1876-1936), Winner of Nobel Prize for Medicine, 1914 — A447

Photo. & Engr.
1976, Apr. 22   *Perf. 14x13½*
1031 A447 3s blue & brown   .45 .15

Ammonite
A448

1976, Apr. 30 Photo.   *Perf. 13½x14*
1032 A448 3s red & multi   .45 .15
Vienna Museum of Natural History, Centenary Exhibition.

Carinthian Dukes' Coronation Chair — A449

Siege of Linz, 17th Century Etching — A450

Photo. & Engr.
1976, May 6   *Perf. 14x13½*
1033 A449 3s grnsh blk & org   .45 .15
Millennium of Carinthia.

1976, May 14
1034 A450 4s blk & gray grn   .55 .20
Upper Austrian Peasants' War, 350th anniv.

Skittles — A451

1976, May 14   *Perf. 13½x14*
1035 A451 4s black & org   .55 .20
11th World Skittles Championships, Vienna.

Duke Heinrich II, Stained-glass Window — A452

1976, May 14   *Perf. 14*
1036 A452 3s multicolored   .45 .15
Babenberg Exhibition, Lilienfeld.

St. Wolfgang, from Pacher Altar — A453

1976, May 26 Engr.   *Perf. 13½*
1037 A453 6s bright violet   .75 .40
Intl. Art Exhibition at St. Wolfgang.

Europa Issue 1976

Tassilo Cup, Kremsmunster, 777 — A454

Photo. & Engr.
1976, Aug. 13   *Perf. 14x13½*
1038 A454 4s ultra & multi   .60 .20

Timber Fair Emblem — A455

Constantin Economo, M.D. — A456

1976, Aug. 13   **Photo.**
1039 A455 3s green & multi   .35 .15
Austrian Timber Fair, Klagenfurt, 25th anniv.

1976, Aug. 23   **Engr.**
1040 A456 3s dark red brown   .35 .15
Dr. Economo (1876-1931), neurologist.

Administrative Court, by Salomon Klein — A457

1976, Oct. 25 Engr.   *Perf. 13½x14*
1041 A457 6s deep brown   .80 .30
Austrian Central Administrative Court, cent.

Souvenir Sheet

Coats of Arms of Austrian Provinces — A458

Millennium of Austria: a, Lower Austria. b, Upper Austria. c, Styria. d, Carinthia. e, Tyrol. f, Voralberg. g, Salzburg. h, Burgenland. i, Vienna.

Photo. & Engr.
1976, Oct. 25   *Perf. 14*
1042   Sheet of 9   3.00 3.00
  a.-i. A458 2s any single   .30 .30

"Cancer"
A459

1976, Nov. 17 Photo.   *Perf. 14x13½*
1043 A459 2.50s multicolored   .35 .15
Fight against cancer.

UN Emblem and Bridge — A460

1976, Nov. 17
1044 A460 3s blue & gold   .45 .15
UN Industrial Development Org. (UNIDO), 10th anniv.

Punched Tape, Map of Europe — A461

1976, Nov. 17   *Perf. 14*
1045 A461 1.50s multicolored   .15 .15
Austrian Press Agency (APA), 30th anniv.

Viktor Kaplan, Kaplan Turbine — A462

Photo. & Engr.
1976, Nov. 26   *Perf. 13½x14*
1046 A462 2.50s multicolored   .35 .15
Viktor Kaplan (1876-1934), inventor of Kaplan turbine, birth centenary.

Nativity, by Konrad von Friesach, c. 1450
A463

1976, Nov. 26   *Perf. 13½*
1047 A463 3s multicolored   .40 .15
Christmas.

Augustin, the Piper — A464

Photo. & Engr.
1976, Dec. 29   *Perf. 13½*
1048 A464 6s multicolored   .75 .25
Modern Austrian art.

Rainer Maria Rilke (1875-1926), Poet A465

Vienna City Synagogue A466

1976, Dec. 29 Engr.   *Perf. 14x13½*
1049 A465 3s deep violet   .40 .15

1976, Dec. 29 Photo.   *Perf. 13½*
1050 A466 1.50s multicolored   .20 .15
Sesquicentennial of Vienna City Synagogue.

Nikolaus Joseph von Jacquin (1727-1817), Botanist — A467

1977, Feb. 16 Engr.   *Perf. 14x13½*
1051 A467 4s chocolate   .55 .20

Oswald von Wolkenstein (1377-1445), Poet — A468

Photo. & Engr.
1977, Feb. 16   *Perf. 14*
1052 A468 3s multicolored   .35 .15

Handball A469

1977, Feb. 25 Photo.   *Perf. 13½x14*
1053 A469 1.50s multicolored   .15 .15
World Indoor Handball Championships, Austria, Feb. 5-Mar. 6.

A470   A471

1977, Apr. 12   **Engr.**   *Perf. 14x13¹/₂*
1054 A470 6s dk violet blue   .70 .25

Alfred Kubin (1877-1959), illustrator and writer.

1977, Apr. 22   **Engr.**   *Perf. 13¹/₂*
Designs: 2.50s, Great Spire, St. Stephen's Cathedral. 3s, Heathen Tower and Frederick's Gable. 4s, Interior view with Albertinian Choir.

1055 A471	2.50s dark brown	.35	.15
1056 A471	3s dark blue	.40	.25
1057 A471	4s rose lake	.50	.35
	Nos. 1055-1057 (3)	1.25	.75

Restoration and re-opening of St. Stephen's Cathedral, Vienna, 25th anniversary.

Fritz Hermanovsky-Orlando (1877-1954), Poet and Artist — A472

Photo. & Engr.
1977, Apr. 29   *Perf. 13¹/₂x14*
1058 A472 6s Prus green & gold   .70 .25

IAEA Emblem   Arms of
A473   Schwanenstadt
   A474

1977, May 2   **Photo.**   *Perf. 14*
1059 A473 3s brt bl, lt bl & gold   .35 .15

Intl. Atomic Energy Agency (IAEA), 20th anniv.

1977, June 10   **Photo.**   *Perf. 14x13¹/₂*
1060 A474 3s dk brown & multi   .35 .15

Town of Schwanenstadt, 350th anniv.

Europa Issue 1977

Attersee, Upper Austria — A475

1977, June 10   **Engr.**   *Perf. 14*
1061 A475 6s olive green   .90 .30

Globe, by Vincenzo Coronelli, 1688 — A476

Photo. & Engr.
1977, June 29   *Perf. 14*
1062 A476 3s black & buff   .35 .15

5th Intl. Symposium of the Coronelli World Fed. of Friends of the Globe, Austria, June 29-July 3.

Kayak Race — A477

1977, July 15   **Photo.**   *Perf. 13¹/₂x14*
1063 A477 4s multicolored   .50 .20

3rd Kayak Slalom White Water Race on Lieser River, Spittal.

The Good Samaritan, by Francesco Bassano — A478

1977, Sept. 16   **Photo. & Engr.**
1064 A478 1.50s brown & red   .20 .15

Workers' Good Samaritan Org., 50th anniv.

Papermakers' Coat   Man with Austrian
of Arms — A479   Flag Lifting Barbed
   Wire — A480

1977, Oct. 10   *Perf. 14x13¹/₂*
1065 A479 3s multicolored   .35 .15

17th Conf. of the European Committee of Pulp and Paper Technology (EUCEPA), Vienna.

1977, Nov. 3   *Perf. 14*
1066 A480 2.50s slate & red   .35 .15

Honoring the martyrs for Austria's freedom.

"Austria," First Steam Locomotive in Austria — A481

Designs: 2.50s, Steam locomotive 214. 3s, Electric locomotive 1044.

Photo. & Engr.
1977, Nov. 17   *Perf. 13¹/₂*
1067 A481	1.50s multicolored	.20	.15
1068 A481	2.50s multicolored	.40	.15
1069 A481	3s multicolored	.45	.20
	Nos. 1067-1069 (3)	1.05	
	Set value		.40

140th anniversary of Austrian railroads.

A482   A483

Virgin and Child, wood statue, Mariastein, Tyrol.

1977, Nov. 25   *Perf. 14x13¹/₂*
1070 A482 3s multicolored   .30 .15

Christmas.

1977, Dec. 2   *Perf. 13¹/₂x14*
The Danube Maiden, by Wolfgang Hutter.
1071 A483 6s multicolored   .75 .20

Modern Austrian art.

Egon Friedell (1878-1938), Writer and Historian A484

1978, Jan. 23   **Photo. & Engr.**
1072 A484 3s lt blue & blk   .40 .15

Subway Train — A485

1978, Feb. 24   **Photo.**   *Perf. 13¹/₂x14*
1073 A485 3s multicolored   .45 .15

New Vienna subway system.

Biathlon Competition A486

1978, Feb. 28   **Photo. & Engr.**
1074 A486 4s multicolored   .45 .20

Biathlon World Championships, Hochfilzen, Tyrol, Feb. 28-Mar. 5.

Leopold Kunschak (1871-1953), Political Leader — A487

1978, Mar. 13   **Engr.**   *Perf. 14x13¹/₂*
1075 A487 3s violet blue   .40 .15

Coyote, Aztec Feather Shield — A488

1978, Mar. 13   **Photo.**   *Perf. 13¹/₂x14*
1076 A488 3s multicolored   .40 .15

Ethnographical Museum, 50th anniv. exhibition.

Alpine Farm, Woodcut by Suitbert Lobisser — A489

1978, Mar. 23   **Engr.**   *Perf. 13¹/₂*
1077 A489 3s dark brown, *buff*   .40 .15

Lobisser (1878-1943), graphic artist.

Capercaillie, Hunting Bag, 1730, and Rifle, 1655 — A490

Photo. & Engr.
1978, Apr. 28   *Perf. 13¹/₂*
1078 A490 6s multicolored   .75 .35

Intl. Hunting Exhibition, Marchegg.

Europa Issue 1978

Riegersburg, Styria — A491

1978, May 3   **Engr.**
1079 A491 6s deep rose lilac   .75 .35

Parliament, Vienna, and Map of Europe — A492   Admont Pietà, c. 1410 — A493

1978, May 3   **Photo.**   *Perf. 14x13¹/₂*
1080 A492 4s multicolored   .45 .20

3rd Interparliamentary Conference for European Cooperation and Security, Vienna.

1978, May 26   **Photo. & Engr.**
1081 A493 2.50s ocher & black   .25 .15

Gothic Art in Styria Exhibition, St. Lambrecht, 1978.

Ort Castle, Gmunden — A494

1978, June 9
1082 A494 3s multicolored   .30 .15

700th anniversary of Gmunden City.

Child with Flowers and Fruit — A495   Lehar and his Home, Bad Ischl — A496

Photo. & Engr.
1978, June 30   *Perf. 14x13½*
1083 A495 6s gold & multi   .85 .35
25 years of Social Tourism.

1978, July 14   **Engr.**   *Perf. 14x13½*
1084 A496 6s slate   .75 .30
International Lehar Congress, Bad Ischl. Franz Lehar (1870-1948), operetta composer.

Congress Emblem A497

1978, Aug. 21   **Photo.**   *Perf. 13½x14*
1085 A497 1.50s black, red & yel   .20 .15
Cong. of Intl. Fed. of Building Construction and Wood Workers, Vienna, Aug. 20-24.

Ottokar of Bohemia and Rudolf of Hapsburg A498

1978, Aug. 25   **Photo. & Engr.**
1086 A498 3s multicolored   .35 .15
Battle of Durnkrut and Jedenspeigen (Marchfeld), which established Hapsburg rule in Austria, 700th anniversary.

First Documentary Reference to Villach, "ad pontem uillah" A499

1978, Sept. 8   **Litho.**   *Perf. 13½x14*
1087 A499 3s multicolored   .35 .15
1100th anniversary of Villach, Carinthia.

Seal of Graz, 1440 — A500   Emperor Maximilian Fishing — A501

Photo. & Engr.
1978, Sept. 13   *Perf. 14x13½*
1088 A500 4s multicolored   .50 .25
850th anniversary of Graz.

1978, Sept. 15   *Perf. 14x13½*
1089 A501 4s multicolored   .50 .20
World Fishing Championships, Vienna, Sept. 1978.

"Aid to the Handicapped" A502

1978, Oct. 2   **Photo.**   *Perf. 13½x14*
1090 A502 6s orange brn & blk   .75 .30

Symbolic Column — A503

1978, Oct. 9   **Photo.**   *Perf. 13½*
1091 A503 2.50s orange, blk & gray   .30 .15
9th Intl. Congress of Concrete and Prefabrication Industries, Vienna, Oct. 8-13.

Grace, by Albin Egger-Lienz A504

1978, Oct. 27   *Perf. 13½x14*
1092 A504 6s multicolored   .75 .30
European Family Congress, Vienna, Oct. 26-29.

Lise Meitner (1878-1968), Physicist, and Atom Symbol — A505

1978, Nov. 7   **Engr.**   *Perf. 14x13½*
1093 A505 6s dark violet   .75 .30

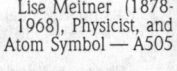

Viktor Adler, by Anton Hanak A506

Photo. & Engr.
1978, Nov. 10   *Perf. 13½x14*
1094 A506 3s vermilion & black   .40 .15
Viktor Adler (1852-1918), leader of Social Democratic Party, 60th death anniversary.

Franz Schubert, by Josef Kriehuber — A507   Virgin and Child, Wilhering Church — A508

1978, Nov. 17   **Engr.**   *Perf. 14*
1095 A507 6s reddish brown   .65 .35
Franz Schubert (1797-1828), composer.

Perf. 12½x13½
1978, Dec. 1   **Photo. & Engr.**
1096 A508 3s multicolored   .35 .15
Christmas.

Archduke Johann Shelter, Grossglockner A509

1978, Dec. 6   *Perf. 13½x14*
1097 A509 1.50s gold & dk vio bl   .20 .15
Austrian Alpine Club, centenary.

A510   A511

Adam, by Rudolf Hausner.

1978, Dec. 6   **Photo.**   *Perf. 13½x14*
1098 A510 6s multicolored   .75 .35
Modern Austrian art.

1978, Dec. 6   **Photo.**   *Perf. 14x13½*
1099 A511 6s Bound Hands   .75 .30
Universal Declaration of Human Rights, 30th anniv.

Type of 1973
Designs: 20g, Freistadt, Upper Austria. 3s, Bishofsmutze, Salzburg. 4.20s, Hirschegg, Kleinwalsertal. 5.50s, Peace Chapel, Stoderzinken. 5.60s, Riezlern, Kleinwalsertal. 9s, Asten Carinthia. 12s, Kufstein Fortress. 14s, Weiszsee, Salzburg.

Photo. & Engr.
1978-83   *Perf. 13½x14*
Size: 23x29mm
1100 A395 20g vio bl & dk bl   .15 .15
Size: 17x21mm
1102 A395 3s lt ultra & vio bl   .45 .15
Size: 23x29mm
1104 A395 4.20s blk & grysh bl   .55 .15
1105 A395 5.50s lilac & pur   .75 .20
1106 A395 5.60s yel grn & ol grn   .75 .20
1107 A395 9s red   1.25 .45
1108 A395 12s ocher & vio brn   1.75 .15
1109 A395 14s lt green & green   2.00 .20
Nos. 1100-1109 (8)   7.65 1.65
Issued: 3s, 12/7/78; 4.20s, 6/22/79; 20g, 6/27/80; 12s, 10/3/80; 14s, 1/27/82; 5.50s, 5.60s, 7/1/82; 9s, 2/9/83.

Child and IYC Emblem A512

Photo. & Engr.
1979, Jan. 16   *Perf. 14*
1110 A512 2.50s dk blue, blk & brn   .30 .15
International Year of the Child.

CCIR Emblem A513

1979, Jan. 16   **Photo.**   *Perf. 13½x14*
1111 A513 6s multicolored   .75 .30
Intl. Radio Consultative Committee (CCIR) of the ITU, 50th anniv.

Air Rifle, Air Pistol and Club Emblem A514

Photo. & Engr.
1979, Mar. 7   *Perf. 13½*
1112 A514 6s multicolored   .75 .30
Austrian Shooting Club, cent., and European Air Rifle and Air Pistol Championships, Graz.

Figure Skater — A515

1979, Mar. 7   **Photo.**   *Perf. 14x13½*
1113 A515 4s multicolored   .55 .25
World Ice Skating Championships, Vienna.

Steamer Franz I A516

Designs: 2.50s, Tugboat Linz. 3s, Passenger ship Theodor Körner.

1979, Mar. 13   **Engr.**   *Perf. 13½*
1114 A516 1.50s violet blue   .20 .15
1115 A516 2.50s sepia   .30 .15
1116 A516 3s magenta   .35 .20
Nos. 1114-1116 (3)   .85
Set value   .40
1st Danube Steamship Company, 150th anniv.

Fashion Design, by Theo Zasche, 1900 — A517

Photo. & Engr.
1979, Mar. 26   *Perf. 13x13½*
1117 A517 2.50s multicolored   .30 .15
50th Intl. Fashion Week, Vienna.

Wiener Neustadt Cathedral A518

1979, Mar. 27   **Engr.**   *Perf. 13½*
1118 A518 4s violet blue   .50 .25
Cathedral of Wiener Neustadt, 700th anniv.

Teacher and Pupils, by Franz A. Zauner — A519   Population Chart and Barock Angel — A520

Photo. & Engr.
1979, Mar. 30   *Perf. 14x13¹/₂*
1119 A519 2.50s multicolored   .30 .15
Education of the deaf in Austria, 200th anniv.

1979, Apr. 6
1120 A520 2.50s multicolored   .30 .15
Austrian Central Statistical Bureau, 150th anniv.

Laurenz   Diesel
Koschier — A521   Motor — A522

Europa Issue, 1979
1979, May 4
1121 A521 6s ocher & purple   .80 .30

1979, May 4   **Photo.**
1122 A522 4s multicolored   .45 .20
13th CIMAC Congress (Intl. Org. for Internal
Combustion Machines).

Arms of Ried,
Schärding and
Braunau — A523

Photo. & Engr.
1979, June 1   *Perf. 14x13¹/₂*
1123 A523 3s multicolored   .30 .15
200th anniversary of Innviertel District.

Flood and
City — A524

1979, June 1   *Perf. 13¹/₂x14*
1124 A524 2.50s multicolored   .30 .15
Control and eliminate water pollution.

Arms of   Jodok Fink
Rottenmann   A526
A525

Photo. & Engr.
1979, June 22   *Perf. 14x13¹/₂*
1125 A525 3s multicolored   .30 .15
700th anniversary of Rottenmann.

1979, June 29   **Engr.**   *Perf. 14*
1126 A526 3s brown carmine   .40 .15
Jodok Fink (1853-1929), governor of Vorarlberg.

Arms of Wels,
Returnees' Emblem,
"Europa Sail" — A527

1979, July 6   **Photo.**   *Perf. 14x13¹/₂*
1127 A527 4s yellow grn & blk   .45 .20
5th European Meeting of the Intl. Confederation
of Former Prisoners of War, Wels, July 6-8.

Symbolic Flower,
Conference
Emblem — A528

1979, Aug. 20   **Litho.**   *Perf. 14x13¹/₂*
1128 A528 4s turq blue   .45 .20
UN Conf. for Science and Technology, Vienna,
Aug. 20-31.

Donaupark,
UNIDO and
IAEA Emblems
A529

1979, Aug. 24   **Engr.**   *Perf. 13¹/₂x14*
1129 A529 6s grayish blue   .75 .30
Opening of the Donaupark Intl. Center in
Vienna, seat of the UN Industrial Development Org.
(UNIDO) and the Intl. Atomic Energy Agency
(IAEA).

Diseased Eye
and Blood
Vessels
A530

1979, Sept. 10   **Photo.**   *Perf. 14*
1130 A530 2.50s multicolored   .35 .15
10th World Congress of Intl. Diabetes Federation, Vienna, Sept. 9-14.

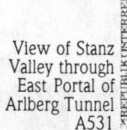

View of Stanz
Valley through
East Portal of
Arlberg Tunnel
A531

1979, Sept. 14   **Photo. & Engr.**
1131 A531 4s multicolored   .45 .20
16th World Road Cong., Vienna, Sept. 16-21.

3s   Steam
          Printing Press
REPUBLIK ÖSTERREICH A532

Photo. & Engr.
1979, Sept. 18   *Perf. 13¹/₂x14*
1132 A532 3s multicolored   .40 .20
Austrian Government Printing Office, 175th
anniv.

Richard Zsigmondy
(1865-1929),
Chemist — A533

1979, Sept. 21   **Engr.**   *Perf. 14x13¹/₂*
1133 A533 6s multicolored   .75 .30

"Save
Energy"
A534

1979, Oct. 1   **Photo.**   *Perf. 14x13¹/₂*
1134 A534 2.50s multicolored   .30 .15

Festival and
Convention
Center,
Bregenz
(Model)
A535

1979, Oct. 1   **Engr.**   *Perf. 14*
1135 A535 2.50s purple   .30 .15

Lions International
Emblem — A536

1979, Oct. 11   **Photo. & Engr.**
1136 A536 4s multicolored   .45 .25
25th Lions Europa Forum, Vienna, Oct. 11-13.

A537   A538

Photo. & Engr.
1979, Oct. 19   *Perf. 13¹/₂x14*
1137 A537 2.50s Wilhelm Exner   .30 .15
Centenary of Technological Handicraft Museum,
founded by Wilhelm Exner.

1979, Oct. 23   **Litho.**   *Perf. 13¹/₂x14*
The Compassionate Christ, by Hans Fronius.
1138 A538 4s olive & ol blk   .50 .25
Modern Austrian art.

Locomotive
and Arms
A539

1979, Oct. 24   **Photo.**   *Perf. 13¹/₂x14*
1139 A539 2.50s multicolored   .30 .15
Raab-Odenburg-Ebenfurt railroad, cent.

August
Musger — A540

Photo. & Engr.
1979, Oct. 30   *Perf. 14x13¹/₂*
1140 A540 2.50s bl gray & blk   .30 .15
August Musger (1868-1929), developer of slow-
motion film technique.

Nativity, St.
Barbara's
Church
A541

1979, Nov. 30   *Perf. 13¹/₂x14*
1141 A541 4s multicolored   .45 .25
Christmas.

Arms of
Baden — A542

1980, Jan. 25   *Perf. 14*
1142 A542 4s multicolored   .45 .25
Baden, 500th anniversary.

A543   A544

1980, Feb. 21   *Perf. 13¹/₂*
1143 A543 2.50s red & aqua   .30 .15
Fight rheumatism.

1980, Feb. 21   **Photo.**   *Perf. 14x13¹/₂*
1144 A544 4s dark blue & red   .45 .25
Austrian exports.

Austrian Red
Cross
Centenary
A545

1980, Mar. 14   **Photo.**   *Perf. 13¹/₂x14*
1145 A545 2.50s multicolored   .30 .15

Rudolph
Kirchschlager — A546

Photo. & Engr.
1980, Mar. 20   *Perf. 14x13¹/₂*
1146 A546 4s sepia & red   .45 .25

Robert Hamerling (1830-1889), Poet — A547

1980, Mar. 24   Engr.   Perf. 13½x14
1147 A547 2.50s olive green .35 .15

Seal of Hallein — A548

Maria Theresa, by Andreas Moller — A549

Photo. & Engr.
1980, Apr. 30   Perf. 14x13½
1148 A548 4s red & black .45 .25
Hallein, 750th anniversary.

1980, May 13   Engr.   Perf. 13½
Empress Maria Theresa (1717-1780) Paintings by: 4s, Martin van Meytens. 6s, Josef Ducreux.
1149 A549 2.50s violet brown .30 .25
1150 A549 4s dark blue .45 .40
1151 A549 6s rose lake .65 .75
　　Nos. 1149-1151 (3) 1.40 1.40

Flags of Austria and Four Powers — A550

1980, May 14   Photo.   Perf. 13½x14
1152 A550 4s multicolored .45 .25
State Treaty, 25th anniversary.

St. Benedict, by Meinrad Guggenbichler A551

1980, May 16   Engr.   Perf. 14½
1153 A551 2.50s olive green .30 .15
Congress of Benedictine Order of Austria.

Hygieia by Gustav Klimt — A552

1980, May 20   Photo.   Perf. 14
1154 A552 4s multicolored .45 .25
Academic teaching of hygiene, 175th anniv.

Aflenz Ground Satellite Receiving Station Inauguration — A553

1980, May 30   Photo.   Perf. 14
1155 A553 6s multicolored .85 .30

Steyr, Etching, 1693 A554

Photo. & Engr.
1980, June 4   Perf. 13½
1156 A554 4s multicolored .45 .25
Millennium of Steyr.

Worker, Oil Drill Head — A555

1980, June 12
1157 A555 2.50s multicolored .30 .15
Austrian oil production, 25th anniversary.

Seal of Innsbruck, 1267 — A556

1980, June 23   Perf. 13½x14½
1158 A556 2.50s multicolored .35 .15
Innsbruck, 800th anniversary.

Duke's Hat — A557

Bible Illustration, Book of Genesis — A559

Leo Ascher (1880-1942), Composer A558

Perf. 14½x13½
1980, June 23   Photo.
1159 A557 4s multicolored .45 .20
800th anniversary of Styria as a Duchy.

1980, Aug. 18   Engr.   Perf. 14
1160 A558 3s dark purple .45 .20

1980, Aug. 25   Perf. 13½
1161 A559 4s multicolored .45 .25
10th Intl. Cong. of the Org. for Old Testament Studies.

Europa Issue 1980

Robert Stolz (1880-1975), Composer — A560

1980, Aug. 25   Engr.   Perf. 14x13½
1162 A560 6s red brown .85 .30

Old and Modern Bridges A561

1980, Sept. 1   Photo.   Perf. 13½
1163 A561 4s multicolored .45 .25
11th Congress of the Intl. Assoc. for Bridge and Structural Engineering, Vienna.

Moon Figure, by Karl Brandstätter A562

Customs Service, Sesquicentennial A563

Photo. & Engr.
1980, Oct. 10   Perf. 14x13½
1164 A562 4s multicolored .45 .25

1980, Oct. 13   Photo.
1165 A563 2.50s multicolored .30 .15

Gazette Masthead, 1810 A564

1980, Oct. 23   Photo.   Perf. 13½
1166 A564 2.50s multicolored .30 .15
Official Gazette of Linz, 350th anniversary.

Waidhofen Town Book Title Page, 14th Century — A565

Photo. & Engr.
1980, Oct. 24   Perf. 14
1167 A565 2.50s multicolored .30 .15
Waidhofen on Thaya, 750th anniversary.

Federal Austrian Army, 25th Anniversary A566

1980, Oct. 24   Photo.   Perf. 13½x14
1168 A566 2.50s grnsh black & red .30 .15

Alfred Wegener A567

1980, Oct. 31   Engr.
1169 A567 4s violet blue .55 .25
Alfred Wegener (1880-1930), scientist, formulated theory of continental drift.

A568　　　　A569

1980, Nov. 6   Perf. 14x13½
1170 A568 4s dark red brown .55 .25
Robert Musil (1880-1942), poet.

Photo. & Engr.
1980, Nov. 28   Perf. 13½
Nativity, stained glass window, Klagenfurt.
1171 A569 4s multicolored .55 .25
Christmas.

25th Anniversary of Social Security A570

1981, Jan. 19   Litho.   Perf. 13½x14
1172 A570 2.50s multicolored .30 .15

Niebelungen Saga, 1926, by Dachauer A571

Machinist in Wheelchair A572

1981, Apr. 6   Engr.   Perf. 14x13½
1173 A571 3s sepia .40 .15
Wilhelm Dachauer (1881-1951), artist and engraver.

1981, Apr. 6   Photo. & Engr.
1174 A572 6s multicolored .75 .35
Rehabilitation Intl., 3rd European Regional Conf.

Sigmund Freud — A573

Congress, Vienna — A574

1981, May 6   Engr.
1175 A573 3s rose violet .40 .15
Sigmund Freud (1856-1939), psychoanalyst.

1981, May 11   Photo.
1176 A574 4s multicolored .55 .25

A575   Europa — A576

Azzo (founder of House of Kuenringer) and his
followers, bear-skin manuscript.

1981, May 15   **Photo. & Engr.**
1177 A575 3s multicolored   .35 .15
Kuenringer Exhibition, Zwettl Monastery.

1981, May 22   **Photo.**
1178 A576 6s Maypole   .80 .35

Telephone
Service
Centenary
A577

Photo. and Engr.
1981 May 29   **Perf. 13½x14**
1179 A577 4s multicolored   .45 .25

Seibersdorf
Research
Center, 25th
Anniv.
A578

1981, June 29   **Photo.**   **Perf. 13½**
1180 A578 4s multicolored   .45 .25

The Frog King
(Child's
Drawing)
A579

1981, June 29   **Perf. 13½x14**
1181 A579 3s multicolored   .35 .15

Town Hall and
Town Seal of
1250 — A580

Photo. & Engr.
1981, July 17   **Perf. 13½x14**
1182 A580 4s multicolored   .45 .25
St. Veit an der Glan, 800th anniv.

Johann Florian Heller
(1813-1871), Pioneer
of Urinalysis — A581

1981, Aug. 31   **Perf. 14x13½**
1183 A581 6s red brown   .75 .35
11th Intl. Clinical Chemistry Congress.

Ludwig Boltzmann   Scale — A583
(1844-1906),
Physicist — A582

1981, Sept. 4   **Engr.**   **Perf. 14x13½**
1184 A582 3s dark green   .45 .15

1981, Sept. 7   **Photo. & Engr.**
1185 A583 6s multicolored **Perf. 14** .75 .35
Intl. Pharmaceutical Federation World Congress,
Vienna, Sept. 6-11.

Otto Bauer,   Escher's Impossible
Politician, Birth   Cube
Centenary   A585
A584

1981, Sept. 7   **Photo.**   **Perf. 14x13½**
1186 A584 4s multicolored   .45 .25

1981, Sept. 14
1187 A585 4s dk blue & brt blue   .45 .25
10th Intl. Mathematicians' Cong., Innsbruck.

Kneeling Virgin,
Detail of Coronation
of Mary Altarpiece,
St. Wolfgang, 500th
Anniv. — A586

1981, Sept. 25   **Engr.**   **Perf. 14x13½**
1188 A586 3s dark blue   .35 .15

South-East Fair,
Graz, 75th
Anniv. — A587

1981, Sept. 25   **Photo.**   **Perf. 13½x14**
1189 A587 4s multicolored   .45 .25

Holy Trinity,
12th Cent.
Byzantine
Miniature
A588

1981, Oct. 5
1190 A588 6s multicolored   .75 .35
16th Intl. Byzantine Congress.

Hans Kelsen
(1881-1973), Co-
author of Federal
Constitution
A589

1981, Oct. 9   **Engr.**
1191 A589 3s dark carmine   .35 .15

Edict of Tolerance
Bicen. — A590

1981, Oct. 9   **Photo. & Engr.**   **Perf. 14**
1192 A590 4s Joseph II   .45 .25

World Food
Day — A591

1981, Oct. 16   **Photo.**   **Perf. 13½**
1193 A591 6s multicolored   .75 .35

Between the
Times, by
Oscar Asboth
A592

1981, Oct. 22   **Litho.**   **Perf. 13½x14**
1194 A592 4s multicolored   .55 .25

Intl. Catholic
Workers'
Day — A593

Photo. & Engr.
1981, Oct. 23   **Perf. 14x13½**
1195 A593 3s multicolored   .35 .15

Baron Josef Hammer-Purgstall, Founder of
Oriental Studies, 125th Death
Anniv. — A594

Photo. & Engr.
1981, Nov. 23   **Perf. 14**
1196 A594 3s multicolored   .35 .15

Julius Raab (1891-
1964),
Politician — A595

1981, Nov. 27   **Engr.**   **Perf. 13½**
1197 A595 6s rose lake   .75 .35

Nativity,
Corn Straw
Figures
A596

1981, Nov. 27   **Photo. & Engr.**
1198 A596 4s multicolored   .50 .20
Christmas.

Stefan Zweig (1881-
1942), Poet — A597

1981, Nov. 27   **Engr.**   **Perf. 14x13½**
1199 A597 4s dull violet   .50 .20

800th Anniv. of St.
Nikola on the
Danube — A598

1981, Dec. 4   **Photo. & Engr.**
1200 A598 4s multicolored   .55 .20

Vienna
Emergency
Medical Service
Centenary
A599

1981, Dec. 9   **Photo.**   **Perf. 13½x14**
1201 A599 3s multicolored   .35 .15

Schladming-Haus
Alpine World Skiing
Championship
A600

1982, Jan. 27   **Perf. 14**
1202 A600 4s multicolored   .45 .20

Dorotheum (State
Auction Gallery),
275th
Anniv. — A601

Photo. & Engr.
1982, Mar. 12   **Perf. 14**
1203 A601 4s multicolored   .45 .20

A602   A603

1982, Mar. 19 Photo. *Perf. 14x13¹/₂*
1204 A602 5s multicolored   .60 .30
Water Rescue Service, 25th anniv.

Photo. & Engr.
1982, Apr. 23   *Perf. 14x13¹/₂*
1205 A603 3s St. Severin   .35 .15
St. Severin and the End of the Roman Era
exhibition.

A604   A605

1982, May 4   *Perf. 14*
1206 A604 4s multicolored   .55 .20
Intl. Kneipp Hydropathy Congress, Vienna.

1982, May 7
1207 A605 4s Printers' guild arms   .55 .20
Printing in Austria, 500th anniv.

A606   A607

Design: Urine analysis, Canone di Avicenna
manuscript.

1982, May 12   Photo.
1208 A606 6s multicolored   .75 .35
5th European Urology Soc. Cong., Vienna.

1982, May 14   Photo. & Engr.
1209 A607 3s multicolored   .35 .15
800th birth anniv. of St. Francis of Assisi.

A608   A609

1982, May 19   Engr.   *Perf. 13¹/₂*
1210 A608 3s olive green   .35 .15
Haydn and His Time Exhibition, Rohrau.

1982, May 25 Photo. *Perf. 14x13¹/₂*
1211 A609 7s multicolored   .90 .40
25th World Milk Day.

800th Anniv of
Gfohl (Market
Town) — A610

Photo. & Engr.
1982, May 28   *Perf. 14*
1212 A610 4s multicolored   .45 .20

Tennis Player and
Austrian Tennis
Federation
Emblem — A611

1982, June 11
1213 A611 3s multicolored   .35 .15

900th Anniv.
of City of
Langenlois
A612

Photo. & Engr.
1982, June 11   *Perf. 13¹/₂x14*
1214 A612 4s multicolored   .45 .20

800th Anniv. of   Ignaz Seipel (1876-
City of   1932),
Weiz — A613   Statesman — A614

1982, June 18 Photo. *Perf. 14x13¹/₂*
1215 A613 4s Arms   .45 .20

1982, July 30   Engr.   *Perf. 14x13¹/₂*
1216 A614 3s brown violet   .35 .15

Europa Issue 1982

Sesquicentennial of Linz-Freistadt-Budweis
Horse-drawn Railroad — A615

1982, July 30   *Perf. 13¹/₂*
1217 A615 6s brown   .90 .35

Mail Bus Service,   Rocket Lift-
75th   off — A617
Anniv. — A616

1982, Aug. 6 Photo. *Perf. 14x13¹/₂*
1218 A616 4s multicolored   .50 .20

1982, Aug. 9   *Perf. 14*
1219 A617 4s multicolored   .50 .20
2nd UN Conference on Peaceful Uses of Outer
Space, Vienna, Aug. 9-21.

Geodesists'
Day — A618

Photo. & Engr.
1982, Sept. 1   *Perf. 13¹/₂x14*
1220 A618 3s Tower, Office of Standards   .35 .15

Protection of
Endangered
Species — A619

1982, Sept. 9   *Perf. 14*
1221 A619 3s Bustard   .45 .25
1222 A619 4s Beaver   .60 .30
1223 A619 6s Capercaillie   .90 .45
  Nos. 1221-1223 (3)   1.95 1.00

10th Anniv. of
Intl. Institute
for Applied
Systems
Anaysis,
Vienna
A620

1982, Oct. 4   Photo.
1224 A620 3s Laxenburg Castle   .35 .15

St. Apollonia
(Patron Saint
of Dentists)
A621

1982, Oct. 11   Photo. & Engr.
1225 A621 4s multicolored   .45 .20
70th Annual World Congress of Dentists.

Emmerich Kalman
(1882-1953),
Composer
A622

1982, Oct. 22   Engr.   *Perf. 13¹/₂*
1226 A622 3s dark blue   .35 .15

Max Mell (1882-   Christmas — A624
1971),
Poet — A623

1982, Nov. 10 Photo. *Perf. 14x13¹/₂*
1227 A623 3s multicolored   .35 .15

Photo. & Engr.
1982, Nov. 25   *Perf. 13¹/₂*
Design: Christmas crib, Damuls Church,
Vorarlberg, 1630.
1228 A624 4s multicolored   .45 .20

Centenary of St.   Portrait of a Girl, by
George's College,   Ernst Fuchs — A626
Istanbul — A625

1982, Nov. 26 Litho. *Perf. 14*
1229 A625 4s Bosporus   .45 .20

1982, Dec. 10   Photo. & Engr.
1230 A626 4s multicolored   .45 .20

Postal Savings
Bank Centenary
A627

Photo. & Engr.
1983, Jan. 12   *Perf. 14*
1231 A627 4s Bank   .55 .20

Hildegard Burjan
(1883-1933),
Founder of Caritas
Socialis — A628

1983, Jan. 28   Engr.
1232 A628 4s rose lake   .55 .20

World Communications Year — A629

1983, Feb. 18 Photo. *Perf. 13¹/₂x14*
1233 A629 7s multicolored   .95 .40

75th Anniv. Children's Friends Org. — A630

Photo. & Engr.
1983, Feb. 23 *Perf. 14x13½*
1234 A630 4s multicolored .55 .20

Josef Matthias Hauer (1883-1959), Composer A631

1983, Mar. 18 Engr. *Perf. 14*
1235 A631 3s deep lilac rose .40 .15

25th Anniv. of Austrian Airlines A632

1983, Mar. 31 Photo. *Perf. 13½x14*
1236 A632 6s multicolored .85 .35

Work Inspection Centenary A633

1983, Apr. 8 Photo. *Perf. 13½*
1237 A633 4s multicolored .55 .20

Upper Austria Millennium Provincial Exhibition A634

1983, Apr. 28 Photo. *Perf. 13½*
1238 A634 3s Wels Castle, by Matthaus Merian .40 .15

Gottweig Monastery, 900th Anniv. A635

7th World Pacemakers Symposium A636

Photo. & Engr.
1983, Apr. 29 *Perf. 13½*
1239 A635 3s multicolored .40 .15

1983, Apr. 29 Photo. *Perf. 14x13½*
1240 A636 4s multicolored .55 .20

Catholic Students' Org. — A637

1983, May 20 Photo. *Perf. 14*
1241 A637 4s multicolored .55 .20

Weitra, 800th Anniv. A638

Photo. & Engr.
1983, May 20 *Perf. 13½*
1242 A638 4s multicolored .55 .20

Granting of Town Rights to Hohenems, 650th Anniv. — A639

1983, May 27 Photo. *Perf. 14*
1243 A639 4s multicolored .55 .20

25th Anniv. of Stadthall, Vienna A640

1983, June 24 Photo. *Perf. 14*
1244 A640 4s multicolored .55 .20

Europa Issue 1983

A641 A642

1983, June 24 Engr. *Perf. 14x13½*
1245 A641 6s dark green .95 .35
Europa: Viktor Franz Hess (1883-1964), 1936 Nobel Prize winner in physics.

1983, July 1 Photo. *Perf. 13½*
1246 A642 5s multicolored .70 .30
Kiwanis Intl. Convention, Vienna, July 3-6.

7th World Congress of Psychiatry, Vienna — A643

1983, July 11 Photo. *Perf. 14*
1247 A643 4s Emblem, St. Stephen's Cathedral .55 .20

Baron Carl von Hasenauer (1833-1894), Architect A644

1983, July 20 Engr. *Perf. 13½x14*
1248 A644 3s Natural History Museum, Vienna .45 .15

27th Intl. Chamber of Commerce Professional Competition, Linz — A645

1983, Aug. 16 Photo.
1249 A645 4s Chamber building .55 .20

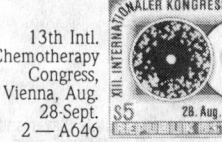

13th Intl. Chemotherapy Congress, Vienna, Aug. 28-Sept. 2 — A646

1983, Aug. 26
1250 A646 5s Penicillin test on cancer .70 .30

Catholics' Day — A647

Visit of Pope John Paul II — A648

1983, Sept. 9 Photo. *Perf. 14x13½*
1251 A647 3s multicolored .40 .15

Photo. & Engr.
1983, Sept. 9 *Perf. 13½*
1252 A648 6s multicolored .90 .35

Souvenir Sheet

Battle of 1683 to Relieve Vienna, by Frans Geffel A649

1983, Sept. 9 *Perf. 14*
1253 A649 6s multicolored .95 .50
300th anniv. of Vienna's rescue from Turkey.

Vienna Rathaus Centenary — A650

1983, Sept. 23 *Perf. 13½x14*
1254 A650 4s multicolored .55 .20

Karl von Terzaghi (1883-1963), Founder of Scientific Subterranean Engineering A651

1983, Oct. 3 Engr.
1255 A651 3s dark blue .40 .15

10th Trade Unions Federal Congress, Oct. 3-8 — A652

1983, Oct. 3 Photo. *Perf. 13½*
1256 A652 3s black & red .40 .15

Evening Sun in Burgenland, by Gottfried Kumpf — A653

Photo. & Engr.
1983, Oct. 7 *Perf. 13½x14*
1257 A653 4s multicolored .55 .20

Modling-Hinterbruhl Electric Railroad Centenary — A654

1983, Oct. 21 Photo.
1258 A654 3s multicolored .40 .15

Provincial Museum of Upper Austria Sesquicentennial — A655

1983, Nov. 4 Photo. & Engr.
1259 A655 4s Francisco-Carolinum Museum .55 .20

Creche, St. Andreas Parish Church, Kitzbuhel A656

1983, Nov. 25 *Perf. 14*
1260 A656 4s multicolored .55 .20
Christmas.

Parliament Bldg. Vienna, 100th Anniv. — A657

1983, Dec. 2 Engr.
1261 A657 4s slate blue .55 .20

A658   A659

Altar picture, St. Nikola/Pram Church.

1983, Dec. 6   Photo.   Perf. 14x13½
1262 A658 3s multicolored   .40 .15

**   Perf. 14½x13½**
1983, Dec. 15   Engr.
1263 A659 6s dark red brn   .90 .35
Wolfgang Pauli (1900-58), physicist, Nobel Prize winner.

Gregor Mendel (1822-1884), Genetics Founder — A660

**   Photo. & Engr.**
1984, Jan. 5   Perf. 13½
1264 A660 4s multicolored   .55 .20

Anton Hanak (1875-1934), Sculptor — A661

1984, Jan. 5
1265 A661 3s red brown & blk   .40 .15

50th Anniv. of 1934 Uprising — A662

1984, Feb. 10   Photo.   Perf. 14
1266 A662 4.50s Memorial, Woellers-dorf   .65 .30

Wernher von Reichersberg Family, Bas-relief, 15th Cent. — A663

**   Photo. & Engr.**
1984, Apr. 25   Perf. 14x13½
1267 A663 3.50s brown & blue   .50 .25
900th anniv. of Reichersberg Monastery.

Tobacco Monopoly Bicentenary A665

1984, May 4   Perf. 13½
1269 A665 4.50s Cigar wrapper, tobac-co plant   .65 .30

1200th Anniv. of Kostendorf Municipality — A666

1984, May 4
1270 A666 4.50s View, arms   .65 .30

Automobile Engineers World Congress A667

1984, May 4   Photo.   Perf. 13½x14
1271 A667 5s Wheel bearing cross-sec-tion   .70 .30

Europa (1959-1984) A668

1984, May 4   Perf. 13½
1272 A668 6s multicolored   .90 .35

A669   Aragonite — A670

Archduke Johann (1782-1859) by S. von Carolsfeld.

**   Photo. & Engr.**
1984, May 11   Perf. 14
1273 A669 4.50s multicolored   .65 .30

1984, May 11   Perf. 13½
1274 A670 3.50s multicolored   .50 .20
Ore and Iron Provincial Exhibition.

Era of Emperor Francis Joseph Exhibition — A671

Design: Cover of Viribus Unitis, publ. by Max Herzig, 1898.

1984, May 18
1275 A671 3.50s red & gold   .50 .20

A672   A673

**   Photo. & Engr.**
1984, May 30   Perf. 14x13½
1276 A672 4.50s Tower, arms   .65 .30
City of Vocklabruck, 850th anniv.

1984, June 1   Perf. 13½
Dionysius, Virinum mosaic.
1277 A673 3.50s multicolored   .50 .20
Museum of Carinthia, centenary.

Erosion Prevention Systems Centenary A674

1984, June 5   Engr.   Perf. 14
1278 A674 4.50s Stone reinforcement wall   .65 .30

Tyrol Provincial Celebration, 1809-1984 — A675

Art Exhibition: Meeting of Imperial Troops with South Tyrolean Reserves under Andreas Hofer near Sterzing in April 1809, by Ludwig Schnorr von Carolsfeld, 1830.

**   Photo. & Engr.**
1984, June 5   Perf. 14x13½
1279 A675 3.50s multicolored   .50 .20

A676   A677

1984, June 5   Engr.
1280 A676 4s violet brown   .55 .25
Ralph Benatzky (1884-1957), composer.

1984, June 22   Photo.   Perf. 14
1281 A677 3.50s multicolored   .50 .20
Christian von Ehrenfels (1859-1932), philosopher.

25th Anniv. of Minimundus (Model City) — A678

1984, June 22   Perf. 13½x14
1282 A678 4s Eiffel Tower, Tower of Pisa, ferris wheel   .55 .25

Blockheide Eibenstein Nature Park — A679

1984   Photo. & Engr.
1283 A679 4s shown   .55 .25
1284 A679 4s Lake Neusiedl   .55 .25
Issued: #1283, June 29; #1284, Aug. 13.

See Nos. 1349-1354, 1492-1496.

Monasteries and Abbeys — A679a

Designs: 3.50s, Geras Monastery, Lower Austria. 4s, Stams. 4.50s, Schlagl. 5s, Benedictine Abbey of St. Paul Levanttal. 6s, Rein-Hohenfurth.

1984-85   Perf. 14
1285 A679a 3.50s multicolored   .50 .20
1286 A679a 4s multicolored   .50 .20
1287 A679a 4.50s multicolored   .65 .30
1288 A679a 5s multicolored   .65 .30
1288A A679a 6s multicolored   .90 .35
    Nos. 1285-1288A (5)   3.20 1.35

Issued: 3.50s, 4/27/84; 4s, 9/28/84; 4.50s, 5/18/84; 5s, 9/27/85; 6s, 10/4/84.
See Nos. 1361-1365, 1464A-1468.

Schanatobel Railroad Bridge A680

Railroad Anniversaries: 3.50s, Arlberg cente-nary. 4.50s, Tauern, 75th.

1984, July 6   Perf. 14
1289 A680 3.50s shown   .50 .20
1290 A680 4.50s Falkenstein Bridge   .65 .20

A681   A682

1984, July 6   Photo.
1291 A681 6s Johan Stuwer's balloon   .90 .35
Balloon flight in Austria bicentenary.

1984, Aug. 31   Photo. & Engr.
1292 A682 7s Vienna Palace of Justice, emblem   .95 .45
Intl. Lawyers' Congress, Vienna.

A683   A684

1984, Sept. 3   Photo.
1293 A683 6s Josef Hyrtl, anatomist   .90 .35
7th European Anatomy Congress, Innsbruck, Sept. 3-7.

1984, Oct. 12
1294 A684 4s Window, by Karl Korab   .55 .20

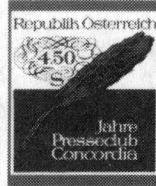

A685   A686

1984, Oct. 18
1295 A685 3.50s Clock (Immset Uhr),
1555   .50 .20

Johannes of Gmunden, mathematician, 600th
birth anniv.

1984, Nov. 9   Photo.   Perf. 13½
1296 A686 4.50s Quill   .65 .30

Concordia Press Club, 125th anniv.

Fanny Eissler, Dancer,
Birth
Centenary — A687

1984, Nov. 23   Photo. & Engr.
1297 A687 4s multicolored   .55 .30

Christmas
A688

Design: Christ is Born, Aggsbacher Altar,
Herzogenburg Monastery.

1984, Nov. 30   Perf. 14
1298 A688 4.50s multicolored   .65 .20

A689   A690

1985, Jan. 4   Perf. 14x13½
1299 A689 3.50s Seal   .50 .15

Karl Franzens University, Graz, 400th anniv.

1985, Jan. 15   Engr.
1300 A690 4.50s dk rose lake   .60 .20

Dr. Lorenz Bohler, Surgeon, birth cent.

Nordic Events, Ski Championships,
Seefeld — A691

1985, Jan. 17   Photo.   Perf. 13½
1301 A691 4s Ski jumper, cross country
racer   .55 .15

Linz Diocese
Bicentenary
A692

1985, Jan. 25
1302 A692 4.50s Linz Cathedral interi-
or   .60 .20

Alban Berg (1885-
1935),
Composer — A693

1985, Feb. 8   Engr.
1303 A693 6s bluish black   .80 .25

Vocational
Training Inst.,
25th
Anniv. — A694

1985, Feb. 15 Photo.   Perf. 13½x14
1304 A694 4.50s multicolored   .60 .20

City of Bregenz,
Bimillennium — A695

1985, Feb. 22   Perf. 14x13½
1305 A695 4s multicolored   .55 .15

Austrian
Registration
Labels
Cent. — A696

1985, Mar. 15   Perf. 13½x14
1306 A696 4.50s Label, 1885   .60 .20

Josef Stefan
(1835-1893),
Physicist — A697

Photo. & Engr.
1985, Mar. 22   Perf. 14x13½
1307 A697 6s buff, dl red brn & dk brn .80 .25

A698   A699

St. Leopold 16th-17th cent. embroidery.

1985, Mar. 29
1308 A698 3.50s multicolored   .50 .15

St. Leopold Exhibition, Klosterneuberg.

1985, Apr. 26   Photo.
1309 A699 4.50s multicolored   .60 .20

Liberation from German occupation forces, 40th
anniv.

Painter Franz von
Defregger (1835-
1921)
A700

1985, Apr. 26
1310 A700 3.50s Fairy tale teller   .50 .15

Europa Issue 1985

Johann Joseph
Fux (1660-1741),
Composer, Violin
and Trombone
A701

Photo. & Engr.
1985, May 3   Perf. 13½
1311 A701 6s lil gray & dk brn   .90 .25

Boheimkirchen (Market Town)
Millennium — A702

1985, May 10   Perf. 14
1312 A702 4.50s View, coat of arms   .60 .20

A703   A704

Mercury staff, flags of member and affiliate
nations.

1985, May 10   Photo.   Perf. 13½
1313 A703 4s multicolored   .55 .15

European Free Trade Assoc., 25th anniv.

1985, May 15   Photo. & Engr.
Episcopal residence gate, St. Polten diocese arms.
1314 A704 4.50s multicolored   .60 .20

St. Polten Diocese, bicentenary.

The Gumpp Family
of Builders,
Innsbruck — A705

Perf. 14½x13½
1985, May 17   Photo.
1315 A705 3.50s multicolored   .50 .20

Garsten Market
Town Millennium
A706

Design: 17th century engraving by George Matthaus Fischer (1628-1696).

Photo. & Engr.
1985, June 7   Perf. 13½x14
1316 A706 4.50s multicolored   .60 .20

UN, 40th
Anniv.
A707

Perf. 13½x14½
1985, June 26   Photo.
1317 A707 4s multicolored   .55 .20

Austrian membership, 30th anniv.

Intl. Assoc. for the
Prevention of
Suicide, 13th
Congress — A708

Photo. & Engr.
1985, June 28   Perf. 14
1318 A708 5s brn, lt ap grn & yel   .70 .30

Souvenir Sheet

Year of the
Forest
A709

1985, June 28   Perf. 13½
1319 A709 6s Healthy and damaged
woodland   1.00 .35

Kurhaus, Bad
Ischl Operetta
Activities
Emblem
A710

1985, July 5   Perf. 14
1320 A710 3.50s multicolored   .50 .15

Bad Ischl Festival, 25th anniv.

Intl. Competition of Fire Brigades, Vocklabruck — A711

1985, July 18 Photo. Perf. 14x13½
1321 A711 4.50s Fireman, emblem .60 .20

Grossglockner Alpine Motorway, 50th Anniv. — A712

Photo. & Engr.
1985, Aug. 2 Perf. 13½
1322 A712 4s View of Fuschertorl .55 .20

World Chess Federation Congress, Graz — A713

1985, Aug. 28 Photo. Perf. 13½
1323 A713 4s Checkered globe, emblem .55 .20

The Legendary Foundation of Konigstetten by Charlemagne, by Auguste Stephan, c. 1870 — A714

Photo. & Engr.
1985, Aug. 30 Perf. 14
1324 A714 4.50s multicolored .60 .20
Konigstetten millennium.

Hofkirchen-Taufkirchen-Weibern Municipalities, 1200th Anniv. — A715

1985, Aug. 30 Perf. 13½x14
1325 A715 4.50s View of Weiburn, municipal arms .60 .20

Dr. Adam Politzer (1835-1923), Physician — A716

1985, Sept. 12 Engr. Perf. 14
1326 A716 3.50s blue violet .50 .15
Politzer pioneered aural therapy for auditory disorders.

Intl. Assoc. of Forwarding Agents, World Congress, Vienna — A717

1985, Oct. 7 Photo. Perf. 13½
1327 A717 6s multicolored .85 .35

Carnival Figures Riding High Bicycles, By Paul Flora A718

Photo. & Engr.
1985, Oct. 25 Perf. 14
1328 A718 4s multicolored .55 .20

St. Martin on Horseback A719

1985, Nov. 8 Photo.
1329 A719 4.50s multicolored .60 .30
Eisenstadt Diocese, 25th anniv.

Creche, Marble Bas-relief, Salzburg — A720

Photo. & Engr.
1985, Nov. 29 Perf. 13½
1330 A720 4.50s gold, dl vio & buff .60 .30
Christmas.

Hanns Horbiger (1860-1931), Inventor — A721

1985, Nov. 29 Perf. 14
1331 A721 3.50s gold & sepia .50 .20

Aqueduct, Hundsau Brook, Near Gostling A722

1985, Nov. 29 Perf. 13½x14½
1332 A722 3.50s red, bluish blk & brt ultra .50 .20
Vienna Aqueduct, 75th anniv.

Chateau de la Muette, Paris Headquarters A723

1985, Dec. 13
1333 A723 4s sep, rose lil & gold .55 .25
Org. for Economic Cooperation and Development, 25th anniv.

Johann Bohm (1886-1959), Pres. Austrian Trade Fed. — A724

1986, Jan. 24 Photo. Perf. 14
1334 A724 4.50s blk, ver & grayish black .65 .30

Intl. Peace Year — A725

Perf. 13½x14½
1986, Jan. 24 Photo.
1335 A725 6s multicolored .85 .35

Digital Telephone Service Introduction A726

1986, Jan. 29 Photo.
1336 A726 5s Push-button keyboard .75 .30

Johann Georg Albrechtsberger (b. 1736), Composer — A727

Perf. 13½x14½
1986, Jan. 31 Photo. & Engr.
1337 A727 3.50s Klosterneuberg organ .50 .20

Korneuberg, 850th Anniv. A728

1986, Feb. 7 Photo. Perf. 14
1338 A728 5s multicolored .75 .30

A729 A730

Self-portrait, by Oskar Kokoschka (b.1886).

Perf. 14½x13½
1986, Feb. 28 Photo.
1339 A729 4s multicolored .60 .30

1986, Feb. 28 Photo. Perf. 13x13½
1340 A730 6s multicolored .85 .35
Admission to Council of Europe, 30th anniv.

Clemens Holzmeister (b. 1886), Architect, Salzburg Festival Theater, 1926 — A731

Photo. & Engr.
1986, Mar. 27 Perf. 13½
1341 A731 4s sepia & redsh brn .60 .30

3rd Intl. Geotextile Congress, Vienna A732

Perf. 13½x14½
1986, Apr. 7 Photo.
1342 A732 5s multicolored .75 .30

Prince Eugen and Schlosshof Castle — A733

Photo. & Engr.
1986, Apr. 21 Perf. 14
1343 A733 4s multicolored .60 .30
Prince Eugen Exhibition, Schlosshof and Niederweiden.

St. Florian Monastery, Upper Austria A734

1986, Apr. 24
1344 A734 4s multicolored .60 .30
The World of Baroque provincial exhibition, St. Florian.

Herberstein Castle, Arms of Styria — A735

1986, May 2 Perf. 13½x14½
1345 A735 4s multicolored .60 .30

Europa
1986 — A736

1986, May 2   *Perf. 13¹/₂*
1346 A736 6s Pasque flower   .85 .45

Wagner,
Scene
from
Opera
Lohengrin
A737

1986, May 21
1347 A737 4s multicolored   .60 .30
    Intl. Richard Wagner Congress, Vienna.

Antimonite
A738

1986, May 23   *Perf. 13¹/₂x14¹/₂*
1348 A738 4s multicolored   .60 .30
    Burgenland Provincial Minerals Exhibition.

Scenery Type of 1984

1986-89   Photo. & Engr.   *Perf. 14*
1349 A679 5s Martinswall, Tyrol   .65 .35
1350 A679 5s Tschauko Falls, Carin-
              thia   .65 .35
1351 A679 5s Dachstein Ice Caves   .80 .45
1352 A679 5s Gauertal, Montafon   .80 .60
1353 A679 5s Krimmler Waterfalls   .80 .60
1354 A679 5s Lusthauswasser   .80 .60
       Nos. 1349-1354 (6)   4.50 2.80
    Issued: #1351, 6/11/87; #1352, 8/21/87;
#1353, 8/19/88; #1354, 9/1/89.

Waidhofen
on Ybbs
Township,
800th
Anniv.
A739

1986, June 20   Photo.   *Perf. 13¹/₂*
1355 A739 4s multicolored   .50 .30

Salzburg
Local Railway,
Cent.
A740

1986, Aug. 8   Photo.   *Perf. 14*
1356 A740 4s multicolored   .55 .30

Seals of
Dukes
Leopold Of
Austria,
Otakar of
Styria, and
Georgenberg
Church
A741

1986, Aug. 14   Photo. & Engr.
1357 A741 5s multicolored   .70 .30
    Georgenberg Treaty, 800th anniv.

Julius Tandler
(1869-1936), Social
Reformer — A742

1986, Aug. 22
1358 A742 4s multicolored   .60 .30

Sonnblick
Observatory,
Cent. — A743

Perf. 13¹/₂x14¹/₂
1986, Aug. 27   Photo. & Engr.
1359 A743 4s Observatory, 1886   .60 .30

Discovery of Mandrake
Root — A744

1986, Aug. 27   *Perf. 14¹/₂x13¹/₂*
1360 A744 5s multicolored   .75 .30
    European Assoc. for Anesthesiology, 7th cong.

Monasteries and Abbeys Type of 1984

    Designs: 5.50s, St. Gerold's Provostry,
Vorarlberg. 7s, Loretto Monastery, Burgenland.
7.50s, Dominican Convent, Vienna. 8s, Zwettl
Monastery. 10s, Wilten Monastery.

1986-88   Photo. & Engr.   *Perf. 14*
1361 A679a 5.50s multicolored   .80 .60
1362 A679a 7s multicolored   1.10 .90
1363 A679a 7.50s multicolored   1.10 .85
1364 A679a 8s multicolored   1.40 1.00
1365 A679a 10s multicolored   1.75 1.25
       Nos. 1361-1365 (5)   6.15 4.60
    Issued: 5.50s, 9/12/86; 7.50s, 10/3; 7s,
8/14/87; 8s, 5/27/88; 10s, 3/18/88.

A745   A746

Photo. & Engr.
1986, Sept. 3   *Perf. 14*
1366 A745 4s multicolored   .60 .30
    Otto Stoessl (d. 1936), writer.

1986, Sept. 3   Photo.
1367 A746 4s Fireman, 1686   .60 .30
    Vienna fire brigade, 300th anniv.

Silk Viennese
Hunting
Tapestry — A747

Photo. & Engr.
1986, Sept. 3   *Perf. 14*
1368 A747 5s multicolored   .75 .40
    Intl. conf. on Oriental Carpets, Vienna, Budapest.

A748   A749

Photo. & Engr.
1986, Oct. 10   *Perf. 14*
1369 A748 5s Minister at pulpit   .70 .40
    Protestant Act, 25th anniv., and Protestant Pat-
ent of Franz Josef I ensuring religious equality,
125th anniv.

1986, Oct. 17   *Perf. 13¹/₂x14*
    Disintegration, by Walter Schmogner.
1370 A749 4s multicolored   .60 .30

Franz Liszt,
Composer, and
Birthplace,
Burgenland
A750

1986, Oct. 17   *Perf. 13¹/₂*
1371 A750 5s green & sepia   .70 .40

Souvenir Sheet

European Security Conference,
Vienna — A751

Illustration reduced.

1986, Nov. 4   *Perf. 13¹/₂x14*
1372 A751 6s Vienna   .95 .65

Strettweg
Cart, 7th
Cent.
B.C. — A752

Photo. & Engr.
1986, Nov. 26   *Perf. 14*
1373 A752 4s multicolored   .65 .30
    Joanneum Styrian Land Museum, 175th anniv.

Christmas
A753

    Design: The Little Crib, bas-relief by
Schwanthaler (1740-1810), Schlierbach Monastery.

1986, Nov. 28
1374 A753 5s gold & rose lake   .80 .40

Federal Chamber of
Commerce, 40th
Anniv. — A754

1986, Dec. 2   Photo.
1375 A754 5s multicolored   .80 .40

Industry
A755

1986-91   *Perf. 14x13¹/₂*
1376 A755 4s Steel workers   .80 .30
1377 A755 4s Office worker,
              computer   .80 .35
1378 A755 4s Lab assistant   .80 .30
1378A A755 4.50s Textile worker   .75 .60
1379 A755 5s Bricklayer   .80 .60
       Nos. 1376-1379 (5)   3.95 2.15
    Issued: #1376, 12/4/86; #1377, 10/5/87;
#1378, 10/21/88; 5s, 10/10/89; 4.50s,
10/11/91.
    This is an expanding set. Numbers will change if
necessary.

The Educated Eye, by
Arnulf Rainer — A756

1987, Jan. 13   Photo.   *Perf. 13¹/₂x14*
1386 A756 5s multicolored   .80 .40
    Adult education in Vienna, cent.

The Large
Blue
Madonna, by
Anton
Faistauer
(1887-1970)
A757

    Paintings: 6s, Self-portrait, 1922, by A. Paris
Gutersloh (1887-1973).

1987, Jan. 29   *Perf. 14*
1387 A757 4s multicolored   .55 .20
1388 A757 6s multicolored   .90 .40

Europa
1987 — A758

Photo. & Engr.
1987, Apr. 6   *Perf. 13¹/₂x14*
1389 A758 6s Hundertwasser House .95 .55

World Ice
Hockey
Championships,
Vienna — A759

Perf. 13½x14½
1987, Apr. 17   Photo.
1390 A759 5s multicolored   .80   .60

Opening of the
Austria Center,
Vienna
A760

1987, Apr. 22
1391 A760 5s multicolored   .80   .60

Salzburg City
Charter, 700th
Anniv.
A761

1987, Apr. 24
1392 A761 5s multicolored   .80   .60

A762   A763

Photo. & Engr.
1987, Apr. 29   **Perf. 14**
1393 A762 4s Factory, 1920   .65   .50
Work-Men-Machines, provincial exhibition,
Upper Austria.

1987, Apr. 29   Photo.   **Perf. 13½**
1394 A763 5s multicolored   .80   .60
Equal rights for men and women.

A764   A765

Adele Block-Bauer I, abstract by Gustav Klimt.
Photo. & Engr.
1987, May 8   **Perf. 13½**
1395 A764 4s multicolored   .65   .50
The Era of Emperor Franz Joseph, provincial
exhibition, Lower Austria.

1987, May 15   **Perf. 14½x13½**
1396 A765 6s multicolored   1.00   .75
Arthur Schnitzler (1862-1931), poet.

Von
Raitenau,
View of
Salzburg
A766

1987, May 15   **Perf. 14**
1397 A766 4s multicolored   .65   .50
Prince Archbishop Wolf Dietrich von Raitenau,
patron of baroque architecture in Salzburg, provincial exhibition.

Lace, Lustenau
Municipal
Arms — A767

1987, May 22
1398 A767 5s multicolored   .80   .60
Lustenau, 1100th anniv.

Souvenir Sheet

Austrian Railways Sesquicentenary — A768

1987, June 5   Photo.   **Perf. 13½**
1399 A768 6s multicolored   1.00   .75

8th Intl.
Congress of
Engravers,
Vienna
A769

Photo. & Engr.
1987, June 17   **Perf. 14**
1400 A769 5s gray, gray brn & dull
rose   .80   .60

Dr. Karl Josef Bayer   Shipping on
(1847-1904),   Achensee,
Chemist — A770   Cent. — A771

1987, June 22   **Perf. 14x13½**
1401 A770 5s multicolored   .80   .60
Eighth Intl. Light Metals Congress, June 22-26,
Leoben and Vienna; Bayer Technique for producing
aluminum oxide from bauxite, cent.

1987, June 26   Photo.
1402 A771 4s multicolored   .65   .50

A772   A773

1987, July 1
1403 A772 5s Palais Rottal, Vienna   .80   .60
Ombudsmen's office, 10th anniv.

1987, Aug. 11   Photo. & Engr.
1404 A773 5s dull olive bister, choc &
buff   .80   .60
Dr. Erwin Schrodinger (1887-1961), 1933 Nobel
laureate in physics.

Freistadt
Exhibitions,
125th Anniv.
A774

1987, Aug. 11   **Perf. 14x14½**
1405 A774 5s multicolored   .80   .60

Arbing, 850th
Anniv. — A775

1987, Aug. 21   **Perf. 13½**
1406 A775 5s multicolored   .80   .60

1987 World Cycling
Championships,
Villach to
Vienna — A776

1987, Aug. 25   **Perf. 14**
1407 A776 5s multicolored   .80   .60

World
Congress of
Savings Banks,
Vienna
A777

Perf. 13½x14½
1987, Sept. 9   Photo.
1408 A777 5s multicolored   .80   .60

Johann Michael
Haydn (1737-
1806),
Composer
A778

Perf. 13½x14½
1987, Sept. 14   Engr.
1409 A778 4s dull violet   .65   .50

Paul Hofhaymer
(1459-1537),
Composer
A779

Photo. & Engr.
1987, Sept. 11   **Perf. 14**
1410 A779 4s gold, blk & ultra   .65   .50

Bearded
Vulture — A780

1987, Sept. 25
1411 A780 4s multicolored   .65   .50
Innsbruck Zoo, 25th anniv.

Baumgottinnen, by Arnulf
Neuwirth — A781

1987, Oct. 9   **Perf. 14x13½**
1412 A781 5s multicolored   .80   .60
Modern Art.

Gambling Monopoly,
200th
Anniv. — A782

Perf. 14½x13½
1987, Oct. 30   Photo.
1413 A782 5s Lottery drum   .80   .60

Christoph
Willibald Gluck
(1714-1787),
Composer
A784

Photo. & Engr.
1987, Nov. 13   **Perf. 14**
1415 A784 5s cream & blk   .88   .65

Oskar Helmer
(b. 1887),
Politician — A785

1987, Nov. 13
1416 A785 4s multicolored   .70   .50

Joseph Mohr (1792-1848) and Franz
Gruber (1787-1863), Opening Bars of
"Silent Night, Holy Night" — A786

1987, Nov. 27
1417 A786 5s multicolored   .90   .65
Christmas.

A787   A788

Photo. & Engr.
1988, Jan. 12   *Perf. 13¹/₂*
1418 A787 5s St. John Bosco, children   .90   .65
Intl. Education Congress of Salesian Fathers.

Perf. 14¹/₂x13¹/₂
1988, Feb. 19   **Photo. & Engr.**
1419 A788 6s multicolored   1.05   .80
Ernst Mach (1838-1916), physicist.

Village with Bridge (1904), by Franz von Zulow (1883-1963), Painter — A789

1988, Feb. 25   **Photo.**   *Perf. 14¹/₂x14*
1420 A789 4s multicolored   .70   .50

Biedermeier Provincial Exhibition, Vormarz in Vienna A790

Painting: Confiscation, by Ferdinand Georg Waldmuller (1793-1865).

Photo. & Engr.
1988, Mar. 11   *Perf. 14*
1421 A790 4s multicolored   .70   .50

Anschluss of March 11, 1938 A791

1988, Mar. 11   **Photo.**   *Perf. 13¹/₂*
1422 A791 5s gray olive, brn blk & ver   .85   .65

No. 2 Aigen Steam Locomotive, 1887 — A792

1988, Mar. 22   *Perf. 13¹/₂x14¹/₂*
1423 A792 4s shown   .70   .50
1424 A792 5s Electric train, Josepsplatz   .85   .65
Muhlkreis Railway, cent. (4s); Vienna Local Railway, cent. (5s).

World Wildlife Fund — A793

Photo. & Engr.
1988, Apr. 15   *Perf. 13¹/₂x14*
1425 A793 5s Bee eater   .90   .65

Styrian Provincial Exhibition on Glass and Coal, Barnbach A794

1988, Apr. 29   *Perf. 13¹/₂*
1426 A794 4s Frosted glass   .70   .50

Intl. Red Cross, 125th Anniv. — A795

1988, May 6   **Photo.**   *Perf. 14*
1427 A795 12s grn, brt red & blk   2.25   1.65

Gothic Silver Censer — A796

1988, May 6   **Photo. & Engr.**
1428 A796 4s multicolored   .70   .50
Art and Monasticism at the Birth of Austria, lower Austrian provincial exhibition, Seitenstetten.

Europa 1988 A797

Communication and transportation.

1988, May 13   **Photo.**
1429 A797 6s multicolored   1.10   .80

Mattsee Monastery and Lion of Alz — A798

1988, May 18   **Photo. & Engr.**
1430 A798 4s multicolored   .70   .50
Provincial exhibition at Mattsee Monastery: Bavarian Tribes in Salzburg.

Weinberg Castle — A799

Perf. 13¹/₂x14¹/₂
1988, May 20   **Photo.**
1431 A799 4s multicolored   .70   .50
Upper Austrian provincial exhibition: Weinberg Castle.

Odon von Horwath (1901-1938), Dramatist — A800

Perf. 14¹/₂x13¹/₂
1988, June 1   **Photo. & Engr.**
1432 A800 6s olive bis & slate grn   1.10   .80

Stockerau Festival, 25th Anniv. — A801

1988, June 17   *Perf. 14*
1433 A801 5s Stockerau Town Hall   .80   .60

Tauern Motorway Opening — A802

1988, June 24   **Photo.**   *Perf. 13¹/₂x14*
1434 A802 4s multicolored   .65   .50

Brixlegg, 1200th Anniv. — A803

Perf. 13¹/₂x14¹/₂
1988, July 1   **Photo. & Engr.**
1435 A803 5s multicolored   .80   .60

View of Klagenfurt, Engraving by Matthaus Merian (1593-1650) A804

Photo. & Engr.
1988, Aug. 12   *Perf. 14*
1436 A804 5s multicolored   .80   .60
Carinthian Postal Service, 400th Anniv.

Brixen-im-Thale, 1200th Anniv. — A805

1988, Aug. 12
1437 A805 5s multicolored   .80   .60

Feldkirchen, 1100th Anniv. — A806

1988, Sept. 2   *Perf. 13¹/₂*
1438 A806 5s multicolored   .80   .60

Feldbach, 800th Anniv. A807

1988, Sept. 15   **Photo. & Engr.**
1439 A807 5s multicolored   .80   .60

Ansfelden, 1200th Anniv. — A808

1988, Sept. 23   *Perf. 14*
1440 A808 5s multicolored   .80   .60

Exports — A809

1988, Oct. 18   **Photo.**   *Perf. 14x13¹/₂*
1441 A809 8s multicolored   1.50   1.25
No. 1441 has a holographic image. Soaking in water may affect the hologram.

Vienna Concert Hall, 75th Anniv. A810

Photo. & Engr.
1988, Oct. 19   *Perf. 13¹/₂*
1442 A810 5s multicolored   .80   .60

The Watchmen, by Giselbert Hoke — A811

1988, Oct. 21   *Perf. 14*
1443 A811 5s multicolored   .80   .60

Social Democrats Unification Party Congress, Cent. — A812

1988, Nov. 11 Photo. *Perf. 14¹/₂x14*
1444 A812 4s multicolored .65 .50

Leopold Schonbauer (1888-1963), Physician — A813

Perf. 14¹/₂x13¹/₂
1988, Nov. 11 Photo. & Engr.
1445 A813 4s multicolored .65 .50

Christmas A814

Nativity painting from St. Barbara's Church.

1988, Nov. 25 Perf. 14
1446 A814 5s multicolored .80 .60

Benedictine Monastery, Melk, 900th Anniv. A815

Design: Fresco by Paul Troger.

1989, Mar. 17 Photo. & Engr.
1447 A815 5s multicolored .80 .60

Madonna and Child, by Lucas Cranach (1472-1553) A816

Marianne Hainisch (1839-1936), Women's Rights Activist A817

1989, Mar. 17 *Perf. 14¹/₂x13¹/₂*
1448 A816 4s multicolored .60 .50
Diocese of Innsbruck, 25th anniv.

1989, Mar. 24 *Perf. 14x13¹/₂*
1449 A817 6s multicolored .95 .70

Glider Plane and Parachutist A818

1989, Mar. 31 Photo. *Perf. 14*
1450 A818 6s multicolored 1.00 .75
World Gliding Championships, Wiener Neustadt, and World Parachuting Championships, Damuls.

Bruck an der Leitha Commune, 750th Anniv. A819

Painting by Georg Matthaus Vischer (1628-1696).

1989, Apr. 21
1451 A819 5s multicolored .85 .60

A820 A821

Die Malerei, 1904, by Rudolf Jettmar (1869-1939).

Perf. 14¹/₂x13¹/₂
1989, Apr. 21 Photo.
1452 A820 5s multicolored .85 .60

1989, Apr. 26 Photo. & Engr.
Holy Trinity Church, Stadl-Paura.
1453 A821 5s multicolored .85 .60
Michael Prunner (1669-1739), baroque architect.

A822 A823

Eduard Suess (1831-1914, structural geologist) portrait by J. Krieher (1800-1876) and map.

1989, Apr. 26
1454 A822 6s multicolored 1.00 .75

1989, Apr. 26
1455 A823 5s multicolored .85 .60
Ludwig Wittgenstein (1889-1951), philosopher.

Styrian Provincial Exhibition, Judenburg A824

Design: Judenberg, 17th cent., an engraving by Georg Matthaus Vischer.

1989, Apr. 28 *Perf. 14x13¹/₂*
1456 A824 4s multicolored .70 .50

Industrial Technology Exhibition, Pottenstein — A825

1989, Apr. 28 Photo. *Perf. 13¹/₂*
1457 A825 4s Steam engine .70 .50

Radstadt Township, 700th Anniv. A826

1989, May 3 Photo. *Perf. 13¹/₂x14¹/₂*
1458 A826 5s multicolored .85 .60

Europa 1989 — A827

1989, May 5
1459 A827 6s Toy boat 1.00 .75

Monastery Church at Lambach, 900th Anniv. — A828

Photo. & Engr.
1989, May 19 *Perf. 14*
1460 A828 4s multicolored .70 .50

Paddle Steamer *Gisela* — A829

1989, May 19 Photo. *Perf. 13¹/₂*
1461 A829 5s multicolored .85 .60
Shipping on the Traunsee, 150th anniv.

St. Andra im Lavanttal, 650th Anniv. A830

Period cityscape by Matthaus Merian.

1989, May 26 Photo. & Engr.
1462 A830 5s multicolored .85 .60

Richard Strauss (1864-1949), Composer — A831

Perf. 14¹/₂x13¹/₂
1989, June 1 Photo. & Engr.
1463 A831 6s dark brn, gold & red brn 1.00 .75

Achensee Railway, Cent. — A832

1989, June 8 Photo. *Perf. 13¹/₂*
1464 A832 5s multicolored .85 .60

Monastery Type of 1984

Design: 50g, Vorau Abbey, Styria. 1s, Monastery of Mehrerau, Vorarlberg. 1.50s, Monastery of the German Order in Vienna. 2s, Bendictine Monastery, Michaelbeuern. 11s, Engelszell Abbey. 12s, Monastery of the Hospitalers, Eisenstadt. 17s, St. Peter, Salzburg. 20s, Wernberg Monastery.

1989-92 Photo. & Engr. *Perf. 14*
1464A A679a 50g multicolored .15 .15
1465 A679a 1s multicolored .15 .15
1465A A679a 1.50s multicolored .30 .25
1466 A679a 2s multicolored .35 .25
1467 A679a 11s multicolored 1.90 1.40
1467A A679a 12s multicolored 2.25 1.75
1468 A679a 17s multicolored 2.75 2.00
1469 A679a 20s multicolored 2.75 2.00
Nos. 1464A-1469 (8) 10.60 7.95

Issued: 1s, 9/1/89; 17s, 6/29/89; 11s, 3/9/90; 50g, 10/12/90; 20s, 5/3/91; 2s, 9/27/91; 1.50s, 10/23/92; 12s, 6/17/92.
This is an expanding set. Numbers will change if necessary.

Interparliamentary Union, Cent. — A833

Photo. & Engr.
1989, June 30 *Perf. 14*
1475 A833 6s Parliament, Vienna 1.00 .75

Social Security in Austria, Cent. — A834

1989, Aug. 1 Photo.
1476 A834 5s multicolored .70 .50

UN Offices in Vienna, 10th Anniv. A835

1989, Aug. 23
1477 A835 8s multicolored 1.10 .85

Wildalpen, 850th Anniv. A836

Photo. & Engr.
1989, Sept. 15 *Perf. 13¹/₂x14*
1478 A836 5s Foundry, coat of arms .80 .60

33rd Congress of the Association for Quality Assurance (EOQC) — A837

1989, Sept. 18 Photo. *Perf. 14x13¹/₂*
1479 A837 6s multicolored   .90 .70

14th World Congress of the Soc. for Criminal Law (AIDP) A838

Photo. & Engr.
1989, Oct. 2   *Perf. 13¹/₂*
1480 A838 6s Justice Palace, Vienna   .90 .70

Lebensbaum, by Ernst Steiner — A839

1989, Oct. 10   *Perf. 13¹/₂x14*
1481 A839 5s multicolored   .80 .60

A840   A841

Perf. 14¹/₂x13¹/₂
1989, Nov. 6   Photo.
1482 A840 4s Trakl   .60 .45
1483 A840 4s Anzengruber   .60 .45
  Georg Trakl (1887-1914), expressionist poet; Ludwig Anzengruber (1839-1889), playwright and novelist.

1989, Nov. 10   Photo. & Engr.
1484 A841 6s multicolored   .90 .70
  Alfred Fried (1864-1921), pacifist and publisher awarded the Nobel peace prize for 1911 with Tobias Asser.

Parish Church Christ Child, by Johann Carl Reslfeld A842

1989, Dec. 1   *Perf. 13¹/₂x14¹/₂*
1485 A842 5s multicolored   .75 .60
  Christmas.

A843   A844

The Young Post Rider, an Engraving by Albrecht Durer

1990, Jan. 12 Photo. & Engr. *Perf. 14*
1486 A843 5s multicolored   .80 .60
  Postal communications in Europe, 500th anniv. See Belgium No. 1332, Germany No. 1592, Berlin No. 9N584 and German Democratic Republic No. 2791.

Perf. 13¹/₂x14¹/₂
1990, Jan. 12   Photo.
1487 A844 5s multicolored   .80 .60
  Hahnenkamm alpine competition, Kitzbuhel, 50th anniv.

A845   A846

Perf. 14¹/₂x13¹/₂
1990, Jan. 17   Photo.
1488 A845 4.50s multicolored   .70 .55
  Salomon Sulzer (1804-90), cantor and composer.

1990, Jan. 22   Photo. & Engr.
1489 A846 6s claret & pale green   .95 .70
  Friedrich Emich (1860-1940), chemist.

Miniature from the *Market Book of Grein,* by Ulrich Schreier, c. 1490 A847

1990, Mar. 9   *Perf. 14*
1490 A847 5s sepia, buff & gray   .80 .60
  City of Linz, 500th anniv.

University Seals — A848

1990, Apr. 6
1491 A848 5s multicolored   .85 .65
  625th Anniv. of Vienna University and 175th anniv. of Vienna Technical University.

Scenery Type of 1984

1990-97			***Perf. 14***	
1492	A679	5s Styrian Vineyards	.85	.65
1493	A679	5s Obir Caverns	.95	.70
1494	A679	5s Natural Bridge, Vorarlberg	.90	.75
1495	A679	6s Wilder Kaiser Mountain, Tyrol	1.25	.95
1496	A679	6s Peggau Cave, Styria	1.00	.80
1497	A679	6s Moorland, swamp, Heidenreichstein	1.25	1.00
1498	A679	6s Hohe Tauern Natl. Park	1.25	1.00
1499	A679	6s Nussberg Vineyards	1.00	.80
		Nos. 1492-1499 (8)	8.45	6.65

  Issued: #1492, 4/27; #1493, 3/26/91; #1494, 2/5/92; #1495, 2/19/93; #1496, 4/29/94; #1497, 5/19/95; #1498, 3/29/96; #1499, 2/21/97.

A849   A850

Church and municipal arms.

1990, Apr. 27 Photo. *Perf. 14x13¹/₂*
1500 A849 7s multicolored   1.25 .25
  1200th anniv. of Anthering.

1990, Apr. 30   Photo.   *Perf. 13¹/₂*
1501 A850 4.50s multicolored   .80 .60
  Labor Day, cent.

Seckau Abbey, 850th Anniv. — A851   Ebene Reichenau Post Office — A852

1990, May 4   Engr.   *Perf. 14x13¹/₂*
1502 A851 4.50s bluish black   .80 .60

1990, May 4   Photo. *Perf. 13¹/₂x14*
1503 A852 7s multicolored   1.25 .25

A853   A854

  Self Portraits: 4.50s, Hans Makart (1840-84). 5s, Egon Schiele (1890-1918).

Photo. & Engr.
1990, May 29   *Perf. 14*
1504 A853 4.50s multicolored   .80 .60
1505 A853 5s multicolored   .85 .65

1990, June 1   Photo. *Perf. 14x13¹/₂*
1506 A854 4.50s multicolored   .80 .60
  Ferdinand Raimund (1790-1836), actor.

Christ Healing the Sick by Rembrandt A855

1990, June 5 Photo. & Engr. *Perf. 14*
1507 A855 7s multicolored   1.25 1.00
  2nd Intl. Christus Medicus Cong., Bad Ischl.

Hardegg, 700th Anniv. — A856

1990, June 8   *Perf. 13¹/₂x14*
1508 A856 4.50s multicolored   .80 .60

Oberdrauburg, 750th Anniv. A857

1990, June 8   Photo.
1509 A857 5s multicolored   .85 .65

Gumpoldskirchen, 850th Anniv. — A858

Photo. & Engr.
1990, June 15   *Perf. 13¹/₂*
1510 A858 5s multicolored   .85 .65

Mathias Zdarsky (1856-1940), Alpine Skier — A859

1990, June 20   *Perf. 14x13¹/₂*
1511 A859 5s multicolored   .85 .65

Telegraph, 1880, Anton Tschechow, 1978 — A860

1990, June 28   Photo.   *Perf. 14*
1512 A860 9s multicolored   1.50 1.10
  Modern shipbuilding in Austria, 150th anniv.

A861   A862

Photo. & Engr.
1990, Aug. 3   *Perf. 14x13¹/₂*
1513 A861 5s gold & brown   .85 .65
  Joseph Friedrich Perkonig (1890-1959), poet.

Photo. & Engr.
1990, Aug. 30   *Perf. 13¹/₂x14*
  Herr des Regenbogens, by Robert Zeppel-Sperl.
1514 A862 5s gold & brown   .85 .65

European Dialysis and Transplantation
Society, 27th Congress — A863

1990, Sept. 4   Photo.   *Perf. 14*
1515 A863 7s multicolored   1.25 1.00

Franz Werfel (1890-
1945), Writer — A864

Photo. & Engr.
1990, Sept. 11   *Perf. 14x13½*
1516 A864 5s multicolored   .95 .70

Austrian
Forces in
UN Peace
Keeping
Forces,
30th Anniv.
A865

1990, Sept. 20   Photo.   *Perf. 13½*
1517 A865 7s multicolored   1.25 1.00

Federal
and State
Arms
A866

1990, Sept. 24   **Photo. & Engr.**
1518 A866 5s multicolored   .95 .70
Federalism in Austria.

A867   A868

1990, Oct. 22   Photo & Engr.   *Perf. 14*
1519 A867 4.50s blk, bl grn & red   .85 .65
Mining Univ., Leoben, 150th anniv.

Photo. & Engr.
1990, Nov. 8   *Perf. 14x13½*
1520 A868 4.50s multicolored   .85 .65
Karl Freiherr von Vogelsang (1818-90), politician.

Metalworkers and Miners Trade Union,
Cent. — A869

1990, Nov. 16   *Perf. 14*
1521 A869 5s multicolored   .95 .70

3rd World Curling
Championships
A870

1990, Nov. 23   Photo.   *Perf. 14x13½*
1522 A870 7s multicolored   1.40 1.00

Palmhouse at
Schonbrunn
A871

1990, Nov. 30   *Perf. 14*
1523 A871 5s multicolored   .95 .70

A872   A873

Christmas: Altar in Klosterneuburg Abbey by the
Master from Verdun.

Photo. & Engr.
1990, Nov. 23   *Perf. 13½*
1524 A872 5s multicolored   .95 .70

Photo. & Engr.
1991, Jan. 15   *Perf. 14x13½*
1525 A873 4.50s multicolored   .85 .65
Franz Grillparzer (1791-1872), dramatic poet.

A874   A875

1991, Jan. 21   *Perf. 13½*
1526 A874 5s multicolored   .95 .70
Alpine Skiing World Championship, Saalbach-
Hinterglemm.

1991, Jan. 21   Photo.   *Perf. 14x13½*
1527 A875 5s multicolored   .95 .70
Bruno Kreisky (1911-90), chancellor.

Friedrich
Freiherr von
Schmidt
(1825-1891),
Architect
A876

1991, Jan. 21   *Perf. 14*
1528 A876 7s multicolored   1.35 1.00

Visual
Arts — A877

Designs: 4.50s, Donner Fountain, Vienna, by
Raphael Donner (1693-1741), sculptor. 5s,
Kitzbuhel in Winter, by Alfons Walde (1891-1958),
painter. 7s, Vienna Stock Exchange, Theophil Hansen (1813-1891), architect.

1991, Feb. 8
1529 A877 4.50s multicolored   .85 .65
1530 A877 5s multicolored   .95 .70
1531 A877 7s multicolored   1.40 1.00
Nos. 1529-1531 (3)   3.20 2.35
See No. 1543.

Marie von
Ebner
Eschenbach
(1830-1916),
Poet — A878

Perf. 13½x14½
1991, Mar. 12   Engr.
1532 A878 4.50s rose violet   .85 .65

Miniature Sheet

Wolfgang Amadeus
Mozart (1756-1791),
Composer — A879

Design: b, Magic Flute Fountain, Vienna.

1991, Mar. 22   *Perf. 13½*
1533   Sheet of 2 + label   1.65 1.25
a.-b. A879 5s any single   .80 .60

Spittal an der
Drau, 800th
Anniv.
A880

1991, Apr. 11   *Perf. 14*
1534 A880 4.50s multicolored   .75 .60

Europa
A881

1991, May 3   Photo.   *Perf. 14*
1535 A881 7s ERS-1 satellite   1.10 .80

Garden
Banquet
by
Anthony
Bays
A882

1991, May 10   Photo.   *Perf. 13½*
1536 A882 5s multicolored   .75 .60
Vorarlberg Provincial Exhibition, Hohenems.

Museum of
Military
History,
Cent.
A883

Design: 7s, Interior of Museum of Art History.

Photo. & Engr.
1991, May 24   *Perf. 13½*
1537 A883 5s multicolored   .95 .80
1538 A883 7s multicolored   1.25 1.00
Museum of Art History, Cent. (#1538).

Grein,
500th
Anniv.
A884

1991, May 24   Photo.   *Perf. 14*
1539 A884 4.50s multicolored   .90 .45

Tulln, 1200th
Anniv.
A885

1991, May 24   *Perf. 13½x14*
1540 A885 5s multicolored   .95 .80

Completion of
Karawanken
Tunnels — A886

1991, May 31   *Perf. 14x13½*
1541 A886 7s multicolored   1.25 1.00

5th Anniv. of
St. Polten as
Provincial
Capital of
Lower Austria
A887

1991, July 5   Photo.   *Perf. 14*
1542 A887 5s multicolored   .80 .65

Visual Arts Type of 1991

Design: 4.50s, Karlsplatz Station of Vienna Subway by Otto Wagner (1841-1918), Architect.

1991, July 12   **Photo. & Engr.**
1543 A877 4.50s multicolored   .75 .60

Rowing and Junior Canoeing World
Championships, Vienna — A888

1991, Aug. 20   Photo.   *Perf. 13½x14*
1544 A888 5s multicolored   .85 .70

European
Congress of
Radiologists
A889

1991, Sept. 13 *Perf. 14*
1545 A889 7s multicolored   1.10 .95

Paracelsus (1493-
1541),
Physician — A890

1991, Sept. 27 *Perf. 14x13¹/₂*
1546 A890 4.50s multicolored   .75 .60

Joint Austrian-
Soviet Space
Mission — A891

1991, Oct. 2 *Perf. 14*
1547 A891 9s multicolored   1.50 1.25

Austrian Folk
Festivals — A892

Designs: 4.50s, Almabtrieb, Tyrol. 5s, Winzer-
krone, Vienna. 7s, Ernte-Monstranz, Styria.

1991, Oct. 4 *Photo. & Engr.*
1548 A892 4.50s multicolored   .75 .60
1549 A892 5s multicolored   .85 .70
1550 A892 7s multicolored   1.10 .95
   Nos. 1548-1550 (3)   2.70 2.25

See Nos. 1577-1579, 1619-1621, 1671-1673,
1694, 1705-1706, 1714, 1730, 1741.

The General by
Rudolph
Pointner — A893

Photo. & Engr.
1991, Oct. 11 *Perf. 13¹/₂x14*
1551 A893 5s multicolored   .85 .70

Birth of Christ, Baumgartenberg
Church — A894

1991, Nov. 29
1552 A894 5s multicolored   .85 .70
   Christmas.

Julius Raab, Politician,
Birth Cent. — A895,

1991, Nov. 29 *Perf. 14x13¹/₂*
1553 A895 4.50s red brn & brn   .75 .60

1992
Winter and
Summer
Olympic
Games
A897

1992, Jan. 14 *Photo.* *Perf. 14*
1555 A897 7s multicolored   1.25 1.00

Trade Union
of Clerks in
Private
Enterprises,
Cent. — A898

1992, Jan. 14
1556 A898 5.50s multicolored   .95 .80

A899   A900

1992, Jan. 29 *Perf. 14x13¹/₂*
1557 A899 5s multicolored   .90 .75
8th Natural Run Toboggan World Championships.

1992, Feb. 5 *Engr.* *Perf. 14x13¹/₂*
1558 A900 5.50s brown   .95 .80
   George Saiko, Poet, birth cent.

Worker's Sports,
Cent. — A901

1992, Feb. 5 *Photo.* *Perf. 14*
1559 A901 5.50s multicolored   .95 .80
Souvenir Sheet

Vienna Philharmonic Orchestra, 150th
Anniv. — A902

Photo. & Engr.
1992, Mar. 27 *Perf. 14*
1560 A902 5.50s multicolored   .95 .80

Scientists — A903

Designs: 5s, Franz Joseph Muller von Reichen-
stein (1742-1825), discoverer of tellurium. 5.50s,
Dr. Paul Kitaibel (1757-1817), botanist. 6s, Christian Johann Doppler (1803-1853), physicist. 7s,
Richard Kuhn (1900-1967), chemist.

1992, Mar. 27 *Photo.*
1561 A903   5s multicolored   .85 .70
1562 A903   5.50s multicolored   .95 .80
1563 A903   6s multicolored   1.00 .85
1564 A903   7s multicolored   1.25 .95
   Nos. 1561-1564 (4)   4.05 3.30

Railway
Workers
Union, Cent.
A904

1992, Apr. 2 *Perf. 14x13¹/₂*
1565 A904 5.50s black & red   .95 .80

Norbert Hanrieder
(1842-1913),
Poet — A905

Photo. & Engr.
1992, Apr. 30 *Perf. 14x13¹/₂*
1566 A905 5.50s purple & buff   .95 .80

Carl Zeller (1842-
1898) and Karl
Millocker (1842-
1899), Operetta
Composers
A906

Photo. & Engr.
1992, Apr. 30 *Perf. 14*
1567 A906 6s multicolored   1.00 .85

LD Steel
Mill, 40th
Anniv.
A907

1992, May 8 *Photo.* *Perf. 14x13¹/₂*
1568 A907 5s multicolored   .85 .70

Discovery of
America,
500th
Anniv.
A908

1992, May 8 *Photo. & Engr.* *Perf. 14*
1569 A908 7s multicolored   1.25 .95
   Europa.

Austro-Swiss
Treaty on
Regulation of
Rhine River,
Cent. — A909

1992, May 8 *Photo.* *Perf. 13¹/₂x14*
1570 A909 7s multicolored   1.25 .95

Protection of the
Alps — A910

1992, May 22 *Perf. 14x13¹/₂*
1571 A910 5.50s multicolored   .95 .80

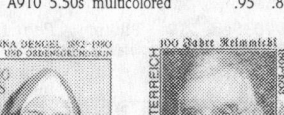

Dr. Anna Dengel   Sebastian Rieger
(1892-1980),   (1867-1953),
Physician — A911   Poet — A912

1992, May 22 *Photo. & Engr.*
1572 A911 5.50s multicolored   .95 .80

1992, May 22 *Engr.*
1573 A912 5s red brown   .85 .70

Lienz, 750th
Anniv.
A913

1992, June 17 *Photo.* *Perf. 14x13¹/₂*
1574 A913 5s Town Hall   .90 .70

Intl. Congress of
Austrian Society
of
Surgeons — A914

Photo. & Engr.
1992, June 17 *Perf. 14*
1575 A914 6s multicolored   1.10 .90

Dr. Kurt Waldheim, President of Austria, 1986-92 — A915

1992, June 22   *Perf. 14x13¹/₂*
1576 A915 5.50s multicolored   .95   .75

Folk Festivals Type of 1991

Designs: 5s, Marksman's target, Lower Austria. 5.50s, Peasant's chest, Carinthia. 7s, Votive icon, Vorarlberg.

Photo. & Engr.
                          1992, Sept. 18   *Perf. 14*
1577 A892 5s multicolored   .90   .70
1578 A892 5.50s multicolored   .95   .75
1579 A892 7s multicolored   1.25 1.00
     Nos. 1577-1579 (3)   3.10 2.45

Marchfeld Canal — A917

1992, Oct. 9   Photo.   *Perf. 13¹/₂x14*
1580 A917 5s multicolored   .90   .70

5th Intl. Ombudsman Conference, Vienna A918

1992, Oct. 9   Photo & Engr.   *Perf. 14*
1581 A918 5.50s multicolored   .95   .75

The Clearance of Seawater, by Peter Pongratz A919

1992, Oct. 9
1582 A919 5.50s multicolored   .95   .75

Academy of Fine Arts, 300th Anniv. — A920

Photo. & Engr.
1992, Oct. 23   *Perf. 14*
1583 A920 5s red & blue   1.00   .85

Birth of Christ, by Johann Georg Schmidt A921

1992, Nov. 27   *Perf. 14x13¹/₂*
1584 A921 5.50s multicolored   1.10   .90

Christmas.

Veit Koniger, Sculptor, Death Bicent. — A922

Photo. & Engr.
1992, Nov. 27   *Perf. 14*
1585 A922 5s multicolored   1.00   .80

Herman Potocnik, Theoretician of Geosynchronous Satellite Orbit, Birth Cent. — A923

1992, Nov. 27   Photo.
1586 A923 10s multicolored   2.00 1.65

Famous Buildings A924

Designs: 5s, Statues and dome of Imperial Palace, Vienna, designed by Joseph Emanuel Fischer von Erlach. 5.50s, Kinsky Palace, designed by Lukas von Hildebrandt. 7s, Vienna State Opera, designed by Eduard van der Null and August Siccard von Siccardsburg.

1993, Jan. 22   Photo. & Engr.
1587 A924 5s multicolored   1.00   .80
1588 A924 5.50s multicolored   1.10   .90
1589 A924 7s multicolored   1.40 1.10
    Nos. 1587-1589 (3)   3.50 2.80

Joseph Emanuel Fischer von Erlach, 300th birth anniv. (#1587). Johann Lukas von Hildebrandt, 325th birth anniv. (#1588). Eduard van der Null, August Siccard von Siccardsburg, 125th death anniv. (#1589).

Radio Dispatched Medical Service, 25th Anniv. — A925

1993, Feb. 19   Photo.
1590 A925 5s multicolored   1.00   .80

Typewriter Made by Peter Mitterhofer (1822-1893) A926

1993, Feb. 19   *Perf. 13¹/₂x14*
1591 A926 17s multicolored   3.50 2.75

Popular Entertainers — A927

5.50s, Strada del Sole, by Rainhard Fendrich.

1993, Mar. 19   Photo.   *Perf. 14*
1592 A927 5.50s multicolored   1.00   .80
     See Nos. 1626, 1639.

Charles Sealsfield (1793-1864), Writer A928

Photo. & Engr.
1993, Mar. 19   *Perf. 13¹/₂x14*
1593 A928 10s multicolored   1.75 1.40

Rights of the Child — A930

1993, Apr. 16   Photo.   *Perf. 13¹/₂x14*
1595 A930 7s multicolored   1.25 1.00

Flying Harlequin, by Paul Flora — A931

1993, Apr. 16   Photo. & Engr.
1596 A931 7s multicolored   1.25 1.00

Europa.

Monastery of Admont — A932

Designs: 1s, Detail of abbesse's crosier, St. Gabriel Abbey, Styria. 5.50s, Death, wooden statue by Josef Stammel (1695-1765). 6s, Stained glass, Mariastern-Gwiggen Monastery. 7s, Marble lion, Franciscan Monastery, Salzburg. 8s, Gothic entry, Wilhering Monastery, Upper Austria. 7.50s, Cupola fresco, by Paul Troger, Monastery of Altenburg. 10s, Altarpiece, St. Peregrinus praying, Maria Luggau Monastery. 20s, Crosier, Fiecht Monastery. 26s, Sculpture of Mater Dolorosa, Franciscan Monastery, Schwaz, Tirol. 30s, Madonna of Scottish Order, Schottenstift Monastery, Vienna.

Perf. 14x13¹/₂, 13¹/₂x14 (8s, 26s), 14 (1s, 30s)

1993-95   Photo. & Engr.
1599 A932   1s multicolored   .20   .15

1603 A932 5.50s green, black &   yel   1.00   .80
               Perf. 14
1606 A932 6s multicolored   1.10   .90
1606A A932 7s gray, blk & yel   1.25 1.00
1607 A932 7.50s brown, blk & bl   1.25 1.00
1608 A932 8s multicolored   1.60 1.25
1609 A932 10s multicolored   1.75 1.40
1613 A932 20s multicolored   3.50 1.75
1613A A932 26s multicolored   5.25 4.25
1614 A932 30s multicolored   5.50 4.50
    Nos. 1599-1614 (10)   22.40 17.00

Issued: 5.50s, 4/16; 6s, 9/17; 20s, 10/8; 7.50s, 4/4/94; 10s, 8/26/94; 30s, 10/7/94; 7s, 11/18/94; 8s, 9/15/95; 26s, 10/6/95; 1s, 4/28/95.

This is an expanding set. Numbers may change.

Peter Rosegger (1843-1918), Writer — A933

1993, May 5   Photo.   *Perf. 14x13¹/₂*
1617 A933 5.50s green & black   1.00   .80

Lake Constance Steamer Hohentwiel A934

1993, May 5   Photo.   *Perf. 14*
1618 A934 6s multicolored   1.10   .85
See Germany No. 1786, Switzerland No. 931.

Folk Festivals Type of 1991

Designs: 5s, Corpus Christi Day Procession, Upper Austria. 5.50s, Blockdrawing, Burgenland. 7s, Cracking whip when snow is melting, Salzburg.

Photo. & Engr.
1993, June 11   *Perf. 14*
1619 A892 5s multicolored   .90   .70
1620 A892 5.50s multicolored   1.00   .80
1621 A892 7s multicolored   1.25 1.00
    Nos. 1619-1621 (3)   3.15 2.50

UN Conference on Human Rights, Vienna — A935

1993, June 11   Photo.
1622 A935 10s multicolored   1.75 1.40

Franz Jagerstatter (1907-1943), Resistance Fighter — A936

1993, Aug. 6   Photo.   *Perf. 14x13¹/₂*
1623 A936 5.50s multicolored   1.00   .80

Schafberg Railway, Cent. — A937

1993, Aug. 6   *Perf. 13¹/₂x14*
1624 A937 6s multicolored   1.10   .90

Self-portrait with Puppet, by Rudolf Wacker (1893-1939) A938

Birth of Christ, by Master of the Krainburger Altar — A945

Lake Rudolph, Teleki-Hohnel Expedition — A950

Karl Seitz (1869-1950) Politician — A955

Karl Bohm (1894-1981), Conductor — A956

1993, Aug. 6 Photo. & Engr. *Perf. 14*
1625 A938 6s multicolored   1.10   .90

Popular Entertainers Type of 1993

Design: 5.50s, Granny, by Ludwig Hirsch.

1993, Sept. 3 Photo. *Perf. 14*
1626 A927 5.50s multicolored   1.00   .80

Vienna Mens' Choral Society, 150th Anniv. A940

1993, Sept. 17 Photo. *Perf. 14*
1627 A940 5s multicolored   .90   .75

Easter, by Max Weiler A941

99 Heads, by Hundertwasser A942

Photo. & Engr.
1993, Oct. 8 *Perf. 13½x14*
1628 A941 5.50s multicolored   1.00   .80

1993, Oct. 8
1629 A942 7s multicolored   1.25 1.00

Council of Europe Conference, Vienna.

Austrian Republic, 75th Anniv. — A943

Design: 5.50s, Statue of Pallas Athena.

Photo. & Engr.
1993, Nov. 12 *Perf. 13½x14*
1630 A943 5.50s multicolored   1.00   .80

Trade Unions in Austria, Cent. A944

1993, Nov. 12 Photo. *Perf. 14*
1631 A944 5.50s multicolored   1.00   .80

Photo. & Engr.
1993, Nov. 26 *Perf. 13½x14*
1632 A945 5.50s multicolored   1.00   .80
Christmas.

Folklore and Customs Type of 1991

Antiques: 5.50s, Dolls, cradle, Vorarlberg. 6s, Sled, Steiermark. 7s, Godparent's bowl, Upper Austria.

1994, Jan. 28 Photo. & Engr. *Perf. 14*
1633 A892 5.50s multicolored   1.00   .80
1634 A892 6s multicolored   1.10   .90
1635 A892 7s multicolored   1.25 1.00
    Nos. 1633-1635 (3)   3.35 2.70

1994 Winter Olympics, Lillehammer, Norway — A946

1994, Feb. 9
1636 A946 7s multicolored   1.25 1.00

Vienna Mint, 800th Anniv. A947

1994, Feb. 18
1637 A947 6s multicolored   1.10   .90

Lying Lady, by Herbert Boeckl (1894-1966) A948

1994, Mar. 18 Photo. *Perf. 14x13½*
1638 A948 5.50s multicolored   .95   .70

Popular Entertainers Type of 1993

Design: 6s, Rock Me Amadeus, by Falco.

1994, Mar. 18 *Perf. 14*
1639 A927 6s multicolored   1.00   .80

Wiener Neustadt, 800th Anniv. — A949

1994, Mar. 18
1640 A949 6s multicolored   1.00   .80

Photo. & Engr.
1994, May 27 *Perf. 14x13½*
1641 A950 7s multicolored   1.25 1.00
Europa.

Daniel Gran, 300th Birth Anniv. A951

Fresco: 20s, Allegory of Theology, Jurisprudence and Medicine.

1994, May 27
1642 A951 20s multicolored   3.50 2.75

Carinthian Summer Festival, 25th Anniv. — A952

Design: 5.50s, Scene from The Prodigal Son.

Photo. & Engr.
1994, June 17 *Perf. 14*
1643 A952 5.50s lake & gold   .95   .75

Railway Centennials — A953

1994 **Photo. & Engr.** *Perf. 14*
1647 A953 5.50s Gailtal   .95   .75
1648 A953 6s Murtal   1.00   .80
    Issued: 5.50s, 6s, 6/17/94.

Hermann Gmeiner, 75th Birth Anniv. — A954

1994, June 17 *Perf. 14x13½*
1656 A954 7s multicolored   1.25 1.00

1994, Aug. 12 Photo. *Perf. 14*
1657 A955 5.50s multicolored   1.00   .80

Photo. & Engr.
1994, Aug. 26 *Perf. 14x13½*
1658 A956 7s gold & dk blue   1.25 1.00

Ethnic Minorities in Austria A957

1994, Sept. 9 Photo. *Perf. 13½*
1659 A957 5.50s multicolored   1.00   .80

Franz Theodor Csokor (1885-1969), Writer — A958

Design: 7s, Joseph Roth (1894-1939), writer.

1994, Sept. 9 *Perf. 14x13½*
1660 A958 6s multicolored   1.00   .80
1661 A958 7s multicolored   1.25 1.00

Coin Bank — A959   Modern Art — A960

Photo. & Engr.
1994, Oct. 7 *Perf. 14x13½*
1662 A959 7s multicolored   1.25 1.00
Savings banks in Austria, 175th anniv.

1994, Oct. 7 *Perf. 13½x14*
Design: 6s, "Head," by Franz Ringel.
1663 A960 6s multicolored   1.10   .90

Austrian Working Environment — A961

1994, Nov. 18 Photo. *Perf. 14*
1664 A961 6s Stewardess, child   1.10   .90
    See Nos. 1690, 1703, 1736.

Richard
Coudenhove
Kalergi, Founder
of PanEuropean
Union, Birth
Cent. — A962

Photo. & Engr.
1994, Nov. 18   *Perf. 13 1/2*
1665 A962 10s multicolored   1.90 1.50

Birth of Christ, by
Anton Wollenek
A963

1994, Nov. 25   *Perf. 14*
1666 A963 6s multicolored   1.10 .90

Christmas.

Membership in
European
Union — A964

1995, Jan. 13   Photo.   *Perf. 14*
1667 A964 7s multicolored   1.25 1.00

Adolf Loos (1870-
1933),
Architect — A965

1995, Jan. 13
1668 A965 10s House, Vienna   1.90 1.50

Official Representation for Workers, 75th
Anniv. — A966

1995, Feb. 24   *Perf. 14x13 1/2*
1669 A966 6s multicolored   1.10 .90

Austrian
Gymnastics
and Sports
Assoc., 50th
Anniv.
A967

1995, Feb. 24
1670 A967 6s multicolored   1.10 .90

Folklore and Customs Type of 1991

Designs: 5.50s, Belt, Gailtal, Carinthia. 6s, Vineyard watchman's costume, Vienna. 7s, Bonnet,
Wachau, Lower Austria.

Photo. & Engr.
1995, Mar. 24   *Perf. 14*
1671 A892 5.50s multicolored   1.10 .90
1672 A892 6s multicolored   1.25 1.00
1673 A892 7s multicolored   1.40 1.10
      Nos. 1671-1673 (3)   3.75 3.00

Second Republic,
50th Anniv. — A968

1995, Apr. 27
1674 A968 6s State seal   1.25 1.00

History of
Mining &
Industry
A969

Design: Blast furnaces, old Heft ironworks.

1995, Apr. 28   *Perf. 13 1/2x14*
1675 A969 5.50s multicolored   1.10 .90

Carinthian Provincial Exhibition.

Nature Lovers Club, Cent. — A970

1995, Apr. 28   *Perf. 14*
1676 A970 5.50s multicolored   1.10 .90

Europa — A971

1995, May 19   *Perf. 14*
1677 A971 7s multicolored   1.50 1.25

1995 Conference of
Ministers of
Transportation,
Vienna — A972

1995, May 26   Photo.   *Perf. 14*
1678 A972 7s multicolored   1.40 1.25

Bregenz
Festival, 50th
Anniv.
A973

1995, June 9
1679 A973 6s multicolored   1.25 1.00

St. Gebhard (949-
995) — A974

Design: Stained glass window, by Martin Hausle.

1995, June 9
1680 A974 7.50s multicolored   1.50 1.25

UN, 50th
Anniv. — A975

1995, June 26   Photo.   *Perf. 14*
1681 A975 10s multicolored   2.00 2.00

Josef Loschmidt
(1821-95),
Chemist — A976

Photo. & Engr.
1995, June 26   *Perf. 14x13 1/2*
1682 A976 20s multicolored   4.00 4.00

A977   A978

Photo. & Engr.
1995, Aug. 18   *Perf. 13 1/2x14*
1683 A977 6s multicolored   1.25 1.00

Salzburg Festival, 75th anniv.

1995, Aug. 18   *Perf. 14x13 1/2*
1684 A978 6s buff, black & red   1.25 1.00

Kathe Leichter, resistance member, birth cent.

Europaisches Landschaftsbild, by Adolf
Frohner — A979

1995, Aug. 18
1685 A979 6s multicolored   1.25 1.00

Operetta
Composers
A980

Designs: 6s, Franz von Suppe (1819-95), scene
from "The Beautiful Galathea." 7s, Nico Dostal (b.
1895), scene from "The Hungarian Wedding."

1995, Sept. 15   *Perf. 14*
1686 A980 6s multicolored   1.25 1.00
1687 A980 7s multicolored   1.40 1.00

University of
Klagenfurt, 25th
Anniv. — A981

1995, Oct. 6   Photo.   *Perf. 14*
1688 A981 5.50s multicolored   1.10 .90

Carinthian
Referendum,
75th Anniv.
A982

1995, Oct. 6   Photo. & Engr.
1689 A982 6s multicolored   1.25 1.00

Austria Working Environment Type of
1994

1995, Oct. 20
1690 A961 6s Post office official   1.25 1.00

Composers — A983

Designs: 6s, Anton von Webern (1883-1945). 7s,
Ludwig van Beethoven (1770-1827).

1995, Oct. 20   *Perf. 13 1/2x14*
1691 A983 6s orange & blue   1.25 1.00
1692 A983 7s orange & red   1.40 1.10

Christmas — A984

Photo. & Engr.
1995, Dec. 1   *Perf. 13 1/2*
1693 A984 6s Christ Child   1.25 1.00

Folklore and Customs Type of 1991

Design: Roller and Scheller in "Procession of
Masked Groups in Imst," Tyrol.

1996, Feb. 9 Photo. & Engr. *Perf. 14*
1694 A892 6s multicolored   1.25 1.00

Maria Theresa Academy, 250th
Anniv. — A985

1996, Feb. 9
1695 A985 6s multicolored   1.25 1.00

1996 World Ski
Jumping
Championships
A986

1996, Feb. 9   Photo.
1696 A986 7s multicolored   1.40 1.10

New Western
Pier, Vienna Intl.
Airport — A987

1996, Mar. 28   Photo.   *Perf. 14*
1697 A987 7s multicolored   1.40 1.10

Mother with Child,
by Peter Fendi
(1796-1842)
A988

Designs: 7s, Self-portrait, by Leopold Kupelwieser
(1795-1862).

1996, Mar. 29
1698 A988 6s multicolored   1.25 1.00
1699 A988 7s multicolored   1.40 1.10

Anton Bruckner
(1824-96),
Composer,
Organist — A989

Photo. & Engr.
1996, Apr. 26   *Perf. 14*
1700 A989 5.50s Organ, music   1.15 .90

Georg
Matthäus
Vischer,
300th Death
Anniv.
A990

1996, Apr. 26
1701 A990 10s Kollmitz Castle   2.00 1.50

City of
Klagenfurt,
800th Anniv.
A991

1996, May 3
1702 A991 6s Ancient square   1.25 1.00

Austrian Working Environment Type of
1994

1996, May 17
1703 A961 6s Chef, waitress   1.25 1.00

Paula von
Preradovic,
Author
A992

1996, May 17   *Perf. 13¹/₂x14*
1704 A992 7s black, gray & buff   1.40 1.10
    Europa.

Folklore and Customs Type of 1991

Designs: 5.50s, Corpus Christi poles, Salzburg.
7s, Tyrolian riflemen.

Photo. & Engr.
1996, June 21   *Perf. 14*
1705 A892 5.50s multicolored   1.00 .80
1706 A892   7s multicolored   1.30 1.00

1996
Summer
Olympic
Games,
Atlanta
A993

1996, June 21
1707 A993 10s multicolored   1.90 1.50

Burgenland
Province,
75th Anniv.
A994

1996, Sept. 20
1708 A994 6s multicolored   1.10 .90

Austrian Mountain
Rescue Service,
Cent. — A995

1996, Sept. 27
1709 A995 6s multicolored   1.10 .90

Austria Millenium
A996

Designs: a, Deed by Otto III. b, Empress Maria
Theresa, Josef II. c, Duke Henry II. d, 1848 Revolution. e, Rudolf IV. f, Dr. Karl Renner, 1st Republic.
g, Emperor Maximilian I. h, State Treaty of 1955,
2nd Republic. i, Imperial Crown of Rudolf II. j,
Austria, Europe.

Photo. & Engr.
1996, Oct. 25   *Perf. 14*
1710   Sheet of 10   19.00 19.00
  a.-b. A996 6s any single   1.10   1.10
  c.-f. A996 7s any single   1.30   1.30
  g.-h. A996 10s any single   1.90   1.90
  i.-j. A996 20s any single   3.80   3.80

Power
Station, by
Reinhard
Artberg
A997

1996, Nov. 22
1711 A997 7s multicolored   1.30 1.30

UNICEF, 50th Anniv. — A998

1996, Nov. 22   Photo.
1712 A998 10s multicolored   1.90 1.90

Christmas — A999

1996, Nov. 29   Photo. & Engr.
1713 A999 6s multicolored   1.25 1.00

Folklore and Customs Type of 1991

Design: Epiphany Carol Singers, Burgenland.

1997, Jan. 17 Photo. & Engr. Perf. 14
1714 A892 7s multicolored   1.25 1.00

Theodor Kramer, Poet, Birth
Cent. — A1000

1997, Jan. 17
1715 A1000 5.50s deep blue   1.00 .80

Austrian Academy of Sciences, 150th
Anniv. — A1001

1997, Feb. 21   Photo.   *Perf. 14*
1716 A1001 10s multicolored   1.65 1.35

Austrian
Electricity
Board, 50th
Anniv.
A1002

1997, Mar. 21
1717 A1002 6s multicolored   1.00 .80

The Cruel Lady of   Erich Wolfgang
Forchtenstein   Korngold (1897-
Castle, Burgenland   1957), Composer
A1003   A1004

Photo. & Engr.
1997, Mar. 21   *Perf. 14*
1718 A1003 7s multicolored   1.15 .95
    See Nos. 1731, 1733.

1997, Mar. 21

Design: Scene from opera, "The Dead City. "
1719 A1004 20s blue, black & gold   3.30 1.65

Vienna
Rapid,
Austrian
Soccer
Champions
A1005

1997, Apr. 25   Photo.   *Perf. 14*
1720 A1005 7s multicolored   1.25 1.00

Deer Feeding
in Wintertime
A1006

1997, Apr. 25
1721 A1006 7s multicolored   1.25 1.00

St. Peter Canisius
(1521-97)
A1007

1997, Apr. 25   Photo. & Engr.
1722 A1007 7.50s Canisius Altar,
                    Innsbruck   1.25 1.10

Composers
A1008

Designs: 6s, Johannes Brahms (1833-1897). 10s,
Franz Schubert (1797-1828).

1997, May 9
1723 A1008 6s gold & violet blue   1.00 .80
1724 A1008 10s purple & gold   1.75 1.40

Stamp
Day — A1009

1997, May 9 *Perf. 13½*
1725 A1009 7s "A" and "E" 1.25 1.00
See Nos. B357-B362. The first letters will spell
"Briefmarke," the second "Philatelie."

Child's View of
"Town Band of
Bremen" — A1010

1997, May 23 Photo.
1726 A1010 7s multicolored 1.25 1.00
Europa.

Technical
Surveyance
Assoc., 125th
Anniv. — A1011

1997, June 13 Photo. *Perf. 14*
1727 A1011 7s multicolored 1.40 1.15

Railways
A1012

Designs: 6s, Hochschneeberg Cog Railway.
7.50s, Wiener Neustadt-Odenburg Railway.

1997, June 13 Photo. & Engr.
1728 A1012 6s multicolored 1.20 .95
1729 A1012 7.50s multicolored 1.50 1.20

Folklore and Customs Type of 1991

1997, July 11 Photo. & Engr. *Perf. 14*
1730 A892 6.50s Marching band,
Tyrol 1.30 1.00

Stories and Legends Type

Design: Dragon of Klagenfurt.

1997, July 11
1731 A1003 6.50s multicolored 1.30 1.00

Karl Heinrich
Waggerl, Birth
Cent. — A1013

1997, July 11
1732 A1013 7s multicolored 1.40 1.00

Stories and Legends Type of 1997

Design: Danube water nymph rescuing ferryman,
Upper Austria.

Photo. & Engr.
1997, Sept. 19 *Perf. 14*
1733 A1003 14s multicolored 2.75 2.10

1997
Orthopedics
Congress,
Vienna
A1014

1997, Sept. 19 Photo. *Perf. 14*
1734 A1014 8s Adolph Lorenz 1.60 1.20

Vienna
Agricultural
University, 125th
Anniv. — A1015

1997, Sept. 19
1735 A1015 9s multicolored 1.80 1.40

Austrian Working Environment Type of
1994

Photo. & Engr.
1997, Oct. 17 *Perf. 14*
1736 A961 6.50s Nurse, patient 1.30 1.00

"House in
Wind," by
Helmut
Schickhofer
A1016

1997, Oct. 17
1737 A1016 7s multicolored 1.40 1.00

Blind Persons
Assocs. in Austria,
Cent. — A1017

1997, Oct. 17 Photo. & Embossed
1738 A1017 7s multicolored 1.40 1.00

No. 1738 contains embossed Braille inscription.

A1018 A1019

Photo. & Engr.
1997, Oct. 31 *Perf. 14x13½*
1739 A1018 7s multicolored 1.40 1.00

Dr. Thomas Klestil, Pres. of Austria, 65th
birthday.

1997, Oct. 31 *Perf. 14*
1740 A1019 7s multicolored 1.40 1.00

Oskar Werner (1922-84), actor.

Folklore and Customs Type of 1991
Upper Austria tower wind players, Steyr.

Photo. & Engr.
1997, Nov. 21 *Perf. 14*
1741 A892 6.50s multicolored 1.30 1.00

Light For All Relief Organization, 25th
Anniv. — A1020

1997, Nov. 28 Photo. *Perf. 14*
1742 A1020 7s multicolored 1.40 1.00

Christmas
A1021

Photo. & Engr.
1997, Nov. 28 *Perf. 14*
1743 A1021 7s Mariazell Madonna 1.40 1.00

SEMI-POSTAL STAMPS

Issues of the Monarchy

Emperor Franz   The Firing
Josef — SP1   Step — SP2

Perf. 12½
1914, Oct. 4 Typo. Unwmk.
B1 SP1 5h green .15 .15
B2 SP1 10h rose .15 .15
Set value .20 .15
Set, never hinged .40

Nos. B1-B2 were sold at an advance of 2h each
over face value. Exist imperf.; value, set $60.

1915, May 1
Designs: 5h+2h, Cavalry. 10h+2h, Siege gun.
20h+3h, Battleship. 35h+3h, Airplane.
B3 SP2 3h + 1h violet brn .15 .30
B4 SP2 5h + 2h green .15 .15
B5 SP2 10h + 2h deep rose .15 .15
B6 SP2 20h + 3h Prus blue .15 .70
B7 SP2 35h + 3h ultra 1.75 1.10
Nos. B3-B7 (5) 2.35 2.40
Set, never hinged 5.00

Exist imperf. Value, set $110.

Issues of the Republic

Kärnten

Types of Austria, 1919-
20, Overprinted in
Black

Abstimmung

1920, Sept. 16 *Perf. 12½*
B11 A44 5h gray, *yellow* .25 .55
B12 A44 10h red, *pink* .50 .85
B13 A43 15h bister, *yel* .25 .55
B14 A45 20h dark grn, *bl* .25 .55
B15 A43 25h violet, *pink* .25 .55
B16 A45 30h brown, *buff* .55 1.75
B17 A45 40h carmine, *yel* .35 .75
B18 A45 50h dark bl, *blue* .35 .75
B19 A43 60h ol grn, *azure* .95 1.90
B20 A47 80h red .25 .55
B21 A47 1k orange brown .30 .60
B22 A47 2k pale blue .25 .55

Granite Paper
Imperf
B23 A46 2½k brown red .30 .70
B24 A46 3k dk blue & green .30 .70
B25 A46 4k carmine & violet .50 1.10
B26 A46 5k blue .60 1.25
B27 A46 7½k yellow green .60 1.25
B28 A46 10k gray grn & red .60 1.25
B29 A46 20k lilac & orange .60 1.25
Nos. B11-B29 (19) 8.00 17.40
Set, never hinged 20.00

Carinthia Plebiscite. Sold at three times face
value for the benefit of the Plebiscite Propaganda
Fund.
Nos. B11-B19 exist imperf. Value, set $125.

Hochwasser

Types of Regular Issues
of 1919-21 Overprinted *1920*

1921, Mar. 1 *Perf. 12½*
B30 A44 5h gray, *yellow* .20 .35
B31 A44 10h orange brown .20 .35
B32 A43 15h gray .20 .35
B33 A43 20h green, *yellow* .20 .35
B34 A43 25h blue, *yellow* .20 .35
B35 A45 30h violet, *bl* .20 .35
B36 A45 40h org brn, *pink* .25 .60
B37 A45 50h green, *blue* .75 2.00
B38 A43 60h lilac, *yellow* .20 .35
B39 A47 80h pale blue .20 .35
B40 A47 1k red org, *blue* .50 1.50
B41 A47 1½k green, *yellow* .25 .35
B42 A47 2k lilac brown .25 .35

Hochwasser

Overprinted *1920*

B43 A46 2½k light blue .25 .35
B44 A46 3k ol grn & brn red .25 .35
B45 A46 4k lilac & orange .55 1.75
B46 A46 5k olive green .30 .85
B47 A46 7½k brown red .30 .85
B48 A46 10k blue & olive grn .45 1.25
B49 A46 20k car rose & vio .80 1.50
Nos. B30-B49 (20) 6.50 14.50
Set, never hinged 15.00

Nos. B30-B49 were sold at three times face
value, the excess going to help flood victims. Exists
imperf. Value, set $175.

Franz Joseph   View of
Haydn — SP9   Bregenz — SP16

Musicians: 5k, Mozart. 7½k, Beethoven. 10k,
Schubert. 25k, Anton Bruckner. 50k, Johann
Strauss (son). 100k, Hugo Wolf.

1922, Apr. 24 Engr. *Perf. 12½*
B50 SP9 2½k brown 5.00 6.00
a. Perf. 11½ 4.25 4.50
B51 SP9 5k dark blue 1.10 1.50
B52 SP9 7½k black 1.25 2.25
a. Perf. 11½ 65.00 110.00
B53 SP9 10k dark violet 1.90 2.50
a. Perf. 11½ 2.00 2.50
B54 SP9 25k dark green 2.50 3.75
a. Perf. 11½ 3.25 4.00
B55 SP9 50k claret 1.75 3.50
B56 SP9 100k brown olive 6.00 7.50
a. Perf. 11½ 6.00 8.75
Nos. B50-B56 (7) 19.50 27.00
Set, never
hinged 47.50

These stamps were sold at 10 times face value,
the excess being given to needy musicians.
All values exist imperf. on both regular and hand-
made papers. Value, set $425.
A 1969 souvenir sheet without postal validity
contains reprints of the 5k in black, 7½k in claret
and 50k in dark blue, each overprinted

"NEUDRUCK" in black at top. It was issued for the Vienna State Opera Centenary Exhibition.

1923, May 22   Perf. 12½

Designs: 120k, Mirabelle Gardens, Salzburg. 160k, Church at Eisenstadt. 180k, Assembly House, Klagenfurt. 200k, "Golden Roof," Innsbruck. 240k, Main Square, Linz. 400k, Castle Hill, Graz. 600k, Abbey at Melk. 1000k, Upper Belvedere, Vienna.

Various Frames

B57	SP16	100k dk green	2.50	5.00
B58	SP16	120k deep blue	2.50	5.00
B59	SP16	160k dk violet	2.50	5.00
B60	SP16	180k red violet	2.50	5.00
B61	SP16	200k lake	2.50	5.00
B62	SP16	240k red brown	2.50	5.00
B63	SP16	400k dark brown	2.50	5.00
B64	SP16	600k olive brn	2.50	5.00
B65	SP16	1000k black	2.50	5.00
		Nos. B57-B65 (9)	22.50	45.00
		Set, never hinged	52.50	

Nos. B57-B65 were sold at five times face value, the excess going to needy artists.
All values exist imperf. on both regular and handmade papers. Value, set $350.

Feebleness
SP25

Siegfried Slays the Dragon
SP30

Designs: 300k+900k, Aid to industry. 500k+1500k, Orphans and widow. 600k+1800k, Indigent old man. 1000k+3000k, Alleviation of hunger.

1924, Sept. 6   Photo.

B66	SP25	100k + 300k yel green	3.25	3.25
B67	SP25	300k + 900k red brn	4.50	9.00
B68	SP25	500k + 1500k brn vio	4.50	9.00
B69	SP25	600k + 1800k pck bl	4.50	9.00
B70	SP25	1000k + 3000k brn org	7.50	12.50
		Nos. B66-B70 (5)	24.25	42.75
		Set, never hinged	52.50	

The surtax was for child welfare and anti-tuberculosis work. Set exists imperf. Value, $300.

1926, Mar. 8   Engr.

Designs: 8g+2g, Gunther's voyage to Iceland. 15g+5g, Brunhild accusing Kriemhild. 20g+5g, Nymphs telling Hagen the future. 24g+6g, Rudiger von Bechelaren welcomes the Nibelungen. 40g+10g, Dietrich von Bern vanquishes Hagen.

B71	SP30	3g + 2g olive blk	1.00	.35
B72	SP30	8g + 2g indigo	.25	.35
B73	SP30	15g + 5g dk claret	.25	.35
B74	SP30	20g + 5g olive grn	.40	.75
B75	SP30	24g + 6g dk violet	.40	.75
B76	SP30	40g + 10g red brn	3.00	2.75
		Nos. B71-B76 (6)	5.30	5.30
		Set, never hinged	12.50	

Nibelungen issue.
The surtax was for child welfare. Set exists imperf. Value, $225.

Pres. Michael Hainisch — SP36

Pres. Wilhelm Miklas — SP37

1928, Nov. 5

B77	SP36	10g dark brown	5.00	9.00
B78	SP36	15g red brown	5.00	9.00
B79	SP36	30g black	5.00	9.00
B80	SP36	40g indigo	5.00	9.00
		Nos. B77-B80 (4)	20.00	36.00
		Set, never hinged	35.00	

Tenth anniversary of Austrian Republic. Sold at double face value, the premium aiding war orphans and children of war invalids.
Set exists imperf. Value $300.

1930, Oct. 4

B81	SP37	10g light brown	7.50	12.50
B82	SP37	20g red	7.50	12.50
B83	SP37	30g brown violet	7.50	12.50
B84	SP37	40g indigo	7.50	12.50

B85	SP37	50g dark green	7.50	12.50
B86	SP37	1s black brown	7.50	12.50
		Nos. B81-B86 (6)	45.00	75.00
		Set, never hinged	85.00	

Nos. B81-B86 were sold at double face value. The excess aided the anti-tuberculosis campaign and the building of sanatoria in Carinthia.
Set exists imperf. Value, $325.

Regular Issue of 1929-30 Overprinted in Various Colors

1931, June 20

B87	A56	10g bister (Bl)	30.00	35.00
B88	A56	20g dk gray (R)	30.00	35.00
B89	A56	30g dk violet (Gl)	30.00	35.00
B90	A56	40g dk blue (Gl)	30.00	35.00
B91	A56	50g gray vio (O)	30.00	35.00
B92	A57	1s black brn (Bk)	30.00	35.00
		Nos. B87-B92 (6)	180.00	210.00
		Set, never hinged	350.00	

Rotary convention, Vienna.
Nos. B87 to B92 were sold at double their face values. The excess was added to the beneficent funds of Rotary International.
Exists imperf.

Ferdinand Raimund — SP38

Poets: 20g, Franz Grillparzer. 30g, Johann Nestroy. 40g, Adalbert Stifter. 50g, Ludwig Anzengruber. 1s, Peter Rosegger.

1931, Sept. 12

B93	SP38	10g dark violet	12.00	17.50
B94	SP38	20g gray black	12.00	17.50
B95	SP38	30g orange red	12.00	17.50
B96	SP38	40g dull blue	12.00	17.50
B97	SP38	50g gray green	12.00	17.50
B98	SP38	1s yellow brown	12.00	17.50
		Nos. B93-B98 (6)	72.00	105.00
		Set, never hinged	130.00	

Nos. B93-B98 were sold at double face value. The surtax aided unemployed young people.
Set exists imperf. Value, $500.

Chancellor Ignaz Seipel
SP44

Ferdinand Georg Waldmüller
SP45

1932, Oct. 12   Perf. 13

B99	SP44	50g ultra	10.00	16.00
		Never hinged	18.00	

Msgr. Ignaz Seipel, Chancellor of Austria, 1922-29. Sold at double face value, the excess aiding wounded veterans of World War I.
Exists imperf. Value, $150.

1932, Nov. 21

Artists: 24g, Moritz von Schwind. 30g, Rudolf von Alt. 40g, Hans Makart. 64g, Gustav Klimt. 1s, Albin Egger-Lienz.

B100	SP45	12g slate green	17.50	30.00
B101	SP45	24g dp violet	17.50	30.00
B102	SP45	30g dark red	17.50	30.00
B103	SP45	40g dark gray	17.50	30.00
B104	SP45	64g dark brown	17.50	30.00
B105	SP45	1s claret	17.50	30.00
		Nos. B100-B105 (6)	105.00	180.00
		Set, never hinged	180.00	

Nos. B100 to B105 were sold at double their face values. The surtax was for the assistance of charitable institutions.
Set exists imperf. Value, $600.

Mountain Climbing
SP51

Designs: 24g, Ski gliding. 30g, Walking on skis. 50g, Ski jumping.

1933, Jan. 9   Photo.   Perf. 12½

B106	SP51	12g dark green	6.50	12.50
B107	SP51	24g dark violet	55.00	85.00
B108	SP51	30g brown red	12.50	17.50
B109	SP51	50g dark blue	55.00	85.00
		Nos. B106-B109 (4)	129.00	200.00
		Set, never hinged	325.00	

Meeting of the Intl. Ski Federation, Innsbruck, Feb. 8-13.
These stamps were sold at double their face value. The surtax was for the benefit of "Youth in Distress."
#B106-B109 exist imperf. Value $1,500.

Stagecoach, after Painting by Moritz von Schwind
SP55

1933, June 23   Engr.   Perf. 12½
Ordinary Paper

B110	SP55	50g deep ultra	150.00	190.00
		Never hinged	225.00	
a.		Granite paper	300.00	425.00
		Never hinged	450.00	

Sheets of 25.
Nos. B110 and B110a exist imperf. Values $750 and $1,500.

Souvenir Sheet
Perf. 12
Granite Paper

B111		Sheet of 4	2,000.	2,750.
		Never hinged	2,500.	
a.		SP55 50g deep ultra	350.	550.
		Never hinged	525.	

Intl. Phil. Exhib., Vienna, 1933. In addition to the postal value of 50g the stamp was sold at a premium of 50g for charity and of 1.60s for the admission fee to the exhibition.
Size of No. B111: 126x103mm.
A 50g dark red in souvenir sheet, with dark blue overprint ("NEUDRUCK WIPA 1965"), had no postal validity.
Even though the margins No. B111 have no gum, the sheet sells for a premium when definitely never hinged.

St. Stephen's Cathedral in 1683 — SP56

Marco d'Aviano, Papal Legate — SP57

Designs: 30g, Count Ernst Rudiger von Starhemberg. 40g, John III Sobieski, King of Poland. 50g, Karl V, Duke of Lorraine. 64g, Burgomaster Johann Andreas von Liebenberg.

1933, Sept. 6   Photo.   Perf. 12½

B112	SP56	12g dark green	20.00	25.00
B113	SP57	24g dark violet	19.00	22.50
B114	SP57	30g brown red	19.00	22.50
B115	SP57	40g blue black	22.50	37.50
B116	SP57	50g dark blue	19.00	22.50
B117	SP57	64g olive brown	22.50	35.00
		Nos. B112-B117 (6)	122.00	165.00
		Set, never hinged	240.00	

Deliverance of Vienna from the Turks, 250th anniv., and Pan-German Catholic Congress, Sept. 6, 1933.
The stamps were sold at double their face value, the excess being for the aid of Catholic works of charity.
Set exists imperf. Value, $750.

Types of Regular Issue of 1925-30 Surcharged:

+2g   WINTERHILFE

Winterhilfe   **+6g**

  a   b

+50g

WINTERHILFE
c

1933, Dec. 15

B118	A52(a)	5g + 2g olive grn	.30	.65
B119	A56(b)	12g + 3g lt blue	.30	.70
B120	A56(b)	24g + 6g brn orange	.30	.65
B121	A57(c)	1s + 50g orange red	27.50	40.00
		Nos. B118-B121 (4)	28.40	42.00
		Set, never hinged	50.00	

Winterhelp. Exists imperf. Value, set $175.

12 GROSCHEN Anton Pilgram — SP62

Architects: 24g, J. B. Fischer von Erlach. 30g, Jakob Prandtauer. 40g, A. von Siccardsburg & E. van der Null. 60g, Heinrich von Ferstel. 64g, Otto Wagner.

1934, Dec. 2   Engr.   Perf. 12½
Thick Yellowish Paper

B122	SP62	12g black	9.00	15.00
B123	SP62	24g dull violet	9.00	15.00
B124	SP62	30g carmine	9.00	15.00
B125	SP62	40g brown	9.00	15.00
B126	SP62	60g blue	9.00	15.00
B127	SP62	64g dull green	9.00	15.00
		Nos. B122-B127 (6)	54.00	90.00
		Set, never hinged	100.00	

Exist imperf. Value, set $500.
Nos. B124-B127 exist in horiz. pairs imperf. between. Value, $175 to $225.
These stamps were sold at double their face value. The surtax on this and the following issues was devoted to general charity.

Types of Regular Issue of 1934 Surcharged in Black:

+50g

Winterhilfe
+2g   WINTERHILFE

  a   b

1935, Nov. 11   Perf. 12, 12½

B128	A67(a)	5g + 2g emerald	.45	1.00
B129	A67(a)	12g + 3g blue	.75	1.00
B130	A67(a)	24g + 6g lt brown	.45	1.00
B131	A68(b)	1s + 50g ver	19.00	35.00
		Nos. B128-B131 (4)	20.65	38.00
		Set, never hinged	55.00	

Winterhelp. Set exists imperf. Value, $140.

Prince Eugene of Savoy — SP68

Slalom Turn — SP74

Military Leaders: 24g, Field Marshal Laudon. 30g, Archduke Karl. 40g, Field Marshal Josef Radetzky. 60g, Admiral Wilhelm Tegetthoff. 64g, Field Marshal Franz Conrad Hotzendorff.

1935, Dec. 1   Perf. 12½

B132	SP68	12g brown	9.00	14.00
B133	SP68	24g dark green	9.00	14.00
B134	SP68	30g claret	9.00	14.00
B135	SP68	40g slate	9.00	14.00
B136	SP68	60g deep ultra	9.00	14.00
B137	SP68	64g dark violet	9.00	14.00
		Nos. B132-B137 (6)	54.00	84.00
		Set, never hinged	100.00	

These stamps were sold at double their face value. Set exists imperf. Value, $500.

1936, Feb. 20 — Photo.

Designs: 24g, Jumper taking off. 35g, Slalom turn. 60g, Innsbruck view.

B138	SP74	12g Prus green	2.50	3.00
B139	SP74	24g dp violet	4.50	4.50
B140	SP74	35g rose car	22.50	32.50
B141	SP74	60g sapphire	22.50	35.00
	Nos. B138-B141 (4)		52.00	75.00
	Set, never hinged		100.00	

Ski concourse issue. These stamps were sold at twice face value. Set exists imperf. Value, $475.

St. Martin of Tours — SP78

Designs: 12g+3g, Medical clinic. 24g+6g, St. Elizabeth of Hungary. 1s+1s, "Flame of Charity."

1936, Nov. 2 — Unwmk.

B142	SP78	5g + 2g dp green	.25	.25
B143	SP78	12g + 3g dp violet	.25	.40
B144	SP78	24g + 6g dp blue	.25	.40
B145	SP78	1s + 1s dk carmine	5.50	10.00
	Nos. B142-B145 (4)		6.25	11.20
	Set, never hinged		12.00	

Winterhelp. Set exists imperf. Value, $175.

Josef Ressel — SP82   Nurse and Infant — SP88

Inventors: 24g, Karl von Ghega. 30g, Josef Werndl. 40g, Carl Auer von Welsbach. 60g, Robert von Lieben. 64g, Viktor Kaplan.

1936, Dec. 6 — Engr.

B146	SP82	12g dk brown	2.00	5.00
B147	SP82	24g dk violet	2.00	5.00
B148	SP82	30g dp claret	2.00	5.00
B149	SP82	40g gray violet	2.00	5.00
B150	SP82	60g vio blue	2.00	5.00
B151	SP82	64g dk slate green	2.00	5.00
	Nos. B146-B151 (6)		12.00	30.00
	Set, never hinged		25.00	

These stamps were sold at double their face value. Exists imperf. Value, set $325.

1937, Oct. 18 — Photo.

12g+3g, Mother and child. 24g+6g, Nursing the aged. 1s+1s, Sister of Mercy with patient.

B152	SP88	5g + 2g dk green	.20	.25
B153	SP88	12g + 3g dk brown	.20	.25
B154	SP88	24g + 6g dk blue	.20	.25
B155	SP88	1s + 1s dk carmine	3.00	6.00
	Nos. B152-B155 (4)		3.60	6.75
	Set, never hinged		7.50	

Winterhelp. Set exists imperf. Value, $85.

Gerhard van Swieten — SP92   The Dawn of Peace — SP101

Physicians: 8g, Leopold Auenbrugger von Auenbrugg. 12g, Karl von Rokitansky. 20g, Joseph Skoda. 24g, Ferdinand von Hebra. 30g, Ferdinand von Arlt. 40g, Joseph Hyrtl. 60g, Theodor Billroth. 64g, Theodor Meynert.

1937, Dec. 5 — Engr. — Perf. 12½

B156	SP92	5g choc	1.75	4.00
B157	SP92	8g dk red	1.75	4.00
B158	SP92	12g brown blk	1.75	4.00
B159	SP92	20g dk green	1.75	4.00
B160	SP92	24g dk violet	1.75	4.00
B161	SP92	30g brown car	1.75	4.00
B162	SP92	40g dp olive grn	1.75	4.00

B163	SP92	60g indigo	1.75	4.00
B164	SP92	64g brown vio	1.75	4.00
	Nos. B156-B164 (9)		15.75	36.00
	Set, never hinged		30.00	

These stamps were sold at double their face value. Set exists imperf. Value, $450.

> Catalogue values for unused stamps in this section, from this point to the end of the section, are for Never Hinged items.

1945, Sept. 10 — Photo. — Perf. 14

B165	SP101	1s + 10s dk green	.85	1.40

No. 467 Surcharged in Black

1946, June 25

B166	A110	30g + 20g dk red	3.00	5.00

First anniversary of United Nations.

Pres. Karl Renner SP102

1946 — Engr. — Perf. 13½x14

B167	SP102	1s + 1s dk slate grn	2.00	4.00
B168	SP102	2s + 2s dk blue vio	2.00	4.00
B169	SP102	3s + 3s dk purple	2.00	4.00
B170	SP102	5s + 5s dk violet brn	2.00	4.00
	Nos. B167-B170 (4)		8.00	16.00

See Nos. B185-B188.

Nazi Sword Piercing Austria — SP103   Sweeping Away Fascist Symbols — SP104

Designs: 8g+6g, St. Stephen's Cathedral in Flames. 12g+12g, Pleading hand in concentration camp. 30g+30g, Hand choking Nazi serpent. 42g+42g, Hammer breaking Nazi pillar. 1s+1s, Oath of allegiance. 2s+2s, Austrian eagle and burning swastika.

1946, Sept. 16 — Unwmk. Photo. — Perf. 14

B171	SP103	5g + (3g) dk brown	.45	.65
B172	SP104	6g + (4g) dk slate grn	.30	.55
B173	SP104	8g + (6g) orange red	.30	.55
B174	SP104	12g + (12g) slate blk	.30	.55
B175	SP104	30g + (30g) violet	.30	.55
B176	SP104	42g + (42g) dull brn	.30	.55
B177	SP104	1s + 1s dk red	.45	.65
B178	SP104	2s + 2s dk car rose	.60	.65
	Nos. B171-B178 (8)		3.00	4.70

Anti-fascist propaganda.

Race Horse with Foal — SP111

Various Race Horses.

1946, Oct. 20 — Engr. — Perf. 13½x14

B179	SP111	16g + 16g rose brown	2.00	3.00
B180	SP111	24g + 24g dk purple	2.00	3.00
B181	SP111	60g + 60g dk green	2.00	3.00
B182	SP111	1s + 1s dk blue gray	2.00	3.00
B183	SP111	2s + 2s yel brown	2.00	3.00
	Nos. B179-B183 (5)		10.00	15.00

Austria Prize race, Vienna.

St. Ruprecht's Church, Vienna — SP116

1946, Oct. 30 — Perf. 14x13½

B184	SP116	30g + 70g dark red	.35	.70

Founding of Austria, 950th anniv. The surtax aided the Stamp Day celebration.

Renner Type of 1946 Souvenir Sheets

1946, Sept. 5 — Imperf.

B185	Sheet of 8		500.00	900.00
a.	SP102 1s+1s dk slate grn		55.00	100.00
B186	Sheet of 8		500.00	900.00
a.	SP102 2s+2s dk blue vio		55.00	100.00
B187	Sheet of 8		500.00	900.00
a.	SP102 3s+3s dark purple		55.00	100.00
B188	Sheet of 8		500.00	900.00
a.	SP102 5s+5s dk vio brown		55.00	100.00

1st anniv. of Austria's liberation. Sheets of 8 plus center label showing arms.

Statue of Rudolf IV the Founder — SP118   Reaping Wheat — SP128

Designs: 5g+20g, Tomb of Frederick III. 6g+24g, Main pulpit. 8g+32g, Statue of St. Stephen. 10g+40g, Madonna of the Domestics statue. 12g+48g, High altar. 30g+1.20s, Organ, destroyed in 1945. 50g+1.80s, Anton Pilgram statue. 1s+5s, Cathedral from northeast. 2s+10s, Southwest corner of cathedral.

1946, Dec. 12 — Engr. — Perf. 14x13½

B189	SP118	3g + 12g brown	.25	.50
B190	SP118	5g + 20g dk vio brown	.25	.50
B191	SP118	6g + 24g dk blue	.25	.50
B192	SP118	8g + 32g dk green	.25	.50
B193	SP118	10g + 40g dp blue	.40	.75
B194	SP118	12g + 48g dk vio	.45	.80
B195	SP118	30g + 1.20s car	1.10	1.90
B196	SP118	50g + 1.80s dk bl	1.25	2.00
B197	SP118	1s + 5s brn vio	1.75	3.25
B198	SP118	2s + 10s vio brn	3.50	7.50
	Nos. B189-B198 (10)		9.45	18.20

The surtax aided reconstruction of St. Stephen's Cathedral, Vienna.

1947, Mar. 23 — Perf. 14x13½

Designs: 8g+2g, Log raft. 10g+5g, Cement factory. 12g+8g, Coal mine. 18g+12g, Oil derricks. 30g+10g, Textile machinery. 35g+15g, Iron furnace. 60g+20g, Electric power lines.

B199	SP128	3g + 2g yel brown	.40	.50
B200	SP128	8g + 2g dk bl grn	.40	.50
B201	SP128	10g + 5g slate blk	.40	.50
B202	SP128	12g + 8g dark pur	.40	.50
B203	SP128	18g + 12g ol green	.40	.50
B204	SP128	30g + 10g deep cl	.40	.50
B205	SP128	35g + 15g crimson	.40	.50
B206	SP128	60g + 20g dk blue	.40	.50
	Nos. B199-B206 (8)		3.20	4.00

Vienna International Sample Fair, 1947.

Race Horse and Jockey SP136

1947, June 29 — Perf. 13½x14

B207	SP136	60g + 20g deep blue, pale pink	.15	.20

Cup of Corvinus — SP137   Prisoner of War — SP147

Designs: 8g+2g, Statue of Providence, Vienna. 10g+5g, Abbey at Melk. 12g+8g, Picture of a Woman, by Kriehuber. 18g+12g, Children at the Window, by Waldmuller. 20g+10g, Entrance, Upper Belvedere Palace. 30g+10g, Nymph Egeria, Schönbrunn Castle. 35g+15g, National Library, Vienna. 48g+12g, "Workshop of a Printer of Engravings," by Schmutzer. 60g+20g, Girl with Straw Hat, by Amerling.

1947, June 20 — Perf. 14x13½

B208	SP137	3g + 2g brown	.30	.40
B209	SP137	8g + 2g dk blue grn	.30	.40
B210	SP137	10g + 5g dp claret	.30	.40
B211	SP137	12g + 8g dk purple	.30	.40
B212	SP137	18g + 12g golden brn	.30	.40
B213	SP137	20g + 10g sepia	.30	.40
B214	SP137	30g + 10g dk yel grn	.30	.40
B215	SP137	35g + 15g deep car	.30	.40
B216	SP137	48g + 12g dk brn vio	.30	.40
B217	SP137	60g + 20g dp blue	.30	.40
	Nos. B208-B217 (10)		3.00	4.00

1947, Aug. 30

Designs: 12g+8g, Prisoners' Mail. 18g+12g, Prison camp visitor. 35g+15g, Family reunion. 60g+20g, "Industry" beckoning. 1s+40g, Sower.

B218	SP147	8g + 2g dk green	.20	.30
B219	SP147	12g + 8g dk vio brn	.20	.30
B220	SP147	18g + 12g black brn	.20	.30
B221	SP147	35g + 15g rose brn	.20	.30
B222	SP147	60g + 20g dp blue	.20	.30
B223	SP147	1s + 40g redsh brn	.20	.30
	Nos. B218-B223 (6)		1.20	1.80

Olympic Flame and Emblem SP153   Laabenbach Bridge Neulengbach SP154

1948, Jan. 16 — Engr.

B224	SP153	1s + 50g dark blue	.35	.35

The surtax was used to help defray expenses of Austria's 1948 Olympics team.

1948, Feb. 18 — Perf. 14x13½

Designs: 20g+10g, Dam, Vermunt Lake. 30g+10g, Danube Port, Vienna. 40g+20g, Mining, Erzberg. 45g+20g, Tracks, Southern Railway Station, Vienna. 60g+30g, Communal housing project, Vienna. 75g+35g, Gas Works, Vienna. 80g+40g, Oil refinery. 1s+50g, Gesäuse Highway, Styria. 1.40s+70g, Parliament Building, Vienna.

B225	SP154	20g + 10g slate blk	.20	.20
B226	SP154	20g + 10g lilac	.20	.20
B227	SP154	30g + 10g dull grn	.50	.50
B228	SP154	40g + 20g ol brn	.20	.20
B229	SP154	45g + 20g dk blue	.20	.20
B230	SP154	60g + 30g dk red	.20	.20
B231	SP154	75g + 35g dk vio brn	.15	.15
B232	SP154	80g + 40g vio brn	.20	.20
B233	SP154	1s + 50g dp blue	.20	.20
B234	SP154	1.40s + 70g dp car	.50	.50
	Set value		1.60	1.55

The surtax was for the Reconstruction Fund.

Violet — SP155   Hans Makart — SP156

Designs: 20g+10g, Anemone. 30g+10g, Crocus. 40g+20g, Yellow primrose. 45g+20g, Pasque-flower. 60g+30g, Rhododendron. 75g+35g, Dog-rose. 80g+40g, Cyclamen. 1s+50g, Alpine Gentian. 1.40s+70g, Edelweiss.

1948, May 14   **Engr. & Typo.**

B235	SP155	10g + 5g multi	.35	.25
B236	SP155	20g + 10g multi	.15	.20
B237	SP155	30g + 10g multi	2.50	2.00
B238	SP155	40g + 20g multi	.50	.25
B239	SP155	45g + 20g multi	.15	.20
B240	SP155	60g + 30g multi	.15	.20
B241	SP155	75g + 35g multi	.15	.20
B242	SP155	80g + 40g multi	.30	.20
B243	SP155	1s + 50g multi	.40	.30
B244	SP155	1.40s + 70g multi	.65	.55
		Nos. B235-B244 (10)	5.30	4.35

1948, June 15   **Unwmk.**   **Engr.**

Designs: 20g+10g, Künstlerhaus, Vienna. 40g+20g, Carl Kundmann. 50g+25g, A. S. von Sic-cardsburg. 60g+30g, Hans Cannon. 1s+50g, William Unger. 1.40s+70g, Friedrich von Schmidt.

B245	SP156	20g + 10g dp yel green	6.25	5.00
B246	SP156	30g + 15g dark brown	3.00	1.90
B247	SP156	40g + 20g indigo	3.00	1.90
B248	SP156	50g + 25g dk vio	3.50	2.75
B249	SP156	60g + 30g dk red	3.50	2.75
B250	SP156	1s + 50g dk blue	6.25	5.00
B251	SP156	1.40s + 70g red brown	8.50	7.50
		Nos. B245-B251 (7)	34.00	26.80

Kunstlerhaus, home of the leading Austrian Art-ists Association, 80th anniv.

St. Rupert — SP157

Easter — SP158

Designs: 30g+15g, Cathedral and Fountain. 40g+20g, Facade of Cathedral. 50g+25g, Cathedral from South. 60g+30g, Abbey of St. Peter. 80g+40g, Inside Cathedral. 1s+50g, Salzburg Cathedral and Castle. 1.40s+70g, Madonna by Michael Pacher.

1948, Aug. 6   **Perf. 14x13½**

B252	SP157	20g + 10g dp grn	6.00	5.50
B253	SP157	30g + 15g red brn	2.50	2.50
B254	SP157	40g + 20g sl blk	1.90	1.75
B255	SP157	50g + 25g choc	.40	.40
B256	SP157	60g + 30g dk red	.40	.40
B257	SP157	80g + 40g dk brn vio	.40	.40
B258	SP157	1s + 50g dp blue	.75	.50
B259	SP157	1.40s + 70g dk grn	1.50	1.25
		Nos. B252-B259 (8)	13.85	12.70

The surtax was to aid in the reconstruction of Salzburg Cathedral.

1949, Apr. 13   **Unwmk.**

Designs: 60g+20g, St. Nicholas Day. 1s+25g, Birthday. 1.40s+35g, Christmas.

Inscribed: "Gluckliche Kindheit"

B260	SP158	40g + 10g brn vio	17.00	12.50
B261	SP158	60g + 20g brn red	17.00	12.50
B262	SP158	1s + 25g dp ultra	17.00	12.50
B263	SP158	1.40s + 35g dk grn	17.00	12.50
		Nos. B260-B263 (4)	68.00	50.00

The surtax was for Child Welfare.

Arms of Austria, 1230 — SP159

SP160

1949, Aug. 17   **Engr. & Photo.**

B264	SP159	40g + 10g 1230	7.00	6.00

Engraved and Typographed

B265	SP159	60g + 15g 1450	7.00	6.00
B266	SP159	1s + 25g 1600	7.00	6.00
B267	SP159	1.60s + 40g 1945	7.00	6.00
		Nos. B264-B267 (4)	28.00	24.00

Surtax was for returned prisoners of war.

1949, Dec. 3   **Engr.**

Laurel Branch, Stamps and Magnifier
B268	SP160	60g + 15g dark red	2.25	1.50

Stamp Day, Dec. 3-4.

Arms of Austria and Carinthia — SP161

Carinthian with Austrian Flag — SP162

Design: 1.70s+40g, Casting ballot.

1950, Oct. 10   **Photo.**   **Perf. 14x13½**

B269	SP161	60g + 15g	26.00	18.00
B270	SP162	1s + 25g	35.00	20.00
B271	SP162	1.70s + 40g	40.00	30.00
		Nos. B269-B271 (3)	101.00	68.00

Plebiscite in Carinthia, 30th anniv.

Collector Examining Cover — SP163

Miner and Mine — SP164

1950, Dec. 2   **Engr.**

B272	SP163	60g + 15g blue grn	8.50	6.00

Stamp Day.

1951, Mar. 10   **Unwmk.**

Designs: 60g+15g, Mason holding brick and trowel. 1s+25g, Bridge builder with hook and chain. 1.70s+40g, Electrician, pole and insulators.

B273	SP164	40g + 10g dark brown	13.00	11.00
B274	SP164	60g + 15g dk grn	13.00	11.00
B275	SP164	1s + 25g red brown	13.00	11.00
B276	SP164	1.70s + 40g vio bl	13.00	11.00
		Nos. B273-B276 (4)	52.00	44.00

Issued to publicize Austrian reconstruction.

Laurel Branch and Olympic Circles SP165

1952, Jan. 26   **Perf. 13½x14**

B277	SP165	2.40s + 60g grnsh black	15.00	13.00

The surtax was used to help defray expenses of Austria's athletes in the 1952 Olympic Games.

Cupid as Postman — SP166

1952, Mar. 10   **Perf. 14x13½**

B278	SP166	1.50s + 35g dark brn car	17.50	16.00

Stamp Day.

Sculpture, "Christ, The Almighty" SP167

1952, Sept. 6   **Perf. 13½x14**

B279	SP167	1s + 25g grnsh gray	11.00	9.00

Austrian Catholic Conv., Vienna, Sept. 11-14.

Type of 1945-46 Overprinted in Gold

1953, Aug. 29   **Unwmk.**

B280	A124	1s + 25g on 5s dl bl	2.50	2.00

60th anniv. of labor unions in Austria.

Bummerlhaus Steyr SP168

Globe and Philatelic Accessories SP169

Designs: 1s+25g, Johannes Kepler. 1.50s+40g, Lutheran Bible, 1st edition. 2.40s+60g, Theophil von Hansen. 3s+75g, Reconstructed Lutheran School, Vienna.

1953, Nov. 5   **Engr.**   **Perf. 14x13½**

B281	SP168	70g + 15g vio brn	.30	.30
B282	SP168	1s + 25g dk gray blue	.30	.30
B283	SP168	1.50s + 40g choc	.90	.90
B284	SP168	2.40s + 60g dk grn	2.50	2.25
B285	SP168	3s + 75g dk pur	6.00	5.75
		Nos. B281-B285 (5)	10.00	9.50

The surtax was used toward reconstruction of the Lutheran School, Vienna.

1953, Dec. 5

B286	SP169	1s + 25g choc	5.00	3.75

Stamp Day.

Type of 1945-46 with Denomination Replaced by Asterisks

Overprinted in Brown

1954, Feb. 19   **Perf. 13½x14**

B287	A124	1s + 20g blue gray	.15	.15

Surtax for aid to avalanche victims.

Patient Under Sun Lamp — SP170

Designs: 70g+15g, Physician using microscope. 1s+25g, Mother and children. 1.45s+35g, Operating room. 1.50s+35g, Baby on scale. 2.40s+60g, Nurse.

1954   **Engr.**   **Perf. 14x13½**

B288	SP170	30g + 10g purple	1.50	1.10
B289	SP170	70g + 15g dk brn	.25	.25
B290	SP170	1s + 25g dk bl	.30	.25

B291	SP170	1.45s + 35g dk bl green	.45	.40
B292	SP170	1.50s + 35g dk red	5.00	4.50
B293	SP170	2.40s + 60g dk red brown	6.00	5.50
		Nos. B288-B293 (6)	13.50	12.00

The surtax was for social welfare.

Early Vienna-Ulm Ferryboat SP171

1954, Dec. 4   **Perf. 13½x14**

B294	SP171	1s + 25g dk gray grn	4.50	4.00

Stamp Day.

"Industry" Welcoming Returned Prisoner of War — SP172

1955, June 29

B295	SP172	1s + 25g red brn	2.00	1.50

Surtax for returned prisoners of war and relatives of prisoners not yet released.

Collector Looking at Album — SP173

Ornamental Shield and Letter — SP174

1955, Dec. 3   **Perf. 14x13½**

B296	SP173	1s + 25g vio brn	3.00	2.75

Stamp Day. The surtax was for the promotion of Austrian philately.

1956, Dec. 1   **Engr.**

B297	SP174	1s + 25g scarlet	2.75	2.50

Stamp Day. See note after No. B296.

Arms of Austria, 1945 — SP175

Perf. 14x13½

1956, Dec. 21   **Engr. & Typo.**

B298	SP175	1.50s + 50g on 1.60s + 40g gray & red	.25	.20

The surtax was for Hungarian refugees.

New Post Office, Linz 2 — SP176

Design: 2.40s+60g, Post office, Kitzbuhel.

1957-58   **Engr.**   **Perf. 13½x14**

B299	SP176	1s + 25g dk sl grn	2.75	2.50
B300	SP176	2.40s + 60g blue	.65	.60

Stamp Day. See note after B296. Issue dates: 1s, Nov. 30, 1957. 2.40s, Dec. 6, 1957. See No. B303.

Roman Carriage from Tomb at Maria Saal — SP177

Perf. 13¹/₂x14
1959, Dec. 5   Litho. & Engr.
B301 SP177 2.40s + 60g pale lil & blk   .55 .50
Stamp Day.

Progressive Die Proof under Magnifying Glass — SP178

1960, Dec. 2   Engr.   Perf. 13¹/₂x14
B302 SP178 3s + 70g vio brn   .85 .70
Stamp Day.

Post Office Type of 1957
Design: 3s+70g, Post Office, Rust.

1961, Dec. 1   Unwmk.   Perf. 13¹/₂
B303 SP176 3s + 70g dk bl grn   .90 .70
Stamp Day. See note after No. B296.

Hands of Stamp Engraver at Work — SP179

1962, Nov. 30   Perf. 13¹/₂x14
B304 SP179 3s + 70g dull pur   1.25 .90
Stamp Day.

Railroad Exit, Post Office Vienna 101 — SP180

1963, Nov. 29   Litho. & Engr.
B305 SP180 3s + 70g tan & blk   .80 .80
Stamp Day.

View of Vienna, North SP181

Designs: Various view of Vienna with compass indicating direction.

1964, July 20   Litho.   Perf. 13¹/₂x14
B306 SP181 1.50s + 30g ("N")   .20 .15
B307 SP181 1.50s + 30g ("NO")   .20 .15
B308 SP181 1.50s + 30g ("O")   .20 .15
B309 SP181 1.50s + 30g ("SO")   .20 .15
B310 SP181 1.50s + 30g ("S")   .20 .15
B311 SP181 1.50s + 30g ("SW")   .20 .15
B312 SP181 1.50s + 30g ("W")   .20 .15
B313 SP181 1.50s + 30g ("NW")   .20 .15
     Nos. B306-B313 (8)   1.60 1.20
Vienna Intl. Phil. Exhib. (WIPA 1965).

Post Bus Terminal, St. Gilgen, Wolfgangsee SP182

1964, Dec. 4   Unwmk.   Perf. 13¹/₂
B314 SP182 3s + 70g multi   .45 .45
Stamp Day.

Wall Painting, Tomb at Thebes — SP183

Development of Writing: 1.80s+50g, Cuneiform writing on stone tablet and man's head from Assyrian palace. 2.20s+60g, Wax tablet with Latin writing, Corinthian column. 3s+80g, Gothic writing on sealed letter, Gothic window from Munster Cathedral. 4s+1s, Letter with seal and postmark and upright desk. 5s+1.20s, Typewriter.

Perf. 14x13¹/₂
1965, June 4   Litho. & Engr.
B315 SP183 1.50s + 40g multi   .15 .15
B316 SP183 1.80s + 50g multi   .15 .15
B317 SP183 2.20s + 60g multi   .35 .35
B318 SP183 3s + 80g multi   .20 .20
B319 SP183 4s + 1s multi   .45 .45
B320 SP183 5s + 1.20s multi   .60 .60
     Nos. B315-B320 (6)   1.90 1.90
Vienna Intl. Phil. Exhib., WIPA, June 4-13.

Mailman Distributing Mail — SP184

1965, Dec. 3   Engr.   Perf. 13¹/₂x14
B321 SP184 3s + 70g blue grn   .40 .35
Stamp Day.

Letter Carrier, 16th Century SP185

Letter Carrier, 16th Century Playing Card SP186

Litho. & Engr.
1966, Dec. 2   Perf. 13¹/₂
B322 SP185 3s + 70g multi   .40 .35
Stamp Day. Design is from Ambras Heroes' Book, Austrian National Library.

Engr. & Photo.
1967, Dec. 1   Perf. 13x13¹/₂
B323 SP186 3.50s + 80g multi   .40 .35
Stamp Day.

Mercury, Basrelief from Purkersdorf SP187

Unken Post Station Sign, 1710 SP188

1968, Nov. 29   Engr.   Perf. 13¹/₂
B324 SP187 3.50s + 80g slate green   .40 .35
Stamp Day.

Engr. & Photo.
1969, Dec. 5   Perf. 12
B325 SP188 3.50s + 80g tan, red & blk .40 .35
Stamp Day. Design is from a watercolor by Friedrich Zeller.

Saddle, Bag, Harness and Post Horn — SP189

Perf. 13¹/₂x14
1970, Dec. 4   Engr. & Litho.
B326 SP189 3.50s + 80g gray blk & yel .40 .35
Stamp Day.

"50 Years" SP190

Engr. & Photo.
1971, Dec. 3   Perf. 13¹/₂
B327 SP190 4s + 1.50s gold & red brn .60 .45
50th anniversary of the Federation of Austrian Philatelic Societies.

Local Post Carrier — SP191

Gabriel, by Lorenz Luchsperger, 15th Century — SP192

1972, Dec. 1   Engr.   Perf. 14x13¹/₂
B328 SP191 4s + 1s olive green   .60 .45
Stamp Day.

1973, Nov. 30
B329 SP192 4s + 1s maroon   .60 .45
Stamp Day.

Mail Coach Leaving Old PTT Building — SP193

1974, Nov. 29   Engr.   Perf. 14x13¹/₂
B330 SP193 4s + 2s violet blue   .70 .70
Stamp Day.

Alpine Skiing, Women's SP194

Designs: 1.50s+70g, Ice hockey. 2s+90g, Ski jump. 4s+1.90s, Bobsledding.

1975, Mar. 14   Photo.   Perf. 13¹/₂x14
B331 SP194 1s + 50g multi   .25 .25
B332 SP194 1.50s + 70g multi   .30 .30
B333 SP194 2s + 90g multi   .35 .35
B334 SP194 4s + 1.90s multi   .70 .70
     Nos. B331-B334 (4)   1.60 1.60

1975, Nov. 14
Designs: 70g+30g, Figure skating, pair. 2s+1s, Cross-country skiing. 2.50s+1s, Luge. 4s+2s, Biathlon.

B335 SP194   70g + 30g multi   .15 .15
B336 SP194   2s + 1s multi   .30 .30
B337 SP194   2.50s + 1s multi   .40 .40
B338 SP194   4s + 2s multi   .70 .70
     Nos. B335-B338 (4)   1.55 1.55
12th Winter Olympic Games, Innsbruck, Feb. 4-15, 1976.

Austria Nos. 5, 250, 455 — SP195

Photo. & Engr.
1975, Nov. 28   Perf. 14
B339 SP195 4s + 2s multi   .65 .65
Stamp Day; 125th anniv. of Austrian stamps.

Postilion's Gala Hat and Horn — SP196

1976, Dec. 3   Perf. 13¹/₂x14
B340 SP196 6s + 2s blk & lt vio   .80 .80
Stamp Day.

Emanuel Herrmann — SP197

1977, Dec. 2   Perf. 14x13¹/₂
B341 SP197 6s + 2s multi   .80 .80
Stamp Day. Emanuel Herrmann (1839-1902), economist, invented postal card. Austria issued first postal card in 1869.

Post Bus, 1913 — SP198

1978, Dec. 1   Photo.   Perf. 13¹/₂x14
B342 SP198 10s + 5s multi   1.40 1.40
Stamp Day.

Heroes' Square, Vienna SP199

Photo. & Engr.
1979, Nov. 30   Perf. 13¹/₂
B343 SP199 16s + 8s multi   2.75 2.50

No. B343 Inscribed "2. Phase"
1980, Nov. 21
B344 SP199 16s + 8s multi   2.75 2.50

Souvenir Sheet
1981, Feb. 20
B345 SP199 16s + 8s multi   3.00 2.50
WIPA 1981 Phil. Exhib., Vienna, May 22-31. No. B345 contains one stamp without inscription.

Mainz-Weber Mailbox, 1870 — SP200

1982, Nov. 26　　　　Photo. & Engr.
B346 SP200 6s + 3s multi　　　　1.00 1.00
Stamp Day.

Boy Examining
Cover — SP201

Photo. & Engr.
1983, Oct. 21　　　　　　　*Perf. 14*
B347 SP201 6s + 3s multi　　　　1.10 1.10
Stamp Day. See Nos. B349-B352, B354-B355.

World Winter
Games for the
Handicapped
— SP202

1984, Jan. 5　Photo.　*Perf. 13½x13*
B348 SP202 4s + 2s Downhill skier　.75 .75

Stamp Day Type of 1983

Designs: No. B349, Seschemnofer III burial chamber detail, pyramid of Cheops, Gizeh. No. B350, Roman messenger on horseback. No. B351, Nuremberg messenger, 16th cent. No. B352, *The Postmaster* (detail), 1841, lithograph by Carl Schuster.

1984-87　　Photo. & Engr.　*Perf. 14*
B349 SP201 6s + 3s multi　　　　1.25 1.25
B350 SP201 6s + 3s multi　　　　1.25 1.25
B351 SP201 6s + 3s multi　　　　1.25 1.25
B352 SP201 6s + 3s multi　　　　1.40 1.40
　　　Nos. B349-B352 (4)　　　5.15 5.15

Issue: #B349, 11/30/84; #B350, 11/28/85; #B351, 11/28/86; #B352, 11/19/87.

4th World Winter Sports Championships
for the Disabled, Innsbruck — SP203

1988, Jan. 15　Photo.　*Perf. 13½*
B353 SP203 5s + 2.50s multi　　1.10 1.10

Stamp Day Type of 1983

Designs: No. B354, Railway mail car. No. B355, Hansa-Brandenburg CI mail plane.

1988-89　　Photo. & Engr.　*Perf. 14*
B354 SP201 6s + 3s multi　　　　1.40 1.40
B355 SP201 6s + 3s multi　　　　1.40 1.40
Issued: #B354, Nov. 17; #B355, May 24, 1989.

Stamp
Day — SP204

1990, May 25　Photo.　*Perf. 13½*
B356 SP204 7s + 3s multi　　　1.65 1.65

SP205　　　　　　　　Stamp
　　　　　　　　　　Day — SP205a

1991, May 29　　　　Photo. & Engr.
B357 SP205　7s +3s "B" and "P"　1.75 1.75
1992, May 22
B358 SP205　7s +3s "R" and
　　　　　　　　"H"　　　　1.65 1.65
1993, May 5
B359 SP205　7s +3s "I" and "I"　1.75 1.75
1994, May 27
B360 SP205　7s +3s "E" and "L"　1.65 1.65
1995, May 26
B361 SP205a 10s +5s "F" & "A"　3.00 3.00
1996, May 17
B362 SP205a 10s +5s "M" & "T"　3.00 3.00
　　　Nos. B357-B362 (6)　　12.80 12.80

The first letters will spell "Briefmarke," the second "Philatelie."
The 1997 stamp with letters "A" and "E" is No. 1725.

Special
Olympics
Winter Games
SP206

1993, Mar. 19　Photo.　*Perf. 13½x14*
B367 SP206 6s +3s multi　　　1.65 1.65

WIPA
2000
SP207

Design: #5, postman on bicycle.

Photo. & Engr.
1997, May 23　　　　　　*Perf. 14*
B368 SP207 27s +13s multi　　6.75 6.75

AIR POST STAMPS

Issues of the Monarchy

FLUGPOST

Types of Regular
Issue of 1916
Surcharged

2·50 K 2·50

1918, Mar. 30　Unwmk.　*Perf. 12½*
C1　A40 1.50k on 2k lilac　　2.25 3.00
C2　A40 2.50k on 3k ocher　　8.00 16.00
　a.　Inverted surcharge　　　　　1,250.
　b.　Perf. 11½　　　　　　325.00 240.00
　c.　Perf. 12½x11½　　　　27.50 37.50

Overprinted **FLUGPOST**

C3　A40 4k gray　　　　　5.00 10.00
　Set, never hinged　　　　　　30.00

Set exists imperf. Value, $325.
Nos. C1-C3 also exist without surcharge or overprint. Value, set perf., $625; imperf., $625.
Nos. C1-C3 were printed on grayish and on white paper.
A 7k on 10k red brown was prepared but not regularly issued. Value, perf. or imperf., $400.

Issues of the Republic

Hawk — AP1　　　　Wilhelm
　　　　　　　　Kress — AP2

1922-24　　Typo.　　*Perf. 12½*
C4　AP1　300k claret　　　　.35 1.25
C5　AP1　400k green ('24)　4.50 12.50
C6　AP1　600k bister　　　　.15 .55
C7　AP1　900k brn orange　　.15 .55
　　　　　　Engr.
C8　AP2 1200k brn violet　　.15 .55
C9　AP2 2400k slate　　　　.15 .55
C10 AP2 3000k dp brn ('23)　1.75 3.50
C11 AP2 4800k dark bl ('23)　2.25 3.75
　　Nos. C4-C11 (8)　　　9.45 23.20
　Set, never hinged　　　　20.00

Set exists imperf. Value, $300.

Plane and Pilot's　　Airplane
Head — AP3　　　　Passing
　　　　　　　　Crane — AP4

1925-30　　Typo.　　*Perf. 12½*
C12 AP3　2g gray brown　　.40 1.00
C13 AP3　5g red　　　　　.25 .25
　a.　Horiz. pair, imperf. btwn.　205.00
C14 AP3　6g dark blue　　.90 1.50
C15 AP3　8g yel green　　1.00 1.75
C16 AP3 10g dp org ('26)　1.00 1.75
　a.　Horiz. pair, imperf. btwn.　275.00
C17 AP3 15g red vio ('26)　.40 .90
　a.　Horiz. pair, imperf. btwn.　275.00
C18 AP3 20g org brn ('30)　10.00 4.25
C19 AP3 25g blk vio ('30)　2.25 6.50
C20 AP3 30g bister ('26)　6.50 6.50
C21 AP3 50g bl gray ('30)　12.50 10.00
C22 AP3 80g dk grn ('30)　1.25 4.50
　　　　　　Photo.
C23 AP4 10g orange red　.90 2.75
　a.　Horiz. pair, imperf. btwn.　275.00
C24 AP4 15g claret　　　.60 1.50
C25 AP4 30g brn violet　.80 2.75
C26 AP4 50g gray black　.75 2.75
C27 AP4　1s deep blue　1.75 4.00
C28 AP4　2s dark green　1.50 4.00
　a.　Vertical pair, imperf. btwn.　275.00
C29 AP4　3s red brn ('26)　40.00 37.50
C30 AP4　5s indigo ('26)　12.50 22.50

　　　　Size: 25½x32mm

C31 AP4 10s blk brown, *gray*
　　　　　　('26)　　　10.00 17.50
　　Nos. C12-C31 (20)　105.25 134.15
　Set, never hinged　　　225.00

Exists imperf. Value, set $900.

Airplane over　　Airplane over the
Güssing　　　　Danube — AP6
Castle — AP5

Designs (each includes plane): 10g, Maria-Worth. 15g, Durnstein. 20g, Hallstatt. 25g, Salzburg. 30g, Upper Dachstein and Schladminger Glacier. 40g, Lake Wetter. 50g, Arlberg. 60g, St. Stephen's Cathedral. 80g, Church of the Minorites. 2s, Railroad viaduct, Carinthia. 3s, Gross Glockner mountain. 5s, Aerial railway. 10s, Seaplane and yachts.

1935, Aug. 16　　Engr.　　*Perf. 12½*
C32 AP5　5g rose violet　　.15 .15
C33 AP5 10g red orange　　.15 .15
C34 AP5 15g yel green　　.55 .30
C35 AP5 20g gray blue　　.15 .20
C36 AP5 25g violet brn　　.15 .20
C37 AP5 30g brn orange　　.15 .25
C38 AP5 40g gray green　　.15 .25
C39 AP5 50g light sl bl　　.15 .25
C40 AP5 60g black brn　　.30 .40
C41 AP5 80g light brown　.30 .40
C42 AP6　1s rose red　　.30 .55
C43 AP6　2s olive green　1.75 4.00
C44 AP6　3s yellow brn　7.50 12.50

C45 AP6　5s dark green　　5.00 12.50
C46 AP6 10s slate blue　37.50 75.00
　　Nos. C32-C46 (15)　54.25 107.10
　Set, never hinged　　　90.00

Set exists imperf. Value, $275.

> **Catalogue values for unused stamps in this section, from this point to the end of the section, are for Never Hinged items.**

Windmill, Neusiedler
Lake Shore — AP20

Designs: 1s, Roman arch, Carnuntum. 2s, Town Hall, Gmund. 3s, Schieder Lake, Hinterstoder. 4s, Praegraten, Eastern Tyrol. 5s, Torsäule, Salzburg. 10s, St. Charles Church, Vienna.

1947　Unwmk.　　*Perf. 14x13½*
C47 AP20 50g black brown　　.15 .20
C48 AP20　1s dark brn vio　　.30 .25
C49 AP20　2s dark green　　.35 .40
C50 AP20　3s chocolate　　2.25 2.75
C51 AP20　4s dark green　　1.40 2.00
C52 AP20　5s dark blue　　1.40 2.00
C53 AP20 10s dark blue　　.75 1.50
　　Nos. C47-C53 (7)　　6.60 9.10

Rooks — AP27

Birds: 1s, Barn swallows. 2s, Blackheaded gulls. 3s, Great cormorants. 5s, Buzzard. 10s, Gray heron. 20s, Golden eagle.

1950-53　　　　　　*Perf. 13½x14*
C54 AP27 60g dark bl vio　　2.50 1.10
C55 AP27　1s dark vio blue
　　　　　　('53)　　　17.50 15.00
C56 AP27　2s dark blue　　15.00 6.00
C57 AP27　3s dk slate green
　　　　　　('53)　　　100.00 65.00
C58 AP27　5s red brn ('53)　100.00 65.00
C59 AP27 10s gray vio ('53)　45.00 30.00
C60 AP27 20s brn blk ('53)　10.00 4.00
　　Nos. C54-C60 (7)　290.00 186.10
　Set, hinged　　　　180.00

Value at lower left on Nos. C59 and C60. No. C60 exists imperf.

Etrich "Dove"
AP28

Designs: 3.50s, Twin-engine jet airliner. 5s, Four-engine jet airliner.

1968, May 31　Engr.　*Perf. 13½x14*
C61 AP28　2s olive bister　　.30 .25
C62 AP28 3.50s slate green　.50 .40
C63 AP28　5s dark blue　　.75 .60
　　Nos. C61-C63 (3)　　1.55 1.25

IFA WIEN 1968 (International Air Post Exhibition), Vienna, May 30-June 4.

POSTAGE DUE STAMPS

Issues of the Monarchy

D1　　　　　　　　D2

Perf. 10 to 13½

1894-95	Typo.		Wmk. 91	
J1	D1	1kr brown	1.75	1.40
a.		Perf. 13½	25.00	30.00
J2	D1	2kr brown ('95)	3.75	2.00
a.		Pair, imperf. btwn.	175.00	200.00
J3	D1	3kr brown	3.00	1.00
J4	D1	5kr brown	2.75	1.50
a.		Perf. 13½	16.00	15.00
b.		Pair, imperf. btwn.	160.00	175.00
J5	D1	6kr brown ('95)	2.75	5.00
J6	D1	7kr brown ('95)	.80	4.00
a.		Vert. pair, imperf. btwn.	250.00	300.00
b.		Horiz. pair, imperf. btwn.	275.00	
J7	D1	10kr brown	4.50	.50
J8	D1	20kr brown	.80	4.50
J9	D1	50kr brown	35.00	55.00
		Nos. J1-J9 (9)	55.10	74.90

See Nos. J204-J231.

1899-1900			Imperf.	
J10	D2	1h brown	.20	.40
J11	D2	2h brown	.25	.15
J12	D2	3h brown ('00)	.20	.40
J13	D2	4h brown	2.00	1.50
J14	D2	5h brown ('00)	3.00	1.25
J15	D2	6h brown	.30	.95
J16	D2	10h brown	.25	.40
J17	D2	12h brown	.40	1.75
J18	D2	15h brown	.40	.90
J19	D2	20h brown	18.50	3.00
J20	D2	40h brown	.80	2.50
J21	D2	100h brown	4.25	2.50
		Nos. J10-J21 (12)	30.55	16.10

Perf. 10½, 12½, 13½ and Compound

J22	D2	1h brown	.55	.20
J23	D2	2h brown	.45	.20
J24	D2	3h brown ('00)	.40	.15
J25	D2	4h brown	.40	.15
J26	D2	5h brown ('00)	.40	.15
J27	D2	6h brown	.40	.15
J28	D2	10h brown	.45	.15
J29	D2	12h brown	.45	.60
J30	D2	15h brown	.70	.80
J31	D2	20h brown	.55	.30
J32	D2	40h brown	1.00	.75
J33	D2	100h brown	22.50	4.00
		Nos. J22-J33 (12)	28.25	4.00

Nos. J10-J33 exist on unwmkd. paper.
For surcharges see Offices in the Turkish Empire Nos. J1-J5.

D3

1908-13		Unwmk.	Perf. 12½	
J34	D3	1h carmine	1.10	.65
J35	D3	2h carmine	.35	.25
J36	D3	4h carmine	.35	.15
J37	D3	6h carmine	.35	.15
J38	D3	10h carmine	.35	.15
J39	D3	14h carmine ('13)	3.75	.75
J40	D3	20h carmine	5.25	.15
J41	D3	25h carmine ('10)	9.50	1.25
J42	D3	30h carmine	5.50	.15
J43	D3	50h carmine	7.50	.15
J44	D3	100h carmine	15.00	.20
		Nos. J34-J44 (11)	49.00	3.60

All values exist on ordinary paper, #J34-J38, J40, J42-J44 on chalky paper and #J34-J38, J40, J44 on thin ordinary paper. Thin paper copies sell for 5-10 times the listed values. All values exist imperf.
See Offices in the Turkish Empire type D3.

1911, July 16

J45	D3	5k violet	40.00	6.00
J46	D3	10k violet	200.00	3.00

Regular Issue of 1908 Overprinted or Surcharged in Carmine or Black:

a   b

1916, Oct. 21

J47	A22	1h gray (C)	.15	.15
a.		Pair, one without overprint	125.00	
J48	A22	15h on 2h vio (Bk)	.20	.25
		Set value	.30	.35
		Set, never hinged	.90	

D4   D5

1916, Oct. 1

J49	D4	5h rose red	.15	.15
J50	D4	10h rose red	.15	.15
J51	D4	15h rose red	.15	.15
J52	D4	20h rose red	.15	.15
J53	D4	25h rose red	.35	.25
J54	D4	30h rose red	.15	.15
J55	D4	40h rose red	.20	.15
J56	D4	50h rose red	.90	.90
J57	D5	1k ultramarine	.30	.15
a.		Horiz. pair, imperf. btwn.	350.00	350.00
J58	D5	5k ultramarine	1.25	1.40
J59	D5	10k ultramarine	1.25	.90
		Nos. J49-J59 (11)	5.00	4.50
		Set, never hinged	16.00	

Exists imperf. Value, set $80.
For overprints see Western Ukraine Nos. 54-55, NJ1-NJ6, Poland Nos. J1-J10.

PORTO

Type of Regular Issue of 1916 Surcharged

15   ✱   15

1917

J60	A38	10h on 24h blue	1.25	.20
J61	A38	15h on 36h violet	.20	.15
J62	A38	20h on 54h orange	.20	.20
J63	A38	50h on 42h chocolate	.20	.15
		Nos. J60-J63 (4)	1.85	.70
		Set, never hinged	5.00	

All values of this issue are known imperforate, also without surcharge, perforated and imperforate.
For overprints see Western Ukraine Nos. 57-58.

Issues of the Republic

Postage Due Stamps of 1916 Overprinted

Deutschösterreich

1919

J64	D4	5h rose red	.15	.15
a.		Inverted overprint	200.00	225.00
J65	D4	10h rose red	.15	.15
J66	D4	15h rose red	.15	.30
J67	D4	20h rose red	.20	.20
J68	D4	25h rose red	4.75	12.00
J69	D4	30h rose red	.15	.15
J70	D4	40h rose red	.15	.25
J71	D4	50h rose red	.30	.80
J72	D5	1k ultramarine	8.00	7.00
J73	D5	5k ultramarine	9.00	8.00
J74	D5	10k ultramarine	8.00	3.00
		Nos. J64-J74 (11)	31.00	32.00
		Set, never hinged	70.00	

Nos. J64, J65, J67 and J70 exist imperforate.

D6   D7

1920-21			Perf. 12½	
J75	D6	5h bright red	.15	.15
J76	D6	10h bright red	.15	.15
J77	D6	15h bright red	.15	.30
J78	D6	20h bright red	.15	.15
J79	D6	25h bright red	.15	.30
J80	D6	30h bright red	.15	.15
J81	D6	40h bright red	.15	.15
J82	D6	50h bright red	.15	.15
J83	D6	80h bright red	.15	.15
J84	D7	1k ultramarine	.15	.15
J85	D7	1½k ultra ('21)	.15	.15
J86	D7	2k ultra ('21)	.15	.15

J87	D7	3k ultra ('21)	.15	.15
J88	D7	4k ultra ('21)	.15	.15
J89	D7	5k ultramarine	.15	.15
J90	D7	8k ultramarine	.15	.15
J91	D7	10k ultramarine	.15	.15
J92	D7	20k ultramarine	.15	.35
		Set value	.95	2.00
		Set, never hinged	3.00	

Nos. J84 to J92 exist on white paper and on grayish white paper. They also exist imperf.; value, set $65.

Imperf

J93	D6	5h bright red	.15	.15
J94	D6	10h bright red	.15	.15
J95	D6	15h bright red	.15	.25
J96	D6	20h bright red	.15	.15
J97	D6	25h bright red	.15	.30
J98	D6	30h bright red	.15	.15
J99	D6	40h bright red	.15	.15
J100	D6	50h bright red	.15	.20
J101	D6	80h bright red	.15	.15
		Set value	.50	.15
		Set, never hinged	1.25	

Nachmarke

No. 207a Surcharged in Dark Blue

7½ K

1921, Dec.			**Perf. 12½**
J102	A43	7½k on 15h bister	.15	.20
		Never hinged	.15	
a.		Inverted surcharge	185.00	185.00

D8   D9

1922

J103	D8	1k reddish buff	.15	.15
J104	D8	2k reddish buff	.15	.15
J105	D8	4k reddish buff	.15	.15
J106	D8	5k reddish buff	.15	.15
J107	D8	7½k reddish buff	.15	.15
J108	D8	10k blue green	.15	.15
J109	D8	15k blue green	.15	.15
J110	D8	20k blue green	.15	.15
J111	D8	25k blue green	.15	.15
J112	D8	40k blue green	.15	.15
J113	D8	50k blue green	.15	.15
		Set value	.60	1.50
		Set, never hinged	1.00	

Issue date: Nos. J108-J113, June 2.

1922-24

J114	D9	10k cobalt blue	.15	.15
J115	D9	15k cobalt blue	.15	.15
J116	D9	20k cobalt blue	.15	.15
J117	D9	50k cobalt blue	.15	.20
J118	D10	100k plum	.15	.15
J119	D10	150k plum	.15	.15
J120	D10	200k plum	.15	.15
J121	D10	400k plum	.15	.15
J122	D10	600k plum ('23)	.15	.15
J123	D10	800k plum	.15	.15
J124	D10	1,000k plum ('23)	.15	.15
J125	D10	1,200k plum ('23)	.50	1.50
J126	D10	1,500k plum ('24)	.15	.15
J127	D10	1,800k plum ('24)	1.50	4.25
J128	D10	2,000k plum ('23)	.20	.50
J129	D10	3,000k plum ('24)	5.75	7.50
J130	D10	4,000k plum ('24)	3.75	9.75
J131	D10	6,000k plum ('24)	3.75	15.00
		Nos. J114-J131 (18)	17.25	40.35
		Set, never hinged	40.00	
		Value, Nos. J103-J131 imperf, $200.		

D11   D12

1925-34			**Perf. 12½**
J132	D11	1g red	.15	.15
J133	D11	2g red	.15	.15
J134	D11	3g red	.15	.15
J135	D11	4g red	.15	.15

J136	D11	5g red ('27)	.15	.15
J137	D11	6g red	.15	.30
J138	D11	8g red	.15	.15
J139	D11	10g dark blue	.15	.15
J140	D11	12g dark blue	.15	.15
J141	D11	14g dark blue ('27)	.15	.15
J142	D11	15g dark blue	.25	.15
J143	D11	16g dark blue ('29)	.25	.15
J144	D11	18g dark blue ('34)	.90	3.00
J145	D11	20g dark blue	.15	.15
J146	D11	23g dark blue	.55	.15
J147	D11	24g dark blue ('32)	.80	.15
J148	D11	28g dark blue ('27)	.35	.30
J149	D11	30g dark blue	.15	.15
J150	D11	31g dark blue ('29)	.70	.15
J151	D11	35g dark blue ('30)	.45	.15
J152	D11	39g dark blue ('32)	.75	.15
J153	D11	40g dark blue	.75	1.50
J154	D11	60g dark blue	.55	.85
J155	D12	1s dark green	6.00	.85
J156	D12	2s dark green	30.00	3.00
J157	D12	5s dark green	75.00	24.00
J158	D12	10s dark green	50.00	3.50
		Nos. J132-J158 (27)	169.00	40.00
		Set, never hinged	300.00	

Issues of 1925-27 (21 values) imperf, value, set $400.

Issue dates: 3g, 2s-10s, Dec. 5g, 28g, Jan. 1. 14g, June. 31g, Feb. 1. 35g, Jan. 24g, 39g, Sept. 16g, May. 18g, June 25. Others, June 1.

Coat of Arms

D13   D14

1935, June 1

J159	D13	1g red	.15	.15
J160	D13	2g red	.15	.15
J161	D13	5g red	.15	.15
J162	D13	5g red	.15	.15
J163	D13	10g blue	.15	.15
J164	D13	12g blue	.15	.15
J165	D13	15g blue	.15	.40
J166	D13	20g blue	.15	.15
J167	D13	24g blue	.15	.15
J168	D13	30g blue	.15	.15
J169	D13	39g blue	.20	.15
J170	D13	60g blue	.40	1.10
J171	D14	1s green	.65	.40
J172	D14	2s green	1.00	.50
J173	D14	5s green	2.50	1.10
J174	D14	10s green	3.75	.60
		Nos. J159-J174 (16)	10.00	
		Set value		5.00
		Set, never hinged	40.00	

On #J163-J170, background lines are horiz.
Nos. J159-J174 exist imperf. Value, set $125.

Catalogue values for unused stamps in this section, from this point to the end of the section, are for Never Hinged items.

D15

1945	Unwmk.	Typo.	Perf. 10½	
J175	D15	1g vermilion	.15	.15
J176	D15	2g vermilion	.15	.15
J177	D15	3g vermilion	.15	.15
J178	D15	5g vermilion	.15	.15
J179	D15	10g vermilion	.15	.15
J180	D15	12g vermilion	.15	.15
J181	D15	20g vermilion	.15	.15
J182	D15	24g vermilion	.15	.15
J183	D15	30g vermilion	.15	.15
J184	D15	60g vermilion	.15	.20
J185	D15	1s violet	.15	.35
J186	D15	2s violet	.15	.45
J187	D15	5s violet	.15	.20
J188	D15	10s violet	.15	.20
		Set value	1.00	2.25

Issue dates: 1g-60g, Sept. 10, 1s-10s, Sept. 24.

Occupation Stamps of the Allied Military Government Overprinted in Black

PORTO

1946			**Perf. 11**
J189	OS1	3g deep orange	.15	.15
J190	OS1	5g bright green	.15	.15
J191	OS1	6g red violet	.15	.15
J192	OS1	8g rose pink	.15	.15
J193	OS1	10g light gray	.15	.20
J194	OS1	12g pale buff brown	.15	.15
J195	OS1	15g rose red	.15	.20
J196	OS1	20g copper brown	.15	.15
J197	OS1	25g deep blue	.15	.15

J198	OS1	30g bright violet	.15 .15
J199	OS1	40g light ultra	.15 .15
J200	OS1	60g light olive grn	.15 .15
J201	OS1	1s dark violet	.15 .20
J202	OS1	2s yellow	.25 .30
J203	OS1	5s deep ultra	.25 .30
		Set value	1.40 1.88

Nos. J189-J203 were issued by the Renner Government. Inverted overprints exist on about half of the denominations.
Issue dates: 3g-60g, Apr. 23, 1s-5s, May 20.

Type of 1894-95
Inscribed "Republik Österreich"

1947		Typo.	Perf. 14
J204	D1	1g chocolate	.15 .15
J205	D1	2g chocolate	.15 .15
J206	D1	3g chocolate	.15 .15
J207	D1	5g chocolate	.15 .15
J208	D1	8g chocolate	.15 .15
J209	D1	10g chocolate	.15 .15
J210	D1	12g chocolate	.15 .15
J211	D1	15g chocolate	.15 .15
J212	D1	16g chocolate	.20 .40
J213	D1	17g chocolate	.20 .40
J214	D1	18g chocolate	.20 .40
J215	D1	20g chocolate	.50 .15
J216	D1	24g chocolate	.30 .30
J217	D1	30g chocolate	.20 .15
J218	D1	36g chocolate	.50 .60
J219	D1	40g chocolate	.15 .15
J220	D1	42g chocolate	.50 .60
J221	D1	48g chocolate	.50 .60
J222	D1	50g chocolate	.55 .15
J223	D1	60g chocolate	.20 .15
J224	D1	70g chocolate	.15 .15
J225	D1	80g chocolate	3.75 1.65
J226	D1	1s blue	.20 .15
J227	D1	1.15s blue	2.50 .30
J228	D1	1.20s blue	3.00 1.00
J229	D1	2s blue	.40 .40
J230	D1	5s blue	.40 .40
J231	D1	10s blue	.40 .40
		Nos. J204-J231 (28)	16.00 9.75

Issue dates: 1g, 20g, 50g, 80g, 1.15s, 1.20s, Sept. 25, others, Aug. 14.

D16   D17

1949-57			
J232	D16	1g carmine	.20 .15
J233	D16	2g carmine	.20 .15
J234	D16	4g carmine ('51)	1.00 .15
J235	D16	5g carmine	2.25 .25
J236	D16	8g carmine ('51)	2.75 1.50
J237	D16	10g carmine	.15 .15
J238	D16	20g carmine	.15 .15
J239	D16	30g carmine	.15 .15
J240	D16	40g carmine	.15 .15
J241	D16	50g carmine	.15 .15
J242	D16	60g carmine ('50)	7.50 .15
J243	D16	63g carmine ('57)	4.75 4.00
J244	D16	70g carmine	.15 .15
J245	D16	80g carmine	.15 .15
J246	D16	90g carmine ('50)	.20 .15
J247	D16	1s purple	.20 .15
J248	D16	1.20s purple	.35 .15
J249	D16	1.35s purple	.30 .15
J250	D16	1.40s purple ('51)	.45 .20
J251	D16	1.50s purple ('53)	.20 .15
J252	D16	1.65s purple ('50)	.40 .15
J253	D16	1.70s purple	.40 .15
J254	D16	2s purple	.35 .15
J255	D16	2.50s purple ('51)	.45 .15
J256	D16	3s purple ('51)	1.00 .15
J257	D16	4s purple ('51)	1.00 .40
J258	D16	5s purple	1.75 .20
J259	D16	10s purple	2.75 .20
		Nos. J232-J259 (28)	29.50
		Set value	8.25

Issued: 60g, 90g, 1.65s, 8/7; 4g, 8g, 1.40s, 2.50s-4s, 12/4; 1.50s, 2/18; 63g, 4/30; others, 11/17.

1985-89		Photo.	Perf. 14
		Background Color	
J260	D17	10g brt yel ('86)	.15 .15
J261	D17	20g pink ('86)	.15 .15
J262	D17	50g orange ('86)	.15 .15
J263	D17	1s lt blue ('86)	.15 .15
J264	D17	2s pale brn ('86)	.30 .20
J265	D17	3s violet ('86)	.40 .30
J266	D17	5s ocher	.60 .40
J267	D17	10s pale grn ('89)	1.50 1.10
		Nos. J260-J267 (8)	3.40 2.60

Issue dates: 5s, Dec. 12. 20g, 1s, 3s, Mar. 19. 10g, 50g, 2s, Oct. 3. 10s, June 30.
This is an expanding set. Numbers will change if necessary.

MILITARY STAMPS

Issues of the Austro-Hungarian Military Authorities for the Occupied Territories in World War I

See Bosnia and Herzegovina for similar designs inscribed "MILITARPOST" instead of "FELDPOST."

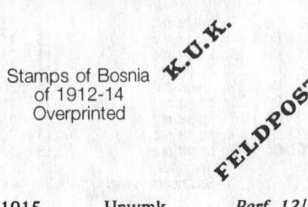

Stamps of Bosnia of 1912-14 Overprinted

1915		Unwmk.	Perf. 12½
M1	A23	1h olive green	.15 .20
M2	A23	2h bright blue	.15 .20
M3	A23	3h claret	.15 .20
M4	A23	5h green	.15 .15
M5	A23	6h dark gray	.15 .20
M6	A23	10h rose carmine	.15 .15
M7	A23	12h deep ol grn	.20 .30
M8	A23	20h orange brn	.30 .35
M9	A23	25h ultramarine	.30 .30
M10	A23	30h orange red	2.75 5.00
M11	A24	35h myrtle grn	2.50 4.00
M12	A24	40h dark violet	2.50 4.00
M13	A24	45h olive brown	2.75 4.50
M14	A24	50h slate blue	2.50 4.00
M15	A24	60h brn violet	.30 .45
M16	A24	72h dark blue	2.50 4.00
M17	A25	1k brn vio, straw	2.75 5.00
M18	A25	2k dk gray, blue	2.75 4.00
M19	A26	3k car, green	20.00 24.00
M20	A25	5k dk vio, gray	20.00 24.00
M21	A25	10k dk ultra, gray	175.00 150.00
		Nos. M1-M21 (21)	238.00 235.00

Exists imperf. Value, set $300.
Nos. M1-M21 also exist with overprint double, inverted and in red. These varieties were made by order of an official but were not regularly issued.

Emperor Franz Josef
M1   M2

Perf. 11½, 12½ and Compound

1915-17			Engr.
M22	M1	1h olive green	.15 .15
M23	M1	2h dull blue	.15 .15
M24	M1	3h claret	.15 .15
M25	M1	5h green	.15 .15
a.		Perf. 11½	35.00 40.00
b.		Perf. 11½x12½	47.50 70.00
c.		Perf. 12½x11½	75.00 100.00
M26	M1	6h dark gray	.15 .15
M27	M1	10h rose carmine	.15 .15
M28	M1	10h gray bl ('17)	.15 .15
M29	M1	12h dp olive grn	.15 .15
M30	M1	15h car rose ('17)	.15 .15
a.		Perf. 11½	7.50 7.50
M31	M1	20h orange brn	.35 .15
M32	M1	20h ol green ('17)	.35 .15
M33	M1	25h ultramarine	.15 .15
M34	M1	30h vermilion	.15 .15
M35	M1	35h dark green	.35 .35
M36	M1	40h dark violet	.35 .35
M37	M1	45h olive brown	.25 .35
M38	M1	50h myrtle green	.25 .20
M39	M1	60h brown violet	.25 .35
M40	M1	72h dark blue	.25 .35
M41	M1	80h org brn ('17)	.15 .15
M42	M1	90h magenta ('17)	.70 .75
M43	M2	1k brn vio, straw	1.25 1.75
M44	M2	2k dk gray, blue	1.10 .65
M45	M2	3k car, green	.80 .90
M46	M2	4k dark violet, gray ('17)	.70 .90
M47	M2	5k dk vio, gray	18.00 20.00
M48	M2	10k dk ultra, gray	2.75 5.25
		Nos. M22-M48 (27)	29.50 34.25

Nos. M22-M48 exist imperf. Value, set $75.

Emperor Karl I
M3   M4

1917-18			Perf. 12½
M49	M3	1h grnsh blue ('18)	.15 .15
a.		Perf. 11½	3.50 4.00
M50	M3	2h red org ('18)	.15 .15
M51	M3	3h olive gray	.15 .15
a.		Perf. 11½	12.00 15.00
b.		Perf. 11½x12½	18.00 27.50
M52	M3	5h olive green	.15 .15
M53	M3	6h violet	.15 .15
M54	M3	10h orange brn	.15 .15
M55	M3	12h blue	.15 .15
a.		Perf. 11½	2.75 3.50
M56	M3	15h bright rose	.15 .15
M57	M3	20h red brown	.15 .15
M58	M3	25h ultramarine	.35 .35
M59	M3	30h slate	.15 .15
M60	M3	40h olive bister	.15 .15
a.		Perf. 11½	1.40 1.50
M61	M3	50h deep green	.15 .15
a.		Perf. 11½	4.25 6.00
M62	M3	60h car rose	.15 .15
M63	M3	80h dull blue	.15 .15
M64	M3	90h dk violet	.45 .45
M65	M4	2k rose, straw	.15 .15
a.		Perf. 11½	2.25 3.50
M66	M4	3k green, blue	.95 .95
M67	M4	4k rose, green	15.00 12.00
a.		Perf. 11½	27.50 35.00
M68	M4	10k dl vio, gray	2.25 3.50
a.		Perf. 11½	11.00 17.50
		Nos. M49-M68 (20)	21.25 19.50

Nos. M49-M68 exist imperf. Value, set $36.
See No. M82. For overprints see Western Ukraine Nos. 34-53, 75-81.

Emperor Karl I — M5

1918		Typo.	Perf. 12½
M69	M5	1h grnsh blue	20.00
M70	M5	2h orange	10.00
M71	M5	3h olive gray	8.00
M72	M5	5h yellow green	.30
M73	M5	10h dark brown	.30
M74	M5	20h red	.80
M75	M5	25h blue	.80
M76	M5	30h bister	75.00
M77	M5	45h dark slate	75.00
M78	M5	50h deep green	50.00
M79	M5	60h violet	100.00
M80	M5	80h rose	50.00
M81	M5	90h brown violet	2.00
			Engr.
M82	M4	1k ol bister, blue	.30
		Nos. M69-M82 (14)	392.50

Nos. M69-M82 were on sale at the Vienna post office for a few days before the Armistice signing. They were never issued at the Army Post Offices. They exist imperf.; value, set $400.

MILITARY SEMI-POSTAL STAMPS

Emperor Karl I — MSP7   Empress Zita — MSP8

Perf. 12½x13

1918, July 20		Unwmk.	Typo.
MB1	MSP7	10h gray green	.20 .20
MB2	MSP8	20h magenta	.20 .20
MB3	MSP7	45h blue	.20 .20
		Nos. MB1-MB3 (3)	.60 .60
		Set, never hinged	1.25

These stamps were sold at a premium of 10h each over face value. The surtax was for "Karl's Fund."
For overprints see Western Ukraine Nos. 31-33. Exist imperf. Value, set $8.

MILITARY NEWSPAPER STAMPS

Mercury — MN1

1916		Unwmk. Typo.	Perf. 12½
MP1	MN1	2h blue	.15 .15
a.		Perf. 11½	1.50 1.00
b.		Perf. 12½x11½	125.00 125.00
MP2	MN1	6h orange	.55 .50
MP3	MN1	10h orange	.70 .50
MP4	MN1	20h brown	.40 .45
a.		Perf. 11½	1.90 1.25
		Nos. MP1-MP4 (4)	1.80 1.60
		Set, never hinged	4.50

Exist imperf. Values, Nos. MP2-MP3, $1 each, Nos. MP1, MP4, $18 each.

NEWSPAPER STAMPS

From 1851 to 1866, the Austrian Newspaper Stamps were also used in Lombardy-Venetia.

Values for unused stamps 1851-67 are for fine copies with original gum. Specimens without gum sell for about a third or less of the figures quoted.

Issues of the Monarchy

Mercury — N1

Three Types
Type I - The "G" has no crossbar.
Type II - The "G" has a crossbar.
Type IIa - as type II but the rosette is deformed. Two spots of color in the "G."

1851-56		Unwmk. Typo.	Imperf.
		Machine-made Paper	
P1	N1	(0.6kr) bl, type IIa	130.00 70.00
a.		Blue, type I	175.00 85.00
b.		Ribbed paper	400.00 145.00
c.		Blue, type II	375.00 165.00
P2	N1	(6kr) yel, type I	10,000. 7,500.
P3	N1	(30kr) rose, type I	12,000. 10,000.
P4	N1	(6kr) scar, type II ('56)	37,500. 40,000.

From 1852 No. P3 and from 1856 No. P2 were used as 0.6 kreuzer values.
Values for Nos. P2-P3 unused are for stamps without gum. Pale shades sell at considerably lower values.
Originals of Nos. P2-P3 are usually in pale colors and poorly printed. Values are for stamps clearly printed and in bright colors. Numerous reprints of Nos. P1-P4 were made between 1866 and 1904. Those of Nos. P2-P3 are always well printed and in much deeper colors. All reprints are in type I, but occasionally show faint traces of a crossbar on "G" of "ZEITUNGS."

N2   N3

Two Types of the 1858-59 Issue
Type I - Loops of the bow at the back of the head broken.
Type II - Loops complete. Wreath projects further at top of head.

1858-59			Embossed
P5	N2	(1kr) blue, type I	500.00 550.00
P6	N2	(1kr) lilac, type II ('59)	700.00 275.00

1861			
P7	N3	(1kr) gray	140.00 140.00
a.		(1kr) gray lilac	350.00 200.00
b.		(1kr) deep lilac	1,500. 575.00

The embossing on the reprints of the 1858-59 and 1861 issues is not as sharp as on the originals.

N4

Wmk. 91, or, before July 1864, Unwmkd.

1863			
P8	N4	(1.05kr) gray	35.00 13.00
a.		Tete beche pair	20,000.
b.		(1.05kr) gray lilac	60.00 17.50

The embossing of the reprints is not as sharp as on the originals.

Mercury

N5   N6

Three Types

Type I - Helmet not defined at back, more or less blurred. Two thick short lines in front of wing of helmet. Shadow on front of face not separated from hair.

Type II - Helmet distinctly defined. Four thin short lines in front of wing. Shadow on front of face clearly defined from hair.

Type III - Outer white circle around head is open at top (closed on types I and II). Greek border at top and bottom is wider than on types I and II.

1867-73		Typo.		Wmk. 91
P9	N5	(1kr) vio, type I	37.50	4.00
a.		(1kr) violet, type II ('73)	120.00	18.00

1874-76

Fine Print

P9B	N5	(1kr) violet, type III		
		('76)	.50	.20
c.		(1kr) gray lilac, type I ('76)	100.00	25.00
d.		(1kr) violet, type II	30.00	5.00
e.		Double impression, type III	175.00	

Stamps of this issue, except No. P9c, exist in many shades, from gray to lilac brown and deep violet. Stamps in type III exist also privately perforated or rouletted.

1880				
P10	N6	½kr green	5.00	.90

Nos. P9B and P10 also exist on thicker paper without sheet watermark and No. P10 exists with unofficial perforation.

N7

1899		Unwmk.		Imperf.
		Without Varnish Bars		
P11	N7	2h dark blue	.20	.15
P12	N7	6h orange	2.00	1.75
P13	N7	10h brown	.90	.75
P14	N7	20h rose	1.75	1.75
		Nos. P11-P14 (4)	4.85	4.40

1901				
		With Varnish Bars		
P11a	N7	2h dark blue	.70	.20
P12a	N7	6h orange	9.50	12.50
P13a	N7	10h brown	10.00	7.50
P14a	N7	20h rose	20.00	25.00
		Nos. P11a-P14a (4)	40.20	45.20

Nos. P11 to P14 were re-issued in 1905.

Mercury

N8   N9

1908				Imperf.
P15	N8	2h dark blue	1.50	.15
a.		Tete beche pair	190.00	275.00
P16	N8	6h orange	2.25	.30
P17	N8	10h carmine	2.25	.30
P18	N8	20h brown	2.25	.25
		Nos. P15-P18 (4)	8.25	1.00

All values are found on chalky, regular and thin ordinary paper. They exist privately perforated.

1916				Imperf.
P19	N9	2h brown	.15	.15
P20	N9	4h green	.20	.30
P21	N9	6h dark blue	.20	.60
P22	N9	10h orange	.20	.30
P23	N9	30h claret	.25	.30
		Nos. P19-P23 (5)	1.00	1.65
		Set, never hinged	2.00	

Issues of the Republic

Newspaper Stamps of 1916 Overprinted

1919				
P24	N9	2h brown	.15	.15
P25	N9	4h green	.15	.45
P26	N9	6h dark blue	.15	.70
P27	N9	10h orange	.25	.45
P28	N9	30h claret	.15	.70
		Set value	.60	
		Set, never hinged	1.65	

Mercury

N10   N11

1920-21				Imperf.
P29	N10	2h violet	.15	.15
P30	N10	4h brown	.15	.15
P31	N10	5h slate	.15	.15
P32	N10	6h turq blue	.15	.15
P33	N10	8h green	.15	.15
P34	N10	9h yellow ('21)	.15	.15
P35	N10	10h red	.15	.15
P36	N10	12h blue	.15	.15
P37	N10	15h lilac ('21)	.15	.15
P38	N10	18h blue grn ('21)	.15	.15
P39	N10	20h orange	.15	.15
P40	N10	30h yellow brn ('21)	.15	.15
P41	N10	45h green ('21)	.15	.15
P42	N10	60h claret	.15	.20
P43	N10	72h chocolate ('21)	.15	.35
P44	N10	90h violet ('21)	.15	.35
P45	N10	1.20k red ('21)	.15	.35
P46	N10	2.40k yellow grn ('21)	.15	.35
P47	N10	3k gray ('21)	.15	.35
		Set value	1.10	3.00
		Set, never hinged	1.75	

Nos. P37-P40, P42, P44 and P47 exist also on thick gray paper.

1921-22				
P48	N11	45h gray	.15	.15
P49	N11	75h brown org ('22)	.15	.15
P50	N11	1.50k ol bister ('22)	.15	.15
P51	N11	1.80k gray blue ('22)	.15	.15
P52	N11	2.25k light brown	.15	.15
P53	N11	3k dull green ('22)	.15	.35
P54	N11	6k claret ('22)	.15	.35
P55	N11	7.50k bister	.18	.35
		Set value	.60	
		Set, never hinged	1.25	

Nos. P24-P55 exist privately perforated.

NEWSPAPER TAX STAMPS

Values for unused stamps 1853-59 are for copies in fine condition with gum. Specimens without gum sell for about one-third or less of the figures quoted.

Issues of the Monarchy

NT1   NT2

		Unwmk.		
1853, Mar. 1		**Typo.**		**Imperf.**
PR1	NT1	2kr green	1,500.	50.00

The reprints are in finer print than the more coarsely printed originals, and on a smooth toned paper.

Wmk. 91, or, before July 1864, Unwmkd.

1858-59

Two Types.

Type I - The banderol on the Crown of the left eagle touches the beak of the eagle.

Type II - The banderol does not touch the beak.

PR2	NT2	1kr blue, type II ('59)	32.50	6.00
a.		1kr blue, type I	600.00	150.00
b.		Printed on both sides, type II		
PR3	NT2	2kr brown, type II		
		('59)	20.00	7.50
a.		2kr red brown, type II	400.00	1,000.
PR4	NT2	4kr brn, type I	400.00	1,000.

Nos. PR2a, PR3a, and PR4 were printed only on unwatermarked paper. Nos. PR2 and PR3 exist on unwatermarked and watermarked paper.

Nos. PR2 and PR3 exist in coarse and (after 1874) in fine print, like the contemporary postage stamps.

The reprints of the 4kr brown are of type II and on a smooth toned paper.

Issue date: 4kr, Nov. 1.

See Lombardy-Venetia for the 1kr in black and the 2kr, 4fk in red.

NT3   NT4

1877			Redrawn	
PR5	NT3	1kr blue	14.00	1.50
a.		1kr pale ultramarine		1,500.
PR6	NT3	2kr brown	14.00	1.50

In the redrawn stamps the shield is larger and the vertical bar has eight lines above the white square and nine below, instead of five.

Nos. PR5 and PR6 exist also watermarked "WECHSEL" instead of "ZEITUNGS-MARKEN."

1890, June 1				
PR7	NT4	1kr brown	10.00	1.20
PR8	NT4	2kr green	11.00	1.50

#PR5-PR8 exist with private perforation.

NT5

Perf. 13, 12½

1890, June 1			Wmk. 91	
PR9	NT5	25kr carmine	100.00	400.00

Nos. PR1-PR9 did not pay postage, but were a fiscal tax, collected by the postal authorities on newspapers.

SPECIAL HANDLING STAMPS

(For Printed Matter Only)
Issues of the Monarchy

Mercury — SH1

1916		Unwmk.	Perf. 12½	
QE1	SH1	2h claret, yel	.30	.40
QE2	SH1	5h dp green, yel	.30	.40
		Set, never hinged	1.75	

SH2

1917			Perf. 12½	
QE3	SH2	2h claret, yel	.15	.15
a.		Pair, imperf. between	200.00	200.00
b.		Perf. 11½x12½	45.00	60.00
c.		Perf. 12½x11½	60.00	90.00
d.		Perf. 11½	.95	1.40
QE4	SH2	5h dp green, yel	.15	.15
a.		Pair, imperf. between	175.00	175.00
b.		Perf. 11½x12½	45.00	60.00
c.		Perf. 12½x11½	60.00	90.00
d.		Perf. 11½	.95	1.40
		Set value	.20	.20
		Set, never hinged	.35	

Nos. QE1-QE4 exist imperforate.

Issues of the Republic

Nos. QE3 and QE4 Overprinted

1919				
QE5	SH2	2h claret, yel	.15	.15
a.		Inverted overprint	175.00	
b.		Perf. 11½x12½	5.00	8.00
c.		Perf. 12½x11½	65.00	85.00
d.		Perf. 11½	.22	.70
QE6	SH2	5h deep green, yel	.15	.20
a.		Perf. 11½x12½	2.25	3.75
b.		Perf. 12½x11½	25.00	35.00
c.		Perf. 11½	.18	.48
		Set value	.15	
		Set, never hinged	.20	

Nos. QE5 and QE6 exist imperforate.

SH3

Dark Blue Surcharge

1921				
QE7	SH3	50h on 2h claret, yel	.15	.15
		Never hinged	.15	

SH4

1922			Perf. 12½	
QE8	SH4	50h lilac, yel	.15	.20
		Never hinged	.15	

#QE5-QE8 exist in vertical pairs, imperf between. No. QE8 exists imperf.

OCCUPATION STAMPS

Issued under Italian Occupation

Issued in Trieste

Austrian Stamps of 1916-18 Overprinted

Regno d'Italia Venezia Giulia 3. XI. 18,

1918		Unwmk.	Perf. 12½	
N1	A37	3h bright vio	.20	.20
a.		Double overprint	7.00	9.00
b.		Inverted overprint	7.00	9.00
N2	A37	5h light grn	.20	.20
a.		Inverted overprint	7.00	9.00
b.		"3.XI." omitted	7.00	7.00
c.		Double overprint		9.00
N3	A37	6h dp orange	.25	.30
N4	A37	10h magenta	.20	.25
a.		Inverted overprint	5.00	6.00
N5	A37	12h light bl	.55	.70
a.		Double overprint	7.00	9.00
N6	A42	15h dull red	.20	.25
a.		Inverted overprint	6.00	8.25
b.		Double overprint	7.00	9.00
c.		"3.XI." omitted	7.00	7.00
N7	A42	20h dark green	.20	.25
a.		Inverted overprint	5.00	6.00
b.		"3.XI." omitted	7.00	8.25
c.		Double overprint	14.00	
N8	A42	25h deep blue	1.40	1.75
a.		Inverted overprint	20.00	25.00
b.		"3.XI." omitted	40.00	40.00
N9	A42	30h dl violet	.40	.55
N10	A39	40h olive grn	14.00	17.50
N11	A39	50h dark green	.60	.80
N12	A39	60h deep blue	1.00	1.40
N13	A39	80h orange brn	.70	.80
a.		Inverted overprint		
N14	A39	1k car, yel	.60	.80
a.		Double overprint	14.00	14.00
N15	A40	2k light bl	25.00	27.50
N16	A40	4k yellow grn	55.00	72.50

Handstamped

N17	A40	10k dp violet	8,000.	10,000.

Granite Paper

N18	A40	2k light blue		
N19	A40	3k car rose	40.00	72.50
		Nos. N1-N16,N19 (17)	140.50	198.25

Some authorities question the authenticity of No. N18. Counterfeits of Nos. N10, N15-N19 are plentiful.

Venezia Giulia

Italian Stamps of 1901-18 Overprinted

Wmk. 140   Perf. 14

N20	A42	1c brown	.20	.40
a.		Inverted overprint	3.25	5.00
N21	A43	2c orange brn	.20	.40
a.		Inverted overprint	2.50	3.75
N22	A48	5c green	.15	.30
a.		Inverted overprint	5.00	7.00
b.		Double overprint	14.00	
N23	A48	10c claret	.15	.30
a.		Inverted overprint	7.00	10.00
b.		Double overprint	14.00	
N24	A50	20c brn orange	.15	.30
a.		Inverted overprint	10.00	15.00
b.		Double overprint	14.00	20.00
N25	A49	25c blue	.15	.30
			40.00	
a.		Double overprint	14.00	20.00
N26	A49	40c brown	.80	2.00
			35.00	
N27	A45	45c olive grn	.25	.50
a.		Inverted overprint	14.00	20.00
N28	A49	50c violet	.30	.75
N29	A49	60c brown car	3.25	8.25
N30	A46	1 l brn & green	1.40	3.50
		Nos. N20-N30 (11)	7.00	17.00

Venezia Giulia

Italian Stamps of 1901-18 Surcharged

5 Heller

N31	A48	5h on 5c green	.15	.30
a.		"5" omitted	10.00	15.00
b.		Inverted surcharge	12.50	17.50
N32	A50	20h on 20c brn org	.15	.30
a.		Double surcharge	12.50	17.50

Issued in the Trentino

Regno d Italia

Austrian Stamps of 1916-18 Overprinted

Trentino

3 nov 1918

1918   Unwmk.   Perf. 12½

N33	A37	3h bright vio	.50	.70
a.		Double overprint	14.00	20.00
b.		Inverted overprint	12.50	16.00
N34	A37	5h light grn	.30	.45
a.		"8 nov. 1918"	750.00	
b.		Inverted overprint	12.50	16.00
N35	A37	6h dp orange	13.00	17.50
N36	A37	10h magenta	.40	.60
a.		"8 nov. 1918"	16.00	22.50
N37	A37	12h light blue	40.00	60.00
N38	A42	15h dull red	1.10	1.65
N39	A42	20h dark green	.20	.30
a.		"8 nov. 1918"	20.00	32.50
b.		Double overprint	14.00	20.00
c.		Inverted overprint	5.00	14.00
N40	A42	25h deep blue	9.00	13.00
N41	A42	30h dl violet	2.00	3.00
N42	A39	40h olive grn	13.00	17.50
N43	A39	50h dark green	5.00	7.25
a.		Inverted overprint	20.00	26.00
N44	A39	60h deep blue	9.00	13.00
a.		Double overprint	25.00	32.50
N45	A39	80h orange brn	14.00	20.00
N46	A39	90h red violet	200.00	300.00
N47	A39	1k car, yel	14.00	20.00
N48	A40	2k light blue	62.50	92.50
N49	A40	4k yel green	375.00	700.00
N50	A40	10k dp violet	25,000.	

Granite Paper

N51	A40	2k light blue	100.00	

Counterfeits of Nos. N33-N51 are plentiful.

Venezia Tridentina

Italian Stamps of 1901-18 Overprinted

Wmk. 140   Perf. 14

N52	A42	1c brown	.20	.50
a.		Inverted overprint	6.00	9.00
N53	A43	2c orange brn	.20	.50
a.		Inverted overprint	6.00	9.00
N54	A48	5c green	.20	.50
a.		Inverted overprint	6.00	9.00
b.		Double overprint	8.25	12.50
N55	A48	10c claret	.20	.50
a.		Inverted overprint	8.25	12.50
b.		Double overprint	8.25	12.50
N56	A50	20c brn orange	.20	.50
a.		Inverted overprint	8.25	12.50
N57	A49	40c brown	4.00	10.50
N58	A45	45c olive grn	2.50	6.00
a.		Double overprint	26.00	40.00
N59	A49	50c violet	2.50	6.00
N60	A46	1 l brn & green	2.50	6.00
a.		Double overprint	26.00	40.00
		Nos. N52-N60 (9)	12.50	31.00

Venezia Tridentina

Italian Stamps of 1906-18 Surcharged

5 Heller

N61	A48	5h on 5c green	.15	.25
N62	A48	10h on 10c claret	.15	.25
a.		Inverted surcharge	9.50	13.00
N63	A50	20h on 20c brn org	.15	.25
a.		Double surcharge	9.50	13.00
		Set value	.25	

General Issue

Italian Stamps of 1901-18 Surcharged

5 centesimi di corona

1919

N64	A42	1c on 1c brown	.15	.15
a.		Inverted surcharge	1.80	2.75
N65	A43	2c on 2c org brn	.15	.15
a.		Double surcharge	32.50	
b.		Inverted surcharge	.95	1.50
N66	A48	5c on 5c green	.15	.15
a.		Inverted surcharge	4.50	6.50
b.		Double surcharge	9.00	9.00
N67	A48	10c on 10c claret	.15	.15
a.		Inverted surcharge	4.50	6.50
b.		Double surcharge	9.00	13.00
N68	A50	20c on 20c brn org	.15	.15
a.		Double surcharge	13.00	19.00
N69	A49	25c on 25c blue	.15	.15
a.		Inverted surcharge	13.00	13.00
N70	A49	40c on 40c brown	.15	.15
a.		"ccrona"	15.00	22.50
N71	A45	45c on 45c ol grn	.15	.15
a.		Inverted surcharge	13.00	19.00
N72	A49	50c on 50c violet	.15	.15
N73	A49	60c on 60c brn car	.15	.15
a.		"00" for "60"	15.00	22.50

1 corona

Surcharged

N74	A46	1cor on 1 l brn & grn	.15	.15
		Set value, N64-N74	.90	.90

Surcharges similar to these but differing in style or arrangement of type were used in Dalmatia.

OCCUPATION SPECIAL DELIVERY STAMPS

Issued in Trieste

Special Delivery Stamp of Italy of 1903 Overprinted

Venezia Giulia

1918   Wmk. 140   Perf. 14

NE1	SD1	25c rose red	2.50	6.00
a.		Inverted overprint	16.00	25.00

General Issue

Special Delivery Stamps of Italy of 1903-09 Surcharged

25 centesimi di corona

1919

NE2	SD1	25c on 25c rose	.15	.20
a.		Double surcharge	8.25	12.50
NE3	SD2	30c on 30c bl & rose	.15	.40
		Set value	.25	

OCCUPATION POSTAGE DUE STAMPS

Issued in Trieste

Postage Due Stamps of Italy, 1870-94, Overprinted

Venezia Giulia

1918   Wmk. 140   Perf. 14

NJ1	D3	5c buff & mag	.15	.30
a.		Inverted overprint	3.75	3.00
b.		Double overprint	25.00	
NJ2	D3	10c buff & mag	.15	.30
a.		Inverted overprint	7.25	10.50
NJ3	D3	20c buff & mag	.15	.30
a.		Double overprint	25.00	
b.		Inverted overprint	7.25	10.50

NJ4	D3	30c buff & mag	.25	.50
NJ5	D3	40c buff & mag	2.00	5.00
a.		Inverted overprint	37.50	55.00
NJ6	D3	50c buff & mag	5.00	12.50
a.		Inverted overprint	37.50	55.00
NJ7	D3	1 l bl & mag	13.00	32.50
		Nos. NJ1-NJ7 (7)	20.70	51.40

General Issue

Postage Due Stamps of Italy, 1870-1903 Surcharged

5 centesimi di corona

1919

Buff & Magenta

NJ8	D3	5c on 5c	.15	.30
a.		Inverted overprint	2.00	3.00
NJ9	D3	10c on 10c	.15	.30
a.		Center and surcharge invtd.	10.00	15.00
NJ10	D3	20c on 20c	.15	.30
a.		Double overprint	20.00	30.00
NJ11	D3	30c on 30c	.15	.30
NJ12	D3	40c on 40c	.15	.30
NJ13	D3	50c on 50c	.15	.30

una corona

Surcharged

NJ14	D3	1cor on 1 l bl & mag	.15	.30
NJ15	D3	2cor on 2 l bl & mag	4.50	11.00
NJ16	D3	5cor on 5 l bl & mag	4.50	11.00
		Nos. NJ8-NJ16 (9)	10.05	24.10

A. M. G. ISSUE FOR AUSTRIA

Catalogue values for unused stamps in this section are for Never Hinged items.

Issued jointly by the Allied Military Government of the US and Great Britain, for civilian use in areas under American, British and French occupation. (Upper Austria, Salzburg, Tyrol, Vorarlberg, Styria and Carinthia).

 OS1

1945   Unwmk.   Litho.   Perf. 11

4N1	OS1	1g aquamarine	.15	.15
4N2	OS1	3g deep orange	.15	.15
4N3	OS1	4g buff	.15	.15
4N4	OS1	5g bright green	.15	.15
4N5	OS1	6g red violet	.15	.15
4N6	OS1	8g rose pink	.15	.15
4N7	OS1	10g light gray	.15	.15
4N8	OS1	12g pale buff brown	.15	.15
4N9	OS1	15g rose red	.15	.15
4N10	OS1	20g copper brown	.15	.15
4N11	OS1	25g deep blue	.15	.15
4N12	OS1	30g bright violet	.15	.15
4N13	OS1	40g light ultra	.15	.15
4N14	OS1	60g light olive grn	.15	.18
4N15	OS1	1s dark violet	.15	.30
4N16	OS1	2s yellow	.20	.30
4N17	OS1	5s deep ultra	.40	.45
		Set value	1.40	1.90

For Nos. 4N2, 4N4-4N17 overprinted "PORTO" see Nos. J189-J203.

AUSTRIAN OFFICES ABROAD

These stamps were on sale and usable at all Austrian post-offices in Crete and in the Turkish Empire.

100 Centimes = 1 Franc

OFFICES IN CRETE

Used values are italicized for stamps often found with false cancellations.

Stamps of Austria of 1899-1901 Issue, Surcharged in Black:

CENTIMES
a

CENTIMES
b

CENTIMES
c

FRANC
d

1903-04   Unwmk.   Perf. 12½, 13½

On Nos. 73a, 75a, 77a, 81a

Granite Paper

With Varnish Bars

1	A15(a)	5c on 5h blue green	1.50	3.50
2	A16(a)	10c on 10h rose	.70	3.75
3	A16(b)	25c on 25h ultra	35.00	22.50
4	A17(c)	50c on 50h gray blue	6.75	110.00

On Nos. 83, 83a, 84, 85

Without Varnish Bars

5	A18(d)	1fr on 1k car rose	2.25	90.00
a.		1fr on 1k carmine	175.00	
b.		Horiz. or vert. pair, imperf. between	175.00	
6	A18(d)	2fr on 2k ('04)	9.50	225.00
7	A18(d)	4fr on 4k ('04)	10.50	400.00
		Nos. 1-7 (7)	66.20	

Surcharged on Austrian Stamps of 1904-05

1905

On Nos. 89, 97

Without Varnish Bars

8	A19(a)	5c on 5h green	45.00	18.00
9	A20(b)	10c on 10h car	.80	6.00

On Nos. 89a, 97a, 99a, 103a

With Varnish Bars

8a	A19(a)	5c on 5h blue green	4.00	6.00
9a	A20(b)	10c on 10h carmine	20.00	14.00
10	A20(b)	25c on 25h ultra	1.25	35.00
11	A21(b)	50c on 50h dl bl	4.00	150.00

Surcharged on Austrian Stamps and Type of 1906-07

1907   Perf. 12½, 13½

Without Varnish Bars

12	A19(a)	5c on 5h yel green (#90)	1.25	7.50
13	A20(b)	10c on 10h car (#92)	1.10	15.00
14	A20(b)	15c on 15h vio	1.25	15.00
		Nos. 12-14 (3)	3.60	

A5   A6

1908   Typo.   Perf. 12½

15	A5	5c green, yellow	.35	.20
16	A5	10c scarlet, rose	.40	.30
17	A5	15c brown, buff	.45	2.75
18	A5	25c dp blue, blue	11.50	2.75

Engr.

19	A6	50c lake, yellow	1.75	18.00
20	A6	1fr brown, gray	2.25	25.00
a.		Vert pair, imperf. btwn.	175.00	
		Nos. 15-20 (6)	16.95	49.00

Nos. 15 to 18 are on paper colored on the surface only. All values exist imperforate.

60th year of the reign of Emperor Franz Josef, for permanent use.

Paper Colored Through

1914   Typo.

21	A5	10c rose, rose	1.65	575.00
22	A5	25c ultra, blue	.65	65.00

Nos. 21 and 22 exist imperforate.

OFFICES IN THE TURKISH EMPIRE

From 1863 to 1867 the stamps of Lombardy-Venetia (Nos. 15 to 24) were used at the Austrian Offices in the Turkish Empire.

100 Soldi = 1 Florin
40 Paras = 1 Piaster

Values for unused stamps are for copies with gum. Specimens without gum sell for about one-third or less of the figures quoted.

Used values are italicized for stamps often found with false cancellations.

For similar designs in Kreuzers, see early Austria.

A1

A2

Two different printing methods were used, as in the 1867-74 issues of Austria. They may be distinguished by the coarse or fine lines of the hair and whiskers and by the paper, which is more transparent on the later issue.

1867   Typo.   Wmk. 91   Perf. 9½
Coarse Print

1	A1	2sld orange	1.75	22.50
a.		2sld yellow	55.00	30.00
2	A1	3sld green	100.00	40.00
a.		3sld dark green	125.00	70.00
3	A1	5sld red	100.00	11.00
a.		5sld carmine	110.00	16.00
4	A1	10sld blue	100.00	1.75
a.		10sld light blue	110.00	2.50
b.		10sld dark blue	110.00	3.00
5	A1	15sld brown	16.00	6.00
a.		15sld dark brown	45.00	20.00
b.		15sld reddish brown	16.00	10.00
6	A1	25sld gray lilac	50.00	40.00
a.		25sld brown violet	16.00	40.00
7	A2	50sld brn, perf. 10½	5.00	45.00
a.		Perf. 12	90.00	70.00
b.		Perf. 13	250.00	
k.		Perf. 9	25.00	50.00
l.		50sld pale red brn, perf. 12	55.00	60.00
m.		Vert. pair, imperf. btwn.	325.00	650.00
n.		Horiz. pair, imperf. btwn.	325.00	750.00
o.		Perf. 10½x9	65.00	100.00

Perf. 9, 9½, 10½ and Compound
1876-83
Fine Print

7C	A1	2sld yellow ('83)	.20	1,375.
7D	A1	3sld green ('78)	1.00	20.00
7E	A1	5sld red ('78)	.40	15.00
7F	A1	10sld blue	55.00	1.00
7I	A1	15sld org brn ('81)	9.00	125.00
7J	A1	25sld gray lilac ('83)	.50	275.00
		Nos. 7C-7J (6)	66.10	

The 10 soldi has been reprinted in deep dull blue, perforated 10½.

A3

1883   Perf. 9½, 10, 10½

8	A3	2sld brown	.20	115.00
9	A3	3sld green	.20	27.50
10	A3	5sld rose	.20	16.00
11	A3	10sld blue	.75	.50
12	A3	20sld gray, perf. 10	1.00	60.00
a.		Perf. 9½	5.50	7.50
13	A3	50sld red lilac	1.50	17.50
		Nos. 8-13 (6)	4.65	

No. 9 Surcharged   **10 PARA 10**

10 PARAS ON 3 SOLDI:
Type I - Surcharge 16½/2mm across. "PARA" about ½mm above bottom of "10." 2mm space between "10" and "P"; 1½mm between "A" and "10." Perf. 9½ only.
Type II - Surcharge 15¼ to 16mm across. "PARA" on same line with figures or slightly higher or lower. 1½mm space between "10" and "P"; 1mm between "A" and "10." Perf. 9½ and 10.

1886   Perf. 9½ and 10

14	A3	10pa on 3sld green, type II	.30	6.00
a.		Surcharge type I	185.00	350.00
b.		Inverted surcharge, type I		1,850.

Same Surcharge on Austria Nos. 42-46
1888

15	A11	10pa on 3kr grn	3.00	7.50
a.		"01 PARA 10"		400.00
16	A11	20pa on 5kr rose	.60	8.00
17	A11	1pi on 10kr blue	45.00	1.10
a.		Perf. 13½		225.00
b.		Double surcharge		275.00
18	A11	2pi on 20kr gray	1.50	4.50
19	A11	5pi on 50kr vio	2.25	15.00
		Nos. 15-19 (5)	52.35	

Austria Nos. 52-55, 58, 61 Surcharged   **10 PARA 10**

1890-92   Unwmk.   Perf. 9 to 13½
Granite Paper

20	A12	8pa on 2kr brn ('92)	.15	.15
a.		Perf. 9½	10.00	15.00
21	A12	10pa on 3kr green	.65	.15
a.		Pair, imperf. between		
22	A12	20pa on 5kr rose	.15	.15
23	A12	1pi on 10kr ultra	.35	.15
24	A12	2pi on 20kr ol grn	5.50	25.00
25	A12	5pi on 50kr violet	11.00	60.00
		Nos. 20-25 (6)	17.80	

See note after Austria No. 65 on missing numerals, etc.

Austria Nos. 66, 69 Surcharged   **2 PIASTER 2**

1891   Perf. 10 to 13½

26	A14	2pi on 20kr green	4.75	1.25
a.		Perf. 9½	110.00	70.00
27	A14	5pi on 50kr violet	2.75	2.50

Two types of the surcharge on No. 26 exist.

Austria Nos. 62-65 Surcharged   **10 PIAST. 10**

1892   Perf. 10½, 11½

28	A13	10pi on 1gld blue	11.00	25.00
29	A13	20pi on 2gld car	13.00	35.00
a.		Double surcharge		

1896   Perf. 10½, 11½, 12½

30	A13	10pi on 1gld pale lilac	13.00	20.00
31	A13	20pi on 2gld gray grn	42.50	65.00

Austria Nos. 73, 75, 77, 81, 83-85 Surcharged

10 PARA 10   **5 PIASTER 5**
#32-35   #36-38

Perf. 10½, 12½, 13½ and Compound
1900
Without Varnish Bars

32	A15	10pa on 5h bl grn	4.50	.75
33	A16	20pa on 10h rose	5.00	.75
a.		Perf. 12½x10½	250.00	85.00
34	A16	1pi on 25h ultra	3.50	.25
35	A17	2pi on 50h gray bl	7.25	3.00
36	A18	5pi on 1k car rose	1.10	.30
a.		5pi on 1k carmine	1.25	1.00
b.		Horiz. or vert. pair, imperf. btwn.	115.00	
37	A18	10pi on 2k gray lil	3.00	2.25
a.		Horiz. pair, imperf. btwn.		
38	A18	20pi on 4k gray grn	2.50	6.00
		Nos. 32-38 (7)	26.85	13.30

In the surcharge on Nos. 37 and 38 "piaster" is printed "PIAST."

1901
With Varnish Bars

32a	A15	10pa on 5h blue green	2.00	2.50
33a	A16	20pa on 10h rose	2.50	175.00
34a	A16	1pi on 25h ultra	1.65	.40
35a	A17	2pi on 50h gray blue	3.75	3.50
		Nos. 32a-35a (4)	9.90	

A4

A5

A6

1906   Perf. 12½ to 13½
Without Varnish Bars

39	A4	10pa dark green	12.00	1.00
40	A5	20pa rose	.80	.35
41	A5	1pi ultra	.35	.35
42	A6	2pi gray blue	.90	.40
		Nos. 39-42 (4)	14.05	1.90

1903
With Varnish Bars

39a	A4	10pa dark green	4.75	.75
40a	A5	20pa rose	2.25	.35
41a	A5	1pi ultra	2.25	.35
42a	A6	2pi gray blue	125.00	2.25

1907
Without Varnish Bars

43	A4	10pa yellow green	.35	1.25
45	A5	30pa violet	.50	2.25

A7

A8

1908   Typo.   Perf. 12½

46	A7	10pa green, yellow	.15	.15
47	A7	20pa scarlet, rose	.20	.15
48	A7	30pa brown, buff	.30	.40
49	A7	1pi deep bl, blue	12.00	.15
50	A7	60pa vio, bluish	.60	2.25

Engr.

51	A8	2pi lake, yellow	.40	.15
52	A8	5pi brown, gray	.60	.40
53	A8	10pi green, yellow	.90	1.10
54	A8	20pi blue, gray	1.50	2.25
		Nos. 46-54 (9)	16.65	7.00

Nos. 46 to 50 are on paper colored on the surface only. 60th year of the reign of Emperor Franz Josef I, for permanent use. All values exist imperforate.

1913-14   Typo.
Paper Colored Through

57	A7	20pa rose, rose ('14)	.80	300.00
58	A7	1pi ultra, blue	.35	.30

Nos. 57 and 58 exist imperforate.

POSTAGE DUE STAMPS

Type of Austria D2 Surcharged   **10 PARA**

Black Surcharge
1902   Unwmk.   Perf. 12½, 13½

J1	D2	10pa on 5h green	1.25	2.75
J2	D2	20pa on 10h green	1.25	2.50
J3	D2	1pi on 20h green	2.00	3.50
J4	D2	2pi on 40h green	2.00	2.75
J5	D2	5pi on 100h green	3.00	1.65
		Nos. J1-J5 (5)	9.50	13.15

Shades of Nos. J1-J5 exist, varying from yellowish green to dark green.

D3

1908   Typo.   Perf. 12½

J6	D3	¼pi green	3.25	5.50
J7	D3	½pi green	1.50	4.00
J8	D3	1pi green	2.00	5.50
J9	D3	1½pi green	.75	10.00
J10	D3	2pi green	2.25	10.00
J11	D3	5pi green	2.25	6.00
J12	D3	10pi green	18.00	90.00
J13	D3	20pi green	17.50	115.00
J14	D3	30pi green	12.50	10.00
		Nos. J6-J14 (9)	60.00	256.00

Nos. J6 to J14 exist in distinct shades of green and on thick chalky, regular and thin ordinary paper. Values are for the least expensive variety. No. J6-J14 exist imperforate. Forgeries exist.

LOMBARDY-VENETIA

Formerly a kingdom in the north of Italy forming part of the Austrian Empire. Milan and Venice were the two principal cities. Lombardy was annexed to Sardinia in 1859, and Venetia to the kingdom of Italy in 1866.

100 Centesimi = 1 Lira
100 Soldi = 1 Florin (1858)

Unused examples without gum of Nos. 1-24 are worth approximately 20% of the values given, which are for stamps with original gum as defined in the catalogue introduction.

For similar designs in Kreuzers, see early Austria.

Coat of Arms — A1

15 CENTESIMI:
Type I- "5" is on a level with the "1." One heavy line around coat of arms center.
Type II- As type I, but "5" is a trifle sideways and is higher than the "1."
Type III- As type II, but two, thinner, lines around center.

45 CENTESIMI:
Type I- Lower part of "45" is lower than "Centes." One heavy line around coat of arms center. "45" varies in height and distance from "Centes."
Type II- One heavy line around coat of arms center. Lower part of "45" is on a level with lower part of "Centes."
Type III- As type II, but two, thinner, lines around center.

Wmk. K.K.H.M. in Sheet or Unwmkd.
1850   **Typo.**   *Imperf.*
Thick to Thin Paper

1	A1	5c buff	2,250.	125.00
a.		Printed on both sides	8,500.	225.00
b.		5c yellow	4,500.	325.00
c.		5c orange	2,500.	175.00
d.		5c lemon yellow		1,450.
3	A1	10c black	2,250.	110.00
a.		10c gray black	2,250.	100.00
4	A1	15c red, type III	1,000.	5.00
b.		15c red, type I	2,500.	20.00
c.		Ribbed paper, type II		750.00
d.		Ribbed paper, type I	11,000.	200.00
f.		15c red, type II	1,200.	11.00
5	A1	30c brown	2,900.	8.00
a.		Ribbed paper	4,500.	125.00
6	A1	45c blue, type III	10,500.	30.00
a.		45c blue, type I	11,000.	45.00
b.		Ribbed paper, type I	—	375.00
c.		45c blue, type II		55.00

1854   **Machine-made Paper, Type III**

3c	A1	10c black	6,000.	225.00
4g	A1	15c pale red	650.00	3.50
5b	A1	30c brown	2,750.	3.50
6d	A1	45c blue	8,000.	35.00

See note about the paper of the 1850 issue of Austria. *The reprints are type III, in brighter colors.*

A2   A3

A4   A5

A6

Two Types of Each Value.
Type I- Loops of the bow at the back of the head broken.
Type II- Loops complete. Wreath projects further at top of head.

1858-62   **Embossed**   *Perf. 14½*

7	A2	2s yel, type II	650.00	125.00
a.		2s yellow, type I	3,500.	600.00
8	A3	3s black, type II	6,500.	150.00
a.		3s black, type I	2,500.	300.00
b.		Perf. 16, type I		1,100.
c.		Perf. 15x16 or 16x15, type I	4,500.	400.00
9	A3	3s grn, type II ('62)	500.00	100.00
10	A4	5s red, type II	275.00	5.00
a.		5s red, type I	850.00	
b.		Printed on both sides, type II		6,000.
11	A5	10s brown, type II	1,900.	11.00
a.		10s brown, type I		35.00
12	A6	15s blue, type II	2,250.	24.00
a.		15s blue, type I		100.00
b.		Printed on both sides, type II	3,500.	15,000.

The reprints are of type II and are perforated 10½, 11, 11½, 12, 12½ and 13. There are also imperforate reprints of Nos. 7-9.

A7   A8

1861-62   *Perf. 14*

13	A7	5s red	2,750.	3.00
14	A7	10s brown ('62)	4,000.	30.00

The reprints are perforated 9, 9 ½, 10½, 11, 12, 12½ and 13. There are also imperforate reprints of the 2 and 3s.
The 2, 3 and 15s of this type exist only as reprints.

1863

15	A8	2s yellow	150.00	150.00
16	A8	3s green	2,250.	100.00
17	A8	5s rose	2,750.	15.00
18	A8	10s blue	5,000.	85.00
19	A8	15s yellow brown	3,500.	140.00

1864-65   **Wmk. 91**   *Perf. 9½*

20	A8	2s yellow ('65)	200.00	500.00
21	A8	3s green	30.00	21.00
22	A8	5s rose	4.50	3.00
23	A8	10s blue	30.00	9.00
24	A8	15s yellow brown	275.00	100.00

Nos. 15-24 reprints are perforated 10½ and 13. There are also imperforate reprints of the 2s and 3s.

NEWSPAPER TAX STAMPS

From 1853 to 1858 the Austrian Newspaper Tax Stamp 2kr green (No. PR1) was also used in Lombardy-Venetia, at the value of 10 centesimi.

 NT1

Type I - The banderol of the left eagle touches the beak of the eagle.
Type II - The banderol does not touch the beak.

1858-59   **Unwmk. Typo.**   *Imperf.*

PR1	NT1	1kr black, type I ('59)	3,200.	3,200.
PR2	NT1	2kr red, type II ('59)	325.00	60.00
PR3	NT1	4kr red, type II	10,000.	3,500.

No. PR2 exists with watermark 91.
The reprints are on a smooth toned paper and are all of type II.

AZERBAIJAN

ˌa-zər-ˌbī-ˈjän

(Azerbaidjan)

LOCATION — Southernmost part of Russia in Eastern Europe, bounded by Georgia, Dagestan, Caspian Sea, Persia and Armenia
GOVT. — A Soviet Socialist Republic
AREA — 32,686 sq. mi.
POP. — 2,096,973 (1923)
CAPITAL — Baku

100 Kopecks = 1 Ruble

Catalogue values for unused stamps in this country are for Never Hinged items, beginning with Scott 350 in the regular postage section.

National Republic

Standard Bearer — A1   Farmer at Sunset — A2

Baku — A3

Temple of Eternal Fires — A4

1919   **Unwmk.**   **Litho.**   *Imperf.*

1	A1	10k multicolored	.15	.30
2	A1	20k multicolored	.15	.30
3	A2	40k green, yellow & blk	.15	.30
4	A2	60k red, yellow & blk	.25	.30

5	A2	1r blue, yellow & blk	.35	.50
6	A3	2r red, bister & blk	.35	.50
7	A3	5r blue, bister & blk	.45	.85
8	A3	10r olive grn, bis & blk	.65	.95
9	A4	25r blue, red & black	1.10	9.00
10	A4	50r ol grn, red & black	1.40	1.75
		Nos. 1-10 (10)	5.00	14.75

The two printings of Nos. 1-10 are distinguished by the grayish or thin white paper. Both have yellowish gum. White paper copies are worth five times the above values.
For surcharges see Nos. 57-64, 75-80.

Soviet Socialist Republic

Symbols of Labor — A5   Oil Well — A6

Bibi Eibatt Oil Field — A7   Khan's Palace, Baku — A8

Globe and Workers — A9   Maiden's Tower, Baku — A10

Goukasoff House A11   Blacksmiths A12

Hall of Judgment, Baku — A13

1922

15	A5	1r gray green	.20	.35
16	A6	2r olive black	.50	.50
17	A7	5r gray brown	.20	.35
18	A8	10r gray	.50	.65
19	A9	25r orange brown	.20	.40
20	A10	50r violet	.20	.40
21	A11	100r dull red	.35	.50
22	A12	150r blue	.35	.50
23	A9	250r violet & buff	.35	.50
24	A13	400r dark blue	.35	.50
25	A12	500r gray vio & blk	.35	.50
26	A13	1000r dk blue & rose	.35	.50
27	A8	2000r blue & black	.35	.50
28	A7	3000r brown & blue	.35	.50
a.		Tete beche pair	13.00	14.00
29	A11	5000r black, ol grn	.60	.75
		Nos. 15-29 (15)	5.20	7.50

Counterfeits exist of Nos. 1-29. They generally sell for more than genuine copies.
For overprints and surcharges see Nos. 32-41, 43, 45-55, 65-72, 300-304, 307-333.

Nos. 15, 17, 23, 28, 27 Handstamped from Metal Dies in a Numbering Machine

15000

1922

32	A5	10,000r on 1r	8.00	8.00
33	A7	15,000r on 5r	9.50	10.00
34	A9	33,000r on 250r	5.00	5.00

35	A7	50,000r on 3000r	5.00	5.00
36	A8	66,000r on 2000r	11.00	10.00
		Nos. 32-36 (5)	38.50	38.00

Same Surcharges on Regular Issue and Semi-Postal Stamps of 1922
1922-23

36A	A7	500r on 5r	60.00	67.50
37	A6	1000r on 2r	15.00	15.00
38	A8	2000r on 10r	5.00	5.00
39	A8	5000r on 2000r	5.00	3.00
40	A11	15,000r on 5000r	12.00	10.00
41	A5	20,000r on 1r	10.00	9.00
42	SP1	25,000r on 500r	35.00	
43	A7	50,000r on 5r	12.50	12.50
44	SP2	50,000r on 1000r	26.00	
45	A11	50,000r on 5000r	5.00	4.50
45A	A8	60,000r on 2000r	12.50	14.00
46	A11	70,000r on 5000r	20.00	20.00
47	A6	100,000r on 2r	15.00	15.00
48	A8	200,000r on 10r	10.00	10.00
49	A9	200,000r on 25r	15.00	15.00
50	A7	300,000r on 3000r	15.00	15.00
51	A8	500,000r on 2000r	15.00	10.00

Revalued

52	A7	500r on #33	30.00	52.50
53	A11	15,000r on #46	30.00	52.50
54	A7	300,000r on #35	45.00	55.00
55	A8	500,000r on #36	50.00	75.00

The surcharged semi-postal stamps were used for regular postage.

Same Surcharges on Stamps of 1919

57	A1	25,000r on 10k	.70	1.00
58	A1	50,000r on 20k	.70	1.00
59	A2	75,000r on 60k	1.75	2.50
60	A2	100,000r on 60k	.70	.95
61	A2	200,000r on 1r	.70	.95
62	A3	300,000r on 2r	.88	1.50
63	A3	500,000r on 5r	1.00	1.10
64	A2	750,000r on 40k	3.50	2.75
		Nos. 57-64 (8)	9.93	11.35

Handstamped from Settings of Rubber Type in Black or Violet

100000   200.000
Nos. 65-66, 71-80   Nos. 67-70

On Stamps of 1922

65	A6	100,000r on 2r	12.00	12.00
66	A8	200,000r on 10r	13.00	14.00
67	A8	200,000r on 10r (V)	17.50	15.00
68	A9	200,000r on 25r (V)	15.00	11.00
a.		Black surcharge	26.00	27.50
69	A7	300,000r on 3000r (V)	25.00	25.00
70	A8	200,000r on 2000r (V)	20.00	20.00
a.		Black surcharge	27.50	29.00
72	A11	1,500,000r on 5000r (V)	16.00	15.00
a.		Black surcharge	16.00	15.00

On Stamps of 1919

75	A1	50,000r on 20k		1.00
76	A2	75,000r on 40k		.65
77	A2	100,000r on 60k		1.25
78	A2	200,000r on 1r	.15	.15
79	A3	300,000r on 5r		1.10
80	A3	500,000r on 5r		1.25

Inverted and double surcharges of Nos. 32-80 sell for twice the normal price.
Counterfeits exist of Nos. 32-80.

Baku Province
Regular and Semi-Postal Stamps of 1922 Handstamped in Violet or Black

БАКИНСКОИ П. К.

The overprint reads "Bakinskoi P(ochtovoy) K(ontory)," meaning Baku Post Office.

1922   **Unwmk.**   *Imperf.*

300	A5	1r gray green	13.00
301	A7	5r gray brown	13.00
302	A12	150r blue	4.00
303	A9	250r violet & buff	6.00
304	A13	400r dark blue	5.25
305	SP1	500r blue & pale blue	6.00
306	SP2	1000r brown & bister	8.00
307	A8	2000r blue & black	8.00
308	A7	3000r brown & blue	13.00
309	A11	5000r black, ol grn	13.00
		Nos. 300-309 (10)	89.25

Stamps of 1922 Handstamped in Violet

Бакинскаго Г.-П.-Т.О.Х₀ 1

Ovpt. reads: Baku Post, Telegraph Office No. 1.

1924

Overprint 24x2mm

312	A12	150r blue	6.00
313	A9	250r violet & buff	6.00
314	A13	400r dark blue	6.00
317	A8	2000r blue & black	6.50

318	A7	3000r brown & blue	6.50
319	A11	5000r black, ol grn	6.50

Overprint 30x3¹/₂mm

323	A12	150r blue	6.00
324	A9	250r violet & buff	6.00
325	A13	400r dark blue	6.00
328	A8	2000r blue & black	6.00
329	A7	3000r brown & blue	6.50
330	A11	5000r black, ol grn	6.00

Overprinted on Nos. 32-33, 35

331	A5	10,000r on 1r	22.50
332	A7	15,000r on 5r	22.50
333	A7	50,000r on 3000r	27.50
		Nos. 312-333 (15)	146.50

The overprinted semipostal stamps were used for regular postage.

A 24x2mm handstamp on #17, B1-B2, and 30x3¹/₂mm on #15, 17, B1-B2, was of private origin.

With the breakup of the Soviet Union on Dec. 26, 1991, Azerbaijan and ten former Soviet republics established the Commonwealth of Independent States.

100 Kopecks = 1 Ruble
100 Giapiks = 1 Manat (1992)

> Catalogue values for unused stamps in this section, from this point to the end of the section, are for Never Hinged items.

Flag, Map — A20

Unwmk.
1992, Mar. 26   Litho.   Perf. 14
350	A20	35k multicolored	1.40

Park — A21

1992, May 7   Perf. 12
351	A21	25g on 15k multicolored	.35
a.		Booklet pane of 12	4.25
		Complete booklet, #351a	4.25
352	A21	35g on 15k multicolored	.40
353	A21	50g on 15k multicolored	.60
354	A21	1.50m on 15k multicolored	1.75
355	A21	2.50m on 15k multicolored	2.00
		Nos. 351-355 (5)	6.10

Nos. 351-355 are overprinted or surcharged on a National Park series prepared for the Soviet Union with one stamp for each republic. Not issued without surcharge.
For additional surcharges see Nos. 435, 501-504.

Iran-Azerbaijan
Telecommunications — A21a

1992   Photo.   Perf. 13x13¹/₂
355A	A21a	15g multicolored	1.65

See Iran No. 2544.
For surcharges see Nos. 403-406.

20q Horses — A22

1993, Feb. 1   Litho.   Perf. 13
356	A22	20g shown	.15
357	A22	30g Kabarda	.15
358	A22	50g Qarabair	.15
359	A22	1m Don	.25
360	A22	2.50m Yakut	.60
361	A22	5m Orlov	1.25
362	A22	10m Diliboz	2.50
		Nos. 356-362 (7)	5.05

Perf. 12¹/₂
Souvenir Sheet
362A	A22	8m Qarabag	.90

For overprints see Nos. 629-636.

Ruins — A23   Government
Building — A24

1992-93   Litho.   Perf. 12¹/₂x12
363	A23	10g blk & blue grn	.15
365	A23	20g black & red	.20
367	A23	50g black & blue grn	.15
368	A23	50g black & yellow	.50
370	A23	1m black & rose lilac	.25
372	A23	1.50m black & blue	1.50
373	A23	2.50m black & yellow	.50
374	A23	5m black & green	1.00
		Nos. 363-374 (8)	4.25

Issued: 10g, 20g, 1.50m, #367, Dec. 20; #368, 1m, 2.50m, 5m, June 20, 1993.
For surcharges see Nos. 550-557.
This is an expanding set. Numbers may change.

1993, Oct. 12   Litho.   Perf. 12¹/₂
375	A24	25g yellow & black	.15
376	A24	30g green & black	.20
377	A24	50g blue & black	.30
378	A24	1m red & black	.55
		Nos. 375-378 (4)	1.20

For surcharges see No. 407-414.

Flowers — A25

1993, Aug. 12   Litho.   Perf. 12¹/₂
379	A25	25g Tulipa eichleri	.15
380	A25	50g Puschkinia scilloides	.15
381	A25	1m Iris elegantissima	.20
382	A25	1.50m Iris acutiloba	.30
383	A25	5m Tulipa florenskyii	1.10
384	A25	10m Iris reticulata	2.00
		Nos. 379-384 (6)	3.90

Souvenir Sheet
Perf. 13
385	A25	10m Muscari elecostomum	2.00

No. 385 contains one 32x40mm stamp.

Fish
25q A26

25g, Acipenser guldenstadti. 50g, Acipenser stellatus. 1m, Rutilus frisii kutum. 1.50m, Rutilus rutilus caspicus. 5m, Salmo trutta caspius. No. 391, Alosa kessleri. #392, Huso huso.

1993, Aug. 27   Perf. 12¹/₂
386	A26	25g multicolored	.15
387	A26	50g multicolored	.15
388	A26	1m multicolored	.20
389	A26	1.50m multicolored	.30
390	A26	5m multicolored	1.10
391	A26	10m multicolored	2.00
		Nos. 386-391 (6)	3.90

Souvenir Sheet
Perf. 13
392	A26	10m multicolored	2.00

No. 392 contains one 40x32mm stamp.

Pres. Geidar A.
Aliyev — A27

Design: No. 394, Map of Nakhichevan.

1993, Sept. 12   Litho.   Perf. 12¹/₂x13
393	A27	25m multicolored	2.00
394	A27	25m multicolored	2.00
a.		Pair, #393-394	4.00
b.		Souv. sheet, #393-394, perf. 12	4.00
c.		Souv. sheet, #393-394, perf. 12	4.00

Name on map spelled "Naxcivan" on #394c. It is spelled "Haxcivan" on #394b-394b.
No. 394c issued Sept. 20, 1993.

Historic Buildings,
Baku — A28

Style of tombs: 2m, Fortress, 13th-14th cent. 4m, Moorish gate, 15th cent. 8m, Oriental-style columns, 15th cent.

1994, Jan. 17   Litho.   Perf. 11
395	A28	2m red, silver & black	.20
396	A28	4m green, silver & black	.35
397	A28	8m blue, silver & black	.75
		Nos. 395-397 (3)	1.30

A29   A30

1994, Jan. 17   Perf. 12¹/₂
398	A29	5m Natl. Colors, Star, Crescent	.60
399	A29	8m Natl. coat of arms	1.00

1994, Jan. 17   Perf. 12¹/₂
400	A30	10m multi + label	.80

Mohammed Fizuli (1494-1556), poet.

Mammed
Amin
Rasulzade
(1884-1955),
Politician
A31

Jalil Mamedkulizade,
Politician, 125th
Birth Anniv. — A32

1994, May 21   Perf. 12¹/₂, 13 (#402)
401	A31	15m black, yellow & brown	.95
402	A32	20m black, blue & gold	.95

No. 402 printed se-tenant with label.

No. 355A Surcharged

 2 m.

1994, Jan. 18   Photo.   Perf. 13x13¹/₂
403	A21a	2m on 15g	.15
404	A21a	20m on 15g	.55
405	A21a	25m on 15g	.70
406	A21a	50m on 15g	1.40
		Nos. 403-406 (4)	2.80

5 m.

Nos. 375-378
Surcharged

1994, Feb. 22   Litho.   Perf. 12¹/₂
407	A24	5m on 1m #375	.15
408	A24	10m on 30g #377	.15
409	A24	15m on 30g #377	.20
a.		Pair, #408-409	.35
410	A24	20m on 50g #378	.30
411	A24	25m on 1m #375	.35
a.		Pair, #407, 411	.50
412	A24	40m on 50g #378	.55
a.		Pair, #410, 412	.85
413	A24	50m on 25g #376	.65
414	A24	100m on 25g #376	1.40
a.		Pair, #413-414	2.05
		Nos. 407-414 (8)	3.75

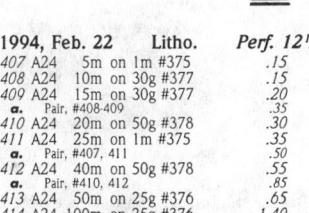

Baku Oil Fields — A33

Designs: 15m, Temple of Eternal Fires. 20m, Oil derricks. 25m, Early tanker. 50m, Ludwig Nobel, Robert Nobel, Petr Bilderling, Alfred Nobel.

1994, June 10   Photo.   Perf. 13
415	A33	15m multicolored	.40
416	A33	20m multicolored	.55
417	A33	25m multicolored	.65
418	A33	50m multicolored	1.40
a.		Souvenir sheet of 1	1.40
		Nos. 415-418 (4)	3.00

See Turkmenistan Nos. 39-43.

Minerals — A34   Posthorn — A35

1994, June 15   Litho.   Perf. 13
419	A34	5m Laumontite	.40
420	A34	10m Epidot calcite	.70
421	A34	15m Andradite	1.10
422	A34	20m Amethyst	1.40
a.		Souvenir sheet, #420-423 + 2 labels, perf. 12	4.75
		Nos. 419-422 (4)	3.60

1994   Litho.   Perf. 12½
426 A35 5m black & red   .15
427 A35 10m black & green   .15
428 A35 20m black & blue   .15
429 A35 25m black & yellow   .25
431 A35 40m black & brown   .35
    Nos. 426-431 (5)   1.05
For surcharges see Nos. 487-489A.

400 м.

No. 351 Surcharged

25q

Unwmk.
1994, Oct. 17   Litho.   Perf. 12
435 A21 400m on 25g multi   .85

Souvenir Sheet

Pres. Geidar A. Aliyev — A36

Illustration reduced.

1994, Oct. 28   Litho.   Perf. 14
436 A36 150m multicolored   3.50

Ships of
the
Caspian
Sea
A37

Designs: a, Tugboat, "Captain Racebov." b,
"Azerbaijan." c, Balt Ro Ro line, "Merkuri I." d,
Tanker, "Tovuz." e, Tanker.

1994, Oct. 28
437 A37 50m Strip of 5, #a.-e.   2.75
Issued in sheets of 15 stamps. The background of
the sheet shows a nautical chart, giving each stamp
a different background.

1994 World Cup Soccer Championships,
US — A38

Various soccer plays. Denominations: 5m, 10m,
20m, 25m, 30m, 50m, 80m.

1994, June 17   Litho.   Perf. 13
438-444 A38 Set of 7   5.25
Souvenir Sheet
445 A38 100m multicolored   2.25
No. 445 contains one 32x40mm stamp and is a
continuous design.

Dinosaurs
A39

Designs: 5m, Coelophysis, segisaurus. 10m,
Pentaceratops, tyrannosaurids. 20m, Segnosaurus,
oviraptor. 25m, Albertosaurus, corythosaurus. 30m,
Iguanodons. 50m, Stegosaurus, allosaurus. 80m,
Tyrannosaurus, saurolophus.

100m, Phobetor.

1994, Sept. 15
446-452 A39 Set of 7   5.25
Souvenir Sheet
Perf. 12½
453 A39 100m multicolored   2.25
No. 453 contains one 40x32mm stamp and is a
continuous design.

Lyrurus Mlokosiewickzi — A40

a, 50m, Female on nest. b, 80m, Female on
mountain cliff. c, 100m, 2 males. d, 120m, Male.

1994, Dec. 15   Litho.   Perf. 12½
454 A40 Block of 4, #a.-d.   3.25
World Wildlife Fund.

Raptors
A41 10m.

Designs: 10m, Haliaeetus albicilla. 15m, Aguila
heliaca. 20m, Aguila rapax. 25m, Gypaetus
barbatus, vert. 50m, Falco cherrug, vert.
100m, Aguila chrysaetos.

1994, Nov. 15   Litho.   Perf. 13
458-462 A41 Set of 5   5.25
Souvenir Sheet
Perf. 12½
463 A41 100m multicolored   2.25
No. 463 contains one 40x32mm stamp and is a
continuous design.

25m. Cats
A42

Designs: 10m, Felis libica, vert. 15m, Felis
otocolobus, vert. 20m, Felis lyns. 25m, Felis
pardus. 50m, Panthera tigrus.
100m, Panthera tigrus adult and cub, vert.

1994, Dec. 14   Perf. 13
464-468 A42 Set of 5   5.25
Souvenir Sheet
469 A42 100m multicolored   2.25
No. 469 contains one 32x40mm stamp and is a
continuous design.
For overprints see Nos. 637-642.

Butterflies
A43 10m.

Designs: 10m, Parnassius apollo. 25m, Zegris
menestho. 50m, Manduca atropos. 60m, Pararge
adrastoides.

1995, Jan. 23   Litho.   Perf. 14
470 A43 10m multicolored   .42
471 A43 25m multicolored   1.00
472 A43 50m multicolored   2.00
473 A43 60m multicolored   2.50
a.   Souvenir sheet of 4, #470-473   6.00
    Nos. 470-473 (4)   5.92

Intl. Olympic Committee, Cent. — A44

Designs: No. 474, Pierre de Coubertin. No. 475,
Discus. No. 476, Javelin.

1994, Dec. 15   Litho.   Perf. 12
474-476 A44 100m Set of 3   3.30

A45   A46

1994 Winter Olympic medalists, Lillehammer:
10m, Aleksei Urnamov, Russia, figure skating. 25,
Nancy Kerrigan, US, figure skating. 40m Bonnie
Blair, US, speed skating, horiz. 50m, Takanori
Kano, Japan, ski jumping, horiz. 80m, Philip Laros,
Canada, freestyle skiing. 100m, Four-man bobsled,
Germany.
200m, Katja Seizinger, skiing, Germany, vert.

1995, Feb. 10   Litho.   Perf. 14
478-483 A45 Set of 6   5.00
Souvenir Sheet
484 A45 200m multicolored   4.50

1995, Feb. 21
Women in space: No. 485a, Mary Kliv, US. b,
Valentina Tereshkova, Russia. c, Tamara Cernigan,
US. d, Wendy Lourens, US.
No. 486a, Meg Jamison, US. b, Kitty Coleman,
US. c, Ellen Sulman, US. d, M.I. Weber, US.
Miniature Sheets of 4
485-486 A46 100m each, #a.-d.   7.00
First manned moon landing, 25th anniv. (in
1994).

Nos. 426-428
Surcharged

100 м.

1995   Litho.   Perf. 12½
487 A35 100m on 5m #426   .20
488 A35 250m on 10m #427   .55
488A A35 400m on 25m No. 429   .75
489 A35 500m on 20m #428   1.10
489A A35 900m on 40m No. 431   1.65
    Nos. 487-489A (5)   4.25
Issued: #488A, 7/7; #487-488, 489, 2/28.

Mushrooms — A47

Designs: 100m, Gymnopilus spectabilis. 250m,
Fly agaris. 300m, Lepiota procera. 400m,
Hygrophorus spectosus.
500m, Fly agaris, diff.

1995, Sept. 1   Litho.   Perf. 14
490-493 A47 Set of 4   4.50
Souvenir Sheet
494 A47 500m multicolored   4.50

Singapore
'95
A48

Orchids: 100m, Paphiopedilum argus, paphiopedilum barbatum. 250m, Maxillaria picta. 300m,
Laeliocattleya. 400m, Dendrobium nobile.
500m, Cattleya gloriette.

1995, Sept. 1
495-498 A48 Set of 4   4.50
Souvenir Sheet
499 A48 500m multicolored   4.50

UN, 50th
Anniv.
A49

Design: 250m, Azerbaijan Pres. Geidar A. Aliyev,
UN Sec. Gen. Boutros Boutros-Ghali.

1995, Sept. 15
500 A49 250m multicolored   2.25

200 м.

Nos. 352-355
Surcharged

1995   Litho.   Perf. 12
501 A21 200m on 2.50m #355   .30
502 A21 600m on 35g #352   .85
503 A21 800m on 50g #353   1.10
504 A21 1000m on 1.50m #354   1.40
    Nos. 501-504 (4)   3.65

Uzeyir Hacibeyov
(1885-1948) — A50

Design: 400m, Oglu Iskenderov (1895-1965).

1995, June 30   Litho.   Perf. 12x12½
505 A50 250m silver gray & black .45
506 A50 400m gold bister & brown .75

Balloons
and
Airships
A51

Designs: 100m, First hydrogen balloon, 1784,
vert. 150m, First motorized balloon, 1883, vert.
250m, First elliptical balloon, 1784. 300m, First
Scott Baldwin dirigible, 1904. 400m, US Marine
balloon, 1917. 500m, Pedal-powered dirigible,
1909.
800m, First rigid dirigible designed by Hugo Eckener, 1924.

1995, July 20   Litho.   Perf. 13
507 A51 100m multicolored   .20
508 A51 150m multicolored   .30
509 A51 250m multicolored   .45
510 A51 300m multicolored   .55
511 A51 400m multicolored   .75
512 A51 500m multicolored   .90
    Nos. 507-512 (6)   3.15
Souvenir Sheet
513 A51 800m multicolored   1.50

Marine
Life
A52

Designs: 50m, Loligo vulgaris. 100m, Orchis-
toma pileus. 150m, Pegea confoederata. 250m,

Polyorchis karafutoensis, vert. 300m, Agalma okeni, vert.
500m, Corolla spectabillis.

1995, June 2   **Litho.**   **Perf. 13**
514	A52	50m multicolored	.45
515	A52	100m multicolored	.85
516	A52	150m multicolored	1.25
517	A52	250m multicolored	2.25
518	A52	300m multicolored	2.50
		Nos. 514-518 (5)	7.30

Souvenir Sheet
519	A52	500m multicolored	4.25

Turtles
A53

Designs: 50m, Chelus fimbriatus. 100m, Caretta caretta. 150m, Geochelone pardalis. 250m, Geochelone elegans. 300m, Testudo hermanni.
500m, Macroclemys temmincki.

1995, June 12   **Litho.**   **Perf. 13**
520	A53	50m multicolored	.45
521	A53	100m multicolored	.90
522	A53	150m multicolored	1.25
523	A53	250m multicolored	2.25
524	A53	300m multicolored	2.50
		Nos. 520-524 (5)	7.35

Souvenir Sheet
525	A53	500m multicolored	4.50

1998 World Cup
Soccer
Championships,
France — A54

Various soccer plays.

1995, Sept. 30   **Litho.**   **Perf. 12½**
526	A54	100m orange & multi	.20
527	A54	150m green & multi	.30
528	A54	250m yellow orange & multi	.45
529	A54	300m yellow & multi	.55
530	A54	400m blue & multi	.75
		Nos. 526-530 (5)	2.25

Souvenir Sheet
Perf. 13
531	A54	600m multicolored	1.10

Domestic
Cats — A55

1995, Oct. 30   **Perf. 12½**
532	A55	100m Persian	.20
533	A55	150m Chartreux	.30
534	A55	250m Somali	.45
535	A55	300m Longhair Scottish fold	.55
536	A55	400m Cumric	.75
537	A55	500m Turkish angora	.90
		Nos. 532-537 (6)	3.15

Souvenir Sheet
538	A55	800m Birman	1.50

No. 538 contains one 32x40mm stamp.

Fauna and
Flora — A56

Designs: 100m, Horse. 200m, Muscari elecostomum, vert. 250m, Huso huso. 300m, Aquila chrysaetos. 400m, Panthera tigrus. 500m, Lyrurus

miokosiewickzi, facing right. 1000m, Lyrurus miokosiewickzi, facing left.

1995, Nov. 30
539	A56	100m multicolored	.20
540	A56	200m multicolored	.40
541	A56	250m multicolored	.45
542	A56	300m multicolored	.55
543	A56	400m multicolored	.75
544	A56	500m multicolored	.90
545	A56	1000m multicolored	2.00
		Nos. 539-545 (7)	5.25

John
Lennon
(1940-80)
A57

1995, Dec. 8   **Perf. 14½**
546	A57	500m multicolored	.90

Miniature Sheet

Locomotives — A58

Designs: No. 547a, 4-4-0, America. b, J3 Hudson, US. c, 2-8-2. d, 2-6-2, Germany. e, 2-8-2, Germany. f, 2-6-2, Italy. g, G-C5, Japan. h, 2-10-2 QJ, China. i, 0-10-0, China.
500m, Electric passenger train, vert.

1996, Feb. 1   **Perf. 14**
547	A58	100m Sheet of 9, #a.-i.	12.00

Souvenir Sheet
548	A58	500m multicolored	6.00

AZƏRBAYCAN POÇTU 1995
Dr. M. Topcubasov, Surgeon — A59

1996, Feb. 1
549	A59	300m multicolored	4.00

Nos. 363, 365, 367-368,
370, 372-374 Surcharged **250 M.**

1995, Jan. 4   **Litho.**   **Perf. 12½x12**
550	A23	250m on 10g #363	.25
551	A23	250m on 20g #365	.25
552	A23	250m on 50g #368	.25
553	A23	250m on 1.50m #372	.25
554	A23	500m on 50g #367	.50
555	A23	500m on 1m #370	.50
556	A23	500m on 2.50m #373	.50
557	A23	500m on 5m #374	.50
		Nos. 550-557 (8)	3.00

1996
Olympic
Games,
Atlanta
A60

1996, Apr. 9   **Litho.**   **Perf. 14**
568	A60	50m Carl Lewis	.35
569	A60	100m Muhammed Ali	.70
570	A60	150m Li Ning	1.10
571	A60	200m Said Aouita	1.40
572	A60	250m Olga Korbut	1.75
573	A60	300m Nadia Comaneci	2.00
574	A60	400m Greg Louganis	2.75
		Nos. 568-574 (7)	10.05

Souvenir Sheet
575	A60	500m Nazim Hüseynov, vert.	3.50

Husein
Aliyev
(1911-91),
Artist
A61

Paintings: 100m, Water bird, swamp. 200m, Landscape.

1996, Apr. 16   **Litho.**   **Perf. 14**
576	A61	100m multicolored	.90
577	A61	200m multicolored	1.75
a.		Pair, #576-577 + label	2.60

No. 577a issued in sheets of 6 stamps.

Resid Behbudov (1915-89), Singer — A62

1996, Apr. 22   **Perf. 12½**
578	A62	100m multicolored	1.30

A63   A64

1996, Mar. 20
579	A63	250m multicolored	2.50

Novruz Bayrami, natl. holiday.

1996, May 28   **Litho.**   **Perf. 14**
580	A64	250m multicolored	2.50

Independence, 5th anniv.

A65   A66

1996, Apr. 22   **Litho.**   **Perf. 12½**
581	A65	100m multicolored	1.25 1.25

Yusif Memmedeliyev (1905-95), chemist.

1996, June 7   **Perf. 14**

Jerusalem, 3000th Anniv.: a, 100m, Wailing Wall. b, 250m, Inside cathedral. c, 300m, Dome of the Rock.
500m, Windmill.
582	A66	Sheet of 3, #a.-c.	5.00 5.00

Souvenir Sheet
583	A66	500m multicolored	5.00 5.00

For overprints see Nos. 643-644.

Dogs
A67

Designs: 50m, German shepherd. 100m, Basset hound. 150m, Collie. 200m, Bull terrier. 300m, Boxer. 400m, Cocker spaniel.
500m, Sharpei.

1996, June 18   **Perf. 13**
584-589	A67	Set of 6	6.00 6.00

Souvenir Sheet
590	A67	500m multicolored	3.00 3.00

Birds — A68

Designs: 50m, Tetraenura regia. 100m, Coliuspasser macrourus. 150m, Oriolus xanthornus. 200m, Oriolus oriolus. 300m, Sturnus vulgaris. 400m, Serinus mozambicus.
500m, Merops apiaster.

1996, June 19   **Perf. 13**
591-596	A68	Set of 6	6.00 6.00

Souvenir Sheet
597	A68	500m multicolored	3.00 3.00

Roses — A69

Designs: 50m, Burgundy. 100m, Virgo. 150m, Rose gaujard. 200m, Luna. 300m, Lady rose. 400m, Landora.
500m, Lougsor, horiz.

1996, June 19
598-603	A69	Set of 6	6.00 6.00

Souvenir Sheet
604	A69	500m multicolored	3.00 3.00

A70   A71

1996, July 8   **Litho.**   **Perf. 14**
605	A70	500m multicolored	1.50 1.50

UNICEF, 50th anniv.

1996, July 22

Competing teams: 100m, Spain, Bulgaria. 150m, Romania, France. 200m, Czech Republic, Germany. 250m, England, Israel. 300m, Croatia, Turkey. 400m, Italy, Russia.
500m, Trophy cup.
606-611	A71	Set of 6	3.25 3.25

Souvenir Sheet
612	A71	500m multicolored	1.50 1.50

Euro '96, European Soccer Championships, Great Britain.

Ships
A72

Ship, home country: 100m, Chinese junk. 150m, Danmark, Denmark. 200m, Nippon Maru, Japan. 250m, Mircea, Romania. 300m, Kruzenshtern, Russia. 400m, Ariadne, Germany.
500m, Tovarishch, Russia, vert.

1996, Aug. 26   Litho.   *Perf. 14*
613-618 A72 Set of 6   5.00 5.00
Souvenir Sheet
619 A72 500m multicolored   4.00 4.00
For overprints see Nos. 645-651.

Sculpture — A73

1997, Mar. 6   Litho.   *Perf. 13½x13*
620 A73 250m black & yellow   .15 .15
621 A73 400m black & vermilion   .20 .20
622 A73 500m black & green   .25 .25
623 A73 1000m black & purple   .50 .50
Nos. 620-623 (4)   1.10 1.10

Famous Personalities — A74

Designs: No. 624, Mamed-Kerim Ogli Aliyev (1897-1962), politician. No. 625, Illyas Efendiyev (1914-96), writer. No. 626, Fatali Xan-Xoyskiy (1875-1920), politician. No. 627, Nariman Narimanov (1870-1925), politician, writer.

1997, Mar. 25   Litho.   *Perf. 14*
Background Color
624 A74 250m tan   1.10 1.10
625 A74 250m gray blue   1.10 1.10
626 A74 250m pale red   1.10 1.10
627 A74 250m pale olive   1.10 1.10
Nos. 624-627 (4)   4.40 4.40

Qobustan Prehistoric Art — A75

Rock carvings: a, Oxen. b, Large horned animals. c, Six figures.

1997, May 19   Litho.   *Perf. 14*
628 A75 500m Sheet of 3, #a.-c.   4.25 4.25

#356-362A, 464-469 Ovptd. in Red

✚
Red Cross

1997, June 2   Litho.   *Perf. 13*
Denominations as Before
629-635 A22 Set of 7   8.00 8.00
Souvenir Sheet
636 A22 8m multicolored   5.00 5.00
Location of overprint varies. No. 636 is ovptd. both on stamp and in sheet margin.

1997, June 2
Denominations as Before
637-641 A42 Set of 5   6.00 6.00
Souvenir Sheet
642 A42 100m multicolored   5.00 5.00
Location of overprint varies. No. 642 is ovptd. both on stamp and in sheet margin.

Nos. 582-583, 613-619 Ovptd.

1997, June 2   *Perf. 14*
643 A66 Sheet of 3, #a.-c.   5.00 5.00
Souvenir Sheet
644 A66 500m multicolored   5.00 5.00
Size and location of overprint varies. Overprint appears both on stamp and in sheet margin.

1997, June 2   *Perf. 14*
Denominations as Before
645-650 A72 Set of 6   5.00 5.00
Souvenir Sheet
651 A72 500m multicolored   5.00 5.00
Location of overprint varies. No. 651 is ovptd. both on stamp and in sheet margin.

Grimm's Fairy Tales — A76

Bremen Musical: No. 652: a, Dog. b, Dancing horse, cat. c, Rooster.
500m, Animals looking through window at treaure chest, man.

1997, July 1   *Perf. 13½x14*
652 A76 250m Sheet of 3, #a.-c.   2.00 2.00
Souvenir Sheet
653 A76 500m multicolored   1.40 1.40

Caspian Seals A77

Designs: a, Seal looking right. b, Mountain top, seal looking forward. c, Seal, seagull. d, Seal looking left. e, Seal looking forward. f, Small seal.
500m, Mother nursing pup.

1997, July 1
654 A77 250m Sheet of 6, #a.-f.   4.25 4.25
Souvenir Sheet
655 A77 500m multicolored   1.40 1.40

Traditional Musical Instruments A77a

1997, Aug. 4   Litho.   *Perf. 14*
656 A77a 250m Qaval   .75 .75
657 A77a 250m Tanbur   .75 .75
658 A77a 500m Cenq   1.50 1.50
Nos. 656-658 (3)   3.00 3.00

A78   A79

Azerbaijan Oil Industry: a, Early oil derricks, building. b, Off-shore oil drilling platform.

1997, Aug. 18   *Perf. 14½*
Souvenir Sheet
659 A78 500m Sheet of 2, #a.-b.   3.00 3.00

1997, Sept. 12   *Perf. 14x13½*
660 A79 250m Hagani Shirvany, poet 1.00 1.00
No. 660 was issued in sheets of 4 + 5 labels.

Mosques A80

#661, Ashaqi mechet Qovqar-agi, Shusha, 1874-75. #662, Momuna-Zatun, Naxcivan, 1187. #663, Taza-pir, Baku (1905-14).

1997, Sept. 18   Litho.   *Perf. 14*
661 A80 250m multicolored   .85 .85
662 A80 250m multicolored   .85 .85
663 A80 250m multicolored   .85 .85
Nos. 661-663 (3)   2.55 2.55

H.C. Rasul Beyov (1917-1984), Communications Official — A81

1997, Oct. 6   Litho.   *Perf. 14*
664 A81 250m multicolored   2.00 2.00

1998 World Cup Soccer Championships, France — A82

Winning team photos: No. 665: a, Italy, 1938. b, Argentina, 1986. c, Uruguay, 1980. d, Brazil, 1994. e, England, 1966. f, Germany, 1990.
1500m, Tofiq Bahramov, "Golden Whistle" prize winner, 1966, vert.

1997, Oct. 15
665 A82 250m Sheet of 6, #a.-f.   5.00 5.00
Souvenir Sheet
666 A82 1500m multicolored   4.00 4.00

SEMI-POSTAL STAMPS

Carrying Food to Sufferers — SP1

1922   Unwmk.   *Imperf.*
B1 SP1 500r blue & pale blue   .40 .75
For overprint and surcharge see Nos. 42, 305.

Widow and Orphans — SP2

1922
B2 SP2 1000r brown & bister   .50 1.25
Counterfeits exist.

For overprint and surcharge see Nos. 44, 306.

OCCUPATION AZIRBAYEDJAN

Russian stamps of 1909-18 were privately overprinted as above in red, blue or black by a group of Entente officers working with Russian soldiers returning from Persia. Azerbaijan was not occupied by the Allies. There is evidence that existing covers (some seemingly postmarked at Baku, dated Oct. 19, 1917, and at Tabriz, Russian Consulate, Apr. 25, 1917) are fakes.

AIR POST STAMP

Catalogue values for all stamps in this section are for never hinged items.

Eagle — AP1

1995, Oct. 16   Litho.   *Perf. 14*
C1 AP1 2200m multicolored   6.00

AZORES
'ā–zōrz

LOCATION — Group of islands in the North Atlantic Ocean, due west of Portugal
GOVT. — Integral part of Portugal, former colony
AREA — 922 sq. mi.
POP. — 253,935 (1930)
CAPITAL — Ponta Delgada

Azores stamps were supplanted by those of Portugal in 1931.

1000 Reis = 1 Milreis
100 Centavos = 1 Escudo (1912)

See Portugal for other recent issues.

Stamps of Portugal Overprinted in Black or Carmine

AÇORES
a

A second type of this overprint has a broad "O" and open "S."

1868		**Unwmk.**	*Imperf.*	
1	A14	5r black	3,250.	1,750.
2	A14	10r yellow	13,500.	7,500.
3	A14	20r bister	250.00	125.00
4	A14	50r green	250.00	125.00
5	A14	80r orange	250.00	125.00
6	A14	100r lilac	250.00	125.00

The reprints are on thick chalky white wove paper, ungummed, and on thin ivory paper with shiny white gum. Value $20 each.

1868-70   *Perf. 12½*
5 REIS:
Type I - The "5" at the right is 1mm from end of label.
Type II - The "5" is 1½mm from end of label.
7	A14	5r black (C)	70.00	50.00
8	A14	10r yellow	90.00	50.00
a.		Inverted overprint	250.00	150.00

AZORES

9	A14	20r bister	70.00	45.00
10	A14	25r rose	70.00	8.00
a.		Inverted overprint	—	
11	A14	50r green	200.00	140.00
12	A14	80r orange	200.00	140.00
13	A14	100r lilac	200.00	140.00
14	A14	120r blue	170.00	90.00
15	A14	240r violet	600.00	300.00

The reprints are on thick chalky white paper ungummed, perf 13½, and on thin ivory paper with shiny white gum, perf 13½. Value $10 each.

1871-75			*Perf. 12½, 13½*	
21	A15	5r black (C)	12.50	6.00
a.		Inverted overprint	47.50	30.00
23	A15	10r yellow	27.50	20.00
a.		Inverted overprint		
24	A15	20r bister	25.00	19.00
25	A15	25r rose	16.00	5.00
a.		Inverted overprint		
b.		Double overprint	35.00	25.00
c.		Perf. 14	165.00	55.00
d.		Dbl. impression of stamp		
26	A15	50r green	80.00	30.00
27	A15	80r orange	110.00	50.00
28	A15	100r lilac	90.00	45.00
a.		Perf. 14	165.00	100.00
29	A15	120r blue	165.00	95.00
30	A15	240r violet	800.00	500.00

Nos. 21-29 exist with overprint "b."

The reprints are of type "b." They are on thick chalky white paper ungummed, perf 13½, and also on thin white paper with shiny white gum, perforated 13½.

Overprinted in Black

AÇORES
b

1875-80

15 REIS:

Type I - The figures of value, 1 and 5, at the right in upper label are close together.
Type II - The figures of value at the right in upper label are spaced.

31	A15	10r blue green	175.00	100.00
32	A15	10r yellow green	100.00	60.00
33	A15	15r lilac brown	17.50	12.00
a.		Inverted overprint	125.00	
34	A15	50r blue	150.00	60.00
35	A15	150r blue	160.00	100.00
36	A15	150r yellow	200.00	175.00
37	A15	300r violet	80.00	60.00

The reprints have the same papers, gum and perforations as those of the preceding issue.

Black Overprint

1880			*Perf. 12½, 13½*	
38	A17	25r gray	125.00	30.00
39	A18	25r red lilac	50.00	6.00
a.		25r gray		
b.		Double overprint	50.00	6.00

Overprinted in Carmine or Black

1881-82				
40	A16	5r black (C)	21.00	7.50
41	A23	25r brown ('82)	45.00	5.00
a.		Inverted overprint		
42	A19	50r blue	150.00	30.00
		Nos. 40-42 (3)	216.00	42.50

Reprints of Nos. 38, 39, 39a, 40 and 42 have the same papers, gum and perforations as those of preceding issues.

Overprinted in Red or Black

AÇORES
c

1882-85   *Perf. 11½, 12½, 13½*

15, 20 REIS

Type I - The figures of value are some distance apart and close to the end of the label.
Type II - The figures are closer together and farther from the end of the label. On the 15 reis this is particularly apparent in the upper right figures.

43	A16	5r black (R)	25.00	10.00
44	A21	5r slate	15.00	3.00
a.		Double overprint		
c.		Inverted overprint		
45	A15	10r green	75.00	50.00
a.		Inverted overprint		
46	A22	10r green	25.00	10.00
a.		Double overprint		
47	A15	15r lilac brn	65.00	35.00
b.		Inverted overprint		
48	A15	20r bister	90.00	50.00
a.		Inverted overprint		
49	A15	20r carmine	125.00	80.00
a.		Inverted overprint	165.00	100.00
50	A23	25r brown	19.00	3.00
51	A15	50r blue	1,200.	1,000.
52	A24	50r blue	24.00	3.00
53	A15	80r yellow	70.00	40.00
a.		80r orange	110.00	70.00
b.		Double overprint		

54	A15	100r lilac	55.00	35.00
55	A15	150r blue	1,000.	750.00
56	A15	150r yellow	100.00	60.00
57	A15	300r violet	100.00	60.00

Reprints of the 1882-85 issues have the same papers, gum and perforations as those of preceding issues.

Red Overprint

58	A21	5r slate	20.00	4.00
59	A24a	500r black	160.00	110.00
60	A15	1000r black	125.00	85.00

1887			**Black Overprint**	
61	A25	20r pink	25.00	10.00
a.		Inverted overprint		
b.		Double overprint		
62	A26	25r lilac rose	25.00	2.00
a.		Inverted overprint		
b.		Double ovpt., one invtd.		
63	A26	25r red violet	25.00	2.00
a.		Double overprint		
64	A24a	500r red violet	125.00	75.00
a.		Perf. 13½	400.00	200.00
		Nos. 61-64 (4)	200.00	89.00

Nos. 58-64 inclusive have been reprinted on thin white paper with shiny white gum and perforated 13½.

Prince Henry the Navigator Issue

Portugal Nos. 97-109   AÇORES
Overprinted

1894, Mar. 4			*Perf. 14*	
65	A46	5r orange yel	3.00	3.00
a.		Inverted overprint	45.00	45.00
66	A46	10r violet rose	3.00	2.00
a.		Double overprint		
b.		Inverted overprint	—	
67	A46	15r brown	3.50	2.50
68	A46	20r violet	3.50	2.50
a.		Double overprint		
69	A47	25r green	4.00	3.00
a.		Double overprint	50.00	50.00
b.		Inverted overprint	50.00	50.00
70	A47	50r blue	10.00	4.25
71	A47	75r dp carmine	20.00	6.00
72	A47	80r yellow grn	21.00	6.00
73	A47	100r lt brn, *pale buff*	21.00	5.00
a.		Double overprint		
74	A48	150r lt car, *pale rose*	30.00	10.00
75	A48	300r dk bl, *sal buff*	40.00	17.50
76	A48	500r brn vio, *pale lil*	60.00	25.00
77	A48	1000r gray blk, *yelsh*	125.00	45.00
a.		Double overprint		
		Nos. 65-77 (13)	344.00	130.75

St. Anthony of Padua Issue

Portugal Nos. 132-146   AÇORES
Overprinted in Red or Black

1895, June 13			*Perf. 12*	
78	A50	2½r black (R)	2.50	1.50
79	A51	5r brown yel	8.00	2.00
80	A51	10r red lilac	8.00	2.50
81	A51	15r red brown	12.50	4.00
82	A51	20r gray lilac	12.50	5.00
83	A51	25r green & vio	8.00	2.75
84	A52	50r blue & brn	25.00	14.00
85	A52	75r rose & brn	25.00	25.00
86	A52	80r lt green & brn	40.00	25.00
87	A52	100r choc & blk	50.00	25.00
88	A53	150r vio rose & bis	80.00	65.00
89	A53	200r blue & bis	100.00	60.00
90	A53	300r slate & bis	125.00	70.00
91	A53	500r vio brn & grn	200.00	100.00
92	A53	1000r violet & grn	400.00	200.00
		Nos. 78-92 (15)	1,096.	601.75

7th cent. of the birth of Saint Anthony of Padua.

Vasco da Gama Issue
Common Design Types

1898, Apr. 1			*Perf. 14, 15*	
93	CD20	2½r blue green	3.00	.80
94	CD21	5r red	3.00	1.00
95	CD22	10r gray lilac	5.00	2.00
96	CD23	25r yellow green	5.00	2.00
97	CD24	50r dark blue	8.00	6.00
98	CD25	75r violet brown	16.00	9.00
99	CD26	100r bister brown	20.00	9.00
100	CD27	150r bister	32.50	18.00
		Nos. 93-100 (8)	92.50	47.80

For overprints and surcharges see Nos. 141-148.

King
Carlos — A28

King Manuel
II — A29

1906		**Typo.**	*Perf. 11½x12*	
101	A28	2½r gray	.40	.15
a.		Inverted overprint	25.00	25.00
102	A28	5r orange yel	.40	.15
a.		Inverted overprint	25.00	25.00

103	A28	10r yellow grn	.40	.15
104	A28	20r gray vio	.50	.30
105	A28	25r carmine	.40	.15
106	A28	50r ultra	4.50	3.00
107	A28	75r brown, *straw*	1.50	.80
108	A28	100r dk blue, *bl*	1.50	.90
109	A28	200r red lilac, *pnksh*	1.50	1.00
110	A28	300r dk blue, *rose*	5.00	3.25
111	A28	500r black, *blue*	11.00	8.00
		Nos. 101-111 (11)	27.10	17.85

"Açores" and letters and figures in the corners are in red on the 2½, 10, 20, 75 and 500r and in black on the other values.

1910, Apr. 1			*Perf. 14x15*	
112	A29	2½r violet	.25	.20
113	A29	5r black	.25	.20
114	A29	10r dk green	.30	.25
115	A29	15r lilac brn	.40	.50
116	A29	20r carmine	.45	.45
117	A29	25r violet brn	.25	.20
a.		Perf. 11½	1.25	
118	A29	50r blue	1.00	.70
119	A29	75r bister brn	1.75	1.25
120	A29	80r slate	1.75	1.25
121	A29	100r brown, *lt grn*	2.25	1.75
122	A29	200r green, *sal*	2.25	1.75
123	A29	300r black, *blue*	3.50	2.50
124	A29	500r olive & brown	7.00	7.00
125	A29	1000r blue & black	12.00	12.00
		Nos. 112-125 (14)	33.40	30.00

The errors of color 10r black, 15r dark green, 25r black and 50r carmine are considered to be proofs.

Stamps of 1910
Overprinted in
Carmine or Green

REPUBLICA

1910

126	A29	2½r violet	.15	.15
a.		Inverted overprint	9.00	9.00
127	A29	5r black	.20	.15
a.		Inverted overprint	9.00	9.00
128	A29	10r dk green	.20	.20
a.		Inverted overprint	9.00	9.00
129	A29	15r lilac brn	.80	.65
a.		Inverted overprint	9.00	9.00
130	A29	20r carmine (G)	1.00	.80
a.		Inverted overprint	16.00	16.00
b.		Double overprint	16.00	16.00
131	A29	25r violet brn	.25	.15
a.		Perf. 11½	40.00	30.00
132	A29	50r blue	.60	.50
133	A29	75r bister brn	.35	.20
a.		Double overprint	9.00	9.00
134	A29	80r slate	.45	.35
135	A29	100r brown, *grn*	.40	.25
136	A29	200r green, *sal*	.60	.60
137	A29	300r black, *blue*	1.25	1.25
138	A29	500r olive & brn	1.25	*1.75*
139	A29	1000r blue & blk	3.50	*4.00*
		Nos. 126-139 (14)	11.00	*11.00*

Vasco da Gama Issue Overprinted or
Surcharged in Black:

REPUBLICA
d

REPUBLICA   **REPUBLICA**

REIS **15** REIS		1$000	
e		f	

1911   *Perf. 14, 15*

141	CD20(d)	2½r blue green	.35	.30
142	CD21(e)	15r on 5r red	.20	.20
143	CD23(e)	25r yellow grn	.40	.25
144	CD24(d)	50r dk blue	1.00	.70
145	CD25(e)	75r violet brn	.60	.60
146	CD27(e)	80r on 150r bister	.60	.60
147	CD26(d)	100r yellow brn	.60	.60
a.		Double surcharge	35.00	35.00
148	CD22(f)	1000r on 10r lilac	8.50	6.50
		Nos. 141-148 (8)	12.25	9.75

Postage Due Stamps of Portugal
Overprinted or Surcharged in Black
"ACORES" and

REPUBLICA

REPUBLICA   Rˢ **300** Rˢ

1911			*Perf. 12*	
149	D1	5r black	.75	.35
150	D1	10r magenta	1.75	1.25
a.		"Acores" double	20.00	20.00
151	D1	20r orange	2.00	2.00
152	D1	200r brn, *buff*	7.25	6.00
a.		"Acores" inverted		
153	D1	300r on 50r slate	7.25	6.00
154	D1	500r on 100r car, *pink*	7.25	6.00
		Nos. 149-154 (6)	26.25	21.60

Ceres — A30

Ceres Issue of Portugal Overprinted
"ACORES" in Black or Carmine
With Imprint

1912-31			*Perf. 12x11½, 15x14*	
155	A30	¼c olive brown	.15	.15
a.		Inverted overprint	9.00	
156	A30	½c black (C)	.15	.15
157	A30	1c deep green	.55	.35
a.		Inverted overprint	9.00	
158	A30	1c deep brown ('18)	.15	.15
a.		Inverted overprint		
159	A30	1½c choc ('13)	.50	.40
a.		Inverted overprint	9.00	
160	A30	1½c deep green ('18)	.35	.15
a.		Inverted overprint		
161	A30	2c carmine	.30	.20
a.		Inverted overprint	14.00	
162	A30	2c orange ('18)	.20	.15
a.		Inverted overprint	18.00	
163	A30	2½c violet	.25	.15
164	A30	3c rose ('18)	.20	.15
165	A30	3c dull ultra ('25)	.20	.15
166	A30	3½c lt green ('18)	.30	.15
167	A30	4c lt green ('19)	.15	.15
168	A30	4c orange ('30)	.25	.20
169	A30	5c dp blue	.25	.15
170	A30	5c yellow brn ('18)	.25	.20
171	A30	5c olive brn ('23)	.15	.15
172	A30	5c black brn ('30)	2.75	2.50
173	A30	6c dull rose ('20)	.20	.15
174	A30	6c choc ('25)	.20	.15
175	A30	6c red brn ('31)	.35	.80
176	A30	7½c yel brn	4.75	1.25
177	A30	7½c deep blue ('18)	.60	.40
178	A30	8c slate ('13)	.55	.20
179	A30	8c blue grn ('22)	.25	.15
180	A30	8c orange ('25)	.50	.25
181	A30	10c orange brown	.30	.15
182	A30	12c blue gray ('20)	1.00	.70
183	A30	12c deep green ('22)	.45	.35
184	A30	13½c chlky bl ('20)	1.00	3.25
185	A30	14c dk bl, *yel* ('20)	3.25	6.00
186	A30	15c plum ('13)	.60	.60
187	A30	15c blk (R) ('23)	.40	.40
188	A30	16c brt ultra ('24)	.80	.40
189	A30	16c dp bl ('30)	1.25	*1.50*
190	A30	20c vio brn, *grn* ('13)	8.00	3.25
191	A30	20c choc ('20)	.60	.20
192	A30	20c deep green ('23)	.80	.80
a.		Double overprint		
193	A30	20c gray ('24)	.60	.20
194	A30	24c grnsh bl ('21)	.60	.40
195	A30	25c salmon ('23)	.30	.20
196	A30	30c brn, *pink* ('13)	40.00	22.50
197	A30	30c brn, *yel* ('19)	2.25	2.25
198	A30	30c gray brn ('21)	.80	.65
199	A30	32c dp green ('25)	4.00	1.00
200	A30	36c red ('21)	.40	.20
201	A30	40c dp blue ('23)	.40	.40
202	A30	40c black brn ('24)	.20	.15
203	A30	40c brt green ('30)	1.50	.40
204	A30	48c brt rose ('24)	1.50	1.00
205	A30	48c dull pink ('31)	6.25	6.00
206	A30	50c grn, *sal* ('13)	5.25	1.00
207	A30	50c yellow ('23)	1.25	1.00
208	A30	50c bister ('30)	2.50	1.75
209	A30	50c red brn ('31)	2.00	1.50
210	A30	60c blue ('21)	1.00	.70
211	A30	64c pale ultra ('24)	1.50	1.00
212	A30	64c brown rose ('31)	45.00	45.00
213	A30	75c dull rose ('23)	4.25	4.00
214	A30	75c car rose ('30)	1.50	1.25
215	A30	80c dull rose ('21)	1.25	.65
216	A30	80c violet ('24)	1.25	.90
217	A30	80c dk green ('31)	1.50	1.25
218	A30	90c chlky bl ('21)	1.25	.75
219	A30	96c dp rose ('26)	8.25	4.50
220	A30	1e dp grn, *bl*	4.75	1.50
221	A30	1e violet ('21)	1.25	.75
222	A30	1e gray vio ('24)	1.50	1.00
223	A30	1e brn lake ('30)	12.50	10.00
224	A30	1.10e yel brn ('21)	1.25	1.25
225	A30	1.20e yel grn ('21)	1.50	1.00
226	A30	1.20e buff ('24)	3.75	1.75
227	A30	1.25e dk blue ('30)	1.50	.75
228	A30	1.50e blk vio ('23)	2.75	1.75
229	A30	1.50e dp bl ('25)	2.75	1.75
230	A30	1.60e dp bl ('25)	2.75	1.75
231	A30	2e slate grn ('21)	4.25	2.00
232	A30	2.40e apple grn ('26)	60.00	50.00

233	A30	3e lilac pink ('26)	60.00	55.00
234	A30	3.20e gray grn ('25)	10.00	4.50
235	A30	5e emerald ('24)	20.00	12.00
236	A30	10e pink ('24)	40.00	20.00
237	A30	20e pale turq ('25)	125.00	75.00
		Nos. 155-237 (83)	525.00	369.00

For same overprint on surcharged stamps see Nos. 300-306. For same design without imprint see Nos. 307-313.

Castello-Branco Issue
Stamps of Portugal, 1925, Overprinted in Black or Red AÇORES

1925, Mar. 29   *Perf. 12½*

238	A73	2c orange	.20	.50
239	A73	3c green	.20	.50
240	A73	4c ultra (R)	.20	.50
241	A73	5c scarlet	.20	.50
242	A74	10c pale blue	.20	.45
243	A74	16c red orange	.25	.75
244	A75	25c car rose	.25	.75
245	A74	32c green	.55	.80
246	A75	40c grn & blk (R)	.25	.75
247	A74	48c red brn	1.25	2.25
248	A76	50c blue green	.80	2.25
249	A76	64c orange brn	1.40	2.25
250	A76	75c gray blk (R)	1.00	3.00
251	A75	80c brown	1.00	3.00
252	A76	96c car rose	1.25	3.00
253	A77	1.50e dk bl, *bl* (R)	1.25	2.25
254	A75	1.60e indigo (R)	1.25	2.25
255	A77	2e dk grn, *grn* (R)	1.50	3.00
256	A77	2.40e red, *org*	2.00	3.25
257	A77	3.20e blk, *grn* (R)	3.00	5.00
		Nos. 238-257 (20)	18.00	37.00

First Independence Issue
Stamps of Portugal, 1926, Overprinted in Red AÇORES

1926, Aug. 13   *Perf. 14, 14½*
Center in Black

258	A79	2c orange	.25	.70
259	A80	3c ultra	.25	.70
260	A79	4c yellow grn	.25	.70
261	A80	5c black brn	.25	.70
262	A79	6c ocher	.25	.70
263	A80	15c dk green	.50	.90
264	A81	20c dull violet	.50	.90
265	A82	25c scarlet	.50	.90
266	A81	32c deep green	.50	.90
267	A82	40c yellow brn	.50	.90
268	A82	50c olive bis	1.25	2.00
269	A82	75c red brown	1.25	2.00
270	A83	1e black violet	1.75	3.25
271	A84	4.50e olive green	2.00	6.75
		Nos. 258-271 (14)	10.00	22.00

The use of these stamps instead of those of the regular issue was obligatory on Aug. 13th and 14th, Nov. 30th and Dec. 1st, 1926.

Second Independence Issue
Same Overprint on Stamps of Portugal, 1927, in Red

1927, Nov. 29
Center in Black

272	A86	2c lt brown	.25	.70
273	A87	3c ultra	.25	.70
274	A86	4c orange	.25	.70
275	A88	5c dk brown	.25	.70
276	A89	6c orange brn	.25	.70
277	A87	15c black brn	.25	.70
278	A86	25c gray	1.00	3.00
279	A89	32c blue grn	1.00	3.00
280	A90	40c yellow grn	1.00	3.00
281	A90	96c red	2.50	5.75
282	A88	1.60e myrtle grn	2.50	5.75
283	A91	4.50e bister	4.50	8.00
		Nos. 272-283 (12)	14.00	32.70

Third Independence Issue
Same Overprint on Stamps of Portugal, 1928, in Red

1928, Nov. 27
Center in Black

284	A93	2c lt blue	.25	.70
285	A94	3c lt green	.25	.70
286	A95	4c lake	.25	.70
287	A96	5c olive grn	.25	.70
288	A97	6c orange brn	.25	.70
289	A94	15c slate	.40	1.25
290	A95	16c dk violet	.65	2.25
291	A93	25c ultra	.65	2.00
292	A97	32c dk green	.65	2.00
293	A96	40c olive brn	.65	2.00
294	A95	50c red orange	1.25	3.00
295	A92	80c lt gray	1.25	6.00
296	A97	96c carmine	1.75	6.00
297	A96	1e claret	1.75	6.00
298	A93	1.60e dk blue	1.75	6.00
299	A98	4.50e yellow	4.00	8.50
		Nos. 284-299 (16)	16.00	45.50

 A31   A32

1929-30   *Perf. 12x11½, 15x14*

300	A31	4c on 25c pink ('30)	.35	.35
301	A31	4c on 60c dp blue	.35	.35
302	A31	10c on 25c pink	.80	.40
303	A31	12c on 25c pink	.80	.40
304	A31	15c on 25c pink	.65	.60
305	A31	20c on 25c pink	.80	.65
306	A31	40c on 1.10e yel brn	2.75	2.25
		Nos. 300-306 (7)	6.50	5.00

Black or Red Overprint

1930   *Perf. 14*

Without Imprint at Foot

307	A32	4c orange	.35	.40
308	A32	5c dp brown	1.50	1.00
309	A32	10c vermilion	.80	.55
310	A32	15c black (R)	.80	.55
311	A32	40c brt green	.80	.55
312	A32	80c violet	11.00	8.75
313	A32	1.60e dk blue	1.75	1.00
		Nos. 307-313 (7)	17.00	12.80

POSTAGE DUE STAMPS

 D2   D3

Portugal Nos. J7-J13 Overprinted in Black

1904   Unwmk.   *Perf. 12*

J1	D2	5r brown	.45	.65
J2	D2	10r orange	.45	.65
J3	D2	20r lilac	.85	1.10
J4	D2	30r gray green	1.00	1.10
a.		Double overprint		
J5	D2	40r gray violet	1.75	1.75
J6	D2	50r carmine	2.75	3.00
J7	D2	100r dull blue	4.25	4.50
		Nos. J1-J7 (7)	11.50	12.75

Same Overprinted in Carmine or Green (Portugal Nos. J14-J20)

 REPUBLICA

1911

J8	D2	5r brown	.20	.20
J9	D2	10r orange	.20	.20
J10	D2	20r lilac	.20	.20
J11	D2	30r gray green	.20	.20
J12	D2	40r gray violet	.45	.45
J13	D2	50r carmine (G)	2.00	2.00
J14	D2	100r dull blue	1.25	1.25
		Nos. J8-J14 (7)	4.50	4.50

Portugal Nos. J21-J27 Overprinted in Black

1918

J15	D3	½c brown	.15	.15
a.		Inverted overprint	4.00	4.00
b.		Double overprint	4.00	4.00
J16	D3	1c orange	.15	.15
a.		Inverted overprint	4.00	4.00
b.		Double overprint	4.00	4.00
J17	D3	2c red lilac	.15	.15
a.		Inverted overprint	4.00	4.00
b.		Double overprint	4.00	4.00
J18	D3	3c green	.15	.15
a.		Inverted overprint	4.00	4.00
b.		Double overprint	4.00	4.00
J19	D3	4c gray	.15	.15
a.		Inverted overprint	4.00	4.00
b.		Double overprint	4.00	4.00
J20	D3	5c rose	.15	.15
b.		Double overprint	4.00	4.00
J21	D3	10c dark blue	.20	.20
		Nos. J15-J21 (7)	1.10	1.10

Stamps and Type of Portugal Postage Dues, 1921-27, Overprinted in Black

1922-24   *Perf. 11½x12*

J30	D3	½c gray green ('23)	.15	.15
J31	D3	1c gray green ('23)	.15	.15
J32	D3	2c gray green ('23)	.15	.15
J33	D3	3c gray green ('24)	.35	.35
J34	D3	8c gray green ('24)	.20	.20
J35	D3	10c gray green ('24)	.20	.20
J36	D3	12c gray green ('24)	.20	.20

J37	D3	16c gray green ('24)	.20	.20
J38	D3	20c gray green	.60	.50
J39	D3	24c gray green	.20	.20
J40	D3	32c gray green ('24)	.20	.20
J41	D3	36c gray green	.20	.20
J42	D3	40c gray green ('24)	.50	.50
J43	D3	48c gray green ('24)	.30	.30
J44	D3	50c gray green	.60	.50
J45	D3	60c gray green	.65	.35
J46	D3	72c gray green ('24)	.65	.35
J47	D3	80c gray green ('24)	1.75	1.40
J48	D3	1.20e gray green ('24)	1.75	1.40
		Nos. J30-J48 (19)	9.00	7.50

NEWSPAPER STAMPS

Newspaper Stamps of Portugal, Nos. P1, P1a, Overprinted Types b & c in Black or Red and:

 N3

Perf. 11½, 12½ and 13½

1876-88			Unwmk.	
P1	N1	2½r (a) olive	11.00	3.50
a.		Inverted overprint		
P2	N1	2½r (b) olive ('82)	5.00	1.00
a.		Inverted overprint		
b.		Double overprint		
P3	N3	2r black ('85)	5.00	2.00
a.		Inverted overprint		
b.		Double overprint, one inverted		
P4	N1	2½r (b) bister ('82)	5.00	1.00
a.		Double overprint		
P5	N3	2r black (R) ('88)	15.00	10.00
		Nos. P1-P5 (5)	41.00	17.50

Reprints of the newspaper stamps have the same papers, gum and perforations as reprints of the regular issues. Value $2 each.

PARCEL POST STAMPS

Portugal Nos. Q1-Q17 Overprinted Like Nos. 155-237 in Black or Red

1921-22			Unwmk.	*Perf. 12*
Q1	PP1	1c lilac brown	.15	.15
a.		Inverted overprint	4.00	4.00
Q2	PP1	2c orange	.15	.15
a.		Inverted overprint	4.00	4.00
Q3	PP1	5c light brown	.15	.15
a.		Inverted overprint	5.00	5.00
b.		Double overprint	5.00	5.00
Q4	PP1	10c red brown	.15	.25
a.		Inverted overprint	5.00	5.00
b.		Double overprint	5.00	5.00
Q5	PP1	20c gray blue	.30	.25
a.		Inverted overprint	5.00	5.00
b.		Double overprint	5.00	5.00
Q6	PP1	40c carmine	.30	.30
a.		Double overprint	6.50	6.50
Q7	PP1	50c black (R)	.55	.55
Q8	PP1	60c dark blue (R)	.55	.55
Q9	PP1	70c gray brown	2.50	1.25
Q10	PP1	80c ultra	2.50	1.25
Q11	PP1	90c light violet	2.50	1.25
Q12	PP1	1e light green	3.00	1.25
Q13	PP1	2e pale lilac	4.00	2.50
Q14	PP1	3e olive	6.00	3.25
Q15	PP1	4e ultra	7.00	5.00
Q16	PP1	5e gray	7.00	5.00
Q17	PP1	10e chocolate	20.00	13.00
		Nos. Q1-Q17 (17)	56.80	36.10

POSTAL TAX STAMPS

These stamps represent a special fee for the delivery of postal matter on certain days in the year. The money derived from their sale is applied to works of public charity.

Nos. 114 and 157 Overprinted in Carmine   ASSISTENCIA

1911-13		Unwmk.	*Perf. 14x15*	
RA1	A29	10r dark green	.55	.40

The 20r of this type was for use on telegrams.

Perf. 15x14

RA2	A30	1c deep green	1.25	1.25

The 2c of this type was for use on telegrams.

Postal Tax Stamp of Portugal, No. RA4, Overprinted Like Nos. 155-237 in Black

1915   *Perf. 12*

RA3	PT2	1c carmine	.15	.15

The 2c of this type was for use on telegrams.

Postal Tax Stamp of 1915 Surcharged **15 ctvs.**

1924

RA4	PT1	15c on 1c rose	.75	1.25

Comrades of the Great War Issue
Postal Tax Stamps of Portugal, 1925, Overprinted AÇORES

1925, Apr. 8   *Perf. 11*

RA5	PT3	10c brown	.40	.30
RA6	PT3	10c green	.40	.30
RA7	PT3	10c black	.40	.30
RA8	PT3	10c ultra	.40	.30
		Nos. RA5-RA8 (4)	1.60	1.20

The use of Nos. RA5-RA11 in addition to the regular postage was compulsory on certain days. If the tax represented by these stamps was not prepaid, it was collected by means of Postal Tax Due Stamps.

In 1934-45, #RA5-RA11, RAJ1-RAJ4 were used for regular postage in Portugal.

Pombal Issue
Common Design Types

1925   *Perf. 12½*

RA9	CD28	20c dp green & black	.35	.30
RA10	CD29	20c dp green & black	.35	.30
RA11	CD30	20c dp green & black	.35	.30
		Nos. RA9-RA11 (3)	1.05	.90

POSTAL TAX DUE STAMPS

Postal Tax Due Stamp of Portugal Overprinted like Nos. RA5-RA8

1925, Apr. 8   Unwmk.   *Perf. 11x11½*

RAJ1	PTD1	20c brown orange	.40	.40

See note after No. RA8.

Pombal Issue
Common Design Types

1925, May 8   *Perf. 12½*

RAJ2	CD28	40c dp green & black	.60	4.00
RAJ3	CD29	40c dp green & black	.60	4.00
RAJ4	CD30	40c dp green & black	.60	4.00
		Nos. RAJ2-RAJ4 (3)	1.80	

See note after No. RA8.

See Portugal for later issues.

BAHAMAS
bə-ˈhä-məs

LOCATION — A group of about 700 islands and 2,000 rocks in the West Indies, off the coast of Florida. Only 30 islands are inhabited.

GOVT. — Independent state in British Commonwealth

AREA — 5,353 sq. mi.

POP. — 209,505 (1980)

CAPITAL — Nassau

The principal island, on which the capital is located, is New Providence. The Bahamas obtained internal self-government on January 7, 1964, and independence on July 10, 1973.

12 Pence = 1 Shilling
20 Shillings = 1 Pound
100 Cents = 1 Dollar (1966)

Values for unused stamps are for examples with original gum as defined in the catalogue introduction. Very fine examples of Nos. 2-26 will have perforations touching the design or frameline on at least one side due to the narrow spacing of the stamps on the plates. Stamps with perfs clear of the design or framelines on all four sides are extremely scarce and will command higher prices.

Pen cancellations usually indicate revenue use. Such stamps sell for much less than postally canceled copies. Beware of stamps with revenue or pen cancellations removed and forged postal cancellations added.

Queen Victoria
A1   A2

1859-60   Unwmk.   Engr.   Imperf.

1	A1	1p dull lake ('60)	50.	1,500.
a.		1p reddish lake	4,500.	2,000.
b.		1p brownish lake	4,500.	2,250.

Most unused copies of #1 are remainders, and false cancellations are plentiful. #1a and 1b are on thicker paper than #1.

1861   Rough Perf. 14 to 16

2	A1	1p lake	925.	275.
a.		Clean-cut perf. ('60)	2,100.	700.
3	A2	4p dull rose	1,600.	500.
		Imperf. between, pair	—	
4	A2	6p gray lilac	3,000.	575.
a.		Pale lilac	3,250.	575.

1862   Engr.   Perf. 11½, 12

5	A1	1p lake	800.	175.
a.		Pair, imperf. between	5,000.	
6	A2	4p dull rose	3,000.	425.
7	A2	6p gray violet	4,500.	500.

No. 5a was not issued in the Bahamas. It is unique and faulty.
Nos. 5-7 exist with perf. 11½ or 12 compound with 11.

**   Perf. 13**

8	A1	1p brown lake	550.	125.
a.		1p carmine lake	550.	150.
9	A2	4p rose	2,750.	400.
10	A2	6p gray violet	3,250.	400.
a.		6p dull violet	3,250.	500.

Queen Victoria — A3

1863-65   Typo.   Wmk. 1   Perf. 12½

11	A1	1p lake	85.00	70.00
a.		1p brown lake	85.00	70.00
b.		1p rose lake	95.00	70.00
12	A1	1p vermilion	65.00	50.00
13	A2	4p rose	375.00	70.00
a.		4p rose lake	400.00	90.00
b.		4p bright rose	250.00	70.00
14	A2	6p dk violet	160.00	90.00
a.		6p rose lilac	5,000.	3,750.
c.		6p lilac	300.00	75.00
15	A3	1sh green ('65)	2,500.	325.00

For surcharge see No. 26.

1863-81   Perf. 14

16	A1	1p vermilion	45.00	20.00
17	A1	1p car lake (anil)	1,600.	
18	A2	4p rose	400.00	50.00
a.		4p deep rose ('76)	400.00	50.00
b.		4p dull rose	1,750.	50.00
19	A3	1sh green ('80)	7.50	7.50
a.		1shp dark green	120.00	45.00

Some copies of No. 16 show a light aniline appearance and care should be taken not to confuse these with No. 17. All known used copies of No. 17 bear fiscal cancels.

1882-98   Wmk. 2

20	A1	1p vermilion	325.00	65.00
21	A2	4p rose	800.00	65.00
22	A3	1sh green	30.00	17.50
23	A3	1sh blue grn ('98)	35.00	22.50

**   Perf. 12**

| 24 | A1 | 1p vermilion | 37.50 | 25.00 |
| 25 | A2 | 4p rose | 500.00 | 60.00 |

No. 14a Surcharged in Black *FOURPENCE*

1883   Wmk. 1   Perf. 12½

| 26 | A2 | 4p on 6p violet | 675. | 500. |
| a. | | Inverted surcharge | 7,000. | 4,500. |

The surcharge, being handstamped, is found in various positions. Counterfeit overprints exist.

Queen Victoria A5   Queen's Staircase A6

1884-90   Typo.   Wmk. 2   Perf. 14

27	A5	1p carmine rose	5.00	2.00
a.		1p pale rose	40.00	10.00
28	A5	2½p ultra	8.00	2.00
		2½p dull blue	35.00	12.50
29	A5	4p yellow	8.00	5.00
30	A5	6p violet	5.00	25.00
31	A5	5sh olive green	60.00	70.00
32	A5	£1 brown	325.00	275.00
		Revenue cancellation		55.00
		Nos. 27-32 (6)	411.00	379.00

Cleaned fiscally used copies of No. 32 are often found with postmarks of small post offices added.

1901-03   Engr.   Wmk. 1

33	A6	1p carmine & blk	5.00	4.50
34	A6	5p org & blk ('03)	10.00	35.00
35	A6	2sh ultra & blk ('03)	17.50	40.00
36	A6	3sh green & blk ('03)	21.00	40.00
		Nos. 33-36 (4)	53.50	119.50

See Nos. 48, 58-62, 71, 78, 81-82.

Edward VII A7   George V A8

1902   Wmk. 2   Typo.

37	A7	1p carmine rose	2.25	2.25
38	A7	2½p ultra	7.00	1.75
39	A7	4p orange	9.50	15.00
40	A7	6p bister brn	6.50	10.00
41	A7	1sh gray blk & car	11.00	20.00
42	A7	5sh violet & ultra	45.00	55.00
43	A7	£1 green & blk	350.00	350.00
		Nos. 37-43 (7)	431.25	454.00

1906-11   Wmk. 3

44	A7	½p green	4.00	2.00
45	A7	1p car rose	5.50	2.00
46	A7	2½p ultra ('07)	17.50	20.00
47	A7	6p bister brn ('11)	42.50	50.00
		Nos. 44-47 (4)	69.50	74.00

1910-16   Engr.

| 48 | A6 | 1p red & gray blk ('16) | 2.00 | 1.75 |
| a. | | 1p carmine & black | 5.50 | 5.50 |

For overprints see Nos. B1-B2.

1912-19   Typo.

49	A8	½p green	.85	1.25
50	A8	1p carmine rose	1.50	.50
50A	A8	2p gray ('19)	2.00	2.50
51	A8	2½p ultra	4.00	6.00
52	A8	4p orange	2.75	3.50
53	A8	6p bister brn	2.00	3.75

Chalky Paper

54	A8	1sh black & red	3.00	4.00
55	A8	5sh violet & ultra	27.50	27.50
56	A8	£1 green & blk	250.00	325.00
		Nos. 49-56 (9)	293.60	374.00

1917-19   Engr.

58	A6	3p purple, yel	7.75	8.50
59	A6	3p brown & blk ('19)	3.00	6.00
60	A6	5p violet & blk	4.00	11.00
61	A6	2sh ultra & black	15.00	27.50
62	A6	3sh green & black	30.00	40.00
		Nos. 58-62 (5)	59.75	93.00

Peace Commemorative Issue

King George V and Seal of Bahamas — A9

1920, Mar. 1   Engr.   Perf. 14

65	A9	½p gray green	.60	2.25
66	A9	1p deep red	1.75	1.25
67	A9	2p gray	3.75	5.50
68	A9	3p brown	3.50	9.50
69	A9	1sh dark green	27.50	30.00
		Nos. 65-69 (5)	37.10	48.50

Types of 1901-12

1921-34   Typo., Engr. (A6)   Wmk. 4

70	A8	½p green ('24)	.20	.20
71	A6	1p car & black	1.00	1.00
72	A8	1p car rose	.20	.20
73	A8	1½p fawn ('34)	1.00	1.50
74	A8	2p gray ('27)	.90	2.50
75	A8	2½p ultra ('22)	.90	2.50
76	A8	3p violet, yel ('31)	6.00	15.00
77	A8	4p yellow ('24)	1.75	5.75
78	A6	5p red vio & gray blk ('29)	7.00	11.00
79	A8	6p bister brn ('22)	1.50	3.50
80	A8	1sh blk & red ('26)	3.50	9.00
81	A6	2sh ultra & blk ('22)	37.50	62.50
82	A6	3sh grn & blk ('24)	55.00	70.00
83	A6	5sh vio & ultra ('24)	30.00	40.00
84	A8	£1 grn & blk ('26)	175.00	275.00
		Nos. 70-84 (15)	321.45	499.65

The 3p, 1sh, 5sh and £1 are on chalky paper.

Seal of Bahamas — A10

1930, Jan. 2   Engr.   Perf. 12

85	A10	1p red & black	1.00	2.50
86	A10	3p dp brown & blk	3.00	7.50
87	A10	5p dk vio & blk	3.50	7.50
88	A10	2sh ultra & black	22.50	35.00
89	A10	3sh dp green & blk	27.50	55.00
		Nos. 85-89 (5)	57.50	107.50

The dates on the stamps commemorate important events in the history of the colony. The 1st British occupation was in 1629. The Bahamas were ceded to Great Britain in 1729 and a treaty of peace was signed by that country, France and Spain.

**Type of 1930 Issue
Without Dates at Top**

1931-42

90	A10	2sh ultra & black ('42)	.70	.70
a.		2sh ultra & slate purple ('42)	12.00	11.00
91	A10	3sh dp green & blk	.80	.80
a.		3sh deep grn & slate purple ('42)	12.00	11.00

Nos. 90-91 are on thick paper with yellowish gum, Nos. 90a-91a are on thin white paper with colorless gum.
For overprints see Nos. 126-127.

**Silver Jubilee Issue
Common Design Type**

1935, May 6   Perf. 13½x14

92	CD301	1½p car & blue	.45	.40
93	CD301	2½p blue & brn	1.50	2.50
94	CD301	6p grn & lt bl	4.00	6.50
95	CD301	1sh brt vio & ind	6.50	9.00
		Nos. 92-95 (4)	12.45	18.40
		Set, never hinged	30.00	

Flamingos in Flight — A11

1935, May 22   Perf. 12½

| 96 | A11 | 8p car & ultra | 5.00 | 3.50 |
| | | Never hinged | 8.50 | |

**Coronation Issue
Common Design Type**

1937, May 12   Perf. 13½x14

97	CD302	½p dp green	.15	.15
98	CD302	1½p brown	.25	.20
99	CD302	2½p brt ultra	.65	.60
		Nos. 97-99 (3)	1.05	.95
		Set, never hinged	1.65	

George VI — A12   Sea Gardens, Nassau — A13

Fort Charlotte A14

Flamingos in Flight — A15

1938-46   Typo.   Wmk. 4   Perf. 14

100	A12	½p green	.20	.20
101	A12	1p carmine	1.50	1.25
101A	A12	1p gray ('41)	.20	.20
102	A12	1½p red brown	.20	.20
103	A12	2p gray	12.00	19.00
103B	A12	2p carmine ('41)	.25	.25
c.		"TWO PENCE" double		1,750.
104	A12	2½p ultra	1.90	1.25
104A	A12	2½p lt violet ('43)	.30	.30
105	A12	3p lt violet	7.50	10.00
105A	A12	3p ultra ('43)	.40	.50

**   Engr.
                     Perf. 12½**

106	A13	4p red org & blue	.70	.60
107	A14	6p blue & ol grn	.50	.40
108	A15	8p car & ultra	.95	.80

**   Typo.
                     Perf. 14**

109	A12	10p yel org ('46)	.70	.70
110	A12	1sh black & car	1.25	.95
112	A12	5sh pur & ultra	10.00	8.00
a.		5sh lilac & light ultra	40.00	40.00
113	A12	£1 green & blk	37.50	35.00
		Nos. 100-113 (17)	76.05	79.60
		Set, never hinged	150.00	

#110-113 printed on chalky & ordinary paper. See Nos. 154-156. For overprints see Nos. 116-125, 128-129.

No. 104 Surcharged in Black **3d.**

1940, Nov. 28   Perf. 14

| 115 | A12 | 3p on 2½p ultra | .30 | .25 |
| | | Never hinged | .45 | |

**1 4 9 2
LANDFALL
OF
COLUMBUS
1 9 4 2**

Stamps of 1931-42 Overprinted in Black

1942, Oct. 12   Perf. 14, 12½, 12

116	A12	½p green	.15	.15
117	A12	1p gray	.15	.15
118	A12	1½p red brn	.15	.15
119	A12	2p carmine	.15	.15
120	A12	2½p ultra	.15	.15
121	A12	3p ultra	.15	.15
122	A13	4p red org & blue	.25	.20
123	A14	6p blue & ol grn	.35	.25
124	A15	8p car & ultra	.50	.30
125	A12	1sh black & car	.65	.40
126	A10	2sh dk ultra & blk	6.00	9.50
a.		2sh ultra & slate purple	8.25	13.00
127	A10	3sh dp grn & sl pur	3.25	9.00
a.		3sh deep green & black	10.00	17.00
128	A12	5sh lilac & ultra	4.75	9.00
129	A12	£1 green & black	22.50	30.00
		Nos. 116-129 (14)	39.15	59.55
		Set, never hinged	60.00	

450th anniv. of the discovery of America by Columbus.
Nos. 125, 128-129 printed on chalky and ordinary paper.

Two printings of the basic stamps were overprinted, the first with dark gum, the second with white gum.

> Catalogue values for unused stamps in this section, from this point to the end of the section, are for Never Hinged items.

Peace Issue
Common Design Type
Perf. 13½x14

1946, Nov. 11		**Engr.**		**Wmk. 4**
130 CD303	1½p brown		.15	.15
131 CD303	3p deep blue		.20	.20

Infant Welfare Clinic — A16

Designs: 1p, Modern agriculture. 1½p, Sisal. 2p, Native straw work. 2½p, Modern dairying. 3p, Fishing fleet. 4p, Out island settlement. 6p, Tuna fishing. 8p, Paradise Beach. 10p, Modern hotel. 1sh, Yacht racing. 2sh, Water skiing. 3sh, Shipbuilding. 5sh, Modern transportation. 10sh, Modern salt production. £1, Parliament Building.

1948, Oct. 11		**Unwmk.**		**Perf. 12**
132 A16	½p orange		.15	.15
133 A16	1p olive green		.15	.15
134 A16	1½p olive bister		.35	.15
135 A16	2p vermilion		.25	.20
136 A16	2½p red brown		.65	.60
137 A16	3p brt ultra		.45	.45
138 A16	4p gray black		.45	.75
139 A16	6p emerald		.65	.75
140 A16	8p violet		.65	.75
141 A16	10p rose car		.70	.75
142 A16	1sh olive brn		1.25	1.10
143 A16	2sh claret		6.25	6.00
144 A16	3sh brt blue		6.25	6.00
145 A16	5sh purple		5.00	6.00
146 A16	10sh dk gray		5.00	7.00
147 A16	£1 red orange		10.00	12.00
Nos. 132-147 (16)			38.20	43.00

300th anniv., in 1947, of the settlement of the colony.

Silver Wedding Issue
Common Design Type
Perf. 14x14½

1948, Dec. 1		**Wmk. 4**		**Photo.**
148 CD304	1½p red brown		.20	.15
	Engr.; Name Typo.			
	Perf. 11½x11			
149 CD305	£1 gray green		30.00	40.00

UPU Issue
Common Design Types
Engr.; Name Typo. on #151 & 152

1949, Oct. 10		*Perf. 13½, 11x11½*		
150 CD306	2½p violet		.25	.25
151 CD307	3p indigo		.50	.50
152 CD308	6p blue gray		1.00	1.00
153 CD309	1sh rose car		1.65	1.65
Nos. 150-153 (4)			3.40	3.40

George VI Type of 1938
Perf. 13½x14

1951-52		**Wmk. 4**		**Typo.**
154 A12	½p claret ('52)		.20	.20
a.	Wmk. 4a (error)		1,250.	
155 A12	2p green		.40	.40
156 A12	3p rose red ('52)		.80	3.00
Nos. 154-156 (3)			1.40	3.60

Coronation Issue
Common Design Type

1953, June 3		**Engr.**		*Perf. 13½x13*
157 CD312	6p blue & black		.60	.60

Infant Welfare Clinic — A17

Designs: 1p, Modern Agriculture. 1½p, Out island settlement. 2p, Native strawwork. 3p, Fishing fleet. 4p, Water skiing. 5p, Modern dairying. 6p, Modern transportation. 8p, Paradise Beach. 10p, Modern hotels. 1sh, Yacht racing. 2sh, Sisal. 2sh6p, Shipbuilding. 5sh, Tuna fishing. 10sh, Modern salt production. £1, Parliament Building.

1954, Jan. 1		*Perf. 11x11½*		
158 A17	½p red org & blk		.15	.15
159 A17	1p org brn & ol grn		.15	.15
a.	Booklet pane of 4		.55	
160 A17	1½p black & blue		.15	.15
a.	Booklet pane of 4		.70	
161 A17	2p dk grn & brn org		.15	.15
a.	Booklet pane of 4		.70	
162 A17	3p dp car & blk		.20	.15
163 A17	4p lil rose & bl green		.30	.15
a.	Booklet pane of 4		1.75	
164 A17	5p dp ultra & brn		.65	1.75
165 A17	6p blk & aqua		.45	.25
a.	Booklet pane of 4		2.25	
166 A17	8p rose vio & blk		.50	.25
a.	Booklet pane of 4		2.50	
167 A17	10p ultra & blk		.55	.35
168 A17	1sh ol brn & ultra		.65	.50
169 A17	2sh blk & brn org		1.10	.75
170 A17	2sh6p dp bl & blk		2.50	1.10
171 A17	5sh dp org & emer		5.00	2.50
172 A17	10sh grnsh blk & blk		7.00	5.00
173 A17	£1 vio & grnsh black		15.00	11.00
Nos. 158-173 (16)			34.50	24.45

See No. 203. For types overprinted or surcharged see Nos. 181-182, 185-200, 202.

Queen Elizabeth II — A18

Wmk. 314

1959, June 10		**Engr.**		*Perf. 13*
174 A18	1p dk red & black		.15	.15
175 A18	2p green & black		.15	.15
176 A18	6p blue & black		.30	.30
177 A18	10p brown & black		.55	.55
Nos. 174-177 (4)			1.15	1.15

Cent. of the 1st postage stamp of Bahamas.

Christ Church Cathedral, Nassau — A19

Perf. 14x13

1962, Jan. 30		**Photo.**		**Unwmk.**
178 A19	8p shown		.60	.60
179 A19	10p Public library		.60	.60

Centenary of the city of Nassau.

Freedom from Hunger Issue
Common Design Type
Perf. 14x14½

1963, June 4		**Wmk. 314**		
180 CD314	8p sepia		1.25	1.10
a.	"8d" and "BAHAMAS" omitted		875.00	

Nos. 166-167 Overprinted: "BAHAMAS TALKS/ 1962"
Perf. 11x11½

1963, July 15		**Engr.**		**Wmk. 4**
181 A17	8p rose vio & black		1.00	.85
182 A17	10p vio & black		1.75	1.65

Meeting of Pres. Kennedy and Prime Minister Harold Macmillan, Dec. 1962.

Red Cross Centenary Issue
Common Design Type

1963, Sept. 2		**Wmk. 314**		
		Litho.		*Perf. 13*
183 CD315	1p black & red		.20	.15
184 CD315	10p ultra & red		2.00	1.40

Type of 1954 Overprinted: "NEW CONSTITUTION/ 1964"

Designs as Before

Perf. 11x11½

1964, Jan. 7		**Engr.**		**Wmk. 314**
185 A17	½p red org & blk		.15	.15
186 A17	1p org brn & ol green		.15	.15
187 A17	1½p black & blue		.15	.15
188 A17	2p dk grn & brn org		.15	.15
189 A17	3p dp car & blk		.15	.15
190 A17	4p lil rose & bl green		.20	.15
191 A17	5p dp ultra & brn		.20	.20
192 A17	6p blk & aqua		.25	.20
193 A17	8p rose vio & blk		.35	.30
194 A17	10p ultra & black		.45	.35
195 A17	1sh ol brn & ultra		.60	.45
196 A17	2sh blk & brn org		1.25	.95
197 A17	2sh6p dp bl & blk		1.50	1.25
198 A17	5sh dp org & emer		3.00	2.50

---

199 A17	10sh grnsh blk & black		5.50	4.75
200 A17	£1 vio & grnsh black		11.50	9.50
Nos. 185-200 (16)			25.55	21.35

Shakespeare Issue
Common Design Type
Perf. 14x14½

1964, Apr. 23		**Photo.**		**Wmk. 314**
201 CD316	6p greenish blue		.45	.35

Type of 1954 Surcharged with Olympic Rings, New Value and Bars
Perf. 11x11½

1964, Oct. 1		**Engr.**		**Wmk. 314**
202 A17	8p on 1sh ol brn & ultra		.45	.45

18th Olympic Games, Tokyo, Oct. 10-25.

Queen Type of 1954

1964, Oct. 6		**Wmk. 314**		
203 A17	2p dk grn & brn org		.50	.50

Out Island Regatta A21 BAHAMAS

Designs: ½p, Colony badge. 1½p, Princess Margaret Hospital. 2p, High School. 3p, Flamingo. 4p, Island development. 6p, Liner "Queen Elizabeth." 8p, Island development. 10p, Public Square, Nassau. 1sh, Sea Garden, Nassau. 2sh, Cannons at Fort Charlotte. 2sh6p, Sea plane and jetliner. 5sh, 1914 Williamson film project and 1939 underwater post office. 10sh, Conch shell. £1, Columbus' flagship.

1965, Jan. 7		**Engr. and Litho.**		
		Perf. 13½x13		
204 A21	½p multi, *bluish*		.15	.15
205 A21	1p multi		.15	.15
a.	Booklet pane of 4		.40	
206 A21	1½p multi		.15	.15
a.	Booklet pane of 4		.45	
207 A21	2p multi		.15	.15
a.	Booklet pane of 4		.55	
208 A21	3p multi		.20	.15
209 A21	4p multi		.25	.15
a.	Booklet pane of 4		1.10	
210 A21	6p multi		.30	.15
a.	Booklet pane of 4		1.25	
211 A21	8p multi		.40	.30
a.	Booklet pane of 4		1.65	
212 A21	10p multi		.35	.15
213 A21	1sh multi, *grnsh*		.55	.25
214 A21	1sh multi, *grnsh*		1.10	.65
215 A21	2sh6p multi		1.50	.80
216 A21	5sh multi		3.00	1.60
217 A21	10sh multi		6.00	3.75
218 A21	£1 multi		12.00	7.25
Nos. 204-218 (15)			26.25	15.80

Booklet panes were issued Mar. 23, 1965.
See Nos. 252-266. For surcharges see Nos. 221, 230-244.

ITU Issue
Common Design Type
Perf. 11x11½

1965, May 17		**Litho.**		**Wmk. 314**
219 CD317	1p emerald & org		.20	.20
220 CD317	2sh lilac & olive		2.25	2.25

No. 211 Surcharged 9d.

Perf. 13½x13

1965, July 12		**Engr. & Litho.**		
221 A21	9p on 8p multi		.60	.60

Intl. Cooperation Year Issue
Common Design Type
Perf. 14½

1965, Oct. 25		**Wmk. 314**		**Litho.**
222 CD318	1p blue grn & claret		.15	.15
223 CD318	1sh lt violet & grn		.85	.70

Churchill Memorial Issue
Common Design Type

1966, Jan. 24		**Photo.**		*Perf. 14*
224 CD319	½p multicolored		.15	.15
225 CD319	2p multicolored		.20	.20
226 CD319	10p multicolored		1.00	1.00
227 CD319	1sh multicolored		1.50	1.50
Nos. 224-227 (4)			2.85	2.85

Royal Visit Issue
Common Design Type Inscribed "Royal Visit / 1966"

1966, Feb. 4		**Litho.**		*Perf. 11x12*
228 CD320	6p violet blue		.65	.65
229 CD320	1sh dk car rose		1.65	1.65

Nos. 204-218 Surcharged ☰ 2¢

Perf. 13½x13

1966, May 25		**Engr. & Litho.**		**Wmk. 314**
230 A21	1c on ½p multi		.15	.15
231 A21	2c on 1p multi		.15	.15
232 A21	3c on 2p multi		.15	.15
233 A21	4c on 3p multi		.15	.15
234 A21	4c on 3p multi		.15	.15
a.	Surch. omitted, vert. strip of 7-10		3,000.	
235 A21	8c on 6p multi		.20	.20
236 A21	8c on 8p multi		.25	.25
237 A21	11c on 1½p multi		.35	.25
238 A21	12c on 10p multi		.40	.20
239 A21	15c on 1sh multi		.48	.35
240 A21	22c on 2sh multi		.65	.45
241 A21	50c on 2sh6p multi		1.40	1.25
242 A21	$1 on 5sh multi		2.50	2.50
243 A21	$2 on 10sh multi		5.50	5.00
244 A21	$3 on £1 multi		8.00	7.50
Nos. 230-244 (15)			20.48	18.75

The denominations are next to the bars instead of below on Nos. 232, 235-240; the length of the bars varies to cover old denomination.
No. 234a, if single, is identical with No. 209, but distinguishable if in vertical strip of 7 to 10. No. 234 was printed in sheets of 100 (10x10); No. 209 in sheets of 60 (10x6).

World Cup Soccer Issue
Common Design Type

1966, July 1		**Litho.**		*Perf. 14*
245 CD321	8c multicolored		.30	.30
246 CD321	15c multicolored		.60	.60

WHO Headquarters Issue
Common Design Type

1966, Sept. 20		**Litho.**		*Perf. 14*
247 CD322	11c multicolored		.50	.50
248 CD322	15c multicolored		.70	.70

UNESCO Anniversary Issue
Common Design Type

1966, Dec. 1		**Litho.**		*Perf. 14*
249 CD323	3c "Education"		.15	.15
250 CD323	15c "Science"		.65	.65
251 CD323	$1 "Culture"		3.25	3.25
Nos. 249-251 (3)			4.05	4.05

Type of 1965
Values in Cents and Dollars
Perf. 13½x13

1967, May 25		**Engr. & Litho.**		

Designs: 1c, Colony badge. 2c, Out Island Regatta. 3c, High School. 4c, Flamingo. 5c, Liner "Oceanic." 8c, Island development. 10c, Yachting. 11c, Princess Margaret Hospital. 12c, Public Square, Nassau. 15c, Sea Garden, Nassau. 22c, Cannon at Fort Charlotte. 50c, Sea plane and jetliner. $1, 1914 Williamson film project and 1939 underwater post office. $2, Conch shell. $3, Columbus' flagship.

252 A21	1c brown & multi		.15	.15
253 A21	2c grn, slate & bl		.15	.15
254 A21	3c grn, indigo & vio		.15	.15
255 A21	4c ultra, blue & red		.15	.15
256 A21	5c pur, bl & indigo		.15	.15
257 A21	8c dk brn, bl & dl grn		.20	.20
258 A21	10c car rose, bl & pur		.25	.20
259 A21	11c bl, grn & rose red		.35	.25
260 A21	12c ol grn, bl & lt brn		.40	.20
261 A21	15c rose & multi		.50	.30
262 A21	22c rose red, brn & bl		.60	.25
263 A21	50c emer, ol & bl		1.40	.90
264 A21	$1 sep, brn org & dk blue		2.75	1.75
265 A21	$2 green & multi		5.50	4.25
266 A21	$3 pur, bl & brn org		8.50	6.75
Nos. 252-266 (15)			21.20	15.95

Nos. 252-266 are on toned paper. Printings on very white, untinted paper appeared between late 1969 and May, 1971. Value, set $500.

Seal of Bahamas, Queen Elizabeth II and Lord Baden-Powell A22

60th anniv. of world Scouting: 15c, Scout emblem and portraits as on 3c.

Perf. 14x13½

1967, Sept. 1		**Photo.**		**Wmk. 314**
267 A22	3c multicolored		.25	.25
268 A22	15c multicolored		.85	.85

Human
Rights Flame
and Globe
A23

Intl. Human Rights Year: 12c, Human rights flame and scales of justice. $1, Human rights flame and Seal of Bahamas.

1968, May 13   Litho.   Perf. 14
269	A23	3c multicolored	.15	.15
270	A23	12c multicolored	.50	.50
271	A23	$1 multicolored	2.25	2.25
		Nos. 269-271 (3)	2.90	2.90

Golf — A24

Tourist Publicity: 11c, Yachting. 15c, Horse racing. 50c, Water skiing.

1968, Aug. 20   Unwmk.   Perf. 13½
272	A24	5c multicolored	.25	.25
273	A24	11c multicolored	.52	.52
274	A24	15c multicolored	.65	.65
275	A24	50c multicolored	2.25	2.25
		Nos. 272-275 (4)	3.67	3.67

Olympic Monument and Sailboat — A25

Olympic Monument, San Salvador Island, Bahamas, and: 11c, Long jump. 50c, Running. $1, Sailing.

1968, Sept. 30   Photo.   Perf. 14½x14
276	A25	5c multicolored	.20	.20
277	A25	11c multicolored	.40	.40
278	A25	50c multicolored	1.65	1.65
279	A25	$1 multicolored	3.50	3.50
		Nos. 276-279 (4)	5.75	5.75

19th Olympic Games, Mexico City, Oct. 12-27.

Legislative
Building
A26

Designs: 10c, Bahamas mace and Big Ben, London, vert. 12c, Local straw market, vert. 15c, Horse-drawn surrey.

Perf. 14½
1968, Nov. 1   Unwmk.   Litho.
280	A26	3c brt blue & multi	.15	.15
281	A26	10c yel, blk & blue	.40	.40
282	A26	12c brt rose & multi	.45	.45
283	A26	15c green & multi	.50	.50
		Nos. 280-283 (4)	1.50	1.50

14th Commonwealth Parliamentary Conf., Nassau, Nov. 1-8.

$100 Coin with Queen Elizabeth II and
Landing of Columbus — A27

Gold Coins with Elizabeth II on Obverse: 12c, $50 coin and Santa Maria flagship. 15c, $20 coin and Nassau Harbor Lighthouse. $1, $10 coin and Fort.

Engr. on Gold Paper
1968, Dec. 2   Unwmk.   Perf. 13½
284	A27	3c dark red	.20	.20
285	A27	12c dark green	.65	.65
286	A27	15c lilac	.75	.75
287	A27	$1 black	4.50	2.50
		Nos. 284-287 (4)	6.10	4.10

First gold coinage in the Bahamas.

Bahamas
Postal Card
and
Airplane
Wing
A28

Design: 15c, Seaplane, 1929.

Perf. 14½x14
1969, Jan. 30   Litho.   Unwmk.
288	A28	12c multicolored	.90	.90
289	A28	15c multicolored	1.10	1.10

50th anniv. of the 1st flight from Nassau, Bahamas, to Miami, Fla., Jan. 30, 1919.

Game
Fishing
Boats
A29

Designs: 11c, Paradise Beach. 12c, Sunfish sailboats. 15c, Parade on Rawson Square.

1969, Aug. 26   Litho.   Wmk. 314
290	A29	3c multicolored	.20	.20
291	A29	11c multicolored	.60	.60
292	A29	12c multicolored	.65	.65
293	A29	15c multicolored	.80	.80
a.		Souvenir sheet of 4, #290-293	4.25	4.25
		Nos. 290-293 (4)	2.25	2.25

Tourist publicity.

Holy Family, by
Nicolas
Poussin — A30

Paintings: 3c, Adoration of the Shepherds, by Louis Le Nain. 12c, Adoration of the Kings, by Gerard David. 15c, Adoration of the Kings, by Vincenzo Foppa.

1969, Oct. 15   Photo.   Perf. 12
294	A30	3c red & multi	.15	.15
295	A30	11c emerald & multi	.60	.60
296	A30	12c ultra & multi	.70	.70
297	A30	15c multicolored	.90	.90
		Nos. 294-297 (4)	2.35	2.35

Christmas.

Girl Guides,
Globe and
Flags — A31

Designs: 12c, Yellow elder and Brownie emblem. 15c, Ranger emblem.

1970, Feb. 23   Wmk. 314   Perf. 14½
298	A31	3c vio blue & multi	.20	.20
299	A31	12c dk brn, grn & yel	.60	.60
300	A31	15c vio bl, bluish grn & yel	.80	.80
		Nos. 298-300 (3)	1.60	1.60

60th anniversary of the Girl Guides.

Opening of UPU Headquarters,
Bern — A32

1970, May 20   Litho.   Perf. 14½
301	A32	3c ver & multi	.15	.15
302	A32	15c orange & multi	.75	.75

Bus and
Globe
A33

Globe and: 11c, Train. 12c, Sailboat and ship. 15c, Plane.

1970, July 14   Perf. 13½x13
303	A33	3c orange & multi	.20	.20
304	A33	11c emerald & multi	.65	.65
305	A33	12c multicolored	.70	.70
306	A33	15c blue & multi	1.00	1.00
a.		Souvenir sheet of 4, #303-306	9.00	9.00
		Nos. 303-306 (4)	2.55	2.55

Issued to promote good will through world-wide travel and tourism.

People,
Palms and
Flamingo
A34

15c, Red Cross Headquarters, Nassau & marlin.

1970, Aug. 18   Perf. 14x14½
307	A34	3c multicolored	.15	.15
308	A34	15c multicolored	.80	.80

Centenary of British Red Cross Society.

Nativity by G. B.
Pittoni — A35

Christmas: 11c, Holy Family, by Anton Raphael Mengs. 12c, Adoration of the Shepherds, by Giorgione. 15c, Adoration of the Shepherds, School of Seville.

Perf. 12½x13
1970, Nov. 3   Litho.   Wmk. 314
309	A35	3c multicolored	.20	.20
310	A35	11c red org & multi	.55	.55
311	A35	12c emerald & multi	.65	.65
312	A35	15c blue & multi	.80	.80
a.		Souv. sheet of 4, #309-312 + 3 labels	2.25	2.25
		Nos. 309-312 (4)	2.20	2.20

International
Airport — A36

Designs: 2c, Breadfruit. 3c, Straw market. 4c, 6c, Hawksbill turtle. 5c, Grouper. 8c, Yellow elder. 10c, Bahamian sponge boat. 11c, Flamingos. 7c, 12c, Hibiscus. 15c, Bonefish. 18c, 22c, Royal poinciana. 50c, Post office, Nassau. $1, Pineapple, vert. $2, Crayfish, vert. $3, "Junkanoo" (costumed drummer), vert.

Wmk. 314 Upright (Sideways on $1, $2, $3)
1971   Perf. 14½x14, 14x14½
313	A36	1c blue & multi	.15	.15
314	A36	2c red & multi	.15	.15
315	A36	3c lilac & multi	.15	.15
316	A36	4c brown & multi	.42	.42
317	A36	5c dp org & multi	.30	.28
318	A36	6c brown & multi	.15	.15
319	A36	7c green & multi	.30	.28
320	A36	8c yel & multi	.65	.40
321	A36	10c red & multi	.38	.38
322	A36	11c red & multi	.40	.40
323	A36	12c green & multi	1.10	1.10
324	A36	15c gray & multi	.32	.32
325	A36	18c multicolored	.40	.40
326	A36	22c green & multi	1.40	1.40
327	A36	50c multicolored	1.65	1.40
328	A36	$1 red & multi	3.50	2.75
329	A36	$2 blue & multi	6.75	5.50
330	A36	$3 vio bl & multi	10.00	8.75
		Nos. 313-330 (18)	28.17	24.38

See Nos. 398-401, 426-443.

Wmk. 314 Sideways (Upright on $1, $2, $3)
1973
317a	A36	5c	.16	.16
320a	A36	8c	.24	.24
327a	A36	50c	1.40	1.40
328a	A36	$1	3.00	3.00
329a	A36	$2	5.50	5.50
330a	A36	$3	7.50	7.50
		Nos. 317a-330a (6)	18.80	18.80

1976   Wmk. 373
313a	A36	1c	.15	.15
314a	A36	2c	.15	.15
315a	A36	3c	.15	.15
317b	A36	5c	.15	.15
320b	A36	8c	.15	.15
321a	A36	10c	.18	.18
327b	A36	50c	1.25	1.25
328b	A36	$1	2.50	2.50
329b	A36	$2	4.75	4.75
330b	A36	$3	7.50	7.50
		Nos. 313a-330b (10)	16.93	16.93

Snowflake
with Peace
Signs — A37

Christmas: 11c, "Peace on Earth" with doves. 15c, Christmas wreath around old Bahamas coat of arms. 18c, Star of Bethlehem over palms.

Perf. 14x14½
1971   Photo.   Wmk. 314
331	A37	3c dp lil rose, gold & org	.15	.15
332	A37	11c violet & gold	.45	.45
333	A37	15c gold embossed & multi	.65	.65
334	A37	18c brt bl, gold & vio bl	.90	.90
a.		Souv. sheet of 4, #331-334, perf. 15	2.50	2.50
		Nos. 331-334 (4)	2.15	2.15

High
Jump,
Arms of
Bahamas
A38

Olympic Rings, Compass, Arms of Bahamas and: 11c, Bicycling. 15c, Running. 18c, Sailing.

1972, June 27   Litho.   Perf. 13x13½
335	A38	10c lt violet & multi	.40	.40
336	A38	11c ocher & multi	.48	.48
337	A38	15c yel green & multi	.70	.70
338	A38	18c blue & multi	.95	.95
a.		Souvenir sheet of 4, #335-338	3.25	4.50
		Nos. 335-338 (4)	2.53	2.53

20th Olympic Games, Munich, Aug. 26-Sept. 10.

Shepherd and Star of
Bethlehem — A39

Designs: 6c, Bells. 15c, Holly and monstrance. 20c, Poinsettia.

1972, Oct. 3   Wmk. 314   Perf. 14
339	A39	3c gold & multi	.15	.15
340	A39	6c black & multi	.28	.28
341	A39	15c black & multi	.70	.70

342 A39 20c gold & multi .95 .95
  a. Souvenir sheet of 4, #339-342 2.75 3.25
    Nos. 339-342 (4) 2.08 2.08
Christmas. Gold on 15c is embossed.

Souvenir Sheet

Map of Bahama Islands — A40

1972, Nov. 1   Litho.   **Perf. 15**
343 A40 Sheet of 4 3.75 4.75
  a. 11c blue & multi .35 .35
  b. 15c blue & multi .45 .45
  c. 18c blue & multi .52 .52
  d. 50c blue & multi 1.50 1.50
Tourism Year of the Americas.

Silver Wedding Issue, 1972
Common Design Type

Design: Queen Elizabeth II, Prince Philip, mace and galleon.

Perf. 14x14½
1972, Nov. 13   Photo.   **Wmk. 314**
344 CD324 11c car rose & multi .35 .35
345 CD324 18c violet & multi .55 .55

Weather Satellite, WMO Emblem A41

1973, Apr. 3   Litho.   **Perf. 14**
346 A41 15c shown .65 .65
347 A41 18c Weather radar .90 .90
Intl. meteorological cooperation, cent.

Clarence A. Bain — A42   Virgin in Prayer, by Sassoferrato — A43

Independence: 11c, New Bahamian coat of arms. 15c, New flag and Government House. $1, Milo B. Butler, Sr.

1973   **Wmk. 314**   **Perf. 14½x14**
348 A42 3c lilac & multi .15 .15
349 A42 11c lt blue & multi .30 .30
350 A42 15c lt green & multi .45 .45
351 A42 $1 yel & multi 2.25 2.25
  a. Souvenir sheet of 4, #348-351 3.50 4.50
    Nos. 348-351 (4) 3.15 3.15
Issued: #348-350, July 10; #351, 351a, Aug. 1.

1973, Oct. 16   Litho.   **Perf. 14**
Christmas: 11c, Virgin and Child with St. John, by Filippino Lippi. 15c, Choir of Angels, by Marmion. 18c, The Two Trinities, by Murillo.

352 A43 3c blue & multi .18 .18
353 A43 11c multicolored .60 .60
354 A43 15c gray grn & multi .80 .80
355 A43 18c lil rose & multi 1.10 1.10
  a. Souvenir sheet of 4, #352-355 2.75 3.75
    Nos. 352-355 (4) 2.68 2.68

Bahamas stamps can be mounted in the Scott British North and West Caribbean album.

Agriculture, Science and Medicine — A44

18c, Symbols of engineering, art, and law.

1974, Feb. 5   Litho.   **Perf. 13½x14**
356 A44 15c dull grn & multi .48 .48
357 A44 18 multicolored .65 .65
University of the West Indies, 25th anniv.

UPU Emblem A45

Designs: 13c, UPU emblem, vert. 14c, UPU emblem. 18c, UPU monument, Bern, vert.

1974, Apr. 23   **Perf. 14**
358 A45 3c multicolored .15 .15
359 A45 13c multicolored .45 .45
360 A45 14c olive bis & multi .52 .52
361 A45 18c multicolored .80 .80
  a. Souvenir sheet of 4, #358-361 1.90 2.25
    Nos. 358-361 (4) 1.92 1.92
Centenary of Universal Postal Union.

Roseate Spoonbills, Trust Emblem — A46

Protected Birds (National Trust Emblem and): 14c, White-crowned pigeons. 21c, White-tailed tropic birds. 36c, Bahamian parrot.

1974, Sept. 10   Litho.   **Perf. 14**
362 A46 13c multicolored .95 .70
363 A46 14c multicolored .95 .70
364 A46 21c multicolored 1.40 1.10
365 A46 36c multicolored 2.50 1.75
  a. Souvenir sheet of 4, #362-365 7.50 8.50
    Nos. 362-365 (4) 5.80 4.25
Bahamas National Trust, 15th anniv.

Holy Family, by Jacques de Stella A47

Christmas: 10c, Virgin and Child, by Girolamo Romanino. 12c, Virgin and Child with St. John and St. Catherine, by Andrea Previtali. 21c, Virgin and Child with Angels, by Previtali.

1974, Oct. 29   **Wmk. 314**   **Perf. 13**
366 A47 8c black & multi .40 .40
367 A47 10c green & multi .48 .48
368 A47 12c red & multi .60 .60
369 A47 21c ultra & multi 1.00 1.00
  a. Souvenir sheet of 4, #366-369 2.50 2.50
    Nos. 366-369 (4) 2.48 2.48

Anteos Maerula A48

1975, Feb. 4   Litho.   **Perf. 14x13½**
370 A48 3c shown .28 .24
371 A48 14c Eurema nicippe 1.00 .70
372 A48 18c Papilio andraemon 1.25 1.00
373 A48 21c Euptoieta hegesia 1.50 1.40
  a. Souvenir sheet of 4, #370-373 6.00 5.00
    Nos. 370-373 (4) 4.03 3.34

Sheep Raising A49

Designs: 14c, Electric reel fishing, vert. 18c, Growing food. 21c, Crude oil refinery, vert.

Unwmk.
1975, May 27   Litho.   **Perf. 14**
374 A49 3c dull grn & multi .15 .15
375 A49 14c green & multi .50 .50
376 A49 18c brown & multi .65 .65
377 A49 21c vio bl & multi .75 .75
  a. Souvenir sheet of 4, #374-377 2.25 2.25
    Nos. 374-377 (4) 2.05 2.05
Economic diversification.

Rowena Rand, Staff and Chrismon — A50   Plant and IWY Emblem — A51

Wmk. 373
1975, July 22   Litho.   **Perf. 14**
378 A50 14c multicolored .60 .60
379 A51 18c multicolored .80 .80
International Women's Year.

Adoration of the Shepherds, by Perugino — A52

Christmas: 8c, 18c, Adoration of the Kings, by Ghirlandaio. 21c, like 3c.

1975, Dec. 2   Litho.   **Perf. 13½**
380 A52 3c dk green & multi .15 .15
381 A52 8c dk violet & multi .30 .30
382 A52 18c purple & multi .70 .70
383 A52 21c maroon & multi .85 .85
  a. Souvenir sheet of 4, #380-383 2.25 2.25
    Nos. 380-383 (4) 2.00 2.00

Telephones, 1876 and 1976 — A53

Designs: 16c, Radio-telephone link, Deleporte, Nassau (radar). 21c, Alexander Graham Bell. 25c, Communications satellite.

1976, Mar. 23   Litho.   **Perf. 14**
384 A53 3c multicolored .15 .15
385 A53 16c multicolored .40 .40
386 A53 21c multicolored .52 .52
387 A53 25c multicolored .65 .65
    Nos. 384-387 (4) 1.72 1.72
Centenary of first telephone call by Alexander Graham Bell, Mar. 10, 1876.

Bicycling and Olympic Rings — A54

Olympic Rings and: 16c, Long jump. 25c, Sailing. 40c, Boxing.

1976, July 13   Litho.   **Perf. 14**
388 A54 8c magenta & blue .24 .24
389 A54 16c orange & brn .42 .42
390 A54 25c magenta & blue .60 .60
391 A54 40c orange & brn 1.10 1.10
  a. Souvenir sheet of 4, #388-391 2.75 2.75
    Nos. 388-391 (4) 2.36 2.36
21st Olympic Games, Montreal, Canada, July 17-Aug. 1.

John Murray, Earl of Dunmore A55

Design: 16c, Map of US and Bahamas.

1976, June 1   **Wmk. 373**   **Perf. 14**
392 A55 16c multicolored .52 .52
393 A55 $1 multicolored 2.50 2.50
  a. Souvenir sheet of 4, #393 10.00 10.00
American Bicentennial.

Virgin and Child, Filippo Lippi — A56

Christmas: 21c, Adoration of the Shepherds, School of Seville. 25c, Adoration of the Kings, by Vincenzo Foppa. 40c, Virgin and Child, by Vivarini.

1976, Oct. 19   Litho.   **Perf. 14½x14**
394 A56 3c brt blue & multi .15 .15
395 A56 21c dp org & multi .60 .60
396 A56 25c emerald & multi .75 .75
397 A56 40c red lilac & multi 1.10 1.10
  a. Souvenir sheet of 4, #394-397 2.75 2.75
    Nos. 394-397 (4) 2.60 2.60

Type of 1971
Designs: 16c, Hibiscus. 21c, Breadfruit. 25c, Hawksbill turtle. 40c, Bahamian sponge boat.

1976, Nov. 2   Litho.   **Wmk. 373**
398 A36 16c emerald & multi .35 .35
399 A36 21c vermilion & multi .38 .38
400 A36 25c brown & multi .52 .52
401 A36 40c vermilion & multi .70 .70
    Nos. 398-401 (4) 1.95 1.95

Elizabeth II Seated under Gold Canopy — A57

Designs: 16c, Coronation. 21c, Taking and signing of oath. 40c, Queen holding orb and scepter.

1977, Feb. 7   **Perf. 12**
402 A57 8c silver & multi .20 .20
403 A57 16c silver & multi .35 .35
404 A57 21c silver & multi .48 .48
405 A57 40c silver & multi 1.00 1.00
  a. Souvenir sheet of 4, #402-405 3.00 3.50
    Nos. 402-405 (4) 2.03 2.03
Reign of Queen Elizabeth II, 25th anniv. For surcharges see Nos. 412-415.

Featherduster — A58

Marine Life: 8c, Porkfish. 16c, Elkhorn coral. 21c, Soft coral and sponge.

1977, May 24   Litho.   Perf. 13½

406 A58	3c multicolored	.18	.18
407 A58	8c multicolored	.32	.32
408 A58	16c multicolored	.80	.80
409 A58	21c multicolored	1.00	1.00
a.	Souvenir sheet of 4, #406-409, perf. 14½	2.50	3.00
	Nos. 406-409 (4)	2.30	2.30

Campfire and Shower A59

1977, Sept. 27   Litho.   Wmk. 373

410 A59	16c shown	.42	.42
411 A59	21c Boating	.52	.52

6th Caribbean Jamboree, Kingston, Jamaica, Aug. 5-14.

Nos. 402-405a Overprinted: "Royal Visit / October 1977"

1977, Oct. 19   Litho.   Perf. 12

412 A57	8c silver & multi	.16	.16
413 A57	16c silver & multi	.32	.32
414 A57	21c silver & multi	.38	.38
415 A57	40c silver & multi	.80	.80
a.	Souvenir sheet of 4	2.25	2.75
	Nos. 412-415 (4)	1.66	1.66

Caribbean visit of Queen Elizabeth II, Oct. 19-20.

BAHAMAS 3c
Virgin and Child — A60

BAHAMAS 3c
Nassau Public Library — A61

Crèche Figurines: 16c, Three Kings. 21c, Adoration of the Kings. 25c, Three Kings.

1977, Oct. 25   Litho.   Perf. 13½

416 A60	3c gold & multi	.15	.15
417 A60	16c gold & multi	.38	.38
418 A60	21c gold & multi	.48	.48
419 A60	25c gold & multi	.60	.60
a.	Souvenir sheet of 4, #416-419, perf. 14½	1.90	1.90
	Nos. 416-419 (4)	1.61	1.61

Christmas.

1978, Mar. 28   Litho.   Perf. 14½x14

Architectural Heritage: 8c, St. Matthew's Church. 16c, Government House. 18c, The Hermitage, Cat Island.

420 A61	3c black & yel green	.15	.15
421 A61	8c black & lt blue	.18	.18
422 A61	16c black & lilac rose	.32	.32
423 A61	18c black & salmon	.35	.35
a.	Souvenir sheet of 4, #420-423	1.10	1.10
	Nos. 420-423 (4)	1.00	1.00

Scepter, St. Edward's Crown, Orb — A62

Perf. 14x13½

1978, June 27   Litho.   Wmk. 373

424 A62	16c shown	.28	.28
425 A62	$1 Elizabeth II	1.65	1.65
a.	Souvenir sheet of 2, #424-425	2.25	2.25

Coronation of Queen Elizabeth II, 25th anniv.

Type of 1971

Designs as before and: 16c, Hibiscus. 25c, Hawksbill turtle.

Perf. 14½x14, 14x14½

1978, June   Unwmk.

426 A36	1c blue & multi	.15	.15
430 A36	5c dp org & multi	.15	.15
436 A36	16c brt grn & multi	.38	.38
439 A36	25c brown & multi	.60	.60
440 A36	50c lemon & multi	1.10	1.10
441 A36	$1 lemon & multi	2.50	2.50
442 A36	$2 blue & multi	4.75	4.75
443 A36	$3 vio bl & multi	7.25	7.25
	Nos. 426-443 (8)	16.88	16.88

Angels and Palms — A63

Christmas: 5c, Coat of arms within wreath, and sailing ships.

Perf. 14x14½

1978, Nov. 14   Litho.   Wmk. 373

444 A63	5c car, pink & gold	.15	.15
445 A63	21c ultra, dk bl & gold	.32	.32
a.	Souvenir sheet of 2, #444-445	2.50	2.50

Baby Walking, IYC Emblem — A64

IYC Emblem and: 16c, Children playing leapfrog. 21c, Girl skipping rope. 25c, Building blocks with "IYC" and emblem.

Perf. 13½x13

1979, May 15   Litho.   Wmk. 373

446 A64	5c multicolored	.15	.15
447 A64	16c multicolored	.25	.25
448 A64	21c multicolored	.35	.35
449 A64	25c multicolored	.40	.40
a.	Souv. sheet of 4, #446-449, perf. 14	1.10	1.10
	Nos. 446-449 (4)	1.15	1.15

International Year of the Child.

Rowland Hill and Penny Black — A65

Designs: 21c, Stamp printing press, 1840, and Bahamas No. 7. 25c, Great Britain No. 27 with 1850's Nassau cancellation, and Great Britain No. 29. 40c, Early mailboat and Bahamas No. 1.

1979, Aug. 14   Perf. 13½x14

450 A65	10c multicolored	.16	.16
451 A65	21c multicolored	.35	.35
452 A65	25c multicolored	.40	.40
453 A65	40c multicolored	.65	.65
a.	Souvenir sheet of 4, #450-453	1.65	1.65
	Nos. 450-453 (4)	1.56	1.56

Sir Rowland Hill (1795-1879), originator of penny postage.

Commonwealth Plaque over Map of Bahamas — A66

Designs: 21c, Parliament buildings. 25c, Legislative chamber. $1, Senate chamber.

1979, Sept. 27   Litho.   Perf. 13½

454 A66	16c multicolored	.25	.25
455 A66	21c multicolored	.35	.35
456 A66	25c multicolored	.40	.40

457 A66	$1 multicolored	1.65	1.65
a.	Souvenir sheet of 4, #454-457	2.75	2.75
	Nos. 454-457 (4)	2.65	2.65

Parliament of Bahamas, 250th anniv.

Headdress — A67

Christmas: Goombay Carnival costumes.

1979, Nov. 6   Litho.   Perf. 13

458 A67	5c multicolored	.15	.15
459 A67	10c multicolored	.15	.15
460 A67	16c multicolored	.22	.22
461 A67	21c multicolored	.32	.32
462 A67	25c multicolored	.38	.38
463 A67	40c multicolored	.60	.60
a.	Souv. sheet of 6, 458-463, perf 13½	1.90	1.90
	Nos. 458-463 (6)	1.82	1.82

Columbus' Landing, 1492 — A68   1c

1980, July 9   Litho.   Perf. 15

464 A68	1c shown	.15	.15
465 A68	3c Blackbeard	.15	.15
466 A68	5c Articles, 1647, Eleuthera map	.15	.15
467 A68	10c Ceremonial mace	.20	.20
468 A68	12c Col. Andrew Deveaux	.24	.24
469 A68	15c Slave trading, Vendue House	.28	.28
470 A68	16c Shipwreck salvage, 19th cent.	.30	.30
471 A68	18c Blockade runner, 1860s	.32	.32
472 A68	21c Bootlegging, 1919-1929	.40	.40
473 A68	25c Pineapple cultivation	.24	.24
474 A68	40c Sponge clipping	.75	.75
475 A68	50c Victoria & Colonial Hotels	1.00	1.00
476 A68	$1 Modern agriculture	2.00	2.00
477 A68	$2 Ship, jet	3.70	3.70
478 A68	$3 Central Bank, Arms	5.75	5.75
479 A68	$5 Prince Charles, Prime Minister Pindling	9.50	9.50
	Nos. 464-479 (16)	25.13	25.13

For overprints and surcharges see Nos. 496-499, 532-535.

1985, Nov. 6   Wmk. 384

464a A68	1c	.15	.15
465a A68	3c	.15	.15
467a A68	10c	.20	.20
473a A68	25c	.48	.48
	Nos. 464a-473a (4)	.98	.98

Virgin and Child, Straw Figures — A69

1980, Oct. 28   Litho.   Perf. 14½

480 A69	5c shown	.15	.15
481 A69	21c Three kings	.35	.35
482 A69	25c Angel	.40	.40
483 A69	$1 Christmas tree	1.65	1.65
a.	Souvenir sheet of 4, #480-483	2.50	2.50
	Nos. 480-483 (4)	2.55	2.55

Christmas.

Man with Crutch, Sun Rays A70

International Year for Disabled Persons

1981, Feb. 10   Litho.   Perf. 14½

484 A70	5c shown	.15	.15
485 A70	$1 Man in wheelchair	1.65	1.65
a.	Souvenir sheet of 2, #484-485	1.75	1.75

International Year of the Disabled.

Grand Bahama Tracking Station A71

Satellite Views: 20c, Bahamas, vert. 25c, Eleuthera. 50c, Andros and New Providence, vert.

1981, Apr. 21   Litho.   Perf. 13½   Wmk. 373

486 A71	10c multicolored	.18	.18
487 A71	20c multicolored	.35	.35
488 A71	25c multicolored	.45	.45
489 A71	50c multicolored	.90	.90
a.	Souvenir sheet of 4, #486-489	2.00	2.75
	Nos. 486-489 (4)	1.88	1.88

Prince Charles and Lady Diana — A72

Perf. 14½

1981, July 22   Litho.   Wmk. 373

490 A72	30c shown	.52	.52
491 A72	$2 Charles, Prime Minister	3.50	3.50
a.	Souvenir sheet of 2, #490-491	5.00	5.75

Royal wedding.

Bahama Ducks — A73

Wmk. 373

1981, Aug. 25   Litho.   Perf. 14

492 A73	5c multicolored	.25	.25
493 A73	20c Reddish egrets	1.00	1.00
494 A73	25c Brown boobies	1.00	1.00
495 A73	$1 West Indian tree ducks	2.50	2.50
a.	Souvenir sheet of 4, #492-495	5.25	5.25
	Nos. 492-495 (4)	4.75	4.75

See Nos. 514-517.

Nos. 466-467, 473, 475 Overprinted: "COMMONWEALTH FINANCE MINISTERS' MEETING 21-23 SEPTEMBER 1981"

1981, Sept.   Litho.   Perf. 15

496 A68	5c multicolored	.15	.15
497 A68	10c multicolored	.16	.16
498 A68	25c multicolored	.42	.42
499 A68	50c multicolored	.85	.85
	Nos. 496-499 (4)	1.58	1.58

World Food Day — A74

Perf. 13x13½

1981, Oct. 16   Wmk. 373

500 A74	5c Chickens	.18	.18
501 A74	20c Sheep	.40	.40
502 A74	30c Lobster	.60	.60
503 A74	50c Pigs	1.00	1.00
a.	Souvenir sheet of 4, #500-503	2.25	2.75
	Nos. 500-503 (4)	2.18	2.18

5c Bahamas

Christmas — A75

Wmk. 373

1981, Nov. 23		Litho.		Perf. 14	
504		Sheet of 9		5.00	5.00
a.	A75	5c Father Christmas		.20	.20
b.	A75	5c shown		.20	.20
c.	A75	5c St. Nicholas, Holland		.20	.20
d.	A75	25c Lussibruden, Sweden		.40	.40
e.	A75	25c Mother and child		.40	.40
f.	A75	25c King Wenceslas, Czechoslovakia		.40	.40
g.	A75	30c Mother and child		.45	.45
h.	A75	30c Mother and child standing		.45	.45
i.	A75	$1 Christkindl angel, Germany		1.75	1.75

TB Bacillus
Centenary
A76

1982, Feb. 3		Litho.	Perf. 14	
505	A76	5c Koch	.15	.15
506	A76	16c X-ray	.30	.30
507	A76	21c Microscopes	.42	.42
508	A76	$1 Mantoux test	1.90	1.90
a.		Souvenir sheet of 4, #505-508, perf. 14½	3.50	4.00
		Nos. 505-508 (4)	2.77	2.77

BAHAMAS 25c

Flamingoes — A77

Designs: a, Females. b, Males. c, Nesting. d, Juvenile birds. e, Immature birds. No. 509 in continuous design.

Wmk. 373

1982, Apr. 28	Litho.		Perf. 14	
509	Strip of 5, multicolored		4.00	4.00
a.-e.	A77 25c any single		.80	.80

Princess Diana Issue
Common Design Type

1982, July 1		Litho.	Perf. 14	
510	CD333	16c Arms	.25	.25
511	CD333	25c Diana	.38	.38
512	CD333	40c Wedding	.60	.60
513	CD333	$1 Portrait	1.50	1.50
		Nos. 510-513 (4)	2.73	2.73

Bird Type of 1981
Wmk. 373

1982, Aug. 18		Litho.	Perf. 14	
514	A73	10c Bat	.18	.18
515	A73	16c Hutia	.28	.28
516	A73	21c Racoon	.35	.35
517	A73	$1 Dolphins	1.75	1.75
a.		Souvenir sheet of 4, #514-517	3.25	3.25
		Nos. 514-517 (4)	2.56	2.56

28th
Commonwealth
Parliamentary
Conference — A78

	Perf. 14x13½			
1982, Oct. 16		Litho.	Wmk. 373	
518	A78	5c Plaque	.15	.15
519	A78	25c Assoc. arms	.50	.50
520	A78	40c Natl. arms	.80	.80
521	A78	50c House of Assembly	1.00	1.00
		Nos. 518-521 (4)	2.45	2.45

Christmas
A79

Designs: 5c, Wesley Methodist Church, Baillou Hill Road. 12c, Centerville Seventh Day Adventist Church. 15c, Church of God of Prophecy, East Street. 21c, Bethel Baptist Church, Meeting Street. 25c, St. Francis Xavier Catholic Church, West Hill Street. $1, Holy Cross Anglican Church, Highbury Park.

1982, Nov. 3		Perf. 14		
522	A79	5c multicolored	.15	.15
523	A79	12c multicolored	.24	.24
524	A79	15c multicolored	.28	.28
525	A79	21c multicolored	.40	.40
526	A79	25c multicolored	.48	.48
527	A79	$1 multicolored	1.90	1.90
		Nos. 522-527 (6)	3.45	3.45

A80

1983, Mar. 14		Litho.		
528	A80	5c Lynden O. Pindling	.15	.15
529	A80	25c Flags	.40	.40
530	A80	35c Map	.55	.55
531	A80	$1 Ocean liner	1.65	1.65
		Nos. 528-531 (4)	2.75	2.75

Commonwealth Day.

Nos. 469-472 Surcharged

1983, Apr. 5		Litho.	Perf. 15	
532	A68	20c on 15c multi	.35	.35
533	A68	31c on 21c multi	.55	.55
534	A68	35c on 16c multi	.65	.65
535	A68	80c on 18c multi	1.50	1.50
		Nos. 532-535 (4)	3.05	3.05

30th Anniv. of
Customs
Cooperation Council
A81

10th Anniv. of
Independence
A82

	Perf. 14x13½			
1983, May 31			Wmk. 373	
536	A81	31c Officers, ship	.52	.52
537	A81	$1 Officers, jet	1.65	1.65

1983, July 6		Litho.	Perf. 14	
538	A82	$1 Flag raising	1.50	1.50
a.		Souvenir sheet, perf. 12	1.50	1.50

Local Butterflies
A83

1983, Aug. 24			Perf. 14½x14	
539	A83	5c Carters skipper	.18	.18
540	A83	25c Giant southern white	.90	.90
541	A83	31c Large orange sulphur	1.10	1.10
542	A83	50c Flambeau	1.75	1.75
a.		Souvenir sheet of 4	4.25	4.25
		Nos. 539-542 (4)	3.93	3.93

No. 542a contains Nos. 539-542, perf. 14 and perf. 14½x14.

American
Loyalists
Arrival
Bicentenary
A84

Paintings by Alton Lowe.

1983, Sept. 28			Perf. 14	
543	A84	5c Loyalist Dreams	.15	.15
544	A84	31c New Plymouth, Abaco	.55	.55
545	A84	35c New Plymouth Hotel	.60	.60

546	A84	50c Island Hope		.90	.90
a.		Souvenir sheet of 4, #543-546		2.25	2.25
		Nos. 543-546 (4)		2.20	2.20

Christmas — A85

125th Anniv. of
Bahamas
Stamps — A86

Children's designs: 5c, Christmas Bells, by Monica Pinder. 20c, The Flamingo by Cory Bullard. 25c, The Yellow Hibiscus with Christmas Candle by Monique A. Bailey. 31c, Santa goes a Sailing by Sabrina Seiler, horiz. 35c, Silhouette scene with palm trees by James Blake. 50c, Silhouette scene with Pelicans, by Erik Russell, horiz.

1983, Nov. 1			Perf. 14	
547	A85	5c multicolored	.15	.15
548	A85	20c multicolored	.32	.32
549	A85	25c multicolored	.42	.42
550	A85	31c multicolored	.50	.50
551	A85	35c multicolored	.60	.60
552	A85	50c multicolored	.80	.80
		Nos. 547-552 (6)	2.79	2.79

1984, Feb. 22		Litho.	Perf. 14	
553	A86	5c No. 3	.15	.15
554	A86	$1 No. 1	1.65	1.65

Lloyd's List Issue
Common Design Type
Perf. 14½

1984, Apr. 25		Litho.	Wmk. 373	
555	CD335	5c Trent	.15	.15
556	CD335	31c Orinoco	.55	.55
557	CD335	35c Nassau Harbor	.60	.60
558	CD335	50c Container ship Oropesa	.85	.85
		Nos. 555-558 (4)	2.15	2.15

1984 Summer
Olympics
A87

1984, June 20		Litho.	Perf. 14x14½	
559	A87	5c Running	.15	.15
560	A87	25c Discus	.42	.42
561	A87	31c Boxing	.52	.52
562	A87	$1 Basketball	1.65	1.65
a.		Souvenir sheet of 4, #559-562	2.75	2.75
		Nos. 559-562 (4)	2.74	2.74

Flags of Bahamas and
Caribbean
Community — A88

Wmk. 373

1984, July 4		Litho.	Perf. 14	
563	A88	50c multicolored	.90	.90

Conference of Heads of Government of Caribbean Community, 5th Meeting.

Allen's Cay
Iguana — A89

1984, Aug. 15			Perf. 14	
564	A89	5c shown	.15	.15
565	A89	25c Curly-tailed lizard	.60	.60
566	A89	35c Greenhouse frog	.80	.80
567	A89	50c Atlantic green turtle	1.00	1.00
a.		Souvenir sheet of 4, #564-567	3.00	3.00
		Nos. 564-567 (4)	2.55	2.55

25th Anniv. of
Natl. Trust — A90

Christmas — A91

Wildlife: a, Calliphlox evelynae. b, Megaceryle alcyon, Eleutherodactylus planirostris. c, Phoebis sennae, Phoenicopterus ruber, Himantopus himantopus, Phoebus sennae. d, Urbanus proteus, Chelonia mydas. e, Pandion haliaetus. Continuous design.

1984, Aug. 15		Litho.	Perf. 14	
568		Strip of 5	5.25	5.25
a.-e.	A90 31c any single		1.10	1.10

1984, Nov. 7		Litho.	Perf. 13½x13	
Madonna and Child Paintings.				
569	A91	5c Titian	.15	.15
570	A91	31c Anais Colin	.55	.55
571	A91	35c Elena Caula	.60	.60
a.		Souvenir sheet of 3, #569-571	1.40	1.40
		Nos. 569-571 (3)	1.30	1.30

Girl Guides,
75th Anniv.,
Intl. Youth
Year — A92

1985, Feb. 22		Litho.	Perf. 14	
572	A92	5c Brownies	.15	.15
573	A92	25c Camping	.40	.40
574	A92	31c Girl Guides	.50	.50
575	A92	35c Rangers	.55	.55
a.		Souvenir sheet of 4, #572-575	1.65	1.65
		Nos. 572-575 (4)	1.60	1.60

Audubon
Birth
Bicentenary
A93

Wmk. 373

1985, Apr. 24		Litho.	Perf. 14	
576	A93	5c Killdeer	.15	.15
577	A93	31c Mourning dove, vert.	.85	.85
578	A93	35c Mourning doves, diff., vert.	.90	.90
579	A93	$1 Killdeers, diff.	2.50	2.50
		Nos. 576-579 (4)	4.40	4.40

Queen Mother 85th Birthday
Common Design Type
Perf. 14½x14

1985, June 7		Litho.	Wmk. 384	
580	CD336	5c Portrait, 1927	.15	.15
581	CD336	25c At christening of Peter Phillips	.42	.42
582	CD336	35c Portrait, 1985	.60	.60
583	CD336	50c Holding Prince Henry	.85	.85
		Nos. 580-583 (4)	2.02	2.02

Souvenir Sheet

584	CD336	$1.25 In a pony and trap	2.00	2.00

UN and UN
Food and
Agriculture
Org., 40th
Annivs.
A94

Wmk. 373

1985, Aug. 26		Litho.	Perf. 14	
585	A94	25c Wheat, emblems	.42	.42

Commonwealth
Heads of Government
Meeting,
1985 — A95

1985, Oct. 16   Wmk. 373   *Perf. 14¹/₂*
586 A95 31c Queen Elizabeth II   .48 .48
587 A95 35c Flag, Commonwealth em-
              blem   .55 .55

Christmas
A96

Paintings by Alton Roland Lowe: 5c, Grandma's
Christmas Bouquet. 25c, Junkanoo Romeo and
Juliet, vert. 31c, Bunce Girl, vert. 35c, Home for
Christmas.

1985, Nov. 5   *Perf. 13*
588 A96 5c multicolored   .15 .15
589 A96 25c multicolored   .48 .48
590 A96 31c multicolored   .62 .62
591 A96 35c multicolored   .65 .65
   a. Souv. sheet of 4, #588-591, perf. 14 1.90 1.90
        Nos. 588-591 (4)   1.90 1.90

Queen Elizabeth II 60th Birthday
Common Design Type

Designs: 10c, Age 1, 1927. 25c, Coronation,
Westminster Abbey, 1953. 35c, Giving speech,
royal visit, Bahamas. 40c, At Djakova, Yugoslavia,
state visit, 1972. $1, Visiting Crown Agents, 1983.

1986, Apr. 21   Wmk. 384   *Perf. 14¹/₂*
592 CD337 10c scar, blk & sil   .16 .16
593 CD337 25c ultra & multi   .40 .40
594 CD337 35c green & multi   .55 .55
595 CD337 40c violet & multi   .65 .65
596 CD337 $1 rose vio & multi   1.65 1.65
        Nos. 592-596 (5)   3.41 3.41

AMERIPEX '86 — A97

1986, May 19   *Perf. 14*
597 A97 5c Nos. 464, 471   .15 .15
598 A97 25c Nos. 288-289   .45 .45
599 A97 31c No. 392   .55 .55
600 A97 50c No. 489a   .90 .90
601 A97 $1 Statue of Liberty, vert.   1.75 1.75
   a. Souvenir sheet of one   1.75 1.75
        Nos. 597-601 (5)   3.80 3.80

Statue of Liberty, cent.

Royal Wedding Issue, 1986
Common Design Type

Designs: 10c, Formal engagement. $1, Andrew
in dress uniform.

1986, July 23   *Perf. 14¹/₂x14*
602 CD338 10c multicolored   .16 .16
603 CD338 $1 multicolored   1.65 1.65

Fish — A98

1986-87   Wmk. 384   *Perf. 14*
604 A98 5c Rock beauty   .15 .15
605 A98 10c Stoplight parrotfish   .15 .15
606 A98 15c Jacknife fish   .22 .22
607 A98 20c Flamefish   .28 .28
608 A98 25c Swissguard basslet   .35 .35
609 A98 30c Spotfin butterflyfish   .42 .42
610 A98 35c Queen triggerfish   .52 .52
611 A98 40c Four-eyed butterf-
              lyfish   .55 .55
612 A98 45c Fairy basslet   .65 .65
613 A98 50c Queen angelfish   .70 .70
614 A98 60c Blue chromis   .85 .85
615 A98 $1 Spanish hogfish   1.40 1.40

616 A98 $2 Harlequin bass   2.75 2.75
617 A98 $3 Blackbar soldierfish   4.50 4.50
618 A98 $5 Pygmy angelfish   7.25 7.25
618A A99 $10 Red hind ('87)   16.00 16.00
        Nos. 604-618A (16)   36.74 36.74

Nos. 605, 608, 611-613, 615, 617-618 exist
inscribed "1990." Nos. 611, 615, 616 "1988."
Issue dates: $10, Jan. 2, others, Aug. 5.

1987, June 25   Wmk. 373
604a   5c   .15 .15
605a 10c   .15 .15
606a 15c   .22 .22
611a 40c   .55 .55
612a 45c   .65 .65
613a 50c   .70 .70
614a 60c   .85 .85
615a $1   1.40 1.40
616a $2   2.75 2.75
        Nos. 604a-616a (9)   7.42 7.42

Nos. 604a-616a dated 1987. No. 605a "1988."
No. 604a "1989."

Christ Church
Cathedral — A99

**   *Perf. 14¹/₂***
1986, Sept. 16   Wmk. 373
619 A99 10c View, 19th cent.   .16 .16
620 A99 40c View, 1986   .65 .65
   a. Souvenir sheet of 2, #619-620   .85 .85

City of Nassau, Diocese of Nassau and the Bahamas and Christ Church, 125th anniv.

Christmas, Intl.
Peace
Year — A100

**   Wmk. 384**
1986, Nov. 4   Litho.   *Perf. 14*
621 A100 10c Nativity   .16 .16
622 A100 40c Flight to Egypt   .65 .65
623 A100 45c Children praying   .75 .75
624 A100 50c Exchanging gifts   .80 .80
   a. Souvenir sheet of 4, #621-624   2.50 2.50
        Nos. 621-624 (4)   2.36 2.36

Pirates of the   Map of the
Caribbean — A101   Bahamas — A102

**   *Perf. 14¹/₂***
1987, June 2   Litho.   Wmk. 373
625 A101 10c Anne Bonney   .22 .22
626 A101 40c Blackbeard (d. 1718)   .90 .90
627 A101 45c Capt. Edward England   1.00 1.00
628 A101 50c Capt. Woodes Rogers
              (c. 1679-1732)   1.25 1.25
        Nos. 625-628 (4)   3.37 3.37

Souvenir Sheet
629 A102 $1.25 shown   2.75 2.75

Paintings of
Lighthouses
by Alton
Roland
Lowe — A103

1987, Mar. 31   Wmk. 384
630 A103 10c Great Isaac   .30 .30
631 A103 40c Bird Rock   1.25 1.25
632 A103 45c Castle Is.   1.50 1.50
633 A103 $1 Hole in the Wall   3.25 3.25
        Nos. 630-633 (4)   6.30 6.30

Tourist
Transportation
A104

Ships: No. 634a, Cruise ship, sailboat. b, Cruise
ships, tugboat, speedboat. c, Pleasure boat leaving
harbor, sailboat. d, Pleasure boat docked, sailboats.
e, Sailboats.
Aircraft: No. 635a, Bahamasair plane. b,
Bahamasair and Pan Am aircraft. c, Aircraft, radar
tower. d, Control tower, aircraft. e, Helicopter,
planes.

1987, Aug. 26   Wmk. 373   *Perf. 14*
634   Strip of 5   3.75 3.75
   a.-e. A104 40c any single   .75 .75
635   Strip of 5   3.75 3.75
   a.-e. A104 40c any single   .75 .75

Orchids
Painted by
Alton Roland
Lowe — A105

1987, Oct. 20   Wmk. 384   *Perf. 14¹/₂*
636 A105 10c Cattleyopis lindenii   .16 .16
637 A105 40c Encyclia lucayana   .65 .65
638 A105 45c Encyclia hodgeana   .75 .75
639 A105 50c Encyclia lleidae   .80 .80
   a. Souvenir sheet of 4, #636-639   2.50 2.50
        Nos. 636-639 (4)   2.36 2.36

Christmas.

Discovery of America,
500th Anniv. (in
1992) — A106

10c, Ferdinand & Isabella. 40c, Columbus before
the Talavera Committee. 45c, Lucayan village. 50c,
Lucayan potters. $1.50, Map, c. 1500.

**   *Perf. 14x14¹/₂***
1988, Feb. 23   Litho.   Wmk. 373
640 A106 10c multicolored   .16 .16
641 A106 40c multicolored   .65 .65
642 A106 45c multicolored   .75 .75
643 A106 50c multicolored   .80 .80
        Nos. 640-643 (4)   2.36 2.36

Souvenir Sheet
644 A106 $1.50 multicolored   3.00 3.00

See Nos. 663-667, 688-692, 725-729, 749-753,
762.

World Wildlife
Fund — A107

Whistling ducks, Dendrocygna arborea.

1988, Apr. 29   *Perf. 14¹/₂*
645 A107 5c Ducks in flight   .18 .15
646 A107 10c Among marine plants   .16 .16
647 A107 20c Adults, ducklings   .32 .32
648 A107 45c Wading   .75 .75
        Nos. 645-648 (4)   1.41 1.38

Abolition of
Slavery, 150th
Anniv.
A108

1988, Aug. 9   *Perf. 14*
649 A108 10c African hut   .20 .20
650 A108 40c Basket weavers in hut,
              Grantstown   .80 .80

1988
Summer
Olympics,
Seoul
A109

Games emblem and details of painting by James
Martin: 10c, Olympic flame, high jump, hammer
throw, basketball and gymnastics. 40c, Swimming,
boxing, weight lifting, fencing and running. 45c,
Gymnastics, shot put and javelin. $1, Running,
cycling and gymnastics.

**   Wmk. 384**
1988, Aug. 30   Litho.   *Perf. 14*
651 A109 10c multicolored   .20 .20
652 A109 40c multicolored   .80 .80
653 A109 45c multicolored   .90 .90
654 A109 $1 multicolored   2.00 2.00
   a. Souvenir sheet of 4, #651-654   4.00 4.00
        Nos. 651-654 (4)   3.90 3.90

Lloyds of London, 300th Anniv.
Common Design Type

Designs: 10c, Lloyds List No. 560, 1740. 40c,
Freeport Harbor, horiz. 45c, Space shuttle over the
Bahamas, horiz. $1, Supply ship Yarmouth Castle
on fire.

1988, Oct. 4   Wmk. 373
655 CD341 10c multicolored   .20 .20
656 CD341 40c multicolored   .80 .80
657 CD341 45c multicolored   .90 .90
658 CD341 $1 multicolored   2.00 2.00
        Nos. 655-658 (4)   3.90 3.90

Christmas
Carols — A110

Designs: 10c, O' Little Town of Bethlehem. 40c,
Little Donkey. 45c, Silent Night. 50c, Hark! The
Herald Angels Sing.

1988, Nov. 21   Wmk. 384   *Perf. 14¹/₂*
659 A110 10c multicolored   .20 .20
660 A110 40c multicolored   .80 .80
661 A110 45c multicolored   .90 .90
662 A110 50c multicolored   1.00 1.00
   a. Souvenir sheet of 4, #659-662   2.90 2.90
        Nos. 659-662 (4)   2.90 2.90

Discovery of America Type of 1988

Design: 10c, Columbus as chartmaker. 40c,
Development of the caravel. 45c, Navigational
tools. 50c, Arawak artifacts. $1.50, Caravel under
construction, an illumination from the Nuremburg
Chronicles, 15th cent.

**   *Perf. 14¹/₂x14***
1989, Jan. 25   Litho.   Wmk. 373
663 A106 10c multicolored   .20 .20
664 A106 40c multicolored   .80 .80
665 A106 45c multicolored   .90 .90
666 A106 50c multicolored   1.00 1.00
        Nos. 663-666 (4)   2.90 2.90

Souvenir Sheet
667 A106 $1.50 multicolored   3.00 3.00

---

*The index in each volume of the
Scott Catalogue contains many listings that help identify stamps.*

Hummingbirds
A111

1989, Mar. 29   Perf. 14½
Litho.   Wmk. 384
668	A111	10c Cuban emerald	.20	.20
669	A111	40c Ruby-throated	.80	.80
670	A111	45c Bahama woodstar	.90	.90
671	A111	50c Rufous	1.00	1.00
		Nos. 668-671 (4)	2.90	2.90

Intl. Red Cross
and Red
Crescent
Organizations,
125th Anniv.
A112

1989, May 31   Perf. 14x14½
672	A112	10c Water safety	.20	.20
673	A112	$1 Dunant, Battle of Sol-ferino	2.00	2.00

Moon Landing, 20th Anniv.
Common Design Type

Apollo 8: 10c, Apollo Communications System, Grand Bahama Is. 40c, James Lovell Jr., William Anders and Frank Borman. 45c, Mission emblem. $1, The Rising Earth (photograph). $2, Astronaut practicing lunar surface activities at Manned Spacecraft Center, Houston, in training for Apollo 11 mission.

1989, July 20   Perf. 14x13½
Size of Nos. 674-675: 29x29mm
674	CD342	10c multicolored	.20	.20
675	CD342	40c multicolored	.80	.80
676	CD342	45c multicolored	.90	.90
677	CD342	$1 multicolored	2.00	2.00
		Nos. 674-677 (4)	3.90	3.90

Souvenir Sheet
678	CD342	$2 multicolored	4.00	4.00

Christmas — A113

Designs: 10c, Church of the Nativity, Bethlehem. 40c, Basilica of the Annunciation, Nazareth. 45c, By the Sea of Galilee, Tabgha. $1, Church of the Holy Sepulcher, Jerusalem.

**   Perf. 14½x14**
1989, Oct. 16   Wmk. 373
679	A113	10c multicolored	.20	.20
680	A113	40c multicolored	.80	.80
681	A113	45c multicolored	.90	.90
682	A113	$1 multicolored	2.00	2.00
a.		Souvenir sheet of 4, #679-682	4.00	4.00
		Nos. 679-682 (4)	3.90	3.90

World
Stamp
Expo '89
A114

Expo emblem and: 10c, Earth, #359. 40c, UPU Headquarters, #301. 45c, US Capitol, #601. $1, Passenger jet, #150. $2, Washington, DC, on map.

1989, Nov. 17   Wmk. 384   Perf. 14
683	A114	10c multicolored	.20	.20
684	A114	40c multicolored	.80	.80
685	A114	45c multicolored	.90	.90
686	A114	$1 multicolored	2.00	2.00
		Nos. 683-686 (4)	3.90	3.90

Souvenir Sheet
Perf. 14½x14
687	A114	$2 multicolored	4.00	4.00

No. 687 contains one 31x38mm stamp.

Discovery of America Type of 1988
10c, Caravel launch. 40c, Provisioning ships. 45c, Shortening sails. 50c, Lucayan fishermen. $1.50, Columbus's fleet departing from Cadiz.

**   Perf. 14½x14**
1990, Jan. 24   Litho.   Wmk. 373
688	A106	10c multicolored	.20	.20
689	A106	40c multicolored	.80	.80
690	A106	45c multicolored	.90	.90
691	A106	50c multicolored	1.00	1.00
		Nos. 688-691 (4)	2.90	2.90

Souvenir Sheet
692	A106	$1.50 multicolored	3.00	3.00

Organization of American States,
Cent. — A115

1990, Mar. 14   Wmk. 384   Perf. 14
693	A115	40c multicolored	.80	.80

Souvenir Sheet

Stamp World London '90 — A116

Aircraft: a, Spitfire I. b, Hurricane IIc.

1990, May 3   Wmk. 384
694	A116	Sheet of 2	4.00	4.00
a.-b.		$1 any single	2.00	2.00

For surcharge see No. B3.

Intl.
Literacy
Year
A117

10c, Teacher helping student. 40c, Children reading to each other. 50c, Children reading aloud.

1990, June 27   Wmk. 384   Perf. 14
695	A117	10c multicolored	.20	.20
696	A117	40c multicolored	.80	.80
697	A117	50c multicolored	1.00	1.00
		Nos. 695-697 (3)	2.00	2.00

Queen Mother, 90th Birthday
Common Design Types
1990, Aug. 4   Perf. 14x15
698	CD343	40c Portrait, c. 1938	.80	.80

Perf. 14½
699	CD344	$1.50 At garden party, 1938	3.00	3.00

Bahamian
Parrot — A118

1990, Sept. 26   Wmk. 373   Perf. 14
700	A118	10c shown	.20	.20
701	A118	40c In flight	.80	.80
702	A118	45c Head	.90	.90
703	A118	50c On branch	1.00	1.00
		Nos. 700-703 (4)	2.90	2.90

Souvenir Sheet
704	A118	$1.50 On branch, diff.		

Christmas — A119   Birds — A120

**   Perf. 13½**
1990, Nov. 5   Litho.   Wmk. 373
705	A119	10c Angel appears to Mary	.20	.20
706	A119	40c Nativity	.80	.80
707	A119	45c Angel appears to shep-herds	.90	.90
708	A119	$1 Three kings	2.00	2.00
a.		Souvenir sheet of 4, #705-708	3.90	3.90
		Nos. 705-708 (4)	3.90	3.90

**   Wmk. 384**
1991, Feb. 4   Litho.   Perf. 14
709	A120	5c Green heron	.15	.15
710	A120	10c Turkey vulture	.20	.20
711	A120	15c Osprey	.30	.30
712	A120	20c Clapper rail	.40	.40
713	A120	25c Royal tern	.50	.50
714	A120	30c Key West quail dove	.60	.60
715	A120	40c Smooth-billed ani	.80	.80
716	A120	45c Burrowing owl	.90	.90
717	A120	50c Hairy woodpecker	1.00	1.00
718	A120	55c Mangrove cuckoo	1.10	1.10
719	A120	60c Bahama mocking-bird	1.20	1.20
720	A120	70c Red-winged blackbird	1.40	1.40
721	A120	$1 Thick-billed vireo	2.00	2.00
722	A120	$2 Bahama yellow-throat	4.00	4.00
723	A120	$5 Stripe-headed tana-ger	10.00	10.00
724	A120	$10 Greater Antillean bullfinch	20.00	20.00
		Nos. 709-724 (16)	44.55	44.55

Issued: $10, July 1; others, Feb. 4.

1993   Wmk. 373
710a	10c	.20	.20
713a	25c	.50	.50
714a	30c	.60	.60
715a	40c	.80	.80
718a	55c	1.10	1.10
723a	$5	10.00	10.00
	Nos. 710a-723a (6)	13.20	13.20

Nos. 710a-723a dated 1993. 40c, 55c exist dated 1995.
Issued: 40c, 12/31/93; others, 9/23/93.

Discovery of America Type of 1988

Designs: 15c, Columbus practices celestial navigation. 40c, The fleet in rough seas. 55c, Natives on the beach. 60c, Map of voyage. $1.50, Pinta's crew sights land.

**   Perf. 14½x14**
1991, Apr. 9   Litho.   Wmk. 384
725	A106	15c multicolored	.30	.30
726	A106	40c multicolored	.80	.80
727	A106	55c multicolored	1.10	1.10
728	A106	60c multicolored	1.20	1.20
		Nos. 725-728 (4)	3.40	3.40

Souvenir Sheet
729	A106	$1.50 multicolored	3.00	3.00

Elizabeth & Philip, Birthdays
Common Design Types
**   Perf. 14½**
1991, June 17   Litho.   Wmk. 384
730	CD346	15c multicolored	.30	.30
731	CD345	$1 multicolored	2.00	2.00
a.		Pair, #730-731 + label	2.30	2.30

Hurricane
Awareness
A121

Designs: 15c, Weather radar image of Hurricane Hugo. 40c, Anatomy of hurricane rotating around eye. 55c, Flooding caused by Hurricane David. 60c, Lockheed WP-3D Orion.

1991, Aug. 28   Perf. 14
732	A121	15c multicolored	.30	.30
733	A121	40c multicolored	.80	.80
734	A121	55c multicolored	1.10	1.10
735	A121	60c multicolored	1.20	1.20
		Nos. 732-735 (4)	3.40	3.40

Christmas
A122

Designs: 15c, The Annunciation. 55c, Mary and Joseph traveling to Bethlehem. 60c, Angel appearing to shepherds. $1, Adoration of the Magi.

1991, Oct. 28   Wmk. 373   Perf. 14
736	A122	15c multicolored	.30	.30
737	A122	55c multicolored	1.10	1.10
738	A122	60c multicolored	1.20	1.20
739	A122	$1 multicolored	2.00	2.00
a.		Souvenir sheet of 4, #736-739	4.60	4.60
		Nos. 736-739 (4)	4.60	4.60

Majority
Rule, 25th
Anniv.
A123

Designs: 15c, First Progressive Liberal Party cabinet. 40c, Signing of Independence Constitution. 55c, Handing over constitutional instrument, vert. 60c, First Bahamian Governor-General, Sir Milo Butler, vert.

**   Wmk. 373**
1992, Jan. 10   Litho.   Perf. 14
740	A123	15c multicolored	.28	.28
741	A123	40c multicolored	.75	.75
742	A123	55c multicolored	1.00	1.00
743	A123	60c multicolored	1.10	1.10
		Nos. 740-743 (4)	3.13	3.13

Queen Elizabeth II's Accession to the
Throne, 40th Anniv.
Common Design Type
**   Wmk. 373**
1992, Feb. 6   Litho.   Perf. 14
744	CD349	15c multicolored	.28	.28
745	CD349	40c multicolored	.75	.75
746	CD349	55c multicolored	1.00	1.00
747	CD349	60c multicolored	1.10	1.10
748	CD349	$1 multicolored	1.85	1.85
		Nos. 744-748 (5)	4.98	4.98

Discovery of America Type of 1988

Designs: 15c, Lucayans first sight of fleet. 40c, Approaching Bahamas coastline. 55c, Lucayans about to meet Columbus. 60c, Columbus gives thanks for safe arrival. $1.50, Monument to Columbus' landing.

**   Perf. 14½x14**
1992, Mar. 17   Litho.   Wmk. 384
749	A106	15c multicolored	.28	.28
750	A106	40c multicolored	.75	.75
751	A106	55c multicolored	1.00	1.00
752	A106	60c multicolored	1.10	1.10
		Nos. 749-752 (4)	3.13	3.13

Souvenir Sheet
753	A106	$1.50 multicolored	2.75	2.75

Templeton, Galbraith and Hansberger Ltd.
Building — A124

**   Perf. 14½**
1992, Apr. 22   Litho.   Wmk. 384
754	A124	55c multicolored	1.00	1.00

Templeton Prize for Progress in Religion, 20th Anniv.

1992 Summer Olympics, Barcelona — A125

Perf. 14½x14
1992, June 2 **Wmk. 373**
755 A125 15c Pole vault .28 .28
756 A125 40c Javelin .75 .75
757 A125 55c Hurdling 1.00 1.00
758 A125 60c Basketball 1.15 1.15
Nos. 755-758 (4) 3.18 3.18

Souvenir Sheet
759 A125 $2 Sailing 3.75 3.75

Intl. Conference on Nutrition A126

Designs: 15c, Drought-affected earth, starving child. 55c, Hand holding plant, stalks of grain.

Perf. 14½x13
1992, Aug. 11 **Litho.** **Wmk. 373**
760 A126 15c multicolored .28 .28
761 A126 55c multicolored 1.00 1.00

Discovery of America Type of 1988
Souvenir Sheet
Perf. 14x13½
1992, Oct. 12 **Litho.** **Wmk. 384**
762 A106 $2 Coming ashore 3.75 3.75

Christmas — A127

1992, Nov. 2 **Wmk. 373** **Perf. 14**
763 A127 15c The Annunciation .28 .28
764 A127 55c Nativity Scene 1.00 1.00
765 A127 60c Angel, shepherds 1.10 1.10
766 A127 70c The Magi 1.30 1.30
a. Souvenir sheet of 4, #763-766 3.75 3.75
Nos. 763-766 (4) 3.68 3.68

The Contract, Farm Labor Program, 50th Anniv. — A128

Bahamian, American flags and: 15c, Silhouette of worker's head. 55c, Onions. 60c, Citrus fruits. 70c, Apples.

Perf. 14x14½
1993, Mar. 16 **Litho.** **Wmk. 384**
767 A128 15c multicolored .28 .28
768 A128 55c multicolored 1.00 1.00
769 A128 60c multicolored 1.10 1.10
770 A128 70c multicolored 1.30 1.30
Nos. 767-770 (4) 3.68 3.68

Royal Air Force, 75th Anniv.
Common Design Type
Designs: 15c, Westland Wapiti. 40c, Gloster Gladiator. 55c, DeHavilland Vampire. 70c, English Electric Lightning.
No. 775a, Avro Shackleton. b, Fairey Battle. c, Douglas Boston. d, DeHavilland DH9a.

Wmk. 373
1993, Apr. 1 **Litho.** **Perf. 14**
771 CD350 15c multicolored .26 .26
772 CD350 40c multicolored .70 .70
773 CD350 55c multicolored .95 .95
774 CD350 $1.25 multicolored 1.25 1.25
Nos. 771-774 (4) 3.16 3.16

Souvenir Sheet
775 CD350 60c Sheet of 4, #a.-d. 4.50 4.50

Coronation of Queen Elizabeth II, 40th Anniv. — A129

Perf. 13½
1993, June 2 **Litho.** **Wmk. 373**
776 A129 15c Nos. 424-425 .28 .28
777 A129 55c No. 157 1.00 1.00
778 A129 60c Nos. 402-403 1.10 1.10
779 A129 70c Nos. 404-405 1.30 1.30
Nos. 776-779 (4) 3.68 3.68

A130 A131

Natl. symbols: 15c, Lignum vitae. 55c, Yellow elder. 60c, Blue marlin. 70c, Flamingo.

1993, July 8 **Litho.** **Perf. 14**
780 A130 15c multicolored .28 .28
781 A130 55c multicolored 1.00 1.00
782 A130 60c multicolored 1.10 1.10
783 A130 70c multicolored 1.30 1.30
Nos. 780-783 (4) 3.68 3.68

Independence, 20th anniv.

1993, Sept. 8 **Litho.** **Perf. 14**
Wildflowers.
784 A131 15c Cordia .30 .30
785 A131 55c Seaside morning glory 1.10 1.10
786 A131 60c Poinciana 1.25 1.25
787 A131 70c Spider lily 1.40 1.40
Nos. 784-787 (4) 4.05 4.05

Christmas A132

1993, Nov. 1 **Litho.** **Perf. 14**
788 A132 15c Angel, Mary .28 .28
789 A132 55c Shepherds, angel 1.00 1.00
790 A132 60c Holy family 1.10 1.10
791 A132 70c Three wise men 1.25 1.25
Nos. 788-791 (4) 3.63 3.63

Souvenir Sheet
792 A132 $1 Madonna and Child 1.90 1.90

Intl. Year of the Family A133

Perf. 13½
1994, Feb. 18 **Litho.** **Wmk. 384**
793 A133 15c shown .28 .28
794 A133 55c Children studying 1.00 1.00
795 A133 60c Son, father fishing 1.10 1.10
796 A133 70c Children, grandmother 1.25 1.25
Nos. 793-796 (4) 3.63 3.63

Hong Kong '94.

Royal Visit — A134

Designs: 15c, Bahamas, United Kingdom flags. 55c, Royal Yacht Britannia. 60c, Queen Elizabeth II. 70c, Prince Philip, Queen.

Perf. 14x13½
1994, Mar. 7 **Wmk. 373**
797 A134 15c multicolored .28 .28
798 A134 55c multicolored 1.00 1.00
799 A134 60c multicolored 1.10 1.10
800 A134 70c multicolored 1.25 1.25
Nos. 797-800 (4) 3.63 3.63

Natl. Family Island Regatta, 40th Anniv. A135

Designs: 15c, 55c, 60c, 70c, Various sailing boats at sea. $2, Beached yacht, vert.

Wmk. 373
1994, Apr. 27 **Litho.** **Perf. 14**
801 A135 15c multicolored .28 .28
802 A135 55c multicolored 1.00 1.00
803 A135 60c multicolored 1.10 1.10
804 A135 70c multicolored 1.25 1.25
Nos. 801-804 (4) 3.63 3.63

Souvenir Sheet
805 A135 $2 multicolored 3.75 3.75

Intl. Olympic Committee, Cent. — A136

Flag, Olympic rings, and: 15c, Nos. 276-279, horiz. 55c, Nos. 388-391. 60c, Nos. 559-562, horiz. 70c, Nos. 755-758.

Wmk. 373
1994, May 31 **Litho.** **Perf. 14**
806 A136 15c multicolored .28 .28
807 A136 55c multicolored 1.00 1.00
808 A136 60c multicolored 1.10 1.10
809 A136 70c multicolored 1.25 1.25
Nos. 806-809 (4) 3.63 3.63

Souvenir Sheet

First Recipients of the Order of the Caribbean Community — A137

Illustration reduced.

Perf. 13x14
1994, July 5 **Litho.** **Wmk. 373**
810 A137 $2 multicolored 4.00 4.00

A138 A139

Butterfly, flower: 15c, Canna skipper, canna. 55c, Cloudless sulphur, cassia. 60c, White peacock, passion flower. 70c, Devillier's swallowtail, calico flower.

1994, Aug. 16 **Litho.** **Perf. 14**
811 A138 15c multicolored .30 .30
812 A138 55c multicolored 1.10 1.10
813 A138 60c multicolored 1.25 1.25
814 A138 70c multicolored 1.40 1.40
Nos. 811-814 (4) 4.05 4.05

1994, Sept. 13 **Perf. 13½x14**
Marine Life: a, Cuban hogfish, Spanish hogfish. b, Tomate, squirrelfish. c, French angelfish. d, Queen angelfish. e, Rock beauty.
$2, Rock beauty, queen angelfish.
815 A139 40c Strip of 5, #a.-e. 4.00 4.00

Souvenir Sheet
816 A139 $2 multicolored 4.00 4.00

Christmas A140

Wmk. 384
1994, Oct. 31 **Litho.** **Perf. 14**
817 A140 15c Angel .30 .30
818 A140 55c Holy family 1.10 1.10
819 A140 60c Shepherds 1.25 1.25
820 A140 70c Magi 1.40 1.40
Nos. 817-820 (4) 4.05 4.05

Souvenir Sheet
821 A140 $2 Christ Child, vert. 3.75 3.75

College of the Bahamas, 20th Anniv. — A141

Designs: 15c, Lion. 70c, Queen Elizabeth II, college facade.

Wmk. 373
1995, Feb. 8 **Litho.** **Perf. 14**
822 A141 15c multicolored .30 .30
823 A141 70c multicolored 1.40 1.40

End of World War II, 50th Anniv.
Common Design Types
Designs: 15c, Bahamian soldiers on parade. 55c, Neutrality patrols flown by PBY-5A flying boats. 60c, Bahamian women in all three services. 70c, B-24 Liberator, Bahamians in RAF.
$2, Reverse of War Medal 1939-45.

Perf. 13½
1995, May 8 **Wmk. 373**
824 CD351 15c multicolored .30 .30
825 CD351 55c multicolored 1.10 1.10
826 CD351 60c multicolored 1.25 1.25
827 CD351 70c multicolored 1.40 1.40
Nos. 824-827 (4) 4.05 4.05

Souvenir Sheet
Perf. 14
828 CD352 $2 multicolored 4.00 4.00

Kirtland's Warbler — A142

Designs: No. 829a, 25c, Female feeding young. b, 25c Immature bird feeding, prior to migration. c, 15c, Female at nest. d, 15c, Singing male. $2, Female on branch overlooking lake.

Perf. 13¹/₂

1995, June 7		Litho.	Wmk. 373	
829	A142	Strip of 4, #a.-d.	1.90	1.90

Souvenir Sheet
Perf. 13

830	A142	$2 multicolored	4.00	4.00

World Wildlife Fund (#829). No. 830 contains one 42x28mm stamp and has continuous design.

Tourism A143

Designs: 15c, Eleuthera Cliffs. 55c, Clarence Town, Long Island. 60c, Albert Lowe Museum. 70c, Yachting.

Perf. 14¹/₂

1995, July 18		Litho.	Wmk. 384	
831	A143	15c multicolored	.30	.30
832	A143	55c multicolored	1.10	1.10
833	A143	60c multicolored	1.25	1.25
834	A143	70c multicolored	1.40	1.40
		Nos. 831-834 (4)	4.05	4.05

FAO, 50th Anniv. A144

Designs: 15c, Pig, poultry farming. 55c, Horticultural methods. 60c, Healthy eating. 70c, Sustainable fishing.

Perf. 13¹/₂x13

1995, Sept. 5		Litho.	Wmk. 373	
835	A144	15c multicolored	.30	.30
836	A144	55c multicolored	1.10	1.10
837	A144	60c multicolored	1.25	1.25
838	A144	70c multicolored	1.40	1.40
		Nos. 835-838 (4)	4.05	4.05

UN, 50th Anniv.
Common Design Type

Designs: 15c, Sikorsky S-55, UNEF, Sinai, 1957. 55c, Ferret armored car, UNEF, Sinai, 1957. 60c, Fokker F-27, UNAMIC/UNTAC, Cambodia, 1991-93. 70c, Lockheed Hercules.

Wmk. 373

1995, Oct. 25		Litho.	Perf. 14	
839	CD353	15c multicolored	.30	.30
840	CD353	55c multicolored	1.10	1.10
841	CD353	60c multicolored	1.25	1.25
842	CD353	70c multicolored	1.40	1.40
		Nos. 839-842 (4)	4.05	4.05

Christmas A145

Designs: 15c, St. Agnes Anglican Church. 55c, Church of God. 60c, Sacred Heart Roman Catholic Church. 70c, Salem Union Baptist Church.

1995, Nov. 17				
843	A145	15c multicolored	.30	.30
844	A145	55c multicolored	1.10	1.10
845	A145	60c multicolored	1.25	1.25
846	A145	70c multicolored	1.40	1.40
		Nos. 843-846 (4)	4.05	4.05

World AIDS Day A146

1995, Dec. 1				
847	A146	25c Virus in blood	.50	.50
848	A146	70c Scientific research	1.40	1.40

Shells · A147

Designs: 5c, Sunrise tellin. 10c, Queen conch. 15c, Angular triton. 20c, True tulip. 25c, Reticulated cowrie-helmet. 30c, Sand dollar. 40c, Lace short-frond murex. 45c, Inflated sea biscuit. 50c, West Indian top shell (magpie). 55c, Spiny oyster. 60c, King helmet. 70c, Lion's paw. $1, Crown cone. $2, Atlantic partridge tun. $5, Wide-mouthed purpura. $10, Triton's trumpet.

1996	Litho.	Wmk. 373	Perf. 14	
849	A147	5c multicolored	.15	.15
850	A147	10c multicolored	.20	.20
851	A147	15c multicolored	.30	.30
852	A147	20c multicolored	.40	.40
853	A147	25c multicolored	.50	.50
854	A147	30c multicolored	.60	.60
855	A147	40c multicolored	.80	.80
856	A147	45c multicolored	.90	.90
857	A147	50c multicolored	1.00	1.00
858	A147	55c multicolored	1.10	1.10
859	A147	60c multicolored	1.25	1.25
860	A147	70c multicolored	1.40	1.40
a.		Souvenir sheet of 1	1.40	1.40
861	A147	$1 multicolored	2.00	2.00
a.		A147 $1 Sheet of 1	2.00	2.00

862	A147	$2 multicolored	4.00	4.00
863	A147	$5 multicolored	10.00	10.00
864	A147	$10 multicolored	20.00	20.00
		Nos. 849-864 (16)	44.60	44.60

No. 860a issued 6/20/97 for return of Hong Kong to China.
No. 861a issued 2/3/97 for Hong Kong '97.
Nos. 850, 861-864 exist dated "1997."
Issued: 5c, 10c, 15c, 20c, 25c, 30c, 40c, 45c, 50c, 55c, 60c, 70c, $1, $2, $5, 1/2/96.

Radio, Cent. — A148

Designs: 15c, East Goodwin Lightship, Marconi apparatus suspended from masthead. 55c, Arrest of Dr. Crippen, newspaper headline telling of wireless message from SS Montrose. 60c, SS Philadelphia, first readable transatlantic messages. 70c, Yacht Elettra, Guglielmo Marconi. $2, SS Titantic, SS Carpathia.

1996, Feb. 4		Litho.	Perf. 13¹/₂	
865	A148	15c multicolored	.30	.30
866	A148	55c multicolored	1.10	1.10
867	A148	60c multicolored	1.20	1.20
868	A148	70c multicolored	1.40	1.40
		Nos. 865-868 (4)	4.00	4.00

Souvenir Sheet

869	A148	$2 multicolored	4.00	4.00

A149　　　　　A150

Perf. 13¹/₂

1996, June 25		Litho.	Wmk. 384	
870	A149	15c Swimming	.30	.30
871	A149	55c Track	1.10	1.10
872	A149	60c Basketball	1.20	1.20
873	A149	70c Long jump	1.40	1.40
		Nos. 870-873 (4)	4.00	4.00

Souvenir Sheet

874	A149	$2 Javelin, 1896	4.00	4.00

Modern Olympic Games, cent.

Wmk. 384

1996, Sept. 3		Litho.	Perf. 14	

Reptiles: 15c, Green anole. 55c, Fowl snake. 60c, Inagua freshwater turtle. 70c, Acklins rock iguana.

875	A150	15c multicolored	.30	.30
876	A150	55c multicolored	1.10	1.10
877	A150	60c multicolored	1.20	1.20
878	A150	70c multicolored	1.40	1.40
a.		Souvenir sheet, #875-878	4.00	4.00
		Nos. 875-878 (4)	4.00	4.00

Environmental protection.

Christmas — A151

Designs: 15c, Angel Gabriel and Mary. 55c, Mary and Joseph. 60c, Shepherds. 70c, Magi. $2, Prensentation at the Temple.

Wmk. 373

1996, Nov. 4		Litho.	Perf. 14	
879	A151	15c multicolored	.30	.30
880	A151	55c multicolored	1.10	1.10
881	A151	60c multicolored	1.20	1.20
882	A151	70c multicolored	1.40	1.40
		Nos. 879-882 (4)	4.00	4.00

Souvenir Sheet

883	A151	$2 multicolored	4.00	4.00

Archives Dept., 25th Anniv. — A152

Perf. 14¹/₂x14

1996, Dec. 9			Wmk. 384	
884	A152	55c shown	1.10	1.10

Souvenir Sheet
Perf. 14x13¹/₂

885	A152	$2 Building, horiz.	4.00	4.00

Queen Elizabeth II and Prince Philip, 50th Wedding Anniv. — A153

Designs: No. 886, Queen. No. 887, Grenadier Guards. No. 888, Prince Philip. No. 889, Queen reviewing Grenadier Guards. No. 890, Prince holding trophy, Queen opening jewel box. No. 891, Prince on polo pony.
$2, Queen, Prince riding in open carriage, horiz.

Wmk. 373

1997, July 9		Litho.	Perf. 13	
886	A153	50c multicolored	1.00	1.00
887	A153	50c multicolored	1.00	1.00
a.		Pair, #886-887	2.00	2.00
888	A153	60c multicolored	1.20	1.20
889	A153	60c multicolored	1.20	1.20
a.		Pair, #888-889	2.40	2.40
890	A153	70c multicolored	1.40	1.40
891	A153	70c multicolored	1.40	1.40
a.		Pair, #890-891	2.80	2.80
		Nos. 886-891 (6)	7.20	7.20

Souvenir Sheet

892	A153	$2 multicolored	4.00	4.00

Intl. Year of the Reefs A154

Various pictures of marine life and coral.

Perf. 14x14¹/₂

1997, Sept. 3		Litho.	Wmk. 384	
893	A154	15c multicolored	.30	.30
894	A154	55c multicolored	1.10	1.10
895	A154	60c multicolored	1.20	1.20
896	A154	70c multicolored	1.40	1.40
		Nos. 893-896 (4)	4.00	4.00

Christmas — A155

Perf. 13x13¹/₂

1997, Oct. 6		Litho.	Wmk. 373	
897	A155	15c Angel	.30	.30
898	A155	55c Madonna & Child	1.10	1.10
899	A155	60c Shepherd	1.20	1.20
900	A155	70c Magi	1.40	1.40
		Nos. 897-900 (4)	4.00	4.00

Souvenir Sheet

901	A155	$2 Christ Child	4.00	4.00

SEMI-POSTAL STAMPS

No. 48 Overprinted in Red

1.1.17.

1917, May 18   Wmk. 3   Perf. 14
B1 A6 1p car & black   .42 .42

Type of 1911 Overprinted **WAR**
in Red **CHARITY**

3.6.18.

1919, Jan. 1
B2 A6 1p red & black   .45 .45
  a. Double overprint   1,800.

This stamp was originally scheduled for release in 1918.

Souvenir Sheet

No. 694 Surcharged **HURRICANE RELIEF +$1**

Wmk. 384
1992, Nov. 16   Litho.   Perf. 14
B3 A116 Sheet of 2, #a.-b.   8.00 8.00

AIR POST STAMPS

Catalogue values for all unused stamps in this section are for Never Hinged items.

Manned Flight Bicentenary AP1

Airplanes.

Wmk. 373
1983, Oct. 13   Litho.   Perf. 14
C1 AP1 10c Consolidated Catalina   .18 .18
  a. Without emblem ('85)   .18 .18
  b. Without emblem, wmk. 384 ('86)   .18 .18
C2 AP1 25c Avro Tudor IV   .42 .42
  a. Without emblem ('85)   .45 .45
  b. Without emblem, wmk. 384 ('86)   .45 .45
C3 AP1 31c Avro Lancastrian   .55 .55
  a. Without emblem ('85)   .55 .55
C4 AP1 35c Consolidated Commo-
      dore   .60 .60
  a. Without emblem ('85)   .65 .65
     Nos. C1-C4 (4)   1.75 1.75

Aircraft AP2

1987, July 7
C5 AP2 15c Bahamasair Boeing 737   .25 .25
C6 AP2 40c Eastern Boeing 757   .65 .65
C7 AP2 45c Pan Am Airbus A300
      B4   .75 .75
C8 AP2 50c British Airways Boeing
      747   .85 .85
     Nos. C5-C8 (4)   2.50 2.50

SPECIAL DELIVERY STAMPS

No. 34 Overprinted **SPECIAL DELIVERY**

1916   Wmk. 1   Perf. 14
E1 A6 5p orange & black   7.00 7.00
  a. Double overprint   1,000. 1,000.
  b. Inverted overprint   1,500. 1,500.
  c. Double ovpt., one invtd.   1,900. 1,900.
  d. Pair, one without overprint   12,000. 12,000.

The No. E1 overprint exists in two types. Type I (illustrated) is much scarcer. Type II shows "SPE-CIAL" farther right, so that the letter "I" is slightly right of the vertical line of the "E" below it.

Type of Regular Issue of **SPECIAL**
1903 Overprinted **DELIVERY**

1917, July 2   Wmk. 3
E2 A6 5p orange & black   .90 1.25

No. 60 Overprinted in **SPECIAL**
Red **DELIVERY**

1918
E3 A6 5p violet & black   .65 1.25

WAR TAX STAMPS

Stamps of 1912-18 **WAR TAX**
Overprinted

1918, Feb. 21   Wmk. 3   Perf. 14
MR1 A8 ½p green   3.00 4.00
  a. Double overprint   1,000. 1,000.
  b. Inverted overprint   1,000. 1,000.
MR2 A8 1p car rose   .80 1.10
  a. Double overprint   1,000. 1,000.
  b. Inverted overprint   1,000. 1,000.
MR3 A8 3p brown, yel   3.75 4.75
  a. Inverted overprint   1,100. 1,100.
  b. Double overprint   1,000. 1,000.
MR4 A8 1sh black & red   75.00 100.00
  a. Double overprint   2,750. 2,500.
     Nos. MR1-MR4 (4)   82.55 109.85

Same Overprint on No. 48a

1918, July 10
MR5 A6 1p car & black   3.50 6.00
  a. Double overprint   1,200.
  b. Double ovpt., one invtd.   1,300.
  c. Inverted overprint   1,100. 1,100.

Nos. 49-50, 54 Overprinted **WAR TAX**
in Black or Red

MR6 A8 ½p green   .20 .20
MR7 A8 1p car rose   .20 .20
  a. Watermarked sideways   850.00
MR8 A8 1sh black & red (R)   1.25 2.00
     Nos. MR6-MR8 (3)   1.65 2.40

Nos. 58-59 **WAR TAX**
Overprinted

1918-19
MR9 A6 3p brown, yel   1.00 3.50
MR10 A6 3p brown & blk ('19)   1.00 3.50

W A R

Nos. 49-50, 54 Overprinted
in Red or Black

T A X

1919, July 14
MR11 A8 ½p green (R)   .32 .55
MR12 A8 1p car rose   .32 .55
MR13 A8 1sh black & red (R)   3.00 10.50
     Nos. MR11-MR13 (3)   3.64 11.60

W A R

No. 59 Overprinted

T A X

MR14 A6 3p brown & black   .90 1.50

BAHRAIN
bä-′rān

LOCATION — An archipelago in the Persian Gulf, including the islands of Bahrain, Muharraq, Sitra, Nebi Saleh, Kasasifeh and Arad.
GOVT. — Independent sheikdom

AREA — 255 sq. mi.
POP. — 350,798 (1981)
CAPITAL — Manama

Bahrain was a British-protected territory until it became an independent state on August 15, 1971.

12 Pies = 1 Anna
16 Annas = 1 Rupee
100 Naye Paise = 1 Rupee (1957)
1000 Fils = 1 Dinar (1966)

Catalogue values for unused stamps in this country are for Never Hinged items, beginning with Scott 62 in the regular postage section and Scott MR2 in the postal tax section.

Indian Postal Administration
Stamps of India, 1926-32, Overprinted in Black

BAHRAIN
a

Wmk. Multiple Stars (196)
1933, Aug. 10   Perf. 14
1 A46 3p gray   1.40 .15
2 A47 ½a green   3.50 .70
3 A68 9p dark green   2.75 .70
4 A48 1a dark brown   4.25 1.65
5 A69 1a3p violet   3.00 .40
6 A60 2a vermilion   3.00 3.25
7 A51 3a blue   14.00 14.00
8 A70 3a6p deep blue   1.50 .60
9 A61 4a olive green   10.50 10.50
10 A54 8a red violet   3.25 1.00
11 A55 12a claret   4.25 1.65
     Nos. 1-14 (14)   181.40 182.10

Overprinted in Black

b **BAHRAIN**

12 A56 1r green & brown   15.00 7.50
13 A56 2r brn org & car rose   30.00 30.00
14 A56 5r dk violet & ultra   85.00 110.00
     Nos. 1-14 (14)   181.40 182.10

Stamps of India, 1926-32, Overprinted Type "a" in Black

1934
15 A72 1a dark brown   5.75 .15
16 A51 3a carmine rose   4.50 .20
17 A52 4a olive green   4.00 .30
     Nos. 15-17 (3)   14.25 .65

India Nos. 138, 111, 111a Overprinted Type "a" in Black

1935-37   Perf. 13½x14, 14
18 A71 ½a green   3.75 .15
19 A49 2a vermilion   22.50 2.00
  a. Small die ('37)   25.00 2.50

India Stamps of 1937 Overprinted Type "a" in Black

1938-41   Wmk. 196   Perf. 13½x14
20 A80 3p slate   2.50 .90
21 A80 ½a brown   .45 .90
22 A80 9p green   1.00 .20
23 A80 1a carmine   1.00 .15
24 A81 2a scarlet   2.25 .35
26 A81 3a yel grn ('41)   12.50 2.50
27 A81 3a6p ultra   1.75 2.00
28 A81 4a dk brn ('41)   45.00 30.00
30 A81 8a bl vio ('40)   55.00 35.00
31 A81 12a car lake ('40)   45.00 42.50
Overprinted Type "b" in Black
32 A82 1r brn & slate   1.90 .90
33 A82 2r dk brn & dk vio   12.00 2.50
34 A82 5r dp ultra & dk grn   35.00 13.00
35 A82 10r rose car & dk vio
      ('41)   60.00 18.00
36 A82 15r dk grn & dk brn
      ('41)   30.00 27.50
37 A82 25r dk vio & bl vio
      ('41)   75.00 62.50
     Nos. 20-37 (16)   380.35 238.15

India Stamps of 1941-43 Overprinted Type "a" in Black

1942-44   Wmk. 196   Perf. 13½x14
38 A83 3p slate   .25 .15
39 A83 ½a rose vio ('44)   1.40 .15
40 A83 9p lt green ('43)   4.00 4.25
41 A83 1a car rose ('44)   1.40 .40
42 A84 1a3p bister ('43)   4.00 7.00
43 A84 1½a dk pur ('43)   2.50 1.25
45 A84 2a scarlet ('43)   1.40 .55
46 A84 3a violet ('43)   5.75 1.75
47 A84 3½a ultra   3.25 7.00
48 A85 4a chocolate   .85 .50
49 A85 6a peacock blue   5.75 3.50

50 A85 8a blue vio ('43)   .85 .85
51 A85 12a car lake   1.75 1.75
     Nos. 38-51 (13)   33.15 29.10
     Set, never hinged   55.00

British Postal Administration

See Oman (Muscat) for similar stamps with surcharge of new value only.

Great Britain Nos. 258 to 263, 243 and 248 Surcharged in Black

BAHRAIN
c
½ ANNA

1948-49   Wmk. 251   Perf. 14½x14
52 A101 ½a on ½p green   .25 .25
53 A101 1a on 1p vermilion   .15 .15
54 A101 1½a on 1½p lt red brn   .15 .15
55 A101 2a on 2p lt orange   .30 .15
56 A101 2½a on 2½p ultra   .40 .40
57 A101 3a on 3p violet   .25 .15
58 A102 6a on 6p rose lilac   .25 .15
59 A103 1r on 1sh brown   1.40 .55

Great Britain Nos. 249A, 250 and 251A Surcharged in Black

BAHRAIN
2 RUPEES

Wmk. 259   Perf. 14
60 A104 2r on 2sh6p yel grn   4.00 3.25
61 A104 5r on 5sh dull red   6.50 6.50
61A A105 10r on 10sh ultra   35.00 30.00
     Nos. 52-61A (11)   48.65 41.70
     Set, never hinged   70.00

Surcharge bars at bottom on No. 61A.
Issued: 10r, 7/4/49; others, 4/1/48.

Catalogue values for unused stamps in this section, from this point to the end of the section, are for Never Hinged items.

Silver Wedding Issue

Great Britain Nos. 267 and **BAHRAIN**
268 Surcharged in Black **2½ ANNAS**

Perf. 14½x14, 14x14½
1948, Apr. 26   Wmk. 251
62 A109 2½a on 2½p   .20 .20
63 A110 15r on £1   37.50 42.50

Three bars obliterate the original denomination on No. 63.

Olympic Issue

Great Britain Nos. 271 to 274 Surcharged "BAHRAIN" and New Value in Black

1948, July 29   Perf. 14½x14
64 A113 2½a on 2½p brt ul-
      tra   .20 .20
  a. Double surcharge   425.00 525.00
65 A114 3a on 3p dp vio   .30 .25
66 A115 6a on 6p red vio   .45 .40
67 A116 1r on 1sh dk brn   .90 .75
     Nos. 64-67 (4)   1.85 1.60

A square of dots obliterates the original denomination on No. 67.

UPU Issue

Great Britain Nos. 276 to 279 Surcharged "BAHRAIN," New Value and Square of Dots in Black

1949, Oct. 10   Photo.   Perf. 14½x14
68 A117 2½a on 2½p brt ultra   .30 .30
69 A118 3a on 3p dp vio   .45 .35
70 A119 6a on 6p red vio   .75 .65
71 A120 1r on 1sh brown   1.90 1.40
     Nos. 68-71 (4)   3.40 2.70

Great Britain Nos. 280, 281, 283-285 Surcharged Type "c" in Black

1950-51   Wmk. 251
72 A101 ½a on ½p lt org   .25 .20
73 A101 1a on 1p ultra   .35 .30
74 A101 1½a on 1½p green   .55 1.25

75 A101 2a on 2p lt red brn .35 .30
76 A101 2½a on 2½p ver .80 .70
77 A102 4a on 4p ultra .70 .50

Great Britain Nos. 286-288 Surcharged in Black ▬ **BAHRAIN**

2 RUPEES

Wmk. 259   Perf. 11x12
78 A121 2r on 2sh6p green 18.00 5.75
79 A121 5r on 5sh dl red 15.00 8.00
80 A122 10r on 10sh ultra 30.00 17.50
Nos. 72-80 (9) 66.00 34.50

Longer bars, at lower right, on No. 80.
Issue dates: 4a, Nov. 2, 1950; others, May 3, 1951.

Stamps of Great Britain, 1952-54, Surcharged "BAHRAIN" and New Value in Black or Dark Blue

1952-54   Wmk. 298   Perf. 14½x14
81 A126 ½a on ½p red org ('53) .25 .25
  a. "½" omitted 200.00 225.00
82 A126 1a on 1p ultra .25 .15
83 A126 1½a on 1½p grn .25 .25
84 A126 2a on 2p red brn .25 .25
85 A127 2½a on 2½p scar .55 .25
86 A127 3a on 3p dk pur (Dk Bl) .65 .25
87 A128 4a on 4p ultra 1.50 .75
88 A129 6a on 6p lil rose 1.25 .65
89 A132 12a on 1sh3p dk grn 4.00 1.50
90 A131 1r on 1sh6p dk bl 5.50 2.00
Nos. 81-90 (10) 14.45 6.30

Issued: #83, 85, 12/5; #81-82, 84, 8/31/53; #87, 89-90, 11/2/53; #86, 88, 1/18/54.

Six stamps of this design picturing Sheik Sulman bin Hamad Al Kalifah were for local use in 1953-57.
Six stamps of similar design (same sheik, "Bahrain" vertical at left) were issued in 1961 for local use.

Coronation Issue
Great Britain Nos. 313-316 Surcharged "BAHRAIN" and New Value in Black
Perf. 14½x14
1953, June 3   Wmk. 298
92 A134 2½a on 2½p scar 1.10 1.10
93 A135 4a on 4p brt ultra 1.75 1.75
94 A136 12a on 1sh3p dk grn 4.00 4.00
95 A137 1r on 1sh6p dk bl 5.25 5.25
Nos. 92-95 (4) 12.10 12.10

Squares of dots obliterate the original denominations on Nos. 94-95.

Great Britain Nos. 309-311 Surcharged "BAHRAIN" and New Value in Black
1955   Wmk. 308   Engr.   Perf. 11x12
96 A133 2r on 2sh6p dk brn 3.00 1.25
97 A133 5r on 5sh crimson 9.50 4.00
98 A133 10r on 10sh brt ultra 20.00 6.50
Nos. 96-98 (3) 32.50 11.75

Three slightly different types of surcharge are found on the 2r; two on 5r and 10r.

Great Britain Nos. 317, 323, 325, 332-333 Surcharged "BAHRAIN" and New Value
Perf. 14½x14
1956-57   Wmk. 308   Photo.
99 A126 ½a on ½p red org .25 .20
100 A128 4a on 4p ultra 5.00 6.25
101 A129 6a on 6p lil rose .50 .40
102 A132 12a on 1sh3p dk green 6.25 12.00
103 A131 1r on 1sh6p dk bl ('57) 1.50 .75
Nos. 99-103 (5) 13.50 19.60

Great Britain Nos. 317-325, 328, 332 Surcharged "BAHRAIN" and New Value
1957, Apr. 1
104 A129 1np on 5p lt brown .15 .15
105 A126 3np on ½p red org .25 .25
106 A126 6np on 1p ultra .25 .25
107 A126 9np on 1½p green .25 .25
108 A126 12np on 2p red brn .30 .25
109 A127 15np on 2½p scar, type I .35 .15
  a. Type II .40 .50
110 A127 20np on 3p dk pur .25 .15
111 A128 25np on 4p ultra .65 1.00
112 A129 40np on 6p lil rose .65 .35
113 A130 50np on 9p dp ol grn 1.75 1.75
114 A132 75np on 1sh3p dk grn 1.50 .55
Nos. 104-114 (11) 6.35 5.10

The arrangement of the surcharge varies on different values: there are three bars through value on No. 113.

Jubilee Jamboree Issue
Great Britain Nos. 334-336 Surcharged "BAHRAIN," New Value and Square of Dots in Black
Perf. 14½x14
1957, Aug. 1   Photo.   Wmk. 308
115 A138 15np on 2½p scar .35 .35
116 A138 25np on 4p ultra .65 .40
117 A138 75np on 1sh3p dk grn .80 .80
Nos. 115-117 (3) 1.80 1.55

Great Britain No. 357 Surcharged "BAHRAIN/ NP 15 NP" in Black
1960   Wmk. 322   Perf. 14½x14
118 A127 15np on 2½p scar, type II 4.50 7.25

Sheik Sulman bin Hamad Al Khalifah
A1   A2
Perf. 14½x14
1960, July 1   Photo.   Unwmk.
119 A1 5np lt ultra .15 .15
120 A1 15np orange .15 .15
121 A1 20np lt violet .20 .15
122 A1 30np olive bister .25 .15
123 A1 40np gray .30 .15
124 A1 50np emerald .30 .15
125 A1 75np red brown .60 .15
Engr.
Perf. 13x13½
126 A2 1r gray .90 .20
127 A2 2r carmine 1.75 .50
128 A2 5r ultra 4.50 1.75
129 A2 10r olive green 12.00 2.25
Nos. 119-129 (11) 21.10 5.75

Sheik Isa bin Sulman Al Khalifah — A3
Bahrain Airport — A4

Designs: 5r, 10r, Deep water jetty.

1964, Feb. 22   Photo.   Perf. 14½x14
130 A3 5np ultra .15 .15
131 A3 15np orange .15 .15
132 A3 20np brt purple .15 .15
133 A3 30np brown olive .20 .15
134 A3 40np slate .20 .15
135 A3 50np emerald .30 .15
136 A3 75np chestnut .60 .25
Engr.
Perf. 13½x13
137 A4 1r black 1.00 .35
138 A4 2r rose red 5.00 .85
139 A4 5r violet blue 8.50 1.75
140 A4 10r dull green 14.00 5.00
Nos. 130-140 (11) 30.25 12.35

Bahrain Postal Administration

Sheik Isa bin Sulman Al Khalifah — A5
Sheik and Bahrain International Airport — A6

Pearl Divers — A7

Bab al Bahrain, Suq Al-Khamis Mosque, Sheik, Emblem, etc. — A8

Designs: 50f, 75f, Pier, Mina Sulman harbor. 200f, Falcon and horse race. 500f, "Hospitality," pouring coffee and Sheik's Palace.

Perf. 14½x14
1966, Jan. 1   Photo.   Unwmk.
141 A5 5f green .15 .15
142 A5 10f dark red .15 .15
143 A5 15f ultra .15 .15
144 A5 20f magenta .20 .15
Perf. 13½x14
145 A6 30f green & black .28 .16
146 A6 40f blue & black .32 .20
147 A6 50f dp car rose & blk .42 .25
148 A6 75f violet & black .60 .35
Perf. 14½x14
149 A7 100f dk blue & yel 1.00 .50
150 A7 200f dk green & org 3.00 1.00
151 A7 500f red brown & yel 6.25 2.50
152 A8 1d multicolored 12.50 5.00
Nos. 141-152 (12) 25.02 10.56

Produce, Date Palm, Ship, Truck and Plane — A9
Map of Bahrain and WHO Emblem — A10

1966, Mar. 28   Litho.   Perf. 13x13½
153 A9 10f red & blue green .32 .32
154 A9 20f green & vio .65 .65
155 A9 40f olive bis & lt bl 1.25 1.25
156 A9 200f vio blue & pink 6.25 6.25
Nos. 153-156 (4) 8.47 8.47

6th Bahrain Trade Fair & Agricultural Show.

1968, June   Unwmk.   Perf. 13½x14
157 A10 20f gray & black .55 .55
158 A10 40f blue grn & black 1.40 1.40
159 A10 150f dp rose & black 5.50 5.50
Nos. 157-159 (3) 7.45 7.45

20th anniv. of the WHO.

Isa Town A11

1968, Nov. 18   Litho.   Perf. 14½
160 A11 50f shown 1.65 1.65
161 A11 80f Market 2.50 2.50
162 A11 120f Stadium 4.25 4.25
163 A11 150f Mosque 6.75 6.75
Nos. 160-163 (4) 15.15 15.15

Education Symbol A12

1969, Apr.   Litho.   Perf. 13
164 A12 40f multicolored 1.25 1.25
165 A12 60f multicolored 2.00 2.00
166 A12 120f multicolored 4.25 4.25
Nos. 164-166 (3) 7.50 7.50

50th anniversary of education in Bahrain.

Map of Arabian Gulf, Radar and Emblem A13

Designs: 40f, 150f, Radar installation and emblem of Cable & Wireless Ltd., vert.

Perf. 14x13½, 13½x14
1969, July 14   Litho.
167 A13 20f lt green & multi 1.00 1.00
168 A13 40f vio blue & multi 2.25 2.25
169 A13 100f ocher & multi 5.25 5.25
170 A13 150f rose lilac & multi 9.00 9.00
Nos. 167-170 (4) 17.50 17.50

Opening of the satellite earth station (connected through the Indian Ocean satellite Intelsat III) at Ras Abu Jarjur, July 14.

Municipal Building, Arms and Map of Bahrain A14

1970, Feb. 23   Litho.   Perf. 12x12½
171 A14 30f blue & multi 2.75 2.75
172 A14 150f multicolored 10.00 10.00

2nd Conf. of the Arab Cities' Org.

Copper Bull's Head A15

Conf. Emblem and: 80f, Gateway to Qalat al Bahrain, 7th cent. B.C. 120f, Aerial view of grave mounds, Bahrain. 150f, Dilmun seal, 2000 B.C.

1970, Mar. 1   Photo.   Perf. 14½
173 A15 60f multicolored 2.00 2.00
174 A15 80f multicolored 2.25 2.25
175 A15 120f multicolored 3.50 3.50
176 A15 150f multicolored 4.25 4.25
Nos. 173-176 (4) 12.00 12.00

3rd Intl. Asian Archaeological Conf., Bahrain.

Vickers VC 10, Big Ben and Minaret A16

1970, Apr. 5 Litho. Perf. 14½x14

177	A16	30f multicolored	.90	.90
178	A16	60f multicolored	1.90	1.90
179	A16	120f multicolored	6.25	6.25
		Nos. 177-179 (3)	9.05	9.05

1st flight to London from the Arabian Gulf Area by Gulf Aviation Company.

Intl. Education Year Emblem A17

120f, Education Year emblem & students.

1970, Nov. 1 Litho. Perf. 14½x14

180	A17	60f blk, blue & org	3.25	3.25
181	A17	120f multicolored	8.00	8.00

Independent State

Government House, Manama — A18

UN Emblem and Sails — A19

Designs: 30f, "Freedom" with dove and torch, and globe. 120f, 150f, Bahrain coat of arms.

1971, Oct. 2 Photo. Perf. 14½x14

182	A18	30f gold & multi	1.65	1.65
183	A18	60f gold & multi	3.25	3.25
184	A18	120f gold & multi	6.50	6.50
185	A18	150f gold & multi	8.25	8.25
		Nos. 182-185 (4)	19.65	19.65

Declaration of Bahrain independence, Aug. 15, 1971.

Perf. 14x14½, 14½x14

1972, Feb. 1 Litho.

Designs: 30f, 60f, Dhow with sails showing UN and Arab League emblems, horiz. 150f, as 120f.

186	A19	30f multicolored	2.50	2.50
187	A19	60f red, gray & multi	6.00	6.00
188	A19	120f dull blue & multi	12.50	12.50
189	A19	150f multicolored	14.00	14.00
		Nos. 186-189 (4)	35.00	35.00

Bahrain's admission to the Arab League and the United Nations.

"Your Heart is your Health" — A20

1972, Apr. 7 Litho. Perf. 14½x14

190	A20	30f black & multi	3.75	3.75
191	A20	60f gray & multi	7.50	7.50

World Health Day.

UN and FAO Emblems A21

1973, May 12 Litho. Perf. 12½x13

192	A21	30f org red, pur & grn	3.75	3.75
193	A21	60f ocher, brn & grn	6.50	6.50

World Food Programs, 10th anniversary.

People of Various Races, Human Rights Flame A22

1973, Nov. Litho. Perf. 14x14½

194	A22	30f blue, blk & brn	4.00	4.00
195	A22	60f lake, blk & brn	7.75	7.75

25th anniversary of the Universal Declaration of Human Rights.

Flour Mill — A23

60f, Intl. Airport. 120f, Sulmaniya Medical Center. 150f, ALBA aluminum smelting plant.

1973, Dec. 16 Photo. Perf. 14½

196	A23	30f multicolored	1.00	1.00
197	A23	60f multicolored	1.75	1.75
198	A23	120f multicolored	3.50	3.50
199	A23	150f multicolored	4.25	4.25
		Nos. 196-199 (4)	10.50	10.50

National Day.

Letters and UPU Emblem A24

Carrier Pigeon and UPU Emblem A25

60f, UPU emblem & letters. 150f, Like 120f.

1974, Feb. 4 Litho. Perf. 13½

200	A24	30f blue & multi	1.00	1.00
201	A24	60f emerald & multi	1.75	1.75

Perf. 12½x13½

202	A25	120f ultra & multi	3.00	3.00
203	A25	150f yellow & multi	4.25	4.25
		Nos. 200-203 (4)	10.00	10.00

Bahrain's admission to UPU.

Traffic Signals — A26

1974, May 4 Litho. Perf. 14½

204	A26	30f org brown & multi	2.75	2.75
205	A26	60f brt blue & multi	6.25	6.25

International Traffic Day.

Jet, Globe, Mail Coach and UPU Emblem A27

1974, Sept. 1 Photo. Perf. 14x14½

206	A27	30f multicolored	.80	.80
207	A27	60f multicolored	1.65	1.65
208	A27	120f multicolored	3.25	3.25
209	A27	150f multicolored	4.00	4.00
		Nos. 206-209 (4)	9.70	9.70

Centenary of Universal Postal Union.

National Day Emblem, Sitra Power Station — A28

Woman's Silk Gown — A29

National Day: 120f, 150f, Bahrain dry dock.

1974, Dec. 16 Litho. Perf. 14½

210	A28	30f blue & multi	.90	.90
211	A28	60f green & multi	1.50	1.50
212	A28	120f lil rose & multi	3.50	3.50
213	A28	150f ver & multi	4.25	4.25
		Nos. 210-213 (4)	10.15	10.15

Photo.; Gold Embossed

1975, Feb. 1 Perf. 14½x14

Design: Various women's costumes.

214	A29	30f blue grn & multi	.70	.70
215	A29	60f vio blue & multi	1.10	1.10
216	A29	120f rose red & multi	2.75	2.75
217	A29	150f multicolored	3.50	3.50
		Nos. 214-217 (4)	8.05	8.05

Pendant — A30

Woman Planting Flower, IWY Emblem — A31

Designs: Various jewelry.

1975, Apr. 1 Photo. Perf. 14½x14

218	A30	30f olive & multi	.60	.60
219	A30	60f dp pur & multi	1.40	1.40
220	A30	120f dp car & multi	2.75	2.75
221	A30	150f dp blue & multi	3.50	3.50
		Nos. 218-221 (4)	8.25	8.25

1975, July 28 Litho. Perf. 14½

60f, Educated woman holding IWY emblem.

222	A31	30f multicolored	1.50	1.50
223	A31	60f multicolored	3.50	3.50

International Women's Year.

Miniature Sheet

Arabian Stallion A32

Arabian horses: a, Brown head. b, White mare. c, Mare and foal. d, White head. e, White mare. f, Mare and stallion. g, Bedouins on horseback. #224a, 224b, 224d are vert.

Perf. 14x14½, 14½x14

1975, Sept. 1 Photo.

224		Sheet of 8	52.50	32.50
a.-h.		A32 60f any single	5.25	3.50

Flag of Bahrain — A33

Map of Bahrain — A34

Sheik Isa — A35

1976-80 Litho. Perf. 14½

225	A33	5f red & ultra	.15	.15
226	A33	10f red & green	.15	.15
227	A33	15f red & black	.15	.15
228	A33	20f red & brown	.15	.15
228A	A34	25f gray & blk ('79)	.15	.15
229	A34	40f blue & black	.25	.25
229A	A34	50f yel grn & blk ('79)	.30	.30
230	A34	60f dl grn & blk ('77)	.35	.35
231	A34	80f rose lil & blk	.45	.45
232	A34	100f lt red brn & blk ('77)	.55	.55
233	A34	150f org & black	.85	.85
234	A34	200f yel & black	1.10	1.10

Engr.

Perf. 12x12½

235	A35	300f lt grn & grn	1.65	1.65
236	A35	400f pink & red brn	2.25	2.25
237	A35	500f lt bl & dk bl	2.75	2.75
238	A35	1d gray & sepia	5.50	5.50
239	A35	2d rose & vio ('80)	11.50	9.25
240	A35	3d buff & brn ('80)	17.00	14.00
		Nos. 225-240 (18)	45.25	39.50

A later printing of the 100f-200f, and possibly others, has a larger printers imprint at bottom.

Concorde at London Airport — A36

Designs: No. 245, Concorde at Bahrain Airport. No. 246, Concorde over London to Bahrain map. No. 247, Concorde on runway at night.

1976, Jan. 22 Photo. Perf. 13x14

244	A36	80f gold & multi	2.25	2.25
245	A36	80f gold & multi	2.25	2.25
246	A36	80f gold & multi	2.25	2.25
247	A36	80f gold & multi	2.25	2.25
a.		Souvenir sheet of 4	8.00	8.00
b.		Block of 4, #244-247	9.00	9.00

1st commercial flight of supersonic jet Concorde, London to Bahrain, Jan. 21. No. 247a contains 4 stamps with simulated perfs.

Soldier, Flag and Arms of Bahrain — A37

1976, Feb. 5 Litho. Perf. 14½

248	A37	40f yellow & multi	2.00	2.00
249	A37	80f lt blue & multi	4.00	4.00

Defense Force Day.

Sheik Isa, King Khalid, Bahrain and Saudi Flags A38

1976, Mar. 23   Litho.   Perf. 14½
250 A38 40f gold & multi   1.75 1.75
251 A38 80f silver & multi   3.00 3.00
Visit of King Khalid of Saudi Arabia.

New Housing, Housing
Ministry's Seal — A39

1976, Dec. 16   Litho.   Perf. 14½
252 A39 40f rose & multi   1.65 1.65
253 A39 80f blue & multi   3.25 3.25
National Day.

APU
Emblem
A40

1977, Apr. 12   Litho.   Perf. 14½
254 A40 40f silver & multi   1.50 1.50
255 A40 80f rose & multi   3.00 3.00
Arab Postal Union, 25th anniversary.

Miniature Sheet

Dogs on
Beach
and
Dhow
A41

Saluki dogs: b, Dog and camels. c, Dog and gazelles. d, Dog and Ruler's Palace. e, Dog's head. f,
Heads of two dogs. g, Dog in dunes. h, Playing
dogs.

1977, July   Photo.   Perf. 14x14½
256   Sheet of 8   28.00 28.00
a.-h. A41 80f any single   2.75 2.75

Students
and Candle
A42

1977, Sept. 8   Litho.   Perf. 14½
257 A42 40f multicolored   1.50 1.50
258 A42 80f multicolored   3.00 3.00
International Literacy Day.

Shipyard
and Flags
A43

1977, Dec. 16   Litho.   Perf. 14½
259 A43 40f multicolored   1.50 1.50
260 A43 80f multicolored   3.00 3.00
Inauguration of Arab Shipbuilding and Repair
Yard Co.

Antenna,
ITU
Emblem
A44

1978, May 17   Litho.   Perf. 14½
261 A44 40f yellow & multi   1.50 1.50
262 A44 80f silver & multi   3.00 3.00
10th World Telecommunications Day.

Ghanja
Dhow
A45

Dhows of the Arabian Gulf. #267-270 vertical.

Perf. 14x14½, 14½x14
1979, June 16   Photo.
263 A45 100f shown   3.25 3.25
264 A45 100f Zarook   3.25 3.25
265 A45 100f Shu'ai   3.25 3.25
266 A45 100f Jaliboot   3.25 3.25
267 A45 100f Baghla   3.25 3.25
268 A45 100f Sambuk   3.25 3.25
269 A45 100f Boom   3.25 3.25
270 A45 100f Kotia   3.25 3.25
a.   Block of 8, #263-270   26.00 26.00
        Nos. 263-270 (8)   26.00 26.00

Learning to   Hegira, 1,500th
Walk — A46   Anniv. — A47

IYC Emblem and: 100f, Hands surrounding girl,
UN emblem.

1979   Litho.   Perf. 14½
271 A46 50f multicolored   1.50 1.50
272 A46 100f multicolored   3.00 3.00
International Year of the Child.

1980   Photo.   Perf. 13x13½
273 A47 50f multicolored   .65   .65
274 A47 100f multicolored   1.25 1.25
a.   Miniature sheet of 1   6.00 6.00
275 A47 150f multicolored   2.00 2.00
276 A47 200f multicolored   2.75 2.75
        Nos. 273-276 (4)   6.65 6.65

Falcon
A48

Designs: Falcons.

Perf. 13½x14, 14x13½
1980, Nov. 1   Photo.
277   Block of 8   15.00 15.00
a.-h. A48 100f any single   1.75 1.75

IYD
Emblem,
Sheik
Isa — A49

1981, Mar. 21   Litho.   Perf. 14½
278 A49 50f multicolored   1.65 1.65
279 A49 100f multicolored   3.25 3.25
International Year of the Disabled.

50th
Anniversary
of Electricity
in Bahrain
A50

1981, Apr. 26   Litho.   Perf. 14½
280 A50 50f multicolored   1.65 1.65
281 A50 100f multicolored   3.25 3.25

Stone
Cutting — A51

1981, July 1   Photo.   Perf. 14x13½
282 A51 50f shown   .75   .75
283 A51 100f Pottery   1.25 1.25
284 A51 150f Weaving   2.75 2.75
285 A51 200f Basket making   3.00 3.00
        Nos. 282-285 (4)   7.75 7.75

Hegira (Pilgrimage
Year) — A52

Designs: Various mosques.

1981, Oct. 1   Photo.   Perf. 14x13½
286 A52 50f multicolored   .80   .80
287 A52 100f multicolored   1.65 1.65
288 A52 150f multicolored   2.25 2.25
289 A52 200f multicolored   3.25 3.25
        Nos. 286-289 (4)   7.95 7.95

Sheik Isa, 20th
Anniv. of
Coronation — A53

1981, Dec. 16   Photo.   Perf. 14x13½
290 A53 15f multicolored   .25   .25
291 A53 50f multicolored   .80   .80
292 A53 100f multicolored   1.75 1.75
293 A53 150f multicolored   2.50 2.50
294 A53 200f multicolored   3.50 3.50
        Nos. 290-294 (5)   8.80 8.80

Wildlife
in al
Areen
Park
A54

Designs: a, Gazelle. b, Oryx. c, Dhub lizard. d,
Arabian hares. e, Oryxes. f, Reems.

1982, Mar. 1   Photo.   Perf. 13½x14
295   Sheet of 6   14.00 14.00
a.-f. A54 100f any single   2.25 2.25

3rd Session of Gulf
Supreme Council,
Nov. — A55

1982, Nov. 9   Litho.   Perf. 14½
296 A55 50f blue & multi   .85   .85
297 A55 100f green & multi   2.25 2.25

Opening of Madinat Hamad Housing
Development — A56

1983, Dec. 1   Litho.   Perf. 14½
298 A56 50f multicolored   .85   .85
299 A56 100f multicolored   2.25 2.25

Al Khalifa Dynasty Bicentenary — A57

Sheiks or Emblems: a, 500fr, Isa bin Sulman. b,
Emblem (tan & multi). c, Isa bin Ali, 1869-1932. d,
Hamad bin Isa, 1932-42. e, Sulman bin Hamad,
1942-61. f, Emblem (pale green & multi). g,
Emblem (lemon & multi). h, Emblem (light blue &
multi). i, Emblem (gray & multi).

1983, Dec. 16   Litho.   Perf. 14½
300   Sheet of 9   9.00 9.00
a.-i. A57 100f any single   .80   .80

Souvenir Sheet
301 A57 500f multicolored   8.50 8.50
No. 301 contains one stamp 60x38mm.

Gulf Co-operation Council Traffic
Week — A58

1984, Apr. 30   Litho.   Perf. 14½
302 A58 15f multicolored   .30   .30
303 A58 50f multicolored   1.00 1.00
304 A58 100f multicolored   2.00 2.00
        Nos. 302-304 (3)   3.30 3.30

1984
Summer
Olympics
A59

1984, Sept. 15   Perf. 14½
305 A59 15f Hurdles   .26   .26
306 A59 50f Equestrian   .80   .80
307 A59 100f Diving   1.65 1.65
308 A59 150f Fencing   2.00 2.00
309 A59 200f Shooting   3.50 3.50
        Nos. 305-309 (5)   8.21 8.21

Postal Service
Cent.
A60

1984, Dec. 8   Photo.   Perf. 12x11½
310	A60	15f multicolored	.40	.40
311	A60	50f multicolored	1.25	1.25
312	A60	100f multicolored	2.25	2.25
		Nos. 310-312 (3)	3.90	3.90

Miniature Sheet

Coastal Fish A61

1985, Feb. 10   Photo.   Perf. 13½x14
313		Sheet of 10	12.00	12.00
a.-j.	A61	100f any single	1.40	1.40

1st Arab Gulf States Week for Social Work A62

1985, Oct. 15   Litho.   Perf. 14½
314	A62	15f multicolored	.25	.25
315	A62	50f multicolored	.85	.85
316	A62	100f multicolored	1.90	1.90
		Nos. 314-316 (3)	3.00	3.00

Intl. Youth Year A63

1985, Nov. 16
317	A63	15f multicolored	.25	.25
318	A63	50f multicolored	.85	.85
319	A63	100f multicolored	1.90	1.90
		Nos. 317-319 (3)	3.00	3.00

Bahrain-Saudi Arabia Causeway Opening — A64

1986, Nov.   Litho.   Perf. 14½
320	A64	15f Causeway, aerial view	.25	.25
321	A64	50f Island	.85	.85
322	A64	100f Causeway	1.90	1.90
		Nos. 320-322 (3)	3.00	3.00

Sheik Isa, 25th Anniv. as the Emir — A65

1986, Dec. 16
323	A65	15f multicolored	.25	.25
324	A65	50f multicolored	.85	.85
325	A65	100f multicolored	1.90	1.90
a.		Souvenir sheet of 3, #323-325	5.50	5.50
		Nos. 323-325 (3)	3.00	3.00

WHO, 40th Anniv. A66

1988, Apr. 30   Litho.   Perf. 14½
326	A66	50f multicolored	.50	.50
327	A66	150f multicolored	1.40	1.40

Opening of Ahmed Al Fateh Islamic Center A67

1988, June 2   Litho.   Perf. 14½
328	A67	50f multicolored	.50	.50
329	A67	150f multicolored	1.40	1.40

1988 Summer Olympics, Seoul A68

1988, Sept. 17   Litho.   Perf. 14½
330	A68	50f Running	.28	.28
331	A68	80f Equestrian	.45	.45
332	A68	150f Fencing	.80	.80
333	A68	200f Soccer	1.10	1.10
		Nos. 330-333 (4)	2.63	2.63

Gulf Cooperation Council Supreme Council 9th Regular Session, Bahrain A69

1988, Dec. 19   Litho.   Perf. 14½
334	A69	50f multicolored	.50	.50
335	A69	150f multicolored	1.40	1.40

Miniature Sheets

Camels A70

No. 336: a, Close-up of head, rider in background. b, Camel kneeling at rest. c, Two adults, calf. d, Three adults. e, Camel facing right. f, Mount and rider (facing left).
No. 337: a, Man walking in front of camel, oil well. b, Man walking in front of camel. c, Oil well, camel's head. d, Mount and rider (facing forward). e, Mount and rider (facing right). f, Two dromedaries at a run. Nos. 337a-337f vert.

Perf. 13½x14, 14x13½
1989, June 15
336		Sheet of 6	6.00	6.00
a.-f.	A70	150f any single	1.00	1.00
337		Sheet of 6	6.00	6.00
a.-f.	A70	150f any single	1.00	1.00

Sheik Isa — A71

1989, Dec. 16   Litho.   Perf. 13½x14
338	A71	25f multicolored	.15	.15
339	A71	40f multicolored	.24	.24
340	A71	50f multicolored	.30	.30
341	A71	60f multicolored	.35	.35
342	A71	75f multicolored	.45	.45
343	A71	80f multicolored	.48	.48
344	A71	100f multicolored	.60	.60
345	A71	120f multicolored	.72	.72
346	A71	150f multicolored	.90	.90
347	A71	200f multicolored	1.20	1.20
a.		Souvenir sheet of 10, #338-347	6.00	6.00
		Nos. 338-347 (10)	5.39	5.39

Houbara (Bustard) — A72

Designs: a, Two birds facing right. b, Two birds facing each other. c, Chicks. d, Adult, chick. e, Adult, facing right, vert. f, In flight. g, Adult facing right. h, Chick, facing left, vert. i, Adult facing left. j, Adult male, close-up. k, Courtship display. l, Two birds facing left.

1990, Feb. 17   Photo.   Perf. 14
348		Sheet of 12	10.80	10.80
a.-l.	A72	150f any single	.90	.90

Gulf Air, 40th Anniv. A73

1990, Mar. 24   Litho.   Perf. 14½
360	A73	50f multicolored	.30	.30
361	A73	80f multicolored	.48	.48
362	A73	150f multicolored	.90	.90
363	A73	200f multicolored	1.20	1.20
		Nos. 360-363 (4)	2.88	2.88

Chamber of Commerce, 50th Anniv. A74

1990, May 26
364	A74	50f multicolored	.30	.30
365	A74	80f multicolored	.48	.48
366	A74	150f multicolored	.90	.90
367	A74	200f multicolored	1.20	1.20
		Nos. 364-367 (4)	2.88	2.88

Intl. Literacy Year A75

1990, Sept. 8   Litho.   Perf. 14½
368	A75	50f multicolored	.30	.30
369	A75	80f multicolored	.48	.48
370	A75	150f multicolored	.90	.90
371	A75	200f multicolored	1.20	1.20
		Nos. 368-371 (4)	2.88	2.88

Miniature Sheet

Indigenous Birds — A76

Designs: a, Galerida cristata. b, Upupa epops. c, Pycnonotus leucogenys. d, Streptopelia turtur. e, Streptopelia decaocto. f, Falco tinnunculus. g, Passer domesticus, horiz. h, Lanius excubitor, horiz. i, Psittacula krameri.

1991, Sept. 15   Litho.   Perf. 14½
372		Sheet of 9	9.00	9.00
a.-i.	A76	150f any single	1.10	1.10

See Nos. 382, 407.

Coronation of Sheik Isa, 30th Anniv. A77

Design: Nos. 374, 376, 378, 380, 381a, Portrait at left, leaves.

Litho. & Embossed
1991, Dec. 16   Perf. 14½
373	A77	50f multicolored	.35	.35
374	A77	50f multicolored	.35	.35
375	A77	80f multicolored	.55	.55
376	A77	80f multicolored	.55	.55
377	A77	150f multicolored	1.10	1.10
378	A77	150f multicolored	1.10	1.10
379	A77	200f multicolored	1.50	1.50
380	A77	200f multicolored	1.50	1.50
		Nos. 373-380 (8)	7.00	7.00

Souvenir Sheet
Perf. 14x14½
381		Sheet of 2	7.50	7.50
a.-b.	A77	500f any single	3.75	3.75

No. 381 contains 41x31mm stamps.

Miniature Sheet
Indigenous Birds Type of 1991

Designs: No. 382a, Ciconia ciconia. b, Merops apiaster. c, Sturnus vulgaris. d, Hypocolius ampelinus. e, Cuculus canorus. f, Turdus viscivorus. g, Coracias garrulus. h, Carduelis carduelis. i, Lanius collurio. j, Turdus iliacus, horiz. k, Motacilla alba, horiz. l, Oriolus oriolus, horiz. m, Erithacus rubecula. n, Luscinia luscinia. o, Muscicapa striata. p, Hirundo rustica.

1992, Mar. 21   Litho.   Perf. 14½
382		Sheet of 16	13.50	13.50
a.-p.	A76	150f any single	.80	.80

Miniature Sheet

Horse Racing A78

Designs: No. 383a, Horses leaving starting gate. b, Trainers leading horses. c, Horses racing around turn. d, Horses in stretch racing by flags. e, Two horses racing by grandstand. f, Five horses galloping. g, Two brown horses racing. h, Black horse, gray horse racing.

1992, May 22
383		Sheet of 8	7.20	7.20
a.-h.	A78	150f any single	.90	.90

1992 Summer Olympics, Barcelona A79

1992, July 25   Litho.   Perf. 14½
384	A79	50f Equestrian	.35	.35
385	A79	80f Running	.60	.60
386	A79	150f Judo	1.10	1.10
387	A79	200f Cycling	1.40	1.40
		Nos. 384-387 (4)	3.45	3.45

Bahrain Intl. Airport, 60th Anniv. A80

1992, Oct. 27   Litho.   Perf. 14½
388	A80	50f multicolored	.35	.35
389	A80	80f multicolored	.55	.55
390	A80	150f multicolored	1.00	1.00
391	A80	200f multicolored	1.25	1.25
		Nos. 388-391 (4)	3.15	3.15

Children's Art — A81

Designs: 50f, Girl jumping rope, vert. 80f, Women in traditional dress, vert. 150f, Women stirring kettle. 200f, Fishermen.

1992, Nov. 28   Litho.   Perf. 14½
392	A81	50f multicolored	.30 .30
393	A81	80f multicolored	.50 .50
394	A81	150f multicolored	.95 .95
395	A81	200f multicolored	1.25 1.25
		Nos. 392-395 (4)	3.00 3.00

Inauguration of Expansion of Aluminum Bahrain — A82

Designs: 50f, Ore funicular. 80f, Smelting pot. 150f, Mill. 200f, Cylindrical aluminum ingots.

1992, Dec. 16
396	A82	50f multicolored	.30 .30
397	A82	80f multicolored	.50 .50
398	A82	150f multicolored	.95 .95
399	A82	200f multicolored	1.25 1.25
		Nos. 396-399 (4)	3.00 3.00

Bahrain Defense Force, 25th Anniv. — A83

Designs: 50f, Artillery forces, vert. 80f, Fighters, tanks, and ship, vert. 150f, Frigate. 200f, Jet fighter.

Perf. 13½x13, 13x13½

1993, Feb. 5   Litho.
400	A83	50f multicolored	.30 .30
401	A83	80f multicolored	.50 .50
402	A83	150f multicolored	.95 .95
403	A83	200f multicolored	1.25 1.25
		Nos. 400-403 (4)	3.00 3.00

World Meteorology Day — A84

Designs: 50f, Satellite image of Bahrain, vert. 150f, Infrared satellite map of world. 200f, Earth, seen from space, vert.

1993, Mar. 23   Litho.   Perf. 14½
404	A84	50f multicolored	.45 .45
405	A84	150f multicolored	1.40 1.40
406	A84	200f multicolored	1.75 1.75
		Nos. 404-406 (3)	3.60 3.60

Bird Type of 1991 Miniature Sheet

Designs: a, Ardea purpurea. b, Gallinula chloropus. c, Phalacrocorax nigrogularis. d, Dromas ardeola. e, Alcedo atthis. f, Vanellus vanellus. g, Haematopus ostralegus, horiz. h, Nycticorax nycticorax. i, Sterna caspia, horiz. j, Arenaria interpres, horiz. k, Rallus aquaticus, horiz. l, Anas platyrhychos, horia. m, Larus fuscus, horiz.

1993, May 22   Litho.   Perf. 14½
407		Sheet of 13 + 2 labels	11.00 11.00
a.-m.	A76	150f any single	.85 .85

Gazella Subgutturosa Marica — A85

1993, July 24   Litho.   Perf. 14½
408	A85	25f Calf	.15 .15
409	A85	50f Female standing	.30 .30
410	A85	50f Female walking	.30 .30
411	A85	150f Male	.95 .95
		Nos. 408-411 (4)	1.70 1.70

World Wildlife Federation.

Wild Flowers — A86   A87

Designs: a, Lycium shawii. b, Alhagi maurorum. c, Caparis spinosa. d, Cistanche phelypae. e, Asphodelus tenuifolius. f, Limonium axillare. g, Cynomorium coccineum. h, Calligonum polygonoides.

1993, Oct. 16   Litho.   Perf. 13½x13
412	A86	150f Sheet of 8, #a.-h.	6.50 6.50

1994, Jan. 22   Litho.   Perf. 14½
Background Color
413	A87	50f yellow	.30 .30
414	A87	80f blue green	.50 .50
415	A87	150f purple	.95 .95
416	A87	200f blue	1.25 1.25
		Nos. 413-416 (4)	3.00 3.00

Intl. Year of the Family.

A88   A89

Butterflies: No. 417a, Lepidochrysops arabicus. b, Ypthima bolanica. c, Eurema brigitta. d, Precis limnoria. e, Aglais urticae. f, Colotis protomedia. g, Salamis anacardii. h, Byblia ilithyia.

No. 418a, Papilio machaon. b, Agrodiaetus loewii. c, Vanessa cardui. d, Papilio demoleus. e, Hamanumida daedalus. f, Funonia orithya. g, Funonia chorimine. h, Colias croceus.

Perf. 13½x13, 13x13½

1994, Mar. 21   Litho.
417	A88	50f Sheet of 8, #a.-h.	2.50 2.50
418	A88	150f Sheet of 8, #a.-h.	7.50 7.50

No. 418 is horiz.

1994, May 8   Litho.   Perf. 14½
419	A89	50f lilac & multi	.30 .30
420	A89	80f yellow & multi	.50 .50
421	A89	150f salmon & multi	.95 .95
422	A89	200f green blue & multi	1.25 1.25
		Nos. 419-422 (4)	3.00 3.00

Intl. Red Cross & Red Crescent Societies, 75th anniv.

1994 World Cup Soccer Championships, US — A90

Designs: 50f, Goalkeeper. 80f, Heading ball. 150f, Dribbling ball. 200f, Slide tackle.

1994, June 17   Litho.   Perf. 14
423	A90	50f multicolored	.30 .30
424	A90	80f multicolored	.50 .50
425	A90	150f multicolored	.95 .95
426	A90	200f multicolored	1.25 1.25
		Nos. 423-426 (4)	3.00 3.00

Bahrain's First Satellite Earth Station, 25th Anniv. A91

1994, July 14
427	A91	50f blue & multi	.30 .30
428	A91	80f yellow & multi	.50 .50
429	A91	150f violet & multi	.95 .95
430	A91	200f pink, yellow & multi	1.25 1.25
		Nos. 427-430 (4)	3.00 3.00

Education in Bahrain, 75th Anniv. — A92

1994, Nov. 19   Litho.   Perf. 14½
431	A92	50f yellow & multi	.30 .30
432	A92	80f buff & multi	.50 .50
433	A92	150f salmon & multi	.95 .95
434	A92	200f pink & multi	1.25 1.25
		Nos. 431-434 (4)	3.00 3.00

Gulf Cooperation Council Supreme Council, 15th Regular Session, Bahrain — A93

1994, Dec. 19   Perf. 14
435	A93	50f blue green & multi	.30 .30
436	A93	80f brown & multi	.50 .50
437	A93	150f lilac rose & multi	.95 .95
438	A93	200f blue & multi	1.25 1.25
		Nos. 435-438 (4)	3.00 3.00

Date Palm A94

Designs: 80f, Flowering stage. 100f, Dates beginning to ripen. 200f, Dates up close. 250f, Trees from distance. 500f, Pitcher, basket of dates.

1995, Mar. 21   Litho.   Perf. 14
439	A94	80f multicolored	.48 .48
440	A94	100f multicolored	.60 .60
441	A94	200f multicolored	1.25 1.25
442	A94	250f multicolored	1.50 1.50
		Nos. 439-442 (4)	3.83 3.83
		Souvenir Sheet	
443	A94	500f multicolored	3.00 3.00

No. 443 contains one 65x48mm stamp.

Fight Against Polio — A95

1995, Apr. 22   Litho.   Perf. 13x13½
444	A95	80f pink & multi	.42 .42
445	A95	200f blue & multi	1.00 1.00
446	A95	250f lt brown & multi	1.40 1.40
		Nos. 444-446 (3)	2.82 2.82

World Health Day.

1st Natl. Industries Exhibition A96

1995, May 15
447	A96	80f blue green & multi	.42 .42
448	A96	200f lilac & multi	1.00 1.00
449	A96	250f lt brown & multi	1.40 1.40
		Nos. 447-449 (3)	2.82 2.82

FAO, 50th Anniv. A97

Fields of various crops.

1995, June 17   Litho.   Perf. 14
450	A97	80f lilac & multi	.42 .42
451	A97	200f blue & multi	1.00 1.00
452	A97	250f lt pink & multi	1.40 1.40
		Nos. 450-452 (3)	2.82 2.82

Arab League, 50th Anniv. — A98

1995, Sept. 14   Litho.   Perf. 14½
453	A98	80f pink & multi	.40 .40
454	A98	200f blue & multi	1.10 1.10
455	A98	250f yellow & multi	1.40 1.40
		Nos. 453-455 (3)	2.90 2.90

UN, 50th Anniv. A99

1995, Oct. 24   Litho.   Perf. 14½
456	A99	80f yellow & multi	.40 .40
457	A99	100f green & multi	.55 .55
458	A99	200f pink & multi	1.10 1.10
459	A99	250f blue & multi	1.40 1.40
		Nos. 456-459 (4)	3.45 3.45

Miniature Sheet

Traditional Architecture — A100

Example of architecture, detail: a, Tower with balcony. b, Arched windows behind balcony. c, Double doors under arch. d, Four rows of square windows above row of arched windows. e, Door flanked by two windows. f, Three windows.

1995, Nov. 20   Litho.   Perf. 14¹/₂
460 A100 200f Sheet of 6, #a.-f.   6.50 6.50

National Day — A101

1995, Dec. 16   Litho.   Perf. 14¹/₂
461 A101 80f blue & multi   .40 .40
462 A101 100f green & multi   .55 .55
463 A101 200f violet & multi   1.10 1.10
464 A101 250f blue green & multi 1.40 1.40
    Nos. 461-464 (4)   3.45 3.45

Public Library,
50th
Anniv. — A102

1996, Mar. 23   Litho.   Perf. 14
465 A102 80f pink & multi   .40 .40
466 A102 200f green & multi   1.10 1.10
467 A102 250f blue & multi   1.40 1.40
    Nos. 465-467 (3)   2.90 2.90

Pearl
Diving — A103

Designs: 80f, Group of divers on ship, three in water. 100f, Five divers in water, ship. 200f, Diver underneath water. 250f, Diver being pulled up, underwater scene.
500f, Lantern, weight, scales, pearls, knife. Illustration reduced.

1996, May 8   Litho.   Perf. 14
468 A103 80f multicolored   .40 .40
469 A103 100f multicolored   .55 .55
470 A103 200f multicolored   1.10 1.10
471 A103 250f multicolored   1.40 1.40
    Nos. 468-471 (4)   3.45 3.45
    Souvenir Sheet
    Perf. 14¹/₂
472 A103 500f multicolored   2.75 2.75

No. 472 contains one 70x70mm stamp.

1996
Summer
Olympics,
Atlanta
A104

1996, July 19   Litho.   Perf. 14
473 A104 80f olive & multi   .40 .40
474 A104 100f pink & multi   .55 .55
475 A104 200f blue green & multi 1.10 1.10
476 A104 250f orange & multi   1.40 1.40
    Nos. 473-476 (4)   3.45 3.45

Interpol, Intl. Criminal Police
Organization — A105

1996, Sept. 25   Litho.   Perf. 14
477 A105 80f blue & multi   .40 .40
478 A105 100f yellow & multi   .55 .55
479 A105 200f green & multi   1.10 1.10
480 A105 250f green & multi   1.40 1.40
    Nos. 477-480 (4)   3.45 3.45

Aluminum
Production
in Bahrain,
25th
Anniv.
A106

1996, Nov. 20   Litho.   Perf. 14
481 A106 80f bister & multi   .40 .40
482 A106 100f orange & multi   .55 .55
483 A106 200f blue & multi   1.10 1.10
484 A106 250f green & multi   1.40 1.40
    Nos. 481-484 (4)   3.45 3.45

Accession to the Throne by Sheik Isa Bin
Salman Al Khalifa, 35th Anniv.
A107

1996, Dec. 16
485 A107 80f gray & multi   .40 .40
486 A107 100f green & multi   .55 .55
487 A107 200f pink & multi   1.10 1.10
488 A107 250f blue & multi   1.40 1.40
    Nos. 485-488 (4)   3.45 3.45

Bahrain
Refinery,
60th
Anniv.
A108

1997, Jan. 15   Litho.   Perf. 14
489 A108 80f red & multi   .45 .45
490 A108 200f blue & multi   1.10 1.10
491 A108 250f yellow & multi   1.30 1.30
    Nos. 489-491 (3)   2.85 2.85

Pure
Breeds of
Arabian
Horses,
Amiri
Stud
A109

Designs: a, Musannaan, Al-Jellabieh, Rabdaan. b, Kuheilaan weld umm zorayr. c, Al-Jellaby. d, Musannaan. e, Kuheilaan aladiyat. f, Kuheilaan aafas. g, Al-Dhahma. h, Mlolshaan. i, Al-Kray. j, Krush. k, Al Hamdaany. l, Hadhfaan. m, Rabda. n, Al-Suwaitieh. o, Al-Obeyah. p, Al-Shuwaimeh. q, Al-Ma'anaghieh. r, Al-Tuwaisah. s, Wadhna. t, Al-Saqlawieh. u, Al-Shawafah.

1997, Apr. 23   Litho.   Perf. 14x14¹/₂
492 A109 200f Sheet of 21, #a.-u. 22.50 22.50

9th Men's Junior World Volleyball
Championship — A110

1997, Aug. 21   Litho.   Perf. 14x14¹/₂
493 A110 80f brown & multi   .45 .45
494 A110 100f green & multi   .55 .55
495 A110 200f gray brown & multi 1.10 1.10
496 A110 250f blue & multi   1.30 1.30
    Nos. 493-496 (4)   3.40 3.40

Montreal Protocol
on Substances that
Deplete Ozone
Layer, 10th
Anniv. — A111

1997, Sept. 16   Litho.   Perf. 14¹/₂
497 A111 80f yellow & multi   .45 .45
498 A111 100f purple & multi   .55 .55
499 A111 200f red & multi   1.10 1.10
500 A111 250f green & multi   1.30 1.30
    Nos. 497-500 (4)   3.40 3.40

WAR TAX STAMPS

WT1   WT2

1973, Oct. 21   Litho.   Perf. 14¹/₂
MR1 WT1 5f sky blue

Catalogue values for all unused stamps in this section, from this point to the end of the section, are for **Never Hinged** items.

1974   Litho.   Perf. 14¹/₂
MR2 WT2 5f light blue   1.75 .25
    a. Perf. 14¹/₂x13¹/₂   2.50

No. MR2a was issued around 1988.

BANGKOK

'baŋ-,käk

LOCATION — Capital of Siam (Thailand)

Stamps were issued by Great Britain under rights obtained in the treaty of 1855. These were in use until July 1, 1885, when the stamps of Siam were designated as the only official postage stamps to be used in the kingdom.

100 Cents = 1 Dollar

Excellent counterfeits of Nos. 1-22 are plentiful.

Stamps of Straits Settlements
Overprinted in Black   **B**

1882		**Wmk. 1**		**Perf. 14**
1	A2	2c brown	2,250.	1,200.
2	A2	4c rose	2,500.	1,200.
a.		Inverted overprint		
3	A6	5c brown violet	300.00	150.00
4	A6	6c violet	225.00	125.00
5	A3	8c yel orange	2,000.	165.00
6	A7	10c slate	200.00	125.00
7	A3	12c blue	500.00	250.00
8	A3	24c green	650.00	125.00
9	A4	30c claret	40,000.	25,000.
10	A5	96c olive gray	4,000.	2,250.

The existence of No. 2a is questioned. See note after No. 20. No. 2 with two clear impressions: $6,000 used.

1882-83		**Wmk. 2**		
11	A2	2c brown	325.00	250.00
12	A2	2c rose ('83)	40.00	40.00
a.		Inverted overprint	20,000.	10,000.
b.		Double overprint	1,750.	
c.		Triple overprint	10,000.	
13	A2	4c rose	400.00	250.00
14	A2	4c brown ('83)	60.00	60.00
a.		Double overprint		—
15	A6	5c ultra ('83)	165.00	165.00
16	A2	6c violet ('83)	100.00	100.00
a.		Double overprint		
17	A3	8c yel orange	125.00	80.00
a.		Inverted overprint	17,500.	10,000.
18	A7	10c slate	125.00	80.00
a.		Double overprint		
19	A3	12c violet brn ('83)	175.00	140.00
20	A3	24c green	3,250.	2,250.

Partial double overprints exist on a number of values of these issues. They sell for a modest premium over catalogue value depending on how much of the impression is present.

1883		**Wmk. 1**		
21	A5	2c on 32c pale red	2,250.	2,250.

On Straits Settlements No. 9
1885		**Wmk. 38**		
22	A7	32c on 2a yel (B+B)	40,000.	50,000.

BANGLADESH

,bän–glə-'desh

LOCATION — In southern, central Asia, touching India, Burma, and the Bay of Bengal
GOVT. — Republic in the British Commonwealth
AREA — 55,598 sq. mi.
POP. — 87,052,024 (1981)
CAPITAL — Dacca (Dhaka)

Bangladesh, formerly East Pakistan, broke away from Pakistan in April 1971, proclaiming its independence. It consists of 14 former eastern districts of Bengal and the former Sylhet district of Assam province of India.

100 Paisas = 1 Rupee
100 Paisas (Poishas) = 1 Taka (1972)

Catalogue values for all unused stamps in this country are for **Never Hinged** items.

Various stamps of Pakistan were handstamped locally for use in Bangladesh from March 26, 1971 until April 30, 1973.

Map of
Bangladesh
A1

Sheik Mujibur
Rahman
A2

Designs: 20p, "Dacca University Massacre." 50p, "A Nation of 75 Million People." 1r, Flag of Independence (showing map). 2r, Ballot box. 3r, Broken chain. 10r, "Support Bangladesh" and map.

Perf. 14x14½

1971, July 29   Litho.   Unwmk.
1	A1	10p red, dk pur & lt bl	.15	.15
2	A1	20p bl, grn, red & yel	.15	.15
3	A1	50p dp org, gray & brn	.15	.15
4	A1	1r red, emer & yel	.20	.20
5	A1	2r lil rose, lt & dk bl	.40	.40
6	A1	3r blue, emer & grn	.50	.50
7	A2	5r dp org, tan & blk	1.00	1.00
8	A1	10r gold, dk bl & lil rose	1.65	1.65
		Nos. 1-8 (8)	4.20	4.20

A set of 15 stamps of types A1 and A2 in new paisa-taka values and colors was rejected by Bangladesh officials and not issued. Bangladesh representatives in England released these stamps, which were not valid, on Feb. 1, 1972.
Imperfs of Nos. 1-8 were in the Format International liquidation. They are not errors.

Nos. 1-8 Overprinted in	BANGLADESH
Black or Red	LIBERATED
	বাংলাদেশের মুক্তি

1971, Dec. 20
9	A1	10p multicolored	.15	.15
10	A1	20p multicolored	.15	
11	A1	50p multicolored	.15	
12	A1	1r multicolored	.30	
13	A1	2r multicolored	.50	
14	A1	3r multicolored	.90	
15	A2	5r multicolored (R)	1.25	1.25
16	A1	10r multicolored	2.50	2.50
		Nos. 9-16 (8)	5.90	

Liberation of Bangladesh.
The 10p, 5r and 10r were issued in Dacca, but Nos. 10-14 were not put on sale in Bangladesh.

Monument
A3

"Independence"
A4

1972, Feb. 21   Litho.   Perf. 13
32	A3	20p green & rose	.70	.30

Language Movement Martyrs.

1972, Mar. 26   Photo.   Perf. 13
33	A4	20p maroon & red	.15	.15
34	A4	60p dark blue & red	.30	.30
35	A4	75p purple & red	.30	.30
		Nos. 33-35 (3)	.75	.75

First anniversary of independence.

Doves of
Peace — A5

Flower Growing
from Ruin — A6

1972, Dec. 16   Litho.   Perf. 13
36	A5	20p ocher & multi	.15	.15
37	A5	60p lilac & multi	.30	.30
38	A5	75p yellow green & multi	.35	.35
		Nos. 36-38 (3)	.80	.80

Victory Day, Dec. 16.

1973, Mar. 25   Litho.   Perf. 13
39	A6	20p ocher & multi	.20	.20
40	A6	60p brown & multi	.40	.40
41	A6	1.35t violet blue & multi	1.00	1.00
		Nos. 39-41 (3)	1.60	1.60

Martyrs of the war of liberation.

Embroidered
Quilt — A7

Hilsa — A8

Court of
Justice — A9

Designs: 3p, Jute field. 5p, Jack fruit. 10p, Farmer plowing with ox team. 20p, Hibiscus rosenensis. 25p, Tiger. 60p, Bamboo and water lilies. 75p, Women picking tea. 90p, Handicraft. 2t, Collecting date palm juice, vert. 5t, Net fishing. 10t, Sixty-dome Mosque.

Perf. 14x14½, 14½x14
1973, Apr. 30   Litho.
Size: 21x28mm, 28x21mm
42	A7	2p black	.15	.15
43	A7	3p bright green	.15	.15
44	A7	5p light brown	.15	.15
45	A7	10p black	.15	.15
46	A7	20p olive	.70	.70
47	A7	25p red lilac	1.90	1.90
48	A8	50p rose lilac	1.50	1.50
49	A7	60p gray	.70	.70
50	A7	75p orange	1.25	1.25
51	A7	90p red brown	1.25	1.25

Taka Expressed as "TA"
Size: 35x22mm
52	A9	1t violet	3.50	3.50
53	A9	2t greenish gray	4.50	4.50
54	A9	5t grayish blue	6.00	6.00
55	A9	10t rose	6.50	6.50
		Nos. 42-55 (14)	28.40	28.40

See Nos. 82-85, 95-106, 165-176. For overprints see Nos. O1-O10, O13.

 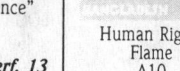

Human Rights
Flame
A10

Family, Chart,
Map of
Bangladesh
A11

1973, Dec. 10   Litho.   Perf. 13x13½
56	A10	10p blue & multi	.15	.15
57	A10	1.25t violet & multi	.60	.60

25th anniversary of the Universal Declaration of Human Rights.

1974, Feb. 10   Litho.   Perf. 13½
58	A11	20p blue grn & multi	.15	.15
59	A11	25p brt blue & multi	.15	.15
60	A11	75p red & multi	.45	.45
		Nos. 58-60 (3)	.75	.75

First census in Bangladesh.
For overprints see Nos. 194-196.

Copernicus,
Heliocentric
System
A12

Flag and UN
Headquarters
A13

1974, July 22   Litho.   Perf. 13½
61	A12	25p violet, blk & org	.20	.20
62	A12	75p emerald, blk & org	.60	.60

Nicolaus Copernicus (1473-1543), Polish astronomer.

1974, Sept. 25   Litho.   Perf. 13½
63	A13	25p lilac & multi	.15	.15
64	A13	1t blue & multi	.50	.50

Admission of Bangladesh to the UN.

A14

A15

Designs: 25p, 1.75t, UPU emblem. 1.25t, 5t, Mail runner. 25p, 1.25t, country and denomination appear on a yellow background. 1.75t, 5t, blue background.

1974, Oct. 9   Perf. 13½
65	A14	25p multicolored	.15	.15
66	A14	1.25t multicolored	.20	.20
67	A14	1.75t multicolored	.35	.35
68	A14	5t multicolored	.95	.95
a.		Souv. sheet of 4, #65-68, imperf.	35.00	
		Nos. 65-68 (4)	1.65	1.65

1974, Nov. 4   Litho.
69	A15	25p Royal bengal tiger	.30	.30
70	A15	50p Tiger cub	1.25	1.25
71	A15	2t Swimming tiger	3.50	3.50
		Nos. 69-71 (3)	5.05	5.05

"Save the Tiger," World Wildlife Fund.

Type of 1973
Taka Expressed in Bengali
1974-75   Perf. 14½x14, 14x14½
Size: 35x22mm
82	A9	1t violet	1.65	1.65
83	A9	2t grayish green	3.25	3.25
84	A9	5t grayish blue ('75)	4.50	4.50
85	A9	10t rose ('75)	8.00	8.00
		Nos. 82-85 (4)	17.40	17.40

For overprints see Nos. O11-O12, O14.

Family — A16

Children — A17

Family — A18

1974, Dec. 30   Litho.   Perf. 14
86	A16	25p ocher & multi	.15	.15
87	A17	70p claret & multi	.35	.35
88	A18	1.25t multicolored	.50	.50
		Nos. 86-88 (3)	1.00	1.00

Family planning. The numerals on No. 87 look like "90" but mean "70."

Betbunia Satellite
Earth Station — A19

1975, June 14   Litho.   Perf. 14
89	A19	25p red, black & silver	.15	.15
90	A19	1t vio blue, blk & silver	.60	.60

Opening of Betbunia Satellite Earth Station.

Allegory, IWY
Emblem
A20

1975, Dec. 31   Litho.   Perf. 15
91	A20	50p rose & multi	.15	.15
92	A20	2t lt lilac & multi	.70	.70

International Women's Year.

Types of 1973 Redrawn
1976-77   Litho.   Perf. 15x14½
Size: 18x23mm, 23x18mm
95	A7	5p green	.15	.15
96	A7	10p black	.15	.15
97	A7	20p olive green	.20	.20
98	A7	25p rose lilac	.30	.30
99	A8	50p rose lilac	.45	.45
100	A7	60p gray	.60	.60
101	A7	75p olive	.70	.70
102	A7	90p red brown	.90	.90

Taka Expressed in Bengali
Size: 32x20mm, 20x32mm
103	A9	1t violet	.95	.95
104	A9	2t greenish gray	2.00	2.00
105	A9	5t grayish blue	5.25	5.25
106	A9	10t rose ('77)	10.00	10.00
		Nos. 95-106 (12)	21.65	21.65

For overprints see Nos. O16-O25.

Telephones, 1876
and 1976 — A21

Alexander Graham
Bell — A22

1976, Mar. 10   Litho.   Perf. 15
107	A21	2.25t multicolored	.40	.40
108	A22	5t multicolored	1.00	1.00

Centenary of first telephone call by Alexander Graham Bell, Mar. 10, 1876.

Eye and
Healthful
Food — A23

1976, Apr. 7   Litho.   Perf. 15
109	A23	30p yellow & multi	.35	.35
110	A23	2.25t orange & multi	1.65	1.65

World Health Day: Foresight prevents blindness.

Liberty
Bell — A24

Designs: 2.25t, Statue of Liberty, New York Skyline. 5t, Mayflower. 10t, Mt. Rushmore, presidents' heads.

1976, May 29   Photo.   Perf. 13½x14

111	A24	30p multicolored	.15	.15
112	A24	2.25t multicolored	.30	.30
113	A24	5t multicolored	.70	.70
114	A24	10t multicolored	1.40	1.40
a.		Souv. sheet of 4, #111-114, perf. 13	3.25	3.25
		Nos. 111-114 (4)	2.55	2.55

American Bicentennial. Sheet exists imperf.

Weaver, Chemist, Farmer, Student and Emblem — A25

1976, July 29   Litho.   Perf. 15

115	A25	30p multicolored	.15	.15
116	A25	2.25t multicolored	.75	.75

25th anniversary of Colombo Plan.
For overprint see No. 252.

Hurdles — A26

Montreal Olympic Emblem and: 30p, Running, horiz. 1t, High jump. 2.25t, Swimming, horiz. 3.50t, Gymnastics. 5t, Soccer.

1976, Nov. 29   Litho.   Perf. 15

117	A26	25p multicolored	.15	.15
118	A26	30p multicolored	.15	.15
119	A26	1t multicolored	.20	.20
120	A26	2.25t multicolored	.50	.50
121	A26	3.50t multicolored	.70	.70
122	A26	5t multicolored	1.10	1.10
		Nos. 117-122 (6)	2.80	2.80

21st Olympic Games, Montreal, Canada, July 17-Aug. 1.

Coronation Ceremony — A27

Designs: 2.25t, Queen Elizabeth II. 10t, Queen and Prince Philip.

1977, Feb. 7   Perf. 14x15

123	A27	30p multicolored	.15	.15
124	A27	2.25t multicolored	.25	.25
125	A27	10t multicolored	1.10	1.10
a.		Souv. sheet of 3, #123-125, perf. 14½	1.65	1.65
		Nos. 123-125 (3)	1.50	1.50

25th anniv. of the reign of Elizabeth II.

Qazi Nazrul Islam — A28

Nazrul A29

1977, Aug. 29   Litho.   Perf. 14

126	A28	40p lt green & black	.15	.15
127	A29	2.25t multicolored	.65	.65

Qazi Nazrul Islam (1899-1976), natl. poet.

Pigeon Carrying Letter A30

1977, Sept. 29   Litho.   Perf. 14

128	A30	30p multicolored	.15	.15
129	A30	2.25t multicolored	.60	.60

Asian-Oceanic Postal Union (AOPU), 15th anniversary.

Leopard A31

40p and 1t are vert.

1977, Nov. 9   Litho.   Perf. 13

130	A31	40p Asiatic black bear	.15	.15
131	A31	1t Axis deer	.60	.60
132	A31	2.25t shown	.70	.70
133	A31	3.50t Gayal	.95	.95
134	A31	4t Elephant	1.50	1.50
135	A31	5t Bengal tiger	1.75	1.75
		Nos. 130-135 (6)	5.65	5.65

Campfire, Tent, Scout Emblem — A32

Designs: 3.50t, Emblem, first aid, signaling, horiz. 5t, Scout emblem and oath.

1978, Jan. 22   Litho.   Perf. 13

136	A32	40p multicolored	.15	.15
137	A32	3.50t multicolored	.90	.90
138	A32	5t multicolored	1.65	1.65
		Nos. 136-138 (3)	2.70	2.70

1st National Boy Scout Jamboree, Jan. 22.
For overprint see No. 269.

Champac A33

Flowers and Flowering Trees: 1t, Pudding pipe tree. 2.25t, Flamboyant tree. 3.50t, Water lilies. 4t, Butea. 5t, Anthocephalus indicus.

1978, Mar. 31   Litho.   Perf. 13

139	A33	40p multicolored	.20	.20
140	A33	1t multicolored	.50	.50
141	A33	2.25t multicolored	.85	.85
142	A33	3.50t multicolored	1.10	1.10
143	A33	4t multicolored	1.25	1.25
144	A33	5t multicolored	1.40	1.40
		Nos. 139-144 (6)	5.30	5.30

For overprints see Nos. 259A-259F.

Crown, Scepter and Staff of State — A34

Designs: 3.50t, Royal family on balcony. 5t, Queen Elizabeth II and Prince Philip. 10t, Queen in coronation regalia, Westminster Abbey.

1978, May 20   Perf. 14

145	A34	40p multicolored	.15	.15
146	A34	3.50t multicolored	.20	.20
147	A34	5t multicolored	.30	.30
148	A34	10t multicolored	.55	.55
a.		Souv. sheet of 4, #145-148, perf. 14½	1.40	1.40
		Nos. 145-148 (4)	1.20	1.20

Coronation of Queen Elizabeth II, 25th anniv.
For overprint see No. 228B.

Alan Cobham's DH50, 1926 A35

Planes: 2.25t, Capt. Hans Bertram's Junkers W33 Atlantis, 1932-33. 3.50t, Wright brothers' plane. 5t, Concorde.

1978, June 15   Litho.   Perf. 13

149	A35	40p multicolored	.20	.20
150	A35	2.25t multicolored	1.25	1.25
151	A35	3.50t multicolored	1.90	1.90
152	A35	5t multicolored	2.50	2.50
		Nos. 149-152 (4)	5.85	5.85

75th anniversary of powered flight.

Holy Kaaba, Mecca — A37

Design: 3.50t, Pilgrims at Mt. Arafat, horiz.

1978, Nov. 9   Litho.   Perf. 13

154	A37	40p multicolored	.15	.15
155	A37	3.50t multicolored	.75	.75

Pilgrimage to Mecca.

Jasim Uddin, Poet — A38

1979, Mar. 14   Litho.   Perf. 14

156	A38	40p multicolored	.40	.40

Rowland Hill — A39   Moulana Bhashani — A40

Hill and Stamps of Bangladesh: 3.50t, No. 1, horiz. 10t, No. 66, horiz.

1979, Aug. 27   Litho.   Perf. 14

157	A39	40p multicolored	.15	.15
158	A39	3.50t multicolored	.35	.35
159	A39	10t multicolored	1.10	1.10
a.		Souvenir sheet of 3, #157-159	2.75	2.75
		Nos. 157-159 (3)	1.60	1.60

Sir Rowland Hill (1795-1879), originator of penny postage.

1979, Nov. 17   Perf. 12½

160	A40	40p multicolored	.55	.55

Moulana Abdul Hamid Khan Bhashani (1880-1976), philosopher and statesman.

A41   A42

IYC Emblem and: 40p, Boys and Hoops. 3.50t, Boys flying kites. 5t, Children jumping.

1979, Dec. 17   Litho.   Perf. 14x14½

161	A41	40p multicolored	.15	.15
162	A41	3.50t multicolored	.45	.45
163	A41	5t multicolored	.65	.65
a.		Souv. sheet of 3, #161-163, perf. 14½	2.50	2.50
		Nos. 161-163 (3)	1.25	1.25

International Year of the Child.

Type of 1973

Designs: 5p, Lalbag Fort. 10p, Fenchungan Fertilizer Factory, vert. 15p, Pineapple. 20p, Gas well. 25p, Jute on boat. 30p, Banana tree. 40p, Baitul Mukarram Mosque. 50p, Baitul Mukarram Mosque. 80p, Garh excavations. 1ta, Dotara (musical instrument.) 2t, Karnaphuli Dam.

1979-82   Photo.   Perf. 14½
Size: 18x23mm, 23x18mm

165	A7	5p brown ('79)	.15	.15
166	A7	10p Prus blue	.15	.15
167	A7	15p yellow org ('81)	.20	.15
168	A7	20p dk carmine ('79)	.30	.15
169	A7	25p dk blue ('82)	.35	.15
170	A7	30p lt olive grn ('80)	.45	.15
171	A8	40p rose magenta ('79)	.55	.15
172	A9	50p black & gray ('81)	.75	.15
173	A7	80p dk brown ('80)	1.10	.15
174	A7	1t red lilac ('81)	1.50	.15
175	A7	2t brt ultra ('81)	2.75	1.00
		Nos. 165-175 (11)	8.25	
		Set value		2.00

For overprints see Nos. O27-O36.

1980, Feb. 23   Litho.   Perf. 14

Rotary Intl., 75th Anniv.: 40p, Rotary emblem, diff.

179	A42	40p multicolored	.15	.15
180	A42	5t ultra & gold	.90	.90

For overprints see Nos. 285-286.

15-Cent Minimum Value
The minimum value for a single stamp is 15 cents. This value reflects the costs of handling inexpensive stamps.

Canal
Digging
A43

1980, Mar. 27   Litho.   Perf. 14
181 A43 40p multicolored   .55   .55

Sher-e-Bangla A.K.
Fazlul Huq (1873-
1962), Natl.
Leader — A44

1980, Apr. 27   Litho.   Perf. 14
182 A44 40p multicolored   .55   .55

Early Mail Transport, London 1980
Emblem — A45

1980, May 5
183 A45 1t shown   .15   .15
184 A45 10t Modern mail transport   1.40 1.40
  a. Souvenir sheet of 2, #183-184   1.75 1.75
   London 80 Intl. Stamp Exhib., May 6-14.

Dome of the   Adult
Rock — A46   Education — A47

1980, Aug. 21   Litho.   Perf. 14½
185 A46 50p violet rose   .85   .85
   For the families of Palestinians.

1980, Aug. 23   Perf. 13½
186 A47 50p multicolored   .55   .55

Beach Scene
A48

1980, Sept. 27   Litho.   Perf. 14
187 A48 50p shown   .15   .15
188 A48 5t Beach scene, diff.   1.40 1.40
  a. Souvenir sheet of 2, #187-188   1.50 1.50
  b. Pair, #187-188   1.50 1.50
   World Tourism Conference, Manila, Sept. 27.
No. 188b has continuous design.
For overprints see Nos. 243-244.

Hegira (Pilgrimage
Year) — A49

1980, Nov. 11   Photo.   Perf. 14
189 A49 50p multicolored   .40   .40

A50   A51

Design: Deer and Boy Scout emblem.

1981, Jan. 1   Litho.   Perf. 14
190 A50 50p multicolored   .15   .15
191 A50 5t multicolored   1.40 1.40
   5th Asia-Pacific and 2nd Bangladesh Scout Jamboree, 1980-1981.

1980, Dec. 9   Litho.   Perf. 14
192 A51 50p multicolored   .15   .15
193 A51 2t multicolored   .55   .55
   Begum Roquiah (1880-1932), educator.

Nos. 58-60 Overprinted:
2nd / CENSUS / 1981

1981, Mar. 6   Perf. 13½
194 A11 20p multicolored   .15   .15
195 A11 25p multicolored   .15   .15
196 A11 75p multicolored   .35   .35
           Set value   .55   .55

A52   A53

1981, Mar. 16   Litho.   Perf. 14
197 A52 1t multicolored   .15   .15
198 A52 15t multicolored   2.50 2.50
  a. Souvenir sheet of 2, #197-198   3.25 3.25
   Queen Mother Elizabeth, 80th birthday (1980).

1981, Mar. 26
199 A53 50p Citizen Holding Rifle &
            Flag   .15   .15
200 A53 2t People, map   .60   .60
   10th anniversary of independence.

UN Conference on Least-developed
Countries, Paris — A54

1981, Sept. 1   Litho.   Perf. 14x13½
201 A54 50p multicolored   .70   .70

Birth Centenary of
Kemal Ataturk (First
President of
Turkey) — A55

1981, Nov. 10   Litho.   Perf. 14
202 A55 50p Portrait   .50   .50
203 A55 1t Portrait, diff.   .70   .70

Intl. Year of
the Disabled
A56

1981, Dec. 26   Litho.   Perf. 14
204 A56 50p Sign language, vert.   .35   .35
205 A56 2t Amputee   1.10 1.10

World Food Day,
Oct. 16 — A57

1981, Dec. 31   Litho.   Perf. 13½x14
206 A57 50p multicolored   .80   .80

A58   A59

1982, May 22   Litho.   Perf. 13½x14
207 A58 50p Boat hauling rice straw   .70   .70
   10th Anniv. of UN Conf. on Human
Environment.
For overprint see No. 281.

1982, Oct. 9
208 A59 50p multicolored   .95   .95
   Dr. Kazi Motahar Hossain, educator and
statistician.

Scouting
Year — A60

1982, Oct. 21   Litho.   Perf. 14
209 A60 50p Emblem, knots   .75   .75
210 A60 2t Baden-Powell, vert.   3.25 3.25

Capt.
Mohiuddin
Jahangir
A61

Liberation Heroes (Tablet Color): b, Sepoy
Hamidur Rahman (pale green). c, Sepoy Mohammed Mustafa Kamal (rose claret). d, Mohammad
Ruhul Amin (yellow). e, M. Matiur Rahman (olive
bister). f, Lance-Naik Munshi Abdur Rob (brown
orange). g, Lance-Naik Nur Mouhammad (bright
yellow green).

1982, Dec. 16   Litho.   Perf. 14
211   Strip of 7   1.90 1.90
  a.-g. A61 50p multicolored   .25   .25

Metric
System
A62

1983, Jan. 10   Litho.   Perf. 14
212 A62 50p Mail scale, vert.   .60   .60
213 A62 2t Weights, measures   2.25 2.25

TB Bacillus
Centenary — A63

1983, Feb. 20   Litho.   Perf. 14
214 A63 50p Koch   1.00 1.00
215 A63 1t Slides, microscope   2.00 2.00

A64

1983, Mar. 14   Litho.   Perf. 14
216 A64 1t Open stage theater   .15   .15
217 A64 3t Boat race   .20   .20
218 A64 10t Snake dance   .65   .65
219 A64 15t Tea garden   1.00 1.00
       Nos. 216-219 (4)   2.00 2.00
   Commonwealth Day.

Jnantapash
Shahidullah (1885-
1969), Educator and
Linguist — A65

1983, July 10   Litho.   Perf. 14
220 A65 50p multicolored   .95   .95

Birds — A66

1983, Aug. 17   Litho.   Perf. 14
221 A66 50p Copsychus saulari   1.25   .65
222 A66 2t Halcyon smyrnen-
            sis, vert.   2.00 2.00
223 A66 3.75t Dinopium
            benghalense, vert.   2.25 2.25
224 A66 5t Carina scutulata   3.00 3.00
  a. Souvenir sheet of 4, #221-224   11.00 11.00
       Nos. 221-224 (4)   8.50 7.90
   No. 224a sold for 13t.

Local
Fish — A67

1983, Oct. 31   Litho.   Perf. 14
225 A67 50p Macrobrachium
            rosengergii   .60   .25
226 A67 2t Stromateus ciner-
            eus   1.90 1.40
227 A67 3.75t Labeo rohita   2.25 1.75
228 A67 5t Anabas testudineus   2.75 2.25
  a. Souv. sheet of 4, #225-228, imp-
       perf.   7.50 7.50
       Nos. 225-228 (4)   7.50 5.65
   No. 228a sold for 13t.

No. 148 Ovptd. "Nov. '83/Visit of Queen"
in Red

1983, Nov. 14   Litho.   Perf. 14
228B A34 10t multicolored   5.25 5.25

World Communications Year — A68

1983, Dec. 21   Litho.   Perf. 14
229 A68 50p Messenger, vert.   .20 .20
230 A68 5t Jet, train, ship, vert.   1.90 1.90
231 A68 10t Dish antenna, messenger   3.50 3.50
Nos. 229-231 (3)   5.60 5.60

Hall — A69

A70

1983, Dec. 5   Litho.   Perf. 14
232 A69 50p Sangsad Bhaban   .20 .20
233 A69 5t Shait Gumbaz   2.25 2.25
14th Islamic Foreign Ministers Conference.

Perf. 11¹⁄₂x12¹⁄₂, 12¹⁄₂x11¹⁄₂
1983, Dec. 21
234 A70 5p Mailboat   .15 .15
235 A70 10p Dacca P.O. counter   .15 .15
236 A70 15p IWTA Terminal   .15 .15
237 A70 20p Sorting mail   .15 .15
238 A70 25p Mail delivery   .15 .15
239 A70 30p Postman at mailbox   .15 .15
240 A70 50p Mobile post office   .20 .20

Size: 30¹⁄₂x18¹⁄₂mm
Perf. 12x11¹⁄₂
241 A70 1t Kamalapur Railway Station   .25 .25
242 A70 2t Zia Intl. Airport   .50 .50
242A A70 5t Khulna P.O.   1.25 1.25
Nos. 234-242A (10)   3.10 3.10

Nos. 235-237, 239-242A horiz.
Nos. 234-240 reprinted on cream paper.
See #270-271. For overprints see #O37-O46, O48.

No. 188b Overprinted in English

First Bangladesh National Philatelic Exhibition 1984
50P   ৫০প

or Bengali in Red
প্রথম বাংলাদেশ জাতীয় ডাকটিকিট প্রদর্শনী - ১৯৮৪
৫৫   ৫৫

1984, Feb. 1   Litho.   Perf. 14
243 A48 50p Beach Scene   .25 .25
244 A48 5t Beach Scene, diff.   2.25 2.25
a. Pair, #243-244   2.50 2.50
1st Bangladesh Natl. Philatelic Exhibition, 1984.
No. 244a has continuous design.

A71

1984, May 17   Perf. 14¹⁄₂
245 50p Girl examining stamp album   .15 .15
246 7.50t Boy updating collection   1.75 1.75
a. Souvenir sheet of 2, #245-246   3.75 3.75
b. A71 Pair, #245-246   1.90 1.90
c. As "a," overprinted   9.25 9.25
#246a sold for 10t.
Overprint in sheet margin of No. 246c reads: "SILVER JUBILEE / BANGLADESH POSTAGE STAMPS 1971-96."

Dacca Zoo — A72   Postal Life Insurance, Cent. — A73

1984, July 17   Litho.   Perf. 14
247 A72 1t Sarus crane, gavial   1.40 1.40
248 A72 2t Peafowl, royal Bengal tiger   2.75 2.75

1984, Dec. 3   Litho.
249 A73 1t Chicken hawk, hen   .40 .40
250 A73 5t Beneficiaries   1.90 1.90

Abbasudin Ahmad, Bengali Singer — A74

1984, Dec. 24
251 A74 3t multicolored   1.00 1.00

No. 116 Ovptd. for KHULNAPEX '84 Stamp Exhibition
খুলনাপেক্স—৮৪

1984, Dec. 29   Litho.   Perf. 15
252 A25 2.25t multicolored   1.10 1.10

1984 Summer Olympics, Los Angeles — A75

1984, Dec. 31   Perf. 14
253 A75 1t Bicycling   .85 .15
254 A75 5t Field hockey   2.00 2.00
255 A75 10t Volleyball   2.75 2.75
Nos. 253-255 (3)   5.60 4.90

Islamic Development Bank, 9th Annual Congress, Dacca — A76

1985, Feb. 2
256 A76 1t Farmer   .40 .40
257 A76 5t Four Asian races   1.90 1.90

UN Child Survival Campaign — A77   UN Decade for Women — A78

1985, Mar. 14
258 A77 1t Breastfeeding   .30 .30
259 A77 10t Growth monitoring   2.75 2.75

Nos. 139-144 Ovptd. in Bengali for Local Elections
উপজেলা নির্বাচন ১৯৮৫

1985, May 16   Litho.   Perf. 13
259A A33 40p multicolored   .15 .15
259B A33 1t multicolored   .15 .15
259C A33 2.25t multicolored   .25 .25
259D A33 3.50t multicolored   .40 .40
259E A33 4t multicolored   .45 .45
259F A33 5t multicolored   .55 .55
Nos. 259A-259F (6)   1.95 1.95

1985, July 18   Perf. 14
260 A78 1t shown   .15 .15
261 A78 10t Technology   1.65 1.65

UN, 40th Anniv. A79

1985, Sept. 15
262 A79 1t UN building   .15 .15
263 A79 10t World map, natl. flag   1.25 1.25
11th anniv. of UN admission.

Intl. Youth Year — A80

1985, Nov. 2   Litho.   Perf. 14
264 A80 1t Scissors, pencil   .15 .15
265 A80 5t Hammer, wrenches   .70 .70

Seven Doves, Council Emblem — A81

1985, Dec. 8   Litho.   Perf. 14
266 A81 1t shown   .15 .15
267 A81 5t Flags, lotus blossom   .80 .80
1st South Asian Regional Council Summit, SARC, Dacca.

Shilpacharya Zainul Abedin (1914-1976), Founder, Dacca College of Art — A82

1985, Dec. 28
268 A82 3t multicolored   .85 .85

No. 138 Overprinted Reading Up

1985, Dec. 29   Perf. 13
269 A32 5t multicolored   2.75 2.75
3rd Natl. Scout Jamboree.
The overprint comes in two types.

Postal Services Type of 1983-84
1986, Jan. 11   Litho.   Perf. 12x11¹⁄₂
Size: 30¹⁄₂x19mm
270 A70 3t Sorting machine   .30 .30
Perf. 12x12¹⁄₂
Size: 33¹⁄₂x22¹⁄₂mm
271 A70 4t Chittagong Port   .55 .55
Issue dates: 3t, Jan. 11, 1986. 4t, Apr. 22, 1993.
For overprint see No. O46.
This is an expanding set. Numbers will change if necessary.

Fishing Net, by Safiuddin Ahmed A83

Paintings by Bengali artists: 5t, Happy Return, by Quamrul Hassan. 10t, Levelling the Plowed Field, by Zainul Abedin.

1986, Apr. 6   Litho.   Perf. 14
275 A83 1t multicolored   .15 .15
276 A83 5t multicolored   .55 .55
277 A83 10t multicolored   1.10 1.10
Nos. 275-277 (3)   1.80 1.80

1986 World Cup Soccer Championships, Mexico — A84

1986, June 29   Perf. 15x14
278 A84 1t Stealing the ball   .30 .30
279 A84 10t Goal   3.00 3.00
Souvenir Sheet
Imperf
279A A84 20t multicolored   5.50 5.50
No. 279A contains one stamp 62x45mm with simulated perfs.

Gen. M.A.G. Osmani (1918-1984), Liberation Forces Commander-in-Chief — A85

1986, Sept. 10   Litho.   Perf. 14
280 A85 3t multicolored   1.50 1.50

No. 207 Ovptd. SAARC SEMINAR '86
1986, Dec. 3   Litho.   Perf. 13¹⁄₂x14
281 A58 50p on #207   1.75 1.75

Intl. Peace Year
A86   A87

1986, Dec. 25 Litho.   Perf. 12x12¹/₂
282 A86 1t shown   .30 .15
283 A86 10t City ruins, flower   3.00 3.00

Souvenir Sheet
284 A87 20t shown   2.50 2.50

Nos. 179-180 Ovptd. or Surcharged
"CONFERENCE FOR DEVELOPMENT
'87"

1987, Jan. 12   Perf. 14
285 A42 1t on 40p multicolored   .15 .15
286 A42 5t multicolored   .65 .65

Language Movement, 35th Anniv. — A88

Illustration reduced.

1987, Feb. 21   Perf. 12¹/₂x12
287 A88 3t Protestors   1.00 1.00
288 A88 3t Memorial   1.00 1.00
  a.   Pair, Nos. 287-288   2.00 2.00

World Health   Bengali New
Day — A89   Year — A90

1987, Apr. 7   Perf. 11¹/₂x12
289 A89 1t Child immunization   2.50 2.50

See No. 318.

1987, Apr. 16   Perf. 12x12¹/₂
290 A90 1t Bengali script, embroi-
            dery   .15 .15
291 A90 10t shown   .75 .75

Jute Carpet
A91

Exports: 1t, Jute shika (wall hanging, bowl-
holder and mats), vert. 10t, Table lamp and shade,
vert.

Perf. 12x12¹/₂, 12¹/₂x12
1987, May 18   Litho.
292 A91 1t multicolored   .15 .15
293 A91 5t shown   .35 .35
294 A91 10t multicolored   .75 .75
  Nos. 292-294 (3)   1.25 1.25

Ustad Ayet Ali
Khan (1884-
1967),
Composer, and
Surbahar — A92

1987, Sept. 8   Perf. 12x12¹/₂
295 A92 5t multicolored   .80 .80

Palanquin
A93

Transportation.

1987, Oct. 24 Litho.   Perf. 12¹/₂x12
296 A93 2t shown   .20 .20
297 A93 3t Bicycle rickshaw   .30 .30
298 A93 5t Paddle steamer   .55 .55
299 A93 7t Train   .75 .75
300 A93 10t Ox cart   1.10 1.10
  Nos. 296-300 (5)   2.90 2.90

For overprint see No. 424.

Hossain Shahid
Suhrawardy (1893-
1963),
Politician — A94

1987, Dec. 5 Litho.   Perf. 12x12¹/₂
301 A94 3t multicolored   .40 .40

Intl. Year of
Shelter for
the
Homeless
A95

1987, Dec. 15   Perf. 12¹/₂x12
302 A95 5t shown   .50 .50
303 A95 5t Prosperous community   .50 .50

Nos. 302-303 are printed se-tenant in a continuous design.

Natl. Democracy, 1st Anniv. — A96

Design: Pres. Hossain Mohammed Ershad
addressing parliament.

1987, Dec. 31
304 A96 10t multicolored   1.90 1.90

Woman
Tending
Crop — A97

1988, Jan. 26
305 A97 3t shown   .35 .35
306 A97 5t Milking cow, village   .50 .50
  Intl. Fund for Agricultural Development (IFAD)
Seminar on Loans for Women in Rural Areas.

1988 Summer Olympics, Seoul — A98

1988 Summer Games emblem and Sports: a, Basketball. b, Weight lifting. c, Women's tennis. d,
Shooting. e, Boxing.

1988, Sept. 29 Litho.   Perf. 11¹/₂
307   Strip of 5   3.00 3.00
  a.-e. A98 5t any single   .60 .60

Historical
Sites — A99

Designs: 1t, Shait Gumbaz Mosque (interior),
Bagerhat. 4t, Paharpur Monastery. 5t, Kantanagar
Temple, Dinajpur. 10t, Lalbag Fort, Dacca.

1988, Oct. 9   Perf. 12¹/₂x12
308 A99 1t multicolored   .15 .15
309 A99 4t multicolored   .15 .15
310 A99 5t multicolored   .25 .25
311 A99 10t multicolored   .50 .50
  Nos. 308-311 (4)   1.05 1.05

Qudrat-i-Khuda   Asia Cup
(1900-1977),   Cricket — A101
Scientist — A100

1988, Nov. 3   Perf. 12x12¹/₂
312 A100 5t multicolored   .55 .55

1988, Nov. 27
313   Strip of 3   3.25 3.25
  a.   A101 1t Wicketkeeper   .15 .15
  b.   A101 5t Batsman   .95 .95
  c.   A101 10t Bowler   2.00 2.00

Intl. Red Cross and
Red Crescent
Organizations, 125th
Annivs. — A102

1988, Oct. 26 Litho.   Perf. 12x12¹/₂
314 A102 5t Emblems, Dunant   .50 .50
315 A102 10t Blood donation   1.00 1.00

Dacca G.P.O., 25th Anniv. — A103

1988, Dec. 6   Perf. 12
316 A103 1t Exterior   .15 .15
317 A103 5t Sales counter   .65 .65

World Health Day Type of 1987

1988, Jan. 16 Litho.   Perf. 11¹/₂x12
318 A89 25p Oral rehydration   .70 .70

32nd Meeting of the
Colombo Plan
Consultative
Committee,
Dacca — A104

1988, Nov. 29   Perf. 12x12¹/₂
319 A104 3t multicolored   .25 .25
320 A104 10t multicolored   .75 .75

No. 191   ৫ম জাতীয় রোভার মুট
Ovptd.   ১৯৮৮-৮৯

1989, Dec. 29 Litho.   Perf. 14
321 A50 5t multicolored   1.10 1.10

5th Natl. Rover Moot (Scouting).

No. 277   চতুর্থ দ্বিবার্ষিক এশীয়
Ovptd.   চারুকলা প্রদর্শনী
           বাংলাদেশ ১৯৮৯

1989, Mar. 1
322 A83 10t multicolored   1.10 1.10

4th Asiatic Exposition.

A106   A107

1989, Mar. 13 Litho.   Perf. 12x12¹/₂
324 A106 10t multicolored   .85 .85

Police academy, Sardah, 75th anniv.

1989, Mar. 7 Litho.   Perf. 12x12¹/₂
Modernizing water supply services.
325 A107 10t multicolored   .85 .85

12th Natl. Science & Technology Week.

A108

French Revolution, Bicent. — A109

Scenes from the revolution: 5t, Close-up of revolutionaries destroying the Bastille, vert. No. 326b, Liberty guiding the people. No. 326c, Women's march on Versailles, vert. No. 327a, Celebration of the Federation on the Champ de Mars. No. 327b, Storming of the Bastille. 25t, Montage of scenes, #326a-326c.

1989, July 12   *Perf. 14*
326   Sheet of 3 + label   2.25 2.25
  a.   A108 5t multicolored   .45 .45
  b.-c.   A108 10t any single   .90 .90
     Perf. 14x15
327   Strip of 2 + label   2.25 2.25
  a.-b.   A109 17t any single   1.10 1.10
     Size: 152x88mm
     Imperf
328   A108 25t multicolored   2.25 2.25
   Nos. 326-328 (3)   6.75 6.75

Labels picture the revolution anniv. emblem.

Rural Development in Asia and the Pacific (CIRDAP), 10th Anniv. — A110

1989, Aug. 10   Litho.   *Perf. 12½x12*
329 A110   5t shown   .45 .45
330 A110   10t multi, diff.   .85 .85
  a.   Pair, Nos. 329-330   1.50 1.50

No. 330a has a continuous design.

Child Survival A111

1989, Aug. 22
331 A111   1t shown   .15 .15
332 A111   10t Women and children, diff.   .90 .90

SOS Children's Village, 40th anniv.

Involvement of the Bangladesh Army in UN Peace-keeping Operations, 1st Anniv. — A112

1989, Sept. 12   *Perf. 12x12½*
333 A112   4t shown   .65 .65
334 A112   10t Camp, two soldiers   1.65 1.65

2nd Asian Poetry Festival, Dacca — A113

1989, Nov. 17   Litho.   *Perf. 12x12½*
335 A113   2t multicolored   .20 .20
336 A113   10t multicolored   .90 .90

State Printing Office A114

1989, Dec. 7   *Perf. 13½*
337 A114 10t multicolored   1.25 1.25

Bangladesh Television, 25th Anniv. A115

1989, Dec. 25   Litho.   *Perf. 12½x12*
338 A115   5t shown   .45 .45
339 A115   10t Emblem, flowers, diff.   .95 .95

World Wildlife Fund A116

Various gavials, (Gavialis gangeticus).

1990, Jan. 31   Litho.   *Perf. 14*
340 A116   50p shown   .15 .15
341 A116   2t Reptile's jaws   .55 .55
342 A116   4t 4 reptiles   1.00 1.00
343 A116   10t 2 reptiles resting   2.75 2.75
  a.   Block of 4, #340-343   4.50 4.50

A117   A118

1990, Feb. 2   *Perf. 14*
344 A117 6t multicolored   .85 .85
    Natl. Population Day.

1990, May 6   *Perf. 14*
345 A118   7t shown   1.65 1.65
346 A118   10t Penny Black, No. 230   2.50 2.50
    Penny Black, 150th anniv.

Justice Syed Mahbub Murshed, (1911-1979) — A119

1990, Apr. 3   Litho.   *Perf. 12½x12*
347 A119 5t multicolored   1.10 1.10

Intl. Literacy Year — A120

Design: 10t, Boy teaching girl to write.

1990, Apr. 10   *Perf. 12x12½*
348 A120   6t multicolored   1.40 1.40
349 A120   10t multicolored   2.00 2.00

Loading Cargo Plane — A121   Curzon Hall — A122

Fertilizer Plant — A123   Postal Academy, Rajshahi — A124

Salimullah Hall — A125

Bangla Academy — A126

1989-93   *Perf. 12x11½, 12, 12x12½*
350 A121   3t multicolored   .15 .15
351 A122   5t gray blk & red brn   .25 .25
352 A123   10t carmine   .50 .50
353 A124   20t multicolored   1.10 1.10
    Perf. 14½x14
354 A125   6t blue gray & yel   .55 .55
    Perf. 14x14½
355 A126   2t brown & green   .15 .15
   Nos. 350-355 (6)   2.70 2.70

Issue dates: 5t, Mar. 31. 3t, Apr. 30. 10t, 20t, July 8. 6t, Jan. 30, 1991. 2t, Dec. 3, 1993.
For overprint see No. O47B.
This is an expanding set. Numbers will change.

World Cup Soccer Championships, Italy — A133

1990, June 12   Litho.   *Perf. 14*
362 A133   8t shown   1.65 1.65
363 A133   10t Soccer player, diff.   2.25 2.25
    Size: 115x79mm
    Imperf
364 A133   25t Colosseum, soccer ball   5.50 5.50
   Nos. 362-364 (3)   9.40 9.40

Fruits — A134

1990, July 16   *Perf. 12x12½*
365 A134   1t Mangifera indica   .15 .15
366 A134   2t Psidium guayava   .35 .35
367 A134   3t Citrullus vulgaris   .50 .50
368 A134   4t Carica papaya   .70 .70
369 A134   5t Artocarpus heterophyllus   .90 .90
370 A134   10t Averrhoa carambola   1.75 1.75
   Nos. 365-370 (6)   4.35 4.35

UN Conference on Least Developed Nations, Paris A135

1990, Sept. 3   Litho.   *Perf. 14*
371 A135 10t multicolored   1.90 1.90

Asia-Pacific Postal Training Center, 20th Anniv. — A136

Design: 6t, Map of Western Pacific, letters.

1990, Sept. 10   *Perf. 13½x14*
372 A136   2t shown   .45 .45
373 A136   6t multicolored   1.25 1.25
  a.   Pair, #372-373   1.75 1.75

No. 373a has continuous design.

11th Asian Games, Beijing A137

1990, Sept. 22   *Perf. 14*
374 A137   2t Rowing   .40 .40
375 A137   4t Kabaddi   .80 .80
376 A137   8t Wrestling   1.65 1.65
377 A137   10t Badminton   2.00 2.00
   Nos. 374-377 (4)   4.85 4.85

Lalan Shah, Poet — A138

1990, Oct. 17   Litho.   *Perf. 14*
378 A138 6t multicolored   1.40 1.40

UN Development Program, 40th Anniv. — A139

1990, Oct. 24   Litho.   *Perf. 14*
379 A139 6t multicolored   1.25 1.25

Immunization Program — A139a

1990, Nov. 29   Litho.   *Perf. 14½x14*
379A A139a 2t brown   .40 .40

Butterflies — A140

1990, Dec. 24   Litho.   Perf. 13½x12
380 A140 6t Danaus chrysippus   1.50 1.50
381 A140 6t Precis almana   1.50 1.50
382 A140 10t Ixias pyrene   2.50 2.50
383 A140 10t Danaus plexippus   2.50 2.50
  a.   Block of 4, #380-383   8.00 8.00

UN Decade
Against
Drugs
A141

1991, Jan 1   Litho.   Perf. 14x13½
384 A141 2t Drugs, map   .75   .75
385 A141 4t shown   1.50 1.50

Third National
Census — A142

1991, Mar. 12   Litho.   Perf. 14
386 A142 4t multicolored   .80   .80

Independence,
20th Anniv.
A143

Designs: a, Invincible Bangla statue. b, Freedom
Fighter statue. c, Mujibnagar Memorial. d, Eternal
flame. e, National Martyrs' Memorial.

1991, Mar. 26   Perf. 13½
387 A143 4t Strip of 5, #a.-e.   2.75 2.75
  No. 387 printed in continuous design.

Pres. Ziaur Rahman, 10th Death Anniv.
A144   A145

1991, May 30   Perf. 14
388 A144 50p multicolored   .20   .20
389 A145 2t multicolored   .90   .90
  a.   Souvenir sheet of 2, #388-389 1.75 1.75
  No. 389a sold for 10t.

Endangered Animals — A146

1991, June 16   Perf. 12
390 A146 2t Petaurista petaurista   .30   .30
391 A146 4t Presbytis entellus, vert. .60   .60
392 A146 6t Buceros bicornis, vert.   .90   .90
  a.   Pair, #391-392   1.50 1.50
393 A146 10t Manis crassicaudata   1.50 1.50
  a.   Pair, #390, 393   1.90 1.90
         Nos. 390-393 (4)   3.30 3.30

Kaikobad (1857-
1951),
Poet — A147

1991, July 21   Litho.   Perf. 14
394 A147 6t multicolored   .85   .85

Rabindranath Tagore, Poet, 50th Anniv. of
Death — A148

1991, Aug. 7
395 A148 4t multicolored   .85   .85

Blood and Eye
Donations — A149

1991, Sept. 19
396 A149 3t shown   .60   .60
397 A149 5t Blind man and eye   .95   .95
  Sandhani, Medical Students Association, 14th
anniversary.

Shahid Naziruddin,
Leader of
Democratic
Movement, 1st
Anniv. of
Death — A150

1991, Oct. 10
398 A150 2t multicolored   .80   .80

Shaheed Noor
Hossain, 4th Death
Anniv. — A151

1991, Nov. 10   Litho.   Perf. 14
399 A151 2t multicolored   .80   .80

Archaeological Treasures of
Mainamati — A152

Designs: a, Bronze Stupa with images of Buddha.
b, Bowl and pitcher. c, Ruins of Salban Vihara
Monastery. d, Gold coins. e, Terra-cotta plaque.

1991, Nov. 26   Litho.   Perf. 13½
400 A152 4t Strip of 5, #a.-e.   3.50 3.50

Mass
Uprising,
First
Anniv.
A153

1991, Dec. 6   Perf. 14
401 A153 4t multicolored   .80   .80

Miniature Sheets

Independence,
20th
Anniv. — A154

Martyred intellectuals who died in 1971: No.
402a, A.N.M. Munier Chowdhury. b, Ghyasuddin
Ahmad. c, S.M.A. Rashidul Hasan. d, Muhammad
Anwar Pasha. e, Dr. Md. Mortaza. f, Shahid Saber.
g, Fazlur Rahman Khan. h, Ranada Prasad Saha. i,
Adhyaksha Joges Chandra Ghose. j, Santosh Chan-
dra Bhattacharyya.
  No. 403a, Dr. Gobinda Chandra Deb. b, A.N.M.
Muniruzzaman. c, Mufazzal Haider Chaudhury. d,
Dr. Abdul Alim Choudhury. e, Sirajuddin Hossain.
f, Shahidulla Kaiser. g, Altaf Mahmud. h, Dr. Jyo-
tirmay Guha Thakurta. i, Dr. Md. Abul Khair. j, Dr.
Serajul Haque Khan.
  No. 404a, Dr. Mohammad Fazle Rabbi. b, Mir
Abdul Quyyum. c, A.N.M. Golam Mostafa. d,
Dhirendranath Dutta. e, S.A. Mannan (Ladu Bhai).
f, Nizamuddin Ahmad. g, Abul Bashar Chowdhury.
h, Selina Parveen. i, Dr. Abul Kalam Azad. j, Saidul
Hassan.
  No. 404 l, LCDR. Moazzam Hussain. m,
Muhammad Habibur Rahman. n, Khandoker Abu
Taleb. o, Moshiur Rahman. p, Md. Abdul Muktadir.
q, Nutan Chandra Sinha. r, Syed Nazmul Haque. s,
Dr. Mohammed Amin Uddin. t, Dr. N.A.M. Faizul
Mohee. u, Sukha Ranjan Somaddar.

1991-93   Litho.   Perf. 13½
                Sheets of 10
402 A154 2t #a.-j. + 5 labels   1.90 1.90
403 A154 2t #a.-j. + 5 labels   1.90 1.90
404 A154 2t #a.-j. + 5 labels   1.90 1.90
                Perf. 14½
404K A154 2t #l.-u. + 5 labels   3.00 3.00
Issued: #402-404, 12/14/91; #404K, 12/14/93.
See Nos. 470-471, 499-500, 534-535.

Shrimp
A155

1991, Dec. 31   Perf. 14
405 A155 6t Penaeus monodon   1.25 1.25
406 A155 6t Metapenaeus monoceros   1.25 1.25
  a.   Pair, #405-406   2.50 2.50

Shaheed
Mirze Abu
Raihan
Jaglu, 5th
Death
Anniv.
A156

1992, Feb. 8   Litho.   Perf. 14x13½
407 A156 2t multicolored   .95   .95

World Environment Day — A157

Design: 4t, Scenes of environmental protection
and pollution control, vert.

1992, June 5   Litho.   Perf. 14
408 A157 4t multicolored   .45   .45
409 A157 10t multicolored   1.10 1.10

Nawab
Sirajuddaulah of
Bengal (1733-1757)
A158

1992, July 2   Litho.   Perf. 14
410 A158 10t multicolored   1.00 1.00

Syed Ismail
Hossain Sirajee
(1880-1931),
Social Reformer
A159

1992, July 17
411 A159 4t multicolored   .80   .80

Tree Week — A160

1992, July 17   Litho.   Perf. 14
412 A160 2t Couple planting tree,
             horiz.   .50   .50
413 A160 4t Birds, trees   1.00 1.00

1992
Summer
Olympics,
Barcelona
A161

Olympic rings and: a, 4t, Rowing. b, 6t, Hands
holding Olympic torch. c, 10t, Peace doves. d, 10t,
Clasped hands.

1992, July 25   Litho.   Perf. 14
414 A161 Block of 4, #a.-d.   2.75 2.75

The Star Mosque, 18th Cent. A162

1992, Oct. 29   Litho.   Perf. 14¹/₂x14
415 A162 10t multicolored   1.10 1.10

Masnad-E-Ala Isa Khan, 393rd Anniv. of Death — A163

1992, Sept. 15   Perf. 14x14¹/₂
416 A163 4t multicolored   .80 .80

7th SAARC Summit, Dacca — A164

1992, Dec. 5
417 A164 6t Flags of members   .50 .50
418 A164 10t Emblem   .85 .85

1992 Bangladesh Natl. Philatelic Exhibition — A165

Designs: No. 419a, Elephant and mahout, ivory work, 19th cent. b, Post rider, mail box and postman delivering mail to villager.

1992, Sept. 26   Perf. 14¹/₂x14
419 A165 10t Pair, #a.-b. + label 2.25 2.25
  c.   Souv. sheet, imperf.   2.50 2.50
No. 419c contains one strip of No. 419 with simulated perforations and sold for 25t.

1992 Intl. Conference on Nutrition, Rome — A166

1992, Dec. 5
420 A166 4t multicolored   .55 .55

Meer Nisar Ali Titumeer (1782-1831) — A167

1992, Nov. 19   Litho.   Perf. 14¹/₂x14
421 A167 10t multicolored   1.00 1.00

Archaeological Relics, Mahasthan — A168

Relics from 3rd century B.C.-15th century A.D.: No. 422a, Terracotta seal and head. b, Terracotta hamsa. c, Terracotta Surya image. d, Gupta stone columns.

1992, Nov. 30   Litho.   Perf. 14¹/₂x14
422 A168 10t Strip of 4, #a.-d.   4.00 4.00

Canal Digging A169

a, Workers digging canal. b, Completed project.

1993, Mar. 31   Litho.   Perf. 14¹/₂x14
423 A169 2t Pair, #a.-b.   1.40 1.40

No. 300 Ovptd.   বাংলাপেক্স '৯২
                  Banglapex '92

1992, Aug. 18   Litho.   Perf. 12¹/₂x12
424 A93 10t multicolored   1.10 1.10

Syed Abdus Samad (1895-1964), Soccer Player — A170

1993, Feb. 2   Perf. 14x14¹/₂
425 A170 2t multicolored   .80 .80

A171

1993, Apr. 14
426 A171 2t multicolored   .70 .70
Completion of 14th cent. Bengali era.

Haji Shariat Ullah (1770-1839), Social Reformer, Religious and Political Leader — A172

1993, Mar. 10   Litho.   Perf. 14x14¹/₂
427 A172 2t multicolored   .70 .70

World Health Day A173

1993, Apr. 7   Perf. 14¹/₂x14, 14x14¹/₂
428 A173 6t Prevent accidents   .60 .60
429 A173 10t Prevent violence, vert. 1.00 1.00

Compulsory Primary Education — A174

1993, May 26
430 A174 2t Slate, chalk, books .20 .20
431 A174 2t Hand writing, children, vert. .20 .20

Nawab Sir Salimullah (1871-1915), Social Reformer — A175

1993, June 7   Litho.   Perf. 14¹/₂x14
432 A175 4t multicolored   .55 .55

Fishing Industry A176

1993, Aug. 15   Litho.   Perf. 14¹/₂x14
433 A176 2t multicolored   .55 .55

Tomb of Sultan Ghiyasuddin Azam Shah — A177

1993, Dec. 30   Litho.   Perf. 14¹/₂x14
434 A177 10t multicolored   1.10 1.10

Scenic Views A178

Designs: No. 435, Sunderban. No. 436, Madhabkunda Waterfall, vert. No. 437, River, mountains, vert. No. 438, Beach, Kuakata.

Perf. 14¹/₂x14, 14x14¹/₂
1993, Oct. 30
435 A178 10t multicolored   1.10 1.10
436 A178 10t multicolored   1.10 1.10
437 A178 10t multicolored   1.10 1.10
438 A178 10t multicolored   1.10 1.10
  a.   Souv. sheet of 4, #435-438, imperf.   4.50 4.50
       Nos. 435-438 (4)   4.40 4.40
#438a sold for 50t and has simulated perfs.

6th Asian Art Biennial, Bangladesh A179

1993, Nov. 7   Litho.   Perf. 14x14¹/₂
439 A179 10t multicolored   .85 .85

Foy's Lake A180

1993, Nov. 6   Perf. 14¹/₂x14
440 A180 10t multicolored   1.10 1.10
Tourism month.

14th Asian Pacific, 5th Bangladesh Natl. Scout Jamboree A181

1994, Jan. 5   Perf. 14x14¹/₂
441 A181 2t multicolored   .55 .55

Oral Rehydration Solution, 25th Anniv. — A182

1994, Feb. 5   Litho.   Perf. 13¹/₂x14
442 A182 2t multicolored   .55 .55

6th SAF Games, Dhaka A183

1993, Dec. 6 Perf. 14x13¹/₂, 13¹/₂x14
443 A183 2t Shot put .30 .30
444 A183 4t Runners, vert. .65 .65

Mosques A184

Mosques: 4t, Interior, Chhota Sona, Nawabgonj. No. 446, Exterior, Chhota Sona. No. 447, Exterior, Baba Adam's, Munshigonj.

1994, Mar. 30 Litho. Perf. 14x13¹/₂
445 A184 4t multicolored .25 .25
446 A184 6t multicolored .40 .40
447 A184 6t multicolored .40 .40
Nos. 445-447 (3) 1.05 1.05

For overprint see No. 509.

ILO, 75th Anniv. A185

Designs: 4t, People, oxen working in fields. 10t, Man rotating gearwheel, vert.

Perf. 14x13¹/₂, 13¹/₂x14
1994, Apr. 11 Litho.
448 A185 4t multicolored .30 .30
449 A185 10t multicolored .80 .80

Bangla Era, 15th Cent. — A186

1994, Apr. 14 Perf. 13¹/₂x14
450 A186 2t multicolored .55 .55

Traditional Festivals A187

1994, May 12 Perf. 14x13¹/₂
451 A187 4t Folk Festival .40 .40
452 A187 4t Baishakhi Festival .40 .40

Intl. Year of the Family — A188

1994, May 15 Perf. 13¹/₂x14
453 A188 10t multicolored 1.50 1.50

Tree Planting Campaign A189

1994, June 15 Litho. Perf. 13¹/₂x14
454 A189 4t Family planting trees .55 .55
455 A189 6t Hands, seedlings .80 .80

1994 World Cup Soccer Championships, US — A190

Soccer player's uniform colors: a, Red, yellow & blue. b, Yellow, green, & red.

1994, June 17 Litho. Perf. 14¹/₂
456 A190 20t Pair, #a.-b. + label 3.25 3.25
Complete booklet, #456 11.50

Jamuna Multi-Purpose Bridge — A191

1994, July 24 Perf. 14¹/₂x14
457 A191 4t multicolored .40 .40

Birds — A192

Designs: 4t, Oriolus xanthornus. No. 459, Gallus gallus. No. 460, Dicrurus paradiseus. No. 461, Dendrocitta vagabunda.

1994, Aug. 31 Perf. 14x14¹/₂
458 A192 4t multicolored .50 .50
459 A192 6t multicolored .75 .75
460 A192 6t multicolored .75 .75
461 A192 6t multicolored .75 .75
a. Souvenir sheet, #458-461 2.75 2.75
Nos. 458-461 (4) 2.75 2.75

No. 461a sold for 25t.

Dr. Mohammad Ibrahim (1911-89), Pioneer in Treatment of Diabetes A193

1994, Sept. 6 Litho. Perf. 14¹/₂x14
462 A193 2t multicolored .40 .40

Nawab Faizunnessa Chowdhurani (1834-1903), Social Reformer A194

1994, Sept. 23 Perf. 14x14¹/₂
463 A194 2t multicolored .40 .40

12th Asian Games, Hiroshima, Japan — A195

1994, Oct. 2 Perf. 14¹/₂x14
464 A195 4t multicolored .55 .55

Shells A196

Designs: No. 465, White, pink pearls, oysters. No. 466, Snail, three other shells. No. 467, Scallop, other shells. No. 468, Spiral shaped shells, vert.

Perf. 14¹/₂x14, 14x14¹/₂
1994, Oct. 30 Litho.
465 A196 6t multicolored .60 .60
466 A196 6t multicolored .60 .60
467 A196 6t multicolored .60 .60
468 A196 6t multicolored .60 .60
Nos. 465-468 (4) 2.40 2.40

Democracy Demonstration, Death of Dr. Shamsul Alam Khan Milon, 4th Anniv. — A197

1994, Nov. 27 Perf. 14¹/₂x14
469 A197 2t multicolored .40 .40

Martyred Intellectual Type of 1991 Miniature Sheets of 8

Martyred intellectuals who died in 1971: No. 470a, Dr. Harinath Dey. b, Dr. Lt. Col. A.F. Ziaur Rahman. c, Mamum Mahmud. d, Mohsin Ali Dewan. e, Dr. Lt. Col. N.A.M. Jahangir. f, Shah Abdul Majid. g, Muhammad Akhter. h, Meherunnesa.
No. 471a, Dr. Kasiruddin Talukder. b, Fazlul Haque Choudhury. c, Md. Shamsuzzaman. d, A.K.M. Shamsuddin. e, Lt. Mohammad Anwarul Azim. f, Nurul Amin Khan. g, Mohammad Sadeque. h, Md. Araz Ali.

1994, Dec. 14 Perf. 14¹/₂
470 A154 2t #a.-h. + 4 labels 1.25 1.25
471 A154 2t #a.-h. + 4 lables 1.25 1.25

Vegetables A199

Perf. 14x14¹/₂, 14¹/₂x14
1994, Dec. 24
472 A199 4t Diplazium esculentum .20 .20
473 A199 4t Momordica charantia .20 .20
474 A199 6t Lagenaria siceraria .40 .40
475 A199 6t Trichosanthes dioica .40 .40
476 A199 10t Solanum melongena .75 .75
477 A199 10t Cucurbita maxima .75 .75
Nos. 472-477 (6) 2.70 2.70

Nos. 472-476 are vert.

World Tourism Organization, 20th Anniv. — A200

1995, Jan. 2 Perf. 14¹/₂x14
478 A200 10t multicolored .95 .95

Intl. Trade Fair, Dhaka — A201

Designs: 4t, Trade products. 6t, Factories, emblems of industry.

1995, Jan. 7 Litho. Perf. 14x14¹/₂
479 A201 4t multicolored .30 .30
480 A201 6t multicolored .60 .60

Bangladesh Rifles, Bicent. — A202

1995, Jan. 10 Litho. Perf. 14¹/₂x14
481 A202 2t shown .30 .30
482 A202 4t Building, battalion .60 .60

Fight Against Cancer — A203

1995, Apr. 7 Litho. Perf. 14x14¹/₂
483 A203 2t multicolored .80 .80

Natl. Diabetes
Awareness
Day — A204

1995, Feb. 28   **Perf. 14**
484 A204 2t multicolored   .80 .80

For overprint see No. O49.

Munshi
Mohammad
Meherullah
(1861-1907),
Educator — A205

1995, June 7   **Litho.**   **Perf. 14x14¹/₂**
485 A205 2t multicolored   .45 .45

FAO, 50th
Anniv. — A206

1995, Oct. 16   **Litho.**   **Perf. 14**
486 A206 10t multicolored   1.10 1.10

UN, 50th
Anniv.
A207

UN emblem, "50," and: 2t, Dove of peace, UN
headquarters. No. 488, "1945," earth from space,
"1995." No. 489, Hands of different nationalities
clasping, UN headquarters.

1995, Oct. 24   **Perf. 14¹/₂x14**
487 A207 2t multicolored   .20 .20
488 A207 10t multicolored   1.00 1.00
489 A207 10t multicolored   1.00 1.00
    Nos. 487-489 (3)   2.20 2.20

Flowers — A208

Designs: No. 490, Bombax ceiba. No. 491,
Lagerstroemia speciosa. No. 492, Gloriosa superba.
No. 493, Canna indica. No. 494, Bauhinia
purpurea. No. 495, Passiflora incarnata.

1995, Oct. 9   **Perf. 14¹/₂x14, 14x14¹/₂**
490 A208 6t multicolored   .65 .65
491 A208 6t multi, vert.   .65 .65
492 A208 10t multi, vert.   1.00 1.00
493 A208 10t multi, vert.   1.00 1.00
494 A208 10t multi, vert.   1.00 1.00
495 A208 10t multi, vert.   1.00 1.00
    Nos. 490-495 (6)   5.30 5.30

18th Eastern Regional Conference on
Tuberculosis and Respiratory Diseases,
Dhaka — A209

1995, Oct. 29   **Litho.**   **Perf. 14¹/₂x14**
497 A209 6t multicolored   1.25 1.25

South Asian
Assoc. for
Regional
Cooperation
(SAARC), 10th
Anniv. — A210

1995, Dec. 8   **Litho.**   **Perf. 14x14¹/₂**
498 A210 2t multicolored   .55 .55

Martyred Intellectual Type of 1991
Sheets of 8

Martyred intellectuals who died in 1971: No.
499a, Shaikh Habibur Rahman. b, Dr. Major
Naimul Islam. c, Md. Shahidullah. d, Ataur Rahman
Khan Khadim. e, A.B.M. Ashraful Islam Bhuiyan. f,
Dr. Md. Sadat Ali. g, Sarafat Ali. h, M.A. Sayeed.
No. 500: a, Abdul Ahad. b, Lt. Col. Mohammad
Abdul Qadir. c, Mozammel Hoque Chowdhury. d,
Rafiqul Haider Chowdhury. e, Dr. Azharul Haque.
f, A.K. Shamsuddin. g, Anudwaipayan Bhat-
tacharjee. h, Lutfunnahar Helena.

1995, Dec. 14   **Litho.**   **Perf. 14¹/₂x14**
499 A154 2t #a.-h. + 4 labels   1.80 1.80
500 A154 2t #a.-h. + 4 labels   1.80 1.80

Second Asian
Pacific
Community
Development
Scout
Camp — A211

1995, Dec. 18   **Litho.**   **Perf. 14x14¹/₂**
501 A211 2t multicolored   .55 .55

Volleyball,
Cent. — A212

1995, Dec. 25
502 A212 6t multicolored   1.00 1.00

Traditional Costumes — A213

Designs: No. 503, Man in punjabi and lungi,
vert. No. 504, Woman in sari, vert. No. 505, Christian bride and groom, vert. No. 506, Muslim bridal
couple, vert. No. 507, Hindu bridal couple. No.
508, Buddhist bridal couple.

Perf. 14x14¹/₂, 14¹/₂x14
1995, Dec. 25
503 A213 6t multicolored   .70 .70
504 A213 6t multicolored   .70 .70
505 A213 10t multicolored   1.15 1.15
506 A213 10t multicolored   1.15 1.15
507 A213 10t multicolored   1.15 1.15
508 A213 10t multicolored   1.15 1.15
    Nos. 503-508 (6)   6.00 6.00

No. 446 Ovptd. in Red

রাজশাহীপেক্স-৯৫

1995   **Litho.**   **Perf. 14x13¹/₂**
509 A184 6t multicolored   4.60 4.60

Shaheed
Amanullah
Mohammad
Asaduzzaman
(1942-69)
A214

1996, Jan. 20   **Perf. 14x14¹/₂**
510 A214 2t multicolored   .50 .50

1996 World Cup Cricket
Championships — A215

Perf. 14x14¹/₂, 14¹/₂x14
1996, Feb. 14
511 A215 4t Pitching, vert.   .60 .60
512 A215 6t At bat, vert.   .85 .85
513 A215 10t shown   1.40 1.40
    Nos. 511-513 (3)   2.85 2.85

Independence, 25th Anniv. — A216

Designs: No. 514, Natl. Martrys' Memorial. No.
515, Industrial development. No. 516, 1971
Destruction of war. No. 517, Educational development. No. 518, Development in communication.
No. 519, Development in health.

1996, Mar. 26   **Litho.**   **Perf. 14x14¹/₂**
514 A216 4t multicolored   .55 .55
515 A216 4t multicolored   .55 .55
516 A216 4t multicolored   .55 .55
517 A216 4t multicolored   .55 .55
518 A216 4t multicolored   .55 .55
519 A216 4t multicolored   .55 .55
    Nos. 514-519 (6)   3.30 3.30

Michael
Madhusudan Dutt
(1824-73),
Writer — A217

1996, June 29   **Litho.**   **Perf. 14x14¹/₂**
520 A217 4t multicolored   .60 .60

1996
Summer
Olympic
Games,
Atlanta
A218

1996, July 19   **Litho.**   **Perf. 14**
521 A218 4t Gymnast, vert.   .60 .60
522 A218 6t Judo, vert.   .90 .90
523 A218 10t High jumper   1.40 1.40
524 A218 10t Runners   1.40 1.40
   a.   Souvenir sheet, #521-524   7.00 7.00
    Nos. 521-524 (4)   4.30 4.30

No. 524a sold for 50t.

Sheikh Mujibur
Rahman (1920-
75), Prime
Minister — A219

Design: No. 527, Maulana Mohammad Akrum
Khan (1868-1968).

1996   **Litho.**   **Perf. 14x14¹/₂**
526 A219 4t multicolored   .60 .60
527 A219 4t multicolored   .60 .60

Issued: No. 526, 8/15/96, No. 527, 8/18/96.

Children's
Paintings
A221

Perf. 14x14¹/₂, 14¹/₂x14
1996, Oct. 9   **Litho.**
529 A221 2t Kingfisher, vert.   .45 .45
530 A221 4t River Crossing   .95 .95

Jailed, 21st Death
Anniv. — A222

a, Syed Nazrul Islam. b, Tajuddin Ahmad. c, M.
Monsoor Ali. d, A.H.M. Quamaruzzaman.

1996, Nov. 3   **Litho.**   **Perf. 14x14¹/₂**
531 A222 4t Block of 4, #a.-d.   2.00 2.00

UNICEF, 50th
Anniv. — A223

Designs: 4t, Children receiving food, medicine,
aid. 10t, Mother holding infant.

1996, Dec. 11
532 A223 4t multicolored   .65 .65
533 A223 10t multicolored   1.65 1.65

Martyred Intellectual Type of 1991

Martyred intellectuals who died in 1971: No.
534: a, Dr. Jekrul Haque. b, Munshi Kabiruddin
Ahmed. c, Md. Abdul Jabbar. d, Mohammad Amir.

e, A.K.M. Shamsul Huq Khan. f, Dr. Siddique Ahmed. g, Dr. Soleman Khan. h, S.B.M. Mizanur Rahman.
No. 535: a, Aminuddin. b, Md. Nazrul Islam. c, Zahirul Islam. d, A.K. Lutfor Rahman. e, Afsar Hossain. f, Abul Hashem Mian. g, A.T.M. Alamgir. h, Baser Ali.

1996, Dec. 14   Litho.   Perf. 14¹/₂x14
Sheets of 8
| 534 | A154 | 2t #a.-h. + 4 labels | 2.25 | 2.25 |
| 535 | A154 | 2t #a.-h. + 4 labels | 2.25 | 2.25 |

Victory Day, 25th Anniv. A224

Designs: 4t, People celebrating, natl. flag. 6t, Soldiers, monument, vert.

Perf. 14¹/₂x14, 14x14¹/₂
1996, Dec. 16
| 536 | A224 | 4t multicolored | .65 | .65 |
| 537 | A224 | 6t multicolored | 1.00 | 1.00 |

OFFICIAL STAMPS

Nos. 42-47, 49-50, 52, 82-84 and 54 Overprinted **SERVICE** in Black or Red

Perf. 14x14¹/₂, 14¹/₂x14
1973-75   **Litho.**
O1	A7	2p black (R)	.15	.15
O2	A7	3p brt green	.15	.15
O3	A7	5p lt brown	.15	.15
O4	A7	10p black (R)	.15	.15
O5	A7	20p olive	1.10	.15
O6	A7	25p red lilac	3.00	.15
O8	A7	60p gray (R)	3.00	.20
O9	A7	75p orange ('74)	1.10	.25
O10	A9	1t violet (#52)	12.00	3.25
O11	A9	1t violet (#82)	2.25	.35
O12	A9	2t grayish grn ('74)	3.75	1.25
O13	A9	5t gray blue (#54)	5.25	4.50
O14	A9	5t grysh bl (#84) ('75)	6.50	5.00
		Nos. O1-O14 (13)	38.55	15.70

Issue date: Apr. 30, 1973.

Nos. 95-101, 103-105 Overprinted "SERVICE" in Black or Red

1976   Litho.   Perf. 15x14¹/₂, 14¹/₂x15
O16	A7	5p green	.30	.30
O17	A7	10p black (R)	.30	.30
O18	A7	20p olive	.30	.30
O19	A7	25p rose	.30	.30
O20	A8	50p rose lilac	.40	.40
O21	A7	60p gray (R)	.50	.50
O22	A7	75p olive	.55	.55

Perf. 15
O23	A9	1t violet	.85	.85
O24	A9	2t greenish gray	1.65	1.65
O25	A9	5t grayish blue	4.25	4.25
		Nos. O16-O25 (10)	9.40	9.40

Nos. 165-169, 171-175 Ovptd. "SERVICE"
1979-82   Photo.   Perf. 14¹/₂
O27	A7	5p brown	.15	.15
O28	A7	10p Prussian blue	.15	.15
O29	A7	15p yellow orange	.15	.15
O30	A7	20p dk carmine	.20	.20
O31	A7	25p dk blue ('82)	.25	.25
O32	A9	40p rose magenta	.45	.45
O33	A9	50p gray ('81)	.55	.55
O34	A7	80p dark brown	.80	.80
O35	A7	1t red lilac ('81)	1.10	1.10
O36	A7	2t brt ultra ('81)	1.90	1.90
		Nos. O27-O36 (10)	5.70	5.70

Nos. 234-242, 271 Ovptd. "Service" in Red, Diagonally Up on No. O43A, 1t, 2t, 4t
Perf. 11¹/₂x12¹/₂, 12¹/₂x11¹/₂
1983, Dec. 21
O37	A70	5p bluish green	.15	.15
O38	A70	10p deep magenta	.15	.15
O39	A70	15p blue	.15	.15
O40	A70	20p dark gray	.15	.15
O41	A70	25p slate	.15	.15
O42	A70	30p gray brown	.15	.15
O43	A70	50p yellow brown	.15	.15
O43A	A70	50p yellow brown	.15	.15
Size: 30¹/₂x28¹/₂mm
Perf. 12x11¹/₂
| O44 | A70 | 1t ultramarine | .30 | .30 |
| O45 | A70 | 2t Prussian blue | .60 | .60 |

Perf. 12
| O46 | A70 | 4t blue | 1.40 | 1.40 |
| | | Set value | 3.00 | 3.00 |

Issue dates: 4t, 1990(?); No. O43A, 1993(?).

No. 354 Ovptd. in Red সার্ভিস
1992, Nov. 22   Litho.   Perf. 14¹/₂x14
| O47B | A125 | 6t blue gray & yel | 6.75 | 6.75 |

No. 241 Ovptd. in Red সার্ভিস
1992, Sept. 16   Litho.   Perf. 12x11¹/₂
| O48 | A70 | 1t ultramarine | .15 | .15 |

No. 484 Ovptd. in Red সার্ভিস
1996   Litho.   Perf. 14
| O49 | A204 | 2t multicolored | 2.75 | 2.75 |

BARBADOS
bär-'bā-(,)dōs

LOCATION — A West Indies island east of the Windwards
GOVT. — Independent state in the British Commonwealth
AREA — 166 sq. mi.
POP. — 270,500 (1981)
CAPITAL — Bridgetown

The British colony of Barbados became an independent state on November 30, 1966.

4 Farthings = 1 Penny
12 Pence = 1 Shilling
20 Shillings = 1 Pound
100 Cents = 1 Dollar (1950)

Catalogue values for unused stamps in this country are for Never Hinged items, beginning with Scott 207 in the regular postage section, Scott B2 in the semi-postal section and Scott J1 in the postage due section.

Values for unused stamps are for examples with original gum as defined in the catalogue introduction. Very fine examples of Nos. 10-42a, 44-59a will have perforations touching the design on at least one side due to the narrow spacing of the stamps on the plates and imperfect perforation methods. Stamps with perfs clear of the design on all four sides are extremely scarce and will command higher prices.

Watermarks

Wmk. 5- Small Star   Wmk. 6- Large Star

Britannia
A1   A2

1852-55   Unwmk.   Engr.   Imperf.
Blued Paper
| 1 | A1 | (¹/₂p) deep green | 100.00 | 300.00 |
| a. | | (¹/₂p) yellow green | 9,000. | 800.00 |

2	A1	(1p) dark blue	18.00	70.00
3	A1	(2p) slate blue	15.00	
a.		(2p) grayish slate	225.00	1,100.
b.		Vert. half (#3a) used as 1p on cover		6,750.
4	A1	(4p) brown red ('55)	50.00	300.00
		Nos. 1-4 (4)	183.00	670.00

No. 3 was not placed in use. No. 3a was used only when bisected.

1855-58
White Paper
5	A1	(¹/₂p) deep green ('58)	85.00	200.00
a.		(¹/₂p) yellow green ('57)	450.00	110.00
6	A1	(1p) blue	21.00	50.00
a.		(1p) pale blue	55.00	60.00

It is believed that the (4p) brownish red on white paper exists only as No. 17b.

1859
| 8 | A2 | 6p rose red | 600.00 | 110.00 |
| 9 | A2 | 1sh black | 140.00 | 70.00 |

Pin-perf. 14
| 10 | A1 | (¹/₂p) pale yel grn | 2,500. | 350.00 |
| 11 | A1 | (1p) blue | 2,500. | 150.00 |

Pin-perf. 12¹/₂
| 12 | A1 | (¹/₂p) pale yel grn | 6,000. | 550. |
| 12A | A1 | (1p) blue | 16,000. | 1,400. |

1861   Clean-Cut Perf. 14 to 16
13	A1	(¹/₂p) dark blue grn	60.00	10.00
14	A1	(1p) pale blue	625.00	35.00
a.		(1p) blue		35.00
b.		Half used as ¹/₂p on cover	725.00	3,500.

Rough Perf. 14 to 16
15	A1	(¹/₂p) green	9.00	9.00
a.		(¹/₂p) blue green	65.00	75.00
b.		Imperf., pair	500.00	
16	A1	(1p) blue	20.00	1.50
a.		Diagonal half used as ¹/₂p on cover		1,750.
b.		Imperf., pair	550.00	
17	A1	(4p) rose red	60.00	25.00
		(4p) brown red	100.00	32.50
b.		As "a", imperf., pair	850.00	
c.		(4p) rose red, imperf., pair	750.00	
18	A1	(4p) vermilion	175.00	60.00
a.		Imperf., pair	850.00	
19	A2	6p rose red	175.00	12.00
20	A2	6p orange ver	55.00	13.00
a.		6p vermilion	55.00	13.00
b.		Imperf., pair	450.00	800.00
21	A2	1sh black	35.00	3.50
a.		Horiz. pair, imperf. btwn.	5,750.	
b.		1sh blue (error)	15,000.	

No. 21b was never placed in use. All copies are pen-marked (some have been removed) and have clipped perfs on one or more sides.

Perf. 11 to 13
| 22 | A1 | (¹/₂p) deep green | 6,500. | |
| 23 | A1 | (1p) blue | 2,250. | |

Nos. 22 and 23 were never placed in use.

1870   Wmk. 6   Rough Perf. 14 to 16
24	A1	(¹/₂p) green	75.00	10.00
a.		Imperf., pair (#24)	675.00	
b.		(¹/₂p) yellow green	90.00	40.00
25	A1	(1p) blue	1,200.	30.00
a.		Imperf., pair	1,500.	
26	A1	(4p) dull red	650.00	75.00
27	A2	6p vermilion	625.00	50.00
28	A2	1sh black	225.00	17.50

1871   **Wmk. 5**
29	A1	(1p) blue	75.00	3.00
30	A1	(4p) rose red	575.00	25.00
31	A2	6p vermilion	350.00	20.00
32	A2	1sh black	125.00	10.00

Clean-Cut Perf. 14¹/₂ to 16
33	A1	(1p) blue	200.00	10.00
a.		Diagonal half used as ¹/₂p on cover		1,500.
34	A2	6p vermilion	550.00	45.00
35	A2	1sh black	125.00	10.00

Perf. 11 to 13x14¹/₂ to 16
| 36 | A1 | (¹/₂p) blue green | 225.00 | 25.00 |
| 37 | A1 | (4p) vermilion | 450.00 | 75.00 |

1873   **Perf. 14**
| 38 | A2 | 3p claret | 475.00 | 110.00 |

Wmk. 6
Clean-Cut Perf. 14¹/₂ to 16
39	A1	(¹/₂p) blue green	175.00	17.50
40	A1	(4p) rose red	725.00	125.00
41	A2	6p vermilion	575.00	60.00
a.		Imperf., pair	90.00	1,500.
b.		Horiz. pair, imperf. btwn.	4,500.	
42	A2	1sh black	90.00	12.00
a.		Horiz. pair, imperf. btwn.		

Britannia — A3   5 SHILLINGS

1873   Wmk. 5   Perf. 15¹/₂x15
| 43 | A3 | 5sh dull rose | 1,100. | 325.00 |

For surcharged bisects see Nos. 57-59.

1874   Wmk. 6   Perf. 14
| 44 | A2 | ¹/₂p blue green | 17.50 | 7.50 |
| 45 | A2 | 1sh blue | 67.50 | 3.00 |

Clean-Cut Perf. 14¹/₂ to 16
| 45A | A2 | 1p blue | | 14,000. |

1875   Wmk. 1   Perf. 12¹/₂
46	A2	¹/₂p yellow green	21.00	3.00
47	A2	4p scarlet	165.00	10.00
48	A2	6p orange	600.00	65.00
49	A2	1sh purple	450.00	17.50
		Nos. 46-49 (4)	1,236.	95.50

1875-78   **Perf. 14**
50	A2	¹/₂p yel green ('76)	6.00	1.75
51	A2	1p ultramarine	30.00	1.00
a.		1p gray blue	30.00	.75
b.		Half used as ¹/₂p on cover		1,200.
c.		Watermarked sideways		1,750.
52	A2	3p violet ('78)	80.00	10.00
53	A2	4p rose red	80.00	8.00
a.		4p scarlet	125.00	5.00
b.		As "a," perf. 14x12¹/₂	4,500.	
54	A2	4p lake	375.00	5.00
55	A2	6p chrome yel	100.00	3.25
a.		6p yellow	300.00	12.50
56	A2	1sh purple ('76)	125.00	5.00
a.		1sh violet	2,100.	45.00
b.		1sh dull mauve	275.00	4.00
c.		1sh used as ¹/₂p on cover		5,000.

#48, 49, 55, 56 have the watermark sideways.
No. 53b was never placed in use.

A4   A5

Large Surcharge, ("1" 7mm High, "D" 2³/₄mm High)
1878   Wmk. 5   Perf. 15¹/₂x15
Slanting Serif
57	A4	1p on half of 5sh	4,000.	650.
a.		Unsevered pair	16,000.	2,500.
b.		Unsevered horiz. pair, #57 + 58		4,000.
d.		Unsevered horiz. pair, #57 + 58, imperf. between		—
e.		Unsevered horiz. pair, #57 + 59, imperf. between	25,000.	8,500.

Straight Serif
| 58 | A4 | 1p on half of 5sh | 4,750. | 950. |
| a. | | Unsevered pair | | 4,250. |

Small Surcharge, ("1" 6mm, "D" 2¹/₂mm High)
| 59 | A5 | 1p on half of 5sh | 5,250. | 1,100. |
| a. | | Unsevered pair | 15,000. | 4,250. |

On Nos. 57, 58 and 59 the surcharge is found reading upwards or downwards.
The perforation, which divides the stamp into halves, measures 11¹/₂ to 13.
The old denomination has been cut off the bottom of the stamps.

BARBADOS   HALFPENNY   Queen Victoria — A6

1882-85   Typo.   Wmk. 2   Perf. 14
60	A6	¹/₂p green	5.25	.80
61	A6	1p carmine rose	4.75	.50
a.		1p rose	30.00	1.50
b.		1p used on cover		750.00
62	A6	2¹/₂p dull blue	52.50	.75
		2¹/₂p ultramarine	47.50	1.00
63	A6	3p magenta	3.00	8.75
a.		3p lilac	70.00	30.00
64	A6	4p slate	175.00	2.00
65	A6	4p brown ('85)	25.75	1.00
66	A6	6p olive gray	52.50	25.00
67	A6	1sh orange brown	17.00	18.00
68	A6	5sh bister	125.00	175.00
		Nos. 60-68 (9)	437.75	231.80

No. 65 Surcharged in **HALF-PENNY** Black

1892
69	A6	½p on 4p brown	1.00	2.00
a.		Without hyphen	6.00	11.00
b.		Double surcharge		
c.		Double surch., red & black	500.00	1,200.
d.		As "c," without hyphen	1,500.	1,500.

Badge of Colony
A8   A9

1892-1903   **Wmk. 2**
70	A8	1f sl & car ('96)	.85	.20
71	A8	½p green	.55	.20
72	A8	1p carmine rose	1.75	.20
73	A8	2p sl & org ('99)	5.25	1.50
74	A8	2½p ultramarine	8.75	.30
75	A8	5p olive brn	4.25	4.25
76	A8	6p vio & car	6.00	3.50
77	A8	8p org & ultra	2.25	15.00
78	A8	10p bl grn & car	4.50	6.00
79	A8	2sh6p slate & org	35.00	35.00
80	A8	2sh6p pur & grn ('03)	47.50	75.00
		Nos. 70-80 (11)	116.65	141.15

See Nos. 90-101. For surcharge see No B1.

Victoria Jubilee Issue
1897   **Wmk. 1**
81	A9	1f gray & car	1.25	.30
82	A9	½p gray green	1.75	.30
83	A9	1p carmine rose	2.00	.35
84	A9	2½p ultra	4.25	.70
85	A9	5p dk olive brn	8.50	9.25
86	A9	6p vio & car	12.00	14.00
87	A9	8p org & ultra	7.00	15.00
88	A9	10p bl grn & car	30.00	35.00
89	A9	2sh6p slate & org	35.00	42.50
		Nos. 81-89 (9)	101.75	117.40

Bluish Paper
81a	A9	1f gray & car	25.00	30.00
82a	A9	½p gray green	25.00	30.00
83a	A9	1p carmine rose	35.00	40.00
84a	A9	2½p ultra	37.50	45.00
85a	A9	5p dk olive brn	225.00	250.00
86a	A9	6p vio & car	100.00	110.00
87a	A9	8p org & ultra	85.00	100.00
88a	A9	10p bl grn & car	140.00	150.00
89a	A9	2sh6p slate & org	90.00	95.00
		Nos. 81a-89a (9)	762.50	850.00

Badge Type of 1892-1903
1904-10   **Wmk. 3**
90	A8	1f gray & car	3.50	1.25
91	A8	1f brown ('09)	.90	.25
92	A8	½p green	7.00	.15
93	A8	1p carmine rose	5.75	.20
94	A8	1p carmine ('09)	4.00	.15
95	A8	2p gray ('09)	4.00	7.75
96	A8	2½p ultramarine	4.00	.40
97	A8	6p vio & car	15.00	12.50
98	A8	6p dl vio & vio ('10)	5.00	12.00
99	A8	8p org & ultra	22.50	52.50
100	A8	1sh blk, grn ('10)	7.50	12.00
101	A8	2sh6p pur & green	27.50	55.00
		Nos. 90-101 (12)	106.65	154.15

Nelson Centenary Issue

Lord Nelson Monument — A10

1906   **Engr.**   **Wmk. 1**
102	A10	1f gray & black	2.00	.60
103	A10	½p green & black	3.00	.40
104	A10	1p car & black	3.50	.30
105	A10	2p org & black	4.00	4.25
106	A10	2½p ultra & black	5.00	4.00
107	A10	6p lilac & black	15.00	17.50
108	A10	1sh rose & black	17.50	27.50
		Nos. 102-108 (7)	50.00	54.55

See Nos. 110-112.

The "Olive Blossom" — A11

1906, Aug. 15   **Wmk. 3**
109	A11	1p blk, green & blue	8.00	1.25

Tercentenary of the 1st British landing.

Nelson Type of 1906
1907, July 6   **Wmk. 3**
110	A10	1f gray & black	2.50	2.00
111	A10	2p org & black	12.50	15.00
112	A10	2½p ultra & black	10.00	12.50
a.		2½p indigo & black	850.00	1,200.
		Nos. 110-112 (3)	25.00	29.50

A12   A13

King George V — A14

1912   **Typo.**
116	A12	¼p brown	.40	.30
117	A12	½p green	1.50	.20
a.		Booklet pane of 6	3.00	.15
118	A12	1p carmine	10.00	1.00
b.		1p scarlet		
b.		Booklet pane of 6		
119	A12	2p gray	1.65	6.50
120	A12	2½p ultramarine	1.00	.50
121	A13	3p violet, yel	1.00	4.00
122	A13	4p blk & scar, yel	1.00	7.50
123	A13	6p vio & red vio	6.00	5.00
124	A14	1sh black, green	4.00	7.00
125	A14	2sh vio & ultra, bl	24.00	32.50
126	A14	3sh grn & violet	47.50	37.50
		Nos. 116-126 (11)	91.05	101.15

Seal of the Colony — A15

1916-18   **Engr.**
127	A15	¼p brown	.30	.25
128	A15	½p green	.75	.20
129	A15	1p red	1.00	.20
130	A15	2p gray	3.50	10.00
131	A15	2½p ultramarine	.85	.75
132	A15	3p violet, yel	2.25	2.50
133	A15	4p red, yel	.60	5.00
134	A15	4p red & black ('18)	.85	2.50
135	A15	6p claret	1.50	2.25
136	A15	1sh black, green	3.50	5.00
137	A15	2sh violet, blue	15.00	8.50
138	A15	3sh dark violet	32.50	70.00
139	A15	3sh dk vio & grn ('18)	15.00	30.00
a.		3sh bright violet & green ('18)	140.00	150.00
		Nos. 127-139 (13)	77.60	137.15

Nos. 134 and 139 are from a re-engraved die. The central medallion is not surrounded by a line and there are various other small alterations.

Victory Issue

Victory
A16   A17

1920, Sept. 9   **Wmk. 3**
140	A16	¼p bister & black	.25	.35
141	A16	½p yel green & blk	.80	.30
a.		Booklet pane of 2		
142	A16	1p org red & blk	1.25	.20
a.		Booklet pane of 2		
143	A16	2p gray & black	1.50	4.50
144	A16	2½p ultra & dk bl	2.00	4.75
145	A16	3p red lilac & blk	.85	2.00
146	A16	4p gray grn & blk	1.40	3.50
147	A16	6p orange & blk	1.75	4.50
148	A17	1sh yel green & blk	5.00	10.00
149	A17	2sh brown & blk	10.00	15.00
150	A17	3sh orange & blk	15.00	20.00
		Nos. 140-150 (11)	39.80	65.10

1921, Aug. 22   **Wmk. 4**
151	A16	1p orange red & blk	8.00	.30
		Nos. 140-151 (12)	47.80	65.40

A18   A19

1921-24   **Wmk. 4**
152	A18	¼p brown	.15	.15
153	A18	½p green	.35	.15
154	A18	1p carmine	.30	.15
155	A18	2p gray	1.00	.30
156	A18	2½p ultramarine	.90	1.50
158	A18	6p claret	1.50	1.50
159	A18	1sh blk, emer ('24)	30.00	32.50
160	A18	2sh dk vio, blue	13.00	17.50
161	A18	3sh dark violet	13.00	22.50

      Wmk. 3
162	A18	3p violet, yel	.75	1.50
163	A18	4p red, yel	.70	3.00
164	A18	1sh black, green	4.00	10.00
		Nos. 152-164 (12)	65.65	90.75

1925-35   **Wmk. 4**   **Perf. 14**
165	A19	¼p brown	.15	.15
166	A19	½p green	.15	.15
a.		Perf. 13½x12½ ('32)	1.25	.15
b.		Booklet pane of 10		
167	A19	1p carmine	.15	.15
a.		Perf. 13½x12½ ('32)	.90	.30
b.		Booklet pane of 10		
168	A19	1½p org, perf. 13½x12½ ('32)	.75	.60
a.		Booklet pane of 6		
b.		Perf. 14	3.50	.80
169	A19	2p gray	.50	1.25
170	A19	2½p ultramarine	.50	.50
a.		Perf. 13½x12½ ('32)	3.00	1.00
171	A19	3p vio brn, yel	.60	.40
172	A19	3p red brn, yel ('35)	6.00	6.00
173	A19	4p red, yel	.80	.80
174	A19	6p claret	.80	.80
175	A19	1sh blk, emerald	1.50	2.50
a.		1sh blk, yel grn ('32)	15.00	10.00
176	A19	1sh brn blk, yel grn ('32)	4.25	7.50
177	A19	2sh violet, bl	5.00	4.00
178	A19	2sh6p car, blue ('32)	15.00	17.50
179	A19	3sh dark violet	8.00	12.50
		Nos. 165-179 (15)	44.15	54.80

Charles I and George V — A20

1927, Feb. 17   **Perf. 12½**
180	A20	1p carmine lake	.75	.60

Tercentenary of the settlement of Barbados.

Silver Jubilee Issue
Common Design Type
1935, May 6   **Perf. 11x12**
186	CD301	1p car & dk bl	.20	.20
187	CD301	1½p blk & ultra	.40	.30
188	CD301	2½p ultra & brn	.85	.85
189	CD301	1sh brn vio & ind	5.00	5.00
		Nos. 186-189 (4)	6.45	6.35
		Set, never hinged	15.00	

Coronation Issue
Common Design Type
1937, May 14   **Perf. 13½x14**
190	CD302	1p carmine	.15	.15
191	CD302	1½p brown	.20	.20
192	CD302	2½p bright ultra	.40	.40
		Nos. 190-192 (3)	.75	.75
		Set, never hinged	1.00	

A21

1938-47   **Perf. 13-14 & Compound**
193	A21	½p green	.40	.15
b.		Perf. 14	22.50	1.40
c.		Booklet pane of 10		
193A	A21	½p bister ('42)	.15	.15
194	A21	1p carmine	1.75	.15
b.		Perf. 13½x13	50.00	1.40
c.		Booklet pane of 10		
194A	A21	1p green ('42)	.15	.15
d.		Perf. 13½x13	.30	.15
195	A21	1½p red orange	.15	.15
d.		Perf. 14	.60	.15
195A	A21	2p rose lake ('41)	1.10	.50
195B	A21	2p bright rose red ('43)	.20	.15
		Perf. 14	.15	.15
196	A21	2½p ultramarine	.20	.15
197	A21	3p brown	.20	.50
b.		Perf. 14	.25	.20
197A	A21	3p deep bl ('47)	.20	.15
198	A21	4p black	.20	.15
a.		Perf. 14	.30	.30
199	A21	6p violet	.20	.15
199A	A21	8p red vio ('46)	.65	.65
200	A21	1sh brn olive	.50	.20
a.		1sh olive green	5.00	1.40
201	A21	2sh6p brown vio	2.75	.65
201A	A21	5sh indigo ('41)	2.75	1.40
		Nos. 193-201A (16)	11.55	
		Set, never hinged	25.00	
		Set value		4.20

For surcharge see No. 209.

Kings Charles I, George VI Assembly Chamber and Mace A22

1939, June 27   **Engr.**   **Wmk. 4**
202	A22	½p deep green	.25	.15
203	A22	1p scarlet	.25	.15
204	A22	1½p deep orange	.35	.25
205	A22	2½p ultramarine	.60	.80
206	A22	3p yellow brown	.65	.80
		Nos. 202-206 (5)	2.10	2.15
		Set, never hinged	5.00	

Tercentenary of the General Assembly.

Catalogue values for unused stamps in this section, from this point to the end of the section, are for Never Hinged items.

Peace Issue
Common Design Type
1946, Sept. 18
207	CD303	1½p deep orange	.15	.15
208	CD303	3p brown	.15	.15

Nos. 195e, 195B, Surcharged in Black **ONE PENNY**

1947, Apr. 21   **Perf. 14**
209	A21	1p on 2p brt rose red	.55	.55
a.		Double surcharge		
b.		Perf. 13½x13	.65	.65

Silver Wedding Issue
Common Design Types
Perf. 14x14½
1948, Nov. 24   **Photo.**   **Wmk. 4**
210	CD304	1½p orange	.15	.15

Engraved; Name Typographed
Perf. 11½x11
211	CD305	5sh dark blue	10.00	10.00

UPU Issue
Common Design Types
1949, Oct. 10   **Perf. 13½, 11x11½**
212	CD306	1½p red orange	.32	.35
213	CD307	3p indigo	.55	.55
214	CD308	4p gray	1.00	1.00
215	CD309	1sh olive	1.40	1.40
		Nos. 212-215 (4)	3.27	3.30

Dover Fort — A23

Admiral Nelson Statue — A24

Designs: 2c, Sugar cane breeding. 3c, Public buildings. 6c, Casting net. 8c, Intercolonial schooner. 12c, Flying Fish. 24c, Old Main Guard Garrison. 48c, Cathedral. 60c, Careenage. $1.20, Map. $2.40, Great Seal, 1660.

Perf. 11x11½ (A23), 13x13½ (A24)
1950, May 1   Engr.   Wmk. 4
216	A23	1c slate	.15	.15
217	A23	2c emerald	.15	.15
218	A23	3c slate & brown	.15	.15
219	A24	4c carmine	.30	.30
220	A23	6c blue	.35	.30
221	A23	8c choc & blue	.60	.40
222	A23	12c olive & aqua	1.25	.15
223	A23	24c gray & red	1.50	1.00
224	A24	48c violet	4.00	2.75
225	A23	60c brn car & bl grn	2.50	3.00
226	A23	$1.20 olive & car	9.00	5.25
227	A24	$2.40 gray	21.00	13.00
		Nos. 216-227 (12)	40.95	27.20

University Issue
Common Design Types
1951, Feb. 16   Perf. 14x14½
228	CD310	3c turq bl & choc	.15	.15
229	CD311	12c ol brn & turq bl	.75	.75

Stamp of 1852 — A25

Perf. 13½
1952, Apr. 15   Wmk. 4   Engr.
230	A25	3c slate bl & dp grn	.15	.15
231	A25	4c rose pink & bl	.25	.25
232	A25	12c emer & slate bl	.40	.40
233	A25	24c gray blk & red brn	.65	.65
		Nos. 230-233 (4)	1.45	1.45

Centenary of Barbados postage stamps.

Coronation Issue
Common Design Type
1953, June 4   Perf. 13½x13
234	CD312	4c red orange & black	.15	.15

Harbor Police — A26

Designs as in 1950 with portrait of Queen Elizabeth II. $2.40, Great Seal, 1660 ("E II R").

Perf. 11x11½ (horiz.), 13x13½ (vert.)
1953-57   Engr.
235	A23	1c slate ('53)	.15	.15
236	A23	2c grnsh blue & deep orng	.15	.15
237	A23	3c emerald & blk	.15	.15
238	A24	4c orange & gray	.15	.15
239	A26	5c dp car & dp bl	.20	.15
240	A23	6c red brown	.20	.15
241	A23	8c brt blue & blk	.30	.15
242	A23	12c brn ol & aqua	.35	.15
243	A23	24c gray & red ('56)	.55	.20
244	A24	48c violet ('56)	1.75	1.10
245	A23	60c brown car & blue grn ('56)	3.00	1.75
246	A24	$1.20 ol & car ('56)	5.25	3.25
247	A23	$2.40 gray ('57)	11.00	6.25
		Nos. 235-247 (13)	23.25	13.75

See Nos. 257-264.

West Indies Federation
Common Design Type
Perf. 11½x11
1958, Apr. 23   Wmk. 314
248	CD313	3c green	.15	.15
249	CD313	6c blue	.40	.40
250	CD313	12c carmine rose	.50	.50
		Nos. 248-250 (3)	1.05	1.05

Deep Water Harbor, Bridgetown A27

1961, May 6   Engr.   Perf. 11x11½
251	A27	4c orange & black	.15	.15
252	A27	8c ultra & black	.30	.30
253	A27	24c black & pink	.65	.65
		Nos. 251-253 (3)	1.10	1.10

Deep Water Harbor at Bridgetown opening.

Scout Emblem and Map of Barbados — A28

Perf. 11½x11
1962, Mar. 9   Wmk. 314
254	A28	4c orange & black	.15	.15
255	A28	12c gray & blue	.30	.30
256	A28	$1.20 greenish gray & carmine rose	2.00	2.00
		Nos. 254-256 (3)	2.45	2.45

50th anniv. of the founding of the Boy Scouts of Barbados.

Queen Types of 1953-57
Perf. 11x11½, 13x13½
1964-65   Engr.   Wmk. 314
257	A23	1c slate	.25	.25
258	A24	4c orange & gray	.35	.35
259	A23	8c brt bl & blk ('65)	.50	.45
260	A23	12c brn ol & aqua ('65)	.60	
261	A23	24c gray & red	.60	.50
262	A24	48c violet	2.50	2.50
263	A23	60c brn car & bl grn	3.50	3.50
264	A23	$2.40 gray ('65)	5.50	5.50
		Nos. 257-264 (8)	13.80	

The 12c was never put on sale in Barbados.

ITU Issue
Common Design Type
Perf. 11x11½
1965, May 17   Litho.   Wmk. 314
265	CD317	2c lilac & ver	.15	.15
266	CD317	48c yellow & gray	1.50	1.50
		Nos. 290-293 (4)	1.75	1.75

Sea Horse — A29

Designs: 1c, Deep sea coral. 2c, Lobster. 4c, Sea urchin. 5c, Staghorn coral. 6c, Butterflyfish. 8c, File shell. 12c, Balloonfish. 15c, Angelfish. 25c, Brain coral. 35c, Brittle star. 50c, Flyingfish. $1, Queen conch shell. $2.50, Fiddler crab.

Wmk. 314 Upright
1965, July 15   Photo.   Perf. 14x13½
267	A29	1c dk blue, pink & black	.15	.15
268	A29	2c car rose, sepia & orange	.15	.15
269	A29	3c org, brn & sep ("Hippocanpus")	.15	.15
270	A29	4c ol grn & dk bl	.15	.15
a.		Imperf. pair	450.00	
271	A29	5c lil, brn & pink	.15	.15
272	A29	6c greenish bl, yel & blk	.15	.15
273	A29	8c ultra, orange, red & black	.25	.20
274	A29	12c rose lil, yel & blk	.40	.25
275	A29	15c red, yel & blk	.75	.50
276	A29	25c yel brn & ultra	1.10	.80
277	A29	35c grn, rose brn & blk	1.75	1.00
278	A29	50c yel grn & ultra	2.75	1.65
279	A29	$1 gray & multi	5.50	4.00
280	A29	$2.50 lt bl & multi	12.00	10.00
		Nos. 267-280 (14)	25.40	19.30

1966-69   Wmk. 314 Sideways
Design: $5, "Dolphin" (coryphaena hippurus).
267a	A29	1c	.15	.15
268a	A29	2c ('67)	.15	.15
269A	A29	3c ("Hippocampus") ('67)	.18	.15
270b	A29	4c	.15	.15
271a	A29	5c	.15	.15
272a	A29	6c ('67)	.20	.15
273a	A29	8c ('67)	.25	.20
274a	A29	12c ('67)	.35	.20
275a	A29	15c	.50	.35
276a	A29	25c	.60	.55
277a	A29	35c	.85	.60
278a	A29	50c	1.25	1.10
279a	A29	$1	2.50	1.90
280a	A29	$2.50	6.25	6.00
280B	A29	$5 dk ol & multi	12.50	12.50
		Nos. 267a-280B (15)	26.03	24.30

For surcharge see No. 327.

Churchill Memorial Issue
Common Design Type
1966, Jan. 24   Wmk. 314   Perf. 14
281	CD319	1c multicolored	.15	.15
282	CD319	4c multicolored	.20	.20
283	CD319	25c multicolored	1.00	1.00
284	CD319	35c multicolored	1.40	1.40
		Nos. 281-284 (4)	2.75	2.75

Royal Visit Issue
Common Design Type
1966, Feb. 4   Litho.   Perf. 11x12
285	CD320	3c violet blue	.20	.20
286	CD320	35c dark car rose	1.75	1.75

UNESCO Anniversary Issue
Common Design Type
1967, Jan. 6   Litho.   Perf. 14
287	CD323	4c "Education"	.15	.15
288	CD323	12c "Science"	.55	.55
289	CD323	25c "Culture"	1.40	1.40
		Nos. 287-289 (3)	2.10	2.10

Arms of Barbados — A30   Policeman and Anchor Monument — A31

Designs: 25c, Hilton Hotel, horiz. 35c, Garfield Sobers, captain of Barbados and West Indies Cricket Team. 50c, Pine Hill Dairy, horiz.

1966, Dec. 2   Unwmk.   Photo.
290	A30	4c multicolored	.15	.15
291	A30	25c multicolored	.35	.35
292	A30	35c multicolored	.50	.50
293	A30	50c multicolored	.75	.75
		Nos. 290-293 (4)	1.75	1.75

Barbados' independence, Nov. 30, 1966.

1967, Oct. 16   Litho.   Perf. 13½x14
Designs: 25c, Policeman with telescope. 35c, Police motor launch, horiz. 50c, Policemen at Harbor Gate.
294	A31	4c multicolored	.15	.15
295	A31	25c multicolored	.30	.30
296	A31	35c multicolored	.50	.50
297	A31	50c multicolored	.80	.80
		Nos. 294-297 (4)	1.75	1.75

Centenary of Bridgetown Harbor Police.
For surcharge see No. 322.

Independence Arch — A32

1st Anniv. of Independence: 4c, Sir Winston Scott, Governor-General, vert. 35c, Treasury Building. 50c, Parliament Building.

Perf. 14½x14, 14x14½
1967, Dec. 4   Photo.   Unwmk.
298	A32	4c multicolored	.15	.15
299	A32	25c multicolored	.25	.25
300	A32	35c multicolored	.40	.40
301	A32	50c multicolored	.60	.60
		Nos. 298-301 (4)	1.40	1.40

UN Building, Santiago, Chile A33

1968, Feb. 27   Perf. 14½x14½
302	A33	15c multicolored	.20	.20

20th anniv. of the UN Economic Commission for Latin America.

Radar Antenna on Top of Old Sugar Mill, Sugar Cane — A34

Designs: 25c, Caribbean Meteorological Institute, Barbados, horiz. 50c, HARP gun used in High Altitude Research Program, at Paragon in Christ Church, Barbados.

Perf. 14x14½, 14½x14
1968, June 4   Photo.   Unwmk.
303	A34	3c violet & multi	.15	.15
304	A34	25c vermilion & multi	.30	.30
305	A34	50c orange & multi	.70	.70
		Nos. 303-305 (3)	1.15	1.15

World Meteorological Day.

Girl Scout at Campfire, Lady Baden-Powell and Queen Elizabeth II — A35

Lady Baden-Powell, Queen Elizabeth II and: 25c, Pax Hill Headquarters. 35c, Girl Scout badge.

Perf. 14x14½
1968, Aug. 29   Photo.   Unwmk.
306	A35	3c dp ultra, blk & gold	.15	.15
307	A35	25c bluish green, black & gold	.35	.35
308	A35	35c org yel, blk & gold	.70	.70
		Nos. 306-308 (3)	1.20	1.20

Barbados Girl Scouts' 50th anniv.

Human Rights Flame and Escape to Freedom A36

Designs: 4c, Human Rights flame, hands, and broken chain. 25c, Human Rights flame, family and broken chain.

Perf. 11x11½
1968, Dec. 10   Litho.   Unwmk.
309	A36	4c violet, gray grn & red brown	.15	.15
310	A36	25c org, blk & blue	.40	.40
311	A36	35c greenish blue, blue, blk & org	.55	.55
		Nos. 309-311 (3)	1.10	1.10

International Human Rights Year.

Horse Racing: 25c, "They're off!" 35c, On the flat. 50c, The Finish.

In the Paddock A37

1969, Mar. 15   Litho.   Perf. 14½

312	A37	4c multicolored	.15 .15
313	A37	25c multicolored	.25 .25
314	A37	35c multicolored	.35 .35
315	A37	50c multicolored	.55 .55
a.		Souvenir sheet of 4, #312-315	2.50 3.00
		Nos. 312-315 (4)	1.30 1.30

Map of Caribbean — A38

Design: 12c, 50c, "Strength in Unity," horiz.

Perf. 14x14½, 14½x14

1969, May 6   Photo.   Wmk. 314

316	A38	5c brown & multi	.15 .15
317	A38	12c ultra & multi	.20 .20
318	A38	25c green & multi	.30 .30
319	A38	50c magenta & multi	.65 .65
		Nos. 316-319 (4)	1.30 1.30

1st anniv. of CARIFTA (Caribbean Free Trade Area).

ILO Emblem A39

Perf. 14x13

1969, Aug. 5   Litho.   Unwmk.

320	A39	4c bl grn, brt grn & blk	.15 .15
321	A39	25c red brn, brt mag & red	.40 .40

50th anniv. of the ILO.

No. 294 Surcharged   **ONE CENT**

1969, Aug. 30   Perf. 13½x14

322	A31	1c on 4c multicolored	.35 .35

Barbados Boy Scout Emblem A40

Designs: 25c, Sea Scouts rowing in Bridgetown harbor. 35c, Campfire. 50c, Various Scouts in front of National Headquarters and Training Center, Hazelwood.

Perf. 13½x13

1969, Dec. 16   Litho.   Unwmk.

323	A40	5c multicolored	.15 .15
324	A40	25c multicolored	.50 .50
325	A40	35c multicolored	.65 .65
326	A40	50c multicolored	1.00 1.00
a.		Souvenir sheet of 4, #323-326	10.00 12.00
		Nos. 323-326 (4)	2.30 2.30

Attainment of independence by the Barbados Boy Scout Assoc.

No. 271a Surcharged   **4 x**

Wmk. 314 Sideways

1970, Mar. 11   Photo.   Perf. 14x13½

327	A29	4c on 5c multicolored	.20 .20

This locally applied surcharge exists in several variations: double, triple, on back, in pair with one missing, etc.

Lion at Gun Hill — A41

Barbados Museum A42

Designs: 2c, Trafalgar Fountain. 3c, Montefiore Drinking Fountain. 4c, St. James' Monument. 5c, St. Ann's Fort. 6c, Old Sugar Mill, Morgan Lewis. 8c, Cenotaph. 10c, South Point Lighthouse. 15c, Sharon Moravian Church. 25c, George Washington House. 35c, St. Nicholas Abbey. 50c, Bowmanston Pumping Station. $1, Queen Elizabeth Hospital. $2.50, Modern sugar factory. $5, Seawell International Airport.

Wmk. 314 Upright (A41), Sideways (A42)

Perf. 12½x13, 13x12½

1970, May 4   Photo.

328	A41	1c blue grn & multi	.15 .15
329	A41	2c crimson & multi	.15 .15
330	A41	3c blue & multi	.15 .15
331	A41	4c yellow & multi	.15 .15
332	A41	5c dp org & multi	.15 .15
333	A41	6c dull yel & multi	.15 .15
334	A41	8c dp blue & multi	.15 .15
335	A41	10c red & multi	.15 .15
336	A42	12c ultra & multi	.20 .20
337	A42	15c yellow & multi	.22 .20
338	A42	25c orange & multi	.40 .40
339	A42	35c pink & multi	.60 .60
340	A42	50c bl grn & multi	.65 .65
341	A42	$1 emerald & multi	1.40 1.40
342	A42	$2.50 ver & multi	3.50 3.50
343	A42	$5 yellow & multi	6.50 6.50
		Nos. 328-343 (16)	14.67 14.65

Nos. 328-332, 334-343 were reissued in 1971 on glazed paper.

Wmk. 314 Sideways (A41), Upright (A42)

1972-74

331a	A41	4c	.15 .15
332a	A41	5c	.15 .15
333a	A41	6c	.15 .15
334a	A41	8c	.15 .15
335a	A41	10c ('74)	.25 .25
336a	A42	12c	.25 .25
337a	A42	15c	.30 .30
338a	A42	25c	.55 .55
339a	A42	35c	.85 .85
340a	A42	50c	1.25 1.25
341a	A42	$1	2.50 2.50
342a	A42	$2.50 ('73)	6.50 6.50
343a	A42	$5 ('73)	13.00 13.00
		Nos. 331a-343a (13)	26.05 26.05

For surcharge, see No. 391.

Primary Education, UN and Education Year Emblems A43

Designs (UN and Education Year Emblems and): 5c, Secondary education (student with microscope). 25c, Technical education (men working with power drill). 50c, University building.

1970, June 26   Litho.   Perf. 14

344	A43	4c multicolored	.15 .15
345	A43	5c multicolored	.15 .15
346	A43	25c multicolored	.35 .35
347	A43	50c multicolored	.75 .75
		Nos. 344-347 (4)	1.40 1.40

UN, 25th anniv., and Intl. Education Year.

Minnie Root A44   5c Barbados

Flowers: 1c, Barbados Easter lily, vert. 10c, Eyelash orchid. 25c, Pride of Barbados, vert. 35c, Christmas hope.

1970, Aug. 24   Litho.   Wmk. 314
Flowers in Natural Colors

348	A44	1c green	.20 .15
349	A44	5c deep magenta	.20 .15
350	A44	10c dark blue	.45 .25
351	A44	25c brt orange brown	1.25 .55
352	A44	35c blue	1.75 .90
a.		Souvenir sheet of 5	3.00 2.25
		Nos. 348-352 (5)	3.85 2.00

No. 352a contains 5 imperf. stamps similar to Nos. 348-352 with simulated perforations.

Christ Carrying Cross — A45

Easter: 10c, 50c, Resurrection, by Benjamin West, St. George's Anglican Church. 35c like 4c, Window from St. Margaret's Anglican Church, St. John.

1971, Apr. 7   Wmk. 314   Perf. 14

353	A45	4c purple & multi	.15 .15
354	A45	10c silver & multi	.15 .15
355	A45	35c brt blue & multi	.50 .50
356	A45	50c gold & multi	.80 .80
		Nos. 353-356 (4)	1.60 1.60

Sailfish Craft — A46

Tourism: 5c, Tennis. 12c, Horseback riding. 25c, Water-skiing. 50c, Scuba diving.

1971, Aug. 17   Perf. 14x14½

357	A46	1c multicolored	.15 .15
358	A46	5c multicolored	.15 .15
359	A46	12c multicolored	.20 .20
360	A46	25c multicolored	.50 .50
361	A46	50c multicolored	1.00 1.00
		Nos. 357-361 (5)	2.00 2.00

Samuel Jackman Prescod — A47

1971, Sept. 26   Perf. 14

362	A47	3c orange & multi	.15 .15
363	A47	35c ultra & multi	.65 .65

Samuel Jackman Prescod (1806-1871), 1st black member of Barbados Assembly.

Coat of Arms — A48

Designs: 15c, 50c, Flag and map of Barbados.

1971, Nov. 23

364	A48	4c light blue & multi	.15 .15
365	A48	15c multicolored	.30 .30
366	A48	25c yel green & multi	.45 .45
367	A48	50c blue & multi	.90 .90
		Nos. 364-367 (4)	1.80 1.80

5th anniv. of independence.

Telegraphy, 1872 and 1972 A49

Designs: 10c, "Stanley Angwin" off St. Lawrence Coast. 35c, Earth station and Intelsat 4. 50c, Mt. Misery tropospheric scatter station.

1972, Mar. 28   Litho.   Perf. 14

368	A49	4c purple & multi	.15 .15
369	A49	10c emerald & multi	.25 .25
370	A49	35c red & multi	.55 .55
371	A49	50c orange & multi	.85 .85
		Nos. 368-371 (4)	1.80 1.80

Centenary of telecommunications to and from Barbados.

Lord Baden-Powell, Charles W. Springer, George B. Burton — A50

Designs: 5c, Map of Barbados and Combermere School, vert. 25c, Photograph of 1922 troop. 50c, Flags of various Boy Scout troops.

1972, Aug. 1

372	A50	5c ultra & multi	.15 .15
373	A50	15c ultra & multi	.40 .40
374	A50	25c ultra & multi	.60 .60
375	A50	50c ultra & multi	1.10 1.10
		Nos. 372-375 (4)	2.25 2.25

60th anniv. of Barbados Boy Scouts and 4th Caribbean Jamboree.

Bookmobile, Open Book — A51

Intl. Book Year: 15c, Visual aids truck. 25c, Central Library, Bridgetown. $1, Codrington College.

1972, Oct. 31   Litho.   Wmk. 314

376	A51	4c brt pink & multi	.15 .15
377	A51	15c dull org & multi	.25 .25
378	A51	25c buff & multi	.40 .40
379	A51	$1 lt violet & multi	1.90 1.90
		Nos. 376-379 (4)	2.70 2.70

Pottery Wheels A52

Barbados pottery industry: 15c, Kiln. 25c, Finished pottery, Chalky Mount. $1, Pottery on sale at market.

1973, Mar. 1   Wmk. 314   Perf. 14

380	A52	5c dull red & multi	.15 .15
381	A52	15c olive grn & multi	.20 .20
382	A52	25c gray & multi	.35 .35
383	A52	$1 yellow & multi	1.40 1.40
		Nos. 380-383 (4)	2.10 2.10

First Flight in Barbados, Wright Box Kite, 1911 A53

Aircraft: 15c, First flight to Barbados, De Havilland biplane, 1928. 25c, Passenger plane, 1939. 50c, Vickers VC-10 over control tower, 1973.

1973, July 25　　　　　　　Perf. 12½x12

384	A53	5c blue & multi	.15	.15
385	A53	15c vio blue & multi	.40	.40
386	A53	25c multicolored	.65	.65
387	A53	50c blue & multi	1.40	1.40
		Nos. 384-387 (4)	2.60	2.60

Chancellor
Sir Hugh
Wooding
A54

Designs: 25c, Sherlock Hall, Cave Hill Campus. 35c, Cave Hill Campus.

1973, Dec. 11　　　　　　　Perf. 13x14

388	A54	5c dp orange & multi	.15	.15
389	A54	25c red brown & multi	.40	.40
390	A54	35c multicolored	.60	.60
		Nos. 388-390 (3)	1.15	1.15

25th anniv. of the Univ. of the West Indies.

No. 338a Surcharged **4c.**

1974, Apr. 30　Photo.　Perf. 13x12½

391	A42	4c on 25c multi	.15	.15
a.		"4c." omitted	20.00	

Old
Sailboat
A55

Designs: 25c, Rowboat. 50c, Motor-powered fishing boat. $1, Trawler "Calamar."

1974, June 11　Wmk. 314　Perf. 14

392	A55	15c blue & multi	.25	.25
393	A55	35c multicolored	.50	.50
394	A55	50c vio blue & multi	.70	.70
395	A55	$1 blue & multi	1.40	1.40
a.		Souvenir sheet of 4, #392-395	3.00	3.75
		Nos. 392-395 (4)	2.85	2.85

Fishing boats of Barbados.

Fire Orchid — A56

Orchids. 1c, 20c, 25c, $2.50, $5 horizontal.

Wmk. 314 Sideways; Upright (1c, 20c, 25c, $1, $10)

1974-77　　　Photo.　　　Perf. 14

396	A56	1c Cattleya gaskelliana alba	.15	.15
397	A56	2c shown	.15	.15
398	A56	3c Rose Marie	.15	.15
399	A56	4c Fiery red orchid	.15	.15
400	A56	5c Schomburgkia humboltii	.15	.15
401	A56	8c Dancing dolls	.15	.15
402	A56	10c Spider orchids	.20	.15
403	A56	12c Dendrobium aggregatum	.25	.20
404	A56	15c Lady slippers	.40	.35
404C	A56	20c Spathoglottis	.45	.40
405	A56	25c Eyelash	.75	.55
406	A56	35c Bletia patula	.80	.65
406B	A56	45c Sunset Glow	1.10	.85
407	A56	50c Sunset Glow	1.10	.85

Perf. 14½x14, 14x14½

408	A56	$1 Ascocenda red gem	2.00	1.50
409	A56	$2.50 Brassolaeliocattleya nugget	4.75	3.75

410	A56	$5 Caularthron bicornutum	9.50	8.00
411	A56	$10 Moon orchid	17.50	15.00
		Nos. 396-411 (18)	39.70	33.15

Issued: 20c, 45c, 5/3/77; others, 9/16/74.
For surcharge see No. B2.

Wmk. 314 Upright; Sideways (1c, 25c, $1)

1976　　　　　　　　　　Perf. 14

396a	A56	1c multicolored	.15	.15
397a	A56	2c multicolored	.15	.15
398a	A56	3c multicolored	.20	.20
399a	A56	4c multicolored	.25	.20
402a	A56	10c multicolored	.45	.40
404a	A56	15c multicolored	.80	.70
405a	A56	25c multicolored	1.00	.90
406a	A56	35c multicolored	1.50	1.25

Perf. 14½x14

408a	A56	$1 multicolored	4.00	3.50
		Nos. 396a-408a (9)	8.50	7.40

1975　　　　Wmk. 373　　Perf. 14

396b	A56	1c multicolored	.15	.15
397b	A56	2c multicolored	.15	.15
398b	A56	3c multicolored	.15	.15
399b	A56	4c multicolored	.25	.22
400b	A56	5c multicolored	.15	.15
402b	A56	10c multicolored	.20	.20
403b	A56	12c multicolored	.25	.25
404b	A56	15c multicolored	.50	.45
406c	A56	45c multicolored	1.10	.90

Perf. 14½x14, 14x14½

408b	A56	$1 multicolored	2.00	1.90
409b	A56	$2.50 multicolored	5.00	4.50
410b	A56	$5 multicolored	10.00	9.50
411b	A56	$10 multicolored	18.00	18.00
		Nos. 396b-411b (13)	37.90	36.52

UPU
Emblem,
Barbados
No. 64
A57

Cent. of the UPU: 35c, Letters encircling globe. 50c, Barbados coat of arms. $1, Map of Barbados, sailing ship and jet.

1974, Oct. 9　　Litho.　　Perf. 14½

412	A57	8c brt rose, org & gray	.15	.15
413	A57	35c red, blk, & ocher	.45	.45
414	A57	50c vio blue, bl & sil	.65	.65
415	A57	$1 ultra, blk & brn	1.25	1.25
a.		Souvenir sheet of 4, #412-415	3.00	3.00
		Nos. 412-415 (4)	2.50	2.50

Yacht
Britannia off
Barbados
A58

Royal Visit, Feb. 1975: 35c, $1, Palms and sunset.

1975, Feb. 18

416	A58	8c brown & multi	.15	.15
417	A58	25c blue & multi	.40	.40
418	A58	35c purple & multi	.60	.60
419	A58	$1 violet & multi	1.65	1.65
		Nos. 416-419 (4)	2.80	2.80

St. Michael's
Cathedral — A59

Designs: 15c, Bishop Coleridge. 50c, All Saint's Church. $1, St. Michael, stained glass window, St. Michael's Cathedral.

Wmk. 314

1975, July 29　　Litho.　　Perf. 14

420	A59	5c blue & multi	.15	.15
421	A59	15c lilac & multi	.20	.20
422	A59	50c green & multi	.55	.55
423	A59	$1 multicolored	1.00	1.00
a.		Souvenir sheet of 4, #420-423	2.25	2.75
		Nos. 420-423 (4)	1.90	1.90

Anglican Diocese in Barbados, sesquicentennial.

Pony Float
A60

Designs: 25c, Stiltsman (band and masqueraders). 35c, Maypole dancing. 50c, Cuban dancers.

1975, Nov. 18　　Litho.　　Wmk. 373

424	A60	8c yellow & multi	.15	.15
425	A60	25c buff & multi	.30	.30
426	A60	35c ultra & multi	.40	.40
427	A60	50c orange & multi	.65	.65
a.		Souvenir sheet of 4, #424-427	1.75	1.75
		Nos. 424-427 (4)	1.50	1.50

Crop-over (harvest) festival.

Sailing Ship, 17th
Cent. — A61

Coat of
Arms — A62

350th Anniv. of 1st Settlement: 10c, Bearded fig tree and fruit. 25c, Ogilvy's 17th cent. map. $1, Capt. John Powell.

1975, Dec. 17　Wmk. 373　Perf. 13½

428	A61	4c lt blue & multi	.15	.15
429	A61	10c lt blue & multi	.20	.15
430	A61	25c yellow & multi	.55	.50
431	A61	$1 dk red & multi	1.90	1.65
a.		Souvenir sheet of 4, #428-431	3.00	2.75
		Nos. 428-431 (4)	2.80	2.45

Coil Stamps

1975, Dec.　　Unwmk.　　Perf. 15x14

432	A62	5c light blue	.15	.15
433	A62	25c violet	.25	.25

Map of West
Indies, Bats,
Wicket and
Ball — A63

Prudential Cup — A64

1976, July 7　　Litho.　　Perf. 14

438	A63	25c lt blue & multi	.85	.50
439	A64	45c lilac rose & black	1.10	1.00

World Cricket Cup, won by West Indies Team, 1975.

Map of South Carolina settled by
Barbadians — A65

American Bicentennial: 25c, George Washington and map of Bridge Town area. 50c, Declaration of Independence. $1, Masonic emblem and Prince Hall, founder and Grand Master of African Grand Lodge, Boston, 1790-1807.

1976, Aug. 17　Wmk. 373　Perf. 13½

440	A65	15c multicolored	.20	.20
441	A65	25c multicolored	.35	.35
442	A65	50c multicolored	.65	.65
443	A65	$1 multicolored	1.40	1.40
		Nos. 440-443 (4)	2.60	2.60

Mailman
with Bicycle
A66

PO Act, 125th anniv.: 35c, Mailman on motor scooter. 50c, Cover with Barbados No. 2. $1, Mail truck.

1976, Oct. 19　　Litho.　　Perf. 14

444	A66	8c rose red, blk & bis	.15	.15
445	A66	35c multicolored	.40	.40
446	A66	50c vio blue & multi	.60	.60
447	A66	$1 red & multi	1.10	1.10
		Nos. 444-447 (4)	2.25	2.25

Coast
Guard
Vessels
A67

Designs: 15c, Bank note, reverse, showing Barbados Parliament. 25c, National anthem by Van Roland Edwards (music) and Irvine Burgie (lyrics). $1, Independence Day parade.

1976, Nov. 30　　　　　　Perf. 13x13½

448	A67	5c multicolored	.15	.15
449	A67	15c multicolored	.15	.15
450	A67	25c yel, brown & blk	.25	.25
451	A67	$1 multicolored	1.00	1.00
a.		Souvenir sheet of 4, #448-451	2.00	2.00
		Nos. 448-451 (4)	1.55	1.55

10th anniv. of independence.

SILVER JUBILEE

Queen Knighting
Garfield Sobers,
1957 Visit — A68

Designs: 50c, Queen arriving at Westminster Abbey. $1, Queen leaving coach.

1977, Feb. 7　　　　　　　Perf. 14x13½

452	A68	15c silver & multi	.20	.20
453	A68	50c silver & multi	.60	.60
454	A68	$1 silver & multi	1.25	1.25
		Nos. 452-454 (3)	2.05	2.05

25th anniv. of the reign of Queen Elizabeth II. See Nos. 467-469.

Underwater
Park — A69

Beauty of Barbados: 35c, Royal palms, vert. 50c, Underwater caves. $1, Stalagmite in Harrison's Cave, vert.

1977, May 3　　Wmk. 373　　Perf. 14

455	A69	5c multicolored	.15	.15
456	A69	35c multicolored	.50	.50
457	A69	50c multicolored	.65	.65
458	A69	$1 multicolored	1.40	1.40
a.		Souvenir sheet of 4, #455-458	2.75	2.75
		Nos. 455-458 (4)	2.70	2.70

House of Commons Maces — A70

Charles I Handing Charter to Carlisle — A71

Designs: 25c, Speaker's chair. 50c, Senate Chamber. $1, Sam Lord's Castle, horiz.

1977, Aug. 2   Litho.   Perf. 13½
459	A70	10c red brown & yel	.15	.15
460	A70	25c slate grn & org	.30	.30
461	A70	50c dk green, grn & yel	.60	.60
462	A70	$1 dk & lt blue & org	1.10	1.10
		Nos. 459-462 (4)	2.15	2.15

13th Regional Conference of Commonwealth Parliamentary Association.

Perf. 13½x13, 13x13½
1977, Oct. 11   Litho.   Wmk. 373

Designs: 12c, Charter scroll. 45c, Charles I and Earl of Carlisle, horiz. $1, Map of Barbados, by Richard Ligon, 1657, horiz.

463	A71	12c buff & multi	.15	.15
464	A71	25c buff & multi	.30	.30
465	A71	45c buff & multi	.55	.55
466	A71	$1 buff & multi	1.10	1.10
		Nos. 463-466 (4)	2.10	2.10

350th anniv. of charter granting Barbados to the Earl of Carlisle.

Silver Jubilee Type, 1977, Inscribed:
"ROYAL VISIT"

1977, Oct. 31   Unwmk.   Roulette 5
Self-adhesive
467	A68	15c silver & multi	.20	.20
468	A68	50c silver & multi	.60	.60
469	A68	$1 silver & multi	1.10	1.10
		Nos. 467-469 (3)	1.90	1.90

Caribbean visit of Queen Elizabeth II. Printed on peelable paper backing inscribed in ultramarine multiple rows: "SILVER JUBILEE ROYAL VISIT BARBADOS." Printed with die-cut label inscribed in black "BEND & PEEL" attached at left of stamp. Sheets of 50 stamps and 50 labels.

Gibson's Map of Bridgetown, 1766 — A72

25c, Bridgetown, engraving by S. Copens, 1695. 45c, Trafalgar Square, Bridgetown, drawing by J. M. Carter, 1835. $1, The Bridges, 1978.

Perf. 14½
1978, Mar. 1   Litho.   Wmk. 373
470	A72	12c gold & multi	.15	.15
471	A72	25c gold & multi	.25	.25
472	A72	45c gold & multi	.45	.45
473	A72	$1 gold & multi	.85	.85
		Nos. 470-473 (4)	1.70	1.70

350th anniv. of founding of Bridgetown.

Elizabeth II Coronation Anniv. Issue
Souvenir Sheet
Common Design Types

1978, Apr. 21   Unwmk.   Perf. 15
474	Sheet of 6	3.00	3.00
a.	CD326 50c Griffin of Edward III	.50	.50
b.	CD327 50c Elizabeth II	.50	.50
c.	CD328 50c Pelican	.50	.50

No. 474 contains 2 se-tenant strips of Nos. 474a-474c, separated by horizontal gutter with commemorative and descriptive inscriptions and showing central part of coronation with coach.

Freak Bridge Hand A73

Designs: 10c, World Bridge Fed. emblem. 45c, Central American and Caribbean Bridge Fed. emblem. $1, Map of Caribbean and cards.

Perf. 14½
1978, June 6   Litho.   Wmk. 373
475	A73	5c multicolored	.15	.15
476	A73	10c multicolored	.15	.15
477	A73	45c multicolored	.50	.50
478	A73	$1 multicolored	1.00	1.00
a.		Souvenir sheet of 4, #475-478	1.50	1.50
		Nos. 475-478 (4)	1.80	1.80

7th Regional Bridge Tournament, Dover Centre, Barbados, June 5-14.

Girl Guides' Camp — A74

Designs: 28c, Girl Guides helping children and handicapped. 50c, Badge with "60," vert. $1, Badge with initials, vert.

1978, Aug. 1   Litho.   Perf. 13½
479	A74	12c multicolored	.15	.15
480	A74	28c multicolored	.30	.30
481	A74	50c multicolored	.50	.50
482	A74	$1 multicolored	1.00	1.00
		Nos. 479-482 (4)	1.95	1.95

Girl Guides of Barbados, 60th anniv.

Garment Industry A75

Industries of Barbados: 28c, Cooper, vert. 45c, Blacksmith, vert. 50c, Wrought iron industry.

1978, Nov. 14   Litho.   Perf. 14
483	A75	12c multicolored	.15	.15
484	A75	28c multicolored	.30	.30
485	A75	45c multicolored	.40	.40
486	A75	50c multicolored	.50	.50
		Nos. 483-486 (4)	1.35	1.35

Early Mail Steamer A76

Ships: 25c, Q.E.II in Deep Water Harbour. 50c, Ra II (raft) nearing Barbados. $1, Early mail steamer.

1979, Feb. 8   Litho.   Perf. 13x13½
487	A76	12c multicolored	.15	.15
488	A76	25c multicolored	.30	.30
489	A76	50c multicolored	.50	.50
490	A76	$1 multicolored	1.00	1.00
		Nos. 487-490 (4)	1.95	1.95

Barbados No. 235 A77

28c, Barbados #430, vert. 45c, Penny Black and Maltese postmark, vert. 50c, Barbados #21b.

Wmk. 373
1979, May 8   Litho.   Perf. 14
491	A77	12c multicolored	.15	.15
492	A77	28c multicolored	.20	.20
493	A77	45c multicolored	.30	.30
		Nos. 491-493 (3)	.65	.65

Souvenir Sheet
494	A77	50c multicolored	.40	.40

Sir Rowland Hill (1795-1879), originator of penny postage.

Birds — A78

Launcher Transported through Barbados — A79

1979-81   Photo.   Wmk. 373   Perf. 14
495	A78	1c Grass canaries	.15	.15
496	A78	2c Rain birds	.15	.15
497	A78	5c Sparrows	.15	.15
498	A78	8c Frigate birds	.15	.15
499	A78	10c Cattle egrets	.15	.15
500	A78	12c Green gaulins	.15	.15
501	A78	20c Hummingbirds	.25	.15
502	A78	25c Ground doves	.25	.25
503	A78	28c Blackbirds	.30	.30
504	A78	35c Green-throated caribs	.40	.40
505	A78	45c Wood doves	.55	.55
506	A78	50c Ramiers	.65	.65
506A	A78	55c Black-breasted plover ('81)	.80	.80
507	A78	70c Yellow breasts	.80	.80
508	A78	$1 Pee whistlers	1.25	1.25
509	A78	$2.50 Christmas birds	3.25	3.25
510	A78	$5 Kingfishers	7.00	2.00
511	A78	$10 Red-seal coot	14.00	14.00
		Nos. 495-511 (18)	30.40	25.30

Issue dates: 55c, Sept. 1; others, Aug. 7.
See #570-572. For surcharges see #563-565.

1979, Oct. 9   Photo.

Designs: 10c, Gun on landing craft, Foul Bay, horiz. 20c, Firing of 16-inch launcher by day. 28c, Bath Station and Intelsat IV-A, horiz. 45c, Intelsat over Caribbean, horiz. 50c, Intelsat IV-A over Atlantic, and globe. $1, Lunar landing module, horiz.

512	A79	10c multicolored	.15	.15
513	A79	12c multicolored	.15	.15
514	A79	20c multicolored	.15	.15
515	A79	28c multicolored	.20	.20
516	A79	45c multicolored	.30	.30
517	A79	50c multicolored	.35	.35
		Nos. 512-517 (6)	1.30	1.30

Souvenir Sheet
518	A79	$1 multicolored	.85	.85

Space exploration. No. 518 commemorates 10th anniversary of first moon landing.

Family, IYC Emblem — A80

IYC Emblem and: 28c, Children holding hands and map of Barbados. 45c, Boy and teacher. 50c, Children playing. $1, Boy and girl flying kite.

1979, Nov. 27   Litho.   Perf. 14
519	A80	12c multicolored	.15	.15
520	A80	28c multicolored	.20	.20
521	A80	45c multicolored	.30	.30
522	A80	50c multicolored	.35	.35
523	A80	$1 multicolored	.65	.65
		Nos. 519-523 (5)	1.65	1.65

Map of Barbados, Anniversary Emblem — A81

Rotary Intl., 75th Anniv.: 28c, Map of district 404. 50c, 75th anniv. emblem. $1, Paul P. Harris, founder.

1980, Feb. 19   Litho.   Perf. 13½
524	A81	12c multicolored	.15	.15
525	A81	28c multicolored	.20	.20
526	A81	50c multicolored	.35	.35
527	A81	$1 multicolored	.65	.65
		Nos. 524-527 (4)	1.35	1.35

Regiment Volunteer, Artillery Company, 1909 — A82

Perf. 14½
1980, Apr. 8   Litho.   Wmk. 373
528	A82	12c shown	.15	.15
529	A82	35c Drum major	.20	.20
530	A82	50c Sovereign's, regimental flags	.35	.35
531	A82	$1 Women's corps	.65	.65
		Nos. 528-531 (4)	1.35	1.35

Barbados Regiment, 75th anniv.

Souvenir Sheets

Early Mailman, London 1980 Emblem — A83

The vignette is a different color for each stamp.

Wmk. 373
1980, May 6   Litho.   Perf. 14
532	Sheet of 6	1.10	1.10
a.-f.	A83 28c any single	.20	.20
533	Sheet of 6	2.25	2.25
a.-f.	A83 50c any single	.35	.35

London 80 Intl. Stamp Exhib., May 6-14.

Underwater Scenes — A84

1980, Sept. 30   Litho.   Perf. 13½
534	A84	12c multicolored	.15	.15
535	A84	25c multicolored	.25	.25
536	A84	50c multicolored	.40	.40
537	A84	$1 multicolored	.75	.75
a.		Souvenir sheet of 4, #534-537	1.50	1.50
		Nos. 534-537 (4)	1.55	1.55

Bathsheba Railroad Station A85

1981, Jan. 13   Litho.   Perf. 14½
538 A85 12c shown   .15   .15
539 A85 28c Cab stand, The Green   .20   .20
540 A85 45c Mule-drawn tram   .30   .30
541 A85 70c Horse-drawn bus   .50   .50
542 A85 $1 Fairchild St. railroad
        station   .65   .65
     Nos. 538-542 (5)   1.80   1.80

Visually Handicapped Girl at
Typewriter — A86

1981, May 19   Litho.   Perf. 14
543 A86 10c shown   .15   .15
544 A86 25c Sign language al-
        phabet, vert.   .15   .15
545 A86 45c Blind people crossing
        street, vert.   .30   .30
546 A86 $2.50 Baseball game   1.65   1.65
     Nos. 543-546 (4)   2.25   2.25
     International Year of the Disabled.

Royal Wedding Issue
Common Design Type
Perf. 13½
1981, July 22   Litho.   Wmk. 373
547 CD331 28c Bouquet   .20   .20
548 CD331 50c Charles   .35   .35
549 CD331 $2.50 Couple   1.65   1.65
     Nos. 547-549 (3)   2.20   2.20

4th Caribbean Arts
Festival
(CARIFESTA), July
19-Aug. 3 — A87

1981, Aug. 11   Litho.   Perf. 14½
550 A87 15c Landship maneuver   .15   .15
551 A87 20c Yoruba dancer   .15   .15
552 A87 40c Tuk band   .30   .30
553 A87 55c Frank Collymore (sculp-
        ture)   .40   .40
554 A87 $1 Barbados Harbor (paint-
        ing)   .75   .75
     Nos. 550-554 (5)   1.75   1.75

Hurricane
Gladys,
View from
Apollo
A88

1981, Sept. 29   Litho.   Perf. 14
555 A88 35c Satellite view over Bar-
        bados   .30   .30
556 A88 50c shown   .40   .40
557 A88 60c Police watch   .50   .50
558 A88 $1 Spotter plane   .85   .85
     Nos. 555-558 (4)   2.05   2.05

Harrison's Cave — A89

Perf. 14x14½
1981, Dec. 1   Litho.   Wmk. 373
559 A89 10c Twin Falls   .15   .15
560 A89 20c Rotunda Room
        Stream   .15   .15
561 A89 55c Rotunda Room forma-
        tion   .35   .35
562 A89 $2.50 Cascade Pool   1.65   1.65
     Nos. 559-562 (4)   2.30   2.30

Nos. 503, 505, 507 Surcharged
1982, Feb. 1   Photo.   Perf. 14
563 A78 15c on 28c multi   .15   .15
564 A78 40c on 45c multi   .40   .40
565 A78 60c on 70c multi   .60   .60
     Nos. 563-565 (3)   1.15   1.15

Black Belly
Sheep
A90

1982, Feb. 9   Litho.
566 A90 40c Ram   .40   .40
567 A90 50c Ewe   .50   .50
568 A90 60c Ewe, lambs   .60   .60
569 A90 $1 Pair, map   1.00   1.00
     Nos. 566-569 (4)   2.50   2.50

Bird Type of 1979
Wmk. 373
1982, Mar. 1   Photo.   Perf. 14
570 A78 15c like #503   .15   .15
571 A78 40c like #506   .40   .40
572 A78 60c like #507   .60   .60
     Nos. 570-572 (3)   1.15   1.15

Early
Marine
Transport
A91

1982, Apr. 6   Litho.   Perf. 14½
577 A91 20c Lighter   .20   .20
578 A91 35c Rowboat   .35   .35
579 A91 55c Speightstown schoon-
        er   .55   .55
580 A91 $2.50 Inter-colonial schoon-
        er   2.50   2.50
     Nos. 577-580 (4)   3.60   3.60

Visit of Pres.
Ronald
Reagan
A92

1982, Apr. 8   Litho.   Perf. 14
581 A92 20c Barbados Flag, arms   .20   .20
582 A92 20c US Flag, arms   .20   .20
  a.   Pair, Nos. 581-582   .40   .40
583 A92 55c like #581   .55   .50
584 A92 55c like #582   .55   .50
  a.   Pair, Nos. 583-584   1.10   1.10
     Nos. 581-584 (4)   1.50   1.40
Printed in sheets of 8 with gutter showing Pres.
Reagan and Prime Minister Tom Adams.

Princess Diana Issue
Common Design Type
1982, July 1   Litho.   Perf. 14½
585 CD333 20c Arms   .15   .15
586 CD333 60c Diana   .45   .45
587 CD333 $1.20 Wedding   .90   .90
588 CD333 $2.50 Portrait   1.75   1.75
     Nos. 585-588 (4)   3.25   3.25

Scouting
Year — A93

Washington's 250th
Birth
Anniv. — A94

1982, Sept. 7   Wmk. 373   Perf. 14
589 A93 15c Helping woman   .15   .15
590 A93 40c Sign, emblem, flag,
        horiz.   .45   .45

---

591 A93 55c Religious service,
        horiz.   .55   .55
592 A93 $1 Flags   1.00   1.00
     Nos. 589-592 (4)   2.15   2.15
Souvenir Sheet
593 A93 $1.50 Laws   1.65   1.65

1982, Nov. 2   Perf. 13½x13
594 A94 10c Arms   .15   .15
595 A94 55c Washington's house,
        Barbados   .55   .55
596 A94 60c Taking command   .60   .60
597 A94 $2.50 Taking oath   2.50   2.50
     Nos. 594-597 (4)   3.80   3.80

A95

1983, Mar. 14   Litho.   Perf. 14
598 A95 15c Map, globe   .15   .15
599 A95 40c Beach   .40   .40
600 A95 60c Sugar cane harvest   .60   .60
601 A95 $1 Cricket game   1.00   1.00
     Nos. 598-601 (4)   2.15   2.15
     Commonwealth day.

Gulf
Fritillary
A96

Perf. 13½x13
1983, Feb. 8   Litho.   Wmk. 373
602 A96 20c shown   .25   .25
603 A96 40c Monarch   .45   .45
604 A96 55c Mimic   .60   .60
605 A96 $2.50 Hanno Blue   3.00   3.00
     Nos. 602-605 (4)   4.30   4.30

Manned
Flight
Bicentenary
A97

1983, June 14   Litho.   Perf. 14
606 A97 20c US Navy dirigible   .30   .30
607 A97 40c Douglas DC-3   .85   .85
608 A97 55c Vickers Viscount   1.25   1.25
609 A97 $1 Lockheed TriStar   2.50   2.50
     Nos. 606-609 (4)   4.90   4.90

Nash 600,
1941
A98

1983, Aug. 9   Litho.   Perf. 14
610 A98 25c shown   .25   .25
611 A98 45c Dodge, 1938   .45   .45
612 A98 75c Ford Model AA,
        1930   .75   .75
613 A98 $2.50 Dodge Four, 1918   2.50   2.50
     Nos. 610-613 (4)   3.95   3.95

A99

A100

1983, Aug. 30   Litho.   Perf. 14
614 A99 20c Players   .20   .20
615 A99 65c Emblem, map   .65   .65
616 A99 $1 Cup   1.00   1.00
     Nos. 614-616 (3)   1.85   1.85
World Cup Table Tennis Championship.

1983, Nov. 1   Perf. 14
Christmas: 10c, 25c, Angel with lute, painting
details. $2, The Virgin and Child, by Masaccio.
617 A100 10c multicolored   .15   .15
618 A100 25c multicolored   .25   .25
Souvenir Sheet
619 A100 $2 multicolored   2.00   2.00

Barbados
Museum,
Golden
Jubilee
A101

Museum Paintings: 45c, by Richard Day. 75c, St.
Ann's Garrison in Barbados by W.S. Hedges. $2.50,
Needham's Point, Carlisle Bay.

1983, Nov. 1   Perf. 14
620 A101 45c multicolored   .45   .45
621 A101 75c multicolored   .75   .75
622 A101 $2.50 multicolored   2.50   2.50
     Nos. 620-622 (3)   3.70   3.70

1984
Olympics,
Los Angeles
A102

1984, Apr. 3   Litho.   Perf. 14
623 A102 50c Track & field   .50   .50
624 A102 65c Shooting   .65   .65
625 A102 75c Sailing   .75   .75
626 A102 $1 Bicycling   1.00   1.00
  a.   Souvenir sheet of 4, #623-626 3.00   3.00
     Nos. 623-626 (4)   2.90   2.90

Lloyd's List Issue
Common Design Type
1984, Apr. 25   Litho.   Perf. 14½
627 CD335 45c World map   .45   .45
628 CD335 50c Bridgetown Harbor   .50   .50
629 CD335 75c Philosopher   .75   .75
630 CD335 $1 Sea Princess   1.00   1.00
     Nos. 627-630 (4)   2.70   2.70

Souvenir Sheet

1984 UPU
Congress
A103

1984, June 6   Litho.   Perf. 13½
631 A103 $2 #213, UPU emblem   2.00   2.00

World Chess
Fed., 60th
Anniv. — A104

1984, Aug. 8   Perf. 14x14½
632 A104 25c Junior match   .30   .30
633 A104 45c Knights   .50   .50
634 A104 65c Queens   .75   .75
635 A104 $2 Rooks   2.25   2.25
     Nos. 632-635 (4)   3.80   3.80

Christmas — A105

1984, Oct. 24   Litho.   Perf. 14
636 A105 50c Poinsettia   .50   .50
637 A105 65c Snow-on-the-mountain   .65   .65
638 A105 75c Christmas candle   .75   .75
639 A105 $1 Christmas hope   1.00 1.00
        Nos. 636-639 (4)   2.90 2.90

Marine Life A106

1985   Litho.   Wmk. 373   Perf. 14
640 A106   1c Bristle worm   .15   .15
641 A106   2c Spotted trunk fish   .15   .15
642 A106   5c Coney fish   .15   .15
643 A106 10c Pink-tipped anem-
              one   .15   .15
645 A106 20c Christmas tree
              worm   .30   .30
646 A106 25c Hermit crab   .35   .35
648 A106 35c Animal flower   .50   .50
649 A106 40c Vase sponge   .60   .60
650 A106 45c Spotted moray   .65   .65
651 A106 50c Ghost crab   .75   .75
653 A106 65c Flaming tongue
              snail   .95   .95
654 A106 75c Sergeant major
              fish   1.10 1.10
656 A106 $1 Caribbean warty
              anemone   1.50 1.50
657 A106 $2.50 Green turtle   3.75 3.75
658 A106 $5 Rock beauty   7.25 7.25
659 A106 $10 Elkhorn coral   15.00 15.00
        Nos. 640-659 (16)   33.30 33.30

Issue dates: 10c, 20c, 25c, 50c, $2.50 and $5, Feb. 26; 5c, 35c, 40c, 65c and $10, Apr. 9; 1c, 2c, 45c, 75c and $1, May 7.
Exist inscribed "1987," etc.

1986 (?)   Wmk. 384
640a A106   1c   .15   .15
641a A106   2c   .15   .15
642a A106   5c   .15   .15
643a A106   10c   .15   .15
645a A106   20c   .30   .30
646a A106   25c   .35   .35
648a A106   35c   .45   .45
649a A106   40c   .60   .60
650a A106   45c   .65   .65
651a A106   50c   .75   .75
653a A106   65c   .95   .95
654a A106   75c   1.10 1.10
656a A106 $1   1.50 1.50
657a A106 $2.50   3.75 3.75
658a A106 $5   7.25 7.25
659a A106 $10   15.00 15.00
        Nos. 640a-659a (16)   33.25 33.25

Some inscribed "1986." Also exist with "1987," "1988," and with no date.

Queen Mother 85th Birthday
Common Design Type
Perf. 14¹/₂x14
1985, June 7   Litho.   Wmk. 384
660 CD336 25c At Buckingham Pal-
               ace, 1930   .25   .25
661 CD336 65c With Lady Diana,
               1981   .65   .65
662 CD336 75c At the docks   .75   .75
663 CD336 $1 Holding Prince Hen-
               ry   1.00 1.00
        Nos. 660-663 (4)   2.65 2.65
Souvenir Sheet
664 CD336 $2 Opening the Garden
               Center, Syon
               House   2.00 2.00

Audubon Birth Bicentenary A107

Illustrations of North American bird species. Nos. 666-668 vert.

Wmk. 373
1985, Aug. 6   Litho.   Perf. 14
665 A107 45c Falco peregrinus   .60   .60
666 A107 65c Dendroica discolor   .90   .90
667 A107 75c Ardea herodias   1.10 1.10
668 A107 $1 Dendroica petechia   1.40 1.40
        Nos. 665-668 (4)   4.00 4.00

Satellite Orbiting Earth A108

1985, Sept. 10
669 A108 75c multicolored   .75   .75

INTELSAT, Intl. Telecommunications Satellite Consortium, 20th anniv.

Royal Barbados Police, 150th Anniv. — A109

1985, Nov. 19
670 A109 25c Traffic Dept.   .25   .25
671 A109 50c Police Band   .50   .50
672 A109 65c Dog Force   .65   .65
673 A109 $1 Mounted Police   1.00 1.00
        Nos. 670-673 (4)   2.40 2.40
Souvenir Sheet
674 A109 $2 Band on parade, horiz. 2.00 2.00

Queen Elizabeth II 60th Birthday
Common Design Type

Designs: 25c, Age 2. 50c, Senate House opening, University College of the West Indies, Jamaica, 1953. 65c, With Prince Philip, Caribbean Tour, 1985. 75c, Banquet, state visit to Sao Paulo, Brazil, 1968. $2, Visiting Crown Agents, 1983.

Perf. 14x14¹/₂
1986, Apr. 21   Litho.   Wmk. 384
675 CD337 25c scar, blk & sil   .20   .20
676 CD337 50c ultra & multi   .45   .45
677 CD337 65c green & multi   .60   .60
678 CD337 75c violet & multi   .70   .70
679 CD337 $2 rose vio & multi   1.90 1.90
        Nos. 675-679 (5)   3.85 3.85

EXPO '86, Vancouver A110

1986, May 2   Perf. 14
680 A110 50c Trans-Canada North
               Star   .50   .50
681 A110 $2.50 Lady Nelson   2.50 2.50

AMERIPEX '86 A111

1986, May 22   Wmk. 373
682 A111 45c No. 441   .45   .45
683 A111 50c No. 442   .50   .50
684 A111 65c No. 558   .65   .65
685 A111 $1 Nos. 583-584   1.00 1.00
        Nos. 682-685 (4)   2.60 2.60
Souvenir Sheet
686 A111 $2 Statue of Liberty, NY
               Harbor   2.00 2.00
Statue of Liberty, cent.

Royal Wedding Issue, 1986
Common Design Type

Designs: 45c, Informal portrait. $1, Andrew in navy uniform.

Perf. 14¹/₂x14
1986, July 23   Litho.   Wmk. 384
687 CD338 45c multicolored   .45   .45
688 CD338 $1 multicolored   1.00 1.00

Electrification of Barbados, 75th Anniv. — A112

Designs: 10c, Transporting utility poles, 1923. 25c, Heathfield ladder, 1935, vert. 65c, Transport fleet, 1941. $2, Bucket truck, 1986, vert.

Wmk. 384
1986, Sept. 16   Litho.   Perf. 14
689 A112 10c multicolored   .15   .15
690 A112 25c multicolored   .25   .25
691 A112 65c multicolored   .65   .65
692 A112 $2 multicolored   2.00 2.00
        Nos. 689-692 (4)   3.05 3.05

Christmas — A113

Church windows and flowers.

1986, Oct. 28   Wmk. 373
693 A113 25c Alpinia purpurata   .25   .25
694 A113 50c Anthurium andrae-
               anum   .50   .50
695 A113 75c Heliconia rostrata   .75   .75
696 A113 $2 Heliconia psittacorum   2.00 2.00
        Nos. 693-696 (4)   3.50 3.50

Natl. Special Olympics, 10th Anniv. A114

1987, Mar. 27   Wmk. 373   Perf. 14
697 A114 15c Shot put   .15   .15
698 A114 45c Wheelchair race   .45   .45
699 A114 65c Girl's long jump   .65   .65
700 A114 $2 Emblem, creed   2.00 2.00
        Nos. 697-700 (4)   3.25 3.25

CAPEX '87 — A115

1987, June 12
701 A115 25c Barn swallow   .35   .35
702 A115 50c Yellow warbler   .75   .75
703 A115 65c Audubon's shearwater   .90   .90
704 A115 75c Black-whiskered vireo 1.10 1.10
705 A115 $1 Scarlet tanager   1.50 1.50
        Nos. 701-705 (5)   4.60 4.60

Natl. Scouting Movement, 75th Anniv. — A116

1987, July 24   Perf. 14x14¹/₂
706 A116 10c Scout sign   .15   .15
707 A116 25c Campfire   .25   .25
708 A116 65c Merit badges, etc.   .65   .65
709 A116 $2 Marching band   2.00 2.00
        Nos. 706-709 (4)   3.05 3.05

Bridgetown Synagogue Restoration A117

1987, Oct. 6   Wmk. 384   Perf. 14¹/₂
710 A117 50c Exterior   .65   .65
711 A117 65c Interior   .85   .85
712 A117 75c Ten Commandments,
               vert.   1.00 1.00
713 A117 $1 Marble laver, vert.   1.40 1.40
        Nos. 710-713 (4)   3.90 3.90

Natl. Independence, 21st Anniv. — A118

E.W. Barrow (1920-87), Father of Independence A119

Designs: 25c, Coat of arms and seal of the colony. 45c, Natl. flag and the Union Jack. 65c, Silver dollar and penny. $2, Old and new regimental flags and Queen Elizabeth's colors.

1987, Nov. 24   Perf. 14¹/₂
714 A118 25c multicolored   .25   .25
715 A118 45c multicolored   .45   .45
716 A118 65c multicolored   .65   .65
717 A118 $2 multicolored   2.00 2.00
        Nos. 714-717 (4)   3.35 3.35
Souvenir Sheet
718 A119 $1.50 multicolored   1.50 1.50

Cricket A120

Bat, wicket posts, ball, 18th cent. belt buckle and batters: 15c, E.A. "Manny" Martindale. 45c, George Challenor. 50c, Herman C. Griffith. 75c, Harold Austin. $2, Frank Worrell.

1988   Litho.   Wmk. 373   Perf. 14
719 A120 15c multicolored   .15   .15
720 A120 45c multicolored   .45   .45
720A A120 50c multicolored   .50   .50
721 A120 75c multicolored   .75   .75
722 A120 $2 multicolored   2.00 2.00
        Nos. 719-722 (5)   3.85 3.85

The 50c was originally printed with the wrong photograph but was not issued. Copies of the error have appeared on the market.
Issued: No. 720A, July 11; others, June 6.

Lizards — A121

1988 Summer Olympics, Seoul — A122

1988, June 13
723 A121 10c Kentropyx borckianus .15 .15
724 A121 50c Hemidactylus mabouia .60 .60
725 A121 65c Anolis extremus .75 .75
726 A121 $2 Gymnophthalmus un-
           derwoodii 2.25 2.25
    Nos. 723-726 (4) 3.75 3.75

Perf. 14½

1988, Aug. 2   Litho.   Wmk. 373
727 A122 25c Cycling .25 .25
728 A122 45c Running .45 .45
729 A122 75c Swimming .75 .75
730 A122 $2 Yachting 2.00 2.00
    a. Souvenir sheet of 4, #727-730 3.50 3.50
    Nos. 727-730 (4) 3.45 3.45

Lloyds of London, 300th Anniv.
Common Design Type

Designs: 40c, Royal Exchange, 1774. 50c, Sugar
mill (windmill), horiz. 65c, Container ship Author,
horiz. $2, Sinking of the Titanic, 1912.

1988, Oct. 18   Litho.   Perf. 14
731 CD341 40c multicolored .40 .40
732 CD341 50c multicolored .50 .50
733 CD341 65c multicolored .65 .65
734 CD341 $2 multicolored 2.00 2.00
    Nos. 731-734 (4) 3.55 3.55

Harry Bayley
Observatory,
25th Anniv.
A123

Designs: 25c, Observatory, crescent Moon,
Venus and Harry Bayley. 65c, Observatory and con-
stellations. 75c, Andromeda Galaxy and telescope.
$2, Orion Constellation.

1988, Nov. 28   Wmk. 384   Perf. 14½
735 A123 25c multicolored .25 .25
736 A123 65c multicolored .65 .65
737 A123 75c multicolored .75 .75
738 A123 $2 multicolored 2.00 2.00
    Nos. 735-738 (4) 3.65 3.65

Commercial Aviation, 50th Anniv. — A124

Designs: 25c, Caribbean Airline Liat BAe748.
65c, Pan American DC-8. 75c, Two British Airways
Concordes, Grantley Adams Intl. Airport. $2, Two
Caribbean Air Cargo Boeing 707-351c.

1989, Mar. 20   Litho.   Perf. 14
739 A124 25c multicolored .25 .25
740 A124 65c multicolored .65 .65
741 A124 75c multicolored .75 .75
742 A124 $2 multicolored 2.00 2.00
    Nos. 739-742 (4) 3.65 3.65

Parliament,
350th
Anniv. — A125

1989, July 19   Litho.   Perf. 13½
743 A125 25c Assembly chamber .25 .25
744 A125 50c The Speaker .50 .50
745 A125 75c Parliament, c. 1882 .75 .75
746 A125 $2.50 Queen in Parliament 2.50 2.50
    Nos. 743-746 (4) 4.00 4.00

Parliament, 350th anniv. See No. 752.

Wildlife Preservation — A126

1989, Aug. 1   Perf. 14x13½
747 A126 10c Wild hare, vert. .20 .20
748 A126 50c Red-footed tortoise .75 .75
749 A126 65c Green monkey, vert. 1.00 1.00
750 A126 $2 Toad 3.00 3.00
    Nos. 747-750 (4) 4.95 4.95

Souvenir Sheet
751 A126 $1 Mongoose, vert. 2.00 2.00

Parliament Anniv. Type of 1989
Souvenir Sheet

1989, Oct. 9   Wmk. 373   Perf. 13½
752 A125 $1 The Mace 1.00 1.00

35th Commonwealth Parliamentary Conf.

Wild
Plants — A127

World Stamp Expo
'89, Washington,
DC — A128

1989-92   Wmk. 373   Perf. 14½
753 A127 2c Bread'n cheese .15 .15
754 A127 5c Scarlet cordia .15 .15
755 A127 10c Columnar cac-
           tus .15 .15
756 A127 20c Spiderlily .20 .20
757 A127 25c Rock balsam .25 .25
758 A127 30c Hollyhock .30 .30
758A A127 35c Red sage .35 .35
759 A127 45c Yellow shak-
           shak .45 .45
760 A127 50c Whitewood .50 .50
761 A127 55c Bluebell .55 .55
762 A127 65c Prickly sage .65 .65
763 A127 70c Seaside sam-
           phire .70 .70
764 A127 80c Flat-hand dildo .80 .80
764A A127 90c Herringbone .90 .90
765 A127 $1.10 Lent tree 1.10 1.10
766 A127 $2.50 Rodwood 2.50 2.50
767 A127 $5 Cowitch 5.00 5.00
768 A127 $10 Maypole 10.00 10.00
    Nos. 753-768 (18) 24.70 24.70

Issue dates: 35c, 90c, June 9, 1992 (inscribed
1991). Others, Nov. 1.
Nos. 754-756, 763, 765 exist inscribed "1991."
For overprints see Nos. 788-790.

1990   Litho.   Wmk. 384
753a A127 2c .15 .15
754a A127 5c .15 .15
755a A127 10c .15 .15
756a A127 20c .20 .20
757a A127 25c .25 .25
759a A127 45c .40 .40
760a A127 50c .45 .45
762a A127 65c .60 .60
766a A127 $2.50 2.25 2.25
767a A127 $5 4.50 4.50
768a A127 $10 9.00 9.00
    Nos. 753a-768a (11) 18.10 18.10

Inscribed 1990.

1989, Nov. 17   Wmk. 384   Perf. 14

Water sports.

769 A128 25c Water skiing .25 .25
770 A128 50c Yachting .50 .50
771 A128 65c Scuba diving .65 .65
772 A128 $2.50 Surfing 2.50 2.50
    Nos. 769-772 (4) 3.90 3.90

Horse
Racing
A129

Wmk. 373
1990, May 3   Litho.   Perf. 14
773 A129 25c Bugler, jockeys .25 .25
774 A129 45c Parade ring .45 .45
775 A129 75c In the straight .75 .75
776 A129 $2 Winner, vert. 2.00 2.00
    Nos. 773-776 (4) 3.45 3.45

Barbados
No. 2 — A130

Stamps on stamps: No. 778, Barbados #61. 65c,
Barbados #73. $2.50, Barbados #121. No. 781a,
Great Britain #1. No. 781b, Barbados #108.

1990, May 3
777 A130 25c shown .25 .25
778 A130 50c multicolored .50 .50
779 A130 65c multicolored .65 .65
780 A130 $2.50 multicolored 2.50 2.50
    Nos. 777-780 (4) 3.90 3.90

Souvenir Sheet
781   Sheet of 2 1.00 1.00
a.-b.   A130 50c any single .50 .50

Stamp World London '90.

Queen Mother, 90th Birthday
Common Design Types
1990, Aug. 8   Wmk. 384   Perf. 14x15
782 CD343 75c At age 23 .75 .75

Perf. 14½
783 CD344 $2.50 Engagement por-
             trait, 1923 2.50 2.50

Insects
A131

Wmk. 373
1990, Oct. 16   Litho.   Perf. 14
784 A131 50c Dragonfly .50 .50
785 A131 65c Black hardback beetle .65 .65
786 A131 75c Green grasshopper .75 .75
787 A131 $2 God-horse 2.00 2.00
    Nos. 784-787 (4) 3.90 3.90

Nos. 757, 764 and
766 Overprinted

VISIT OF
HRH THE
PRINCESS ROYAL
OCTOBER 1990

1990, Nov. 21   Perf. 14½
788 A127 25c on No. 757 .25 .25
789 A127 80c on No. 764 .80 .80
790 A127 $2.50 on No. 766 2.50 2.50
    Nos. 788-790 (3) 3.55 3.55

Christmas — A132

1990, Dec. 4   Perf. 14
791 A132 20c Christmas star .20 .20
792 A132 50c Nativity scene .50 .50
793 A132 $1 Stained glass window 1.00 1.00
794 A132 $2 Angel 2.00 2.00
    Nos. 791-794 (4) 3.70 3.70

Yellow
Warbler
A133

1991, Mar. 4
795 A133 10c shown .25 .25
796 A133 20c Male, female, nest .55 .55
797 A133 45c Female, chicks 1.25 1.25
798 A133 $1 Male, fledgling 2.75 2.75
    Nos. 795-798 (4) 4.80 4.80

World Wildlife Fund.

Fishing
A134

Perf. 13½x14, 14x13½
1991, June 18   Litho.   Wmk. 373
799 A134 5c Daily catch, vert. .15 .15
800 A134 50c Line fishing .50 .50
801 A134 75c Cleaning fish .75 .75
802 A134 $2.50 Game fishing, vert. 2.50 2.50
    Nos. 799-802 (4) 3.90 3.90

Freemasonry in
Barbados, 250th
Anniv. — A135

Designs: 25c, Masonic Building, Bridgetown.
65c, Compass and square. 75c, Royal arch jewel.
$2.50, Columns, apron and centenary badge.

1991, Sept. 17   Perf. 14
803 A135 25c multicolored .25 .25
804 A135 65c multicolored .65 .65
805 A135 75c multicolored .75 .75
806 A135 $2.50 multicolored 2.50 2.50
    Nos. 803-806 (4) 4.15 4.15

Butterflies
A136

1991, Nov. 15   Wmk. 384
807 A136 20c Polydamus swallow-
           tail .25 .25
808 A136 50c Long-tailed skipper,
           vert. .65 .65
809 A136 65c Cloudless sulphur .85 .85
810 A136 $2.50 Caribbean buckeye,
           vert. 3.25 3.25
    Nos. 807-810 (4) 5.00 5.00

Souvenir Sheet
811 A136 $4 Painted lady 6.00 6.00

Phila Nippon '91.

Independence, 25th Anniv. — A137

Governor-General Dame Nita Barrow and: 10c,
Students in classroom. 25c, Barbados Workers Union
headquarters. 65c, Building industry. 75c, Agriculture. $1, Inoculations given at health clinic. $2.50,
Gordon Greenidge, Desmond Haynes, cricket players (no portrait).

1991, Nov. 20   Wmk. 373
812 A137 10c multicolored .15 .15
813 A137 25c multicolored .25 .25
814 A137 65c multicolored .65 .65
815 A137 75c multicolored .75 .75
816 A137 $1 multicolored 1.00 1.00
    Nos. 812-816 (5) 2.80 2.80

Souvenir Sheet
817 A137 $2.50 multi, vert. 2.40 2.50

Easter — A138

Wmk. 384

1992, Apr. 7		**Litho.**	*Perf.*	*14*
818	A138	35c Christ carrying cross	.35	.35
819	A138	70c Christ on cross	.70	.70
820	A138	90c Christ taken down from cross	.90	.90
821	A138	$3 Christ risen	3.00	3.00
		Nos. 818-821 (4)	4.95	4.95

Flowering Trees A139

Perf. 14x13½

1992, June 9	**Litho.**	**Wmk. 373**	
822	A139	10c Cannon ball	.15 .15
823	A139	30c Golden shower	.30 .30
824	A139	80c Frangipani	.80 .80
825	A139	$1.10 Flamboyant	1.10 1.10
		Nos. 822-825 (4)	2.35 2.35

Orchids A140

Designs: 55c, Epidendrum "Costa Rica." 65c, Cattleya guttaca. 70c, Laeliacattleya "Splashing Around." $1.40, Phalaenopsis "Kathy Saegert."

1992, Sept. 8			*Perf. 13½x14*	
826	A140	55c multicolored	.55	.55
827	A140	65c multicolored	.65	.65
828	A140	70c multicolored	.70	.70
829	A140	$1.40 multicolored	1.40	1.40
		Nos. 826-829 (4)	3.30	3.30

For overprints see Nos. 838-841.

Transport and Tourism A141

Designs: 5c, Mini Moke, Gun Hill Signal Station, St. George. 35c, Tour bus, Bathsheba Beach, St. Joseph. 90c, BWIA McDonnell Douglas MD 83, Grantley Adams Airport. $2, Cruise ship Festivale, deep water harbor, Bridgetown.

		Perf. 14½	
1992, Dec. 15	**Litho.**	**Wmk. 373**	
830	A141	5c multicolored	.15 .15
831	A141	35c multicolored	.35 .35
832	A141	90c multicolored	.90 .90
833	A141	$2 multicolored	2.00 2.00
		Nos. 830-833 (4)	3.40 3.40

Cacti and Succulents — A142

		Wmk. 373	
1993, Feb. 9	**Litho.**	*Perf. 14*	
834	A142	10c Barbados gooseberry	.15 .15
835	A142	35c Night-blooming cereus	.35 .35
836	A142	$1.40 Aloe	1.40 1.40
837	A142	$2 Scrunchineel	2.00 2.00
		Nos. 834-837 (4)	3.90 3.90

Nos. 826-829 Ovptd. "WORLD ORCHID CONFERENCE 1993" on 2 or 4 lines

Perf. 13½x14

1993, Apr. 1	**Litho.**	**Wmk. 373**	
838	A140	55c on #826 multi	.55 .55
839	A140	65c on #827 multi	.65 .65
840	A140	70c on #828 multi	.70 .70
841	A140	$1.40 on #829 multi	1.40 1.40
		Nos. 838-841 (4)	3.30 3.30

Royal Air Force, 75th Anniv.
Common Design Type

Designs: 10c, Hawker Hunter. 30c, Handley Page Victor. 70c, Hawker Typhoon. $3, Hawker Hurricane.

No. 846a, Armstrong Whitworth Siskin 3a. b, Supermarine S.6B. c, Supermarine Walrus. d, Hawker Hart.

1993, Apr. 1			*Perf. 14*	
842	CD350	10c multicolored	.15	.15
843	CD350	30c multicolored	.30	.30
844	CD350	70c multicolored	.70	.70
845	CD350	$3 multicolored	3.00	3.00
		Nos. 842-845 (4)	4.15	4.15

Souvenir Sheet

846	CD350	50c Sheet of 4, #a.-d.	2.00 2.00

Cannon A143

Designs: 5c, 18-pounder Culverin, 1625, Denmark Fort. 45c, 6-pounder Commonwealth gun, 1649-1660, St. Ann's Fort. $1, 9-pounder Demi-culverin, 1691, The Main Guard. $2.50, 32-pounder Demi-cannon, 1693-94, Charles Fort.

		Wmk. 373	
1993, June 8	**Litho.**	*Perf. 13*	
847	A143	5c multicolored	.15 .15
848	A143	45c multicolored	.45 .45
849	A143	$1 multicolored	1.00 1.00
850	A143	$2.50 multicolored	2.50 2.50
		Nos. 847-850 (4)	4.10 4.10

Barbados Museum, 60th Anniv. — A144

Designs: 10c, Shell box, carved figure. 75c, Map, print of three people. 90c, Silver cup, print of soldier. $1.10, Map.

		Wmk. 373	
1993, Sept. 14	**Litho.**	*Perf. 14*	
851	A144	10c multicolored	.15 .15
852	A144	75c multicolored	.75 .75
853	A144	90c multicolored	.90 .90
854	A144	$1.10 multicolored	1.10 1.10
		Nos. 851-854 (4)	2.90 2.90

A145 A146

Prehistoric Aquatic Reptiles: a, Plesiosaurus. b, Ichthyosaurus. c, Elasmosaurus. d, Mosasaurus. e, Archelon. Continuous design.

		Wmk. 373	
1993, Oct. 28	**Litho.**	*Perf. 13*	
855	A145	90c Strip of 5, #a.-e.	5.00 5.00

		Wmk. 384	
1994, Jan. 11	**Litho.**	*Perf. 14*	
856	A146	10c Cricket	.15 .15
857	A146	35c Motor racing	.35 .35
858	A146	50c Golf	.50 .50
859	A146	70c Run Barbados 10k	.70 .70
860	A146	$1.40 Swimming	1.40 1.40
		Nos. 856-860 (5)	3.10 3.10

Sports & tourism.

Migratory Birds A147

		Wmk. 373		
1994, Feb. 18		**Litho.**	*Perf. 14*	
861	A147	10c Whimbrel	.15	.15
862	A147	35c American golden plover	.35	.35
863	A147	70c Ruddy turnstone	.70	.70
864	A147	$3 Tricolored heron	3.00	3.00
		Nos. 861-864 (4)	4.20	4.20

Hong Kong '94.

1st UN Conference of Small Island Developing States — A148

1994, Apr. 25			*Perf. 14x14½*	
865	A148	10c Bathsheba	.15	.15
866	A148	65c Pico Tenneriffe	.65	.65
867	A148	90c Ragged Point Lighthouse	.90	.90
868	A148	$2.50 Consett Bay	2.50	2.50
		Nos. 865-868 (4)	4.20	4.20

Order of the Caribbean Community — A149

First award recipients: No. 869, Sir Shridath Ramphal, statesman, Guyana. No. 870, Derek Walcott, writer, Nobel Laureate, St. Lucia. No. 871, William Demas, economist, Trinidad and Tobago.

		Wmk. 373		
1994, July 4		**Litho.**	*Perf. 14*	
869	A149	70c multicolored	.70	.70
870	A149	70c multicolored	.70	.70
871	A149	70c multicolored	.70	.70
		Nos. 869-871 (3)	2.10	2.10

Ships A150

Designs: 5c, Dutch Flyut, 1695. 10c, Geestport, 1994. 25c, HMS Victory, 1805. 30c, Royal Viking Queen, 1994 35c, HMS Barbados, 1945. 45c, Faraday, 1924. 50c, USCG Hamilton, 1974. 65c, HMCS Saguenay, 1939. 70c, Inanda, 1928. 80c, HMS Rodney, 1944. 90c, USS John F. Kennedy, 1982. $1.10, William & John, 1627. $5, USCG Champlain, 1931. $10, Artist, 1877.

		Wmk. 373		
1994, Aug. 16		**Litho.**	*Perf. 14*	
872	A150	5c multicolored	.15	.15
873	A150	10c multicolored	.15	.15
874	A150	25c multicolored	.25	.25
875	A150	30c multicolored	.30	.30
876	A150	35c multicolored	.35	.35
877	A150	45c multicolored	.45	.45
878	A150	50c multicolored	.50	.50
879	A150	65c multicolored	.65	.65
880	A150	70c multicolored	.70	.70
881	A150	80c multicolored	.80	.80
882	A150	90c multicolored	.90	.90
883	A150	$1.10 multicolored	1.10	1.10
884	A150	$5 multicolored	5.00	5.00
885	A150	$10 multicolored	10.00	10.00
		Nos. 872-885 (14)	21.30	21.30

1996		**Litho.**	**Wmk. 384**
872a	A150	5c	.15 .15
873a	A150	10c	.15 .15
878a	A150	50c	.50 .50
883a	A150	$1.10	1.10 1.10
884a	A150	$5	5.00 5.00
		Nos. 872a-884a (5)	6.90 6.90

West India Regiment, Bicent. — A151

Designs: 30c, 2nd Regiment, 1860. 50c, 4th Regiment, Light Company, 1795. 70c, 3rd Regiment, drum major, 1860. $1, 5th Regiment, undress, working dress, 1815. $1.10, 1st, 2nd Regiments, Review Order, 1874.

		Perf. 15x14		
1995, Feb. 21		**Litho.**	**Wmk. 373**	
886	A151	30c multicolored	.30	.30
887	A151	50c multicolored	.50	.50
888	A151	70c multicolored	.70	.70
889	A151	$1 multicolored	1.00	1.00
890	A151	$1.10 multicolored	1.10	1.10
		Nos. 886-890 (5)	3.60	3.60

End of World War II
Common Design Type

Designs: 10c, Barbadians serving in the Middle East. 35c, Lancaster bomber. 55c, Spitfire fighter. $2.50, SS Davisian sunk off Barbados, July 10, 1940.
$2, Reverse of War Medal 1939-45.

		Wmk. 373		
1995, May 8		**Litho.**	*Perf. 14*	
891	CD351	10c multicolored	.15	.15
892	CD351	35c multicolored	.30	.30
893	CD351	55c multicolored	.55	.55
894	CD351	$2.50 multicolored	2.50	2.50
		Nos. 891-894 (4)	3.50	3.50

Souvenir Sheet

895	CD352	$2 multicolored	2.50 2.50

Combermere School, 300th Anniv. — A152

Designs: 5c, Scouting, Combermere 1st Barbados, 1912. 20c, Violin, sheet music. 35c, Cricket, Sir Frank Worrell, vert. 90c, Frank Collymore, #553. $3, Landscape.

		Wmk. 373		
1995, July 25		**Litho.**	*Perf. 14*	
896	A152	5c multicolored	.15	.15
897	A152	20c multicolored	.20	.20
898	A152	35c multicolored	.35	.35
899	A152	$3 multicolored	3.00	3.00
		Nos. 896-899 (4)	3.70	3.70

Souvenir Sheet

900		Sheet of 5, #896-899, 900a	4.50	4.50
a.		A152 90c multicolored	.90	.90

UN, 50th Anniv.
Common Design Type

Designs: 30c, Douglas C-124 Globemaster, Korea 1950-53. 45c, Royal Navy Sea King helicopter. $1.40, Wessex helicopter, UNFICYP, Cyprus 1964. $2, Gazelle helicopter, UNFICYP, Cyprus 1964.

		Wmk. 373		
1995, Oct. 24		**Litho.**	*Perf. 14*	
901	CD353	30c multicolored	.30	.30
902	CD353	45c multicolored	.45	.45
903	CD353	$1.40 multicolored	1.40	1.40
904	CD353	$2 multicolored	2.00	2.00
		Nos. 901-904 (4)	4.15	4.15

Water Lilies — A153

Wmk. 373

1995, Dec. 19   Litho.   Perf. 14

905	A153	10c	Blue beauty	.15 .15
906	A153	65c	White water lily	.65 .65
907	A153	70c	Sacred lotus	.70 .70
908	A153	$3	Water hyacinth	3.00 3.00
		Nos. 905-908 (4)		4.50 4.50

Barbados Philatelic Society, Cent. A154

Magnifying glass, tongs, and: 10c, #70. 55c, #109. $1.10, #148. $1.40, #192.

Wmk. 373

1996, Jan. 30   Litho.   Perf. 14

909	A154	10c	multicolored	.15 .15
910	A154	55c	multicolored	.55 .55
911	A154	$1.10	multicolored	1.10 1.10
912	A154	$1.40	multicolored	1.40 1.40
		Nos. 909-912 (4)		3.20 3.20

A155

Modern Olympic Games, Cent. — A156

1996, Apr. 2   Litho.   Perf. 14

913	A155	20c	Soccer	.20 .20
914	A155	30c	Relay race	.30 .30
915	A155	55c	Basketball	.55 .55
916	A155	$3	Rhythmic gymnastics	3.00 3.00
		Nos. 913-916 (4)		4.05 4.05

Souvenir Sheet

917	A156	$2.50	Discus thrower	2.50 2.50

Olymphilex '96 (No. 917).

CAPEX '96 — A157

Transportation links with Canada: 10c, Canadian Airlines DC10. 90c, Air Canada Boeing 767. $1, Air Canada 320 Airbus. $1.40, Canadian Airlines Boeing 767.

Wmk. 373

1996, June 7   Litho.   Perf. 14

918	A157	10c	multicolored	.15 .15
919	A157	90c	multicolored	.90 .90
920	A157	$1	multicolored	1.00 1.00
921	A157	$1.40	multicolored	1.40 1.40
		Nos. 918-921 (4)		3.45 3.45

Chattel Houses A158

House features: 35c, Shed roof, lattice work. 70c, Pedimented porch, carved wooden trim. $1.10, Decorative, elegant porch. $2, Hip roof, bell pelmet window hoods.

1996, June 7

922	A158	35c	multicolored	.35 .35
923	A158	70c	multicolored	.70 .70
924	A158	$1.10	multicolored	1.10 1.10
925	A158	$2	multicolored	2.00 2.00
		Nos. 922-925 (4)		4.15 4.15

Christmas A159

Children's paintings: 10c, Going to Church on Christmas morning. 30c, The Tuk Band. 55c, Caroling on Christmas. $2.50, Decorated houses.

Perf. 14½

1996, Nov. 12   Litho.   Wmk. 373

926	A159	10c	multicolored	.15 .15
927	A159	30c	multicolored	.30 .30
928	A159	55c	multicolored	.55 .55
929	A159	$2.50	multicolored	2.50 2.50
		Nos. 926-929 (4)		3.50 3.50

UNICEF, 50th anniv.

Hong Kong '97 — A160

Dogs: 10c, Doberman pinscher. 30c, German shepherd. 90c, Japanese akita. $3, Irish red setter.

1997, Feb. 12   Litho.   Wmk. 373

Perf. 14x14½

930	A160	10c	multicolored	.15 .15
931	A160	30c	multicolored	.30 .30
932	A160	90c	multicolored	.90 .90
933	A160	$3	multicolored	3.00 3.00
		Nos. 930-933 (4)		4.35 4.35

Visit of US Pres. Clinton to Barbados, May 1997 A161

35c, Barbados flag, arms. 90c, US flag, arms.

Wmk. 373

1997, May 9   Litho.   Perf. 14

934	A161	35c	multicolored	.35 .35
935	A161	90c	multicolored	.90 .90
a.		Pair, #934-935		1.25 1.25

Issued in sheets of 8 stamps + 2 labels.

Shells — A162

Designs: 5c, Measled cowry. 35c, Trumpet triton. 90c, Scotch bonnet. $2, West Indian murex. $2.50, Sea bottom with miscellaneous shells.

Wmk. 373

1997, July 29   Litho.   Perf. 14

936	A162	5c	multicolored	.15 .15
937	A162	35c	multicolored	.35 .35
938	A162	90c	multicolored	.90 .90
939	A162	$2	multicolored	1.90 1.90
		Nos. 936-939 (4)		3.30 3.30

Souvenir Sheet

940	A162	$2.50	multicolored	2.40 2.40

Public Library, 150th Anniv. A163

Designs: 10c, Lucas manuscripts. 30c, Storytelling to children. 70c, Bookmobile. $3, Information technology.

Wmk. 373

1997, Oct. 1   Litho.   Perf. 14

941	A163	10c	multicolored	.15 .15
942	A163	30c	multicolored	.30 .30
943	A163	70c	multicolored	.70 .70
944	A163	$3	multicolored	3.10 3.10
		Nos. 941-944 (4)		4.25 4.25

SEMI-POSTAL STAMPS

No. 73 Surcharged in Red

Kingston Relief Fund. 1d.

Wmk. 2

1907, Jan. 25   Typo.   Perf. 14

B1	A8	1p on 2p sl & org		1.75 2.50
a.		No period after 1d		15.00 17.50
b.		Inverted surcharge		1.75 2.50
c.		Inverted surcharge, no period after 1d		15.00 17.50
d.		Double surcharge		750.00
e.		Dbl. surch., both invtd.		750.00

> Catalogue values for unused stamps in this section, from this point to the end of the section, are for Never Hinged items.

28c + 4c

No. 406 Surcharged

ST. VINCENT RELIEF FUND

1979, May 29   Photo.   Wmk. 314

B2	A56	28c + 4c on 35c multi		.30 .30

The surtax was for victims of the eruption of Mt. Soufrière.

POSTAGE DUE STAMPS

> Catalogue values for unused stamps in this section are for Never Hinged items.

D1

1934-47   Typo.   Wmk. 4   Perf. 14

J1	D1	½p green ('35)		.75 .75
J2	D1	1p black		1.40 1.40
J3	D1	3p dk car rose ('47)		22.50 22.50
		Nos. J1-J3 (3)		24.65 24.65

A 2nd die of the 1p was introduced in 1947.

1950

J4	D1	1c green		.20 .20
J5	D1	2c black		.40 .40
J6	D1	6c carmine rose		1.50 1.75
		Nos. J4-J6 (3)		2.10 2.35

Values are for 1953 chalky paper printing.

Wmk. 4a (error)

J4a	D1	1c green	140.00
J5a	D1	2c black	190.00
J6a	D1	6c carmine rose	110.00
		Nos. J4a-J6a (3)	440.00

1965, Aug. 3   Wmk. 314   Perf. 14

J7	D1	1c green		.30 .30
J8	D1	2c black		.35 .35
J9	D1	6c carmine rose		.65 .65
a.		Wmk. sideways, perf. 14x13½ ('74)		2.25 2.25
		Nos. J7-J9 (3)		1.30 1.30

Issued: No. J9a, 2/4/74.

Wmk. 314 Sideways

1974, Dec. 4   Perf. 13x13½

J8b	D1	1c		1.50 1.50
J9b	D1	6c		1.50 1.50

POSTAGE DUE

1¢

BARBADOS   D2

Designs: Each stamp shows different stylized flower in background.

Perf. 13½x14

1976, May 12   Litho.   Wmk. 373

J10	D2	1c brt pink & mag		.15 .15
J11	D2	2c lt & dk vio blue		.15 .15
J12	D2	5c yellow & brown		.15 .15
J13	D2	10c lilac & purple		.15 .15
J14	D2	25c yel green & dk grn		.25 .25
J15	D2	$1 rose & red		.90 .90
		Set value		1.35 1.35

1985, July   Perf. 15x14

J10a	D2	1c		.15 .15
J11a	D2	2c		.15 .15
J12a	D2	5c		.15 .15
J13a	D2	10c		.15 .15
J14a	D2	25c		.25 .25
		Set value		.45 .45

WAR TAX STAMP

No. 118 Overprinted   **WAR TAX**

1917   Wmk. 3   Perf. 14

MR1	A12	1p carmine		.15 .15
a.		Imperf., pair		4,000.

BARBUDA

bär-'büd-ə

LOCATION — Northernmost of the Leeward Islands, West Indies
GOVT. — Dependency of Antigua
AREA — 63 sq. mi.
POP. — 1,000 (estimated)
See Antigua.

12 Pence = 1 Shilling

> Catalogue values for unused stamps in this country are for Never Hinged items, beginning with Scott 12 in the regular postage section, and Scott B1 in the semi-postal section.

Watermark

Wmk. 380- "POST OFFICE"

Leeward Islands Stamps and Types of
1912-22 Overprinted in Black or Red

BARBUDA

Die II

For description of dies I and II, see back of this
section of the Catalogue.

1922, July 13   Wmk. 4   Perf. 14

1	A5	½p green	1.50	4.50
2	A5	1p rose red	1.50	4.50
3	A5	2p gray	1.60	4.00
4	A5	2½p ultramarine	1.60	4.50
5	A5	6p vio & red vio	4.00	10.00
6	A5	2sh vio & ultra, *bl*	15.00	30.00
7	A5	3sh green & violet	32.50	50.00
8	A5	4sh blk & scar (R)	35.00	50.00

Wmk. 3

9	A5	3p violet, *yel*	1.50	4.75
10	A5	1sh blk, *emer* (R)	3.25	4.75
11	A5	5sh grn & red, *yel*	95.00	125.00
		Nos. 1-11 (11)	192.45	292.00

Catalogue values for unused
stamps in this section, from this
point to the end of the section, are
for Never Hinged items.

Map — B1

Fish — B2

1968-70   Litho.   Unwmk.   Perf. 14

12	B1	½c blk, salmon pink & red brn	.15	.15
13	B1	1c blk, org & brt org	.15	.15
14	B1	2c blk, brt pink & brt rose	.15	.15
15	B1	3c blk, yel & org yel	.15	.15
16	B1	4c blk, lt grn & brt grn	.15	.15
17	B1	5c blk, bl grn & brt bl grn	.15	.15
18	B1	6c blk, lt lil & red lil	.15	.15
19	B1	10c blk, lt bl & dk bl	.15	.15
20	B1	15c blk, dl grn & grn	.20	.20
21	B2	20c Great barracuda	.75	1.25
22	B2	25c Great amberjack	.30	.25
23	B2	35c French angelfish	.40	.40
24	B2	50c Porkfish	.55	.55
25	B2	75c Striped parrotfish	.80	.80
26	B2	$1 Longspine squirrelfish	1.10	1.10
27	B2	$2.50 Catalufa	2.75	2.75
28	B2	$5 Blue chromis	5.00	6.00
		Nos. 12-28 (17)	13.05	14.50

Issued: ½c-15c, 11/19/68; 20c, 7/22/70; 25c-
75c, 2/5/69; others, 3/6/69.
For surcharge see No. 80.

1968
Summer
Olympics,
Mexico
City — B3

Designs: 25c, Running, Aztec calendar stone.
35c, High jumping, Aztec statue. 75c, Yachting,
Aztec lion mask. $1, Soccer, Aztec carved stone.

1968, Dec. 20

29	B3	25c multicolored	.25	.25
30	B3	35c multicolored	.35	.35
31	B3	75c multicolored	.75	.75
		Nos. 29-31 (3)	1.35	1.35

Souvenir Sheet

32	B3	$1 multicolored	2.75	2.75

The Ascension, by
Orcagna — B4

1969, Mar. 24

33	B4	25c blue & black	.15	.15
34	B4	35c dp carmine & blk	.15	.20
35	B4	75c violet & black	.30	.35
		Nos. 33-35 (3)	.60	.70

Easter.

3rd
Caribbean
Boy Scout
Jamboree
B5

1969, Aug. 7

36	B5	25c Flag ceremony	.45	.45
37	B5	35c Campfire	.65	.65
38	B5	75c Rowing	1.40	1.40
		Nos. 36-38 (3)	2.50	2.50

The Sistine Madonna,
by Raphael — B6

1969, Oct. 20

39	B6	½c multicolored	.15	.15
40	B6	25c multicolored	.15	.15
41	B6	35c multicolored	.25	.25
42	B6	75c multicolored	.55	.55
		Set value	1.00	1.00

Christmas.

English
Monarchs — B7

1970-71   Perf. 14½x14

43	B7	35c William I	.15	.15
44	B7	35c William II	.15	.15
45	B7	35c Henry I	.15	.15
46	B7	35c Stephen	.15	.15
47	B7	35c Henry II	.15	.15
48	B7	35c Richard I	.15	.15
49	B7	35c John	.15	.15
50	B7	35c Henry III	.15	.15
51	B7	35c Edward I	.15	.15
52	B7	35c Edward II	.15	.15
53	B7	35c Edward III	.15	.15
54	B7	35c Richard II	.15	.15
55	B7	35c Henry IV	.15	.15
56	B7	35c Henry V	.15	.15
57	B7	35c Henry VI	.15	.15
58	B7	35c Edward IV	.15	.15
59	B7	35c Edward V	.15	.15
60	B7	35c Richard III	.15	.15
61	B7	35c Henry VII	.15	.15
62	B7	35c Henry VIII	.15	.15
63	B7	35c Edward VI	.15	.15
64	B7	35c Lady Jane Grey	.15	.15
65	B7	35c Mary I	.15	.15
66	B7	35c Elizabeth I	.15	.15
67	B7	35c James I	.15	.15
68	B7	35c Charles I	.15	.15
69	B7	35c Charles II	.15	.15
70	B7	35c James II	.15	.15
71	B7	35c William III	.15	.15
72	B7	35c Mary II	.15	.15
73	B7	35c Anne	.15	.15
74	B7	35c George I	.15	.15
75	B7	35c George II	.15	.15
76	B7	35c George III	.15	.15
77	B7	35c George IV	.15	.15
78	B7	35c William IV	.15	.15
79	B7	35c Victoria	.15	.15
		Nos. 43-79 (37)	5.55	5.55

Issued: 1970, #43, 2/16; #44, 3/2; #45, 3/16;
#46, 4/4; #47, 4/15; #48, 5/1; #49, 5/15; #50,
6/1; #51, 6/15; #52, 7/1; #53, 7/15; #54, 8/1;
#55, 8/15; #56, 9/1; #57, 9/15; #58, 10/1; #59,
10/15; #60, 11/2; #61, 11/16; #62, 12/1; #63,
12/15.
    1971: #64, 1/2; #65, 1/15; #66, 2/1; #67,
2/15; #68, 3/1; #69, 3/15; #70, 4/1; #71, 4/15;
#72, 5/1; #73, 5/15; #74, 6/1; #75, 6/15; #76,
7/1; #77, 7/15; #78, 8/2; #79, 8/16.
    See Nos. 626-631 for other Monarchs.

20c

No. 12 Surcharged

1970, Feb. 26   Perf. 14

80	B1	20c on ½c multicolored	.15	.15

Easter — B8

1970, Mar. 16

81	B8	25c Carrying Cross	.15	.15
82	B8	35c Descent from cross	.15	.20
83	B8	75c Crucifixion	.35	.35
a.		Strip of 3, #81-83	.70	.70

Charles
Dickens
B9

1970, July 10

84	B9	20c Oliver Twist	.15	.15
85	B9	75c Old Curiosity Shop	.40	.50

Christmas
B10

Designs: 20c, Madonna of the Meadow, by Giovanni Bellini. 50c, Madonna, Child and Angels
from Wilton Diptych. 75c, Nativity, by Piero della
Francesca.

1970, Oct. 15

86	B10	20c multicolored	.15	.15
87	B10	50c multicolored	.20	.25
88	B10	75c multicolored	.35	.40
		Nos. 86-88 (3)	.70	.80

British Red
Cross,
Cent.
B11

1970, Dec. 21

89	B11	20c Patient in wheelchair, vert.	.20	.25
90	B11	35c shown	.35	.40
91	B11	75c Child care	.60	.80
		Nos. 89-91 (3)	1.15	1.45

Easter — B12

Details from the Mond Crucifixion, by Raphael.

1971, Apr. 7

92	B12	35c Angel	.20	.30
93	B12	50c Crucifixion	.30	.35
94	B12	75c Angel, diff.	.45	.75
a.		Strip of 3, #92-94	1.00	1.00

Martello
Tower
B13

1971, May 10

95	B13	20c shown	.15	.15
96	B13	25c Sailboats	.15	.15
97	B13	50c Hotel bungalows	.30	.30
98	B13	75c Government House, mystery stone	.45	.45
		Nos. 95-98 (4)	1.05	1.05

Christmas — B14

Paintings: ½c, The Granduca Madonna, by
Raphael. 35c, The Ansidei Madonna, by Raphael.
50c, The Virgin and Child, by Botticelli. 75c, The
Madonna of the Trees, by Bellini.

1971, Oct. 4

99	B14	½c multicolored	.15	.15
100	B14	35c multicolored	.25	.25
101	B14	50c multicolored	.38	.38
102	B14	75c multicolored	.60	.60
		Set value	1.25	1.25

A set of four stamps for Durer (20c,
35c, 50c, 75c) was not authorized.

All stamps are types of Antigua or
overprinted on stamps of Antigua unless
otherwise specified. Many of the "BAR-
BUDA" overprints are vertical.

Nos. 321-322 Ovptd. "BARBUDA"

1973, Nov. 14   Perf. 13½

103	A65	35c multicolored	1.50	1.50
104	A65	$2 multicolored	8.00	8.00

Nos. 313-315a Ovptd. in Red "BARBUDA"

1973, Nov. 26   Perf. 13½x14

105	A63	20c multicolored	.24	.24
106	A63	35c multicolored	.40	.40
107	A63	85c multicolored	.85	.85
		Nos. 105-107 (3)	1.49	1.49

Souvenir Sheet

108		Sheet of 4, #105-107, 108a	4.00	4.00
a.		A63 5c multicolored		

Carnival, 1973.

Nos. 307, 309, 311, 311a Ovptd.
"BARBUDA"

Perf. 14x13½

1973, Nov. 26   Wmk. 314

109	A53	½c multicolored	.15	.15
110	A53	20c multicolored	.20	.20
111	A53	75c multicolored	.80	.80
		Nos. 109-111 (3)	1.15	1.15

Souvenir Sheet

112	Sheet of 5, #109-111, 112a-112b + label		3.50	3.50
a.	A53 10c multicolored			
b.	A53 35c multicolored			

Nos. 241a, 242-243, 244a, 245-248, 249a, 250-254, 255a, 256, 256a, 257 Ovptd. "BARBUDA"

Wmk. 314 Sideways, Upright

1973-74			**Perf. 14**	
113	A51	½c multicolored	.15	.15
114	A51	1c multicolored	.15	.15
115	A51	2c multicolored	.15	.15
116	A51	3c multicolored	.15	.15
117	A51	4c multicolored	.15	.15
118	A51	5c multicolored	.15	.15
119	A51	6c multicolored	.15	.15
120	A51	10c multicolored	.18	.18
121	A51	15c multicolored	.28	.28
122	A51	20c multicolored	.38	.38
123	A51	25c multicolored	.45	.45
124	A51	35c multicolored	.65	.65
125	A51	50c multicolored	.95	.95
126	A51	75c multicolored	1.40	1.40
127	A51	$1 multicolored	1.90	1.90
128	A51	$2.50 multicolored	4.75	4.75
a.	Wmk. upright		9.25	9.25
129	A51	$5 multicolored	9.25	9.25
	Nos. 113-129 (17)		21.24	21.24

Issue dates: ½c, 3c, 15c, $1, $2.50, Feb. 18, 1974. Others, Nov. 26.

Nos. 316-320a Ovptd. in Silver or Red "BARBUDA"

Perf. 14½

1973, Dec. 11		**Photo.**	**Unwmk.**	
130	A64	3c multicolored	.15	.15
131	A64	5c multicolored	.15	.15
132	A64	20c multicolored	.30	.30
133	A64	35c multicolored (R)	.55	.55
134	A64	$1 multicolored (R)	1.50	1.50
	Nos. 130-134 (5)		2.65	2.65

Souvenir Sheet

135	Sheet of 5 + label		9.00	9.00
a.	A64 35c multicolored (S)			
b.	A64 $1 multicolored (S)			

No. 135 contains Nos. 130-132, 135a-135b.

Nos. 323-324a Ovptd. "BARBUDA"

1973, Dec. 16		**Litho.**	**Perf. 13½**	
136	A65	35c multicolored	.32	.32
137	A65	$2 multicolored	1.75	1.75
a.	Souvenir sheet of 2, #136-137		2.50	2.50

Nos. 325-328 Ovptd. "BARBUDA"

1974, Feb. 18			**Wmk. 314**	
138	A66	15c multicolored	.15	.15
139	A66	20c multicolored	.18	.18
140	A66	35c multicolored	.32	.32
141	A66	75c multicolored	.70	.70
	Nos. 138-141 (4)		1.35	1.35

Nos. 329-333 Ovptd. "BARBUDA"

1974, May 1			**Perf. 14x13½**	
142	A53	½c multicolored	.15	.15
143	A53	10c multicolored	.15	.15
144	A53	20c multicolored	.30	.30
145	A53	35c multicolored	.52	.52
146	A53	75c multicolored	1.10	1.10
	Nos. 142-146 (5)		2.22	2.22

No. 333a exists with overprint.

Nos. 334-340 Ovptd. Type "a" or "b" and No. 340 "BARBUDA" in Red

BARBUDA	**BARBUDA**
15 SEPT.	**13 JULY 1922**
1874 G.P.U.	
a	b

1974, July 15   Unwmk.   Perf. 14½
Se-tenant Pairs Overprinted Type "a" on Left Stamp, Type "b" on Right Stamp

148	A67	½c multicolored	.15	.15
149	A67	1c multicolored	.15	.15
150	A67	2c multicolored	.15	.15
151	A67	5c multicolored	.40	.40
152	A67	20c multicolored	1.50	1.50
153	A67	35c multicolored	2.75	2.75
154	A67	$1 multicolored	7.50	7.50
	Nos. 148-154 (7)		12.60	12.60

Souvenir Sheet
Perf. 13

155	Sheet of 7 + label		10.00	10.00
a.	A67 ½c multicolored		.15	.15
b.	A67 1c multicolored		.15	.15
c.	A67 2c multicolored		.15	.15
d.	A67 5c multicolored		.30	.30
e.	A67 20c multicolored		1.25	1.25
f.	A67 35c multicolored		2.00	2.00
g.	A67 $1 multicolored		6.00	6.00

UPU, cent.

Nos. 341-344a Ovptd. "BARBUDA"

1974, Aug. 14		**Wmk. 314**	**Perf. 14**	
156	A68	5c multicolored	.15	.15
157	A68	20c multicolored	.18	.18
158	A68	35c multicolored	.32	.32
159	A68	75c multicolored	.65	.65
a.	Souvenir sheet of 4, #156-159		1.25	1.25
	Nos. 156-159 (4)		1.30	1.30

Nos. 345-348a Ovptd. "BARBUDA" and

World Cup Soccer Championships — B16

Various soccer plays.

1974, Sept. 2		**Unwmk.**	**Perf. 15, 14**	
160	A69	5c multicolored	.15	.15
161	A69	35c multicolored	.30	.30
162	B16	35c multicolored	.16	.16
163	A69	75c multicolored	.65	.65
164	A69	$1 multicolored	.85	.85
a.	Souv. sheet of 4, #160-161, 163-164 + 2 labels, perf. 13½		2.25	2.25
165	B16	$1.20 multicolored	.55	.55
166	B16	$2.50 multicolored	1.25	1.25
a.	Souv. sheet of 3, #162, 165-166		3.00	3.00
	Nos. 160-166 (7)		3.91	3.91

UPU, Cent. — B17   **BARBUDA   35c**

1974, Sept. 30			**Perf. 14x13½**	
167	B17	35c Ship letter, 1833	.15	.15
168	B17	$1.20 #1, 2 on FDC	.48	.48
169	B17	$2.50 Airplane, map	1.00	1.00
a.	Souvenir sheet of 3, #167-169		4.00	4.00
	Nos. 167-169 (3)		1.63	1.63

BARBUDA   Greater Amberjack B18

1974-75			**Perf. 14x14½, 14½x14**	
170	B18	½c Oleander, rose bay	.15	.15
171	B18	1c Blue petrea	.15	.15
172	B18	2c Poinsettia	.15	.15
173	B18	3c Cassia tree	.15	.15
174	B18	4c shown	.15	.15
175	B18	5c Holy Trinity School	.15	.15
176	B18	6c Snorkeling	.15	.15
177	B18	10c Pilgrim Holiness Church	.15	.15
178	B18	15c New Cottage Hospital	.15	.15
179	B18	20c Post Office & Treasury	.16	.16
180	B18	25c Island jetty & boats	.20	.20
181	B18	35c Martello Tower	.28	.28

Size: 39x25mm
Perf. 14

182	B18	50c Warden's House	.40	.40
183	B18	75c Inter-island air service	.60	.60
184	B18	$1 Tortoise	.80	.80

Size: 45x29mm
Perf. 13½x14

185	B18	$2.50 Spiny lobster	2.00	2.00
186	B18	$5 Frigate birds	4.00	4.00
a.	Perf. 14x15			

Size: 34x47mm

187	B18	$10 Hibiscus	8.00	8.00
	Nos. 170-187 (18)		17.79	17.79

Nos. 170-173, 180, 187 vert.
Issued: 4c, 5c, 6c, 10c, 15c, 20c, 25c, 35c, 75c, 10/15/74; ½c, 1c, 2c, 3c, 50c, $1, $2.50, #186, 1/6/75; #186a, 7/24/75; $10, 9/19/75.
For overprints see Nos. 213-214.

Nos. 349-352a Ovptd. "BARBUDA" in Red and

Winston Churchill, Birth Cent. — B19

1974			**Perf. 14½, 13½x14**	
188	A70	5c multicolored	.15	.15
189	B19	5c Making broadcast	.15	.15
190	A70	35c multicolored	.70	.70
191	B19	35c Portrait	.28	.28
192	A70	75c multicolored	1.50	1.50
193	B19	75c Painting	.60	.60
194	A70	$1 multicolored	2.00	2.00
a.	Souv. sheet of 4, #188, 190, 192, 194		8.50	8.50
195	B19	$1 Victory sign	.80	.80
a.	Souv. sheet of 4, #189, 191, 193, 195		3.50	3.50
	Nos. 188-195 (8)		6.18	6.18

Issue dates: Nos. 188, 190, 192, 194, Oct. 15, others, Nov. 20. For overprints see Nos. 213-214.

Nos. 353-360a Ovptd. "BARBUDA"

1974, Nov. 25			**Perf. 14½**	
196	A71	½c multicolored	.15	.15
197	A71	1c multicolored	.15	.15
198	A71	2c multicolored	.15	.15
199	A71	3c multicolored	.15	.15
200	A71	5c multicolored	.15	.15
201	A71	20c multicolored	.20	.20
202	A71	35c multicolored	.38	.38
203	A71	75c multicolored	.80	.80
a.	Souv. sheet of 4, #200-203, perf. 13½		1.40	1.40
	Set value		1.50	1.50

Nos. 369-373a Ovptd. "BARBUDA"

1975, Mar. 17				
204	A72	5c multicolored	.15	.15
205	A72	15c multicolored	.28	.28
206	A72	20c multicolored	.65	.65
207	A72	50c multicolored	.90	.90
208	A72	$1 multicolored	1.75	1.75
a.	Souv. sheet of 5, #204-208 + label, perf. 13½x14		4.50	4.50
	Nos. 204-208 (5)		3.73	3.73

Stamps from No. 208a are 43x28mm.

Battle of the Saints B20

1975, May 30			**Perf. 13½x14**	
209	B20	35c shown	1.00	1.00
210	B20	50c Two ships	1.40	1.40
211	B20	75c Ships firing	2.00	2.00
212	B20	95c Sailors abandoning ship	2.50	2.50
	Nos. 209-212 (4)		6.90	6.90

Barbuda No. 186a Ovptd.

a

b

1975, July 2			**Perf. 14x15**	
213	B18	(a) $5 multicolored		
214	B18	(b) $5 multicolored		

Overprint "a" is in 1st and 3rd vertical rows, "b" 2nd and 4th. The 5th row has no overprint. This can be collected se-tenant either as Nos. 213, 214 or 213, 214 and 186a.

Military Uniforms — B21

Designs: 35c, Officer of 65th Foot, 1763. 50c, Grenadier, 27th Foot, 1701-1710. 75c, Officer of 21st Foot, 1793-1796. 95c, Officer, Royal Regiment of Artillery, 1800.

1975, Sept. 17			**Perf. 14**	
215	B21	35c multicolored	.70	.70
216	B21	50c multicolored	1.00	1.00
217	B21	75c multicolored	1.50	1.50
218	B21	95c multicolored	1.90	1.90
	Nos. 215-218 (4)		5.10	5.10

Barbuda Nos. 189, 191, 193, 195 Ovptd. "30th ANNIVERSARY / UNITED NATIONS / 1945 - 1975"

1975, Oct. 24			**Perf. 13½x14**	
219	B19	5c multicolored	.15	.15
220	B19	35c multicolored	.15	.15
221	B19	75c multicolored	.25	.25
222	B19	$1 multicolored	.60	.60
	Nos. 219-222 (4)		1.15	1.15

Nos. 394-401a Ovptd. "BARBUDA"

1975, Nov. 17			**Perf. 14**	
223	A77	½c multicolored	.15	.15
224	A77	1c multicolored	.15	.15
225	A77	2c multicolored	.15	.15
226	A77	5c multicolored	.15	.15
227	A77	10c multicolored	.15	.15
228	A77	20c multicolored	.20	.20
229	A77	35c multicolored	.20	.20
230	A77	$2 multicolored	1.25	1.25
a.	Souvenir sheet of 4, #227-230		2.50	2.50
	Set value		1.55	1.55

Nos. 402-404 Ovptd. "BARBUDA"

1975, Dec. 15			**Perf. 14**	
231	A78	5c multicolored	.15	.15
232	A78	35c multicolored	.85	.85
233	A78	$2 multicolored	5.00	5.00
	Nos. 231-233 (3)		6.00	6.00

American Revolution, Bicent. — B22

Details from Surrender of Cornwallis at Yorktown, by Trumbull: No. 234a, British officers. b, Gen. Benjamin Lincoln. c, Washington, Allied officers.
The Battle of Princeton: No. 235a, Infantry. b, Battle. c, Cannon fire.
Surrender of Burgoyne at Saratoga by Trumbull: No. 236a, Mounted officer. b, Washington, Burgoyne. c, American officers.
Signing the Declaration of Independence, by Trumbull: No. 237a, Delegates to Continental Congress. b, Adams, Sherman, Livingston, Jefferson and Franklin. c, Hancock, Thomson, Read, Dickinson, and Rutledge. Strips of 3 have continuous designs.

1976, Mar. 8			**Perf. 13½x13**	
234	B22	15c Strip of 3, #a.-c.	.32	.32
235	B22	35c Strip of 3, #a.-c.	.75	.75
d.	Souvenir sheet, #234-235		1.65	1.65
236	B22	$1 Strip of 3, #a.-c.	2.25	2.25
237	B22	$2 Strip of 3, #a.-c.	4.25	4.25
d.	Souvenir sheet, #236-237		10.00	10.00

See Nos. 244-247.

Birds B23

1976, June 30			**Perf. 13½x14**	
238	B23	35c Bananaquits	1.40	1.40
239	B23	50c Blue-hooded euphonia	2.00	2.00
240	B23	75c Royal tern	3.00	3.00
241	B23	95c Killdeer	3.75	3.75

242	B23	$1.25	Glossy cowbird	5.00	5.00
243	B23	$2	Purple gallinule	8.25	8.25
			Nos. 238-243 (6)	23.40	23.40

Barbuda #234-237 With Inscription Added at Top Across the Three Stamps in Blue
"H.M. Queen Elizabeth" "Royal Visit 6th July 1976" "H.R.H. Duke of Edinburgh"

1976, Aug. 12   *Perf. 13¹/₂x14*
Size: 38x31mm

244	B22	15c	Strip of 3, #a.-c.	.30	.30
245	B22	35c	Strip of 3, #a.-c.	.70	.70
d.			Souvenir sheet of 2, #244-245	1.10	1.10
246	B22	$1	Strip of 3, #a.-c.	2.00	2.00
247	B22	$2	Strip of 3, #a.-c.	4.00	4.00
d.			Souvenir sheet, #246-247	7.00	7.00

Nos. 244-247 are perforated on outside edges; imperf. vertically within.

Nos. 448-452 Ovptd. "BARBUDA"

1976, Dec. 2   *Perf. 14*

248	A85	8c	multicolored	.15	.15
249	A85	10c	multicolored	.15	.15
250	A85	15c	multicolored	.15	.15
251	A85	50c	multicolored	.32	.32
252	A85	$1	multicolored	.65	.65
			Set value	1.20	1.20

Nos. 431-437 Ovptd. "BARBUDA"

1976, Dec. 28   *Perf. 15*

253	A82	¹/₂c	yellow & multi	.15	.15
254	A82	1c	purple & multi	.15	.15
255	A82	2c	emerald & multi	.15	.15
256	A82	15c	brt blue & multi	.15	.15
257	A82	30c	olive & multi	.20	.20
258	A82	$1	orange & multi	.65	.65
259	A82	$2	red & multi	1.25	1.25
a.			Souv. sheet of 4, #256-259, perf. 13¹/₂	3.50	3.50
			Set value	2.25	2.25

Telephone, Cent. — B24

1977, Jan. 31   *Perf. 14*

260	B24	75c	shown	.30	.30
261	B24	$1.25	Satellite dish, television	.45	.45
262	B24	$2	Satellites in earth orbit	.75	.75
a.			Souv. sheet of 3, #260-262, perf. 15	3.50	3.50
			Nos. 260-262 (3)	1.50	1.50

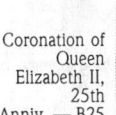

Coronation of Queen Elizabeth II, 25th Anniv. — B25

Designs: Nos. 263a, St. Margaret's Church, Westminster. b, Westminster Abbey entrance. c, Westminster Abbey.
Nos. 264a, Riders on horseback. b, Coronation coach. c, Team of horses. Strips of 3 have continuous designs.

1977, Feb. 7   *Perf. 13¹/₂x13*

263	B25	75c	Strip of 3, #a.-c.	.85	.85
264	B25	$1.25	Strip of 3, #a.-c.	1.35	1.35

Souvenir Sheet

265	B25	Sheet of 6	2.25	2.25

Nos. 263a-264c se-tenant with labels. No. 265 contains Nos. 263a-264c with silver borders.

Nos. 405-422 Ovptd. "BARBUDA"

1977, Apr. 4   *Perf. 15*

266	A79	¹/₂c	multicolored	.15	.15
267	A79	1c	multicolored	.15	.15
268	A79	2c	multicolored	.15	.15
269	A79	3c	multicolored	.15	.15
270	A79	4c	multicolored	.15	.15
271	A79	5c	multicolored	.15	.15
272	A79	6c	multicolored	.15	.15
273	A79	10c	multicolored	.15	.15
274	A79	15c	multicolored	.15	.15
275	A79	20c	multicolored	.15	.15
276	A79	25c	multicolored	.18	.18
277	A79	35c	multicolored	.28	.28
278	A79	50c	multicolored	.38	.38
279	A79	75c	multicolored	.52	.52
280	A79	$1	multicolored	.70	.70

Perf. 13¹/₂x14

281	A80	$2.50	multicolored	1.75	1.75
282	A80	$5	multicolored	3.50	3.50
283	A80	$10	multicolored	7.25	7.25
			Nos. 266-283 (18)	16.06	16.06

For overprints see Nos. 506-516.

Nos. 459-464 Ovptd. "BARBUDA"

1977, Apr. 4   *Perf. 13¹/₂x14, 12*

284	A87	10c	multicolored	.15	.15
285	A87	30c	multicolored	.28	.28
286	A87	50c	multicolored	.45	.45
287	A87	90c	multicolored	.85	.85
288	A87	$2.50	multicolored	2.25	2.25
			Nos. 284-288 (5)	3.98	3.98

Souvenir Sheet

289	A87	$5	multicolored	4.50	4.50

A booklet of self-adhesive stamps contains one pane of six rouletted and die cut 50c stamps in design of 90c (silver overprint), and one pane of one die cut $5 (gold overprint) in changed colors. Panes have marginal inscriptions.
For overprints see Nos. 312-317.

Nos. 465-471a Ovptd. "BARBUDA"

1977, June 13   *Perf. 14*

290	A88	¹/₂c	multicolored	.15	.15
291	A88	1c	multicolored	.15	.15
292	A88	2c	multicolored	.15	.15
293	A88	10c	multicolored	.15	.15
294	A88	30c	multicolroed	.45	.45
295	A88	50c	multicolored	.75	.75
296	A88	$2	multicolored	3.00	3.00
a.			Souvenir sheet of 3, #294-296	5.00	5.00
			Nos. 290-296 (7)	4.80	4.80

Overprint is slightly smaller on No. 296a.

Nos. 472-476a Ovptd. "BARBUDA"

1977, Aug. 12   *Perf. 14*

297	A89	10c	multicolored	.15	.15
298	A89	30c	multicolored	.22	.22
299	A89	50c	multicolored	.38	.38
300	A89	90c	multicolored	.65	.65
301	A89	$1	multicolored	.75	.75
a.			Souvenir sheet of 4, #298-301	2.50	2.50
			Nos. 297-301 (5)	2.15	2.15

Royal Visit B26

1977, Oct. 27   *Perf. 14¹/₂*

302	B26	50c	Royal yacht Britannia	.24	.24
303	B26	$1.50	Jubilee emblem	.65	.65
304	B26	$2.50	Flags	1.10	1.10
a.			Souvenir sheet of 3, #302-304	3.00	3.00
			Nos. 302-304 (3)	1.99	1.99

Nos. 483-489 Ovptd. "BARBUDA"

1977, Nov. 15   *Perf. 14*

305	A90	¹/₂c	multicolored	.15	.15
306	A90	1c	multicolored	.15	.15
307	A90	2c	multicolored	.15	.15
308	A90	8c	multicolored	.15	.15
309	A90	10c	multicolored	.15	.15
310	A90	25c	multicolored	.20	.20
311	A90	$2	multicolored	1.65	1.65
a.			Souvenir sheet of 4, #308-311	2.50	2.50
			Set value	2.00	2.00

Nos. 477-482 Ovptd. "BARBUDA" in Black

1977, Dec. 20   *Perf. 12*

312	A87	10c	multicolored	.15	.15
313	A87	30c	multicolored	.18	.18
314	A87	50c	multicolored	.28	.28
315	A87	90c	multicolored	.52	.52
316	A87	$2.50	multicolored	1.50	1.50
			Nos. 312-316 (5)	2.63	2.63

Nos. 312-316 exist with blue overprint.

1977, Nov. 28   *Perf. 13¹/₂x14*

312a	A87	10c	multicolored	.15	.15
313a	A87	30c	multicolored	.28	.28
314a	A87	50c	multicolored	.38	.38
315a	A87	90c	multicolored	.70	.70
316a	A87	$2.50	multicolored	2.00	2.00
			Nos. 312a-316a (5)	3.51	3.51

Souvenir Sheet

317	A87	$5	multicolored	3.75	3.75

Overprint of Nos. 312a-316a differs from that on Nos. 312-316.

Anniversaries — B27

First navigable airships, 75th anniv: No. 318a, Zeppelin LZ1. b, German Naval airship L31. c, Graf Zeppelin. d, Gondola on military airship.
Soviet space program, 20th anniv: No. 319a, Sputnik, 1957. b, Vostok rocket, 1961. c, Voskhod rocket, 1964. d, Space walk, 1965.
Lindbergh's Atlantic crossing, 50th anniv: No. 320a, Fueling for flight. b, New York take-off. c, Spirit of St. Louis. d, Welcome in England.
Coronation of Queen Elizabeth II, 25th anniv: No. 321a, Lion of England. b, Unicorn of Scotland. c, Yale of Beaufort. d, Falcon of Plantagenet.
Rubens, 400th birth anniv: No. 322a, Two lions. b, Daniel in the Lion's Den. c, Two lions lying down. d, Lion at Daniel's feet. Block of 4 has continuous design.

1977, Dec. 29   *Perf. 14¹/₂x14*

318	B27	75c	Block of 4, #a.-d.	1.25	1.25
319	B27	95c	Block of 4, #a.-d.	1.65	1.65
320	B27	$1.25	Block of 4, #a.-d.	2.00	2.00
321	B27	$2	Block of 4, #a.-d.	3.25	3.25
322	B27	$2	Block of 4, #a.-d.	8.50	8.50
e.			Min. sheet, #318-322 + 4 labels	17.00	17.00
			Nos. 318-322 (5)	16.65	16.65

Nos. 490-494a Ovptd. "BARBUDA"

1978, Feb. 15   *Perf. 13x13¹/₂*

323	A91	10c	multicolored	.15	.15
324	A91	15c	multicolored	.15	.15
325	A91	50c	multicolored	.28	.28
326	A91	90c	multicolored	.52	.52
327	A91	$2	multicolored	1.10	1.10
a.			Souv. sheet of 4, #324-327, perf. 14	2.25	2.25
			Set value	2.00	2.00

Pieta, by Michelangelo — B28

Works by Michelangelo: 95c, Holy Family. $1.25, Libyan Sibyl. $2, The Flood.

1978, Mar. 23   *Perf. 13¹/₂x14*

328	B28	75c	multicolored	.38	.38
329	B28	95c	multicolored	.50	.50
330	B28	$1.25	multicolored	.65	.65
331	B28	$2	multicolored	1.00	1.00
a.			Souvenir sheet of 4, #328-331	2.53	2.53
			Nos. 328-331 (4)	2.53	2.53

Nos. 495-502 Ovptd. "BARBUDA"

1978, Mar. 23   *Perf. 14*

332	A92	¹/₂c	multicolored	.15	.15
333	A92	1c	multicolored	.15	.15
334	A92	2c	multicolored	.15	.15
335	A92	10c	multicolored	.15	.15
336	A92	50c	multicolored	.35	.35
337	A92	90c	multicolored	.60	.60
338	A92	$2	multicolored	1.40	1.40
			Set value	2.45	2.45

Souvenir Sheet

339	A92	$2	multicolored	1.75	1.75

Nos. 503-507 Ovptd. "BARBUDA"

1978, May 22   *Perf. 14¹/₂*

340	A93	10c	multicolored	.15	.15
341	A93	50c	multicolored	.40	.40
342	A93	90c	multicolored	.75	.75
343	A93	$2	multicolored	1.65	1.65
			Nos. 340-343 (4)	2.95	2.95

Souvenir Sheet

344	A93	$2.50	multicolored	2.00	2.00

Coronation of Queen Elizabeth II, 25th Anniv. — B29

Crowns: No. 345a, St. Edward's. b, Imperial State. No. 346a, Queen Mary's. b, Queen Mother's. No. 347a, Queen Consort's. b, Queen Victoria's.

1978, June 2   *Perf. 15*
Miniature Sheets of Two Each Plus Two Labels

345	B29	75c	Sheet of 4	1.30	1.30
346	B29	$1.50	Sheet of 4	2.50	2.50
347	B29	$2.50	Sheet of 4	4.50	4.50

Souvenir Sheet
Perf. 14¹/₂

348	B29	Sheet of 6, #345a-347b	4.00	4.00

Nos. 508-514 Ovptd. in Black or Deep Rose Lilac "BARBUDA"

1978   *Perf. 14*

349	A94	10c	multicolored	.15	.15
350	A94	30c	multicolored	.18	.18
351	A94	50c	multicolored	.28	.28
352	A94	90c	multicolored	.52	.52
353	A94	$2.50	multicolored	1.50	1.50
			Nos. 349-353 (5)	2.63	2.63

Souvenir Sheet

354	A94	$5	multicolored	3.00	3.00

Self-adhesive

355					
a.	A95	Bklt. pane, 3 each 25c and 50c, die cut, rouletted (DRL)			
b.	A95	$5 Bklt. pane of 1, die cut			

Issue dates: #349-354. June 2, #355, Oct. 12.

Nos. 515-518 Ovptd. "BARBUDA"

1978, Sept. 12   *Perf. 14*

356	A96	10c	multicolored	.15	.15
357	A96	15c	multicolored	.15	.15
358	A96	$3	multicolored	2.25	2.25
			Nos. 356-358 (3)	2.55	2.55

Souvenir Sheet

359		Sheet of 4	2.50	2.50
a.	A96	25c multicolored	.18	.18
b.	A96	30c multicolored	.22	.22
c.	A96	50c multicolored	.38	.38
d.	A96	$2 multicolored	1.50	1.50

Nos. 519-523 Ovptd. "BARBUDA"

1978, Nov. 20   *Perf. 14*

360	A97	25c	multicolored	.26	.26
361	A97	50c	multicolored	.52	.52
362	A97	90c	multicolored	.95	.95
363	A97	$2	multicolored	2.25	2.25
			Nos. 360-363 (4)	3.98	3.98

Souvenir Sheet

364	A97	$2.50	multicolored	3.00	3.00

Flora and Fauna B30

1978, Nov. 20   *Perf. 15*

365	B30	25c	Blackbar soldierfish	.50	.50
366	B30	50c	Painted lady	1.00	1.00
367	B30	75c	Dwarf poinciana	1.50	1.50
368	B30	95c	Zebra butterfly	1.90	1.90
369	B30	$1.25	Bougainvillea	2.50	2.50
			Nos. 365-369 (5)	7.40	7.40

Nos. 524-527 Ovptd. in Silver "BARBUDA"

1978, Nov. 20   *Perf. 14*

370	A98	8c	multicolored	.15	.15
371	A98	25c	multicolored	.18	.18
372	A98	$2	multicolored	1.50	1.50
			Nos. 370-372 (3)	1.83	1.83

Souvenir Sheet

373	A98	$4	multicolored	3.25	3.25

Events and Annivs. B31

Designs: 75c, 1978 World Cup Soccer Championships, vert. 95c, Wright Brothers 1st powered flight, 75th anniv. $1.25, First Trans-Atlantic balloon flight, Aug. 1978. $2, Coronation of Elizabeth II, 25th anniv., vert.

1978, Dec. 20   *Perf. 14*

374	B31	75c	multicolored	.40	.40
375	B31	95c	multicolored	.50	.50
376	B31	$1.25	multicolored	.60	.60
377	B31	$2	multicolored	1.00	1.00
a.			Souv. sheet of 4, #374-377, imperf.	4.00	4.00
			Nos. 374-377 (4)	2.50	2.50

No. 377a has simulated perfs.

Nos. 528-532 Ovptd. in Bright Blue
"BARBUDA" and

Sir Rowland
Hill, Death
Cent.
B32

1979, Apr. 4
378 A99	25c multicolored		.16	.16
379 A99	50c multicolored		.35	.35
380 B32	75c Sir Rowland Hill, vert.		.42	.42
381 B32	95c Mail coach, 1840		.52	.52
382 A99	$1 multicolored		.65	.65
383 B32	$1.25 London's first pillar box, 1855		.70	.70
384 B32	$2 St. Martin's Post Office, London, vert.		1.10	1.10
a.	Souvenir sheet of 4, #380-381, 383-384, imperf.		2.75	2.75
385 A99	$2 multicolored		1.40	1.40
	Nos. 378-385 (8)		5.30	5.30

Souvenir Sheet
386 A99	$2.50 multicolored		2.00	2.00

No. 384a has simulated perfs.
For overprints see Nos. 423-426.

Nos. 533-536 Ovptd. "BARBUDA"
1979, Apr. 16
387 A100	10c multicolored		.15	.15
388 A100	50c multicolored		.35	.35
389 A100	$4 multicolored		2.50	2.50
	Nos. 387-389 (3)		3.00	3.00

Souvenir Sheet
390 A100	$2.50 multicolored		1.90	1.90

Intl. Civil Aviation Organization, 30th
Anniv. — B33

1979, May 24   *Perf. 13½x14*
391 B33	75c Passengers leaving 747		.50	.50
392 B33	95c Air traffic controllers		.65	.65
393 B33	$1.25 Plane on runway		.85	.85
a.	Block of 3, #391-393 + label		2.00	2.00

Nos. 537-541 Ovptd. "BARBUDA"
1979, May 24   *Perf. 14*
394 A101	25c multicolored		.18	.18
395 A101	50c multicolored		.38	.38
396 A101	90c multicolored		.65	.65
397 A101	$2 multicolored		1.40	1.40
	Nos. 394-397 (4)		2.61	2.61

Souvenir Sheet
398 A101	$5 multicolored		3.50	3.50

Nos. 542-546 Ovptd. "BARBUDA"
1979, Aug. 1   *Perf. 14½*
399 A102	30c multicolored		.24	.24
400 A102	50c multicolored		.42	.42
401 A102	90c multicolored		.70	.70
402 A102	$3 multicolored		2.50	2.50
	Nos. 399-402 (4)		3.86	3.86

Souvenir Sheet
403 A102	$2.50 multicolored		2.50	2.50

Nos. 547-551 Ovptd. "BARBUDA"
1979, Aug. 1   *Perf. 14*
404 A103	25c multicolored		.16	.16
405 A103	50c multicolored		.38	.38
406 A103	90c multicolored		.65	.65
407 A103	$3 multicolored		2.25	2.25
	Nos. 404-407 (4)		3.44	3.44

Souvenir Sheet
408 A103	$2.50 multicolored		2.00	2.00

Intl. Year of the
Child — B34

Details of the Christ Child from various paintings
by Dürer: 25c, 1512. 50c, 1516. 75c, 1526. $1.25,
1502.

1979, Sept. 24   *Perf. 14x13½*
409 B34	25c multicolored		.18	.18
410 B34	50c multicolored		.38	.38
411 B34	75c multicolored		.58	.58
412 B34	$1.25 multicolored		.90	.90
a.	Souvenir sheet of 4, #409-412		2.25	2.25
	Nos. 409-412 (4)		2.04	2.04

Nos. 552-556 Ovptd. "BARBUDA"
1979, Nov. 21   *Perf. 14*
413 A104	8c multicolored		.15	.15
414 A104	15c multicolored		.15	.15
415 A104	50c multicolored		.30	.30
416 A104	$4 multicolored		2.50	2.50
	Nos. 413-416 (4)		3.10	3.10

Souvenir Sheet
Perf. 12x12½
417 A104	$3 multicolored		2.25	2.25

Nos. 557-561 Ovptd. "BARBUDA"
1980, Mar. 18
418 A105	10c multicolored		.15	.15
419 A105	25c multicolroed		.15	.15
420 A105	$1 multicolored		.52	.52
421 A105	$2 multicolored		1.00	1.00
	Nos. 418-421 (4)		1.82	1.82

Souvenir Sheet
422 A105	$3 multicolored		2.00	2.00

Nos. 571A-571D Overprinted "BARBUDA"
in Dark Blue
1980, May 6   *Perf. 12*
423 A99	25c multicolored		.18	.18
424 A99	50c multicolored		.42	.42
425 A99	$1 multicolored		.75	.75
426 A99	$2 multicolored		1.65	1.65
	Nos. 423-426 (4)		3.00	3.00

First Moon Landing, 10th Anniv. — B35

1980, May 21   *Perf. 13½x14*
427 B35	75c Crew badge		.45	.45
428 B35	95c Plaque left on moon		.60	.60
429 B35	$1.25 Lunar, command modules		.75	.75
430 B35	$2 Lunar module		1.25	1.25
a.	Souvenir sheet of 4, #427-430		3.25	3.25
	Nos. 427-430 (4)		3.05	3.05

American
Widgeon
B36

1980, June 16   *Perf. 14½x14*
431 B36	1c shown		.55	.40
432 B36	2c Snowy plover		.55	.40
433 B36	4c Rose-breasted grosbeak		.65	.40
434 B36	6c Mangrove cuckoo		.65	.40
435 B36	10c Adelaide's warbler		.65	.40
436 B36	15c Scaly-breasted thrasher		.65	.40
437 B36	20c Yellow-crowned night heron		.75	.40
438 B36	25c Bridled quail dove		.75	.40
439 B36	35c Carib grackle		.75	.40
440 B36	50c Northern pintail		.75	.40
441 B36	75c Black-whiskered vireo		.75	.45
442 B36	$1 Blue-winged teal		1.10	.75

Perf. 14x14½
443 B36	$1.50 Green-throated carib		1.40	1.00
444 B36	$2 Red-necked pigeon		2.00	1.40
445 B36	$2.50 Stolid flycatcher		2.75	1.65
446 B36	$5 Yellow-bellied sapsucker		3.25	3.25
447 B36	$7.50 Caribbean elaenia		4.75	4.75
448 B36	$10 Great egret		6.50	6.50
	Nos. 431-448 (18)		29.20	23.75

Nos. 443-448 vert.

Nos. 572-578 Ovptd. "BARBUDA"
Perf. 13½x14, 14x13½
1980, July 29
449 A106a	10c multicolored		.15	.15
450 A106a	30c multicolored		.20	.20
451 A106a	50c multicolored		.35	.35
452 A106a	90c multicolored		.60	.60
453 A106a	$1 multicolored		.60	.60
454 A106a	$4 multicolored		2.50	2.50
	Nos. 449-454 (6)		4.40	4.40

Souvenir Sheet
Perf. 14
455 A106a	$5 multicolored		3.00	3.00

Nos. 579-583 Ovptd. "BARBUDA"
1980, Sept. 8   *Perf. 14*
456 A107	30c multicolored		.20	.20
457 A107	50c multicolored		.35	.35
458 A107	90c multicolored		.60	.60
459 A107	$3 multicolored		2.00	2.00
	Nos. 456-459 (4)		3.15	3.15

Souvenir Sheet
460 A107	$5 multicolored		3.50	3.50

Nos. 584-586 Optd. "BARBUDA"
1980, Oct. 6
461 A108	10c multicolored		.15	.15
462 A108	$2.50 multicolored		2.50	2.50

Souvenir Sheet
Perf. 12
463 A108	$3 multicolored		2.75	2.75

Nos. 587-591 Ovptd. "BARBUDA"
1980, Dec. 8   *Perf. 14*
464 A109	10c multicolored		.20	.20
465 A109	30c multicolored		.55	.55
466 A109	$1 multicolored		1.75	1.75
467 A109	$2 multicolored		3.50	3.50
	Nos. 464-467 (4)		6.00	6.00

Souvenir Sheet
468 A109	$2.50 multicolored		3.25	3.25

Nos. 602-606 Ovptd. "BARBUDA"
1981, Jan. 26
469 A111	25c multicolored		.20	.20
470 A111	50c multicolored		.45	.45
471 A111	90c multicolored		.80	.80
472 A111	$3 multicolored		2.75	2.75
	Nos. 469-472 (4)		4.20	4.20

Souvenir Sheet
473 A111	$2.50 multicolored		2.50	2.50

Famous
Women — B37

1981, Mar. 9   *Perf. 14x13½*
474 B37	50c Florence Nightingale		.25	.25
475 B37	90c Marie Curie		.50	.50
476 B37	$1 Amy Johnson		.55	.55
477 B37	$4 Eleanor Roosevelt		2.25	2.25
	Nos. 474-477 (4)		3.55	3.55

Walt Disney
Characters at
Sea — B38

1981, May 15   *Perf. 13½x14*
478 B38	10c Goofy		.15	.15
479 B38	20c Donald Duck		.30	.30
480 B38	25c Mickey Mouse		.45	.45
481 B38	30c Goofy fishing		.50	.50
482 B38	35c Goofy sailing		.60	.60
483 B38	40c Mickey fishing		.65	.65
484 B38	75c Donald Duck boating		1.25	1.25
485 B38	$1 Minnie Mouse		1.75	1.75
486 B38	$2 Chip 'n Dale		3.50	3.50
	Nos. 478-486 (9)		9.15	9.15

Souvenir Sheet
487 B38	$2.50 Donald Duck, diff.		8.00	8.00

Nos. 618-622 Ovptd. "BARBUDA"
1981, June 9   *Perf. 14*
488 A112	10c multicolored		.15	.15
489 A112	50c multicolored		.35	.35
490 A112	90c multicolored		.60	.60
491 A112	$4 multicolored		2.75	2.75
	Nos. 488-491 (4)		3.85	3.85

Souvenir Sheet
Perf. 14x14½
492 A112	$5 multicolored		4.50	4.50

Miniature Sheets

Royal
Wedding — B39

Designs: $1, Buckingham Palace. $1.50,
Caernarvon Castle. $4, Highgrove House.

1981, July 27   *Perf. 11x11½*
493 B39	Sheet of 6		8.00	8.00
494 B39	Sheet of 6		8.00	8.00
495 B39	Sheet of 6		8.00	8.00

Souvenir Sheet
Perf. 11½x11
496 B39	$5 St. Paul's Cathedral, vert.		2.25	2.25

Sheets of 6 contain two of each denomination.
Stamps of same denomination have continuous
design. For surcharges see Nos. 592-594.

Nos. 623-627 Ovptd. in Black or Silver
"BARBUDA"
1981, Aug. 14   *Perf. 14*
497 CD331	25c multicolored		.15	.15
498 CD331	50c multicolored		.30	.30
499 CD331	$4 multicolored		2.00	2.00
	Nos. 497-499 (3)		2.45	2.45

Souvenir Sheet
500 CD331	$5 multicolored		3.50	3.50

Self-adhesive
501 CD331	Booklet		15.00	15.00
a.	Pane of 6 (2x25c, 2x$1, 2x$2), Charles, die cut, rouletted (S)		8.00	8.00
b.	Pane of 4, $5 Couple, die cut (S)		6.50	6.50

Issued: #497-500, Aug. 24; #501, Oct. 12.
For surcharge see No. B1.

Intl. Year of
the Disabled
B40

1981, Sept. 14   *Perf. 14*
502 B40	50c Travel		.35	.35
503 B40	90c Braille, sign language		.65	.65
504 B40	$1 Helping hands		.70	.70
505 B40	$4 Mobility aids		2.75	2.75
	Nos. 502-505 (4)		4.45	4.45

Nos. 607-617 Ovptd. "BARBUDA"

1981, Nov. 1   *Perf. 15*

506	A79	6c multicolored	.15	.15
507	A79	10c multicolored	.15	.15
508	A79	20c multicolored	.15	.15
509	A79	25c multicolored	.20	.20
510	A79	35c multicolored	.30	.30
511	A79	50c multicolored	.40	.40
512	A79	75c multicolored	.60	.60
513	A79	$1 multicolored	.75	.75

Perf. 13¹/₂x14

514	A80	$2.50 multicolored	1.90	1.90
515	A80	$5 multicolored	3.75	3.75
516	A80	$10 multicolored	7.50	7.50
		Nos. 506-516 (11)	15.85	15.85

Nos. 628-632 Ovptd. "BARBUDA"

1981, Dec. 14   *Perf. 15*

517	A113	10c multicolored	.15	.15
518	A113	50c multicolored	.50	.50
519	A113	90c multicolored	.90	.90
520	A113	$2.50 multicolored	2.50	2.50
		Nos. 517-520 (4)	4.05	4.05

Souvenir Sheet

521	A113	$5 multicolored	4.00	4.00

Nos. 643-647 Ovptd. "BARBUDA"

1981, Dec. 14

522	A116	10c multicolored	.15	.15
523	A116	50c multicolored	.55	.55
524	A116	90c multicolored	1.00	1.00
525	A116	$2 multicolored	2.25	2.25
		Nos. 522-525 (4)	3.95	3.95

Souvenir Sheet

526	A116	$4 multicolored	3.00	3.00

Nos. 638-642 Ovptd. in Black or Silver "BARBUDA"

1981, Dec. 22

527	A115	8c multi	.15	.15
528	A115	30c multi	.20	.20
529	A115	$1 multi (S)	.65	.65
530	A115	$3 multi	2.00	2.00
		Nos. 527-530 (4)	3.00	3.00

Souvenir Sheet

531	A115	$5 multi	3.50	3.50

Birth of Prince William — B41

Various portraits.

1982, June 21   **Wmk. 380**   *Perf. 14*

532	B41	$1 buff & multi	.60	.60
533	B41	$2.50 lt pink & multi	1.50	1.50
534	B41	$5 lt lilac & multi	3.00	3.00
		Nos. 532-534 (3)	5.10	5.10

Souvenir Sheet

535	B41	$5 Couple	4.00	4.00
		See Nos. 540-543.		

The overprint on stamps of Antigua, from here on, read "BARBUDA MAIL" in one or two lines.

#672-675 Ovptd. in Black or Silver

Perf. 14¹/₂x14

1982, Oct. 12   **Unwmk.**

536	CD332	90c multi	.65	.65
537	CD332	$1 multi (S)	.75	.75
538	CD332	$4 multi (S)	3.00	3.00
		Nos. 536-538 (3)	4.40	4.40

Souvenir Sheet

539	CD332	$5 multi	3.50	3.50

Barbuda Nos. 532-535 Inscribed "Twenty First Birthday Greetings to H.R.H. The Princess of Wales"

Various portraits.

Perf. 14x14¹/₂

1982, July 1   **Wmk. 380**

540	B41	$1 lt grn & multi	.60	.60
541	B41	$2.50 pale salmon & multi	1.50	1.50
542	B41	$5 lt bl & multi	3.00	3.00
		Nos. 540-542 (3)	5.10	5.10

Souvenir Sheet

543	B41	$4 Couple	3.50	3.50

#663-666 Ovptd. in Black or Silver

Perf. 14¹/₂x14

1982, Aug. 30   **Unwmk.**

544	CD332	90c multi	.75	.75
545	CD332	$1 multi (S)	.85	.85
546	CD332	$4 multi	3.25	3.25
		Nos. 544-546 (3)	4.85	4.85

Souvenir Sheet

547	CD332	$5 multi	4.50	4.50

Nos. 676-683 Overprinted

1982, Dec. 6   *Perf. 15*

551	A121	10c multicolored	.15	.15
552	A121	25c multicolored	.22	.22
553	A121	45c multicolored	.40	.40
554	A121	60c multicolored	.55	.55
555	A121	$1 multicolored	.90	.90
556	A121	$3 multicolored	2.75	2.75
		Nos. 551-556 (6)	4.97	4.97

Souvenir Sheets

557	A121	$4 on #682	3.25	3.25
558	A121	$4 on #683	3.25	3.25

Nos. 684-688 Overprinted

1982, Dec. 6   *Perf. 14*

559	A122	10c multicolored	.15	.15
560	A122	30c multicolored	.22	.22
561	A122	$1 multicolored	.75	.75
562	A122	$4 multicolored	3.00	3.00
		Nos. 559-562 (4)	4.12	4.12

Souvenir Sheet

563	A122	$5 multicolored	3.75	3.75

Nos. 689-693 Overprinted

1983, Mar. 14   *Perf. 14¹/₂*

564	A123	45c multicolored	.32	.32
565	A123	50c multicolored	.38	.38
566	A123	60c multicolored	.45	.45
567	A123	$4 multicolored	3.00	3.00
		Nos. 564-567 (4)	4.15	4.15

Souvenir Sheet

568	A123	$5 multicolored	3.75	3.75

Nos. 694-697 Overprinted

1983, Mar. 14   *Perf. 14*

569	A124	25c multicolored	.22	.22
570	A124	45c multicolored	.42	.42
571	A124	60c multicolored	.55	.55
572	A124	$3 multicolored	2.75	2.75
		Nos. 569-572 (4)	3.94	3.94

Nos. 698-702 Overprinted

1983, Apr. 12

573	A125	15c multicolored	.15	.15
574	A125	50c multicolored	.48	.48
575	A125	60c multicolored	.55	.55
576	A125	$3 multicolored	3.00	3.00
		Nos. 573-576 (4)	4.18	4.18

Souvenir Sheet

577	A125	$5 multicolored	4.00	4.00

First Manned Balloon Flight, Bicent. — B43

1983, June 13

578	B43	$1 Vincenzo Lunardi, 1785	1.00	1.00
579	B43	$1.50 Montgolfier brothers, 1783	1.50	1.50
580	B43	$2.50 Blanchard & Jeffries, 1785	2.50	2.50
		Nos. 578-580 (3)	5.00	5.00

Souvenir Sheet

581	B43	$5 Graf Zeppelin, 1928	3.75	3.75

Nos. 703-707 Overprinted

1983, July 4   *Perf. 15*

582	A126	15c multicolored	.15	.15
583	A126	50c multicolored	.45	.45
584	A126	60c multicolored	.55	.55
585	A126	$3 multicolored	2.75	2.75
		Nos. 582-585 (4)	3.90	3.90

Souvenir Sheet

586	A126	$5 multicolored	4.50	4.50

Nos. 726-730 Overprinted

1983, Sept. 12

587	A128	30c multicolored	.26	.26
588	A128	50c multicolored	.45	.45
589	A128	50c multicolored	.52	.52
590	A128	$4 multicolored	3.50	3.50
		Nos. 587-590 (4)	4.73	4.73

Souvenir Sheet

591	A128	$5 multicolored	4.50	4.50

Barbuda Nos. 493-495 Surcharged 45c on $1, 50c on $1.50, or 60c on $4

1983, Oct. 21   *Perf. 11¹/₂x11*

592		Sheet of 6	11.00	11.00
593		Sheet of 6	11.00	11.00
594		Sheet of 6	11.00	11.00

Nos. 708-725 Overprinted

1983, Oct. 28   *Perf. 14*

595	A127	1c multicolored	.15	.15
596	A127	2c multicolored	.15	.15
597	A127	3c multicolored	.15	.15
598	A127	5c multicolored	.15	.15
599	A127	10c multicolored	.15	.15
600	A127	15c multicolored	.15	.15
601	A127	20c multicolored	.15	.15
602	A127	25c multicolored	.20	.20
603	A127	30c multicolored	.25	.25
604	A127	40c multicolored	.35	.35
605	A127	45c multicolored	.35	.35
606	A127	50c multicolored	.45	.45
607	A127	60c multicolored	.50	.50
608	A127	$1 multicolored	.85	.85
609	A127	$2 multicolored	1.75	1.75
610	A127	$2.50 multicolored	2.25	2.25
611	A127	$5 multicolored	4.25	4.25
612	A127	$10 multicolored	8.00	8.00
		Nos. 595-612 (18)	20.25	20.25

Nos. 731-735 Overprinted

1983, Oct. 28   *Perf. 14*

613	A129	10c multicolored	.15	.15
614	A129	30c multicolored	.20	.20
615	A129	$1 multicolored	.75	.75
616	A129	$4 multicolored	3.00	3.00
		Nos. 613-616 (4)	4.10	4.10

Souvenir Sheet

617	A129	$5 multicolored	3.75	3.75

#736-739 Ovptd. in Black or Silver

1983, Dec. 14   *Perf. 14*

618	A130	15c multicolored (S)	.15	.15
619	A130	45c multicolored (S)	.45	.45
620	A130	60c multicolored	.50	.50
621	A130	$3 multicolored	2.75	2.75
		Nos. 618-621 (4)	3.85	3.85

Members of Royal Family — B44

1984, Feb. 14   *Perf. 14¹/₂x14*

622	B44	$1 Edward VII	1.00	1.00
623	B44	$1 George V	1.00	1.00
624	B44	$1 George VI	1.00	1.00
625	B44	$1 Elizabeth II	1.00	1.00
626	B44	$1 Prince Charles	1.00	1.00
627	B44	$1 Prince William	1.00	1.00
		Nos. 622-627 (6)	6.00	6.00

Nos. 740-744 Overprinted and

1984 Summer Olympics, Los Angeles B45

1984   *Perf. 15, 13¹/₂ (B45)*

628	A131	25c multicolored	.20	.20
629	A131	50c multicolored	.40	.40
630	A131	90c multicolored	.45	.45
631	B45	$1.50 Olympic Stadium, Athens	1.10	1.10
632	B45	$2.50 Olympic Stadium, Los Angeles	1.90	1.90
633	A131	$3 multicolored	2.50	2.50
634	B45	$5 Torch bearer	4.00	4.00
a.		Souv. sheet of 1, perf. 15	4.00	4.00
		Nos. 628-634 (7)	10.55	10.55

Souvenir Sheet

635	A131	$5 multicolored	4.00	4.00

Issue dates: A131, Apr. 26, B45, July 27.

Nos. 755-759 Overprinted

1984, July 12   *Perf. 15*

636	A133	15c multicolored	.15	.15
637	A133	50c multicolored	.45	.45
638	A133	60c multicolored	.55	.55
639	A133	$3 multicolored	2.75	2.75
		Nos. 636-639 (4)	3.90	3.90

Souvenir Sheet

640	A133	$5 multicolored	4.25	4.25

Nos. 745-749 Overprinted

1984, July 12

641	A132	45c multicolored	.40	.40
642	A132	50c multicolored	.45	.45
643	A132	60c multicolored	.50	.50
644	A132	$4 multicolored	3.50	3.50
		Nos. 641-644 (4)	4.85	4.85

Souvenir Sheet

645	A132	$5 multicolored	4.50	4.50

#760-767 Ovptd. in Black or Silver

1984, Oct. 1   *Perf. 14*

646	A134	10c multicolored (S)	.15	.15
647	A134	20c multicolored	.15	.15
648	A134	30c multicolored	.25	.25
649	A134	40c multicolored	.30	.30
650	A134	90c multicolored	.70	.70
651	A134	$1.10 multicolored (S)	.90	.90
652	A134	$1.50 multicolored (S)	1.25	1.25
653	A134	$2 multicolored	1.65	1.65
		Nos. 646-653 (8)	5.35	5.35

Nos. 768-772 Overprinted

1984, Oct. 1

654	A135	40c multicolored	.35	.35
655	A135	50c multicolored	.45	.45
656	A135	60c multicolored	.50	.50
657	A135	$3 multicolored	2.75	2.75
		Nos. 654-657 (4)	4.05	4.05

Souvenir Sheet

658	A135	$5 multicolored	4.25	4.25

Nos. 773-778 Overprinted

1984, Nov. 21   *Perf. 15*

659	A136	40c multicolored	.40	.40
660	A136	50c multicolored	.50	.50
661	A136	60c multicolored	.60	.60
662	A136	$2 multicolored	2.00	2.00
663	A136	$3 multicolored	3.00	3.00
		Nos. 659-663 (5)	6.50	6.50

Souvenir Sheet

664	A136	$5 multicolored	5.00	5.00

Nos. 782-791 Overprinted in Silver

1984   *Perf. 15*

665	A137a	15c multicolored	.15	.15
666	A137a	25c multicolored	.20	.20
667	A137a	50c multicolored	.40	.40
668	A137a	60c multicolored	.50	.50
669	A137a	70c multicolored	.55	.55
670	A137a	90c multicolored	.75	.75
671	A137a	$3 multicolored	2.50	2.50
672	A137a	$4 multicolored	3.25	3.25
		Nos. 665-672 (8)	8.30	8.30

Souvenir Sheets

673	A137a	$5 #790	4.50	4.50
674	A137a	$5 #791, horiz.	4.50	4.50

Issue dates: Correggio, Nov. 21; Degas, Nov. 30.

Nos. 779-781 Overprinted

1984, Nov. 30

675	A137	$1 multicolored	.80	.80
676	A137	$5 multicolored	4.00	4.00

Souvenir Sheet

677	A137	$5 multicolored	4.50	4.50

Nos. 819-827 Overprinted

1985, Feb. 18

678	A139	60c multicolored	.45	.45
679	A139	60c multicolored	.45	.45
680	A139	60c multicolored	.45	.45
681	A139	60c multicolored	.45	.45
682	A139	$1 multicolored	.75	.75
683	A139	$1 multicolored	.75	.75
684	A139	$1 multicolored	.75	.75
685	A139	$1 multicolored	.75	.75
		Nos. 678-685 (8)	4.80	4.80

Souvenir Sheet

686	A139	$5 multicolored	4.50	4.50

Queen Mother (Lady Elizabeth Bowes-Lyon), 1907 — B46

1985, Feb. 26   *Perf. 14x14½*
687	B46	15c shown	.15	.15
688	B46	45c Duchess of York, 1926	.35	.35
689	B46	50c Coronation, 1937	.40	.40
690	B46	60c Queen Mother	.50	.50
691	B46	90c Wearing tiara	.70	.70
692	B46	$2 Wearing blue hat	1.65	1.65
693	B46	$3 With children	2.50	2.50
		Nos. 687-693 (7)	6.25	6.25

For overprints see Nos. 724-728, 733, 735.

Nos. 828-834 Overprinted
1985, May 10   *Perf. 15*
694	A140	25c multicolored	.20	.20
695	A140	30c multicolored	.25	.25
696	A140	50c multicolored	.40	.40
697	A140	90c multicolored	.70	.70
698	A140	$1 multicolored	.80	.80
699	A140	$3 multicolored	2.50	2.50
		Nos. 694-699 (6)	4.85	4.85

Souvenir Sheet
700	A140	$5 multicolored	4.00	4.00

Audubon, Birth Bicentenary — B47

1985, Apr. 4   *Perf. 14*
701	B47	45c Roseate tern	.40	.40
702	B47	50c Mangrove cuckoo	.45	.45
703	B47	60c Yellow-crowned night heron	.55	.55
704	B47	$5 Brown pelican	4.50	4.50
		Nos. 701-704 (4)	5.90	5.90

Nos. 845-849, 910-913 Ovptd. in Black or Silver
1985-86   *Perf. 15, 12½x12*
705	A143	60c on #910 (S)	.48	.48
706	A143	90c on #845	.70	.70
707	A143	90c on #911 (S)	.70	.70
708	A143	$1 on #846	.80	.80
709	A143	$1.50 on #847	1.25	1.25
710	A143	$1.50 on #912	1.25	1.25
711	A143	$3 on #848	2.50	2.50
712	A143	$3 on #913	2.50	2.50

Souvenir Sheet
713	A143	$5 on #849	4.50	4.50

Issue dates: Nos. 706, 708-709, 711, 713, July 18, 1985. Others, Dec. 1986.

Nos. 850-854 Overprinted
1985, July 18   *Perf. 14*
714	A144	25c multicolored	.22	.22
715	A144	60c multicolored	.52	.52
716	A144	95c multicolored	.80	.80
717	A144	$4 multicolored	3.50	3.50
		Nos. 714-717 (4)	5.04	5.04

Souvenir Sheet
718	A144	$5 multicolored	4.50	4.50

Nos. 840-844 Overprinted
1985, Aug. 2
719	A142	10c multicolored	.15	.15
720	A142	30c multicolored	.28	.28
721	A142	60c multicolored	.52	.52
722	A142	$4 multicolored	3.75	3.75
		Nos. 719-722 (4)	4.70	4.70

Souvenir Sheet
723	A142	$5 multicolored	4.50	4.50

Barbuda Nos. 687-693 Ovptd. "4TH AUG 1900-1985" and Antigua Nos. 866A-870 Ovptd. "BARBUDA / MAIL" in Silver or Black

Perf. 14, 12x12½ (#729, 731, 736)
1985-86
724	B46	15c multi	.15	.15
725	B46	45c multi	.35	.35
726	B46	50c multi	.40	.40
727	B46	60c multi	.48	.48
728	B46	90c multi	.70	.70
729	A148	90c multi	.70	.70
730	A148	$1 multi (S)	.80	.80
731	A148	$1 like #730	.80	.80
732	A148	$1.50 multi	1.20	1.20
733	B46	$2 multi	1.65	1.65
734	A148	$2.50 multi	2.00	2.00

735	B46	$3 multi	2.50	2.50
736	B46	$3 multi	2.50	2.50
		Nos. 724-736 (13)	14.23	14.23

Souvenir Sheet
737	A148	$5 multi	4.50	4.50

Queen Mother's 85th birthday.
Issue dates: 15c, 45c, 50c, 60c, No. 728, $2, No. 735, Aug. 2. No. 730, $1.50, $2.50, Nov. 8. Others, Dec. 1986. Nos. 729, 731, 736 issued in sheets of 5 plus label.

Nos. 835-839 Overprinted
1985, Aug. 30   *Perf. 15*
738	A141	15c multicolored	.15	.15
739	A141	50c multicolored	.40	.40
740	A141	60c multicolored	.45	.45
741	A141	$3 multicolored	2.50	2.50
		Nos. 738-741 (4)	3.50	3.50

Souvenir Sheet
742	A141	$5 multicolored	4.00	4.00

Nos. 855-859 Overprinted
1985, Aug. 30   *Perf. 14*
743	A145	30c multicolored	.24	.24
744	A145	90c multicolored	.70	.70
745	A145	$1.50 multicolored	1.25	1.25
746	A145	$3 multicolored	2.50	2.50
		Nos. 743-746 (4)	4.69	4.69

Souvenir Sheet
747	A145	$5 multicolored	4.25	4.25

Nos. 860-861 Overprinted
1985, Nov. 25   *Perf. 14*
748	A146	$2 yellow green	1.65	1.65

Souvenir Sheet
749	A146	$5 deep brown	4.00	4.00

#871-875 Ovptd. in Black or Silver
1985, Nov. 25
750	A149	15c multi (S)	.15	.15
751	A149	45c multi	.40	.40
752	A149	60c multi	.55	.55
753	A149	$3 multi (S)	3.00	3.00
		Nos. 750-753 (4)	4.10	4.10

Souvenir Sheet
754	A149	$5 multi	4.50	4.50

Nos. 862-866 Overprinted
1986, Feb. 17
755	A147	25c multicolored	.20	.20
756	A147	50c multicolored	.40	.40
757	A147	60c multicolored	.48	.48
758	A147	$3 multicolored	2.50	2.50
		Nos. 755-758 (4)	3.58	3.58

Souvenir Sheet
759	A147	$5 multicolored	4.00	4.00

Nos. 886-889 Overprinted
1986, Feb. 17   *Perf. 14½*
760	A152	60c multicolored	.48	.48
761	A152	$1 multicolored	.80	.80
762	A152	$4 multicolored	3.25	3.25
		Nos. 760-762 (3)	4.53	4.53

Souvenir Sheet
763	A152	$5 multicolored	4.00	4.00

Nos. 876-880 Overprinted
1986, Mar. 10   *Perf. 14*
764	A150	25c multicolored	.20	.20
765	A150	50c multicolored	.40	.40
766	A150	$1 multicolored	.80	.80
767	A140	$3 multicolored	2.50	2.50
		Nos. 764-767 (4)	3.90	3.90

Souvenir Sheet
768	A150	$5 multicolored	4.00	4.00

Nos. 881-885 Overprinted
1986, Mar. 10   *Perf. 14*
769	A151	15c multicolored	.15	.15
770	A151	45c multicolored	.35	.35
771	A151	60c multicolored	.48	.48
772	A151	$3 multicolored	2.50	2.50
		Nos. 769-772 (4)	3.48	3.48

Souvenir Sheet
773	A151	$5 multicolored	4.00	4.00

Nos. 905-909 Overprinted
1986, Apr. 4   *Perf. 15*
774	A156	10c multicolored	.15	.15
775	A156	25c multicolored	.20	.20
776	A156	60c multicolored	.48	.48
777	A156	$4 multicolored	3.25	3.25
		Nos. 774-777 (4)	4.08	4.08

Souvenir Sheet
778	A156	$5 multicolored	4.00	4.00

B48 — BARBUDA $1

1986, Apr. 21
779	B48	$1 Shaking hands	.80	.80
780	B48	$2 Talking with woman	1.65	1.65
781	B48	$2.50 With officer	2.00	2.00
		Nos. 779-781 (3)	4.45	4.45

Souvenir Sheet
Perf. 13½x14
782	B48	$5 Portraits	4.00	4.00

No. 782 contains one 34x27mm stamp.

Nos. 925-928 Overprinted in Silver or Black
1986, Aug. 12
783	CD339	60c multi	.48	.48
784	CD339	$1 multi	.80	.80
785	CD339	$4 multi	3.25	3.25
		Nos. 783-785 (3)	4.53	4.53

Souvenir Sheet
786	CD339	$5 multi (Bk)	4.00	4.00

Nos. 920-924 Overprinted and

Halley's Comet B49 — $1 Barbuda

1986   *Perf. 14, 15 (B49)*
787	A158	5c multicolored	.15	.15
788	A158	10c multicolored	.15	.15
789	A158	60c multicolored	.48	.48
790	B49	$1 shown	.80	.80
791	B49	$2.50 Early telescope, dish antenna, vert.	2.00	2.00
792	A158	$4 multicolored	3.25	3.25
793	B49	$5 World map, comet	4.00	4.00
		Nos. 787-793 (7)	10.83	10.83

Souvenir Sheet
794	A159	$5 multicolored	4.00	4.00

Issue dates: Nos. 790-791, 793, July 10, others, Sept. 22.

Nos. 901-904 Overprinted
1986, Aug. 12   *Perf. 13½x14*
795	A156	40c multicolored	.32	.32
796	A156	$1 multicolored	.80	.80
797	A156	$3 multicolored	2.50	2.50
		Nos. 795-797 (3)	3.62	3.62

Souvenir Sheet
Perf. 14x13½
798	A156	$5 multicolored	4.00	4.00

Nos. 915-919 Overprinted
1986, Aug. 28   *Perf. 14*
799	A157	30c multicolored	.24	.24
800	A157	60c multicolored	.48	.48
801	A157	$1 multicolored	.80	.80
802	A157	$4 multicolored	3.25	3.25
		Nos. 799-802 (4)	4.77	4.77

Souvenir Sheet
803	A157	$5 multicolored	4.00	4.00

See Nos. 848-851.

Nos. 934-938 Overprinted
1986, Aug. 28   Litho.   *Perf. 15*
804	A161	25c multicolored	.20	.20
805	A161	50c multicolored	.40	.40
806	A161	$1 multicolored	.80	.80
807	A161	$3 multicolored	2.50	2.50
		Nos. 804-807 (4)	3.90	3.90

Souvenir Sheet
808	A161	$5 multicolored	4.00	4.00

Nos. 939-942 Ovptd. in Silver
1986, Sept. 22   *Perf. 14*
809	CD340	45c multicolored	.42	.42
810	CD340	60c multicolored	.60	.60
811	CD340	$4 multicolored	4.00	4.00
		Nos. 809-811 (3)	5.02	5.02

Souvenir Sheet
812	CD340	$5 multicolored	5.00	5.00

Nos. 943-947 Overprinted in Silver or Black
1986, Nov. 10   *Perf. 15*
813	A162	15c multicolored	.15	.15
814	A162	45c multicolored	.32	.32
815	A162	60c multicolored	.45	.45
816	A162	$3 multicolored	2.25	2.25
		Nos. 813-816 (4)	3.17	3.17

Souvenir Sheet
817	A162	$5 multi (Bk)	4.00	4.00

Nos. 948-957 Overprinted
1986, Nov. 10
818	A163	10c multicolored	.15	.15
819	A163	15c multicolored	.15	.15
820	A163	50c multicolored	.38	.38
821	A163	60c multicolored	.45	.45
822	A163	70c multicolored	.52	.52
823	A163	$1 multicolored	.75	.75
824	A163	$3 multicolored	2.25	2.25
825	A163	$4 multicolored	3.00	3.00
		Nos. 818-825 (8)	7.65	7.65

Souvenir Sheets
826	A163	$4 multicolored	3.25	3.25
827	A163	$5 multicolored	4.00	4.00

Nos. 958-962 Overprinted
1986, Nov. 28
828	A164	10c multicolored	.15	.15
829	A164	50c multicolored	.38	.38
830	A164	$1 multicolored	.75	.75
831	A164	$4 multicolored	3.00	3.00
		Nos. 828-831 (4)	4.28	4.28

Souvenir Sheet
832	A164	$5 multicolored	4.00	4.00

Nos. 929-933 Overprinted
1987, Jan. 12   *Perf. 14*
833	A160	30c multicolored	.28	.28
834	A160	60c multicolored	.55	.55
835	A160	$1 multicolored	.90	.90
836	A160	$3 multicolored	2.75	2.75
		Nos. 833-836 (4)	4.48	4.48

Souvenir Sheet
837	A160	$5 multicolored	4.00	4.00

Nos. 968-972A Overprinted
1987, Jan. 12
838	A165	10c multicolored	.15	.15
839	A165	15c multicolored	.15	.15
840	A165	50c multicolored	.40	.40
841	A165	60c multicolored	.48	.48
842	A165	70c multicolored	.55	.55
843	A165	$1 multicolored	.80	.80
844	A165	$3 multicolored	2.50	2.50
845	A165	$4 multicolored	3.25	3.25
		Nos. 838-845 (8)	8.28	8.28

Souvenir Sheets
846	A165	$5 multi (#972)	4.00	4.00
847	A165	$5 multi (#972A)	4.00	4.00

Automobile, cent.

Nos. 963-966 Overprinted
1987, Mar. 10
848	A157	30c multicolored	.22	.22
849	A157	60c multicolored	.45	.45
850	A157	$1 multicolored	.75	.75
851	A157	$4 multicolored	3.00	3.00
		Nos. 848-851 (4)	4.42	4.42

See Nos. 799-802.

Nos. 1000-1004 Overprinted
1987, Apr. 23   *Perf. 15*
852	A170	30c multicolored	.22	.22
853	A170	60c multicolored	.45	.45
854	A170	$1 multicolored	2.25	2.25
855	A170	$3 multicolored	.75	.75
		Nos. 852-855 (4)	3.67	3.67

Souvenir Sheet
856	A171	$5 multicolored	5.00	5.00

Nos. 1005-1014 Overprinted
1987, July 1   *Perf. 14*
857	A172	15c multicolored	.15	.15
858	A173	30c multicolored	.22	.22
859	A172	40c multicolored	.30	.30
860	A173	50c multicolored	.38	.38
861	A172	60c multicolored	.45	.45
862	A172	$1 multicolored	.75	.75
863	A173	$2 multicolored	1.50	1.50
864	A173	$3 multicolored	2.25	2.25
		Nos. 857-864 (8)	6.00	6.00

Souvenir Sheets
865	A172	$5 multicolored	4.00	4.00
866	A173	$5 multicolored	4.00	4.00

Nos. 1025-1034 Overprinted
1987, July 28   *Perf. 15*
867	A175	10c multicolored	.15	.15
868	A175	15c multicolored	.15	.15
869	A175	30c multicolored	.24	.24
870	A175	50c multicolored	.40	.40

871	A175	60c multicolored	.48 .48
872	A175	70c multicolored	.55 .55
873	A175	90c multicolored	.70 .70
874	A175	$1.50 multicolored	1.20 1.20
875	A175	$2 multicolored	1.65 1.65
876	A175	$3 multicolored	2.25 2.25
		Nos. 867-876 (10)	7.77 7.77

Marine
Life
B50

1987, July 28

877	B50	5c Shore crab	.15 .15
878	B50	10c Sea cucumber	.15 .15
879	B50	15c Stop light parrotfish	.15 .15
880	B50	25c Banded coral shrimp	.18 .18
881	B50	35c Spotted drum	.26 .26
882	B50	60c Thorny star-fish	.45 .45
883	B50	75c Atlantic trumpet triton	.55 .55
884	B50	90c Feather-star, yellow beaker sponge	.65 .65
885	B50	$1 Blue gorgonian, vert.	.75 .75
886	B50	$1.25 Slender filefish, vert.	.90 .90
887	B50	$5 Barred hamlet, vert.	3.75 3.75
888	B50	$7.50 Fairy basslet, vert.	5.50 5.50
889	B50	$10 Fire coral, butterfly fish, vert.	7.50 7.50
		Nos. 877-889 (13)	20.94 20.94

For surcharges see Nos. 1133-1134.

#1048-1052 Ovptd. in Silver or Black

1987, Oct. 12   *Perf. 14*

890	A178	10c multicolored	.15 .15
891	A178	60c multicolored	.48 .48
892	A178	$1 multicolored	.80 .80
893	A178	$3 multicolored	2.25 2.25
		Nos. 890-893 (4)	3.68 3.68

Souvenir Sheet

894	A178	$5 multi (Bk)	4.00 4.00

1988 Summer Olympics, Seoul.

#990-999 Ovptd. in Black or Silver

1987, Oct. 12   *Perf. 13 1/2 x14*

895	A169	10c multicolored	.15 .15
896	A169	30c multicolored	.24 .24
897	A169	40c multicolored	.32 .32
898	A169	60c multicolored	.48 .48
899	A169	90c multicolored	.70 .70
900	A169	$1 multicolored (S)	.80 .80
901	A169	$3 multicolored	2.25 2.25
902	A169	$4 multicolored	3.00 3.00
		Nos. 895-902 (8)	7.94 7.94

Size: 110x95mm
Imperf

903	A169	$5 multicolored	4.00 4.00
904	A169	$5 multicolored (S)	4.00 4.00

#1015-1024 Ovptd. in Silver or Black

1987, Nov. 5   *Perf. 14*

905	A174	15c multicolored	.15 .15
906	A174	30c multicolored	.24 .24
907	A174	45c multicolored	.35 .35
908	A174	50c multicolored (Bk)	.40 .40
909	A174	60c multicolored	.48 .48
910	A174	90c multicolored	.70 .70
911	A174	$1 multicolored	.80 .80
912	A174	$2 multicolored	1.65 1.65
913	A174	$3 multicolored (Bk)	2.25 2.25
914	A174	$5 multicolored	4.00 4.00
		Nos. 905-914 (10)	11.02 11.02

#1040-1047 Ovptd. in Black or Silver

1987, Nov. 5

915	A177	15c multicolored	.15 .15
916	A177	30c multicolored	.28 .28
917	A177	45c multicolored	.42 .42
918	A177	50c multicolored	.48 .48
919	A177	60c multicolored	.55 .55
920	A177	$1 multicolored	.95 .95
921	A177	$2 multicolored	2.00 2.00
922	A177	$3 multicolored (S)	2.75 2.75
		Nos. 915-922 (8)	7.58 7.58

Nos. 1035-1039 Overprinted

1987, Dec. 8

923	A176	30c multicolored	.24 .24
924	A176	60c multicolored	.48 .48
925	A176	$1 multicolored	.80 .80
926	A176	$3 multicolored	2.25 2.25
		Nos. 923-926 (4)	3.77 3.77

Souvenir Sheet

927	A176	$5 multicolored	4.00 4.00

Nos. 1063-1067 Overprinted

1988, Jan. 12

928	A181	45c multicolored	.32 .32
929	A181	60c multicolored	.45 .45
930	A181	$1 multicolored	.75 .75
931	A181	$4 multicolored	3.00 3.00
		Nos. 928-931 (4)	4.52 4.52

Souvenir Sheet

932	A181	$5 multicolored	4.00 4.00

Nos. 1083-1091 Overprinted

1988, Mar. 25

933	A184	25c multicolored	.20 .20
934	A184	30c multicolored	.24 .24
935	A184	40c multicolored	.32 .32
936	A184	45c multicolored	.35 .35
937	A184	50c multicolored	.40 .40
938	A184	60c multicolored	.48 .48
939	A184	$1 multicolored	.80 .80
940	A184	$2 multicolored	1.65 1.65
		Nos. 933-940 (8)	4.44 4.44

Souvenir Sheet

941	A184	$5 multicolored	4.00 4.00

Nos. 1058-1062 Ovptd. in Silver

1988, May 6

942	A180	15c multicolored	.15 .15
943	A180	45c multicolored	.35 .35
944	A180	60c multicolored	.48 .48
945	A180	$4 multicolored	3.25 3.25
		Nos. 942-945 (4)	4.23 4.23

Souvenir Sheet

946	A180	$5 multicolored	4.00 4.00

Nos. 1068-1072 Overprinted

1988, July 4

947	A182	25c multicolored	.20 .20
948	A182	60c multicolored	.48 .48
949	A182	$1 multicolored	1.65 1.65
950	A182	$3 multicolored	2.25 2.25
		Nos. 947-950 (4)	4.58 4.58

Souvenir Sheet

951	A182	$5 multicolored	4.00 4.00

Nos. 1073-1082 Overprinted

1988, July 4

952	A183	10c multicolored	.15 .15
953	A183	15c multicolored	.15 .15
954	A183	50c multicolored	.40 .40
955	A183	60c multicolored	.48 .48
956	A183	70c multicolored	.55 .55
957	A183	$1 multicolored	.80 .80
958	A183	$3 multicolored	2.25 2.25
959	A183	$4 multicolored	3.25 3.25
		Nos. 952-959 (8)	8.03 8.03

Souvenir Sheets

960	A183	$5 multi (#1081)	4.00 4.00
961	A183	$5 multi (#1082)	4.00 4.00

Nos. 1092-1101 Overprinted

1988, July 25

962	A185	10c multicolored	.15 .15
963	A185	30c multicolored	.25 .25
964	A185	45c multicolored	.38 .38
965	A185	50c multicolored	.50 .50
966	A185	90c multicolored	.75 .75
967	A185	$1 multicolored	.85 .85
968	A185	$3 multicolored	2.50 2.50
969	A185	$4 multicolored	3.50 3.50
		Nos. 962-969 (8)	8.88 8.88

Souvenir Sheets

970	A185	$5 multi (#1100)	4.00 4.00
971	A185	$5 multi (#1101)	4.00 4.00

Nos. 1102-1111 Overprinted

1988, July 25   *Perf. 13 1/2 x14*

972	A187	30c multicolored	.24 .24
973	A187	40c multicolored	.32 .32
974	A187	45c multicolored	.35 .35
975	A187	50c multicolored	.40 .40
976	A187	$1 multicolored	.80 .80
977	A187	$2 multicolored	1.65 1.65
978	A187	$3 multicolored	2.25 2.25
979	A187	$4 multicolored	3.25 3.25
		Nos. 972-979 (8)	9.26 9.26

Souvenir Sheets

980	A187	$5 multi (#1110)	4.00 4.00
981	A187	$5 multi (#1111)	4.00 4.00

Nos. 1053-1057 Overprinted

1988, Aug. 25   *Perf. 15*

982	A179	10c multicolored	.15 .15
983	A179	45c multicolored	.45 .45
984	A179	$1 multicolored	.75 .75
985	A179	$3 multicolored	2.25 2.25
		Nos. 982-985 (4)	3.60 3.60

Souvenir Sheet

986	A179	$5 multicolored	4.00 4.00

Nos. 1112-1116 Overprinted

1988, Aug. 25

987	A188	30c multicolored	.24 .24
988	A188	60c multicolored	.48 .48
989	A188	$1 multicolored	.80 .80
990	A188	$3 multicolored	2.25 2.25
		Nos. 987-990 (4)	3.77 3.77

Souvenir Sheet

991	A188	$5 multicolored	4.00 4.00

Nos. 1127-1136 Overprinted

1988, Sept. 16   *Perf. 14*

992	A190	10c multicolored	.15 .15
993	A190	30c multicolored	.22 .22
994	A190	50c multicolored	.38 .38
995	A190	90c multicolored	.65 .65
996	A190	$1 multicolored	.75 .75
997	A190	$2 multicolored	1.65 1.65
998	A190	$3 multicolored	2.25 2.25
999	A190	$4 multicolored	3.00 3.00
		Nos. 992-999 (8)	9.05 9.05

Souvenir Sheets

1000	A191	$5 multi (#1135)	4.00 4.00
1001	A191	$5 multi (#1136)	4.00 4.00

Nos. 1140-1144 Overprinted

1988, Sept. 16

1002	A192	40c multicolored	.32 .32
1003	A192	60c multicolored	.48 .48
1004	A192	$1 multicolored	.80 .80
1005	A192	$3 multicolored	2.25 2.25
		Nos. 1002-1005 (4)	3.85 3.85

Souvenir Sheet

1006	A192	$5 multicolored	4.00 4.00

Nos. 1145-1162 Overprinted

1988-90

1007	A193	1c multicolored	.15 .15
1008	A193	2c multicolored	.15 .15
1009	A193	3c multicolored	.15 .15
1010	A193	5c multicolored	.15 .15
1011	A193	10c multicolored	.15 .15
1012	A193	15c multicolored	.15 .15
1013	A193	20c multicolored	.16 .16
1014	A193	25c multicolored	.20 .20
1015	A193	30c multicolored	.24 .24
1016	A193	40c multicolored	.32 .32
1017	A193	45c multicolored	.35 .35
1018	A193	50c multicolored	.40 .40
1019	A193	60c multicolored	.48 .48
1020	A193	$1 multicolored	.80 .80
1021	A193	$2 multicolored	1.65 1.65
1022	A193	$2.50 multicolored	2.00 2.00
1023	A193	$5 multicolored	4.00 4.00
1024	A193	$10 multicolored	8.00 8.00
1025	A193	$20 mult ('90)	16.00 16.00
		Nos. 1007-1025 (19)	35.50 35.50

Issue dates: $20, May 4, others Dec. 8.

Nos. 1162A-1167 Overprinted

1989, Apr. 28

1026	A194	1c multicolored	.15 .15
1027	A194	2c multicolored	.15 .15
1028	A194	3c multicolored	.15 .15
1029	A194	4c multicolored	.15 .15
1030	A194	30c multicolored	.24 .24
1031	A194	60c multicolored	.48 .48
1032	A194	$1 multicolored	.80 .80
1033	A194	$4 multicolored	3.25 3.25
		Nos. 1026-1033 (8)	5.37 5.37

Souvenir Sheet

1034	A194	$5 multicolored	4.00 4.00

Nos. 1175-1176 Overprinted

1989, May 24

1035	A196	$1.50 Strip of 4, #a.-d.	4.75 4.75

Souvenir Sheet

1036	A196	$6 multicolored	4.75 4.75

Nos. 1177-1186 Overprinted

1989, May 29

1037	A197	10c multicolored	.15 .15
1038	A197	30c multicolored	.35 .35
1039	A197	40c multicolored	.48 .48
1040	A197	60c multicolored	.70 .70
1041	A197	$1 multicolored	1.20 1.20
1042	A197	$2 multicolored	2.25 2.25
1043	A197	$3 multicolored	3.50 3.50
1044	A197	$4 multicolored	4.75 4.75
		Nos. 1037-1044 (8)	13.38 13.38

Souvenir Sheets

1045	A197	$7 multi (#1185)	5.50 5.50
1046	A197	$7 multi (#1186)	5.50 5.50

Nos. 1187-1196 Overprinted

1989, Sept. 18

1047	A198	25c multicolored	.18 .18
1048	A198	45c multicolored	.32 .32
1049	A198	50c multicolored	.38 .38
1050	A198	60c multicolored	.45 .45
1051	A198	75c multicolored	.55 .55
1052	A198	90c multicolored	.65 .65
1053	A198	$3 multicolored	2.25 2.25
1054	A198	$4 multicolored	3.00 3.00
		Nos. 1047-1054 (8)	7.78 7.78

Souvenir Sheets

1055	A198	$6 multi (#1195)	4.50 4.50
1056	A198	$6 multi (#1196)	4.50 4.50

Nos. 1197-1206 Overprinted

1989, Dec. 14   *Perf. 14x13 1/2*

1057	A199	25c multicolored	.18 .18
1058	A199	45c multicolored	.32 .32
1059	A199	50c multicolored	.38 .38
1060	A199	60c multicolored	.45 .45
1061	A199	$1 multicolored	.75 .75
1062	A199	$2 multicolored	1.50 1.50
1063	A199	$3 multicolored	2.25 2.25
1064	A199	$4 multicolored	3.00 3.00
		Nos. 1057-1064 (8)	8.83 8.83

Souvenir Sheets

1065	A199	$5 multi (#1205)	3.75 3.75
1066	A199	$5 multi (#1206)	3.75 3.75

Nos. 1217-1222 Overprinted

1989, Dec. 20   *Perf. 14*

1067	A201	15c multicolored	.15 .15
1068	A201	18c multicolored	.18 .18
1069	A201	$1 multicolored	.75 .75
1070	A201	$4 multicolored	3.00 3.00
		Nos. 1067-1070 (4)	4.08 4.08

Souvenir Sheets

1071	A201	$5 multi (#1221)	3.75 3.75
1072	A201	$5 multi (#1222)	3.75 3.75

Nos. 1264-1273 Overprinted

1989, Dec. 20

1073	A208	10c multicolored	.15 .15
1074	A208	25c multicolored	.18 .18
1075	A208	30c multicolored	.22 .22
1076	A208	50c multicolored	.38 .38
1077	A208	60c multicolored	.45 .45
1078	A208	70c multicolored	.52 .52
1079	A208	$4 multicolored	3.00 3.00
1080	A208	$5 multicolored	3.75 3.75
		Nos. 1073-1080 (8)	8.65 8.65

Souvenir Sheets

1081	A208	$5 multi (#1272)	3.75 3.75
1082	A208	$5 multi (#1273)	3.75 3.75

Nos. 1223-1232 Overprinted

1990, Feb. 21

1083	A202	10c multicolored	.15 .15
1084	A202	25c multicolored	.18 .18
1085	A202	50c multicolored	.38 .38
1086	A202	60c multicolored	.45 .45
1087	A202	75c multicolored	.55 .55
1088	A202	$1 multicolored	.75 .75
1089	A202	$3 multicolored	2.25 2.25
1090	A202	$4 multicolored	3.00 3.00
		Nos. 1083-1090 (8)	7.71 7.71

Souvenir Sheets

1091	A202	$6 multi (#1231)	4.50 4.50
1092	A202	$6 multi (#1232)	4.50 4.50

Nos. 1233-1237 Overprinted

1990, Mar. 30

1093	A203	25c multicolored	.18 .18
1094	A203	45c multicolored	.32 .32
1095	A203	60c multicolored	.45 .45
1096	A203	$4 multicolored	3.00 3.00
		Nos. 1093-1096 (4)	3.95 3.95

Souvenir Sheet

1097	A203	$5 multicolored	3.75 3.75

Nos. 1258-1262 Overprinted

1990, Mar. 30

1098	A206	10c multicolored	.15 .15
1099	A206	45c multicolored	.32 .32
1100	A206	$1 multicolored	.75 .75
1101	A206	$4 multicolored	3.00 3.00
		Nos. 1098-1101 (4)	4.22 4.22

Souvenir Sheet

1102	A206	$5 multicolored	3.75 3.75

Nos. 1275-1284 Overprinted

1990, June 6

1103	A210	10c multicolored	.15 .15
1104	A210	20c multicolored	.15 .15
1105	A210	25c multicolored	.18 .18
1106	A210	45c multicolored	.32 .32
1107	A210	60c multicolored	.45 .45
1108	A210	$2 multicolored	1.50 1.50
1109	A210	$3 multicolored	2.25 2.25
1110	A210	$4 multicolored	3.00 3.00
		Nos. 1103-1110 (8)	8.00 8.00

Souvenir Sheets

1111	A210	$5 multi (#1283)	3.75 3.75
1112	A210	$5 multi (#1284)	3.75 3.75

Nos. 1285-1294 Overprinted

1990, July 12

1113	A211	15c multicolored	.15 .15
1114	A211	45c multicolored	.32 .32
1115	A211	50c multicolored	.38 .38
1116	A211	60c multicolored	.45 .45
1117	A211	$1 multicolored	.75 .75
1118	A211	$2 multicolored	1.50 1.50

1119 A211	$3 multicolored	2.25	2.25
1120 A211	$5 multicolored	3.75	3.75
	Nos. 1113-1120 (8)	9.55	9.55

Souvenir Sheets

1121 A211	$6 multi (#1293)	4.50	4.50
1122 A211	$6 multi (#1294)	4.50	4.50

Nos. 1295-1304 Overprinted

1990, Aug. 14

1123 A212	10c multicolored	.15	.15
1124 A212	15c multicolored	.15	.15
1125 A212	50c multicolored	.38	.38
1126 A212	60c multicolored	.45	.45
1127 A212	$1 multicolored	.75	.75
1128 A212	$2 multicolored	1.50	1.50
1129 A212	$3 multicolored	2.25	2.25
1130 A212	$4 multicolored	3.00	3.00
	Nos. 1123-1130 (8)	8.63	8.63

Souvenir Sheets

1131 A212	$5 multi (#1303)	3.75	3.75
1132 A212	$5 multi (#1304)	3.75	3.75

Barbuda Nos. 888-889 Surcharged "1st Anniversary / Hurricane Hugo / 16th September, 1989-1990"

1990, Sept. 17   *Perf. 15*

1133 A50	$5 on $7.50	3.75	3.75
1134 A50	$7.50 on $10	5.50	5.50

Nos. 1324-1328 Overprinted

1990, Oct. 12   *Perf. 14*

1135 A217	15c multicolored	.15	.15
1136 A217	35c multicolored	.28	.28
1137 A217	75c multicolored	.55	.55
1138 A217	$3 multicolored	2.25	2.25
	Nos. 1135-1138 (4)	3.23	3.23

Souvenir Sheet

1139 A217	$6 multicolored	4.50	4.50

No. 1313 Ovptd. in Silver
Miniature Sheet

1990, Dec. 14

1140 A215	45c Sheet of 20, #a.-t.	6.75	6.75

Nos. 1360-1369 Overprinted

Perf. 14x13½, 13½x14

1990, Dec. 14

1141 A221	25c multicolored	.18	.18
1142 A221	30c multicolored	.22	.22
1143 A221	40c multicolored	.30	.30
1144 A221	60c multicolored	.45	.45
1145 A221	$1 multicolored	.75	.75
1146 A221	$2 multicolored	1.50	1.50
1147 A221	$4 multicolored	3.00	3.00
1148 A221	$5 multicolored	3.75	3.75
	Nos. 1141-1148 (8)	10.15	10.15

Souvenir Sheets

1149 A221	$6 multi (#1368)	4.50	4.50
1150 A221	$6 multi (#1369)	4.50	4.50

Nos. 1305-1308 Overprinted

1991, Feb. 4   *Perf. 15x14*

1151 A213	45c green	.35	.35
1152 A213	60c bright rose	.45	.45
1153 A213	$5 bright ultra	3.75	3.75
	Nos. 1151-1153 (3)	4.55	4.55

Souvenir Sheet

1154 A213	$6 black	4.50	4.50

Nos. 1309-1312 Overprinted

1991, Feb. 4   *Perf. 13½*

1155 A214	50c red & deep grn	.38	.38
1156 A214	75c red & vio brn	.55	.55
1157 A214	$4 red & brt ultra	3.00	3.00
	Nos. 1155-1157 (3)	3.93	3.93

Souvenir Sheet

1158 A214	$6 red & black	4.50	4.50

BARBUDA

Birds — B52

1991, Mar. 25   Litho.   *Perf. 14*

1164 B52	60c Troupial	.45	.45
1168 B52	$2 Christmas bird	1.50	1.50
1169 B52	$4 Rose-breasted gros-beak	3.00	3.00
1171 B52	$7 Stolid flycatcher	5.25	5.25
	Nos. 1164-1171 (4)	10.20	10.20

This is an expanding set. Numbers will change.

Nos. 1329-1333 Overprinted

1991, Apr. 23   Litho.   *Perf. 14*

1173 A218	38c multicolored	.38	.38
1174 A218	50c multicolored	.55	.55
1175 A218	$1 multicolored	.75	.75
1176 A218	$5 multicolored	3.75	3.75
	Nos. 1173-1176 (4)	5.43	5.43

Souvenir Sheet

1177 A218	$6 multicolored	4.50	4.50

Nos. 1350-1359 Overprinted

1991, Apr. 23

1178 A220	10c multicolored	.15	.15
1179 A220	25c multicolored	.18	.18
1180 A220	50c multicolored	.38	.38
1181 A220	60c multicolored	.45	.45
1182 A220	$1 multicolored	.75	.75
1183 A220	$2 multicolored	1.50	1.50
1184 A220	$3 multicolored	2.25	2.25
1185 A220	$4 multicolored	3.00	3.00
	Nos. 1178-1185 (8)	8.66	8.66

Souvenir Sheets

1186 A220	$6 multi (#1358)	4.50	4.50
1187 A220	$6 multi (#1359)	4.50	4.50

Nos. 1370-1379 Overprinted

1991, June 21   *Perf. 14x13½*

1188 A222	25c multicolored	.18	.18
1189 A222	45c multicolored	.35	.35
1190 A222	50c multicolored	.38	.38
1191 A222	60c multicolored	.45	.45
1192 A222	$1 multicolored	.75	.75
1193 A222	$2 multicolored	1.50	1.50
1194 A222	$3 multicolored	2.25	2.25
1195 A222	$4 multicolored	3.00	3.00
	Nos. 1188-1195 (8)	8.86	8.86

Souvenir Sheets

1196 A222	$6 multi (#1378)	4.50	4.50
1197 A222	$6 multi (#1379)	4.50	4.50

Nos. 1380-1390 Overprinted

1991, July 25   Litho.   *Perf. 14*

1198 A223	10c multicolored	.15	.15
1199 A223	15c multicolored	.15	.15
1200 A223	25c multicolored	.18	.18
1201 A223	45c multicolored	.35	.35
1202 A223	50c multicolored	.38	.38
1203 A223	$1 multicolored	.75	.75
1204 A223	$2 multicolored	1.50	1.50
1205 A223	$4 multicolored	3.00	3.00
1206 A223	$5 multicolored	3.75	3.75
	Nos. 1198-1206 (9)	10.21	10.21

Souvenir Sheets

1207 A223	$6 multi (#1389)	4.50	4.50
1208 A223	$6 multi (#1390)	4.50	4.50

Nos. 1411-1420 Overprinted

1991, Aug. 26   Litho.   *Perf. 14*

1209 A226	10c multicolored	.15	.15
1210 A226	15c multicolored	.15	.15
1211 A226	45c multicolored	.35	.35
1212 A226	60c multicolored	.45	.45
1213 A226	$1 multicolored	.75	.75
1214 A226	$2 multicolored	1.50	1.50
1215 A226	$4 multicolored	3.00	3.00
1216 A226	$5 multicolored	3.75	3.75
	Nos. 1209-1216 (8)	10.10	10.10

Souvenir Sheets

1217 A226	$6 multi (#1419)	4.50	4.50
1218 A226	$6 multi (#1420)	4.50	4.50

Nos. 1401-1410 Overprinted

1991, Oct. 18

1219 A225	10c multicolored	.15	.15
1220 A225	35c multicolored	.26	.26
1221 A225	50c multicolored	.38	.38
1222 A225	75c multicolored	.55	.55
1223 A225	$1 multicolored	.75	.75
1224 A225	$2 multicolored	1.50	1.50
1225 A225	$4 multicolored	3.00	3.00
1226 A225	$5 multicolored	3.75	3.75
	Nos. 1219-1226 (8)	10.34	10.34

Souvenir Sheets

1227 A225	$6 multi (#1409)	4.50	4.50
1228 A225	$6 multi (#1410)	4.50	4.50

Nos. 1446-1455 Overprinted

1991, Nov. 18

1229 CD347	10c multicolored	.15	.15
1230 CD347	15c multicolored	.15	.15
1231 CD347	20c multicolored	.15	.15
1232 CD347	40c multicolored	.30	.30
1233 CD347	$1 multicolored	.75	.75
1234 CD347	$2 multicolored	1.50	1.50
1235 CD347	$4 multicolored	3.00	3.00
1236 CD347	$5 multicolored	3.75	3.75
	Nos. 1229-1236 (8)	9.75	9.75

Souvenir Sheets

1237 CD347	$4 multi (#1454)	3.00	3.00
1238 CD347	$4 multi (#1455)	3.00	3.00

Nos. 1503-1510 Overprinted

1991, Dec. 24   *Perf. 12*

1239 A238	10c multicolored	.15	.15
1240 A238	30c multicolored	.22	.22
1241 A238	40c multicolored	.30	.30
1242 A238	60c multicolored	.45	.45
1243 A238	$1 multicolored	.75	.75
1244 A238	$3 multicolored	2.25	2.25
1245 A238	$4 multicolored	3.00	3.00
1246 A238	$5 multicolored	3.75	3.75
	Nos. 1239-1246 (8)	10.87	10.87

Nos. 1421-1435 Overprinted

1992, Feb. 20   *Perf. 13½*

1249 A227	5c multicolored	.15	.15
1250 A227	10c multicolored	.15	.15
1251 A227	15c multicolored	.15	.15
1252 A227	25c multicolored	.18	.18
1253 A227	30c multicolored	.22	.22
1254 A227	40c multicolored	.30	.30
1255 A227	50c multicolored	.38	.38
1256 A227	75c multicolored	.55	.55
1257 A227	$2 multicolored	1.50	1.50
1258 A227	$3 multicolored	2.25	2.25
1259 A227	$4 multicolored	3.00	3.00
1260 A227	$5 multicolored	3.75	3.75
	Nos. 1249-1260 (12)	12.58	12.58

Size: 102x76mm

Imperf

1261 A227	$5 multi (#1433)	3.75	3.75
1262 A227	$5 multi (#1434)	3.75	3.75
1263 A227	$6 multi	4.50	4.50

Nos. 1476-1483 Overprinted

1992, Apr. 7   Litho.   *Perf. 14*

1264 A231	10c multi	.15	.15
1265 A231	15c multi, vert.	.15	.15
1266 A231	45c multi, vert.	.35	.35
1267 A231	60c multi, vert.	.45	.45
1268 A231	$1 multi	.75	.75
1269 A231	$2 multi	1.50	1.50
1270 A231	$4 multi	3.00	3.00
1271 A231	$5 multi, vert.	3.75	3.75
	Nos. 1264-1271 (8)	10.10	10.10

Nos. 1484-1485 Overprinted

1992, Apr. 7   Litho.   *Perf. 14*

Souvenir Sheet

1272 A231	$6 multi (#1484)	5.00	5.00
1273 A231	$6 multi (#1485)	5.00	5.00

Nos. 1551-1560 Overprinted

1992, Apr. 16   Litho.   *Perf. 14x13½*

1274 A242	10c multicolored	.15	.15
1275 A242	15c multicolored	.15	.15
1276 A242	30c multicolored	.25	.25
1277 A242	40c multicolored	.35	.35
1278 A242	$1 multicolored	.85	.85
1279 A242	$2 multicolored	1.65	1.65
1280 A242	$4 multicolored	3.30	3.30
1281 A242	$5 multicolored	4.15	4.15
	Nos. 1274-1281 (8)	10.85	10.85

Souvenir Sheets

1282 A242	$6 multi (#1559)	5.00	5.00
1283 A242	$6 multi (#1560)	5.00	5.00

Nos. 1489-1492 Overprinted

1992, June 19   Litho.   *Perf. 14*

1284 A234	75c multi	.55	.55
1285 A234	$2 multi, vert.	1.50	1.50
1286 A234	$3.50 multi	2.65	2.65
	Nos. 1284-1286 (3)	4.70	4.70

Souvenir Sheet

1287 A234	$5 multi, vert.	4.25	4.25

Nos. 1493-1494 Overprinted

1992, June 19

1288 A235	$1.50 multi	1.10	1.10
1289 A235	$4 multi	3.00	3.00

Nos. 1495-1496 Overprinted

1992, June 19

1290 A236	$2 multi	1.50	1.50
1291 A236	$2.50 multi, vert.	1.90	1.90

Nos. 1499-1502 Overprinted

1992, June 19

1292 A237	25c multicolored	.18	.18
1293 A237	$2 multicolored	1.50	1.50
1294 A237	$3 multicolored	2.25	2.25
1295 A237	$4 multicolored	3.50	3.50
	Nos. 1292-1295 (4)	7.43	7.43

Nos. 1571-1578 Overprinted

1992, Oct. 12   Litho.   *Perf. 14*

1296 A244	15c multicolored	.15	.15
1297 A244	30c multicolored	.22	.22
1298 A244	40c multicolored	.30	.30
1299 A244	$1 multicolored	.75	.75
1300 A244	$2 multicolored	1.50	1.50
1301 A244	$4 multicolored	3.00	3.00
	Nos. 1296-1301 (6)	5.92	5.92

Souvenir Sheets

1302 A244	$6 multicolored	4.50	4.50
1303 A244	$6 multicolored	4.50	4.50

Nos. 1599-1600 Overprinted

1992, Oct. 12   *Perf. 14½*

1304 A247	$1 multicolored	.75	.75
1305 A247	$2 multicolored	1.50	1.50

Nos. 1513-1518 Overprinted

1992, Nov. 3   *Perf. 14*

1306 CD348	10c multicolored	.15	.15
1307 CD348	30c multicolored	.22	.22
1308 CD348	$1 multicolored	.75	.75
1309 CD348	$5 multicolored	3.75	3.75
	Nos. 1306-1309 (4)	4.87	4.87

Souvenir Sheets

1310 CD348	$6 multi (#1517)	4.50	4.50
1311 CD348	$6 multi (#1518)	4.50	4.50

Nos. 1541-1550 Ovptd. "BARBUDA / MAIL"

1992, Dec. 8

1312 A241	10c multicolored	.15	.15
1313 A241	15c multicolored	.15	.15
1314 A241	30c multicolored	.22	.22
1315 A241	50c multicolored	.38	.38
1316 A241	$1 multicolored	.75	.75
1317 A241	$2 multicolored	1.50	1.50
1318 A241	$4 multicolored	3.00	3.00
1319 A241	$5 multicolored	3.75	3.75
	Nos. 1312-1319 (8)	9.90	9.90

Souvenir Sheets

1320 A241	$6 multi (#1549)	5.50	5.50
1321 A241	$6 multi (#1550)	5.50	5.50

Nos. 1608-1617 Ovptd. "BARBUDA MAIL"

1992, Dec. 8   Litho.   *Perf. 13½x14*

1322 A251	10c multicolored	.15	.15
1323 A251	25c multicolored	.18	.18
1324 A251	30c multicolored	.22	.22
1325 A251	40c multicolored	.30	.30
1326 A251	60c multicolored	.45	.45
1327 A251	$1 multicolored	.75	.75
1328 A251	$4 multicolored	3.00	3.00
1329 A251	$5 multicolored	3.75	3.75
	Nos. 1322-1329 (8)	8.80	8.80

Souvenir Sheets

1330 A251	$6 multi (#1616)	5.50	5.50
1331 A251	$6 multi (#1617)	5.50	5.50

No. 1601 Ovptd. "BARBUDA MAIL"

1992   Litho.   *Perf. 14*

Souvenir Sheet

1332 A248	$6 multicolored	4.50	4.50

Nos. 1519-1528 Ovptd.

1993, Jan. 25   Litho.   *Perf. 14*

1333 A239	10c multicolored	.15	.15
1334 A239	15c multicolored	.15	.15
1335 A239	30c multicolored	.28	.28
1336 A239	40c multicolored	.35	.35
1337 A239	$1 multicolored	.90	.90
1338 A239	$2 multicolored	1.80	1.80
1339 A239	$4 multicolored	3.50	3.50
1340 A239	$5 multicolored	4.50	4.50
	Nos. 1332-1339 (8)	11.63	11.63

Souvenir Sheets

1341 A239	$6 multi (#1527)	5.50	5.50
1342 A239	$6 multi (#1528)	5.50	5.50

Nos. 1561-1570 Ovptd.

1993, Mar. 22   Litho.   *Perf. 13*

1343 A243	10c multicolored	.15	.15
1344 A243	15c multicolored	.15	.15
1345 A243	30c multicolored	.22	.22
1346 A243	40c multicolored	.30	.30
1347 A243	$1 multicolored	.75	.75
1348 A243	$2 multicolored	1.50	1.50
1349 A243	$4 multicolored	3.00	3.00
1350 A243	$5 multicolored	3.75	3.75
	Nos. 1343-1350 (8)	9.82	9.82

Imperf

Size: 120x95mm

1351 A243	$6 multi (#1569)	5.50	5.50
1352 A243	$6 multi (#1570)	5.50	5.50

Nos. 1589-1598 Ovptd.

1993, May 10   Litho.   *Perf. 14*

1353 A246	10c multicolored	.15	.15
1354 A246	25c multicolored	.18	.18
1355 A246	45c multicolored	.35	.35
1356 A246	60c multicolored	.45	.45
1357 A246	$1 multicolored	.75	.75
1358 A246	$2 multicolored	1.50	1.50
1359 A246	$4 multicolored	3.00	3.00
1360 A246	$5 multicolored	3.75	3.75
	Nos. 1353-1360 (8)	10.13	10.13

Souvenir Sheets

1361 A246	$6 multi (#1597)	5.50	5.50
1362 A246	$6 multi (#1598)	5.50	5.50

Nos. 1603-1608 Ovptd.

1993, June 29	**Litho.**		**Perf. 14**
1363 A250	10c multicolored	.15	.15
1364 A250	25c multicolored	.22	.22
1365 A250	30c multicolored	.28	.28
1366 A250	40c multicolored	.35	.35
1367 A250	60c multicolored	.55	.55
1368 A250	$1 multicolored	.90	.90
1369 A250	$4 multicolored	3.60	3.60
1370 A250	$5 multicolored	4.50	4.50
Nos. 1363-1370 (8)		10.55	10.55

Souvenir Sheets

1371 A250	$6 multi (#1607)	5.50	5.50
1372 A250	$6 multi (#1608)	5.50	5.50

Nos. 1619-1632 Ovptd.

1993, Aug. 16	**Litho.**		**Perf. 14**
1373 A252	10c multicolored	.15	.15
1374 A252	40c multicolored	.30	.30
1375 A253	45c multicolored	.35	.35
1376 A252	75c multicolored	.58	.58
1377 A252	$1 multicolored	.75	.75
1378 A252	$1.50 multicolored	1.15	1.15
1379 A252	$2 multicolored	1.50	1.50
1380 A253	$2 multi (#1626)	1.50	1.50
1381 A253	$2 multi (#1627)	1.50	1.50
1382 A252	$2.25 multicolored	1.70	1.70
1383 A253	$3 multicolored	2.25	2.25
1384 A252	$4 multi (#1630)	3.00	3.00
1385 A253	$4 multi (#1631)	3.00	3.00
1386 A252	$6 multicolored	4.50	4.50
Nos. 1373-1386 (14)		22.23	22.23

Numbers have been reserved for four souvenir sheets in this set.

Nos. 1650-1657 Ovptd.

1993, Sept. 21	**Litho.**		**Perf. 14**
1391 A256	15c multicolored	.15	.15
1392 A256	25c multicolored	.18	.18
1393 A256	30c multicolored	.22	.22
1394 A256	40c multicolored	.30	.30
1395 A256	$1 multicolored	.75	.75
1396 A256	$2 multicolored	1.50	1.50
1397 A256	$4 multicolored	3.00	3.00
1398 A256	$5 multicolored	3.75	3.75
Nos. 1391-1398 (8)		9.85	9.85

Numbers have been reserved for two souvenir sheets with this set.

No. 1660 Ovptd.

1993, Nov. 11	**Litho.**		**Perf. 14**
1401 A257	$1 Sheet of 12, #a.-l.	9.00	9.00

Numbers have been reserved for two souvenir sheets in this set.

Nos. 1697-1710 Ovptd.

1994, Mar. 3	**Litho.**		**Perf. 14**
1404-1415 A267	$2 Set of 12	18.00	18.00

Souvenir Sheets

1416-1417 A267	$6 each	4.50	4.50

Nos. 1676-1678 Ovptd.

1994, Apr. 21	**Litho.**		**Perf. 14**
1418 A260	40c multicolored	.30	.30
1419 A260	$3 multicolored	2.25	2.25

Souvenir Sheet

1420 A260	$6 multicolored	4.50	4.50

Nos. 1679-1682 Ovptd.

1994, Apr. 21			
1421-1423 A261	Set of 3	4.50	4.50

Souvenir Sheet

1424 A261	$6 multicolored	4.50	4.50

Nos. 1683-1685 Ovptd.

1994, Apr. 21			
1425 A262	40c multicolored	.32	.32
1426 A262	$4 multicolored	3.25	3.25

Souvenir Sheet

1427 A262	$5 multicolored	3.75	3.75

Nos. 1686-1688 Ovptd.

1994, Apr. 21			
1428 A263	30c multicolored	.25	.25
1429 A263	$4 multicolored	3.25	3.25

Souvenir Sheet

1430 A263	$6 multicolored	4.50	4.50

Nos. 1692-1693 Ovptd.

1994, Apr. 21			
1431 A265	$5 multicolored	4.00	4.00

Souvenir Sheet

1432 A265	$6 multicolored	4.50	4.50

Nos. 1694-1696 Ovptd.

1994, Apr. 21			
1433 A266	15c multicolored	.15	.15
1434 A266	$5 multicolored	4.00	4.00

Souvenir Sheet

1435 A266	$6 multicolored	4.50	4.50

Nos. 1732-1735 Ovptd.

1994, Apr. 21			
1436-1439 A270	Set of 4	1.10	1.10

Nos. 1711-1720 Ovptd.

1994, June 15			
1440-1446 A268	Set of 7	12.00	12.00

Souvenir Sheets

1447-1449 A268	$6 each	4.50	4.50

Nos. 1736-1741 Ovptd.

1994, June 15			
1450-1453 A271	30c Set of 4	7.25	7.25

Souvenir Sheets

1454-1455 A271	$6 each	4.50	4.50

Nos. 1689-1691 Ovptd.

1994, Sept. 21	**Litho.**		**Perf. 14**
1456 A264	$1 multicolored	.75	.75
1457 A264	$3 multicolored	2.25	2.25

Souvenir Sheet

1458 A264	$6 multicolored	4.50	4.50

Nos. 1786-1795 Ovptd.

1994, Sept. 21	**Litho.**		**Perf. 14**
1459-1466 A279	Set of 8	10.00	10.00

Souvenir Sheet

1467-1468 A279	$6 each	4.50	4.50

Nos. 1776-1779 Ovptd.

1994, Nov. 3	**Litho.**		**Perf. 14**
1469 A277	$1.50 multi (#1776)	9.00	9.00
1470 A277	$1.50 multi (#1777)	9.00	9.00

Souvenir Sheets

1471 A277	$1.50 multi (#1778)	1.10	1.10
1472 A277	$1.50 multi (#1779)	1.10	1.10

Nos. 1835-1842 Ovptd.

1995, Jan. 12	**Litho.**		**Perf. 14**
1473-1478 A291	Set of 6	8.50	8.50

Souvenir Sheets

1479 A291	$6 multi (#1841)	4.50	4.50
1480 A291	$6 multi (#1842)	4.50	4.50

Nos. 1857-1866 Ovptd.

1995, Jan. 12	**Litho.**		**Perf. 14**
1481-1488 A295	Set of 8	6.75	6.75

Souvenir Sheets
Perf. 13 1/2x14

1489 A295	$6 multi (#1865)	4.50	4.50
1490 A295	$6 multi (#1866)	4.50	4.50

Nos. 1829-1834 Ovptd.

1996, Feb. 14	**Litho.**		**Perf. 14**
1491 A290	75c multi (#1829)	5.50	5.50
1492 A290	75c multi (#1830)	5.50	5.50
1493 A290	75c multi (#1831)	5.50	5.50

Souvenir Sheets

1494 A290	$6 multi (#1832)	5.50	5.50
1495 A290	$6 multi (#1833)	5.50	5.50
1496 A290	$6 multi (#1834)	5.50	5.50

Nos. 1867-1881 Ovptd.

1995	**Litho.**		**Perf. 14 1/2x14**
1497 A296	15c multi (#1867)	.15	.15
1498 A296	25c multi (#1868)	.20	.20
1499 A296	35c multi (#1869)	.30	.30
1500 A296	40c multi (#1870)	.35	.35
1501 A296	45c multi (#1871)	.40	.40
1502 A296	60c multi (#1872)	.55	.55
1503 A296	65c multi (#1873)	.60	.60
1504 A296	70c multi (#1873)	.65	.65
1505 A296	75c multi (#1874)	.70	.70
1506 A296	90c multi (#1875)	.80	.80
1507 A296	$1.20 multi (#1876)	1.10	1.10
1508 A296	$2 multi (#1877)	1.80	1.80
1509 A296	$5 multi (#1878)	4.50	4.50
1510 A296	$10 multi (#1879)	9.00	9.00
1511 A296	$20 multi (#1880)	18.00	18.00
Nos. 1497-1511 (15)		39.10	39.10

Nos. 1806-1808 Ovptd.

1996, Jan. 22	**Litho.**		**Perf. 14**
1512 A281	50c Sheet of 9, #a.-i.	3.50	3.50

Souvenir Sheets

1513 A281	$6 multi (#1807)	4.50	4.50
1514 A281	$6 multi (#1808)	4.50	4.50

Nos. 1949-1956 Ovptd.

1996, Jan. 22			**Perf. 13 1/2x14**
1515-1520 A314	Set of 6	6.75	6.75

1521 A314	$5 multi (#1955)	3.75	3.75
1522 A314	$6 multi (#1956)	4.50	4.50

Nos. 1848, 1851, 1854-1856 Ovptd.

1996, Feb. 14	**Litho.**		**Perf. 14**
1553 A294	15c multi (#1848)	.15	.15
1554 A294	75c multi (#1851)	.75	.75
1555 A294	$4 multi (#1854)	3.00	3.00
Nos. 1553-1555 (3)		3.90	3.90

Souvenir Sheets

1556 A294	$6 multi (#1855)	4.50	4.50
1557 A294	$6 multi (#1856)	4.50	4.50

Nos. 1882-1890 Ovptd.

1996, June 13	**Litho.**		**Perf. 14**
1558-1563 A297	Set of 6	7.50	7.50
1564 A297	75c Sheet of 12, #a.-l.	8.25	8.25

Souvenir Sheets

1565 A297	$6 multi (#1889)	5.50	5.50
1566 A297	$6 multi (#1890)	5.50	5.50

Nos. 1891-1898 Ovptd.

1996, July 16	**Litho.**		**Perf. 14**
1567-1572 A298	Set of 6	7.00	7.00

Souvenir Sheets

1573 A298	$6 multi (#1897)	5.10	5.10
1574 A298	$6 multi (#1898)	5.10	5.10

Nos. 1930-1933 Ovptd.

1996, Sept. 10			
1575-1576 A310	Strip of 3, #a.-c., each	3.10	3.10

Souvenir Sheets

1577 A310	$6 multi (#1932)	5.10	5.10
1578 A310	$6 multi (#1933)	5.10	5.10

Nos. 1945-1948 Ovptd.

1996, Oct. 25	**Litho.**		**Perf. 14**
1579 A313	$1 Sheet of 9, #a.-i. (#1945)	8.00	8.00
1580 A313	$1 Sheet of 9, #a.-i. (#1946)	8.00	8.00

Souvenir Sheets

1581 A313	$6 multi (#1947)	5.25	5.25
1582 A313	$6 multi (#1948)	5.25	5.25

Nos. 2001-2002 Ovptd.

1996, Nov. 14			**Perf. 13 1/2x14**
1583 A323	$2 Strip of 3, #a.-c.	5.25	5.25

Souvenir Sheet

1584 A323	$6 multicolored	5.25	5.25

Nos. 2018-2025 Ovptd.

1997, Jan. 28	**Litho.**		**Perf. 13 1/2x14**
1585-1590 A328	Set of 6	6.50	6.50

Souvenir Sheets

1591 A328	$6 multi (#2024)	5.50	5.50
1592 A328	$6 multi (#2025)	5.50	5.50

Nos. 1905-1906 Ovptd.

1997, Feb. 24			**Perf. 14**
1593 A301	Strip of 3, #a.-c.	2.60	2.60

Souvenir Sheet

1594 A301	$6 multicolored	5.50	5.50

Nos. 1907-1908 Ovptd.

1997, Feb. 24			
1595 A302	$5 multicolored	4.50	4.50

Souvenir Sheet

1596 A302	$6 multicolored	5.50	5.50

Nos. 1899-1902 Ovptd.
Sheets of 6 or 8 + Label

1997, Apr. 4	**Litho.**		**Perf. 14**
1597 A299	$1.20 #a.-f.	6.50	6.50
1598 A299	$1.20 #a.-h.	8.50	8.50

Souvenir Sheets

1599 A299	$3 multicolored	2.75	2.75
1600 A299	$6 multicolored	5.50	5.50

Nos. 1903-1904 Ovptd.

1997	**Litho.**		**Perf. 14**
1601 A300	Strip of 3, #a.-c.	2.50	2.50

Souvenir Sheet

1602 A300	$6 multicolored	5.50	5.50

Nos. 1909-1910 Ovptd.

1997			**Perf. 13 1/2x14**
1603 A303	$1.50 Strip or block of 4, #a.-d.	5.50	5.50

Souvenir Sheet

1604 A303	$6 multicolored	5.50	5.50

Nos. 1913-1917 Ovptd.

1997	**Litho.**		**Perf. 14**
1605-1608 A305	Set of 4	5.00	5.00

Souvenir Sheet

1609 A305	$6 multicolored	5.50	5.50

Nos. 1918-1919 Ovptd.

1997			
1610 A306	45c Sheet of 12, #a.-l.	4.75	4.75

Souvenir Sheet

1611 A306	$6 multicolored	5.50	5.50

Nos. 1928-1929 Ovptd.

1997			
1612 A309	75c Sheet of 12, #a.-l.	8.00	8.00

Souvenir Sheet

1613 A309	$6 multicolored	5.50	5.50

Nos. 1940-1942 Ovptd.

1997			
1619 A311	$1.20 Sheet of 9, #a.-i.	9.75	9.75

Souvenir Sheets

1620 A311	$6 multi (#1941)	5.50	5.50
1621 A311	$6 multi (#1942)	5.50	5.50

Numbers have been reserved for additional values in this set.

Nos. 1911-1912 Ovptd.

1997			**Perf. 14**
1622 A304	75c Sheet of 12, #a.-l.	8.00	8.00

Souvenir Sheet

1623 A304	$6 multicolored	5.50	5.50

Nos. 1943-1944 Ovptd.

1997			
1624 A312	75c Sheet of 12, #a.-l.	8.00	8.00

Souvenir Sheet

1625 A312	$6 multicolored	5.50	5.50

Nos. 1967-1970 Ovptd.

1997			
1626-1627 A317	75c Strips of 4, #a.-d., each	2.75	2.75

Souvenir Sheets

1628 A317	$6 multi (#1969)	5.50	5.50
1629 A317	$6 multi (#1970)	5.50	5.50

SEMI-POSTAL STAMP

Catalogue values for unused stamps in this section are for Never Hinged items.

Barbuda No. 501 Crudely Surcharged

S. Atlantic Fund + 50c

1982, June 28			
	Self-Adhesive		
B1 CD331	Booklet		16.00

BASUTOLAND

bə-'sü-tə-ˌland

LOCATION — An enclave in the state of South Africa
GOVT. — Former British Crown Colony
AREA — 11,716 sq. mi.
POP. — 733,000 (est. 1964)
CAPITAL — Maseru

The Colony, a former independent native state, was annexed to the Cape Colony in 1871. In 1883 control was transferred directly to the British Crown. Stamps of the Cape of Good Hope were used from 1871 to 1910 and those of the Union of South Africa from 1910 to 1933. Basutoland became the independent state of Lesotho on Oct. 4, 1966.

12 Pence = 1 Shilling
100 Cents = 1 Rand (1961)

Catalogue values for unused stamps in this country are for Never Hinged items, beginning with Scott 29 in the regular postage section and Scott J1 in the postage due section.

George V — A1   George VI — A2

Crocodile and River Scene

Perf. 12 1/2

1933, Dec. 1   Engr.   Wmk. 4
1	A1	1/2p emerald	.20	.60
2	A1	1p carmine	.30	.20
3	A1	2p red violet	.50	1.10
4	A1	3p ultra	.50	1.75
5	A1	4p slate	1.75	2.50
6	A1	6p yellow	2.25	2.50
7	A1	1sh red orange	3.50	5.25
8	A1	2sh6p dk brown	17.50	22.50
9	A1	5sh violet	35.00	50.00
10	A1	10sh olive green	100.00	125.00
		Nos. 1-10 (10)	161.50	211.40

Silver Jubilee Issue
Common Design Type

1935, May 4   Perf. 13 1/2x14
11	CD301	1p car & blue	.25	.25
12	CD301	2p gray blk & ultra	.60	2.00
13	CD301	3p blue & brown	2.50	3.25
14	CD301	6p brt vio & indigo	3.50	6.50
		Nos. 11-14 (4)	6.85	12.00
		Set, never hinged	14.50	

Common Design Types pictured following the introduction.

Coronation Issue
Common Design Type

1937, May 12   Perf. 13 1/2x14
15	CD302	1p carmine	.15	.15
16	CD302	2p rose violet	.30	.30
17	CD302	3p bright ultra	.40	.40
		Nos. 15-17 (3)	.85	.85
		Set, never hinged	1.40	

1938, Apr. 1   Perf. 12 1/2
18	A2	1/2p emerald	.30	.30
19	A2	1p rose car	.30	.15
20	A2	1 1/2p light blue	.30	.20
21	A2	2p rose lilac	.30	.30
22	A2	3p ultra	.35	.35
23	A2	4p gray	.45	1.25
24	A2	6p yel ocher	.55	.60
25	A2	1sh red orange	.75	.85
26	A2	2sh6p black brown	2.75	2.75
27	A2	5sh violet	11.00	11.00
28	A2	10sh olive green	15.00	17.00
		Nos. 18-28 (11)	32.05	34.75
		Set, never hinged	60.00	

Catalogue values for unused stamps in this section, from this point to the end of the section, are for Never Hinged items.

Peace Issue
South Africa Nos. 100-102 Overprinted **Basutoland**

Basic stamps inscribed alternately in English and Afrikaans.

1945, Dec. 3   Wmk. 201   Perf. 14
29	A42	1p rose pink & choc, pair	.25	.25
a.		Single, English	.15	.15
b.		Single, Afrikaans	.15	.15
30	A43	2p vio & slate blue, pair	.30	.30
a.		Single, English	.15	.15
b.		Single, Afrikaans	.15	.15
31	A43	3p ultra & dp ultra, pair	.45	.45
a.		Single, English	.15	.15
b.		Single, Afrikaans	.15	.15
		Nos. 29-31 (3)	1.00	1.00

King George VI — A3

King George VI and Queen Elizabeth A4

Princess Margaret Rose and Princess Elizabeth A5

Royal British Family — A6

Perf. 12 1/2

1947, Feb. 17   Wmk. 4   Engr.
35	A3	1p red	.15	.15
36	A4	2p green	.15	.15
37	A5	3p ultra	.15	.15
38	A6	1sh dark violet	.25	.25
		Set value	.45	.45

Visit of the British Royal Family, Mar. 11-12, 1947.

Silver Wedding Issue
Common Design Types

1948, Dec. 1   Photo.   Perf. 14x14 1/2
39	CD304	1 1/2p brt violet	.15	.15

Engr.; Name Typo.
Perf. 11 1/2
40	CD305	10sh dk brown olive	40.00	32.00

UPU Issue
Common Design Types
Engr.; Name Typo. on 3p, 6p
Perf. 13 1/2, 11x11 1/2

1949, Oct. 10   Wmk. 4
41	CD306	1 1/2p blue	.30	.30
42	CD307	3p indigo	.75	.65
43	CD308	6p orange yel	1.00	.90
44	CD309	1sh red brown	1.10	1.10
		Nos. 41-44 (4)	3.15	2.95

Coronation Issue
Common Design Type

1953, June 3   Engr.   Perf. 13 1/2x13
45	CD312	2p red violet & black	.25	.25

Qiloane Hill — A7   Shearing Angora Goats — A8

Designs: 1p, Orange River. 2p, Mosotho horseman. 3p, Basuto household. 4 1/2p, Maletsunyane

falls. 6p, Herdboy with lesiba. 1sh, Pastoral scene. 1sh3p, Plane at Lancers Gap. 2sh6p, Old Fort Leribe. 5sh, Mission cave house.

1954, Oct. 18   Wmk. 4   Perf. 13 1/2
46	A7	1/2p dk brown & gray	.15	.15
47	A7	1p dp grn & gray blk	.15	.15
48	A7	2p org & dp blue	.30	.25
49	A7	3p car & ol green	.35	.30
50	A7	4 1/2p dp blue & ind	.80	.65
51	A7	6p dk grn & org brn	.75	.60
52	A7	1sh rose vio & dk ol green	1.40	1.10
53	A7	1sh3p aqua & brown	1.75	1.40
54	A7	2sh6p lilac rose & dp ultra	6.25	5.00
55	A7	5sh dp car & black	9.00	7.50
56	A8	10sh dp cl & black	19.00	15.00
		Nos. 46-56 (11)	39.90	32.10

See Nos. 72-82, 87-91. For surcharges see Nos. 57, 61-71.

No. 48 Surcharged **1/2d.**

1959, Aug. 1
57	A7	1/2p on 2p org & dp blue	.20	.20

Chief Moshoeshoe (Moshesh) — A9

Designs: 1sh, Council chamber. 1sh3p, Mosotho on horseback.

Perf. 13x13 1/2

1959, Dec. 15   Wmk. 314
58	A9	3p lt yel, grn & blk	.15	.15
59	A9	1sh green & pink	.35	.35
60	A9	1sh3p orange & ultra	.60	.60
		Nos. 58-60 (3)	1.10	1.10

Institution of the Basutoland National Council.

2 1/2c	2 1/2c	3 1/2c	3 1/2c
I	II	I	II
5c	**5c**	**10c**	**10c**
I	II	I	II
12 1/2c	**12 1/2c**		
I	II		
25c	**25c**	**25c**	
I	II	III	
50c	**50c**	**R1**	**R1**	**R1**
I	II	I	II	III

1961, Feb. 14   Wmk. 4   Perf. 13 1/2
61	A7	1/2c on 1/2p dk brn & gray	.15	.15
a.		Double surcharge	250.00	
62	A7	1c on 1p dp grn & gray blk	.15	.15
63	A7	2c on 2p org & dp bl	.15	.15
a.		Inverted surcharge	125.00	
64	A7	2 1/2c on 3p (II)	.15	.15
a.		Type I	.15	.15
b.		Inverted surcharge (II)	1,750.	1,000.
65	A7	3 1/2c on 4 1/2p (I)	.15	.15
a.		Type II	4.50	4.50
66	A7	5c on 6p (II)	.15	.15
a.		Type I	.15	.15
67	A7	10c on 1sh (I)	.20	.20
a.		Type II	40.00	40.00
68	A7	12 1/2c on 1sh3p (II)	.35	.35
a.		Type I	.65	.65
69	A7	25c on 2sh6p (I)	.65	.65
a.		Type II	12.00	12.00
b.		Type III	.65	.65
70	A7	50c on 5sh (II)	1.40	1.40
a.		Type I	2.25	2.25
71	A8	1r on 10sh (III)	2.75	2.75
a.		Type I	12.00	12.00
b.		Type II	12.00	12.00
		Nos. 61-71 (11)	6.25	6.25

Surcharge types on Nos. 64-71 are numbered chronologically.

Types of 1954
Value in Cents and Rands

Designs: 1/2c, Qiloane Hill. 1c, Orange River. 2c, Mosotho horseman. 2 1/2c, Basuto household. 3 1/2c, Maletsunyane Falls. 5c, Herdboy with lesiba. 10c, Pastoral scene. 12 1/2c, Plane at Lancers Gap.

25c, Old Fort Leribe. 50c, Mission cave house. 1r, Shearing Angora goats.

1961-63   Wmk. 4   Engr.   Perf. 13 1/2
72	A7	1/2c dk brn & gray ('62)	.15	.15
73	A7	1c dp grn & gray blk ('62)	.15	.15
74	A7	2c org & dp bl ('62)	.15	.15
75	A7	2 1/2c car & ol grn	.45	.15
76	A7	3 1/2c dp bl & ind ('62)	.40	.15
77	A7	5c dk grn & org brn ('62)	.60	.30
78	A7	10c rose vio & dk ol	.95	.40
79	A7	12 1/2c aqua & brn ('62)	1.25	.55
80	A7	25c lilac rose & dp ultra ('62)	2.25	1.00
81	A7	50c dp car & blk ('62)	9.00	4.00
		Perf. 11 1/2		
82	A8	1r dp cl & blk ('63)	15.00	6.50
		Nos. 72-82 (11)	30.35	13.50

See Nos. 87-91. For overprints on stamps and types see Lesotho Nos. 5-14, 20a.

Freedom from Hunger Issue
Common Design Type
Perf. 14x14 1/2

1963, June 4   Photo.   Wmk. 314
83	CD314	12 1/2c lilac	.50	.40

Red Cross Centenary Issue
Common Design Type

1963, Sept. 2   Litho.   Perf. 13
84	CD315	2 1/2c black & red	.20	.15
85	CD315	12 1/2c ultra & red	.70	.70

Queen Type of 1961-63

1964   Engr.   Perf. 13 1/2
87	A7	1c grn & gray blk	.15	.15
88	A7	2 1/2c car & ol green	.30	.15
89	A7	5c dk green & org brn	.70	.60
90	A7	12 1/2c aqua & brown	1.50	1.40
91	A7	50c dp car & black	6.00	4.75
		Nos. 87-91 (5)	8.65	7.05

Mosotho Woman and Child — A10

Designs: 3 1/2c, Maseru border post. 5c, Mountains. 12 1/2c, Legislative Building.

Perf. 14x13 1/2

1965, May 10   Photo.   Wmk. 314
97	A10	2 1/2c ultra & multi	.15	.15
98	A10	3 1/2c blue & bister	.20	.15
99	A10	5c blue & ocher	.20	.20
100	A10	12 1/2c lt blue, blk & buff	.40	.40
		Nos. 97-100 (4)	.95	.90

Attainment of self-government.

ITU Issue
Common Design Type

1965, May 17   Litho.   Perf. 11x11 1/2
101	CD317	1c ver & red lilac	.15	.15
102	CD317	20c grnsh bl & org brn	.85	.65

Intl. Cooperation Year Issue
Common Design Type

1965, Oct. 25   Wmk. 314   Perf. 14 1/2
103	CD318	1/2c blue grn & cl	.15	.15
104	CD318	12 1/2c lt vio & green	.90	.70

Churchill Memorial Issue
Common Design Type

1966, Jan. 24   Photo.   Perf. 14
Design in Black, Gold and Carmine Rose
105	CD319	1c bright blue	.15	.15
106	CD319	2 1/2c rose car	.15	.15
107	CD319	10c brown	.50	.50
108	CD319	22 1/2c violet	1.25	1.25
		Nos. 105-108 (4)	2.05	2.05

POSTAGE DUE STAMPS

Catalogue values for all unused stamps in this section are for Never Hinged items.

D1

Coat of
Arms — D2

1933-38   Wmk. 4   Typo.   Perf. 14

J1	D1	1p dark red ('38)	.20	.20
a.		1p dark carmine	1.00	1.10
b.		Wmk. 4a (error)	67.50	
J2	D1	2p lt violet	.20	.20
a.		Wmk. 4a (error)	67.50	

Nos. J1-J2 valued on chalky paper.

1956, Dec. 1

J3	D2	1p carmine	.25	.25
J4	D2	2p dark purple	.25	.25

Nos. J2-J4 Surcharged with New Value

1961

J5	D2	1c on 1p carmine	.15	.15
J6	D2	1c on 2p dk purple	.15	.15
J7	D1	5c on 2p lt violet	3.00	3.00
a.		Wmk. 4a (error)	275.00	
J8	D2	5c on 2p dark pur ("5" 7½mm high)	.15	.15
a.		"5" 3½mm high	17.50	25.00
		Nos. J5-J8 (4)	3.45	3.45

Value in Cents

1964   Wmk. 314   Perf. 14

J9	D2	1c carmine	.15	.15
J10	D2	5c dark purple	.20	.20

For overprints see Lesotho Nos. J1-J2.

OFFICIAL STAMPS

Nos. 1-3 and 6 Overprinted "OFFICIAL"

1934   Wmk. 4   Engr.   Perf. 12½

O1	A1	½p emerald	4,000.	4,000.
O2	A1	1p carmine	1,100.	1,750.
O3	A1	2p red violet	1,750.	1,750.
O4	A1	6p yellow	4,000.	2,250.

Counterfeits exist.

BATUM

LOCATION — A seaport on the Black Sea

Batum is the capital of Adzhar, a territory which, in 1921, became an autonomous republic of the Georgian Soviet Socialist Republic.

Stamps of Batum were issued under the administration of British forces which occupied Batum and environs between December, 1918, and July, 1920, following the Treaty of Versailles.

100 Kopecks = 1 Ruble

Counterfeits exist of Nos. 1-65.

Basic Russian Designs

A8   A11   A14

A15   A19

A1

1919   Unwmk.   Litho.   Imperf.

1	A1	5k green	.50	.30
2	A1	10k ultramarine	.50	.30
3	A1	50k yellow	.30	.25
4	A1	1r red brown	.45	.35
5	A1	3r violet	1.75	1.75
6	A1	5r brown	2.75	2.75
		Nos. 1-6 (6)	6.25	5.70

For overprints and surcharges see #13-20, 51-65.

БАТУМ. ОБ.

Russian Stamps of 1909-17 Surcharged

Руб 10 Руб.

1919   On Stamps of 1917

7	A14	10r on 1k orange	25.00	13.50
8	A14	10r on 3k red	12.00	15.00

On Stamp of 1909-12   Perf. 14x14½

9	A14	10r on 5k claret	200.00	200.00

On Stamp of 1917

10	A14	10r on 10k on 7k light blue	200.00	200.00
		Nos. 7-10 (4)	437.00	428.50

БАТУМ. ОБ.

Russian Stamps of 1909-13 Surcharged

Коп 35 Коп.

1919

11	A15	35k on 4k carmine	1,650.	
12	A19	35k on 4k dull red	6,500.	

This surcharge was intended for postal cards. A few cards which bore adhesive stamps were also surcharged.

Values are for stamps off card and without gum.

Type of 1919 Issue Overprinted

BRITISH OCCUPATION

1919   Unwmk.   Imperf.

13	A1	5k green	1.25	1.10
14	A1	10k dark blue	1.25	1.10
15	A1	25k orange	1.25	1.10
16	A1	1r pale blue	.90	.85
17	A1	2r salmon pink	.40	.35
18	A1	3r violet	.40	.35
19	A1	5r brown	.40	.35
a.		"CCUPATION"	190.00	190.00
20	A1	7r dull red	1.25	1.10
		Nos. 13-20 (8)	7.10	6.30

Russian Stamps of 1909-17 Surcharged in Various Colors:

БАТУМ ОБЛАС.   БАТУМЪ BRITISH

Р 10 Р.   Р. 15 Р.

BRITISH OCCUPATION   OCCUPATION ОБЛ.
10r & 50r   15r

On Stamps of 1917

1919-20   Imperf.

21	A14	10r on 3k red	25.00	22.50
22	A14	15r on 1k org (R)	50.00	45.00
23	A14	15r on 1k org (Bk)	75.00	65.00
24	A14	15r on 1k org (V)	50.00	45.00
25	A14	50r on 1k org	300.00	275.00
26	A14	50r on 2k green	275.00	250.00

On Stamps of 1909-17   Perf. 14x14½

27	A14	50r on 2k green	300.00	300.00
28	A14	50r on 3k red	450.00	450.00
29	A15	50r on 4k car	275.00	275.00
30	A14	50r on 5k claret	275.00	275.00
31	A15	50r on 10k dk blue (R)	650.00	650.00
32	A11	50r on 15k red brn & blue	250.00	250.00

БАТУМ.ОБЛ.

Surcharged

Р.25Р.

BRITISH OCCUPATION

On Stamps of 1909-17

33	A14	25r on 5k cl (Bk)	50.00	50.00
34	A14	25r on 5k cl (Bl)	50.00	50.00
35	A14	25r on 10k on 7k lt blue (Bk)	50.00	50.00
36	A14	25r on 10k on 7k lt blue (Bl)	42.50	42.50
37	A11	25r on 20k on 14k bl & rose (Bk)	75.00	75.00
38	A11	25r on 20k on 14k bl & rose (Bl)	40.00	40.00
39	A11	25r on 25k grn & gray vio (Bk)	100.00	100.00
40	A11	25r on 25k grn & gray vio (Bl)	100.00	100.00
41	A8	25r on 50k vio & green (Bk)	20.00	20.00
42	A8	25r on 50k vio & green (Bl)	40.00	40.00
43	A14	50r on 2k green	65.00	65.00
44	A14	50r on 3k red	65.00	65.00
45	A15	50r on 4k car	100.00	100.00
46	A14	50r on 5k claret	100.00	100.00

On Stamps of 1917   Imperf

47	A14	50r on 2k green	95.00	95.00
48	A14	50r on 3k red	150.00	150.00
49	A14	50r on 5k claret	600.00	600.00

On Stamp of 1913   Perf. 13½

50	A19	50r on 4k dull red (Bl)	75.00	75.00

Nos. 3, 13 and 15 Surcharged in Black or Blue:

РУБ 25 ПЕН   R. 50 R. BRITISH OCCUPATION

25 РУБ. 25   РУБ.

1920   Imperf.

51	A1	25r on 5k green	20.00	20.00
52	A1	25r on 5k grn (Bl)	22.50	22.50
53	A1	25r on 25k orange	15.00	15.00
54	A1	25r on 25k org (Bl)	60.00	60.00
55	A1	50r on 50k yellow	15.00	15.00
56	A1	50r on 50k yel (Bl)	50.00	50.00
		Nos. 51-56 (6)	182.50	182.50

The surcharges on Nos. 21-56 inclusive are hand-stamped and are known double, inverted, etc.

Tree Type of 1919 Overprinted Like Nos. 13-20.

1920

57	A1	1r orange brown	.15	.15
58	A1	2r gray blue	.15	.15
59	A1	3r rose	.15	.15
60	A1	5r black brown	.15	.15
61	A1	7r yellow	.15	.15
62	A1	10r dark green	.15	.15
63	A1	15r violet	.15	.20
64	A1	25r vermilion	.50	.35
65	A1	50r dark blue	.65	.45
		Nos. 57-65 (9)	2.20	
		Set value		1.50

The variety "BPITISH" occurs on #57-65.

BECHUANALAND

ˌbech-ˈwä-nə-ˌland

(British Bechuanaland)

LOCATION — Southern Africa
GOVT. — A British Crown Colony, annexed in 1895 to the Cape of Good Hope Colony which became a province in the Union of South Africa.
AREA — 51,424 sq. mi.
POP. — 84,210 (1904)
CAPITAL — Mafeking

12 Pence = 1 Shilling
20 Shillings = 1 Pound

Watermarks

Wmk. 29- Orb   Wmk. 14- VR in Italics

Cape of Good Hope Stamps of 1871-85 Overprinted

British Bechuanaland

1886   Wmk. 1   Perf. 14
Black Overprint

1	A6	4p blue	50.00	55.00

Wmk. 2   Black Overprint

3	A6	3p claret	30.00	30.00

Red Overprint

4	A6	½p black	10.00	10.00
a.		Double overprint in red & blk	850.00	

Wmk. Anchor (16)   Black Overprint

5	A6	½p black	6.00	10.00
6	A6	1p rose	8.00	6.50
b.		"ritish"	1,800.	1,600.
7	A6	2p bister	22.50	10.00
		"ritish"	4,500.	4,500.
8	A3	6p violet	60.00	32.50
9	A3	1sh green	215.00	125.00
		"ritish"	10,000.	8,000.

There is no period after Bechuanaland in the genuine stamps.

BRITISH

Black Ovpt. on Great Britain #111

BECHUANALAND

1887   Wmk. 30

10	A54	½p vermilion	.60	1.00
a.		Double overprint	2,250.	

For overprints see Bechuanaland Protectorate Nos. 51-53.

A1

A2   A3

1887   Typo.   Wmk. 29
Country Name in Black

11	A1	1p lilac	12.00	4.75
12	A1	2p lilac	30.00	20.00
13	A1	3p lilac	3.25	4.75
14	A1	4p lilac	35.00	5.50
15	A1	6p lilac	40.00	18.00

Wmk. 14

16	A2	1sh green	30.00	5.00
17	A2	2sh green	45.00	30.00
18	A2	2sh6p green	55.00	40.00
19	A2	5sh green	90.00	90.00
20	A2	10sh green	190.00	225.00

Wmk. 29

21	A3	£1 lilac	900.	725.
22	A3	£5 lilac	2,750.	1,400.
		Pen cancellation		165.

The corner designs and central oval differs on No. 22.

For overprints see Bechuanaland Protectorate Nos. 54-58, 60-66. For surcharges see Nos. 23-28, 30, Cape of Good Hope No. 171.

Nos. 11-12, 14-16 Surcharged **1d.**

1888
Country Name in Black
Black Surcharge

23	A1	1p on 1p lilac	7.00	5.00
a.		Double surcharge		
24	A1	6p on 6p lilac	90.00	22.50

Red Surcharge

25	A1	2p on 2p lilac	12.50	3.00
a.		"2" with curved tail	200.00	150.00
26	A1	4p on 4p lilac	150.00	200.00

Green Surcharge

27	A1	6p on 6p lilac	2,750.

Blue Surcharge

27A	A1	6p on 6p lilac	4,500.

Wmk. 14
Black Surcharge

28	A2	1sh on 1sh green	85.00	47.50

British·

Bechuanaland No. 29

One Half-Penny No. 30

Green Ovpt. on Cape of Good Hope #41

1889   Wmk. 16

29	A4	½p black	4.75	13.00

Vertical overprint, double overprints one inverted or double, and varieties such as "British" omitted probably are from printers waste.

Wmk. 29
Black Surcharge on No. 13

30	A1	½p on 3p lilac & blk	125.00	135.00

British Bechuanaland.

Cape of Good Hope Nos. 43-44 Overprinted in Black

1891   Wmk. 16

31	A4	1p rose	10.00	9.50
a.		Horiz. pair, one without overprint		1,500.
b.		"British" omitted		575.00
c.		"Bechuanaland" omitted	850.00	
32	A4	2p bister	3.00	3.00
a.		Without period	200.00	

See Nos. 38-39.

Stamps of Great Britain Overprinted in Black **BRITISH BECHUANALAND**

1891-94   Wmk. 30

33	A40	1p lilac	5.00	1.00
34	A56	2p green & car	3.00	2.50
35	A59	4p brown & green	2.50	.75
36	A62	6p violet, rose	2.50	1.75
37	A65	1sh green ('94)	11.00	13.00
		Nos. 33-37 (5)	24.00	19.00

For surcharges see Cape of Good Hope Nos. 172, 176-177.

Cape of Good Hope Nos. 43-44 Overprinted Like Nos. 31-32 but Reading Down

1893-95   Wmk. 16

38	A6	1p rose	2.50	2.75
a.		No dots over the "i's" of "British"	75.00	75.00
b.		"British" omitted	650.00	
c.		As "a," reading up		750.00
d.		Pair, one without overprint		
39	A6	2p bister ('95)	4.75	2.75
a.		Double overprint	900.00	900.00
b.		No dots over the "i's" of "British"	125.00	125.00
c.		"British" omitted	350.00	325.00
d.		As "b," reading up		

Cape of Good Hope No. 42 Overprinted

BRITISH

BECHUANALAND

"BECHUANALAND" 16mm Long
Overprint Lines 13mm Apart

1897

40	A6	½p light green	2.50	5.00

"BECHUANALAND" 15mm Long
Overprint Lines 10½mm Apart

41	A6	½p light green	10.00	27.50

"BECHUANALAND" 15mm Long
Overprint Lines 13½mm Apart

42	A6	½p light green	17.50	45.00
		Nos. 40-42 (3)	30.00	77.50

BECHUANALAND PROTECTORATE

ˌbech-ˈwä-nə-ˌland prə-ˈtek-t(ə-)rət

LOCATION — In central South Africa, north of the Republic of South Africa, east of South-West Africa and bounded on the north and east by Angola and Southern Rhodesia

GOVT. — British Protectorate
AREA — 222,000 sq. mi.
POP. — 540,400 (1964)

Bechuanaland Protectorate became the independent republic of Botswana, Sept. 30, 1966.

12 Pence = 1 Shilling
20 Shillings = 1 Pound
100 Cents = 1 Rand (1961)

> Catalogue values for unused stamps in this country are for Never Hinged items, beginning with Scott 137 in the regular postage section and Scott J7 in the postage due section.

Additional Overprint in Black on Bechuanaland No. 10

Protectorate   Protectorate
a   b

Protectorate
c

1888-90   Wmk. 30   Perf. 14

51	A54(a)	½p vermilion	110.00	150.00
a.		Double overprint	575.00	
52	A54(b)	½p vermilion ('89)	2.50	16.00
a.		Double overprint	300.00	
53	A54(c)	½p vermilion	90.00	100.00
a.		Inverted overprint	65.00	80.00
b.		Double overprint	80.00	90.00
c.		As "a," double	600.00	600.00

For surcharge see No. 68.

Bechuanaland Nos. 16-20 Overprinted Type "b" in Black
Wmk. 14
Country Name in Black

54	A2	1sh green	55.00	50.00
a.		First "o" omitted	3,250.	3,000.
55	A2	2sh green	475.00	625.00
a.		First "o" omitted	5,750.	4,250.
56	A2	2sh6p green	500.00	625.00
a.		First "o" omitted	6,000.	4,500.
57	A2	5sh green	1,100.	1,500.
a.		First "o" omitted	6,750.	6,000.
58	A2	10sh green	3,250.	4,000.
a.		First "o" omitted		12,000.

Bechuanaland Nos. 11-15 Overprinted Type "b" and Surcharged in Black

1888   Wmk. 29
Country Name in Black

60	A1	1p on 1p lilac	5.50	10.00
a.		Short "1"	275.00	300.00
61	A1	2p on 2p lilac	17.50	15.00
a.		"2" with curved tail	300.00	300.00

63	A1	3p on 3p lilac	80.00	110.00
64	A1	4p on 4p lilac	175.00	175.00
65	A1	6p on 6p lilac	50.00	40.00

In #60 the "1" is 2½mm high; in #60a, 2mm.

Value Surcharged in Red

66	A1	4p on 4p lilac	50.00	42.50

A7

Cape of Good Hope Type of 1886 Overprinted in Green

1889   Wmk. 16

67	A7	½p black	3.75	20.00
a.		Double overprint	400.00	475.00
b.		"Bechuanaland" omitted	600.00	600.00

Black Surcharge on Bechuanaland Protectorate No. 52
Wmk. 30

68	A54	4p on ½p ver	15.00	3.00
a.		Inverted surcharge		4,500.

Stamps of Great Britain 1881-87, Overprinted in Black **BECHUANALAND PROTECTORATE**

1897, Oct.

69	A54	½p vermilion	1.00	1.00
70	A40	1p lilac	3.50	.50
71	A56	2p green & car	2.00	4.00
72	A58	3p violet, yel	5.00	7.50
73	A59	4p brown & green	10.00	10.00
74	A62	6p violet, rose	17.50	10.50
		Nos. 69-74 (6)	39.00	33.50

For surcharges see Cape of Good Hope Nos. 167-170, 173-175.

Same on Great Britain No. 125

1902, Feb. 25

75	A54	½p blue green	1.50	1.25

Stamps of Great Britain, 1902, Overprinted in Black

BECHUANALAND | **PROTECTORATE**

King Edward VII — A9

1904-12

76	A66	½p gray green ('06)	3.50	3.50
77	A66	1p car ('05)	4.75	1.25
78	A66	2½p ultra	6.25	5.75
79	A74	1sh scar & grn ('12)	12.00	15.00
		Nos. 76-79 (4)	26.50	25.50

Same on Great Britain No. 143

1908

80	A66	½p pale yel green	2.00	3.00

Transvaal No. 274 Overprinted

1910   Wmk. 3

81	A9	6p brn org & blk	180.00	210.00

This stamp was issued for fiscal use, although it is known postally used.

Great Britain No. 154 Overprinted Like Nos. 76-79

1912, Sept.   Wmk. 30   Perf. 15x14

82	A81	1p scarlet	1.10	1.00

Great Britain Stamps of 1912-13 Overprinted Like Nos. 76-79

1914-24   Wmk. Crown and GvR (33)

83	A82	½p green	.95	1.25
84	A83	1p scarlet	2.50	.30
85	A84	1½p red brn ('20)	1.50	2.00
86	A85	2p orange (I)	2.25	2.25
a.		2p orange (II) ('24)	30.00	3.50
87	A86	2½p ultra	2.50	10.00
88	A87	3p bluish violet	4.75	11.00
89	A88	4p slate green	5.25	9.50

90	A89	6p dull violet	5.75	11.00
91	A90	1sh bister	6.50	12.00
		Nos. 83-91 (9)	31.95	59.30

The dies of No. 86 are the same as in Great Britain 1912-13 issue.

Overprinted **BECHUANALAND PROTECTORATE**

Wmk. 34   Perf. 11x12

92	A91	2sh6p dk brown	110.00	140.00
a.		2sh6p light brown ('16)	125.00	140.00
93	A91	5sh rose car	150.00	200.00
a.		5sh carmine ('20)	200.00	250.00

Nos. 92, 93 were printed by Waterlow Bros. & Layton; Nos. 92a, 93a were printed by Thomas De La Rue & Co.

Same Overprint On Retouched Stamps of 1919

1920-23

94	A91	2sh6p gray brown	115.00	125.00
95	A91	5sh car rose	150.00	165.00

Great Britain Stamps of 1924 Overprinted like Nos. 76-79

Wmk. Crown and Block GvR Multiple (35)

1925-26   Perf. 15x14

96	A82	½p green	1.00	1.65
97	A83	1p scarlet	1.25	1.65
99	A85	2p deep org (II)	2.50	2.25
101	A87	3p violet	3.25	6.50
102	A88	4p slate green	4.00	12.00
103	A89	6p dull violet	5.25	16.00
104	A90	1sh bister	14.00	21.00
		Nos. 96-104 (7)	31.25	61.05

George V   George VI, Cattle and
A11   Baobab Tree
                  A12

Perf. 12½

1932, Dec. 12   Engr.   Wmk. 4

105	A11	½p green	.50	.35
106	A11	1p carmine	.50	.35
107	A11	2p red brown	.50	.45
108	A11	3p ultra	1.00	1.00
109	A11	4p orange	1.00	2.00
110	A11	6p red violet	2.50	1.25
111	A11	1sh blk & ol grn	5.00	5.00
112	A11	2sh black & org	22.50	25.00
113	A11	2sh6p black & car	17.50	20.00
114	A11	3sh black & red vio	25.00	27.50
115	A11	5sh black & ultra	35.00	40.00
116	A11	10sh blk & red brown	85.00	95.00
		Nos. 105-116 (12)	196.00	217.90

Common Design Types pictured following the introduction.

Silver Jubilee Issue
Common Design Type

1935, May 4   Perf. 11x12

117	CD301	1p car & blue	.25	.35
118	CD301	2p black & ultra	.55	.45
119	CD301	3p ultra & brown	.55	.60
120	CD301	6p brown vio & ind	1.25	1.25
		Nos. 117-120 (4)	2.60	2.65

Coronation Issue
Common Design Type

1937, May 12   Perf. 13½x14

121	CD302	1p carmine	.15	.15
122	CD302	2p brown	.15	.15
123	CD302	3p brt ultra	.25	.25
		Set value	.45	.45
		Set, never hinged	1.50	

1938, Apr. 1   Perf. 12½

124	A12	½p green	.30	.30
125	A12	1p rose car	.15	.15
126	A12	1½p light blue	.20	.30
127	A12	2p brown	.20	.30
128	A12	3p ultra	.25	.30
129	A12	4p orange	.50	1.00
130	A12	6p rose violet	1.50	2.00
131	A12	1sh blk & ol grn	1.75	2.00
133	A12	2sh6p black & car	9.00	6.50

135 A12	5sh black & ultra	17.50	6.50
136 A12	10sh black & brn	12.00	17.00
	Nos. 124-136 (11)	43.35	36.35
	Set, never hinged	67.50	

> Catalogue values for unused stamps in this section, from this point to the end of the section, are for Never Hinged items.

Peace Issue
South Africa Nos. 100-102 Overprinted **Bechuanaland**

Basic stamps inscribed alternately in English and Afrikaans.

1945, Dec. 3   Wmk. 201   Perf. 14

137 A42	1p rose pink & choc, pair	.30	.30
a.	Single, English	.15	.15
b.	Single, Afrikaans	.15	.15
138 A43	2p vio & slate blue, pair	.40	.40
a.	Single, English	.20	.20
b.	Single, Afrikaans	.20	.20
139 A43	3p vio & dp ultra, pair	.50	.50
a.	Single, English	.25	.25
b.	Single, Afrikaans	.25	.25
	Nos. 137-139 (3)	1.20	1.20

World War II victory of the Allies.

Royal Visit Issue
Types of Basutoland, 1947
Perf. 12½

1947, Feb. 17   Wmk. 4   Engr.

143 A3	1p red	.15	.15
144 A4	2p green	.15	.15
145 A5	3p ultra	.15	.15
146 A6	1sh dark violet	.30	.30
	Set value	.60	.60

Visit of the British Royal Family, Apr. 17, 1947.

Silver Wedding Issue
Common Design Types

1948, Dec. 1   Photo.   Perf. 14x14½

147 CD304	1½p brt ultra	.15	.15

Engr.; Name Typo.
Perf. 11½x11

148 CD305	10sh gray black	19.50	30.00

UPU Issue
Common Design Types
Engr.; Name Typo. on 3p and 6p

1949, Oct. 10   Perf. 13½, 11x11½

149 CD306	1½p blue	.25	.25
150 CD307	3p indigo	.35	.35
151 CD308	6p red lilac	.80	.80
152 CD309	1sh olive	1.50	1.50
	Nos. 149-152 (4)	2.90	2.90

Coronation Issue
Common Design Type

1953, June 3   Engr.   Perf. 13½x13

153 CD312	2p brown & black	.30	.30

Elizabeth II
A13

Victoria, Elizabeth II and Water Hole
A14

1955-58   Perf. 13x13½

154 A13	½p green	.25	.25
155 A13	1p rose car	.25	.25
156 A13	2p brown	.25	.25
157 A13	3p ultra	.35	.35
158 A13	4p orange ('58)	4.25	4.25
159 A13	4½p indigo	1.25	1.25
160 A13	6p rose violet	.80	.80
161 A13	1sh blk & ol grn	1.50	1.50
162 A13	1sh3p blk & rose vio	2.00	6.50
163 A13	2sh6p blk & car	5.50	10.50
164 A13	5sh black & ultra	10.50	16.00
165 A13	10sh black & brn	24.00	30.00
	Nos. 154-165 (12)	50.90	71.90

For surcharges see Nos. 169-179.

Perf. 14½x14

1960, Jan. 21   Photo.   Wmk. 314

166 A14	1p brown & black	.15	.15
167 A14	3p car rose & black	.16	.16
168 A14	6p ultra & black	.32	.32
	Nos. 166-168 (3)	.63	.63

Proclamation of the Protectorate, 75th anniv.

Nos. 155-165 Surcharged

1c	**1c**	**3½c**	**3½c**	**3½c**
I	II	I	II	III
5c	**5c**	**R1**	**R1**	
I	II	I	II	

Perf. 13x13½

1961, Feb. 14   Wmk. 4   Engr.

169	1c on 1p (I)	.15	.15
a.	Type II	.15	.15
170	2c on 2p	.15	.15
171	2½c on 2p	.15	.15
a.	Pair, one without surcharge	700.00	
172	2½c on 3p	.90	.90
173	3½c on 4p (III)	.18	.18
a.	Type I	.52	.52
b.	Type II	1.65	1.65
174	5c on 6p (II)	.22	.22
a.	Type I	.75	.75
175	10c on 1sh	.32	.32
a.	Pair, one without surcharge	700.00	
176	12½c on 1sh3p ("12½c" 11¼mm wide)	.55	.55
a.	"12½c" 12½mm wide	.75	.75
177	25c on 2sh6p	.90	.90
178	50c on 5sh	1.90	1.90
179	1r on 10sh (II, "R1" at lower center)	4.50	4.50
a.	Type II, "R1" at lower left	6.50	6.50
b.	Type I	300.00	110.00
	Nos. 169-179 (11)	9.92	9.92

Nos. 173a and 173b are found in the same sheet; each comes with "3½c" in both wide and narrow settings.
Surcharge types are numbered chronologically.

African Golden Oriole — A15   Baobab Tree — A16

Designs: 2c, African hoopoe. 2½c, Scarlet-chested sunbird. 3½c, Cape widow bird (Yellow bishop). 5c, Swallow-tailed bee-eater. 7½c, Gray hornbill. 10c, Red-headed weaver. 12½c, Brown-hooded kingfisher. 20c, Woman musician. 35c, Woman grinding corn. 50c, Bechuana ox. 1r, Lion. 2r, Police camel patrol.

Perf. 14x14½, 14½x14

1961, Oct. 2   Photo.   Wmk. 314

180 A15	1c lilac, blk & yel	.20	.20
181 A15	2c pale ol, blk & org	.20	.20
182 A15	2½c bis, blk, grn & dp car	.25	.20
183 A15	3½c pink, blk & yel	.35	.25
184 A15	5c dl org, blk, grn & blue	.45	.30
185 A15	7½c yel grn, blk, red & brn	.65	.40
186 A15	10c aqua & multi	.80	.50
187 A15	12½c gray, yel, red & blue	1.10	.55
188 A15	20c gray & brn	1.40	1.10
189 A16	25c yel & dk brn	2.50	1.40
190 A16	35c dp org & ultra	2.75	1.75
191 A16	50c lt ol grn & sep	4.00	2.75
192 A15	1r ocher & black	8.25	5.25
193 A15	2r blue & brn	16.00	10.50
	Nos. 180-193 (14)	38.90	25.35

Freedom from Hunger Issue
Common Design Type

1963, June 4   Perf. 14x14½

194 CD314	12½c green	.48	.48

Red Cross Centenary Issue
Common Design Type

1963, Sept. 2   Litho.   Perf. 13

195 CD315	2½c black & red	.20	.20
196 CD315	12½c ultra & red	.80	.80

Shakespeare Issue
Common Design Type

1964, Apr. 23   Photo.   Perf. 14x14½

197 CD316	12½c red brown	.28	.28

Notwani River Dam, Gaberones Water Supply
A17

Perf. 14½

1965, Mar. 1   Photo.   Wmk. 314

198 A17	2½c dark red & gold	.15	.15
199 A17	5c deep ultra & gold	.15	.15
200 A17	12½c brown & gold	.30	.30
201 A17	25c emerald & gold	.55	.55
	Nos. 198-201 (4)	1.15	1.15

Internal self-government, Mar. 1, 1965.

ITU Issue
Common Design Type
Perf. 11x11½

1965, May 17   Litho.   Wmk. 314

202 CD317	2½c ver & dl yel	.15	.15
203 CD317	12½c red lil & pale brn	.70	.70

Intl. Cooperation Year Issue
Common Design Type

1965, Oct. 25   Perf. 14½

204 CD318	1c bl grn & claret	.16	.16
205 CD318	12½c lt vio & grn	.85	.85

Churchill Memorial Issue
Common Design Type

1966, Jan. 24   Photo.   Perf. 14
Design in Black, Gold and Carmine Rose

206 CD319	1c bright blue	.15	.15
207 CD319	2½c green	.16	.16
208 CD319	12½c brown	.65	.65
209 CD319	20c violet	1.10	1.10
	Nos. 206-209 (4)	2.06	2.06

Haslar Smoke Generator
A18

Perf. 14½

1966, June 1   Photo.   Wmk. 314

210 A18	2½c shown	.15	.15
211 A18	5c Bugler	.15	.15
212 A18	15c Gun site	.38	.38
213 A18	35c Regimental cap badge	.85	.85
	Nos. 210-213 (4)	1.53	1.53

25th anniv. of the Bechuanaland Pioneers and Gunners.

POSTAGE DUE STAMPS

Postage Due Stamps of Great Britain Overprinted [BECHUANALAND PROTECTORATE]

On Stamp of 1914-22

1926   Wmk. 33   Perf. 14x14½

J1 D1	1p carmine	3.75	40.00

On Stamps of 1924-30
Wmk. 35

J2 D1	½p emerald	3.75	40.00

Overprinted   **BECHUANALAND PROTECTORATE**

J3 D1	2p black brown	7.25	80.00
	Nos. J1-J3 (3)	14.75	

D2

1932   Wmk. 4   Typo.   Perf. 14½

J4 D2	½p olive green	6.00	21.00
J5 D2	1p carmine rose	6.00	7.00
J6 D2	2p dull violet	8.00	24.00
	Nos. J4-J6 (3)	20.00	52.00

> Catalogue values for unused stamps in this section, from this point to the end of the section, are for Never Hinged items.

Nos. J4-J6 Surcharged

2c	**2c**
I	II

1961, Feb. 14

J7 D2	1c on 1p car rose (II)	.15	.15
a.	Type I	.28	.28
b.	Double surcharge (II)	140.00	
J8 D2	2c on 2p dull vio (II)	.25	.25
a.	Type I	.35	.35
J9 D2	5c on ½p ol green (I)	.52	.52
	Nos. J7-J9 (3)	.92	.92

Nos. J7, J7a, J8 and J8a are on chalky paper. Nos. J7 and J8 printed on ordinary paper sell for much more.

Denominations in Cents

1961   Wmk. 4   Perf. 14

J10 D2	1c carmine rose	.15	.15
J11 D2	2c dull violet	.16	.16
J12 D2	5c olive green	.40	1.25
	Nos. J10-J12 (3)	.71	1.56

BELARUS
ˌbē-lə-'rüs

(Byelorussia)

(White Russia)

LOCATION — Eastern Europe, bounded by Russia, Latvia, Lithuania and Poland
GOVT. — Independent republic, member of the Commonwealth of Independent States
AREA — 80,200 sq. mi.
POP. — 10,200,000 (1989)
CAPITAL — Minsk

With the breakup of the Soviet Union on Dec. 26, 1991, Belarus and ten former Soviet republics established the Commonwealth of Independent States.

100 Kopecks = 1 Ruble

> Catalogue values for all unused stamps in this country are for Never Hinged items.

Five denominations, perf and imperf, of this design produced in 1920 were not put in use and were probably propaganda labels. They are common.

> Belarus stamps can be mounted in the annual Scott Commonwealth of Independent States supplement.

Cross of Ephrosinia of Polotsk — A1

1992, Mar. 20   Litho.   Perf. 12x12¹/₂
1   A1   1r multicolored   .25

R.R. Schurma (1892-1978), Composer — A2

1992, Apr. 10   Photo.   Perf. 12x11¹/₂
2   A2   20k blue & black   .30

Arms of Polotsk — A3

Designs: No. 13, Stag jumping fence. No. 14, Man's head, sword.

1992-94   Photo.   Perf. 12x11¹/₂
11 A3   2r shown   .25
   Perf. 12x12¹/₂
12 A3   25r Minsk   .15
13 A3   700r Grodno   .20
14 A3   700r Vitebsk   .20
        Nos. 11-14 (4)   .80

Issued: 2r, 6/9/92; 25r, 11/11/93; #13, 14, 10/17/94.
This is an expanding set. Numbers will change if necessary.

National Symbols — A4

Designs: No. 15, Natl. arms. No. 16, Map, flag.

1992, Aug. 31   Litho.   Perf. 12x12¹/₂
15 A4   5r black, red & yellow   .25
16 A4   5r multicolored   .25

For surcharges see Nos. 55-58, 61-64.

No. 1 Overprinted

Cross of Ephrosinia of Polotsk — A5

A5 illustration reduced.

1992, Sept. 25   Litho.   Perf. 12x12¹/₂
17 A1   1r on #1 multi   .20
   Souvenir Sheet
   Perf. 12
18 A5   5r multicolored   .30

Orthodox Church in Belarus, 1000th anniv. No. 18, imperf., was issued Feb. 15, 1993.
Orthodox Church in Belarus, 1000th anniv. For surcharges see Nos. 59-60, 65-66.

Buildings A6

Designs: No. 19, Church of Boris Gleb, Grodno, 12th cent. No. 20, World Castle, 16th cent. No. 21, Nyasvizh Castle, 16th-19th cent. No. 22, Kamyanets Tower, 12th-13th cent, vert. No. 23, Church of Ephrosinia of Polotsk, 12th cent., vert. No. 24, Calvinist Church, Zaslaw, 16th cent., vert.

1992, Oct. 15   Litho.   Perf. 12
19 A6   2r multicolored   .15
20 A6   2r multicolored   .15
21 A6   2r multicolored   .15
22 A6   2r multicolored   .15
23 A6   2r multicolored   .15
24 A6   2r multicolored   .15
        Set value   .75

Centuries of construction are in Roman numerals.

Natl. Arms — A7

1992-94   Litho.   Perf. 12x12¹/₂
25 A7   30k light blue   .15
26 A7   45k olive green   .15
27 A7   50k green   .15
28 A7   1r brown   .15
29 A7   2r red brown   .15
30 A7   3r org yellow   .15
31 A7   5r blue   .15
32 A7   10r red   .45
33 A7   17r violet   .25
34 A7   25r yellow green   .40
35 A7   50r bright pink   .15
36 A7   100r henna brown   .40
37 A7   150r plum   .40
38 A7   200r blue green   .15
39 A7   300r salmon pink   .15
40 A7   600r light lilac   .25
40A A7 1000r rose carmine   .35
40B A7 3000r gray blue   1.15
        Nos. 25-40B (18)   5.00

Issued: 30k, 45k, 50k, 11/10; 1r-3r, 10r, 1/4/93; 5r, 15r, 25r, 2/9/93; 50r, 100r, 150r, 6/16/93; 200r-3,000r, 12/28/94; others, 1992.
For surcharges see Nos. 141-142.
This is an expanding set. Numbers may change.

Ceramics — A8

Designs: No. 41, Pitcher and bowl. No. 42, Four pieces on tree branches. No. 43, Two large pitchers. No. 44, One large pitcher.

1992, Dec. 24   Litho.   Perf. 11¹/₂
41 A8   1r multicolored   .15
42 A8   1r multicolored   .15
43 A8   1r multicolored   .15
44 A8   1r multicolored   .15
        Set value   .40

M. I. Garetzky (1893-1938), Writer — A9

1993, June 22   Photo.   Perf. 12x11¹/₂
45 A9   50r magenta   .30

Straw Figures — A10

Designs: 5r, Chickens. 10r, Child, mother, vert. 15r, Woman, vert. 25r, Man with scythe, woman with rake, vert.

   Perf. 12x11¹/₂, 11¹/₂x12
1993, Apr. 22   Litho.
47 A10 5r multicolored   .15
48 A10 10r multicolored   .20
49 A10 15r multicolored   .30
50 A10 25r multicolored   .15
        Nos. 47-50 (4)   1.15

First World Congress of White Russians — A11

1993, July 8   Litho.   Perf. 12
51 A11 50r multicolored   1.75

Europa — A12

Paintings by Chagall: No. 52, Promenade, vert. No. 53, Man Over Vitebsk. 2500r, Allegory.

1993, Oct. 12   Litho.   Perf. 14
52 A12 1500r multicolored   3.00
53 A12 1500r multicolored   3.00
a.   Pair, #52-53   6.00
   Souvenir Sheet
54 A12 2500r multicolored   45.00

Nos. 15-16, 18 Surcharged

XVII ЗІМОВЫЯ АЛІМПІЙСКІЯ ГУЛЬНІ ЛІЛЕХАМЕР, НАРВЕГІЯ, 1994

WINTER PRE-OLYMPICS GAMES LILLEHAMMER, NORWAY

Size and location of surcharge varies.

1993, Oct. 15   Litho.   Perf. 12x12¹/₂
55 A4(a) 1500r on 5r #15   3.50
56 A4(b) 1500r on 5r #15   3.50
a.   Pair, #55-56   7.00
57 A4(a) 1500r on 5r #16   3.50
58 A4(b) 1500r on 5r #16   3.50
a.   Pair, #57-58   7.00
          Nos. 55-58 (4)   14.00
   Souvenir Sheets
   Perf. 12
59 A5(a) 1500r on 5r #18   3.50
60 A5(b) 1500r on 5r #18   3.50

No. 59 exists imperf.

Nos. 15-16, 18 Surcharged

ЧЭМПІЯНАТ СВЕТУ ПА ФУТБОЛУ, ЗША, 1994

WORLD CUP USA 94

Size and location of surcharge varies.

1993, Oct. 15   Litho.   Perf. 12x12¹/₂
61 A4(c) 1500r on 5r #15   3.50
62 A4(d) 1500r on 5r #15   3.50
a.   Pair, #61-62   7.00
63 A4(c) 1500r on 5r #16   3.50
64 A4(d) 1500r on 5r #16   3.50
a.   Pair, #63-64   7.00
          Nos. 61-64 (4)   14.00
   Souvenir Sheets
   Perf. 12
65 A5(c) 1500r on 5r #18   3.50
66 A5(d) 1500r on 5r #18   3.50

Stansilavski Church A13

1993, Nov. 24   Litho.   Perf. 12
67 A13 150r multicolored   .50

Famous People — A14

Designs: 50r, Kastus Kalinovsky, led 1863 independence movement. No. 69, Prince Rogvold of Polotsk, map of Polotsk. No. 70, Princess Rogneda, daughter of Rogvold, fortress. 100r, Statue of Simon Budny (1530-93), writer and printer, vert.

1993		Perf. 12x12½, 12½x12	
68	A14	50r multicolored	.15
69	A14	75r multicolored	.25
70	A14	75r multicolored	.25
71	A14	100r multicolored	.35
		Nos. 68-71 (4)	1.00

Issued: 50r, 12/29; 75r, 12/30; 100r, 12/31.

Nos. 27, 29, 30 Surcharged

15.00

1994, Feb. 1	Photo.	Perf. 12x12½	
72	A7	15r on 30k light green	.15
73	A7	25r on 45k olive green	.15
74	A7	50r on 50k green	.15
		Set value	.20

Birds
A15

1994, Jan. 19	Litho.	Perf. 11½	
75	A15	20r Aguila chrysaetos	.15
76	A15	40r Cygnus olor	.15
77	A15	40r Alcedo atthis	.15
a.		Block of 3, #75-77 + label	.40

See Nos. 87-89.

Six World Wildlife Fund labels with 1000r denominations depicting 3 different animals and 3 different birds exist. They were not valid for postage.

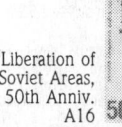

Liberation of
Soviet Areas,
50th Anniv.
A16

Battle maps and: a, Katyusha rockets, liberation of Russia. b, Fighter planes, liberation of Ukraine. c, Combined offensive, liberation of Belarus.

1994, July 3	Litho.	Perf. 12	
78	A16	500r Block of 3 + label	.45

See Russia No. 6213, Ukraine No. 195.

1994 Winter
Olympics,
Lillehammer — A17

1994, Aug. 30	Litho.	Perf. 12x12½	
79	A17	1000r Speed skating	.15
80	A17	1000r Women's figure skating	.15
81	A17	1000r Hockey	.15
82	A17	1000r Cross-country skiing	.15
83	A17	1000r Biathlon	.15
		Set value	.65

Painters — A18

Designs: No. 84, Farmer, oxen in field, by Ferdinand Rushchyts. No. 85, Knight on horseback, by Jasev Drazdovich. No. 86, Couple walking up path, by Petra Sergievich. Illustration reduced.

1994, July 18	Litho.	Perf. 12	
84	A18	300r multicolored	.15
85	A18	300r multicolored	.15
86	A18	300r multicolored	.15
		Set value	.30

For overprint see No. 127.

Bird Type of 1994

1994, Sept. 30		Perf. 11½	
87	A15	300r like #75	.15
88	A15	400r like #76	.15
89	A15	400r like #77	.15
		Set value	.25

Ilya Yefimovich
Repin (1844-1930),
Ukrainian
Painter — A19

Designs: #90, Self-portrait. #91, Repin Museum.

1994, Oct. 31	Litho.	Perf. 12x12½	
90	A19	1000r multicolored	.30
91	A19	1000r multicolored	.30
a.		Pair, #90-91	.60

Churches
A20

Designs: No. 92, Sacred Consolidated Church, Sinkavitsch, 16th cent. No. 93, Sts. Peter and Paul Cathedral, Gomel, 19th cent.

1994, Oct. 20	Litho.	Perf. 12	
92	A20	700r multicolored	.20
93	A20	700r multicolored	.20

Kosciuszko
Uprising,
Bicent. (in
1994)
A21

Battle scene and: No. 94, Tomasz Vaishetcki (1754-1816). No. 95, Jakov Jasinski (1761-94). No. 96, Tadeusz Kosziuszko (1746-1817). No. 97, Mikhail K. Aginski (1765-1833).

1995, Jan. 11		Perf. 12½x12	
94	A21	600r multicolored	.15
95	A21	600r multicolored	.15
96	A21	1000r multicolored	.30
97	A21	1000r multicolored	.30
		Nos. 94-97 (4)	.90

End of World
War II, 50th
Anniv. — A22

1995, May 4	Litho.	Perf. 13½	
98	A22	180r multicolored	.15
99	A22	600r multicolored	.20
		Set value	.25

Radio, Cent. — A23

1995, May 7		Perf. 14	
100	A23	600r multicolored	.20

Exists imperf.

180

Monument — A24

1995-96	Litho.	Perf. 13x14	
102	A24	180r olive brown & red	.15
103	A24	200r gray green & bister	.15
105	A24	280r green & blue	.20
109	A24	600r plum & bister	.20
		Nos. 102-109 (4)	.70

No. 102 exists imperf.

Issued: 180r, 5/10/95; 280r, 5/18/95; 600r, 8/29/95; 200r, 1/30/96.
This is an expanding set. Numbers may change.

Ivan Chersky
(1845-92),
Geographer
A25

1995, May 15	Litho.	Perf. 13½x14	
113	A25	600r multicolored	.20

Exists imperf.

A26   A27

Traditional Costumes: 600r, Woman wearing shawl, coat, ankle length skirt, man with long coat. 1200r, Woman wearing shawl & apron holding child, man wearing vest, knickers.

1995, July 13	Litho.	Perf. 14½x14	
114	A26	180r multicolored	.15
115	A26	600r multicolored	.15
116	A26	1200r multicolored	.35
		Set value	.55

See Nos. 164-167.

1995, July 20		Perf. 12	

World Wildlife Fund: Various pictures of a beaver.

117	A27	300r multi	.15
118	A27	450r multi	.15
119	A27	450r multi, horiz.	.15
120	A27	800r multi, horiz.	.20
		Set value	.50

A28   A29

1995	Litho.	Perf. 14	
121	A28	600r Book Fair	.20

Exists imperf.

1995, Oct. 3	Litho.	Perf. 14	
122	A29	600r Natl. arms	.20
123	A29	600r Flag	.20

New national symbols. Exist imperf.

UN, 50th
Anniv. — A30

1995, Oct. 24	Litho.	Perf. 13½x14	
124	A30	600r bister, black & blue	.20

Exists imperf.

Churches
A31

Designs: No. 125, Mstislav, 17th-19th cent. No. 126, Kamai, 17th cent.

1995, Nov. 21		Perf. 14	
125	A31	600r multicolored	.20
126	A31	600r multicolored	.20

1995

No. 84 Ovptd. **125 год
з дня нараджэння**

1995, Dec. 27	Litho.	Perf. 12	
127	A18	300r multicolored	.20

P. V. Sukhi
(1895-1975),
Airplane
Designer — A32

1995, Dec. 27		Perf. 13½	
128	A32	600r multicolored	.20

Wildlife
A33

Designs: 1000r, Lynx lynx. No. 130, Capreolus capreolus, vert. No. 131, Ursus arctos. 3000r, Alces alces, vert. 5000r, Bison bonasus. 10,000r, Cervus elaphus, vert.

1995-96	Litho.	Perf. 14	
129	A33	1000r multicolored	.25
130	A33	2000r multicolored	.40
131	A33	2000r multicolored	.40
132	A33	3000r multicolored	.65
133	A33	5000r multicolored	1.10
		Nos. 129-133 (5)	2.80

Souvenir Sheet
Imperf

134	A33	10,000r multicolored	2.25

Issued: #129-133, 2/6/96; #134, 12/29/95.

Famous People — A34

Designs: 600r, L. Sapega (1557-1633), statesman. 1200r, K. Semyanovitch (1600-51), military scholar. 1800r, S. Polotzki (1629-80), writer. Illustration reduced.

1995, Dec. 30	Litho.	Perf. 12	
135	A34	600r multicolored	.15
136	A34	1200r multicolored	.30
137	A34	1800r multicolored	.45
		Nos. 135-137 (3)	.90

Miniature Sheet

Butterflies
A35

Designs: No. 138a, Apatura iris. b, Lopinga achine. c, Callimorpha dominula. d, Catocala fraxini. e, Papilio machaon. f, Parnassius apollo. g, Ammobiota hebe. h, Colias palaeno.
No. 139, Proserpinus proserpina. No. 140, Vacciniina optilete.

1996, Mar. 29   Litho.   Perf. 14
138 A35 300r Sheet of 8, #a.-h.   6.00
Souvenir Sheets
139-140 A35 1000r each   6.00
Inscribed 1995.

Nos. 28, 34 Surcharged in Green
or Red

B

1996   Litho.   Perf. 12x12½
141 A7 (B) on 1r #28 (G)   .15
142 A7 (A) on 25r #34 (R)   .15
        Set value   .25

Nos. 141-142 were valued at 200r and 400r, respectively, on day of issue. Issued: No. 141, 2/28/96. No. 142, 3/13/96.

Souvenir Sheet

Beaver — A36

Illustration reduced.

1996, Mar. 26 Litho. Perf. 12½x12
143 A36 1200r multicolored   .35

Kondrat
Krapiva (1896-
1991),
Writer — A37

1996, Mar. 5   Litho.   Perf. 14x14½
144 A37 1000r multicolored   .35

Chernobyl
Disaster, 10th
Anniv. — A38

Radiation symbol and: a, Eye. b, Leaf showing contamination. c, Boarded-up window.

1996, Apr. 10   Litho.   Perf. 14
145 A38 1000r Block of 3, #a.-c. +
         label   .60

Coat of Arms — A39

1996, May 6   Litho.   Perf. 13½
146 A39   100r blue & black   .15
147 A39   500r green & black   .15
148 A39   600r vermilion & black   .15
149 A39 1000r orange & black   .20
150 A39 1500r dp lilac rose & blk   .30
151 A39 1800r violet & black   .35
152 A39 2200r rose violet & black   .45
153 A39 3300r yellow & black   .65
154 A39 5000r green blue & blk   1.00
155 A39 10,000r apple green & blk   2.00
156 A39 30,000r brown & black   6.00
157 A39 50,000r red brown & blk   10.00
        Nos. 146-157 (12)   21.40
See No. 182.

Agreement with
Russia — A40

1996, June 14   Perf. 13½x14
158 A40 1500r multicolored   .30

1996 Summer
Olympic
Games,
Atlanta
A41

1996, July 15   Litho.   Perf. 14
159 A41 3000r Rhythmic gymnastics   .15
160 A41 3000r Discus   .15
161 A41 3000r Wrestling   .15
162 A41 3000r Weight lifting   .15
        Nos. 159-162 (4)   .60
Souvenir Sheet
Imperf
163 A41 5000r Shooting, vert.   1.00
No. 163 has simulated perforations.

Regional Costume Type of 1995

Couples in traditional 19th cent. costumes: 1800r, Kapilska-Kletzky region. 2200r, David-Gorodok-Turai region. 3300r, Kobrin region. 5000r, Naralyan region.

1996, Aug. 13   Litho.   Perf. 14
164 A26 1800r multicolored   .20
165 A26 2200r multicolored   .25
166 A26 3300r multicolored   .40
        Nos. 164-166 (3)   .85
Souvenir Sheet
Imperf
167 A26 5000r multicolored   1.00

Medicinal Plants — A42

No. 168, Sanguisorba officinaus. No. 169, Acorus calamus. 2200r, Potentilla erecta. 3300r, Frangula alnus. 5000r, Menyanthes trifoliata.

1996, Aug. 15   Perf. 14x13½
168 A42 1500r multicolored   .25
169 A42 1500r multicolored   .25
170 A42 2200r multicolored   .40
171 A42 3300r multicolored   .60
        Nos. 168-171 (4)   1.50
Souvenir Sheet
Imperf
172 A42 5000r multicolored   1.00

Birds
A44

No. 173: a, Ardea cinerea. b, Ciconia nigra. c, Phalacrocorax caroo. d, Ciconia ciconia. e, Larus ridibundus. f, Gallinago gallinago. g, Chlidonias

leucopterus. h, Remiz pendulinus. i, Botaurus stellaris. j, Fulica atra. k, Ixobrychus minutus. l, Alcedo atthts.
No. 174: a, Anas crecca. b, Anas strepera. c, Anas acuta. d, Anas platyrhynchos. e, Aythya marila. f, Clangula hyemalis. g, Anas clypeata. h, Anas querquedula. i, Anas penelope. j, Arthya nyroca. k, Bucephala clangula. l, Mergus merganser. m, Mergus albellus. n, Aythya fuligula. o, Mergus serrator. p, Aythya ferina.
No. 175, Aythya ferina, diff. No. 176, Gallinago gallinago, diff.

1996, Sept. 10   Litho.   Perf. 14
173 A44 400r Sheet of 12, #a.-l.   6.00
174 A44 400r Sheet of 16, #a.-p.   8.00
Souvenir Sheets
175-176 A44 1000r each   4.00

Grammar Book,
1596 — A45

1996, Sept. 19 Litho. Perf. 14x13½
177 A45 1500r multicolored   .30

Churches
A46

1996, Sept. 24   Perf. 14x14½
178 A46 3300r Pinsk   .65
179 A46 3300r Mogilev, 17th cent.   .65

Mikola
Shchakatskin
(1896-1940),
Art
Critic — A47

1996, Oct. 16   Litho.   Perf. 14
180 A47 2000r multicolored   .45

Minsk
Telephone
Station,
Cent. — A48

1996, Nov. 14
181 A48 2000r multicolored   .45

Natl. Arms Type of 1996

1996, Nov. 21 Litho. Perf. 13½x14
182 A39 200r gray green & black   .15

Pres. Aleksandr G. Lukashenka, Natl.
Flag — A49

1996, Dec. 6   Litho.   Perf. 13½
183 A49 2500r multicolored   .50

БЕЛАРУСЬ BELARUS 1996 **3000** Famous
Men — A50

Designs: No. 184, Kyril Turovski (1130-81), Bishop of Turov. No. 185, Mikola Gusovski (1470-1533), writer. No. 186, Mikolaj Radziwil (1515-65), chancellor of Lithuania.

1996, Dec. 17   Perf. 13½
184 A50 3000r multicolored   .60
185 A50 3000r multicolored   .60
186 A50 3000r multicolored   .60
        Nos. 184-186 (3)   1.80

New
Year — A51

1500r, Christmas tree, buildings in Minsk.

1996, Dec. 21   Perf. 14
187 A51 1500r multicolored   .30
188 A51 2000r multicolored, vert.   .40

БЕЛАРУСЬ BELARUS 1996 **3500** Natl. Museum of
Art,
Minsk — A52

Icons: No. 189, Madonna and Child, Smolensk, 16th cent. No. 190, Paraskeva, 16th cent. No. 191, Ilya, 17th cent. No. 192, Three saints, 18th cent. 5000r, Birth of Christ, by Peter Yacijevitsch, 1649.

1996, Dec. 26   Perf. 13½
189 A52 3500r multicolored   .70
190 A52 3500r multicolored   .70
191 A52 3500r multicolored   .70
192 A52 3500r multicolored   .70
        Nos. 189-192 (4)   2.80
Souvenir Sheet
Imperf
193 A46 5000r multicolored   1.00

Georgi K.
Zhukov (1896-
1974), Soviet БЕЛАРУСЬ BELARUS 1996 **2000**
Marshal — A53

1997, Jan. 3   Perf. 13½
194 A53 2000r multicolored   .45

Kupala Natl. Theater, Minsk — A54

1997, Jan. 3   *Perf. 13½x14*
195 A54 3500r multicolored   .70

BELGIAN CONGO

'bel–jən 'käŋ–(,)gō

LOCATION — Central Africa
GOVT. — Belgian colony
AREA — 902,082 sq. mi. (estimated)
POP. — 12,660,000 (1956)
CAPITAL — Léopoldville

Congo was an independent state, founded by Leopold II of Belgium, until 1908 when it was annexed to Belgium as a colony. In 1960 it became the independent Republic of the Congo. See Congo Democratic Republic and Zaire.

100 Centimes = 1 Franc

Catalogue values for unused stamps in this country are for Never Hinged items, beginning with Scott 187 in the regular postage section, Scott B32 in the semi-postal section, Scott C17 in the airpost section, and Scott J8 in the postage due section.

Independent State

King Leopold II
A1   A2   A3

1886   **Unwmk.**   **Typo.**   **Perf. 15**
1 A1   5c green   8.00   20.00
2 A1   10c rose   4.00   5.00
3 A2   25c blue   40.00   32.50
4 A3   50c olive green   6.00   6.00
5 A1   5fr lilac   325.00   250.00
a.   Perf. 14   800.00
b.   5fr deep lilac   700.00   475.00

Counterfeits exist.
For surcharge see No. Q1.

King Leopold II — A4

1887-94
6 A4   5c grn ('89)   .75   .75
7 A4   10c rose ('89)   1.25   1.25
8 A4   25c blue ('89)   1.25   1.25
9 A4   50c reddish brown   45.00   20.00
10 A4   50c gray ('94)   2.50   15.00
11 A4   5fr violet   900.00   375.00
12 A4   5fr gray ('92)   110.00   95.00
13 A4   10fr buff ('91)   400.00   275.00

The 25fr and 50fr in gray were not issued. Values, each $20.
Counterfeits exist of Nos. 10-13, 25fr and 50fr, unused, used, genuine stamps with faked cancels and counterfeit stamps with genuine cancels.
For surcharges see Nos. Q3-Q6.

Port Matadi — A5

River Scene on the Congo, Stanley Falls — A6

Inkissi Falls — A7

Railroad Bridge on M'pozo River — A8

Hunting Elephants A9

Bangala Chief and Wife — A10

1894-1901   **Engr.**   *Perf. 12½ to 15*
14 A5   5c pale bl & blk   12.50   12.50
15 A5   5c red brn & blk ('95)   3.25   1.35
16 A5   5c grn & blk ('00)   1.75   .50
17 A6   10c red brn & blk   12.50   12.50
18 A6   10c grnsh bl & blk ('95)   1.50   1.25
a.   Center inverted   1,850.   2,250.
19 A6   10c car & blk ('00)   3.00   .75
20 A7   25c yel org & blk   3.25   2.25
21 A7   25c lt bl & blk ('00)   3.00   1.25
22 A8   50c grn & blk   1.25   1.25
23 A8   50c ol & blk ('00)   3.00   .75
24 A9   1fr lilac & blk   20.00   11.00
a.   1fr rose lilac & black   225.00   22.50
25 A9   1fr car & blk ('01)   200.00   5.00
26 A10   5fr lake & blk   40.00   25.00
a.   5fr carmine rose & black   85.00   35.00
   Nos. 14-26 (13)   305.00   75.35

For overprints see Nos. 31-32, 34, 36-37, 39.

Climbing Oil Palms — A11

Congo Canoe — A12

1896
27 A11   15c ocher & blk   3.25   .50
28 A12   40c bluish grn & blk   3.25   2.50

For overprints see Nos. 33, 35.

Congo Village — A13

River Steamer on the Congo — A14

1898
29 A13   3.50fr red & blk   140.00   80.00
a.   Perf. 14x12   350.00   225.00
30 A14   10fr yel grn & blk   90.00   24.00
a.   Center inverted   25,000.
b.   Perf. 12   525.00   22.50
c.   Perf. 12x14   325.00
   As "c," pen canceled   14.00

For overprints see Nos. 38, 40.

Belgian Congo
Overprinted   **CONGO BELGE**

1908
31 A5   5c green & blk   7.00   7.00
a.   Handstamped   2.50   1.75
32 A6   10c carmine & blk   12.00   12.00
a.   Handstamped   2.50   1.75
33 A11   15c ocher & blk   7.00   7.00
a.   Handstamped   5.50   3.50
34 A7   25c lt blue & blk   3.75   2.50
a.   Handstamped   7.00   3.50
c.   Double overprint (#34)   185.00
35 A12   40c bluish grn & blk   2.25   2.25
a.   Handstamped   7.00   5.50
36 A8   50c olive & blk   4.00   2.25
a.   Handstamped   3.75   3.00
b.   Inverted overprint (#36)   500.00
37 A9   1fr carmine & blk   19.00   2.25
a.   Handstamped   25.00   7.00
38 A13   3.50fr red & blk   25.00   20.00
a.   Handstamped   160.00   110.00
39 A10   5fr carmine & blk   40.00   24.00
a.   Handstamped   60.00   40.00
40 A14   10fr yel grn & blk   85.00   20.00
a.   Perf. 14   225.00
b.   Handstamped   125.00   45.00
c.   Handstamped, perf. 14   275.00   225.00
   Nos. 31-40 (10)   205.00   99.25

Most of the above handstamps are also found inverted and double.
Values for handstamped overprints are for those applied locally.
Counterfeits of the handstamped overprints exist.

Port Matadi — A15

River Scene on the Congo, Stanley Falls — A16

Climbing Oil Palms — A17

Railroad Bridge on M'pozo River — A18

1909   *Perf. 14*
41 A15   5c green & blk   .75   .75
42 A16   10c carmine & blk   .75   .50
43 A17   15c ocher & blk   25.00   15.00
44 A18   50c olive & blk   3.00   2.50
   Nos. 41-44 (4)   29.50   18.75

Port Matadi — A19

River Scene on the Congo, Stanley Falls — A20

Climbing Oil Palms — A21

Inkissi Falls — A22

Congo Canoe — A23

Railroad Bridge on M'pozo River — A24

Hunting Elephants A25

Congo Village — A26

Bangala Chief and Wife — A27

River Steamer
on the
Congo — A28

1910-15   Engr.   Perf. 14, 15

45	A19	5c green & blk	.75	.15
46	A20	10c carmine & blk	.40	.15
47	A21	15c ocher & blk	.40	.15
48	A21	15c grn & blk ('15)	1.50	
a.		Booklet pane of 10	14.00	
49	A22	25c blue & blk	1.50	.30
50	A23	40c bluish grn & blk	2.00	1.75
51	A23	40c brn red & blk ('15)	3.75	1.75
52	A24	50c olive & blk	3.00	1.50
53	A24	50c brn lake & blk ('15)	6.00	1.75
54	A25	1fr carmine & blk	2.75	2.10
55	A25	1fr ol bis & blk ('15)	2.00	.65
56	A26	3fr red & blk	15.00	10.00
57	A27	5fr carmine & blk	17.00	14.00
58	A27	5fr ocher & blk ('15)	1.50	.65
59	A28	10fr green & blk	16.00	12.50
		Nos. 45-59 (15)	72.25	47.55

Nos. 48, 51, 53, 55 and 58 exist imperforate.
For overprints and surcharges see Nos. 64-76,
81-86, B5-B9.

Port
Matadi — A29

Stanley Falls,
Congo
River — A30

Inkissi
Falls — A31

TEN CENTIMES.
Type I - Large white space at top of picture and
two small white spots at lower edge. Vignette does
not fill frame.
Type II - Vignette completely fills frame.

1915

60	A29	5c green & blk	.15	.15
a.		Booklet pane of 10	7.50	
61	A30	10c car & blk (II)	.20	.15
a.		Booklet pane of 10	14.00	
		10c carmine & black (I)	.20	.15
b.		Booklet pane of 10 (II)		
62	A31	25c blue & blk	.85	.25
a.		Booklet pane of 10	65.00	
		Nos. 60-62 (3)	1.20	.55

Nos. 60 to 62 exist imperforate.
For surcharges see Nos. 77-80, 87, B1-B4.

Stamps of 1910 Issue Surcharged in Red
or Black

1921

64	A23	5c on 40c bluish grn & blk (R)	.25	.25
65	A19	10c on 5c grn & blk (R)	.25	.25
66	A24	10c on 50c ol & blk (R)	.25	.25
67	A21	25c on 15c ocher & blk (R)	1.50	1.00
68	A23	30c on 10c car & blk	.35	.35
69	A22	50c on 25c bl & blk (R)	1.40	.90
		Nos. 64-69 (6)	4.00	3.00

The position of the new value and the bars varies
on Nos. 64 to 69.

Overprinted **1921**

1921

70	A25	1fr carmine & blk	.75	.75
a.		Double overprint	20.00	
71	A26	3fr red & blk	2.50	2.50
72	A27	5fr carmine & blk	4.75	4.75
73	A28	10fr green & blk (R)	4.25	2.50
		Nos. 70-73 (4)	12.25	10.50

Belgian Surcharges

Nos. 51, 53, 60-62
Surcharged in Black or Red **·10ᶜ**

1922

74	A24	5c on 50c	.35	.30
75	A29	10c on 5c (R)	.35	.25
76	A23	25c on 40c (R)	2.00	.30
77	A30	30c on 10c (II)	.15	.15
a.		30c on 10c (I)	.15	.15
b.		Double surcharge	4.75	4.75
78	A31	50c on 25c (R)	.40	.25
		Nos. 74-78 (5)	3.25	1.25

No. 74 has the surcharge at each side.

Congo Surcharges
Nos. 60, 51 Surcharged in Red or Black:

10 c.
a

25 c.
b

1922

80	A29	10c on 5c (R)	.55	.55
a.		Inverted surcharge	17.50	17.50
b.		Double surcharge	4.75	
c.		Double surch., one invtd.	40.00	
d.		Pair, one without surcharge	42.50	
e.		On No. 45	125.00	125.00
81	A23	25c on 40c	.70	.35
a.		Inverted surcharge	17.50	17.50
b.		Double surcharge	5.50	
c.		"25c" double		
d.		25c on 5c, No. 60	100.00	100.00

Nos. 55, 58 Surcharged
with vertical bars over
original values **10 c.**

1922

84	A25	10c on 1fr (R)	.55	.55
a.		Double surcharge	14.00	
b.		Inverted surcharge	17.50	17.50
85	A27	25c on 5fr	1.50	1.50

Nos. 68, 77 Handstamped **0,25**

86	A20	25c on 30c on 10c	7.00	8.50
87	A30	25c on 30c on 10c (II)	7.00	8.50

Nos. 86-87 exist with handstamp surcharge
inverted.
Counterfeit handstamped surcharges exist.

Ubangi
Woman — A32

Watusi
Cattle — A44

Designs: 10c, Baluba woman. 15c, Babuende
woman. No. 90, 40c, 1.25fr, 1.50fr, 1.75fr, Ubangi
man. 15c, Basketmaking. 30c, 35c, Nos. 101, 102,
Carving wood. 50c, Archer. No. 92, 100, Weaving. 1fr, Making pottery. 3fr, Working rubber. 5fr,
Making palm oil. 10fr, African elephant.

1923-27   Engr.   Perf. 12

88	A32	5c yellow	.15	.15
89	A32	10c green	.15	.15
90	A32	15c olive brn	.15	.15
91	A32	20c olive grn ('24)	.15	.15
92	A44	20c green ('26)	.15	.15
93	A44	25c red brown	.25	.15
94	A44	30c rose red ('24)	.45	.45
95	A44	30c olive grn ('25)	.15	.15
96	A32	35c green ('27)	.45	.35
97	A32	40c violet ('25)	.15	.15
98	A44	50c gray blue	.25	.15
99	A44	50c buff ('25)	.30	.15
100	A44	75c red orange	.25	.20
101	A44	75c gray bl ('25)	.40	.25
102	A44	75c salmon red ('26)	.20	.15
103	A44	1fr bister brn	.55	.15
104	A44	1fr dl blue ('25)	.35	.15
105	A44	1fr rose red ('27)	.85	.15
106	A32	1.25fr dl blue ('26)	.30	.20
107	A32	1.50fr dl blue ('26)	.30	.15
108	A32	1.75fr dl blue ('26)	3.75	3.25
109	A44	3fr gray brn ('24)	4.00	2.25
110	A44	5fr gray ('24)	10.00	4.75
111	A44	10fr gray blk ('24)	17.50	8.50

1925-26

112	A44	45c dk vio ('26)	.40	.25
113	A44	60c carmine rose	.40	.15
		Nos. 88-113 (26)	42.00	22.85

For surcharges see Nos. 114, 136-138, 157.

No. 107 Surcharged ═══

1ᶠ75

1927, June 14

114	A32	1.75fr on 1.50fr dl bl	.30	.20

Sir Henry Morton
Stanley — A45

1928, June 30   Perf. 14

115	A45	5c gray blk	.15	.15
116	A45	10c dp violet	.15	.15
117	A45	20c orange red	.35	.15
118	A45	35c green	1.00	.75
119	A45	40c red brown	.40	.15
120	A45	60c black brn	.40	.15
121	A45	1fr carmine	.40	.15
122	A45	1.60fr dk gray	4.00	3.25
123	A45	1.75fr dp blue	1.65	.80
124	A45	2fr dk brown	1.10	.30
125	A45	2.75fr red violet	4.50	.45
126	A45	3.50fr rose lake	1.40	.75
127	A45	5fr slate grn	1.10	.30
128	A45	10fr violet blue	1.65	.70
129	A45	20fr claret	6.75	2.25
		Nos. 115-129 (15)	25.00	10.60

Sir Henry M. Stanley (1841-1904), explorer.

═══

Nos. 118, 121-123,
125-126 Surcharged in
Red, Blue or Black

1Fᴬ25

1931, Jan. 15

130	A45	40c on 35c	.50	.40
131	A45	1.25fr on 1fr (Bl)	.40	.15
132	A45	2fr on 1.60fr	.80	.30
133	A45	2fr on 1.75fr	.75	.30
134	A45	3.25fr on 2.75fr (Bk)	2.25	2.00
135	A45	3.25fr on 3.25fr (Bk)	3.00	2.10

Nos. 96, 108, 112 Surcharged in Red

═══ **50ᶜ** ═══

Perf. 12½, 12

136	A44	40c on 35c grn	3.25	3.00
137	A44	50c on 45c dk vio	2.00	1.10

Surcharged **2**

138	A32	2(fr) on 1.75fr dl bl	8.50	7.50
		Nos. 130-138 (9)	21.45	16.85

View of
Sankuru
River — A46

Flute Players — A50

Designs: 15c, Kivu Kraal. 20c, Sankuru River
rapids. 25c, Uele hut. 50c, Musicians of Lake Leopold II. 60c, Batetelas drummers. 75c, Mangbetu
woman. 1fr, Domesticated elephant of Api. 1.25fr,
Mangbetu chief. 1.50fr, Village of Mondimbi.
2.50fr, 3.25fr, Okapi. 4fr, Canoes at Stanleyville.
5fr, Woman preparing cassava. 10fr, Baluba chief.
20fr, Young woman of Irumu.

1931-37   Engr.   Perf. 11½

139	A46	10c gray brn ('32)	.15	.15
140	A46	15c gray ('32)	.15	.15
141	A46	20c brn lil ('32)	.15	.15

142	A46	25c dp blue ('32)	.15	.15
143	A50	40c dp grn ('32)	.20	.20
144	A46	50c violet ('32)	.15	.15
b.		Booklet pane of 8	6.25	
145	A50	60c vio brn ('32)	.15	.15
146	A50	75c rose ('32)	.15	.15
b.		Booklet pane of 8	1.25	
147	A50	1fr rose red ('32)	.15	.15
148	A50	1.25fr red brown	.15	.15
b.		Booklet pane of 8	1.25	
149	A46	1.50fr dk ol gray ('37)	.15	.15
b.		Booklet pane of 8	6.00	
150	A46	2fr ultra ('32)	.20	.15
151	A46	2.50fr dp blue ('37)	.30	.15
b.		Booklet pane of 8	8.50	
152	A46	3.25fr gray blk ('32)	.45	.30
153	A46	4fr dl vio ('32)	.20	.15
154	A50	5fr dp vio ('32)	.50	.25
155	A50	10fr red ('32)	.50	.40
156	A50	20fr blk brn ('32)	1.50	1.25
		Set value	5.00	3.75

3ᶠ25

No. 109
Surcharged in
Red

═══

1932, Mar. 15   Perf. 12

157	A44	3.25fr on 3fr gray brn	2.75	2.25

King Albert Memorial Issue

King Albert — A62

1934, May 7   Photo.   Perf. 11½

158	A62	1.50fr black		.65	.15

Leopold I,
Leopold II,
Albert I,
Leopold III
A63

1935, Aug. 15   Engr.   Perf. 12½x12

159	A63	50c green	.65	.50
160	A63	1.25fr dk carmine	.65	.15
161	A63	1.50fr brown vio	.65	.15
162	A63	2.40fr brown org	2.00	2.00
163	A63	2.50fr lt blue	2.00	.90
164	A63	4fr brt violet	2.00	1.25
165	A63	5fr black brn	2.00	1.50
		Nos. 159-165 (7)	9.95	6.45

Founding of Congo Free State, 50th anniv.
For surcharges see Nos. B21-B22.

Molindi
River — A64

Bamboos — A65

Suza River — A66

Rutshuru
River — A67

Karisimbi — A68

Mitumba Forest — A69

1937-38   Photo.   Perf. 11½

166 A64	5c purple & blk	.15	.15
167 A65	90c car & brn	.40	.30
168 A66	1.50fr dp red brn & blk	.15	.15
169 A67	2.40fr ol blk & brn	.15	.15
170 A68	2.50fr dp ultra & blk	.30	.15
171 A69	4.50fr dk grn & brn	.30	.15
172 A69	4.50fr car & sep	.20	.20
Nos. 166-172 (7)		1.65	
Set value			1.00

National Parks.
No. 172 was issued in sheets of four measuring 140x111mm. It was sold by subscription, the subscription closing Oct. 20, 1937. Value, $1.60.
Nos. 166-171 were issued Mar. 1, 1938.
See No. B26. For surcharges see Nos. 184, 186.

King Albert Memorial, Leopoldville — A70

1941, Feb. 7   Litho.   Perf. 11

173 A70	10c lt gray	.20	.15
174 A70	15c brown vio	.25	.15
175 A70	25c lt blue	.30	.15
176 A70	50c lt violet	.25	.15
177 A70	75c rose pink	.95	.30
178 A70	1.25fr gray	.30	.15
179 A70	1.75fr orange	.95	.45
180 A70	2.50fr carmine	.65	.15
181 A70	2.75fr vio blue	.95	.60
182 A70	5fr lt olive grn	4.00	1.50
183 A70	10fr rose red	2.75	1.75
Nos. 173-183 (11)		11.55	5.50

Exist imperforate.
For surcharge see No. 185.

Nos. 168, 179, 169 Surcharged in Blue or Black

5 c.

75 c.

Nos. 184, 186   No. 185

1941-42   Perf. 11½, 11

184 A66	5c on 1.50fr (Bl)	.15	.15
a.	Inverted surcharge	14.00	14.00
185 A70	75c on 1.75fr ('42)	.35	.35
a.	Inverted surcharge	14.00	14.00
186 A67	2.50(fr) on 2.40fr ('42)	.85	.70
a.	Double surcharge	27.50	27.50
b.	Inverted surcharge	14.00	14.00
Nos. 184-186 (3)		1.35	1.20

> Catalogue values for unused stamps in this section, from this point to the end of the section, are for Never Hinged items.

Oil Palms
A71   A72

Congo Woman — A73   Askari — A75

Leopard A74

Okapi — A76

Inscribed "Congo Belge Belgisch Congo"

1942, May 23   Engr.   Perf. 12½

187 A71	5c red	.15	.15
188 A72	10c olive grn	.15	.15
189 A72	15c brown car	.15	.15
190 A72	20c dp ultra	.15	.15
191 A72	25c brown vio	.15	.15
192 A72	30c blue	.15	.15
193 A72	50c dp green	.15	.15
194 A72	60c chestnut	.15	.15
195 A73	75c dl lil & blk	.15	.15
196 A73	1fr dk brn & blk	.20	.15
197 A73	1.25fr rose red & blk	.20	.15
198 A73	1.75fr dk gray brn	.75	.15
199 A74	2fr ocher	.75	.15
200 A74	2.50fr carmine	.75	.15
201 A75	3.50fr dk ol grn	.35	.15
202 A75	5fr orange	.70	.15
203 A75	6fr brt ultra	.50	.15
204 A75	7fr black	.60	.15
205 A75	10fr dp brown	.75	.15
206 A76	20fr plum & blk	8.00	.65
Nos. 187-206 (20)		14.90	
Set value			2.50

Same Inscribed "Belgisch Congo Congo Belge"

207 A72	10c olive grn	.15	.15
208 A72	15c brown car	.15	.15
209 A72	20c dp ultra	.15	.15
210 A72	25c brown vio	.15	.15
211 A72	30c blue	.15	.15
212 A72	50c dp green	.15	.15
213 A72	60c chestnut	.15	.15
214 A73	75c dl lil & blk	.15	.15
215 A73	1fr dk brn & blk	.20	.15
216 A73	1.25fr rose red & blk	.20	.15
217 A73	1.75fr dk gray brn	.75	.35
218 A74	2fr ocher	.75	.15
219 A74	2.50fr carmine	.75	.15
220 A75	3.50fr dk ol grn	.30	.15
221 A75	5fr orange	.55	.15
222 A75	6fr brt ultra	.55	.15
223 A75	7fr black	.55	.15
224 A75	10fr dp brown	.65	.15
225 A76	20fr plum & blk	7.00	.65
Nos. 207-225 (19)		13.45	
Set value			2.35

Miniature sheets of Nos. 193, 194, 197, 200, 211, 214, 217 and 219 were printed in 1944 by the Belgian Government in London and given to the Belgian political review, Message, which distributed them to its subscribers, one a month. Value per sheet, about $12.50.
Remainders of these eight miniature sheets received marginal overprints in various colors in 1950, specifying a surtax of 100fr per sheet and paying tribute to the UPU. These sheets, together with four of Ruanda-Urundi, were sold by the Committee of Cultural Works (and not at post offices) in sets of 12 for 1,217.15 francs. Set value, about $150.
Nos. 187-227 imperforate had no franking value.
For surcharges see Nos. B34-B37.

Congo Woman — A77   Askari — A78

1943, Jan. 1

226 A77	50fr ultra & blk	6.50	.40
227 A78	100fr car & blk	7.50	.60

Slaves and Arab Guards A79

Auguste Lambermont A80

Design: 10fr, Leopold II.

Perf. 13x11½, 12½x12

1947	Engr.		Unwmk.
228 A79	1.25fr black brown	.25	.15
229 A80	3.50fr dark blue	.40	.15
230 A80	10fr red orange	.75	.15
Nos. 228-230 (3)		1.40	
Set value			.30

50th anniv. of the abolition of slavery in Belgian Congo. See Nos. 261-262.

Baluba Carving of Former King — A82

Carved Figures and Masks of Baluba Tribe: 10c, 50c, 2fr, "Ndoha," figure of tribal king. 15c, 70c, 1.20fr, 2.50fr, "Tshimanyi," an idol. 20c, 75c, 1.60fr, 3.50fr, "Buangakokoma," statue of kneeling beggar. 25c, 1fr, 2.40fr, 5fr, "Mbuta," sacred double cup, carved with two faces, Man and Woman. 40c, 1.25fr, 6fr, 8fr, "Ngadimuashi," female mask. 1.50fr, 3fr, 10fr, 50fr, "Buadi-Muadi," mask with squared features. 6.50fr, 20fr, 100fr, "Mbowa," executioner's mask with buffalo horns.

1947-50   Perf. 12½

231 A82	10c dp org ('48)	.15	.15
232 A82	15c ultra ('48)	.15	.15
233 A82	20c brt bl ('48)	.15	.15
234 A82	25c rose car ('48)	.20	.15
235 A82	40c violet ('48)	.15	.15
236 A82	50c olive grn	.15	.15
237 A82	70c yel grn ('48)	.15	.15
238 A82	75c magenta ('48)	.15	.15
239 A82	1fr yel org & dk vio	1.50	.15
240 A82	1.20fr gray & brn ('50)	.20	.15
241 A82	1.25fr lt bl grn & mag ('48)	.30	.15
242 A82	1.50fr ol & mag ('50)	14.00	1.10
243 A82	1.60fr bl gray & brt bl ('50)	.40	.15
244 A82	2fr org & mag ('48)	.20	.15
245 A82	2.40fr bl grn & dk grn ('50)	.30	.15
246 A82	2.50fr brn red & bl grn ('48)	4.25	.15
247 A82	3fr lt ultra & ind ('49)	4.25	.15
248 A82	3.50fr lt bl & blk ('48)	3.50	.15
249 A82	5fr bis & mag ('48)	1.25	.15
250 A82	6fr brn org & ind ('48)	1.40	.15
251 A82	6.50fr red org & red brn ('49)	1.90	.15
252 A82	8fr gray bl & dk grn ('50)	1.25	.15
253 A82	10fr pale vio & red brn ('48)	4.00	.15
254 A82	20fr red org & vio brn ('48)	1.90	.15
255 A82	50fr dp org & blk ('48)	3.75	.15
256 A82	100fr crim bl & brn ('48)	4.00	.30
Nos. 231-256 (26)		45.65	
Set value			3.75

Railroad Train and Map — A83

1948, July 1   Unwmk.   Perf. 13½

257 A83	2.50fr dp bl & grn	1.00	.15

50th anniv. of railway service in the Congo.

Globe and Ship — A84

1949, Nov. 21   Perf. 11½

Granite Paper

258 A84	4fr violet blue	.85	.15

75th anniv. of the UPU.

Allegorical Figure and Map — A85

1950, Aug. 12   Perf. 12x12½

259 A85	3fr blue & indigo	1.75	.15
260 A85	6.50fr car rose & blk brn	2.00	.25

Establishment of Katanga Province, 50th anniv.

Portrait Type of 1947

1.50fr, Cardinal Lavigerie. 3fr, Baron Dhanis.

Perf. 12½x12

1951, June 25			Unwmk.
261 A80	1.50fr purple	2.00	.25
262 A80	3fr black brown	2.00	.15

Littonia — A86

St. Francis Xavier — A86a

1952-53   Photo.   Perf. 11½

Granite Paper

Flowers in Natural Colors

Size: 21x25½mm

263 A86	10c Dissotis	.15	.15
264 A86	15c Protea	.15	.15
265 A86	20c Vellozia	.15	.15
266 A86	25c shown	.15	.15
267 A86	40c Ipomoea	.20	.15
268 A86	50c Angraecum	.15	.15
269 A86	60c Euphorbia	.15	.15
270 A86	75c Ochna	.15	.15
271 A86	1fr Hibiscus	.15	.15
272 A86	1.25fr Protea ('53)	.65	.45
273 A86	1.50fr Schrizoglossum	.15	.15
274 A86	2fr Ansellia	.25	.15
275 A86	3fr Costus	.25	.15
276 A86	4fr Nymphaea	.30	.15
277 A86	5fr Thunbergia	.45	.15
278 A86	6.50fr Thonningia	.55	.15
279 A86	7fr Gerbera	.55	.15
280 A86	8fr Gloriosa ('53)	.90	.15
281 A86	10fr Silene ('53)	1.65	.15
282 A86	20fr Aristolochia	1.40	.15

Size: 22x32mm

283 A86	50fr Eulophia ('53)	7.00	.45
284 A86	100fr Crytosepalum ('53)	11.00	1.00
Nos. 263-284 (22)		26.50	
Set value			2.90

Nos. 264, 269 and 270 with additional surcharges are varieties of Congo Democratic Republic Nos. 324, 327 and 328.

1953, Jan. 5   Engr.   Perf. 12½x13

285 A86a	1.50fr ultra & gray blk	.75	.30

400th death anniv. of St. Francis Xavier.

Canoe on Lake Kivu — A87

1953, Jan. 5 — *Perf. 14*
286 A87 3fr car & blk — 1.25 .20
287 A87 7fr dp bl & brn org — 1.25 .25
Issued to publicize the Kivu Festival, 1953.

Royal Colonial Institute Jubilee Medal A88

Design: 6.50fr, Same with altered background and transposed inscriptions.

1954, Dec. 27　Photo. — *Perf. 13½*
288 A88 4.50fr indigo & gray — 1.10 .28
289 A88 6.50fr dk grn & brn — .90 .15
25th anniv. of the founding of the Belgian Royal Colonial Institute.

King Baudouin and Tropical Scene — A89

Designs: King and various views.

Inscribed "Congo Belge-Belgisch Congo"
Engr.; Portrait Photo.
1955, Feb. 15　Unwmk. — *Perf. 11½*
Portrait in Black
290 A89 1.50fr rose car — .70 .25
291 A89 3fr green — .25 .15
292 A89 4.50fr ultra — .30 .15
293 A89 6.50fr dp claret — .55 .15

Inscribed "Belgisch Congo-Congo Belge"
294 A89 1.50fr rose car — .30 .16
295 A89 3fr green — .25 .15
296 A89 4.50fr ultra — .30 .15
297 A89 6.50fr deep claret — .55 .15
　Nos. 290-297 (8) — 3.20
　Set value — .90

Map of Africa and Emblem of Royal Touring Club — A90

1955, July 26　Engr. — *Perf. 11½*
Inscription in French
298 A90 6.50fr vio blue — 3.25 .25
Inscription in Flemish
299 A90 6.50fr vio blue — 3.25 .25
5th International Congress of African Tourism, Elisabethville, July 26-Aug. 4. Nos. 298-299 printed in alternate rows.

Kings of Belgium A91

1958, July 1　Unwmk. — *Perf. 12½*
300 A91 1fr rose vio — .22 .15
301 A91 1.50fr ultra — .22 .15
302 A91 3fr rose car — .22 .15
303 A91 5fr green — .70 .32
304 A91 6.50fr brn red — .45 .15
305 A91 10fr dl vio — .65 .15
　Nos. 300-305 (6) — 2.46
　Set value — .73
Belgium's annexation of Congo, 50th anniv.

Roan Antelope — A92　　Black Buffaloes — A93

Animals: 20c, White rhinoceros. 40c, Giraffe. 50c, Thick-tailed bushbaby. 1fr, Gorilla. 2fr, Black-and-white colobus (monkey). 3fr, Elephants. 5fr, Okapis. 6.50fr, Impala. 8fr, Giant pangolin. 10fr, Eland and zebras.

1959, Oct. 15　Photo. — *Perf. 11½*
Granite Paper
306 A92 10c bl & brn — .15 .15
307 A93 20c red org & slate — .15 .15
308 A92 40c brn & bl — .15 .15
309 A93 50c brt ultra, red & sep — .15 .15
310 A92 1fr brn, grn & blk — .15 .15
311 A93 1.50fr blk & org yel — .15 .15
312 A92 2fr crim, blk & brn — .15 .15
313 A93 3fr blk, gray & lil rose — .25 .15
314 A92 5fr brn, dk brn & brt grn — .40 .20
315 A93 6.50fr bl, brn & org yel — .45 .15
316 A92 8fr org brn, ol bis & lil — .50 .30
317 A93 10fr multi — .60 .15
　Set value — 2.80 1.30

Madonna and Child — A94

1959, Dec. 1　Unwmk. — *Perf. 11½*
318 A94 50c golden brn, ocher & red brn — .15 .15
319 A94 1fr dk bl, pur & red brn — .15 .15
320 A94 2fr gray, brt bl & red brn — .20 .15
　Set value — .40 .25

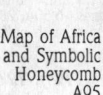

Map of Africa and Symbolic Honeycomb A95

1960, Feb. 19　Unwmk. — *Perf. 11½*
Inscription in French
321 A95 3fr gray & red — .25 .15
Inscription in Flemish
322 A95 3fr gray & red — .25 .15
Commission for Technical Co-operation in Africa South of the Sahara (C. C. T. A.), 10th anniv.

SEMI-POSTAL STAMPS

Types of 1910-15 Issues Surcharged in Red　✚ 10ᶜ

1918, May 15　Unwmk. — *Perf. 14, 15*
B1 A29 5c + 10c grn & bl — .15 .20
B2 A30 10c + 15c car & bl (I) — .15 .20
B3 A21 15c + 20c bl grn & bl — .15 .20
B4 A31 25c + 25c dp bl & pale bl — .20 .20
B5 A23 40c + 40c brn red & bl — .40 .40
B6 A24 50c + 50c brn lake & bl — .40 .40
B7 A25 1fr + 1fr ol bis & bl — 2.00 2.00
B8 A27 5fr + 5fr ocher & bl — 11.00 11.00
B9 A28 10fr + 10fr grn & bl — 85.00 85.00
　Nos. B1-B9 (9) — 99.45 99.60
The position of the cross and the added value varies on the different stamps.
Nos. B1-B9 exist imperforate.

Design: #B11 inscribed "Belgisch Congo."

1925, July 8 — *Perf. 12½*
B10 SP1 25c + 25c carmine & blk — .20 .25
B11 SP1 25c + 25c carmine & blk — .20 .25
　a. Pair, Nos. B10-B11 — .35 .35
Colonial campaigns in 1914-1918. The surtax helped erect at Kinshasa a monument to those who died in World War I.

Nurse Weighing Child — SP3

First Aid Station — SP5

20c+10c, Missionary & Child. 60c+30c, Congo hospital. 1fr+50c, Dispensary service. 1.75fr+75c, Convalescent area. 3.50fr+1.50fr, Instruction on bathing infant. 5fr+2.50fr, Operating room. 10fr+5fr, Students.

1930, Jan. 16　Engr. — *Perf. 11½*
B12 SP3 10c + 5c ver — .55 .55
B13 SP3 20c + 10c dp brn — .70 .70
B14 SP5 35c + 15c dp grn — 1.25 1.25
B15 SP5 60c + 30c dl vio — 1.50 1.50
B16 SP3 1fr + 50c dk car — 2.25 2.25
B17 SP5 1.75fr + 75c dp bl — 4.25 4.50
B18 SP5 3.50fr + 1.50fr rose lake — 8.50 8.50
B19 SP5 5fr + 2.50fr red brn — 7.50 7.50
B20 SP5 10fr + 5fr gray blk — 8.50 8.50
　Nos. B12-B20 (9) — 35.00 35.25
The surtax was intended to aid welfare work among the natives, especially the children.

Nos. 161, 163 Surcharged "+50c" in Blue or Red

1936, May 15 — *Perf. 12½x12*
B21 A63 1.50fr + 50c (Bl) — 2.50 3.00
B22 A63 2.50fr + 50c (R) — 2.00 2.00
Surtax was for the King Albert Memorial Fund.

Queen Astrid with Congolese Children — SP12

1936, Aug. 29　Photo. — *Perf. 12½*
B23 SP12 1.25fr + 5c dark brown — .40 .35
B24 SP12 1.50fr + 10c dull rose — .40 .35
B25 SP12 2.50fr + 25c dark blue — .60 .60
　Nos. B23-B25 (3) — 1.40 1.30
Issued in memory of Queen Astrid. The surtax was for the aid of the National League for Protection of Native Children.

National Park Type of 1937-38 Souvenir Sheet
1938, Oct. 3 — *Perf. 11½*
B26 Sheet of 6 — 18.00 18.00
　a. A64 5c ultra & light brown — 3.00 3.00
　b. A65 90c ultra & light brown — 3.00 3.00
　c. A66 1.50fr ultra & light brown — 3.00 3.00
　d. A67 2.40fr ultra & light brown — 3.00 3.00
　e. A68 2.50fr ultra & light brown — 3.00 3.00
　f. A69 4.50fr ultra & light brown — 3.00 3.00
Intl. Tourist Cong. The star is printed in yellow. A surtax of 3.15fr was for the benefit of the Congo Tourist Service.

Marabou Storks and Vultures — SP14　　Buffon's Kob — SP15

Designs: 1.50fr+1.50fr, Pygmy chimpanzees. 4.50fr+4.50fr, Dwarf crocodiles. 5fr+5fr, Lioness.

1939　Photo. — *Perf. 14*
B27 SP14 1fr + 1fr dp claret — 5.50 5.50
B28 SP15 1.25fr + 1.25fr car — 5.50 5.50
B29 SP15 1.50fr + 1.50fr brt pur — 7.50 7.50
B30 SP14 4.50fr + 4.50fr sl grn — 5.50 5.50
B31 SP15 5fr + 5fr brown — 6.00 6.00
　Nos. B27-B31 (5) — 30.00 30.00
Surtax for the Leopoldville Zoological Gardens. Sold in full sets by subscription.

> Catalogue values for unused stamps in this section, from this point to the end of the section, are for Never Hinged items.

Lion of Belgium and Inscription "Belgium Shall Rise Again" — SP19

1942, Feb. 17　Engr. — *Perf. 12½*
B32 SP19 10fr + 40fr brt grn — 1.50 1.00
B33 SP19 10fr + 40fr vio bl — 1.50 1.00

Nos. 193, 216, 198 and 220 Surcharged in Red

Au profit de la Croix Rouge ✚ 50 Fr. Ten voordeele van het Roode Kruis
a

Ten voordeele van het Roode Kruis ✚ 100 Fr. Au profit de la Croix Rouge
b

Au profit de la Croix Rouge ✚ 100 Fr. Ten voordeele van het Roode Kruis
c

1945
B34 A72 (a) 50c + 50fr — 2.00 2.00
B35 A73 (b) 1.25fr + 100fr — 2.00 2.00
B36 A74 (c) 1.75fr + 100fr — 2.00 2.25
B37 A75 (b) 3.50fr + 100fr — 2.00 2.25
　Nos. B34-B37 (4) — 8.00 8.50
The surtax was for the Red Cross. Sold in full sets by subscription.

Mozart at Age 7 — SP20

Queen Elisabeth and Sonata by Mozart — SP21

1956, Oct. 10　Unwmk. — *Perf. 11½* — **Engr.**
B38 SP20 4.50fr + 1.50fr brt lil — 2.00 1.50
B39 SP21 6.50fr + 2.50fr ultra — 3.00 2.50
200th anniv. of the birth of Wolfgang Amadeus Mozart.
The surtax was for the Pro-Mozart Committee.

Brussels Print
Thick or Thin Paper

1865-66   **Perf. 15, 14½x14**

18	A3	10c slate ('66)	125.00	1.50
a.		Pair, imperf. between	—	
19	A3a	20c blue ('66)	175.00	1.50
a.		20c lilac blue	190.00	1.75
20	A4	30c brown	425.00	11.00
a.		Pair, imperf. between	1,000.	
21	A4a	40c rose ('66)	450.00	20.00
22	A5	1fr violet	1,900.	90.00

Nos. 18 to 22 on thin paper are perf. 14½x14; on thick paper, perf. 15.
The reprints are on thin paper, imperforate and ungummed.

Coat of Arms — A6

1866-67   **Imperf.**

23	A6	1c gray	250.00	150.00

Perf. 15, 14½x14

24	A6	1c gray	45.00	16.00
25	A6	2c blue ('67)	135.00	90.00
a.		2c ultramarine	150.00	110.00
26	A6	5c brown	150.00	90.00

Nos. 23-26 were valid for postage on newspapers and printed matter only.
Nos. 24 to 26 on thin paper are perf. 14½ x 14; on thick paper, perf. 15.
Counterfeits exist.
Reprints of Nos. 24 to 26 are on thin paper, imperforate and ungummed.

Imperf. varieties of 1869-1912 (between Nos. 28-105) are without gum.

A7   A8   A9

A10   A11   A12

King Leopold II
A13   A14   A15

1869-70   **Perf. 15**

28	A7	1c green	6.00	.30
29	A7	2c ultra ('70)	20.00	1.50
30	A7	5c buff ('70)	45.00	.70
31	A7	8c lilac ('70)	80.00	50.00
32	A8	10c green	20.00	.40
33	A9	20c lt ultra ('70)	140.00	.75
34	A10	30c buff ('70)	80.00	4.00
35	A11	40c brt rose ('70)	110.00	6.00
36	A12	1fr dull lilac ('70)	350.00	17.00
a.		1fr rose lilac	350.00	20.00
		Nos. 28-36 (9)	851.00	80.65

The frames and inscriptions of Nos. 30, 31 and 42 differ slightly from the illustration.
Minor "broken letter" varieties exist on several values.
Nos. 28-30, 32-33, 35-38 also were printed in aniline colors. These are not valued separately.
See Nos. 40-43, 49-51, 55.

1875-78

37	A13	25c olive bister	135.00	1.25
a.		25c ocher	135.00	1.50
38	A14	50c gray	200.00	8.50
		Roller cancel		12.50
a.		50c gray black	325.00	55.00
b.		50c deep black	1,750.	175.00
39	A15	5fr dp red brown	1,500.	1,150.
		Roller cancel		525.00
a.		5fr pale brown ('78)	3,750.	1,250.
		Roller cancel		500.00

Dangerous counterfeits of No. 39 exist.

Printed in Aniline Colors

1881   **Perf. 14**

40	A7	1c gray green	20.00	.60
41	A7	2c lt ultra	12.50	2.25
42	A7	5c orange buff	57.50	1.10
a.		5c red orange	57.50	1.10
43	A8	10c gray green	30.00	.80
44	A13	25c olive bister	75.00	1.75
		Nos. 40-44 (5)	195.00	6.50

See note following No. 36.

A16   A17

A18   A19

1883

45	A16	10c carmine	27.50	2.00
46	A17	20c gray	115.00	5.00
47	A18	25c blue	260.00	35.00
		Roller cancel		15.00
48	A19	50c violet	260.00	35.00
		Roller cancel		15.00

A20   A21

A22

1884-85   **Perf. 14**

49	A7	1c olive green	10.00	.85
50	A7	1c gray	3.75	.15
51	A7	5c green	25.00	.20
52	A20	10c rose, *bluish*	7.25	.35
a.		Grayish paper	8.00	.45
c.		Yellowish paper	175.00	20.00
53	A21	25c blue, *pink* ('85)	10.00	.75
54	A22	1fr brown, *grnsh*	575.00	17.50

The frame and inscription of No. 51 differ slightly from the illustration.
See note after No. 36.

A23   A24

A25   A26

1886-91

55	A7	2c purple brn ('88)	12.00	1.00
56	A23	20c olive, *grnsh*	125.00	1.00
57	A24	35c vio brn, *brnsh* ('91)	18.00	2.75
58	A25	50c bister, *yelsh*	9.50	2.00
59	A26	2fr violet, *pale lil*	90.00	40.00
		Roller cancel		6.00

Coat of Arms   King Leopold
A27   A28

1893-1900

60	A27	1c gray	1.10	.20
61	A27	2c yellow	1.25	1.10
a.		Wmkd. coat of arms in sheet ('95)	—	
62	A27	2c violet brn ('94)	1.65	.25
63	A27	2c red brown ('98)	3.25	.35
64	A27	5c yellow grn	5.00	.25
65	A28	10c orange brn	5.00	.25
66	A28	10c brt rose ('00)	3.50	.25
67	A28	20c olive green	22.50	.55
68	A28	25c ultra	20.00	.45
a.		No ball to "5" in upper left corner	32.50	12.00
69	A28	35c violet brn	37.50	1.25
a.		35c red brown	42.50	1.65
70	A28	50c bister	62.50	20.00
71	A28	50c gray ('97)	57.50	2.25
72	A28	1fr car, *lt grn*	75.00	20.00
73	A28	10c orange ('00)	105.00	5.00
74	A28	2fr lilac, *rose*	110.00	82.50
75	A28	2fr lilac ('00)	150.00	13.50

Values quoted for Nos. 60-107 are for stamps with label attached. Stamps without label sell for much less.

Antwerp Exhibition Issue

Arms of Antwerp — A29

1894

76	A29	5c green, *rose*	4.75	3.25
77	A29	10c carmine, *bluish*	3.75	2.25
78	A29	25c blue, *rose*	1.00	1.00
		Nos. 76-78 (3)	9.50	6.50

Brussels Exhibition Issue

St. Michael and Satan
A30   A31

1896-97   **Perf. 14x14½**

79	A30	5c deep violet	1.00	.40
80	A31	10c orange brown	8.50	3.25
81	A31	10c lilac brown	.50	.35
		Nos. 79-81 (3)	10.00	4.00

A32   A33

A34   A35

A36   A37

A38   A39

Two types of 1c:

I - Periods after "Dimanche" and "Zondag" in label.

II - No period after "Dimanche." Period often missing after "Zondag."

1905-07			Perf. 14	
82	A32	1c gray (I) ('07)	1.50	.20
a.		Type II ('08)	2.00	.25
83	A32	2c red brown ('07)	11.00	5.50
84	A32	5c green ('07)	9.00	.50
85	A33	10c dull rose	1.75	.20
86	A34	20c olive grn	18.00	.90
87	A35	25c ultra	10.00	.75
a.		25c deep blue	13.50	1.25
88	A36	35c purple brn	20.00	1.90
89	A37	50c bluish gray	70.00	2.50
90	A38	1fr yellow orange	100.00	8.50
91	A39	2fr violet	70.00	22.50
		Bar cancellation		4.00
		Nos. 82-91 (10)	311.25	43.45

A40   A41

Lion of Belgium — A42   A43

King Albert I — A44

1912				
92	A40	1c orange	.20	.15
93	A41	2c orange brn	.45	.50
94	A42	5c green	.35	.15
95	A43	10c red	1.00	.40
96	A43	20c olive grn	8.50	1.75
97	A43	35c bister brn	1.25	.80
98	A43	40c green	13.00	8.75
99	A43	50c gray	1.25	1.00
100	A43	1fr orange	6.00	5.50
101	A43	2fr violet	14.00	15.00
102	A44	5fr plum	90.00	24.00
		Nos. 92-102 (11)	136.00	58.00

Counterfeits exist of Nos. 97-102. Those of No. 102 are common.

For overprints see Nos. Q49-Q50, Q52, Q55-Q55A, Q57-Q60.

A45

1912-13				
Larger Head				
103	A45	10c red	.35	.20
a.		Without engraver's name	.25	.15
104	A45	20c olive grn ('13)	.50	.50
a.		Without engraver's name	1.10	1.10
105	A45	25c ultra	.35	.45
a.		With engraver's name	2.75	1.90
107	A45	40c green ('13)	.60	.75
		Nos. 103-107 (4)	1.80	1.90

For overprints see #Q51, Q53-Q54, Q56.

Albert I   Cloth Hall of Ypres
A46   A47

Bridge of Dinant — A48

Library of Louvain — A49

Scheldt River at Antwerp A50

Anti-slavery Campaign in the Congo — A51

King Albert I at Furnes — A52

Kings of Belgium Leopold I, Albert I, Leopold II A53

1915-20			Typo.	Perf. 14, 14½
108	A46	1c orange	.15	.15
109	A46	2c chocolate	.15	.15
110	A46	3c gray blk ('20)	.20	.15
111	A46	5c green	.40	.15
112	A46	10c carmine	.75	.15
113	A46	15c purple	.90	.15
114	A46	20c red violet	.90	.15
115	A46	25c blue	1.10	.20

			Engr.	
116	A47	35c brown org & blk	.75	.20
117	A48	40c green & black	1.25	.20
a.		Vert. pair, imperf. btwn.		
118	A49	50c car rose & blk	4.00	.25
119	A50	1fr violet	15.00	.40
120	A51	2fr slate	20.00	1.50
121	A52	5fr dp blue	200.00	80.00
		Telegraph or railroad cancel		55.00
122	A53	10fr brown	20.00	17.50
		Nos. 108-122 (15)	265.55	101.30

Two types each of the 1c, 10c and 20c; three of the 2c and 15c; four of the 5c, differing in the top left corner.

Nos. 108-120, 122 exist imperforate. See No. 138. For surcharges see Nos. B34-B47.

Perron of Liege (Fountain) A54   King Albert in Trench Helmet A55

1919			Perf. 11½	
123	A54	25c deep blue	1.75	.30
a.		Sheet of 10	5,750.	5,750.

Perf. 11, 11½, 11½x11, 11x11½

1919				
		Size: 18½x22mm		
124	A55	1c lilac brn	.15	.15
125	A55	2c olive	.15	.15
		Size: 23x26mm		
126	A55	5c green	.20	.15
127	A55	10c carmine	.15	.15
128	A55	15c gray vio	.25	.20
129	A55	20c olive blk	.80	.95
130	A55	25c deep blue	.80	.65
131	A55	35c bister brn	1.50	1.50
132	A55	40c red	2.50	3.50
133	A55	50c red brn	8.50	10.00
134	A55	1fr lt orange	30.00	40.00
135	A55	2fr violet	375.00	375.00
		Size: 28x33½mm		
136	A55	5fr car lake	100.00	100.00
137	A55	10fr claret	110.00	110.00
		Nos. 124-137 (14)	630.00	642.40

Type of 1915 Inscribed: "FRANK" instead of "FRANKEN"

1919, Dec.			Perf. 14, 15	
138	A52	5fr deep blue	1.75	1.25

Town Hall at Termonde
A56   A57

1920			Perf. 11½	
139	A56	65c claret & black	1.10	.20
a.		Center inverted	25,000.	

For surcharge see No. 143.

Semi-Postal Stamps of 1920 Surcharged in Red or Black   **20ᶜ**   **20ᶜ**

1921			Perf. 12	
140	SP6	20c on 5c (R)	.60	.25
a.		Inverted surcharge	185.00	185.00
141	SP7	20c on 10c	.42	.15
142	SP8	20c on 15c (R)	.45	.25
a.		Inverted surcharge	185.00	185.00

Red Surcharge

143	A57	55c on 65c claret & blk	1.10	.35
a.		Pair, one without surcharge	1.75	.85
		Nos. 140-143 (4)	2.57	1.10

A58   A59

1922-27			Typo.	Perf. 14
144	A58	1c orange	.15	.15
145	A58	2c olive ('26)	.15	.15
146	A58	3c fawn	.15	.15
147	A58	5c gray	.15	.15
148	A58	10c blue grn	.15	.15
149	A58	15c plum ('23)	.15	.15
150	A58	20c black brn	.20	.15
151	A58	25c dull violet	.15	.15
152	A58	30c vermilion	.55	.15
153	A58	30c rose ('25)	.40	.15
154	A58	35c red brown	.35	.15
155	A58	35c blue grn ('27)	.60	.30
156	A58	40c rose	.55	.15
157	A58	50c bister ('25)	.55	.15
158	A58	60c olive brn ('27)	2.25	.15
159	A58	1.25fr dp blue ('26)	.65	.85
160	A58	1.50fr brt blue ('26)	1.60	.40
161	A58	1.75fr ultra ('27)	1.10	.15
a.		Tete beche pair	8.00	5.00
c.		Bklt. pane of 4 + 2 labels	40.00	
		Nos. 144-161 (18)	9.85	
		Set value		3.00

See Nos. 185-190. For overprints and surcharges see Nos. 191-195, 197, B56, O1-O6.

Perf. 11½, 11½x11, 11½x12, 11½x12½

1921-25				Engr.
162	A59	50c dull blue	.35	.15
163	A59	75c scarlet ('22)	.15	.15
164	A59	75c ultra ('24)	.50	.15
165	A59	1fr black brn ('22)	.90	.15

166	A59	1fr dk blue ('25)	.70	.15
167	A59	2fr dk green ('22)	.90	.30
168	A59	5fr brown vio ('23)	15.00	15.00
169	A59	10fr magenta ('22)	9.00	6.50
		Nos. 162-169 (8)	27.50	22.55

No. 162 measures 18x20¾mm and was printed in sheets of 100.

Philatelic Exhibition Issues

1921, May 26			Perf. 11½	
170	A59	50c dark blue	3.50	3.50
a.		Sheet of 25	225.00	200.00

No. 170 measures 17½x21¼mm, was printed in sheets of 25 and sold at the Philatelic Exhibition at Brussels.

The sheet normally has pin holes and a cancellation-like marking in the margin. These are considered unused and the condition valued here.

Souvenir Sheet

1924, May 24			Perf. 11½	
171		Sheet of 4	140.00	125.00
	A59	5fr red brown	12.00	12.00

Sold only at the Intl. Phil. Exhib., Brussels. Sheet size: 130x145mm.

The sheet normally has pin holes and a cancellation-like marking in the margin. These are considered unused and the condition valued here.

Kings Leopold I and Albert I — A60

1925			Perf. 14	
172	A60	10c dp green	5.75	6.25
173	A60	15c dull blue	3.75	4.50
174	A60	20c red brown	3.75	4.50
175	A60	25c grnsh black	3.75	4.50
176	A60	30c vermilion	3.75	4.50
177	A60	35c lt blue	3.75	4.50
178	A60	40c brnsh blk	3.75	4.50
179	A60	50c yellow brn	3.75	4.50
180	A60	75c dk blue	3.75	4.50
181	A60	1fr dk violet	5.75	6.75
182	A60	2fr ultra	3.75	4.50
183	A60	5fr blue blk	3.75	4.50
184	A60	10fr dp rose	6.00	8.00
		Nos. 172-184 (13)	55.00	66.00

75th anniv. of Belgian postage stamps.
Nos. 172-184 were sold only in sets and only by The Administration of Posts, not at post offices.

A61

1926-27			Typo.	
185	A61	75c dk violet	.75	.70
186	A61	1fr pale yellow	.65	.25
187	A61	1fr rose red ('27)	.85	.15
a.		Tete beche pair	8.25	5.00
c.		Bklt. pane 4 + 2 labels	25.00	
188	A61	2fr Prus blue	2.25	.15
189	A61	5fr emerald ('27)	15.00	1.00
190	A61	10fr dk brown ('27)	27.50	4.50
		Nos. 185-190 (6)	47.00	6.75

For overprints and surcharge see Nos. 196, Q174-Q175.

Stamps of 1921-27 Surcharged in Carmine, Red or Blue   **1ᶠ75**

1927				
191	A58	3c on 2c olive (C)	.15	.15
192	A58	10c on 15c plum (R)	.15	.15
193	A58	35c on 40c rose (Bl)	.50	.15
194	A58	1.75fr on 1.50fr brt bl (C)	2.50	.80
		Nos. 191-194 (4)	3.30	1.25

Nos. 153, 185 and 159 Surcharged in Black

BRUXELLES 1929 BRUSSEL **5ᶜ**

1929, Jan. 1

195	A58	5c on 30c rose	.15	.15
196	A61	5c on 75c dk violet	.30	.30
197	A58	5c on 1.25fr dp blue	.15	.15
		Nos. 195-197 (3)	.60	.60

The surcharge on Nos. 195 to 197 is a precancelation which alters the value of the stamp to which it is applied.

Values for precanceled stamps in unused column are for those which have not been through the post and have original gum. Values in second column are for postally used, gumless stamps.

A63   A64

1929-32   **Typo.**   **Perf. 14**

198	A63	1c orange	.15	.15
199	A63	2c emerald ('31)	.20	.35
200	A63	3c red brown	.15	.15
201	A63	5c slate	.15	.15
c.		Bklt. pane of 4 + 2 labels	8.25	
202	A63	10c olive grn	.15	.15
c.		Bklt. pane of 4 + 2 labels	4.50	
203	A63	20c brt violet	1.00	.15
204	A63	25c rose red	.45	.15
c.		Bklt. pane of 4 + 2 labels	8.25	
205	A63	35c green	.65	.15
c.		Bklt. pane of 4 + 2 labels	9.75	
206	A63	40c red vio ('30)	.30	.15
c.		Bklt. pane of 4 + 2 labels	9.75	
207	A63	50c dp blue	.50	.15
c.		Bklt. pane of 4 + 2 labels	8.25	
208	A63	60c rose ('30)	1.10	.20
c.		Bklt. pane of 4 + 2 labels	30.00	
209	A63	70c org brn ('30)	.70	.15
c.		Bklt. pane of 4 + 2 labels	22.50	
210	A63	75c dk blue ('30)	1.75	.15
211	A63	75c dp brown ('32)	6.00	.15
b.		Bklt. pane of 4 + 2 labels	100.00	
		Nos. 198-211 (14)	13.25	
		Set value		1.75

For overprints and surcharges see Nos. 225-226, 240-241, 254-256, 309, O7-O15.

Tete Beche Pairs

201a	A63	5c	1.00	.90
202a	A63	10c	.65	.60
204a	A63	25c	2.00	2.00
205a	A63	35c	3.00	3.00
206a	A63	40c	3.00	3.00
207a	A63	50c	2.50	2.50
208a	A63	60c	9.00	8.50
209a	A63	70c	6.50	5.50
210a	A63	75c	10.00	9.50
211a	A63	75c	32.50	27.50
		Nos. 201a-211a (10)	70.15	63.00

1929, Jan. 25   **Engr.**   **Perf. 14½, 14**

212	A64	10fr dk brown	15.00	4.50
213	A64	20fr dk green	85.00	16.00
214	A64	50fr red violet	7.50	9.00
a.		Perf. 14½	37.50	40.00
215	A64	100fr rose lake	14.00	15.00
a.		Perf. 14½	37.50	40.00
		Nos. 212-215 (4)	121.50	44.50

Peter Paul   Zenobe
Rubens — A65   Gramme — A66

1930, Apr. 26   **Photo.**   **Perf. 12½x12**

216	A65	35c blue green	.45	.25
217	A66	35c blue green	.45	.25

No. 216 issued for the Antwerp Exhibition, No. 217 the Liege Exhibition.

Leopold I, by   Leopold II, by
Jacques de   Joseph
Winne — A67   Lempoels — A68

Design: 1.75fr, Albert I.

1930, July 1   **Engr.**   **Perf. 11½**

218	A67	60c brown violet	.25	.15
219	A68	1fr carmine	1.25	1.25
220	A68	1.75fr dk blue	3.00	.95
		Nos. 218-220 (3)	4.50	2.35

Centenary of Belgian independence.
For overprints see Nos. 222-224.

Antwerp Exhibition Issue
Souvenir Sheet

Arms of
Antwerp — A70

1930, Aug. 9   **Perf. 11½**

221	A70	4fr Sheet of 1	175.00	175.00

Size: 142x141mm. Inscription in lower margin "ATELIER DU TIMBRE-1930-ZEGELFABRIEK." Each purchaser of a ticket to the Antwerp Phil. Exhib., Aug. 9-15, was allowed to purchase one stamps. The ticket cost 6 francs.

The sheet normally has pin holes and a cancellation-like marking in the margin. These are considered unused and the condition valued here.

Nos. 218-220
Overprinted in Blue or Red

B.I.T.
OCT. 1930

1930, Oct.

222	A67	60c brown vio (Bl)	1.75	1.50
223	A68	1fr carmine (Bl)	8.25	7.50
224	A68	1.75fr dk blue (R)	14.00	14.00
		Nos. 222-224 (3)	24.00	23.00

50th meeting of the administrative council of the Intl. Labor Bureau at Brussels.

The names of the painters and the initials of the engraver have been added at the foot of these stamps.

Stamps of 1929-30 Surcharged in Blue or Black:

BELGIQUE
1931
BELGIË
≡ 2c ≡

1931, Feb. 20   **Perf. 14**

225	A63	2c on 3c red brown (Bl)	.15	.15
226	A63	10c on 60c rose (Bk)	.50	.20

The surcharge on No. 226 is a precancelation which alters the denomination. See note after No. 197.

King Albert
A71   A71a

1931, June 15   **Photo.**

227	A71	1fr brown carmine	.85	.15

1932, June 1

228	A71a	75c bister brown	.65	.15
a.		Tete beche pair	11.00	11.00
c.		Bklt. pane 4 + 2 labels	27.50	

See No. 257. For overprint see No. O18.

A72   1fr, Belgian

1931-32   **Engr.**

229	A72	1.25fr gray black	.85	.35
230	A72	1.50fr brown vio	1.25	.30
231	A72	1.75fr dp blue	.90	.15
232	A72	2fr red brown	1.25	.15
233	A72	2.45fr dp violet	.75	.35
234	A72	2.50fr black brn ('32)	11.50	.35
235	A72	5fr dp green	12.50	.90
236	A72	10fr claret	30.00	11.00
		Nos. 229-236 (8)	60.00	13.50

Nos. 206 and 209 Surcharged as No. 226, but dated "1932"

1932, Jan. 1

240	A63	10c on 40c red vio	2.75	.30
241	A63	10c on 70c org brn	2.25	.20

See note after No. 197.

Gleaner   Mercury
A73   A74

1932, June 1   **Typo.**   **Perf. 13½x14**

245	A73	2c pale green	.15	.45
246	A74	5c dp orange	.15	.15
247	A73	10c olive grn	.25	.15
a.		Tete beche pair	4.50	4.50
c.		Bklt. pane 4 + 2 labels	15.00	
248	A74	20c brt violet	.45	.15
249	A73	25c deep red	.45	.15
a.		Tete beche pair	4.00	4.00
c.		Bklt. pane 4 + 2 labels	15.00	
250	A74	35c dp green	1.75	.15
		Nos. 245-250 (6)	3.20	
		Set value		.95

For overprints see Nos. O16-O17.

Auguste Piccard's
Balloon — A75

1932, Nov. 26   **Engr.**   **Perf. 11½**

251	A75	75c red brown	3.50	.30
252	A75	1.75fr dk blue	8.00	1.75
253	A75	2.50fr dk violet	10.00	8.50
		Nos. 251-253 (3)	21.50	10.55

Issued in commemoration of Prof. Auguste Piccard's two ascents to the stratosphere.

Nos. 206 and 209 Surcharged as No. 226, but dated "1933"

1933, Nov.   **Perf. 14**

254	A63	10c on 40c red vio	14.00	4.00
255	A63	10c on 70c org brn	11.00	1.50

No. 206 Surcharged as No. 226, but dated "1934"

1934, Feb.

256	A63	10c on 40c red vio	11.00	1.50

For Nos. 254 to 256 see note after No. 197. Regummed copies of Nos. 254-256 abound.

King Albert Memorial Issue
Type of 1932 with Black Margins

1934, Mar. 10   **Photo.**

257	A71a	75c black	.30	.15

See No. 228. For overprint see No. O18.

Congo Pavilion — A76

Designs: 1fr, Brussels pavilion. 1.50fr, "Old Brussels." 1.75fr, Belgian pavilion.

1934, July 1   **Perf. 14x13½**

258	A76	35c green	.50	.15
259	A76	1fr dk carmine	.65	.20
260	A76	1.50fr brown	1.75	.75
261	A76	1.75fr blue	4.00	1.25
		Nos. 258-261 (4)	6.90	1.25

Brussels Intl. Exhib. of 1935.

King Leopold III
A80   A81

1934-35   **Perf. 13½x14**

262	A80	70c ol blk ('35)	.35	.15
a.		Tete beche pair	1.75	1.00
c.		Bklt. pane 4 + 2 labels	6.25	
263	A80	75c brown	.70	.15

Perf. 14x13½

264	A81	1fr rose car ('35)	3.50	.35
		Nos. 262-264 (3)	4.55	
		Set value		.55

For overprint see No. O19.

Coat of Arms — A82

1935-48   **Typo.**   **Perf. 14**

265	A82	2c green ('37)	.15	.15
266	A82	5c orange	.15	.15
267	A82	10c olive bister	.15	.15
a.		Tete beche pair	.35	.30
b.		Bklt. pane 4 + 2 labels	4.50	
268	A82	15c dk violet	.15	.15
269	A82	20c lilac	.15	.15
270	A82	25c carmine rose	.15	.15
a.		Tete beche pair	.59	.45
c.		Bklt. pane 4 + 2 labels	4.50	
271	A82	25c yel org ('46)	.15	.15
272	A82	30c brown	.15	.15
273	A82	35c green	.15	.15
a.		Tete beche pair	.30	.20
c.		Bklt. pane 4 + 2 labels	3.00	
274	A82	40c red vio ('38)	.20	.15
275	A82	50c blue	.25	.15
276	A82	60c slate ('41)	.15	.15
277	A82	65c red lilac ('46)	.30	.15
278	A82	70c lt blue grn ('45)	.15	.15
279	A82	75c lilac rose ('45)	.25	.15
280	A82	80c green ('48)	3.50	.45
281	A82	90c dull vio ('46)	.20	.15
282	A82	1fr red brown ('45)	.15	.15
		Nos. 265-282 (18)	6.50	
		Set value		1.25

Several stamps of type A82 exist in various shades.

Nos. 265, 361 were privately overprinted and surcharged "+10FR." by the Association Belgo-Americaine for the dedication of the Bastogne Memorial, July 16, 1950. The overprint is in six types.

See design O1. For overprints and surcharges see Nos. 312-313, 361-364, 390-394, O20-O22, O24, O26-O28, O33.

A83   A83a

Perf. 14, 14x13½, 11½

1936-51   **Photo.**

Size: 17½x21¾mm

283	A83	70c brown	.35	.15
a.		Tete beche pair	.75	.65
c.		Bklt. pane 4 + 2 labels	7.50	

Size: 20¾x24mm

284	A83a	1fr rose car	.30	.15
285	A83a	1.20fr dk brown ('51)	.90	.15
286	A83a	1.50fr brt red vio ('43)	.25	.15
287	A83a	1.75fr dp ultra ('43)	.15	.20
288	A83a	1.75fr dk car ('50)	.15	.15
289	A83a	2fr dk pur ('43)	.90	.85
290	A83a	2.25fr grnsh blk ('43)	.25	.15
291	A83a	2.50fr org red ('51)	1.90	.15
292	A83a	3.25fr chestnut ('43)	.15	.15
293	A83a	5fr dp green ('43)	.90	.40
		Nos. 283-293 (11)	6.20	
		Set value		2.00

Nos. 287-288, 290-291, 293 inscribed "Belgie-Belgique."

See designs A85, A91. For overprints and surcharges see #314, O23, O25, O29, O31, O34.

A84   A85

1936-51   Engr.   Perf. 14x13½
294	A84	1.50fr rose lilac	.30	.15
295	A84	1.75fr dull blue	.20	.15
296	A84	2fr dull vio	.30	.15
297	A84	2.25fr gray vio ('41)	.25	.15
298	A84	2.45fr black	22.50	.15
299	A84	2.50fr ol blk ('40)	2.00	.25
300	A84	3.25fr org brn ('41)	.30	.15
301	A84	5fr dull green	1.50	.15
302	A84	10fr dk vio brn	.60	.15
a.		10fr light brown	22.50	.15
303	A84	20fr vermilion	1.00	.15

Perf. 11½
304	A84	3fr yel brn ('51)	.60	.15
305	A84	4fr bl, bluish ('50)	1.50	.15
a.		White paper	5.50	
306	A84	6fr brt rose car ('51)	3.00	.15
307	A84	10fr brn vio ('51)	.60	.15
308	A84	20fr red ('51)	1.25	.15
		Nos. 294-308 (15)	35.90	
		Set value		2.00

See No. 1159. For overprint and surcharges see Nos. 316-317, O32.

No. 206 Surcharged as No. 226, but dated "1937"

1937   Unwmk.   Perf. 14
309	A63	10c on 40c red vio	.15	.20

See note after No. 197.

1938-41   Photo.   Perf. 13½x14
310	A85	75c olive gray	.30	.15
a.		Tete beche pair	1.50	1.25
c.		Bklt. pane 4 + 2 labels	6.75	
311	A85	1fr rose pink ('41)	.15	.15
a.		Tete beche pair	.35	.25
b.		Booklet pane of 6	2.25	
c.		Bklt. pane 4 + 2 labels	2.25	
		Set value		.15

For overprints and surcharges see Nos. 315, O25, O30, O35.

Nos. 272, 274, 283, 310, 299, 298 Surcharged in Blue, Black, Carmine or Red

1938-42
312	A82 (a)	10c on 30c (Bl)	.15	.15
313	A82 (a)	10c on 40c (Bl)	.15	.15
314	A83 (b)	10c on 70c (Bk)	.15	.15
315	A85 (b)	50c on 75c (C)	.15	.15
316	A84 (c)	2.25fr on 2.50fr (C)	.40	.60
317	A84 (c)	2.50fr on 2.45fr (R)	12.00	.15
		Nos. 312-317 (6)	13.00	1.35

Issue date: No. 317, Oct. 31, 1938.

Basilica and Bell Tower — A86   Water Exhibition Buildings — A87

Designs: 1.50fr, Albert Canal and Park. 1.75fr, Eygenbilsen Cut in Albert Canal.

Perf. 14x13½, 13½x14
1938, Oct. 31
318	A86	35c dk blue grn	.15	.15
319	A87	1fr rose red	.50	.20
320	A87	1.50fr vio brn	1.25	.70
321	A87	1.75fr ultra	1.40	.20
		Nos. 318-321 (4)	3.30	1.25

Intl. Water Exhibition, Liège, 1939.

> Catalogue values for unused stamps in this section, from this point to the end of the section, are for Never Hinged items.

Lion Rampant A90   Leopold III, Crown and V A91

1944   Unwmk.   Photo.   Perf. 12½
Inscribed: "Belgique-Belgie"
322	A90	5c chocolate	.15	.15
323	A90	10c green	.15	.15
324	A90	25c lt blue	.15	.15
325	A90	35c brown	.15	.15
326	A90	50c lt bl grn	.15	.15
327	A90	75c purple	.15	.15
328	A90	1fr vermilion	.15	.15
329	A90	1.25fr chestnut	.20	.15
330	A90	1.50fr orange	.45	.40
331	A90	1.75fr brt ultra	.15	.15
332	A90	2fr aqua	3.75	1.90
333	A90	2.75fr dp mag	.20	.15
334	A90	3fr claret	.75	.60
335	A90	3.50fr sl blk	.75	.60
336	A90	5fr dk olive	6.75	4.75
337	A90	10fr black	1.25	1.10
		Nos. 322-337 (16)	15.30	10.85

Inscribed: "Belgie-Belgique"
338	A90	5c chocolate	.15	.15
339	A90	10c green	.15	.15
340	A90	25c lt bl	.15	.15
341	A90	35c brown	.15	.15
342	A90	50c lt bl grn	.15	.15
343	A90	75c purple	.15	.15
344	A90	1fr vermilion	.15	.20
345	A90	1.25fr chestnut	.15	.20
346	A90	1.50fr orange	.30	.45
347	A90	1.75fr brt ultra	.15	.15
348	A90	2fr aqua	2.00	2.00
349	A90	2.75fr dp magenta	.20	.15
350	A90	3fr claret	.65	.75
351	A90	3.50fr slate blk	.65	.75
352	A90	5fr dark olive	5.75	5.00
353	A90	10fr black	1.00	1.25
		Nos. 338-353 (16)	11.90	11.75

1944-57   Perf. 14x13½
354	A91	1fr brt rose red	.35	.15
355	A91	1.50fr magenta	.50	.15
356	A91	1.75fr dp ultra	.50	.55
357	A91	2fr dp vio	1.50	.15
358	A91	2.25fr grnsh blk	.55	.65
359	A91	3.25fr chnt brn	.75	.15
360	A91	5fr dk bl grn	3.00	.15
a.		Perf. 11½ ('57)	75.00	.15
		Nos. 354-360 (7)	7.15	
		Set value		1.50

Nos. 355, 357, 359 inscribed "Belgique-Belgie." For surcharges see Nos. 365-367 and footnote following No. 367.

Stamps of 1935-41 Overprinted in Red

V

1944   Perf. 14
361	A82	2c pale green	.15	.15
362	A82	15c indigo	.15	.15
363	A82	20c brt violet	.15	.15
364	A82	60c slate	.25	.15
		Set value		.50	.35

See note following No. 282.

Nos. 355, 357, and 360 Surcharged Typographically in Black or Carmine   **—10%**

1946   Perf. 14x13½
365	A91	On 1.50fr magenta	.40	.15
366	A91	On 2fr dp vio (C)	1.50	.45
367	A91	On 5fr dk bl grn (C)	2.00	.30
		Nos. 365-367 (3)	3.90	.90

To provide denominations created by a reduction in postal rates, the Government produced Nos. 365-367 by surcharging typographically. Also, each post office was authorized on May 20, 1946, to surcharge its stock of 1.50fr, 2fr and 5fr stamps "-10 percent." Hundreds of types and sizes of this surcharge exist, both hand-stamped and typographed. These include the "1,35," "1,80" and "4,50" applied at Ghislenghien.

M. S. Prince Baudouin — A92

2.25fr, S.S. Marie Henriette. 3.15fr, S.S. Diamant.

Perf. 14x13½, 13½x14
1946, June 15   Photo.   Unwmk.
368	A92	1.35fr brt bluish grn	.15	.15
369	A92	2.25fr slate green	.30	.15
370	A92	3.15fr slate black	.30	.15
		Nos. 368-370 (3)	.75	.45

Centenary of the steamship line between Ostend and Dover.
#368 exists in two sizes: 21¼x18¼mm and 21x17mm. #369-370 are 24½x20mm.

Capt. Adrien de Gerlache A95   Belgica and Explorers A96

1947, June   Perf. 14x13½, 11½
371	A95	1.35fr crimson rose	.45	.15
372	A96	2.25fr gray black	2.75	2.00

50th anniv. of Capt. Adrien de Gerlache's Antarctic Expedition.

Joseph A. F. Plateau — A97

1947, June   Perf. 14x13½
373	A97	3.15fr deep blue	.80	.15

Issued to mark the World Film and Fine Arts Festival, Brussels, June, 1947.

Chemical Industry — A98   Industrial Arts — A99

Agriculture — A100   Textile Industry — A102

Communications Center — A101

Iron Manufacture A103

Photogravure (#374-376, 378), Typographed (#377, 380), Engraved
1948   Unwmk.   Perf. 11½
374	A98	60c blue grn	.85	.20
375	A98	1.20fr brown	2.25	.15
376	A99	1.35fr red brown	.85	.15
377	A100	1.75fr brt red	1.65	.15
378	A99	1.75fr dk gray grn	1.10	.15
379	A101	2.25fr gray blue	2.00	1.75
380	A100	2.50fr dk car rose	6.75	.20
381	A101	3fr brt red vio	9.00	.30
382	A102	3.15fr deep blue	2.00	.20
383	A102	4fr brt ultra	8.25	.20
384	A103	6fr blue green	13.00	.20
385	A103	6.30fr brt red vio	4.00	3.75
		Nos. 374-385 (12)	51.70	7.40

See Nos. O42-O46.

Leopold I — A104

1949, July 1   Engr.   Perf. 14x13½
386	A104	90c dk green	1.10	.60
387	A104	1.75fr brown	.90	.15
388	A104	3fr red	3.50	3.00
389	A104	4fr deep blue	5.00	1.25
		Nos. 386-389 (4)	10.50	5.00

Cent. of Belgium's 1st postage stamps. See note on souvenir sheet below No. 2.

Stamps of 1935-45 Precanceled and Surcharged in Black

1949   Perf. 14
390	A82	5c on 15c dk vio	.15	.15
391	A82	5c on 30c brown	.15	.15
392	A82	5c on 40c red vio	.15	.15
393	A82	20c on 70c lt bl grn	.30	.35
394	A82	20c on 75c lil rose	.20	.15

Similar Surcharge and Precancellation in Black on Nos. B455-B458
Perf. 14x13½
395	SP251	10c on #B455	3.50	3.00
396	SP251	40c on #B456	1.10	.85
397	SP251	80c on #B457	.65	.50
398	SP251	1.20fr on #B458	2.25	1.50
		Nos. 390-398 (9)	8.45	6.80

See note after No. 197.

St. Mary Magdalene, from Painting by Gerard David — A105

1949, July 15   Photo.   Perf. 11
399	A105	1.75fr dark brown	.70	.35

Gerard David Exhibition at Bruges, 1949.

Allegory of UPU — A106

1949, Oct. 1   Engr.   Perf. 11½
400	A106	4fr deep blue	4.50	2.50

75th anniv. of the UPU.

Symbolical of
Pension Fund
A107

Lion
Rampant
A108

Perf. 11½

1950, May 1   Unwmk.   Photo.
401 A107 1.75fr dark brown   .50 .25
General Pension Fund founding, cent.

1951, Feb. 15   Engr.   Perf. 11½
402 A108 20c blue   .25 .15

1951-75   Typo.   Perf. 13½x14
Size: 17½x21mm
403 A108 2c org brn ('60)   .15 .15
404 A108 3c brt lil ('60)   .15 .15
405 A108 5c pale violet   .15 .15
406 A108 5c brt pink ('74)   .15 .15
407 A108 10c red orange   .15 .15
408 A108 15c brt pink ('59)   .15 .15
409 A108 20c claret   .15 .15
410 A108 25c green   1.75 .25
411 A108 25c lt bl grn ('66)   .15 .15
412 A108 30c gray grn ('57)   .15 .15
413 A108 40c brown olive   .15 .15
414 A108 50c ultra   .15 .15
  a. 50c light blue   .15 .15
415 A108 60c lilac rose   .20 .15
416 A108 65c violet brn   12.50 .55
417 A108 75c bluish lilac   .15 .15
418 A108 80c emerald   .75 .15
419 A108 90c deep blue   .75 .15
420 A108 1fr rose   .20 .15
421 A108 2fr emerald ('73)   .15 .15
422 A108 2.50fr brown ('70)   .20 .15
423 A108 3fr brt pink ('70)   .15 .15
424 A108 4fr brt rose lil ('74) .25 .15
425 A108 4.50fr blue ('74)   .30 .15
426 A108 5fr brt lilac ('75)   .30 .15
Size: 17x20½mm
427 A108 1.50fr dk sl grn ('69) .15 .15

Perf. 13½x13
428 A108 2fr emerald ('68)   .15 .15

Photo.   Perf. 11½
Size: 20½x24mm
429 A108 50c lt blue ('61)   .45 .15
430 A108 60c lil rose ('66)   1.10 .70
431 A108 1fr car rose ('59)   .15 .15

Perf. 13½x12½
Size: 17½x22mm
432 A108 50c lt blue ('75)   .15 .15
  a. Booklet pane of 4 (#432, 784 and
    2 #785) + labels   1.00
  b. Booklet pane of 4 (#432 and 3
    #787) + labels   1.35
433 A108 1fr rose ('69)   2.00 .90
434 A108 2fr emerald ('72)   .50 .30
  e. Booklet pane of 6 (4 #434 + 2
    #475)   5.50
  f. Booklet pane of 5 (#434, 4 #476 +
    label)   8.00
    Nos. 403-434 (32)   23.95
    Set value   5.00

Counterfeits exist of No. 416. Nos. 429, 431 also issued in coils with black control number on back of every fifth stamp. Nos. 432-434 issued in booklet panes only. No. 432 has one straightedge, and stamps in the pane are tete-beche. Each pane has 2 labels showing Belgian postal emblem and a large selvage with postal code instructions.
Nos. 433-434 have 1 or 2 straight-edges. Panes have a large selvage with inscription or map of Belgium showing postal zones.
See designs A386, O5. For surcharges see Nos. 477-478, 563-567.

Francois de Tassis
(Franz von
Taxis) — A109

Portraits: 1.75fr, Jean-Baptiste of Thurn & Taxis. 2fr, Baron Leonard I. 2.50fr, Count Lamoral I. 3fr, Count Leonard II. 4fr, Count Lamoral II. 5fr, Prince Eugene Alexander. 5.75fr, Prince Anselme Francois. 8fr, Prince Alexander Ferdinand. 10fr, Prince Charles Anselme. 20fr, Prince Charles Alexander.

1952, May 14   Engr.   Perf. 11½
Laid Paper
435 A109 80c olive grn   .75 .30
436 A109 1.75fr red org   .75 .30
437 A109 2fr violet brn   1.50 .40
438 A109 2.50fr carmine   2.25 1.65
439 A109 3fr olive bis   2.00 1.00
440 A109 4fr ultra   3.00 .85
441 A109 5fr red brn   4.00 1.75
442 A109 5.75fr blue vio   6.75 2.25
443 A109 8fr gray   12.50 2.75
444 A109 10fr rose vio   22.50 4.50
445 A109 20fr brown   60.00 22.50
    Nos. 435-445,B514 (12) 291.00 213.25
13th UPU Cong., Brussels, 1952.

King Baudouin
A110   A111

1952-58   Engr.   Perf. 11½
Size: 21x24mm
446 A110 1.50fr gray   .55 .15
447 A110 2fr crimson   .40 .15
448 A110 4fr ultra   3.50 .20
Size: 24½x35mm
449 A110 50fr gray brn   1.75 .20
  a. 50fr violet brown   35.00 .60
450 A110 100fr rose red ('58)   5.00 .25

1953-72   Photo.   Perf. 11½
451 A111 1.50fr gray   .25 .15
452 A111 2fr rose carmine   6.75 .15
453 A111 2fr green   .25 .15
454 A111 2.50fr red brn ('57)   .60 .15
  a. 2.50fr orange brown ('70)   .25 .15
455 A111 3fr rose lilac ('58)   .40 .15
456 A111 3.50fr brt yel grn ('58) .75 .15
457 A111 4fr brt ultra   .50 .15
458 A111 4.50fr dk red brn ('62) 3.00 .15
459 A111 5fr violet ('57)   1.25 .15
460 A111 6fr dp pink ('58)   .75 .15
461 A111 6.50fr gray ('60)   62.50 15.00
462 A111 7fr blue ('60)   .90 .15
463 A111 7.50fr grysh brn ('58) 47.50 14.00
464 A111 8fr bluish gray ('58) 1.25 .15
465 A111 8.50fr claret ('58)   15.00 .30
466 A111 9fr gray ('58)   47.50 .75
467 A111 12fr lt bl grn ('66)   .90 .15
468 A111 30fr red org ('58)   5.50 .15
Redrawn
469 A111 2.50fr orange brn ('71) .35 .15
470 A111 4.50fr brown ('72)   2.25 .60
471 A111 7fr blue ('71)   .60 .15

Perf. 13½x12½
Size: 17½x22mm
472 A111 1.50fr gray ('70)   .60 .30
  b. Bklt. pane of 10   6.50
  c. Bklt. pane, 3 #472, 3 #475 15.00
473 A111 2.50fr org brn ('70)   9.00 6.25
  h. Bklt. pane, 1 #473, 5 #475 16.00
474 A111 3fr ultra ('72)   .60 .15
  a. Bklt. pane of 5 + label   25.00
  b. Bklt. pane 2 #433, 6 #474 18.00
475 A111 3.50fr brt yel grn ('70) .60 .25
476 A111 4.50fr dull red brn
    ('72)   .75 .45
    Nos. 446-476 (31)   221.50 41.40

Nos. 451, 453, 454a, 455, 456, 458 also issued in coils with black control number on back of every fifth stamp. These coils, except for No. 451, are on luminescent paper.
On Nos. 469-471, the 2, 4 and 7 are 3mm high. The background around the head is white. On Nos. 454, 458, 462 the 2, 4 and 7 are 2½mm high and the background is tinted.
Nos. 472-476 issued in booklets only and have 1 or 2 straight-edges. All panes have a large selvage with inscription or map.
See designs M1, O3.

Luminescent Paper
Stamps issued on both ordinary and luminescent paper include: Nos. 307-308, 430-431, 449-451, 453-460, 462, 464, 467-468, 472, 643-644, 650-651, 837, Q385, Q410.
Stamps issued only on luminescent paper include: Nos. 433, 454a, 472b, 473-474, 649, 652-658, 664-670, 679-682, 688-690, 694-696, 698-703, 705-711, 713-726, 729-747, 751-754, 756-757, 759, 761-762, 764, 766, 769, 772, 774, 778, 789, 791-793, 795, 797-799, 801-807, 809-811, 814-818, 820-834, 836, 838-848.
See note after No. 857.

20c
I-I-54
31-XII-54

Nos. 416 and 419
Surcharged and
Precanceled in Black

1954, Jan. 1   Unwmk.   Perf. 13½x14
477 A108 20c on 65c vio brn   1.75 .30
478 A108 20c on 90c dp blue   1.75 .20
See note after No. 197.

Map and
Rotary Emblem
A112

Designs: 80c, Mermaid and Mercury holding emblem. 4fr, Rotary emblem and two globes.

1954, Sept. 10   Engr.   Perf. 11½
479 A112 20c red   .25 .15
480 A112 80c dark green   .65 .35
481 A112 4fr ultra   1.40 .50
    Nos. 479-481 (3)   2.30 1.00
5th regional conf. of Rotary Intl. at Ostend. No. 481 for Rotary 50th Anniv. (in 1955).
A souv. sheet containing one each, imperf., was sold for 500 francs. It was not valid for postage.

The Rabot and
Begonia — A113

Designs: 2.50fr, The Oudeburg and azalea. 4fr, "Three Towers" and orchid.

1955, Feb. 15   Photo.
482 A113 80c brt carmine   .85 .35
483 A113 2.50fr black brn   5.25 2.75
484 A113 4fr dk rose brn   5.00 .90
    Nos. 482-484 (3)   11.10 4.00
Ghent Intl. Flower Exhibition, 1955.

Homage to Charles V as a
Child, by Albrecht de
Vriendt — A114

Charles V, by
Titian — A115

4fr, Abdication of Charles V, by Louis Gallait.

1955, Mar. 25   Unwmk.   Perf. 11½
485 A114 20c rose red   .25 .20
486 A115 2fr dk gray green   1.90 .15
487 A114 4fr blue   5.00 1.25
    Nos. 485-487 (3)   7.15 1.60
Charles V Exhibition, Ghent, 1955.

Emile Verhaeren, by
Montald
Constant — A116

1955, May 11   Engr.
488 A116 20c dark gray   .15 .15
Birth cent. of Verhaeren, poet.

Allegory of
Textile
Manufacture
A117

1955, May 11
489 A117 2fr violet brown   1.00 .15
2nd Intl. Textile Exhibition, Brussels, June 1955.

"The Foolish
Virgin" by Rik
Wouters — A118

"Departure of
Volunteers from
Liege, 1830" by
Charles
Soubre — A119

1955, June 10
490 A118 1.20fr olive green   1.10 1.10
491 A118 2fr violet   1.65 .15
3rd biennial exhibition of sculpture, Antwerp, June 11-Sept. 10, 1955.

1955, Sept. 10   Photo.
492 A119 20c grnsh slate   .20 .15
493 A119 2fr chocolate   .90 .20
Exhibition "The Romantic Movement in Liege Province," Sept. 10-Oct. 31, 1955; and 125th anniv. of Belgium's independence from the Netherlands.

Pelican Giving
Blood to
Young — A120

Buildings of
Tournai, Ghent
and
Antwerp — A121

1956, Jan. 14   Engr.
494 A120 2fr brt carmine   .35 .18
Blood donor service of the Belgian Red Cross.

1956, July 14   Photo.
495 A121 2fr brt ultra   .30 .18
The Scheldt exhibition (Scaldis) at Tournai, Ghent and Antwerp, July-Sept. 1956.

Europa Issue

"Rebuilding
Europe" — A122

1956, Sept. 15   Engr.
496 A122 2fr lt green   1.75 .15
497 A122 4fr purple   8.75 .70
Issued to symbolize the cooperation among the six countries comprising the Coal and Steel Community.

Train on Map of Belgium and Luxembourg A123

1956, Sept. 29
498 A123 2fr dark blue .45 .20

Issued to mark the electrification of the Brussels-Luxembourg railroad.

Edouard Anseele — A124

"The Atom" and Exposition Emblem — A125

1956, Oct. 27
499 A124 20c violet brown .15 .15

Cent. of the birth of Edouard Anseele, statesman, and in connection with an exhibition held in his honor at Ghent.

1957-58 Unwmk.
500 A125 2fr carmine rose .25 .15
501 A125 2.50fr green ('58) .40 .15
502 A125 4fr brt violet blue .95 .20
503 A125 5fr claret ('58) .85 .50
Nos. 500-503 (4) 2.45 1.00

1958 World's Fair at Brussels.

Emperor Maximilian I Receiving Letter — A126

1957, May 19
504 A126 2fr claret .40 .15

Day of the Stamp, May 19, 1957.

Sikorsky S-58 Helicopter A127

1957, June 15
505 A127 4fr gray grn & brt bl .80 .45

100,000th passenger carried by Sabena helicopter service, June 15, 1957.

Zeebrugge Harbor A128

1957, July 6
506 A128 2fr dark blue .40 .15

50th anniv. of the completion of the port of Zeebrugge-Bruges.

Leopold I Entering Brussels, 1831 — A129

Leopold I Arriving at Belgian Border — A130

1957, July 17 Photo.
507 A129 20c dk gray grn .15 .15
508 A130 2fr lilac .50 .20

126th anniv. of the arrival in Belgium of King Leopold I.

Boy Scout and Girl Scout Emblems A131

Design: 4fr, Robert Lord Baden-Powell, painted by David Jaggers, vert.

Perf. 11½
1957, July 29 Unwmk. Engr.
509 A131 80c gray .25 .15
510 A131 4fr light green 1.00 .45

Cent. of the birth of Lord Baden-Powell, founder of the Boy Scout movement.

"Kneeling Woman" by Lehmbruck A132

"United Europe" A133

1957, Aug. 20 Photo.
511 A132 2.50fr dk blue grn 1.10 .85

4th Biennial Exposition of Sculpture, Antwerp, May 25-Sept. 15.

1957, Sept. 16 Engr. *Perf. 11½*
512 A133 2fr dk violet brn 1.00 .15
513 A133 4fr dark blue 1.90 .45

Europa: United Europe for peace and prosperity.

Queen Elisabeth Assisting at Operation, by Allard L'Olivier A134

Perf. 11½
1957, Nov. 23 Unwmk. Engr.
514 A134 30c rose lilac .15 .15

50th anniv. of the founding of the Edith Cavell-Marie Depage and St. Camille schools of nursing.

Post Horn and Historic Postal Insignia A135

1958, Mar. 16 Photo. *Perf. 11½*
515 A135 2.50fr gray .25 .15

Postal Museum Day.

United Nations Issue

International Labor Organization A136

Allegory of UN — A137

Designs: 1fr, FAO. 2fr, World Bank. 2.50fr, UNESCO. 3fr, UN Pavilion. 5fr, ITU. 8fr, Intl. Monetary Fund. 11fr, WHO. 20fr, UPU.

Perf. 11½
1958, Apr. 17 Unwmk. Engr.
516 A136 50c gray .90 1.40
517 A136 1fr claret .30 .45
518 A137 1.50fr dp ultra .30 .45
519 A137 2fr gray brown .85 1.25
520 A136 2.50fr olive grn .30 .45
521 A136 3fr grnsh blue .85 1.25
522 A137 5fr rose lilac .55 .90
523 A136 8fr red brown 1.00 1.65
524 A136 11fr dull lilac 1.25 2.00
525 A136 20fr car rose 1.65 2.50
Nos. 516-525,C15-C20 (16) 10.25 14.75

World's Fair, Brussels, Apr. 17-Oct. 19.

Postally valid only from the UN pavilion at the Brussels Fair. Proceeds went toward financing the UN exhibits.

Eugène Ysaye — A138

1958, Sept. 1
526 A138 30c dk blue & plum .15 .15

Ysaye (1858-1931), violinist, composer.

Common Design Types pictured in section at front of book.

Europa Issue, 1958
Common Design Type
1958, Sept. 13 Photo.
Size: 24½x35mm
527 CD1 2.50fr brt red & blue .20 .15
528 CD1 5fr brt blue & red .35 .35

Issued to show the European Postal Union at the service of European integration.

Infant and UN Emblem — A140

Charles V and Jean-Baptiste of Thurn and Taxis — A141

1958, Dec. 10 Engr.
529 A140 2.50fr blue gray .30 .15

10th anniv. of the signing of the Universal Declaration of Human Rights.

1959, Mar. 15 Unwmk.
530 A141 2.50fr green .35 .15

Issued for the Day of the Stamp. Design from painting by J.-E. van den Bussche.

NATO Emblem A142

City Hall, Audenarde A143

1959, Apr. 3 Photo. *Perf. 11½*
531 A142 2.50fr dp red & dk bl .45 .15
532 A142 5fr emerald & dk bl 1.25 1.40

10th anniv. of NATO. See No. 720.

1959, Aug. 17 Engr.
533 A143 2.50fr deep claret .30 .15

Pope Adrian VI, by Jan van Scorel — A144

1959, Aug. 31 *Perf. 11½*
534 A144 2.50fr dark red .20 .15
535 A144 5fr Prus blue .55 .55

500th anniv. of the birth of Pope Adrian VI.

Europa Issue, 1959
Common Design Type
1959, Sept. 19 Photo.
Size: 24x35½mm
536 CD2 2.50fr dark red .20 .15
537 CD2 5fr brt grnsh blue .45 .45

Boeing 707 A146

Engraved and Photogravure
1959, Dec. 1 *Perf. 11½*
538 A146 6fr dk bl gray & car 1.75 .80

Inauguration of jet flights by Sabena Airlines.

Countess of Taxis — A147

Indian Azalea — A148

1960, Mar. 21 Engr. *Perf. 11½*
539 A147 3fr dark blue .85 .15

Alexandrine de Rye, Countess of Taxis, Grand Mistress of the Netherlands Posts, 1628-1645, and day of the stamp, Mar. 21, 1960. The painting of the Countess is by Nicholas van der Eggermans.

1960, Mar. 28 Unwmk.
540 A148 40c shown .20 .15
541 A148 3fr Begonia .90 .15
542 A148 6fr Anthurium, bromelia 1.00 .90
Nos. 540-542 (3) 2.10 1.20

24th Ghent Intl. Flower Exhibition, Apr. 23-May 2, 1960.

Steel Workers, by
Constantin
Meunier — A149

Design: 3fr, The sower, field and dock workers,
from "Monument to Labor," Brussels, by Constantin Meunier, horiz.

Engraved and Photogravure
1960, Apr. 30   Perf. 11½
543 A149 40c claret & brt red   .15 .15
544 A149 3fr brown & brt red   .85 .25
Socialist Party of Belgium, 75th anniv.

Congo River
Boat
Pilot — A150

Designs: 40c, Medical team. 1fr, Planting tree.
2fr, Sculptors. 2.50fr, Shot put. 3fr, Congolese
officials. 6fr, Congolese and Belgian girls playing
with doll. 8fr, Boy pointing on globe to independent
Congo.

1960, June 30   Photo.   Perf. 11½
Size: 35x24mm
545 A150   10c bright red   .30 .15
546 A150   40c rose claret   .45 .15
547 A150   1fr brt lilac   .85 .75
548 A150   2fr gray green   .95 .85
549 A150   2.50fr blue   .85 .75
550 A150   3fr dk bl gray   1.00 .45
Size: 51x35mm
551 A150   6fr violet bl   3.00 1.90
552 A150   8fr dk brown   5.00 4.00
     Nos. 545-552 (8)   12.40 9.00
Independence of Congo.

Europa Issue, 1960
Common Design Type
1960, Sept. 17
Size: 35x24½mm
553 CD3 3fr claret   .60 .15
554 CD3 6fr gray   1.25 .40

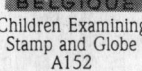

Children Examining
Stamp and Globe
A152

H. J. W. Frère-
Orban
A153

1960, Oct. 1   Photo.   Perf. 11½
555 A152 40c bister & blk + label   .15 .15
Promoting stamp collecting among children.

Engraved and Photogravure
1960, Oct. 17   Unwmk.
Portrait in Brown
556 A153   10c orange yel   .15 .15
557 A153   40c blue grn   .15 .15
558 A153   1.50fr brt violet   .70 .70
559 A153   3fr red   1.10 .15
     Nos. 556-559 (4)   2.10 1.15
Centenary of Communal Credit Society.

King Baudouin
and Queen
Fabiola
A154

1960, Dec. 13   Photo.   Perf. 11½
Portraits in Dark Brown
560 A154 40c green   .15 .15
561 A154 3fr red lilac   .30 .15
562 A154 6fr dull blue   1.25 .60
     Nos. 560-562 (3)   1.70 .90
Wedding of King Baudouin and Dona Fabiola de
Mora y Aragon, Dec. 15, 1960.

15ᶜ
Nos. 412, 414 Surcharged
═══════

1961-68   Typo.   Perf. 13½x14
563 A108 15c on 30c gray grn   .15 .15
564 A108 15c on 50c blue ('68)   .15 .15
565 A108 20c on 30c gray grn   .15 .15
     Nos. 563-565 (3)   .45
     Set value   .30

**15ᶜ
1961
═══
1962**
No. 412 Surcharged and
Precanceled

1961
566 A108 15c on 30c gray grn   .90 .15
567 A108 20c on 30c gray grn   1.90 1.40
     See note after No. 197.

Nicolaus Rockox,
by Anthony Van
Dyck — A155

Seal of Jan Bode,
Alderman of
Antwerp,
1264 — A156

Engraved and Photogravure
1961, Mar. 18   Perf. 11½
568 A155 3fr bister, blk & brn   .35 .15
400th anniv. of the birth of Nicolaus Rockox,
mayor of Antwerp.

1961, Apr. 16   Photo.
569 A156 3fr buff & brown   .35 .15
Issued for Stamp Day, April 16.

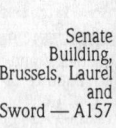

Senate
Building,
Brussels, Laurel
and
Sword — A157

Engraved and Photogravure
1961, Sept. 14   Unwmk.   Perf. 11½
570 A157 3fr brn & Prus blue   .30 .15
571 A157 6fr dk brn & dk car   2.75 1.00
50th Conference of the Interparliamentary
Union, Brussels, Sept. 14-22.

Europa Issue, 1961
Common Design Type
1961, Sept. 16   Photo.
572 CD4 3fr yel grn & dk grn   .25 .20
573 CD4 6fr org brn & blk   .35 .25

Atomic Reactor
Plant, BR2,
Mol — A159

Designs: 3fr, Atomic Reactor BR3, vert. 6fr,
Atomic Reactor plant BR3.

1961, Nov. 8   Unwmk.   Perf. 11½
574 A159 40c dk blue grn   .15 .15
575 A159 3fr red lilac   .15 .15
576 A159 6fr bright blue   .35 .25
     Nos. 574-576 (3)   .65
     Set value   .40
Aatomic nuclear research center at Mol.

Horta
Museum — A160

1962, Feb. 15   Engr.
577 A160 3fr red brown   .25 .15
Baron Victor Horta (1861-1947), architect.

Postrider, 16th
Century
A161

Engraved and Photogravure
1962, Mar. 25   Perf. 11½
Chalky Paper
578 A161 3fr brn & slate grn   .30 .15
Stamp Day. See No. 677.

Gerard
Mercator — A162

Bro. Alexis-Marie
Gochet — A163

Engraved and Photogravure
1962, Apr. 14   Unwmk.
579 A162 3fr sepia & gray   .30 .15
Mercator (Gerhard Kremer, 1512-1594), geographer and map maker.

1962, May 19   Engr.   Perf. 11½
Portrait: 3fr, Canon Pierre-Joseph Triest.
580 A163 2fr dark blue   .30 .15
581 A163 3fr golden brown   .30 .15
Brother Alexis-Marie Gochet (1835-1910), geographer and educator, and Canon Pierre-Joseph Triest (1760-1836), educator and founder of hospitals
and orphanages.

Europa Issue, 1962
Common Design Type
1962, Sept. 15   Photo.
582 CD5 3fr dp car, citron & blk   .25 .15
583 CD5 6fr olive, citron & blk   .35 .35

Hand with Barbed
Wire and Freed
Hand — A165

1962, Sept. 16   Engr. & Photo.
584 A165 40c lt blue & blk   .15 .15
Issued in memory of concentration camp victims.

Adam, by
Michelangelo,
Broken Chain
and UN Emblem
A166

1962, Nov. 24   Perf. 11½
585 A166 3fr gray & blk   .25 .15
586 A166 6fr lt redsh brn & dk brn   .40 .30
UN Declaration of Human Rights.

Henri Pirenne (1862-
1935),
Historian — A167

1963, Jan. 15   Engr.
587 A167 3fr ultramarine   .35 .15

Swordsmen and
Ghent
Belfry — A168

Designs: 3fr, Modern fencers. 6fr, Arms of the
Royal and Knightly Guild of St. Michael, vert.

Engraved and Photogravure
1963, Mar. 23   Unwmk.   Perf. 11½
588 A168 1fr brn red & pale bl   .15 .15
589 A168 3fr dk vio & yel grn   .15 .15
590 A168 6fr gray, blk, red, bl & gold   .30 .15
     Nos. 588-590 (3)   .60
     Set value   .40
350th anniv. of the granting of a charter to the
Ghent guild of fencers.

Stagecoach
A169

1963, Apr. 7
591 A169 3fr gray & ocher   .25 .15
Stamp Day. See No. 678.

Hotel des
Postes, Paris,
Stagecoach
and Stamp,
1863
A170

Perf. 11½
1963, May 7   Unwmk.   Engr.
592 A170 6fr dk brn, gray & yel grn   .40 .35
Cent. of the 1st Intl. Postal Conf., Paris, 1863.

"Peace," Child in Rye
Field — A171

1963, May 8   Engr. & Photo.
593 A171 3fr grn, blk, yel & brn   .15 .15
594 A171 6fr buff, blk, brn & org   .35 .25
May 8th Movement for Peace. (On May 8,
1945, World War II ended in Europe).

Allegory and Shields of 17 Member Nations
A172

1963, June 13   Unwmk.   Perf. 11½
595 A172 6fr blue & black .40 .30
10th anniversary of the Conference of European Transport Ministers.

Seal of Union of Belgian Towns — A173

1963, June 17
596 A173 6fr grn, red, blk & gold .40 .35
Intl. Union of Municipalities, 50th anniv.

Caravelle over Brussels National Airport
A174

Photogravure and Engraved
1963, Sept. 1   Unwmk.   Perf. 11½
597 A174 3fr green & gray .25 .15
40th anniversary of SABENA airline.

Europa Issue, 1963
Common Design Type
1963, Sept. 14   Photo.   Size: 35x24mm
598 CD6 3fr blk, dl red & lt brn .60 .15
599 CD6 6fr blk, lt bl & lt brn 1.65 .35

Jules Destrée A176

Design: No. 601, Henry Van de Velde.

Perf. 11½
1963, Nov. 16   Unwmk.   Engr.
600 A176 1fr rose lilac .15 .15
601 A176 1fr green .15 .15
Set value .20 .20
Jules Destrée (1863-1936), statesman and founder of the Royal Academy of French Language and Literature, and of Henry Van de Velde (1863-1957), architect.
No. 600 incorrectly inscribed "1864."

Development of the Mail, Bas-relief A177

1963, Nov. 23   Engr. & Photo.
602 A177 50c dl red, slate & blk .15 .15
50th anniversary of the establishment of postal checking service.

Dr. Armauer G. Hansen A178

Fight Against Leprosy: 2fr, Leprosarium. 5fr, Father Joseph Damien.

1964, Jan. 25   Unwmk.   Perf. 11½
603 A178 1fr brown org & blk .15 .15
604 A178 2fr brown org & blk .20 .15
605 A178 5fr brown org & blk .25 .20
a. Souvenir sheet of 3, #603-605 1.90 1.90
Nos. 603-605 (3) .60
Set value .40
No. 605a sold for 12fr.

Andreas Vesalius (1514-64), Anatomist — A179

Jules Boulvin (1855-1920), Mechanical Engineer A180

Design: 2fr, Henri Jaspar (1870-1939), statesman and lawyer.

Engraved and Photogravure
1964, Mar. 2   Unwmk.   Perf. 11½
606 A179 50c pale grn & blk .15 .15
607 A180 1fr pale grn & blk .15 .15
608 A180 2fr pale grn & blk .15 .15
Set value .35 .30

Postilion of Liege, 1830-40 — A181

1964, Apr. 5   Engr.   Perf. 11½
609 A181 3fr black .20 .15
Issued for Stamp Day 1964.

Arms of Ostend A182

1964, May 16   Photo.
610 A182 3fr ultra, ver, gold & blk .20 .15
Millennium of Ostend.

Flame, Hammer and Globe — A183

1fr, "SI" and globe. 2fr, Flame over wavy lines.

1964, July 18   Unwmk.   Perf. 11½
611 A183 50c dark blue & red .15 .15
612 A183 1fr dark blue & red .15 .15
613 A183 2fr dark blue & red .15 .15
Set value .30 .25
Centenary of the First Socialist International, founded in London, Sept. 28, 1864.

Europa Issue, 1964
Common Design Type
1964, Sept. 12   Photo.   Perf. 11½
Size: 24x35½mm
614 CD7 3fr yel grn, dk car & gray .25 .15
615 CD7 6fr car rose, yel grn & bl .40 .40

Benelux Issue

King Baudouin, Queen Juliana and Grand Duchess Charlotte — A185

1964, Oct. 12
616 A185 3fr olive, lt grn & mar .15 .15
20th anniv. of the customs union of Belgium, Netherlands and Luxembourg.

Hand, Round & Pear-shaped Diamonds A186   Symbols of Textile Industry A187

1965, Jan. 23   Unwmk.   Perf. 11½
617 A186 2fr ultra, dp car & blk .15 .15
Diamond Exhibition "Diamantexpo," Antwerp, July 10-28, 1965.

1965, Jan. 25   Photo.
618 A187 1fr blue, red & blk .15 .15
Eighth textile industry exhibition "Textirama," Ghent, Jan. 29-Feb. 2, 1965.

Vriesia — A188   Paul Hymans — A189

Designs: 2fr, Echinocactus. 3fr, Stapelia.

1965, Feb. 13   Engr. & Photo.
619 A188 1fr multicolored .15 .15
620 A188 2fr multicolored .15 .15
621 A188 3fr multicolored .15 .15
a. Souvenir sheet of 3, #619-621 1.75 1.75
Set value .30 .30
25th Ghent International Flower Exhibition, Apr. 24-May 3, 1965.
No. 621a was issued Apr. 26 and sold for 20fr.

1965, Feb. 24   Engr.   Perf. 11½
622 A189 1fr dull purple .15 .15
Paul Hymans (1865-1941), Belgian Foreign Minister and first president of the League of Nations.

Peter Paul Rubens A190   Sir Rowland Hill as Philatelist A191

Portraits: 2fr, Frans Snyders. 3fr, Adam van Noort. 6fr, Anthony Van Dyck. 8fr, Jacob Jordaens.

1965, Mar. 15   Photo. & Engr.
Portraits in Sepia
623 A190 1fr carmine rose .15 .15
624 A190 2fr blue green .15 .15
625 A190 3fr plum .15 .15
626 A190 6fr deep carmine .25 .15
627 A190 8fr dark blue .35 .35
Nos. 623-627 (5) 1.05 .95
Issued to commemorate the founding of the General Savings and Pensions Bank.

1965, Mar. 27   Engr.   Perf. 11½
628 A191 50c blue green .15 .15
Issued to publicize youth philately. The design is from a mural by J. E. Van den Bussche in the General Post Office, Brussels.

Postmaster, c. 1833 — A192   Staircase, Affligem Abbey — A194

Telephone, Globe and Teletype Paper — A193

1965, Apr. 26   Unwmk.   Perf. 11½
629 A192 3fr emerald .15 .15
Issued for Stamp Day.

1965, May 8   Photo.
630 A193 2fr dull purple & blk .15 .15
Cent. of the ITU.

1965, May 27   Engr.
631 A194 1fr gray blue .15 .15

St. Jean Berchmans and his Birthplace A195

1965, May 27   Engr. & Photo.
632 A195 2fr dk brn & red brn .15 .15
Issued to honor St. Jean Berchmans (1599-1621), Jesuit "Saint of the Daily Life."

TOC H Lamp and Arms of Poperinge A196   Farmer with Tractor A197

1965, June 19   Photo.   Perf. 11½
633 A196 3fr ol bis, blk & car .15 .15
50th anniv. of the founding of Talbot House in Poperinge, which served British soldiers in World War I, and where the TOC H Movement began (Christian Social Service; TOC H is army code for Poperinge Center).

Engraved and Photogravure
1965, July 17   Unwmk.   Perf. 11½
Design: 3fr, Farmer with horse-drawn roller.
634 A197 50c bl, ol, bis brn & blk .15 .15
635 A197 3fr bl, ol grn, ol & blk .15 .15
Set value .20 .15
75th anniv. of the Belgian Farmers' Association (Boerenbond).

Europa Issue, 1965
Common Design Type

1965, Sept. 25   *Perf. 11½*
Size: 35½x24mm

636 CD8	1fr dl rose & blk	.15 .15
637 CD8	3fr grnsh gray & blk	.15 .15
	Set value	.25 .20

Leopold I
A199

Joseph Lebeau
A200

1965, Nov. 13   **Engr.**

638 A199	3fr sepia	.20 .15
639 A199	6fr bright violet	.25 .25
	Set value	.30

King Leopold I (1790-1865). The designs of the vignettes are similar to A4 and A5.

1965, Nov. 13   **Photo.**

640 A200	1fr multicolored	.15 .15

Joseph Lebeau (1794-1865), Foreign Minister.

Tourist Issue

Grapes and
Houses,
Hoeilaart
A201

Bridge and Castle,
Huy
A202

Designs: No. 643, British War Memorial, Ypres. No. 644, Castle Spontin. No. 645, City Hall, Louvain. No. 646, Ourthe Valley. No. 647, Romanesque Cathedral, gothic fountain, Nivalles. No. 648, Water mill, Kasterlee. No. 649, City Hall, Cloth Guild and Statue of Margarethe of Austria, Malines. No. 650, Town Hall, Lier. No. 651, Castle Bouillon. No. 652, Fountain and Kursaal Spa. No. 653, Windmill, Bokrijk. No. 654, Mountain road, Vielsalm. No. 655, View of Furnes. No. 656, City Hall and Belfry, Mons. No. 657, St. Martin's Church, Aalst. No. 658, Abbey and fountain, St. Hubert.

1965-71   **Engr.**   *Perf. 11½*

641 A201	50c vio bl, lt bl & yel grn	.15 .15
642 A202	50c sl grn, lt bl & red brn	.15 .15
643 A202	1fr grn, lt bl, sal & brn	.15 .15
644 A202	1fr ind, lt bl & ol	.15 .15
645 A201	1fr brt rose lil, lt bl & blk	.15 .15
646 A202	1fr blk, grnsh bl & ol	.15 .15
647 A201	1.50fr sl, sky bl & bis	.15 .15
648 A202	1.50fr blk, bl & ol	.15 .15
649 A202	1.50fr dk bl & buff	.18 .15
650 A201	2fr brn, bl & ind	.18 .15
651 A202	2fr dk brn, grn & ocher	.18 .15
652 A202	2fr bl, brt grn & blk	.15 .15
653 A202	2fr bl, lt bl & yel	.15 .15
654 A202	2fr blk, lt bl & yel	.15 .15
655 A202	2fr car, lt bl & dk brn	.15 .15
656 A201	2.50fr vio, buff & blk	.18 .15
657 A201	2.50fr vio, lt bl, blk & ol	.25 .15
658 A201	2.50fr vio bl & yel	.25 .15
	Nos. 641-658 (18)	3.02
	Set value	1.50

Issued: #641-642, 11/13/65; #643-644, 7/15/67; #645-646, 12/16/68; #647-648, 7/6/70; #649, 656, 12/11/71; #650-651, 11/11/66; #652-653, 6/24/68; #654-655, 9/6/69; #657-658, 9/11/71.

Queen Elisabeth Type of Semi-Postal Issue, 1956

1965, Dec. 23   **Photo.**   *Perf. 11½*

659 SP305	3fr dark gray	.22 .15

Queen Elisabeth (1876-1965).

A dark frame has been added in design of No. 659; 1956 date has been changed to 1965; inscription in bottom panel is Koningin Elisabeth Reine Elisabeth 3F.

"Peace on
Earth" — A203

Arms of Pope
Paul VI — A204

Rural Mailman,
19th
Century — A205

Design: 1fr, "Looking toward a Better Future" (family, new buildings, sun and landscape).

1966, Feb. 12   **Photo.**   *Perf. 11½*

660 A203	50c multicolored	.15 .15
661 A203	1fr ocher, blk & bl	.15 .15
662 A204	3fr gray, gold, car & blk	.15 .15
	Set value	.25 .19

75th anniv. of the encyclical by Pope Leo XIII "Rerum Novarum," which proclaimed the general principles for the organization of modern industrial society.

1966, Apr. 17   **Photo.**   **Unwmk.**

663 A205	3fr blk, dl yel & pale lil	.18 .15

Stamp Day. For overprint see No. 673.

Iguanodon,
Natural
Science
Institute
A206

Arend-Roland Comet,
Observatory — A207

Designs: No. 665, Ancestral head and spiral pattern, Kasai; Central Africa Museum. No. 666, Snowflakes, Meteorological Institute. No. 667, Seal of Charles V, Royal Archives. No. 668, Medieval scholar, Royal Library. 8fr, Satellite and rocket, Space Aeronautics Institute.

1966, May 28   **Engr. & Photo.**

664 A206	1fr green & blk	.15 .15
665 A206	2fr gray, blk & brn org	.15 .15
666 A206	3fr blue, blk & yel	.15 .15
667 A207	3fr dp rose, blk & gold	.15 .15
668 A207	3fr multicolored	.15 .15
669 A207	6fr ultra, yel & blk	.22 .15
670 A207	8fr multicolored	.30 .30
	Set value	1.00 .78

National scientific heritage.

Atom Symbol
and
Retort — A208

August Kekulé,
Benzene
Ring — A209

Engraved and Photogravure

1966, July 9   **Unwmk.**   *Perf. 11½*

671 A208	6fr gray, blk & red	.30 .18

Issued to publicize the European chemical plant, EUROCHEMIC, at Mol.

1966, July 9

672 A209	3fr brt blue & blk	.18 .15

August Friedrich Kekule (1829-96), chemistry professor at University of Ghent (1858-67).

No. 663 Overprinted with Red and Blue Emblem

1966, July 11   **Photo.**

673 A205	3fr multicolored	.18 .15

19th Intl. P.T.T. Cong., Brussels, July 11-15.

Rik Wouters (1882-
1916), Self-
portrait — A210

1966, Sept. 6   **Photo.**   *Perf. 11½*

674 A210	60c multicolored	.15 .15

Europa Issue, 1966
Common Design Type

1966, Sept. 24   **Engr.**   *Perf. 11½*
Size: 24x34mm

675 CD9	3fr brt green	.15 .15
676 CD9	6fr brt rose lilac	.32 .28

Types of 1962-1963 Overprinted in Black and Red

1966, Nov. 11   **Engr. & Photo.**

677 A161	60c sepia & grnsh gray	.15 .15
678 A169	3fr sepia & pale bister	.15 .15
	Set value	.19 .16

75th anniv., Royal Fed. of Phil. Circles of Belgium. Overprint shows emblem of F.I.P.

Lions Emblem — A214

1967, Jan. 14   *Perf. 11½*

679 A214	3fr gray, blk & bl	.15 .15
680 A214	6fr lt green, blk & vio	.28 .15
	Set value	.23

Lions Club Intl., 50th anniv.

Pistol by
Leonhard
Cleuter
A215

1967, Feb. 11   **Photo.**

681 A215	2fr dp car, blk & cream	.15 .15

Fire Arms Museum in Liege.

International
Tourist Year
Emblem
A216

1967, Feb. 11

682 A216	6fr ver, ultra & blk	.28 .15

International Tourist Year, 1967.

Birches and
Trientalis
A217

Design: No. 684, Dunes, beach grass, privet and blue thistles.

1967, Mar. 11   **Photo.**   *Perf. 11½*

683 A217	1fr multicolored	.15 .15
684 A217	1fr multicolored	.15 .15
	Set value	.16 .16

Issued to publicize the nature preserves at Hautes Fagnes and Westhoek.

Paul E. Janson — A218

1967, Apr. 15   **Engr.**   *Perf. 11½*

685 A218	10fr blue	.35 .18

Issued in memory of Paul Emile Janson (1872-1944), lawyer and statesman.

Postilion
A219

1967, Apr. 16   **Photo. & Engr.**

686 A219	3fr rose red & claret	.18 .15

Issued for Stamp Day, 1967.

Inscribed: "FITCE"

1967, June 24   *Perf. 11½*

687 A219	10fr ultra, sep & emer	.42 .30

Issued to commemorate the meeting of the Federation of Common Market Telecommunications Engineers, Brussels, July 3-8.

Europa Issue, 1967
Common Design Type

1967, May 2   **Photo.**
Size: 24x35mm

688 CD10	3fr blk, lt bl & red	.18 .15
689 CD10	6fr blk, grnsh gray & yel	.30 .28

Flax, Shuttle and
Mills — A221

1967, June 3   **Photo.**   *Perf. 11½*

690 A221	6fr tan & multi	.28 .20

Belgian linen industry.

Old Kursaal, Ostend — A222

1967, June 3   **Engr. & Photo.**
691 A222 2fr dk brn, lt bl & yel   .15 .15
700th anniversary of Ostend as a city.

A223   A224

Designs: #692, Caesar Crossing Rubicon, 15th Century Tapestry. #693, Emperor Maximilian Killing a Boar, 16th cent. tapestry.

1967, Sept. 2   **Photo.**   **Perf. 11½**
692 A223 1fr multicolored   .15 .15
693 A223 1fr multicolored   .15 .15
     Set value   .20 .16

Issued for the Charles Plisnier and Lodewijk de Raet Foundations.

Engraved and Photogravure
1967, Sept. 30   **Perf. 11½**
Arms of Universities: #694, Ghent. #695, Liege.
694 A224 3fr gray & multi   .15 .15
695 A224 3fr gray & multi   .15 .15
     Set value   .20

Universities of Ghent and Liège, 150th anniv.

Princess Margaret of York — A225   "Virga Jesse," Hasselt — A226

1967, Sept. 30   **Photo.**
696 A225 6fr multicolored   .28 .24
British Week, Sept. 28-Oct. 2.

1967, Nov. 11   **Engr.**   **Perf. 11½**
697 A226 1fr slate blue   .15 .15
Christmas, 1967.

Hand Guarding Worker — A227   Military Mailman, 1916, by James Thiriar — A228

1968, Feb. 3   **Photo.**   **Perf. 11½**
698 A227 3fr multicolored   .18 .15
Issued to publicize industrial safety.

Engraved and Photogravure
1968, Mar. 17   **Perf. 11½**
699 A228 3fr sepia, lt bl & brn   .18 .15
Issued for Stamp Day, 1968.

View of Grammont and Seal of Baudouin VI — A229   Stamp of 1866, No. 23 — A230

Historic Sites: 3fr, Theux-Franchimont fortress, sword and seal. 6fr, Neolithic cave and artifacts, Spiennes. 10fr, Roman oil lamp and St. Medard's Church, Wervik.

1968, Apr. 13   **Photo.**   **Perf. 11½**
700 A229 2fr bl, blk, lil & rose   .15 .15
701 A229 3fr orange, blk & car   .15 .15
702 A229 6fr ultra, ind & bis   .25 .15
703 A229 6fr tan, blk, yel & gray   .40 .28
     Nos. 700-703 (4)   .95 .73

1968, Apr. 13   **Engr.**   **Perf. 13**
704 A230 1fr black   .15 .15
Centenary of the Malines Stamp Printery.

Europa Issue, 1968
Common Design Type
1968, Apr. 27   **Photo.**   **Perf. 11½**
     Size: 35x24mm
705 CD11 3fr dl grn, gold & blk   .15 .15
706 CD11 6fr carmine, sil & blk   .35 .25

St. Laurent Abbey, Liège A232

Designs: 3fr, Gothic Church, Lisseweghe. No. 709. Barges in Zandvliet locks. No. 710, Ship in Neuzen lock, Ghent Canal. 10fr, Ronquieres canal ship lift.

Engraved and Photogravure
1968, Sept. 7   **Perf. 11½**
707 A232 2fr ultra, gray ol & sep   .15 .15
708 A232 3fr ol bis, gray & sep   .15 .15
709 A232 6fr ind, brt bl & sep   .30 .15
710 A232 6fr black, grnsh bl & ol   .22 .15
711 A232 10fr bister, brt bl & sep   .50 .32
     Nos. 707-711 (5)   1.32 .92

No. 710 issued Dec. 14 for opening of lock at Neuzen, Netherlands.

Christmas Candle — A233

1968, Dec. 7   **Perf. 11½**
712 A233 1fr multicolored   .15 .15
Christmas, 1968.

St. Albertus Magnus — A234

1969, Feb. 15   **Engr.**   **Perf. 11½**
713 A234 2fr sepia   .15 .15
The Church of St. Paul in Antwerp (16th century) was destroyed by fire in Apr. 1968.

Ruins of Aulne Abbey, Gozee A235

1969, Feb. 15   **Engr. & Photo.**
714 A235 3fr brt pink & blk   .15 .15
Aulne Abbey was destroyed in 1794 during the French Revolution.

The Travelers, Roman Sculpture — A236   Broodjes Chapel, Antwerp — A237

1969, Mar. 15   **Engr.**   **Perf. 11½**
715 A236 2fr violet brown   .15 .15
2,000th anniversary of city of Arlon.

1969, Mar. 15   **Engr. & Photo.**
716 A237 3fr gray & blk   .15 .15
150th anniv. of public education in Antwerp.

Post Office Train — A238

1969, Apr. 13   **Photo.**   **Perf. 11½**
717 A238 3fr multicolored   .15 .15
Issued for Stamp Day.

Europa Issue, 1969
Common Design Type
1969, Apr. 26
     Size: 35x24mm
718 CD12 3fr lt grn, brn & blk   .20 .15
719 CD12 6fr salmon, rose car & blk   .30 .30

NATO Type of 1959 Redrawn and Dated "1949-1969"
1969, May 31   **Photo.**   **Perf. 11½**
720 A142 6fr org brn & ultra   .28 .28

20th anniv. of NATO. No. 720 inscribed Belgique-Belgie and OTAN-NAVO.

Construction Workers, by F. Leger A240   Bicyclist A241

1969, May 31
721 A240 3fr multicolored   .15 .15
50th anniversary of the ILO.

1969, July 5   **Photo.**   **Perf. 11½**
722 A241 6fr rose & multi   .28 .24
World Bicycling Road Championships, Terlaemen to Zolder, Aug. 10.

Ribbon in Benelux Colors — A242

1969, Sept. 6   **Photo.**   **Perf. 11½**
723 A242 3fr blk, red, ultra & yel   .20 .15
25th anniv. of the signing of the customs union of Belgium, Netherlands and Luxembourg.

Annevoie Garden and Pascali Rose — A243

Design: No. 725, Lochristi Garden and begonia.

1969, Sept. 6
724 A243 2fr multicolored   .15 .15
725 A243 2fr multicolored   .15 .15
     Set value   .20 .16

Armstrong, Collins, Aldrin and Map Showing Tranquillity Base — A245

1969, Sept. 20   **Photo.**
726 A245 6fr black   .28 .24
See note after Algeria #427. See #B846.

Wounded Veteran — A246   Mailman — A247

1969, Oct. 11   **Engr.**   **Perf. 11½**
727 A246 1fr blue gray   .15 .15
Natl. war veterans' aid organization (O.N.I.G.). The design is similar to type SP10.

1969, Oct. 18   **Photo.**
728 A247 1fr deep rose & multi   .15 .15
Issued to publicize youth philately. Design by Danielle Saintenoy, 14.

Kennedy Tunnel Under the Schelde, Antwerp A248

6fr, Three highways crossing near Loncin.

1969, Nov. 8   **Engr.**   **Perf. 11½**
729 A248 3fr multicolored   .22 .15
730 A248 6fr multicolored   .28 .28

Issued to publicize the John F. Kennedy Tunnel under the Schelde and the Walloon auto route and interchange near Loncin.

"The Letter Box," by
T. Lobrichon — A271

1971, Mar. 13   Engr.   Perf. 11½
800 A271 1.50fr dark brown   .15 .15
Youth philately.

Albert I, Jules Destrée and
Academy — A272

Engraved and Photogravure
1971, Apr. 17   Perf. 11½
801 A272 7fr gray & blk   .30 .20
50th anniversary of the founding of the Royal
Academy of Language and French Literature.

BELGIE·BELGIQUE Stamp Day — A273

1971, Apr. 25
802 A273 3.50fr Mailman   .15 .15

Europa Issue, 1971
Common Design Type
1971, May 1   Photo.
Size: 35x24mm
803 CD14 3.50fr olive & blk   .24 .15
804 CD14 7fr dk ol grn & blk   .35 .15
Set value   .20

Radar
Ground
Station
A275

1971, May 15   Photo.   Perf. 11½
805 A275 7fr multicolored   .30 .15
3rd World Telecommunications Day.

Antarctic Explorer, Ship and
Penguins — A276

1971, June 19   Photo.   Perf. 11½
806 A276 10fr multicolored   .50 .50
Tenth anniversary of the Antarctic Treaty pledging peaceful uses of and scientific cooperation in Antarctica.

ORVAL   2F50

A277   G.HUBIN 1F50
A278

1971, June 26   Engr.   Perf. 11½
807 A277 2.50fr Orval Abbey   .15 .15
9th cent. of the Abbey of Notre Dame, Orval.

1971, June 26   Engr. & Photo.
808 A278 1.50fr vio bl & blk   .15 .15
Georges Hubin (1863-1947), socialist leader and Minister of State.

Mr. and Mrs. Goliath,
the Giants of
Ath — A279

View
of
Ghent
A280

1971, Aug. 7   Photo.
809 A279 2.50fr multicolored   .15 .15

Engr.
810 A280 2.50fr gray brown   .15 .15

Test Tubes and Insulin Molecular
Diagram — A281

1971, Aug. 7   Photo.
811 A281 10fr lt gray & multi   .40 .30
50th anniversary of the discovery of insulin.

Family and
"50" — A283

1971, Sept. 11   Photo.
812 A283 1.50fr green & multi   .15 .15
Belgian Large Families League, 50th anniv.

Achaemenidaen Tomb, Buzpar, and
Persian Coat of Arms — A284

Engraved and Photogravure
1971, Oct. 2   Perf. 11½
813 A284 7fr multicolored   .30 .15
2500th anniversary of the founding of the Persian empire by Cyrus the Great.

Dr. Jules Bordet
A285   Flight into Egypt,
Anonymous
A286

Portrait: No. 815, Stijn Streuvels.

1971, Oct. 2   Engr.
814 A285 3.50fr slate green   .15 .15
815 A285 3.50fr dark brown   .15 .15
Set value   .16

No. 814 honors Dr. Jules Bordet (1870-1945), serologist and immunologist; No. 815, Stijn Streuvels (1871-1945), novelist whose pen name was Frank Lateur.

1971, Nov. 13   Photo.
816 A286 1.50fr multicolored   .15 .15
Christmas 1971.

Federation
Emblem — A287   Book Year
Emblem — A288

1971, Nov. 13
817 A287 3.50fr black, ultra & gold   .18 .15
25th anniversary of the Federation of Belgian Industries (FIB).

1972, Feb. 19
818 A288 7fr bister, blk & bl   .30 .20
International Book Year 1972.

Coins of Belgium and
Luxembourg — A289   Traffic Signal and
Road
Signs — A290

1972, Feb. 19   Engr. & Photo.
819 A289 1.50fr orange, blk & sil   .15 .15
Economic Union of Belgium and Luxembourg, 50th anniversary.

1972, Feb. 19   Photo.
820 A290 3.50fr blue & multi   .15 .15
Via Secura (road safety), 25th anniversary.

Belgica '72
Emblem
A291

1972, Mar. 27
821 A291 3.50fr choco, bl & lil   .15 .15
International Philatelic Exhibition, Brussels, June 24-July 9.

"Your Heart is
your Health"
A292   Auguste
Vermeylen
A293

1972, Mar. 27
822 A292 7fr blk, gray, red & bl   .25 .18
World Health Day.

1972, Mar. 27
823 A293 2.50fr multicolored   .15 .15
Centenary of the birth of Auguste Vermeylen (1872-1945), Flemish writer and educator. Portrait by Isidore Opsomer.

A294   A296

1972, Apr. 23
824 A294 3.50fr Astronaut on Moon   .15 .15
Stamp Day 1972.

Europa Issue 1972
Common Design Type
1972, Apr. 29
Size: 24x35mm
825 CD15 3.50fr light blue & multi   .20 .15
826 CD15 7fr rose & multi   .40 .30

1972, May 13   Photo.   Perf. 11½
827 A296 2.50fr "Freedom of the Press"   .15 .15
50th anniv. of the BELGA news information agency and 25th Congress of the Intl. Federation of Newspaper Editors (F.I.E.J.), Brussels, May 15-19.

Freight Cars
with Automatic
Coupling
A297

1972, June 3
828 A297 7fr blue & multi   .30 .20
Intl. Railroad Union, 50th anniv.

View of
Couvin — A298

Design: No. 830, Aldeneik Church, Maaseik, vert.

1972, June 24   Engr.   Perf. 13½x14
829 A298 2.50fr bl, vio brn & sl grn   .20 .20
830 A298 2.50fr dk brown & bl   .20 .20

Beatrice, by Gustave de Smet — A299

Radar Station, Intelsat 4 — A300

1972, Sept. 9   Photo.   Perf. 11½
831 A299 3fr multicolored   .18 .15
Youth philately.

1972, Sept. 16
832 A300 3.50fr lt bl, sil & blk   .18 .15
Opening of the Lessive satellite earth station.

Frans Masereel, Self-portrait A301

Adoration of the Kings, by Felix Timmermans A302

1972, Oct. 21
833 A301 4.50fr lt olive & blk   .18 .15
Frans Masereel (1889-1972), wood engraver.

1972, Nov. 11   Photo.   Perf. 11½
834 A302 3.50fr black & multi   .18 .15
Christmas 1972.

Maria Theresa, Anonymous A303

1972, Dec. 16   Photo.   Perf. 11½
835 A303 2fr multicolored   .15 .15
200th anniversary of the Belgian Academy of Science, Literature and Art, founded by Empress Maria Theresa.

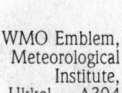

WMO Emblem, Meteorological Institute, Ukkel — A304

1973, Mar. 24   Photo.   Perf. 11½
836 A304 9fr blue & multi   .38 .18
Cent. of intl. meteorological cooperation.

"Fire" — A305

Man and WHO Emblem — A306

1973, Mar. 24
837 A305 2fr multicolored   .15 .15
Natl. industrial fire prevention campaign.

1973, Apr. 7
838 A306 8fr dk red, ocher & blk   .32 .24
25th anniv. of WHO.

Europa Issue 1973
Common Design Type
1973, Apr. 28
Size: 35x24mm
839 CD16 4.50fr multicolored   .22 .15
840 CD16 8fr olive, dk bl & yel   .55 .45

Thurn and Taxis Courier — A308

Arrows Circling Globe — A309

Engraved and Photogravure
1973, Apr. 28   Perf. 11½
841 A308 4.50fr black & red brn   .20 .15
Stamp Day.

1973, May 12   Photo.
842 A309 3.50fr dp ocher & multi   .16 .15
5th International Telecommunications Day.

Workers' Sports Exhibition Poster, Ghent, 1913 — A310

1973, May 12
843 A310 4.50fr multicolored   .20 .15
60th anniversary of the International Workers' Sports Movement.

Fair Emblem A311

1973, May 12   Photo.   Perf. 11½
844 A311 4.50fr multicolored   .18 .15
25th International Fair, Liege, May 12-27.

DC-10 and 1923 Biplane over Brussels Airport A312

Design: 10fr, Tips biplane, 1908.

1973, May 19   Engr. & Photo.
845 A312 8fr gray bl, blk & ultra   .28 .20
846 A312 10fr grn, lt bl & blk   .45 .35
50th anniv. of SABENA, Belgian airline (8fr) and 25th anniv. of the "Vieilles Tiges" Belgian flying pioneers' society (10fr).

Adolphe Sax and Tenor Saxophone A313

Fresco from Bathhouse, Ostend A314

1973, Sept. 15   Photo.
847 A313 9fr green, blk & bl   .40 .20
Adolphe Sax (1814-1894), inventor of saxophone.

1973, Sept. 15
848 A314 4.50fr multicolored   .22 .15
Year of the Spa.

St. Nicholas Church, Eupen A315

Charley, by Henri Evenepoel A316

Designs: No. 850, Town Hall, Leau. No. 851, Aarshot Church. No. 852, Chiman Castle. No. 853, Gemmenich Border: Belgium, Germany, Netherlands. No. 854, St. Monan and church, Nassogne. No. 855, Church tower, Dottignes. No. 856, Grand-Place, Sint-Truiden.

1973-75   Engr.   Perf. 13
849 A315 2fr plum, sep & lt vio   .20 .15
850 A315 3fr black, lt bl & mar   .50 .15
851 A315 3fr brn blk & yel   .32 .15
852 A315 4fr grnsh blk & grnsh bl   .35 .15
853 A315 4fr grnsh blk & bl   .40 .18
854 A315 4fr grnsh blk & bl   .40 .18
855 A315 4.50fr multicolored   .50 .20
856 A315 5fr multicolored   .50 .18
Nos. 849-856 (8)   3.17 1.34
Nos. 851, 855 not luminescent. Nos. 850, 852-854, 856 horiz.

1973, Oct. 13   Photo.   Perf. 11½
857 A316 3fr multicolored   .18 .15
Youth philately.

Luminescent Paper
Starting with No. 858, all stamps are on luminescent paper unless otherwise noted.

Jean-Baptiste Moens A317

1973, Oct. 13   Engr. & Photo.
858 A317 10fr gray & multi   .42 .20
50th anniversary of the Belgian Stamp Dealers' Association. Printed in sheets of 12 stamps and 12 labels showing association emblem.

Adoration of the Shepherds, by Hugo van der Goes A318

Louis Pierard, by M. I. Ianchelevici A319

1973, Nov. 17   Engr.   Perf. 11½
859 A318 4fr blue   .18 .15
Christmas 1973.

1973, Nov. 17   Engr. & Photo.
860 A319 4fr vermilion & buff   .25 .15
Louis Pierard (1886-1952), journalist, member of Parliament.

Highway, Automobile Club Emblem A320

1973, Nov. 17   Photo.
861 A320 5fr yellow & multi   .25 .15
Flemish Automobile Club, 50th anniv.

Early Microphone, Emblem of Radio Belgium — A321

1973, Nov. 24   Engr. & Photo.
862 A321 4fr blue & black   .18 .15
50th anniversary of Radio Belgium.

Felicien Rops, Self-portrait A323

Engraved and Photogravure
1973, Dec. 8   Perf. 11½
863 A323 7fr tan & black   .32 .15
Felicien Rops (1833-1898), painter and engraver.

King Albert, (1875-
1934) — A324

Sun, Bird, Flowers
and Girl — A325

1974, Feb. 16   Photo.   Perf. 11½
864 A324 4fr Prus green & blk   .22 .15

1974, Mar. 25   Photo.   Perf. 11½
865 A325 3fr violet & multi   .15 .15

Protection of the environment.

NATO Emblem
A326

1974, Apr. 20   Photo.   Perf. 11½
866 A326 10fr dp to lt blue   .45 .25

25th anniversary of the signing of the North
Atlantic Treaty.

Hubert
Krains — A327

"Destroyed City,"
by Ossip
Zadkine — A328

1974, Apr. 27   Engr. & Photo.
867 A327 5fr black & gray   .20 .15

Stamp Day.

Europa Issue 1974

1974, May 4

Design: 10fr, Solidarity, by Georges Minne.

868 A328 5fr black & red   .24 .15
869 A328 10fr black & ultra   .60 .30

Children
A329

1974, May 18   Photo.   Perf. 11½
870 A329 4fr lt blue & multi   .20 .15

10th Lay Youth Festival.

Planetarium,
Brussels
A330

Soleilmont Abbey Ruins — A331

Designs: 4fr, Pillory, Braine-le-Chateau. 7fr,
Fountain, Ghent (procession symbolic of Chamber
of Rhetoric). 10fr, Belfry, Bruges, vert.

Engr. and Photo.

1974, June 22   Perf. 11½
871 A330 3fr sky blue & blk   .15 .15
872 A330 4fr lilac rose & blk   .18 .15
873 A331 5fr lt green & blk   .28 .15
874 A331 7fr dull yellow & blk   .35 .20
875 A330 10fr black, blue & brn   .45 .15
      Nos. 871-875 (5)   1.41
      Set value   .55

Historic buildings and monuments.

"BENELUX"
A332

1974, Sept. 7   Photo.   Perf. 11½
876 A332 5fr bl grn, dk grn & lt bl   .25 .15

30th anniversary of the signing of the customs
union of Belgium, Netherlands and Luxembourg.

Jan Vekemans, by
Cornelis de
Vos — A333

1974, Sept. 14
877 A333 3fr multicolored   .18 .15

Youth philately.

Leon
Tresignies,
Willebroek
Canal Bridge
A334

1974, Sept. 28   Engr. & Photo.
878 A334 4fr brn & ol grn   .18 .15

60th death anniversary of Corporal Leon
Tresignies (1886-1914), hero of World War I.

Montgomery
Blair, UPU
Emblem
A335

10fr, Heinrich von Stephan and UPU emblem.

1974, Oct. 5   Perf. 11½
879 A335 5fr green & blk   .20 .15
880 A335 10fr brick red & blk   .40 .28

Centenary of Universal Postal Union.

Symbolic
Chart — A336

1974, Oct. 12   Photo.   Perf. 11½
881 A336 7fr multicolored   .30 .20

Central Economic Council, 25th anniv.

Rotary
Emblem
A337

1974, Oct. 19
882 A337 10fr multicolored   .42 .20

Rotary International of Belgium.

A338

A341

Wild boar (regiment's emblem).

1974, Oct. 26
883 A338 3fr multicolored   .18 .15

Granting of the colors to the Ardennes Chasseurs
Regiment, 40th anniversary.

1974, Nov. 16   Perf. 11½
884 A341 4fr rose lilac   .20 .15

Christmas 1974. The Angel shown is from the
triptyque "The Mystical Lamb" in the Saint-Bavon
Cathedral, Ghent.

A342

A343

Adolphe Quetelet, by J. Odevaere.

1974, Dec. 14   Engr. & Photo.
885 A342 10fr black & buff   .42 .20

Death centenary of Adolphe Quetelet (1796-
1874), statistician, astronomer and Secretary of
Royal Academy of Brussels.

1975, Feb. 15   Photo.   Perf. 11½
912 A343 6.50fr Themabelga emblem   .30 .15

Themabelga, International Thematic Stamp Exhibition, Brussels, Dec. 13-21, 1975.

A344

A345

1975, Feb. 22
913 A344 4.50fr Neoregelia carolinae   .22 .15

Photogravure and Engraved

914 A344 5fr Coltsfoot   .25 .16
915 A344 6.50fr Azalea   .30 .15
      Nos. 913-915 (3)   .77 .46

Ghent Intl. Flower Exhib., Apr. 26-May 5.

1975, Mar. 15   Perf. 11½

School emblem, man Leading boy.

916 A345 4.50fr black & multi   .20 .15

Centenary of the founding of the Charles Buls
Normal School for Boys, Brussels.

Davids
Foundation
Emblem
A346

1975, Mar. 22   Photo.
917 A346 5fr yellow & multi   .25 .15

Centenary of the Davids Foundation, a Catholic
organization for the promotion of Flemish through
education and books.

King Albert
(1875-1934)
A347

Mailman, 1840,
by James Thiriar
A348

1975, Apr. 5   Engr. & Photo.
918 A347 10fr black & maroon   .45 .25

1975, Apr. 19   Engr.   Perf. 11½
919 A348 6.50fr dull magenta   .30 .15

Stamp Day 1975.

St. John, from
Last Supper, by
Bouts — A349

Concentration
Camp
Symbols — A350

Europa: 10fr, Woman's Head, detail from "Trial
by Fire," by Dirk Bouts.

1975, Apr. 26   Engr. & Photo.
920 A349 6.50fr black, grn & blue   .35 .15
921 A349 10fr black, ocher & red   .60 .32

1975, May 3   Photo.

Design: "B" denoted political prisoners, "KG"
prisoners of war.

922 A350 4.50fr multicolored   .20 .15

Liberation of concentration camps, 30th
anniversary.

Hospice of St.
John, Bruges
A351

Church of St. Loup,
Namur — A352

Design: 10fr, Martyrs' Square, Brussels.

1975, May 12   Engr.   Perf. 11½
926 A351 4.50fr deep rose lilac   .22 .20
927 A352 5fr slate green   .22 .15
928 A351 10fr bright blue   .45 .32
      Nos. 926-928 (3)   .89 .67

European Architectural Heritage Year.

Library,
Louvain
University,
Ryckmans and
Cerfaux
A355

1975, June 7   Photo.   Perf. 11½
931 A355 10fr dull blue & sepia   .40 .20
25th anniversary of Louvain Bible Colloquium, founded by Professors Gonzague Ryckmans (1887-1969) and Lucien Cerfaux (1883-1968).

"Metamorphose" by Pol Mara — A356

Marie Popelin, Palace of Justice, Brussels — A357

1975, June 14
932 A356 7fr multicolored   .30 .20
Queen Fabiola Mental Health Foundation.

1975, June 21   Engr. & Photo.
933 A357 6.50fr green & claret   .30 .15
International Women's Year 1975. Marie Popelin (1846-1913), first Belgian woman doctor of law.

Assia, by Charles Despiau — A358

Cornelia Vekemans, by Cornelis de Vos — A359

1975, Sept. 6   Perf. 11½
934 A358 5fr yellow grn & blk   .24 .15
Middelheim Outdoor Museum, 25th anniv.

1975, Sept. 20   Photo.
935 A359 4.50fr multicolored   .20 .15
Youth philately.

Map of Schelde-Rhine Canal — A360

1975, Sept. 20
936 A360 10fr multicolored   .45 .22
Opening of connection between the Schelde and Rhine, Sept. 23, 1975.

National Bank, W. F. Orban, Founder A361

Photogravure and Engraved
1975, Oct. 11   Perf. 12½x13
937 A361 25fr multicolored   1.00 .30
Natl. Bank of Belgium, 125th anniv.

Edmond Thieffry and Plane, 1925 — A362

1975, Oct. 18   Perf. 11½
938 A362 7fr black & lilac   .30 .20
First flight Brussels to Kinshasa, Congo, 50th anniversary.

"Seat of Wisdom" St. Peter's, Louvain — A363

1975, Nov. 8   Perf. 11½
939 A363 6.50fr blue, blk & grn   .28 .15
University of Louvain, 550th anniversary.

Angels, by Rogier van der Weyden A364

1975, Nov. 15
940 A364 5fr multicolored   .24 .15
Christmas 1975.

Willemsfonds Emblem — A365

American Bicentennial Emblem — A366

1976, Feb. 21   Photo.   Perf. 11½
941 A365 5fr multicolored   .24 .15
125th anniversary of the Willems Foundation, which supports Flemish language and literature.

1976, Mar. 13   Photo.   Perf. 11½
942 A366 14fr gold, red, bl & blk   .60 .30
American Bicentennial. No. 942 printed checkerwise in sheets of 30 stamps and 30 gold and black labels which show medal with 1626 seal of New York. Black engraved inscription on labels commemorates arrival of first Walloon settlers in Nieu Nederland.

Cardinal Mercier — A367

Symbolic of V.E.V. — A368

1976, Mar. 20   Engr.
943 A367 4.50fr brt rose lilac   .20 .15
Desire Joseph Cardinal Mercier (1851-1926), professor at Louvain University, spiritual and patriotic leader during World War I, 50th death anniversary.

1976, Apr. 3   Photo.   Perf. 11½
944 A368 6.50fr multicolored   .28 .15
Flemish Economic Organization (Vlaams Ekonomisch Verbond), 50th anniversary.

General Post Office, Brussels A369

1976, Apr. 24   Engr.   Perf. 11½
945 A369 6.50fr sepia   .28 .15
Stamp Day.

Potter's Hands — A370

Europa: 6.50fr, Basket maker, vert.

1976, May 8   Photo.
946 A370 6.50fr multicolored   .45 .15
947 A370 14fr multicolored   .65 .38

Truck on Road — A371

1976, May 8
948 A371 14fr black, yel & red   .65 .35
15th International Road Union Congress, Brussels, May 9-13.

Queen Elisabeth (1876-1965) — A372

1976, May 24   Perf. 11½
949 A372 14fr green   .60 .30

Ardennes Draft Horses — A373

1976, June 19
950 A373 5fr multicolored   .22 .15
Ardennes Draft Horses Association, 50th anniversary.

Souvenir Sheets

King Baudouin — A374

1976, June 26
951 A374   Sheet of 3   2.50 .50
a.   4.50fr gray   .70 .70
b.   6.50fr ocher   .70 .70
c.   10fr brick red   .70 .70
952 A374   Sheet of 2   3.50 3.50
a.   20fr yellow green   .85 .85
b.   30fr Prussian blue   .85 .85
25th anniv. of the reign of King Baudouin. No. 951 sold for 30fr, No. 952 for 70fr. The surtax went to a new foundation for the improvement of living conditions in honor of the King.

Electric Train and Society Emblem A375

1976, Sept. 11   Photo.   Perf. 11½
953 A375 6.50fr multi   .30 .15
Natl. Belgian Railroad Soc., 50th anniv.

William of Nassau, Prince of Orange — A376

1976, Sept. 11   Engr.
954 A376 10fr slate green   .42 .20
400th anniv. of the pacification of Ghent.

New Subway Train — A377

1976, Sept. 18   Photo.
955 A377 6.50fr multi   .30 .15
Opening of first line of Brussels subway.

Young Musician, by W. C. Duyster — A378

1976, Oct. 2   Photo.   Perf. 11½
956 A378 4.50fr multi   .20 .15
Young musicians and youth philately.

Charles Bernard — A379

St. Jerome in the Mountains, by Le Patinier — A380

Blind Leading the Blind, by Breughel the Elder — A381

#958, Fernand Victor Toussaint van Boelaere.

1976, Oct. 16   Engr.
957 A379   5fr violet   .15 .15
958 A379   5fr red brn & sepia   .15 .15
959 A380   6.50fr dark brown   .30 .15
960 A381   6.50fr slate green   .30 .15
      Nos. 957-960 (4)   .90
      Set value   .50
Charles Bernard (1875-1961), Frenchspeaking journalist; Toussaint van Boelaere (1875-1947), Flemish journalist; No. 959, Charles Plisnier Belgian-French Cultural Society. No. 960, Assoc. for Language Promotion.

Remouchamps
Caves — A382

Hunnegem
Priory,
Gramont, and
Madonna
A383

Designs: No. 963, River Lys and St. Martin's
Church. No. 964, Ham-sur-Heure Castle.

1976, Oct. 23   Engr.   Perf. 13
961 A382 4.50fr multi   .15 .15
962 A383 4.50fr multi   .15 .15
963 A383 5fr multi   .22 .15
964 A383 5fr multi   .22 .15
        Nos. 961-964 (4)   .74
        Set value   .48

Tourism. #961-962 are not luminescent.

Nativity, by Master of
Flemalle — A384

1976, Nov. 20   Perf. 11½
965 A384 5fr violet   .22 .18

Christmas 1976.

Rubens' Monogram — A385

1977, Feb. 12   Photo. & Engr.
966 A385 6.50fr lilac & blk   .30 .15

Peter Paul Rubens (1577-1640), painter.

Heraldic Lion — A386

1977-85   Typo.   Perf. 13½x14
                Size: 17x20mm
967 A386 50c brn ('80)   .15 .15
  a.   50c orange brown ('85)   .15 .15
968 A386 1fr brt lil   .15 .15
  a.   1fr bright rose lilac ('84)   .15 .15
969 A386 1.50fr gray ('78)   .15 .15
970 A386 2fr yel ('78)   .15 .15
970A A386 2.50fr yel grn ('81)   .15 .15
971 A386 2.75fr Prus bl ('80)   .30 .15
972 A386 3fr vio ('78)   .30 .15
  a.   3fr dull violet ('84)   .18 .15
973 A386 4fr red brn ('80)   .25 .15
  a.   4fr rose brown ('85)   .25 .15
974 A386 4.50fr lt ultra   .30 .15
975 A386 5fr grn ('80)   .30 .15
  a.   5fr emerald green ('84)   .20 .15
976 A386 6fr dl red brn   .35 .15
  a.   6fr light red brown ('85)   .35 .15
        Nos. 967-976 (11)   2.55
        Set value   .60

Perf. 13½x12½, 12½x13½
1978, Aug.   Photo.
        Size: 17x22mm, 22x17mm
              Booklet Stamps
977 A386 1fr brt lilac   .15 .15
  a.   Bklt. pane, #977-978, 2 #786   1.50
  b.   Bklt. pane, #977, 979, 2 #788   2.00

978 A386 2fr yellow   .30 .30
979 A386 3fr violet   .45 .45
        Nos. 977-979 (3)   .90 .90

Each pane has 2 labels showing Belgian Postal
emblem, also a large selvage with zip code instructions. No. 977-979 not luminescent.
See Nos. 1084-1088, design O5.

Anniversary
Emblem
A387

1977, Mar. 14   Photo.   Perf. 11½
982 A387 6.50fr sil & multi   .30 .15

Royal Belgian Association of Civil and Agricultural Engineers, 50th anniversary.

Birds and Lions
Emblem
A388

1977, Mar. 28
983 A388 14fr multi   .60 .30

Belgian District No. 112 of Lions International,
25th anniversary.

Pillar Box,
1852 — A389

1977, Apr. 23   Engr.
984 A389 6.50fr slate green   .45 .15

Stamp Day 1977.

Gileppe Dam,
Jalhay — A390

Europa: 14fr, War Memorial, Yser at Nieuport.

1977, May 7   Photo.   Perf. 11½
985 A390 6.50fr multi   .40 .15
986 A390 14fr multi   .90 .15
        Set value   .20

Mars and Mercury
Association
Emblem — A391

1977, May 14
987 A391 5fr multi   .25 .15

Mars and Mercury Association of Reserve and
Retired Officers, 50th anniversary.

Prince de Hornes
Coat of
Arms — A392

Conversion of St.
Hubertus — A394

Battle of the Golden Spur, from Oxford
Chest
A393

Design: 6.50fr, Froissart writing book.

1977, June 11   Engr.   Perf. 11½
988 A392 4.50fr violet   .30 .15
989 A393 5fr red   .35 .15
990 A394 6.50fr dark brown   .40 .15
991 A394 14fr slate green   .75 .35
        Nos. 988-991 (4)   1.80
        Set value   .65

300th anniv. of the Principality of Overijse
(4.50fr); 675th anniv. of the Battle of the Golden
Spur (5fr); 600th anniv. of publication of 1st volume
of the Chronicles of Jehan Froissart (6.50fr); 1250th
anniv. of the death of St. Hubertus (14fr).

Rubens, Self-
portrait — A395

1977, June 25   Photo.
992 A395 5fr multi   .25 .15
  a.   Souvenir sheet of 3   1.25 .90

Peter Paul Rubens (1577-1640), painter. No.
992a sold for 20fr.

Open Book, from The Lamb of God, by
Van Eyck Brothers
A396

1977, Sept. 3   Photo.   Perf. 11½
993 A396 10fr multi   .45 .25

Intl. Federation of Library Associations (IFLA),
50th Anniv. Congress, Brussels, Sept. 5-10.

Gymnast and Soccer
Player — A397

Designs: 6.50fr, Fencers in wheelchairs, horiz.
10fr, Basketball players. 14fr, Hockey players.

1977, Sept. 10
994 A397 4.50fr multi   .25 .15
995 A397 6.50fr multi   .40 .15
996 A397 10fr multi   .60 .20
997 A397 14fr multi   .80 .30
        Nos. 994-997 (4)   2.05
        Set value   .65

Workers' Gymnastics and Sports Center, 50th
anniversary (4.50fr); sport for the Handicapped

(6.50fr); 20th European Basketball Championships
(10fr); First World Hockey Cup (14fr).

Europalia 77 Emblem — A398

1977, Sept. 17
998 A398 5fr gray & multi   .22 .15

5th Europalia Arts Festival, featuring German
Federal Republic, Belgium, Oct.-Nov. 1977.

The Egg Farmer, by
Gustave De
Smet — A399

1977, Oct. 8   Engr. & Photo.
999 A399 4.50fr bister & blk   .22 .15

Publicity for Belgian eggs.

Mother and
Daughter with
Album, by
Constant
Cap — A400

1977, Oct. 15   Engr.
1000 A400 4.50fr dark brown   .22 .15

Youth Philately.

Bailiff's House,
Gembloux — A401

Market
Square, St.
Nicholas
A402

No. 1002, St. Aldegonde Church and Cultural
Center. No. 1004, Statue and bridge, Liège.

1977, Oct. 22
1001 A401 4.50fr multi   .22 .15
1002 A401 4.50fr multi   .22 .15
1003 A402 5fr multi   .22 .18
1004 A402 5fr multi   .22 .18
        Nos. 1001-1004 (4)   .88
        Set value   .56

Tourism. Nos. 1001-1004 not luminescent.
See Nos. 1017-1018, 1037-1040.

Nativity, by Rogier van
der Weyden — A403

1977, Nov. 11   Engr.
1005 A403 5fr rose red   .30 .15

Christmas 1977.

Symbols of Transportation and Map — A404

Parliament of Europe, Strasbourg, and Emblem — A405

Campidoglio Palace, Rome, and Map — A406

Design: No. 1009, Paul-Henri Spaak and map of 19 European member countries.

1978, Mar. 18   Photo.   Perf. 11½
1006 A404 10fr blue & multi   .55 .20
1007 A405 10fr blue & multi   1.10 .20
1008 A406 14fr blue & multi   .65 .55
1009 A406 14fr blue & multi   .65 .55
    Nos. 1006-1009 (4)   2.95 1.50

European Action: 25th anniversary of the European Transport Ministers' Conference; 1st general elections for European Parliament; 20th anniversary of the signing of the Treaty of Rome; Paul Henri Spaak (1899-1972), Belgian statesman who worked for the establishment of European Community.

Grimbergen Abbey — A407

1978, Apr. 1   Engr.
1010 A407 4.50fr red brown   .22 .15
850th anniversary of the Premonstratensian Abbey at Grimbergen.

Emblem — A408

No. 39 with First Day Cancel — A409

1978, Apr. 8   Photo.
1011 A408 8fr multicolored   .50 .15
Ostend Chamber of Commerce and Industry, 175th anniversary.

1978, Apr. 15
1012 A409 8fr multicolored   .35 .15
Stamp Day.

Europa Issue

Pont des Trous, Tournai — A410

Design: 8fr, Antwerp Cathedral, by Vaclav Hollar, vert.

Photogravure and Engraved
1978, May 6   Perf. 11½
1013 A410 8fr multicolored   .50 .15
1014 A410 14fr multicolored   .75 .30

Virgin of Ghent, Porcelain Plaque — A411

Paul Pastur Workers' University, Charleroi — A412

1978, Sept. 16   Photo.   Perf. 11½
1015 A411 6fr multicolored   .42 .15
1016 A412 8fr multicolored   .55 .15
    Set value   .20

Municipal education in Ghent, 150th anniversary; Paul Pastur Workers' University, Charleroi, 75th anniv. #1015-1016 are not luminescent.

Types of 1977 and

Tourist Guide, Brussels A413

#1017, Jonathas House, Enghien. #1018, View of Wetteren and couple in local costume. #1020, Prince Carnival, Eupen-St. Vith.

1978, Sept. 25   Photo. & Engr.
1017 A401 4.50fr multi   .16 .15
1018 A402 4.50fr multi   .16 .15
1019 A413   6fr multi   .25 .15
1020 A413   6fr multi   .25 .15
    Nos. 1017-1020 (4)   .82
    Set value   .50

Tourism. #1017-1020 are not luminescent.

Emblem A414

1978, Oct. 7   Photo.
1021 A414 8fr red & blk   .35 .15
Royal Flemish Engineer's Organization, 50th anniversary.

Young Philatelist A415

1978, Oct. 14   Engr.   Perf. 11½
1022 A415 4.50fr dk violet   .22 .15
Youth philately.

Nativity, Notre Dame, Huy — A416

1978, Nov. 18   Engr.   Perf. 11½
1023 A416 6fr black   .28 .15
Christmas 1978.

Tyll Eulenspiegel, Lay Action Emblem — A417

European Parliament Emblem — A418

1979, Mar. 3   Photo.   Perf. 11½
1024 A417 4.50fr multi   .28 .15
10th anniversary of Lay Action Centers.

1979, Mar. 3
1025 A418 8fr multicolored   .50 .15
European Parliament, first direct elections, June 7-10.

St. Michael Banishing Lucifer — A419

1979, Mar. 17   Photo. & Engr.
1026 A419 4.50fr rose red & blk   .20 .15
1027 A419   8fr brt green & blk   .30 .15
    Set value   .20
Millennium of Brussels.

NATO Emblem and Monument A420

1979, Mar. 31   Photo.
1028 A420 3fr multicolored   1.75 .45
NATO, 30th anniv.

Prisoner's Head — A421

1979, Apr. 7   Photo. & Engr.
1029 A421 6fr orange & blk   .25 .15
25th anniversary of the National Political Prisoners' Monument at Breendonk.

Belgium No. Q2 — A422

1979, Apr. 21   Photo.   Perf. 11½
1030 A422 8fr multicolored   .50 .15
Stamp Day 1979.

Mail Coach and Truck A423

Europa: 14fr, Chappe's heliograph, Intelsat satellite and dish antenna.

1979, Apr. 28   Photo. & Engr.
1031 A423 8fr multicolored   .45 .15
1032 A423 14fr multicolored   .90 .40

Chamber of Commerce Emblem — A424

1979, May 19   Photo.   Perf. 11½
1033 A424 8fr multicolored   .35 .15
Verviers Chamber of Commerce and Industry, 175th anniversary.

"50" Emblem A425

1979, June 9   Photo.   Perf. 11½
1034 A425 4.50fr gold & ultra   .30 .15
Natl. Fund for Professional Credit, 50th anniv.

Merchants, Roman Bas-relief A426

1979, June 9
1035 A426 10fr multicolored   .60 .16
Belgian Chamber of Trade and Commerce, 50th anniversary.

"Tintin" as Philatelist A427

1979, Sept. 29   Photo.   Perf. 11½
1036 A427 8fr multicolored   1.10 .15
Youth philately.

Tourism Types of 1977

Designs: No. 1037, Belfry, Thuin. No. 1038, Royal Museum of Central Africa, Tervuren. No. 1039, St. Nicholas Church and cattle, Ciney. No. 1040, St. John's Church and statue of Our Lady, Poperinge.

Perf. 11½ (A401), 13 (A402)
1979, Oct. 22   Photo. & Engr.
1037 A401 5fr multicolored   .20 .15
1038 A402 5fr multicolored   .20 .15
1039 A401 6fr multicolored   .35 .15
1040 A402 6fr multicolored   .35 .15
    Nos. 1037-1040 (4)   1.10
    Set value   .45

Francois Auguste Gevaert A429

Piano, String Instruments A430

Design: 6fr, Emmanuel Durlet.

1979, Nov. 3   *Perf. 11½*

1041	A429	5fr brown	.35 .15
1042	A429	6fr brown	.42 .15
1043	A430	14fr brown	.90 .35
	Nos. 1041-1043 (3)		1.67
	Set value		.55

Francois Auguste Gevaert (1828-1908), musicologist and composer; Emmanuel Durlet (1893-1977), pianist; Queen Elisabeth Musical Chapel Foundation, 40th anniv.

Virgin and Child, Notre Dame, Foy — A431

1979, Nov. 24   **Photo. & Engr.**

1044	A431	6fr lt grnsh blue	.30 .15

Christmas 1979.

Independence, 150th Anniversary A432

1980, Jan. 26   **Photo.**   *Perf. 11½*

1045	A432	9fr purple	.40 .15

Frans van Cauwelaert A433   Spring Flowers A434

1980, Feb. 25   **Engr.**

1046	A433	5fr gray	.22 .15

Frans van Cauwelaert (1880-1961), Minister of State.

1980, Mar. 10   **Photo.**

1047	A434	5fr shown	.24 .15
1048	A434	6.50fr Summer flowers	.32 .15
1049	A434	9fr Autumn flowers	.45 .15
	Nos. 1047-1049 (3)		1.01
	Set value		.30

Ghent Flower Show, Apr. 19-27.

P.T.T., 50th Anniv. A435

1980, Apr. 14   **Photo.**   *Perf. 11½*

1050	A435	10fr multicolored	.45 .22

Belgium No. C4 — A436

1980, Apr. 21

1051	A436	9fr multicolored	.50 .15

Stamp Day.

A437   A438

Europa: 9fr, St. Benedict, by Hans Memling. 14fr, Margaret of Austria (1480-1530).

1980, Apr. 28

1052	A437	9fr multicolored	.45 .15
1053	A437	14fr multicolored	.70 .24

1980, May 10   **Photo.**   *Perf. 11½*

1054	A438	5fr Palais des Nations, Brussels	.25 .15

4th Interparliamentary Conference for European Cooperation and Security, Brussels, May 12-18.

Golden Carriage, 1780, Mons — A439

Tourism: #1056, Canal landscape, Damme.

1980, May 17

1055	A439	6.50fr multi	.32 .20
1056	A439	6.50fr multi	.32 .20

Souvenir Sheet

Royal Mint Theater, Brussels — A440

Photo. & Engr.

1980, May 31   *Perf. 11½*

1057	A440	50fr black	3.25 3.25

150th anniv. of independence. Sold for 75fr.

King Baudouin, 50th Birthday — A441

1980, Sept. 6   **Photo.**   *Perf. 11½*

1058	A441	9fr rose claret	.42 .15

View of Chiny A442

Portal and Court, Diest — A443

1980   **Engr.**   *Perf. 13*

1059	A442	5fr multicolored	.25 .15
1060	A443	5fr multicolored	.25 .15
	Set value		.20

Tourism. Nos. 1059-1060 are not luminescent. Issue dates: No. 1059, Sept. 27; No. 1060, Dec. 13. See Nos. 1072-1075, 1120-1125.

Emblem of Belgian Heart League A444

1980, Oct. 4   **Photo.**   *Perf. 11½*

1061	A444	14fr blue & magenta	.55 .25

Heart Week, Oct. 20-25.

Rodenbach Statue, Roulers — A445

1980, Oct. 11

1062	A445	9fr multicolored	.40 .15

Albrecht Rodenbach (1856-1880), poet.

Youth Philately — A446

1980, Oct. 27   **Photo.**   *Perf. 11½*

1063	A446	5fr multicolored	.22 .15

National Broadcasting Service, 50th Anniversary — A447

1980, Nov. 10

1064	A447	10fr gray & blk	.45 .22

Garland and Nativity, by Daniel Seghers, 17th Century A448

1980, Nov. 17

1065	A448	6.50fr multicolored	.40 .15

Christmas 1980.

Baron de Gerlache, by F.J. Navez — A449   Leopold I, By Geefs — A450

Design: 9fr, Baron de Stassart, by F.J. Navez.

1981, Mar. 16   **Photo.**   *Perf. 11½*

1066	A449	6fr multicolored	.35 .15
1067	A449	9fr multicolored	.55 .15

Photogravure and Engraved

1068	A450	50fr multicolored	3.00 .55

Sesquicentennial of Chamber of Deputies, Senate and Dynasty.

Europa Issue 1981

Tchantchès and Op-Signoorke, Puppets — A451

Photogravure and Engraved

1981, May 4   *Perf. 11½*

1069	A451	9fr shown	.40 .15
1070	A451	14fr d'Artagnan and Woltje	.65 .35

Impression of M.A. de Cock (Founder of Post Museum) — A452

1981, May 18   **Photo.**

1071	A452	9fr multicolored	.40 .15

Stamp Day.

Tourism Types of 1980

Designs: No. 1072, Virgin and Child statue, Our Lady's Church, Tongre-Notre Dame. No. 1073, Egmont Castle, Zottegem. No. 1074, Eau d'Heure River. No. 1075, Tongerlo Abbey, Antwerp.

1981, June 15   **Engr.**   *Perf. 11½*

1072	A442	6fr multi	.35 .15
1073	A442	6fr multi	.35 .20
1074	A443	6.50fr multi	.35 .20
1075	A443	6.50fr multi	.35 .20
	Nos. 1072-1075 (4)		1.40 .75

Soccer Player — A453   E. Remouchamps, Founder — A454

1981, Sept. 5   **Photo.**   *Perf. 11½*

1076	A453	6fr multicolored	.35 .15

Soccer in Belgium centenary; Royal Antwerp Soccer Club.

1981, Sept. 5   **Photo. & Engr.**

1077	A454	6.50fr multi	.40 .15

Walloon Language and Literature Club 125th anniv.

Audit Office Sesquicentennial — A455

1981, Sept. 12   **Engr.**
1078 A455 10fr tan & dk brn   .60 .24

French
Horn — A456

1981, Sept. 12   **Photo.**
1079 A456 6.50fr multi   .40 .15
Vredekring (Peace Circle) Band of Antwerp centenary.

Souvenir Sheet

20F Pieta, by Ben
Genaux — A457

1981, Sept. 19   **Photo.**   *Perf. 11½*
1080 A457 20fr multicolored   1.75 1.40
Mining disaster at Marcinelle, 25th anniv. Sold for 30fr.

Mausoleum of Marie of Burgundy and Charles the Bold, Bruges — A458

1981, Oct. 10   **Photo. & Engr.**
1081 A458 50fr multi   2.75 .60

Youth
Philately — A459

1981, Oct. 24   **Photo.**
1082 A459 6fr multi   .28 .15

Type of 1977 and

A459a   A460

King Baudouin
A460a

Photo. and Engr.; Photo.
1980-86   *Perf. 13½x14, 11½*

1084	A386	65c brt rose	.20	.15
1085	A386	1fr on 5fr grn	.20	.15
1086	A386	7fr brt rose	.55	.15
1087	A386	8fr grnsh bl	.60	.15
1088	A386	9fr dl org	.55	.15
1089	A459a	10fr blue	.85	.15
1090	A459a	11fr dl red	.90	.15
1091	A459a	12fr grn	.90	.15
1092	A459a	13fr scar	.85	.15
1093	A459a	15fr red org	1.25	.20
1094	A459a	20fr dk bl	1.50	.28
1095	A459a	22fr lilac	1.65	.30
1096	A459a	23fr gray grn	1.00	.55
1097	A459a	30fr brown	2.25	.40
1098	A459a	40fr red org	2.50	.55
1099	A460	50fr lt grnsh bl & bl	3.25	.30
1100	A460a	50fr tan & dk brn	3.25	.60
1101	A460	65fr pale lil & blk	4.50	.90
1102	A460	100fr lt bis brn & dk bl	6.75	1.25
1103	A460a	100fr lt bl & dk bl	6.75	1.25
		Nos. 1084-1103 (20)	40.25	7.93

Issued: 65c, 4/14/80; 1fr, 5/3/82; 7fr, 5/17/82; 8fr, 5/9/83; 9fr, 2/11/85; 65fr, No. 1099, 1102, 11/5/81; 10fr, 11/15/82; 11fr, 4/5/83; 12fr, 1/23/84; 15fr, 22fr, 30fr, No. 1100, 3/26/84; 20fr, 40fr, No. 1103, 6/12/84; 23fr, 2/25/85; 13fr, 3/10/86. See Nos. 1231-1234.

Max Waller,   The Spirit
Movement   Drinkers, by
Founder   Gustave van de
A461   Woestyne
           A462

Fernand Severin,   Jan van
Poet, 50th Death   Ruusbroec,
Anniv. — A463   Flemish Mystic,
            500th Birth
            Anniv. — A464

Thought and Man   Nativity, 16th
TV Series, 25th   Cent. Engraving
Anniv.   A466
A465

1981, Nov. 7

1104	A461	6fr multi	.30	.15
1105	A462	6.50fr multi	.35	.18
1106	A463	9fr multi	.50	.15
1107	A464	10fr multi	.80	.22
1108	A465	14fr multi	.75	.35
		Nos. 1104-1108 (5)	2.70	1.05

La Jeune Belgique cultural movement cent. (6fr).

1981, Nov. 21
1109 A466 6.50fr multi   .30 .15
Christmas 1981.

Royal Conservatory of Music
Sesquicentennial — A467

Design: 9fr, Judiciary sesquicentennial.

1982, Jan. 25   **Photo.**   *Perf. 11½*
1110 A467 6.50fr multi   .30 .15
1111 A467 9fr multi   .40 .15
        Set value   .22

A468   A469

1982, Mar. 1
1112 A468 6fr Cyclotron   .35 .15
1113 A468 14fr Galaxy, telescope   .85 .35
1114 A468 50fr Koch   3.00 .65
     Nos. 1112-1114 (3)   4.20 1.15
Radio-isotope production, Natl. Radio-elements Institute, Fleurus (6fr); Royal Belgian Observatory (14fr); centenary of TB bacillus discovery (50fr).

1982, Apr. 17   **Photo.**   *Perf. 11½*
1115 A469 6.50fr multi   .32 .15
Joseph Lemaire (1882-1966), Minister of State.

Europa
1982 — A470

1982, May 1
1116 A470 10fr Universal suffrage   .48 .15
1117 A470 17fr Edict of Tolerance,
           1781   .80 .40

Stamp Day — A471

1982, May 22   **Photo. & Engr.**
1118 A471 10fr multi   .50 .15

67th World
Esperanto
Congress,
Anvers
A472

1982, June 7   **Photo.**   *Perf. 11½*
1119 A472 12fr Tower of Babel   .60 .30

Tourism Type of 1980

Designs: No. 1120, Tower of Gosselies. No. 1121, Zwijveke Abbey, Dendermonde. No. 1122, Stavelot Abbey. No. 1123, Villers-la-Ville Abbey ruins. No. 1124, Geraardsbergen Abbey entrance. No. 1125, Beveren Pillory.

1982, June 21   **Photo. & Engr.**

1120	A443	7fr lt bl & blk	.50	.15
1121	A443	7fr lt grn & blk	.50	.15
1122	A442	7.50fr tan & dk brn	.55	.25
1123	A442	7.50fr lt vio & pur	.55	.25
1124	A443	7.50fr slate & blk	.55	.25
1125	A443	7.50fr beige & blk	.55	.25
		Nos. 1120-1125 (6)	3.20	1.30

Self Portrait, by   Abraham Hans,
L.P. Boon (b.   Writer (1882-
1912)   1932)
A473   A474

Designs: 10fr, Adoration of the Shepherds, by Hugo van der Goes (1440-1482). 12fr, The King on His Throne, carving by M. de Gheldrode (1898-1962). 17fr, Madonna and Child, by Pieter Paulus (1881-1959).

1982, Sept. 13   **Photo.**   *Perf. 11½*

1126	A473	7fr multicolored	.50	.15
1127	A473	10fr multicolored	.60	.15
1128	A473	12fr multicolored	.70	.35
1129	A473	17fr multicolored	1.00	.35
		Nos. 1126-1129 (4)	2.80	
		Set value		.82

1982, Sept. 27
1130 A474 17fr multicolored   1.10 .35

Youth Philately
and Scouting
A475

1982, Oct. 2   **Photo.**   *Perf. 11½*
1131 A475 7fr multicolored   .50 .15

Grand Orient Lodge
of Belgium
Sesquicentennial
A476

1982, Oct. 16   **Photo. & Engr.**
1132 A476 10fr Man taking oath   .60 .15

Cardinal Joseph
Cardijn (1882-
1967)
A477

1982, Nov. 13   **Photo.**
1133 A477 10fr multicolored   .48 .15

St. Francis of Assisi
(1182-1226) — A478

1982, Nov. 27
1134 A478 20fr multicolored   .90 .30

Horse-drawn
Trolley
A479

1983, Feb. 12   **Photo.**   *Perf. 11½*
1135 A479 7.50fr shown   .38 .22
1136 A479 10fr Electric trolley   .50 .15
1137 A479 50fr Trolley, diff.   2.50 .50
     Nos. 1135-1137 (3)   3.38 .87

Intl. Fed. for Periodical Press, 24th World Congress, Brussels, May 11-13 — A480

1983, Mar. 19   Photo.   Perf. 11½
1138 A480 20fr multicolored   1.00 .25

Homage to Women
A481

1983, Apr. 16
1139 A481 8fr Operator   .45 .15
1140 A481 11fr Homemaker   .55 .15
1141 A481 20fr Executive   .95 .25
      Nos. 1139-1141 (3)   1.95
      Set value   .40

Stamp Day — A482

1983, Apr. 23
1142 A482 11fr multicolored   .60 .15

Procession of the Precious Blood, Bruges
A483

1983, Apr. 30   Photo.   Perf. 11½
1143 A483 8fr multi   .60 .15

Europa 1983
A484

Paintings by P. Delvaux. 11fr vert.

1983, May 14
1144 A484 11fr Common Man   .65 .15
1145 A484 20fr Night Train   1.25 .45

Manned Flight Bicentenary
A485

1983, June 11   Photo.   Perf. 11½
1146 A485 11fr Balloon over city   .65 .15
1147 A485 22fr Country   1.40 .45

Our Lady's Church, Hastiere
A486

1983, June 25
1148 A486 8fr shown   .40 .18
1149 A486 8fr Landen   .40 .18
1150 A486 8fr Park, Mouscron   .40 .18
1151 A486 8fr Wijnendale Castle, Torhout   .40 .18
      Nos. 1148-1151 (4)   1.60 .72

Tineke Festival, Heule — A487

1983, Sept. 10   Photo.
1152 A487 8fr multi   .40 .15

Enterprise Year Emblem
A488

1983, Sept. 24
1153 A488 11fr multicolored   .55 .15
European year for small and medium-sized enterprises and craft industry.

Youth Philately — A489

1983, Oct. 10   Photo.   Perf. 11½
1154 A489 8fr multicolored   .40 .15

Belgian Exports — A490

1983, Oct. 24   Perf. 11½
1155 A490 10fr Diamond industry   .55 .15
1156 A490 10fr Metallurgy   .55 .15
1157 A490 10fr Textile industry   .55 .15
      Nos. 1155-1157 (3)   1.65
      Set value   .30
See Nos. 1161-1164.

A491   A492

1983, Nov. 7
1158 A491 20fr multicolored   1.00 .25
Hendrik Conscience, novelist (1812-1883).

Leopold III Type of 1936

1983, Dec. 12   Engr.   Perf. 12x11½
1159 A84 11fr black   .55 .15
Leopold III memorial (1901-1983), King 1934-1951.

Photogravure and Engraved
1984, Jan. 14   Perf. 11½
1160 A492 11fr multicolored   .55 .15
Free University of Brussels, sesquicentennial.

Exports Type of 1983

1984, Jan. 28   Photo.
1161 A490 11fr Chemicals   .55 .15
1162 A490 11fr Food   .55 .15
1163 A490 11fr Transportation equipment   .55 .15
1164 A490 11fr Technology   .55 .15
      Nos. 1161-1164 (4)   2.20
      Set value   .48

A494   A495

1984, Feb. 11   Photo. & Engr.
1165 A494 8fr tan & dk brn   .40 .15
50th death anniv. of King Albert I.

1984, Mar. 3   Photo.
Souvenir Sheet
1166   Sheet of 2   2.00 2.00
   a. A495 10fr Archery   .55 .55
   b. A495 24fr Dressage   1.40 1.40
1984 Olympics. See Nos. B1029-B1030.

Family, Globe, Birds   St. John Bosco
A496   Canonization
                              A497

1984, Mar. 24   Photo.   Perf. 11½
1167 A496 12fr multicolored   .60 .15
"Movement without a Name" peace org.

1984, Apr. 7
1168 A497 8fr multicolored   .40 .15

Europa (1959-84)
A498

1984, May 5   Photo.   Perf. 11½
1169 A498 12fr black & red   .75 .15
1170 A498 22fr black & ultra   1.40 .30

Stamp Day — A499

1984, May 19
1171 A499 12fr No. 52   .60 .15

2nd European Parliament Elections
A500

1984, May 26
1172 A500 12fr multicolored   .60 .15

Royal Military School, 150th Anniv. — A501

1984, June 9   Photo.   Perf. 11½
1173 A501 22fr Hat   1.10 .25

Notre-Dame de la Chappelle, Brussels
A502

Churches: No. 1175, St. Martin's, Montignyle-Tilleul. No. 1176, Tielt, vert.

Perf. 11½x12, 12x11½
1984, June 23   Photo. & Engr.
1174 A502 10fr multicolored   .55 .15
1175 A502 10fr multicolored   .55 .15
1176 A502 10fr multicolored   .55 .15
      Nos. 1174-1176 (3)   1.65 .45

50th Anniv. of Chirojeugd (Christian Youth Movement)
A503

1984, Sept. 15   Photo.   Perf. 11½
1177 A503 10fr Emblem   .50 .15

Affligem Abbey
A504

1984, Oct. 6   Photo. & Engr.
1178 A504 8fr Averbode, vert.   .40 .25
1179 A504 22fr Chimay, vert.   1.25 .25
1180 A504 24fr Rochefort, vert.   1.25 .38
1181 A504 50fr shown   2.50 .50
      Nos. 1178-1181 (4)   5.40 1.38

Youth Philately
A505

1984, Oct. 20   Photo.
1182 A505 8fr Postman smurf   .45 .15

Arthur Meulemans (1884-1966), Composer — A506

1984, Nov. 17   Photo. & Engr.
1183 A506 12fr multi   .60 .15

St. Norbert, 850th   Europalia
Death   '85 — A508
Anniv. — A507

1985, Jan. 14   Photo. & Engr.
1184 A507 22fr sepia & beige   1.10 .30

1985, Jan. 21   Photo.
1185 A508 12fr Virgin of Louvain   .65 .15

Belgian Assoc. of Professional Journalists, Cent. — A509

1985, Feb. 11   **Photo.**
1186 A509 9fr multicolored   .42 .15

Ghent Flower Festival, Orchids A510

Visit of Pope John Paul II A511

Photogravure and Engraved
1985, Mar. 18   *Perf. 11½*
1187 A510 12fr Vanda coerules   .70 .15
1188 A510 12fr Phalaenopsis   .70 .15
1189 A510 12fr Suphrolaelio cattlea
            riffe   .70 .15
        Nos. 1187-1189 (3)   2.10 .45

1985, Apr. 1   **Photo.**
1190 A511 12fr multicolored   .60 .15

Belgian Worker's Party Cent. — A512

1985, Apr. 15   **Photo.**
1191 A512 9fr Chained factory gate   .42 .15
1192 A512 12fr Broken wall, red flag   .60 .15
        Set value   .24

Jean de Bast (1883-1975), Engraver A513

1985, Apr. 22   **Engr.**
1193 A513 12fr blue black   .60 .15
        Stamp Day.

Public Transportation Year — A514

Design: 9fr, Steam tram locomotive Type 18, 1896. 12fr, Locomotive Elephant and tender, 1835. 23fr, Type 23 tank engine, 1904. 24fr, Type I Pacific locomotive, 1935. 50fr, Type 27 electric locomotive, 1975.

1985, May 6   **Photo.**
1194 A514 9fr multicolored   .65 .20
1195 A514 12fr multicolored   .85 .20
1196 A514 23fr multicolored   1.50 .35
1197 A514 24fr multicolored   1.90 .40
        Nos. 1194-1197 (4)   4.90 1.15
        Souvenir Sheet
1198 A514 50fr multicolored   4.50 3.75

Europa 1985 — A515

1985, May 13   **Photo.**
1199 A515 12fr Cesar Franck at or-
            gan, 1887   .80 .15
1200 A515 23fr Folk figures   1.50 .25

26th Navigation Congress, Brussels A516

1985, June 10   **Photo.**   *Perf. 11½*
1201 A516 23fr Zeebruge Harbor   1.25 .25
1202 A516 23fr Projected lock at
            Strepy-Thieu   1.25 .25

St. Martin's Church, Marcinelle A517

Tourism: No. 1203, Church of the Assumption of Our Lady, Avernas-le-Baudouin, vert. No. 1204, Church of the Old Beguinage, Tongres, vert. No. 1206, Private residence, Puyenbroeck.

1985, June 24   *Perf. 11½*
1203 A517 12fr multicolored   .60 .15
1204 A517 12fr multicolored   .60 .15
1205 A517 12fr multicolored   .60 .15
1206 A517 12fr multicolored   .60 .15
        Nos. 1203-1206 (4)   2.40
        Set value   .48

Queen Astrid (1905-1935) A518

Baking Pies for the Mattetart of Geraardsbergen A519

1985, Sept. 2   *Perf. 11½*
1207 A518 12fr brown   .60 .15

1985, Sept. 16
Folk events: 24fr, Children dancing, centenary of the St. Lambert de Hermalle-Argenteau Le Rouges youth organization.
1208 A519 12fr multicolored   .60 .15
1209 A519 24fr multicolored   .95 .28

Liberation from German Occupation, 40th Anniv. — A520

Allegories: 9fr, Dove, liberation of concentration camps. 23fr, Battle of Ardennes. 24fr, Destroyer, liberation of the River Scheldt estuary.

1985, Sept. 30   **Photo.**   *Perf. 11½*
1210 A520 9fr multicolored   .50 .25
1211 A520 23fr multicolored   1.25 .65
1212 A520 24fr multicolored   1.25 .68
        Nos. 1210-1212 (3)   3.00 1.58

Ernest Claes (1885-1968), Author A521

1985, Oct. 7
1213 A521 9fr Portrait, book character   .48 .25

Intl. Youth Year — A522

1985, Oct. 21
1214 A522 9fr Nude in repose, angel   .50 .25

King Baudouin & Queen Fabiola, 25th Wedding Anniv. — A523

1985, Dec. 9
1215 A523 12fr multicolored   .52 .38

Birds — A524

Photo. (50c-2fr, No. 1220, 4.50fr-6fr, No. 1229, 10fr), Typo. (Others)
1985-91   *Perf. 11½*
1216 A524 50c Roitelet huppe   .15 .15
1217 A524 1fr Pic Epechette   .15 .15
1218 A524 2fr Moineau friquet   .15 .15
1219 A524 3fr Gros bec   .15 .15
1220 A524 3fr Bruant des roseax   .25 .15
1221 A524 3.50fr Rouge gorge   .20 .15
1222 A524 4fr Gorge bleue   .25 .15
1223 A524 4.50fr Traquet Patre   .35 .15
1224 A524 5fr Sittele tporchepot   .35 .15
1225 A524 6fr Bouvreuil   .40 .15
1226 A524 7fr Mesange bleue   .45 .15
1227 A524 8fr Martin-pechuer   .45 .15
1228 A524 9fr Chardonneret   .35 .15
1229 A524 9fr Grive musicienne   .65 .15
1230 A524 10fr Pinson   .65 .15
        Nos. 1216-1230 (15)   4.95
        Set value   2.00

Issued: 7fr, 9/7/87; 5fr, 6fr, 9/12/88; 4fr, 4/17/89; 2fr, 12/4/89; 1fr, 1/8/90; 10fr, 1/15/90; 50c, #1220, 1229, 9/30/91; others, 9/30/85.
See Nos. 1432-1447, 1627, 1641, 1645, 1651, 1660.

King Type of 1981

1986-90   **Photo.**   *Perf. 11½*
1231 A459a 14fr black   .80 .20
1232 A459a 24fr dk grysh green   1.10 .85
1233 A459a 25fr blue black   1.45 .38
1234 A460a 200fr sage grn & dl
            gray grn   11.00 2.00
        Nos. 1231-1234 (4)   14.35 3.43

Issued: 24fr, 4/7/86; 200fr, 11/3/86; 14fr, 1/15/90; 25fr, 2/19/90.

Congo Stamp Cent. — A525

1986, Jan. 27   **Photo.**   *Perf. 11½*
1236 A525 10fr Belgian Congo #3   .42 .15
        See Zaire No. 1230.

Carnival Cities of Aalst and Binche A526

Folklore: masks, giants.

1986, Feb. 3
1237 A526 9fr Aalst Belfry   .48 .15
1238 A526 12fr Binche Gilles   .60 .18

Intl. Peace Year — A527

1986, Mar. 10
1239 A527 23fr Emblem, dove   1.25 .35

Stamp Day — A528

1986, Apr. 21   **Photo.**   *Perf. 11½*
1240 A528 13fr Artifacts   .65 .42

Europa 1986 — A529

1986, May 5
1241 A529 13fr Fish   .65 .65
1242 A529 24fr Flora   1.40 .85

Dogs — A530

St. Ludger's Church, Zele — A531

1986, May 26   **Photo.**   *Perf. 11½*
1243 A530 9fr Malines sheepdog   .65 .30
1244 A530 13fr Tervueren sheepdog   .85 .45
1245 A530 24fr Groenendael sheep-
            dog   1.65 .82
1246 A530 26fr Flemish cattle dog   1.65 .85
        Nos. 1243-1246 (4)   4.80 2.42

1986, June 30   **Photo. & Engr.**
Designs: No. 1248, Waver Town Hall. No. 1249, Nederzwalm Canal, horiz. No. 1250, Chapel of Our Lady of the Dunes, Bredene. No. 1251, Licot Castle, Viroinval, horiz. No. 1252, Eynenbourg Castle, La Calamine, horiz.
1247 A531 9fr multicolored   .60 .30
1248 A531 9fr multicolored   .60 .30
1249 A531 13fr multicolored   .80 .45
1250 A531 13fr multicolored   .80 .45
1251 A531 13fr multicolored   .80 .45
1252 A531 13fr multicolored   .80 .45
        Nos. 1247-1252 (6)   4.40 2.40

Youth Philately
A532

1986, Sept. 1 **Photo.** *Perf. 11¹/₂*
1253 A532 9fr dl ol grn, blk & dk red .50 .32
Cartoon Exhibition, Knokke.

Famous
Men — A533

Designs: 9fr, Constant Permeke, painter, sculptor. 13fr, Baron Michel-Edmond de Selys Longchamps, scientist. 24fr, Felix Timmermans, writer. 26fr, Maurice Careme, poet.

1986, Sept. 29
1254 A533 9fr multicolored .52 .32
1255 A533 13fr multicolored .75 .45
1256 A533 24fr multicolored 1.40 .82
1257 A533 26fr multicolored 1.50 .90
  Nos. 1254-1257 (4) 4.17 2.49

Royal
Academy for
Dutch
Language and
Literature,
Cent. — A534

1986, Oct. 6 **Engr.**
1258 A534 9fr dark blue .52 .32

Natl. Beer
Industry
A535

Perf. 12¹/₂x11¹/₂
1986, Oct. 13 **Photo.**
1259 A535 13fr Glass, barley, hops .70 .50

Provincial Law
and Councils,
150th Anniv.
A536

1986, Oct. 27 *Perf. 11¹/₂*
1260 A536 13fr Stylized map .70 .50

Christian
Trade Union,
Cent. — A537

1986, Dec. 13 **Photo.** *Perf. 11¹/₂*
1261 A537 9fr shown .45 .35
1262 A537 13fr design reversed .65 .50

Flanders Technology
Intl. — A538

1987, Mar. 2 **Photo.**
1263 A538 13fr multi .70 .50

EUROPALIA '87, Austrian Cultural
Events — A539

Design: Woman, detail of a fresco by Gustav Klimt, Palais Stoclet, Brussels.

1987, Apr. 4 **Photo.** *Perf. 11¹/₂*
1264 A539 13fr multicolored .70 .50

Stamp Day
1987 — A540

Portrait: Jakob Wiener (1815-1899), 1st engraver of Belgian stamps.

1987, Apr. 11 **Photo. & Engr.**
1265 A540 13fr lt greenish blue & sage
   grn .70 .50

Folklore
A541

1987, Apr. 25 **Photo.**
1266 A541 9fr Penitents procession,
   Veurne .45 .35
1267 A541 13fr Play of John and Alice,
   Wavre .65 .50

Europa 1987 — A542

Modern architecture: 13fr, Louvain-la-Neuve Church. 24fr, Regional Housing Assoc. Tower, St. Maartensdal at Louvain.

1987, May 9 **Photo.**
1268 A542 13fr multicolored .85 .55
1269 A542 24fr multicolored 1.50 1.00

Statue of
Andre-Ernest
Gretry (1741-
1813), French
Composer
A543

1987, May 23
1270 A543 24fr multicolored 1.50 1.00
Wallonie Royal Opera, Liege, 20th anniv.

Tourism — A544

Designs: No. 1271, Statues of Jan Breydel and Pieter de Conin, Bruges. No. 1272, Boondael Chapel, Brussels. No. 1273, Windmill, Keerbergen. No. 1274, St. Christopher's Church, Racour. No. 1275, Virelles Lake, Chimay.

1987, June 13
1271 A544 13fr multicolored 1.00 .55
1272 A544 13fr multicolored 1.00 .55
1273 A544 13fr multicolored 1.00 .55
1274 A544 13fr multicolored 1.00 .55
1275 A544 13fr multicolored 1.00 .55
  Nos. 1271-1275 (5) 5.00 2.75

Royal Belgian Rowing Assoc.,
Cent. — A545

European Volleyball
Championships
A546

1987, Sept. 5
1276 A545 9fr multicolored .50 .38
1277 A546 13fr multicolored .75 .55

Foreign Trade
Year — A547

1987, Sept. 12
1278 A547 13fr multi .75 .55

Belgian Social
Reform,
Cent. — A548

1987, Sept. 19
1279 A548 26fr Leisure, by P. Paulus 1.45 1.10

Youth Philately
A549

1987, Oct. 3
1280 A549 9fr multi .50 .38

Newspaper
Centennials
A550

1987, Dec. 12
1281 A550 9fr Le Soir .55 .42
1282 A550 9fr Hett Lattste Nieuws,
   vert. .55 .42

The Sea — A551

Designs: a, Lighthouse, trawler, rider and mount. b, Trawler, youths playing volleyball on beach. c, Cruise ship, sailboat, beach and cabana. d, Shore, birds.

1988, Feb. 6 **Photo.** *Perf. 11¹/₂*
1283 Strip of 4 + label 2.50 1.80
a.-d. A551 10fr any single .62 .45
No. 1283 has a continuous design.

Dynamism of
the Regions
A552

1988, Mar. 5 **Photo.** *Perf. 11¹/₂*
1284 A552 13fr Operation Athena .80 .58
1285 A552 13fr Flanders Alive Campaign .80 .58

Stamp Day — A553   Europa
1988 — A554

Painting: 19th Cent. Postman, by James Thiriar.

1988, Apr. 16 **Photo. & Engr.**
1286 A553 13fr buff & sepia .80 .58

1988, May 9 **Photo.** *Perf. 11¹/₂*
Transport and communication.
1287 A554 13fr Satellite dish 1.10 .58
1288 A554 24fr Non-polluting combustion engine 1.90 1.10

Tourism
A555

Designs: No. 1289, Romanesque watchtower, ca. 12th-13th cent., Amay, vert. No. 1290, Our Lady of Hanswijk Basilica, 988, Mechelen, vert. No. 1291, St. Sernin's Church, 16th cent., Waimes. No. 1292, Old Town Hall, 1637, and village water pump, 1761, Peer, vert. No. 1293, Our Lady of Bon-Secours Basilica, 1892, Peruwelz.

Photo. & Engr.
1988, June 20 *Perf. 11¹/₂*
1289 A555 9fr beige & blk .50 .38
1290 A555 9fr lt blue & blk .50 .38
1291 A555 9fr pale blue grn & blk .50 .38
1292 A555 13fr pale pink & blk .75 .55
1293 A555 13fr pale gray & blk .75 .55
  Nos. 1289-1293 (5) 3.00 2.24
Our Lady of Hanswijk Basilica millennium (No. 1290); Waimes village, 1100th anniv. (No. 1291).

15

BELGIQUE-BELGIE
Jean Monnet
(1888-1979),
French
Economist — A556

1988, Sept. 12   *Perf. 11½*
1294 A556 13fr black   .70 .52

1988, Sept. 17   **Photo.**
Academies building and: No. 1296, Lyre, quill pen, open book and atomic symbols.

1295 A557 9fr shown   .50 .38
1296 A557 9fr multi   .50 .38
Royal Academy of Medicine (#1295); Royal Academy of Science, Literature and Fine Arts (#1296).

Cultural
Heritage
A558

Artifacts: 9fr, Statue and mask in the Antwerp Ethnographical Museum. 13fr, Sarcophagus, St. Martin's Church, Trazegnies. 24fr, Church organ, Geraardsbergen. 26fr, Shrine, St. Hadelin's Church, Vise.

1988, Sept. 24
1297 A558   9fr multi   .50 .38
1298 A558 13fr multi   .70 .52
1299 A558 24fr multi   1.30 1.00
1300 A558 26fr multi   1.40 1.05
Nos. 1297-1300 (4)   3.90 2.95

Youth
Philately
A559

1988, Oct. 10
1301 A559 9fr multi   .50 .38

Natl. Postal
Savings
Bank, 75th
Anniv.
A560

1988, Nov. 7
1302 A560 13fr multi   .70 .52

Christmas
1988 and
New Year
1989 — A561

1988, Nov. 21
1303 A561 9fr Winter landscape   .50 .38

Royal
Mounted
Guard, 50th
Anniv.
A562

1988, Dec. 12
1304 A562 13fr multi   .75 .55

Printing
Presses
A563

9fr, J. Moretus I, Antwerp Museum, vert. 24fr, Stanhope, Printing Museum, Brussels, vert. 26fr, Litho Krause, Royal Museum, Mariemont.

1988, Dec. 19   **Engr.**
1305 A563   9fr bl blk & blk   .52 .40
1306 A563 24fr dark red brn   1.40 1.05
1307 A563 26fr grn & slate grn   1.50 1.15
Nos. 1305-1307 (3)   3.42 2.60

Lace — A564

1989, Mar. 20   **Photo.**
1308 A564   9fr Marche-en-Famenne   .50 .38
1309 A564 13fr Brussels   .70 .52
1310 A564 13fr Brugge   .70 .52
Nos. 1308-1310 (3)   1.90 1.42

Stamp
Day — A565

1989, Apr. 24   **Photo. & Engr.**
1311 A565 13fr Mail coach, post chaise   .75 .55

Europa
1989 — A566

Royal Academy of
Fine Arts,
Antwerp, 325th
Anniv. — A567

Children's toys.

1989, May 8   **Photo.**
1312 A566 13fr Marbles, horiz.   .75 .52
1313 A566 24fr Jumping-jack   1.35 1.00

1989, May 22   *Perf. 11½*
1314 A567 13fr multi   .75 .52

European Parliament 3rd
Elections — A568

Illustration reduced.

1989, June 5   **Photo.**
1315 A568 13fr Brussels   .75 .52

Declaration of Rights of Man and the
Citizen, Bicent. — A569

1989, June 12   *Perf. 11½*
1316 A569 13fr multi + label   .75 .52

Tourism
A570

Designs: No. 1317, St. Tillo's Church, Izegem. No. 1318, Logne Castle, Ferrieres. No. 1319, St. Laurentius's Church, Lokeren. No. 1320, Antoing Castle, Antoing. Nos. 1318-1320 vert.

1989, June 26   **Photo. & Engr.**
1317 A570   9fr shown   .50 .38
1318 A570   9fr multi   .50 .38
1319 A570 13fr multi   .75 .52
1320 A570 13fr multi   .75 .52
Nos. 1317-1320 (4)   2.50 1.80

Ducks — A571

1989, Sept. 4   **Photo.**   *Perf. 12*
Booklet Stamps
1321 A571 13fr Mallard (8a)   1.25 .50
1322 A571 13fr Winter teal (8b)   1.25 .50
1323 A571 13fr Shoveller (8c)   1.25 .50
1324 A571 13fr Pintail (8d)   1.25 .50
   a.   Bklt. pane of 4, #1321-1324   5.00

Shigefusa
Uesugi, a
Seated
Japanese
Warrior,
13th Cent.
A572

1989, Sept. 18   *Perf. 11½*
1325 A572 24fr multicolored   1.50 .50
Europalia.

Education League,
125th
Anniv. — A573

1989, Sept. 25
1326 A573 13fr multicolored   .80 .20

Treaty of London,
150th
Anniv. — A574

Mr.
Nibbs — A575

1989, Oct. 2   **Photo.**
1327 A574 13fr Map of Limburg Provinces   .80 .52
See Netherlands No. 750.

1989, Oct. 9   *Perf. 11½*
1328 A575 9fr multicolored   .60 .20
Youth philately promotion.

Christmas,
New Year
1990
A576

1989, Nov. 20   **Photo.**
1329 A576 9fr Salvation Army band   .60 .15

Fr. Damien
(1840-89),
Missionary,
Molokai Is.
Leper Colony,
Hawaii
A577

1989, Nov. 27   **Photo.**
1330 A577 24fr multicolored   1.50 .50

Father Adolf
Daens — A578

1989, Dec. 11   **Photo. & Engr.**
1331 A578 9fr pale & dk grn   .55 .15

The Young Post Rider, an
Engraving by Albrecht
Durer
A579

Ghent Flower
Festival
A580

1990, Jan. 12   **Photo. & Engr.**
1332 A579 14fr buff & red blk   .75 .55
Postal communications in Europe, 500th anniv.
See Austria No. 1486, Germany No. 1592, Berlin No. 9N584 and German Democratic Republic No. 2791.

1990, Mar. 3   **Photo.**
1333 A580 10fr Iris florentina   .55 .40
1334 A580 14fr Cattleya harrisoniana   .75 .55
1335 A580 14fr Lilium bulbiferum   .75 .55
Nos. 1333-1335 (3)   2.05 1.50

Intl. Women's Day — A581

1990, Mar. 12   Photo.   Perf. 11½
1336 A581 25fr Emilienne Brunfaut   1.45 1.05

Wheelchair
Basketball — A582

Sports.

1990, Mar. 19
1337 A582 10fr multicolored   .58 .42
1338 A582 14fr multicolored   .80 .60
1339 A582 25fr shown   1.45 1.05
    Nos. 1337-1339 (3)   2.83 2.07

Special Olympics (10fr); and 1990 World Cup
Soccer Championships, Italy (14fr).

Natl. Water
Supply Soc.,
75th Anniv.
A583

1990, Apr. 2
1340 A583 14fr Water means life   .80 .60

Postman Roulin, by
Van Gogh — A584

1990, Apr. 9
1341 A584 14fr multicolored   .80 .60
    Stamp Day.

Labor Day,
Cent.
A585

1990, Apr. 30
1342 A585 25fr multicolored   1.45 1.05

Europa 1990
A586

Post offices.

1990, May 7   Photo. & Engr.
1343 A586 14fr Ostend 1   .80 .60
1344 A586 25fr Liege 1, vert.   1.45 1.05

18-Day Campaign, 1940 — A587

1990, May 14   Photo.   Perf. 11½
1345 A587 14fr Lys Monument,
    Courtrai   .80 .60
    Resistance of German occupation.

Stamp Collecting Promotion Type of 1988
Souvenir Sheet

Various flowers from *Sixty Roses for a Queen,* by
P.J. Redoute (1759-1840): a, *Rose tricolore.* b,
Belle Rubaree. c, *Mycrophylla.* d, Amelie rose. e,
Adelaide rose. f, Helene rose.

1990, June 2   Photo. & Engr.
1346   Sheet of 6   40.00 40.00
a.-c. SP487 14fr any single   1.40 1.40
d.-f. SP487 25fr any single   2.50 2.50

BELGICA '90, Brussels, June 2-10. sold for 220fr.

Battle of Waterloo, 1815 — A588

Design: Marshal Ney leading the French cavalry.
(Illustration reduced.)

1990, June 18   Photo.
1352 A588 25fr multi + label   1.60 1.15

Tourism
A589

1990, July 9
1353 A589 10fr Antwerp   .58 .45
1354 A589 10fr Dendermonde   .58 .45
1355 A589 14fr Gerpinnes, vert.   .80 .60
1356 A589 14fr Lommel   .80 .60
1357 A589 14fr Watermael   .80 .60
    Nos. 1353-1357 (5)   3.56 2.70

A590   A590a

King Baudouin
A590b

1990-92   Photo.   Perf. 11½
1364 A590 14fr multicolored   .80 .60
1365 A590a 15fr rose car   .85 .65
1366 A590a 28fr blue green   1.75 1.30
1367 A590b 100fr slate green   6.00 1.50
    Nos. 1364-1367 (4)   9.40 4.05
    Issue dates: 14fr, Sept. 7; 15fr, Apr. 1; 28fr, Aug.
3, 1992; 100fr, Sept. 14, 1992.

Fish — A591

Designs: No. 1383, Perch (Perche). No. 1384,
Minnow (Vairon). No. 1385, Bitterling (Bouviere).
No. 1386, Stickleback (Epinoche).

1990, Sept. 8   Perf. 12
1383 A591 14fr multicolored   1.25 .60
1384 A591 14fr multicolored   1.25 .60
1385 A591 14fr multicolored   1.25 .60
1386 A591 14fr multicolored   1.25 .60
a.   Bklt. pane of 4, #1383-1386   5.00

Youth
Philately
A592

1990, Oct. 13   Perf. 11½
1387 A592 10fr multicolored   .58 .45

St. Bernard, 900th
Birth Anniv. — A593

1990, Nov. 5   Photo & Engr.
1388 A593 25fr black & buff   1.45 1.10

Winter
Scene by
Jozef Lucas
A594

1990, Nov. 12   Photo.
1389 A594 10fr   .58 .42
    Christmas.

Self-Portrait
A595

Paintings by David Teniers (1610-1690).

1990, Dec. 3
1390 A595 10fr shown   .58 .42
1391 A595 14fr Dancers   .82 .62
1392 A595 25fr Bowlers   1.45 1.10
    Nos. 1390-1392 (3)   2.85 2.14

A596   A597

Designs: 14fr, The Sower by Constantin Meunier
(1831-1905). 25fr, Brabo Fountain by Jef
Lambeaux (1852-1908).

Photo. & Engr.

1991, Mar. 18   Perf. 11½
1393 A596 14fr buff & blk   .82 .62
1394 A596 25fr lt bl & dk bl   1.45 1.10

1991, Apr. 8   Photo.   Perf. 11½
1395 A597 14fr Rhythmic gymnastics   .65 .50
1396 A597 10fr Korfball   .65 .50

No. 1395, European Youth Olympics. No. 1396,
Korfball World Championships.

Stamp Printing Office, Mechlin — A598

1991, Apr. 22
1397 A598 14fr multicolored   .90 .65
    Stamp Day.

Liberal Trade
Union, Cent.
A599

1991, Apr. 29
1398 A599 25fr blue & lt blue   1.50 1.15

Europa
A600

1991, May 6
1399 A600 14fr Olympus-1 satellite   .90 .65
1400 A600 25fr Hermes space shuttle   1.50 1.15

Rerum
Novarum
Encyclical,
Cent.
A601

1991, May 13   Photo.   Perf. 11½
1401 A601 14fr multicolored   .85 .65

Princess Isabel & Philip le Bon — A602

1991, May 27   Photo.   Perf. 11½
1402 A602 14fr multicolored   .85 .65

Europalia '91. See Portugal No. 1861.

Tourism A603

Designs: No. 1403, Neptune's Grotto, Couvin. No. 1404, Dieleghem Abbey, Jette. No. 1405, Town Hall, Niel, vert. No. 1406, Nature Reserve, Hautes Fagnes. No. 1407, Legend of giant Rolarius, Roeselare, vert.

1991, June 17   **Photo. & Engr.**
1403	A603	14fr multicolored	.85	.65
1404	A603	14fr multicolored	.85	.65
1405	A603	14fr multicolored	.85	.65
1406	A603	14fr multicolored	.85	.65
1407	A603	14fr multicolored	.85	.65
		Nos. 1403-1407 (5)	4.25	3.25

King Baudouin, Coronation, 40th Anniv. and 60th Birthday A604

1991, June 24   **Photo.**
1408	A604	14fr multicolored	.85	.65

Royal Academy of Medicine, 150th Anniv. — A605

Photo. & Engr.
1991, Sept. 2   **Perf. 11½**
1409	A605	10fr multicolored	.65	.50

The English Coast at Dover by Alfred W. Finch (1854-1930) — A606

1991, Sept. 9   **Photo.**
1410	A606	25fr multicolored	1.50	1.15

See Finland Nos. 868-869.

Mushrooms — A607

1991, Sept. 16   **Photo.**
Booklet Stamps   **Perf. 12**
1411	A607	14fr Amanita phalloides (13A)	1.25	.65
1412	A607	14fr Amanita rubescens (13B)	1.25	.65
1413	A607	14fr Boletus erythropus (13C)	1.25	.65
1414	A607	14fr Hygrocybe persistens (13D)	1.25	.65
a.		Bklt. pane of 4, #1411-1414	5.00	

Doctors Without Borders A608

Design: No. 1415, Amnesty Intl.

1991, Sept. 23   **Perf. 11½**
1415	A608	25fr multicolored	1.50	1.15
1416	A608	25fr multicolored	1.50	1.15

Telecom '91 — A609

1991, Oct. 7   **Photo.**   **Perf. 11½**
1417	A609	14fr multicolored	.90	.70

6th World Forum and Exposition on Telecommunications, Geneva, Switzerland.

Youth Philately — A610

Cartoon characters: No. 1418, Blake and Mortimer, by Edgar P. Jacobs (16a). No. 1419, Cori the ship boy, by Bob De Moor (16b). No. 1420, Cities of the Fantastic, by Francois Schuiten (16c). No. 1421, Boule and Bill, by Jean Roba (16d).

1991, Oct. 14   **Perf. 12**
Booklet Stamps
1418	A610	14fr multicolored	.90	.70
1419	A610	14fr multicolored	.90	.70
1420	A610	14fr multicolored	.90	.70
1421	A610	14fr multicolored	.90	.70
a.		Bklt. pane of 4, #1418-1421	3.60	

Belgian Newspapers, Cent. A611

1991, Nov. 4   **Photo.**   **Perf. 11½**
1422	A611	10fr Gazet Van Antwerpen	.65	.50
1423	A611	10fr Het Volk	.65	.50

Icon of Madonna and Child, Chevetogne Abbey — A612

1991, Nov. 25   **Photo.**   **Perf. 11½**
1424	A612	10fr multicolored	.65	.50

Christmas.

Wolfgang Amadeus Mozart, Death Bicent. — A613

1991, Dec. 2   **Photo.**   **Perf. 11½**
1425	A613	25fr multicolored	1.70	1.30

A614   A615

1992, Feb. 10   **Photo.**   **Perf. 11½**
1426	A614	14fr Fire fighting	.80	.60

1992, Feb. 24
1427	A615	14fr multicolored	.80	.60

Belgian resistance in WWII.

Belgian Carpet Industry — A616

Antwerp Diamond Club, Cent. A617

Design: 14fr, Chef's hat, cutlery.

1992, Mar. 9
1428	A616	10fr multicolored	.55	.42
1429	A616	14fr multicolored	.80	.60
1430	A617	27fr multicolored	1.50	1.15
		Nos. 1428-1430 (3)	2.85	2.17

Belgian Association of Master Chefs.

Expo '92, Seville A618

1992, Mar. 23
1431	A618	14fr multicolored	.80	.60

Bird Type of 1985

1992-96   **Photo.**   **Perf. 11½**
1432	A524	1fr Sizerin flamme	.15	.15
1433	A524	2fr Merle noir	.15	.15
1434	A524	2fr Grive mauvis	.15	.15
1435	A524	4fr Gobe mouche noir	.30	.22
1436	A524	4fr Bergeronette grise	.25	.15
1437	A524	5fr Etourneau sansonnet	.35	.15
1438	A524	5fr Hirondelle de cheminee	.32	.15
1439	A524	5.50fr Geai des chenes	.35	.15
1440	A524	6fr Cincle plongeur	.35	.15
1441	A524	6.50fr Phragmite des jongs	.45	.30
1442	A524	7fr Loriot	.45	.15
1443	A524	8fr Mesange charbonniere	.45	.15
1444	A524	10fr Verdier	.58	.15
1445	A524	11fr Troglodyte mignon	.65	.15
1446	A524	13fr Moineau domestique	.70	.18
1446A	A524	14fr Pouillot fitis	.95	.20
1447	A524	16fr Jaseur boreal	.90	.22
		Nos. 1432-1447 (17)	7.45	2.99

Issued: 11fr, 4/1/92; 1fr, 2fr, 6fr, 8fr, 10fr, 6/92; 4fr, 5fr, 7fr, 9/7/92; 5.50fr, 9/27/93; 13fr, 16fr, 1/3/94; 6.50fr, 10/3/94; 14fr, 12/18/95; #1435A, 5/6/96; #1433A, 1434, 7/1/96.

Jean Van Noten (1903-1982), Stamp Designer — A619

Photo. & Engr.
1992, Apr. 13   **Perf. 11½**
1448	A619	15fr ver & black	.90	.70

Stamp Day.

Abstract Painting by Jo Delahaut — A620

Design: No. 1449, Witte Magie No. 6, by Roger Raveel, vert.

1992, Apr. 27   **Photo.**   **Perf. 11½**
1449	A620	15fr multicolored	.85	.65
1450	A620	15fr multicolored	.85	.65

Discovery of America, 500th Anniv. — A621

1992, May 4
1451	A621	15fr shown	.85	.65
1452	A621	28fr 500, globe, astrolabe	1.60	1.20

Europa.

Fight Racism — A622

1992, May 18   **Photo.**   **Perf. 11½**
1453	A622	15fr black, gray & pink	.90	.70

Paintings from Orsay Museum, Paris — A623

Paintings by Belgian artists: 11fr, The Hamlet, by Jacob Smits. 15fr, The Bath, by Alfred Stevens.

30fr, The Man at the Helm, by Theo Van Rysselberghe.

1992, June 15   Photo.   Perf. 11½
1454 A623 11fr multicolored .65 .48
1455 A623 15fr multicolored .90 .70
1456 A623 30fr multicolored 1.75 1.35
Nos. 1454-1456 (3) 3.30 2.53

Tourism — A624

Designs: No. 1457, Manneken Pis Fountain, Brussels. No. 1458, Landcommander Castle Alden Biesen, Bilzen, horiz. No. 1459, Building facade, Andenne. No. 1460, Fools' Monday Carnival, Renaix, horiz. No. 1461, Great Procession, Tournai, horiz.

Photo. & Engr.
1992, July 6   Perf. 11½
1457 A624 15fr multicolored .90 .70
1458 A624 15fr multicolored .90 .70
1459 A624 15fr multicolored .90 .70
1460 A624 15fr multicolored .90 .70
1461 A624 15fr multicolored .90 .70
Nos. 1457-1461 (5) 4.50 3.50

Village of Andenne, 1300th anniv. (#1459). Grand Procession of Tournai, 900th anniv. (#1461).

Animals — A625

1992, Sept. 7   Photo.   Perf. 12
Booklet Stamps
1462 A625 15fr Polecat (13a) 1.05 .80
1463 A625 15fr Squirrel (13b) 1.05 .80
1464 A625 15fr Hedgehog (13c) 1.05 .80
1465 A625 15fr Dormouse (13d) 1.05 .80
a. Bklt. pane of 4, #1462-1465 4.25

Brabant Revolution — A626

Design: 15fr, Troops fighting and Henri Van der Noot, Jean Andre Van der Meersch, and Jean Francois Vonck, rebel leaders.

Photo. & Engr.
1992, Sept. 21   Perf. 11½
1466 A626 15fr multicolored .90 .70

Arms of Thurn and Taxis — A627

1992, Oct. 5   Photo.   Perf. 11½
1467 A627 15fr multicolored .90 .70

Gaston Lagaffe, by Andre Franquin A628

1992, Oct. 12
1468 A628 15fr multicolored .90 .70
Youth philately.

Single European Market — A629

1992, Oct. 26
1469 A629 15fr multicolored .90 .70

Antwerp Zoo, 150th Anniv. — A630

1992, Nov. 16
1470 A630 15fr Okapi .90 .70
1471 A630 30fr Tamarin 1.80 1.40

The Brussels Place Royale in Winter, by Luc De Decker A631

1992, Nov. 23
1472 A631 11fr multicolored .70 .52
Christmas.

History A632

Designs: 11fr, Council of Leptines, 1250th anniv. 15fr, 28fr, Missale Romanum of Matthias Corvinus (Matyas Hunyadi, King of Hungary) (diff. details). 30fr, Battles of Neerwinden (1693, 1793).

1993, Mar. 15   Photo.   Perf. 11½
1473 A632 11fr multicolored .65 .48
1474 A632 15fr multicolored .90 .70
1475 A632 30fr multicolored 1.80 1.35
Nos. 1473-1475 (3) 3.35 2.53
Souvenir Sheet
1476 A632 28fr multicolored 1.75 1.30
Size of No. 1474, 80x28mm. No. 1476 contains one 55x40mm stamp.
See Hungary No. 3385-3386.

A633

A634

Antwerp, Cultural City of Europe A635

Designs: No. 1477, Panoramic view of Antwerp (illustration reduced). No. 1478, Antwerp Town Hall, designed by Cornelis Floris. No. 1479, Woman's Head and Warrior's Torso, by Jacob Jordaens. No. 1480, St. Job's Altar (detail), Schoonbroek. No. 1481, Angels on stained glass window, Mater Dei Chapel of Institut Marie-Josee, by Eugeen Yoors, vert.

1993, Mar. 22
1477 A633 15fr multicolored .90 .70
1478 A634 15fr multicolored .90 .70
1479 A635 15fr gray & multi .90 .70
1480 A635 15fr green & multi .90 .70
1481 A635 15fr blue & multi .90 .70
Nos. 1477-1481 (5) 4.50 3.50
Antwerp '93.

Stamp Day — A636

1993, Apr. 5
1482 A636 15fr No. 74 .90 .70

Contemporary Paintings — A637

Europa: 15fr, Florence 1960, by Gaston Bertrand. 28fr, De Sjees, by Constant Permeke.

1993, Apr. 26   Photo.   Perf. 11½
1483 A637 15fr multicolored .90 .70
1484 A637 28fr multicolored 1.70 1.35

Butterflies — A638

1993, May 10
1485 A638 15fr Vanessa atalanta .90 .70
1486 A638 15fr Apatura iris .90 .70
1487 A638 15fr Inachis io .90 .70
1488 A638 15fr Aglais urticae .90 .70
Nos. 1485-1488 (4) 3.60 2.80

Alumni Assoc. (UAE), Free University of Brussels, 150th Anniv. A639

1993, May 17
1489 A639 15fr blue & black .90 .70

Europalia '93 — A640

1993, May 24
1490 A640 15fr Mayan statuette .90 .70

Folklore A641

Designs: 11fr, Ommegang Procession, Brussels. 15fr, Royal Moncrabeau Folk Group, Namur. 28fr, Stilt walkers of Merchtem, vert.

1993, June 7   Photo.   Perf. 11½
1491 A641 11fr multicolored .65 .48
1492 A641 15fr multicolored .90 .70
1493 A641 28fr multicolored 1.65 1.30
Nos. 1491-1493 (3) 3.20 2.48

Tourism A642

Castles: No. 1494, La Hulpe. No. 1495, Cortewalle (Beveren). No. 1496, Jehay. No. 1497, Arenberg (Heverlee), vert. No. 1498, Raeren.

Photo. & Engr.
1993, June 21   Perf. 11½
1494 A642 15fr pale green & black .90 .70
1495 A642 15fr pale lilac & black .90 .70
1496 A642 15fr pale blue & black .90 .70
1497 A642 15fr pale brown & black .90 .70
1498 A642 15fr pale olive & black .90 .70
Nos. 1494-1498 (5) 4.50 3.50

Intl. Triennial Exhibition of Tournai A643

1993, July 5   Photo.   Perf. 11½
1499 A643 15fr black, blue & red .90 .70

Belgian Presidency of European Community Council A644

1993, Aug. 9   Photo.   Perf. 11½
1500 A644 15fr multicolored .90 .70

Rene Magritte
(1898-1967),
Artist
A645

1993, Aug. 9
1501 A645 30fr multicolored   1.75 1.40

King Baudouin (1930-
1993) — A646

1993, Aug. 17   Photo.   Perf. 11½
1502 A646 15fr black & gray   .90   .70

European House Cats — A647

1993, Sept. 6   Photo.   Perf. 12
Booklet Stamps
1503 A647 15fr Brown & white (10a)   .90   .70
1504 A647 15fr Black & white (10b)   .90   .70
1505 A647 15fr Gray tabby (10c)   .90   .70
1506 A647 15fr Calico (10d)   .90   .70
   a.   Booklet pane of 4, #1503-1506 3.75

Publication of De
Humani Corporis
Fabrica, by Andreas
Vesalius, 1543 — A648

1993, Oct. 4   Photo.   Perf. 11½
1507 A648 15fr multicolored   .90   .70

Air Hostess Natacha, by Francois
Waltherty — A649

1993, Oct. 18
1508 A649 15fr multicolored   .85   .65
               Youth philately.

Publication of "Faux
Soir," 50th
Anniv. — A650

1993, Nov. 8   Photo.   Perf. 11½
1509 A650 11fr multicolored   .60   .45

Notre-Dame de
la Chapelle,
Brussels
A651

1993, Nov. 22   Photo.   Perf. 11½
1510 A651 11fr multicolored   .65   .48
          Christmas, New Year.

Children, Future Decisionmakers — A652

1993, Dec. 13   Photo.   Perf. 11½
1511 A652 15fr multicolored   .90   .70

A653   A654

King Albert II — A655

1993-97   Photo.   Perf. 11½
1519 A653 16fr lt gray & multi   .95   .25
1520 A653 16fr lt & dk blue
                    green   1.00   .75
1521 A655 16fr multicolored   1.10   .80
1521A A655 16fr blue   1.10   .80
1521B A655 17fr blue   1.10   .80
1521C A655 18fr olive black   1.00   .75
1521D A655 19fr dp gray violet   1.35 1.00
1522 A653 20fr cream & brown   1.25   .32
1524 A655 28fr claret   1.90 1.40
1526 A653 30fr red lilac   1.65   .40
1527 A653 32fr cream & org
                    brn   1.90   .48
1527A A655 34fr dark blue gray   2.00 1.50
1527B A655 36fr dark slate blue   2.20 1.65
1528 A655 40fr pink & carmine   2.50   .60
1529 A653 50fr green   3.00   .75
1530 A655 50fr green   3.30 2.50
1533 A654 100fr multicolored   6.25 4.75
1535 A654 200fr multicolored   14.00 3.50
       Nos. 1519-1535 (18)   47.55 23.00
Issued: No. 1519, 12/15/93; No. 1520,
1/17/94; 30fr, 2/4/94; 32fr, 3/7/94; 50fr,
4/18/94; 20fr, 6/6/94; 40fr, 6/20/94; 100fr,
10/3/94; 200fr, 5/2/95; No. 1521, 6/6/96; Nos.
1521A, 1530, 28fr, 9/2/96; 17fr, 12/16/96; 34fr,
36fr, 2/10/97; 18fr, 4/7/97; 19fr, 7/7/97.
This is part of an expanding set. Numbers may
change.

Paintings
A656

Designs: No. 1537, The Malleable Darkness, by
Octave Landuyt. No. 1538, Ma Toute Belle, by
Serge Vandercam, vert.

1994, Jan. 31   Photo.   Perf. 11½
1537 A656 16fr multicolored   .90   .70
1538 A656 16fr multicolored   .90   .70

Airplanes
A657

13fr, Hanriot-Dupont HD-1. 15fr, Spad XIII. 30fr,
Schreck FBA-H. 32fr, Stampe-Vertongen SV-4B.

1994, Feb. 28
1539 A657 13fr multicolored   .70   .52
1540 A657 15fr multicolored   .85   .65
1541 A657 30fr multicolored   1.65 1.25
1542 A657 32fr multicolored   1.75 1.40
       Nos. 1539-1542 (4)   4.95 3.82

Daily
Newspapers
A658

Designs: No. 1543, "Le Jour-Le Courier," cent.,
vert. No. 1544, "La Wallonie," 75th anniv.

1994, Mar. 21   Photo.   Perf. 11½
1543 A658 16fr multicolored   .95   .70
1544 A658 16fr multicolored   .95   .70

Fall of the Golden Calf (Detail), by
Fernand Allard l'Olivier — A659

1994, Mar. 28
1545 A659 16fr multicolored   .95   .70
          Charter of Quaregnon, cent.

Stamp Day — A660

1994, Apr. 11   Photo.   Perf. 11½
1546 A660 16fr No. 102   .95   .70

History
A661

Scenes from Brabantse Yeesten, 15th cent. illuminated manuscript: 13fr, Reconciliation between
John I and Arnold, squire of Wezemaal. 16fr, Tournament at wedding of John II and Margaret of York.
30fr, Battle of Woeringen.

1994, Apr. 25
1547 A661 13fr multicolored   .75   .55
1548 A661 16fr multicolored   .95   .70
1549 A661 30fr multicolored   1.75 1.25
       Nos. 1547-1549 (3)   3.45 2.50
          No. 1549 is 81x28mm.

Europa — A662

Designs: 16fr, Abbe Georges Lemaitre (1894-
1966), proposed "big-bang" theory of origins of universe. 30fr, Gerardus Mercator (1512-94), cartographer, astronomer.

1994, May 9   Photo.   Perf. 11½
1550 A662 16fr multicolored   .95   .70
1551 A662 30fr multicolored   1.75 1.25

Papal Visit
A663

#1552, Father Damien (1840-89). #1553, St.
Mutien-Marie (1841-1917), Christian educator.

1994, May 16   Perf. 11½x12
1552 A663 16fr multicolored   .95   .70
1553 A663 16fr multicolored   .95   .70

Tourism
A664

Churches: No. 1554, St. Peter's, Bertem. No.
1555, St. Bavo's, Kanegem, vert. No. 1556, Royal
St. Mary's, Schaarbeek. No. 1557, St. Gery's, Aube-
chies. No. 1558, Sts. Peter and Paul, Saint-Severin,
Condroz, vert.

1994, June 13   Photo.   Perf. 11½
1554 A664 16fr multicolored   .95   .70
1555 A664 16fr multicolored   .95   .70
1556 A664 16fr multicolored   .95   .70
1557 A664 16fr multicolored   .95   .70
1558 A664 16fr multicolored   .95   .70
       Nos. 1554-1558 (5)   4.75 3.50

Guillaume
Lekeu (1870-
94),
Composer
A665

Design: No. 1560, Detail of painting by Hans
Memling (c.1430-94).

1994, Aug. 16   Photo.   Perf. 11½
1559 A665 16fr multicolored   1.10   .75
1560 A665 16fr multicolored   1.10   .75

Liberation of Belgium, 50th
Anniv. — A666

Design: 16fr, General Crerar, Field Marshal
Montgomery, Gen. Bradley, Belgium landscape.
Illustration reduced.

1994, Sept. 5   Photo.   Perf. 11x11½
1561 A666 16fr multicolored   .95   .70

Wildflowers — A667

Designs: No. 1562, Caltha palustris. No. 1563, Cephalanthera damasonium. No. 1564, Calystegia soldanella. No. 1565, Epipactis helleborine.

1994, Sept. 26   Photo.   Perf. 12
Booklet Stamps
1562	A667	16fr multi (14a)	1.10 .75
1563	A667	16fr multi (14b)	1.10 .75
1564	A667	16fr multi (14c)	1.10 .75
1565	A667	16fr multi (14d)	1.10 .75
a.		Booklet pane of 4, #1562-1565	4.50

Cubitus the Dog, by Luc Dupanloup — A668

1994, Oct. 10   Perf. 11½
1566 A668 16fr multicolored   1.10 .75
Youth philately.

Georges Simenon (1903-89), Writer A669

Photo. & Engr.
1994, Oct. 17   Perf. 11½
1567 A669 16fr multicolored   1.10 .75
See France No. 2443, Switzerland No. 948.

Christmas A670

1994, Dec. 5   Photo.   Perf. 11½
1568 A670 13fr multicolored   .85 .65

Anniversaries and Events A671

Designs: No. 1569, August Vermeylen Fund, 50th anniv. No. 1570, Belgian Touring Club, cent. No. 1571, Assoc. of Belgian Enterprises, cent. No. 1572, Dept. of Social Security, 50th anniv.

1995, Feb. 13   Photo.   Perf. 11½
1569	A671	16fr multicolored	1.10 .75
1570	A671	16fr multicolored	1.10 .75
1571	A671	16fr multicolored	1.10 .75
1572	A671	16fr multicolored	1.10 .75
		Nos. 1569-1572 (4)	4.40 3.00

Flowers of Ghent A672

1995, Mar. 6
1573	A672	13fr Hibiscus rosa-sinensis	.95	.70
1574	A672	16fr Rhododendron simsii	1.10	.75
1575	A672	30fr Fuchsia hybrida	2.25	1.65
		Nos. 1573-1575 (3)	4.30	3.10

Games — A673   Stamp Day — A674

1995, Mar. 20
1576	A673	13fr Crossword puzzles	.95	.70
1577	A673	16fr Chess	1.10	.75
1578	A673	30fr Scrabble	2.25	1.65
1579	A673	34fr Cards	2.50	1.75
		Nos. 1576-1579 (4)	6.80	4.85

1995, Apr. 10   Photo. & Engr.
1580 A674 16fr Frans de Troyer   1.10 .75

Peace & Freedom A675

Europa: 16fr, Broken barbed wire, prison guard tower. 30fr, Mushroom cloud, "Never again."

1995, Apr. 24   Photo.   Perf. 11½
1581 A675 16fr multicolored   1.10 .75
1582 A675 30fr multicolored   2.25 1.75
Liberation of concentration camps, 50th anniv. (#1581). Nuclear Non-Proliferation Treaty, 25th anniv. (#1582).

Battle of Fontenoy, 250th Anniv. — A676

Design: 16fr, Irish soldiers, Cross of Fontenoy.

1995, May 15   Perf. 11½
1583 A676 16fr multicolored   1.10 .75
See Ireland No. 967.

UN, 50th Anniv. A677

1995, May 22   Photo.   Perf. 11½
1584 A677 16fr multicolored   1.10 .75

"Sauvagemont, Maransart," by Pierre Alechinsky — A678

No. 1586: "Telegram-style," by Pol Mara.

1995, June 6
1585 A678 16fr multicolored   1.10 .75
1586 A678 16fr multicolored   1.10 .75

Tourism A679

Architectural designs: No. 1587, Cauchie house, Brussels, by Paul Cauchie (1875-1952). No. 1588, De Viif Werelddelen, corner building, Antwerp, by Frans Smet-Verhas (1851-1925). No. 1589, House, Liege, by Paul Jaspar (1859-1945).

1995, June 26
1587	A679	16fr multicolored	1.10	.75
1588	A679	16fr multicolored	1.10	.75
1589	A679	16fr multicolored	1.10	.75
		Nos. 1587-1589 (3)	3.30	2.25

Sailing Ships — A680

1995, Aug. 21   Photo.   Perf. 12
Booklet Stamps
1590	A680	16fr Mercator	1.10 .80
1591	A680	16fr Kruzenstern	1.10 .80
1592	A680	16fr Sagres II	1.10 .80
1593	A680	16fr Amerigo Vespucci	1.10 .80
a.		Booklet pane of 4, #1590-1593	4.50
		Complete booklet, #1593a	4.50

Classic Motorcycles A681

1995, Sept. 25   Photo.   Perf. 11½
1594	A681	13fr 1908 Minerva	.90	.65
1595	A681	16fr 1913 FN, vert.	1.10	.80
1596	A681	30fr 1929 La Mondiale	2.00	1.50
1597	A681	32fr 1937 Gillet, vert.	2.25	1.65
		Nos. 1594-1597 (4)	6.25	4.60

Comic Character, Sammy, by Arthur Berckmans A682

1995, Oct. 9   Photo.   Perf. 11½
1598 A682 16fr multicolored   1.10 .80
Youth philately.

King's Day A683

Design: 16fr, King Albert II and Queen Paola.

1995, Nov. 15   Photo.   Perf. 11½
1599 A683 16fr multicolored   1.10 .80

A684　　　　　　　　A685

Christmas: 13fr, Nativity scene from "Breviary," book of devotions, c. 1500.

1995, Nov. 20
1600 A684 13fr multicolored　　　　　.90　.70

1996, Mar. 4　Photo.　Perf. 11½
1601 A685 16fr multicolored　　　　　1.10　.80
Liberal Party, 150th anniv.

Portrait of Emile Mayrisch (1862-1928), by Théo Van Rysselberghe (1862-1926)
A686

1996, Mar. 4
1602 A686 (A) multicolored　　　　　1.10　.80
No. 1602 was valued at 16fr on day of issue. See Luxembourg No. 939.

Oscar Bonnevalle, Stamp Designer — A687

1996, Apr. 1
1603 A687 16fr multicolored　　　　　1.10　.80
Stamp Day.

Insects
A688

Designs: No. 1604, Sympetrum sanguineum. No. 1605, Bombus terrestris. No. 1606, Lucanus cervus. No. 1607, Melolontha melolontha. No. 1608, Gryllus campestris. No. 1609, Coccinella septempunctata.

1996, Apr. 1　Photo.　Perf. 12
Booklet Stamps
1604 A688 16fr multicolored　　　　　1.10　.80
1605 A688 16fr multicolored　　　　　1.10　.80
1606 A688 16fr multicolored　　　　　1.10　.80
1607 A688 16fr multicolored　　　　　1.10　.80
1608 A688 16fr multicolored　　　　　1.10　.80
1609 A688 16fr multicolored　　　　　1.10　.80
a. Booklet pane, #1604-1609　　　6.60
　　　Complete booklet, #1609a　　　6.60

Famous Women
A689

Europa: 16fr, Yvonne Nevejean (1900-87), saved Jewish children during World War II. 30fr, Marie Gevers (1883-1975), poet.

1996, May 6　Photo.　Perf. 11½
1610 A689 16fr multicolored　　　　　1.10　.80
1611 A689 30fr multicolored　　　　　2.00　1.50

Tourism — A690　　Architecture in
　　　　　　　　　Brussels — A691

Designs: No. 1612, Grotto of Han-Sur-Lesse, horiz. No. 1613, Village of Begijnendijk as separate community, bicent.

1996, June 10　Photo.　Perf. 11½
1612 A690 16fr multicolored　　　　　1.10　.80
1613 A690 16fr multicolored　　　　　1.10　.80

Designs: No. 1614, La Maison du Roi (Grand Place). No. 1615, Galeries Royales Saint-Hubert. No. 1616, Le Palais d'Egmont, Le Petit Sablon, horiz. No. 1617, Le Cinquantenaire, horiz.

1996, June 10
1614 A691 16fr multi (7a)　　　　　1.10　.80
1615 A691 16fr multi (7b)　　　　　1.10　.80
1616 A691 16fr multi (7c)　　　　　1.10　.80
1617 A691 16fr multi (7d)　　　　　1.10　.80
　　Nos. 1614-1617 (4)　　　　　4.40　3.20

Auto Races at
Spa, Cent.
A692

1996, July 1
1618 A692 16fr 1900 German 6CV　1.10　.80
1619 A692 16fr 1925 Alfa Romeo P2 1.10　.80
1620 A692 16fr 1939 Mercedes
　　　　　　　Benz W154　　　　1.10　.80
1621 A692 16fr 1967 Ferrari 330P　1.10　.80
　　Nos. 1618-1621 (4)　　　　　4.40　3.20

Paintings of Historical
Figures — A693

Portraits from town hall triptych, Zierikzee, Netherlands: No. 1622, Philip I, the Handsome (1478-1506). No. 1623, Juana of Castile, the Mad (1479-1555).

1996, Sept. 2　Photo.　Perf. 11½
1622 A693 16fr multicolored　　　　　1.10　.80
1623 A693 16fr multicolored　　　　　1.10　.80

A694　　　　　　　A695

Paintings from National Gallery, London: 14fr, Reading Man, by Rogier Van Der Weyden (1399-1464). 16fr, Susanna Fourment, by Peter Paul Rubens (1577-1640). 30fr, A Man in a Turban, by Jan Van Eyck (1390-1441).

1996, Sept. 2
1624 A694 14fr multicolored　　　　　.95　.70
1625 A694 16fr multicolored　　　　　1.10　.80
1626 A694 30fr multicolored　　　　　2.00　1.50
　　Nos. 1624-1626 (3)　　　　　4.05　3.00

Bird Type of 1985
1996, Oct. 7　Photo.　Perf. 11½
1627 A524 6fr Tarin des aulnes　　　　.40　.30

1996, Oct. 7
Comic Character, Cloro, by Raymond Macherot.
1628 A695 16fr multicolored　　　　　1.10　.80
Youth Philately.

Almanac of
Mons, by Fr.
Charles
Letellier,
150th Anniv.
A696

1996, Oct. 7
1629 A696 16fr multicolored　　　　　1.10　.80

Music and
Literature
A697

Designs: No. 1630, Arthur Grumiaux (1921-86), violinist. No. 1631, Flor Peeters (1903-86), organist. No. 1632, Christian Dotremont (1922-79), poet, artist. No. 1633, Paul Van Ostaijen (1896-1928), writer.

Photo. & Engr.
1996, Oct. 28　　　　　Perf. 11½
1630 A697 16fr multicolored　　　　　1.10　.80
1631 A697 16fr multicolored　　　　　1.10　.80
1632 A697 16fr multicolored　　　　　1.10　.80
1633 A697 16fr multicolored　　　　　1.10　.80
　　Nos. 1630-1633 (4)　　　　　4.40　3.20

Christmas and New Year — A698

Scenes from Christmas Market: a, Decorated trees, rooftops. b, Lighted greeting signs. c, Church. d, Selling desert items. e, Selling Nativity scenes. f, Selling meat. g, Santa ringing bell. h, Man smoking pipe, people with presents. i, People shopping.

1996, Nov. 18　Photo.　Perf. 11½
1634 A698 14fr Sheet of 9, #a.-i.　8.25　6.25

Catholic
Faculty
University,
Mons,
Cent. — A699

1997, Jan. 20　Photo.　Perf. 11½
1635 A699 17fr multicolored　　　　　1.10　.80

Opera at Theatre Royal de la Monnaie,
Brussels — A700

#1636, Marie Sasse (1834-1907), soprano.
#1637, Ernest Van Dijck (1861-1923), tenor.
#1638, Hector Dufranne (1870-1951), baritone.
#1639, Clara Clairbert (1899-1970), soprano.

1997, Feb. 10
1636 A700 17fr multicolored　　　　　1.00　.75
1637 A700 17fr multicolored　　　　　1.00　.75
1638 A700 17fr multicolored　　　　　1.00　.75
1639 A700 17fr multicolored　　　　　1.00　.75
　　Nos. 1636-1639 (4)　　　　　4.00　3.00

Eastern Cantons — A701

Illustration reduced.

1997, Feb. 10　Photo.　Perf. 11½
1640 A701 17fr multicolored　　　　　1.00　.75

Bird Type of 1985
1997, Mar. 10
1641 A524 15fr Mesange boreale　　　.90　.70

UN Peace-Keeping Forces — A702

1997, Mar. 10
1642 A702 17fr multicolored　　　　　1.00　.75

Stories and
Legends
A703

Europa: 17fr, "De Bokkenrijders" (The Goat Riders). 30fr, Jean de Berneau.

1997, Mar. 10　Photo.　Perf. 11½
1643 A703 17fr multicolored　　　　　1.00　.75
1644 A703 30fr multicolored　　　　　1.75　1.30

Bird Type of 1985
1997, Apr. 7
Size: 35x25mm
1645 A524 150fr Ekster　　　　　8.50　6.25

Constant Spinoy (1924-93), Stamp
Engraver — A704

1997, Apr. 7　　Photo. & Engr.
1646 A704 17fr multicolored　　　　　1.00　.75
Stamp Day.

Intl. Flower Show,　Paintings by Paul
Liege　　　　　　　Delvaux (1897-
A705　　　　　　　1994)
　　　　　　　　　A706

1997, Apr. 21　　　　Photo.
1647 A705 17fr multicolored　　　　　1.00　.75

1997, Apr. 21

Details or entire paintings: 15fr, Woman with garland of leaves in hair. 17fr, Nude, horiz. 32fr, Woman wearing hat, trolley.

1648 A706 15fr multicolored	.85	.65
1649 A706 17fr multicolored	1.00	.75
1650 A706 32fr multicolored	1.75	1.35
Nos. 1648-1650 (3)	3.60	2.75

Bird Type of 1985

1997, May 7   Photo.   Perf. 11½

1651 A524 3fr Alouette des champs   .25   .20

Queen Paola, 60th Birthday
A707

1997, May 26

1652 A707 17fr multicolored   1.00   .75

See Italy No.

Cartoon Character, "Jommeke," by Jef Nys — A708

1997, May 26

1653 A708 17fr multicolored   1.00   .75

A709   A710

Roses: No. 1654, Rosa damascena coccinea. No. 1655, Rosa sulfurea. No. 1656, Rosa centifolia.

1997, July 7   Photo.   Perf. 11½

1654 A709 17fr multicolored	1.20	.90
1655 A709 17fr multicolored	1.20	.90
1656 A709 17fr multicolored	1.20	.90
Nos. 1654-1656 (3)	3.60	2.70

World Congress of Rose Societies.

1997, July 7   Photo. & Engr.

Churches: No. 1657, Basilica of St. Martin, Halle. No. 1658, Notre Dame Church, Laeken, horiz. No. 1659, Basilica of St. Martin, Liège.

1657 A710 17fr multicolored	1.20	.90
1658 A710 17fr multicolored	1.20	.90
1659 A710 17fr multicolored	1.20	.90
Nos. 1657-1659 (3)	3.60	2.70

Bird Type of 1985

1997, Sept. 1   Photo.   Perf. 11½

1660 A525 7fr Bergeronnette printaniere   .40   .30

Bees and Apiculture — A711

Designs: No. 1661, Queen, workers. No. 1662, Development of the larvae. No. 1663, Bee exiting cell. No. 1664, Bee collecting nectar. No. 1665, Two bees. No. 1666, Two bees on honeycomb.

1997, Sept. 1   Photo.   Perf. 12
Booklet Stamps

1661 A711 17fr multicolored (15a)	1.00	.75
1662 A711 17fr multicolored (15b)	1.00	.75
1663 A711 17fr multicolored (15c)	1.00	.75
1664 A711 17fr multicolored (15d)	1.00	.75
1665 A711 17fr multicolored (15e)	1.00	.75

1666 A711 17fr multicolored (15f)	1.00	.75
a. Booklet pane of 6, #1661-1666	6.00	
Complete booklet, #1666a	6.00	

Craftsmen
A712

1997, Sept. 1   Perf. 11½

1667 A712 17fr Stone cutter	.75	.60
1668 A712 17fr Mason	.75	.60
1669 A712 17fr Carpenter	.75	.60
1670 A712 17fr Blacksmith	.75	.60
Nos. 1667-1670 (4)	3.00	2.40

Antarctic Expedition by the Belgica, Cent. — A713

1997, Sept. 22   Photo.   Perf. 11½

1671 A713 17fr multicolored   1.00   .75

A714   A715

Royal Museum of Central Africa, Cent.: No. 1672, Mask, Shaba, Congo. No. 1673, Outside view of museum, horiz. 34fr, Dish Bearer sculpture, Buli area, Congo.

1997, Sept. 22   Photo.   Perf. 11½

1672 A714 17fr multicolored	1.00	.75
1673 A714 17fr multicolored	1.00	.75
1674 A714 34fr multicolored	1.00	.75
Nos. 1672-1674 (3)	3.00	2.25

No. 1673 is 25x73mm.

1997, Oct. 25   Photo.   Perf. 11½

Christmas: "Fairon," by Pierre Grahame.

1675 A715 15fr multicolored   .90   .70

SEMI-POSTAL STAMPS

Values quoted for Nos. B1-B24 are for stamps with label attached. Copies without label sell for one-tenth or less.

St. Martin of Tours Dividing His Cloak with a Beggar
SP1   SP2

Unwmk.
1910, June 1   Typo.   Perf. 14

B1	SP1 1c gray	1.65	1.25
B2	SP1 2c purple brn	13.00	9.25
B3	SP1 5c peacock blue	3.50	2.50
B4	SP1 10c brown red	3.50	2.50
B5	SP2 1c gray green	3.50	2.50
B6	SP2 2c violet brn	10.00	7.25

B7	SP2 5c peacock blue	3.50	2.50
B8	SP2 10c carmine	3.50	2.50
Nos. B1-B8 (8)		42.15	30.25

Overprinted "1911" in Black

1911, Apr. 1

B9	SP1 1c gray	20.00	14.00
a.	Inverted overprint		
B10	SP1 2c purple brn	50.00	45.00
B11	SP1 5c peacock blue	5.75	4.00
B12	SP1 10c brown red	5.75	4.00
B13	SP2 1c gray green	40.00	35.00
B14	SP2 2c violet brn	36.00	27.50
B15	SP2 5c peacock blue	5.75	4.00
B16	SP2 10c carmine	5.75	4.00
Nos. B9-B16 (8)		169.00	137.50

Overprinted "CHARLEROI-1911"

1911, June

B17	SP1 1c gray	5.00	5.00
B18	SP1 2c purple brn	17.00	17.00
B19	SP1 5c peacock blue	8.00	8.00
B20	SP1 10c brown red	7.50	7.50
B21	SP2 1c gray green	5.00	5.00
B22	SP2 2c violet brn	16.00	16.00
B23	SP2 5c peacock blue	6.75	6.75
B24	SP2 10c carmine	5.00	5.00
Nos. B17-B24 (8)		70.25	70.25

Nos. B1-B24 were sold at double face value, except the 10c denominations which were sold for 15c. The surtax benefited the national anti-tuberculosis organization.

SP3

Merode Monument — SP4   King Albert I — SP5

1914, Oct. 3   Litho.

B25	SP3 5c green & red	1.65	2.00
B26	SP3 10c red	.45	.50
B27	SP3 20c violet & red	10.50	13.00
Nos. B25-B27 (3)		12.60	15.50

Counterfeits of Nos. B25-B27 abound. Probably as many as 90% of the stamps on the market are counterfeits. Competently certified copies sell for much more.

1914, Oct. 3

B28	SP4 5c green & red	4.50	5.00
B29	SP4 10c red	4.50	5.00
B30	SP4 20c violet & red	42.50	47.50
Nos. B28-B30 (3)		51.50	57.50

Counterfeits of Nos. B28-B30 abound. Probably as many as 90% of the stamps on the market are counterfeits. Competently certified copies sell for much more.

1915, Jan. 1   Perf. 12, 14

B31	SP5 5c green & red	5.00	3.00
a.	Perf. 12x14	16.00	12.00
B32	SP5 10c rose & red	20.00	6.00
B33	SP5 20c violet & red	25.00	14.00
a.	Perf. 14x12	500.00	250.00
b.	Perf. 12	50.00	32.50
Nos. B31-B33 (3)		50.00	23.00

Nos. B25-B33 were sold at double face value. The surtax benefited the Red Cross.

Types of Regular Issue of 1915 Surcharged in Red:

✚ 1c   Nos. B34-B40   ✚ 35c   Nos. B41-B43

✚ 1F   Nos. B44-B47

1918, Jan. 15   Typo.   Perf. 14

B34	A46 1c + 1c dp orange	.50	.50
B35	A46 2c + 2c brown	.60	.60
B36	A46 5c + 5c blue grn	1.25	1.25
B37	A46 10c + 10c red	2.25	2.25
B38	A46 15c + 15c brt violet	3.25	3.25
B39	A46 20c + 20c plum	7.50	7.50
B40	A46 25c + 25c ultra	7.50	7.50

Engr.

B41	A47	35c + 35c lt vio & blk	10.00	10.00
B42	A48	40c + 40c dull red & blk	10.00	10.00
B43	A49	50c + 50c turq blue & blk	12.00	12.00
B44	A50	1fr + 1fr bluish slate	35.00	35.00
B45	A51	2fr + 2fr dp gray grn	100.00	100.00
B46	A52	5fr + 5fr brown	250.00	250.00
B47	A53	10fr + 10fr dp blue	500.00	500.00
	Nos. B34-B47 (14)		939.85	939.85

Discus Thrower — SP6

Racing Chariot — SP7

Runner — SP8

1920, May 20   Engr.   Perf. 12

B48	SP6	5c + 5c dp green	1.40	1.40
B49	SP7	10c + 5c carmine	1.40	1.40
B50	SP8	15c + 15c dk brown	3.00	3.00
	Nos. B48-B50 (3)		5.80	5.80

7th Olympic Games, 1920. Surtax benefited wounded soldiers. Exists imperf.
For surcharges see Nos. 140-142.

Allegory: Asking Alms from the Crown — SP9

Wounded Veteran — SP10

1922, May 20

B51	SP9	20c + 20c brown	1.40	1.40

1923, July 5

B52	SP10	20c + 20c slate gray	1.75	1.75

Surtax on #B51-B52 was to aid wounded veterans.

SP11

SP12

St. Martin, by Van Dyck

SP13   SP14

1925, Dec. 15   Typo.   Perf. 14

B53	SP11	15c + 15c dull vio & red	.50	.20
B54	SP11	30c + 5c gray & red	.25	.20
B55	SP11	1fr + 10c chalky blue & red	1.25	1.40
	Nos. B53-B55 (3)		2.00	1.80

Surtax for the Natl. Anti-Tuberculosis League.

1926, Feb. 10

B56	SP12	30c + 30c bluish grn (red surch.)	.50	.55
B57	SP13	1fr + 1fr lt blue	7.25	7.25
B58	SP14	1fr + 1fr lt blue	1.10	1.25
	Nos. B56-B58 (3)		8.85	9.05

The surtax aided victims of the Meuse flood.

Lion and Cross of Lorraine SP15

Queen Elisabeth and King Albert SP16

1926, Dec. 6   Typo.   Perf. 14

B59	SP15	5c + 5c dk brown	.25	.20
B60	SP15	20c + 5c red brown	.45	.40
B61	SP15	50c + 5c dull violet	.30	.20

Engr.   Perf. 11½

B62	SP16	1.50fr + 25c dk blue	.75	.70
B63	SP16	5fr + 1fr rose red	6.50	6.00
	Nos. B59-B63 (5)		8.25	7.50

Surtax was used to benefit tubercular war veterans.

Boat Adrift — SP17

1927, Dec. 15   Engr.   Perf. 11½, 14

B64	SP17	25c + 10c dk brown	.70	.70
B65	SP17	35c + 10c yel grn	.70	.70
B66	SP17	60c + 10c dp violet	.60	.40
B67	SP17	1.75fr + 25c dk blue	1.50	2.00
B68	SP17	5fr + 1fr plum	4.50	4.75
	Nos. B64-B68 (5)		8.00	8.55

The surtax on these stamps was divided among several charitable associations.

Ogives of Orval Abbey — SP18

Monk Carving Capital of Column — SP19

Ruins of Orval Abbey — SP20

Design: 60c+15c, 1.75fr+25c, 3fr+1fr, Countess Matilda recovering her ring.

1928, Sept. 15   Photo.   Perf. 11½

B69	SP18	5c + 5c red & gold	.25	.30
B70	SP18	25c + 5c dk vio & gold	.45	.50

Engr.

B71	SP19	35c + 10c dp green	1.10	1.10
B72	SP19	60c + 15c red brown	1.65	1.65
B73	SP19	1.75fr + 25c dk blue	3.50	3.50
B74	SP19	2fr + 40c dp violet	13.00	13.00
B75	SP19	3fr + 1fr red	15.00	15.00

Perf. 14

B76	SP20	5fr + 5fr rose lake	15.00	15.00
B77	SP20	10fr + 10fr ol green	15.00	15.00
	Nos. B69-B77 (9)		64.95	65.05

Surtax for the restoration of the ruined Orval Abbey.
For overprints see Nos. B84-B92.

St. Waudru, Mons — SP22

St. Rombaut, Malines — SP23

Designs: 25c + 15c, Cathedral of Tournal. 60c + 15c, St. Bavon, Ghent. 1.75fr + 25c, St. Gudule, Brussels. 5fr + 5fr, Louvain Library.

1928, Dec. 1   Photo.   Perf. 14, 11½

B78	SP22	5c + 5c carmine	.20	.20
B79	SP22	25c + 15c ol brn	.35	.38

Engr.

B80	SP23	35c + 10c dp green	1.25	1.25
B81	SP23	60c + 15c red brn	.25	.25
B82	SP23	1.75fr + 25c vio blue	8.50	7.00
B83	SP23	5fr + 5fr red vio	16.00	15.00
	Nos. B78-B83 (6)		26.80	24.08

The surtax was for anti-tuberculosis work.

19-8-29

Nos. B69-B77 with this overprint in blue or red was privately produced. They are for the laying of the 1st stone toward the restoration of the ruined Abbey of Orval. Forgeries of the overprint exist. Value, set, $650.

Waterfall at Coo — SP28

Bayard Rock, Dinant — SP29

Designs: 35c+10c, Menin Gate, Ypres. 60c+15c, Promenade d'Orleans, Spa. 1.75fr+25c, Antwerp Harbor. 5fr+5fr, Quai Vert, Bruges.

1929, Dec. 2   Engr.   Perf. 11½

B93	SP28	5c + 5c red brown	.20	.25
B94	SP29	25c + 15c gray blk	.65	.60
B95	SP28	35c + 10c green	.80	.95
B96	SP28	60c + 15c rose lake	.55	.50
B97	SP28	1.75fr + 25c dp blue	4.50	4.50

Perf. 14

B98	SP29	5fr + 5fr dl vio	27.50	27.50
	Nos. B93-B98 (6)		34.20	34.30

Bornhem — SP34

Beloeil — SP35

Gaesbeek SP36

Designs: 25c + 15c, Wynendaele. 70c + 15c, Oydonck. 1fr + 25c, Ghent. 1.75fr + 25c, Bouillon.

1930, Dec. 1   Photo.   Perf. 14

B99	SP34	10c + 5c violet	.25	.30
B100	SP34	25c + 15c olive brn	.60	.60

Engr.

B101	SP35	40c + 10c brown vio	.80	1.00
B102	SP35	70c + 15c gray blk	.55	.55
B103	SP35	1fr + 25c rose lake	3.50	3.50
B104	SP35	1.75fr + 25c dp blue	4.50	2.75
B105	SP36	5fr + 5fr gray grn	27.50	32.50
	Nos. B99-B105 (7)		37.70	41.20

Prince Leopold SP41

Queen Elisabeth SP42

Philatelic Exhibition Issue
Souvenir Sheet

1931, July 18   Photo.   Perf. 14

B106	SP41	2.45fr + 55c car brn	140.00	140.00

Sold exclusively at the Brussels Phil. Exhib., July 18-21, 1931. Size: 122x159mm. Surtax for the Veterans' Relief Fund.
The sheet normally has pin holes and a cancellation-like marking in the margin. These are considered unused and the condition valued here.

1931, Dec. 1   Engr.

B107	SP42	10c + 5c red brown	.30	.52
B108	SP42	25c + 15c dk violet	1.10	1.25
B109	SP42	50c + 10c dk green	.95	1.00
B110	SP42	75c + 15c black brn	.90	.65
B111	SP42	1fr + 25c rose lake	6.75	6.00
B112	SP42	1.75fr + 25c ultra	4.75	4.00
B113	SP42	5fr + 5fr brown vio	55.00	55.00
	Nos. B107-B113 (7)		69.75	68.42

The surtax was for the National Anti-Tuberculosis League.

Désiré Cardinal Mercier SP43

Mercier Protecting Children and Aged at Malines SP44

Mercier as Professor at Louvain University — SP45

Mercier in Full Canonicals, Giving His Blessing SP46

1932, June 10   Photo.   Perf. 14½x14

B114	SP43	10c + 10c dk violet	.40	.60
B115	SP43	50c + 30c brt violet	2.25	2.50
B116	SP43	75c + 25c olive brn	2.25	2.25
B117	SP43	1fr + 2fr brown red	6.00	6.00

Engr.   Perf. 11½

B118	SP44	1.75fr + 75c dp blue	70.00	82.50
B119	SP45	2.50fr + 2.50fr dk brn	70.00	70.00
B120	SP44	3fr + 4.50fr dull grn	70.00	70.00
B121	SP45	5fr + 20fr vio brn	80.00	82.50
B122	SP46	10fr + 40fr brn lake	175.00	210.00
	Nos. B114-B122 (9)		475.90	526.35

Issued in commemoration of Cardinal Mercier and to obtain funds to erect a monument to his memory.

Belgian Infantryman SP47

Sanatorium at Waterloo SP48

1932, Aug. 4   Perf. 14½x14

B123	SP47	75c + 3.25fr red brn	55.00	55.00
B124	SP47	1.75fr + 4.25fr dk blue	55.00	55.00

Honoring Belgian soldiers who fought in WWI and to obtain funds to erect a natl. monument to their glory.

1932, Dec. 1   Photo.   Perf. 13½x14

B125	SP48	10c + 5c dk vio	.30	.90
B126	SP48	25c + 15c red vio	1.00	1.00
B127	SP48	50c + 10c red brn	1.00	1.25
B128	SP48	75c + 15c ol brn	1.00	.80
B129	SP48	1fr + 25c dp red	13.00	10.50
B130	SP48	1.75fr + 25c dp blue	10.50	9.25
B131	SP48	5fr + 5fr gray grn	85.00	90.00
		Nos. B125-B131 (7)	111.80	113.95

Surtax for the assistance of the Natl. Anti-Tuberculosis Society at Waterloo.

View of Old Abbey — SP49

Ruins of Old Abbey — SP50

Count de Chiny Presenting First Abbey to Countess Matilda SP56

Restoration of Abbey in XVI and XVII Centuries SP57

Abbey in XVIII Century, Maria Theresa and Charles V — SP58

Madonna and Arms of Seven Abbeys — SP60

Designs: 25c+15c, Guests, courtyard, 50c+25c, Transept. 75c+50c, Bell Tower. 1fr+1.25fr, Fountain. 1.25fr+1.75fr, Cloisters. 5fr+20fr, Duke of Brabant placing 1st stone of new abbey.

1933, Oct. 15   Perf. 14

B132	SP49	5c + 5c dull grn	35.00	40.00
B133	SP50	10c + 15c ol grn	32.50	35.00
B134	SP49	25c + 15c dk brn	32.50	35.00
B135	SP50	50c + 25c red brn	32.50	35.00
B136	SP50	75c + 50c dp grn	32.50	35.00
B137	SP50	1fr + 1.25fr cop red	32.50	35.00
B138	SP49	1.25fr + 1.75fr gray blk	32.50	35.00
B139	SP56	1.75fr + 2.75fr blue	37.50	40.00
B140	SP57	2fr + 3fr mag	37.50	40.00
B141	SP58	2.50fr + 5fr dull brn	37.50	40.00
B142	SP56	5fr + 20fr vio	40.00	40.00

Perf. 11½

B143	SP60	10fr + 40fr blue	225.00	225.00
		Nos. B132-B143 (12)	607.50	635.00

The surtax was for a fund to aid in the restoration of Orval Abbey. Counterfeits exist.

"Tuberculosis Society" SP61

Peter Benoit SP62

1933, Dec. 1   Engr.   Perf. 14x13½

B144	SP61	10c + 5c black	.85	.85
B145	SP61	25c + 15c violet	3.00	3.00
B146	SP61	50c + 10c red brn	2.25	2.25
B147	SP61	75c + 15c blk brn	9.25	9.00
B148	SP61	1fr + 25c claret	10.50	10.50
B149	SP61	1.75fr + 25c vio bl	12.50	12.50
B150	SP61	5fr + 5fr lilac	115.00	115.00
		Nos. B144-B150 (7)	153.35	153.10

The surtax was for anti-tuberculosis work.

1934, June 1   Photo.

B151	SP62	75c + 25c olive brn	5.50	5.50

The surtax was to raise funds for the Peter Benoit Memorial.

King Leopold III SP63   SP64

1934, Sept. 15

B152	SP63	75c + 25c ol blk	18.00	17.00
a.		Sheet of 20	750.00	750.00
B153	SP64	1fr + 25c red vio	17.00	16.00
a.		Sheet of 20	750.00	750.00

The surtax aided the National War Veterans' Fund. Sold for 4.50fr a set at the Exhibition of War Postmarks 1914-18, held at Brussels by the Royal Philatelic Club of Veterans. The price included an exhibition ticket. Sold at Brussels post office Sept. 18-22. No. B152 printed in sheets of 20 (4x5) and 100 (10x10). No. B153 printed in sheets of 20 (4x5) and 150 (10x15).

1934, Sept. 24

B154	SP63	75c + 25c violet	1.25	1.25
B155	SP64	1fr + 25c red brn	7.00	7.00

The surtax aided the National War Veterans' Fund. No. B154 printed in sheets of 100 (10x10); No. B155 in sheets of 150 (10x15). These stamps remained in use one year.

Crusader — SP65

1934, Nov. 17   Engr.   Perf. 13½x14
Cross in Red

B156	SP65	10c + 5c black	1.25	1.25
B157	SP65	25c + 15c brown	1.75	1.75
B158	SP65	50c + 10c dull grn	1.75	1.75
B159	SP65	75c + 15c vio brn	.85	.85
B160	SP65	1fr + 25c rose	8.50	8.50
B161	SP65	1.75fr + 25c ultra	7.50	7.50
B162	SP65	5fr + 5fr brn vio	105.00	105.00
		Nos. B156-B162 (7)	126.60	126.60

The surtax was for anti-tuberculosis work.

Prince Baudouin, Princess Josephine and Prince Albert SP66

1935, Apr. 10   Photo.

B163	SP66	35c + 15c dk green	.85	.75
B164	SP66	70c + 30c red brn	.85	.60
B165	SP66	1.75fr + 50c dk blue	3.00	3.50
		Nos. B163-B165 (3)	4.70	4.85

Surtax was for Child Welfare Society.

Stagecoach SP67

Franz von Taxis — SP68

Queen Astrid — SP69

1935, Apr. 27

B166	SP67	10c + 10c ol blk	.55	.65
B167	SP67	25c + 25c bis brn	1.90	1.75
B168	SP67	35c + 25c dk green	2.50	2.25
		Nos. B166-B168 (3)	4.95	4.65

Printed in sheets of 10. Value, set of 3, $175.

Souvenir Sheet

1935, May 25   Engr.   Perf. 14

B169	SP68	5fr + 5fr grnsh blk	125.00	125.00

Sheets measure 91½x117mm.
Nos. B166-B169 were issued for the Brussels Philatelic Exhibition (SITEB).
The sheet normally has pin holes and a cancellation-like marking in the margin. These are considered unused and the condition valued here.

1935   Photo.   Perf. 11½
Borders in Black

B170	SP69	10c + 5c ol blk	.15	.15
B171	SP69	25c + 15c brown	.15	.30
B172	SP69	35c + 5c dk green	.20	.25
B173	SP69	50c + 10c rose lil	.65	.55
B174	SP69	70c + 5c gray blk	.15	.15
B175	SP69	1fr + 25c red	.90	.70
B176	SP69	1.75fr + 25c blue	2.00	1.50
B177	SP69	2.45fr + 55c dk vio	2.50	2.75
		Nos. B170-B177 (8)	6.70	6.35

Queen Astrid Memorial issue. The surtax was divided among several charitable organizations. Issued: #B174, 10/31; others, 12/1.

Borgerhout Philatelic Exhibition Issue
Souvenir Sheet

Town Hall, Borgerhout — SP70

1936, Oct. 3

B178	SP70	70c + 30c pur brn	50.00	35.00

Sheet measures 115x126mm.
The sheet normally has pin holes and a cancellation-like marking in the margin. These are considered unused and the condition valued here.

Town Hall and Belfry of Charleroi SP71

Prince Baudouin SP72

Charleroi Youth Exhibition
Souvenir Sheet

1936, Oct. 18   Engr.

B179	SP71	2.45fr + 55c gray blue	42.50	40.00

Sheet measures 95x120mm.
The sheet normally has pin holes and a cancellation-like marking in the margin. These are considered unused and the condition valued here.

1936, Dec. 1   Photo.   Perf. 14x13½

B180	SP72	10c + 5c dk brown	.15	.20
B181	SP72	25c + 5c violet	.20	.25
B182	SP72	35c + 5c dk green	.20	.25
B183	SP72	50c + 5c vio brn	.30	.35
B184	SP72	70c + 5c ol grn	.20	.20
B185	SP72	1fr + 25c cerise	.65	.45
B186	SP72	1.75fr + 25c ultra	1.10	.65
B187	SP72	2.45fr + 2.55fr vio rose	3.00	4.00
		Nos. B180-B187 (8)	5.80	6.35

The surtax was for the assistance of the National Anti-Tuberculosis Society.

1937, Jan. 10

B188	SP72	2.45fr + 2.55fr slate	1.50	1.50

Intl. Stamp Day. Surtax for the benefit of the Brussels Postal Museum, the Royal Belgian Phil. Fed. and the Anti-Tuberculosis Soc.

Queen Astrid and Prince Baudouin SP73

Queen Mother Elisabeth SP74

1937, Apr. 15   Perf. 11½

B189	SP73	10c + 5c magenta	.15	.15
B190	SP73	25c + 5c ol blk	.20	.25
B191	SP73	35c + 5c dk grn	.20	.25
B192	SP73	50c + 5c violet	.50	.55
B193	SP73	70c + 5c slate	.20	.30
B194	SP73	1fr + 25c dk car	.65	.45
B195	SP73	1.75fr + 25c dp ultra	1.10	1.10
B196	SP73	2.45fr + 1.55fr dk brn	2.75	2.75
		Nos. B189-B196 (8)	5.75	6.00

The surtax was to raise funds for Public Utility Works.

1937, Sept. 15   Perf. 14x13½

B197	SP74	70c + 5c int black	.30	.30
B198	SP74	1.75fr + 25c brt ultra	.70	.70

Souvenir Sheet
Perf. 11½

B199		Sheet of 4	26.00	15.00
a.		SP74 1.50fr+2.50fr red brown	3.75	3.25
b.		SP74 2.45fr+3.55fr red violet	3.25	2.00

Issued for the benefit of the Queen Elisabeth Music Foundation in connection with the Eugene Ysaye intl. competition.
No. B199 contains two se-tenant pairs of Nos. B199a and B199b. Size: 111x145mm. On sale one day, Sept. 15, at Brussels.
The sheet normally has pin holes and a cancellation-like marking in the margin. These are considered unused and the condition valued here.

Princess Josephine-Charlotte SP75

1937, Dec. 1　　　　　　Perf. 14x13½

B200	SP75	10c + 5c sl grn	.15	.20
B201	SP75	25c + 5c lt brn	.20	.20
B202	SP75	35c + 5c yel grn	.20	.20
B203	SP75	50c + 5c ol gray	.40	.35
B204	SP75	70c + 5c brn red	.15	.50
B205	SP75	1fr + 25c red	.70	.55
B206	SP75	1.75fr + 25c vio bl	.80	.70
B207	SP75	2.45fr + 2.55fr mag	3.25	3.50
		Nos. B200-B207 (8)	5.85	5.90

King Albert Memorial Issue
Souvenir Sheet

King Albert Memorial — SP76

1938, Feb. 17　　　　　　Perf. 11½

B208 SP76 2.45fr + 7.55fr brn vio　13.00 11.00

Dedication of the monument to King Albert.

The sheet normally has pin holes and a cancellation-like marking in the margin. These are considered unused and the condition valued here.

King Leopold III in Military Plane — SP77

1938, Mar. 15

B209	SP77	10c + 5c car brn	.20	.30
B210	SP77	35c + 5c dp grn	.35	.90
B211	SP77	70c + 5c gray blk	.65	.50
B212	SP77	1.75fr + 25c ultra	1.50	1.40
B213	SP77	2.45fr + 2.55fr pur	3.50	3.00
		Nos. B209-B213 (5)	6.20	6.10

The surtax was for the benefit of the National Fund for Aeronautical Propaganda.

Basilica of Koekelberg SP78

Interior View of the Basilica of Koekelberg — SP79

1938, June 1　　　　　　Photo.

B214	SP78	10c + 5c lt brn	.15	.20
B215	SP78	35c + 5c grn	.20	.20
B216	SP78	70c + 5c gray grn	.20	.20
B217	SP78	1fr + 25c car	.65	.55
B218	SP78	1.75fr + 25c car	.65	.65
B219	SP78	2.45fr + 2.55fr brn vio	2.75	3.50

Engr.

B220	SP79	5fr + 5fr dl grn	11.00	10.50
		Nos. B214-B220 (7)	15.60	15.80

Souvenir Sheet

1938, July 21　　Engr.　　Perf. 14

B221 SP79 5fr + 5fr lt vio　14.00 14.00

The surtax was for a fund to aid in completing the National Basilica of the Sacred Heart at Koekelberg.

Nos. B214, B216 and B218 are different views of the exterior of the Basilica.

The sheet normally has pin holes and a cancellation-like marking in the margin. These are considered unused and the condition valued here.

Stamps of 1938 Surcharged in Black:

Nos. B222-B223

No. B224

1938, Nov. 10　　　　　　Perf. 11½

B222	SP78	40c on 35c+5c grn	.35	.40
B223	SP78	75c on 70c+5c gray grn	.50	.65
B224	SP78	2.50 +2.50fr on 2.45+2.55fr	4.50	5.00
		Nos. B222-B224 (3)	5.35	6.05

Prince Albert of Liege — SP81

1938, Dec. 10　　Photo.　Perf. 14x13½

B225	SP81	10c + 5c brown	.15	.20
B226	SP81	30c + 5c magenta	.20	.30
B227	SP81	40c + 5c olive gray	.20	.30
B228	SP81	75c + 5c slate grn	.15	.20
B229	SP81	1fr + 25c dk car	.55	.75
B230	SP81	1.75fr + 25c ultra	.55	.75
B231	SP81	2.50fr + 2.50fr dp grn	3.50	5.50
B232	SP81	5fr + 5fr brn lake	11.00	8.50
		Nos. B225-B232 (8)	16.30	16.50

Henri Dunant SP82

Florence Nightingale SP83

Queen Mother Elisabeth and Royal Children — SP84

Queen Astrid — SP86

King Leopold and Royal Children SP85

Queen Mother Elisabeth and Wounded Soldier — SP87

1939, Apr. 1　　Photo.　Perf. 11½
Cross in Carmine

B233	SP82	10c + 5c brn	.15	.20
B234	SP83	30c + 5c brn car	.30	.30
B235	SP84	40c + 5c ol gray	.20	.30
B236	SP85	75c + 5c slate blk	.40	.20
B237	SP84	1fr + 25c brt rose	1.90	1.10
B238	SP85	1.75fr + 25c brt ultra	.60	.85

B239	SP86	2.50fr + 2.50fr dl vio	1.25	1.65
B240	SP87	5fr + 5fr gray grn	4.25	5.50
		Nos. B233-B240 (8)	9.05	10.10

75th anniversary of the founding of the International Red Cross Society.

Rubens' House, Antwerp SP88

"Albert and Nicolas Rubens" — SP89

Arcade, Rubens' House SP90

"Helena Fourment and Her Children" — SP91

Rubens and Isabelle Brandt — SP92

Peter Paul Rubens — SP93

"The Velvet Hat" — SP94

"Descent from the Cross" SP95

1939, July 1

B241	SP88	10c + 5c brn	.15	.20
B242	SP89	40c + 5c brn car	.30	.30
B243	SP90	75c + 5c ol blk	.60	.50
B244	SP91	1fr + 25c rose	1.65	1.50
B245	SP92	1.50fr + 25c sep	1.65	1.50
B246	SP93	1.75fr + 25c dp ultra	2.25	1.65
B247	SP94	2.50fr + 2.50fr brt red vio	9.25	10.50
B248	SP95	5fr + 5fr slate gray	14.00	14.00
		Nos. B241-B248 (8)	29.85	30.15

Issued to honor Peter Paul Rubens. The surtax was used to restore Rubens' home in Antwerp.

"Martin van Nieuwenhove" by Hans Memling (1430?-1495), Flemish Painter — SP96

1939, July 1

B249 SP96 75c + 75c olive blk　2.75 2.75

Twelfth Century Monks at Work — SP97

Reconstructed Tower Seen through Cloister — SP98

Monks Laboring in the Fields — SP99

Orval Abbey, Aerial View — SP100

Bishop Heylen of Namur, Madonna and Abbot General Smets of the Trappists — SP101

King Albert I and King Leopold III and Shrine — SP102

1939, July 20

B250	SP97	75c + 75c ol blk	2.50	2.75
B251	SP98	1fr + 1fr rose red	1.65	1.65
B252	SP99	1.50fr + 1.50fr dl brn	1.65	1.65
B253	SP100	1.75fr + 1.75fr saph	1.65	1.65
B254	SP101	2.50fr + 2.50fr brt red vio	7.25	6.50
B255	SP102	5fr + 5fr brn car	7.25	7.25
		Nos. B250-B255 (6)	21.95	21.45

The surtax was used for the restoration of the Abbey of Orval.

Bruges
SP103

Furnes
SP104

Belfries: 30c+5c, Thuin. 40c+5c, Lierre. 75c+5c, Mons. 1.75fr+25c, Namur. 2.50fr+2.50fr, Alost. 5fr+5fr, Tournai.

1939, Dec. 1   Photo.   Perf. 14x13½

B256 SP103	10c + 5c ol gray	.15	.25
B257 SP103	30c + 5c brn org	.25	.35
B258 SP103	40c + 5c brt red vio	.40	.45
B259 SP103	75c + 5c olive blk	.15	.25

Engr.

B260 SP104	1fr + 25c rose car	1.00	1.25
B261 SP104	1.75fr + 25c dk blue	1.00	1.25
B262 SP104	2.50fr + 2.50fr dp red brn	7.25	8.00
B263 SP104	5fr + 5fr purple	10.00	11.00
Nos. B256-B263 (8)		20.20	22.80

Mons
SP111

Ghent
SP112

Coats of Arms: 40c+10c, Arel. 50c+10c, Bruges. 75c+15c, Namur. 1fr+25c, Hasselt. 1.75fr+50c, Brussels. 2.50fr+2.50fr, Antwerp. 5fr+5fr, Liege.

1940-41   Typo.   Perf. 14x13½

B264 SP112	10c + 5c multi	.15	.15
B265 SP112	30c + 5c multi	.20	.15
B266 SP111	40c + 10c multi	.20	.15
B267 SP112	50c + 10c multi	.20	.15
B268 SP111	75c + 15c multi	.15	.15
B269 SP111	1fr + 25c multi	.30	.30
B270 SP111	1.75fr + 50c multi	.45	.40
B271 SP112	2.50fr + 2.50fr multi	1.25	1.25
B272 SP111	5fr + 5fr multi	1.50	1.50
Nos. B264-B272 (9)		4.40	4.20

Nos. B264, B269-B272 issued in 1941. Surtax for winter relief. See No. B279.

Queen Elisabeth Music Chapel
SP120

Bust of Prince Albert of Liege — SP121

1940, Nov.   Photo.   Perf. 11½

B273 SP120	75c + 75c slate	1.25	1.25
B274 SP120	1fr + 1fr rose red	1.25	1.25
B275 SP121	1.50fr + 1.50fr Prus grn	1.25	1.25
B276 SP120	1.75fr + 1.75fr ultra	1.25	1.25
B277 SP120	2.50fr + 2.50fr brn org	2.50	2.50
B278 SP121	5fr + 5fr red vio	3.00	3.00
Nos. B273-B278 (6)		10.50	10.50

The surtax was for the Queen Elisabeth Music Foundation. Nos. B273-B278 were not authorized for postal use, but were sold to advance subscribers either mint or canceled to order. See Nos. B317-B318.

Arms Types of 1940-41
Souvenir Sheets
Perf. 14x13½, Imperf.

1941, May   Typo.
Cross and City Name in Carmine
Arms in Color of Stamp

B279	Sheet of 9	13.00	13.00
a.	SP111 10c + 5c slate	1.10	1.25
b.	SP112 30c + 5c emerald	1.10	1.25
c.	SP111 40c + 10c chocolate	1.10	1.25
d.	SP112 50c + 10c light violet	1.10	1.25
e.	SP111 75c + 15c dull purple	1.10	1.25
f.	SP112 1fr + 25c carmine	1.10	1.25
g.	SP111 1.75fr + 50c dull blue	1.10	1.25
h.	SP112 2.50fr + 2.50fr olive gray	1.10	1.25
i.	SP111 5fr + 5fr dull violet	4.00	4.25

The sheets measure 106x148mm. The surtax was used for relief work.

Painting
SP123

Sculpture
SP124

Monks Studying Plans of Orval Abbey — SP128

Designs: 40c+60c, 2fr+3.50fr, Monk carrying candle. 50c+65c, 1.75fr+2.50fr, Monk praying. 75c+1fr, 3fr+5fr, Two monks singing.

1941, June   Photo.   Perf. 11½

B281 SP123	10c + 15c brn org	.35	.40
B282 SP124	30c + 30c ol gray	.35	.40
B283 SP124	40c + 60c dp brn	.35	.40
B284 SP124	50c + 65c vio	.35	.40
B285 SP124	75c + 1fr brt red vio	.35	.40
B286 SP124	1fr + 1.50fr rose red	.35	.40
B287 SP123	1.25fr + 1.75fr dp yel grn	.35	.40
B288 SP123	1.75fr + 2.50fr dp ultra	.35	.40
B289 SP123	2fr + 3.50fr red vio	.35	.40
B290 SP124	2.50fr + 4.50fr dl red brn	.35	.40
B291 SP124	3fr + 5fr dk ol grn	.35	.40
B292 SP128	5fr + 10fr grnsh blk	1.25	1.25
Nos. B281-B292 (12)		5.10	5.65

The surtax was used for the restoration of the Abbey of Orval.

Maria Theresa — SP129

Charles the Bold — SP130

Portraits (in various frames): 35c+5c, Charles of Lorraine. 50c+10c, Margaret of Parma. 60c+10c, Charles V. 1fr+15c, Johanna of Castile. 1.50fr+1fr, Philip the Good. 1.75fr+1.75fr, Margaret of Austria. 3.25fr+3.25fr, Archduke Albert. 5fr+5fr, Archduchess Isabella.

1941-42   Photo.

B293 SP129	10c + 5c ol blk	.15	.15
B294 SP129	35c + 5c dl grn	.15	.15
B295 SP129	50c + 10c brn	.15	.15
B296 SP129	60c + 10c pur	.15	.15
B297 SP129	1fr + 15c brt car rose	.15	.15
B298 SP129	1.50fr + 1fr red vio	.20	.20
B299 SP129	1.75fr + 1.75fr ryl bl	.20	.20
B300 SP130	2.25fr + 2.25fr dl red brn	.30	.30
B301 SP129	3.25fr + 3.25fr lt brn	.35	.45
B302 SP129	5fr + 5fr sl grn	.40	.45
Nos. B293-B302 (10)		2.20	2.35

Souvenir Sheet

Archduke Albert and Archduchess Isabella — SP139

B302A SP139	Sheet of 2 ('42)	6.00	6.00
b.	3.25fr+6.75fr turquoise blue	2.25	2.25
c.	5fr+10fr dark carmine	2.25	2.25

The surtax was for the benefit of National Social Service Work among soldiers' families.

Souvenir Sheets

Monks Studying Plans of Orval Abbey
SP140

1941, Oct.   Photo.   Perf. 11½
Inscribed "Belgie-Belgique"

B303 SP140	5fr + 15fr ultra	7.00	7.00

Inscribed "Belgique-Belgie"

B304 SP140	5fr + 15fr ultra	7.00	7.00

Surtax for the restoration of Orval Abbey. No. B304 exists perforated.
In 1942 these sheets were privately trimmed and overprinted "1142 1942" and ornament.

St. Martin Statue, Church of Dinant
SP141

Lennik, Saint-Quentin
SP142

St. Martin's Church, Saint-Trond
SP146

Statues of St. Martin: 50c+10c, 3.25fr+3.25fr, Beck, Limburg. 60c+10c, 2.25fr+2.25fr, Dave on the Meuse. 1.75fr+50c, Hal, Brabant.

1941-42   Photo.   Perf. 11½

B305 SP141	10c + 5c chestnut	.15	.15
B306 SP142	35c + 5c dk bl grn	.15	.15
B307 SP142	50c + 10c violet	.15	.15
B308 SP142	60c + 10c dp brn	.15	.15
B309 SP142	1fr + 15c carmine	.15	.15
B310 SP141	1.50fr + 25c sl grn	.20	.20
B311 SP142	1.75fr + 50c dk ultra	.30	.30
B312 SP142	2.25fr + 2.25fr red vio	.30	.30
B313 SP142	3.25fr + 3.25fr brn	.30	.30
B314 SP146	5fr + 5fr dk ol grn	.45	.45
Nos. B305-B314 (10)		2.30	2.30

Souvenir Sheets
Inscribed "Belgie-Belgique"

B315 SP146	5fr + 20fr vio brn ('42)	12.50	12.50

Inscribed "Belgique-Belgie"

B316 SP146	5fr + 20fr vio brn ('42)	12.50	12.50

In 1956, the Bureau Europeen de la Jeunesse et de l'Enfance privately overprinted Nos. B315-B316: "Congres Europeen de l'education 7-12 Mai 1956," in dark red and dark green respectively. A black bar obliterates "Winterhulp-Secours d'Hiver."

Souvenir Sheets

Queen Elisabeth Music Chapel — SP147

1941, Dec. 1   Photo.   Perf. 11½
Inscribed "Belgique-Belgie"

B317 SP147	10fr + 15fr ol blk	4.50	4.00

Inscribed "Belgie-Belique"

B318 SP147	10fr + 15fr ol blk	4.50	4.00

The surtax was for the Queen Elisabeth Music Foundation. These sheets were perforated with the monogram of Queen Elisabeth in 1942.
In 1954 Nos. B317-B318 were overprinted to for the birth cent. of Edgar Tinel, composer. These overprinted sheets were not postally valid.

Jean Bollandus
SP148

Christophe Plantin
SP156

Designs: 35c+5c, Andreas Vesalius. 50c+10c, Simon Stevinus. 60c+10c, Jean Van Helmont. 1fr+15c, Rembert Dodoens. 1.75fr+50c, Gerardus Mercator. 3.25fr+3.25fr, Abraham Ortelius. 5fr+5fr, Justus Lipsius.

1942, May 15   Photo.   Perf. 14x13½

B319 SP148	10c + 5c dl brn	.15	.15
B320 SP148	35c + 5c gray grn	.15	.15
B321 SP148	50c + 10c fawn	.15	.15
B322 SP148	60c + 10c grnsh blk	.15	.15

Engr.

B323 SP148	1fr + 15c brt rose	.15	.15
B324 SP148	1.75fr + 50c dl bl	.20	.20
B325 SP148	3.25fr + 3.25fr lil rose	.20	.20
B326 SP148	5fr + 5fr vio	.25	.25

Perf. 13½x14

B327 SP156	10fr + 30fr red org	.95	1.00
Nos. B319-B327 (9)		2.35	2.40

The surtax was used to help fight tuberculosis.
No. B327 was sold by subscription at the Brussels Post Office, July 1-10, 1942.

Belgian Prisoner — SP158

1942, Oct. 1   Perf. 11½

B331 SP158	5fr + 45fr olive gray	5.50	5.50

The surtax was for prisoners of war. Value includes a brown label, inscribed "1942 POUR NOS PRISONNIERS/VOOR ONZE GEVANGENEN," which alternates with the stamps in the sheet.

SP159

SP164

SP162

SP168

Various Statues of St. Martin.

1942-43

B332	SP159	10c + 5c org	.15	.15
B333	SP159	35c + 5c dk bl grn	.15	.15
B334	SP159	50c + 10c dp brn	.15	.15
B335	SP162	60c + 10c blk	.15	.15
B336	SP159	1fr + 15c brt rose	.15	.15
B337	SP164	1.50fr + 25c grnsh blk	.20	.20
B338	SP164	1.75fr + 50c dk bl	.20	.20
B339	SP162	2.25fr + 2.25fr brn	.30	.25
B340	SP162	3.25fr + 3.25fr brt red vio	.35	.30
B341	SP168	5fr + 10fr hn brn	.50	.45
B342	SP168	10fr + 20fr rose brn & vio brn ('43)	.65	.65

Inscribed "Belgique-Belgie"

B343	SP168	10fr + 20fr gldn brn & vio brn ('43)	.65	.65
		Nos. B332-B343 (12)	3.60	3.45

The surtax was for winter relief.
Issue dates: Nos. B332-B341, Nov. 12, 1942.
Nos. B342-B343, Apr. 3, 1943.

Prisoners of War — SP170

#B345, 2 prisoners with package from home.

1943, May　　Photo.　　Perf. 11½

B344	SP170	1fr + 30fr ver	2.50	2.50
B345	SP170	1fr + 30fr brn rose	2.50	2.50

The surtax was used for prisoners of war.

Roof Tiler
SP172

Coppersmith
SP173

Statues in Petit Sablon Park, Brussels: 35c+5c, Blacksmith. 60c+10c, Gunsmith. 1fr+15c, Armsmith. 1.75fr+75c, Goldsmith. 3.25fr+3.25fr, Fishdealer. 5fr+25fr, Watchmaker.

1943, June 1

B346	SP172	10c + 5c chnt brn	.15	.15
B347	SP172	35c + 5c grn	.15	.15
B348	SP173	50c + 10c dk brn	.15	.15

B349	SP173	60c + 10c slate	.15	.15
B350	SP173	1fr + 15c dl rose brn	.15	.15
B351	SP173	1.75fr + 75c ultra	.20	.20
B352	SP173	3.25fr + 3.25fr brt red vio	.30	.40
B353	SP173	5fr + 25fr dk pur	.50	.55
		Set value	1.45	1.75

Surtax for the control of tuberculosis.

"O" — SP180

"ORVAL" — SP185

1943, Oct. 9

B354	SP180	50c + 1fr "O"	.50	.50
B355	SP180	60c + 1.90fr "R"	.30	.25
B356	SP180	1fr + 3fr "V"	.30	.25
B357	SP180	1.75fr + 5.25fr "A"	.30	.25
B358	SP180	3.25fr + 16.75fr "L"	.40	.40
B359	SP185	5fr + 30fr dp brn	.75	.75
		Nos. B354-B359 (6)	2.55	2.40

Surtax aided restoration of Orval Abbey.

St. Leonard Church, Leau — SP186

St. Martin Church, Courtrai
SP190

Basilica of St. Martin, Angre
SP191

Notre Dame, Hal — SP193

St. Martin
SP194

Designs: 35c+5c, St. Martin Church, Dion-le-Val. 50c+15c, St. Martin Church, Alost. 60c+20c, St. Martin Church, Liege. 3.25fr+11.75fr, St. Martin Church, Loppem. No. B369, St. Martin, beggar and Meuse landscape.

1943-44

B360	SP186	10c + 5c dp brn	.15	.15
B361	SP186	35c + 5c dk bl grn	.20	.20
B362	SP186	50c + 15c ol blk	.30	.30
B363	SP186	60c + 20c brt red vio	.30	.40
B364	SP190	1fr + 1fr rose brn	.40	.40
B365	SP191	1.75fr + 4.25fr dp ultra	.90	.60
B366	SP186	3.25fr + 11.75fr red lil	.90	.65

B367	SP193	5fr + 25fr dk bl	1.25	1.25
B368	SP194	10fr + 30fr gray grn ('44)	.90	.90
B369	SP194	10fr + 30fr blk brn ('44)	.90	.90
		Nos. B360-B369 (10)	6.20	5.75

Surtax for winter relief.

```
Catalogue values for unused
stamps in this section, from this
point to the end of the section, are
for Never Hinged items.
```

"Daedalus and Icarus"
SP196

Sir Anthony Van Dyck, Self-portrait
SP200

Paintings by Van Dyck: 50c+2.50fr. "The Good Samaritan." 60c+3.40fr, Detail of "Christ Healing the Paralytic." 1fr+5fr, "Madonna and Child." 5fr+30fr, "St. Sebastian."

1944, Apr. 16　　Photo.　　Perf. 11½
Crosses in Carmine

B370	SP196	35c + 1.65fr dk sl grn	.40	.30
B371	SP196	50c + 2.50fr grnsh blk	.40	.30
B372	SP196	60c + 3.40fr blk brn	.40	.30
B373	SP196	1fr + 5fr dk car	.60	.45
B374	SP200	1.75fr + 8.25fr int bl	.75	.60
B375	SP196	5fr + 30fr cop brn	.75	.60
		Nos. B370-B375 (6)	3.30	2.55

The surtax was for the Belgian Red Cross.

Jan van Eyck
SP202

Godfrey of Bouillon
SP203

Designs: 50c+25c, Jacob van Maerlant. 60c+40c, Jean Joses de Dinant. 1fr+50c, Jacob van Artevelde. 1.75fr+4.25fr, Charles Joseph de Ligne. 2.25fr+8.25fr, Andre Gretry. 3.25fr+11.25fr, Jan Moretus-Plantin. 5fr+35fr, Jan van Ruysbroeck.

1944, May 31

B376	SP202	10c + 15c dk pur	.40	.25
B377	SP203	35c + 15c green	.40	.25
B378	SP203	50c + 25c chnt brn	.40	.25
B379	SP203	60c + 40c ol blk	.40	.25
B380	SP203	1fr + 50c rose brn	.40	.25
B381	SP203	1.75fr + 4.25fr ultra	.40	.25
B382	SP203	2.25fr + 8.25fr grnsh blk	1.00	.55
B383	SP203	3.25fr + 11.25fr dk brn	.40	.25
B384	SP203	5fr + 35fr sl bl	.70	.70
		Nos. B376-B384 (9)	4.50	3.00

The surtax was for prisoners of war.

Sons of Aymon Astride Bayard
SP211

Brabo Slaying the Giant Antigoon
SP212

Till Eulenspiegel Singing to Nele
SP214

Designs: 50c+10c, St. Hubert converted by stag with crucifix. 1fr+15fr, St. George slaying the dragon. 1.75fr+5.25fr, Genevieve of Brabant with son and roe-deer. 3.25fr+11.75fr, Tchantches wrestling with the Saracen. 5fr+25fr, St. Gertrude rescuing the knight with the cards.

1944, June 25

B385	SP211	10c + 5c choc	.15	.20
B386	SP212	35c + 5c dk bl grn	.15	.20
B387	SP211	50c + 10c dl vio	.15	.20
B388	SP214	60c + 10c blk brn	.15	.20
B389	SP214	1fr + 15c rose brn	.15	.20
B390	SP214	1.75fr + 5.25fr ultra	.20	.30
B391	SP211	3.25fr + 11.75fr grnsh blk	.35	.50
B392	SP211	5fr + 25fr dk bl	.45	.70
		Nos. B385-B392 (8)	1.75	2.50

The surtax was for the control of tuberculosis.
Nos. B385-B389 were overprinted "Breendonk+10fr." in 1946 by the Union Royale Philatelique for an exhibition at Brussels. They had no postal validity.

Union of the Flemish and Walloon Peoples in their Sorrow — SP219

Union in Reconstruction — SP220

Perf. 11½

1945, May 1　　Unwmk.　　Photo.

B395	SP219	1fr + 30fr carmine	1.25	.90
B396	SP220	1¾fr + 30fr brt ultra	1.25	.90

1945, July 21
Size: 34½x23½mm

B397	SP219	1fr + 9fr scarlet	.25	.20
B398	SP220	1fr + 9fr car rose	.25	.20
		Nos. B395-B398 (4)	3.00	2.20

Surtax for the postal employees' relief fund.

Prisoner of War — SP221

Reunion
SP222

Awaiting Execution
SP223

Symbolical Figures "Recovery of Freedom"
SP225

Design: 70c+30c, 3.50fr+3.50fr, Member of Resistance Movement.

1945, Sept. 10

B399	SP221	10c + 15c orange	.15	.15
B400	SP222	20c + 20c dp purple	.15	.15
B401	SP223	60c + 25c sepia	.15	.15
B402	SP221	70c + 30c dp yel grn	.15	.15
B403	SP221	75c + 50c org brn	.15	.15
B404	SP222	1fr + 75c brt bl grn	.25	.20
B405	SP223	1.50fr + 1fr brt red	.25	.20
B406	SP221	3.50fr + 3.50fr brt bl	1.10	1.00
B407	SP225	5fr + 40fr brown	.90	.90
		Nos. B399-B407 (9)	3.25	3.05

The surtax was for the benefit of prisoners of war, displaced persons, families of executed victims and members of the Resistance Movement.

Arms of West Flanders — SP226

Arms of Provinces: 20c+20c, Luxembourg. 60c+25c, East Flanders. 70c+30c, Namur. 75c+50c, Limburg. 1fr+75c, Hainaut. 1.50fr+1fr, Antwerp. 3.50fr+1.50fr, Liege. 5fr+45fr, Brabant.

1945, Dec. 1

B408	SP226	10c + 15c sl blk & sl gray	.15	.15
B409	SP226	20c + 20c rose car & rose	.15	.15
B410	SP226	60c + 25c dk brn & pale brn	.15	.15
B411	SP226	70c + 30c dk grn & lt grn	.15	.15
B412	SP226	75c + 50c org brn & pale org brn	.25	.20
B413	SP226	1fr + 75c pur & lt pur	.15	.15
B414	SP226	1.50fr + 1fr car & rose	.15	.15
B415	SP226	3.50fr + 1.50fr dp bl & gray bl	.30	.20
B416	SP226	5fr + 45fr dp mag & cerise	2.25	1.90
		Nos. B408-B416 (9)	3.70	3.20

The surtax was for tuberculosis prevention.

Father Joseph Damien — SP227

Father Damien Comforting Leper — SP229

Leper Colony, Molokai Island, Hawaii SP228

Symbols of Wisdom and Patriotism SP230

"In Memoriam" SP232

François Bovesse SP231

Emile Vandervelde SP233

Sower SP235

Vandervelde, Laborer and Family SP234

Perf. 11½

1946, July 15   Unwmk.   Photo.

B417	SP227	65c + 75c dk blue	1.00	.65
B418	SP228	1.35fr + 2fr brown	1.00	.65
B419	SP229	1.75fr + 18fr rose brn	1.65	1.10

The surtax was for the erection of a museum in Louvain.

1946, July 15

B420	SP230	65c + 75c violet	1.00	.65
B421	SP231	1.35fr + 2fr dk org brn	1.40	.80
B422	SP232	1.75fr + 18fr car rose	1.90	1.10

The surtax was for the erection of a "House of the Fine Arts" at Namur.

1946, July 15

B423	SP233	65c + 75c dk sl grn	1.25	.65
B424	SP234	1.35fr + 2fr dk vio bl	1.40	.80
B425	SP235	1.75fr + 18fr dp car	1.90	1.10
		Nos. B417-B425 (9)	12.50	7.50

The surtax was for the Emile Vandervelde Institute, to promote social, economic and cultural activities.
For surcharges see Nos. CB4-CB12.

Pepin of Herstal — SP236

Malines — SP241

1fr+50c, Charlemagne. 1.50fr+1fr, Godfrey of Bouillon. 3.50fr+1.50fr, Robert of Jerusalem. #B430-B431, Baldwin of Constantinople.

1946, Sept. 15   Engr.   *Perf. 11½x11*

B426	SP236	75c + 25c green	.60	.35
B427	SP236	1fr + 50c violet	.90	.50
B428	SP236	1.50fr + 1fr plum	1.25	.65
B429	SP236	3.50fr + 1.50fr brt bl	1.50	.75
B430	SP236	5fr + 45fr red vio	12.00	7.00
B431	SP236	5fr + 45fr red org	15.00	7.75
		Nos. B426-B431 (6)	31.25	17.00

The surtax on Nos. B426-B429 was for the benefit of former prisoners of war, displaced persons, the families of executed patriots, and former members of the Resistance Movement.
The surtax on Nos. B430-B431 was divided among several welfare, national celebration and educational organizations.
Issue dates: Nos. B426-B429, Apr. 15; No. B430, Sept. 15; No. B431, Nov. 15.
See Nos. B437-B441, B465-B466, B472-B476.

1946, Dec. 2   *Perf. 11½*

Coats of Arms: 90c+60c, Dinant. 1.35fr+1.15fr, Ostend. 3.15fr+1.85fr, Verviers. 4.50fr+45.50fr, Louvain.

B432	SP241	65c + 35c rose car	.50	.50
B433	SP241	90c + 60c lemon	.50	.50
B434	SP241	1.35fr + 1.15fr dp grn	.50	.50
B435	SP241	3.15fr + 1.85fr blue	1.50	1.25
B436	SP241	4.50fr + 45.50fr dk vio brn	13.00	12.00
		Nos. B432-B436 (5)	16.00	14.75

The surtax was for anti-tuberculosis work. See Nos. B442-B446.

Type of 1946

Designs: 65c+35c, John II, Duke of Brabant. 90c+60c, Count Philip of Alsace. 1.35fr+1.15fr, William the Good. 3.15fr+1.85fr, Bishop Notger of Liege. 20fr+20fr, Philip the Noble.

1947, Sept. 25   Engr.   Perf. 11½x11

B437	SP236	65c + 35c Prus grn	.60	.50
B438	SP236	90c + 60c yel grn	1.00	.75
B439	SP236	1.35fr + 1.15fr car	1.40	1.10
B440	SP236	3.15fr + 1.85fr ultra	2.00	1.65
B441	SP236	20fr + 20fr red vio	52.50	42.50
		Nos. B437-B441 (5)	57.50	46.50

The surtax was for victims of World War II.

Arms Type of 1946 Dated "1947"

Coats of Arms: 65c+35c, Nivelles. 90c+60c, St. Trond. 1.35fr+1.15fr, Charleroi. 3.15fr+1.85fr, St. Nicolas. 20fr+20fr, Bouillon.

1947, Dec. 15   *Perf. 11½*

B442	SP241	65c + 35c orange	.80	.65
B443	SP241	90c + 60c dk cl	.70	.65
B444	SP241	1.35fr + 1.15fr dk brn	1.00	.70
B445	SP241	3.15fr + 1.85fr dp bl	2.50	1.75
B446	SP241	20fr + 20fr dk grn	20.00	12.50
		Nos. B442-B446 (5)	25.00	16.25

The surtax was for anti-tuberculosis work.

St. Benedict and King Totila — SP247

Achel Abbey SP248

Designs: 3.15fr+2.85fr, St. Benedict, legislator and builder. 10fr+10fr, Death of St. Benedict.

1948, Apr. 5   Photo.

B447	SP247	65c + 65c red brn	1.25	.55
B448	SP248	1.35fr + 1.35fr gray	1.75	.55
B449	SP247	3.15fr + 2.85fr dp ultra	2.50	1.90
B450	SP247	10fr + 10fr brt red vio	12.50	10.00
		Nos. B447-B450 (4)	18.00	13.00

The surtax was to aid the Abbey of the Trappist Fathers at Achel.

St. Begga and Chevremont Castle — SP249

Chevremont Basilica and Convent SP250

Designs: 3.15fr+2.85fr, Madonna of Chevremont and Chapel. 10fr+10fr, Madonna of Mt. Carmel.

1948, Apr. 5   Unwmk.

B451	SP249	65c + 65c bl grn	1.00	.55
B452	SP250	1.35fr + 1.35fr dk car rose	1.65	.55
B453	SP249	3.15fr + 2.85fr dp bl	2.25	1.90
B454	SP249	10fr + 10fr dp brn	12.00	10.00
		Nos. B451-B454 (4)	16.90	13.00

The surtax was to aid the Basilica of the Carmelite Fathers of Chèvremont.

Anseele Monument Showing French Inscription — SP251

90c+60c, View of Ghent. 1.35fr+1.15fr, Van Artevelde monument, Ghent. 3.15fr+1.85fr. Anseele Monument, Flemish inscription.

1948, June 21   *Perf. 14x13½*

B455	SP251	65c + 35c rose red	2.75	1.10
B456	SP251	90c + 60c gray	3.50	1.90
B457	SP251	1.35fr + 1.15fr hn brn	2.25	1.50
B458	SP251	3.15fr + 1.85fr brt bl	8.50	5.00
a.		Souv. sheet of 4, #B455-B458	140.00	55.00
		Nos. B455-B458 (4)	17.00	9.50

Issued to honor Edouard Anseele, statesman, founder of the Belgian Socialist Party.
No. B458a sold for 50fr.
For surcharges see Nos. 395-398.

Statue "The Unloader" SP252

Underground Fighter SP253

1948, Sept. 4   *Perf. 11½x11*

B460	SP252	10fr + 10fr gray grn	35.00	19.00
B461	SP253	10fr + 10fr red brn	20.00	11.00

The surtax was used toward erection of monuments at Antwerp and Liege.

Portrait Type of 1946 and

Double Barred Cross — SP254

Designs: 4fr+3.25fr, Isabella of Austria. 20fr+20fr, Archduke Albert of Austria.

1948, Dec. 15   Photo.   *Perf. 13½x14*

B462	SP254	20c + 5c dk sl grn	.50	.15
B463	SP254	1.20fr + 30c magenta	1.25	.70
B464	SP254	1.75fr + 25c red	1.75	.60

Engr.   *Perf. 11½x11*

B465	SP236	4fr + 3.25fr ultra	9.50	6.50
B466	SP236	20fr + 20fr Prus grn	42.50	30.00
		Nos. B462-B466 (5)	55.50	37.95

The surtax was divided among several charities.

Souvenir Sheets

Rogier van der Weyden Paintings — SP255

Paintings by van der Weyden (No. B466A): 90c, Virgin and Child. 1.75fr, Christ on the Cross. 4fr, Mary Magdalene.
Paintings by Jordaens (No. B466B): 90c, Woman Reading. 1.75fr, The Flutist. 4fr, Old Woman Reading Letter.

1949, Apr. 1   Photo.   *Perf. 11½*

B466A	SP255	Sheet of 3	125.00	110.00
c.		90c deep brown	37.50	32.50
d.		1.75fr deep rose lilac	37.50	32.50
e.		4fr dark violet blue	37.50	32.50

B466B	SP255	Sheet of 3	125.00	110.00
f.		90c dark violet	37.50	32.50
g.		1.75fr red	37.50	32.50
h.		4fr blue	37.50	32.50

The surtax went to various cultural and philanthropic organizations. Sheets sold for 50fr each. Gum on Nos. B466A-B466B is irregularly applied.

Guido Gezelle — SP256

1949, Nov. 15   Photo.   Perf. 14x13½

B467	SP256	1.75fr + 75c dk Prus grn	2.50	1.75

50th anniversary of the death of Guido Gezelle, poet. The surtax was for the Guido Gezelle Museum, Bruges.

Portrait Type of 1946 and

Arnica — SP257

Designs: 65c+10c, Sand grass. 90c+10c, Wood myrtle. 1.20fr+30c, Field poppy. 1.75fr+25c, Philip the Good. 3fr+1.50fr, Charles V. 4fr+2fr, Maria-Christina. 6fr+3fr, Charles of Lorraine. 8fr+4fr, Maria-Theresa.

1949, Dec. 20   Typo.   Perf. 13½x14

B468	SP257	20c + 5c multi	.50	.50
B469	SP257	65c + 10c multi	1.25	1.10
B470	SP257	90c + 10c multi	2.00	1.50
B471	SP257	1.20fr + 30c multi	2.50	1.75

Engr.   Perf. 11½x11

B472	SP236	1.75fr + 25c red org	1.40	.80
B473	SP236	3fr + 1.50fr dp claret	10.00	6.75
B474	SP236	4fr + 2fr ultra	10.00	8.00
B475	SP236	6fr + 3fr choc	16.00	11.00
B476	SP236	8fr + 4fr dl grn	16.00	8.75
		Nos. B468-B476 (9)	59.65	40.15

The surtax was apportioned among several welfare organizations.

Arms of Belgium and Great Britain SP258

British Memorial SP260

Design: 2.50fr+50c, British tanks at Hertain.

Perf. 13½x14, 11½

1950, Mar. 15   Engr.

B477	SP258	80c + 20c green	1.50	1.00
B478	SP258	2.50fr + 50c red	5.00	3.75
B479	SP260	4fr + 2fr dp bl	9.25	6.25
		Nos. B477-B479 (3)	15.75	11.00

6th anniv. of the liberation of Belgian territory by the British army.

Hurdling SP261

Relay Race SP262

Designs: 90c+10c, Javelin throwing. 4fr+2fr, Pole vault. 8fr+4fr, Foot race.

Perf. 14x13½, 13½x14

1950, July 1   Engr.   Unwmk.

B480	SP261	20c + 5c brt grn	.90	.75
B481	SP261	90c + 10c vio brn	3.75	1.90
B482	SP262	1.75fr + 25c car	4.50	1.90
a.		Souvenir sheet of 1	55.00	42.50
B483	SP261	4fr + 2fr lt bl	35.00	19.00
B484	SP261	4fr + 4fr dp grn	40.00	24.00
		Nos. B480-B484 (5)	84.15	47.55

Issued to publicize the European Athletic Games, Brussels, August 1950.

The margins of No. B482a were trimmed in April, 1951, and an overprint ("25 Francs pour le Fonds Sportif-25e Fofre Internationale Bruxelles") was added in red in French and in black in Flemish by a private committee. These pairs of altered sheets were sold at the Brussels Fair.

Gentian SP263

Sijsele Sanatorium SP264

Tombeek Sanatorium — SP265

Designs: 65c+10c, Cotton Grass. 90c+10c, Foxglove. 1.20fr+30c, Limonia. 4fr+2fr, Jauche Sanatorium.

1950, Dec. 20   Typo.   Perf. 14x13½

B485	SP263	20c + 5c multi	.80	.40
B486	SP263	65c + 10c multi	1.50	.80
B487	SP263	90c + 10c multi	1.65	1.10
B488	SP263	1.20fr + 30c multi	2.75	2.25

Perf. 11½

Engr.

Cross in Red

B489	SP264	1.75fr + 25c car	2.50	1.40
B490	SP264	4fr + 2fr blue	13.00	7.00
B491	SP265	8fr + 4fr bl grn	21.00	15.00
		Nos. B485-B491 (7)	43.20	27.95

The surtax was for tuberculosis prevention and other charitable purposes.

Chemist — SP266

Allegory of Peace — SP268

Colonial Instructor and Class — SP267

1951, Mar. 27   Unwmk.

B492	SP266	80c + 20c grn	1.40	1.00
B493	SP267	2.50fr + 50c vio brn	9.50	5.00
B494	SP268	4fr + 2fr dp bl	10.25	6.00
		Nos. B492-B494 (3)	21.15	12.00

Surtax for the reconstruction fund of the UNESCO.

Monument to Political Prisoners SP269

Fort of Breendonk SP270

8fr+4fr, Monument: profile of figure on pedestal.

1951, Aug. 20   Photo.   Perf. 11½

B495	SP269	1.75fr + 25c blk brn	2.50	1.75
B496	SP270	4fr + 2fr bl & sl gray	17.00	14.00
B497	SP269	8fr + 4fr dk bl grn	22.50	17.00
		Nos. B495-B497 (3)	42.00	32.75

The surtax was for the erection of a national monument.

Queen Elisabeth — SP271

1951, Sept. 22

B498	SP271	90c + 10c grnsh gray	1.75	.75
B499	SP271	1.75fr + 25c plum	2.25	1.50
B500	SP271	3fr + 1fr green	21.00	9.25
B501	SP271	4fr + 2fr gray bl	24.00	12.00
B502	SP271	8fr + 4fr sepia	30.00	14.00
		Nos. B498-B502 (5)	79.00	37.50

The surtax was for the Queen Elisabeth Medical Foundation.

Cross, Sun Rays and Dragon SP272

Beersel Castle SP273

Horst Castle — SP274

Castles: 4fr+2fr, Lavaux St. Anne. 8fr+4fr, Veves.

1951, Dec. 17   Engr.   Unwmk.

B503	SP272	20c + 5c red	.25	.20
B504	SP272	65c + 10c dp ultra	.85	.60
B505	SP272	90c + 10c sepia	.90	.80
B506	SP272	1.20fr + 30c rose vio	1.25	.90
B507	SP273	1.75fr + 75c red brn	1.75	1.50
B508	SP274	3fr + 1fr yel grn	12.00	7.50
B509	SP274	4fr + 2fr blue	14.00	8.50
B510	SP274	8fr + 4fr gray	19.00	11.00
		Nos. B503-B510 (8)	50.00	31.00

The surtax was for anti-tuberculosis work. See Nos. B523-B526, B547-B550.

Main Altar SP275

Basilica of the Sacred Heart Koekelberg SP276

Procession Bearing Relics of St. Albert of Louvain — SP277

1952, Mar. 1   Photo.   Perf. 11½

B511	SP275	1.75fr + 25c blk brn	1.50	1.25
B512	SP276	4fr + 2fr indigo	11.00	7.50

Engr.

B513	SP277	8fr + 4fr vio brn	15.00	9.25
a.		Souvenir sheet, #B511-B513	250.00	125.00
		Nos. B511-B513 (3)	27.50	18.00

25th anniv. of the Cardinalate of J. E. Van Roey, Primate of Belgium. The surtax was for the Basilica. No. B513a sold for 30fr.

Beaulieu Castle, Malines SP278

August Vermeylen SP279

1952, May 14   Engr.

Laid Paper

B514	SP278	40fr + 10fr lt grnsh bl	175.00	175.00

Issued on the occasion of the 13th Universal Postal Union Congress, Brussels, 1952.

Perf. 11½

1952, Oct. 24   Unwmk.   Photo.

Portraits: 80c+40c, Karel Van de Woestijne. 90c+45c, Charles de Coster. 1.75fr+75c, M. Maeterlinck. 4fr+2fr, Emile Verhaeren. 8fr+4fr, Hendrik Conscience.

B515	SP279	65c + 30c purple	1.75	.90
B516	SP279	80c + 40c dk grn	3.75	1.10
B517	SP279	90c + 45c sepia	2.75	1.25
B518	SP279	1.75fr + 75c cer	3.00	1.95
B519	SP279	4fr + 2fr bl vio	30.00	19.00
B520	SP279	8fr + 4fr dk brn	30.00	21.00
		Nos. B515-B520 (6)	72.00	45.00

1952, Nov. 15

4fr, Emile Verhaeren. 8fr, Hendrik Conscience.

B521	SP279	4fr (+ 9fr) blue	100.00	67.50
B522	SP279	8fr (+ 9fr) dk car rose	100.00	67.50

On Nos. B521-B522, the denomination is repeated at either side of the stamp. The surtax is expressed on se-tenant labels bearing quotations of Verhaeren (in French) and Conscience (in Flemish). Value is for stamp with label.

A 9-line black overprint was privately applied to these labels: "Conference Internationale de la Musique Bruxelles UNESCO International Music Conference Brussels 1953*"

Type of 1951 Dated "1952," and

Arms of Malmédy — SP281

Castle Ruins, Burgreuland SP282

Designs: 4fr+2fr, Vesdre Dam, Eupen. 8fr+4fr, St. Vitus, patron saint of Saint-Vith.

1952, Dec. 15   Engr.

B523	SP272	20c + 5c red brn	.40	.40
B524	SP272	40c + 20c green	.85	.60
B525	SP272	1.20fr + 30c lil rose	1.75	1.00
B526	SP272	1.50fr + 50c ol brn	1.75	1.00
B527	SP281	2fr + 75c carmine	3.25	2.25
B528	SP282	3fr + 1.50fr choc	14.00	8.75
B529	SP281	4fr + 2fr blue	12.00	8.00
B530	SP281	8fr + 4fr vio brn	21.00	11.00
		Nos. B523-B530 (8)	55.00	33.00

The surtax on Nos. B523-B530 was for anti-tuberculosis and other charitable works.

Walthère Dewé
SP283

Princess Josephine-
Charlotte
SP284

1953, Feb. 16   Photo.
B531 SP283 2fr + 1fr brn car   3.25   1.75

The surtax was for the construction of a memorial to Walthère Dewé, Underground leader in World War II.

1953, Mar. 14   Cross in Red
B532 SP284 80c + 20c ol grn   1.25   .70
B533 SP284 1.20fr + 30c brown   1.75   .80
B534 SP284 2fr + 50c rose lake   1.25   1.25
  a.   Booklet pane of 8   80.00   65.00
B535 SP284 2.50fr + 50c crimson   14.00   6.75
B536 SP284 4fr + 1fr brt blue   9.25   5.25
B537 SP284 5fr + 2fr sl grn   11.00   6.75
   Nos. B532-B537 (6)   38.50   21.50

The surtax was for the Belgian Red Cross.
The selvage of No. B534a is inscribed in French or Dutch. The value is for the French.

Boats at
Dock — SP285

Bridge and Citadel,
Namur — SP286

Allegory — SP287

Designs: 1.20fr+30c, Bridge at Bouillon. 2fr+50c, Antwerp waterfront. 4fr+2fr, Wharf at Ghent. 8fr+4fr, Meuse River at Freyr.

1953, June 22   Unwmk.   *Perf. 11½*
B538 SP285 80c + 20c green   1.00   .85
B539 SP285 1.20fr + 30c redsh brn   1.75   1.65
B540 SP285 2fr + 50c sepia   2.25   2.00
B541 SP286 2.50fr + 50c dp mag   11.00   8.50
B542 SP286 4fr + 2fr vio bl   16.00   8.50
B543 SP286 8fr + 4fr gray blk   20.00   8.50
   Nos. B538-B543 (6)   52.00   30.00

The surtax was used to promote tourism in the Ardenne-Meuse region and for various cultural works.

1953, Oct. 26   Engr.
B544 SP287 80c + 20c green   3.50   2.50
B545 SP287 2.50fr + 1fr rose car   32.50   24.00
B546 SP287 4fr + 1.50fr blue   37.50   30.00
   Nos. B544-B546 (3)   73.50   56.50

The surtax was for the European Bureau of Childhood and Youth.

Type of 1951 Dated "1953," and

Ernest
Malvoz — SP288

Robert
Koch — SP289

Portraits: 3fr+1.50fr, Carlo Forlanini. 4fr+2fr, Leon Charles Albert Calmette.

1953, Dec. 15
B547 SP272 20c + 5c blue   .50   .45
B548 SP272 80c + 20c rose vio   1.00   .60
B549 SP272 1.20fr + 30c choc   1.25   .80
B550 SP272 1.50fr + 50c dk gray   1.75   1.00
B551 SP288 2fr + 75c dk grn   3.00   1.65
B552 SP288 3fr + 1.50fr dk red   13.00   8.50
B553 SP288 4fr + 2fr ultra   11.00   7.00
B554 SP289 8fr + 4fr choc   17.50   10.00
   Nos. B547-B554 (8)   49.00   30.00

The surtax was for anti-tuberculosis and other charitable works.

King Albert I
Statue — SP290

Albert I
Monument,
Namur
SP291

Design: 9fr+4.50fr, Cliffs of Marche-les-Dames.

1954, Feb. 17   Photo.
B555 SP290 2fr + 50c chnt brn   2.50   1.75
B556 SP291 4fr + 2fr blue   15.00   11.00
B557 SP290 9fr + 4.50fr ol blk   22.50   12.00
   Nos. B555-B557 (3)   40.00   24.75

20th anniv. of the death of King Albert I. The surtax aided in the erection of the monument pictured on #B556.

Political Prisoners'
Monument — SP292

Camp and Fort,
Breendonk
SP293

Design: 9fr+4.50fr, Political prisoners' monument (profile).

1954, Apr. 1   Unwmk.   *Perf. 11½*
B558 SP292 2fr + 1fr red   12.50   7.00
B559 SP293 4fr + 2fr dk brn   30.00   17.50
B560 SP292 9fr + 4.50fr ol grn   32.50   17.50
   Nos. B558-B560 (3)   75.00   42.00

The surtax was used toward the creation of a monument to political prisoners.

Gatehouse and
Gateway
SP294

Nuns in
Courtyard — SP295

Our Lady of
the Vine — SP296

Designs: 2fr+1fr, Swans in stream. 7fr+3.50fr Nuns at well. 8fr+4fr, Statue above door.

1954, May 15
B561 SP294 80c + 20c dk bl grn   1.00   .75
B562 SP294 2fr + 1fr crimson   11.00   1.50
B563 SP295 4fr + 2fr violet   16.00   9.25
B564 SP295 7fr + 3.50fr lil rose   35.00   22.50
B565 SP295 8fr + 4fr brown   32.50   19.00
B566 SP296 9fr + 4.50fr gray bl   55.00   30.00
   Nos. B561-B566 (6)   150.50   83.00

The surtax was for the Friends of the Beguinage of Bruges.

Child's Head
SP297

"The Blind Man and
the Paralytic," by
Antoine Carte
SP298

1954, Dec. 1   Engr.
B567 SP297 20c + 5c dk grn   .50   .50
B568 SP297 80c + 20c dk gray   1.00   .85
B569 SP297 1.20fr + 30c org brn   1.50   1.00
B570 SP297 1.50fr + 50c purple   1.75   1.65
B571 SP298 2fr + 75c rose car   7.25   3.50
B572 SP298 4fr + 1fr brt blue   16.00   9.50
   Nos. B567-B572 (6)   28.00   17.00

The surtax was for anti-tuberculosis work.

Ernest Solvay
SP299

Jean-Jacques
Dony — SP300

Portraits: 1.20fr+30c, Egide Walschaerts. 25fr+50c, Leo H. Baekeland. 3fr+1fr, Jean-Etienne Lenoir. 4fr+2fr, Emile Fourcault and Emile Gobbe.

Perf. 11½
1955, Oct. 22   Unwmk.   Photo.
B573 SP299 20c + 5c brn & dk brn   .40   .35
B574 SP300 80c + 20c violet   1.00   .50
B575 SP299 1.20fr + 30c indigo   1.10   .65
B576 SP300 2fr + 50c dp car   4.00   2.50
B577 SP300 3fr + 1fr dk grn   12.50   6.25
B578 SP299 4fr + 2fr brown   12.50   6.25
   Nos. B573-B578 (6)   31.50   16.50

Issued in honor of Belgian scientists.
The surtax was for the benefit of various cultural organizations.

"The Joys of
Spring" by E.
Canneel — SP301

Einar
Holböll — SP302

Portraits: 4fr+2fr, John D. Rockefeller. 8fr+4fr, Sir Robert W. Philip.

1955, Dec. 5   Unwmk.   *Perf. 11½*
B579 SP301 20c + 5c red lilac   .70   .30
B580 SP301 80c + 20c green   1.00   .65
B581 SP301 1.20fr + 30c redsh brn   1.40   .80
B582 SP301 1.50fr + 50c vio bl   1.40   1.00
B583 SP302 2fr + 50c carmine   8.50   4.75
B584 SP302 4fr + 2fr ultra   17.50   10.00
B585 SP302 8fr + 4fr ol gray   21.00   12.50
   Nos. B579-B585 (7)   51.50   30.00

The surtax was for anti-tuberculosis work.

Palace of Charles of
Lorraine — SP303

Queen Elisabeth and Sonata by
Mozart — SP304

Design: 2fr+1fr, Mozart at age 7.

1956, Mar. 5   Engr.
B586 SP303 80c + 20c steel bl   1.00   1.00
B587 SP303 2fr + 1fr rose lake   4.25   3.00
B588 SP304 4fr + 2fr dull pur   6.75   3.75
   Nos. B586-B588 (3)   12.00   7.75

200th anniversary of the birth of Wolfgang Amadeus Mozart, composer.
The surtax was for the benefit of the Pro-Mozart Committee in Belgium.

Queen
Elisabeth — SP305

1956, Aug. 16   Photo.
B589 SP305 80c + 20c slate grn   1.00   1.00
B590 SP305 2fr + 1fr deep plum   2.75   1.50
B591 SP305 4fr + 2fr brown   4.25   2.50
   Nos. B589-B591 (3)   8.00   5.00

Issued in honor of the 80th birthday of Queen Elisabeth. The surtax went to the Queen Elisabeth Foundation. See No. 659.

Ship with
Cross
SP306

Infant on Scales
SP307

Rehabilitation — SP308

Design: 4fr+2fr, X-Ray examination.

1956, Dec. 17			Engr.	
B592	SP306	20c + 5c redsh brn	.35	.30
B593	SP306	80c + 20c green	.75	.60
B594	SP306	1.20fr + 30c dl lil	.90	.60
B595	SP306	1.5fr + 50c lt sl bl	.95	.90
B596	SP307	2fr + 50c ol grn	2.25	1.65
B597	SP307	4fr + 2fr dl pur	11.00	6.25
B598	SP308	8fr + 4fr dp car	11.00	7.25
		Nos. B592-B598 (7)	27.20	17.55

The surtax was for anti-tuberculosis work.

Charles Plisnier and Albrecht Rodenbach SP309

80c+20c, Emiel Vliebergh & Maurice Wilmotte. 1.20fr+30c, Paul Pastur & Julius Hoste. 2fr+50c, Lodewijk de Raet & Jules Destree. 3fr+1fr, Constantin Meunier & Constant Permeke. 4fr+2fr, Lieven Gevaert & Edouard Empain.

1957, June 8		Perf. 11½ Unwmk.		Photo.
B599	SP309	20c + 5c brt vio	.40	.35
B600	SP309	80c + 20c lt red brn	.55	.35
B601	SP309	1.20f + 30c blk brn	.65	.60
B602	SP309	2fr + 50c claret	1.65	.95
B603	SP309	3fr + 1fr dk ol grn	2.25	1.75
B604	SP309	4fr + 2fr vio bl	3.25	2.50
		Nos. B599-B604 (6)	8.75	6.50

The surtax was for the benefit of various cultural organizations.

Dogs and Antarctic Camp SP310

1957, Oct. 18		Engr.	Perf. 11½	
B605	SP310	5fr + 2.50fr gray, org & vio brn	3.00	2.25
a.		Sheet of 4, #B605b	140.00	125.00
b.		Blue, slate & red brown	30.00	25.00

Surtax for Belgian Antarctic Expedition, 1957-58.

Gen. Patton's Grave and Flag — SP311

Gen. George S. Patton, Jr. — SP312

Designs: 2.50fr+50c, Memorial, Bastogne. 3fr+1fr, Gen. Patton decorating Brig. Gen. Anthony C. McAuliffe. 6fr+3fr, Tanks of 1918 and 1944.

1957, Oct. 28		Photo.	
Size: 36x25mm, 25x36mm			
B606	SP311	1fr + 50c dk gray	1.25	.85
B607	SP311	2.50fr + 50c ol grn	1.75	1.50
B608	SP311	3fr + 1fr red brn	2.75	1.65
B609	SP312	5fr + 2.50fr grysh bl	6.25	5.00

Size: 53x35mm				
B610	SP311	6fr + 3fr pale brn car	10.00	6.00
		Nos. B606-B610 (5)	22.00	15.00

The surtax was for the General Patton Memorial Committee and Patriotic Societies.

Adolphe Max — SP313

1957, Nov. 10			Engr.	
B611	SP313	2.50fr + 1fr ultra	1.25	.75

18th anniversary of the death of Adolphe Max, mayor of Brussels. The surtax was for the national "Adolphe Max" fund.

"Chinels," Fosses SP314

"Op Signoorken," Malines SP315

Infanta Isabella Shooting Crossbow SP316

Legends: 1.50fr+50c, St. Remacle and the wolf. 2fr+1fr, Longman and the pea soup. 5fr+2fr, The Virgin with Inkwell, vert. 6fr+2.50fr, "Gilles" (clowns), Binche.

1957, Dec. 14			Engr. & Photo.	
B612	SP314	30c + 20c	.20	.30
B613	SP315	1fr + 50c	.40	.30
B614	SP314	1.50fr + 50c	.80	.50
B615	SP315	2fr + 1fr	1.10	1.00
B616	SP316	2.50fr + 1fr	1.25	.90
B617	SP316	5fr + 2fr	3.25	2.25
B618	SP316	6fr + 2.50fr	4.50	3.25
		Nos. B612-B618 (7)	11.50	8.50

The surtax was for anti-tuberculosis work. See Nos. B631-B637.

Benelux Gate — SP317

Designs: 1fr+50c, Civil Engineering Pavilion. 1.50fr+50c, Ruanda-Urundi Pavilion. 2.50fr+1fr, Belgium 1900. 3fr+1.50fr, Atomium. 5fr+3fr, Telexpo Pavilion.

1958, Apr. 15		Perf. 11½ Unwmk.		Engr.
Size: 35½x24½mm				
B619	SP317	30c + 20c multi	.15	.15
B620	SP317	1fr + 50c multi	.15	.15
B621	SP317	1.50fr + 50c multi	.25	.25
B622	SP317	2.50fr + 1fr multi	.45	.45
B623	SP317	3fr + 1.50fr multi	.90	.50
Size: 49x33mm				
B624	SP317	5fr + 3fr multi	1.10	.50
		Nos. B619-B624 (6)	3.00	2.00

World's Fair, Brussels, Apr. 17-Oct. 19.

Marguerite van Eyck by Jan van Eyck — SP318

Christ Carrying Cross, by Hieronymus Bosch — SP319

Paintings: 1.50fr+50c, St. Donatien, Jan Gossart. 2.50fr+1fr, Self-portrait, Lambert Lombard. 3fr+1.50fr, The Rower, James Ensor. 5fr+3fr, Henriette, Henri Evenepoel.

1958, Oct. 30		Photo.	Perf. 11½	
Various Frames in Ocher and Brown				
B625	SP318	30c + 20c dk ol grn	.25	.30
B626	SP319	1fr + 50c mar	.75	.70
B627	SP318	1.50fr + 50c vio bl	1.00	.75
B628	SP318	2.50fr + 1fr dk brn	2.00	1.25
B629	SP319	3fr + 1.50fr dl red	2.75	2.00
B630	SP318	5fr + 3fr brt bl	5.25	5.00
		Nos. B625-B630 (6)	12.00	10.00

The surtax was for the benefit of various cultural organizations.

Type of 1957

Legends: 40c+10c, Elizabeth, Countess of Hoogstraten. 1fr+50c, Jean de Nivelles. 1.50fr+50c, St. Evermare play, Russon. 2fr+1fr, The Penitents of Furnes. 2.50fr+1fr, Manger and "Pax." 5fr+2fr, Sambre-Meuse procession. 6fr+2.50fr, Our Lady of Peace and "Pax," vert.

Engraved and Photogravure

1958, Dec. 6		Unwmk.	Perf. 11½	
B631	SP314	40c + 10c ultra & brt grn	.30	.20
B632	SP315	1fr + 50c gray brn & org	.40	.30
B633	SP315	1.50fr + 50c cl & brt grm	.60	.35
B634	SP314	2fr + 1fr brn & red	.70	.50
B635	SP316	2.50fr + 1fr vio brn & bl grn	2.50	1.90
B636	SP316	5fr + 2fr cl & bl	3.75	3.00
B637	SP316	6fr + 2.50fr bl & rose red	4.75	4.50
		Nos. B631-B637 (7)	13.00	10.75

The surtax was for anti-tuberculosis work.

"Europe of the Heart" SP320

1959, Feb. 25		Photo.	Unwmk.	
B638	SP320	1fr + 50c red lilac	.55	.30
B639	SP320	2.50fr + 1fr dk green	.95	.90
B640	SP320	5fr + 2.50fr dp brn	1.25	1.10
		Nos. B638-B640 (3)	2.75	2.30

The surtax was for aid for displaced persons.

Engraved and Photogravure

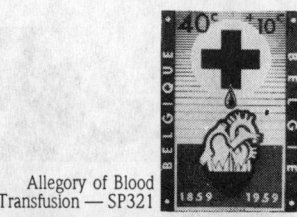

Allegory of Blood Transfusion — SP321

Henri Dunant and Battlefield at Solferino — SP322

Design: 2.50fr+1fr, 3fr+1.50fr, Red Cross, broken sword and drop of blood, horiz.

1959, June 10		Photo.	Perf. 11½	
B641	SP321	40c + 10c	.60	.30
B642	SP321	1fr + 50c	1.10	.45
B643	SP321	1.50fr + 50c	1.40	.60
B644	SP321	2.50fr + 1fr	1.90	1.10
B645	SP321	3fr + 1.50fr	4.75	2.50
B646	SP322	5fr + 3fr (6)	7.25	3.25
		Nos. B641-B646 (6)	17.00	8.20

Cent. of the Intl. Red Cross idea. Surtax for the Red Cross and patriotic organizations.

Philip the Good — SP323

Arms of Philip the Good SP324

Designs: 1fr+50c, Charles the Bold. 1.50fr+50c, Emperor Maximilian of Austria. 2.50fr+1fr, Philip the Fair. 3fr+1.50fr, Charles V. Portraits from miniatures by Simon Bening (c. 1483-1561).

1959, July 4			Engr.	
B647	SP323	40c + 10c multi	.50	.35
B648	SP323	1fr + 50c multi	.80	.50
B649	SP323	1.50fr + 50c multi	.95	.75
B650	SP323	2.50fr + 1fr multi	1.25	1.40
B651	SP323	3fr + 1.50fr multi	3.25	3.00
B652	SP324	5fr + 3fr multi	5.25	4.00
		Nos. B647-B652 (6)	12.00	10.00

The surtax was for the Royal Library, Brussels. Portraits show Grand Masters of the Order of the Golden Fleece.

Whale, Antwerp SP325

Carnival, Stavelot SP326

Designs: 1fr+50c, Dragon, Mons. 2fr+50c, Prince Carnival, Eupen. 3fr+1fr, Jester and cats, Ypres. 6fr+2fr, Holy Family, horiz. 7fr+3fr, Madonna, Liége, horiz.

Engraved and Photogravure

1959, Dec. 5			Perf. 11½	
B653	SP325	40c + 10c cit, Prus bl & red	.45	.40
B654	SP325	1fr + 50c ol & grn	.75	.60
B655	SP325	2fr + 50c lt brn, org & cl	.50	.40
B656	SP326	2.50fr + 1fr gray, pur & ultra	.80	.60
B657	SP326	3fr + 1fr gray, mar & yel	1.75	1.25
B658	SP326	6fr + 2fr ol, brt bl & hn brn	3.25	2.50
B659	SP326	7fr + 3fr chlky bl & org yel	5.00	4.25
		Nos. B653-B659 (7)	12.50	10.00

The surtax was for anti-tuberculosis work.

Child
Refugee — SP327

Designs: 3fr+1.50fr, Man. 6fr+3fr, Woman.

1960, Apr. 7 Engr.
B660	SP327	40c + 10c rose claret	.20	.15
B661	SP327	3fr + 1.50fr gray brn	.65	.50
B662	SP327	6fr + 3fr dk bl	1.65	1.10
a.		Souvenir sheet of 3	50.00	45.00
		Nos. B660-B662 (3)	2.90	1.75

World Refugee Year, July 1, 1959-June 30, 1960. No. B662a contains Nos. B660-B662 with colors changed: 40c+10c, dull purple; 3fr+1.50fr, red brown; 6fr+3fr, henna brown.

Parachutists
and Plane
SP328

Designs: 2fr+50c, 2.50fr+1fr, Parachutists coming in for landing, vert 3fr+1fr, 6fr+2fr, Parachutist walking with parachute.

Photogravure and Engraved
1960, June 13 Perf. 11½
B663	SP328	40c + 10c lt ultra	.15	.15
B664	SP328	1fr + 50c bl & blk	.85	.60
B665	SP328	2fr + 50c bl, blk & ol	2.75	1.25
B666	SP328	2.50fr + 1fr grnsh bl, blk & gray ol	3.00	2.00
B667	SP328	3fr + 1fr bl, blk & sl grn	3.00	2.00
B668	SP328	6fr + 2fr lt vio bl, blk & ol	6.25	4.00
		Nos. B663-B668 (6)	16.00	10.00

The surtax was for various patriotic and cultural organizations.

Mother and
Child, Planes
and Rainbow
SP329

Designs: 40c+10c, Brussels Airport, planes and rainbow. 6fr+3fr, Rainbow connecting Congo and Belgium, and planes, vert

Perf. 11½
1960, Aug. 3 Unwmk. Photo.
Size: 35x24mm
B669	SP329	40c + 10c grnsh blue	.15	.15
B670	SP329	3fr + 1.50fr brt red	2.50	2.25

Size: 35x52mm
B671	SP329	6fr + 3fr violet	3.75	3.00
		Nos. B669-B671 (3)	6.40	5.40

The surtax was for refugees from Congo.

Infant, Milk Bottle and
Mug — SP330

UNICEF: 1fr+50c, Nurse and children of 3 races. 2fr+50c, Refugee woman carrying gift clothes. 2.50fr+1fr, Negro nurse weighing infant. 3fr+1fr, Children of various races dancing. 6fr+2fr, Refugee boys.

Photogravure and Engraved
1960, Oct. 8 Perf. 11½
B672	SP330	40c + 10c gldn brn, yel & bl grn	.15	.15
B673	SP330	1fr + 50c ol gray, mar & slate	1.40	.75
B674	SP330	2fr + 50c vio, pale brn & brt grn	1.50	1.10

B675	SP330	2.50fr + 1fr dk red, sep & lt bl	1.75	1.40
B676	SP330	3fr + 1fr bl grn, red org & dl vio	.95	.85
B677	SP330	6fr + 2fr ultra, emer & brn	3.75	3.25
		Nos. B672-B677 (6)	9.50	7.50

Tapestry
SP331

Belgian handicrafts: 1fr+50c, Cut crystal vases, vert. 2fr+50c, Lace, vert. 2.50fr+1fr, Metal plate & jug. 3fr+1fr, Diamonds. 6fr+2fr, Ceramics.

1960, Dec. 5 Perf. 11½
B678	SP331	40c + 10c bl, bis & brn	.15	.15
B679	SP331	1fr + 50c ind & org brn	1.10	1.00
B680	SP331	2fr + 50c dk red brn, blk & cit	2.00	1.50
B681	SP331	2.50fr + 1fr choc & yel	2.50	2.25
B682	SP331	3fr + 1fr org brn, blk & ultra	1.25	1.10
B683	SP331	6fr + 2fr dp blk & yel	5.00	4.00
		Nos. B678-B683 (6)	12.00	10.00

The surtax was for anti-tuberculosis work.

Jacob Kats and
Abbe Nicolas
Pietkin
SP332

Portraits: 1fr+50c, Albert Mockel and J. F. Willems. 2fr+50c, Jan van Rijswijck and Xavier M. Neujean. 2.50fr+1fr, Joseph Demarteau and A. Van de Perre. 3fr+1fr, Canon Jan-Baptist David and Albert du Bois. 6fr+2fr, Henri Vieuxtemps and Willem de Mol.

1961, Apr. 22 Unwmk. Perf. 11½
Portraits in Gray Brown
B684	SP332	40c + 10c ver & mar	.15	.15
B685	SP332	1fr + 50c bis brn & mar	1.50	1.10
B686	SP332	2fr + 50c yel & crim	1.75	1.50
B687	SP332	2.50fr + 1fr pale cit & dk grn	2.75	1.50
B688	SP332	3fr + 1fr lt & dk bl	2.75	2.50
B689	SP332	6fr + 2fr lil & ultra	5.00	4.25
		Nos. B684-B689 (6)	13.90	11.00

The surtax was for the benefit of various cultural organizations.

White Rhinoceros
SP333

Antonius Cardinal
Perrenot de
Granvelle
SP334

Animals: 1fr+50c, Przewalski horses. 2fr+50c, Okapi. 2.50fr+1fr, Giraffe, horiz. 3fr+1fr, Lesser panda, horiz. 6fr+2fr, European elk, horiz.

Perf. 11½
1961, June 5 Unwmk. Photo.
B690	SP333	40c + 10c bis brn & dk brn	.15	.15
B691	SP333	1fr + 50c gray & brn	.90	.90
B692	SP333	2fr + 50c dp rose & blk	1.40	1.25
B693	SP333	2.50fr + 1fr red org & brn	1.10	1.10
B694	SP333	3fr + 1fr org & blk	1.00	1.00
B695	SP333	6fr + 2fr bl & bis brn	2.25	1.50
		Nos. B690-B695 (6)	6.80	5.90

The surtax was for various philanthropic organizations.

1961, July 29 Engr.
Designs: 3fr+1.50fr, Arms of Cardinal de Granville. 6fr+3fr, Tower and crosier, symbolic of collaboration between Malines and the Archbishopric.
B696	SP334	40c + 10c magenta, car & brn	.15	.15
B697	SP334	3fr + 1.50fr multi	.65	.50
B698	SP334	6fr + 3fr mag pur & bis	1.25	1.10
		Nos. B696-B698 (3)	2.05	1.75

400th anniv. of Malines as an Archbishopric.

Mother and
Child by Pierre
Paulus — SP335

Castle of the
Counts of
Male — SP336

Plaintings: 1fr+50c, Mother Love, Francois-Joseph Navez. 2fr+50c, Motherhood, Constant Permeke. 2.50fr+1fr, Madonna and Child, Rogier van der Weyden. 3fr+1fr, Madonna with Apple, Hans Memling. 6fr+2fr, Madonna of the Forget-me-not, Peter Paul Rubens.

1961, Dec. 2 Photo. Perf. 11½
Gold Frame
B699	SP335	40c + 10c dp brn	.15	.15
B700	SP335	1fr + 50c brt bl	.40	.30
B701	SP335	2fr + 50c rose red	.60	.45
B702	SP335	2.50fr + 1fr magenta	.85	.75
B703	SP335	3fr + 1fr vio bl	1.00	.85
B704	SP335	6fr + 2fr dk sl grn	1.75	1.50
		Nos. B699-B704 (6)	4.75	4.00

The surtax was for anti-tuberculosis work.

1962, Mar. 12 Engr. Perf. 11½
Designs: 90c+10c, Royal library, horiz. 1fr+50c, Church of Our Lady, Tongres. 2fr+50c, Collegiate Church, Soignies, horiz. 2.50fr+1fr, Church of Our Lady, Malines. 3fr+1fr, St. Denis Abbey, Broqueroi. 6fr+2fr, Cloth Hall, Ypres, horiz.
B705	SP336	40c + 10c brt grn	.15	.15
B706	SP336	90c + 10c lil rose	.20	.20
B707	SP336	1fr + 50c dl vio	.45	.45
B708	SP336	2fr + 50c violet	.70	.60
B709	SP336	2.50fr + 1fr red brn	1.00	.85
B710	SP336	3fr + 1fr bl grn	1.00	.85
B711	SP336	6fr + 2fr car rose	1.50	1.40
		Nos. B705-B711 (7)	5.00	4.50

The surtax was for various cultural and philanthropic organizations.

Andean Cock of
the Rock — SP337

Handicapped
Child — SP338

Birds: 1fr+50c, Red lory. 2fr+50c, Guinea touraco. 2.50fr+1fr, Keel-billed toucan. 3fr+1fr, Great bird of paradise. 6fr+2fr, Congolese peacock.

Engraved and Photogravure
1962, June 23 Unwmk. Perf. 11½
B712	SP337	40c + 10c multi	.15	.15
B713	SP337	1fr + 50c multi	.45	.30
B714	SP337	2fr + 50c multi	.50	.40
B715	SP337	2.50fr + 1fr multi	.55	.45
B716	SP337	3fr + 1fr multi	1.10	.95
B717	SP337	6fr + 1fr multi	2.00	1.75
		Nos. B712-B717 (6)	4.75	4.00

The surtax was for various philanthropic organizations.

1962, Sept. 22 Photo.
Handicapped Children: 40c+10c, Reading Braille. 2fr+50c, Deaf-mute girl with earphones and electronic equipment, horiz. 2.50fr+1fr, Child with ball (cerebral palsy). 3fr+1fr, Girl with crutches (polio). 6fr+2fr, Sitting boys playing ball, horiz.
B718	SP338	40c + 10c choc	.15	.15
B719	SP338	1fr + 50c rose red	.30	.30
B720	SP338	2fr + 50c brt lil	.60	.60
B721	SP338	2.50fr + 1fr dl grn	.65	.45

B722	SP338	3fr + 1fr dk blue	.80	.80
B723	SP338	6fr + 2fr dk brn	1.50	1.25
		Nos. B718-B723 (6)	4.00	3.75

The surtax was for various institutions for handicapped children.

Queen Louise-
Marie — SP339

Belgian Queens: No. B725, like No. B724 with "ML" initials. 1fr+50c, Marie-Henriette. 2fr+1fr, Elisabeth. 3fr+1.50fr, Astrid. 8fr+2.50fr, Fabiola.

1962, Dec. 8 Photo. & Engr.
Gray, Black & Gold
B724	SP339	40c + 10c ("L")	.15	.15
B725	SP339	40c + 10c ("ML")	.15	.15
B726	SP339	1fr + 50c	.50	.50
B727	SP339	2fr + 1fr	.85	.85
B728	SP339	3fr + 1.50fr	.95	.85
B729	SP339	8fr + 2.50fr	1.40	1.00
		Nos. B724-B729 (6)	4.00	3.50

The surtax was for anti-tuberculosis work.

British War
Memorial
(Porte de
Menin),
Ypres — SP340

1962, Dec. 26 Engr. Perf. 11½
B730	SP340	1fr + 50c multi	.50	.50

Millennium of the city of Ypres. Issued in sheets of eight.

Peace Bell
Ringing over
Globe
SP341

The Sower by
Brueghel
SP342

Engraved and Photogravure
1963, Feb. 18 Perf. 11½
B731	SP341	1fr + 1.50fr blk, bl, org & grn	1.50	1.50
a.		Sheet of 4	7.25	7.25
B732	SP341	6fr + 3fr blk, brn & org	.75	.75

The surtax was for the installation of the Peace Bell (Bourdon de la Paix) at Koekelberg Basilica and for the benefit of various cultural organizations.
No. B731 was issued in sheets of 4. No. B732 was issued in sheets of 30.

1963, Mar. 21 Perf. 11½
Designs: 3fr+1fr, The Harvest, by Brueghel, horiz. 6fr+2fr, "Bread," by Anton Carte, horiz.
B733	SP342	2fr + 1fr grn, ocher & blk	.15	.15
B734	SP342	3fr + 1fr red lil, ocher & blk	.40	.35
B735	SP342	6fr + 2fr red brn, cit & blk	.55	.50
		Nos. B733-B735 (3)	1.10	1.00

FAO "Freedom from Hunger" campaign.

Speed Racing — SP343

2fr+1fr, Bicyclists at check point, horiz.
3fr+1.50fr, Team racing, horiz. 6fr+3fr, Pace
setters.

1963, July 13   Unwmk.   Engr.   *Perf. 11½*

B736	SP343	1fr + 50c multi	.15 .15
B737	SP343	2fr + 1fr bl, car, blk & ol gray	.20 .20
B738	SP343	3fr + 1.50fr multi	.35 .35
B739	SP343	6fr + 3fr multi	.50 .50
		Nos. B736-B739 (4)	1.20 1.20

80th anniversary of the founding of the Belgian
Bicycle League. The surtax was for athletes at the
1964 Olympic Games.

Princess Paola with
Princess
Astrid — SP344

Prince Albert
and
Family
SP345

Designs: 40c+10c, Prince Philippe. 2fr+50c,
Princess Astrid. 2.50fr+1fr, Princess Paola. 6fr+2fr,
Prince Albert.

1963, Sept. 28   Photo.

B740	SP344	40c + 10c	.15 .15
B741	SP344	1fr + 50c	.35 .30
B742	SP344	2fr + 50c	.45 .40
B743	SP344	2.50fr + 1fr	.45 .45
B744	SP345	3fr + 1fr	.45 .45
B745	SP345	3fr + 1fr	1.50 1.40
a.		Booklet pane of 8	17.00 17.00
B746	SP344	6fr + 2fr	.90 .85
		Nos. B740-B746 (7)	4.25 4.00

Cent. of the Intl. Red Cross. No. B745 issued in
booklet panes of 8, which are in two forms: French
and Flemish inscriptions in top and bottom margins
transposed.

Daughter of Balthazar
Gerbier, Painted by
Rubens — SP346

Jesus, St. John and Cherubs by
Rubens — SP347

Portraits (Rubens' sons): 1fr+40c, Nicolas, 2 yrs.
old. 2fr+50c, Franz. 2.50fr+1fr, Nicolas, 6 yrs. old.
3fr+1fr, Albert.

Photogravure and Engraved
1963, Dec. 7   Unwmk.   *Perf. 11½*

B747	SP346	50c + 10c	.15 .15
B748	SP346	1fr + 10c	.15 .15
B749	SP346	2fr + 50c	.20 .20
B750	SP346	2.50fr + 1fr	.45 .45
B751	SP346	3fr + 1fr	.35 .35
B752	SP347	6fr + 2fr	.45 .45
		Nos. B747-B752 (6)	1.75 1.75

The surtax was for anti-tuberculosis work. See
No. B771.

John Quincy Adams and Lord Gambier
Signing Treaty of Ghent, by Amédée
Forestier — SP348

1964, May 16   Photo.   *Perf. 11½*

B753	SP348	6fr + 3fr dk blue	.75 .75

Signing of the Treaty of Ghent between the US
and Great Britain, Dec. 24, 1814.

Philip van
Marnix — SP349

Portraits: 3fr+1.50fr, Ida de Bure Calvin. 6fr+3fr,
Jacob Jordaens.

1964, May 30   Engr.

B754	SP349	1fr + 50c blue gray	.15 .15
B755	SP349	3fr + 1.50fr rose pink	.25 .25
B756	SP349	6fr + 3fr redsh brn	.45 .45
		Nos. B754-B756 (3)	.85 .85

Issued to honor Protestantism in Belgium. The
surtax was for the erection of a Protestant church.

Foot Soldier,
1918 — SP350

Battle of
Bastogne — SP351

Designs: 2fr+1fr, Flag bearer, Guides Regiment,
1914. 3fr+1.50fr, Trumpeter of the Grenadiers and
drummers, 1914.

1964, Aug. 1   Photo.   *Perf. 11½*

B757	SP350	1fr + 50c multi	.15 .15
B758	SP350	1fr multi	.24 .24
B759	SP350	3fr + 1.50fr multi	.24 .24
		Nos. B757-B759 (3)	.63 .63

50th anniversary of the German aggression
against Belgium in 1914. The surtax aided patriotic
undertakings.

1964, Aug. 1   Unwmk.

6fr+3fr, Liberation of the estuary of the Escaut.

B760	SP351	1fr + 1fr multi	.18 .18
B761	SP351	6fr + 3fr multi	.28 .28

Belgium's Resistance and liberation of World War
II. The surtax was to help found an International
Student Center at Antwerp and to aid cultural
undertakings.

Souvenir Sheets

Rogier van der Weyden Paintings — SP352

Descent From the Cross — SP353

1964, Sept. 19   Photo.   *Perf. 11½*

B762	SP352	Sheet of 3	2.25 2.25
a.		1fr Philip the Good	.52 .52
b.		2fr Portrait of a Lady	.52 .52
c.		3fr Man with Arrow	.52 .52

Engr.

B763	SP353	8fr red brown	2.25 2.25

Rogier van der Weyden (Roger de La Pasture,
1400-64). The surtax went to various cultural organizations. #B762 sold for 14fr, #B763 for 16fr.

Ancient
View of
the
Pand
SP354

3fr+1fr, Present view of the Pand from Lys River.

1964, Oct. 10   Photo.

B764	SP354	2fr + 1fr blk, grnsh bl & ultra	.40 .40
B765	SP354	3fr + 1fr lil rose, bl & dk brn	.40 .40

The surtax was for the restoration of the Pand
Dominican Abbey in Ghent.

Type of 1963 and

Child of Charles I,
Painted by Van
Dyck — SP355

Designs: 1fr+40c, William of Orange with his
bride, by Van Dyck. 2fr+1fr, Portrait of a small boy
with dogs by Erasmus Quellin and Jan Fyt. 3fr+1fr,
Alexander Farnese by Antonio Moro. 4fr+2fr, William II, Prince of Orange by Van Dyck. 6fr+3fr,
Artist's children by Cornelis De Vos.

1964, Dec. 5   *Perf. 11½*

B766	SP355	50c + 10c rose cl	.15 .15
B767	SP355	1fr + 40c car rose	.15 .15
B768	SP355	2fr + 1fr vio brn	.15 .15
B769	SP355	3fr + 1fr gray	.15 .15
B770	SP355	4fr + 2fr vio bl	.24 .24
B771	SP347	6fr + 3fr brt pur	.24 .24
		Nos. B766-B771 (6)	1.08 1.08

The surtax was for anti-tuberculosis work.

Liberator, Shaking
Prisoner's Hand,
Concentration
Camp — SP356

Designs: 1fr+50c, Prisoner's hand reaching for
the sun. 3fr+1.50fr, Searchlights and tank breaking
down barbed wire, horiz. 8fr+5fr, Rose growing
amid the ruins, horiz.

Engraved and Photogravure
1965, May 8   Unwmk.   *Perf. 11½*

B772	SP356	50c + 50c tan, blk & buff	.15 .15
B773	SP356	1fr + 50c multi	.15 .15
B774	SP356	3fr + 1.50fr dl lil & blk	.18 .18
B775	SP356	8fr + 5fr multi	.35 .35
		Nos. B772-B775 (4)	.83 .83

20th anniv. of the liberation of the concentration
camps for political prisoners and prisoners of war.

Stoclet House,
Brussels
SP357

Stoclet House: 6fr+3fr, Hall with marble foundation, vert. 8fr+4fr, View of house from garden.

1965, June 21

B776	SP357	3fr + 1fr slate & tan	.22 .22
B777	SP357	6fr + 3fr sepia	.32 .32
B778	SP357	8fr + 4fr vio brn & tan	.42 .42
		Nos. B776-B778 (3)	.96 .96

Austrian architect Josef Hoffmann (1870-1956),
builder of the art nouveau residence of Adolphe
Stoclet, engineer and financier.

Jackson's
Chameleon
SP358

Animals from Antwerp Zoo: 2fr+1fr, Common
iguanas. 3fr+1.50fr, African monitor. 6fr+3fr,
Komodo monitor. 8fr+4fr, Nile softshell turtle.

1965, Oct. 16   Photo.   *Perf. 11½*

B779	SP358	1fr + 50c multi	.15 .15
B780	SP358	2fr + 1fr multi	.16 .16
B781	SP358	3fr + 1.50fr multi	.22 .22
B782	SP358	6fr + 3fr multi	.45 .45
		Nos. B779-B782 (4)	.98 .98

Miniature Sheet

B783	SP358	8fr + 4fr multi	1.75 1.75

The surtax was for various cultural and philanthropic organizations. No. B783 contains one
stamp, size: 52x35mm.

Boatmen's and
Archers' Guild
Halls — SP359

Buildings on Grand-Place, Brussels: 1fr+40c,
Brewers' Hall. 2fr+1fr, "King of Spain." 3fr+1.50fr,
"Dukes of Brabant." 10fr+4.50fr, Tower of City
Hall and St. Michael.

1965, Dec. 4   Engr.   *Perf. 11½*
Size: 35x24mm

B784	SP359	50c + 10c ultra	.15 .15
B785	SP359	1fr + 40c bl grn	.15 .15
B786	SP359	2fr + 1fr rose claret	.18 .18
B787	SP359	3fr + 1.50fr vio	.20 .20

Size: 24x44mm

B788	SP359	10fr + 4.50fr sep & gray	.32 .32
		Nos. B784-B788 (5)	1.00 1.00

The surtax was for anti-tuberculosis work.

Souvenir Sheets

Queen Elisabeth — SP360

Design: No. B790, Types of 1931 and 1956.

1966, Apr. 16   Photo.   *Perf. 11½*
B789 SP360 Sheet of 2 + label   1.50 1.50
   a.   SP74 3fr dk brn & gray grn   .60 .60
   b.   SP87 3fr dk brn, yel grn & gold   .60 .60
B790 SP360 Sheet of 2 + label   1.50 1.50
   a.   SP42 3fr dk brn & dl bl   .60 .60
   b.   SP304 3fr dk brn & gray   .60 .60

The surtax went to various cultural organizations. Each sheet sold for 20fr.

Luminescent Paper
was used in printing Nos. B789-B790, B801-B806, B808-B809, B811-B823, B825-B831, B833-B835, B837-B840, B842-B846, B848-B850, B852-B854, B856-B863, and from B865 onward unless otherwise noted.

Diver — SP361

Design: 10fr+4fr, Swimmer at start.

1966, May 9   Engr.
B791 SP361 60c + 40c Prus grn, ol & org brn   .15 .15
B792 SP361 10fr + 4fr ol grn, org brn & mag   .38 .38

Issued to publicize the importance of swimming instruction.

Minorites' Convent, Liège — SP362

Designs: 1fr+50c, Val-Dieu Abbey, Aubel. 2fr+1fr, View and seal of Huy. 10fr+4.50fr, Statue of Ambiorix by Jules Bertin, and tower, Tongeren.

1966, Aug. 27   Engr.   *Perf. 11½*
B793 SP362 60c + 40c multi   .15 .15
B794 SP362 1fr + 50c multi   .15 .15
B795 SP362 2fr + 1fr multi   .15 .15
B796 SP362 10fr + 4.50fr multi   .42 .42
   Set value   .70 .70

The surtax was for various patriotic and cultural organizations.

Surveyor and Dog Team — SP363

Designs: 3fr+1.50fr, Adrien de Gerlache and "Belgica." 6fr+3fr, Surveyor, weather balloon and ship. 10fr+5fr, Penguins and "Magga Dan" (ship used for 1964, 1965 and 1966 expeditions).

1966, Oct. 8   Engr.   *Perf. 11½*
B797 SP363 1fr + 50c bl grn   .15 .15
B798 SP363 3fr + 1.50fr pale vio   .20 .20
B799 SP363 6fr + 3fr dk car   .35 .35
   Nos. B797-B799 (3)   .70 .70

Souvenir Sheet
Engraved and Photogravure
B800 SP363 10fr + 5fr dk gray, sky bl & dk red   .70 .70

Belgian Antarctic expeditions. #B800 contains one 52x35mm stamp.

Boy with Ball and Dog — SP364

Designs: 2fr+1fr, Girl skipping rope. 3fr+1.50fr, Girl and boy blowing soap bubbles. 6fr+3fr, Girl and boy rolling hoops, horiz. 8fr+3.50fr, Four children at play and cat, horiz.

1966, Dec. 3   *Perf. 11½*
B801 SP364 1fr + 1fr pink & blk   .15 .15
B802 SP364 2fr + 1fr lt bluish grn & blk   .15 .15
B803 SP364 3fr + 1.50fr lt vio & blk   .15 .15
B804 SP364 6fr + 3fr pale sal & dk brn   .24 .24
B805 SP364 8fr + 3.50fr lt yel grn & dk brn   .28 .28
   Nos. B801-B805 (5)   .97 .97

The surtax was for anti-tuberculosis work.

Souvenir Sheet

Refugees — SP365

Designs: 1fr, Boy receiving clothes. 2fr, Tibetan children. 3fr, African mother and children.

1967, Mar. 11   Photo.   *Perf. 11½*
B806 SP365   Sheet of 3   1.25 1.25
   a.   1fr black & yellow   .28 .28
   b.   2fr black & blue   .28 .28
   c.   3fr black & orange   .40 .40

Issued to help refugees around the world. Sheet has black border with Belgian P.T.T. and UN Refugee emblems. Sold for 20fr.

Robert Schuman — SP366

Colonial Brotherhood Emblem — SP368

Kongolo Memorial, Gentinnes SP367

1967, June 24   Engr.   *Perf. 11½*
B807 SP366 2fr + 1fr gray blue   .24 .24

Engraved and Photogravure
B808 SP367 5fr + 2fr brn & olive   .28 .28
B809 SP368 10fr + 5fr multi   .45 .35

Robert Schuman (1886-1963), French statesman, one of the founders of European Steel and Coal Community, 1st pres. of European Parliament (2fr+1fr); Kongolo Memorial, erected in memory of missionary and civilian victims in the Congo (5fr+2fr); a memorial for African Troops, Brussels (10fr+5fr).

Preaching Fool from "Praise of Folly" by Erasmus — SP369

Erasmus, by Quentin Massys — SP370

Designs: 2fr+1fr, Exhorting Fool from Praise of Folly. 5fr+2fr, Thomas More's Family, by Hans Holbein, horiz. 6fr+3fr, Pierre Gilles (Aegidius), by Quentin Massys.

Photogravure and Engraved (SP369); Photogravure (SP370)
1967, Sept. 2   Unwmk.   *Perf. 11*
B810 SP369 1fr + 50c tan, blk & car   .15 .15
B811 SP369 2fr + 1fr tan, blk & car   .15 .15
B812 SP370 3fr + 1.50fr multi   .15 .15
B813 SP369 5fr + 2fr tan, blk & car   .18 .18
B814 SP370 6fr + 3fr multi   .24 .24
   Nos. B810-B814 (5)   .87 .87

Issued to commemorate Erasmus (1466(?)-1536), Dutch scholar and his era.

Souvenir Sheet

Pro-Post Association Emblem — SP371

Engraved and Photogravure
1967, Oct. 21   *Perf. 11½*
B815 SP371 10fr + 5fr multi   .75 .75

Issued to publicize the POSTPHILA Philatelic Exhibition, Brussels, Oct. 21-29.

Detail from Brueghel's "Children's Games" — SP372

Designs: Various Children's Games. Singles of Nos. B816-B821 arranged in 2 rows of 3 show complete painting by Pieter Brueghel.

1967, Dec. 9   Photo.   *Perf. 11½*
B816 SP372 1fr + 50c multi   .15 .15
B817 SP372 2fr + 50c multi   .18 .18
B818 SP372 3fr + 1fr multi   .18 .18
B819 SP372 6fr + 3fr multi   .30 .30
B820 SP372 10fr + 4fr multi   .40 .40
B821 SP372 13fr + 6fr multi   .60 .60
   Nos. B816-B821 (6)   1.81 1.81

Queen Fabiola Holding Refugee Child from Congo — SP373

6fr+3fr, Queen Elisabeth & Dr. Depage.

1968, Apr. 27   Photo.   *Perf. 11½*
Cross in Red
B822 SP373 6fr + 3fr sepia & gray   .25 .25
B823 SP373 10fr + 5fr sepia & gray   .45 .45

The surtax was for the Red Cross.

Woman Gymnast and Calendar Stone SP374

Yachting and "The Swimmer" by Andrien SP375

"Explosion" SP376

Designs: 2fr+1fr, Weight lifter and Mayan motif. 3fr+1.50fr, Hurdler, colossus of Tula and animal head from Kukulkan. 6fr+2fr, Bicyclists and Chichen Itza Temple.

Engraved and Photogravure
1968, May 27   *Perf. 11½*
B824 SP374 1fr + 50c multi   .15 .15
B825 SP374 2fr + 1fr multi   .15 .15
B826 SP374 3fr + 1.50fr multi   .15 .15
B827 SP374 6fr + 3fr multi   .24 .24
Photo.
B828 SP375 13fr + 5fr multi   .52 .52
   Nos. B824-B828 (5)   1.21 1.21

Issued to publicize the 19th Olympic Games, Mexico City, Oct. 12-27.

1968, June 22   Photo.
Designs (Paintings by Pol Mara): 12fr+5fr, "Fire." 13fr+5fr, "Tornado."
B829 SP376 10fr + 5fr multi   .40 .40
B830 SP376 12fr + 5fr multi   .65 .65
B831 SP376 13fr + 5fr multi   .70 .70
   Nos. B829-B831 (3)   1.75 1.75

The surtax was for disaster victims.

Undulate Triggerfish SP377

Tropical Fish: 3fr+1.50fr, Angelfish. 6fr+3fr, Turkeyfish (Pterois volitans). 10fr+5fr, Orange butterflyfish.

1968, Oct. 19   Engr. & Photo.
B832 SP377 1fr + 50c multi   .15 .15
B833 SP377 3fr + 1.50fr multi   .15 .15
B834 SP377 6fr + 3fr multi   .30 .30
B835 SP377 10fr + 5fr multi   .42 .42
   Nos. B832-B835 (4)   1.02 1.02

King Albert and Queen Elisabeth Entering Brussels SP378

Tomb of the Unknown Soldier and Eternal Flame, Brussels — SP379

Designs: 1fr+50c, King Albert, Queen Elisabeth and Crown Prince Leopold on balcony, Bruges, vert. 6fr+3fr, King and Queen entering Liège.

1968, Nov. 9   Photo.   *Perf. 11½*
B836 SP378 1fr + 50c multi   .15 .15
B837 SP378 3fr + 1.50fr multi   .15 .15
B838 SP378 6fr + 3fr multi   .30 .30

Engraved and Photogravure
B839 SP379 10fr + 5fr multi   .40 .40
   Nos. B836-B839 (4)   1.00 1.00

50th anniv. of the victory in World War I.

Souvenir Sheet

The Painter and the Amateur, by Peter Brueghel — SP380

1969, May 10   Engr.   Perf. 11½
B840 SP380 10fr + 5fr sepia   1.10 1.10
Issued to publicize the POSTPHILA 1969 Philatelic Exhibition, Brussels, May 10-18.

Huts, by Ivanka D. Pancheva, Bulgaria SP381

Msgr. Victor Scheppers SP382

Children's Drawings and UNICEF Emblem: 3fr+1.50fr, "My Art" (Santa Claus), by Claes Patric, Belgium. 6fr+3fr, "In the Sun" (young boy), by Helena Rejchlova, Czechoslovakia. 10fr+5fr, "Out for a Walk" by Phillis Sporn, US, horiz.

1969, May 31   Photo.   Perf. 11½
B841 SP381 1fr + 50c multi   .15 .15
B842 SP381 3fr + 1.50fr multi   .16 .16
B843 SP381 6fr + 3fr multi   .35 .35
B844 SP381 10fr + 5fr multi   .52 .52
    Nos. B841-B844 (4)   1.18 1.18
The surtax was for philanthropic purposes.

1969, July 5   Engr.
B845 SP382 6fr + 3fr rose claret   .45 .45
Msgr. Victor Scheppers (1802-77), prison reformer and founder of the Brothers of Mechlin (Scheppers).

Moon Landing Type of 1969
Souvenir Sheet

Design: 20fr+10fr, Armstrong, Collins and Aldrin and moon with Tranquillity Base, vert.

1969, Sept. 20   Photo.   Perf. 11½
B846 A245 20fr + 10fr indigo   3.00 3.00
See note after No. 726.

Heads from Alexander the Great Tapestry, 15th Century — SP383

Designs from Tapestries: 3fr+1.50fr, Fiddler from "The Feast," c. 1700. 10fr+4fr, Head of beggar from "The Healing of the Paralytic," 16th century.

1969, Sept. 20
B847 SP383 1fr + 50c multi   .15 .15
B848 SP383 3fr + 1.50fr multi   .18 .18
B849 SP383 10fr + 4fr multi   .45 .45
    Nos. B847-B849 (3)   .78 .78
The surtax was for philanthropic purposes.

Bearded Antwerp Bantam SP384

1969, Nov. 8   Engr. & Photo.
B850 SP384 10fr + 5fr multi   .70 .70

Angel Playing Lute — SP385

Designs from Stained Glass Windows: 1.50fr+50c, Angel with trumpet, St. Waudru's, Mons. 7fr+3fr, Angel with viol, St. Jacques', Liege. 9fr+4fr, King with bagpipes, Royal Art Museum, Brussels.

1969, Dec. 13   Photo.
Size: 24x35mm
B851 SP385 1.50fr + 50c multi   .15 .15
B852 SP385 3.50fr + 1.50fr multi   .18 .18
B853 SP385 7fr + 3fr multi   .35 .35
Size: 35x52mm
B854 SP386 9fr + 4fr multi   .52 .52
    Nos. B851-B854 (4)   1.20 1.20
The surtax was for philanthropic purposes.

Farm and Windmill, Open-air Museum, Bokrijk SP386

Belgian Museums: 3.50fr+1.50fr, Stage Coach Inn, Courcelles. 7fr+3fr, "The Thresher of Trevires," Gallo-Roman sculpture, Gaumais Museum, Virton. 9fr+4fr, "The Sovereigns," by Henry Moore, Middelheim Museum, Antwerp.

Engraved and Photogravure
1970, May 30   Perf. 11½
B855 SP386 1.50fr + 50c multi   .15 .15
B856 SP386 3.50fr + 1.50fr multi   .25 .25
B857 SP386 7fr + 3fr multi   .35 .35
B858 SP386 9fr + 4fr multi   .40 .40
    Nos. B855-B858 (4)   1.15 1.15
The surtax went to various culture organizations.

"Resistance" — SP387

Design: 7fr+3fr, "Liberation of Camps." The designs were originally used as book covers.

1970, July 4   Photo.   Perf. 11½
B859 SP387 3.50fr + 1.50fr blk, gray
    grn & dp car   .20 .20
B860 SP387 7fr + 3fr blk, lil & dp
    car   .40 .40
Honoring the Resistance Movement and 25th anniv. of the liberation of concentration camps.

Fishing Rod and Reel — SP388

Design: 9fr+4fr, Hockey stick and puck, vert.

1970, Sept. 19   Engr. & Photo.
B861 SP388 3.50fr + 1.50fr multi   .28 .28
B862 SP388 9fr + 4fr multi   .48 .48

Souvenir Sheet

Belgium Nos. 31, 36, 39 — SP389

1970, Oct. 10   Perf. 11½
B863 SP389   Sheet of 3   4.75 4.75
  a. 1.50fr + 50c black & dull lilac   1.40 1.40
  b. 3.50fr + 1.50fr black & lilac   1.40 1.40
  c. 9fr + 4fr black & red brown   1.40 1.40
BELGICA 72 International Philatelic Exhibition, Brussels, June 24-July 9.

Camille Huysmans (1871-1968) SP390

"Anxious City" (Detail) by Paul Delvaux SP391

Portraits: 3.50fr+1.50fr, Joseph Cardinal Cardijn (1882-1967). 7fr+3fr, Maria Baers (1883-1959). 9fr+4fr, Paul Pastur (1866-1938).

1970, Nov. 14   Perf. 11½
Portraits in Sepia
B864 SP390 1.50fr + 50c car rose   .15 .15
B865 SP390 3.50fr + 1.50fr lilac   .20 .20
B866 SP390 7fr + 3fr green   .40 .40
B867 SP390 9fr + 4fr blue   .48 .48
    Nos. B864-B867 (4)   1.23 1.23

1970, Dec. 12   Photo.
7fr+3fr, "The Memory," by Rene Magritte.
B868 SP391 3.50fr + 1.50fr multi   .18 .18
B869 SP391 7fr + 3fr multi   .38 .38

Notre Dame du Vivier, Marche-les-Dames — SP392

7fr+3fr, Turnhout Beguinage and Beguine.

1971, Mar. 13   Perf. 11½
B870 SP392 3.50fr + 1.50fr multi   .20 .20
B871 SP392 7fr + 3fr multi   .40 .40
The surtax was for philanthropic purposes.

Red Cross — SP393

1971, May 22   Photo.   Perf. 11½
B872 SP393 10fr + 5fr crim & blk   .75 .75
Belgian Red Cross.

Discobolus and Munich Cathedral SP394

Festival of Flanders SP395

1971, June 19   Engr. & Photo.
B873 SP394 7fr + 3fr bl & blk   .42 .42
Publicity for the 20th Summer Olympic Games, Munich 1972.

1971, Sept. 11   Photo.   Perf. 11½
Design: 7fr+3fr, Wallonia Festival.
B874 SP395 3.50fr + 1.50fr multi   .18 .18
B875 SP395 7fr + 3fr multi   .38 .38

Attre Palace — SP396

Steen Palace, Elewijt — SP397

Design: 10fr+5fr, Royal Palace, Brussels.

1971, Oct. 23   Engr.
B876 SP396 3.50fr + 1.50fr sl grn   .30 .30
B877 SP397 7fr + 3fr red brn   .50 .50
B878 SP396 10fr + 5fr vio bl   .70 .70
    Nos. B876-B878 (3)   1.50 1.50
Surtax was for BELGICA 72, International Philatelic Exposition.

Ox Fly — SP398

Insects: 1.50fr+50c, Luna moth, vert. 7fr+3fr, Wasp, polistes gallicus. 9fr+4fr, Tiger beetle, vert.

1971, Dec. 11   Photo.   Perf. 11½
B879 SP398 1.50fr + 50c multi   .20 .20
B880 SP398 3.50fr + 1.50fr multi   .20 .20
B881 SP398 7fr + 3fr multi   .40 .40
B882 SP398 9fr + 4fr multi   .60 .60
    Nos. B879-B882 (4)   1.40 1.40
Surtax was for philanthropic purposes.

Leopold I on #1 — SP399

Epilepsy Emblem — SP400

Designs: 2fr+1fr, Leopold I on No. 5. 2.50fr+1fr, Leopold II on No. 45. 3.50fr+1.50fr, Leopold II on No. 48. 6fr+3fr, Albert I on No. 135. 7fr+3fr, Albert I on No. 214. 10fr+5fr, Albert I on No. 231. 15fr+7.50fr, Leopold III on No. 290. 20fr+10fr, King Baudouin on No. 718.

Engraved and Photogravure

1972, June 24   *Perf. 11½*

B883	SP399	1.50fr + 50c	.16	.16
B884	SP399	2fr + 1fr	.16	.16
B885	SP399	2.50 + 1fr	.20	.20
B886	SP399	3.50fr + 1.50fr	.32	.32
B887	SP399	6fr + 3fr	.52	.52
B888	SP399	7fr + 3fr	.70	.70
B889	SP399	10fr + 5fr	.90	.90
B890	SP399	15fr + 7fr	1.10	1.10
B891	SP399	20fr + 10fr	2.00	2.00
		Nos. B883-B891 (9)	6.06	6.06

Belgica 72, Intl. Philatelic Exhibition, Brussels, June 24-July 9. Nos. B883-B891 issued in sheets of 10 and of 20 (2 tete beche sheets with gutter between). Sold in complete sets.

1972, Sept. 9   **Photo.**   *Perf. 11½*

B892	SP400	10fr + 5fr multi	.55	.55

The surtax was for the William Lennox Center for epilepsy research and treatment.

Gray Lag Goose — SP401

Designs: 4.50fr+2fr, Lapwing. 8fr+4fr, Stork. 9fr+4.50fr, Kestrel, horiz.

1972, Dec. 16   **Photo.**   *Perf. 11½*

B893	SP401	2fr + 1fr multi	.22	.22
B894	SP401	4.50fr + 2fr multi	.32	.32
B895	SP401	8fr + 4fr multi	.60	.60
B896	SP401	9fr + 4.50fr multi	.60	.60
		Nos. B893-B896 (4)	1.74	1.74

Bijloke Abbey, Ghent — SP402

Designs: 4.50fr+2fr, St. Ursmer Collegiate Church, Lobbes. 8fr+4fr, Park Abbey, Heverle. 9fr+4.50fr, Floreffe.

1973, Mar. 24   **Engr.**   *Perf. 11½*

B897	SP402	2fr + 1fr slate grn	.16	.16
B898	SP402	4.50fr + 2fr brown	.24	.24
B899	SP402	8fr + 4fr rose lil	.48	.48
B900	SP402	9fr + 4.50fr brt bl	.60	.60
		Nos. B897-B900 (4)	1.48	1.48

Basketball SP403

1973, Apr. 7   **Photo. & Engr.**

B901	SP403	10fr + 5fr multi	.60	.60

First World Basketball Championships of the Handicapped, Bruges, Apr. 16-21.

Dirk Martens' Printing Press — SP404

Lady Talbot, by Petrus Christus — SP405

Hadrian and Marcus Aurelius Coins — SP406

Council of Malines, by Coussaert — SP407

Designs: 3.50fr+1.50fr, Head of Amon and Tutankhamen's cartouche. 10fr+5fr, Three-master of Ostend Merchant Company.

Photogravure and Engraved; Photogravure (#B906)

1973, June 23   *Perf. 11½*

B902	SP404	2fr + 1fr multi	.15	.15
B903	SP404	3.50fr + 1.50fr multi	.15	.15
B904	SP405	4.50fr + 2fr multi	.20	.20
B905	SP406	8fr + 4fr multi	.60	.60
B906	SP407	9fr + 4.50fr multi	.85	.85
B907	SP407	10fr + 5fr multi	1.50	1.50
		Nos. B902-B907 (6)	3.45	3.45

500th anniv. of 1st book printed in Belgium (#B902); 50th anniv. of Queen Elisabeth Egyptological Foundation (#B903); 500th anniv. of death of painter Petrus Christus (#B904); Discovery of Roman treasure at Luttre-Liberchies (#B905); 500th anniv. of Great Council of Malines (#B906); 250th anniv. of the Ostend Merchant Company (#B907). No. B902 is not luminescent.

Queen of Hearts SP408

Symbol of Blood Donations SP409

Old Playing Cards: #B909, King of Clubs. #B910, Jack of Diamonds. #B911, King of Spades.

1973, Dec. 8   **Photo.**   *Perf. 11½*

B908	SP408	5fr + 2.50fr multi	.38	.38
B909	SP408	5fr + 2.50fr multi	.38	.38
B910	SP408	5fr + 2.50fr multi	.38	.38
B911	SP408	5fr + 2.50fr multi	.38	.38
a.		Block of 4, #B908-B911	1.60	1.60

Surtax was for philanthropic purposes.

1974, Feb. 23   **Photo.**   *Perf. 11½*

Design: 10fr+5fr, Traffic lights, Red Cross (symbolic of road accidents).

B912	SP409	4fr + 2fr multi	.24	.24
B913	SP409	10fr + 5fr multi	.55	.55

The Red Cross as blood collector and aid to accident victims.

Armand Jamar, Self-portrait SP410

Van Gogh, Self-portrait and House at Cuesmes SP411

Designs: 5fr+2.50fr, Anton Bergmann and view of Lierre. 7fr+3.50fr, Henri Vieuxtemps and view of Verviers. 10fr+5fr, James Ensor, self-portrait, and masks.

1974, Apr. 6   **Photo.**   *Perf. 11½*
Size: 24x35mm

B914	SP410	4fr + 2fr multi	.24	.24
B915	SP410	5fr + 2.50fr multi	.32	.32
B916	SP410	7fr + 3.50fr multi	.40	.40

Size: 35x52mm

B917	SP410	10fr + 5fr multi	.65	.65
		Nos. B914-B917 (4)	1.61	1.61

1974, Sept. 21   **Photo.**   *Perf. 11½*

B918	SP411	10fr + 5fr multi	.55	.55

Opening of Vincent van Gogh House at Cuesmes, where he worked as teacher.

Gentian — SP412

Spotted Cat's Ear — SP414

Badger SP413

Design: 7fr+3.50fr, Beetle.

1974, Dec. 8   **Photo.**   *Perf. 11½*

B919	SP412	4fr + 2fr multi	.25	.25
B920	SP413	5fr + 2.50fr multi	.30	.30
B921	SP413	7fr + 3.50fr multi	.40	.40
B922	SP414	10fr + 5fr multi	.60	.60
		Nos. B919-B922 (4)	1.55	1.55

Pesaro Palace, Venice SP415

St. Bavon Abbey, Ghent SP416

Virgin and Child, by Michelangelo — SP417

Frans Hemerijckx and Leprosarium, Kasai — SP418

1975, Apr. 12   **Engr.**   *Perf. 11½*

B923	SP415	6.50fr + 2.50fr brn	.35	.35
B924	SP416	10fr + 4.50 vio brn	.60	.60
B925	SP417	15fr + 6.50fr brt bl	.80	.80
		Nos. B923-B925 (3)	1.75	1.75

Surtax was for various cultural organizations.

1975, Sept. 13   **Photo.**   *Perf. 11½*

B926	SP418	20fr + 10fr multi	1.40	1.40

Dr. Frans Hemerijckx (1902-1969), tropical medicine and leprosy expert.

Emile Moyson — SP419

Beheading of St. Dympna — SP420a

Hand Reading Braille SP420

6.50fr+3fr, Dr. Ferdinand Augustin Snellaert.

1975, Nov. 22   **Engr.**   *Perf. 11½*

B927	SP419	4.50fr + 2fr lilac	.24	.24
B928	SP419	6.50fr + 3fr green	.35	.35

Engraved and Photogravure

B929	SP420	10fr + 5fr multi	.50	.50

Photo.

B930	SP420a	13fr + 6fr multi	.70	.70
		Nos. B927-B930 (4)	1.79	1.79

Emile Moyson (1838-1868), freedom fighter for the rights of Flemings and Walloons; Dr. Snellaert (1809-1872), physician and Flemish patriot; Louis Braille (1809-1852), sesquicentennial of invention of Braille system of writing for the blind; St. Dympna, patron saint of Geel, famous for treatment of mentally ill.

The Cheese Vendor — SP421

Designs (THEMABELGA Emblem and): No. B932, Potato vendor. No. B933, Basket carrier. No. B934, Shrimp fisherman with horse, horiz. No. B935, Knife grinder, horiz. No. B936, Milk vendor with dog cart, horiz.

1975, Dec. 13   **Engr. & Photo.**

B931	SP421	4.50fr + 1.50fr multi	.15	.15
B932	SP421	6.50fr + 3fr multi	.32	.32
B933	SP421	6.50fr + 3fr multi	.32	.32
B934	SP421	10fr + 5fr multi	.45	.45
B935	SP421	10fr + 5fr multi	.45	.45
B936	SP421	30fr + 15fr multi	1.50	1.50
		Nos. B931-B936 (6)	3.19	3.19

THEMABELGA International Topical Philatelic Exhibition, Brussels, Dec. 13-21. Issued in sheets of 10 (5x2).

Blackface Fund Collector — SP422

1976, Feb. 14   Photo.   Perf. 11½
B937 SP422 10fr + 5fr multi   .55 .55

Centenary of the "Conservatoire Africain" philanthropic society, and to publicize the Princess Paola creches.

Swimming and Olympic Emblem SP423

Montreal Olympic Games Emblem and: 5fr+2fr, Running, vert. 6.50fr+2.50fr, Equestrian.

1976, Apr. 10   Photo.   Perf. 11½
B938 SP423 4.50fr + 1.50fr multi   .18 .18
B939 SP423 5fr + 2fr multi   .25 .25
B940 SP423 6.50fr + 2.50fr multi   .45 .45
  Nos. B938-B940 (3)   .88 .88

21st Olympic Games, Montreal, Canada, July 17-Aug. 1.

Queen Elisabeth Playing Violin SP424

Perf. 11½
1976, May 1   Engr.   Photo.
B941 SP424 14fr + 6fr blk & claret   .95 .95

Queen Elisabeth International Music Competition, 25th anniversary.

Souvenir Sheet

Jan Olieslagers, Bleriot Monoplane, Aero Club Emblem SP425

Engraved and Photogravure
1976, June 12   Perf. 11½
B942 SP425 25fr + 10fr multi   2.25 2.25

Royal Belgian Aero Club, 75th anniversary, and Jan Olieslagers (1883-1942), aviation pioneer.

Adoration of the Shepherds (detail), by Rubens SP426

Dwarf, by Velazquez SP427

Rubens Paintings (Details): 4.50fr, Descent from the Cross. No. B945, The Virgin with the Parrot. No. B946, Adoration of the Kings. No. B947, Last Communion of St. Francis. 30fr+15fr, Virgin and Child.

1976, Sept. 4   Photo.   Perf. 11½
Size: 35x52mm
B943 SP426 4.50fr + 1.50fr multi   .35 .35
Size: 24x35mm
B944 SP426 6.50fr + 3fr multi   .55 .55
B945 SP426 6.50fr + 3fr multi   .55 .55
B946 SP426 10fr + 5fr multi   .85 .85
B947 SP426 10fr + 5fr multi   .85 .85
Size: 35x52mm
B948 SP426 30fr + 15fr multi   1.75 1.75
  Nos. B943-B948 (6)   4.90 4.90

Peter Paul Rubens (1577-1640), Flemish painter, 400th birth anniversary.

1976, Nov. 6   Photo.   Perf. 11½
B949 SP427 14fr + 6fr multi   .80 .80

Surtax was for the National Association for the Mentally Handicapped.

Dr. Albert Hustin — SP428

Red Cross and Rheumatism Year Emblem — SP429

1977, Feb. 19   Photo.   Perf. 11½
B950 SP428 6.50fr + 2.50 multi   .38 .38
B951 SP429 14fr + 7fr multi   .75 .75

Belgian Red Cross.

Bordet Atheneum, Empress Maria Theresa — SP430

Conductor and Orchestra, by E. Tytgat — SP431

Lucien Van Obbergh, Stage — SP432

Humanistic Society Emblem SP433

Camille Lemonnier SP434

Design: No. B953, Marie-Therese College, Herve, and coat of arms.

1977, Mar. 21   Photo.   Perf. 11½
B952 SP430 4.50fr + 1fr multi   .20 .20
B953 SP430 4.50fr + 1fr multi   .20 .20
B954 SP431 5fr + 2fr multi   .24 .24
B955 SP432 6.50fr + 2fr multi   .32 .32
B956 SP433 6.50fr + 2fr blk & red   .32 .32

Engr.
B957 SP434 10fr + 5fr slate bl   .48 .48
  Nos. B952-B957 (6)   1.76 1.76

Bicentenaries of the Jules Bordet Atheneum, Brussels, and the Marie-Therese College, Herve (#B952-B953); 50th anniv. of the Brussels Philharmonic Soc., and Artists' Union (#B954-B955); 25th anniv. of the Flemish Humanistic Organization (#B956); 75th anniv. of the French-speaking Belgian writers' organization (#957).

Young Soccer Players — SP435

Albert-Edouard Janssen, Financier — SP436

1977, Apr. 18   Photo.
B958 SP435 10fr + 5fr multi   .55 .55

30th Intl. Junior Soccer Tournament.

1977, Dec. 3   Engr.   Perf. 11½
Famous Men: No. B960, Joseph Wauters (1875-1929), editor of Le Peuple, and newspaper. No. B961, Jean Capart (1877-1947), Egyptologist, and hieroglyph. No. B962, August de Boeck (1865-1937), composer, and score.

B959 SP436 5fr + 2.50fr brown   .28 .28
B960 SP436 5fr + 2.50fr red   .28 .28
B961 SP436 10fr + 5fr magenta   .55 .55
B962 SP436 10fr + 5fr blue gray   .55 .55
  Nos. B959-B962 (4)   1.66 1.66

Abandoned Child — SP437

Checking Blood Pressure — SP438

De Mick Sanatorium, Brasschaat — SP439

1978, Feb. 18   Photo.   Perf. 11½
B963 SP437 4.50fr + 1.50fr multi   .15 .15
B964 SP438 6fr + 3fr multi   .38 .38
B965 SP439 10fr + 5fr multi   .60 .60
  Nos. B963-B965 (3)   1.13 1.13

Help for abandoned children (No. B963); fight against hypertension (No. B964); fight against tuberculosis (No. B965).

Actors and Theater SP440

Karel van de Woestijne SP441

Designs: No. B967, Harquebusier, Harquebusier Palace and coat of arms. 10fr+5fr, John of Austria and his signature.

Engraved and Photogravure
1978, June 17   Perf. 11½
B966 SP440 6fr + 3fr multi   .38 .38
B967 SP440 6fr + 3fr multi   .38 .38

Engr.
B968 SP441 8fr + 4fr black   .45 .45
B969 SP441 10fr + 5fr black   .55 .55
  Nos. B966-B969 (4)   1.76 1.76

Cent. of Royal Flemish Theater, Brussels (#B966); 400th anniv. of Harquebusiers' Guild of Vise, Liege (#967); Karel van de Woestijne (1878-1929), poet (#B968); 400th anniv. of signing of Perpetual Edict by John of Austria (#969).

Lake Placid '80 and Belgian Olympic Emblems — SP442

Designs (Moscow '80 Emblem and): 8fr+3.50fr, Kremlin Towers and Belgian Olympic Committee emblem. 7fr+3fr, Runners from Greek vase, Lake Placid '80 emblem and Olympic rings. 14fr+6fr, Olympic flame, Lake Placid '80 and Belgian emblems, Olympic rings.

1978, Nov. 4   Photo.   Perf. 11½
B970 SP442 6fr + 2.50fr multi   .30 .30
B971 SP442 8fr + 3.50fr multi   .45 .45
Souvenir Sheet
B972   Sheet of 2   1.40 1.40
  a.   SP442 7fr + 3fr multi   .55 .55
  b.   SP442 14fr + 6fr multi   .90 .90

Surtax was for 1980 Olympic Games.

Great Synagogue, Brussels — SP443

Dancers SP444

Father Pire, African Village SP445

Young People Giving First Aid — SP446

Skull with Bottle, Cigarette, Syringe — SP447

1978, Dec. 2   Engr.   Perf. 11½
B973 SP443 6fr + 2fr sepia   .45 .45
Photo.
B974 SP444 8fr + 3fr multi   .35 .35
B975 SP445 14fr + 7fr multi   .65 .65
  Nos. B973-B975 (3)   1.45 1.45

Centenary of Great Synagogue of Brussels; Flemish Catholic Youth Action Organization, 50th anniversary; Nobel Peace Prize awarded to Father Dominique Pire for his "Heart Open to the World" movement, 20th anniversary.

1979, Feb. 10 Photo. Perf. 11½
B976 SP446 8fr + 3fr multi .35 .35
B977 SP447 16fr + 8fr multi .85 .85
Belgian Red Cross.

Beatrice Soetkens with Statue of Virgin Mary — SP448

Details from Tapestries, 1516-1518, Showing Legend of Our Lady of Sand: 8fr+3fr, Francois de Tassis accepting letter from Emperor Frederick III (beginning of postal service). 14fr+7fr, Arrival of statue, Francois de Tassis and Philip the Fair. No. B981, Statue carried in procession by future Emperor Charles V and his brother Ferdinand. No. B982, Ship carrying Beatrice Soetkens with statue to Brussels, horiz.

1979, May 5 Photo. Perf. 11½
B978 SP448 6fr + 2fr multi .25 .25
B979 SP448 8fr + 3fr multi .40 .40
B980 SP448 14fr + 7fr multi .65 .65
B981 SP448 20fr + 10fr multi 1.10 1.10
Nos. B978-B981 (4) 2.40 2.40

Souvenir Sheet
B982 SP448 20fr + 10fr multi .90 .90
The surtax was for festivities in connection with the millennium of Brussels.

Notre Dame Abbey, Brussels SP449

Designs: 8fr+3fr, Beauvoorde Castle. 14fr+7fr, 1st issue of "Courrier de L'Escaut" and Barthelemy Dumortier, founder. 20fr+10fr, Shrine of St. Hermes, Renaix.

Engraved and Photogravure
1979, Sept. 15 Perf. 11½
B983 SP449 6fr + 2fr multi .35 .35
B984 SP449 8fr + 3fr multi .50 .50
B985 SP449 14fr + 7fr multi .60 .60
B986 SP449 20fr + 10fr multi 1.10 1.10
Nos. B983-B986 (4) 2.55 2.55

50th anniv. of restoration of Notre Dame de la Cambre Abbey; historic Beauvoorde Castle, 15th cent. sesquicentennial of the regional newspaper "Le Courrier de L'Escaut"; 850th anniv. of the consecration of the Collegiate Church of St. Hermes, Renaix.

Grand-Hornu Coal Mine — SP450

1979, Oct. 22 Engr. Perf. 11½
B987 SP450 10fr + 5fr blk .55 .55

Henry Heyman — SP451 Veterans Organization Medal — SP452

16F,8F

Boy and IYC Emblem SP453

1979, Dec. 8 Photo. Perf. 11½
B988 SP451 8fr + 3fr multi .45 .45
B989 SP452 10fr + 5fr multi .55 .55
B990 SP453 16fr + 8fr multi .75 .75
Nos. B988-B990 (3) 1.75 1.75

Henri Heyman (1879-1958), Minister of State; Disabled Veterans' Organization, 50th anniv.; Intl. Year of the Child.

Ivo Van Damme, Olympic Rings — SP454

1980, May 3 Photo. Perf. 11½
B991 SP454 20fr + 10fr multi 1.10 1.10
Ivo Van Damme (1954-1976), silver medalist, 800-meter race, Montreal Olympics, 1976. Surtax was for Van Damme Memorial Foundation.

Queen Louis, King Leopold I SP455

150th Anniversary of Independence (Queens and Kings): 9fr+3fr, Marie Henriette. Leopold II. 14fr+6fr, Elisabeth, Albert I. 17fr+8fr, Astrid, Leopold III. 25fr+10fr, Fabiola, Baudouin.

Photogravure and Engraved
1980, May 31 Perf. 11½
B992 SP455 6.50 + 1.50fr multi .28 .28
B993 SP455 9 + 3fr multi .50 .50
B994 SP455 14 + 6fr multi .70 .70
B995 SP455 17 + 8fr multi 1.00 1.00
B996 SP455 25 + 10fr multi 1.25 1.25
Nos. B992-B996 (5) 3.73 3.73

Miner, by Constantine Meunier SP456

Seal of Bishop Notger, First Prince-Bishop — SP457

9fr+3fr, Brewer, 16th century, from St. Lambert's reliquary, vert. 25fr+10fr, Virgin and Child, 13th century, St. John's Collegiate Church, Liege.

1980, Sept. 13 Photo. Perf. 11½
B997 SP456 9 + 3fr multi .35 .35
B998 SP456 17 + 6fr multi .70 .70
B999 SP456 25 + 10fr multi 1.10 1.10
Nos. B997-B999 (3) 2.15 2.15

Souvenir Sheet
B1000 SP457 20 + 10fr multi 1.25 1.25
Millennium of the Principality of Liege.

Visual and Oral Handicaps SP458

Intl. Year of the Disabled: 10fr+5fr, Cerebral handicap, vert.

1981, Feb. 9 Photo. Perf. 11½
B1001 SP458 10 + 5fr multi .70 .70
B1002 SP458 25 + 10fr multi 1.65 1.65

Dove with Red Cross Carrying Globe SP459

Design: 10fr+5fr, Atomic model, vert.

1981, Apr. 6 Photo. Perf. 11½
B1003 SP459 10 + 5fr multi .70 .70
B1004 SP459 25 + 10fr multi 1.65 1.65
Red Cross and: 15th Intl. Radiology Congress, Brussels, June 24-July 1 (#B1003); intl. disaster relief (#B1004).

Ovide Decroly SP460

1981, June 1 Photo. Perf. 11½
B1005 SP460 35 + 15fr multi 2.00 2.00
Ovide Decroly (1871-1932), developer of educational psychology.

Mounted Police Officer — SP461 Billiards — SP462

Anniversaries: 9fr+4fr, Gendarmerie (State Police Force), 150th. 20fr+7fr, Carabineers Regiment, 150th. 40fr+20fr, Guides Regiment.

1981, Dec. 7 Photo. Perf. 11½
B1006 SP461 9 + 4fr multi .60 .60
B1007 SP461 20 + 7fr multi 1.25 1.25
B1008 SP461 40 + 20fr multi 2.75 2.75
Nos. B1006-B1008 (3) 4.60 4.60

1982, Mar. 29 Photo. Perf. 11½
B1009 SP462 6 + 2fr shown .38 .38
B1010 SP462 9 + 4fr Cycling .60 .60
B1011 SP462 10 + 5fr Soccer .70 .70
B1012 SP462 50 + 14fr Yachting 3.00 3.00
Nos. B1009-B1012 (4) 4.68 4.68

Souvenir Sheet
B1013 Sheet of 4 5.00 5.00
a. SP462 25fr like #B1009 1.40 1.40
b. SP462 25fr like #B1010 1.40 1.40
c. SP462 25fr like #B1011 1.40 1.40
d. SP462 25fr like #B1012 1.40 1.40
#B1013 shows designs in changed colors.

Christmas SP463

1982, Nov. 6
B1014 SP463 10 + 1fr multi .60 .45
Surtax was for tuberculosis research.

Belgica '82 Intl. Stamp Exhibition, Brussels, Dec. 11-19 SP464

Messengers (Prints). Nos. B1016-B1018 vert.

Photogravure and Engraved
1982, Dec. 11 Perf. 11½
B1015 SP464 7 + 2fr multi .38 .38
B1016 SP464 7.50 + 2.50fr multi .45 .45
B1017 SP464 10 + 3fr multi .55 .55
B1018 SP464 17 + 7fr multi 1.10 1.10
B1019 SP464 20 + 9fr multi 1.25 1.25
B1020 SP464 25 + 10fr multi 1.50 1.50
Nos. B1015-B1020 (6) 5.23 5.23

Souvenir Sheet
B1021 SP464 50 + 25fr multi 6.00 6.00
No. B1021 contains one 48x37mm stamp.

50th Anniv. of Catholic Charities SP465 Mountain Climbing SP466

1983, Jan. 22 Photo. Perf. 11½
B1022 SP465 10 + 2fr multi .65 .65

1983, Mar. 7 Photo.
B1023 SP466 12 + 3fr shown .80 .80
B1024 SP466 20 + 5fr Hiking 1.25 1.25
Surtax was for Red Cross.

Madonna by Jef Wauters — SP467 Rifles Uniform — SP468

1983, Nov. 21 Photo. Perf. 11½
B1025 SP467 11 + 1fr multi .60 .60

1983, Dec. 5 Photo. Perf. 11½
B1026 SP468 8 + 2fr shown .50 .50
B1027 SP468 11 + 2fr Lancers uniform .75 .75
B1028 SP468 50 + 12fr Grenadiers uniform 3.50 3.50
Nos. B1026-B1028 (3) 4.75 4.75

Type of 1984
1984, Mar. 3 Photo. Perf. 11½
B1029 A495 8 + 2fr Judo, horiz. .55 .55
B1030 A495 12 + 3fr Wind surfing .85 .85

50th Anniv. of Natl. Lottery SP469

1984, Mar. 31 Photo. Perf. 11½
B1031 SP469 12 + 3fr multi .75 .75

Brussels Modern Art Museum Opening SP470

Paintings: 8fr+2fr, Les Masques Singuliers, by James Ensor. 12fr+3fr, Empire des Lumieres, by Rene Magritte. 22fr+5fr, The End, by Jan Cox. 50fr+13fr, Rhythm No. 6, by Jo Delahaut.

1984, Sept. 1   **Photo.**
B1032	SP470	8 + 2fr multi	.60 .60
B1033	SP470	12 + 3fr multi	.90 .90
B1034	SP470	22 + 5fr multi	1.65 1.65
B1035	SP470	50 + 13fr multi	3.75 3.75
	Nos. B1032-B1035 (4)		6.90 6.90

Child with Parents — SP471

1984, Nov. 3   **Photo.**
B1036	SP471	10 + 2fr shown	.60 .60
B1037	SP471	12 + 3fr Siblings	.75 .75
B1038	SP471	15 + 3fr Merry-go-round	.85 .85
	Nos. B1036-B1038 (3)		2.20 2.20

Surtax was for children's programs.

Christmas 1984 SP472

1984, Dec. 1
B1039	SP472	12 + 1fr Three Kings	.75 .75

Belgian Red Cross Blood Transfusion Service, 50th Anniv. — SP473

1985, Mar. 4   **Photo.**   **Perf. 11½**
B1040	SP473	9 + 2fr Tree	.60 .60
B1041	SP473	23 + 5fr Hearts	1.40 1.40

Surtax was for the Belgian Red Cross.

Solidarity SP474

Castles.

1985, Nov. 4   **Photo. & Engr.**
B1042	SP474	9 + 2fr Trazegnies	.60 .60
B1043	SP474	12 + 3fr Laarne	.80 .80
B1044	SP474	23 + 5fr Turnhout	1.40 1.40
B1045	SP474	50 + 12fr Colonster	3.50 3.50
	Nos. B1042-B1045 (4)		6.30 6.30

Christmas 1985, New Year 1986 — SP475

Painting: Miniature from the Book of Hours, by Jean duc de Berry.

1985, Nov. 25   **Photo.**
B1046	SP475	12 + 1fr multi	.70 .70

King Baudouin Foundation SP476

1986, Mar. 24   **Photo.**
B1047	SP476	12 + 3fr Emblem	.80 .80

Surtax for the foundation.

Madonna SP477

Adoration of the Mystic Lamb, St. Bavon Cathedral Altarpiece, Ghent — SP478

Paintings by Hubert van Eyck (c. 1370-1426).

1986, Apr. 5   **Photo.**   **Perf. 11½**
B1048	SP477	9 + 2fr shown	.65 .65
B1049	SP477	13 + 3fr Christ in Majesty	.95 .95
B1050	SP477	24 + 6fr St. John the Baptist	1.75 1.75
	Nos. B1048-B1050 (3)		3.35 3.35

Souvenir Sheet
B1051	SP478	50 + 12fr multi	5.25 5.25

Surtax for cultural organizations.

Antique Automobiles SP479

1986, Nov. 3   **Photo.**
B1052	SP479	9 + 2fr Lenoir, 1863	.65 .65
B1053	SP479	13 + 3fr Pipe de Tourisme, 1911	.90 .90
B1054	SP479	24 + 6fr Minerva 22 HP, 1930	1.75 1.75
B1055	SP479	26 + 6fr FN 8 Cylinder, 1931	1.90 1.90
	Nos. B1052-B1055 (4)		5.20 5.20

Christmas 1986, New Year 1987 — SP480

1986, Nov. 24   **Photo.**
B1056	SP480	13 + 1fr Village in winter	.75 .75

Natl. Red Cross — SP482   European Conservation Year — SP483

Nobel Prize winners for physiology (1938) and medicine (1974): No. B1058, Corneille Heymans (1892-1968). No. B1059, A. Claude (1899-1983).

Photogravure and Engraved
1987, Feb. 16   **Perf. 11½**
B1058	SP482	13 + 3fr dk brn & red	.90 .90
B1059	SP482	24 + 6fr dk brn & red	1.65 1.65

1987, Mar. 16   **Photo.**
B1060	SP483	9 + 2fr Bee orchid	.60 .60
B1061	SP483	24 + 6fr Horseshoe bat	1.65 1.65
B1062	SP483	26 + 6fr Peregrine falcon	1.75 1.75
	Nos. B1060-B1062 (3)		4.00 4.00

Castles — SP484

1987, Oct. 17   **Photo. & Engr.**
B1063	SP484	9 + 2fr Rixensart	.60 .60
B1064	SP484	13 + 3fr Westerlo	.90 .90
B1065	SP484	26 + 5fr Fallais	1.75 1.75
B1066	SP484	50 + 12fr Gaasbeek	3.50 3.50
	Nos. B1063-B1066 (4)		6.75 6.75

Christmas 1987 — SP485   White and Yellow Cross of Belgium, 50th Anniv. — SP486

Painting: Holy Family, by Rev. Father Lens.

1987, Nov. 14   **Photo.**
B1067	SP485	13 + 1fr multi	.85 .85

1987, Dec. 5
B1068	SP486	9 + 2fr multi	.70 .70

Promote Philately — SP487

Various flowers from Sixty Roses for a Queen, by P. J. Redoute (1759-1840).

1988, Apr. 25   **Photo.**   **Perf. 11½**
B1069	SP487	13 + 3fr shown	1.00 1.00
B1070	SP487	24 + 6fr multi, diff.	1.75 1.75

Souvenir Sheet
B1071	SP487	50 + 12fr multi, diff.	3.75 3.75

See Nos. B1081-B1083, B1089-B1091, 1346.

1988 Summer Olympics, Seoul — SP488

1988, June 6   **Photo.**   **Perf. 11½**
B1072	SP488	9fr + 2fr Table tennis	.65 .65
B1073	SP488	13fr + 3fr Cycling	.95 .95

Souvenir Sheet
B1074	SP488	50fr + 12fr Marathon runners	3.70 3.70

Solidarity — SP489

1988, Oct. 24   **Photo.**   **Perf. 12x11½**
B1075	SP489	9fr + 2fr Jacques Brel	.60 .60
B1076	SP489	13fr + 3fr Jef Denyn	.90 .90
B1077	SP489	26fr + 6fr Fr. Ferdinand Verbiest	1.75 1.75
	Nos. B1075-B1077 (3)		3.25 3.25

Belgian Red Cross SP490

Paintings: No. B1078, Crucifixion of Christ, by Rogier van der Weyden (c. 1399-1464). No. B1079, Virgin and Child, by David (c. 1460-1523). No. B1089, The Good Samaritan, by Denis van Alsloot.

1989, Feb. 20   **Perf. 11½**
B1078	SP490	9fr + 2fr multi	.60 .60
B1079	SP490	13fr + 3fr multi	.90 .90
B1080	SP490	24fr + 6fr multi	1.65 1.65
	Nos. B1078-B1080 (3)		3.15 3.15

Stamp Collecting Promotion Type of 1988

Various flowers from Sixty Roses for a Queen, by P.J. Redoute (1759-1840) and inscriptions: No. B1081, "Centfeuille unique melee de rouge." No. B1082, "Bengale a grandes feuilles." No. B1083, Aeme vibere (tea roses).

1989, Apr. 7
B1081	SP487	13fr + 5fr multi	1.00 1.00
B1082	SP487	24fr + 6fr multi	1.65 1.65

Souvenir Sheet
B1083	SP487	50fr + 17fr multi	3.75 3.75

Solidarity SP491

Royal Greenhouses of Laeken.

1989, Oct. 23
B1084	SP491	9fr + 3fr Exterior	.60 .60
B1085	SP491	13fr + 4fr Interior, vert.	.85 .85
B1086	SP491	24fr + 5fr Dome exterior, vert.	1.40 1.40
B1087	SP491	26fr + 6fr Dome interior, vert.	1.50 1.50
	Nos. B1084-B1087 (4)		4.35 4.35

B1134 SP511 17fr +4fr multi   1.30 1.30
Souvenir Sheet
B1135 SP511 41fr +9fr multi   3.10 3.10
  Surtax for "Pro-Post" association.

Judo — SP512   Solidarity — SP513

1997, May 5   Photo.   Perf. 11½
B1136 SP512 17fr +4fr Men's (10a) 1.25 1.25
B1137 SP512 17fr +4fr Women's
                         (10b)   1.25 1.25
  Surtax for Belgian Olympic Committee.

1997, Oct. 25
B1138 SP513 17fr +4fr multi   1.25 1.25
  Surtax for Multiple Sclerosis research.

AIR POST STAMPS

Fokker
FVII/3m over
Ostend — AP1

  Designs: 1.50fr, Plane over St. Hubert. 2fr, over
Namur. 5fr, over Brussels.

            Perf. 11½
1930, Apr. 30   Unwmk.   Photo.
C1 AP1 50c blue   .40   .40
C2 AP1 1.50fr black brn   2.25 2.50
C3 AP1 2fr deep green   2.00   .55
C4 AP1 5fr brown lake   1.75   .95
       Nos. C1-C4 (4)   6.40 4.40
              Exist imperf.

1930, Dec. 5
C5 AP1 5fr dark violet   30.00 30.00
  Issued for use on a mail carrying flight from Brus-
sels to Leopoldville, Belgian Congo, starting Dec. 7.
Exists imperf.

Nos. C2 and C4 Surcharged in Carmine or
              Blue

1935, May 23
C6 AP1 1fr on 1.50fr (C)   .55   .40
C7 AP1 4fr on 5fr (Bl)   7.50 7.00

  Catalogue values for unused
  stamps in this section, from this
  point to the end of the section, are
  for Never Hinged items.

DC-4
Skymaster,
Sabena Airline
AP5

1946, Apr. 20   Engr.   Perf. 11½
C8   AP5 6fr blue   .75   .25
C9   AP5 8.50fr violet brn 1.00   .35
C10 AP5 50fr yellow grn   5.00   .60
  a.   Perf. 12x11½ ('54)   325.00 1.00
C11 AP5 100fr gray   8.25   .80
  a.   Perf. 12x11½ ('54)   65.00 1.10
       Nos. C8-C11 (4)   15.00 2.00

Evolution of Postal Transportation — AP6

1949, July 1
C12 AP6 50fr dark brown   42.50 15.00
  Centenary of Belgian postage stamps.

Glider — AP7

  Design: 7fr, "Tipsy" plane.

1951, June 18   Photo.   Perf. 13½
C12A   Strip of 2 + label 70.00 60.00
  b. AP7 6fr dark violet   25.00 17.50
  c. AP7 7fr carmine rose   25.00 17.50
  For the 50th anniv. of the Aero Club of Belgium.
The strip sold for 50fr.

1951, July 25   Perf. 13½
C13 AP7 6fr sepia   4.50   .15
C14 AP7 7fr Prus green   3.50   .95

    UN Types of Regular Issue, 1958
  Designs: 5fr, ICAO. 6fr, World Meteorological
Organization. 7.50fr, Protection of Refugees. 8fr,
General Agreement on Tariffs and Trade. 9fr,
UNICEF. 10fr, Atomic Energy Agency.

                          Perf. 11½
1958, Apr. 17   Unwmk.   Engr.
C15 A137 5fr dull blue   .25   .30
C16 A136 6fr yellow grn   .30   .45
C17 A137 7.50fr lilac   .30   .30
C18 A136 8fr sepia   .30   .30
C19 A137 9fr carmine   .40   .50
C20 A136 10fr redsh brown .75   .60
       Nos. C15-C20 (6)   2.30 2.45
  World's Fair, Brussels, Apr. 17-Oct. 19. See note
after No. 476.

AIR POST SEMI-POSTAL STAMPS

  Catalogue values for unused
  stamps in this section are for Never
  Hinged items.

American Soldier in Combat — SPAP1

            Perf. 11x11½
1946, June 15   Unwmk.   Engr.
CB1 SPAP1 17.50fr + 62.50fr dl brn   1.25 .90
CB2 SPAP1 17.50fr + 62.50fr dl gray
                         grn   1.25 .90
  Surtax for an American memorial at Bastogne.
  An overprint, "Hommage a Roosevelt," was pri-
vately applied to Nos. CB1-CB2 in 1947 by the
Association Belgo-Americaine.
  In 1950 another private overprint was applied, in
red, to Nos. CB1-CB2. It consists of "16-12-1944,
25-1-1945, Dedication July 16, 1950" and outlines
of the American eagle emblem and the Bastogne
Memorial. Similar overprints were applied to Nos.
265 and 345.

Flight Allegory
SPAP2

1946, Sept. 7   Perf. 11½
CB3 SPAP2 2fr + 8fr brt vio   .60 1.00
  The surtax was for the benefit of aviation.

Nos. B417-B425 Surcharged in Various
  Arrangements in Red or Dark Blue
POSTE AERIENNE
LUCHTPOST   +   LUCHTPOST
1F   2F+1F   POSTE AERIENNE
                      +2F

Type I- Top line "POSTE AERIENNE"
Type II- Top line "LUCHTPOST"

1947, May 18   Photo.   Perf. 11½
                Type I
CB4   1fr + 2fr on #B417 (R)   .60   .90
CB5   1.50fr + 2.50fr on #B418   .60   .90
CB6   2fr + 45fr on #B419   .60   .90
CB7   1fr + 2fr on #B420 (R)   .60   .90
CB8   1.50fr + 2.50fr on #B421   .60   .90
CB9   2fr + 45fr on #B422   .60   .90
CB10 1fr + 2fr on #B423 (R)   .60   .90
CB11 1.50fr + 2.50fr on #B424
                         (R)   .60   .90
CB12 2fr + 45fr on #B425   .60   .90
                Type II
CB4A   1fr + 2fr on #B417 (R)   .60   .90
CB5A   1.50fr + 2.50fr on #B418 .60   .90
CB6A   2fr + 45fr on #B419   .60   .90
CB7A   1fr + 2fr on #B420 (R)   .60   .90
CB8A   1.50fr + 2.50fr on #B421 .60   .90
CB9A   2fr + 45fr on #B422   .60   .90
CB10A 1fr + 2fr on #B423 (R)   .60   .90
CB11A 1.50fr + 2.50fr on #B424
                         (R)   .60   .90
CB12A 2fr + 45fr on #B425   .60   .90
       Nos. CB4-CB12A (18)   10.80 16.20
  Issued for CIPEX, NYC. In 1948 Nos. CB4-CB12
and CB4A-CB12A were punched with the letters
"IMABA," and the inscription "Imaba du 21 au 29
aout 1948" was applied to the backs. Value $20.

Helicopter
Leaving Airport
SPAP3

1950, Aug. 7
CB13 SPAP3 7fr + 3fr blue   9.00 5.25
  Surtax for the Natl. Aeronautical Committee.

SPECIAL DELIVERY STAMPS

  From 1874 to 1903 certain hexagonal
telegraph stamps were used as special
delivery stamps.

Town Hall,   Eupen — SD2
Brussels — SD1

  Designs: 2.35fr, Street in Ghent. 3.50fr, Bishop's
Palace, Liege. 5.25fr, Notre Dame Cathedral,
Antwerp.

1929   Unwmk.   Photo.   Perf. 11½
E1 SD1 1.75fr dark blue   .80   .32
E2 SD1 2.35fr carmine   1.50   .45
E3 SD1 3.50fr dark violet 10.00 9.00
E4 SD1 5.25fr olive green 5.50   5.25

1931
E5 SD2 2.45fr dark green   11.00 2.50
       Nos. E1-E5 (5)   28.80 17.52

No. E5 Surcharged in
Red   2Fr50   ✕

1932
E6 SD2 2.50fr on 2.45fr dk grn 9.00 1.25

POSTAGE DUE STAMPS

D1   D2

1870   Unwmk.   Typo.   Perf. 15
J1 D1 10c green   4.50 1.75
J2 D1 20c ultra   32.50 3.50
  In 1909 many bisects of Nos. J1-J2 were created.
The 10c bisect used as 5c on piece sells for $3.50.
No. J2 was also printed in aniline ink on thin
paper. Value about the same.

1895-09   Perf. 14
J3   D2 5c yellow grn   .15   .15
J4   D2 10c orange brn   15.00 1.50
J5   D2 10c carmine ('00)   .15   .15
J6   D2 20c olive green   .15   .15
J7   D2 30c pale blue ('09) .30   .25
J8   D2 50c yellow brn   17.50 4.50
J9   D2 50c gray ('00)   .75   .45
J10 D2 1fr carmine   20.00 13.00
J11 D2 1fr ocher ('00)   6.50 6.00
       Nos. J3-J11 (9)   60.50 26.15

1916   Redrawn
J12 D2 5c blue grn   16.00 7.00
J13 D2 10c carmine   35.00 11.00
J14 D2 20c dp gray grn   35.00 15.00
J15 D2 30c brt blue   6.00 5.00
J16 D2 50c gray   100.00 60.00
       Nos. J12-J16 (5)   192.00 98.00
  In the redrawn stamps the lions have a heavy,
colored outline. There is a thick vertical line at the
outer edge of the design on each side.

D3   D4

1919   Perf. 14
J17 D3 5c green   .40   .50
J18 D3 10c carmine   .95   .40
J19 D3 20c gray green   7.25 1.25
J20 D3 30c bright blue   1.40   .40
J21 D3 50c gray   2.75   .50
       Nos. J17-J21 (5)   12.75 3.05

1922-32
J22 D4 5c dk gray   .15   .15
J23 D4 10c green   .15   .15
J24 D4 20c deep brown   .15   .15
J25 D4 30c ver ('24)   .65   .15
  a.   30c rose red   1.00   .45
J26 D4 40c red brn ('25)   .25   .15
J27 D4 50c ultra   1.90   .15
J28 D4 70c red brn ('29)   .30   .15
J29 D4 1fr violet ('25)   .45   .15
J30 D4 1fr rose lilac ('32) .55 .15
J31 D4 1.20fr ol grn ('29) .65   .45
J32 D4 1.50fr ol grn ('29) .65   .45
J33 D4 2fr violet ('29)   .75   .20
J34 D4 3.50fr dp blue ('29) 1.00 .25
       Nos. J22-J34 (13)   7.60
       Set value   2.25

1934-46   Perf. 14x13½
J35   D4 35c green ('35)   .40   .45
J36   D4 50c slate   .20   .15
J37   D4 60c carmine ('38) .40   .30
J38   D4 80c slate ('38)   .30   .15
J39   D4 1.40fr gray ('35) .65   .45
J39A D4 3fr org brn ('46) 1.50   .60
J39B D4 7fr brt red vio ('46) 2.25 3.25
       Nos. J35-J39B (7)   5.70 5.35
       See Nos. J54-J61.

  Catalogue values for unused
  stamps in this section, from this
  point to the end of the section, are
  for Never Hinged items.

D5   D6

1945   Typo.   *Perf. 12¹/₂*
Inscribed "TE BETALEN" at Top

J40	D5	10c gray olive	.15	.15
J41	D5	20c ultramarine	.15	.15
J42	D5	30c carmine	.15	.15
J43	D5	40c black violet	.15	.15
J44	D5	50c dl bl grn	.15	.15
J45	D5	1fr sepia	.15	.15
J46	D5	2fr red orange	.15	.15

Inscribed "A PAYER" at Top

J47	D5	10c gray olive	.15	.15
J48	D5	20c ultramarine	.15	.15
J49	D5	30c carmine	.15	.15
J50	D5	40c black vio	.15	.15
J51	D5	50c dl bl grn	.15	.15
J52	D5	1fr sepia	.15	.15
J53	D5	2fr red orange	.15	.15
		Set value	1.75	1.75

Type of 1922-32

1949-53   Typo.   *Perf. 14x13¹/₂*

J54	D4	65c emerald	7.00	3.75
J55	D4	1.60fr lilac rose ('53)	14.00	6.50
J56	D4	1.80fr red	15.00	6.50
J57	D4	2.40fr gray lilac ('53)	9.00	4.00
J58	D4	4fr deep blue ('53)	11.00	.50
J59	D4	5fr red brown	3.50	.40
J60	D4	8fr lilac rose	7.25	3.75
J61	D4	10fr dark violet	7.25	3.75
		Nos. J54-J61 (8)	74.00	29.15

Numerals 6¹/₂mm or More High

1966-70   Photo.

J62	D6	1fr brt pink	.15	.15
J63	D6	2fr blue green	.15	.15
J64	D6	3fr blue	.15	.15
J65	D6	5fr purple	.25	.15
J66	D6	6fr bister brn	.40	.25
J67	D6	7fr red org ('70)	.45	.30
J68	D6	20fr slate grn	1.50	1.00
		Nos. J62-J68 (7)	3.05	2.15

Printed on various papers.

Numerals 4¹/₂-5¹/₂mm High

1985-87   Photo.   *Perf. 14x13¹/₂*

J69	D6	1fr lilac rose	.15	.15
J70	D6	2fr dull blue grn	.15	.15
J71	D6	3fr greenish blue	.15	.15
J72	D6	4fr green	.20	.15
J73	D6	5fr lt violet	.25	.20
J74	D6	7fr brt orange	.35	.30
J75	D6	8fr pale gray	.40	.30
J76	D6	9fr rose lake	.45	.35
J77	D6	10fr lt red brown	.50	.40
J78	D6	20fr lt olive grn	1.10	1.10
		Nos. J69-J78 (10)	3.70	3.25

Printed on various papers.
Issue dates: 3fr, 4fr, 8fr-10fr, Mar. 25, 1985. 2fr, 20fr, 1986. 1fr, 5fr, 7fr, 1987.
This is an expanding set. Numbers will change again if necessary.

MILITARY STAMPS

> Catalogue values for unused stamps in this section are for Never Hinged items.

King Baudouin
M1   M2

1967, July 17   Photo.   *Perf. 11*
Unwmk.
M1   M1   1.50fr greenish gray   .25   .25

1971-75   Engr.   *Perf. 11¹/₂*

M2	M2	1.75fr green	.50	.45
M3	M2	2.25fr gray green ('72)	.30	.30
M4	M2	2.50fr gray green ('74)	.20	.20
M5	M2	3.25fr vio brown ('75)	.25	.20
		Nos. M2-M5 (4)	1.25	1.15

#M1-M3 are luminescent, #M4-M5 are not.

MILITARY PARCEL POST STAMP

Type of Parcel Post Stamp of 1938 Surcharged with New Value and "M" in Blue.

1939   Unwmk.   *Perf. 13¹/₂*
MQ1   PP19   3fr on 5.50fr copper red   .30   .20

OFFICIAL STAMPS

For franking the official correspondence of the Administration of the Belgian National Railways.

Counterfeits exist of Nos. O1-O25.

Regular Issue of 1921-27 Overprinted in Black

1929-30   Unwmk.   *Perf. 14*

O1	A58	5c gray	.20	.20
O2	A58	10c blue green	.30	.40
O3	A58	35c blue green	.40	.30
O4	A58	60c olive green	.45	.30
O5	A58	1.50fr brt blue	8.00	6.25
O6	A58	1.75fr ultra ('30)	1.75	2.00
		Nos. O1-O6 (6)	11.10	9.45

Same Overprint, in Red or Black, on Regular Issues of 1929-30

1929-31

O7	A63	5c slate (R)	.25	.35
O8	A63	10c olive grn (R)	.50	.40
O9	A63	25c rose red (Bk)	1.50	.85
O10	A63	35c dp green (R)	1.75	.50
O11	A63	40c red vio (Bk)	1.25	.45
O12	A63	50c dp blue (R) ('31)	.80	.35
O13	A63	60c rose (Bk)	6.00	6.00
O14	A63	70c orange brn (Bk)	4.25	1.25
O15	A63	75c black vio (R) ('31)	4.00	.85
		Nos. O7-O15 (9)	20.30	11.00

Overprinted on Regular Issue of 1932

1932

O16	A73	10c olive grn (R)	.55	.60
O17	A74	35c dp green	9.00	.75
O18	A71a	75c bister brn (R)	1.50	.30
		Nos. O16-O18 (3)	11.05	1.65

Overprinted on No. 262 in Red

1935   *Perf. 13¹/₂x14*
O19   A80   70c olive black   2.75   .25

Regular Stamps of 1935-36 Overprinted in Red

1936-38   *Perf. 13¹/₂, 13¹/₂x14, 14*

O20	A82	10c olive bister	.15	.35
O21	A82	35c green	.25	.40
O22	A82	50c dark blue	.45	.35
O23	A83	70c brown	1.50	.65

Overprinted in Black or Red on Regular Issue of 1938
Perf. 13¹/₂x14

O24	A82	40c red violet (Bk)	.30	.35
O25	A85	75c olive gray (R)	.65	.30
		Nos. O20-O25 (6)	3.30	2.40

Regular Issues of 1935-41 Overprinted in Red or Dark Blue

1941-44   *Perf. 14, 14x13¹/₂, 13¹/₂x14*

O26	A82	10c olive bister	.15	.15
	a.	Inverted overprint		40.00
O27	A82	40c red violet	.55	.75
O28	A82	50c dark blue	.15	.15
	a.	Inverted overprint		
O29	A83a	1fr rose car (Bl)	.45	.35
O30	A85	1fr rose pink (Bl)	.15	.15
O31	A83a	2.25fr grnsh blk ('44)	.30	.50
O32	A84	2.25fr gray violet	.45	.70
		Nos. O26-O32 (7)	2.20	2.75

Nos. O21, O23 and O25 Surcharged with New Values in Black or Red

1942

O33	A82	10c on 35c green	.20	.35
O34	A83	50c on 70c brown	.15	.20
O35	A85	50c on 75c ol gray (R)	.15	.20
		Nos. O33-O35 (3)	.50	.75

> Catalogue values for unused stamps in this section, from this point to the end of the section, are for Never Hinged items.

O1   O2

1946-48   Unwmk.   *Perf. 14*

O36	O1	10c olive bister	.25	.15
O37	O1	20c brt violet	2.00	.50
O38	O1	50c dk blue	.25	.15
O39	O1	65c red lilac ('48)	3.25	.75
O40	O1	75c lilac rose	.25	.20
O41	O1	90c brown violet	4.25	.35
		Nos. O36-O41 (6)	10.25	2.10

Types A99, A101 and A102 with "B" Emblem Added to Design

1948   *Perf. 11¹/₂*

O42	A99	1.35fr red brown	4.25	.75
O43	A99	1.75fr dk gray green	4.75	.25
O44	A101	3fr brt red violet	25.00	3.50
O45	A102	3.15fr deep blue	11.00	7.00
O46	A102	4fr brt ultra	20.00	13.00
		Nos. O42-O46 (5)	65.00	24.50

1953-66   Typo.   *Perf. 13¹/₂x14*

O47	O2	10c orange	.65	.15
O48	O2	20c red lilac	.80	.25
O49	O2	30c gray green ('58)	.80	.55
O50	O2	40c olive gray	.50	.15
O51	O2	50c light blue	.75	.15
O51A	O2	60c lilac rose ('66)	1.10	.55
O52	O2	65c red lilac	27.50	21.00
O53	O2	80c emerald	4.50	.70
O54	O2	90c deep blue	6.00	.85
O55	O2	1fr rose	.40	.15
		Nos. O47-O55 (10)	43.00	24.50

See Nos. O66, O68.

King Baudouin
O3   O4

1954-70   Photo.   *Perf. 11¹/₂*

O56	O3	1.50fr gray	.30	.15
O57	O3	2fr rose red	37.50	.15
O58	O3	2fr blue grn ('59)	.30	.15
O59	O3	2.50fr red brown ('58)	27.50	.15
O60	O3	3fr red lilac ('58)	1.25	.15
O61	O3	3.50fr yel green ('70)	.75	.15
O62	O3	4fr brt blue	.90	.25
O63	O3	6fr car rose ('58)	1.50	.60
		Nos. O56-O63 (8)	70.00	2.45

Type of 1953-66 Redrawn

1970-75   Typo.   *Perf. 13¹/₂x14*

O66	O2	1.50fr grnsh gray ('75)	.20	.15
O68	O2	2.50fr brown	.20	.15
		Set value		.20

1971-73   Engr.   *Perf. 11¹/₂*

O71	O4	3.50fr org brn ('73)	.25	.25
O72	O4	4.50fr brown ('73)	.25	.25
O73	O4	7fr red	.40	.50
O74	O4	15fr violet	.75	.30
		Nos. O71-O74 (4)	1.65	1.30

Nos. O71-O74 are on luminescent paper.

1974-80

O75	O4	3fr yellow grn	1.50	1.00
O76	O4	4fr blue	1.50	.50
O77	O4	4.50fr grnsh bl ('75)	.30	.15
O78	O4	5fr lilac	.30	.15
O79	O4	6fr carmine ('78)	.35	.20
O80	O4	6.50fr black ('76)	.40	.35
O81	O4	8fr bluish blk ('78)	.50	.20
O82	O4	9fr lt red brn ('80)	.55	.25
O83	O4	10fr rose carmine	.60	.25
O84	O4	25fr lilac ('76)	1.50	.50
O85	O4	30fr org brn ('78)	1.75	.50
		Nos. O75-O85 (11)	9.25	4.10

Heraldic Lion — O5

1977-82   Typo.   *Perf. 13¹/₂x14*

O87	O5	50c brown ('82)	.15	.15
O92	O5	1fr lilac ('82)	.15	.15
O94	O5	2fr orange ('82)	.20	.15

O95	O5	4fr red brown	.25	.20
O96	O5	5fr green ('80)	.25	.25
		Set value	.85	.80

NEWSPAPER STAMPS

Counterfeits exist of Nos. P1-P40.

Parcel Post Stamps of 1923-27 Overprinted **JOURNAUX DAGBLADEN 1928**

Perf. 14¹/₂x14, 14x14¹/₂

1928   Unwmk.

P1	PP12	10c vermilion	.25	.40
P2	PP12	20c turq blue	.25	.40
P3	PP12	40c olive grn	.25	.40
P4	PP12	60c orange	.70	.90
P5	PP12	70c dk brown	.45	.40
P6	PP12	80c violet	.60	.70
P7	PP12	90c slate	2.25	2.00
P8	PP13	1fr brt blue	.90	.60
a.		1fr ultramarine	12.00	5.00
P10	PP13	2fr olive grn	1.50	.60
P11	PP13	3fr orange red	1.65	.90
P12	PP13	4fr rose	2.25	1.10
P13	PP13	5fr violet	2.25	1.00
P14	PP13	6fr bister brn	4.50	1.75
P15	PP13	7fr orange	5.00	2.25
P16	PP13	8fr dk brown	6.00	2.75
P17	PP13	9fr red violet	10.00	3.00
P18	PP13	10fr blue green	9.00	2.75
P19	PP13	20fr magenta	15.00	7.00
		Nos. P1-P8,P10-P19 (18)	62.80	28.90

Parcel Post Stamps of 1923-28 Overprinted **JOURNAUX DAGBLADEN**

1929-31

P20	PP12	10c vermilion	.25	.20
P21	PP12	20c turq blue	.25	.20
P22	PP12	40c olive green	.30	.20
a.		Inverted overprint		
P23	PP12	60c orange	.55	.35
P24	PP12	70c dk brown	.55	.20
P25	PP12	80c violet	.60	.25
P26	PP12	90c gray	2.00	1.00
P27	PP13	1fr ultra	.60	.25
a.		1fr bright blue	4.00	2.50
P28	PP13	1.10fr org brn ('31)	6.25	1.40
P29	PP13	1.50fr gray vio ('31)	6.25	1.90
P30	PP13	2fr olive green	2.00	.25
P31	PP13	2.10fr sl gray ('31)	17.00	12.00
P32	PP13	3fr orange red	2.25	.45
P33	PP13	4fr rose	2.25	.70
P34	PP13	5fr violet	3.00	.55
P35	PP13	6fr bister brn	3.75	1.00
P36	PP13	7fr orange	3.75	1.00
P37	PP13	8fr dk brown	3.75	1.10
P38	PP13	9fr red violet	5.25	1.50
P39	PP13	10fr blue green	3.75	1.10
P40	PP13	20fr magenta	13.00	4.50
		Nos. P20-P40 (21)	77.35	30.10

PARCEL POST AND RAILWAY STAMPS

> Values for used Railway Stamps (Chemins de Fer) stamps are for copies with railway cancellations. Railway Stamps with postal cancellations sell for twice as much.

Coat of Arms — PP1

1879-82   Unwmk.   Typo.   *Perf. 14*

Q1	PP1	10c violet brown	40.00	5.00
Q2	PP1	20c blue	125.00	17.00
Q3	PP1	25c green ('81)	165.00	10.00
Q4	PP1	50c carmine	1,250.	10.00
Q5	PP1	80c yellow	1,300.	57.50
Q6	PP1	1fr gray ('82)	125.00	16.00

Used copies of Nos. Q1-Q6 with pinholes, a normal state, sell for approximately one third the values given.

Most of the stamps of 1882-1902 (Nos. Q7 to Q28) are without watermark. Twice in each sheet of 100 stamps they have one of three watermarks: (1) A winged wheel and "Chemins de Fer de l'Etat Belge," (2) Coat of Arms of Belgium and "Royaume de Belgique," (3) Larger Coat of Arms, without inscription.

PP2

		1882-94		Perf. 15½x14½	
Q7	PP2	10c brown ('86)		20.00	1.25
Q8	PP2	15c gray ('94)		8.00	6.50
Q9	PP2	20c blue ('86)		65.00	2.50
a.		20c ultra ('90)		70.00	3.00
Q10	PP2	25c yel grn ('91)		65.00	3.75
a.		25c blue green ('87)		65.00	3.50
Q11	PP2	50c carmine		70.00	.65
Q12	PP2	80c brnsh buff		70.00	.75
Q13	PP2	80c lemon		75.00	1.75
Q14	PP2	1fr lavender		350.00	2.25
Q15	PP2	2fr yel buff ('94)		210.00	65.00

Counterfeits exist.

PP3

Name of engraver below frame

1895-97

Numerals in Black, except 1fr, 2fr

Q16	PP3	10c red brown ('96)	11.00	.55
Q17	PP3	15c gray	11.00	7.00
Q18	PP3	20c blue	17.50	.90
Q19	PP3	25c green	17.50	1.25
Q20	PP3	50c carmine	25.00	.55
Q21	PP3	60c violet ('96)	50.00	1.00
Q22	PP3	80c ol yel ('96)	50.00	1.00
Q23	PP3	1fr lilac brown	165.00	2.25
Q24	PP3	2fr yel buff ('97)	200.00	15.00

Counterfeits exist.

1902

Numerals in Black

Q25	PP3	30c orange	21.00	2.00
Q26	PP3	40c green	26.00	1.75
Q27	PP3	70c blue	50.00	1.00
a.		Numerals omitted	750.00	
b.		Numerals printed on reverse	750.00	
Q28	PP3	90c red	65.00	1.65
		Nos. Q25-CQ28 (4)	162.00	6.40

Winged Wheel — PP4

Without engraver's name

		1902-14		Perf. 15	
Q29	PP3	10c yel brn & slate		.15	.15
Q30	PP3	15c slate & vio		.20	.15
Q31	PP3	20c ultra & yel brn		.15	.15
Q32	PP3	25c yel grn & red		.20	.15
Q33	PP3	30c orange & bl grn		.20	.15
Q34	PP3	35c bister & bl grn ('12)		.35	.20
Q35	PP3	40c blue grn & vio		.20	.15
Q36	PP3	50c pale rose & vio		.15	.15
Q37	PP3	55c lilac brn & ultra ('14)		.35	.20
Q38	PP3	60c violet & red		.20	.15
Q39	PP3	70c blue & red		.15	.15
Q40	PP3	80c lemon & vio brn		.15	.15
Q41	PP3	90c red & yel grn		.20	.15
Q42	PP4	1fr vio brn & org		.20	.15
Q43	PP4	1.10fr rose & blk ('06)		.20	.15
Q44	PP4	2fr ocher & bl grn		.20	.15
Q45	PP4	3fr black & ultra		.35	.20
Q46	PP4	4fr yel grn & red ('13)		1.25	.70
Q47	PP4	5fr org & bl grn ('13)		.55	.55
Q48	PP4	10fr ol yel & brn vio ('13)		.90	.55
		Nos. Q29-Q48 (20)		6.30	
		Set value			3.70

Exist imperforate.

Regular Issues of 1912-13 Handstamped in Violet

		1915		Perf. 14	
Q49	A42	5c green		165.00	165.00
Q50	A43	10c red		800.00	800.00
Q51	A45	10c red		175.00	175.00
a.		With engraver's name		750.00	750.00
Q52	A43	20c olive grn		1,200.	1,200.
Q53	A45	20c olive grn		200.00	200.00
a.		With engraver's name		750.00	750.00
Q54	A45	25c ultra		200.00	200.00
a.		With engraver's name		750.00	750.00
Q55	A43	35c bister brn		250.00	250.00
Q55A	A43	40c green		1,750.	1,750.
Q56	A43	40c green		250.00	250.00
Q57	A43	50c gray		250.00	250.00
Q58	A43	1fr orange		200.00	200.00
Q59	A43	2fr violet		1,650.	1,650.
Q60	A44	5fr plum		3,500.	3,500.

Excellent forgeries of this overprint exist.

PP5   PP6

		1916	Litho.	Perf. 13½	
Q61	PP5	10c pale blue		1.10	.20
Q62	PP5	15c olive grn		1.40	.50
Q63	PP5	20c red		2.25	.50
Q64	PP5	25c lt brown		2.25	.50
Q65	PP5	30c lilac		1.40	.45
Q66	PP5	35c gray		1.40	.45
Q67	PP5	40c orange yel		3.00	1.50
Q68	PP5	50c bister		2.25	.45
Q69	PP5	55c brown		3.00	2.25
Q70	PP5	60c gray vio		2.25	.45
Q71	PP5	70c green		2.25	.45
Q72	PP5	80c red brown		2.25	.45
Q73	PP5	90c blue		2.25	.45
Q74	PP6	1fr gray		2.25	.45
Q75	PP6	1.10fr ultra (Franken)		27.50	21.00
Q76	PP6	2fr red		25.00	.45
Q77	PP6	3fr violet		25.00	.45
Q78	PP6	4fr emerald		45.00	1.50
Q79	PP6	5fr brown		45.00	3.00
Q80	PP6	10fr orange		45.00	1.50
		Nos. Q61-Q80 (20)		241.80	36.95

Type of 1916 Inscribed "FRANK" instead of "FRANKEN"

1920

Q81	PP6	1.10fr ultra	2.00	.45

PP7   PP8

		1920		Perf. 14	
Q82	PP7	10c blue grn		1.75	.75
Q83	PP7	15c olive grn		1.75	1.10
Q84	PP7	20c red		1.75	.75
Q85	PP7	25c gray brn		2.50	.75
Q86	PP7	30c red vio		27.00	22.50
Q87	PP7	40c pale org		11.00	.75
Q88	PP7	50c bister		9.00	.75
Q89	PP7	55c pale brown		5.50	4.50
Q90	PP7	60c dk violet		10.00	.75
Q91	PP7	70c green		18.00	1.10
Q92	PP7	80c red brown		40.00	1.50
Q93	PP7	90c dull blue		10.00	.75
Q94	PP7	1fr gray		85.00	1.50
Q95	PP8	1.10fr ultra		26.00	2.00
Q96	PP8	1.20fr dk green		11.00	.75
Q97	PP8	1.40fr black brn		11.00	.45
Q98	PP8	2fr vermilion		110.00	1.25
Q99	PP8	3fr red vio		120.00	.85
Q100	PP8	4fr yel grn		120.00	.75
Q101	PP8	5fr bister brn		120.00	.75
Q102	PP8	10fr brown org		120.00	.75
		Nos. Q82-Q102 (21)		861.25	45.30

PP9   PP10

Types PP7 and PP9 differ in the position of the wheel and the tablet above it.
Types PP8 and PP10 differ in the bars below "FR."
There are many other variations in the designs.

		1920-21		Typo.	
Q103	PP9	10c carmine		.30	.15
Q104	PP9	15c yel grn		.30	.15
Q105	PP9	20c blue grn		.70	.20
Q106	PP9	25c ultra		.65	.20
Q107	PP9	30c chocolate		.85	.20
Q108	PP9	35c orange brn		.90	.30
Q109	PP9	40c orange		1.10	.15
Q110	PP9	50c rose		1.10	.15
Q111	PP9	55c yel ('21)		4.50	3.25
Q112	PP9	60c dull rose		1.10	.20
Q113	PP9	70c emerald		3.00	.40
Q114	PP9	80c violet		2.25	.15
Q115	PP9	90c lemon		37.50	21.00
Q116	PP9	90c claret		4.50	.40
Q117	PP10	1fr buff		4.50	.35
Q118	PP10	1fr red brown		4.00	.30
Q119	PP10	1.10fr ultra		1.65	.45
Q120	PP10	1.20fr orange		6.25	.30
Q121	PP10	1.40fr yellow		10.00	1.75
Q122	PP10	1.60fr turq blue		18.00	.70
Q123	PP10	1.60fr emerald		40.00	.70
Q124	PP10	2fr pale rose		26.00	.30
Q125	PP10	3fr dp rose		24.00	.30
Q126	PP10	4fr emerald		24.00	.30
Q127	PP10	5fr lt violet		17.50	.30
Q128	PP10	10fr lemon		110.00	9.00
Q129	PP10	10fr dk brown		22.50	.30
Q130	PP10	15fr dp rose ('21)		22.50	.30
Q131	PP10	20fr dk blue ('21)		325.00	3.00
		Nos. Q103-Q131 (29)		714.65	45.25

PP11

		1922	Engr.	Perf. 11½	
Q132	PP11	2fr black		4.00	.15
Q133	PP11	3fr brown		37.50	.20
Q134	PP11	4fr green		9.00	.15
Q135	PP11	5r claret		9.00	.15
Q136	PP11	10fr yel brown		10.00	.15
Q137	PP11	15fr rose red		10.00	.25
Q138	PP11	20fr blue		67.50	.25
		Nos. Q132-Q138 (7)		147.00	1.30

PP12

PP13

Perf. 14x13½, 13½x14

		1923-40		Typo.	
Q139	PP12	5c red brown		.20	.25
Q140	PP12	10c vermilion		.15	.15
Q141	PP12	15c ultra		.20	.30
Q142	PP12	20c turq blue		.15	.15
Q143	PP12	30c brn vio ('27)		.20	.15
Q144	PP12	40c olive grn		.15	.15
Q145	PP12	50c magenta ('27)		.20	.15
Q146	PP12	60c orange		.25	.15
Q147	PP12	70c dk brown ('24)		.15	.15
Q148	PP12	80c violet		.15	.15
Q149	PP12	90c slate ('27)		1.25	.15
Q150	PP13	1fr gray		.35	.15
Q151	PP13	1fr brt blue ('28)		.55	.15
Q152	PP13	1.10fr orange		3.00	.30
Q153	PP13	1.50fr turq blue		3.25	.30
Q154	PP13	1.70fr dp brown ('31)		.75	.60
Q155	PP13	1.80fr claret		4.25	.60
Q156	PP13	2fr olive grn ('24)		.35	.20
Q157	PP13	2.10fr gray grn		7.50	.85

Q158	PP13	2.40fr dp violet		4.00	.85
Q159	PP13	2.70fr gray ('24)		12.00	.75
Q160	PP13	3fr orange red		.45	.15
Q161	PP13	3.30fr brown ('24)		12.50	.75
Q162	PP13	4fr rose ('24)		.55	.15
Q163	PP13	5fr violet ('24)		.90	.15
Q163A	PP13	5fr brn vio ('40)		.45	.30
Q164	PP13	6fr bis brn ('27)		.50	.15
Q165	PP13	7fr orange ('27)		.90	.15
Q166	PP13	8fr dp brown ('27)		.75	.15
Q167	PP13	9fr red vio ('27)		2.50	.15
Q168	PP13	10fr blue grn ('27)		1.10	.15
Q168A	PP13	10fr black ('40)		4.00	3.75
Q169	PP13	20fr magenta ('27)		1.90	.15
Q170	PP13	30fr turq green ('31)		6.00	.40
Q171	PP13	40fr gray ('31)		55.00	.75
Q172	PP13	50fr bister ('27)		9.00	.30
		Nos. Q139-Q172 (36)		135.65	
		Set value			7.75

See Nos. Q239-Q262. For overprints see Nos. Q216-Q238. Stamps overprinted "Bagages Reisgoed" are revenues.

No. Q158 Surcharged

1924

Green Surcharge

Q173	PP34	2.30fr on 2.40fr violet	3.00	.50
a.		Inverted surcharge	57.50	

Type of Regular Issue of 1926-27 Overprinted

		1928		Perf. 14	
Q174	A61	4fr buff		6.50	.90
Q175	A61	5fr bister		6.50	1.10

Central P.O., Brussels
PP15

		1929-30	Engr.	Perf. 11½	
Q176	PP15	3fr black brn		1.40	.20
Q177	PP15	4fr gray		1.40	.20
Q178	PP15	5fr carmine		1.40	.20
Q179	PP15	6fr vio brn ('30)		22.50	25.00
		Nos. Q176-Q179 (4)		26.70	25.60

No. Q179 Surcharged in Blue

1933

Q180	PP15	4(fr) on 6fr vio brn	25.00	.25

Modern Locomotive
PP16

		1934	Photo.	Perf. 13½x14	
Q181	PP16	3fr dk green		15.00	2.25
Q182	PP16	4fr red violet		4.00	.20
Q183	PP16	5fr dp rose		14.00	.20
		Nos. Q181-Q183 (3)		33.00	2.65
		Set, never hinged		150.00	

Modern Railroad Train — PP17

Old Railroad Train — PP18

1935 Engr. Perf. 14x13½, 13½x14

Q184	PP17	10c rose car	.30	.15
Q185	PP17	20c violet	.35	.15
Q186	PP17	30c black brn	.45	.30
Q187	PP17	40c dk blue	.55	.15
Q188	PP17	50c orange red	.55	.15
Q189	PP17	60c green	.65	.15
Q190	PP17	70c ultra	.70	.15
Q191	PP17	80c olive blk	.65	.15
Q192	PP17	90c rose lake	.85	.45
Q193	PP18	1fr brown vio	.85	.15
Q194	PP18	2fr gray blk	2.00	.15
Q195	PP18	3fr red org	2.50	.15
Q196	PP18	4fr violet brn	3.00	.15
Q197	PP18	5fr plum	3.25	.15
Q198	PP18	6fr dp green	3.50	.15
Q199	PP18	7fr dp violet	17.00	.15
Q200	PP18	8fr olive blk	17.00	.20
Q201	PP18	9fr dk blue	17.00	.15
Q202	PP18	10fr car lake	17.00	.15
Q203	PP18	20fr green	90.00	.20
Q204	PP18	30fr violet	90.00	2.00
Q205	PP18	40fr black brn	90.00	2.50
Q206	PP18	50fr rose car	100.00	2.00
Q207	PP18	100fr ultra	250.00	45.00
		Nos. Q184-Q207 (24)	708.15	55.05
		Set, never hinged	1,750.	

Centenary of Belgian State Railway.

Winged Wheel — PP19

Surcharge in Red or Blue

1938 Photo. Perf. 13½

Q208	PP19	5fr on 3.50fr dk grn	6.50	.45
Q209	PP19	5fr on 4.50fr rose vio (Bl)	.15	.15
Q210	PP19	6fr on 5.50fr cop red (Bl)	.35	.15
a.		Half used as 3fr on piece		1.50
		Nos. Q208-Q210 (3)	7.00	
		Set, never hinged	50.00	
		Set value		.60

See Nos. MQ1, Q297-Q299.

Symbolizing Unity Achieved Through Railroads PP20

1939 Engr. Perf. 13½x14

Q211	PP20	20c redsh brn	3.50	3.75
Q212	PP20	50c vio bl	3.50	3.75
Q213	PP20	2fr rose red	3.50	3.75
Q214	PP20	9fr slate grn	3.50	3.75
Q215	PP20	10fr dk vio	3.50	3.75
		Nos. Q211-Q215 (5)	17.50	18.75
		Set, never hinged	22.50	

Issued in commemoration of the Railroad Exposition and Congress held at Brussels.

Parcel Post Stamps of 1925-27 Overprinted in Blue or Carmine

Perf. 14½x14, 14x14½

1940 Unwmk.

Q216	PP12	10c vermilion	.15	.15
Q217	PP12	20c turq bl (C)	.15	.15
Q218	PP12	30c brn vio	.15	.15
Q219	PP12	40c ol grn (C)	.15	.15
Q220	PP12	50c magenta	.15	.15
Q221	PP12	60c orange	.15	.15
Q222	PP12	70c dk brn	.15	.25
Q223	PP12	80c vio (C)	.15	.15
Q224	PP12	90c slate (C)	.25	.15
Q225	PP13	1fr ultra (C)	.25	.15
Q226	PP13	2fr ol grn (C)	.25	.15
Q227	PP13	3fr org red	.25	.15
Q228	PP13	4fr rose	.25	.15
Q229	PP13	5fr vio (C)	.25	.15
Q230	PP13	6fr bis brn	.35	.25
Q231	PP13	7fr orange	.35	.15
Q232	PP13	8fr dp grn	.35	.15

Q233	PP13	9fr red vio	.35	.15
Q234	PP13	10fr bl grn (C)	.35	.25
Q235	PP13	20fr magenta	.60	.25
Q236	PP13	30fr turq grn (C)	1.10	.75
Q237	PP13	40fr gray (C)	1.40	2.00
Q238	PP13	50fr bister	1.65	1.10
		Nos. Q216-Q238 (23)	9.20	7.35
		Set, never hinged	16.00	

Types of 1923-40

1941

Q239	PP12	10c dl olive	.15	.15
Q240	PP12	20c lt vio	.15	.15
Q241	PP12	30c fawn	.15	.15
Q242	PP12	40c dull blue	.15	.15
Q243	PP12	50c lt grn	.15	.15
Q244	PP12	60c gray	.15	.15
Q245	PP12	70c chalky grn	.15	.15
Q246	PP12	80c orange	.15	.15
Q247	PP12	90c rose lilac	.15	.15
Q248	PP13	1fr lt yel grn	.15	.15
Q249	PP13	2fr vio brn	.40	.15
Q250	PP13	3fr slate	.45	.15
Q251	PP13	4fr dl olive	.50	.15
Q252	PP13	5fr rose lilac	.50	.15
Q253	PP13	5fr black	.80	.15
Q254	PP13	6fr org ver	.75	.30
Q255	PP13	7fr lilac	.75	.15
Q256	PP13	8fr chalky grn	.75	.15
Q257	PP13	9fr blue	.90	.15
Q258	PP13	10fr rose lilac	.90	.15
Q259	PP13	20fr milky blue	2.00	.15
Q260	PP13	30fr orange	4.50	.35
Q261	PP13	40fr rose	5.00	.35
Q262	PP13	50fr brt red vio	6.75	.15
		Nos. Q239-Q262 (24)	26.45	4.30
		Set, never hinged	90.00	

Adjusting Tie Plates — PP21

Engineer at Throttle — PP22

Freight Station Interior — PP23

Signal and Electric Train — PP24

1942 Engr. Perf. 14x13½

Q263	PP21	9.20fr red org	.60	.80
Q264	PP22	12.30fr dp grn	.60	.85
Q265	PP23	14.30fr dk car	.85	1.25

Perf. 11½

Q266	PP24	100fr ultra	20.00	17.00
		Nos. Q263-Q266 (4)	22.05	19.90
		Set, never hinged	25.00	

Catalogue values for unused stamps in this section, from this point to the end of the section, are for Never Hinged items.

PP25 PP26

PP27

1945-46		**Photo.**	**Unwmk.**	
Q267	PP25	10c ol blk ('46)	.30	.15
Q268	PP25	20c dp vio	.30	.15
Q269	PP25	30c chnt brn ('46)	.30	.15
Q270	PP25	40c dp bl ('46)	.30	.15
Q271	PP25	50c peacock grn	.30	.15
Q272	PP25	60c blk	.30	.15
Q273	PP25	70c emer ('46)	.45	.15
Q274	PP25	80c orange	.75	.20
Q275	PP25	90c brn vio ('46)	.30	.25
Q276	PP26	1fr bl grn ('46)	.30	.15
Q277	PP26	2fr blk brn	.30	.15
Q278	PP26	3fr grnsh blk ('46)	2.00	.20
Q279	PP26	4fr dark blue	.45	.20
Q280	PP26	5fr sepia	.45	.15
Q281	PP26	6fr dl ol grn ('46)	2.25	.15
Q282	PP26	7fr dk vio ('46)	.75	.25
Q283	PP26	8fr red org	.75	.15
Q284	PP26	9fr dp bl ('46)	.90	.15
Q285	PP27	10fr dk red ('46)	3.25	.15
Q286	PP27	10fr sepia ('46)	1.65	.25
Q287	PP27	20fr dk yel grn ('46)	.75	.15
Q288	PP27	30fr dp vio	1.00	.15
Q289	PP27	40fr rose pink	.90	.15
Q290	PP27	50fr brt bl ('46)	12.00	.15
		Nos. Q267-Q290 (24)	31.00	
		Set value		3.00

Mercury — PP28

1945-46 Perf. 13½x13

Q291	PP28	3fr emer ('46)	.25	.25
Q292	PP28	5fr ultra	.15	.15
Q293	PP28	6fr red	.15	.15

Inscribed "Belgique-Belgie"

Q294	PP28	3fr emer ('46)	.25	.25
Q295	PP28	5fr ultra	.15	.15
Q296	PP28	6fr red	.15	.15
		Nos. Q291-Q296 (6)	1.10	1.10

Winged Wheel Type of 1938
Carmine Surcharge

1946 Perf. 13½x14

Q297	PP19	8fr on 5.50fr brn	.65	.15
Q298	PP19	10fr on 5.50fr dk bl	.75	.20
Q299	PP19	12fr on 5.50fr vio	1.10	.20
		Nos. Q297-Q299 (3)	2.50	.55

Railway Crossing PP29

1947 Engr. Perf. 12½

Q300	PP29	100fr dark green	7.00	.25

Crossbowman with Train — PP30

1947 Photo. Perf. 11½

Q301	PP30	8fr dark olive brn	1.00	.20
Q302	PP30	10fr gray & blue	1.10	.25
Q303	PP30	12fr dark violet	1.65	.45
		Nos. Q301-Q303 (3)	3.75	.90

Surcharged with New Value and Bars in Carmine

1948

Q304	PP30	9fr on 8fr	1.25	.15
Q305	PP30	11fr on 10fr	1.25	.25
Q306	PP30	13.50fr on 12fr	2.00	.25
		Nos. Q304-Q306 (3)	4.50	.65

Delivery of Parcel — PP31

1948

Q307	PP31	9fr chocolate	6.50	.15
Q308	PP31	11fr brown car	7.00	.15
Q309	PP31	13.50fr gray	10.50	.25
		Nos. Q307-Q309 (3)	24.00	.55

Locomotive of 1835 — PP32

Various Locomotives.
Lathe Work in Frame Differs

1949 Engr. Perf. 12½

Q310	PP32	½fr dark brown	.60	.15
Q311	PP32	1fr carmine rose	.70	.15
Q312	PP32	2fr deep ultra	.95	.15
Q313	PP32	3fr dp magenta	2.00	.15
Q314	PP32	4fr blue green	2.75	.15
Q315	PP32	5fr orange red	2.75	.15
Q316	PP32	6fr brown vio	3.00	.25
Q317	PP32	7fr yellow grn	4.00	.15
Q318	PP32	8fr grnsh blue	5.00	.15
Q319	PP32	9fr yellow brn	6.00	.25
Q320	PP32	10fr citron	7.25	.15
Q321	PP32	20fr orange	11.00	.15
Q322	PP32	30fr blue	15.00	.15
Q323	PP32	40fr lilac rose	21.00	.25
Q324	PP32	50fr violet	21.00	.30
Q325	PP32	100fr red	65.00	.25

Engraved; Center Typographed

Q326	PP32	10fr car rose & blk	9.00	.80
		Nos. Q310-Q326 (17)	177.00	3.75

See No. Q337.

1949 Engr.

Design: Electric locomotive.

Q327	PP32	60fr black brown	20.00	.20

Opening of Charleroi-Brussels electric railway line, Oct. 15, 1949.

Mailing Parcel Post — PP33

Sorting PP34

Loading PP35

1950-52 Perf. 12, 12½

Q328	PP33	11fr red orange	6.00	.20
Q329	PP33	12fr red vio ('51)	20.00	1.50
Q330	PP34	13fr dk blue grn	6.00	.20
Q331	PP34	15fr ultra ('51)	15.00	.30
Q332	PP35	16fr gray	6.00	.20
Q333	PP33	17fr brown ('52)	8.00	.20
Q334	PP35	18fr brt car ('51)	16.00	.45
Q335	PP35	20fr brn org ('52)	8.00	.20
		Nos. Q328-Q335 (8)	85.00	3.25

For surcharges see Nos. Q338-Q340.

Mercury and Winged Wheel — PP36

1951

Q336	PP36	25fr dark blue	10.00	8.50

25th anniv. of the founding of the Natl. Soc. of Belgian Railroads.

Type of 1949

Design: Electric locomotive.

1952 Unwmk. Perf. 11½

Q337	PP32	300fr red violet	150.00	.50

Nos. Q331, Q328 and Q334 Surcharged with New Value and "X" in Red, Blue or Green

1953   *Perf. 12*
Q338	PP34	13fr on 15fr (R)	60.00	3.00
Q339	PP33	17fr on 11fr (Bl)	35.00	2.25
Q340	PP35	20fr on 18fr (G)	30.00	2.50
	Nos. Q338-Q340 (3)		125.00	7.75

Electric Train, 1952 — PP37

1953   Engr.
Q341	PP37	200fr dk yel grn & vio brn	250.00	4.00
Q342	PP37	200fr dk green	225.00	1.00

No. Q341 was issued to commemorate the opening of the railway link connecting Brussels North and South Stations, Oct. 4, 1952.

New North Station, Brussels — PP38

Chapelle Station, Brussels PP39

Designs: No. Q348, 15fr, Congress Station. 10fr, 20fr, 30fr, 40fr, 50fr, South Station. 100fr, 200fr, 300fr, Central Station.

1953-57   Unwmk.   *Perf. 11½*
Q343	PP38	1fr bister	.30	.15
Q344	PP38	2fr slate	.40	.15
Q345	PP38	3fr blue grn	.60	.15
Q346	PP38	4fr orange	.80	.15
Q347	PP38	5fr red brn	.80	.15
Q348	PP38	5fr dk red brn	10.00	.25
Q349	PP38	6fr rose vio	1.10	.15
Q350	PP38	7fr brt green	1.10	.15
Q351	PP38	8fr rose red	1.40	.15
Q352	PP38	9fr brt grnsh bl	2.00	.15
Q353	PP38	10fr lt grn	2.25	.15
Q354	PP38	15fr dl red	13.00	.15
Q355	PP38	20fr blue	4.00	.15
Q356	PP38	30fr purple	6.25	.15
Q357	PP38	40fr brt purple	8.00	.15
Q358	PP38	50fr lilac rose	10.00	.15
Q359	PP39	60fr brt purple	20.00	.15
Q360	PP39	80fr brown vio	30.00	.15
Q361	PP39	100fr emerald	18.00	.15
Q361A	PP39	200fr brt vio bl	95.00	1.65
Q361B	PP39	300fr lilac rose	175.00	2.25
	Nos. Q343-Q361B (21)		400.00	
	Set value			5.25

Issued: #Q347, 20fr, 30fr, 1953; 80fr, 1955; 200fr, 1956; 300fr, 1957; others, 1954.
See Nos. Q407, Q431-Q432.

Electric Train — PP40

Mercury and Winged Wheel — PP41

1954
Q362	PP40	13fr chocolate	14.00	.15
Q363	PP40	18fr dark blue	17.00	.15
Q364	PP40	21fr lilac rose	18.00	.45
	Nos. Q362-Q364 (3)		49.00	.75

Nos. Q362-Q364 Surcharged with New Value and "X" in Blue, Red or Green

1956
Q365	PP40	14fr on 13fr (B)	8.00	.15
Q366	PP40	19fr on 18fr (R)	8.25	.15
Q367	PP40	22fr on 21fr (G)	8.75	.45
	Nos. Q365-Q367 (3)		25.00	.85

1957   Engr.   *Perf. 11½*
Q368	PP41	14fr brt green	7.75	.15
Q369	PP41	19fr olive gray	8.00	.20
Q370	PP41	22fr carmine rose	8.75	.30
	Nos. Q368-Q370 (3)		24.50	.65

Nos. Q369-Q370 Surcharged with New Value and "X" in Pink or Green

1959
Q371	PP41	20fr on 19fr (P)	22.50	.35
Q372	PP41	20fr on 22fr (G)	27.50	.55

Old North Station, Brussels PP42

1959   Engr.   *Perf. 11½*
Q373	PP42	20fr olive green	14.00	.20

See Nos. Q381, Q383. For surcharges see Nos. Q378, Q382, Q384.

Diesel and Electric Locomotives and Association Emblem PP43

1960   Unwmk.   *Perf. 11½*
Q374	PP43	20fr red	42.50	30.00
Q375	PP43	50fr dark blue	42.50	30.00
Q376	PP43	60fr red lilac	42.50	30.00
Q377	PP43	70fr emerald	42.50	30.00
	Nos. Q374-Q377 (4)		170.00	120.00

Intl. Assoc. of Railway Congresses, 75th anniv.

No. Q373 Surcharged with New Value and "X" in Red

1961
Q378	PP42	24fr on 20fr ol grn	65.00	.25

South Station, Brussels — PP44

1962   Unwmk.   *Perf. 11½*
Q379	PP44	24fr dull red	6.25	.25

No. Q379 Surcharged with New Value and "X" in Light Green

1963
Q380	PP44	26fr on 24fr dl red	6.50	.25

Type of 1959
Design: 26fr, Central Station, Antwerp.

1963   Engr.   *Perf. 11½*
Q381	PP42	26fr blue	6.25	1.75

No. Q381 Surcharged in Red

1964, Apr. 20
Q382	PP42	28fr on 26fr blue	6.25	.25

Type of 1959
Design: 28fr, St. Peter's Station, Ghent.

1965   Engr.   *Perf. 11½*
Q383	PP42	28fr red lilac	6.25	1.40

Nos. Q383 Surcharged with New Value and "X" in Green

1966
Q384	PP42	35fr on 28fr red lil	6.25	.20

Arlon Railroad Station — PP45

        Perf. 11½
1967, Aug.   Unwmk.   Engr.
Q385	PP45	25fr bister	10.00	.15
Q386	PP45	30fr blue green	5.00	.20
Q387	PP45	35fr deep blue	7.00	.35
	Nos. Q385-Q387 (3)		22.00	.70

See #Q408. For surcharges see #Q410-Q412.

Electric Train — PP46

1968-73   Engr.   *Perf. 11½*
Q388	PP46	1fr olive bis	.20	.20
Q389	PP46	2fr slate	.25	.20
Q390	PP46	3fr blue green	.55	.20
Q391	PP46	4fr orange	.55	.20
Q392	PP46	5fr brown	.65	.20
Q393	PP46	6fr plum	.55	.20
Q394	PP46	7fr brt green	.65	.20
Q395	PP46	8fr carmine	.80	.20
Q396	PP46	9fr blue	1.40	.20
Q397	PP46	10fr green	2.75	.20
Q398	PP46	20fr dk blue	1.65	.20
Q399	PP46	30fr dk purple	4.00	.20
Q400	PP46	40fr brt lilac	5.50	.20
Q401	PP46	50fr brt pink	6.75	.20
Q402	PP46	60fr brt violet	8.25	.30
Q402A	PP46	70fr dp bister ('73)	6.75	.30
Q403	PP46	80fr dk brown	6.75	.30
Q403A	PP46	90fr yel grn ('73)	5.50	.30
Q404	PP46	100fr emerald	11.00	.25
Q405	PP46	200fr violet blue	13.00	.50
Q406	PP46	300fr lilac rose	22.50	1.25
	Nos. Q388-Q406 (21)		100.00	5.90

See No. Q409.

Types of 1953-68
Designs: 10fr, Congress Station, Brussels. 40fr, Arlon Station. 500fr, Electric train going left.

1968, June   Engr.   *Perf. 11½*
Q407	PP38	10fr gray	1.50	.20
Q408	PP45	40fr vermilion	22.50	.15
Q409	PP46	500fr yellow	30.00	1.90
	Nos. Q407-Q409 (3)		54.00	2.25

Nos. Q385, Q387 and Q408 Surcharged with New Value and "X"

1970, Dec.
Q410	PP45	37fr on 25fr bister	45.00	3.00
Q411	PP45	48fr on 35fr dp bl	13.00	5.00
Q412	PP45	53fr on 40fr ver	15.00	6.00
	Nos. Q410-Q412 (3)		73.00	14.00

Ostend Station PP47

1971, Mar.   Engr.   *Perf. 11½*
Q413	PP47	32fr bis & blk	2.50	2.25
Q414	PP47	37fr gray & blk	2.50	2.50
Q415	PP47	42fr bl & blk	4.00	3.00
Q416	PP47	44fr brt rose & blk	4.50	3.00
Q417	PP47	46fr vio & blk	4.50	3.00
Q418	PP47	50fr brick red & blk	5.25	3.25
Q419	PP47	52fr sep & blk	5.25	3.25
Q420	PP47	54fr yel grn & blk	5.75	3.25
Q421	PP47	61fr grnsh bl & blk	5.75	4.00
	Nos. Q413-Q421 (9)		40.00	27.50

Nos. Q413-Q416, Q419-Q421 Surcharged with New Value and "X"

1971, Dec. 15
Denomination in Black
Q422	PP47	34fr on 32fr bister	2.00	.55
Q423	PP47	40fr on 37fr gray	2.50	.70
Q424	PP47	47fr on 44fr brt rose	2.75	.80
Q425	PP47	53fr on 42fr blue	3.25	.85
Q426	PP47	57fr on 52fr sepia	3.25	1.00
Q427	PP47	59fr on 54fr yel grn	3.25	1.00
Q428	PP47	66fr on 61fr grnsh blue	4.00	1.10
	Nos. Q422-Q428 (7)		21.00	6.00

Track, Underpinning of Railroad Car and Emblems PP48

1972, Mar.   Photo.
Q429	PP48	100fr emer, red & blk	10.00	1.10

Centenary of International Railroad Union.

Congress Emblem — PP49

1974, Apr.   Photo.   *Perf. 11½*
Q430	PP49	100fr yel, blk & red	8.00	1.25

4th International Symposium on Railroad Cybernetics, Washington, DC, Apr. 1974.

Type of 1953-1957
1975, June 1   Engr.   *Perf. 11½*
Q431	PP38	20fr emerald	1.75	.20
Q432	PP38	50fr blue	3.75	.55

Railroad Tracks — PP50

1976, June 10   Photo.   *Perf. 11½*
Q433	PP50	20fr ultra & multi	3.00	.20
Q434	PP50	50fr brt grn & multi	1.75	.50
Q435	PP50	100fr dp org & multi	4.00	1.00
Q436	PP50	150fr brt lil & multi	6.25	1.75
	Nos. Q433-Q436 (4)		15.00	3.45

Railroad Station — PP51

1977   Photo.   *Perf. 11½*
Q437	PP51	1000fr multi	45.00	8.00

Freight Car — PP52

Designs: 1fr-9fr, Freight car. 10fr-40fr, Hopper car. 50fr-90fr, Maintenance car. 100fr-500fr, Liquid fuel car.

1980, Dec. 16   Engr.   *Perf. 11½*
Q438	PP52	1fr bis brn & blk	.15	.15
Q439	PP52	2fr claret & blk	.15	.15
Q440	PP52	3fr brt bl & blk	.15	.15
Q441	PP52	4fr grnsh blk & blk	.15	.15
Q442	PP52	5fr sepia & blk	.20	.15
Q443	PP52	6fr dp org & blk	.35	.15
Q444	PP52	7fr purple & blk	.40	.15
Q445	PP52	8fr black	.40	.15
Q446	PP52	9fr green & blk	.45	.15
Q447	PP52	10fr yel bis & blk	.50	.15
Q448	PP52	20fr grnsh bl & blk	1.10	.20
Q449	PP52	30fr bister & blk	2.25	.35
Q450	PP52	40fr lt lil & blk	2.50	.40
Q451	PP52	50fr dk brn & blk	2.75	.55
Q452	PP52	60fr olive & blk	2.75	.75
Q453	PP52	70fr vio bl & blk	3.50	.75
Q454	PP52	80fr vio bl & blk	4.00	.85
Q455	PP52	90fr lil rose & blk	5.00	.95
Q456	PP52	100fr crim rose & blk	5.25	1.00
Q457	PP52	200fr brn & blk	10.00	2.00
Q458	PP52	300fr ol gray & blk	14.00	3.00
Q459	PP52	500fr dl pur & blk	25.00	5.00
	Nos. Q438-Q459 (22)		81.00	17.50

Train in Station
PP53

Electric Locomotives
PP54

1982		Engr.	Perf. 11½	
Q460	PP53	10fr red & blk	1.75	.25
Q461	PP53	20fr green & blk	1.25	.50
Q462	PP53	50fr sepia & blk	4.25	.75
Q463	PP53	100fr blue & blk	7.25	2.75
		Nos. Q460-Q463 (4)	14.50	4.25

1985, May 3		Photo.	Perf. 11½	
Q464	PP54	250fr BB-150	11.00	2.00
Q465	PP54	500fr BB-120	24.00	10.00

Stylized Castle, Gabled
Station and Electric Rail
Car — PP55

1987, Oct. 12		Engr.	Perf. 11½	
Q466	PP55	10fr dk red & blk	.50	.40
Q467	PP55	20fr dk grn & blk	1.00	.75
Q468	PP55	50fr dk brn & blk	2.50	1.90
Q469	PP55	100fr dk lil & blk	5.25	3.75
Q470	PP55	150fr dark olive bister & blk	7.75	5.65
		Nos. Q466-Q470 (5)	17.00	12.45

High Speed
Trains
PP56

1996, June 2		Litho.	Perf. 11½	
Q471	PP56	100fr shown	6.00	4.50
Q472	PP56	300fr Train going left	18.50	13.50

Electric Trains
PP57

Designs: 50fr, Passenger railcars. 100fr, End car.
200fr, Front car.

1997, Oct. 14		Photo.	Perf. 11½	
Q473	PP57	50fr multicolored	2.75	2.10
Q474	PP57	100fr multicolored	5.50	4.25
Q475	PP57	200fr multicolored	11.00	8.50
		Nos. Q473-Q475 (3)	19.25	14.85

ISSUED UNDER GERMAN OCCUPATION

German Stamps of 1906-11 Surcharged

Belgien
3 Centimes
Nos. N1-N6

✱ 1Fr.25C. ✱

Belgien
Nos. N7-N9

Wmk. Lozenges (125)

1914-15			Perf. 14, 14½	
N1	A16	3c on 3pf brown	.45	.25
N2	A16	5c on 5pf green	.40	.25
N3	A16	10c on 10pf car	.50	.25
N4	A16	25c on 20pf ultra	.55	.35
N5	A16	50c on 40pf lake & blk	2.25	1.65
N6	A16	75c on 60pf mag	.90	1.25
N7	A16	1fr on 80pf lake & blk, rose	2.50	2.00
N8	A17	1fr25c on 1m car	22.50	18.00
N9	A21	2fr50c on 2m gray bl	20.00	22.50
		Nos. N1-N9 (9)	50.05	46.50

German Stamps of 1906-18 Surcharged

Belgien
3 Cent.
Nos. N10-N21

Belgien
1 F.
No. N22

✱ 1F.25Cent. ✱

Belgien
Nos. N23-N25

1916-18				
N10	A22	2c on 2pf drab	.25	.25
N11	A16	3c on 3pf brn	.35	.25
N12	A16	5c on 5pf grn	.35	.25
N13	A22	8c on 7½pf org	.65	.45
N14	A16	10c on 10pf car	.25	.25
N15	A22	15c on 15pf yel brn	.65	.45
N16	A22	15c on 15pf dk vio	.65	.45
N17	A16	20c on 25pf org & blk, yel	.35	.35
N18	A16	25c on 20pf ultra	.35	.25
a.		25c on 20pf blue	.40	.25
N19	A16	40c on 30pf org & blk, buff	.40	.35
N20	A16	50c on 40pf lake & blk	.35	.35
N21	A16	75c on 60pf mag	.65	8.50
N22	A16	1fr on 80pf lake & blk, rose	2.00	2.50
N23	A17	1fr25c on 1m car	3.25	3.25
N24	A21	2fr50c on 2m gray bl	30.00	30.00
a.		2fr50c on 1m carmine (error)		3,500.
N25	A20	6fr25c on 5m sl & car	40.00	37.50
		Nos. N10-N25 (16)	80.50	85.10

A similar series of stamps without "Belgien" was
used in parts of Belgium and France while occupied
by German forces. See France Nos. N15-N26.

BELIZE

bə-'lēz

LOCATION — Central America bordering
on Caribbean Sea to east, Mexico to
north, Guatemala to west
GOVT. — Independent state
AREA — 8,867 sq. mi.
POP. — 152,000 (1982 est.)
CAPITAL — Belmopan

Belize was known as British Honduras
until 1973. The former British colony
achieved independence in September 1981.

100 Cents = 1 Dollar

> **Catalogue values for all unused
> stamps in this country are for Never
> Hinged items.**

Fish-Animal Type of British Honduras
Regular Issue 1968-72 Overprinted in
Black on Silver Panel

✱ B E L I Z E ✱

Wmk. 314 (½c, 5c, $5), Unwmkd.

1973, June 1			Perf. 13x12½	
312	A37	½c multi (#235)	.15	.15
313	A37	1c multi (#214)	.15	.15
314	A37	2c multi (#215)	.15	.15
315	A37	3c multi (#216)	.15	.15
316	A37	4c multi (#217)	.15	.15
317	A37	5c multi (#238)	.15	.15
318	A37	10c multi (#219)	.15	.15
319	A37	15c multi (#220)	.15	.15
320	A37	25c multi (#221)	.30	.30
321	A37	50c multi (#222)	.50	.50
322	A37	$1 multi (#223)	.90	1.25

323	A37	$2 multi (#224)	2.00	2.50
324	A37	$5 multi (#240)	5.50	7.00
		Nos. 312-324 (13)	10.40	12.75

No. 315 with silver panel omitted exists canceled. Nos. 313 and 319 exist with silver panel
double.

Common Design Types
pictured following the introduction.

Princess Anne's Wedding Issue
Common Design Type

1973, Nov. 14		Wmk. 314	Perf. 14	
325	CD325	25c blue grn & multi	.15	.25
326	CD325	50c ocher & multi	.35	.50

Crana — A50

1974, Jan. 1		Litho.	Perf. 13½	
327	A50	½c shown	.15	.15
328	A50	1c Jewfish	.15	.15
329	A50	2c White-lipped pecca-ry	.15	.15
330	A50	3c Grouper	.15	.15
331	A50	4c Collared anteater	.15	.15
332	A50	5c Bonefish	.15	.15
333	A50	10c Paca	.15	.15
334	A50	15c Dolphinfish	.15	.15
335	A50	25c Kinkajou	.25	.25
336	A50	50c Muttonfish	.55	.55
337	A50	$1 Tayra	1.00	1.00
338	A50	$2 Great barracudas	2.00	2.00
339	A50	$5 Mountain lion	5.25	5.25
		Nos. 327-339 (13)	10.25	10.25

BELIZE

Stag,
Mayan
Pottery
A51

Designs: Mayan pottery decorations.

1974, May 1			Perf. 14½	
340	A51	3c shown	.15	.15
341	A51	6c Fire snake	.15	.15
342	A51	16c Mouse	.20	.20
343	A51	26c Eagle	.30	.30
344	A51	50c Parrot	.65	.65
		Nos. 340-344 (5)	1.45	1.45

Parides
Arcas
A52

Designs: Butterflies of Belize.

Wmk. 314 Sideways

1974-77			Perf. 14	
345	A52	½c shown	.15	.15
346	A52	1c Thecla regalis	.15	.15
347	A52	2c Colobura dirce	.15	.15
348	A52	3c Catonephele numilia	.15	.15
349	A52	4c Battus belus	.15	.15
350	A52	5c Callicore patelina	.35	.20
351	A52	10c Callicore astala	.70	.35

Perf. 14x15; 14 (26, 35c)

352	A52	15c Nessaea aglaura	.80	.50
a.		Watermark upright ('75)	.70	.40
353	A52	16c Prepona pseudojoiceyi	.45	.25
354	A52	25c Papilio thoas	1.10	.65
a.		Watermark upright ('77)	.80	.45
355	A52	26c Hamadryas arethusa	7.00	7.50
356	A52	50c Thecla bathildis	2.25	1.25
a.		Watermark upright ('77)	1.00	.60
357	A52	$1 Caligo uranus	2.25	1.20
358	A52	$2 Heliconius sapho	4.25	2.40
359	A52	$5 Eurytides philolaus	13.00	7.50
a.		Watermark upright ('75)		
360	A52	$10 Philaethria dido	21.00	12.00
		Nos. 345-360 (16)	53.90	34.55

Issue dates: No. 355A, July 25, 1977; No. 360,
Jan. 2, 1975; others Sept. 2, 1974.

For surcharges, see Nos. 380, 386. For overprint,
see No. 395.

1975-78			Wmk. 373	
345a	A52	½c multicolored	.15	.15
347a	A52	2c multi ('77)	.15	.15
348a	A52	3c multi ('77)	.20	.20

349a	A52	4c multi ('77)	.25	.25
350a	A52	5c multi ('77)	.30	.30
351a	A52	10c multicolored	.65	.65
352b	A52	15c multi ('77)	.90	.90
354b	A52	25c multi ('78)	1.25	1.25
355A	A52	35c Parides arcas ('77)	2.00	2.00
		Nos. 345a-355A (9)	5.85	5.85

For overprints and surcharges see Nos. 395-396,
424, 426-427.

Churchill
and
Coronation
Coach of
Queen
Elizabeth
II — A53

$1, Churchill & Williamsburg, VA Liberty Bell.

1974, Nov. 30		Wmk. 373	Litho.	Perf. 14	
363	A53	50c multicolored		.15	.15
364	A53	$1 multicolored		.35	.35

Sir Winston Churchill (1874-1965).

Mayan Urn — A54   Maya art

Designs: Various Mayan vessels.

1975, June 2		Wmk. 314	Perf. 14	
365	A54	3c lt green & multi	.15	.15
366	A54	6c lt blue & multi	.15	.15
367	A54	16c dull yel & multi	.20	.20
368	A54	26c lilac & multi	.30	.30
369	A54	50c lt brown & multi	.65	.65
		Nos. 365-369 (5)	1.45	1.45

Musicians
A55

Christmas: 26c, Nativity (Thatched hut and children). 50c, Drummers, vert. $1, Map of Belize,
star, fleeing family, vert.

Perf. 14x14½, 14½x14

1975, Nov. 17		Litho.	Wmk. 314	
370	A55	6c multicolored	.15	.15
371	A55	26c multicolored	.15	.15
372	A55	50c multicolored	.25	.25
373	A55	$1 multicolored	.55	.55
		Nos. 370-373 (4)	1.10	1.10

William
Wrigley,
Jr.,
Sapodilla
Tree
A56

Bicentennial Emblem and: 35c, Charles
Lindbergh and "Spirit of St. Louis." $1, John Lloyd
Stephens and Mayan temple.

1976, Mar. 29		Wmk. 373	Perf. 14½	
374	A56	10c multicolored	.15	.15
375	A56	35c multicolored	.25	.25
376	A56	$1 multicolored	.65	.65
		Nos. 374-376 (3)	1.05	1.05

American Bicentennial.

Bicycling
A57

Perf. 14½

1976, July 17   Litho.   Wmk. 373
377	A57	35c	shown	.20	.20
378	A57	45c	Running	.20	.20
379	A57	$1	Shooting	.45	.45
			Nos. 377-379 (3)	.85	.85

21st Olympic Games, Montreal, Canada, July 17-Aug. 1.

No. 355 Surcharged with New Value and Bar
Wmk. 314

1976, Aug. 30   Litho.   Perf. 14
380	A52	20c on 26c multi	1.40	1.40

Map of West Indies, Bats, Wicket and Ball — A57a

BELIZE Prudential Cup — A57b

1976, Oct. 18   Unwmk.   Perf. 14
381	A57a	35c	lt blue & multi	.45	.45
382	A57b	$1	lilac rose & blk	1.25	1.25

World Cricket Cup, won by West Indies Team, 1975.

Royal Visit, 1975 A58

Designs: 35c, Rose window and Queen's head. $2, Queen surrounded by bishops.

1977, Feb. 7   Litho.   Perf. 13½x14
383	A58	10c	multicolored	.15	.15
384	A58	35c	multicolored	.25	.25
385	A58	$2	multicolored	1.10	1.10
			Nos. 383-385 (3)	1.50	1.50

25th anniv. of the reign of Elizabeth II.

No. 352 Surcharged with New Value and Bar

1977   Wmk. 314   Perf. 14x15
386	A52	5c on 15c multi	.30	.30

The first setting has the "5c" close to the right edge of the block (varies). The second, and more common, setting has about 7mm from the right edge to the "5c."

Red-capped Manakin — A59

Designs: Birds of Belize.

Perf. 14½

1977, Sept. 3   Litho.   Wmk. 373
387	A59	8c	shown	.30	.15
388	A59	10c	Hooded oriole	.30	.20
389	A59	25c	Blue-crowned motmot	.90	.45
390	A59	35c	Slaty-breasted tinamou	1.00	.60
391	A59	45c	Ocellated turkey	1.50	.75
392	A59	$1	White hawk	3.00	1.75
a.		Souvenir sheet of 6. #387-392	8.50	4.25
		Nos. 387-392 (6)	7.00	3.90

See Nos. 398-403, 416-421, 500-501. For overprints and surcharges see No. 502.

Medical Laboratory A60   BELIZE 35c

Design: $1, Mobile medical unit and children receiving treatment.

1977, Dec. 2   Perf. 13½
393	A60	35c	multicolored	.30	.30
394	A60	$1	multicolored	.75	.75
a.		Souvenir sheet of 2, #393-394	1.10	1.10

Pan American Health Org., 75th anniv.

Nos. 351 and 355A Overprinted in Gold: "BELIZE DEFENCE FORCE / 1ST JANUARY 1978"
Wmk. 314, 373

1978, Feb. 15   Litho.   Perf. 14
395	A52	10c	multicolored	.15	.15
396	A52	10c	multicolored	.35	.35

Elizabeth II Coronation Anniversary Issue
Common Design Types
Souvenir Sheet

1978, Apr. 21   Unwmk.   Perf. 15
397		Sheet of 6	1.25	1.25
a.	CD326	75c White lion of Mortimer	.20	.20
b.	CD327	75c Elizabeth II	.20	.20
c.	CD328	75c Jaguar (Maya god)	.20	.20

No. 397 contains 2 se-tenant strips of Nos. 397a-397c, separated by horizontal gutter with commemorative and descriptive inscriptions and showing central part of coronation procession with coach.

Bird Type of 1977
Perf. 14½

1978, July 31   Litho.   Wmk. 373
398	A59	10c	White-crowned parrot	.40	.20
399	A59	25c	Crimson-collared tanager	.90	.45
400	A59	35c	Citreoline trogon	1.00	.50
401	A59	45c	Sungrebe	1.10	.60
402	A59	50c	Muscovy duck	1.25	.65
403	A59	$1	King vulture	2.25	1.25
a.		Souvenir sheet of 6, #398-403	9.50	4.00
		Nos. 398-403 (6)	6.90	3.65

Russelia Sarmentosa — A61

Wild Flowers and Ferns: 15c, Lygodium polymorphum. 35c, Heliconia aurantiaca. 45c, Adiantum tetraphyllum. 50c, Angelonia ciliaris. $1, Thelypteris obliterata.

1978, Oct. 16   Litho.   Perf. 14x13½
404	A61	10c	multicolored	.15	.15
405	A61	15c	multicolored	.20	.20
406	A61	35c	multicolored	.40	.40
407	A61	45c	multicolored	.50	.50
408	A61	50c	multicolored	.55	.55
409	A61	$1	multicolored	1.10	1.10
			Nos. 404-409 (6)	2.90	2.90

Christmas.

Internal Airmail Service, 1937 A62

Mail Service: 10c, MV Heron, 1949. 35c, Dugout canoe on river, 1920. 45c, Stann Creek railroad, 1910. 50c, Mounted courier, 1882. $2, RMS Eagle, 1856, and "paid" cancel.

Perf. 13½x14

1979, Jan. 15   Litho.   Wmk. 373
410	A62	5c	multicolored	.15	.15
411	A62	10c	multicolored	.15	.15
412	A62	35c	multicolored	.30	.30
413	A62	45c	multicolored	.40	.40
414	A62	50c	multicolored	.45	.45
415	A62	$2	multicolored	1.75	1.75
			Nos. 410-415 (6)	3.20	3.20

Centenary of membership in UPU.

Bird Type of 1977

1979, Apr. 16   Unwmk.   Perf. 14½
416	A59	10c	Boat-billed heron	.25	.25
417	A59	25c	Gray-necked wood rail	.70	.60
418	A59	35c	Lineated woodpecker	.85	.85
419	A59	45c	Blue gray tanager	1.10	1.10
420	A59	50c	Laughing falcon	1.25	1.20
421	A59	$1	Long-tailed hermit	2.50	2.50
a.		Souvenir sheet of 6. #416-421	7.25	7.00
		Nos. 416-421 (6)	6.65	6.50

Nos. 477, 354b, 595, 355A, 599, 651 Surcharged with New Value and Bar

10c $1.25

1979-83   Litho.   Perf. 14
422	A67	10c on 15c multi	.65	.65
423	A67	10c on 15c multi	.65	.65
424	A52	10c on 25c multi	.65	.65
424A	A67	10c on 35c multi		
b.		Round obliterator		
425	A76	10c on 35c multi		
426	A52	10c on 35c multi		
427	A52	15c on 35c multi	.30	.30
428	A76	$1.25 on $2 multi	2.00	2.00
429	A81	$1.25 on $2 multi	2.00	2.00

No. 422 has a square the width of the "10c" obliterating the old value. No. 423 has a rectangle that is wider than the "10c."

No. 424A has a square obliterator.

No. 426 has "15c" at top of stamp, No. 427 has "15c" at right of rectangle. Type differs.

No. 429 has rectangular obliterator with new value at top of stamp.

Many errors exist from printer's waste.

Issue dates: #426, Mar. 1979. #427, June, 1979. #424, Mar. 31, 1980. #422, Aug. 22, 1981. #423, Jan. 28, 1983. #425, Apr. 15, 1983. #428-429, June 9, 1983.

Used Stamps
Most used stamps from No. 430-679 exist CTO. Most of these appeared on the market after the contract was canceled and were not authorized. The cancellations are printed and the paper differs from the issued stamps. Postally used copies are valued the same as unused. CTO's are of minimal value.

Imperforate Stamps
Stamps from No. 430-679 exist imperforate in small quantities.

Queen Elizabeth II, 25th Anniv. of Coronation — A63

Designs: 25c, No. 439, Paslow Bldg., #397c. 50c, Parliament, London, #397a. 75c, Coronation coach. $1, Queen on horseback, vert. $2, Prince of Wales, vert. $3, Queen and Prince Philip, vert. $4, Queen Elizabeth II, portrait, vert. No. 437, St. Edward's Crown, vert. No. 438a, $5, Princess Anne on horseback, vert. No. 438b, $10, Queen, Montreal Olympics, vert.

Unwmk.

1979, May 31   Litho.   Perf. 14
430	A63	25c	multicolored	.20	
431	A63	50c	multicolored	.45	
432	A63	75c	multicolored	.70	
433	A63	$1	multicolored	.90	
434	A63	$2	multicolored	1.75	
435	A63	$3	multicolored	2.75	
436	A63	$4	multicolored	3.75	
437	A63	$5	multicolored	4.50	
			Nos. 430-437 (8)	15.00	

Souvenir Sheets
438	A63	Sheet of 2, #a.-b.	10.00	
439	A63	$15	multicolored	10.00	

Powered Flight, 75th Anniv. — A64

1979, July 30
440	A64	4c	Safety, 1909	
441	A64	25c	Boeing 707	
442	A64	50c	Concorde	
443	A64	75c	Handley Page W8b, 1922	
444	A64	$1	AVRO F, 1912	
445	A64	$1.50	Cody, 1910	
446	A64	$2	Triplane Roe II, 1909	
447	A64	$3	Santos-Dumont, 1906	
448	A64	$4	Wright Brothers Flyer, 1903	

Souvenir Sheets
Perf. 14½
449		Sheet of 2		
a.	A64	$5 Dunne D.5, 1910		
b.	A64	$5 Great Britain #581		
450	A64	$10 Belize Airways Jet		

Sir Rowland Hill, death cent., "75th anniv." of ICAO.

1980 Summer Olympics, Moscow — A65

1979, Oct. 10   Perf. 14
451	A65	25c	Handball	.20	
452	A65	50c	Weight lifting	.45	
453	A65	75c	Track	.70	
454	A65	$1	Soccer	.90	
455	A65	$2	Sailing	1.75	
456	A65	$3	Swimming	2.75	
457	A65	$4	Boxing	3.75	
458	A65	$5	Cycling	4.50	
			Nos. 451-458 (8)	15.00	

Souvenir Sheets
Perf. 14½
459		Sheet of 2	12.00	
a.	A65	$5 Track, diff.	4.00	
b.	A65	$10 Boxing, diff.	8.00	
460	A65	$15 Cycling, diff.	12.00	

1980 Winter Olympics, Lake Placid — A66

1979, Dec. 4   Perf. 14
461	A66	25c	Torch	.20	
462	A66	50c	Slalom skiing	.40	
463	A66	75c	Figure skating	.65	
464	A66	$1	Downhill skiing	.85	
465	A66	$2	Speed skating	1.75	
466	A66	$3	Cross country skiing	2.50	
467	A66	$4	Biathlon	3.50	
468	A66	$5	Olympic medals	4.25	
			Nos. 461-468 (8)	14.10	

Souvenir Sheets
Perf. 14½
469		Sheet of 2	12.00	
a.	A66	$5 Torch bearers	4.00	
b.	A66	$10 Medals, diff.	8.00	
470	A66	$15 Torch, diff.	12.00	

See Nos. 503-512.

Cypraea
Zebra
A67

1980, Jan. 7   Litho.   Perf. 14

471 A67	1c shown	.15	.15
472 A67	2c Macrocallista macu-lata	.15	.15
473 A67	3c Arca zebra, vert.	.15	.15
474 A67	4c Chama macerophyl-la, vert.	.15	.15
475 A67	5c Latirus cariniferus	.15	.15
476 A67	10c Conus spurius, vert.	.15	.15
477 A67	15c Murex cabritii, vert.	.20	.15
478 A67	20c Atrina rigida	.25	.15
479 A67	25c Chlamys imbricata, vert.	.30	.15
480 A67	35c Conus granulatus	.40	.15
481 A67	45c Tellina radiata, vert.	.55	.15
482 A67	50c Leucozonia nassa	.60	.20
483 A67	85c Tripterotyphis tri-angularis	1.05	.30
484 A67	$1 Strombus gigas, vert.	1.25	.35
485 A67	$2 Strombus gallus, vert.	2.50	.75
486 A67	$5 Fasciolaria tulipa	6.25	1.75
487 A67	$10 Arene cruentata	12.50	3.50
	Nos. 471-487 (17)	26.75	8.50

Souvenir Sheets

488 A67	Sheet of 2, 85c,$5	7.50	7.50
489 A67	Sheet of 2, $2,$10	15.00	17.50

Stamps in Nos. 488-489 have different color border and are of a slightly different size than the sheet
stamps.
The 10c, 50c, 85c, $1 exist dated 1981.
For overprints and surcharges see Nos. 422-423,
424A, 572-589, 592-593.

Intl. Year of the
Child — A68

Various children. No. 498a, Three children. No.
498b, Madonna and Child by Durer. No. 499, Children before Christmas tree.

1980, Mar. 15   Litho.   Perf. 14

490 A68	25c multicolored	.15
491 A68	50c multicolored	.35
492 A68	75c multicolored	.50
493 A68	$1 multicolored	.65
494 A68	$1.50 multicolored	1.00
495 A68	$2 multicolored	1.40
496 A68	$3 multicolored	2.00
497 A68	$4 multicolored	2.75
	Nos. 490-497 (8)	8.80

Souvenir Sheets
Perf. 13 1/2

498 A68	$5 Sheet of 2, #a.-b.	6.00	
499 A68	$10 multicolored	6.00	

No. 498 contains two 35x54mm stamps. No.
499 contains one 73x110mm stamp.

Bird Type of 1977
Souvenir Sheets

1980, June 16   Unwmk.   Perf. 13 1/2

500	Sheet of 6	5.50	4.50
a.	A59 10c Jabiru	.20	.15
b.	A59 25c Barred antshrike	.50	.35
c.	A59 35c Royal flycatcher	.65	.50
d.	A59 45c White-necked puffbird	.75	.65
e.	A59 50c Ornate hawk-eagle	.85	.75
f.	A59 $1 Golden-masked tanager	1.90	1.50
g.	Sheet of 12	11.00	9.00
501	Sheet of 2	8.00	8.00
a.	A59 $2 Jabiru	3.00	3.00
b.	A59 $3 Golden-masked tanager	5.00	5.00

No. 500g contains 2 each Nos. 500a-500f with
gutter between; inscribed "Protection of Environment" and "Wildlife Protection."

**No. 500 Overprinted or Surcharged with
Exhibition Emblem**

1980, Oct. 3   Litho.   Perf. 13 1/2

502	Sheet of 6	4.00	4.00
a.	A59 10c multicolored	.20	.20
b.	A59 25c multicolored	.50	.50
c.	A59 35c multicolored	.65	.65

---

d.	A59 40c on 45c multi	.85	.85
e.	A59 40c on 50c multi	.85	.85
f.	A59 40c on $1 multi	.85	.85

ESPAMER '80 Stamp Exhibition, Madrid, Spain,
Oct. 3-12.

1980 Winter
Olympics, Lake
Placid — A69

Events and winning country: 25c, Men's speed
skating, US. 50c, Ice hockey, US. 75c, No. 512,
Men's figure skating, Great Britain. $1, Alpine ski-
ing, Austria. $1.50, Women's giant slalom, Ger-
many. $2, Women's speed skating, Netherlands.
$3, Cross country skiing, Sweden. $5, Men's giant
slalom, Sweden. Nos. 511a ($5), 511b ($10), Speed
skating, US.

1980, Aug. 20   Litho.   Perf. 14

503 A69	25c multicolored	.25
504 A69	50c multicolored	.50
505 A69	75c multicolored	.75
506 A69	$1 multicolored	.95
507 A69	$1.50 multicolored	1.50
508 A69	$2 multicolored	1.90
509 A69	$3 multicolored	3.00
510 A69	$5 multicolored	4.75
	Nos. 503-510 (8)	13.60

Souvenir Sheets
Perf. 14 1/2

511 A69	Sheet of 2, #a.-b.	9.50	
512 A69	$10 multicolored	9.50	

Nos. 503-510 issued with se-tenant label.

Intl. Year of the
Child — A70

Nos. 513-521: Scenes from Sleeping Beauty. $8,
Detail from Paumgartner Family Altarpiece by
Albrecht Durer.

1980, Nov. 24   Perf. 14

513 A70	35c multicolored	.30
514 A70	40c multicolored	.35
515 A70	50c multicolored	.40
516 A70	75c multicolored	.65
517 A70	$1 multicolored	.85
518 A70	$1.50 multicolored	1.25
519 A70	$3 multicolored	2.50
520 A70	$4 multicolored	3.50
	Nos. 513-520 (8)	9.80

Souvenir Sheets
Perf. 14 1/2

521	Sheet of 2	9.50	
a.	A70 $5 Marriage	4.25	
b.	A70 $5 Couple on horseback	4.25	
522 A70	$8 multicolored	7.50	

Nos. 513-520 issued with se-tenant label.

Queen
Mother
Elizabeth,
80th
Birthday
A71

1980, Dec. 12

523 A71	$1 multicolored	1.00	1.00

Souvenir Sheet
Perf. 14 1/2

524 A71	$5 multicolored	

No. 524 contains one 46x31mm stamp.
No. 523 issued in sheet of 6.

Christmas — A72

1980, Dec. 30   Litho.   Perf. 14

525 A72	25c Annunciation	.20
526 A72	50c Bethlehem	.40
527 A72	75c Holy Family	.65
528 A72	$1 Nativity	.85
529 A72	$1.50 Flight into Egypt	1.25
530 A72	$2 Shepards	1.65
531 A72	$3 With angel	2.50
532 A72	$4 Adoration	3.25
	Nos. 525-532 (8)	10.75

Souvenir Sheets
Perf. 14 1/2

533 A72	$5 Nativity	5.00	
534 A72	$10 Madonna & Child	6.00	

Nos. 525-532 each issued in sheets of 20 + 10
labels. The 2nd and 5th vertical rows consist of
labels.

Nos. 529, 532, $2
534
Surcharged

1981, May 22

535 A72	$1 on $1.50 multi	
536 A72	$2 on $4 multi	

Souvenir Sheet
Perf. 14 1/2

537 A72	$2 on $10 multi	

Location of overprint and surcharge varies.

Intl. Rotary
Club — A73

Designs: 25c, Paul P. Harris, founder. 50c, No.
546, Rotary, project emblem. $1, No. 545b, 75th
anniv. emblem. $1.50 Diploma, horiz. $2, No.
545a, Project Hippocrates. $3, 75th anniv. project
emblems, horiz. No. 544, Hands reach out, horiz.

1981, May 26   Perf. 14

538 A73	25c multicolored	.25
539 A73	50c multicolored	.50
540 A73	$1 multicolored	.95
541 A73	$1.50 multicolored	1.40
542 A73	$2 multicolored	1.90
543 A73	$3 multicolored	2.75
544 A73	$5 multicolored	4.75
	Nos. 538-544 (7)	12.50

Souvenir Sheets
Perf. 14 1/2

545	Sheet of 2	18.00	
a.	A73 $5 multicolored	5.75	
b.	A73 $10 multicolored	12.00	
546 A73	$10 multicolored	12.00	

Originally scheduled to be issued Mar. 30, the
set was postponed and issued without a 75c stamp.
Supposedly some of the 75c were sold to the
public.
For overprints and surcharges see Nos. 563-571,
590-591.

Royal Wedding of Prince
Charles and Lady
Diana — A74

1981, July 16   Perf. 13 1/2x14

548 A74	50c Coat of Arms	.20
549 A74	$1 Prince Charles	.40
550 A74	$1.50 Couple	.65

Size: 25x43mm
Perf. 13 1/2

551 A74	50c like No. 548	.20
552 A74	$1 like No. 549	.40
553 A74	$1.50 like No. 550	.65
	Nos. 548-553 (6)	2.50

Miniature Sheet
Perf. 14 1/2

554	Sheet of 3, #554a-554c	5.00	
a.	A74 $3 like No. 550	1.65	
b.	A74 $3 like No. 548	1.65	
c.	A74 $3 like No. 549	1.65	

Nos. 551-553 issued in sheets of 6 + 3 labels.
No. 554 contains three 35x50mm stamps.
For overprints see Nos. 659-665.

1984
Olympics — A75

1981, Sept. 14   Perf. 14

555 A75	85c Track	.75
556 A75	$1 Cycling	.90
557 A75	$1.50 Boxing	1.40
558 A75	$2 Emblems	1.90
559 A75	$3 Baron Coubertin	2.75
560 A75	$5 Torch, emblems	4.50
	Nos. 555-560 (6)	12.20

Souvenir Sheets
Perf. 13 1/2

561	Sheet of 2	10.00	
a.	A75 $5 like No. 559	3.25	
b.	A75 $10 like No. 560	6.75	
	Perf. 14 1/2		
562 A75	$15 like No. 558	10.00	

No. 561 contains two 35x54mm stamps. No.
562 contains one 46x68mm stamp.
Nos. 561-562 exist with gold background.

Nos. 538-546   **INDEPENDENCE**
Overprinted in
Black or Gold   **21 SEPT.,1981**

1981, Sept. 21   Perf. 14

563 A73	25c multicolored (G)	
564 A73	50c multicolored	
565 A73	$1 multicolored	
566 A73	$1.50 multicolored	
567 A73	$2 multicolored (G)	
568 A73	$3 multicolored	
569 A73	$5 multicolored	

Souvenir Sheets
Perf. 14 1/2

570 A73	Sheet of 2, #a.-b. (G)	
571 A73	$10 multicolored	

Size of overprint varies.

Nos. 471-483, 485-   *Independence*
489 Overprinted   *21 Sept.,1981*

1981, Sept. 21

572 A67	1c multicolored	
573 A67	2c multicolored	
574 A67	3c multicolored	
575 A67	4c multicolored	
576 A67	5c multicolored	
577 A67	10c multicolored	
578 A67	15c multicolored	
579 A67	20c multicolored	
580 A67	25c multicolored	
581 A67	35c multicolored	

582 A67 45c multicolored
583 A67 50c mulitcolored
584 A67 85c multicolored
585 A67 $2 multicolored
586 A67 $5 multicolored
587 A67 $10 multicolored

Souvenir Sheets

588 A67 Sheet of 2, #488
589 A67 Sheet of 2, #489

Size and style of overprint varies, italic on horiz. stamps, upright on vert. stamps and upright capitals on souvenir sheets.

The 10c is dated 1981. Less than 16 sheets dated 1980 were also overprinted.

Nos. 541, 545 Surcharged

1981, Nov. 13   *Perf. 14*
590 A73 $1 on $1.50 multi

Souvenir Sheet
Perf. 14¹/₂

591   Sheet of 2
a. A73 $1 on $5 multicolored
b. A73 $1 on $10 multicolored
Espamer '81.

Nos. 488, 489
Surcharged in Red

1981, Nov. 14   *Perf. 14¹/₂*

Souvenir Sheets

592   Sheet of 2   2.50
a. A67 $1 on 85c
b. A67 $1 on $5
593   Sheet of 2   2.50
a. A67 $1 on $2
b. A67 $1 on $10

Independence — A76

1981-82   *Perf. 14*
594 A76 10c Flag
595 A76 35c Map, vert.
596 A76 50c Black orchid, vert.
597 A76 85c Tapir
598 A76 $1 Mahogany tree, vert.
599 A76 $2 Keel-billed toucan

Souvenir Sheet
Perf. 14¹/₂

600 A76 $5 like 10c

Issued: 50c-$2, 12/18; 10c, 35c, $5, 2/10/82.
For surcharges see Nos. 425, 428, 616.

1982 World Cup
Soccer
Championships,
Spain — A77

1981, Dec. 28   *Perf. 14*
601 A77 10c Uruguay '30, '50   .15
602 A77 25c Italy '34, '38   .15
603 A77 50c Germany '54, '74   .40
604 A77 $1 Brazil '58, '62, '70   .75

605 A77 $1.50 Argentina '78   1.25
606 A77 $2 England '66   1.75

Souvenir Sheets
Perf. 14¹/₂

607 A77 $2 Emblem   1.75
608 A77 $3 Player   2.50

No. 608 contains one 46x78mm stamp.
For surcharge see No. 617.

Sailing
Ships
A78

1982, Mar. 15   *Perf. 14*
609 A78 10c Man of war, 19th cent.
610 A78 25c Madagascar, 1837
611 A78 35c Whitby, 1838
612 A78 50c China, 1838
613 A78 85c Swiftsure, 1850
614 A78 $2 Windsor Castle, 1857

Souvenir Sheet
Perf. 14¹/₂

615 A78 $5 19th cent. ships

Nos. 599 and 606 Surcharged

1982, Apr. 28
616 A76 $1 on $2 multi   2.25
617 A77 $1 on $2 multi   2.25

Essen '82 Philatelic Exhibition.

Princess of Wales, 21st
Birthday — A79

Various portraits.

1982, May 20   *Perf. 13¹/₂x14*
618 A79 50c multicolored   .25
619 A79 $1 multicolored   .50
620 A79 $1.50 multicolored   .75

Size: 25x42mm
Perf. 13¹/₂

621 A79 50c like No. 618   .25
622 A79 $1 like No. 619   .50
623 A79 $1.50 like No. 620   .75
      Nos. 618-623 (6)   3.00

Souvenir Sheet
Stamp Size: 31x47mm
Perf. 14¹/₂

624 A79 $3 Sheet of 3, #a.-c. like
          #618-620   4.00

Nos. 618-620 also exist with gold borders, size: 30x45mm.

BIRTH OF H.R.H.

Overprinted in Silver

PRINCE
WILLIAM ARTHUR
PHILIP LOUIS
21ST JUNE 1982

1982, Oct. 21   *Perf. 13¹/₂x14*
628 A79 50c multicolored   .40
629 A79 $1 multicolored   .80
630 A79 $1.50 multicolored   1.25

Size: 25x42mm
Perf. 13¹/₂

631 A79 50c multicolored   .40
632 A79 $1 multicolored   .80
633 A79 $1.50 multicolored   1.25
      Nos. 628-633 (6)   4.90

Souvenir Sheet
Perf. 14¹/₂

634 A79 $3 Sheet of 3, #a.-c.   8.50

Size of overprint varies. The overprint exists on the gold bordered stamps. No. 634 exists with a second type of overprint.

Boy
Scouts
A80

1982, Aug. 31   *Perf. 14*
638 A80 10c Building camp fire   .15
639 A80 25c Bird watching   .35
640 A80 35c Playing guitar   .50
641 A80 50c Hiking   .75
642 A80 85c Flag, scouts   1.25
643 A80 $2 Salute   2.00
      Nos. 638-643 (6)   5.75

Souvenir Sheets
Perf. 14¹/₂

644 A80 $2 Scout holding flag, vert. 4.00
645 A80 $3 Lord Baden Powell,
           vert.   6.00

Scouting, 75th anniv. and Lord Baden Powell, 125th birth anniv.
For overprints see Nos. 653-658.

Marine Life — A81

1982, Sept. 20   *Perf. 14*
646 A81 10c Gorgonia ventalina
647 A81 35c Carpilius corallinus
648 A81 50c Plexaura flexuosa
649 A81 85c Condylactis gigantea
650 A81 $1 Stenopus hispidus
651 A81 $2 Abudefduf saxatilis

Souvenir Sheet
Perf. 14¹/₂

652 A81 $5 Scyllarides aequinoctial-
             is

For surcharge see No. 429.

Nos. 638-643 Ovptd. in Gold:
BELGICA 82
INT. YEAR OF THE CHILD
SIR ROWLAND HILL 1795 1879
Picasso CENTENARY OF BIRTH
and Emblems

1982, Oct. 1   *Perf. 14*
653 A80 10c Building camp fire
654 A80 25c Bird watching
655 A80 35c Playing guitar
656 A80 50c Hiking
657 A80 85c Flag, scouts
658 A80 $2 Salute

Overprint is different on Nos. 654-655.
Sheets include labels with native Christmas themes.

Nos. 548-554 Overprinted in Gold Similar
to Nos. 628-634

1982, Oct. 25   *Perf. 13¹/₂x14*
659 A74 50c Coat of Arms   1.40
660 A74 $1 Prince Charles   2.75
661 A74 $1.50 Couple   4.25

Size: 25x43mm
Perf. 13¹/₂

662 A74 50c like No. 659   1.40
663 A74 $1 like No. 660   2.75
664 A74 $1.50 like No. 661   4.25
      Nos. 659-664 (6)   16.80

Miniature Sheet
Perf. 14¹/₂

665   Sheet of 3, #665a-665c   14.00
a. A74 $3 like No. 661   3.50
b. A74 $3 like No. 659   3.50
c. A74 $3 like No. 660   3.50

Nos. 662-664 issued in sheets of 6 plus 3 labels. No. 665 contains three 35x50mm stamps. Size and style of overprint varies.

Visit by
Pope
John
Paul II
A82

1983, Mar. 7   *Perf. 13¹/₂*
666 A82 50c Belize Cathedral   1.90

Souvenir Sheet
Perf. 14¹/₂

667 A82 $2.50 Pope John Paul II   4.75

No. 667 contains one 30x47mm stamp.
No. 666 issued in sheet of 6.

Commonwealth Day — A83

1983, Mar. 14   *Perf. 13¹/₂*
668 A83 35c Map, vert.   .30
669 A83 50c Maya Stella   .40
670 A83 85c Supreme Court Bldg.   .80
671 A83 $2 University Center   2.00
      Nos. 668-671 (4)   3.50

Issued in miniature sheets of 4. Other formats are suspect.

First Manned Flight, Bicent. — A84

1983, May 16   *Perf. 14*
672 A84 10c Flying boat, 1670   .15
673 A84 25c Flying machine, 1709   .16
674 A84 50c Airship Guyton de
            Morveau   .30
675 A84 85c Dirigible   .52
676 A84 $1 Clement Bayard   .60
677 A84 $1.50 Great Britain R-34   .95
      Nos. 672-677 (6)   2.68

Souvenir Sheets
Perf. 14¹/₂

678 A84 $3 Nassau Balloon   1.65
679 A84 $3 Montgolfier Brothers
           balloon, vert.   1.65

"Errors"
Many "errors" exist of Nos. 680-898. These unauthorized varieties were printed without the knowledge of the Belize postal service. There may be large quantities of them.

Mayan Monuments — A85

1983, Nov. 14   Litho.   *Perf. 13½x14*

680	A85	10c Altun Ha	.15	.15
681	A85	15c Xunantunich	.15	.15
682	A85	75c Cerros	.60	.60
683	A85	$2 Lamanai	1.40	1.40
		Nos. 680-683 (4)	2.30	2.30

Souvenir Sheet

684	A85	$3 Xunantunich, diff.	2.75	2.75

World Communications Year — A86

1983, Nov. 28   *Perf. 14*

685	A86	10c Belmopan Earth Station	.15	.15
686	A86	15c Telstar 2	.15	.15
687	A86	75c UPU monument	.75	.75
688	A86	$2 Mail boat	2.00	2.00
		Nos. 685-688 (4)	3.05	3.05

Jaguar, World Wildlife Fund Emblem A87

1983, Dec. 9

689	A87	5c Sitting	.15	.15
690	A87	15c Standing	.15	.15
691	A87	85c Swimming	1.10	1.10
692	A87	$1 Walking	1.40	1.40
		Nos. 689-692 (4)	2.80	2.80

Souvenir Sheet

693	A87	$3 Sitting in tree	3.25	3.25

No. 693 contains one stamp 45x28mm.

Christmas — A88

Scenes from mass celebrated by Pope John Paul II during visit, Mar.

1983, Dec. 22

694	A88	10c multicolored	.15	.15
695	A88	15c multicolored	.15	.15
696	A88	75c multicolored	.75	.75
697	A88	$2 multicolored	2.00	2.00
		Nos. 694-697 (4)	3.05	3.05

Souvenir Sheet

698	A88	$3 multicolored	3.25	3.25

Foureye Butterflyfish A89

1984, Feb. 27   *Perf. 15*

699	A89	1c shown	.15	.15
700	A89	2c Cushion star	.15	.15
701	A89	3c Flower coral	.15	.15
702	A89	4c Fairy basslets	.15	.15
703	A89	5c Spanish hogfish	.15	.15
704	A89	6c Star-eyed hermit crab	.15	.15
705	A89	10c Sea fans, fire sponge	.15	.15
706	A89	15c Blueheads	.15	.15
707	A89	25c Blue-striped grunt	.25	.25
708	A89	50c Coral crab	.50	.50
709	A89	60c Tube sponge	.60	.60
710	A89	75c Brain coral	.75	.75
711	A89	$1 Yellow-tail snapper	1.00	1.00
712	A89	$2 Common lettuce slug	2.00	2.00
713	A89	$5 Yellow damselfish	5.00	5.00
714	A89	$10 Rock beauty	10.00	10.00
		Nos. 699-714 (16)	21.30	21.30

For overprints and surcharge see Nos. 715-716, 762A-762C, 922.
The 50c, 60c, 75c, $1 exist inscribed "1986."

1988, July   *Perf. 13½*

705a	A89	10c	.15	.15
706a	A89	15c	.15	.15
707a	A89	25c	.25	.25
708a	A89	50c	.48	.48

709a	A89	60c	.58	.58
711a	A89	$1	.95	.95
		Nos. 705a-711a (6)	2.56	2.56

Nos. 705, 708 Overprinted: "VISIT OF THE LORD / ARCHBISHOP OF CANTERBURY / 8th-11th MARCH 1984"

1984, Mar. 8

715	A89	10c multicolored	.15	.15
716	A89	50c multicolored	.60	.60

1984 Summer Olympics — A90

1984, Apr. 30   *Perf. 13½x14*

717	A90	25c Shooting	.25	.25
718	A90	75c Boxing	.75	.75
719	A90	$1 Running	1.10	1.10
720	A90	$2 Bicycling	1.90	1.90
		Nos. 717-720 (4)	4.00	4.00

Souvenir Sheet

721	A90	$3 Discus	2.25	2.25

1984 Summer Olympics A91

1984, Apr. 30   Litho.   *Perf. 14½*
Booklet Stamps

722	A91	5c Running	.15	.15
a.		Booklet pane of 4	.30	
723	A91	20c Javelin	.25	.25
a.		Booklet pane of 4	1.10	
724	A91	25c Shot put	.35	.35
a.		Booklet pane of 4	1.50	
725	A91	$2 Torch	2.50	2.50
a.		Booklet pane of 4	10.50	
		Nos. 722-725 (4)	3.25	3.25

Ausipex '84 — A92

1984, Sept. 26   Litho.   *Perf. 15*

726	A92	15c Br. Honduras #3	.15	.15
727	A92	30c Bath-Bristol mail coach, 1784	.30	.30
728	A92	65c Penny Black, Rowland Hill	.65	.65
729	A92	75c Railroad Pier, Commerce Bight	.75	.75

Perf. 14

730	A92	$2 Royal Exhibition Bldgs.	2.00	2.00
		Nos. 726-730 (5)	3.85	3.85

Souvenir Sheet

731	A92	$3 Australia #132, Br. Hond. #3	3.00	3.00

House of Tudor, 500th Anniv. — A93

White-fronted Parrot — A94

1984, Oct. 15   *Perf. 14*

732	A93	50c Queen Victoria	.35	.35
733	A93	50c Prince Albert	.35	.35
a.		Sheet of 4, 2 each, #732-733	1.50	
734	A93	75c King George VI	.55	.55
735	A93	75c Queen Elizabeth	.55	.55
a.		Sheet of 4, 2 each, #734-735	2.25	

736	A93	$1 Prince Charles	.75	.75
737	A93	$1 Princess Diana	.75	.75
a.		Sheet of 4, 2 each, #736-737	3.00	
		Nos. 732-737 (6)	3.30	3.30

Souvenir Sheet

738		Sheet of 2	2.00	2.00
a.		A93 $1.50 Prince Philip	1.00	1.00
b.		A93 $1.50 Queen Elizabeth II	1.00	1.00

1984, Nov. 1   *Perf. 11*

Parrots: b, White-capped. c, Red-lored. d, Mealy. b, d, horiz.

739		Block of 4	4.00	4.00
a.-d.	A94	$1 any single	1.00	1.00

Miniature Sheet
Perf. 14

740	A94	$3 Scarlet macaw	3.00	3.00

No. 740 contains one 48x32mm stamp.

Mayan Artifacts — A95

1984, Nov. 30   *Perf. 15*

741	A95	25c Incense holder, 1450	.25	.25
742	A95	75c Cylindrical vase, 675	.75	.75
743	A95	$1 Tripod vase, 500	1.00	1.00
744	A95	$2 Kinich Ahau (sun god)	2.00	2.00
		Nos. 741-744 (4)	4.00	4.00

Girl Guides 75th Anniv., Intl. Youth Year A96

1985, Mar. 15   Litho.   *Perf. 15*

745	A96	25c Gov.-Gen. Gordon	.25	.25
746	A96	50c Camping	.50	.50
747	A96	90c Map reading	.90	.90
748	A96	$1.25 Students in laboratory	1.25	1.25
749	A96	$2 Lady Baden-Powell	2.00	2.00
		Nos. 745-749 (5)	4.90	4.90

Each stamp shows the scouting and IYY emblems. For overprints see Nos. 777-781.

Audubon Birth Bicentenary A97

Illustrations by Audubon. 10c, 25c, 75c, $1, $5 vert.

Perf. 14, 15 ($1)
1985, May 30-1988   Litho.

750	A97	10c White-tailed kite	.15	.15
751	A97	15c Cuvier's kinglet	.15	.15
752	A97	25c Painted bunting	.35	.35
752A	A97	60c like #752 ('88)		
753	A97	75c Belted kingfisher	1.00	1.00
754	A97	$1 Northern cardinal	1.40	1.40
755	A97	$3 Long-billed curlew	4.00	4.00
		Nos. 750-752,753-755 (6)	7.05	7.05

Souvenir Sheet
Perf. 13½x14

756	A97	$5 Portrait of Audubon, 1826, by John Syme	5.00	5.00

No. 756 contains one 38x51mm stamp.

Queen Mother, 85th Birthday A98

Designs: 10c, The Queen Consort and Princess Elizabeth, 1928. 15c, Queen Mother, Elizabeth. 75c, Queen Mother waving a greeting. No: 760, Royal family photograph, christening of Prince

Henry. $2, Holding the infant Prince Henry. No. 762, Queen Mother, diff.

1985, June 20

757	A98	10c shown	.15	.15
758	A98	15c multicolored	.15	.15
759	A98	75c multicolored	.75	.75
760	A98	$5 multicolored	5.00	5.00
		Nos. 757-760 (4)	6.05	6.05

Souvenir Sheets

761	A98	$2 multicolored	1.75	1.75
762	A98	$5 multicolored	4.25	4.25

Nos. 761-762 contain one 38x51mm stamp. For overprints see Nos. 771-776.

Nos. 705-706, 708 Ovptd.:
INAUGURATION OF
NEW GOVERNMENT
21st. DECEMBER 1984

1985, June 24   *Perf. 15*

762A	A89	10c multicolored	.30	.30
762B	A89	15c multicolored	.45	.45
762C	A89	50c multicolored	1.25	1.25
		Nos. 762A-762C (3)	2.00	2.00

Miniature Sheet

Commonwealth Stamp Omnibus, 50th Anniv. — A99

British Honduras Nos. 111-112, 127, 129, 143, 194, 307 and Belize Nos. 326, 385 and 397b on: a, George V and Queen Mary in an open carriage. b, George VI and Queen Consort Elizabeth crowned. c, Civilians celebrating the end of WWII. d, George VI and Queen Consort at mass service. e, Elizabeth II wearing robes of state and the imperial crown. f, Winston Churchill, WWII fighter planes. g, Bridal photograph of Elizabeth II and Prince Philip. h, Bridal photograph of Princess Anne and Capt. Mark Phillips. i, Elizabeth II. j, Imperial crown.

1985, July 25   *Perf. 14½x14*

763		Sheet of 10	5.00	5.00
a.-j.	A99	50c any single	.50	.50

Souvenir Sheet
Perf. 14

764	A99	$5 Elizabeth II coronation photograph	5.00	5.00

No. 764 contains one 38x51mm stamp. For overprints see Nos. 796-797.

British Post Office, 350th Anniv. A100

1985, Aug. 1   *Perf. 15*

765	A100	10c Postboy, letters	.15	.15
766	A100	15c Packet, privateer	.15	.15
767	A100	25c Duke of Marlborough	.25	.25
768	A100	75c Diana	.75	.75
769	A100	$1 Falmouth P.O. packet	1.00	1.00
770	A100	$3 S. S. Conway	3.00	3.00
		Nos. 765-770 (6)	5.30	5.30

Nos. 757-762 Ovptd. in Silver
"COMMONWEALTH SUMMIT /
CONFERENCE, BAHAMAS / 16th-22nd
OCTOBER 1985"

1985, Sept. 5   Litho.   *Perf. 15*

771	A98	10c multicolored	.15	.15
772	A98	15c multicolored	.15	.15
773	A98	75c multicolored	.75	.75
774	A98	$5 multicolored	5.00	5.00
		Nos. 771-774 (4)	6.05	6.05

Souvenir Sheets

775	A98	$2 multicolored	1.90	1.90
776	A98	$5 multicolored	4.75	4.75

Nos. 745-749 Ovptd. "80th
ANNIVERSARY OF / ROTARY
INTERNATIONAL"

1985, Sept. 25   *Perf. 15*

777	A96	25c multicolored	.25	.25
778	A96	50c multicolored	.50	.50
779	A96	90c multicolored	.90	.90
780	A96	$1.25 multicolored	1.25	1.25
781	A96	$2 multicolored	2.00	2.00
		Nos. 777-781 (5)	4.90	4.90

BELIZE 25c Royal Visit — A101

1985, Oct. 9   *Perf. 15x14¹/₂*
782 A101 25c Royal and natl. flags   .25   .25
783 A101 75c Elizabeth II   .75   .75
Size: 81x38mm
784 A101 $4 Britannia   4.00   4.00
a.   Strip of 3, #782-784   5.00
Nos. 782-784 (3)   5.00   5.00
Souvenir Sheet
Perf. 13¹/₂x14
785 A101 $5 Elizabeth II, diff.   5.00   5.00
No. 785 contains one 38x51mm stamp.

Disneyland,
30th Anniv.
A102

Characters from "It's a Small World."

1985, Nov. 1   *Perf. 11*
786 A102   1c Royal Canadian
     Mounted Police   .15   .15
787 A102   2c American Indian   .15   .15
788 A102   3c Inca of the Andes   .15   .15
789 A102   4c Africa   .15   .15
790 A102   5c Far East   .15   .15
791 A102   6c Belize   .15   .15
792 A102   50c Balkans   .50   .50
793 A102 $1.50 Saudi Arabia   1.50   1.50
794 A102 $3 Japan   3.00   3.00
Set value   5.25   5.25
Souvenir Sheet
Perf. 14
795 A102 $4 Montage   4.00   4.00
Christmas.

Nos. 763-764 Ovptd. "PRE 'WORLD CUP
FOOTBALL' / MEXICO 1986"
1985, Dec. 20   *Perf. 14¹/₂x14*
796   Sheet of 10   5.00   5.00
a.-j.   A99 50c, any single   .50   .50
Souvenir Sheet
797 A99 $5 multicolored   5.00   5.00

BELIZE 5c Women in Folk
Costumes — A103

1986, Jan. 15   *Perf. 15*
798 A103   5c India   .15   .15
799 A103   10c Maya   .15   .15
800 A103   15c Garifuna   .15   .15
801 A103   25c Creole   .30   .30
802 A103   50c China   .65   .65
803 A103   75c Lebanon   1.00   1.00
804 A103 $1 Europe   1.25   1.25
805 A103 $2 South America   2.50   2.50
Nos. 798-805 (8)   6.15   6.15
Souvenir Sheet
Perf. 14
806 A103 $5 Maya, So. America   6.25   6.25
No. 806 contains one 38x51mm stamp.

Miniature Sheet

A104

BELIZE Easter — A105

Papal arms, crucifix and: a, Pius X. b, Benedict
XV. c, Pius XI. d, Pius XII. e, John XXIII. f, Paul VI.
g, John Paul I. h, John Paul II. No. 573, John Paul II
saying mass in Belize.

1986, Apr. 15   *Litho.*   *Perf. 11*
807   Sheet of 8 + label   6.25   6.25
a.-h.   A104 50c, any single   .80   .80
Souvenir Sheet
Perf. 14
808 A105 $4 multi   6.50   6.50
No. 807 contains center label picturing the Vatican, and papal crest.

A106

Queen
Elizabeth II,
60th Birthday
A107

1986, Apr. 21   *Perf. 14*
809   Strip of 3   1.50   1.50
a.   A106 25c Age 2   .25   .25
b.   A106 50c Coronation   .50   .50
c.   A106 75c Riding horse   .75   .75
810 A106 $3 Wearing crown jewels   3.00   3.00
Souvenir Sheet
811 A107 $4 Portrait   3.25   3.25

A108

Halley's Comet
A109

1986, Apr. 30
812   Strip of 3   .75   .75
a.   A108 10c Planet-A probe   .15   .15
b.   A108 15c Sighting, 1910   .15   .15
c.   A108 50c Giotto probe   .50   .50
813   Strip of 3   3.75   3.75
a.   A108 75c Weather bureau   .75   .75
b.   A108 $1 US space telescope, shuttle   1.00   1.00
c.   A108 $2 Edmond Halley   2.00   2.00
Souvenir Sheet
814 A109 $4 Computer graphics   4.00   4.00

Miniature Sheet

A110 BELIZE 10c

US Presidents
A111

1986, May   *Perf. 11*
815   Sheet of 6 + 3 labels   3.75   3.75
a.   A110 10c George Washington   .15   .15
b.   A110 20c John Adams   .15   .15
c.   A110 30c Thomas Jefferson   .25   .25
d.   A110 50c James Madison   .40   .40
e.   A110 $1.50 James Monroe   1.10   1.10
f.   A110 $2 John Quincy Adams   1.65   1.65
Souvenir Sheet
Perf. 14
816 A111 $4 Washington   4.00   4.00
No. 815 contains 3 center labels picturing the
great seal of the US.
Issue dates: #815, May 5. #816, May 7.

A112 BELIZE

Statue of
Liberty,
Cent. — A113

Designs: 25c, Bartholdi, statue. 50c, Statue, US
centennial celebration, Philadelphia, 1876. 75c,

Statue close-up, flags, 1886 unveiling. $3, Flags,
statue close-up. $4, Statue, New York City skyline.

1986, May 15   *Perf. 14*
817   Strip of 3   4.00   4.00
a.   A112 25c multicolored   .25   .25
b.   A112 75c multicolored   .75   .75
c.   A112 $3 multicolored   3.00   3.00
818 A112 50c multicolored   .50   .50
Souvenir Sheet
819 A113 $4 multicolored   4.00   4.00

A114

AMERIPEX '86, Chicago, May 22-
June 1 — A115

1986, May 22
820   Strip of 3   .75   .75
a.   A114 10c British Honduras No. 3   .15   .15
b.   A114 15c Stamp of 1981   .15   .15
c.   A114 50c US No. C3a   .50   .50
821   Strip of 3   3.75   3.75
a.   A114 75c USS Constitution   .75   .75
b.   A114 $1 Liberty Bell   1.00   1.00
c.   A114 $2 White House   2.00   2.00
Souvenir Sheet
822 A115 $4 Capitol Building   3.50   3.50
For overprints see Nos. 835-837.

1986 World Cup Soccer Championships,
Mexico — A116

Designs: 25c, England vs. Brazil. 50c, Mexican
player, Mayan statues. 75c, Belize players. $3,
Aztec calendar stone, Mexico. $4, Flags composing
soccer balls.

1986, June 16   *Litho.*   *Perf. 11*
823 A116 25c multicolored   .25   .25
824 A116 50c multicolored   .50   .50
825 A116 75c multicolored   .75   .75
826 A116 $3 multicolored   3.00   3.00
Nos. 823-826 (4)   4.50   4.50
Souvenir Sheet
Perf. 14
827 A116 $4 multicolored   4.00   4.00
Nos. 823-826 printed in sheets of 8 plus label
picturing Azteca Stadium, 2 each value per sheet.

Nos. 823-827 Overprinted "ARGENTINA -
/WINNERS 1986"
1986, Aug. 15
828 A116 25c multicolored   .25   .25
829 A116 50c multicolored   .50   .50
830 A116 75c multicolored   .75   .75
831 A116 $3 multicolored   3.00   3.00
Nos. 828-831 (4)   4.50   4.50
Souvenir Sheet
832 A116 $4 multicolored   4.00   4.00

Wedding of Prince Andrew and Sarah Ferguson
A117   A118

1986, July 23   **Perf. 14x14¹/₂**
833		Strip of 3	3.25	3.25
a.	A117	25c Sarah	.20	.20
b.	A117	75c Andrew	.60	.60
c.	A117	$3 Couple	2.25	2.25

Souvenir Sheet
Perf. 14¹/₂
834		Sheet of 2	4.00	4.00
a.	A118	$1 Sarah, diff.	1.00	1.00
b.	A118	$3 Andrew, diff.	3.00	3.00

Size of No. 833c: 92x41mm.

Nos. 820-822 Ovptd. with
STOCKHOLMIA '86 Emblems

1986, Aug. 28   **Litho.**   **Perf. 14**
835		Strip of 3	.75	.75
a.	A114	10c multicolored	.15	.15
b.	A114	15c multicolored	.15	.15
c.	A114	50c multicolored	.50	.50
836		Strip of 3	3.75	3.75
a.	A114	75c multicolored	.75	.75
b.	A114	$1 multicolored	1.00	1.00
c.	A114	$2 multicolored	2.00	2.00

Souvenir Sheet
837	A115	$4 multicolored	4.00	4.00

A119

Intl. Peace Year — A120   BELIZE $4

Children.

1986, Oct. 3   **Litho.**   **Perf. 14**
838	A119	25c Infant	.25	.25
839	A119	50c Caucasians	.50	.50
840	A119	75c Oriental	.75	.75
841	A119	$3 Indian, caucasian	3.00	3.00
		Nos. 838-841 (4)	4.50	4.50

Souvenir Sheet
842	A120	$4 shown	4.00	4.00

Nos. 838-841 printed se-tenant in sheets of 8 (2 each) plus center label.

Fungi — A121   Toucans — A122

1986, Oct. 30   **Perf. 14**
843	A121	5c Amanita lilloi	.15	.15
844	A122	10c Keel-billed toucan	.15	.15
845	A121	20c Boletellus cubensis	.30	.30
846	A122	25c Collared aracari	.40	.40
847	A121	75c Psilocybe caerulescens	1.25	1.25

848	A122	$1 Emerald toucanet	1.50	1.50
849	A122	$1.25 Crimson-rumped toucan	1.75	1.75
850	A121	$2 Russula puiggarii	3.00	3.00
		Nos. 843-850 (8)	8.50	8.50

Stamps of the same design printed in sheets of 8 plus center label picturing Audubon Society emblem.

Christmas
A123

Disney characters.

1986, Nov. 14   **Perf. 11**
851		Sheet of 9	6.50	6.50
a.	A123	2c Jose Carioca	.15	.15
b.	A123	3c Carioca, Panchito, Donald	.15	.15
c.	A123	4c Daisy	.15	.15
d.	A123	5c Mickey, Minnie	.15	.15
e.	A123	6c Carioca playing music	.65	.65
f.	A123	50c Panchito, Donald	.65	.65
g.	A123	65c Donald, Carioca	.90	.90
h.	A123	$1.35 Donald	1.75	1.75
i.	A123	$2 Goofy	2.75	2.75

Souvenir Sheet
Perf. 14
852	A123	$4 Donald	6.00	6.00

A124

Marriage of Queen Elizabeth II and the Duke of Edinburgh, 40th Anniv. — A125

1987, Oct. 7   **Litho.**   **Perf. 15**
853	A124	25c Elizabeth, 1947	.20	.20
854	A124	75c Couple, c. 1980	.55	.55
855	A124	$1 Elizabeth, 1986	.75	.75
856	A124	$4 Wearing robes of Order of the Garter	3.00	3.00
		Nos. 853-856 (4)	4.50	4.50

Souvenir Sheet
Perf. 14
857	A125	$6 shown	6.00	6.00

A126

America's Cup 1986-87 — A127

Yachts that competed in the 1987 finals.

1987, Oct. 21   **Perf. 15**
858	A126	25c America II	.25	.25
859	A126	75c Stars and Stripes	.75	.75
860	A126	$1 Australia II	1.00	1.00
861	A126	$4 White Crusader	4.00	4.00
		Nos. 858-861 (4)	6.00	6.00

Souvenir Sheet
Perf. 14
862	A127	$6 Australia II sails	6.00	6.00

A128

Woodcarvings by Sir George Gabb (b. 1928) — A129

1987, Nov. 4   **Perf. 15**
863	A128	25c Mother and Child	.20	.20
864	A128	75c Standing Form	.60	.60
865	A128	$1 Love-Doves	.80	.80
866	A128	$4 Depiction of Music	3.25	3.25
		Nos. 863-866 (4)	4.85	4.85

Souvenir Sheet
Perf. 14
867	A129	$6 African Heritage	4.50	4.50

A130

Indigenous Primates — A131

1987, Nov. 11   **Perf. 15**
868	A130	25c Black spider monkey	.25	.25
869	A130	75c Male black howler	.75	.75
870	A130	$1 Spider monkeys	1.00	1.00
871	A130	$4 Howler monkeys	4.00	4.00
		Nos. 868-871 (4)	6.00	6.00

Souvenir Sheet
Perf. 14
872	A131	$6 Black spider, diff.	6.00	6.00

Natl. Girl Guides Movement, 50th Anniv. A132

Lady Olave Baden-Powell, Founder — A133

1987, Nov. 25   **Perf. 15**
873	A132	25c Flag-bearers	.25	.25
874	A132	75c Camping	.75	.75
875	A132	$1 On parade, camp	1.00	1.00
876	A132	$4 Olave Baden-Powell	4.00	4.00
		Nos. 873-876 (4)	6.00	6.00

Souvenir Sheet
Perf. 14
877	A133	$6 Lady Olave, diff.	6.00	6.00

Intl. Year of Shelter for the Homeless A134

1987, Dec. 3   **Perf. 15**
878	A134	25c Tent dwellings	.25	.25
879	A134	75c Urban slum	.75	.75
880	A134	$1 Tents, diff.	1.00	1.00
881	A134	$4 Construction	4.00	4.00
		Nos. 878-881 (4)	6.00	6.00

Orchids
A135   1c

Designs: Illustrations from Reichenbachia, published by Henry F. Sander in 1886.

1987, Dec. 16   Litho.   Perf. 14

882	A135	1c Laelia euspatha	.15	.15
883	A135	2c Cattleya citrina	.15	.15
884	A135	3c Masdevallia bachousiana	.15	.15
885	A135	4c Cypripedium tautzianum	.15	.15
886	A135	5c Trichopilia suavis alba	.15	.15
887	A135	6c Odontoglossum hebraicum	.15	.15
888	A135	7c Cattleya trianaei schroederiana	.15	.15
889	A135	10c Saccolabium giganteum	.15	.15
890	A135	30c Cattleya warscewiczii	.40	.40
891	A135	50c Chysis bractescens	.65	.65
892	A135	70c Cattleya rochelensis	.95	.95
893	A135	$1 Laelia elegans schilleriana	1.40	1.40
894	A135	$1.50 Laelia anceps percivaliana	2.00	2.00
895	A135	$3 Laelia gouldiana	4.00	4.00
		Nos. 882-895 (14)	10.60	10.60

Miniature Sheets

896	A135	$3 Odontoglossum roezlii	3.00	3.00
897	A135	$5 Cattleya dowiana aurea	5.00	5.00

Nos. 882-887 and 889-894 printed in blocks of six. Sheets of 14 contain 2 blocks of Nos. 882-887 plus 2 No. 888 and center label or 2 blocks of Nos. 889-894 plus center strip containing 2 No. 895 and center label. Center labels picture various illustrations from Reichenbachia.

Nos. 896, 897 contain one 44x51mm stamp.

Miniature Sheet

Easter — A136

Stations of the Cross (in sequential order): a, Jesus condemned to death. b, Carries the cross. c, Falls the first time. d, Meets his mother, Mary. e, Cyrenean takes up the cross. f, Veronica wipes Jesus's face. g, Falls the second time. h, Consoles the women of Jerusalem. i, Falls the third time. j, Stripped of his robes. k, Nailed to the cross. l, Dies. m, Taken down from the cross. n, Laid in the sepulcher.

1988, Mar. 21   Perf. 14

898	Sheet of 14 + label	5.60	5.60
a.-n.	A136 40c, any single	.40	.40

A $6 souvenir sheet was prepared but not issued.

1988 Summer Olympics, Seoul — A137

1988, Aug. 15   Litho.   Perf. 14

899	A137	10c Basketball	.15	.15
900	A137	25c Volleyball	.25	.25
901	A137	60c Table tennis	.60	.60
902	A137	75c Diving	.75	.75
903	A137	$1 Judo	1.00	1.00
904	A137	$2 Field hockey	2.00	2.00
		Nos. 899-904 (6)	4.75	4.75

Souvenir Sheet

905	A137	$3 Women's gymnastics	3.00	3.00

Intl. Red Cross, 125th Anniv. A138

1988, Nov. 18   Litho.   Perf. 14

906	A138	60c Travelling nurse, 1912	.60	.60
907	A138	75c Hospital ship, ambulance boat, 1937	.75	.75
908	A138	$1 Ambulance, 1956	1.00	1.00
909	A138	$2 Ambulance plane, 1940	2.00	2.00
		Nos. 906-909 (4)	4.35	4.35

Indigenous Small Animals A139

1989   Litho.   Wmk. 384   Perf. 14

910	A139	10c Gibnut (agouti)	.25	.25

Unwmk.

911	A139	25c Four-eyed opossum, vert.	.65	.65
a.		Wmk. 384	.65	.65
912	A139	50c Ant bear	1.40	1.40
913	A139	60c like 910	1.65	1.65
914	A139	75c Antelope	2.00	2.00
915	A139	$2 Peccary	5.50	5.50
		Nos. 910-915 (6)	11.45	11.45

Issued: 10c, 7/23; #911a, 12/6; others, 2/24.

Moon Landing, 20th Anniv.
Common Design Type

Apollo 9: 25c, Command service and lunar modules docked in space. 50c, Command service module. 75c, Mission emblem. $1, First manned lunar module in space. $5, Apollo 11 command service module.

Perf. 14x13½

1989, July 20   Wmk. 384
Size of Nos. 680-681: 29x29mm

916	CD342	25c multicolored	.20	.20
917	CD342	50c multicolored	.45	.45
918	CD342	75c multicolored	.65	.65
919	CD342	$1 multicolored	.90	.90
		Nos. 916-919 (4)	2.20	2.20

Souvenir Sheet

920	CD342	$5 multi	5.00	5.00

No. 920 Overprinted

WORLD STAMP EXPO '89™
United States Postal Service
Nov. 17 — 20 and
Nov. 24 — Dec. 3. 1989
Washington Convention Center
Washington, DC

1989, Nov. 17   Perf. 14x13½

921	CD342	$5 multicolored	5.00	5.00

World Stamp Expo '89.

No. 704 Surcharged

5c

1989, Nov. 15   Perf. 15

922	A89	5c on 6c multi	2.00

Christmas — A140   A141

Old churches.

Wmk. 384

1989, Dec. 13   Litho.   Perf. 14

927	A140	10c Wesley	.15	.15
928	A140	25c Baptist	.25	.25
929	A140	60c St. John's Cathedral	.60	.60
930	A140	75c St. Andrew's Presbyterian	.75	.75
931	A140	$1 Holy Redeemer Cathedral	1.00	1.00
		Nos. 927-931 (5)	2.75	2.75

Wmk. 373

1990, Mar. 1   Litho.   Perf. 14

Birds and Butterflies: 5c, Piranga leucoptera, Catonephele numilia female. 10c, Ramphastos sulfuratus, Nessaea aglaura. 15c, Fregata magnificens, Eurytides philolaus. 25c, Jabiru mycteria, Heliconius sapho. 30c, Ardea herodias, Colobura dirce. 50c, Icterus galbula, Hamadryas arethusia. 60c, Ara macao, Thecla regalis. 75c, Cyanerpes cyaneus, Callicore patelina. $1, Pulsatrix perspicillata, Caligo uranus. $2, Cyanocorax yncas, Philaethria dido. $5, Cathartes aura, Battus belus. $10, Pandion haliaetus, Papilio thoas.

932	A141	5c multicolored	.15	.15
933	A141	10c multicolored	.15	.15
934	A141	15c multicolored	.15	.15
935	A141	25c multicolored	.25	.25
936	A141	30c multicolored	.30	.30
937	A141	50c multicolored	.50	.50
938	A141	60c multicolored	.60	.60
939	A141	75c multicolored	.75	.75
940	A141	$1 multicolored	1.00	1.00
941	A141	$2 multicolored	2.00	2.00
942	A141	$5 multicolored	5.00	5.00
943	A141	$10 multicolored	10.00	10.00
		Nos. 932-943 (12)	20.85	20.85

The 10c exists inscribed "1993."
For overprints and surcharge see Nos. 944, 1021, 1030.

No. 940 Overprinted in Gold:
"FIRST DOLLAR / COIN / 1990"

1990, Mar. 1

944	A141	$1 multicolored	1.00	1.00

Turtles A142

Wmk. 373

1990, Aug. 8   Litho.   Perf. 14

945	A142	10c Green	.15	.15
946	A142	25c Hawksbill	.25	.25
947	A142	60c Loggerhead	.60	.60
948	A142	75c Loggerhead, diff.	.75	.75
949	A142	$1 Bocatora	1.00	1.00
950	A142	$2 Hicatee	2.00	2.00
		Nos. 945-950 (6)	4.75	4.75

Battle of Britain, 50th Anniv. A143

Aircraft.

1990, Sept. 15   Wmk. 384   Perf. 13½

951	A143	10c Fairey Battle	.15	.15
952	A143	25c Bristol Beaufort	.25	.25
953	A143	60c Bristol Blenheim	.60	.60
954	A143	75c Armstrong-Whitworth Whitley	.75	.75
955	A143	$1 Vickers-Armstrong Wellington	1.00	1.00
956	A143	$2 Handley-Page Hampden	2.00	2.00
		Nos. 951-956 (6)	4.75	4.75

Orchids — A144

1990, Nov. 1   Wmk. 384   Perf. 14

957	A144	25c Cattleya bowringiana	.25	.25
958	A144	50c Rhyncholaelia digbyana	.50	.50
959	A144	60c Sobralia macrantha	.60	.60
960	A144	75c Chysis bractescens	.75	.75
961	A144	$1 Vanilla planifolia	1.00	1.00
962	A144	$2 Epidendrum polyanthum	2.00	2.00
		Nos. 957-962 (6)	5.10	5.10

Christmas.

Indigenous Fauna A145

1991, Apr. 10

963	A145	25c Iguana	.25	.25
964	A145	50c Crocodile	.50	.50
965	A145	60c Manatee	.60	.60
966	A145	75c Boa constrictor	.75	.75
967	A145	$1 Tapir	1.00	1.00
968	A145	$2 Jaguar	2.00	2.00
		Nos. 963-968 (6)	5.10	5.10

Elizabeth & Philip, Birthdays
Common Design Types

1991, June 17   Perf. 14½

969	CD345	$1 multicolored	1.00	1.00
970	CD346	$1 multicolored	1.00	1.00
a.		Pair, #969-970 + label	2.00	2.00

Hurricanes A146

1991, July 31   Wmk. 373   Perf. 14

971	A146	60c Weather radar	.60	.60
972	A146	75c Weather observation station	.75	.75
973	A146	$1 Scene after hurricane	1.00	1.00
974	A146	$2 Hurricane Gilbert	2.00	2.00
		Nos. 971-974 (4)	4.35	4.35

Independence, 10th Anniv. — A147

Famous Men: 25c, Thomas V. Ramos (1887-1955). 60c, Sir Isaiah Morter (1860-1924). 75c, Antonio Soberanis (1897-1975). $1, Santiago Ricalde (1920-1975).

1991, Sept. 4   Wmk. 384

975	A147	25c multicolored	.28	.28
976	A147	60c multicolored	.65	.65
977	A147	75c multicolored	.80	.80
978	A147	$1 multicolored	1.10	1.10
		Nos. 975-978 (4)	2.83	2.83

Folktales A148

Christmas.

Wmk. 373

1991, Nov. 6   Litho.   Perf. 14

979	A148	25c Anansi	.28	.28
980	A148	50c Jack-O-Lantern	.55	.55
981	A148	60c Tata Duende, vert.	.65	.65
982	A148	75c Xtabai	.80	.80
983	A148	$1 Warrie Massa, vert.	1.10	1.10
984	A148	$2 Old Heg	2.20	2.20
		Nos. 979-984 (6)	5.58	5.58

See Nos. 999-1002.

Orchids — A149

Easter: 25c, Gongora quinquenervis. 50c, Oncidium sphacelatum. 60c, Encyclia bractescens. 75c, Epidendrum ciliare. $1, Psygmorchis pusilla. $2, Galeandra batemanii.

1992, Apr. 1

985	A149	25c multicolored	.28	.28
986	A149	50c multicolored	.55	.55
987	A149	60c multicolored	.65	.65
988	A149	75c multicolored	.80	.80
989	A149	$1 multicolored	1.10	1.10
990	A149	$2 multicolored	2.20	2.20
		Nos. 985-990 (6)	5.58	5.58

Famous
Belizeans
A150

Designs: 25c, Gwendolyn Lizarraga, MBE (1901-75). 60c, Rafael Fonseca, CMG, OBE (1921-78). 75c, Vivian Seay, MBE (1881-1971). $1, Samuel A. Haynes (1898-1971).

1992, Aug. 26   *Perf. 13x12¹/₂*

991	A150	25c multicolored	.28	.28
992	A150	60c multicolored	.65	.65
993	A150	75c multicolored	.80	.80
994	A150	$1 multicolored	1.10	1.10
		Nos. 991-994 (4)	2.83	2.83

See Nos. 1013-1016.

Discovery of America, 500th
Anniv. — A151

Mayan ruins, modern buildings: 25c, Xunantunich, National Assembly. 60c, Altun Ha, Supreme Court Building. 75c, Santa Rita, Tower Hill Sugar Factory. $5, Lamanai, The Citrus Company.

1992, Oct. 1   Litho.   Wmk. 384
Perf. 13¹/₂x14

995	A151	25c multicolored	.28	.28
996	A151	60c multicolored	.65	.65
997	A151	75c multicolored	.80	.80
998	A151	$5 multicolored	5.50	5.50
		Nos. 995-998 (4)	7.23	7.23

Folklore Type of 1991

Christmas.

Perf. 13x12¹/₂

1992, Nov. 16   Litho.   Wmk. 373

999	A148	25c Hashishi Pampi	.25	.25
1000	A148	60c Cadejo	.62	.62
1001	A148	$1 La Sucia, vert.	1.05	1.05
1002	A148	$5 Sisimito	5.00	5.00
		Nos. 999-1002 (4)	6.92	6.92

Royal Air Force, 75th Anniv.
Common Design Type

Designs: 25c, Aerospatiale Puma. 50c, British Aerospace Harrier. 60c, DeHavilland Mosquito. 75c, Avro Lancaster. $1, Consolidated Liberator. $3, Short Stirling.

1993, Apr. 1   Wmk. 373
  Litho.   *Perf. 14*

1003	CD350	25c multicolored	.25	.25
1004	CD350	50c multicolored	.52	.52
1005	CD350	60c multicolored	.65	.65
1006	CD350	75c multicolored	.80	.80
1007	CD350	$1 multicolored	1.05	1.05
1008	CD350	$3 multicolored	3.15	3.15
		Nos. 1003-1008 (6)	6.42	6.42

1993 World Orchid
Conference,
Glasgow — A152

1993, Apr. 24   Litho.   Wmk. 384
Perf. 14¹/₂x14

1009	A152	25c Lycaste aromatica	.28	.28
1010	A152	60c Sobralia decora	.65	.65
1011	A152	$1 Maxillaria alba	1.10	1.10
1012	A152	$2 Brassavola nodosa	2.20	2.20
		Nos. 1009-1012 (4)	4.23	4.23

Famous Belizeans Type of 1992

Designs: 25c, Herbert Watkin Beaumont (1880-1978). 60c, Dr. Selvyn Walford Young (1899-1977). 75c, Cleopatra White (1898-1987). $1, Dr. Karl Heusner (1872-1960).

Wmk. 384

1993, Aug. 11   Litho.   *Perf. 14*

1013	A150	25c multicolored	.28	.28
1014	A150	60c multicolored	.65	.65
1015	A150	75c multicolored	.85	.65
1016	A150	$1 multicolored	1.10	1.10
		Nos. 1013-1016 (4)	2.88	2.68

Christmas
A153

Wmk. 373

1993, Nov. 3   Litho.   *Perf. 14*

1017	A153	25c Boom and chime band	.28	.28
1018	A153	60c John Canoe dance	.65	.65
1019	A153	75c Cortez dance	.80	.80
1020	A153	$2 Maya Musical Group	2.25	2.25
		Nos. 1017-1020 (4)	3.98	3.98

No. 940 Ovptd. with Hong Kong '94
Emblem
Wmk. 373

1994, Feb. 18   Litho.   *Perf. 14*

1021	A141	$1 multicolored	1.10	1.10

Royal Visit — A154

Designs: 25c, Belize, United Kingdom Flags. 60c, Queen Elizabeth II wearing hat. 75c, Queen. $1, Queen, Prince Philip.

Perf. 14¹/₂x14

1994, Feb. 24   Litho.   Wmk. 373

1022	A154	25c multicolored	.28	.28
1023	A154	60c multicolored	.65	.65
1024	A154	75c multicolored	.80	.80
1025	A154	$1 multicolored	1.10	1.10
		Nos. 1022-1025 (4)	2.83	2.83

Bats
A155

Wmk. 384

1994, May 30   Litho.   *Perf. 14*

1026	A155	25c Insect feeder	.25	.25
1027	A155	60c Fruit feeder	.60	.60
1028	A155	75c Fish feeder	.75	.75
1029	A155	$2 Common vampire	2.00	2.00
		Nos. 1026-1029 (4)	3.60	3.60

No. 939 Surcharged

10c
⬜

Wmk. 373

1994, Aug. 18   Litho.   *Perf. 14*

1030	A141	10c on 75c multi	.15	.15

Christmas — A156

Orchids: 25c, Cycnoches chlorochilon. 60c, Brassavolas cucullata. 75c, Sobralia mucronata. $1, Nidema Boothii.

1994, Nov. 7   Wmk. 384

1031	A156	25c multicolored	.25	.25
1032	A156	60c multicolored	.60	.60
1033	A156	75c multicolored	.75	.75
1034	A156	$1 multicolored	1.00	1.00
		Nos. 1031-1034 (4)	2.60	2.60

For overprints see Nos. 1051-1054.

Insects
A157

Wmk. 373

1995, Jan. 11   Litho.   *Perf. 14*

1035	A157	5c Ground beetle	.15	.15
1036	A157	10c Harlequin beetle	.15	.15
1037	A157	15c Giant water bug	.15	.15
1038	A157	25c Peanut-head bug	.25	.25
1039	A157	30c Coconut weevil	.30	.30
1040	A157	50c Mantis	.50	.50
1041	A157	60c Tarantula wasp	.60	.60
1042	A157	75c Rhinoceros beetle	.75	.75
1043	A157	$1 Metallic wood borer	1.00	1.00
1044	A157	$2 Dobson fly	2.00	2.00
1045	A157	$5 Click beetle	5.00	5.00
1046	A157	$10 Long-horned beetle	10.00	10.00
		Nos. 1035-1046 (12)	20.85	20.85

Nos. 1035-1046 exist inscribed "1996."
For overprints see Nos. 1063-1066.

End of World War II, 50th Anniv.
Common Design Type

Designs: 25c, War Memorial Cenotaph. 60c, Remembrance Sunday. 75c, British Honduras Forestry Unit. $1, Wellington Bomber.

Perf. 13¹/₂

1995, May 8   Litho.   Wmk. 373

1047	CD351	25c multicolored	.28	.28
1048	CD351	60c multicolored	.65	.65
1049	CD351	75c multicolored	.80	.80
1050	CD351	$1 multicolored	1.10	1.10
		Nos. 1047-1050 (4)	2.83	2.83

Nos. 1031-1034 Ovptd. in Blue

1995, Sept. 1   Wmk. 384   *Perf. 14*

1051	A156	25c on No. 1031	.25	.25
1052	A156	60c on No. 1032	.60	.60
1053	A156	75c on No. 1033	.75	.75
1054	A156	$1 on No. 1034	1.00	1.00
		Nos. 1051-1054 (4)	2.60	2.60

UN, 50th Anniv.
Common Design Type

Designs: 25c, M113 Light reconnaissance vehicle. 60c, Sultan, armored command vehicle. 75c, Leyland/DAF 8x4 "Drops" vehicle. $2, Warrior infantry combat vehicle.

Wmk. 384

1995, Oct. 24   Litho.   *Perf. 14*

1055	CD353	25c multicolored	.25	.25
1056	CD353	60c multicolored	.60	.60
1057	CD353	75c multicolored	.75	.75
1058	CD353	$2 multicolored	2.00	2.00
		Nos. 1055-1058 (4)	3.60	3.60

Christmas — A158

Doves: 25c, Blue ground dove. 60c, White-fronted dove. 75c, Ruddy ground dove. $1, White-winged dove.

1995, Nov. 6   Wmk. 373

1059	A158	25c multicolored	.25	.25
1060	A158	60c multicolored	.60	.60
1061	A158	75c multicolored	.75	.75
1062	A158	$1 multicolored	1.00	1.00
		Nos. 1059-1062 (4)	2.60	2.60

Nos. 1037, 1039-1040, 1044
Ovptd.

Wmk. 373

1996, May 17   Litho.   *Perf. 14*

1063	A157	15c on #1037	.15	.15
1064	A157	30c on #1039	.30	.30
1065	A157	50c on #1040	.50	.50
1066	A157	$2 on #1044	2.00	2.00
		Nos. 1063-1066 (4)	2.95	2.95

CAPEX '96
A159

Trains: 25c, Unloading banana train onto freighter, Commerce Bight Pier. 60c, Banana train, Stann Creek Station. 75c, Mahogany log train, Hunslet 0-6-0 Side Tank Engine No. 4. $3, LMS Jubilee Class 4-6-0 Locomotive No. 5602 "British Honduras."

Perf. 13¹/₂x13

1996, June 6   Litho.   Wmk. 373

1067	A159	25c multicolored	.25	.25
1068	A159	60c multicolored	.60	.60
1069	A159	75c multicolored	.75	.75
1070	A159	$3 multicolored	3.00	3.00
		Nos. 1067-1070 (4)	4.60	4.60

Christmas — A160

Orchids: 25c, Epidendrum stamfordianum. 60c, Oncidium carthagenense. 75c, Oerstedella verrucosa. $1, Coryanthes speciosa.

Wmk. 373

1996, Nov. 6   Litho.   *Perf. 14*

1071	A160	25c multicolored	.25	.25
1072	A160	60c multicolored	.60	.60
1073	A160	75c multicolored	.75	.75
1074	A160	$1 multicolored	1.00	1.00
		Nos. 1071-1074 (4)	2.60	2.60

Hong Kong
'97 — A161

Cattle: 25c, Red poll. 60c, Brahman. 75c, Longhorn. $1, Charbray.

Wmk. 373
				Perf. 14
1075	A161	25c multicolored	.30	.30
1076	A161	60c multicolored	.70	.70
1077	A161	75c multicolored	.85	.85
1078	A161	$1 multicolored	1.10	1.10
		Nos. 1075-1078 (4)	2.95	2.95

BELIZE

25c   Snakes — A162

Designs: 25c, Coral snake. 60c, Green vine
snake. 75c, Yellow-jawed tommygoff. $1, Speckled
racer.

Wmk. 373
1997, May 28		Litho.	Perf. 14
1079	A162	25c multicolored	.30	.30
1080	A162	60c multicolored	.65	.65
1081	A162	75c multicolored	.80	.80
1082	A162	$1 multicolored	1.10	1.10
		Nos. 1079-1082 (4)	2.85	2.85

Christmas — A164

Orchids: 25c, Maxillaria elatior. 60c, Dimenandra
emarginata. 75c, Macradenia brassavolae. $1,
Ornithocephalus gladiatus.

1997   Litho.   Wmk. 373   Perf. 14
1087	A164	25c multicolored	.25	.25
1088	A164	60c multicolored	.65	.65
1089	A164	75c multicolored	.80	.80
1090	A164	$1 multicolored	1.10	1.10
		Nos. 1087-1090 (4)	2.80	2.80

SEMI-POSTAL STAMPS

World Cup Soccer Championship — SP1

Designs: 20c+10c, 30c+15c, Scotland vs. New
Zealand (diff.). 40c+20c, Kuwait vs. France.
60c+30c, Italy vs. Brazil. No. B5, France vs. Northern Ireland. $1.50+75c, Austria vs. Chile. No. B7,
Italy vs. Germany, vert. $2+$1, England vs. France,
vert.

1982, Dec. 10   Litho.   Perf. 14
B1	SP1	20c +10c multi	.25	.25
B2	SP1	30c +15c multi	.35	.35
B3	SP1	40c +20c multi	.45	.45
B4	SP1	60c +30c multi	.75	.75
B5	SP1	$1 +50c multi	3.00	3.00
B6	SP1	$1.50 +75c multi	5.00	5.00
		Nos. B1-B6 (6)	9.80	9.80

Souvenir Sheets
Perf. 14½
B7	SP1	$1 +50c multi	3.50	3.50
B8	SP1	$2 +$1 multi	6.00	6.00

Nos. B7-B8 each contain one 50x70mm stamp.

POSTAGE DUE STAMPS

Numeral — D2

Each denomination has different border.

1976, July 1   Litho.   Wmk. 373
J6	D2	1c green & red	.15	.15
J7	D2	2c violet & rose lil	.15	.15
J8	D2	5c ocher & brt grn	.15	.15
J9	D2	15c brown org & yel grn	.30	.30
J10	D2	25c slate grn & org	.50	.50
		Nos. J6-J10 (5)	1.25	1.25

CAYES OF BELIZE

> Catalogue values for all unused
> stamps in this country are for Never
> Hinged items.

Spiny
Lobster
A1   1c

Perf. 14½x14, 14x14½
1984, May 30   Litho.   Unwmk.
1	A1	1c shown	.15	.15
2	A1	2c Blue crab	.15	.15
3	A1	5c Red-footed booby	.15	.15
4	A1	10c Brown pelican	.15	.15
5	A1	15c White-tailed deer	.15	.15
6	A1	25c Lighthouse, English Caye	.20	.20
7	A1	75c Spanish galleon, Santa Yaga, c. 1750	.55	.55
8	A1	$3 Map of Ambergris Caye, vert.	2.25	2.25
9	A1	$5 Jetty, windsurfers	3.75	3.75
		Nos. 1-9 (9)	7.50	7.50

The $1 stamp was not issued. Eighteen sheets of
40 were sold for postage by accident.

Lloyd's List Issue
Common Design Type
1984, June 6   Perf. 14½x14
10	CD335	25c Queen Elizabeth 2	.20	.20
11	CD335	75c Lutine Bell	.55	.55
12	CD335	$1 Loss of the Fishburn	.75	.75
13	CD335	$2 Trafalgar Sword	1.50	1.50
		Nos. 10-13 (4)	3.00	3.00

1984 Summer
Olympics, Los
Angeles — A2

1984, Oct. 5   Perf. 15
14	A2	10c Yachting	.15	.15
15	A2	15c Windsurfing	.15	.15
16	A2	75c Swimming	.75	.75
17	A2	$2 Kayaking	2.00	2.00
		Nos. 14-17 (4)	3.05	3.05

No. 17 inscribed Canoeing.

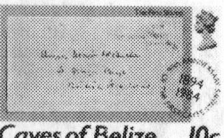

First Cayes
Stamps,
90th
Anniv.
A3   Cayes of Belize   10c

1984, Nov. 5
18	A3	10c 1895 cover	.15	.15
19	A3	15c Sydney Cuthbert	.15	.15
20	A3	75c Cuthbert's steam yacht	.55	.55
21	A3	$2 British Honduras #133	1.50	1.50
		Nos. 18-21 (4)	2.35	2.35

Audubon
Birth
Bicentenary
A4

Illustrations by Audubon.

1985, May 20   Perf. 14
22	A4	25c Blue-winged teal	.20	.20
23	A4	75c Semipalmated sandpiper	.55	.55
24	A4	$1 Yellow-crowned night heron, vert.	.75	.75
25	A4	$3 Common gallinule	2.25	2.25
		Nos. 22-25 (4)	3.75	3.75

Shipwrecks — A5

Designs: a, Oxford, c. 1675. b, Santa Yaga, 1780.
c, No. 27, Comet, 1822. d, Yeldham, 1800.

1985, June 5   Perf. 15
26	A5	$1 Strip of 4+label, #a.-d.	4.00	4.00

Souvenir Sheet
Perf. 13½x14
27	A5	$5 multicolored	5.00	5.00

No. 27 contains one 38x51mm stamp. No. 26
has continuous design.

BENIN
bə-'nin

French Colony

LOCATION — West Coast of Africa
GOVT. — French Possession
AREA — 8,627 sq. mi.
POP. — 493,000 (approx.)
CAPITAL — Benin

In 1895 the French possessions known as
Benin were incorporated into the colony of
Dahomey and postage stamps of Dahomey
superseded those of Benin. Dahomey took
the name Benin when it became a republic
in 1975.

100 Centimes = 1 Franc

> Catalogue values for unused
> stamps in this country are for Never
> Hinged items, beginning with Scott
> 342 in the regular postage section,
> Scott C240 in the airpost section,
> Scott J44 in the postage due sec-
> tion, and Scott Q8 in the parcel
> post section.

Handstamped on
Stamps of French   BÉNIN
Colonies

1892   Unwmk.   Perf. 14x13½
Black Overprint
1	A9	1c blk, bluish	115.00	95.00
2	A9	2c brn, buff	85.00	72.50
3	A9	4c claret, lav	35.00	30.00
4	A9	5c grn, grnsh	13.00	12.00
5	A9	10c blk, lavender	57.50	45.00
6	A9	15c blue	20.00	8.00
7	A9	20c red, grn	165.00	150.00
8	A9	25c blk, rose	67.50	37.50
9	A9	30c brn, yelsh	135.00	110.00
10	A9	35c blk, orange	135.00	100.00
11	A9	40c red, straw	110.00	90.00
12	A9	75c car, rose	275.00	225.00
13	A9	1fr brnz grn, straw	300.00	275.00

Red Overprint
14	A9	15c blue	70.00	45.00

Blue Overprint
15	A9	5c grn, grnsh	1,750.	700.00
15A	A9	15c blue	1,750.	700.00

Nos. 1-13 all exist with overprint inverted, and
several with it double. These sell for slightly more
than normal stamps. The overprints of Nos. 1-15A
are of four types, three without accent mark on
"E." They exist diagonal.
Counterfeits exist of Nos. 1-19.

Additional Surcharge in Red or   **40**
Black

1892
16	A9	01c on 5c grn, grnsh	225.	175.
17	A9	40c on 15c blue	135.	60.
18	A9	75c on 15c blue	625.	425.
19	A9	75c on 15c bl (Bk)	2,500.	1,900.

Counterfeits exist.

Navigation and Commerce
A3   A4

1893   Typo.   Perf. 14x13½
Name of Colony in Blue or Carmine
20	A3	1c blk, bluish	1.90	1.40
21	A3	2c brn, buff	2.25	1.75
22	A3	4c claret, lav	2.50	1.75
23	A3	5c grn, grnsh	3.25	2.00
24	A3	10c blk, lavender	3.25	2.40
25	A3	15c blue, quadrille paper	20.00	14.00
26	A3	20c red, grn	10.00	6.50
27	A3	25c blk, rose	27.50	16.00
28	A3	30c brn, bis	12.50	9.50
29	A3	40c red, straw	3.75	2.25
30	A3	50c car, rose	3.00	2.00
31	A3	75c vio, org	6.25	4.25
32	A3	1fr brnz grn, straw	42.50	35.00
		Nos. 20-32 (13)	138.65	98.80

Perf. 13½x14 stamps are counterfeits.

1894   Perf. 14x13½
33	A4	1c blk, bluish	2.00	1.40
34	A4	2c brn, buff	2.00	1.40
35	A4	4c claret, lav	2.00	1.40
36	A4	5c grn, grnsh	2.50	1.40
37	A4	10c blk, lavender	3.50	2.25
38	A4	15c bl, quadrille paper	4.50	2.25
39	A4	20c red, grn	4.50	3.50
40	A4	25c blk, rose	6.50	2.50
41	A4	30c brn, bis	4.00	2.50
42	A4	40c red, straw	11.00	7.00
43	A4	50c car, rose	15.00	7.50
44	A4	75c vio, org	9.50	8.00
45	A4	1fr brnz grn, straw	9.50	8.00
		Nos. 33-45 (13)	69.50	43.10

Perf. 13½x14 stamps are counterfeits.

PEOPLE'S REPUBLIC OF BENIN

LOCATION — West Coast of Africa
GOVT. — Republic.
AREA — 43,483 sq. mi.
POP. — 3,832,000 (est. 1984)
CAPITAL — Porto Novo

The Republic of Dahomey proclaimed
itself the People's Republic of Benin on Nov.
30, 1975. See Dahomey for stamps issued
before then.

> Catalogue values for unused
> stamps in this section are for Never
> Hinged items.

Allamanda
Cathartica — A83

Flag Bearers, Arms
of Benin — A84

Flowers: 35fr, Ixora coccinea. 45fr, Hibiscus,
60fr, Phaemeria magnifica.

Unwmk.

1975, Dec. 8		Photo.	Perf. 13	
342 A83	10fr lilac & multi		.15	.15
343 A83	35fr gray & multi		.22	.15
344 A83	45fr multi		.35	.22
345 A83	60fr blue & multi		.40	.30
	Nos. 342-345 (4)		1.12	.82

For surcharges see Nos. 618, 719, 723, 788.

1976, Apr. 30		Litho.	Perf. 12	

Design: 60fr, Speaker, wall with "PRPB," flag
and arms of Benin. 100fr, Flag and arms of Benin.

346 A84	50fr ocher & multi		.28	.20
347 A84	60fr ocher & multi		.30	.20
348 A84	100fr multi		.55	.40
	Nos. 346-348 (3)		1.13	.80

Proclamation of the People's Republic of Benin.
Nov. 30, 1975.

A.G. Bell, Satellite and 1876
Telephone — A85

1976, July 9		Litho.	Perf. 13	
349 A985	200fr lilac, red & brn		1.10	.45

Centenary of first telephone call by Alexander
Graham Bell, Mar. 10, 1876.

Dahomey Nos. 277-278 Surcharged

1976, July 19		Photo.	Perf. 12½x13	
350 A57	50fr on 1fr multi		.32	.15
351 A57	60fr on 2fr multi		.42	.15

For overprint and surcharge see Nos. 654A, 711.

African Jamboree, Nigeria 1976 — A86

1976, Aug. 16	Litho.	Perf. 12½x13	
352 A86	50fr Scouts Cooking	.28	.20
353 A86	70fr Three scouts	.38	.28

Blood Bank, Cotonou — A87

Designs: 50fr, Accident and first aid station. 60fr,
Blood donation.

1976, Sept. 24		Litho.	Perf. 13	
354 A87	5fr multicolored		.15	.15
355 A87	50fr multicolored		.28	.20
356 A87	60fr multicolored		.35	.22
	Nos. 354-356 (3)		.78	
	Set value			.47

National Blood Donors Day.

A88

A89

1976, Oct. 4		Litho.	Perf. 13x12½	
357 A88	20fr Manioc		.15	.15
358 A88	50fr Corn		.28	.20
359 A88	60fr Cacao		.30	.20
360 A88	150fr Cotton		.80	.60
	Nos. 357-360 (4)		1.53	1.15

Natl. agricultural production campaign. For
surcharge see No. 565.

1976, Oct. 25				
361 A89	50fr Classroom		.28	.20

Third anniversary of KPARO newspaper, used in
local language studies.

Roan
Antelope — A90

Flags, Wall, Broken
Chains — A91

Penhari National Park: 30fr, Buffalo. 50fr, Hippopotamus, horiz. 70fr, Lion.

1976, Nov. 8			Photo.	
362 A90	10fr multicolored		.15	.15
363 A90	30fr multicolored		.16	.15
364 A90	50fr multicolored		.28	.20
365 A90	70fr multicolored		.38	.22
	Nos. 362-365 (4)		.97	
	Set value			.59

1976, Nov. 30		Litho.	Perf. 12½	

Design: 150fr, Corn, raised hands with weapons.

366 A91	40fr multicolored		.20	.15
367 A91	150fr multicolored		.80	.60

First anniversary of proclamation of the People's
Republic of Benin.

Table Tennis, Map of Africa (Games'
Emblem) — A92

Design: 50fr, Stadium, Cotonou.

1976, Dec. 26		Litho.	Perf. 13	
368 A92	10fr multi		.15	.15
369 A92	50fr multi		.28	.20
	Set value			.35	.25

West African University Games, Cotonou, Dec.
26-31.

Europafrica Issue

Planes over Africa and
Europe — A93

1977, May 13		Litho.	Perf. 13	
370 A93	200fr multi		.70	.55

For surcharge see No. 590.

Snake — A94

1977, June 13		Litho.	Perf. 13x13½	
371 A94	2fr shown		.15	.15
372 A94	3fr Tortoise		.15	.15
373 A94	5fr Zebus		.15	.15
374 A94	10fr Cats		.16	.15
	Set value		.37	.20

Patients at
Clinic — A95

1977, Aug. 2		Litho.	Perf. 12½	
375 A95	100fr multi		.60	.40

World Rheumatism Year.

Karate, Map of
Africa — A96

Designs: 100fr, Javelin, map of Africa, Benin
Flag, horiz. 150fr, Hurdles.

1977, Aug. 30		Litho.	Perf. 12½	
376 A96	90fr multi		.35	.25
377 A96	100fr multi		.45	.35
378 A96	150fr multi		.60	.45
a.	Souvenir sheet of 3, #376-378		2.00	2.00
	Nos. 376-378 (3)		1.40	1.05

2nd West African Games, Lagos, Nigeria.

Chairman
Mao — A97

Lister and
Vaporizer — A98

1977, Sept. 9		Litho.	Perf. 13x12½	
379 A97	100fr multicolored		.50	.40

Mao Tse-tung (1893-1976), Chinese communist
leader.

1977, Sept. 20		Engr.	Perf. 13	

Designs: 150fr, Scalpels and flames, symbols of
antisepsis, and Red Cross.

380 A98	150fr multi		.80	.60
381 A98	210fr multi		1.20	.80

Joseph Lister (1827-1912), surgeon, founder of
antiseptic surgery.

For surcharges see Nos. 560, 566, 919.

Guelege Mask, Ethnographic Museum,
Porto Novo — A99

Designs: 50fr, Jar, symbol of unity, emblem of
King Ghezo, Historical Museum, Abomey, vert.
210fr, Abomey Museum.

1977, Oct. 17			Perf. 13	
382 A99	50fr red & multi		.28	.20
383 A99	60fr blk, bl & bister		.35	.22
384 A99	210fr multi		1.20	.80
	Nos. 382-384 (3)		1.83	1.22

For surcharge see Nos. 562, 920.

Atacora
Falls — A100

Mother and Child,
Owl of
Wisdom — A101

Tourist Publicity: 60fr, Pile houses, Ganvie,
horiz. 150fr, Round huts, Savalou.

1977, Oct. 24		Litho.	Perf. 12½	
385 A100	50fr multi		.32	.24
386 A100	60fr multi		.42	.25
387 A100	150fr multi		1.00	.70
a.	Souvenir sheet of 3, #385-387		2.00	2.00
	Nos. 385-387 (3)		1.74	1.19

		Perf. 12½x13, 13x12½		
1977, Dec. 3			Photo.	

150fr, Chopping down magical tree, horiz.

388 A101	60fr multi		.35	.22
389 A101	150fr multi		.80	.60

Campaign against witchcraft.
For surcharge see No. 576.

Battle
Scene
A102

1978, Jan. 16		Litho.	Perf. 12½	
390 A102	50fr multi		.35	.20

Victory of people of Benin over imperialist forces.

Map, People and
Houses of
Benin — A103

1978, Feb. 1				
391 A103	50fr multi		.35	.20

General population and dwelling census.

600

BENIN — People's Republic of Benin

Alexander Fleming, Microscope and
Penicillin — A104

1978, Mar. 12   Litho.   **Perf. 13**
392 A104 300fr multi   2.00 1.10
Alexnader Fleming (1881-1955), 50th anniversary of discovery of penicillin.

Abdoulaye
Issa, Weapons
and Fighters
— A105

1978, Apr. 1   **Perf. 12½x13**
393 A105 100fr red, blk & gold   .65 .38
First anniversary of death of Abdoulaye Issa and
National Day of Benin's Youth.

Ed Hadj Omar and Horseback
Rider — A106

Design: 90fr, L'Almamy Samory Toure (1830-
1900) and horseback riders.

1976, Apr. 10   **Perf. 13x12½**
394 A106 90fr red & multi   .60 .35
395 A106 100fr multi   .65 .38
African heroes of resistance against colonialism.

ITU Emblem, Satellite,
Landscape — A107

1978, May 17   Litho.   **Perf. 13**
396 A107 100fr multi   .65 .38
10th World Telecommunications Day.

Soccer Player, Stadium, Argentina '78
Emblem — A108

Designs (Argentina '78 Emblem and): 300fr, Soccer players and ball, vert. 500fr, Soccer player,
globe with ball on map.

1978, June 1   Litho.   **Perf. 12½**
397 A108 200fr multi   1.40   .70
398 A108 300fr multi   2.00 1.10
399 A108 500fr multi   3.50 1.75
  a.   Souvenir sheet of 3   7.00 7.00
    Nos. 397-399 (3)   6.90 3.55
11th World Cup Soccer Championship, Argentina, June 1-25. No. 399a contains 3 stamps similar
to Nos. 397-399 in changed colors.
For surcharges see Nos. 591, 593, 595-596.

Nos. 397-399a Overprinted in Red Brown:
  a. FINALE / ARGENTINE: 3 / HOL-
LANDE: 1
  b. CHAMPION / 1978 / ARGENTINE
  c. 3e BRESIL / 4e ITALIE

1978, June 25   Litho.   **Perf. 12½**
400 A108 (a) 200fr multi   1.40   .75
401 A108 (b) 300fr multi   2.00 1.10
402 A108 (c) 500fr multi   3.50 1.75
  a.   Souvenir sheet of 3   7.00 7.00
    Nos. 400-402 (3)   6.90 3.60
Argentina's victory in 1978 Soccer Championship.

Games' Flag over Africa, Basketball
Players — A109

Designs: 60fr, Map of Africa, volleyball players.
80fr, Map of Benin, bicyclists.

1978, July 13   **Perf. 13x12½**
403 A109 50fr lt bl & multi   .35   .20
404 A109 60fr ultra & multi   .40   .22
405 A109 80fr multi   .55   .35
  a.   Souvenir sheet of 3   1.40 1.40
    Nos. 403-405 (3)   1.30   .77
3rd African Games, Algiers, July 13-28. No. 405a
contains 3 stamps in changed colors similar to Nos.
403-405.

Martin Luther King,
Jr. — A110

1978, July 30   **Perf. 12½**
406 A110 300fr multi   2.00 1.10
Martin Luther King, Jr. (1929-1968), American
civil rights leader.
For surcharge see No. 592.

Kanna Taxi,
Oueme
A111

60fr Leatherworker & goods. 70fr, Drummer &
tom-toms. 100fr, Metalworker & calabashes.

1978, Aug. 26
407 A111 50fr multi   .35   .20
408 A111 60fr multi   .40   .22
409 A111 70fr multi   .45   .28
410 A111 100fr multi   .65   .40
    Nos. 407-410 (4)   1.85 1.10
Getting to know Benin through its provinces.

Map of Italy and Exhibition
Poster — A112

1978, Aug. 26   Litho.   **Perf. 13**
411 A112 200fr multi   1.40 .70
Riccione 1978 Philatelic Exhibition.
For overprint see No. 537.

Poultry
Breeding — A113

1978 Oct. 5   Photo.   **Perf. 12½x13**
412 A113 10fr Turkeys   .15   .15
413 A113 20fr Ducks   .15   .15
414 A113 50fr Chicken   .35   .35
415 A113 60fr Guinea fowl .40   .40
    Nos. 412-415 (4)   1.05 1.05

Royal
Messenger,
UPU Emblem
A114

UPU Emblem and: 60fr, Boatsman, ship & car,
vert. 90fr, Special messenger & plane, vert.

Perf. 13x12½, 12½x13
1978, Oct. 16
416 A114 50fr multi   .35   .35
417 A114 60fr multi   .40   .40
418 A114 90fr multi   .60   .60
    Nos. 416-418 (3)   1.35 1.35
Centenary of change of "General Postal Union"
to "Universal Postal Union."

Raoul
Follereau
A115

1978, Dec. 17   Litho.   **Perf. 12½**
419 A115 200fr multi   1.75 1.75
Raoul Follereau (1903-1977), apostle to the lepers and educator of the blind.

IYC Emblem
A116

Intl. Year of the Child: 20fr, Glove as balloon
carrying childern. 50fr, Children of various races
surrounding globe.

1979, Feb. 20   Litho.   **Perf. 12x13**
420 A116 10fr multi   .15   .15
421 A116 20fr multi   .15   .15
422 A116 50fr multi   .35   .35
    Nos. 420-422 (3)   .65 .65

Hydrangea — A117

Flowers: 25fr, Assangokan. 30fr, Geranium. 40fr,
Water lilies, horiz.

Perf. 13x12½, 12½x13
1979, Feb. 28   Litho.
423 A117 20fr multi   .15   .15
424 A117 25fr multi   .16   .16
425 A117 30fr multi   .20   .20
426 A117 40fr mutli   .25   .25
    Nos. 423-426 (4)   .76 .76

Emblem: Map
of Africa and
Members'
Flags — A118

60fr, Map of Benin & flags. 80fr, OCAM flag and
map of Africa showing member states.

1979, Mar. 20   Litho.   **Perf. 12x13**
427 A118 50fr multi   .40   .40
428 A118 60fr multi   .45   .45
429 A118 80fr multi   .65   .65
    Nos. 427-429 (3)   1.50 1.50
OCAM Summit Conf., Cotonou, Mar. 20-28.
For overprints see Nos. 434-436.

Tower,
Waves,
Satellite, ITU
Emblem
A119

1979, May 17   Litho.   **Perf. 12½**
430 A119 50fr multi   .40 .40
World Telecommunications Day.

Bank Building and
Sculpture — A120

1979, May 26   Litho.
431 A120 50fr multi   .35 .35
Opening of Headquarters of West African Savings
Bank in Dakar.

Guelede Mask, Abomey Tapestry, Malaconotus Bird — A121

Design: 50fr, Jet, canoe, satellite, UPU and exhibition emblems.

1979, June 8   Litho.   Perf. 13
432 A121 15fr multi .15 .15
         Engr.
433 A121 50fr multi .35 .35

Philexafrique II, Libreville, Gabon, June 8-17. Nos. 432, 433 each printed in sheets of 10 with 5 labels showing exhibition emblem.

Nos. 427-429 Overprinted: "26 au 28 juin 1979" and Dots

1979, June 26
434 A118 50fr multi .35 .35
435 A118 60fr multi .40 .40
436 A118 80fr multi .55 .55
     Nos. 434-436 (3) 1.30 1.30

2nd OCAM Summit Conf., June 26-28.

Olympic Flame, and Emblems A122

Pre-Olympic Year: 50fr, High jump.

1979, July 1   Litho.
437 A122 10fr multi .15 .15
438 A122 50fr multi .35 .35

Antelope A123

Animals: 10fr, Giraffes, map of Benin, vert 20fr, Chimpanzee. 50fr, Elephants, map of Benin, vert.

1979, Oct. 1   Litho.   Perf. 13
439 A123 5fr multi .15 .15
440 A123 10fr multi .15 .15
441 A123 20fr multi .15 .15
442 A123 50fr multi .35 .35
     Set value .60 .60

Map of Africa, Emblem and Jet — A124

1979, Dec. 12   Litho.   Perf. 12½
443 A124 50fr multi .35 .35
444 A124 60fr multi .40 .40

ASECNA (Air Safety Board), 20th anniv.

Mail Services — A125

Design: 50fr, Post Office and headquarters, vert.

1979, Dec. 19   Litho.   Perf. 13
445 A125 50fr multi .35 .35
446 A125 60fr multi .40 .40

Office of Posts and Telecommunications, 20th anniversary.

Lenin and Globe A126

1980, Apr. 22   Litho.   Perf. 12½
447 A126 50fr shown .25 .25
448 A126 150fr Lenin in library .80 .80

Lenin, 110th birth anniversary.

Monument to King Behanzin A126a

Litho. & Embossed   Perf. 12½
1980, May 31
448A A126a 1000fr gold & multi 5.50 5.50
For overprint see No. Q10A.

Cotonou Club Emblem — A127   Galileo, Astrolabe — A128

1980, Feb. 23   Litho.   Perf. 12½
449 A127 90fr shown .60 .60
450 A127 200fr Rotary emblem on globe, horiz. 1.40 1.40

Rotary International, 75th anniversary.
For surcharge see No. 915.

1980, Apr. 2
451 A128 100fr shown .45 .45
452 A128 100fr Copernicus, solar system .65 .65

Discovery of Pluto, 50th anniversary.

Abu Simbel, UNESCO Emblem — A129

1980, Apr. 15   Perf. 13
453 A129 50fr Column, vert. .35 .35
454 A129 60fr Ramses II, vert. .40 .40
455 A129 150fr shown 1.00 1.00
     Nos. 453-455 (3) 1.75 1.75

UNESCO campaign to save Nubian monuments, 20th anniversary.

Monument, Martyrs' Square, Cotonou A130

Designs: Various monuments in Martyrs' Square. Cotonou. 60fr, 70fr, 100fr, horiz.

1980, May 2   Perf. 12½x13, 13x12½
456 A130 50fr multi .35 .35
457 A130 60fr multi .40 .40
458 A130 70fr multi .45 .45
459 A130 100fr multi .65 .65
     Nos. 456-459 (4) 1.85 1.85

For surcharge see No. 539.

Musical Instruments A131

1980, May 20   Perf. 12½
460 A131 5fr Assan, vert. .15 .15
461 A131 10fr Tinbo .15 .15
462 A131 15fr Tam-tam sato, vert. .15 .15
463 A131 20fr Kora .15 .15
464 A131 30fr Gangan .20 .20
465 A131 50fr Sinhoun .35 .35
     Set value .90 .90

First Non-stop Flight, Paris-New York — A132

1980, June 2   Litho.   Perf. 12½
466 A132 90fr shown .60 .60
467 A132 100fr Dieudonne Coste, Maurice Bellonte .65 .65

For surcharge see No. 564.

Lunokhod I on the Moon — A133

1980, June 15   Engr.   Perf. 13
468 A133 90fr multi .60 .60

Lunokhod I Soviet unmanned moon mission, 10th anniv. See #C290. For surcharge see #C305.

Olympic Flame and Mischa, Moscow '80 Emblem — A134

1980, July 16   Litho.   Perf. 12½
469 A134 50fr shown .35 .35
470 A134 60fr Equestrian, vert. .40 .40
471 A134 70fr Judo .50 .50

472 A134 200fr Flag, sports, globe, vert. 1.40 1.40
473 A134 300fr Weight lifting, vert. 2.25 2.25
     Nos. 469-473 (5) 4.90 4.90

22nd Summer Olympic Games, Moscow, July 19-Aug. 3.
For surcharges see Nos. 559, 561.

Telephone and Rising Sun — A135

World Telecommunications Day: 50fr, Farmer on telephone, vert.

1980, May 17   Litho.   Perf. 12½
474 A135 50fr multi .35 .35
475 A135 60fr multi .40 .40

Cotonou West African Community Village A136

Designs: View of Cotonou.

1980, July 26   Perf. 13x13½
476 A136 50fr multi .35 .35
477 A136 60fr multi .40 .40
478 A136 70fr multi .45 .45
     Nos. 476-478 (3) 1.20 1.20

For surcharge see No. 540.

Agbadja Dancers — A137

Designs: Dancers and musicans.

1980, Aug. 1   Perf. 12½
479 A137 30fr multi .20 .20
480 A137 50fr multi .35 .35
481 A137 66fr multi .40 .40
     Nos. 479-481 (3) .95 .95

Fisherman A138   Philippines under Magnifier A139

Designs: 5fr, Throwing net. 15fr, Canoe and shore fishing. 20fr, Basket traps. 50fr, Hauling net. 60fr, River fishing. All horiz.

1980, Sept. 1
482 A138 5fr multi .15 .15
483 A138 10fr multi .15 .15
484 A138 15fr multi .15 .15
485 A138 20fr multi .15 .15
486 A138 50fr multi .35 .35
487 A138 60fr multi .40 .40
     Set value 1.10 1.10

For surcharge see No. 535.

Perf. 13x13½, 13x½x13
1980, Sept. 27

World Tourism Conference, Manila, Sept. 27: 60fr, Emblem on flag, hand pointing to Manila on globe, horiz.

488 A139 50fr multi .35 .35
489 A139 60fr multi .40 .40

For surcharge see No. 557.

A140   A141

1980, Oct. 1   *Perf. 12¹/₂*
490 A140   40fr Othreis materna   .25   .25
491 A140   50fr Othreis fullonia   .35   .35
492 A140   200fr Oryctes sp.   1.40 1.40
    Nos. 490-492 (3)   2.00 2.00

1980, Oct. 24   Photo.   *Perf. 13¹/₂*
493 A141   75fr multi   .50   .50
    African Postal Union, 5th Anniv.

A142   A143

1980, Nov. 4   *Perf. 12¹/₂x13*
494 A142   30fr shown   .20   .20
495 A142   50fr Freed prisoner   .35   .35
496 A142   60fr Man holding torch   .40   .40
    Nos. 494-496 (3)   .95   .95
    Declaration of human rights, 30th anniv.

1980, Dec. 1   Litho.   *Perf. 13*
    Self-portrait, by Vincent van Gogh, 1888.
497 A143   100fr shown   .75   .75
498 A143   300fr Facteur Roulin   2.25 2.25
    Vincent van Gogh (1853-1890), artist.
    For surcharge see No. 579.

Offenbach and Scene from Orpheus in the
Underworld — A144

1980, Dec. 15   Engr.
499 A144   50fr shown   .40   .40
500 A144   60fr Paris Life   .45   .45
    Jacques Offenbach (1819-1880), composer.

Kepler and Satellites — A145

1980, Dec. 20
501 A145   50fr Kepler, diagram, vert. .35   .35
502 A145   60fr shown   .40   .40
    Johannes Kepler (1571-1630), astronomer.

Intl. Year of the
Disabled — A146

1981, Apr. 10   Litho.   *Perf. 12¹/₂*
503 A146   115fr multi   .75   .75
    For surcharge see No. 582.

20th Anniv. of Manned Space
Flight — A147

1981, May 30   *Perf. 13*
504 A147   500fr multi   3.50 3.50
    For surcharges see Nos. 580, 790.

13th World
Telecommunications
Day — A148

1981, May 30   Litho.   *Perf. 12¹/₂*
505 A148   115fr multi   .75   .75
    For surcharge see No. 583.

Amaryllis
A149

1981, June 20   *Perf. 12¹/₂*
506 A149   10fr shown   .15   .15
507 A149   20fr Eischornia crassipes,
      vert.   .15   .15
508 A149   80fr Parkia biglobosa, vert. .55   .55
    Nos. 506-508 (3)   .85   .85
    For surcharge see No. 542.

Benin Sheraton
Hotel — A150

1981, July
509 A150   100fr multi   .65   .65
    For surcharge see No. 541.

Guinea
Pig — A151

1981, July 31   *Perf. 13x13¹/₂*
510 A151   5fr shown   .15   .15
511 A151   60fr Cat   .40   .40
512 A151   80fr Dogs   .55   .55
    Nos. 510-512 (3)   1.10 1.10
    For surcharges see Nos. 536, 543, 563.

World UPU
Day — A152

1981, Oct. 9   Engr.   *Perf. 13*
513 A152   100fr red brn & blk   .65   .65

25th Intl. Letter Writing Week, Oct. 6-
12 — A153

1981, Oct. 15
514 A153   100fr dk bl & pur   .65   .65
    For surcharge see No. 558.

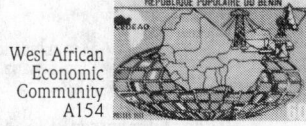

West African
Economic
Community
A154

1981, Nov. 20   Litho.   *Perf. 12¹/₂*
515 A154   60fr multi   .40   .40

West African
Rice
Development
Assoc. 10th
Anniv.
A155

1981, Dec. 10   *Perf. 13x13¹/₂*
516 A155   60fr multi   .40   .40

TB Bacillus
Centenary
A156

1982, Mar. 1   Litho.   *Perf. 13*
517 A156   115fr multi   1.20 1.20
    For surcharge see No. 584.

West African
Economic
Community, 5th
Summit
Conference — A157

1982, May 27   *Perf. 12¹/₂*
518 A157   60fr multi   .40   .40

1982
World
Cup
A158

1982, June 1   *Perf. 13*
519 A158   90fr Players   .65   .65
520 A158   300fr Flags on leg   2.25 2.25
    For overprints and surcharges see #523-524,
594, 789.

France No. B349 Magnified, Map of
France — A159

1982, June 11
521 A159   90fr multi   .60   .60
    For surcharge see No. 916.

    PHILEXFRANCE '82 Stamp Exhibition, Paris,
June 11-21.

George
Washington
A160

1982, Mar. 10   Litho.   *Perf. 14*
522 A160   200fr Washington, flag,
      map   1.00 1.00
    For surcharge see No. 577.

    Nos. 519-520 Overprinted with Finalists
Names

1982, Aug. 16   *Perf. 12¹/₂*
523 A158   90fr multi   .60   .60
524 A158   300fr multi   2.00 2.00
    Italy's victory in 1982 World Cup.
    For surcharge see No. 811.

Bluethroat
A161

Perf. 14x14¹/₂, 14¹/₂x14
1982, Sept. 1
525 A161   5fr Daoelo gigas, vert.   .15   .15
526 A161   10fr shown   .15   .15
527 A161   15fr Swallow, vert.   .15   .15
528 A161   20fr Kingfisher, weaver
      bird, vert.   .16   .16
529 A161   30fr Great sedge warbler   .25   .25
530 A161   60fr Common warbler   .50   .50
531 A161   80fr Owl, vert.   .65   .65
532 A161   100fr Cockatoo, vert.   .80   .80
    Nos. 525-532 (8)   2.81 2.81

ITU Plenipotentiaries Conference, Nairobi,
Sept. — A162

1982, Sept. 26   *Perf. 13*
533 A162   200fr Map   1.00 1.00
    For surcharge see No. 585.

13th World UPU Day
A163

1982, Oct. 9   Engr.   Perf. 13
534 A163 100fr Monument   .65 .65

Nos. 482, 510, 411 Overprinted in Red or Blue:
#535 "Croix Rouge / 8 Mai 1982"
#536 "UAPT 1982"
#537 "RICCONE 1982"

Perf. 13, 12½, 13x13½
1982, Nov.   Litho.
535 A138 60fr on 5fr multi   .40 .40
536 A151 60fr on 5fr multi   .40 .40
537 A112 200fr multi (Bl)   1.40 1.40
      Nos. 535-537 (3)   2.20 2.20

Visit of French Pres. Francois Mitterand
A164

1983, Jan. 15   Litho.   Perf. 12½x13
538 A164 90fr multi   .60 .60

For surcharge see No. 917.

Nos. 458, 476, 508-509, 512 Surcharged
Perf. 13x12½, 13x13½, 12½
1983   Litho.
539 A130 60fr on 70fr multi   .40 .40
540 A136 60fr on 50fr multi   .40 .40
541 A150 60fr on 100fr multi   .40 .40
542 A149 75fr on 80fr multi   .50 .50
543 A151 75fr on 80fr multi   .50 .50
      Nos. 539-543 (5)   2.20 2.20

Seme Oil Rig — A165

1983, Apr. 28   Litho.   Perf. 13x12½
544 A165 125fr multi   .80 .80

World Communications Year — A166

1983, May 17   Litho.   Perf. 13
545 A166 185fr multi   1.00 1.00

For surcharge see No. 898.

Riccione '83, Stamp Show — A167

1983, Aug. 27   Litho.   Perf. 13
546 A167 500fr multi   3.25 3.25

For surcharge see No. 922.

Benin Red Cross, 20th Anniv.
A168

1983, Sept. 5   Photo.   Perf. 13
547 A168 105fr multi   .70 .70

For surcharge see No. 581.

Handicrafts
A169

Designs: 75fr, Handcarved lion chairs and table. 90fr, Natural tree table and stools. 200fr, Monkeys holding jar.

1983, Sept. 18   Litho.   Perf. 13
548 A169 75fr multi   .40 .40
549 A169 90fr multi   .50 .50
550 A169 200fr multi   1.10 1.10
      Nos. 548-550 (3)   2.00 2.00

For surcharge see No. 578.

14th UPU Day — A170

1983, Oct. 9   Engr.   Perf. 13
551 A170 125fr multi   .80 .80

For surcharge see No. 575.

Religious Movements   Plaited Hair Styles
A171   A172

1983, Oct. 31   Litho.   Perf. 14x15
552 A171 75fr Zangbeto   .35 .35
553 A171 75fr Egoun   .35 .35

1983, Nov. 14
554 A172 30fr Rockcoco   .15 .15
555 A172 75fr Serpent   .35 .35
556 A172 90fr Songas   .40 .40
      Nos. 554-556 (3)   .90 .90

Stamps of 1976-81 Surcharged
1983, Nov.
557 A139   5fr on 50fr #488   .15 .15
558 A153 10fr on 100fr #514   .15 .15
559 A134 15fr on 200fr #472   .15 .15
560 A98   15fr on 210fr #381   .15 .15
561 A134 25fr on 70fr #471   .15 .15
562 A99   25fr on 210fr #384   .15 .15
563 A151 75fr on 5fr #510   .35 .35
564 A132 75fr on 100fr #467   .35 .35
565 A88   75fr on 150fr #360   .35 .35
566 A98   75fr on 150fr #380   .35 .35
      Set value   1.85 1.85

Alfred Nobel (1833-96)
A173

1983, Dec. 19   Litho.   Perf. 15x14
567 A173 300fr multi   1.40 1.40

For surcharge see No. 923.

Council of Unity — A174

1984, May 29   Litho.   Perf. 12
568 A174 75fr multi   .35 .35
569 A174 90fr multi   .40 .40

For surcharge see No. 918.

1984 UPU Congress
A175

1984, June 18   Litho.   Perf. 13
570 A175 90fr multi   .40 .40

Abomey Calavi Earth Station
A176

1984, June 29   Litho.   Perf. 12½x13
571 A176 75fr Satellite dish   .35 .35

Traditional Costumes — A177

1984, July 2   Litho.   Perf. 13½x13
572 A177   5fr Koumboro   .15 .15
573 A177 10fr Taka   .15 .15
574 A177 20fr Toko   .15 .15
      Set value   .17 .17

Nos. 389, 498, 503-505, 517, 522, 533, 547, 550 and 551 Surcharged
1984, Sept.
575 A170   5fr on 125fr #551   .15 .15
576 A101   5fr on 150fr #389   .15 .15
577 A100 10fr on 200fr #522   .15 .15
578 A169 10fr on 200fr #550   .15 .15
579 A143 10fr on 300fr #498   .15 .15
580 A147 40fr on 500fr #504   .15 .15
581 A168 75fr on 105fr #547   .35 .35
582 A146 75fr on 115fr #503   .35 .35
583 A148 75fr on 115fr #505   .35 .35
584 A156 75fr on 115fr #517   .35 .35
585 A162 75fr on 200fr #533   .35 .35
      Set value   2.15 2.15

World Food Day — A178   Dinosaurs — A179

1984, Oct. 16   Litho.   Perf. 12½
586 A178 100fr Malnourished child .30 .30

1984, Dec. 14   Litho.   Perf. 13½
587 A179 75fr Anatosaurus   .22 .22
588 A179 90fr Brontosaurus   .25 .25

Cultural & Technical Cooperation Agency, 15th Anniv.
A180

1985, Mar 20   Litho.   Perf. 13
589 A180 300fr Emblem, globe, hands, book   .90 .90

Stamps of 1977-82 Surcharged
1985, Mar.
590 A93   75fr on 200fr No. 370   .20 .20
591 A108 75fr on 200fr No. 397   .20 .20
592 A110 75fr on 300fr No. 406   .20 .20
593 A108 75fr on 300fr No. 398   .20 .20
594 A158 90fr on 300fr No. 520   .25 .25
595 A108 90fr on 500fr No. 399   .25 .25
596 A108 90fr on 500fr No. 402   .25 .25
      Nos. 590-596 (7)   1.55 1.55

End of World War II, 40th Anniv. — A180a

1985, May   Litho.   Perf. 12
596A A180a 100fr multicolored

Traditional Dances
A181

1985, June 1   Litho.   Perf. 15x14½
597 A181 75fr Teke, Borgou Tribe   .20 .20
598 A181 100fr Tipen'ti, L'Atacora Tribe   .28 .28

Intl. Youth Year — A182

1985, July 16   Perf. 13½
599 A182 150fr multi   .45 .45

1986 World Cup Soccer Championships,
Mexico — A183

1985, July 22	Perf. 13x12½
600 A183 200fr multi	.60 .60

Beginning with Scott 601, Benin again surcharged stamps of Dahomey with a variety of surcharges. While the listings that follow contain more than 80 surcharged stamps, the Scott editors still need to examine more than 60 other stamps, in order to list all of those that are currently known to exist.

The size and location of the surcharge varies from stamp to stamp. The type face used in the surcharge may also vary from issue to issue.

REPUBLIQUE POPULAIRE
DU BÉNIN
15 f

a

b

c

d

e   f

g   h

i

j

Dahomey No. 336 Surcharged with Black
Bars and New Value

1985, Aug.	Perf. 12½
601 A78(a) 15fr on 40fr multi	.18 .18

ASECNA Airlines, 25th Anniv. — A184

1985, Sept. 16	Perf. 13
602 A184 150fr multi	.45 .45

UN 40th
Anniv.
A185

1985, Oct. 24	Perf. 12½
603 A185 250fr multi	.90 .90

Benin UN membership, 25th anniv.

ITALIA'85,
Rome — A186

1985, Oct. 25	Perf. 13½
604 A186 200fr multi	.75 .75

PHILEXAFRICA '85, Lome — A187

1985, Nov. 16	Perf. 13
605 A187 250fr #569, labor emblem	.90 .90
606 A187 250fr #C252, Gabon #366, magnified stamp	.90 .90
a. Pair, Nos. 605-606 + label	1.80 1.80

Audubon Birth   Mushrooms and
Bicent. — A188   Toadstools — A189

1985, Oct. 17	Litho.	Perf. 14x15
607 A188 150fr Skua gull		.55 .55
608 A188 300fr Oyster catcher		1.10 1.10

1985, Oct. 17		
609 A189 35fr Boletus edible		.15 .15
610 A189 40fr Amanite phalloide		.15 .15
611 A189 100fr Brown chanterelle		.38 .38
Nos. 609-611 (3)		.68 .68

Dahomey Nos. 282, 292, Benin No. 343
Surcharged

1986, Mar.	Photo.
612 A83(b) 75fr on 35fr #343	.25 .25
613 A57(c) 90fr on 70fr #282	.35 .35
614 A60(b) 90fr on 140fr #292	.35 .35
Nos. 612-614 (3)	.95 .95

African Parliamentary
Union, 10th
Anniv. — A190

1986, May 8	Litho.	Perf. 13x12½
615 A190 100fr multi		.38 .38

9th Conference, Cotonou, May 8-10.

Halley's Comet — A191

1986, May 30	Perf. 12½x12
616 A191 250fr multi	.75 .75

For surcharge see No. 809.

Dahomey No. 283, Benin No. 344
Surcharged
Engraved, Photogravure

1986, June	Perf. 13
617 A58(b) 100fr on 40fr #283	.38 .38
618 A83(b) 150fr on 45fr #344	.55 .55

1986 World Cup Soccer Championships,
Mexico — A192

1986, June 29	Litho.
619 A192 500fr multi	1.75 1.75

For surcharge see No. 792.

Fight against
Desert
Encroachment
A193

1986, July 16	Perf. 13½
620 A193 150fr multi	.55 .55

King   Amazon
Behanzin   A194a
A194

1986-88	Engr.	Perf. 13
621 A194 40fr black		.20 .20
622 A194a 100fr brt blue		.40 .40
623 A194 125fr maroon		.60 .60
624 A194a 150fr violet		.60 .60
625 A194 190fr dark ultra		.90 .90
627 A194 220fr dark grn		1.00 1.00
Nos. 621-627 (6)		3.70 3.70

Issued: 100fr, 150fr, 8/1; others, 10/1/88.
See No. 636. For surcharge see No. 787.

Flowers — A195   Butterflies — A196

Perf. 13x12½, 12½x13	
1986, Sept. 1	Litho.
631 A195 100fr Haemanthus	.42 .42
632 A195 205fr Hemerocalle, horiz.	.90 .90

1986, Sept. 15

#633, Day peacock, little tortoiseshell, morio.
#634, Aurora, machaon and fair lady.

633 A196 150fr multi	.60 .60
634 A196 150fr multi	.60 .60

Dahomey Nos. 290, 307 Overprinted
1985, Oct. 15
Perfs. & Printing Methods as Before

634A A67(b) 50fr on #307	
634B A60(d) 150fr on 100fr #290	

Statue of Liberty, Cent. — A197

King Behanzin — A198

1986, Oct. 28   Litho.   Perf. 12½
635 A197 250fr multi   .90 .90

1986, Oct. 30   Perf. 13½
636 A198 440fr multi   1.60 1.60

Behanzin, leader of resistance movement against French occupation (1886-1894).
For surcharge see No. 921.

Brazilian Cultural Week, Cotonou — A200

1987, Jan. 17   Perf. 12½
638 A200 150fr multi   .88 .88

Rotary Intl. District 910 Conference, Cotonou, Apr. 23-25 — A201

1987, Apr. 23   Litho.   Perf. 13½
639 A201 300fr Center for the Blind,
            Cotonou   1.75 1.75

Automobile Cent. — A202

Modern car and: 150fr, Steam tricycle, by De Dion-Bouton and Trepardoux, 1887. 300fr, Gas-driven Victoria, by Daimler, 1886.

1987, July 1   Perf. 12½
640 A202 150fr multi   .88 .88
641 A202 300fr multi   1.75 1.75

For surcharge see No. 679B.

Snake Temple Baptism — A203

1987, July 20   Perf. 13½
642 A203 100fr multi   .55 .55

Shellfish A204

1987, July 24   Perf. 12½
643 A204 100fr crayfish   .55 .55
644 A204 150fr crab   .90 .90

G. Hansen, R. Follerau — A205

1987, Sept. 4   Perf. 13
645 A205 200fr Cure Leprosy   1.10 1.10

Beginning of Benin Revolution, 15th Anniv. — A205a

1987, Oct. 28   Litho.   Perf. 12x12½
645A A205a 100fr multicolored

Locust Control A206

1987, Dec. 7   Litho.   Perf. 12½x13
646 A206 100fr multi   .72 .72

Christmas 1987 — A207

1987, Dec. 21   Perf. 13
647 A207 150fr multi   1.10 1.10

Dahomey Nos. 268, 284 Ovptd. or Surchd.

1987   Engr.   Perf. 13
647A A58(b) 15fr on 100fr #284
647B A53(b) 40fr on #268
        See Nos. C362, C369.

Intl. Red Cross and Red Crescent Organizations, 125th Anniv. — A208

1988, May 25   Litho.   Perf. 13½
648 A208 200fr multi   1.30 1.30

A209   A210

1988, July 11   Perf. 12½
649 A209 200fr multi   1.30 1.30

Martin Luther King, Jr. (1929-68), American civil rights leader.

1988, May 25   Litho.   Perf. 13½
650 A210 125fr multi   .88 .88

Organization of African Unity, 25th anniv.

WHO, 40th Anniv. — A211

1988, Sept. 1   Litho.   Perf. 13x12½
651 A211 175fr multi   1.15 1.15

Alma Ata Declaration, 10th anniv.; Health Care for All on Earth by the Year 2000.
For surcharge see No. 786.

Ganvie Lake Village A212

1988, Sept. 4   Perf. 13½
652 A212 125fr shown   .85 .85
653 A212 190fr Boatman, village,
            diff.   1.25 1.25

A213   A214

1988, Aug. 14   Perf. 12½
654 A213 125fr multi   .88 .88

1st Benin Scout Jamboree, Aug. 12-19.

Benin No. 351, Dahomey Nos. 296, 328 Surcharged

1988
Printing Method & Perfs as Before
654A A57(d) 10fr on 60fr on 2fr
                                #351
654B A62(d) 10fr on 65fr #296
654E A74(d) 150fr on 200fr #328

1988, Dec. 30   Litho.   Perf. 13
Ritual Offering to Hebiesso, God of Thunder and Lightning.
655 A214 125fr multicolored   .82 .82

Dahomey Nos. 161, 247, 302, 333, 339, 341 Surcharged

1988   Photo.   Perf. 12½x13
655A A19(d) 5fr on 3fr #161
655C A82(d) 30fr on 150fr #341
655D A76(d) 25fr on 100fr #333
655E A45(b) 50fr on 45fr #247
655F A81(d) 55fr on 200fr #339
655G A65(b) 60fr on 85fr #302

These are part of a set of 10. Another set of 19 surcharges also is known to exist. The editors need to see the rest of these stamps before listings can be created.

Rural Development Council, 30th Anniv. A214a

1989, May 29   Litho.   Perf. 15x14
655K A214a 75fr multicolored

World Wildlife Fund — A216

Roseate terns, Sterna dougalli.

1989, Jan. 30   Perf. 13
657 A216 10fr Three terns   .15 .15
658 A216 15fr Feeding on fish   .15 .15
659 A216 50fr Perched   .32 .32
660 A216 125fr In flight   .82 .82
        Nos. 657-660 (4)   1.44 1.44

Eiffel Tower Cent. — A217

1989, Apr. 24   Litho.   Perf. 13x12½
661 A217 190fr multi   1.10 1.10

PHILEXFRANCE '89, French Revolution Bicent. — A218

Design: Bastille, emblems, Declaration of Human Rights and Citizenship, France No. B252-B253.

1989, July 7   *Perf. 13*
662 A218 190fr multicolored   1.10 1.10

Electric Corp.
of Benin,
20th Anniv.
A219

1989, Oct. Litho.   *Perf. 12¹/₂x13*
663 A219 125fr multicolored   .80 .80

Fish — A220

1989, Sept. 22   *Perf. 13¹/₂*
664 A220 125fr Lote   .80 .80
665 A220 190fr Pike, salmon   1.20 1.20

Death of King Glele,
Cent. — A221

1989, Dec. 16 Litho.   *Perf. 13¹/₂*
666 A221 190fr multicolored   1.25 1.25

Christmas
A222

1989, Dec. 25   *Perf. 13*
667 A222 200fr Holy family   1.30 1.30

Benin Posts & Telecommunications,
Cent. — A223

1990, Jan. 1   *Perf. 13¹/₂*
668 A223 125fr multicolored   .82 .82

Fruits and
Flora
A224

1990, Jan. 23 Litho.   *Perf. 11¹/₂*
669 A224 60fr Oranges   .42 .42
670 A224 190fr Kaufmann Tulips,
              vert.   1.40 1.40
671 A224 250fr Cashews, vert.   1.75 1.75
       Nos. 669-671 (3)   3.57 3.57
          Dated 1989.

Moon
Landing,
20th Anniv.
A225

1990, Jan. 23
672 A225 190fr multicolored   1.40 1.40
          Dated 1989.

World Cup Soccer Championships,
Italy — A226

1990, June 8 Litho.   *Perf. 12¹/₂*
673 A226 125fr shown   1.00 1.00
674 A226 190fr Character trademark,
              vert.   1.50 1.50

For overprint see No. 676.

Post, Telephone &
Telegraph
Administration in
Benin,
Cent. — A227

1990, July 1   *Perf. 13*
675 A227 150fr multicolored   1.25 1.25

No. 673   **FINALE**
Ovptd.   **R.F.A. - ARGENTINE**
          1 - 0

1990 Litho.   *Perf. 12¹/₂*
676 A226 125fr multicolored   1.00 1.00

Charles de
Gaulle (1890-
1970)
A228

1990, Nov. 22 Litho.   *Perf. 13*
677 A228 190fr multicolored   1.50 1.50
          See No. 689.

Galileo Probe
and Jupiter
A229

1990, Dec. 1
678 A229 100fr multicolored   .75 .75
For overprint see No. 681.

A230

1990, Dec. 25 Litho.   *Perf. 12¹/₂x13*
679 A230 200fr multicolored   1.75 1.75
          Christmas.

Benin No. 641 Surcharged

1990
Perf. & Printing Method as Before
679B A202(e) 190fr on 300fr #641

A230a   A231

1990 Litho.   *Perf. 11¹/₂x12*
679C A230a 125fr multicolored
       National People's Congress.

1991, Sept. 3 Litho.   *Perf. 13¹/₂*
680 A231 125fr multicolored   1.05 1.05
       Independence, 31st anniv.

No. 678
Ovptd. in   **"Riccione 91"**
Red

1991   *Perf. 13*
681 A229 100fr multicolored   .85 .85

French Open
Tennis
Championships,
Cent. — A232

1991   *Perf. 13¹/₂*
682 A232 125fr multicolored   1.05 1.05

African Tourism Year — A233

1991
683 A233 190fr multicolored   1.65 1.65

Christmas
A234

1991, Dec. 2 Litho.   *Perf. 13¹/₂*
684 A234 125fr multicolored   1.05 1.05

Dancer of   Wolfgang Amadeus
Guelede — A235   Mozart, Death
                  Bicent. — A236

1991, Dec. 2
685 A235 190fr multicolored   1.65 1.65

1991, Dec. 2
686 A236 1000fr multicolored   8.50 8.50
For surcharge see No. 793.

Discovery of
America,
500th Anniv.
A237

Design: 1000fr, Columbus coming ashore, horiz.

1992, Apr. 24 Litho.   *Perf. 13*
687 A237 500fr blk, blue & brn   3.75 3.75
688 A237 1000fr multicolored   7.50 7.50
a.   Souvenir sheet of 2, #687-688   11.25 11.25

De Gaulle Type of 1990
1992 Litho.   *Perf. 13*
689 A228 300fr like #677   2.25 2.25

Intl. Conference on
Nutrition,
Rome — A238

1992, Dec. 5 Litho.   *Perf. 13*
690 A238 190fr multicolored   1.60 1.60

Dahomey Nos. 160, 266, 303, 311, 327, 334, C161 Surcharged

1992

Perfs. & Printing Methods as Before

690A A66(e)	5fr on #303	
690F A19(e)	125fr on 2fr #160	
690G AP54(f)	125fr on 65fr #C161	
690H A77(f)	125fr on 65fr #334	

(G)

690I CD137(e)	125fr on 100fr #311	
690J A52(f)	190fr on 45fr #266	
690K A74(f)	125fr on 100fr #327	

Visit of Pope John Paul II, Feb. 3-5 — A239

Ouidah 92, First Festival of Voodoo Culture — A240

1993, Feb. 3   Litho.   Perf. 13x12½
691 A239 190fr multicolored   1.50 1.50

1993, Feb. 8   Perf. 13½
692 A240 125fr multicolored   1.00 1.00

Well of Possotome, Eurystome A241

1993, May 25   Litho.   Perf. 12½
693 A241 125fr multicolored   1.00 1.00

OAU, 30th Anniv. A242

1993, June 7   Litho.   Perf. 13½
694 A242 125fr multicolored   1.00 1.00

John F. Kennedy — A243

1993, June 24   Perf. 13
695 A243 190fr shown   1.50 1.50
696 A243 190fr Martin Luther King, vert.   1.50 1.50

Assassinations of Kennedy, 30th anniv. (#695), and King, 25th anniv. (#696).

Dahomey Nos. 161, 173, 175, 335 Overprinted or Surcharged

1993

Perfs. & Printing Methods as Before

697 A21(e)	5fr on #175	
700 A19(f)	10fr on 3fr #161	
701 A77(f)	10fr on 100fr #335	
704 A21(f)	25fr on 1fr #173	

Benin Nos. 343, 345, 350, Dahomey Nos. 169, 226-227, 249, 295, 283, 333 Surch.

1994-95

707 A38(f)	5fr on 1fr #226	
711 A57(e)	50fr on 1fr #350	
712 A58(e)	80fr on 40fr #283	
713 A76(g)	100fr on #333	
715 A38(f)	10fr on 3fr #227	
718 A62(e)	135fr on 30fr #295	
719 A83(g)	135fr on 35fr #343	
722 A20(e)	135fr on 60fr #169	
723 A83(g)	135fr on 60fr #345	
725 A45(e)	200fr on 100fr #249	

UNESCO Conference on The Slave Route — A244

1994   Litho.   Perf. 13x13½
730 A244 300fr multicolored

The editors would like to see the 135fr and 200fr values in this set, for which numbers have been reserved.

Intl. Year of the Family A246

1994   Litho.   Perf. 12½
732 A246 200fr multicolored

1996 Summer Olympics, Atlanta A248

Perf. 12½x13, 13x12½

1995, Apr. 30   Litho.
734 A248	45fr	Water polo	.45 .45
735 A248	50fr	Javelin	.50 .50
736 A248	75fr	Weight lifting	.75 .75
737 A248	100fr	Tennis	1.00 1.00
738 A248	135fr	Baseball	1.40 1.40
739 A248	200fr	Synchronized swimming	2.00 2.00
	Nos. 734-739 (6)		6.10 6.10

Souvenir Sheet
740 A248 300fr Diving   4.50 4.50

Nos. 735-740 are vert. No. 740 contains one 32x40mm stamp.

Dogs — A249

1995, Aug. 23   Litho.   Perf. 12½
741 A249	40fr	German shepherd	.40 .40
742 A249	50fr	Beagle	.50 .50
743 A249	75fr	Great dane	.75 .75
744 A249	100fr	Boxer	1.00 1.00
745 A249	135fr	Pointer	1.40 1.40
746 A249	200fr	Fox terrier	2.00 2.00
	Nos. 741-746 (6)		6.05 6.05

Souvenir Sheet
747 A249 300fr Schnauzer   6.50 6.50

Ships A250

Designs: 40fr, Steam driven paddle boat, 1788. 50fr, Paddle steamer Charlotte, 1802. 75fr, Transatlantic steamship, Citta de Catania. 100fr, Hovercraft Mountbatten SR-N4. 135fr, QE II. 200fr, Japanese experimental atomic energy ship, Mutsu-NEF. 300fr, Paddle-steamer Savannah, 1819.

1995, May 20
748 A250	40fr	multicolored	.40 .40
749 A250	50fr	multicolored	.50 .50
750 A250	75fr	multicolored	.75 .75
751 A250	100fr	multicolored	1.00 1.00

752 A250	135fr	multicolored	1.40 1.40
753 A250	200fr	multicolored	2.00 2.00
	Nos. 748-753 (6)		6.05 6.05

Souvenir Sheet
754 A250 300fr multicolored   4.50 4.50

No. 754 contains one 40x32mm stamp.

Primates — A251

1995, June 30
755 A251	50fr	Pan troglodytes	.50 .50
756 A251	75fr	Mandrillus sphinx	.75 .75
757 A251	100fr	Colobus	1.00 1.00
758 A251	135fr	Macaca sylvanus	1.40 1.40
759 A251	200fr	Comopithecus hamadryas	2.00 2.00
	Nos. 755-759 (5)		5.65 5.65

Souvenir Sheet
760 A251 300fr Papio cynocephalus   4.50 4.50

No. 760 contains one 32x40mm stamp.

Domestic Cats A252

1995, July 30   Litho.   Perf. 12½x13
761 A252	40fr	Shorthair tabby	.40 .40
762 A252	50fr	Ruddy red	.50 .50
763 A252	75fr	White longhair	.75 .75
764 A252	100fr	Seal color point	1.00 1.00
765 A252	135fr	Tabby point	1.40 1.40
766 A252	200fr	Black shorthair	2.00 2.00
	Nos. 761-766 (6)		6.05 6.05

Souvenir Sheet
767 A252 300fr Cat in basket   4.50 4.50

No. 767 contains one 40x32mm stamp.

Flowers — A253

Designs: 40fr, Dracunculus vulgaris. 50fr, Narcissus watieri. 75fr, Amaryllis belladonna. 100fr, Nymphaea capensis. 135fr, Chrysanthemum carinatum. 200fr, Iris tingitana.

1995, Oct. 15   Litho.   Perf. 12½
768 A253	40fr	multicolored	.40 .40
769 A253	50fr	multicolored	.55 .55
770 A253	75fr	multicolored	.80 .80
771 A253	100fr	multicolored	1.10 1.10
772 A253	135fr	multicolored	1.40 1.40
773 A253	200fr	multicolored	2.25 2.25
	Nos. 768-773 (6)		6.50 6.50

Wild Animals A254

Designs: 50fr, Panthera leo. 75fr, Syncerus caffer. 100fr, Pan troglodytes. 135fr, Aepyceros melampus. 200fr, Geosciurus inaurus. 300fr, Loxodonta, vert.

Perf. 13x12½, 12½x13

1995, Sept. 20
774 A254	50fr	multicolored	.55 .55
775 A254	75fr	multicolored	.80 .80
776 A254	100fr	multicolored	1.10 1.10
777 A254	135fr	multicolored	1.50 1.50
778 A254	200fr	multicolored	2.25 2.25
	Nos. 774-778 (5)		6.20 6.20

Souvenir Sheet
779 A254 300fr multicolored   4.75 4.75

Nos. 774-777 are vert. No. 779 contains one 32x40mm stamp.

Birds Feeding Their Chicks — A255

Designs: 40fr, Cocothraustes cocothraustes. 50fr, Streptopelia chinensis. 75fr, Falco peregrinus. 100fr, Dendroica fusca. 135fr, Larus ridibundus. 200fr, Pelecanus onocrotalus.

1995, Aug. 28   Perf. 12½x13
780 A255	40fr	multicolored	.40 .40
781 A255	50fr	multicolored	.55 .55
782 A255	75fr	multicolored	.80 .80
783 A255	100fr	multicolored	1.10 1.10
784 A255	135fr	multicolored	1.40 1.40
785 A255	200fr	multicolored	2.25 2.25
	Nos. 780-785 (6)		6.50 6.50

Benin Nos. 344, 504, 520, 619, 627, 651, 686 and Dahomey No. 291 Surch.

1994-95

Printing Method and Perfs as Before
786 A211	25fr on 175fr #651	
787 A194	50fr on 220fr #627	
788 A83(h)	150fr on 45fr #344	
789 A158	150fr on 90fr #520	
790 A147	150fr on 500fr #504	
791 A60(f)	200fr on 135fr #291	
792 A192	200fr on 500fr #619	
793 A236	250fr on 1000fr #686	

Natl. Arms — A256

1995   Litho.   Perf. 12½
793A A256	135fr	yellow & multi	1.30 1.30
793B A256	150fr	yellow green & multi	1.45 1.45
794 A256	200fr	multicolored	

See Nos. 948-951.

Orchids — A257

Designs: 40fr, Angraecum sesquipedale. 50fr, Polystachya virginea. 75fr, Disa uniflora. 100fr, Ansellia africana. 135fr, Angraecum eichlerianum. 200fr, Jumellea confusa.

1995, Nov. 10   Litho.   Perf. 12½
795 A257	40fr	multicolored	.40 .40
796 A257	50fr	multicolored	.50 .50
797 A257	75fr	multicolored	.75 .75
798 A257	100fr	multicolored	1.00 1.00
799 A257	135fr	multicolored	1.35 1.35
800 A257	200fr	multicolored	2.00 2.00
	Nos. 795-800 (6)		6.00 6.00

Butterflies — A258

Designs: 40fr, Graphium policenes. 50fr, Vanessa atalanta. 75fr, Polymmatus icarus. 100fr, Danaus chrysipus. 135fr, Cynthia cardui. 200fr, Argus celbulina.
1000fr, Charaxes jasius.

1996, Mar. 10
801	A258	40fr multicolored	.40	.40
802	A258	50fr multicolored	.50	.50
803	A258	75fr multicolored	.75	.75
804	A258	100fr multicolored	1.00	1.00
805	A258	135fr multicolored	1.35	1.35
806	A258	200fr multicolored	2.00	2.00
		Nos. 801-806 (6)	6.00	6.00

Souvenir Sheet
807	A258	1000fr multicolored	6.00	6.00

CHINA '96, Beijing A259

Designs: a, 40fr, Dancer in traditional Chinese costume. b, 50fr, Exhibition emblem. c, 75fr, Water lily. d, 100fr, Temple of Heaven.

1996, Apr. 8
808	A259	Block of 4, #a.-d.	5.10	5.10

Benin Nos. 523, 616 and
Dahomey No. 306 Surcharged

1996?
Perfs. & Printing Methods as Before
809	A191	5fr on 250fr #616	
810	A67(g)	35fr on #306	
811	A158	150fr on 90fr #523	

15th Lions Intl. District
Convention — A260

1996, May 2   Litho.   Perf. 12½
811A	A260	100fr multicolored	.45	.45
811B	A260	135fr green & multi	1.40	1.40
812	A260	150fr yellow & multi	1.50	1.50
813	A260	200fr red & multi	2.00	2.00
		Nos. 811A-813 (4)	3.96	5.35

La Francoponie
Conference
A261

1995, Dec. 2   Litho.   Perf. 12½
814	A261	150fr pink & multi	1.30	1.30
815	A261	200fr blue & multi	1.75	1.75

Cats — A262

1995, Nov. 2   Litho.   Perf. 13
816	A262	40fr Lynx lynx	.40	.40
817	A262	50fr Felis concolor	.50	.50
818	A262	75fr Acinonyx jubatus	.70	.70
819	A262	100fr Panthera pardus	.95	.95
820	A262	135fr Panthera tigris	1.30	1.30
821	A262	200fr Panthera leo	1.90	1.90
		Nos. 816-821 (6)	5.75	5.75

1998 World Cup
Soccer
Championships,
France — A263

Various soccer players.

1996, Feb. 10   Litho.   Perf. 13
822	A263	40fr multicolored	.40	.40
823	A263	50fr multicolored	.50	.50
824	A263	75fr multicolored	.75	.75
825	A263	100fr multicolored	1.00	1.00
826	A263	135fr multicolored	1.35	1.35
827	A263	200fr multicolored	2.00	2.00
		Nos. 822-827 (6)	6.00	6.00

Souvenir Sheet
Perf. 12½
828	A263	1000fr multicolored	6.00	6.00

No. 828 contains one 32x40mm stamp.

1996 Summer
Olympic Games,
Atlanta — A264

1996, Jan. 28   Litho.   Perf. 13
829	A264	40fr Diving	.40	.40
830	A264	50fr Tennis	.50	.50
831	A264	75fr Running	.75	.75
832	A264	100fr Gymnastics	1.00	1.00
833	A264	135fr Weight lifting	1.35	1.35
834	A264	200fr Shooting	2.00	2.00
		Nos. 829-834 (6)	6.00	6.00

Souvenir Sheet
835	A264	1000fr Water polo	6.00	6.00

No. 835 contains one 32x40mm stamp.

Christmas
Paintings — A265

Entire paintings or details: 40fr, Holy Family Under the Oak Tree, by Raphael. 50fr, The Holy Family, by Raphael. 75fr, St. John the Baptist as a Child, by Murillo. 100fr, The Virgin of Balances, by Leonardo da Vinci. 135fr, The Virgin and the Infant, by Gerard David. 200fr, Adoration of the Magi, by Juan Batista Mayno.
1000fr, Rest on the Flight into Egypt, by Murillo.

1996, May 5   Litho.   Perf. 13
836	A265	40fr multicolored	.40	.40
837	A265	50fr multicolored	.55	.55
838	A265	75fr multicolored	.80	.80
839	A265	100fr multicolored	1.00	1.00
840	A265	135fr multicolored	1.40	1.40
841	A265	200fr multicolored	2.10	2.10
		Nos. 836-841 (6)	6.25	6.25

Souvenir Sheet
842	A265	1000fr multicolored	6.25	6.25

No. 842 contains one 40x32mm stamp.

Wild Cats — A266

Designs: 40fr, Leptailurus serval. 50fr, Profelis temmincki. 75fr, Leopardus pardalis. 100fr, Lynx rufus. 135fr, Prionailurus bengalensis. 200fr, Felis euphtilura.
1000fr, Neofelis nebulosa.

1996, June 10   Litho.   Perf. 12x12½
843	A266	40fr multicolored	.40	.40
844	A266	50fr multicolored	.55	.55
845	A266	75fr multicolored	.80	.80
846	A266	100fr multicolored	1.00	1.00
847	A266	135fr multicolored	1.40	1.40
848	A266	200fr multicolored	2.10	2.10
		Nos. 843-848 (6)	6.25	6.25

Souvenir Sheet
Perf. 12½
849	A266	1000fr multicolored	6.25	6.25

No. 849 contains one 32x40mm stamp.

Sailing
Ships
A267

1996, May 27   Perf. 13x12½
850	A267	40fr Thermopylae	.40	.40
851	A267	50fr 5-masted bark	.55	.55
852	A267	75fr Nightingale	.80	.80
853	A267	100fr Opium clipper	1.00	1.00
854	A267	135fr The Torrens	1.40	1.40
855	A267	200fr English clipper	2.10	2.10
		Nos. 850-855 (6)	6.25	6.25

Souvenir Sheet
Perf. 13
856	A267	1000fr Opium clipper, diff.	6.25	6.25

No. 856 contains one 32x40mm stamp.

Olymphilex
'96 — A268

1996, July 2   Perf. 13
857	A268	40fr Running	.40	.40
858	A268	50fr Kayaking	.55	.55
859	A268	75fr Gymnastics	.80	.80
860	A268	100fr Soccer	1.00	1.00
861	A268	135fr Tennis	1.40	1.40
862	A268	200fr Baseball	2.00	2.00
		Nos. 857-862 (6)	6.15	6.15

Souvenir Sheet
863	A268	1000fr Basketball	6.25	6.25

No. 863 contains one 32x40mm stamp.

Modern Olympic
Games,
Cent. — A269

a, 40fr, Gold medal, woman hurdler. b, 50fr, Runner, Olympic flame. c, 75fr, Pierre de Coubertin, map of US. d, 100fr, Map of US, "1996."

1996, June 20
864	A269	Block of 4, #a.-d.	5.30	5.30

No. 864 is a continuous design.

Horses
A270

Various horses.

1996   Litho.   Perf. 13
865	A270	40fr multi, vert.	.40	.40
866	A270	50fr multi, vert.	.50	.50
867	A270	75fr multi, vert.	.75	.75
868	A270	100fr multi, vert.	1.00	1.00
869	A270	135fr multi, vert.	1.35	1.35
870	A270	200fr multicolored	2.00	2.00
		Nos. 865-870 (6)	6.00	6.00

Flowering
Cacti — A271

40fr, Parodia subterranea. 50fr, Astrophytum senile. 75fr, Echinocereus melanocentrus. 100fr, Turbinicarpus kinkerianus. 135fr, Astrophytum capricorne. 200fr, Nelloydia grandiflora.

1996, July 25
871	A271	40fr multicolored	.40	.40
872	A271	50fr multicolored	.50	.50
873	A271	75fr multicolored	.75	.75
874	A271	100fr multicolored	1.00	1.00
875	A271	135fr multicolored	1.35	1.35
876	A271	200fr multicolored	2.00	2.00
		Nos. 871-876 (6)	6.00	6.00

Mushrooms
A272

Designs: 40fr, Stropharia cubensis. 50fr, Psilocybe zapotecorum. 75fr, Psilocybe mexicana. 100fr, Conocybe siliginoides. 135fr, Psilocybe caerulescens mazatecorum. 200fr, Psilocybe caerulescens nigripes.
1000fr, Psilocybe aztecorum, horiz.

1996, Sept. 30
877	A272	40fr multicolored	.40	.40
878	A272	50fr multicolored	.50	.50
879	A272	75fr multicolored	.75	.75
880	A272	100fr multicolored	1.00	1.00
881	A272	135fr multicolored	1.35	1.35
882	A272	200fr multicolored	2.00	2.00
		Nos. 877-882 (6)	6.00	6.00

Souvenir Sheet
Perf. 12½
883	A272	1000fr multicolored	6.00	6.00

No. 883 contains one 40x32mm stamp.

Prehistoric Animals — A273

1996, Aug. 30   *Perf. 12½*
884	A273	40fr Longisquama, vert.	.40	.40
885	A273	50fr Dimophodon, vert.	.50	.50
886	A273	75fr Dunkleosteus	.75	.75
887	A273	100fr Eryops	1.00	1.00
888	A273	135fr Peloneustes	1.35	1.35
889	A273	200fr Deinonychus	2.00	2.00
		Nos. 884-889 (6)	6.00	6.00

Birds — A274

Designs: 40fr, Campephilus principalis. 50fr, Picathartes oreas. 75fr, Strigops habroptilus. 100fr, Amazona vittata. 135fr, Nipponia nippon. 200fr, Gymnogyps californianus.
1000fr, Paradisea rudolphi.

1996, Sept. 10
890	A274	40fr multicolored	.40	.40
891	A274	50fr multicolored	.50	.50
892	A274	75fr multicolored	.75	.75
893	A274	100fr multicolored	1.00	1.00
894	A274	135fr multicolored	1.35	1.35
895	A274	200fr multicolored	2.00	2.00
		Nos. 890-895 (6)	6.00	6.00

Souvenir Sheet
896	A274	1000fr multicolored	6.00	6.00

No. 896 contains one 32x40mm stamp.

Dahomey No. 235 Overprinted
Benin No. 545 Surcharged

199?
Perfs. & Printing Methods as Before
897	A40(e)	30fr on #235		
898	A166	75fr on 185fr #545		

Dahomey Nos. 208, 239-241, 257-258, 261, 269, 274, 283, 320, 326, 334-336, 337 Surcharged

1996?
Perfs. & Printing Methods as Before
899	A77(f)	100fr on #335		
900	A79(e)	125fr on 15fr #337		
901	A77(h)	135fr on 65fr #334		
902	A42(e)	150fr on 30fr #239		
903	A43(h)	150fr on 30fr #241		
904	A48(h)	150fr on 30fr #257		
905	A50(h)	150fr on 30fr #261		
906	CD132(h)	150fr on 40fr #269		
907	A58(h)	150fr on 40fr #283		
908	A71(e)	150fr on 40fr #320		
909	A74(e)	150fr on 40fr #326		
910	A78(e)	150fr on 40fr #336		
911	A32(e)	150fr on 50fr #208		
912	A42(e)	150fr on 70fr #240		
913	A48(h)	150fr on 70fr #258		
914	A55(h)	150fr on 200fr #274		

Benin Nos. 381, 384, 449, 521, 538, 546, 567, 569, 636, Surcharged

1996?
Perfs. & Printing Methods as Before
915	A127	10fr on 90fr #449		
916	A159	10fr on 90fr #521		
917	A164	10fr on 90fr #538		
918	A174	10fr on 90fr #569		
919	A98	40fr on 210fr #381		
920	A98	40fr on 210fr #384		
921	A198	75fr on 440fr #636		
922	A167	100fr on 500fr #546		
923	A173	125fr on 300fr #567		

Obliterator on No. 922 has either one or two bars. Pairs of No. 922 exist with each stamp having a different obliterator.

Ungulates — A275

Designs: 40fr, Aepyceros melampus. 50fr, Kobus ellipsiprymnus. 75fr, Caffer caffer. 100fr, Connochaetes taurinus. 135fr, Okapia johnstoni. 200fr, Tragelaphus strepsiceros.

1996, Oct. 15   Litho.   *Perf. 12½x12*
930	A275	40fr multicolored	.40	.40
931	A275	50fr multicolored	.50	.50
932	A275	75fr multicolored	.75	.75
933	A275	100fr multicolored	1.00	1.00
934	A275	135fr multicolored	1.35	1.35
935	A275	200fr multicolored	2.00	2.00
		Nos. 930-935 (6)	6.00	6.00

Marine
Mammals
A276

Designs: 40fr, Delphinapterus leucas. 50fr, Tursiops truncatus. 75fr, Belaenoptera musculus. 100fr, Eubalaena australis. 135fr, Gramphidelphis griseus. 200fr, Orcinus orca.

1996, Nov. 5   *Perf. 13*
936	A276	40fr multicolored	.40	.40
937	A276	50fr multicolored	.50	.50
938	A276	75fr multicolored	.75	.75
939	A276	100fr multicolored	1.00	1.00
940	A276	135fr multicolored	1.35	1.35
941	A276	200fr multicolored	2.00	2.00
		Nos. 936-941 (6)	6.00	6.00

Fish
A277

1996   Litho.   *Perf. 12½*
942	A277	50fr Pomacanthidae, vert.	.50	.50
943	A277	75fr Acanthuridae	.75	.75
944	A277	100fr Carangidae	1.00	1.00
945	A277	135fr Chaetodontidae	1.35	1.35
946	A277	200fr Chaetodontidae, diff.	2.00	2.00
		Nos. 942-946 (5)	5.60	5.60

Souvenir Sheet
947	A277	1000fr Scaridae	6.00	6.00

No. 947 contains one 40x32mm stamp.

Coat of Arms Type of 1995

1996-97   *Perf. 12½*
948	A256	100fr multicolored	.45	.45
949	A256	135fr lt yellow & multi	.55	.55
950	A256	150fr lt blue green & multi	.60	.60
951	A256	200fr lt orange & multi	.80	.80
		Nos. 949-951 (3)	1.95	1.95

Issued: 100fr, 1996; 135fr, 150fr, 200fr, 1997.

Military
Uniforms — A278

Regiments of European infantry: 135fr, Grenadier, Glassenapp. 150fr, Officer, Von Groben. 200fr, Musketeer, Comte Dohna. 270fr, Bombardier. 300fr, Gendarme. 400fr, Dragoon, Mollendorf.
1000fr, Soldiers, flag, horses, vert.

1997
952	A278	135fr multicolored	.55	.55
953	A278	150fr multicolored	.60	.60
954	A278	200fr multicolored	.80	.80
955	A278	270fr multicolored	1.10	1.10
956	A278	300fr multicolored	1.25	1.25
957	A278	400fr multicolored	1.60	1.60
		Nos. 952-957 (6)	5.90	5.90

Souvenir Sheet
Perf. 13
958	A278	1000fr multicolored	4.00	4.00

No. 958 contains one 32x40mm stamp.

Trains
A279

135fr, Steam turbine, Reid Macleod, 1920. 150fr, Experimental high speed, 1935. 200fr, Renard Argent, 1935. 270fr, Class No. 21-C-6, 1941. 300fr, Diesel, 1960. 400fr, Diesel, 1960, diff.
1000fr, Coronation Scot, 1937.

1997   Litho.   *Perf. 13*
959	A279	135fr multicolored	.50	.50
960	A279	150fr multicolored	.55	.55
961	A279	200fr multicolored	.75	.75
962	A279	270fr multicolored	1.00	1.00
963	A279	300fr multicolored	1.10	1.10
964	A279	400fr multicolored	1.50	1.50
		Nos. 959-964 (6)	5.40	5.40

Souvenir Sheet
965	A279	1000fr multicolored	3.75	3.75

No. 965 contains one 40x32mm stamp.

1998 World Cup
Soccer
Championship,
France — A280

Various soccer plays.

1997   *Perf. 12½x13*
966	A280	135fr multicolored	.50	.50
967	A280	150fr multicolored	.55	.55
968	A280	200fr multicolored	.75	.75
969	A280	270fr multicolored	1.00	1.00
970	A280	300fr multi, horiz.	1.10	1.10
971	A280	400fr multi, horiz.	1.50	1.50
		Nos. 966-971 (6)	5.40	5.40

Souvenir Sheet
972	A280	1000fr multicolored	3.75	3.75

No. 972 contains one 40x32mm stamp.

Orchids — A281

Phalaenopsis: 135fr, Penetrate. 150fr, Golden sands. 200fr, Sun spots. 270fr, Fuscata. 300fr, Christi floyd. 400fr, Cayanne.
1000fr, Janet kuhn.

1997   Litho.   *Perf. 12½x13*
973	A281	135fr multicolored	.50	.50
974	A281	150fr multicolored	.55	.55
975	A281	200fr multicolored	.70	.70
976	A281	270fr multicolored	1.00	1.00
977	A281	300fr multicolored	1.10	1.10
978	A281	400fr multicolored	1.40	1.40
		Nos. 973-978 (6)	5.25	5.25

Souvenir Sheet
Perf. 12½
979	A281	1000fr multicolored	3.60	3.60

No. 979 contains one 32x40mm stamp.

Dogs — A282

Designs: 135fr, Irish setter. 150fr, Saluki. 200fr, Doberman pinscher. 270fr, Siberian husky. 300fr, Basenji. 400fr, Boxer.
1000fr, Rhodesian ridgeback.

1997   *Perf. 13*
980	A282	135fr multicolored	.50	.50
981	A282	150fr multicolored	.55	.55
982	A282	200fr multicolored	.70	.70
983	A282	270fr multicolored	1.00	1.00
984	A282	300fr multicolored	1.10	1.10
985	A282	400fr multicolored	1.40	1.40
		Nos. 980-985 (6)	5.25	5.25

Souvenir Sheet
Perf. 12½
986	A282	1000fr multicolored	3.60	3.60

No. 986 contains one 32x40mm stamp.

Antique Automobiles — A283

1997   Litho.   *Perf. 13x12½*
987	A283	135fr 1905 Buick	.45	.45
988	A283	150fr 1903 Ford	.50	.50
989	A283	200fr 1913 Stanley	.70	.70
990	A283	270fr 1911 Stoddar-Dayton	.90	.90
991	A283	300fr 1934 Cadillac	1.00	1.00
992	A283	400fr 1931 Cadillac	1.40	1.40
		Nos. 987-992 (6)	4.95	4.95

Souvenir Sheet
Perf. 13
993	A283	1000fr 1928 Ford	3.40	3.40

No. 993 contains one 40x32mm stamp.

Songbirds
A284

Designs: 135fr, Pyrrhula pyrrhula. 150fr, Carduelis spinus. 200fr, Turdus torquatus. 270fr, Parus cristatus. 300fr, Nucifraga caryocatactes. 400fr, Luscinia megarhynchos.
1000fr, Motacilla flava.

1997   *Perf. 13x12½*
994	A284	135fr multicolored	.45	.45
995	A284	150fr multicolored	.50	.50
996	A284	200fr multicolored	.70	.70
997	A284	270fr multicolored	.90	.90
998	A284	300fr multicolored	1.00	1.00
999	A284	400fr multicolored	1.40	1.40
		Nos. 994-999 (6)	4.95	4.95

Souvenir Sheet
Perf. 12½
1000	A284	1000fr multicolored	3.40	3.40

No. 1000 contains one 32x40mm stamp.

Flowering
Cactus — A285

Designs: 135fr, Faucaria lupina. 150fr, Conophytum bilobun. 200fr, Lithops aucampiae. 270fr, Lithops helmutii. 300fr, Stapelia grandiflora. 400fr, Lithops fulviceps. 1000fr, Pleiospilos willowmorensis.

1997   **Litho.**   *Perf. 13x12½*
1001	A285	135fr multicolored	.45 .45
1002	A285	150fr multicolored	.50 .50
1003	A285	200fr multicolored	.70 .70
1004	A285	270fr multicolored	.90 .90
1005	A285	300fr multicolored	1.00 1.00
1006	A285	400fr multicolored	1.30 1.30
		Nos. 1001-1006 (6)	4.85 4.85

Souvenir Sheet
Perf. 12½
1007	A285	1000fr multicolored	3.40 3.40

No. 1007 contains one 32x40mm stamp.

AIR POST STAMPS

PEOPLE'S REPUBLIC

Catalogue values for unused stamps in this section are for Never Hinged items.

Nativity, by Aert van Leyden — AP84

Christmas: 85fr, Adoration of the Kings, by Rubens, vert. 140fr, Adoration of the Shepherds, by Charles Lebrun. 300fr, The Virgin with the Blue Diadem, by Raphael, vert.

1975, Dec. 19   **Litho.**   *Perf. 13*
C240	AP84	40fr gold & multi	.20 .15
C241	AP84	85fr gold & multi	.42 .15
C242	AP84	140fr gold & multi	.60 .25
C243	AP84	300fr gold & multi	1.40 .65
		Nos. C240-C243 (4)	2.62 1.20

For surcharges see Nos. C362, C367, C407.

Slalom, Innsbruck Olympic Emblem — AP85

Innsbruck Olympic Games Emblem and: 150fr, Bobsledding, vert. 300fr, Figure skating, pairs.

1976, June 28   **Litho.**   *Perf. 12½*
C244	AP85	60fr multi	.25 .15
C245	AP85	150fr multi	.65 .25
C246	AP85	300fr multi	1.25 .55
		Nos. C244-C246 (3)	2.15 .95

12th Winter Olympic Games, Innsbruck, Austria, Feb. 4-15.

Dahomey Nos. C263-C265 Overprinted or Surcharged: "POPULAIRE / DU BENIN" and Bars

1976, July 4   **Engr.**   *Perf. 13*
C247	AP86	135fr multi	.55 .55
C248	AP86	210fr on 300fr multi	.90 .35
C249	AP86	380fr on 500fr multi	1.50 .65
		Nos. C247-C249 (3)	2.95 1.25

The overprint includes a bar covering "DU DAHOMEY" in shades of brown; "POPULAIRE DU BENIN" is blue on Nos. C247-C248, red on No. C249. The surcharge and bars over old value are blue on No. C248, red, brown on No. C249.

Long Jump AP86

Designs (Olympic Rings and): 150fr, Basketball, vert. 200fr, Hurdles.

1976, July 16   **Photo.**   *Perf. 13*
C250	AP86	60fr multi	.32 .15
C251	AP86	150fr multi	.85 .30
C252	AP86	200fr multi	1.25 .45
a.		Souv. sheet of 3, #C250-C252	3.00 3.00
		Nos. C250-C252 (3)	2.42 .90

21st Olympic Games, Montreal, Canada, July 17-Aug 1.

Konrad Adenauer and Cologne Cathedral — AP87

Design: 90fr, Konrad Adenauer, vert.

1976, Aug. 27   **Engr.**   *Perf. 13*
C253	AP87	90fr multi	.60 .25
C254	AP87	250fr multi	1.75 .70

Konrad Adenauer (1876-1967), German Chancellor, birth centenary.
For surcharge see No. C289B.

Children's Heads and Flying Fish (Dahomey Type A32) — AP88

210fr, Lion cub's head and Benin type A3, vert.

1976, Sept. 13
C255	AP88	60fr Prus bl & vio bl	.35 .15
C256	AP88	210fr multi	1.10 .45

JUVAROUEN 76, Intl. Youth Phil. Exhib., Rouen, France, Apr. 25-May 2.
For surcharge see No. C300.

Apollo 14 Emblem and Blast-off — AP89

Design: 270fr, Landing craft and man on moon.

1976, Oct. 18   **Engr.**   *Perf. 13*
C257	AP89	130fr multi	.45 .30
C258	AP89	270fr multi	1.00 .65

Apollo 14 Moon Mission, 5th anniversary.
For surcharges see Nos. C312, C454.

Annunciation, by Master of Jativa — AP90

Christmas: 60fr, Nativity, by Gerard David. 270fr, Adoration of the Kings, Dutch School. 300fr, Flight into Egypt, by Gentile Fabriano, horiz.

1976, Dec. 20   **Litho.**   *Perf. 12½*
C259	AP90	50fr gold & multi	.25 .16
C260	AP90	60fr gold & multi	.35 .22
C261	AP90	270fr gold & multi	1.50 .60
C262	AP90	300fr gold & multi	1.60 1.00
		Nos. C259-C262 (4)	3.70 1.98

For surcharges see Nos. C310, C321, C484.

Gamblers and Lottery Emblem — AP91

1977, Mar. 13   **Litho.**   *Perf. 13*
C263	AP91	50fr multi	.25 .20

National lottery, 10th anniversary.

Sassenage Castle, Grenoble — AP92

1977, May 16   *Perf. 12½*
C264	AP92	200fr multi	.80 .60

10th anniv. of Intl. French Language Council.
For surcharge see No. C334.

Concorde, Supersonic Plane — AP93

Designs: 150fr, Zeppelin. 300fr, Charles A. Lindbergh and Spirit of St. Louis. 500fr, Charles Nungesser and François Coli, French aviators lost over Atlantic, 1927.

1977, July 25   **Engr.**   *Perf. 13*
C265	AP93	80fr ultra & red	.40 .35
C266	AP93	150fr multi	.80 .60
C267	AP93	300fr multi	1.60 1.20
C268	AP93	500fr multi	2.50 2.00
		Nos. C265-C268 (4)	5.30 4.15

Aviation history.
For overprint and surcharges see Nos. C274, C316, C336.

Soccer Player — AP94

200fr, Soccer players and Games' emblem.

1977, July 28   **Litho.**   *Perf. 12½x12*
C269	AP94	60fr multi	.35 .20
C270	AP94	200fr multi	1.10 .80

World Soccer Cup elimination games.
For surcharges see Nos. C289A, C308.

Miss Haverfield, by Gainsborough AP95

Designs: 150fr, Self-portrait, by Rubens. 200fr, Anguish, man's head by Da Vinci.

1977, Oct. 3   **Engr.**   *Perf. 13*
C271	AP95	100fr sl grn & mar	.55 .40
C272	AP95	150fr red brn & dk brn	.80 .60
C273	AP95	200fr brn & red	1.10 .80
		Nos. C271-C273 (3)	2.45 1.80

For surcharges see Nos. C309, C317.

No. C265 Overprinted: "1er VOL COMMERCIAL / 22.11.77 PARIS NEW-YORK"

1977, Nov. 22   **Engr.**   *Perf. 13*
C274	AP93	80fr ultra & red	.42 .35

Concorde, 1st commercial flight, Paris to NY.

Viking on Mars AP96

Designs: 150fr, Isaac Newton, apple globe, stars. 200fr, Vladimir M. Komarov, spacecraft and earth. 500fr, Dog Laika, rocket and space.

1977, Nov. 28   **Engr.**   *Perf. 13*
C275	AP96	100fr multi	.55 .40
C276	AP96	150fr multi	.80 .60
C277	AP96	200fr multi	1.10 .80
C278	AP96	500fr multi	2.75 2.00
		Nos. C275-C278 (4)	5.20 3.80

Operation Viking on Mars; Isaac Newton (1642-1727); 10th death anniv. of Russian cosmonaut Vladimir M. Komarov; 20th anniv. of 1st living creature in space.
For surcharges see Nos. C301, C314.

Monument, Red Star Place, Cotonou AP97

Lithographed; Gold Embossed
1977 Nov. 30   *Perf. 12½*
C279	AP97	500fr multi	1.75 1.10

Suzanne Fourment, by Rubens — AP98

Design: 380fr, Nicholas Rubens, By Rubens.

1977, Dec. 12   Engr.   Perf. 13
C280 AP98 200fr multi   1.10 .80
C281 AP98 380fr claret & ocher   2.00 1.40
For surcharges see Nos. C311, C313, C483.

Parthenon and UNESCO Emblem — AP99

Designs: 70fr, Acropolis and frieze showing Pan-Athenaic procession, vert. 250fr, Parthenon and frieze showing horsemen, vert.

1978, Sept. 22   Litho.   Perf. 12½x12
C282 AP99 70fr multi   .35 .20
C283 AP99 250fr multi   1.25 .80
C284 AP99 500fr multi   2.75 1.50
   Nos. C282-C284 (3)   4.35 2.50

Save the Parthenon in Athens campaign.
For surcharge see No. C338.

Philexafrique II—Essen Issue
Common Design Types

Designs: No. C285, Buffalo and Dahomey #C33. No. C286, Wild ducks and Baden #1.

1978, Nov. 1   Litho.   Perf. 12½
C285 CD138 100fr multi   .65 .40
C286 CD139 100fr multi   .65 .40
 a.   Pair, #C285-C286   1.30 1.00

Wilbur and Orville Wright and
Flyer — AP100

1978, Dec. 28   Engr.   Perf. 13
C287 AP100 500fr multi   3.50 2.00

75th anniversary of 1st powered flight.
For surcharge see No. C339.

Cook's Ships, Hawaii, World
Map — AP101

Design: 50fr, Battle at Kowrowa.

1979, June 1   Engr.   Perf. 13
C288 AP101 20fr multi   .20 .20
C289 AP101 50fr multi   .45 .45

Capt. James Cook (1728-1779), explorer.

No. C253, C269 Surcharged
1979
Perfs. & Printing Method as Before
C289A AP94 50fr on 60fr #C269
C289B AP87 50fr on 90fr multi

Lunokhod Type of 1980
1980, June 15   Engr.   Perf. 13
Size: 27x48mm
C290 A133 210fr multi   1.40 1.40
For surcharges see Nos. C305, C450.

Soccer
Players — AP102

1981, Mar. 31   Litho.   Perf. 13
C291 AP102 200fr Ball, globe   .90 .90
C292 AP102 500fr shown   2.50 2.50
ESPANA '82 World Soccer Cup eliminations.
For surcharges see Nos. C335, Q10B.

Prince Charles and Lady Diana, London
Bridge — AP103

1981, July 29   Litho.   Perf. 12½
C293 AP103 500fr multi   3.00 3.00
Royal wedding.
For surcharge see No. C323.

Three Musicians, by Pablo Picasso (1881-1973) — AP104

Perf. 12½x13, 13x12½
1981, Nov. 2   Litho.
C294 AP104 300fr Dance, vert.   2.00 2.00
C295 AP104 500fr shown   3.50 3.50
For surcharges see Nos. C320, C340.

1300th Anniv. of
Bulgaria — AP105

1981, Dec. 2   Litho.   Perf. 13
C296 AP105 100fr multi   .60 .60

Visit of Pope John Paul II — AP106

1982, Feb. 17   Litho.   Perf. 13
C297 AP106 80fr multi   .55 .55

20th Anniv. of John
Glenn's
Flight — AP107

1982, Feb. 21   Litho.   Perf. 13
C298 AP107 500fr multi   3.00 3.00
For surcharge see No. C315.

Scouting Year
AP108

1982, June 1   Perf. 12½
C299 AP108 105fr multi   .70 .70
For surcharge see No. C324.

Nos. C256, C275 Surcharged
1982, Nov.   Engr.   Perf. 13
C300 AP88 50fr on 210fr multi   .35 .35
C301 AP96 50fr on 100fr multi   .35 .35

Monet in Boat, by Claude Monet (1832-1883) — AP109

1982, Dec. 6   Litho.   Perf. 13x12½
C302 AP109 300fr multi   2.00 2.00
For surcharge see No. C326.

Christmas
1982
AP110

Virgin and Child Paintings.

1982, Dec. 20   Perf. 12½x13
C303 AP110 200fr Matthias Grune-
            wald   1.25 1.25
C304 AP110 300fr Correggio   1.75 1.75
For surcharges see Nos. C325, C337.

No. C290 Surcharged
1983   Engr.   Perf. 13
C305 A133 75fr on 210fr multi   .50 .50

Bangkok '83
Stamp
Exhibition
AP111

1983, Aug. 4   Photo.   Perf. 13
C306 AP111 300fr multi   1.50 1.50
For surcharge see No. C322.

Christmas
1983
AP112

1983, Dec. 26   Litho.   Perf. 12½x13
C307 AP112 200fr Loretto Madonna,
            by Raphael   .65 .65
For surcharge see No. C319.

Types of 1976-82 Surcharged
1983, Nov.
C308 AP94 10fr on 200fr C270   .15 .15
C309 AP95 15fr on 200fr C273   .15 .15
C310 AP90 15fr on 270fr C261   .15 .15
C311 AP98 20fr on 200fr C280   .15 .15
C312 AP89 25fr on 270fr C258   .15 .15
C313 AP98 25fr on 380fr C281   .15 .15
C314 AP96 30fr on 100fr C277   .15 .15
C315 AP107 40fr on 500fr C298   .20 .20
C316 AP93 75fr on 150fr C266   .38 .38
C317 AP95 75fr on 150fr C272   .38 .38
           Set value   1.60 1.60

Summer
Olympics — AP113

1984, July 16   Litho.   Perf. 13x13½
C318 AP113 300fr Sam the Eagle,
             mascot   1.00 1.00

Nos. C262, C293-C294, C299, C302-
C303, C306-C307 Surcharged
1984, Sept.
C319 AP112 15fr on 200fr multi   .15 .15
C320 AP104 15fr on 300fr multi   .15 .15
C321 AP90 25fr on 300fr multi   .15 .15
C322 AP111 25fr on 300fr multi   .15 .15
C323 AP103 40fr on 500fr multi   .15 .15
C324 AP108 75fr on 105fr multi   .25 .25
C325 AP110 90fr on 200fr multi   .30 .30
C326 AP109 90fr on 300fr multi   .30 .30
           Set value   1.25 1.25

Christmas
1984
AP114

1984, Dec. 17   Litho.   Perf. 12½x13
C327 AP114 500fr Virgin and Child,
             by Murillo   1.50 1.50
For surcharge see No. C486

Ships — AP115

1984, Dec. 28   Litho.   Perf. 13
C328 AP115 90fr Sidon merchant ship   .30 .30
C329 AP115 125fr Wavertree, vert.   .38 .38

Benin-S.O.M. Postal
Convention
AP116

1985, Apr. 15 Litho. Perf. 13¹/₂
C330 AP116 75fr Benin arms .22 .22
C331 AP116 75fr Sovereign Order of
Malta .22 .22
a. Pair, #C330-C331 .45 .45

PHILEXAFRICA III, Lome — AP117

1985, June 24 Perf. 13
C332 AP117 200fr Oil platform .60 .60
C333 AP117 200fr Soccer players .60 .60
a. Pair, #C332-C333 + label 1.25 1.25

For surcharge see No. C485.

Stamps of 1977-82 Surcharged
1985, Mar.
C334 AP92 75fr on 200fr #C264 .20 .20
C335 AP102 75fr on 200fr #C291 .20 .20
C336 AP93 75fr on 300fr #C267 .20 .20
C337 AP110 75fr on 300fr #C304 .20 .20
C338 AP99 90fr on 500fr #C284 .25 .25
C339 AP100 90fr on 500fr #C287 .25 .25
C340 AP104 90fr on 500fr #C295 .25 .25
Nos. C334-C340 (7) 1.55 1.55

Dahomey Stamps of 1971-75 Surcharged
1985, Aug.
C341 AP87(i) 25fr on 40fr #C266 .15 .15
C342 AP49(a) 40fr #C142 .15 .15
C343 AP56(i) 75fr on 85fr #C164 .20 .20
C344 AP60(a) 75fr on 100fr
#C173 .20 .20
C345 AP64(i) 75fr on 125fr
#C186 .20 .20
C346 AP56(i) 90fr on 20fr #C163 .25 .25
C347 A61(i) 90fr on 150fr
#C153 .25 .25
C348 AP49(a) 90fr on 200fr
#C143 .25 .25
C349 AP78(i) 90fr on 200fr
#C237 .25 .25
C350 AP78(j) 150fr #C236 .45 .45
Nos. C341-C350 (10) 2.35 2.35

Christmas — AP118

1985, Dec. 20 Litho. Perf. 13x12¹/₂
C351 AP118 500fr multi 1.75 1.75

For surcharge see No. C449.

Dahomey Nos. C34-C37, C84, C131
Surcharged or Overprinted
1986 Photo. Perfs. as before
C352 AP33(b) 75fr on 70fr #C84 .25 .25
C353 AP14(b) 75fr on 100fr #C34 .25 .25
C354 AP15(b) 75fr on 200fr #C35 .25 .25
C355 AP15(b) 90fr on 250fr #C36 .35 .35
C356 AP45(b) 100fr #C131 .38 .38
C357 AP14(b) 150fr on 500fr #C37 .55 .55
Nos. C352-C357 (6) 2.03 2.03

Issued: 75fr, 90fr, Mar; 100fr, 150fr, June.

Dahomey Nos. C82, C139, C141, C146
Surcharged
1986
Perfs. & Printing Methods as Before
C357A AP33(d) 15fr on 45fr
#C82
C357B AP48(d) 25fr on 200fr
#C141 (S)
C357D AP48(d) 100fr on #C139
C357E CD135(d) 100fr on #C146

Christmas — AP119

1986, Dec. 24 Litho. Perf. 13x12¹/₂
C358 AP119 300fr multi 1.20 1.20

Air Africa,
25th Anniv.
AP120

1986, Dec. 30 Perf. 12¹/₂
C359 AP120 100fr multi .40 .40

Intl.
Agricultural
Development
Fund (FIDA),
10th Anniv.
AP121

1987, Dec. 14 Litho. Perf. 13¹/₂
C360 AP121 500fr multi 3.50 3.50

Christmas — AP122

1988, Dec. 23 Litho. Perf. 13x12¹/₂
C361 AP122 500fr Adoration of the
Magi, storyteller 3.25 3.25

No. C241 Surcharged

*République
Populaire
du Bénin*

15 f ═

1989, Apr. 24 Litho. Perf. 13
C362 AP84(b) 15fr on 85fr multi .15 .15

Dahomey Nos. C37, C53, C152, C156,
C165, C175, C182, C234,
Benin No. C242 Surcharged or
Overprinted

Dahomey No. ▮▮▮
Overprinted

*République
Populaire
du Bénin*

1987
Perfs. & Printing Methods as Before
C363 AP77 20fr on 250fr #C234
C364 AP48(b) 25fr on 150fr #C175
(S&B)
C365 AP63(b) 40fr on 15fr #C182
C366 AP48(b) 40fr on 100fr #C152
C367 AP84(b) 50fr on 140fr #C242
C368 AP14(b) 50fr on 500fr #C37
C369 AP22(b) 80fr on #C53
C370 AP56(b) 80fr on 150fr #C165
C373 AP52(b) 100fr on #C156

Dahomey Nos. C140, C144, C158, C166,
C177, C185, C188 C191, C195, C207,
C262 Surcharged
1988
Perfs. & Printing Methods as Before
C374 AP50(d) 10fr on 50fr #C144
C375 AP64(d) 10fr on 65fr #C185
C376 AP72(d) 15fr on 150fr #C207
C377 AP67(d) 25fr on 200fr #C191
C378 AP61(d) 40fr on 35fr #C195
C380 AP53(d) 70fr on 250fr #C158
C381 AP48(d) 100fr on #C140
C382 AP65(d) 100fr on #C188
C384 AP61(f) 125fr on #C177
C385 AP86(d) 125fr on 75fr #C262
C386 AP57(d) 150fr on 100fr #C166

Dahomey Nos. C181, C196, C208
Surcharged
1988
Perfs. & Printing Methods as Before
C388 AP61(d) 25fr on 100fr #C196
C390 AP62 40fr on 100fr #C181
C391 AP73(d) 40fr on 150fr #C208

Dahomey Nos. C108, C147-C148, C162,
C167, C178, C187, C194
1992
Perfs. & Printing Methods as Before
C394 AP51(f) 70fr on #C148
C395 AP55(e) 100fr on #C162
C396 AP68(g) 100fr on #C194
C397 AP51(e) 125fr on 40fr #C147
C398 A52(f) 125fr on 70fr #C108
C400 AP64a(e) 125fr on 100fr #C187
C401 AP61(f) 190fr on 140fr #C178
C402 AP58(f) 190fr on 150fr #C167

Dahomey Nos. C145, C149-C150, C182,
C189, C198,
C257, C264-C265 Surcharged
Benin No. C241 Surcharged
1993
Perfs. & Printing Methods as Before
C403 AP51(e) 5fr on 100fr #C149
C404 AP50(f) 10fr on 100fr #C145
C405 AP51(f) 20fr on 200fr #C150
C406 AP83(e) 20fr on 500fr #C257
C407 AP84(e) 25fr on 85fr #C241
C408 AP86(f) 25fr on 500fr #C265
C409 AP63(f) 30fr on 15fr #C182
C410 AP61(f) 30fr on 200fr #C198
C411 AP66(b) 35fr on #C189
C412 AP86(g) 300fr on #C264

Dahomey Nos. C14, C31, C34, C101,
C110, C144, C151, C153, C155, C197,
C222, C234, C250, C254, C256, C261,
Benin C242 Surcharged or Overprinted
1994-95?
Perfs. & Printing Methods as Before
C414 AP52(e) 15fr on 40fr #C155
C415 AP83(f) 25fr on 200fr #C256
C417 AP49(g) 50fr on #C101
C418 AP48(g) 75fr on 40fr #C151
C419 AP4(g) 100fr on #C14
C421 AP50(g) 125fr on 50fr #C144
C422 AP75(e) 125fr on 65fr #C222
C425 AP21(f) 135fr on 45fr #C110
C432 AP81(f) 135fr on 250fr #C250
C432 AP84(f) 150fr on 140fr #C242
C433 A61(b) 150fr on #C153
C434 AP61(b) 150fr on #C197
C435 AP13(e) 200fr on 100fr #C31
C436 AP14(e) 200fr on 100fr #C34

C445 AP61(e) 200fr on 250fr #C234
C446 AP61(e) 200fr on 250fr #C254
C447 AP85(f) 300fr on #C261

Dahomey No. C37, Benin No. C351
Surcharged
1994-95
Printing Method and Perfs as Before
C448 AP14 150fr on 500fr #C37
C449 AP118 200fr on 500fr #C351

Benin No. C290 Surcharged
Dahomey Nos. C206, C257 Surcharged
1996?
Perfs. & Printing Methods as Before
C450 A133 40fr on 210fr #C290
C451 AP83(f) 200fr on 500fr #C257
C452 AP72(f) 1000fr on 150fr #C206

Dahomey No. C265 Surcharged
Benin Nos. C258, C292 Surcharged
1996?
Perfs. & Printing Methods as Before
C453 AP86(g) 25fr on 500fr #C265
C454 AP89 35fr on 270fr #C258
C455 AP102 100fr on 500fr #C292

Dahomey Nos. C61, C74, C85, C88, C94,
C106, C109, C111, C113, C115, C120,
C124-C125, C130, C135-C136, C138,
C142-C143, C150, C157, C204-C205,
C207-C208, C260, C263 Surcharged
1996?
Perfs. & Printing Methods as Before
C456 AP48(e) 70fr on 100fr #C138
C457 AP34(h) 150fr on #C88
C458 AP21(e) 150fr on #C115
C459 AP72(e) 150fr on #C207
C460 AP73(h) 150fr on #C208
C461 AP34(e) 150fr on 30fr #C85
C462 AP31(h) 150fr on 30fr #C74
C463 AP21(e) 150fr on 30fr #C109
C464 AP40(e) 150fr on 40fr on 30fr
#C120
C465 AP47(e) 150fr on 40fr #C136
C466 AP49(e) 150fr on 40fr #C142
C467 CD128(h) 150fr on 50fr #C94
C468 AP38(h) 150fr on 50fr #C106
C469 AP71(e) 150fr on 50fr #C204
C470 AP54(h) 150fr on 70fr #C124
C471 CD124(h) 150fr on 100fr #C61
C472 AP21(e) 150fr on 100fr #C113
C473 AP53(h) 150fr on 100fr #C157
C474 AP84(h) 150fr on 100fr #C260
C475 AP21(e) 150fr on 110fr #C111
C476 AP44(h) 150fr on 110fr #C130
C477 AP54(h) 150fr on 120fr #C125
C478 AP86(g) 150fr on 135fr #C263
C479 AP46(h) 150fr on 200fr #C135
C480 AP49(e) 150fr on 200fr #C143
C481 AP51(h) 150fr on 200fr #C150
C482 AP71(e) 150fr on 200fr #C205

Benin Nos. C261, C281, C327, C332
Surcharged
1996?
Perfs. & Printing Methods as Before
C483 AP98 30fr on 380fr #C281
C484 AP90 35fr on 270fr #C261
C485 AP117 125fr on 200fr #C332
C486 AP114 200fr on 500fr #C327

Dahomey No. C250 Surcharged Type f
1997?
Perf. & Printing Method as Before
C509 AP81(f) 150fr on 250fr #C250

POSTAGE DUE STAMPS

French Colony
Handstamped in Black on Postage Due
Stamps of French Colonies

BENIN

1894		**Unwmk.**		*Imperf.*
J1	D1	5c black	120.00	45.00
J2	D1	10c black	120.00	45.00
J3	D1	20c black	120.00	45.00
J4	D1	30c black	120.00	45.00
		Nos. J1-J4 (4)	480.00	180.00

Nos. J1-J4 exist with overprint in various
positions.

People's Republic

Pineapples
D6

Mail
Delivery — D7

Designs: 20fr, Cashew, vert. 40fr, Oranges. 50fr, Akee. 80fr, Mail delivery by boat.

1978, Sept. 5		Photo.	Perf. 13	
J44	D6	10fr multi	.15	.15
J45	D6	20fr multi	.15	.15
J46	D6	40fr multi	.28	.16
J47	D6	50fr multi	.45	.25

		Engr.		
J48	D7	60fr multi	.32	.22
J49	D7	80fr multi	.45	.28
	Nos. J44-J49 (6)		1.80	1.21

PARCEL POST STAMPS

Catalogue values for unused stamps in this section are for Never Hinged items.

Nos. 448-448A, 459, 473, C292 Overprinted or Surcharged "Colis Postaux"
Perfs. and Printing Methods as Before

1982, Nov.				
Q8	A126	100fr on 150fr	.40	.20
Q9	A130	100fr multi	.40	.20
Q10	A134	300fr multi	1.20	.60
Q10A	A126a	1000fr multi	5.50	5.50
Q10B	AP102	5000fr on 500fr	27.50	27.50
	Nos. Q8-Q10B (5)		35.00	34.00

500 f

République
Populaire
du Bénin

colis postaux

1989	Photo.	Perf. 12½x13	
Q11	AP71	500fr on 200fr multi	3.25 3.25

BERMUDA
(ˌ)bər-ˈmyü–də

LOCATION — A group of about 150 small islands of which only 20 are inhabited, lying in the Atlantic Ocean about 580 miles southeast of Cape Hatteras.
GOVT. — British Crown Colony
AREA — 20.5 sq. mi.
POP. — 54,893 (1980)
CAPITAL — Hamilton

Bermuda achieved internal self-government in 1968.

4 Farthings = 1 Penny
12 Pence = 1 Shilling
20 Shillings = 1 Pound
100 Cents = 1 Dollar (1970)

Catalogue values for unused stamps in this country are for Never Hinged items, beginning with Scott 131.

POSTMASTER STAMPS

PM1

1848-54		Unwmk.	Imperf.
X1	PM1	1p blk, bluish (1848, 1849)	125,000.
X2	PM1	1p red, bluish (1854, 1856)	175,000.
X3	PM1	1p red (1853)	160,000.

PM2

1860			
X4	PM2	(1p) red, yellowish	100,000.

Same inscribed "HAMILTON"

1861			
X5	PM2	(1p) red, bluish	125,000.

Nos. X1-X3 were produced and used by Postmaster William B. Perot of Hamilton. No. X4 is attributed to Postmaster James H. Thies of St. George's. Only a few of each stamp exist. Values reflect actual sales figures for stamps in the condition in which they are found.

GENERAL ISSUES

Values for unused stamps are for examples with original gum as defined in the catalogue introduction. Very fine examples of Nos. 1-1a, 2-15b will have perforations touching the design (or framelines where applicable) on at least one side due to the narrow spacing of the stamps on the plates. Stamps with perfs clear of the design on all four sides are scarce and will command higher prices.

Queen Victoria
A1   A2

A3   A4

A5

1865-74		Typo.	Wmk. 1	Perf. 14	
1	A1	1p rose red		80.00	3.00
a.		1p dull rose		95.00	5.00
b.		Imperf.		20,000.	11,000.
2	A2	2p blue ('66)		130.00	11.00
3	A3	3p buff ('73)		425.00	60.00
4	A4	6p brown lilac		900.00	110.00
5	A4	6p lilac ('74)		21.00	17.50
6	A5	1sh green		175.00	35.00
	Nos. 1-6 (6)			1,731.	236.50

See Nos. 7-9, 19-21, 23, 25. For surcharges see Nos. 10-15.

1882-1903			Perf. 14x12½	
7	A3	3p buff	165.00	50.00
8	A4	6p violet ('03)	15.00	17.50
9	A5	1sh green ('94)	22.50	80.00
a.	Vert. strip of 3, perf. all around & imperf. btwn.		13,000.	
	Nos. 7-9 (3)		202.50	147.50

Handstamped
Diagonally   **THREE PENCE**

1874			Perf. 14	
10	A5	3p on 1sh green	1,400.	950.

Handstamped
Diagonally   *THREE PENCE*

1875				
11	A1	3p on 1p rose	12,000.	
12	A5	3p on 1sh green	2,100.	900.
a.	"P" with top like "R"	2,250.	1,200.

No. 11 is stated to be an essay, but a few copies are known used. Nos. 10-12 are found with double or partly double surcharges.

One
Penny.

Surcharged in Black

1875				
13	A2	1p on 2p blue	700.00	375.00
a.	Without period	11,000.	7,250.
14	A3	1p on 3p buff	450.00	350.00
15	A5	1p on 1sh green	500.00	300.00
a.	Inverted surcharge		
b.	Without period		

A6   A7

1880			Wmk. 1	
16	A6	½p brown	1.75	2.75
17	A7	4p orange	10.00	2.50

See Nos. 18, 24.

BERMUDA

A8

A9

1883-1904   Wmk. 2

18	A6	¼p green ('92)	1.50	1.00
19	A1	1p aniline car ('89)	3.00	.30
a.		1p dull rose	100.00	4.00
b.		1p rose red	60.00	2.25
c.		1p carmine rose ('86)	25.00	1.00
20	A2	2p blue ('86)	35.00	3.00
21	A2	2p aniline pur ('93)	8.50	4.00
a.		2p brown purple ('98)	3.00	2.50
22	A8	2½p ultra ('84)	6.00	.40
23	A3	3p gray ('86)	14.00	5.50
24	A7	4p brown org ('04)	24.00	60.00
25	A5	1sh ol bis ('93)	16.00	12.00
a.		1sh yellow brown	16.00	13.00
		Nos. 18-25 (8)	108.00	86.20

Black Surcharge

1901

26	A9	1f on 1sh gray	.40	.25

Dry Dock — A10

1902-03

28	A10	½p gray grn & blk ('03)	7.25	2.50
29	A10	1p car rose & brown	6.50	.40
30	A10	3p ol grn & violet	1.65	3.75
		Nos. 28-30 (3)	15.40	6.65

1906-10   Wmk. 3

31	A10	¼p pur & brn ('08)	.60	1.25
32	A10	½p gray grn & blk	4.00	1.65
33	A10	½p green ('09)	3.75	2.25
34	A10	1p car rose & brn	4.50	.30
35	A10	1p carmine ('08)	4.50	.40
36	A10	2p orange & gray	4.75	5.75
37	A10	2½p blue & brown	8.75	13.00
38	A10	2½p ultra ('10)	13.00	9.50
39	A10	4p vio brn & blue ('09)	2.75	9.50
		Nos. 31-39 (9)	46.60	43.60

Caravel
A11

King George V
A12

1910-20   Engr.   Perf. 14

40	A11	¼p brown	.45	1.25
41	A11	½p yel green	.90	.30
a.		½p dark green	3.00	1.40
42	A11	1p rose red (I)	7.00	.35
a.		1p carmine (I)	25.00	3.50
43	A11	2p gray	2.00	4.00
44	A11	2½p ultra (I)	2.25	.50
45	A11	3p violet, yel	1.40	5.00
46	A11	4p red, yellow	2.75	6.00
47	A11	6p claret	8.00	8.00
48	A11	1sh blk, green	4.00	5.00
a.		1sh black, olive	3.75	8.00

Typographed
Chalky Paper

49	A12	2sh ultra & dl vio, bl ('20)	9.00	32.50
50	A12	2sh6p red & blk, bl	18.00	42.50
51	A12	4sh car & black ('20)	35.00	70.00
52	A12	5sh red & grn, yellow	45.00	70.00
53	A12	10sh red & grn, green	140.00	125.00
54	A12	£1 black & vio, red	350.00	400.00
		Nos. 40-54 (15)	625.75	820.40

Types I of 1p and 2½p are illustrated above Nos. 81-97.

The 1p was printed from two plates, the 2nd of which, #42a, exists only in carmine on opaque paper with a bluish tinge. Compare #MR1 (as #42) and MR2 (as #42a).

Revenue cancellations are found on Nos. 52-54. See Nos. 81-97.

Seal of the Colony and King
George V — A13

1920-21   Wmk. 3   Ordinary Paper

55	A13	¼p brown	.80	5.00
56	A13	½p green	1.00	6.00
57	A13	2p gray	6.50	17.50

Chalky Paper

58	A13	3p vio & dl vio, yel	6.00	15.00
59	A13	4p red & blk, yellow	6.50	15.00
60	A13	1sh blk, gray grn	14.00	35.00

Ordinary Paper
Wmk. 4

67	A13	1p rose red	1.00	.60
68	A13	2½p ultra	5.50	8.00

Chalky Paper

69	A13	6p red vio & dl vio	12.50	35.00
		Nos. 55-60,67-69 (9)	53.80	137.10

Issued: 6p, Jan. 19, 1921; others, Nov. 11, 1920.

King
George V — A14

1921, May 12   Engr.

71	A14	¼p brown	.45	1.50
72	A14	½p green	3.50	4.00
73	A14	1p carmine	2.50	1.00

Wmk. 3

74	A14	2p gray	6.00	10.00
75	A14	2½p ultra	6.00	4.00
76	A14	3p vio, orange	4.25	10.00
77	A14	4p scarlet, org	8.00	12.00
78	A14	6p claret	8.50	25.00
79	A14	1sh blk, green	16.00	30.00
		Nos. 71-79 (9)	55.20	97.50

Tercentenary of "Local Representative Institutions" (Nos. 55-79).

Types of 1910-20 Issue

Types of 1p: **1d 1d 1d**
           I   II   III

Types of 2½p: **2½d 2½d**
             I   II

1922-34   Wmk. 4

81	A11	¼p brown ('28)	.30	.75
82	A11	½p green	.20	.15
83	A11	1p car, III ('28)	7.50	.30
a.		1p carmine, II ('26)	8.00	.60
b.		1p carmine, I	8.00	.40
84	A11	1½p red brown ('34)	3.00	.30
85	A11	2p gray ('23)	1.00	1.00
86	A11	2½p ap grn ('23)	1.00	1.00
87	A11	2½p ultra, II ('32)	2.00	.35
a.		2½p ultra, I ('26)	1.75	.35
88	A11	3p ultra ('24)	14.00	20.00
89	A11	3p vio, yellow ('26)	.80	.60
90	A11	4p red, yellow ('24)	1.00	1.00
91	A11	6p claret ('24)	.80	.80
92	A11	1sh blk, emer ('27)	5.00	5.00
93	A11	1sh brn blk, yel grn ('34)	30.00	40.00

Chalky Paper

94	A12	2sh ultra & vio, bl ('27)	30.00	40.00
a.		2sh bl & dp vio, dp bl ('31)	35.00	40.00
95	A12	2sh 6p red & blk, bl ('27)	40.00	37.50
a.		2sh6p pale org ver & blk, gray bl ('30)	2,750.	2,250.
b.		2sh6p dp ver & blk, deep blue	50.00	45.00
96	A12	10sh red & grn, emer ('24)	150.00	175.00
a.		10sh dp red & pale grn, dp em- ('31)	150.00	175.00
97	A12	12sh 6p ocher & gray blk ('32)	300.00	350.00
		Nos. 81-97 (17)	586.60	673.75

Revenue cancellations are found on Nos. 94-97.

The 12sh6p with "Revenue" on both sides, was used postally from Feb. 1 to Apr., 1937. Copies with postal cancels in that time period are valued at three times No. 97.

Common Design Types pictured following the introduction.

Silver Jubilee Issue
Common Design Type

1935, May 6   Perf. 11x12

100	CD301	1p car & dk bl	.15	.15
101	CD301	1½p blk & ultra	.45	.45
102	CD301	2½p ultra & brn	1.50	1.50
103	CD301	1sh brn vio & ind	6.00	10.00
		Nos. 100-103 (4)	8.10	12.10
		Set, never hinged	14.00	

Hamilton
Harbor — A15

Yacht
"Lucie" — A17

South Shore — A16

Grape
Bay — A18

Typical Cottage
A19

Scene at Par-la-Ville
A20

1936-40   Perf. 12

105	A15	½p blue green	.15	.15
106	A16	1p car & black	.30	.15
107	A16	1½p choc & black	.30	.15
108	A17	2p lt bl & blk	2.50	2.00
109	A17	2p brn blk & turq bl ('38)	22.50	8.00
109A	A17	2p red & ultra ('40)	.25	.15
110	A17	2½p dk bl & lt bl	.55	.35
111	A19	3p car & black	2.50	1.50
112	A20	6p vio & rose lake	.50	.50
113	A18	1sh deep green	5.50	5.00
114	A15	1sh6p brown	.50	.40
		Nos. 105-114 (11)	35.35	18.05
		Set, never hinged 50.00		

No. 108, blue border and black center.
No. 109, black border, blue center.

Coronation Issue
Common Design Type

1937, May 14   Perf. 13½x14

115	CD302	1p carmine	.15	.15
116	CD302	1½p brown	.20	.15
117	CD302	2½p bright ultra	.50	.25
		Nos. 115-117 (3)	.85	.55
		Set, never hinged	1.50	

Hamilton
Harbor — A21

Grape
Bay — A22

St. David's
Lighthouse
A23

King George VI
A25

Bermudian Water Scene and Yellow-billed Tropic Bird — A24

1938-51   Wmk. 4   Perf. 12

118	A21	1p red & black ('40)	.15	.15
a.		1p rose red & black	12.00	1.00
119	A21	1½p vio brn & blue	.50	.25
a.		1½p dl vio brn & bl ('43)	.20	.15
120	A22	2½p blue & lt bl	2.50	.75
120A	A22	2½p ol brn & lt bl ('41)		
b.		2½p dk ol blk & pale blue ('43)	.30	.15
121	A23	3p car & blk	.30	.15
121A	A23	3p dp ultra & blk	4.50	1.75
c.		3p brt ultra & blk ('41)	.25	.15
121D	A24	7½p ol brn, bl & blk ('41)	.25	.15
122	A22	1sh green	1.25	1.00
			1.00	.35

Typo.
Perf. 13

123	A25	2sh ultra & red vio, bl ('50)	6.00	4.00
a.		2sh ultra & vio, bl, perf. 14	5.00	3.50
b.		2sh ultra & dl vio, bl (mottled paper), perf. 14 ('42)	5.00	3.50
124	A25	2sh 6p red & blk, bl	8.00	6.00
a.		Perf. 14	8.00	3.50
125	A25	5sh red & grn, yel	10.00	7.50
a.		Perf. 14	13.00	7.50
126	A25	10sh red & grn, grn ('51)	20.00	14.00
a.		brn lake & grn, grn, perf. 14	175.00	200.00
b.		red & grn, grn, perf. 14 ('39)	40.00	40.00
127	A25	12sh 6p org & gray blk	55.00	50.00
a.		orange & gray, perf. 14	45.00	35.00
b.		yel & gray, perf. 14 ('47)	600.00	525.00
c.		brn orange & gray, perf. 14	300.00	300.00

Wmk. 3

128	A25	£1 blk & vio, red ('51)	35.00	30.00
a.		£1 blk & pur, red, perf. 14	190.00	100.00
b.		£1 blk & dk vio, salmon, perf. 14 ('42)	40.00	25.00
		Nos. 118-128 (14)	144.45	116.05
		Set, never hinged	220.00	

No. 127b is the so-called "lemon yellow" shade.

Revenue cancellations are found on Nos. 123-128. Copies with removed revenue cancellations and forged postmarks are abundant.

HALF PENNY

No. 118a
Surcharged in Black

X   **X**

1940, Dec. 20   Wmk. 4   Perf. 12

129	A21	½p on 1p rose red & blk	.30	.30
		Never hinged	.50	

Catalogue values for unused stamps in this section, from this point to the end of the section, are for Never Hinged items.

Peace Issue
Common Design Type
Perf. 13½x14

1946, Nov. 6   Engr.   Wmk. 4

131	CD303	1½p brown	.20	.20
132	CD303	3p deep blue	.30	.30

Silver Wedding Issue
Common Design Types

1948, Dec. 1   Photo.   Perf. 14x14½

133	CD304	1½p dp red brown	.15	.15

Engr.; Name Typo.
Perf. 11½x11

134	CD305	£1 rose carmine	47.50	35.00

Postmaster
Stamp of
1848 — A26

1949, Apr. 11   Engr.   Perf. 13x13½

135	A26	2½p dk brown & dp bl	.20 .20
136	A26	3p dp blue & black	.20 .20
137	A26	6p green & rose vio	.45 .45
		Nos. 135-137 (3)	.85 .85

No. 137 shows a different floral arrangement. Bermuda's first postage stamp, cent.

UPU Issue
Common Design Types
Perf. 13½, 11x11½

1949, Oct. 10   Engr.; Name Typo.

138	CD306	2½p slate	.55 .55
139	CD307	3p indigo	.70 .70
140	CD308	6p rose violet	1.10 1.10
141	CD309	1sh blue green	2.25 2.25
		Nos. 138-141 (4)	4.60 4.60

Coronation Issue
Common Design Type

1953, June 4   Engr.   Perf. 13½x13

142	CD312	1½p dk blue & blk	.40 .20

A27

Easter Lilies — A28

Designs: 1p, 4p, Perot stamp. 2p, Racing dinghy. 2½p, Sir George Somers and "Sea Venture." 3p, 1sh3p, Map. 4½p, 9p, "Sea Venture," boat, hog coin and Perot stamp. 6p, 8p, Yellow-billed tropic bird. 1sh, Hog coins. 2sh, Arms of St. George. 2sh6p, Warwick Fort. 5sh, Hog coin. 10sh, Earliest hog coin. £1, Arms of Bermuda.

1953-58   Perf. 13½x13, 13x13½

143	A27	½p olive green	.15 .15
144	A27	1p rose red & blk	.15 .15
145	A28	1½p dull green	.15 .15
146	A27	2p red & ultra	.15 .15
147	A27	2½p carmine rose	.50 .15
148	A27	3p vio (Sandy's)	.45 .25
149	A27	3p violet (Sandys) ('57)	.55 .20
150	A27	4p dp ultra & blk	.25 .25
151	A27	4½p green	.60 .60
152	A27	6p dk bluish grn & blk	2.50 .30
153	A27	8p red & blk ('55)	.95 .35
154	A27	9p violet ('58)	2.00 .95
155	A27	1sh orange	.40 .20
156	A27	1sh3p blue (Sandy's)	2.00 .35
157	A27	1sh3p blue (Sandys) ('57)	4.00 .50
158	A27	2sh yellow brown	.00 .65
159	A28	2sh6p scarlet	2.00 1.25
160	A27	5sh dp car rose	7.50 2.00
161	A27	10sh deep ultra	11.00 4.50

Engr. and Typo.

162	A27	£1 dp ol grn & multi	20.00 17.50
		Nos. 143-162 (20)	57.30 30.60

For overprints, see Nos. 164-167.

Type of 1953 Inscribed "ROYAL VISIT 1953"

Design: 6p, Yellow-billed tropic bird.

1953, Nov. 26   Engr.

163	A27	6p dk bluish grn & blk	.40 .35

Visit of Queen Elizabeth II and the Duke of Edinburgh, 1953.

Nos. 148 and 156 Overprinted in Violet Blue or Red	**Three Power Talks December, 1953**

1953, Dec. 8   Perf. 13½x13

164	A27	3p violet	.20 .20
165	A27	1sh3p blue (R)	.45 .40

Three Power Conference, Tucker's Town, December 1953.

Nos. 153 and 156 Overprinted in Black or Red	**50TH ANNIVERSARY U S — BERMUDA OCEAN RACE 1956**

1956, June 22

166	A27	8p red & black	.25 .30
167	A27	1sh3p blue (R)	.35 .50

Newport-Bermuda Yacht Race, 50th anniv.

Perot Post Office, Hamilton A29

1959, Jan. 1   Engr.   Wmk. 4

168	A29	6p lilac & black	.50 .30

Restoration and reopening of the post office operated at Hamilton by W. B. Perot in the mid-nineteenth century.

Arms of James I and Elizabeth II — A30

Engr. and Litho.

1959, July 29   Wmk. 314   Perf. 13
Coats of Arms in Blue, Yellow & Red

169	A30	1½p dark blue	.15 .15
170	A30	3p gray	.30 .35
171	A30	4p rose violet	.35 .35
172	A30	8p violet gray	.75 .75
173	A30	9p olive green	.95 .95
174	A30	1sh3p orange brown	1.50 1.50
		Nos. 169-174 (6)	4.00 4.05

350th anniv. of the shipwreck of the "Sea Venture" which resulted in the first permanent settlement of Bermuda.

The Old Rectory, St. George's, 1730 — A31

Designs: 2p, Church of St. Peter. 3p, Government House. 4p, Cathedral, Hamilton. 5p, No. 185A, H.M. Dockyard. 6p, Perot's Post Office, 1848. 8p, General Post Office, 1869. 9p, Library and Historical Society. 1sh, Christ Church, Warwick, 1719. 1sh3p, City Hall, Hamilton. 10p, No. 185, Bermuda Cottage, 1705. 2sh, Town of St. George. 2sh3p, Bermuda House, 1710. 2sh6p, Bermuda House, 18th century. 5sh, Colonial Secretariat, 1833. 10sh, Old Post Office, Somerset, 1890. £1, House of Assembly, 1815.

Wmk. 314 Upright

1962-65   Perf. 12½

175	A31	1p org, lil & blk	.15 .15
176	A31	2p sl, lt vio, grn & yel	.15 .15
a.		Light vio omitted	650.00
b.		Green omitted	
d.		Imperf., pair	650.00
177	A31	3p lt bl & yel brn	.15 .15
a.		Yellow brown omitted	1,250.
178	A31	4p car rose & red brn	.15 .15
179	A31	5p dk blue & pink	.32 .32
180	A31	6p emer, lt & dk blue	.18 .15
181	A31	8p orn, dp org & ultra	.35 .30
182	A31	9p org brn & grnsh bl	.32 .28
182A	A31	10p brt vio & bister ('65)	.65 .55
183	A31	1sh multicolored	.42 .26
184	A31	1sh3p sl, lem & rose car	.48 .26
185	A31	1sh6p brt vio & bis	2.75 2.25
186	A31	2sh brown & org	1.25 .85
187	A31	2sh3p brn & brt yel green	2.50 2.00
188	A31	2sh6p grn, yel & sep	1.50 1.10
189	A31	5sh choc & brt green	2.50 1.65
190	A31	10sh dl grn, buff & rose car	4.00 3.50
191	A31	£1 cit, bis, blk & orange	9.50 7.75
		Nos. 175-191 (18)	27.32 21.82

See No. 252a. For surcharges see Nos. 238, 240-244, 247, 250-254.

1966-69   Wmk. 314 Sideways
Unnamed Colors as in 1962-65 Issue

176c	A31	2p ('69)	2.50 1.65
181a	A31	4p ('67)	1.10 .90
182b	A31	10p	1.40 1.10
183a	A31	1sh	1.40 1.25
185A	A31	1sh6p indigo & rose	2.50 3.00
186a	A31	2sh ('67)	4.50 4.50
		Nos. 176c-186a (6)	13.40 12.40

For surcharges see #239, 245-246, 248-249.

Freedom from Hunger Issue
Common Design Type

1963, June 4   Perf. 14x14½

192	CD314	1sh3p sepia	2.75 2.25

Red Cross Centenary Issue
Common Design Type
Wmk. 314

1963, Sept. 2   Litho.   Perf. 13

193	CD315	3p black & red	.50 .30
194	CD315	1sh3p ultra & red	5.50 3.00

Finn Boat — A32

Perf. 13½

1964, Sept. 28   Photo.   Wmk. 314

195	A32	3p blue, vio & red	.28 .28

18th Olympic Games, Tokyo, Oct. 10-25.

ITU Issue
Common Design Type
Perf. 11x11½

1965, May 17   Litho.   Wmk. 314

196	CD317	3p blue & emerald	.42 .30
197	CD317	2sh yel & vio blue	3.50 3.50

Scout Badge and Royal Cipher A33

1965, July 24   Photo.   Perf. 12½

198	A33	2sh multicolored	.85 .85

50th anniversary of Scouting in Bermuda.

Intl. Cooperation Year Issue
Common Design Type

1965, Oct. 25   Litho.   Perf. 14x14½

199	CD318	4p blue grn & cl	.30 .30
200	CD318	2sh6p lt violet & grn	2.25 2.25

Churchill Memorial Issue
Common Design Type

1966, Jan. 24   Photo.   Perf. 14
Design in Black, Gold and Carmine Rose

201	CD319	3p bright blue	.30 .20
202	CD319	6p green	.65 .45
203	CD319	10p brown	1.25 1.00
204	CD319	1sh3p violet	2.50 2.00
		Nos. 201-204 (4)	4.70 3.65

World Cup Soccer Issue
Common Design Type

1966, July 1   Litho.   Perf. 14

205	CD321	10p multicolored	.65 .65
206	CD321	2sh6p multicolored	1.75 1.75

UNESCO Anniversary Issue
Common Design Type

1966, Dec. 1   Litho.   Perf. 14

207	CD323	4p "Education"	.40 .40
208	CD323	1sh3p "Science"	1.50 1.50
209	CD323	2sh "Culture"	2.50 2.50
		Nos. 207-209 (3)	4.40 4.40

Post Office, Hamilton A34

Perf. 14½

1967, June 23   Photo.   Wmk. 314

210	A34	3p vio blue & multi	.15 .15
211	A34	1sh orange & multi	.40 .40
212	A34	1sh6p green & multi	.70 .70
213	A34	2sh6p red & multi	1.10 1.10
		Nos. 210-213 (4)	2.35 2.35

Opening of the new GPO, Hamilton.

Cable Ship Mercury A35

Designs: 1sh, Map of Bermuda and Virgin Islands, telephone and microphone. 1sh6p, Radio tower, television set, telephone and cable. 2sh6p, Cable at sea bottom and ship.

1967, Sept. 14   Photo.   Wmk. 314

214	A35	3p multicolored	.15 .15
215	A35	1sh multicolored	.40 .40
216	A35	1sh6p multicolored	.70 .70
217	A35	2sh6p multicolored	1.10 1.10
		Nos. 214-217 (4)	2.35 2.35

Completion of the Bermuda-Tortola, Virgin Islands, telephone link.

Human Rights Flame, Globe and Doves A36

1968, Feb. 1   Litho.   Perf. 14x14½

218	A36	3p indigo, lt grn & bl	.15 .15
219	A36	1sh brown, lt bl & bl	.45 .45
220	A36	1sh6p black, pink & blue	.75 .75
221	A36	2sh6p green, yellow & bl	.95 .95
		Nos. 218-221 (4)	2.30 2.30

International Human Rights Year.

Mace A37

Design: 1sh6p, 2sh6p, House of Assembly, Bermuda; Parliament, London, and royal cipher.

1968, July 1   Photo.   Perf. 14½

222	A37	3p rose red & multi	.15 .15
223	A37	1sh ultra & multi	.45 .45
224	A37	1sh6p yellow & multi	.75 .75
225	A37	2sh6p multicolored	.95 .95
		Nos. 222-225 (4)	2.30 2.30

New constitution.

Olympic Sports and Rings — A38

1968, Sept. 24   Wmk. 314   Perf. 12½

226	A38	3p lilac & multi	.15 .15
a.		Rose brown omitted ("3d BERMUDA")	2,000.
227	A38	1sh multicolored	.42 .35
228	A38	1sh6p multicolored	.60 .60
229	A38	2sh6p multicolored	1.00 1.00
		Nos. 226-229 (4)	2.17 2.10

19th Olympic Games, Mexico City, Oct. 12-27.

Girl Guides
A39

Designs: 1sh, Like 3p. 1sh6p, 2sh6p, Girl Guides and arms of Bermuda.

1969, Feb. 17   Litho.   Perf. 14
230	A39	3p lilac & multi	.15	.15
231	A39	1sh green & multi	.35	.35
232	A39	1sh6p gray & multi	.55	.55
233	A39	2sh6p red & multi	1.00	1.00
		Nos. 230-233 (4)	2.05	2.05

Bermuda Girl Guides, 50th anniv.

Gold and Emerald Cross — A40

Design: 4p, 2sh, Different background.

1969, Sept. 29   Photo.   Perf. 14¹/₂x14
Cross in Yellow, Brown and Emerald
234	A40	4p violet	.24	.24
235	A40	1sh3p green	.75	.75
236	A40	2sh black	1.10	1.10
237	A40	2sh6p carmine rose	1.40	1.25
		Nos. 234-237 (4)	3.49	3.34

Treasures salvaged off the coast of Bermuda. The cross shown is from the Tucker treasure from the 16th century Spanish galleon San Pedro.

Buildings Issue and Type of 1962-69 Surcharged with New Value and Bar in Black or Brown

1970, Feb. 6   Wmk. 314   Perf. 12¹/₂
238	A31	1c on 1p multi	.15	.15
239	A31	2c on 2p multi	.15	.15
a.		Watermark upright	1.25	1.25
b.		Light violet omitted	650.00	
c.		Pair, one without surch.	2,000.	
240	A31	3c on 3p multi	.15	.15
241	A31	4c on 4p multi (Br)	.15	.15
242	A31	5c on 8p multi	.15	.15
243	A31	6c on 6p multi	.15	.15
244	A31	9c on 9p multi (Br)	.22	.40
245	A31	10c on 10p multi	.28	.50
246	A31	12c on 1sh multi	.32	.60
247	A31	15c on 1sh3p multi	.70	1.10
248	A31	18c on 1sh6p multi	.70	1.25
249	A31	24c on 2sh multi	.85	1.50
250	A31	30c on 2sh6p multi	1.00	1.90
251	A31	36c on 3sh3p multi	1.25	2.50
252	A31	60c on 5sh multi	2.00	3.75
a.		Surcharge omitted	450.00	
253	A31	$1.20 on 10sh multi	4.00	7.50
254	A31	$2.40 on £1 multi	8.00	15.00
		Nos. 238-254 (17)	20.22	36.90

Watermark upright on 1c, 3c to 9c and 36c; sideways on others. Watermark is sideways on No. 252a, upright on No. 189.

Spathiphyllum — A41

Flowers: 2c, Bottlebrush. 3c, Oleander, vert. 4c, Bermudiana. 5c, Poinsettia. 6c, Hibiscus. 9c, Cereus. 10c, Bougainvillea, vert. 12c, Jacaranda. 15c, Passion flower. 18c, Coralita. 24c, Morning glory. 30c, Tecoma. 36c, Angel's trumpet. 60c, Plumbago. $1.20, Bird of paradise. $2.40, Chalice cup.

Wmk. 314, Sideways on Horiz. Stamps
1970, July 6   Perf. 14
255	A41	1c lt green & multi	.15	.15
256	A41	2c pale bl & multi	.26	.19
257	A41	3c yellow & multi	.16	.15
258	A41	4c buff & multi	.18	.15
259	A41	5c pink & multi	.60	.26
a.		Imperf.	800.00	
260	A41	6c orange & multi	.60	.30
261	A41	9c lt green & multi	.35	.16
262	A41	10c pale salmon & multi	.35	.16
263	A41	12c pale yellow & multi	1.65	.85
264	A41	15c buff & multi	1.40	.70
265	A41	18c pale salmon & multi	2.50	1.10
266	A41	24c pink & multi	1.65	.75
267	A41	30c plum & multi	1.65	.75
268	A41	36c dark gray & multi	2.50	1.10
269	A41	60c gray & multi	3.25	1.75
270	A41	$1.20 blue & multi	7.50	3.50
271	A41	$2.40 multicolored	15.00	8.25
		Nos. 255-271 (17)	39.75	20.23

See #322-328. For overprints see #288-291.

1974-76   Wmk. 314 Upright
259b	A41	5c multicolored	1.00	1.00
260a	A41	6c multicolored	2.25	2.25
263a	A41	12c multicolored	1.65	1.65
267a	A41	30c multicolored ('76)	3.00	3.00
		Nos. 259b-267a (4)	7.90	7.90

Issued: 30c, June 11; others, June 13.

1975-76   Wmk. 373
256a	A41	2c multicolored	1.00	1.00
260b	A41	6c multicolored	2.00	2.00

Issued: 2c, Dec. 8; 6c, June 11, 1976.

State House, St. George's, 1622-1815
A42

Designs: 15c, The Sessions House, Hamilton, 1893. 18c, First Assembly House, St. Peter's Church, St. George's. 24c, Temporary Assembly House, Hamilton, 1815-26.

1970, Oct. 12   Litho.   Perf. 14
272	A42	4c multicolored	.15	.15
273	A42	15c multicolored	.45	.45
274	A42	18c multicolored	.65	.65
275	A42	24c multicolored	1.10	1.10
a.		Souvenir sheet of 4, #272-275	3.75	4.25
		Nos. 272-275 (4)	2.35	2.35

350th anniv. of Bermuda's Parliament.

Street in St. George's
A43

"Keep Bermuda Beautiful": 15c, Horseshoe Bay. 18c, Gibb's Hill Lighthouse. 24c, View of Hamilton Harbor.

1971, Feb. 8   Wmk. 314   Perf. 14
276	A43	4c multicolored	.24	.24
277	A43	15c multicolored	.70	.70
278	A43	18c multicolored	.90	.90
279	A43	24c multicolored	1.50	1.50
		Nos. 276-279 (4)	3.34	3.34

Building of "Deliverance" — A44

Designs: 15c, "Deliverance" and "Patience" arriving in Jamestown, Va., 1610, vert. 18c, Wreck of "Sea Venture," vert. 24c, "Deliverance" and "Patience" under sail, 1610.

1971, May 10   Litho.   Wmk. 314
280	A44	4c multicolored	.40	.40
281	A44	15c brown & multi	1.40	1.40
282	A44	18c purple & multi	1.75	1.75
283	A44	24c blue & multi	2.50	2.50
		Nos. 280-283 (4)	6.05	6.05

Voyage of Sir George Somers to Jamestown, Va., from Bermuda, 1610.

> Bermuda stamps can be mounted in the Scott British North and West Caribbean album.

Ocean View Golf Course
A45

Golf Courses: 15c, Port Royal. 18c, Castle Harbour. 24c, Belmont.

1971, Nov. 1   Perf. 13
284	A45	4c multicolored	.18	.18
285	A45	15c multicolored	.65	.65
286	A45	18c multicolored	.75	.75
287	A45	24c multicolored	1.10	1.10
		Nos. 284-287 (4)	2.68	2.68

Golfing in Bermuda.

Nos. 258, 264-266 Overprinted: "HEATH-NIXON / DECEMBER 1971"

1971, Dec. 20   Photo.   Perf. 14
288	A41	4c buff & multi	.15	.15
289	A41	15c buff & multi	.42	.42
290	A41	18c pale sal & multi	.52	.52
291	A41	24c pink & multi	.70	.70
		Nos. 288-291 (4)	1.79	1.79

Meeting of President Richard M. Nixon and Prime Minister Edward Heath of Great Britain, at Hamilton, Dec. 20-21, 1971.

Bonefish
A46

1972, Aug. 7   Litho.   Perf. 13¹/₂x14
292	A46	4c as shown	.26	.26
293	A46	15c Wahoo	.75	.75
294	A46	18c Yellowfin tuna	.90	.90
295	A46	24c Greater amberjack	1.40	1.40
		Nos. 292-295 (4)	3.31	3.31

World fishing records.

Silver Wedding Issue, 1972
Common Design Type

Design: Queen Elizabeth II, Prince Philip, Admiralty oar and mace.

1972, Nov. 20   Photo.   Perf. 14x14¹/₂
296	CD324	4c violet & multi	.15	.15
297	CD324	15c car rose & multi	.52	.52

Palmettos — A47

1973, Sept. 3   Wmk. 314   Perf. 14
298	A47	4c shown	.25	.25
299	A47	15c Olivewood	.75	.75
300	A47	18c Bermuda cedar	1.00	1.20
301	A47	24c Mahogany	1.25	1.25
		Nos. 298-301 (4)	3.25	3.45

Bermuda National Trust, and "Plant a Tree" campaign.

Princess Anne's Wedding Issue
Common Design Type

1973, Nov. 21   Litho.
302	CD325	15c lilac & multi	.35	.35
303	CD325	18c slate & multi	.45	.45

National Tennis Stadium, Pembroke, 1973
A48

15c, Bermuda's 1st tennis court, Pembroke, 1873. 18c, Britain's 1st tennis court, Leamington Spa, 1872. 24c, 1st US tennis club, Staten Island, 1874.

1973, Dec. 17   Wmk. 314
304	A48	4c black & multi	.20	.20
305	A48	15c black & multi	.65	.65
306	A48	18c black & multi	.90	.90
307	A48	24c black & multi	1.25	1.25
		Nos. 304-307 (4)	3.00	3.00

Centenary of tennis in Bermuda.

Rotary Emblem, Weather Vane, City Hall, Hamilton
A49

Rotary Emblem and: 17c, St. Peter's Church, St. George's. 20c, Somerset Drawbridge, Somerset. 25c, Map of Bermuda on globe, 1626.

1974, June 24   Perf. 14
308	A49	5c emerald & multi	.22	.22
309	A49	17c blue & multi	.75	.75
310	A49	20c yel org & multi	.85	.85
311	A49	25c lt violet & multi	1.10	1.10
		Nos. 308-311 (4)	2.92	2.92

50th anniv. of Rotary Intl. in Bermuda.

Jack of Clubs and a Good Bridge Hand — A50

Bermuda Bowl and: 17c, Queen of diamonds. 20c, King of hearts. 25c, Ace of spades.

1975, Jan. 27   Litho.   Wmk. 314
312	A50	5c blue & multi	.24	.24
313	A50	17c dull yel & multi	.75	.75
314	A50	20c ver & multi	.80	.80
315	A50	25c lilac & multi	1.10	1.10
		Nos. 312-315 (4)	2.89	2.89

World Bridge Championship, Bermuda, Jan. 1975.

Queen Elizabeth II and Prince Philip — A51

Perf. 14x14¹/₂
1975, Feb. 17   Photo.   Wmk. 373
316	A51	17c multicolored	.60	.60
317	A51	20c dk blue & multi	.80	.80

Royal Visit, Feb. 16-18, 1975.

British Cavalier Flying Boat, 1937
A52

Designs: 17c, U.S. Navy airship "Los Angeles," 1925, flying from Lakehurst, N.J. to Hamilton, Bermuda. 20c, Constellation over Kindley Field, 1946. 25c, Boeing 747 on tarmac, 1970.

1975, Apr. 28   Litho.   Perf. 14
318	A52	5c lt green & multi	.42	.42
319	A52	17c lt ultra & multi	1.25	1.25
320	A52	20c multicolored	1.75	1.75
321	A52	25c rose lil & multi	2.00	2.00
a.		Souvenir sheet of 4, #318-321	6.00	7.50
		Nos. 318-321 (4)	5.42	5.42

Airmail service to Bermuda, 50th anniv.

Flower Type of 1970

1975, June 2   Photo.   Wmk. 314
322	A41	17c Passion flower	1.25	1.25
323	A41	20c Coralita	1.25	1.25
324	A41	25c Morning glory	1.25	1.25
325	A41	40c Angel's trumpet	1.25	1.25
326	A41	$1 Plumbago	2.00	2.00

Girl Helping Blind Man
Cross Street — A70

1981, Sept. 28   Litho.   Perf. 14
415 A70 10c shown .18 .18
416 A70 25c Kayaking, Paget Island .48 .48
417 A70 30c Mountain climbing, St.
   David's Island .55 .55
418 A70 $1 Duke of Edinburgh 1.90 1.90
 Nos. 415-418 (4) 3.11 3.11

Duke of Edinburgh's Awards, 25th anniv.

Conus
Species
A71

1982, May 13   Wmk. 373   Perf. 14
419 A71 10c shown .20 .20
420 A71 25c Bursa finlayi .50 .50
421 A71 30c Sconsia striata .60 .60
422 A71 $1 Murex pterynotus
   lightbourni 1.90 1.90
 Nos. 419-422 (4) 3.20 3.20

Bermuda
Regiment
A72

1982, June 17   Litho.   Wmk. 373
423 A72 10c Color guard .16 .16
424 A72 25c Queen's birthday
   parade .40 .40
425 A72 30c Governor inspecting
   honor guard .60 .60
426 A72 40c Beating the retreat .75 .75
427 A72 50c Ceremonial gunners 1.00 1.00
428 A72 $1 Royal visit, 1975 2.00 2.00
 Nos. 423-428 (6) 4.91 4.91

Southampton
Fort — A73

1982, Nov. 18   Litho.   Wmk. 373
429 A73 10c Charles Fort, vert. .20 .20
430 A73 25c Pembroks Fort, vert. .50 .50
431 A73 30c shown .60 .60
432 A73 $1 Smiths and Pagets Forts 1.90 1.90
 Nos. 429-432 (4) 3.20 3.20

Arms of Sir Edwin
Sandys (1561-
1629) — A74

Fitted
Dinghies — A75

Coats of Arms: 25c, Bermuda Company. 50c,
William Herbert, 3rd Earl of Pembroke (1584-
1630). $1, Sir George Somers (1554-1610).

1983, Apr. 14   Litho.   Perf. 13½
433 A74 10c multicolored .18 .18
434 A74 25c multicolored .45 .45
435 A74 50c multicolored .90 .90
436 A74 $1 multicolored 1.75 1.75
 Nos. 433-436 (4) 3.28 3.28

See Nos. 457-460, 474-477.

1983, July 21   Wmk. 373   Perf. 14
Old and modern boats.
437 A75 12c multicolored .22 .22
438 A75 30c multicolored .55 .55
439 A75 40c multicolored .70 .70
440 A75 $1 multicolored 1.75 1.75
 Nos. 437-440 (4) 3.22 3.22

Manned
Flight
Bicentenary
A76 12c

Designs: 12c, Curtiss Jenny, 1919 (first flight
over Bermuda). 30c, Stinson Pilot Radio, 1930 (first
completed US-Bermuda flight). 40c, Cavalier, 1937
(first scheduled passenger flight). $1, USS Los Ange-
les airship moored to USS Patoka, 1925.

1983, Oct. 13   Litho.   Perf. 14
441 A76 12c multicolored .28 .28
442 A76 30c multicolored .65 .65
443 A76 40c multicolored .90 .90
444 A76 $1 multicolored 1.75 1.75
 Nos. 441-444 (4) 3.58 3.58

Newspaper and Postal
Services, 200th
Anniv. — A77

1984, Jan. 26   Litho.   Perf. 14
445 A77 12c Joseph Stockdale .22 .22
446 A77 30c First Newspaper .55 .55
447 A77 40c Stockdale's Postal Service, horiz. .70 .70
448 A77 $1 "Lady Hammond,"
   horiz. 1.75 1.75
 Nos. 445-448 (4) 3.22 3.22

375th
Anniv. of
Bermuda
Settlement
A78

Designs: 12c, Thomas Gates, George Somers.
30c, Jamestown, Virginia, US. 40c, Sea Venture
shipwreck. $1, Fleet leaving Plymouth, England.

1984, May 3   Litho.   Wmk. 373
449 A78 12c multicolored .22 .22
450 A78 30c multicolored .55 .55
451 A78 40c multicolored .70 .70
452 A78 $1 multicolored 1.75 1.75
a. Souv. sheet of 2, #450, 452 5.00 5.00
 Nos. 449-452 (4) 3.22 3.22

1984
Summer
Olympics
30c A79

1984, July 19   Litho.   Perf. 14
453 A79 12c Swimming, vert. .20 .20
454 A79 30c Track & field .48 .48
455 A79 40c Equestrian, vert. .65 .65
456 A79 $1 Sailing 1.65 1.65
 Nos. 453-456 (4) 2.98 2.98

Arms Type of 1983

1984, Sept. 27   Litho.   Perf. 13½
457 A74 12c Southampton .20 .20
458 A74 30c Smith .60 .60
459 A74 40c Devonshire .75 .75
460 A74 $1 St. George 1.65 1.65
 Nos. 457-460 (4) 3.20 3.20

Architecture,
Butter — A80   12c

1985, Jan. 24   Litho.   Perf. 13½x13
461 A80 12c shown .35 .35
462 A80 30c Rooftops .75 .75
463 A80 40c Chimneys 1.00 1.00
464 A80 $1.50 Archway 3.50 3.50
 Nos. 461-464 (4) 5.60 5.60

Audubon
Birth
Bicentenary
A81

1985, Mar. 21   Wmk. 373   Perf. 14
465 A81 12c Osprey, vert. .30 .30
466 A81 30c Yellow-crowned night
   heron, vert. .75 .75
467 A81 40c Great egret 1.00 1.00
468 A81 $1.50 Bluebird, vert. 3.50 3.50
 Nos. 465-468 (4) 5.55 5.55

Queen Mother 85th Birthday Issue
Common Design Type

Designs: 12c, Queen Consort, 1937. 30c, With
grandchildren, 80th birthday. 40c, At Clarence
House, 83rd birthday. $1.50, Holding Prince
Henry. No. 473, In coach with Prince Charles.

Perf. 14½x14
1985, June 7   Wmk. 384
469 CD336 12c gray, bl & blk .35 .35
470 CD336 30c multicolored .75 .75
471 CD336 40c multicolored 1.00 1.00
472 CD336 $1.50 multicolored 3.50 3.50
 Nos. 469-472 (4) 5.60 5.60

Souvenir Sheet
473 CD336 $1 multicolored 4.50 4.50

Arms Type of 1983

Coats of Arms: 12c, James Hamilton, 2nd Mar-
quess of Hamilton (1589-1625). 30c, William
Paget, 4th Lord Paget (1572-1629). 40c, Robert
Rich, 2nd Earl of Warwick (1587-1658). $1.50,
Hamilton, 1957.

1985, Sept. 19   Litho.   Perf. 13½
474 A74 12c multicolored .30 .30
475 A74 30c multicolored .75 .75
476 A74 40c multicolored 1.00 1.00
477 A74 $1.50 multicolored 3.75 3.75
 Nos. 474-477 (4) 5.80 5.80

Halley's
Comet — A82

1985, Nov. 21   Wmk. 384   Perf. 14½
478 A82 15c Bermuda Archipelago .38 .38
479 A82 40c Nuremberg Chronicles, 1493 1.00 1.00
480 A82 50c Peter Apian woodcut,
   1532 1.25 1.25
481 A82 $1.50 Painting by Samuel
   Scott (c.1702-72) 3.75 3.75
 Nos. 478-481 (4) 6.38 6.38

Shipwrecks
A83

1986   Wmk. 384   Perf. 14
482 A83 3c Constellation,
   1943 .15 .15
483 A83 5c Early Riser, 1876 .15 .15
484 A83 7c Madiana, 1903 .15 .15
485 A83 10c Curlew, 1856 .20 .20
486 A83 12c Warwick, 1619 .20 .20
487 A83 15c HMS Vixen, 1890 .30 .30

488 A83 20c San Pedro, 1594 .35 .35
489 A83 25c Alert, 1877 .50 .50
490 A83 40c North Carolina,
   1880 .75 .75
491 A83 50c Mark Antonie,
   1777 1.00 1.10
492 A83 60c Mary Celestia,
   1864 1.10 1.10
493 A83 $1 L'Herminie, 1839 1.75 1.75
494 A83 $1.50 Caesar, 1818 2.75 2.75
495 A83 $2 Lord Amherst,
   1778 3.50 3.50
496 A83 $3 Minerva, 1849 5.50 5.50
497 A83 $5 Caraquet, 1923 9.00 9.00
498 A83 $8 HMS Pallas, 1783 14.50 14.50
 Nos. 482-498 (17) 41.85 41.95

Nos. 493, 495-496 exist inscribed "1989." Nos.
482, 488, "1990."
See #545-546. For surcharges see #598-600.

Inscribed "1992"

1992   Litho.   Wmk. 373   Perf. 14
485a A83 10c .18 .18
487a A83 15c .28 .28
488a A83 20c .36 .36
489a A83 25c .45 .45
492a A83 60c 1.10 1.10
497a A83 $5 9.25 9.25
498a A83 $8 14.75 14.75
 Nos. 485a-498a (7) 26.37 26.37

Queen Elizabeth II 60th Birthday
Common Design Type

Designs: 15c, Age 3. 40c, With the Earl of
Roseberry, Oaks May Meeting, Epsom, 1954. 50c,
With Prince Philip, state visit, 1979. 60c, At the
British embassy in Paris, state visit, 1972. $1.50,
Visiting Crown Agents' offices, 1983.

1986, Apr. 21   Wmk. 384   Perf. 14½
499 CD337 15c scar, blk & sil .24 .24
500 CD337 40c ultra & multi .65 .65
501 CD337 50c green & multi .80 .80
502 CD337 60c violet & multi .95 .95
503 CD337 $1.50 rose vio & multi 2.50 2.50
 Nos. 499-503 (5) 5.14 5.14

AMERIPEX
'86 — A84 15c

1986, May 22   Perf. 14
504 A84 15c No. 452a .24 .24
505 A84 40c No. 307 .65 .65
506 A84 50c No. 441 .80 .80
507 A84 $1 No. 339 1.65 1.65
 Nos. 504-507 (4) 3.34 3.34

Souvenir Sheet
508 A84 1.50 Statue of Liberty, S.S.
   Queen of Bermuda 4.50 4.50

Statue of Liberty, cent.

No. 378 Surcharged
Perf. 14x14½
1986, Dec. 4   Photo.   Wmk. 373
509 A62 90c on $3 multi 3.00 3.00

Exists with double surcharge.

Transport Railway, c. 1931-1947 — A85

Wmk. 373
1987, Jan. 22   Litho.   Perf. 14
510 A85 15c Front Street, c. 1940 .24 .24
511 A85 40c Springfield Trestle .65 .65
512 A85 50c No. 101, Bailey's Bay
   Sta. .80 .80
513 A85 $1.50 No. 31, ship Prince
   David 2.50 2.50
 Nos. 510-513 (4) 4.19 4.19

Paintings by
Winslow
Homer (1836-
1910)
A86

1987, Apr. 30 — Perf. 14½

514	A86	15c Bermuda Settlers, 1901	.28	.28
515	A86	30c Bermuda, 1900	.55	.55
516	A86	40c Bermuda Landscape, 1901	.75	.75
517	A86	60c Inland Water, 1901	.95	.95
518	A86	$1.50 Salt Kettle, 1899	3.00	3.00
		Nos. 514-518 (5)	5.53	5.53

Booklet Stamps

519	A86	40c like 15c	.65	.65
520	A86	40c like 30c	.65	.65
521	A86	40c like No. 516	.65	.65
522	A86	40c like 50c	.65	.65
523	A86	40c like $1.50	.65	.65
a.		Bklt. pane, 2 each #519-523	6.50	

Nos. 519-523 printed in strips of 5 within pane. "ER" at lower left.

Intl. Flights Inauguration — A87

1987, June 18 — Perf. 14

524	A87	15c Sikorsky S-42B, 1937	.50	.50
525	A87	40c Shorts S-23 Cavalier	1.40	1.40
526	A87	50c S-42B Bermuda Clipper	1.65	1.65
527	A87	$1.50 Cavalier, Bermuda Clipper	5.00	5.00
		Nos. 524-527 (4)	8.55	8.55

Bermuda Telephone Company, Cent. — A88

1987, Oct. 1 — Litho. — Wmk. 384

528	A88	15c Telephone poles on wagon	.25	.25
529	A88	40c Operators	.70	.70
530	A88	50c Telephones	.85	.85
531	A88	$1.50 Satellite, fiber optics, world	2.50	2.50
		Nos. 528-531 (4)	4.30	4.30

Horse-drawn Commercial Vehicles — A89

1988, Mar. 3 — Litho. — Perf. 14

532	A89	15c Mail wagon, c. 1869	.28	.28
533	A89	40c Open cart, c. 1823	.75	.75
534	A89	50c Closed cart, c. 1823	.95	.95
535	A89	$1.50 Two-wheel wagon, c. 1930	2.75	2.75
		Nos. 532-535 (4)	4.73	4.73

Old Garden Roses — A90

1988, Apr. 21 — Wmk. 373

536	A90	15c Old blush	.26	.26
537	A90	40c Anna Olivier	.52	.52
538	A90	40c Rosa chinensis semperflorens, vert.	.70	.70
539	A90	50c Archduke Charles	.90	.90
540	A90	$1.50 Rosa chinensis viridiflora, vert.	2.75	2.75
		Nos. 536-540 (5)	5.13	5.13

See Nos. 561-575.

Lloyds of London, 300th Anniv.
Common Design Type

Designs: 18c, Loss of the H.M.S. Lutine, 1799. 50c, Cable ship Sentinel, horiz. 60c, The Bermuda, Hamilton, 1931, horiz. $2, Valerian, lost during a hurricane, 1926.

1988, Oct. 13 — Litho. — Wmk. 384

541	CD341	18c multi	.32	.32
542	CD341	50c multi	.90	.90
543	CD341	60c multi	1.10	1.10
544	CD341	$2 multi	3.50	3.50
		Nos. 541-544 (4)	5.82	5.82

Shipwreck Type of 1986

1988 — Litho. — Wmk. 384 — Perf. 14

545	A83	18c like 7c	.35	.35
546	A83	70c like $1.50	1.40	1.40

Issue dates: 18c, Sept. 22; 70c, Oct. 27.

Military Uniforms — A91

Designs: 18c, Devonshire Parish Militia, 1812. 50c, 71st Regiment Highlander, 1831-34. 60c, Cameron Highlander, 1942. $2, Troop of Horse, 1774.

1988, Nov. 10 — Wmk. 373 — Perf. 14½

547	A91	18c multicolored	.30	.30
548	A91	50c multicolored	.85	.85
549	A91	60c multicolored	1.00	1.00
550	A91	$2 multicolored	3.50	3.50
		Nos. 547-550 (4)	5.65	5.65

Ferry Service A92

1989 — Litho. — Wmk. 384 — Perf. 14

551	A92	18c Corona	.30	.30
552	A92	50c Rowboat ferry	.85	.85
553	A92	60c St. George's Ferry	1.00	1.00
554	A92	$2 Laconia	3.50	3.50
		Nos. 551-554 (4)	5.65	5.65

Photography, Sesquicent. A93

Perf. 14x14½

1989, May 11 — Litho. — Wmk. 373

555	A93	18c Morgan's Is.	.35	.35
556	A93	30c Front Street, Hamilton (cannon in square)	.60	.60
557	A93	50c Front Street (seascape)	1.00	1.00
558	A93	60c Crow Lane, Hamilton Harbor	1.20	1.20
559	A93	70c Hamilton Harbor (ship-building)	1.40	1.40
560	A93	$1 Dockyard	2.00	2.00
		Nos. 555-560 (6)	6.55	6.55

Old Garden Roses Type of 1988

1989, July 13 — Perf. 14

561	A90	18c Agrippina	.35	.35
562	A90	30c Smith's Parish	.60	.60
563	A90	50c Champney's pink cluster	1.00	1.00
564	A90	60c Rosette delizy	1.20	1.20
565	A90	$1.50 Rosa bracteata	3.00	3.00
		Nos. 561-565 (5)	6.15	6.15

Nos. 561-562 vert.

Old Garden Roses Type of 1988 with Royal Cipher Instead of Queen's Silhouette

1989, July 13 — Booklet Stamps

566	A90	50c like No. 562	1.00	1.00
567	A90	50c like No. 540	1.00	1.00
568	A90	50c like No. 561	1.00	1.00
569	A90	50c like No. 538	1.00	1.00
570	A90	50c like No. 536	1.00	1.00
571	A90	50c like No. 563	1.00	1.00
572	A90	50c like No. 564	1.00	1.00
573	A90	50c like No. 537	1.00	1.00
574	A90	50c like No. 565	1.00	1.00
575	A90	50c like No. 539	1.00	1.00
a.		Bklt. pane of 10, #566-575	10.00	
		Nos. 566-575 (10)	10.00	10.00

Bermuda Library, 150th Anniv. — A94

1989, Sept. 14 — Perf. 13½x14

576	A94	18c Hamilton Main Library	.30	.30
577	A94	50c St. George's, The Old Rectory	.85	.85
578	A94	60c Springfield, Sommerset Library	1.00	1.00
579	A94	$2 Cabinet Building	3.50	3.50
		Nos. 576-579 (4)	5.65	5.65

Commonwealth Postal Conference — A95

1989, Nov. 3 — Wmk. 384 — Perf. 14

580	A83	18c No. 1	.30	.30
581	A95	50c No. 2	.85	.85
582	A95	60c Type A4	1.00	1.00
583	A95	$2 No. 6	3.50	3.50
		Nos. 580-583 (4)	5.65	5.65

For overprints see Nos. 594-597.

Fairylands, Bermuda, c. 1890, by Ross Sterling Turner — A96

Paintings: 50c, Shinebone Alley, c. 1953, by Ogden M. Pleissner. 60c, Salt Kettle, 1916, by Prosper Senate. $2, St. George's, 1934, by Jack Bush.

1990, Apr. 19

590	A96	18c multicolored	.30	.30
591	A96	50c multicolored	.85	.85
592	A96	60c multicolored	1.00	1.00
593	A96	$2 multicolored	3.50	3.50
		Nos. 590-593 (4)	5.65	5.65

Nos. 580-583 Overprinted

1990, May 3

594	A95	18c multicolored	.35	.35
595	A95	50c multicolored	1.00	1.00
596	A95	60c multicolored	1.20	1.20
597	A95	$2 multicolored	4.00	4.00
		Nos. 594-597 (4)	6.55	6.55

Stamp World London '90.

80c

Nos. 486, 491, 494 Surcharged

1990, Aug. 13

598	A83	30c on 12c No. 486	.55	.55
599	A83	55c on 50c No. 491	1.00	1.00
600	A83	80c on $1.50 No. 494	1.50	1.50
		Nos. 598-600 (3)	3.05	3.05

Nova Scotia-Bermuda Cable, Cent. — A97

1990, Oct. 18 — Litho. — Unwmk.

601	A97	20c Office	.35	.35
602	A97	55c Cableship SS Westmeath	1.00	1.00
603	A97	70c Radio station, 1928	1.25	1.25
604	A97	$2 Cableship Sir Eric Sharp	3.50	3.50
		Nos. 601-604 (4)	6.10	6.10

Nos. 601-602 with Added Inscription: "BUSH-MAJOR / 16 MARCH 1991"

1991, Mar. — Unwmk. — Perf. 14

605	A97	20c like #601	.40	.40
606	A97	55c like #602	1.10	1.10

Carriages A98

Designs: 20c, Two-seat pony cart, c. 1805. 30c, Varnished rockaway, c. 1830. 55c, Vis-a-Vis Victoria, c. 1895. 70c, Semi-formal phaeton, c. 1900. 80c, Pony runabout, c. 1905. $1, Ladies' phaeton, c. 1910.

Perf. 14x14½

1991, Mar. 21 — Litho. — Wmk. 373

607	A98	20c green & multi	.40	.40
608	A98	30c bl gray & multi	.60	.60
609	A98	55c dk car & multi	1.10	1.10
610	A98	70c blue & multi	1.40	1.40
611	A98	80c yel org & multi	1.60	1.60
612	A98	$1 dk gray & multi	2.00	2.00
		Nos. 607-612 (6)	7.10	7.10

Paintings A99

Designs: 20c, Bermuda by Prosper Senat, vert. 55c, Bermuda Cottage by Frank Allison. 70c, Old Maid's Lane by Jack Bush, vert. $2, St. George's by Ogden M. Pleissner.

Perf. 14x13½

1991, May 16 — Litho. — Wmk. 373

613	A99	20c multicolored	.40	.40
614	A99	55c multicolored	1.10	1.10
615	A99	70c multicolored	1.40	1.40
616	A99	$2 multicolored	4.00	4.00
		Nos. 613-616 (4)	6.90	6.90

Elizabeth & Philip, Birthdays
Common Design Types

1991, June 20 — Wmk. 384 — Perf. 14½

617	CD346	55c multicolored	1.10	1.10
618	CD345	70c multicolored	1.40	1.40
a.		Pair, #617-618 + label	2.50	2.50

Bermuda in World War II A100

Designs: 20c, Floating drydock. 55c, Kindley Air Field. 70c, Trans-atlantic air route, Boeing 314. $2, Censored trans-atlantic mail.

1991, Sept. 19 — Wmk. 373 — Perf. 14

619	A100	20c multicolored	.40	.40
620	A100	55c multicolored	1.10	1.10
621	A100	70c multicolored	1.40	1.40
622	A100	$2 multicolored	4.00	4.00
		Nos. 619-622 (4)	6.90	6.90

Queen Elizabeth II's Accession to the Throne, 40th Anniv.
Common Design Type

1992, Feb. 6

623	CD349	20c multicolored	.40	.40
624	CD349	30c multicolored	.60	.60
625	CD349	55c multicolored	1.10	1.10
626	CD349	70c multicolored	1.40	1.40
627	CD349	$1 multicolored	2.00	2.00
		Nos. 623-627 (5)	5.50	5.50

Age of Exploration — A101

Artifacts: 25c, Rings, medallion. 35c, Ink wells. 60c, Gold pieces. 75c, Bishop button, crucifix. 85c, Pearl earrings and buttons. $1, 8-real coin, jug and measuring cups.

1992, July 23   **Perf. 13½**
628	A101	25c multicolored	.50	.50
629	A101	35c multicolored	.70	.70
630	A101	60c multicolored	1.20	1.20
631	A101	75c multicolored	1.50	1.50
632	A101	85c multicolored	1.70	1.70
633	A101	$1 multicolored	2.00	2.00
		Nos. 628-633 (6)	7.60	7.60

Stained Glass Windows — A102

Designs: 25c, Ship wreck. 60c, Birds in tree. 75c, St. Francis feeding bird. $2, Seashells.

1992, Sept. 24   **Perf. 14**
634	A102	25c multicolored	.50	.50
635	A102	60c multicolored	1.20	1.20
636	A102	75c multicolored	1.50	1.50
637	A102	$2 multicolored	4.00	4.00
		Nos. 634-637 (4)	7.20	7.20

7th World Congress of Kennel Clubs — A103

Perf. 13½x14, 14x13½
1992, Nov. 12   Litho.   Wmk. 373
638	A103	25c German shepherd	.48	.48
639	A103	35c Irish setter	.65	.65
640	A103	60c Whippet, vert.	1.15	1.15
641	A103	75c Border terrier, vert.	1.40	1.40
642	A103	85c Pomeranian, vert.	1.60	1.60
643	A103	$1 Schipperke, vert.	1.85	1.85
		Nos. 638-643 (6)	7.13	7.13

Tourist Posters
A104   A105

1993, Feb. 25   Wmk. 373   Perf. 14
644	A104	25c Cyclist, carriage, ship	.48	.48
645	A105	60c Golf course	1.15	1.15
646	A105	75c Coastline	1.40	1.40
647	A104	$2 Dancers	3.70	3.70
		Nos. 644-647 (4)	6.73	6.73

Royal Air Force, 75th Anniv.
Common Design Type

Designs: 25c, Consolidated Catalina. 60c, Supermarine Spitfire. 75c, Bristol Beaufighter. $2, Handley Page Halifax.

1993, Apr. 1
648	CD350	25c multicolored	.48	.48
649	CD350	60c multicolored	1.15	1.15
650	CD350	75c multicolored	1.40	1.40
651	CD350	$2 multicolored	3.70	3.70
		Nos. 648-651 (4)	6.73	6.73

Duchesse de Brabant Rose, Bee — A106

1993, Apr. 1   Wmk. 384
Booklet Stamps
652	A106	10c green & multi	.20	.20
653	A106	25c violet & multi	.48	.48
a.		Booklet pane of 5	2.40	
654	A106	50c sepia & multi	1.00	1.00
a.		Booklet pane, 2 #652, 3 #654	3.50	
655	A106	60c vermilion & multi	1.10	1.10
a.		Booklet pane of 5	5.50	
		Nos. 652-655 (4)	2.78	2.78

Hamilton, Bicent. — A107

Designs: 25c, Modern skyline. 60c, Front Street, ships at left. 75c, Front Street, horse carts. $2, Hamilton Harbor, 1823.

Perf. 14½
1993, Sept. 16   Litho.   Wmk. 373
656	A107	25c multicolored	.48	.48
657	A107	60c multicolored	1.10	1.10
658	A107	75c multicolored	1.40	1.40
659	A107	$2 multicolored	3.75	3.75
		Nos. 656-659 (4)	6.73	6.73

Furness Lines — A108

Designs: 25c, Furness Liv-Aboard Bermuda cruises, vert. 60c, SS Queen of Bermuda entering port. 75c, SS Queen of Bermuda, SS Ocean Monarch. $2, Starlit night aboard ship, vert.

Perf. 15x14, 14x15
1994, Jan. 20   Wmk. 373
660	A108	25c multicolored	.48	.48
661	A108	60c multicolored	1.10	1.10
662	A108	75c multicolored	1.40	1.40
663	A108	$2 multicolored	3.75	3.75
		Nos. 660-663 (4)	6.73	6.73

Royal Visit — A109

Designs: 25c, Queen Elizabeth II. 60c, Queen Elizabeth II, Duke of Edinburgh. 75c, Royal yacht Britannia.

1994, Mar. 9   Litho.   Wmk. 373
664	A109	25c multicolored	.48	.48
665	A109	60c multicolored	1.10	1.10
666	A109	75c multicolored	1.50	1.50
		Nos. 664-666 (3)	3.08	3.08

Flowering Fruits
A110

1994-95   Litho.   Wmk. 373   Perf. 14
668	A110	5c Peach	.15	.15
669	A110	7c Fig	.15	.15
670	A110	10c Calabash, vert.	.20	.20
671	A110	15c Natal plum	.30	.30
672	A110	18c Locust & wild honey	.35	.35
673	A110	20c Pomegranate	.38	.38
674	A110	25c Mulberry, vert.	.48	.48
675	A110	35c Grape, vert.	.70	.70
676	A110	55c Orange, vert.	1.10	1.10
677	A110	60c Surinam cherry	1.25	1.25
678	A110	75c Loquat	1.50	1.50
679	A110	90c Sugar apple	1.75	1.75
680	A110	$1 Prickly pear, vert.	2.00	2.00
681	A110	$2 Paw paw	4.00	4.00
682	A110	$3 Bay grape	6.00	6.00
683	A110	$5 Banana, vert.	10.00	10.00
684	A110	$8 Lemon	16.00	16.00
		Nos. 668-684 (17)	46.31	46.31

Issued: 5c, 7c, 15c, 20c, $8, 7/14/94; 10c, 25c, 35c, 55c, $1, $5, 10/6/94; 18c, 60c, 75c, 90c, $2, $3, 3/23/95.

BERMUDA   Hospital Care, Cent. — A111

1994, Sept. 15   **Perf. 15x14**
685	A111	25c Child birth	.48	.48
686	A111	60c Dialysis	1.10	1.10
687	A111	75c Emergency	1.50	1.50
688	A111	$2 Therapy	4.00	4.00
		Nos. 685-688 (4)	7.08	7.08

Christmas — A112

1994, Nov. 10   **Perf. 14x15**
689	A112	25c Gombey dancers	.48	.48
690	A112	60c Carollers	1.10	1.10
691	A112	75c Marching band	1.50	1.50
692	A112	$2 Natl. dance group	4.00	4.00
		Nos. 689-692 (4)	7.08	7.08

Decimalization, 25th Anniv. — A113

Stamps, 1970 coins: 25c, #255, one cent. 60c, #259, five cents. 75c, #262, ten cents. $2, #324, twenty-five cents.

Wmk. 373
1995, Feb. 6   Litho.   Perf. 14
693	A113	25c multicolored	.48	.48
694	A113	60c multicolored	1.10	1.10
695	A113	75c multicolored	1.50	1.50
696	A113	$2 multicolored	4.00	4.00
		Nos. 693-696 (4)	7.08	7.08

Outdoor Celebrations — A114

Perf. 14x15
1995, May 30   Litho.   Wmk. 373
697	A114	25c Kite flying	.50	.50
698	A114	60c Majorettes	1.10	1.10
699	A114	75c Portuguese dancers	1.50	1.50
700	A114	$2 Floral float	4.00	4.00
		Nos. 697-700 (4)	7.10	7.10

Parliament, 375th Anniv. — A115

Designs: 25c, $1, Bermuda coat of arms.

Perf. 14x13½
1995, Nov. 3   Litho.   Wmk. 373
701	A115	25c blue & multi	.50	.50
702	A115	$1 green & multi	2.00	2.00
		See No. 731.		

Military Bases
A116

Force insignia and: 20c, Ordnance Island Submarine Base. 25c, Royal Naval Dockyard. 60c, Fort Bell and Kindley Field. 75c, Darrell's Island. 90c, US Navy Operating Base. $1, Canadian Forces Station, Daniel's Head.

1995, Dec. 4   **Perf. 14**
703	A116	20c multicolored	.40	.40
704	A116	25c multicolored	.50	.50
705	A116	60c multicolored	1.25	1.25
706	A116	75c multicolored	1.50	1.50
707	A116	90c multicolored	1.75	1.75
708	A116	$1 multicolored	2.00	2.00
		Nos. 703-708 (6)	7.40	7.40

Modern Olympic Games, Cent. — A117

Wmk. 384
1996, May 21   Litho.   Perf. 14
709	A117	25c Track & field	.50	.50
710	A117	30c Cycling	.60	.60
711	A117	65c Sailing	1.30	1.30
712	A117	80c Equestrian	1.60	1.60
		Nos. 709-712 (4)	4.00	4.00

CAPEX '96 — A118

Methods of transportation: 25c, Sommerset Express, c. 1900. 60c, Bermuda Railway, 1930's. 75c, First bus, 1946. $2, Early sightseeing bus, c.1947.

Perf. 13½x14
1996, June 7   Litho.   Wmk. 373
713	A118	25c multicolored	.50	.50
714	A118	60c multicolored	1.20	1.20
715	A118	75c multicolored	1.50	1.50
716	A118	$2 multicolored	4.00	4.00
		Nos. 713-716 (4)	7.20	7.20

Panoramas of Hamilton and St. George's, by E. J. Holland, 1933
A119

Hamilton, looking across water from Bostock Hill: No. 717, Palm trees, Furness Line ship coming through Two Rock Passage. No. 718, House, buildings on other side. No. 719, Sailboats on water, Princess Hotel. No. 720, Island, Bermudiana Hotel,

Cathedral. No. 721, Coral roads on hillside, city of Hamilton.
St. George's, looking across water from St. David's: No. 722, Island, harbor. No. 723, Sailboat, buildings along shore. No. 724, Sailboat, St. George's Hotel, buildings. No. 725, Hillside, ship. No. 726, Homes on hill top, passage out of harbor.

1996   Wmk. 373   Perf. 14x14½
Booklet Stamps

717	A119	60c multicolored	1.20	1.20
718	A119	60c multicolored	1.20	1.20
719	A119	60c multicolored	1.20	1.20
720	A119	60c multicolored	1.20	1.20
721	A119	60c multicolored	1.20	1.20
a.		Strip of 5, #717-721	6.00	6.00
722	A119	60c multicolored	1.20	1.20
723	A119	60c multicolored	1.20	1.20
724	A119	60c multicolored	1.20	1.20
725	A119	60c multicolored	1.20	1.20
726	A119	60c multicolored	1.20	1.20
a.		Strip of 5, #722-726	6.00	6.00
b.		Booklet pane, #721a, 726a	12.00	
		Complete booklet, #726b	12.00	

Lighthouses — A120

Designs: 30c, Hog Fish Beacon. 65c, Gibbs Hill Lighthouse. 80c, St. David's Lighthouse. $2, North Rock Beacon.

Perf. 14x13½
1996, Aug. 15   Litho.   Wmk. 373

727	A120	30c multicolored	.60	.60
728	A120	65c multicolored	1.30	1.30
729	A120	80c multicolored	1.60	1.60
730	A120	$2 multicolored	4.00	4.00
		Nos. 727-730 (4)	7.50	7.50

See Nos. 737-740.

Bermuda Coat of Arms Type of 1995
Inscribed "Commonwealth
Finance Ministers Meeting"
Perf. 14x13½
1996, Sept. 24   Litho.   Wmk. 373

731	A115	$1 red & multi	2.00	2.00

Queen Elizabeth II — A121

1996, Nov. 7

732	A121	$22 blue & org brn	44.00	44.00

Architectural Heritage — A122

Wmk. 384
1996, Nov. 28   Perf. 14

733	A122	30c Waterville	.60	.60
734	A122	65c Bridge House	1.30	1.30
735	A122	80c Fannie Fox's Cottage	1.60	1.60
736	A122	$2.50 Palmetto House	5.00	5.00
		Nos. 733-736 (4)	8.50	8.50

Lighthouse Type of 1996 Redrawn
Wmk. 373
1997, Feb. 12   Litho.   Perf. 14

737	A120	30c Like #727	.60	.60
738	A120	65c Like #728	1.30	1.30
739	A120	80c Like #729	1.60	1.60
740	A120	$2.50 Like #730	5.00	5.00
		Nos. 737-740 (4)	8.50	8.50

Nos. 737-740 each have Hong Kong '97 emblem. No. 738 inscribed "Gibbs Hill Lighthouse c. 1900." No. 739 inscribed "St. David's Lighthouse c. 1900."

Birds A123

Designs: 30c, White-tailed tropicbird. 60c, White-tailed tropicbird, adult, chick, vert. 80c, Cahow, adult, chick, vert. $2.50, Cahow.

Wmk. 384
1997, Apr. 17   Litho.   Perf. 14

741	A123	30c multicolored	.60	.60
742	A123	60c multicolored	1.20	1.20
743	A123	80c multicolored	1.60	1.60
744	A123	$2.50 multicolored	5.00	5.00
		Nos. 741-744 (4)	8.40	8.40

Queen Elizabeth II and Prince Philip, 50th Wedding Anniv. A124

1997   Litho.   Wmk. 373
Perf. 14x14½

745	A124	30c Queen, crowd	.60	.60
746	A124	$2 Queen, Prince	4.00	4.00

WAR TAX STAMPS

No. 42 Overprinted **WAR TAX**

1918   Wmk. 3   Perf. 14

MR1	A11	1p rose red	.50	.40

No. 42a Overprinted **WAR TAX**

1920

MR2	A11	1p carmine	.45	.80

BHUTAN

bü-'tän

LOCATION — Eastern Himalayas
GOVT. — Kingdom
AREA — 18,000 sq. mi.
POP. — 1,250,000 (est. 1983)
CAPITAL — Thimphu

100 Chetrum = 1 Ngultrum or Rupee

Catalogue values for all unused stamps in this country are for Never Hinged items.

Postal Runner — A1

Designs: 3ch, 70ch, Archer. 5ch, 1.30nu, Yak. 15ch, Map of Bhutan, portrait of Druk Gyalpo (Dragon King) Ugyen Wangchuk (1867-1902) and Paro Dzong (fortress-monastery). 33ch, Postal runner. All horiz. except 2ch and 33ch.

Perf. 14x14½, 14½x14
1962   Litho.   Unwmk.

1	A1	2ch red & gray	.15	.15
2	A1	3ch red & ultra	.20	.20
3	A1	5ch green & brown	.80	.80
4	A1	15ch red, blk & org yel	.15	.15
5	A1	33ch blue grn & lil	.20	.20

6	A1	70ch dp ultra & lt blue	.60	.60
7	A1	1.30nu blue & black	1.65	1.65
		Nos. 1-7 (7)	3.75	3.75

Nos. 1-7 were issued for inland use in April, 1962, and became valid for international mail on Oct. 10, 1962.
For overprint and surcharges see #42, 72-73.

Refugee Year Emblem and Arms of Bhutan — A2

1962, Oct. 10   Perf. 14½x14

8	A2	1nu dk blue & dk car rose	.65	.65
9	A2	2nu yel grn & red lilac	1.25	1.25

World Refugee Year. For surcharges see #68-69.

Equipment of Ancient Warrior — A3   Boy Filling Grain Box and Wheat Emblem — A4

1963   Unwmk.   Perf. 14x14½

10	A3	33ch multicolored	.20	.20
11	A3	70ch multicolored	.40	.40
12	A3	1.30nu multicolored	.75	.75
		Nos. 10-12 (3)	1.35	1.35

Bhutan's membership in Colombo Plan.

1963, July 15   Perf. 13½x14

13	A4	20ch lt blue, yel & red brn	.15	.15
14	A4	1.50nu rose lil, bl & red brn	.65	.65

FAO "Freedom from Hunger" campaign.
For surcharge see No. 117M.

Masked Dancer A5

Various Bhutanese Dancers (Five Designs); 2ch, 5ch, 20ch, 1nu, 1.30nu vert.

Perf. 14½x14, 14x14½
1964, Apr. 16

15	A5	2ch multicolored	.15	.15
16	A5	3ch multicolored	.15	.15
17	A5	5ch multicolored	.15	.15
18	A5	20ch multicolored	.15	.15
19	A5	33ch multicolored	.15	.15
20	A5	70ch multicolored	.20	.20
21	A5	1nu multicolored	.35	.35
22	A5	1.30nu multicolored	.40	.40
23	A5	2nu multicolored	.65	.65
		Nos. 15-23 (9)	2.35	2.35

For surcharges see Nos. 70-71, 74-75, 129A, 129G. For overprints see C1-C3, C11-C13.

Stone Throwing — A6

Sport: 5ch, 33ch, Boxing. 1nu, 3nu, Archery. 2nu, Soccer.

1964, Oct. 10   Litho.   Perf. 14½

24	A6	2ch emerald & multi	.15	.15
25	A6	5ch orange & multi	.15	.15
26	A6	15ch brt cit & multi	.15	.15

27	A6	33ch rose lil & multi	.15	.15
28	A6	1nu multicolored	.40	.40
29	A6	2nu rose lilac & multi	.60	.60
30	A6	3nu lt blue & multi	.90	.90
		Set value	2.15	2.15

18th Olympic Games, Tokyo, Oct. 10-25. See No. B4.
Nos. 24-30 exist imperf. Value $4.

Flags of the World at Half-mast — A7

1964, Nov. 22   Unwmk.   Perf. 14½
Flags in Original Colors

31	A7	33ch steel gray	.15	.15
32	A7	1nu silver	.45	.45
33	A7	3nu gold	1.10	1.10
a.		Souv. sheet, perf. 13½ or imperf.	2.75	2.75
		Nos. 31-33 (3)	1.70	1.70

Issued in memory of those who died in the service of their country. Nos. 31-33 exist imperf. No. 33a contains 2 stamps similar to Nos. 32-33.
For overprints see Nos. 44, 46.

Flowers — A8

1965, Jan. 6   Litho.   Perf. 13

34	A8	2ch Primrose	.15	.15
35	A8	5ch Gentian	.15	.15
36	A8	15ch Primrose	.15	.15
37	A8	33ch Gentian	.15	.15
38	A8	50ch Rhododendron	.15	.15
39	A8	75ch Peony	.20	.20
40	A8	1nu Rhododendron	.20	.20
41	A8	2nu Peony	.40	.40
		Set value	1.20	1.20

For overprints see Nos. 43, 45, C4-C5, C14-C15.

Nos. 5, 40, 32, 41 and 33 Overprinted:
"WINSTON CHURCHILL 1874-1965"
1965, Feb. 27

42	A1	33ch bl grn & lilac	.15	.15
43	A8	1nu pink, grn & dk gray	.40	.40
44	A7	1nu silver & multi	.40	.40
45	A8	2nu sepia, yel & grn	.75	.75
46	A7	3nu gold & multi	1.00	1.00
		Nos. 42-46 (5)	2.70	2.70

Issued in memory of Sir Winston Churchill (1874-1965), British statesman. The overprint is in three lines on Nos. 42-43 and 45; in two lines on Nos. 43 and 46.
Nos. 44 and 46 exist imperf. Value, both, $4.50.

Skyscraper, Pagoda and World's Fair Emblem — A9

Designs: 10ch, 2nu, Pieta by Michelangelo and statue of Druk. 20ch, Skyline of NYC and Bhutanese village. 33ch, George Washington Bridge, NY, and foot bridge, Bhutan.

1965, Apr. 21   Litho.   Perf. 14½

47	A9	1ch blue & multi	.15	.15
48	A9	10ch green & multi	.15	.15
49	A9	20ch rose lilac & multi	.15	.15
50	A9	33ch bister & multi	.15	.15
51	A9	1.50nu bister & multi	.50	.50
52	A9	2nu multicolored	.65	.65
a.		Souv. sheet, perf. 13½ or imperf.	2.75	2.75
		Set value	1.45	1.45

Nos. 47-52 exist imperf.; value $3.50.
No. 52a contains two stamps similar to Nos. 51-52.
For overprints see #87-87B, C6-C10, C16-C20.

Telstar, Short-wave Radio and ITU
Emblem — A10

Designs (ITU Emblem and): 2nu, Telstar and
Morse key. 3nu, Syncom and ear phones.

		1966, Mar. 2	**Litho.**	**Perf. 14½**	
53	A10	35ch multicolored		.15	.15
54	A10	2nu multicolored		.55	.55
55	A10	3nu multicolored		.75	.75
		Nos. 53-55 (3)		1.45	1.45

Cent. (in 1965) of the ITU. Souvenir sheets exist
containing two stamps similar to Nos. 54-55, perf.
13½ and imperf. Value, 2 sheets, $5.

Leopard — A11   BHUTAN

Animals: 1ch, 4nu, Asiatic black bear. 4ch, 2nu,
Pigmy hog. 8ch, 75ch, Tiger. 10ch, 1.50nu, Dhole
(Asiatic hunting dog). 1nu, 5nu, Takin (goat).

		1966, Mar. 24	**Litho.**	**Perf. 13**	
56	A11	1ch yellow & blk		.15	.15
57	A11	2ch pale grn & blk		.15	.15
58	A11	4ch lt citron & blk		.15	.15
59	A11	8ch lt blue & blk		.15	.15
60	A11	10ch lt lilac & blk		.15	.15
61	A11	75ch lt yel grn & blk		.20	.20
62	A11	1nu lt green & blk		.50	.50
63	A11	1.50nu lt bl grn & blk		.40	.40
64	A11	2nu dull org & blk		.50	.50
65	A11	3nu bluish lil & blk		.75	.75
66	A11	4nu lt green & blk		1.00	1.00
67	A11	5nu pink & black		1.40	1.40
		Nos. 56-67 (12)		5.50	5.50

For surcharges see Nos. 115C, 115E, 115I,
117N, 117P, 129B, 129J.

Nos. 6-9, 20-23
Surcharged

		1965(?)	**Perf. 14½x14, 14x14½**		
68	A2	5ch on 1nu		26.00	26.00
69	A2	5ch on 2nu		26.00	26.00
70	A5	10ch on 70ch		4.25	4.25
71	A5	10ch on 2nu		4.25	4.25
72	A1	15ch on 70ch		6.25	6.25
73	A1	15ch on 1.30nu		6.25	6.25
74	A5	20ch on 1nu		8.25	8.25
75	A5	20ch on 1.30nu		8.25	8.25
		Nos. 68-75 (8)		89.50	89.50

The surcharges on Nos. 68-69 contain two bars
at left and right obliterating the denomination on
both sides of the design. Four bars on Nos. 72-73.

Simtokha
Dzong
A12

Tashichho Dzong — A13

Daga
Dzong — A14

Designs: 5ch, Rinpung Dzong. 50ch, Tongsa
Dzong. 1nu, Lhuntsi Dzong.

Perf. 14½x14 (A12), 13½ (A13, A14)

		1966-70		**Photo.**	
76	A12	5ch orange brn ('67)		.15	.15
77	A13	10ch dk grn & rose vio ('68)		.15	.15
78	A12	15ch brown		.15	.15
79	A12	20ch green		.15	.15
80	A13	50ch blue grn ('68)		.25	.15
81	A14	75ch dk bl & ol gray ('70)		.25	.25
82	A14	1nu dk vio & vio bl ('70)		.40	.40
		Set value		1.05	.90

Sizes: 5ch, 15ch, 20ch, 37x20½mm. 10ch,
53½x28½mm. 50ch, 35½x25½mm.

King Jigme
Wangchuk
A14a

Coins: 1.30nu, 3nu, 5nu, reverse.

Litho. & Embossed on Gold Foil

		1966, July 8	**Die Cut**	**Imperf.**	
83	A14a	10ch green		.15	.15
83A	A14a	25ch green		.25	.25
83B	A14a	50ch green		.50	.50
83C	A14a	1nu red		1.00	1.00
83D	A14a	1.30nu red		1.15	1.15
83E	A14a	2nu red		1.80	1.80
83F	A14a	3nu red		2.60	2.60
83G	A14a	4nu red		3.75	3.75
83H	A14a	5nu red		4.50	4.50
		Nos. 83-83H (9)		15.70	15.70

See Nos. 98-98B.

Abominable Snowman — A14b

		1966	**Photo.**	**Perf. 13½**	
84	A14b	1ch multicolored		.15	.15
84A	A14b	2ch multi, diff.		.15	.15
84B	A14b	3ch multi, diff.		.15	.15
84C	A14b	4ch multi, diff.		.15	.15
84D	A14b	5ch multi, diff.		.15	.15
84E	A14b	15ch like #84		.15	.15
84F	A14b	30ch like #84A		.15	.15
84G	A14b	40ch like #84B		.15	.15
84H	A14b	50ch like #84C		.15	.15
84I	A14b	1.25nu like #84D		.30	.30
84J	A14b	2.50nu like #84		.65	.65
84K	A14b	3nu like #84A		.75	.75
84L	A14b	5nu like #84B		1.25	1.25
84M	A14b	6nu like #84C		1.50	1.50
84N	A14b	7nu like #84D		1.75	1.75
		Set value		6.50	6.50

Issue dates: 1ch, 2ch, 3ch, 4ch, 5ch, 15ch, 30ch,
40ch, 50ch, Oct. 12. Others, Nov. 15. Exist imperf.
For overprints see Nos. 93-93G. For surcharges
see Nos. 115D, 115K, 115O, 115P, 117I, 117S.

Flowers
A14c

Designs: 3ch, 50ch, Lilium sherriffiae. 5ch, 1nu,
Meconopsis dhwoju. 7ch, 2.50nu, Rhododendron

chaetomallum. 10ch, 4nu, Pleione hookeriana.
5nu, Rhododendron giganteum.

		1967, Feb. 9	**Litho.**	**Perf. 13**	
85	A14c	3ch multicolored		.15	.15
85A	A14c	5ch multicolored		.15	.15
85B	A14c	7ch multicolored		.15	.15
85C	A14c	10ch multicolored		.15	.15

Gray Background

85D	A14c	50ch multicolored		.15	.15
85E	A14c	1nu multicolored		.30	.30
85F	A14c	2.50nu multicolored		.75	.75
85G	A14c	4nu multicolored		1.20	1.20
85H	A14c	5nu multicolored		1.50	1.50
		Nos. 85-85H (9)		4.50	4.50

For surcharges see Nos. 115F, 115L.

Boy Scouts — A14d

		1967, Mar. 28	**Photo.**	**Perf. 13½**	
86	A14d	5ch Planting tree		.15	.15
86A	A14d	10ch Cooking		.15	.15
86B	A14d	15ch Mountain climbing		.15	.15

Emblem, Border in Gold

86C	A14d	50ch like #86		.15	.15
86D	A14d	1.25nu like #86A		.60	.60
86E	A14d	4nu like #86B		1.75	1.75
f.		Souv. sheet of 2, #86D, 86E		2.50	2.50
		Nos. 86-86E (6)		2.95	2.95

Exist imperf.
See Nos. 89-89E for overprints. For surcharges
see Nos. 115G, 117J, 129K.

Nos. 50-52, 52a Ovptd.

expo67

		1967, May 25	**Litho.**	**Perfs. as Before**	
87	A9	33ch on #50		.15	.15
87A	A9	1.50nu on #51		.45	.45
87B	A9	2nu on #52		.60	.60
c.		Souv. sheet of 2, on #52a		1.50	1.50
		Nos. 87-87B (3)		1.20	1.20

Nos. 87-87B exist imperf.

Airplanes — A14f

		1967, June 26	**Litho.**	**Perf. 13½**	
88	A14f	45ch Lancaster		.15	.15
88A	A14f	2nu Spitfire		.45	.45
88B	A14f	4nu Hurricane		.95	.95
c.		Souv. sheet of 2, #88A, 88B		2.00	2.00
		Nos. 88-88B (3)		1.55	1.55

Churchill and Battle of Britain. Exist imperf.
For surcharges see Nos. 117Q, 117T.

Nos. 86-86D, 86e Overprinted "WORLD
JAMBOREE / IDAHO, U.S.A. / AUG. 1-
9,/67"

		1967, Aug. 8	**Photo.**	**Perf. 13½**	
89	A14d	5ch Planting tree		.15	.15
89A	A14d	10ch Cookout		.15	.15
89B	A14d	15ch Mountain climbing		.15	.15
89C	A14d	50ch like #89		.20	.20
89D	A14d	1.25nu like #89A		.60	.60

89E	A14d	4nu like #89B		1.90	1.90
f.		Souv. sheet of 2, #89D, 89E		2.75	2.75
		Nos. 89-89E (6)		3.15	3.15

No. 89f sold for 6.25nu. Exist imperf.

Girl Scouts — A14g

		1967, Sept. 28	**Photo.**	**Perf. 13½**	
90	A14g	5ch Painting		.15	.15
90A	A14g	10ch Making music		.15	.15
90B	A14g	15ch Picking fruit		.15	.15

Emblem, Border in Gold

90C	A14g	1.50nu like #90		.30	.30
90D	A14g	2.50nu like #90A		.45	.45
90E	A14g	5nu like #90B		.90	.90
f.		Souv. sheet of 2, #90A, 90B		2.00	2.00
		Set value		1.50	1.50

Exist imperf.
For surcharge see No. 266.

Astronaut, Space Capsule — A14h

Astronaut walking in space and: 5ch, 30ch, 4nu,
Orbiter, Lunar modules docked. 7ch, 50ch, 5nu,
Lunar module. 10ch, 1.25nu, 9nu, Other
astronauts.

		1967, Oct. 30	**Litho.**	**Imperf.**	
91	A14h	3ch multi		.15	.15
91A	A14h	5ch multi		.15	.15
91B	A14h	7ch multi		.20	.20
91C	A14h	10ch multi		.25	.25
m.		Souv. sheet of 4, #91-91C		.75	.75
91D	A14h	15ch multi		.35	.35
91E	A14h	30ch multi		.75	.75
91F	A14h	50ch multi		1.25	1.25
91G	A14h	1.25nu multi		3.00	3.00
n.		Souv. sheet of 4, #91D-91G		6.75	6.75
91H	A14h	2.50nu multi		1.75	1.75
91I	A14h	4nu multi		3.00	3.00
91J	A14h	5nu multi		3.75	3.75
91K	A14h	9nu multi		6.50	6.50
o.		Souv. sheet of 4, #91H-91K		20.00	20.00
		Nos. 91-91K (12)		21.10	21.10

Nos. 91H-91K are airmail. Simulated 3-dimen-
sions using a plastic overlay.
For other space issues see types A15a, A15e.

Pheasants — A14i

Designs: 1ch, 2nu, Tragopan satyra. 2ch, 4nu,
Lophophorus sclareti. 4ch, 5nu, Lophophorus
impeyanus. 8ch, 7nu, Lophura leucomelana. 15ch,
9nu, Crossoptilon crossoptilon.

		1968	**Photo.**	**Perf. 13½**	
92	A14i	1ch multicolored		.15	.15
92A	A14i	2ch multicolored		.15	.15
92B	A14i	4ch multicolored		.15	.15
92C	A14i	8ch multicolored		.15	.15
92D	A14i	15ch multicolored		.15	.15

Border in Gold

92E	A14i	2nu multicolored	.40	.40
92F	A14i	4nu multicolored	.80	.80
92G	A14i	5nu multicolored	1.00	1.00
92H	A14i	7nu multicolored	1.40	1.40
92I	A14i	9nu multicolored	1.90	1.90
		Nos. 92-92I (10)	6.25	6.25

Issue dates: 1ch, 2ch, 4ch, 8ch, 15ch, 2nu, 4nu, 7nu, Jan 20. 5nu, 9nu, Apr. 23.
Unauthorized imperfs. exist.
For surcharges see Nos. 115H, 117R, 117V, 129D, 129L.

Nos. 84G, 84I, 84K, 84M Ovptd. in Black on Silver

a　　　　　b

1968, Feb. 16 Photo. *Perfs. as Before*

Overprint Type "a"

93	A14b	40ch on #84G	.15	.15
93A	A14b	1.25nu on #84I	.20	.20
93B	A14b	3nu on #84K	.50	.50
93C	A14b	6nu on #84M	1.00	1.00

Overprint Type "b"

93D	A14b	40ch on #84G	.15	.15
93E	A14b	1.25nu on #84I	.20	.20
93F	A14b	3nu on #84K	.50	.50
93G	A14b	6nu on #84M	1.00	1.00
		Nos. 93-93G (8)	3.70	3.70

Exist imperf.

Snow Lion — A14j

1968, Mar. 14 Photo. *Perf. 12½*

94	A14j	2ch Elephant	.15	.15
94A	A14j	3ch Garuda	.15	.15
94B	A14j	4ch Monastery Tiger	.15	.15
94C	A14j	5ch Wind Horse	.15	.15
94D	A14j	15ch Snow Lion	.15	.15
94E	A14j	20ch like #94A	.15	.15
94F	A14j	30ch like #94A	.15	.15
94G	A14j	50ch like #94B	.15	.15
94H	A14j	1.25nu like #94C	.20	.20
94I	A14j	1.50nu like #94	.25	.25
94J	A14j	2nu like #94D	.35	.35
94K	A14j	2.50nu like #94A	.40	.40
94L	A14j	4nu like #94B	.65	.65
94M	A14j	5nu like #94C	.80	.80
94N	A14j	10nu like #94D	1.65	1.65
		Set value	4.75	4.75

Nos. 94I, 94K-94N are airmail. All exist imperf.
For surcharges see Nos. 115, 115M, 115Q, 117-117E, 129C, C35-C36.

Butterflies
A14k

Designs: 15ch, Catagramma sorana. 50ch, Delias hyparete. 1.25nu, Anteos maerula. 2nu, Ornithoptera priamus urvilleanus. 3nu, Euploea mulciber. 4nu, Morpho rhetenor. 5nu, Papilio androgeous. 6nu, Troides magellanus.

1968, May 20 Litho. *Imperf.*

95	A14k	15ch multi	.15	.15
95A	A14k	50ch multi	.45	.45
95B	A14k	1.25nu multi	1.10	1.10
95C	A14k	2nu multi	1.75	1.75
h.		Souv. sheet of 4, #95-95C	3.50	3.50
95D	A14k	3nu multi	1.25	1.25
95E	A14k	4nu multi	1.65	1.65
95F	A14k	5nu multi	2.00	2.00
95G	A14k	6nu multi	2.50	2.50
i.		Souv. sheet of 4, #95D-95G	7.50	7.50
		Nos. 95-95G (8)	10.85	10.85

Souv. sheets issued Oct. 23. Nos. 95D-95G, 95i are airmail. Simulated 3-dimensions using a plastic overlay.

Paintings — A14m

1968 Litho. & Embossed *Imperf.*

96	A14m	2ch Van Gogh	.15	.15
96A	A14m	4ch Millet	.15	.15
96B	A14m	5ch Monet	.15	.15
96C	A14m	10ch Corot	.15	.15
p.		Souv. sheet of 4, #96-96C	.15	.15
96D	A14m	45ch like #96	.20	.20
96E	A14m	80ch like #96A	.35	.35
96F	A14m	1.05nu like #96B	.45	.45
96G	A14m	1.40nu like #96C	.60	.60
q.		Souv. sheet of 4, #96D-96G	1.65	1.65
96H	A14m	1.50nu like #96	.65	.65
96I	A14m	2nu like #96	.85	.85
96J	A14m	2.50nu like #96A	1.10	1.10
96K	A14m	3nu like #96A	1.25	1.25
96L	A14m	4nu like #96B	1.10	1.10
96M	A14m	5nu like #96C	1.40	1.40
r.		Souv. sheet of 4, #96I, 96K-96M	4.75	4.75
96N	A14m	6nu like #96B	1.75	1.75
96O	A14m	8nu like #96C	2.25	2.25
s.		Souv. sheet of 4, #96H, 96J, 96N-96O	12.55	12.55
		Nos. 96-96O (16)	12.55	12.55

Issue dates: Nos. 96-96G, 96I, 96K-96M, July 8. Nos. 96p, 96q, 96r, Aug. 5. Others, Aug. 28. Nos. 96H, 96J, 96N-96O are airmail.
See Nos. 114-114O, 144-144G.

Summer
Olympics,
Mexico,
1968
A14n

1968, Oct. 1 Photo. *Perf. 13½*

97	A14n	5ch Discus	.15	.15
97A	A14n	45ch Basketball	.15	.15
97B	A14n	60ch Javelin	.15	.15
97C	A14n	80ch Shooting	.15	.15
97D	A14n	1.05nu like #97	.15	.15
97E	A14n	2nu like #97B	.20	.20
97F	A14n	3nu like #97C	.35	.35
97G	A14n	5nu Soccer	.60	.60
h.		Souv. sheet of 2, #97D, 97G	2.25	2.25
		Set value	1.50	1.50

Exist imperf.
For surcharges see Nos. 129E, B5-B7.

Coin Type of 1966
Overprinted

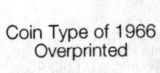

Embossed on Gold Foil

1968, Nov. 12 Die Cut *Imperf.*

98	A14a	15ch green	.15	.15
98A	A14a	33ch green	.25	.25
98B	A14a	9nu green	4.75	4.75
		Nos. 98-98B (3)	5.15	5.15

Human Rights Year.

Birds — A14p

Designs: 2ch, 20ch, 1.50nu, Crimson-winged laughing thrush. 3ch, 30ch, 2.50nu, Ward's trogon, vert. 4ch, 50ch, 4nu, Grey peacock-pheasant. 5ch, 1.25nu, 5nu, Rufous necked hornbill, vert. 15ch, 2nu, 10nu, Myzornis.

1968-69 Photo. *Perf. 12½*

99	A14p	2ch multicolored	.15	.15
99A	A14p	3ch multicolored	.15	.15
99B	A14p	4ch multicolored	.15	.15
99C	A14p	5ch multicolored	.15	.15
99D	A14p	15ch multicolored	.15	.15
99E	A14p	20ch multicolored	.15	.15
99F	A14p	30ch multicolored	.15	.15
99G	A14p	50ch multicolored	.15	.15
99H	A14p	1.25nu multicolored	.30	.30
99I	A14p	1.50nu multicolored	.35	.35
99J	A14p	2nu multicolored	.40	.40
99K	A14p	2.50nu multicolored	.50	.50
99L	A14p	4nu multicolored	.85	.85
99M	A14p	5nu multicolored	1.10	1.10
99N	A14p	10nu multicolored	2.00	2.00
		Nos. 99-99N (15)	6.70	6.70

Issue dates: 2ch, 3ch, 4ch, 5ch, 15ch, 30ch, 50ch, Dec. 7, 1968. 20ch, 1.25nu, 2nu, Dec. 28, 1968. Others, Jan. 29, 1969.
1.50nu, 2.50nu, 4nu, 5nu, 10nu are airmail.
Exist imperf.
For surcharges see Nos. 115A-115B, 115I, 115M, 115R, 117F-117G, 117K, 117O, 129H.

Fish
A14q

1969, Feb. 27 Litho. *Imperf.*

100	A14q	15ch multicolored	.80	.80
100A	A14q	20ch multi, diff.	1.00	1.00
100B	A14q	30ch multi, diff.	1.50	1.50
100C	A14q	5nu multi, diff.	2.00	2.00
100D	A14q	6nu multi, diff.	2.50	2.50
100E	A14q	7nu multi, diff.	3.00	3.00
f.		Souv. sheet of 4, #100B-100E	9.00	9.00
		Nos. 100-100E (6)	10.80	10.80

Nos. 100C-100E are airmail. Simulated 3-dimensions using a plastic overlay.

Insects — A14r

1969, Apr. 10 Litho. *Imperf.*

101	A14r	10ch multicolored	.15	.15
101A	A14r	75ch multi, diff.	.35	.35
101B	A14r	1.25nu multi, diff.	.60	.60
101C	A14r	2nu multi, diff.	1.00	1.00
h.		Souv. sheet of 4, #101-101C	3.75	3.75
101D	A14r	3nu multi, diff.	1.10	1.10
101E	A14r	4nu multi, diff.	1.50	1.50
101F	A14r	5nu multi, diff.	1.90	1.90
101G	A14r	6nu multi, diff.	2.25	2.25
i.		Souv. sheet of 4, #101D-101G	8.00	8.00
		Nos. 101-101G (8)	8.85	8.85

Nos. 101D-101G, 101i are airmail. Stamps from souvenir sheets have inscription at lower right. Simulated 3-dimensions using a plastic overlay.

Admission to UPU — A14s

Illustration reduced.

1969, May 2 Photo. *Perf. 13*

102	A14s	5ch multicolored	.15	.15
102A	A14s	10ch multicolored	.15	.15
102B	A14s	15ch multicolored	.15	.15
102C	A14s	45ch multicolored	.15	.15
102D	A14s	60ch multicolored	.16	.16
102E	A14s	1.05nu multicolored	.25	.25
102F	A14s	1.40nu multicolored	.35	.35
102G	A14s	4nu multicolored	1.00	1.00
		Set value	2.00	2.00

Exist imperf.
For surcharges see #117H, 117L, 117U, 129.

History of Steel Making — A14t

Designs: 2ch, Pre-biblical. 5ch, Damascus sword. 15ch, 3nu, Saugus Mill. 45ch, Beehive coke ovens. 75ch, 4nu, Bessemer converter. 1.50nu, 5nu, Rolling mill. 1.75nu, Steel mill. 2nu, 6nu, Future applications.

Litho. on Steel Foil

1969, June 2 *Imperf.*
Without Gum

103	A14t	2ch multicolored	.15	.15
103A	A14t	5ch multicolored	.15	.15
103B	A14t	15ch multicolored	.15	.15
m.		Souv. sheet of 2, #103A-103B	.15	.15
103C	A14t	45ch multicolored	.15	.15
n.		Souv. sheet of 2, #103, 103C	.30	.30
103D	A14t	75ch multicolored	.20	.20
103E	A14t	1.50nu multicolored	.45	.45
103F	A14t	1.75nu multicolored	.50	.50
o.		Souv. sheet of 2, #103E-103F	2.25	2.25
103G	A14t	2nu multicolored	.60	.60
p.		Souv. sheet of 2, #103D, 103G	1.90	1.90
103H	A14t	3nu multicolored	.85	.85
103I	A14t	4nu multicolored	1.10	1.10
103J	A14t	5nu multicolored	1.40	1.40
q.		Souv. sheet of 2, #103I-103J	3.75	3.75
103K	A14t	6nu multicolored	1.75	1.75
r.		Souv. sheet of 2, #103H,103K	3.75	3.75
		Nos. 103-103K (12)	7.35	7.35

Nos. 103H-103K, 103q, 103r are airmail. Souv. sheets issued June 30.

Birds
A14u

1969, Aug. 5 Litho. *Imperf.*

104	A14u	15ch Owl	.15	.15
104A	A14u	50ch Red birds	.35	.35
104B	A14u	1.25nu Hawk	.95	.95
104C	A14u	2nu Penguin	1.50	1.50
h.		Souv. sheet of 4, #104-104C	3.25	3.25
104D	A14u	3nu Macaws	1.10	1.10
104E	A14u	4nu Bird of paradise	1.40	1.40
104F	A14u	5nu Duck	1.75	1.75
104G	A14u	6nu Pheasant	2.00	2.00
i.		Souv. sheet of 4, #104D-104G	9.20	9.20
		Nos. 104-104G (8)	9.20	9.20

Nos. 104D-104G, 104i are airmail. Simulated 3-dimensions using a plastic overlay. Souv. sheets issued Aug. 28.

Buddhist Prayer Banners — A14v

Litho. on Cloth
1969, Sep. 30   *Imperf.*
Self-adhesive
Sizes: 15ch, 75ch, 2nu, 57x57mm,
5nu, 6nu, 70x37mm

105	A14v	15ch multicolored	.15	.15
105A	A14v	75ch multi, diff.	.25	.25
105B	A14v	2nu multi, diff.	.70	.70
105C	A14v	5nu multi, diff.	1.75	1.75
105D	A14v	6nu multi, diff.	2.25	2.25
		Nos. 105-105D (5)	5.10	5.10

Souvenir Sheet

105E	Sheet of 3	5.00	5.00

No. 105E shows denominations of 75ch, 5nu, 6nu with design elements of Nos. 105A, 105C, 105D with gray frame. Exists perf. 13½.

Mahatma Gandhi — A15

1969, Oct. 2   **Litho.**   *Perf. 13x13½*

106	A15	20ch light blue & brn	.15	.15
107	A15	2nu lemon & brn ol	.75	.75

Mohandas K. Gandhi (1869-1948), leader in India's struggle for independence.

Apollo 11 Moon Landing — A15a

Designs: 3ch, Separation from third stage. 5ch, Entering lunar orbit. 15ch, Lunar module separating from orbiter. 20ch, 3nu, Astronaut standing on lunar module's foot pad. 25ch, Astronaut, lunar module on moon. 45ch, Astronaut, flag. 50ch, 4nu, Setting up experiments. 1.75nu, Lunar module docking with orbiter. 5nu, Lift-off from Cape Canaveral. 6nu, Recovery at sea.

1969   **Litho.**   *Imperf.*

108	A15a	3ch multi	.15	.15
108A	A15a	5ch multi	.15	.15
108B	A15a	15ch multi	.20	.20
108C	A15a	20ch multi	.25	.25
m.		Souv. sheet of 4, #108-108C	.60	.60
108D	A15a	25ch multi	.30	.30
108E	A15a	45ch multi	.50	.50
108F	A15a	50ch multi	.55	.55
108G	A15a	1.75nu multi	1.75	1.75
n.		Souv. sheet of 4, #108D-108G	4.00	4.00
108H	A15a	3nu multi	1.50	1.50
108I	A15a	4nu multi	2.00	2.00
108J	A15a	5nu multi	2.50	2.50
108K	A15a	6nu multi	3.00	3.00
o.		Souv. sheet of 4, #108H-108K	21.00	21.00
		Nos. 108-108K (12)	12.85	12.85

Issue dates: Nos. 108-108G, Nov. 3. Nos. 108H-108K, Nov. 20. Souv. sheets, Dec. 20.
Nos. 108H-108K, 108o are airmail. Simulated 3-dimensions using a plastic overlay.
"Aldrin" misspelled on No. 108o.

Buying Sets
It is often less expensive to purchase complete sets than individual stamps that make up the set. Set values are provided for many such sets.

Paintings
A15b

1970, Jan. 19   **Litho.**   *Imperf.*

109	A15b	5ch Clouet	.15	.15
109A	A15b	10ch van Eyck	.15	.15
109B	A15b	15ch David	.15	.15
109C	A15b	2.75nu Rubens	1.75	1.75
h.		Souv. sheet of 4, #109-109C	2.50	2.50
109D	A15b	3nu Homer	1.10	1.10
109E	A15b	4nu Gentileschi	1.40	1.40
109F	A15b	5nu Raphael	1.75	1.75
109G	A15b	6nu Ghirlandaio	2.25	2.25
i.		Souv. sheet of 4, #109D-109G	7.50	7.50
		Nos. 109-109G (8)	8.70	8.70

Nos. 109D-109G, 109i are airmail. Simulated 3-dimensions using a plastic overlay. Souv. sheets issued Feb. 25.

Various Forms of Mail Transport, UPU Headquarters, Bern — A15c

1970, Feb. 27   **Photo.**   *Perf. 13½*

110	A15c	3ch ol grn & gold	.15	.15
111	A15c	10ch red brn & gold	.15	.15
112	A15c	15ch Prus bl & gold	.15	.15
113	A15c	2.50nu dp mag & gold	.65	.65
		Set value	.75	.75

New Headquarters of Universal Postal Union, Bern, Switzerland.
Exist imperf. Value $5.
For surcharge see No. 129I.

Painting Type of 1968
Paintings of flowers.

Litho. & Embossed
1970, May 6   *Imperf.*

114	A14m	2ch Van Gogh	.15	.15
114A	A14m	3ch Redon	.15	.15
114B	A14m	5ch Kuroda	.15	.15
114C	A14m	10ch Renoir	.15	.15
p.		Souv. sheet of 4, #114-114C	.15	.15
114D	A14m	15ch Renoir, diff.	.15	.15
114E	A14m	75ch Monet	.30	.30
114F	A14m	80ch like #114	.20	.20
114G	A14m	90ch like #114A	.20	.20
114H	A14m	1nu La Tour	.40	.40
114I	A14m	1.10nu like #114B	.30	.30
114J	A14m	1.40nu Oudot	.60	.60
q.		Souv. sheet of 4, #114D, 114E, 114H, 114J	1.90	1.90
114K	A14m	1.40nu like #114C	.35	.35
r.		Souv. sheet of 4, #114F, 114G, 114I, 114K	1.25	1.25
114L	A14m	1.60nu like #114D	.40	.40
114M	A14m	1.70nu like #114E	.40	.40
114N	A14m	3nu like #114H	.75	.75
114O	A14m	3.50nu like #114J	.85	.85
s.		Souv. sheet of 4, #114L-114O	2.75	2.75
		Nos. 114-114O (16)	5.50	5.50

#114F-114G, 114I, 114K-114O are airmail.

Stamps of 1966-69 Surcharged
1970, June 19

115	A14j	20ch on 2nu, #94J	2.50	2.50
115A	A14p	20ch on 2nu, #99J	2.50	2.50
115B	A14p	20ch on 2.50nu, #99K	2.50	2.50
115C	A11	20ch on 3nu, #65	2.50	2.50
115D	A14b	20ch on 3nu, #84K	2.50	2.50
115E	A14i	20ch on 4nu, #66	2.50	2.50
115F	A14c	20ch on 4nu, #85G	2.50	2.50
115G	A14d	20ch on 4nu, #86E	2.50	2.50
115H	A14i	20ch on 4nu, #92F	2.50	2.50
115I	A14b	20ch on 5nu, #84L	2.50	2.50
115J	A11	20ch on 5nu, #67	2.50	2.50
115K	A14b	20ch on 5nu, #85H	2.50	2.50
115L	A14i	20ch on 5nu, #94M	2.50	2.50
115M	A14j	20ch on 5nu, #99M	2.50	2.50
115N	A14b	20ch on 6nu, #84M	2.50	2.50
115O	A14b	20ch on 6nu, #84M	2.50	2.50
115P	A14i	20ch on 7nu, #84N	2.50	2.50
115Q	A14j	20ch on 10nu, #94N	2.50	2.50
115R	A14j	20ch on 10nu, #99N	2.50	2.50
		Nos. 115-115R (19)	47.50	47.50

Nos. 115B, 115I, 115M-115N, 115Q-115R are airmail.

Animals — A15d

1970, Oct. 15   **Litho.**   *Imperf.*

116	A15d	5ch African elephant	.15	.15
116A	A15d	10ch Leopard	.15	.15
116B	A15d	20ch Ibex	.25	.25
116C	A15d	25ch Tiger	.30	.30
116D	A15d	30ch Abominable snowman	.35	.35
116E	A15d	40ch Water buffalo	.50	.50
116F	A15d	65ch Rhinoceros	.80	.80
116G	A15d	75ch Giant pandas	.95	.95
116H	A15d	85ch Snow leopard	1.10	1.10
116I	A15d	2nu Young deer	1.50	1.50
116J	A15d	3nu Wild boar, vert.	2.25	2.25
116K	A15d	4nu Collared bear, vert.	3.00	3.00
116L	A15d	5nu Takin	4.00	4.00
		Nos. 116-116L (13)	15.30	15.30

Nos. 116I-116L are airmail. Simulated 3-dimensions using a plastic overlay.

Stamps of 1963-69 Surcharged
1970, Nov. 2

117	A14j	5ch on 30ch, #94F	.60	.60
117A	A14j	5ch on 50ch, #94G	.60	.60
117B	A14j	5ch on 1.25nu, #94H	.60	.60
117C	A14j	5ch on 1.50nu, #94I	.60	.60
117D	A14j	5ch on 2nu, #94J	.60	.60
117E	A14j	5ch on 2.50nu, #94K	.60	.60
117F	A14p	20ch on 30ch, #99F	2.50	2.50
117G	A14p	20ch on 50ch, #99G	2.50	2.50
117H	A14s	20ch on 1.05nu, #102E	2.50	2.50
117I	A14b	20ch on 1.25nu, #84I	2.50	2.50
117J	A14d	20ch on 1.25nu, #86D	2.50	2.50
117K	A14p	20ch on 1.25nu, #99H	2.50	2.50
117L	A14s	20ch on 1.40nu, #102F	2.50	2.50
117M	A4	20ch on 1.50nu, #14	2.50	2.50
117N	A11	20ch on 1.50nu, #63	2.50	2.50
117O	A14p	20ch on 1.50nu, #99I	2.50	2.50
117P	A11	20ch on 2nu, #64	2.50	2.50
117Q	A14f	20ch on 2nu, #88A	2.50	2.50
117R	A14j	20ch on 2nu, #92E	2.50	2.50
117S	A14b	20ch on 2.50nu, #84J	2.50	2.50
117T	A14b	20ch on 4nu, #88B	2.50	2.50
117U	A14s	20ch on 4nu, #102G	2.50	2.50
117V	A14i	20ch on 7nu, #92H	2.50	2.50
		Nos. 117-117V (23)	46.10	46.10

Nos. 117C, 117E, 117O are airmail.

Conquest of Space — A15e

Designs: 2ch, Jules Verne's "From the Earth to the Moon." 5ch, V-2 rocket. 15ch, Vostok. 25ch, Mariner 2. 30ch, Gemini 7. 50ch, Lift-off. 75ch, Edward White during space walk. 1.50nu, Apollo 13. 2nu, View of Earth from moon. 3nu, Another galaxy. 6nu, Moon, Earth, Sun, Mars, Jupiter. 7nu, Future space station.

1970   **Litho.**   *Imperf.*

118	A15e	2ch multicolored	.15	.15
118A	A15e	5ch multicolored	.15	.15
118B	A15e	15ch multicolored	.15	.15
118C	A15e	25ch multicolored	.20	.20
m.		Souv. sheet of 4, #118-118C	.60	.60
118D	A15e	30ch multicolored	.25	.25
118E	A15e	50ch multicolored	.35	.35
118F	A15e	75ch multicolored	.55	.55
118G	A15e	1.50nu multicolored	1.10	1.10
n.		Souv. sheet of 4, #118D-118G	3.75	3.75
118H	A15e	2nu multicolored	.65	.65
118I	A15e	3nu multicolored	1.00	1.00
118J	A15e	6nu multicolored	2.00	2.00

118K	A15e	7nu multicolored	2.25	2.25
o.		Souv. sheet of 4, #118H-118K	10.00	10.00
		Nos. 118-118K (12)	8.80	8.80

Issue dates: Nos. 118-118G, Nov. 9. Nos. 118H-118K, Nov. 30. Souv. sheets, Dec. 18. Nos. 118H-118K are airmail. Simulated 3-dimensions using a plastic overlay.
See Nos. 127-127C. For surcharge see No. 129F.

Wangdiphodrang Dzong and Bridge — A15f

1971-72   **Photo.**   *Perf. 13½*

119	A15f	2ch gray	.15	.15
120	A15f	3ch deep red lilac	.15	.15
121	A15f	4ch violet	.15	.15
122	A15f	5ch dark green	.15	.15
123	A15f	10ch orange brown	.15	.15
124	A15f	15ch deep blue	.15	.15
125	A15f	20ch deep plum	.15	.15
		Set value	.55	.55

Issued: 5ch-20ch, Feb. 22. 2ch-4ch, Apr. 1972.

Funeral Mask of King Tutankhamen — A15g

History of Sculpture: 75ch, Winged Bull. 1.25nu, Head of Zeus. 2nu, She-wolf Suckling Romulus and Remus, horiz. 3nu, Head of Cicero. 4nu, Head of David, by Michaelangelo. 5nu, Age of Bronze, by Rodin. 6nu, Head of Woman, by Modigliani.

1971, Feb. 27   *Imperf.*
Self-adhesive

126	A15g	10ch multicolored	.15	.15
126A	A15g	75ch multicolored	.35	.35
126B	A15g	1.25nu multicolored	.60	.60
126C	A15g	2nu multicolored	1.00	1.00
h.		Souv. sheet of 4, #126-126C	2.50	2.50
126D	A15g	3nu multicolored	.80	.80
126E	A15g	4nu multicolored	1.10	1.10
126F	A15g	5nu multicolored	1.40	1.40
126G	A15g	6nu multicolored	1.65	1.65
i.		Souv. sheet of 4, #126D-126G	5.50	5.50
		Nos. 126-126G (8)	7.05	7.05

Stamps are plastic heat molded into three dimensions. Nos. 126D-126G are airmail.

Conquest of Space Type of 1970
Designs: 10ch, 2.50nu, Lunokhod 1. 1.70nu, 4nu, Apollo 15.

1971, Mar. 20   **Litho.**   *Imperf.*

127	A15e	10ch multicolored	.15	.15
127A	A15e	1.70nu multicolored	1.00	1.00
127B	A15e	2.50nu multicolored	1.50	1.50
127C	A15e	4nu multicolored	2.25	2.25
d.		Souv. sheet of 4, #127-127C	5.00	5.00
		Nos. 127-127C (4)	4.90	4.90

Nos. 127B-127C are airmail. Simulated 3-dimensions using a plastic overlay.

Antique Automobiles — A15h

1971   **Litho.**   *Imperf.*

128	A15h	2ch Mercedes Benz, Germany	.15	.15

128A	A15h	5ch Ford, US	.15	.15
128B	A15h	10ch Alfa Romeo, Italy	.15	.15
128C	A15h	15ch Cord, US	.15	.15
128D	A15h	20ch Hispano Suiza, Spain	.15	.15
128E	A15h	30ch Invicta, Britain	.15	.15
128F	A15h	60ch Renault, France	.20	.20
128G	A15h	75ch Talbot, Britain	.25	.25
128H	A15h	85ch Mercer, US	.30	.30
128I	A15h	1nu Sunbeam, Britain	.35	.35
128J	A15h	1.20nu Austrian Daimler	.40	.40
128K	A15h	1.55nu Bugatti, Italy	.55	.55
128L	A15h	1.80nu Simplex, US	.60	.60
128M	A15h	2nu Amilcar, France	.65	.65
128N	A15h	2.50nu Bentley, Britain	.85	.85
128O	A15h	4nu Morris Garage, Britain	.85	.85
128P	A15h	6nu Duesenberg, US	1.10	1.10
128Q	A15h	7nu Aston Martin, Britain	1.25	1.25
128R	A15h	9nu Packard, US	1.65	1.65
128S	A15h	10nu Rolls Royce, Britain	1.75	1.75
		Nos. 128-128S (20)	11.65	11.65

Issue dates: Nos. 128-128F, May 20. Nos. 128G-128N, June 10. Nos. 128O-128S, July 5. Nos. 128O-128S are airmail. Simulated 3-dimensions using a plastic overlay.
"Romeo" misspelled.

Stamps of 1964-71 Surcharged
1971, July 1

129	A14s	55ch on 60ch, #102D	.75	.75
129A	A5	55ch on 1.30nu, #22	.40	.40
129B	A11	55ch on 3nu, #65	.40	.40
129C	A14j	55ch on 4nu, #94L	.40	.40
129D	A14i	55ch on 5nu, #92G	.40	.40
129E	A14n	90ch on 1.05nu, #97D	1.90	1.90
129F	A15e	90ch on 1.70nu, #127A	4.25	4.25
129G	A5	90ch on 2nu, #23	.40	.40
129H	A14p	90ch on 2nu, #99J	.75	.75
129I	A15c	90ch on 2.50nu, #88	1.10	1.10
129J	A11	90ch on 4nu, #66	.75	.75
129K	A14d	90ch on 4nu, #86E	1.90	1.90
129L	A14i	90ch on 9nu, #92I	.75	.75
		Nos. 129-129L (13)	14.15	14.15

No. 129C is airmail. No. 129F comes with lines 8mm or 18mm long.

UN Emblem and Bhutan Flag
A16

Designs (Bhutan Flag and): 10ch, UN Headquarters, NY. 20ch, Security Council Chamber and mural by Per Krohg. 3nu, General Assembly Hall.

1971, Sept. 21   Photo.   Perf. 13½

130	A16	5ch gold, bl & multi	.15	.15
131	A16	10ch gold & multi	.15	.15
132	A16	20ch gold & multi	.15	.15
133	A16	3nu gold & multi	.60	.60
		Set value, Nos. 130-133, C21-C23	2.50	2.50

Bhutan's admission to the UN. Exist imperf.
For overprints see Nos. 140-143. For surcharge see No. 252.

Boy Scout Crossing Stream in Rope Sling — A17

Emblem & Boy Scouts: 20ch, 2nu, mountaineering. 50ch, 6nu, reading map. 75ch, as 10ch.

1971, Nov. 30   Litho.   Perf. 13½

134	A17	10ch gold & multi	.15	.15
135	A17	20ch gold & multi	.15	.15
136	A17	50ch gold & multi	.15	.15
137	A17	75ch silver & multi	.16	.16
138	A17	2nu silver & multi	.40	.40
139	A17	6nu silver & multi	1.00	1.00
	a.	Souv. sheet of 2, #138-139 + 2 labels	2.00	2.00
		Nos. 134-139 (6)	2.01	2.01

60th anniv. of the Boy Scouts. Exist imperf.
For overprint and surcharge see #253, 383.

UNHCR UNRWA 1971

Nos. 130-133 Overprinted in Gold

1971, Dec. 23

140	A16	5ch gold & multi	.15	.15
141	A16	10ch gold & multi	.15	.15
142	A16	20ch gold & multi	.15	.15
143	A16	3nu gold & multi	.85	.85
		Nos. 140-143, C24-C26 (7)	5.30	5.30

World Refugee Year. Exist imperf.

The Bathing Girl by Renoir
A17a

Designs: 20ch, A Bar at the Follies, by Monet, horiz. 90ch, Mona Lisa, by da Vinci. 1.70nu, Cart of Father Junier, by Rousseau, horiz. 2.50nu, The Gleaners, by Millet, horiz. 4.60nu, White Horse, by Gaugin. 5.40nu, The Dancing Lesson, by Degas. 6nu, After the Rain, by Gaillauman, horiz.

1972   Litho. & Embossed   Imperf.

144	A17a	15ch multicolored	.15	.15
144A	A17a	20ch multicolored	.15	.15
144B	A17a	90ch multicolored	.35	.35
144C	A17a	1.70nu multicolored	.50	.50
144D	A17a	2.50nu multicolored	1.00	1.00
	h.	Souv. sheet of 4, #144-144B, 144D	3.50	3.50
144E	A17a	4.60nu multicolored	1.40	1.40
144F	A17a	5.40nu multicolored	1.65	1.65
144G	A17a	6nu multicolored	1.90	1.90
	i.	Souv. sheet of 4, #144C, 144E-144G	6.00	6.00
		Nos. 144-144G (8)	7.10	7.10

Issued: #144-144B, 144D, 1/29; others, 2/28.
Nos. 144C, 144E-144G are airmail.

Famous Men
A17b

1972, Apr. 17   Litho.   Imperf.
Self-adhesive

145	A17b	10ch John F. Kennedy	.15	.15
145A	A17b	15ch Gandhi	.15	.15
145B	A17b	55ch Churchill	.45	.45
145C	A17b	2nu De Gaulle	.50	.50
145D	A17b	6nu Pope John XVIII	1.50	1.50
145E	A17b	8nu Eisenhower	2.00	2.00
	f.	Souv. sheet of 4, #145B-145E	5.00	5.00
		Nos. 145-145E (6)	4.75	4.75

Nos. 145C-145E are airmail. Stamps are plastic heat molded into three dimensions.

Book Year Emblem
A17c

1972, May 15   Photo.   Perf. 13½x13

146	A17c	2ch multicolored	.15	.15
146A	A17c	3ch multicolored	.15	.15
146B	A17c	5ch multicolored	.15	.15
146C	A17c	20ch multicolored	.15	.15
		Set value	.30	.30

International Book Year.

1972 Summer Olympics, Munich
A17d

1972, June 6   Photo.   Perf. 13½

147	A17d	10ch Handball	.15	.15
147A	A17d	15ch Archery	.15	.15
147B	A17d	20ch Boxing	.15	.15
147C	A17d	30ch Discus	.15	.15
147D	A17d	35ch Javelin	.15	.15
147E	A17d	45ch Shooting	.15	.15
147F	A17d	1.35nu like #147A	.38	.38
147G	A17d	7nu like #147	1.90	1.90
	h.	Souv. sheet of 3, #147D, 147F-147G	3.00	3.00
		Set value	2.75	2.75

Nos. 147D, 147F-147G are airmail and have a gold border.
Exist imperf.
For overprint see No. 384.

Apollo 11 Type of 1969

Apollo 16: 15ch, Lift-off, vert. 20ch, Achieving lunar orbit. 90ch, Astronauts Young, Mattingly, Duke, vert. 1.70nu, Lunar module. 2.50nu, Walking on moon. 4.60nu, Gathering rock samples. 5.40nu, Apollo 16 on launch pad, vert. 6nu, Looking at earth, vert.

1972, Sept. 1   Litho.   Imperf.

148	A15a	15ch multicolored	.15	.15
148A	A15a	20ch multicolored	.15	.15
148B	A15a	90ch multicolored	.18	.18
148C	A15a	1.70nu multicolored	.35	.35
148D	A15a	2.50nu multicolored	.50	.50
	h.	Souv. sheet of 4, #148-148B, 148D	3.00	3.00
148E	A15a	4.60nu multicolored	.90	.90
148F	A15a	5.40nu multicolored	1.10	1.10
148G	A15a	6nu multicolored	1.20	1.20
	i.	Souv. sheet of 4, #148C, 148E-148G	5.00	5.00
		Nos. 148-148G (8)	4.53	4.53

Nos. 148C, 148E-148G are airmail. Simulated 3-dimensions using a plastic overlay.

Dogs
A17f

1972-73   Photo.   Perf. 13½

149	A17f	2ch Pointer	.15	.15
149A	A17f	3ch Irish Setter	.15	.15
149B	A17f	5ch Lhasa Apso, vert	.15	.15
149C	A17f	10ch Dochi	.15	.15
149D	A17f	15ch Damci	.15	.15
149E	A17f	15ch Collie	.15	.15
149F	A17f	20ch Basset hound	.15	.15
149G	A17f	25ch Damci, diff	.15	.15
149H	A17f	30ch Fox terrier	.15	.15
149I	A17f	55ch Lhasa Apso, diff.	.15	.15
149J	A17f	99ch Boxer	.22	.22
149K	A17f	2.50nu St. Bernard	.55	.55
149L	A17f	4nu Cocker Spaniel	.90	.90
	o.	Souv. sheet of 3, #149J-149L, perf. 14	3.00	3.00
149M	A17f	8nu Damci, diff.	1.90	1.90
	p.	Souv. sheet of 2, #149I, 149M, perf. 14	3.25	3.25
		Set value	4.00	4.00

Souvenir Sheet
Perf. 14

149N	A17f	18nu Poodle	5.00	5.00

Issue dates: Nos. 149B-149D, 149G, 149I, 149M, 149p, Oct. 5. Nos. 149-149A, 149E-149F, 149H, 149J-149L, 149o, Jan. 1. No. 149N, Jan. 15, 1973. No. 149N is airmail. All exist imperf.
For surcharges & overprints see #268-269, 385.

Roses — A17g

1973, Jan. 30   Photo.   Perf. 13½
Scented Paper

150	A17g	15ch Wendy Cussons	.15	.15
150A	A17g	25ch Iceberg	.15	.15
150B	A17g	30ch Marchioness of Urquio	.15	.15
150C	A17g	3nu Pink parfait	.70	.70
150D	A17g	6nu Roslyn	1.40	1.40
150E	A17g	7nu Blue moon	1.65	1.65
	f.	Souv. sheet of 2, #150D-150E	2.50	2.50
		Nos. 150-150E (6)	4.20	4.20

#150D-150E are airmail. Exist imperf.

Apollo 11 Type of 1969

Apollo 17: 10ch, Taking photographs on moon. 15ch, Setting up experiments. 55ch, Earth. 2nu, Driving lunar rover. 7nu, Satellite. 9nu, Astronauts Cernan, Evans, Schmitt.

1973, Feb. 28   Litho.   Imperf.
Size: 50x49mm

151	A15a	10ch multicolored	.15	.15
151A	A15a	15ch multicolored	.15	.15
151B	A15a	55ch multicolored	.20	.20
151C	A15a	2nu multicolored	.70	.70
	f.	Souv. sheet of 4, #151-151C	2.50	2.50
151D	A15a	7nu multicolored	2.25	2.25
151E	A15a	9nu multicolored	3.25	3.25
	g.	Souv. sheet of 2, #151D-151E	10.00	10.00
		Nos. 151-151E (6)	6.70	6.70

Simulated 3-dimensions using a plastic overlay. Nos. 151D-151E are airmail. No. 151g is circular, 160mm in diameter.

Phonograph Records

A17h

Recordings: 10ch, Bhutanese History. 25ch, Royal Bhutan Anthem. 1.25nu, Bhutanese History (English). 3nu, Bhutanese History (Bhutanese). Folk Song #1. 7nu, Folk Song #1. 8nu, Folk Song #2. 9nu, History in English, Folk Songs #1 & 2.

1973, Apr. 15
Self-adhesive
Diameter: #152-152B, 152D-152E, 69mm, #152C, 152F, 100mm

152	A17h	10ch yel on red	.70	.70
152A	A17h	25ch gold on grn	1.00	1.00
152B	A17h	1.25nu sil on bl	4.50	4.50
152C	A17h	3nu sil on pur	10.00	10.00
152D	A17h	7nu sil on blk	22.50	22.50
152E	A17h	8nu red on white	30.00	30.00
152F	A17h	9nu blk on yel	32.50	32.50
		Nos. 152-152F (7)	101.20	101.20

Nos. 152C, 152F are airmail.

King Jigme Dorji Wangchuk (d. 1972) — A17i

Embossed on Gold Foil

1973, May 2   Die Cut   Imperf.

153	A17i	10ch orange	.15 .15
153A	A17i	25ch red	.15 .15
153B	A17i	3nu green	.70 .70
153C	A17i	6nu blue	1.40 1.40
153D	A17i	8nu purple	1.90 1.90
e.	Souv. sheet of 2, #153C-153D		4.50 4.50
	Nos. 153-153D (5)		4.30 4.30

Nos. 153C-153D are airmail.

Mushrooms — A17j

Different mushrooms.

1973, Sept. 25   Litho.   Imperf.

154	A17j	15ch multicolored	.15 .15
154A	A17j	25ch multicolored	.20 .20
154B	A17j	30ch multicolored	.25 .25
154C	A17j	3nu multicolored	2.50 2.50
f.	Souvenir sheet of 4, #154-154C		15.00 15.00
154D	A17j	6nu multicolored	5.75 5.75
154E	A17j	7nu multicolored	6.75 6.75
g.	Souvenir sheet of 2, #154D-154E		35.00 35.00
	Nos. 154-154E (6)		15.60 15.60

Simulated 3-dimensions using a plastic overlay. Nos. 154D-154E are airmail.

Bhutanese Mail Service — A17k

Designs: 5ch, 6nu, Letter carrier at mail box. 10ch, 5nu, Postmaster, letter carrier. 15ch, Sacking mail. 25ch, Mailtruck. 1.25nu, Sorting mail. 3nu, Hand-delivered mail.

1973, Nov. 14   Photo.   Perf. 13½

155	A17k	5ch multicolored	.15 .15
155A	A17k	10ch multicolored	.15 .15
155B	A17k	15ch multicolored	.15 .15
155C	A17k	25ch multicolored	.15 .15
155D	A17k	1.25nu multicolored	.30 .30
155E	A17k	3nu multicolored	.65 .65
155F	A17k	5nu multicolored	1.10 1.10
155G	A17k	6nu multicolored	1.25 1.25
h.	Souv. sheet of 2, #155F-155G		6.00 6.00
	Nos. 155-155G (8)		3.90 3.90

Indipex '73. Nos. 155F-155G are airmail. All exist imperf.

For surcharges and overprint see Nos. 267, 382, C37-C38.

A set of 15 stamps plus souvenir sheet of 3 showing paintings with reading and writing themes was not authorized.

King Jigme Singye Wangchuk and Royal Crest — A18

Designs (King and): 25ch, 90ch, Flag of Bhutan. 1.25nu, Wheel with 8 good luck signs. 2nu, 4nu, Punakha Dzong, former winter capital. 3nu, 5nu, Crown. 5ch, same as 10ch.

1974, June 2   Litho.   Perf. 13½

157	A18	10ch maroon & multi	.15 .15
158	A18	25ch gold & multi	.15 .15
159	A18	1.25nu multi	.35 .35
160	A18	2nu gold & multi	.55 .55
161	A18	3nu multi	.75 .75
	Nos. 157-161 (5)		1.95 1.95

Souvenir Sheets
Perf. 13½, Imperf.

162		Sheet of 2	2.75 2.75
a.	A18 5ch maroon & multi		.15
b.	A18 5nu red orange & multi		2.50
163		Sheet of 2	2.75 2.75
a.	A18 90ch gold & multi		.75
b.	A18 4nu gold & multi		2.00

Coronation of King Jigme Singye Wangchuk, June 2, 1974.

Mailman on Horseback   Old and New Locomotives
A19   A20

Designs (UPU Emblem, Carrier Pigeon and): 3ch, Sailing and steam ships. 4ch, Old biplane and jet. 25ch, Mail runner and jeep.

1974, Oct. 9   Litho.   Perf. 14½

164	A19	1ch grn & multi	.15 .15
165	A20	2ch lilac & multi	.15 .15
166	A20	3ch ocher & multi	.15 .15
167	A20	4ch yel grn & multi	.15 .15
168	A20	5ch salmon & multi	.15 .15
	Set value, #164-168, C27-C29		1.25 1.25

Centenary of Universal Postal Union. Issued in sheets of 50 and sheets of 5 plus label with multicolored margin. Exist imperf.

Family and WPY Emblem — A21

1974, Dec. 17   Perf. 13½

169	A21	25ch bl & multi	.15 .15
170	A21	50ch org & multi	.15 .15
171	A21	90ch ver & multi	.30 .30
172	A21	2.50nu brn & multi	.75 .75
a.	Souvenir sheet of 4, 10nu		2.25 2.25
	Nos. 169-172 (4)		1.35 1.35

For surcharge see No. 254.

Sephisa Chandra A22

Designs: Indigenous butterflies.

1975, Sept. 15   Litho.   Perf. 14½

173	A22	1ch shown	.15 .15
174	A22	2ch Lethe kansa	.15 .15
175	A22	3ch Neope bhadra	.15 .15
176	A22	4ch Euthalia duda	.15 .15
177	A22	5ch Vindula erota	.15 .15
178	A22	10ch Bhutanitis Lidderdale	.15 .15
179	A22	3nu Limenitis zayla	.60 .60
180	A22	5nu Delis thysbe	1.40 1.40
	Set value		2.25 2.25

Souvenir Sheet
Perf. 13

181	A22	10nu Dabasa gyas	2.50 2.50

For surcharges see Nos. 255-256.

Apollo and Apollo-Soyuz Emblem — A23

Design: No. 183, Soyuz and emblem.

1975, Dec. 1   Litho.   Perf. 14x13½

182	A23	10nu multicolored	2.75 2.75
183	A23	10nu multicolored	2.75 2.75
a.	Souvenir sheet of 2, 15nu		7.00 7.00

Apollo Soyuz link-up in space, July 17. Nos. 182-183 printed se-tenant in sheets of 10. No. 183a contains two 15nu stamps similar to Nos 182-183. Exist imperf.
For surcharges see Nos. 257-258.

Jewelry A24

Designs: 2ch, Coffee pot, bell and sugar cup. 3ch, Container and drinking horn. 4ch, Pendants and box cover. 5ch, Painter. 15ch, Silversmith. 20ch, Wood carver with tools. 1.50nu, Mat maker. 5nu, 10nu, Printer.

1975, Dec. 17   Perf. 14½

184	A24	1ch multicolored	.15 .15
185	A24	2ch multicolored	.15 .15
186	A24	3ch multicolored	.15 .15
187	A24	4ch multicolored	.15 .15
188	A24	5ch multicolored	.15 .15
189	A24	15ch multicolored	.15 .15
190	A24	20ch multicolored	.15 .15
191	A24	1.50nu multicolored	.40 .40
192	A24	10nu multicolored	2.50 2.50
	Set value		3.20 3.20

Souvenir Sheet
Perf. 13

193	A24	5nu multicolored	1.40 1.40

Handicrafts and craftsmen.
For surcharges see No. 259, 381.

King Jigme Singye Wangchuk A25

Designs: 25ch, 90ch, 1nu, 2nu, 4nu, like 15ch. 1.30nu, 3nu, 5nu, Coat of arms. Sizes (Diameter): 15ch, 1nu, 1.30nu, 38mm. 25ch, 2nu, 3nu, 49mm. 90ch, 4nu, 5nu, 63mm.

Lithographed, Embossed on Gold Foil

1975, Nov. 11   Imperf.

194	A25	15ch emerald	.15 .15
195	A25	25ch emerald	.15 .15
196	A25	90ch emerald	.35 .35
197	A25	1nu bright carmine	.40 .40
198	A25	1.30nu bright carmine	.45 .45
199	A25	2nu bright carmine	.65 .65
200	A25	3nu bright carmine	1.00 1.00
201	A25	4nu bright carmine	1.65 1.65
202	A25	5nu bright carmine	2.00 2.00
	Nos. 194-202 (9)		6.80 6.80

King Jigme Singye Wangchuk's 20th birthday.

Rhododendron Cinnabarinum — A28

Rhododendron: 2ch, Campanulatum. 3ch, Fortunei. 4ch, Red arboreum. 5ch, Pink arboreum. 1nu, Falconeri. 3nu, Hodgsonii. 5nu, Keysii. 10nu, Cinnabarinum.

1976, Feb. 15   Litho.   Perf. 15

203	A28	1ch rose & multi	.15 .15
204	A28	2ch lt grn & multi	.15 .15
205	A28	3ch gray & multi	.15 .15
206	A28	4ch lil & multi	.15 .15
207	A28	5ch ol gray & multi	.15 .15
208	A28	1nu brn org & multi	.25 .20
209	A28	3nu ultra & multi	.75 .60
210	A28	5nu gray & multi	1.25 .90
	Set value		2.40 1.85

Souvenir Sheet
Perf. 13½

211	A28	10nu multicolored	2.50 2.50

For surcharge see No. 260.

Slalom and Olympic Games Emblem — A29

Designs (Olympic Games Emblem and): 2ch, 4-men bobsled. 3ch, Ice hockey. 4ch, Cross-country skiing. 5ch, Figure skating, women's. 2nu, Downhill skiing. 4nu, Speed skating. 6nu, Ski jump. 10nu, Figure skating, pairs.

1976, Mar. 29   Litho.   Perf. 13½

212	A29	1ch multicolored	.15 .15
213	A29	2ch multicolored	.15 .15
214	A29	3ch multicolored	.15 .15
215	A29	4ch multicolored	.15 .15
216	A29	5ch multicolored	.15 .15
217	A29	2nu multicolored	.40 .35
218	A29	4nu multicolored	.90 .75
219	A29	10nu multicolored	2.50 1.75
	Nos. 212-219 (8)		4.55
	Set value		3.00

Souvenir Sheet

220	A29	6nu multicolored	1.50 1.50

12th Winter Olympic Games, Innsbruck, Austria, Feb. 4-15.
For surcharges see Nos. 261-262.

Ceremonial
Masks
A29a

Various masks.

1976, Apr. 23   Litho.   Imperf.

220A	A29a	5ch multicolored	.15	.15
220B	A29a	10ch multicolored	.15	.15
220C	A29a	15ch multicolored	.15	.15
220D	A29a	20ch multicolored	.15	.15
220E	A29a	25ch multi, horiz.	.15	.15
220F	A29a	30ch multi, horiz.	.15	.15
220G	A29a	35ch multi, horiz.	.15	.15
220H	A29a	1nu multi, horiz.	.45	.45
220I	A29a	2nu multi, horiz.	.90	.90
220J	A29a	2.50nu multi, horiz.	1.10	1.10
220K	A29a	3nu multi, horiz.	1.40	1.40
		Nos. 220A-220K (11)	4.90	4.90

Souvenir Sheets

220L	A29a	5nu like #220C	1.65	1.65
220M	A29a	10nu like #220F	3.25	3.25

Simulated 3-dimensions using a plastic overlay.
Nos. 220H-220M are airmail.
Sizes of stamps: No. 220L, 59x70mm, No.
220M, 69x57mm.

Orchid
A30

Designs: Various flowers.

1976, May 29   Litho.   Perf. 14½

221	A30	1ch multicolored	.15	.15
222	A30	2ch multicolored	.15	.15
223	A30	3ch multicolored	.15	.15
224	A30	4ch multicolored	.15	.15
225	A30	5ch multicolored	.15	.15
226	A30	2nu multicolored	.40	.30
227	A30	4nu multicolored	.80	.60
228	A30	6nu multicolored	1.25	1.00
		Set value	2.60	2.00

Souvenir Sheet
Perf. 13½

229	A30	10nu multicolored	2.75	2.50

For surcharges see Nos. 263-264.

Double Carp
Design
A31

Designs: Various symbolic designs and Colombo
Plan emblem.

1976, July 1   Litho.   Perf. 14½

230	A31	3ch red & multi	.15	.15
231	A31	4ch ver & multi	.15	.15
232	A31	5ch multicolored	.15	.15
233	A31	25ch bl & multi	.20	.15
234	A31	1.25nu multicolored	.35	.30
335	A31	2nu yel & multi	.60	.50
236	A31	2.50nu vio & multi	.75	.60
237	A31	3nu multicolored	.90	.75
		Nos. 230-237 (8)	3.25	2.75

Colombo Plan, 25th anniversary.
For surcharge see No. 265.

Bandaranaike Conference Hall — A32

1976, Aug. 16   Litho.   Perf. 13½

238	A32	1.25nu multicolored	.35	.22
239	A32	2.50nu multicolored	.65	.45

5th Summit Conference of Non-aligned Countries, Colombo, Sri Lanka, Aug. 9-19.

Elizabeth II — A33   Liberty Bell — A34

Spirit of St.   Bhutanese Archer,
Louis — A35   Olympic
                     Rings — A36

Designs: No. 242, Alexander Graham Bell. No.
245, LZ 3 Zeppelin docking, 1907. No. 246, Alfred
B. Nobel.

1978, Nov. 15   Litho.   Perf. 14½

240	A33	20nu multicolored	5.00	5.00
241	A34	20nu multicolored	5.00	5.00
242	A33	20nu multicolored	5.00	5.00
243	A35	20nu multicolored	5.00	5.00
244	A36	20nu multicolored	5.00	5.00
245	A35	20nu multicolored	5.00	5.00
246	A33	20nu multicolored	5.00	5.00
		Nos. 240-246 (7)	35.00	35.00

25th anniv. of coronation of Elizabeth II; American Bicentennial; cent. of 1st telephone call by
Alexander Graham Bell; Charles A. Lindbergh
crossing the Atlantic, 50th anniv.; Olympic Games;
75th anniv. of the Zeppelin; 75th anniv. of Nobel
Prize. Seven souvenir sheets exist, each 25nu,
commemorating same events with different
designs. Size: 103x80mm.

**Issues of 1967-1976 Surcharged with New
Value and Bars**

Perforations and Printing as Before

1978

252	A16	25ch on 3nu (#133)	
253	A17	25ch on 6nu (#139)	
254	A21	25ch on 2.50nu (#172)	
255	A22	25ch on 3nu (#179)	
256	A22	25ch on 5nu (#180)	
257	A23	25ch on 10nu (#182)	
258	A23	25ch on 10nu (#183)	
259	A24	25ch on 10nu (#192)	
260	A28	25ch on 5nu (#210)	
261	A29	25ch on 4nu (#218)	
262	A29	25ch on 10nu (#219)	
263	A30	25ch on 4nu (#227)	
264	A30	25ch on 6nu (#228)	
265	A31	25ch on 2.50nu (#236)	
266	A14g	25ch on 5nu (#90E)	
267	A17k	25ch on 3nu (#155E)	
268	A17f	25ch on 4nu (#149L)	
269	A17f	25ch on 8nu (#149M)	
		Nos. 252-269,	
		C31-C38 (26)	80.00 80.00

Mother and Child, IYC Emblem — A37

IYC Emblem and: 5nu, Mother and two children. 10nu, Boys with blackboards and stylus.

1979, June   Litho.   Perf. 14x13½

289	A37	2nu multicolored	.50	.40
290	A37	5nu multicolored	1.40	1.00
291	A37	10nu multicolored	2.50	2.00
a.		Souv. sheet of 3, #289-291 + label, perf. 15x13½	4.25	3.25
		Nos. 289-291 (3)	4.40	3.40

International Year of the Child.
For overprints see Nos. 761-763.

Conference Emblem and Dove — A38

Design: 10nu, Emblem and Bhutanese symbols.

1979, Sept. 3   Litho.   Perf. 14x13½

292	A38	25ch multicolored	.15	.15
203	A38	10nu multicolored	3.25	2.50

6th Non-Aligned Summit Conference, Havana,
August 1979.

Silver
Rattle,
Dorji
A39

Antiques: 10ch, Silver handell, Dilbu, vert. 15ch,
Cylindrical jar, Jadum, vert. 25ch, Ornamental teapot, Jamjee, vert. 1nu, Leather container, Kem, vert.
1.25nu, Brass teapot, Jamjee. 1.70nu, Vessel with
elephant-head legs, Sangphor, vert. 2nu, Teapot
with ornamental spout, Jamjee, vert. 3nu, Metal
pot on claw-shaped feet, Yangtho, vert. 4nu, Dish
inlaid with precious stones, Battha. 5nu, Metal circular flask, Chhap, vert.

1979, Dec. 17   Photo.   Perf. 14

294	A39	5ch multicolored	.15	.15
295	A39	10ch multicolored	.15	.15
296	A39	15ch multicolored	.15	.15
297	A39	25ch multicolored	.15	.15
298	A39	1nu multicolored	.45	.40
299	A39	1.25nu multicolored	.50	.50
300	A39	1.70nu multicolored	.70	.70
301	A39	2nu multicolored	.90	.75
302	A39	3nu multicolored	1.25	1.10
303	A39	4nu multicolored	1.65	1.50
304	A39	5nu multicolored	2.25	1.90
		Nos. 294-304 (11)	8.30	7.45

Hill, Rinpiang Dzong — A40

Hill Statue, Stamps of Bhutan and: 2nu, Dzong.
5nu, Ounsti Dzong. 10nu, Lingzi Dzong, Gt. Britain Type 81. 20nu, Rope bridge, Penny Black.

1980, May 6   Litho.   Perf. 14x13½

305	A40	1nu multicolored	.30	.25
306	A40	2nu multicolored	.60	.50
307	A40	5nu multicolored	1.60	1.25
308	A40	10nu multicolored	3.00	2.50
		Nos. 305-308 (4)	5.50	4.50

Souvenir Sheet

309	A40	20nu multicolored	5.75	4.25

Sir Rowland Hill (1795-1879), originator of
penny postage.

Kichu Lhakhang Monastery, Phari — A41

Guru Padma Sambhava's Birthday: Monasteries.

1981, July 11   Litho.   Perf. 14

310	A41	1nu Dungtse, Phari, vert.	.35	.25
311	A41	2nu shown	.65	.50
312	A41	2.25nu Kurjey	.75	.55
313	A41	3nu Tangu, Thimphu	1.00	.75
314	A41	4nu Cheri, Thimphu	1.25	1.00
315	A41	5nu Chorten, Kora	1.65	1.25
316	A41	7nu Tak-Tsang, Phari, vert.	2.25	1.75
		Nos. 310-316 (7)	7.90	6.05

Prince Charles and   Orange-bellied
Lady Diana — A42   Chloropsis — A43

1981, Sept. 10   Litho.   Perf. 14½

317	A42	1nu St. Paul's Cathedral	.20	.15
318	A42	5nu like #317	1.00	.65
319	A42	20nu shown	4.00	2.50
320	A42	25nu like #319	4.50	3.50
		Nos. 317-320 (4)	9.70	6.80

Souvenir Sheet

321	A42	20nu Wedding procession	5.00	4.00

Royal wedding. Nos. 318-319 issued in sheets of
5 plus label.
For surcharges see Nos. 471-475.

1982, Apr. 19   Litho.   Perf. 14

322	A43	2nu shown	.55	.40
323	A43	3nu Monal pheasant	.80	.60
324	A43	5nu Ward's trogon	1.40	1.00
325	A43	10nu Mrs. Gould's sunbird	2.50	2.00
		Nos. 322-325 (4)	5.25	4.00

Souvenir Sheet

326	A43	25nu Maroon oriole	7.00	5.00

1982 World
Cup — A44

Designs: Various soccer players.

1982, June 25   Litho.   Perf. 14½x14

327	A44	1nu multicolored	.25	.20
328	A44	2nu multicolored	.55	.40
329	A44	3nu multicolored	.80	.60
330	A44	20nu multicolored	5.25	4.00
		Nos. 327-330 (4)	6.85	5.20

Souvenir Sheets

331	A44	25nu multicolored	12.00	7.50

Nos. 331 have margins continuing design and
listing finalists (Algeria, etc. or Hungary, etc.).
For surcharges see Nos. 481-485.

21st Birthday of Princess Diana — A45

1982, Aug.
332	A45	1nu St. James' Palace	.25	.20
332A	A45	10nu Diana, Charles	2.50	1.75
332B	A45	15nu Windsor Castle	4.00	4.50
333	A45	25nu Wedding	6.50	4.50
		Nos. 332-333 (4)	13.25	10.95

Souvenir Sheet
334	A45	20nu Diana	5.50	4.00

10nu-15nu issued only in sheets of 5 + label.
For overprints and surcharges see Nos. 361-363, 455-459, 476-480.

Scouting Year — A46

1982, Aug. 23   Litho.   Perf. 14
335	A46	3nu Baden-Powell, vert.	.65	.50
336	A46	5nu Eating around fire	1.10	.85
337	A46	15nu Reading map	3.50	2.50
338	A46	20nu Pitching tents	4.50	3.50
		Nos. 335-338 (4)	9.75	7.35

Souvenir Sheet
339	A46	25nu Mountain climbing	6.00	4.50

For surcharges see Nos. 450-454.

Rama and Cubs with Mowgli — A47

Scenes from Walt Disney's The Jungle Book.

1982, Sept. 1   Perf. 11
340	A47	1ch multicolored	.15	.15
341	A47	2ch multicolored	.15	.15
342	A47	3ch multicolored	.15	.15
343	A47	4ch multicolored	.15	.15
344	A47	5ch multicolored	.15	.15
345	A47	10ch multicolored	.15	.15
346	A47	30ch multicolored	.15	.15
347	A47	2nu multicolored	.50	.40
348	A47	5nu multicolored	5.50	4.25
		Nos. 340-348 (9)	7.05	
		Set value		5.00

Souvenir Sheets   Perf. 13½
349	A47	20nu Baloo and Mowgli in forest	5.25	4.00
350	A47	20nu Baloo and Mowgli floating	5.25	4.00

George Washington Surveying A48

1982, Nov. 15   Litho.   Perf. 15
351	A48	50ch shown	.15	.15
352	A48	1nu FDR, Harvard	.16	.15
353	A48	2nu Washington at Valley Forge	.32	.25
354	A48	3nu FDR, family	.50	.38
355	A48	4nu Washington, Battle of Monmouth	.65	.50
356	A48	5nu FDR, White House	.85	.65
357	A48	15nu Washington, Mt. Vernon	2.50	2.00
358	A48	20nu FDR, Churchill, Stalin	3.25	2.50
		Nos. 351-358 (8)	8.38	6.58

Souvenir Sheets
359	A48	25nu Washington, vert.	4.25	3.25
360	A48	25nu FDR, vert.	4.25	3.25

Washington and Franklin D. Roosevelt.

Nos. 332-334 Overprinted: "ROYAL BABY / 21.6.82"

1982, Nov. 19   Perf. 14½x14
361	A45	1nu multicolored	.25	.25
361A	A45	10nu multicolored	2.50	1.75
361B	A45	15nu multicolored	3.75	3.00
362	A45	25nu multicolored	6.25	4.75
		Nos. 361-362 (4)	12.75	9.75

Souvenir Sheet
363	A45	20nu multicolored	5.25	4.25

Birth of Prince William of Wales, June 21.

500th Birth Anniv. of Raphael — A51

Portraits.

1983, Mar. 23   Perf. 13½
375	A51	1nu Angelo Doni	.25	.20
376	A51	4nu Maddalena Doni	1.00	.75
377	A51	5nu Baldassare Castiglione	1.25	.90
378	A51	20nu La Donna Velata	5.00	3.75
		Nos. 375-378 (4)	7.50	5.60

Souvenir Sheets
379	A51	25nu Expulsion of Heliodorus	6.25	4.75
380	A51	25nu Mass of Bolsena	6.25	4.75

Nos. 184, 155F, 139, 184, 147G, 149M Surchd. or Ovptd.: "Druk Air"

1983, Feb. 11
381	A24	30ch on 1ch multi	.15	.15
382	A17k	5nu multicolored	2.00	1.25
383	A17	6nu multicolored	2.25	1.50
384	A17d	7nu multicolored	2.50	1.50
385	A17f	8nu multicolored	2.50	1.75
		Nos. 381-385 (5)	9.40	6.15

Druk Air Service inauguration. Overprint of 8nu all caps. Nos. 382, 384 air mail.

Manned Flight Bicentenary A52

1983, Aug. 15   Litho.   Perf. 15
386	A52	50ch Dornier Wal	.15	.15
387	A52	3nu Savoia-Marchetti S-66	.75	.55
388	A52	10nu Hawker Osprey	2.50	1.75
389	A52	20nu Ville de Paris	5.00	3.75
		Nos. 386-389 (4)	8.40	6.20

Souvenir Sheet
390	A52	25nu Balloon Captif	5.00	3.75

Buddhist Symbols — A53

1983, Aug. 11   Litho.   Perf. 13½
391	A53	25ch Sacred vase	.15	.15
392	A53	50ch Five Sensory Symbols	.15	.15
393	A53	2nu Seven Treasures	.35	.30
394	A53	3nu Five Sensory Organs	.60	.45
395	A53	8nu Five Fleshes	1.50	1.10
396	A53	9nu Sacrificial cake	1.75	1.25
a.		Souv. sheet of 6, #391-396	4.50	3.50
		Nos. 391-396 (6)	4.50	3.40

Size of Nos. 393, 396: 45x40mm.

World Communications Year (1983) — A54

Various Disney characters and history of communications.

1984, Apr. 10   Litho.   Perf. 14½x14
397	A54	4ch multicolored	.15	.15
398	A54	5ch multicolored	.15	.15
399	A54	10ch multicolored	.15	.15
400	A54	20ch multicolored	.15	.15
401	A54	25ch multicolored	.15	.15
402	A54	50ch multicolored	.15	.15
403	A54	1nu multicolored	.30	.25
404	A54	5nu multicolored	1.10	.95
405	A54	20nu multicolored	4.25	3.75
		Nos. 397-405 (9)	6.55	5.85

Souvenir Sheets   Perf. 14x14½
406	A54	20nu Donald Duck on phone, horiz.	4.75	4.00
407	A54	20nu Mickey Mouse on TV	4.75	4.00

1984 Winter Olympics — A55

1984, June 16   Perf. 14
408	A55	50ch Skiing	.15	.15
409	A55	1nu Cross-country skiing	.25	.20
410	A55	3nu Speed skating	.60	.45
411	A55	20nu Bobsledding	3.75	3.00
		Nos. 408-411 (4)	4.75	3.80

Souvenir Sheet
412	A55	25nu Hockey	5.00	3.25

Golden Langur A56   Locomotives A57

1984, June 10   Litho.   Perf. 14½
413	A56	50ch shown	.15	.15
414	A56	1nu Group in tree, horiz.	.20	.15
415	A56	2nu Family, horiz.	.40	.30
416	A56	4nu Group walking	.80	.60
		Nos. 413-416 (4)	1.55	1.20

Souvenir Sheets
417	A56	20nu Snow leopard	4.00	2.00
418	A56	25nu Yak	4.00	2.00
419	A56	25nu Blue sheep, horiz.	4.00	2.00

1984, July 16
420	A57	50ch Sans Pareil, 1829	.15	.15
421	A57	1nu Planet, 1830	.20	.15
422	A57	3nu Experiment, 1832	.60	.45
423	A57	4nu Black Hawk, 1835	.80	.60
424	A57	5.50nu Jenny Lind, 1847	1.10	.85
425	A57	8nu Semmering-Bavaria, 1851	1.60	1.25
426	A57	10nu Great Northern #1, 1870	2.00	1.50
427	A57	25nu German Natl. Tinder, 1880	5.00	3.75
		Nos. 420-427 (8)	11.45	8.70

Souvenir Sheets
428	A57	20nu Darjeeling Himalayan Railway, 1984	4.00	3.00
429	A57	20nu Sondermann Freight, 1896	4.00	3.00
430	A57	20nu Crampton's locomotive, 1846	4.00	3.00
431	A57	20nu Erzsebet, 1870	4.00	3.00

Nos. 424-427 horiz.

Classic Cars A58

1984, Aug. 29   Litho.   Perf. 14
432	A58	50ch Riley Sprite, 1936	.15	.15
433	A58	1nu Lanchester, 1919	.20	.15
434	A58	3nu Itala, 1907	.65	.45
435	A58	4nu Morris Oxford Bullnose, 1913	.90	.60
436	A58	5.50nu Lagonda LG6, 1939	1.25	.85
437	A58	6nu Wolseley, 1903	1.40	.90
438	A58	8nu Buick Super, 1952	1.75	1.20
439	A58	20nu Maybach Zeppelin, 1933	4.50	3.00
		Nos. 432-439 (8)	10.80	7.30

Souvenir Sheets
440	A58	25nu Simplex, 1912	2.50	1.50
441	A58	25nu Renault, 1901	2.50	1.50

For surcharges see Nos. 537-544.

Summer Olympic Games — A59

1984, Oct. 27   Litho.
442	A59	15ch Women's archery	.15	.15
443	A59	25ch Men's archery	.15	.15
444	A59	2nu Table tennis	.40	.30
445	A59	2.25nu Basketball	.45	.35
446	A59	5.50nu Boxing	1.10	.85
447	A59	6nu Running	1.20	.90
448	A59	8nu Tennis	1.60	1.20
		Nos. 442-448 (7)	5.05	3.90

Souvenir Sheet
449	A59	25nu Archery	5.00	3.50

For overprints see Nos. 537-544.

Nos. 335-339 Surcharged with New Values and Bars in Black or Silver

1985   Litho.   Perf. 14
450	A46	10nu on 3nu multi	2.00	1.50
451	A46	10nu on 5nu multi	2.00	1.50
452	A46	10nu on 15nu multi	2.00	1.50
453	A46	10nu on 20nu multi	2.00	1.50
		Nos. 450-453 (4)	8.00	6.00

Souvenir Sheet
454	A46	20nu on 25nu multi	4.00	3.00

Nos. 332, 332A, 332B, 333-334 Surcharged with New Values and Bars

1985, Feb. 28
455	A45	5nu on 1nu multi	1.00	.70
456	A45	5nu on 10nu multi	1.00	.70
457	A45	5nu on 15nu multi	1.00	.70
458	A45	40nu on 25nu multi	8.00	5.25
		Nos. 455-458 (4)	11.00	7.35

Souvenir Sheet
459	A45	25nu on 20nu multi	5.00	4.00

50th Anniv. of Donald Duck — A60

1984, Dec. 10 Litho. Perf. 13½x14
460 A60	4ch Magician Mickey	.15	.15
461 A60	5ch Slide, Donald, Slide	.15	.15
462 A60	10ch Donald's Golf Game	.15	.15
463 A60	20ch Mr. Duck Steps Out	.15	.15
464 A60	25ch Lion Around	.15	.15
465 A60	50ch Alpine Climbers	.15	.15
466 A60	1nu Flying Jalopy	.25	.19
467 A60	5nu Frank Duck	1.10	.75
468 A60	20nu Good Scouts	4.50	3.25
	Nos. 460-468 (9)	6.75	5.05

Souvenir Sheets
469 A60	20nu Three Caballeros	4.50	3.25
470 A60	20nu Sea Scouts	4.50	3.25

Nos. 317-321 Surcharged with New
Values and Bars

1985, Feb. 28 Litho. Perf. 14½
471 A42	10nu on 1nu multi	2.00	1.50
472 A42	10nu on 5nu multi	2.00	1.50
473 A42	10nu on 20nu multi	2.00	1.50
474 A42	10nu on 25nu multi	2.00	1.50
	Nos. 471-474 (4)	8.00	6.00

Souvenir Sheet
475 A42	30nu on 20nu multi	6.00	5.00

Nos. 361, 361A, 361B, 362-363
Surcharged with New Values and Bars

1985, Feb. 28 Litho. Perf. 14½x14
476 A45	5nu on 1nu multi	.75	.75
477 A45	5nu on 10nu multi	.75	.55
478 A45	5nu on 15nu multi	.75	.55
479 A45	40nu on 25nu multi	7.50	5.50
	Nos. 476-479 (4)	9.75	7.35

Souvenir Sheet
480 A45	25nu on 20nu multi	5.00	3.75

Nos. 327-331 Surcharged with New
Values and Bars in Black or Silver

1985, June
481 A44	5nu on 1nu multi	1.50	1.10
482 A44	5nu on 2nu multi	1.50	1.10
483 A44	5nu on 3nu multi	1.50	1.10
484 A44	5nu on 20nu multi	1.50	1.10
	Nos. 481-484 (4)	6.00	4.40

Souvenir Sheets
485 A44	20nu on 25nu multi	7.50	5.50

Mask Dance of
the Judgement of
Death — A61

1985, Apr. 27 Perf. 13½
486 A61	5ch Shinje Choegyel	.15	.15
487 A61	35ch Raksh Lango	.15	.15
488 A61	50ch Druelgo	.15	.15
489 A61	2.50nu Pago	.45	.35
490 A61	3nu Telgo	.55	.40
491 A61	4nu Due Nakcung	.75	.60
492 A61	5nu Lha Karpo	.90	.70
a.	Souv. sheet of 4, #486-487, 491-492	1.90	1.50
493 A61	5.50nu Nyalbum	1.00	.75
494 A61	6nu Khimda Pelkyi	1.10	.85
	Nos. 486-494 (9)	5.20	4.10

For overprints see Nos. 764-772.

Monasteries
A62

1984, Dec. 1 Litho. Perf. 12
495 A62	10ch Domkhar	.15	.15
496 A62	25ch Shemgang	.15	.15
497 A62	50ch Chapcha	.15	.15
498 A62	1nu Tashigang	.15	.15
499 A62	2nu Pungthang Chhug	.30	.30
500 A62	5nu Dechhenphoda	.70	.70
	Set value	1.25	1.25

Veteran's
War
Memorial
Building,
San
Francisco
A63

1985, Oct. 24 Litho. Perf. 14
502 A63	50ch Flags of Bhutan, UN, vert.	.15	.15
503 A63	15ch Headquarters, NY, vert.	2.75	2.00
504 A63	20nu shown	3.75	2.75
	Nos. 502-504 (3)	6.65	4.90

Souvenir Sheet
505 A63	25nu UN Human Rights Declaration	4.25	3.00

UN, 40th anniv.

Audubon
Birth
Bicentenary
A64

Illustrations of North American bird species by
Audubon.

1985
506 A64	50ch Anas breweri	.15	.15
507 A64	1nu Lagopus lagopus	.20	.15
508 A64	2nu Charadrius montanus	.35	.25
509 A64	3nu Cavia stellata	.50	.40
510 A64	4nu Canachites canadensis	.70	.50
511 A64	5nu Mergus cucullatus	.85	.60
512 A64	15nu Olor buccinator	2.50	1.75
513 A64	20nu Bucephala clangula	3.50	2.50
	Nos. 506-513 (8)	8.75	6.30

Souvenir Sheets
514 A64	25nu Accipiter striatus	3.75	2.25
515 A64	25nu Parus bicolor	3.75	2.25

Issue dates: Nos. 507, 510-511, 514 Nov. 15.
Nos. 506, 508-509, 513, 515 Dec. 6.

A Tramp
Abroad, by
Mark Twain
(1835-1910)
A65

Walt Disney animated characters.

1985, Nov. 15
516 A65	50ch multicolored	.15	.15
517 A65	2nu multicolored	.35	.25
518 A65	5nu multicolored	.85	.60
519 A65	9nu multicolored	1.50	1.10
520 A65	20nu multicolored	3.50	2.50
	Nos. 516-520 (5)	6.35	4.60

Souvenir Sheet
521 A65	25nu Goofy, Mickey Mouse	5.00	3.50

Intl. Youth Year.
For overprints see Nos. 554, 556-557.

Rapunzel, by
Jacob and
Wilhelm
Grimm — A66

Walt Disney animated characters.

1985, Nov. 15
522 A66	1nu multicolored	.20	.15
523 A66	4nu multicolored	.70	.50
524 A66	7nu multicolored	1.25	.95
525 A66	8nu multicolored	1.40	1.05
526 A66	15nu multicolored	2.50	1.75
	Nos. 522-526 (5)	6.05	4.40

Souvenir Sheet
527 A66	25nu multicolored	5.00	4.00

No. 525 printed in sheets of 8.
For overprints see Nos. 553, 555, 558.

First South
Asian Regional
Cooperation
Summit, Dec.
7-8, Dacca,
Bangladesh
A67

1985, Dec. 8 Perf. 14
528 A67	50ch multicolored	.15	.15
529 A67	5nu multicolored	.85	.60

Seven Precious
Attributes of the
Universal
King — A68

1986, Feb. 12 Litho. Perf. 13x12½
530 A68	30ch Wheel	.15	.15
531 A68	50ch Gem	.15	.15
532 A68	1.25nu Queen	.20	.20
533 A68	2nu Minister	.30	.30
534 A68	4nu Elephant	.55	.55
535 A68	6nu Horse	.85	.85
536 A68	8nu General	1.10	1.10
	Nos. 530-536 (7)	3.30	3.30

Nos. 442-443, 445-449 Ovptd. with
Medal, Winners' Names and Countries.
No. 449 Ovptd. for Men's and Women's
Events

1986, May 5 Litho. Perf. 14
537 A59	15ch Hyang Soon Seo, So. Korea	.15	.15
538 A59	25ch Darrell Pace, US	.15	.15
539 A59	2.25nu US	.30	.30
540 A59	5.50nu Mark Breland, US	.80	.80
541 A59	6nu Daley Thompson, Britain	.85	.85
542 A59	8nu Stefan Edberg, Sweden	1.10	1.10
	Nos. 537-542 (6)	3.35	3.35

Souvenir Sheets
543 A59	25nu Hyang Soon Seo	3.50	3.50
544 A59	25nu Darrel Pace	3.50	3.50

Kilkhor Mandalas,
Deities — A69

Religious art: 10ch, 1nu, Phurpa, ritual dagger.
25ch, 3nu, Amitayus in wrath. 50ch, 5nu, Over-
powering Deities. 75ch, 7nu, Great Wrathful One,
Guru Rinpoche.

1986, June 17 Perf. 13½
545 A69	10ch multicolored	.15	.15
546 A69	25ch multicolored	.15	.15
547 A69	50ch multicolored	.15	.15
548 A69	75ch multicolored	.15	.15
549 A69	1nu multicolored	.15	.15
550 A69	3nu multicolored	.40	.40
551 A69	5nu multicolored	.70	.70
552 A69	7nu multicolored	1.00	1.00
	Nos. 545-552 (8)	2.85	2.85

Nos. 525, 519, 526, 520, 521 and 527
Ovptd. with AMERIPEX '86 Emblem

1986, June 16 Litho. Perf. 14
553 A66	8nu multi	1.40	1.00
554 A65	9nu multi	1.50	1.10
555 A66	15nu multi	2.50	1.75
556 A65	20nu multi	3.50	2.50
	Nos. 553-556 (4)	8.90	6.35

Souvenir Sheets
557 A65	25nu #521	4.25	3.00
558 A66	25nu #527	4.25	3.00

A70

A71

Halley's
Comet
A72

Designs: 50ch, Babylonian tablet fragments,
2349 B.C. sighting. 1nu, 17th cent. print, A.D. 66
sighting. 2nu, French silhouette art, 1835 sighting.
3nu, Bayeux Tapestry, 1066 sighting. 4nu, Wood-
block, 684 sighting. 5nu, Illustration from Bybel
Printen, 1650. 15nu, 1456 Sighting, Cancer constellation. 20nu, Delft plate, 1910 sighting. No.
572, Comet over Himalayas. No. 573, Comet over
domed temple Dug-gye Jong.

1986, Nov. 4 Litho. Perf. 15
564 A70	50ch multicolored	.15	.15
565 A70	1nu multicolored	.20	.15
566 A71	2nu multicolored	.35	.30
567 A70	3nu multicolored	.50	.35
568 A70	4nu multicolored	.70	.50
569 A71	5nu multicolored	.85	.65
570 A70	15nu multicolored	2.50	2.00
571 A70	20nu multicolored	3.50	2.50
	Nos. 564-571 (8)	8.75	6.60

Souvenir Sheets
572 A72	25nu multicolored	4.25	3.00
573 A72	25nu multicolored	4.25	3.00

A73

Statue of Liberty,
Cent. — A74

Statue and ships: 50ch, Mircea, Romania. 1nu,
Shalom, Israel. 2nu, Leonardo da Vinci, Italy. 3nu,
Libertad, Argentina. 4nu, France, France. 5nu, SS
United States, US. 15nu, Queen Elizabeth II,
England. 20nu, Europa, West Germany. No. 582,
Statue. No. 583, Statue, World Trade Center.

1986, Nov. 4
574 A73	50ch multicolored	.15	.15
575 A73	1nu multicolored	.20	.15
576 A73	2nu multicolored	.35	.30
577 A73	3nu multicolored	.50	.35
578 A73	4nu multicolored	.65	.50
579 A73	5nu multicolored	.85	.65
580 A73	15nu multicolored	2.50	1.90
581 A73	20nu multicolored	3.40	2.50
	Nos. 574-581 (8)	8.60	6.50

Souvenir Sheets
582 A74	25nu multicolored	4.25	3.00
583 A74	25nu multi, diff.	4.25	3.00

Discovery
of
America,
500th
Anniv.
A75

1987, May 25   Litho.   Perf. 14

584	A75	20ch Santa Maria	.40	.40
585	A75	25ch Queen Isabella	.40	.40
586	A75	50ch Ship, flying fish	.40	.40
587	A75	1nu Columbus's coat of arms	.75	.60
588	A75	2nu Christopher Columbus	1.40	1.00
589	A75	3nu Landing in the New World	2.00	2.00
a.		Miniature sheet of 6, #584-589	5.00	5.00
		Nos. 584-589 (6)	5.35	4.80

Souvenir Sheets

590	A75	20ch Pineapple		
591	A75	25ch Indian hammock		
592	A75	50ch Tobacco plant		
593	A75	1nu Flamingo		
594	A75	2nu Navigator, astrolabe, 15th cent.		
595	A75	3nu Lizard		
596	A75	5nu Iguana	1.25	.95

All stamps are vertical except those contained in Nos. 591, 595 and 596. Stamps from No. 589a have white background.

CAPEX '87 — A76

Locomotives.

1987, June 15

597	A76	50ch Canadian Natl. U1-f	.15	.15
598	A76	1nu Via Rail L.R.C.	.20	.15
599	A76	2nu Canadian Natl. GM GF-30t	.35	.25
600	A76	3nu Canadian Natl. 4-8-4	.50	.35
601	A76	8nu Canadian Pacific 4-6-2	1.40	1.00
602	A76	10nu Via Express passenger train	1.75	1.25
603	A76	15nu Canadian Nat. Turbotrain	2.50	1.90
604	A76	20nu Canadian Pacific Diesel-Electric Express	3.25	2.50
		Nos. 597-604 (8)	10.10	7.55

Souvenir Sheet

605	A76	25nu Royal Hudson 4-6-4	4.25	3.00
606	A76	25nu Canadian Natl. 4-8-4, diff.	4.25	3.00

Two Faces, Sculpture by Marc Chagall (1887-1984) — A77

Paintings: 1nu, At the Barber's. 2nu, Old Jew with Torah. 3nu, Red Maternity. 4nu, Eve of Yom Kippur. 5nu, The Old Musician. 6nu, The Rabbi of Vitebsk. 7nu, Couple at Dusk. 9nu, The Artistes. 10nu, Moses Breaking the Tablets of the Law. 12nu, Bouquet with Flying Lovers. 20nu, In the Sky of the Opera. No. 619, Romeo and Juliet. No. 620, Magician of Paris. No. 621, Maternity. No. 622, The Carnival for Aleko: Scene II. No. 623, Visit to the Grandparents. No. 624, The Smolensk Newspaper. No. 625, The Concert. No. 626, Composition with Goat. No. 627, Still Life. No. 628, The Red Gateway. No. 629, Cow with Parasol. No. 630, Russian Village.

1987, Dec. 17   Litho.   Perf. 14

607	A77	50ch multicolored	.15	.15
608	A77	1nu multicolored	.15	.15
609	A77	2nu multicolored	.35	.25
610	A77	3nu multicolored	.45	.35
611	A77	4nu multicolored	.65	.45
612	A77	5nu multicolored	.80	.60
613	A77	7nu multicolored	.95	.70
614	A77	7nu multicolored	1.10	.90
615	A77	9nu multicolored	1.50	1.10
616	A77	10nu multicolored	1.60	1.25
617	A77	12nu multicolored	1.90	1.50
618	A77	20nu multicolored	3.25	2.50

Size: 110x95mm
Imperf

619	A77	25nu multicolored	4.00	3.00
620	A77	25nu multicolored	4.00	3.00
621	A77	25nu multicolored	4.00	3.00
622	A77	25nu multicolored	4.00	3.00
623	A77	25nu multicolored	4.00	3.00

624	A77	25nu multicolored	4.00	3.00
625	A77	25nu multicolored	4.00	3.00
626	A77	25nu multicolored	4.00	3.00
627	A77	25nu multicolored	4.00	3.00
628	A77	25nu multicolored	4.00	3.00
629	A77	25nu multicolored	4.00	3.00
630	A77	25nu multicolored	4.00	3.00
		Nos. 607-630 (24)	60.85	45.90

1988 Winter Olympics, Calgary — A78

Emblem and Disney animated characters as competitors in Olympic events.

1988, Feb. 15   Litho.   Perf. 14

631	A78	50ch Slalom	.15	.15
632	A78	1nu Downhill skiing	.16	.15
633	A78	2nu Ice hockey	.30	.25
634	A78	4nu Biathlon	.65	.50
635	A78	7nu Speed skating	1.10	.85
636	A78	8nu Figure skating	1.25	.95
637	A78	9nu Figure skating, diff.	1.50	1.10
638	A78	20nu Bobsled	3.25	2.50
		Nos. 631-638 (8)	8.36	6.45

Souvenir Sheets

639	A78	25nu Ski jumping	4.00	4.00
640	A78	25nu Ice dancing	4.00	4.00

Transportation Innovations — A79

1988, Mar. 31

641	A79	50ch Pullman Pioneer, 1865	.15	.15
642	A79	1nu Stephenson's Rocket, 1829	.15	.15
643	A79	2nu Pierre L'Allement's Velocipede, 1866	.30	.25
644	A79	3nu Benz Velocipede, 1886	.50	.35
645	A79	4nu Volkswagen Beetle, c. 1960	.65	.50
646	A79	5nu Natchez Vs. Robert E. Lee, 1870	.80	.60
647	A79	6nu American La France, 1910	1.00	.75
648	A79	7nu USS Constitution, 1787, vert.	1.15	.85
649	A79	9nu Bell Rocket Belt, 1961, vert.	1.50	1.10
650	A79	10nu Trevithick Locomotive, 1804	1.60	1.25
		Nos. 641-650 (10)	7.80	5.95

Souvenir Sheets

651	A79	25nu Concorde jet	4.00	4.00
652	A79	25nu Mallard, 1938, vert.	4.00	4.00
653	A79	25nu Shinkansen	4.00	4.00
654	A79	25nu TGV, 1981	4.00	4.00

1988 Summer Olympics, Seoul A80

7nu-20nu vert.

1989, Feb. 15   Litho.

655	A80	50ch Women's gymnastics	.15	.15
656	A80	1nu Tae kwon do	.15	.15
657	A80	2nu Shot put	.30	.25
658	A80	4nu Women's volleyball	.65	.50
659	A80	7nu Basketball	1.10	.85
660	A80	8nu Soccer	1.25	.95
661	A80	9nu Women's high jump	1.50	1.10
662	A80	20nu Running	3.25	2.50
		Nos. 655-662 (8)	8.35	6.45

Souvenir Sheets

663	A80	25nu Archery, vert.	4.00	4.00
664	A80	25nu Fencing	4.00	4.00

Paintings by Titian — A81

Designs: 50ch, Gentleman with a Book. 1nu, Venus and Cupid, with a Lute Player. 2nu, Diana and Actaeon. 3nu, Cardinal Ippolito dei Medici. 4nu, Sleeping Venus. 5nu, Venus Risen from the Waves. 6nu, Worship of Venus. 7nu, Fete Champetre. 10nu, Perseus and Andromeda. 15nu, Danae. 20nu, Venus at the Mirror. 25nu, Venus and the Organ Player. No. 677, The Pardo Venus, horiz. No. 678, Venus and Cupid, with an Organist. No. 679, Miracle of the Irascible Son. No. 680, Diana and Callisto. No. 681, Saint John the Almsgiver. No. 682, Danae with the Shower of Gold, horiz. No. 683, Bacchus and Ariadne. No. 684, Venus Blindfolding Cupid. No. 685, Portrait of Laura Dianti. No. 686, Venus of Urbino. No. 687, Portrait of Johann Friedrich. No. 688, Mater Dolorosa with Raised Hands.

Perf. 13½x14, 14x13½

1989, Feb. 15   Litho.

665	A81	50ch multicolored	.15	.15
666	A81	1nu multicolored	.15	.15
667	A81	2nu multicolored	.30	.25
668	A81	3nu multicolored	.50	.35
669	A81	4nu multicolored	.65	.50
670	A81	5nu multicolored	.80	.60
671	A81	6nu multicolored	.95	.75
672	A81	7nu multicolored	1.10	.85
673	A81	10nu multicolored	1.60	1.25
674	A81	15nu multicolored	2.50	1.75
675	A81	20nu multicolored	3.25	2.50
676	A81	25nu multicolored	4.00	3.00
		Nos. 665-676 (12)	15.95	12.10

Souvenir Sheets

677-688	A81	25nu each	4.00	4.00

Mickey Mouse, 60th Anniv. (in 1988).— A82

Movie posters.

1989, June 20   Litho.   Perf. 13½x14

689	A82	1ch Mickey Mouse, 1930s	.15	.15
690	A82	2ch Barnyard Olympics, 1932	.15	.15
691	A82	3ch Society Dog Show, 1939	.15	.15
692	A82	4ch Fantasia, 1980s re-release	.15	.15
693	A82	5ch The Mad Dog, 1932	.15	.15
694	A82	10ch A Gentleman's Gentleman, 1941	.15	.15
695	A82	50ch Symphony hour, 1942	.15	.15
696	A82	10nu The Moose Hunt, 1931	1.50	1.25
697	A82	15nu Wild Waves, 1929	2.25	1.75
698	A82	20nu Mickey in Arabia, 1932	3.00	2.50
699	A82	25nu Tugboat Mickey, 1940	3.75	3.00
700	A82	30nu Building a Building, 1933	4.25	3.50
		Nos. 689-700 (12)	15.80	13.05

Souvenir Sheets

701	A82	25nu The Mad Doctor, 1933	4.00	4.00
702	A82	25nu The Meller Drammer, 1933	4.00	4.00
703	A82	25nu Ye Olden Days, 1933	4.00	4.00
704	A82	25nu Mickey's Good Deed, 1932	4.00	4.00
705	A82	25nu Mickey's Pal Pluto, 1933	4.00	4.00
706	A82	25nu Trader Mickey, 1932	4.00	4.00
707	A82	25nu Touchdown Mickey, 1932	4.00	4.00

708	A82	25nu Steamboat Willie, 1928	4.00	4.00
709	A82	25nu The Whoopee Party, 1932	4.00	4.00
710	A82	25nu Mickey's Nightmare, 1932	4.00	4.00
711	A82	25nu The Klondike Kid, 1932	4.00	4.00
712	A82	25nu The Wayward Canary, 1932	4.00	4.00

Mushrooms — A83

1989, Aug. 22   Litho.   Perf. 14

713	A83	50ch Tricholoma pardalotum	.15	.15
714	A83	1nu Suillus placidus	.15	.15
715	A83	2nu Boletus regius	.30	.25
716	A83	3nu Gomphidius glutinosus	.50	.35
717	A83	4nu Boletus calopus	.65	.50
718	A83	5nu Suillus grevillei	.80	.60
719	A83	6nu Boletus appendiculatus	.95	.70
720	A83	7nu Lactarius torminosus	1.10	.80
721	A83	10nu Macrolepiota rhacodes	1.60	1.25
722	A83	15nu Amanita rubescens	2.50	1.75
723	A83	20nu Amanita phalloides	3.25	2.50
724	A83	25nu Amanita citrina	4.00	3.00
		Nos. 713-724 (12)	15.95	12.00

Souvenir Sheets

725	A83	25nu Russula aurata	4.00	4.00
726	A83	25nu Gyroporus castaneus	4.00	4.00
727	A83	25nu Cantharellus cibarius	4.00	4.00
728	A83	25nu Boletus rhodoxanthus	4.00	4.00
729	A83	25nu Paxillus involutus	4.00	4.00
730	A83	25nu Gyroporus cyanescens	4.00	4.00
731	A83	25nu Lepista nuda	4.00	4.00
732	A83	25nu Dentinum repandum	4.00	4.00
733	A83	25nu Lepista saeva	4.00	4.00
734	A83	25nu Hydnum imbricatum	4.00	4.00
735	A83	25nu Xerocomus subtomentosus	4.00	4.00
736	A83	25nu Russula olivacea	4.00	4.00

Intl. Maritime Organization, 30th Anniv. — A84

Ships: 50ch, Spanish galleon La Reale, 1680. 1nu, Submersible Turtle, 1776. 2nu, Charlote Dundas, 1802. 3nu, Great Eastern, c. 1858. 4nu, HMS Warrior, 1862. 5nu, Mississippi steamer, 1884. 6nu, Preussen, 1902. 7nu, USS Arizona, 1915. 10nu, Bluenose, 1921. 15nu, Steam trawler, 1925. 20nu, American liberty ship, 1943. No. 748, S.S. United States, 1952. No. 749, Moran tug, c. 1950. No. 750, Sinking of the Titanic, 1912. No. 751, U-boat, c. 1942. No. 752, Japanese warship Yamato, 1944. No. 753, HMS Dreadnought. Not 754, S.S. Normandie, c. 1933, and a Chinese junk. No. 755, HMS Victory, 1805. No. 756, USS Monitor, 1862. No. 757, Cutty Sark, 1869. No. 758, USS Constitution. No. 759, HMS Resolution. No. 760, Chinese junk.

1989, Aug. 24   Litho.   Perf. 14

737	A84	50ch multicolored	.15	.15
738	A84	1nu multicolored	.15	.15
739	A84	2nu multicolored	.30	.25
740	A84	3nu multicolored	.50	.35
741	A84	4nu multicolored	.65	.50
742	A84	5nu multicolored	.80	.60
743	A84	6nu multicolored	.95	.70
744	A84	7nu multicolored	1.10	.80
745	A84	10nu multicolored	1.60	1.25
746	A84	15nu multicolored	2.50	1.75
747	A84	20nu multicolored	3.25	2.50
748	A84	25nu multicolored	4.00	3.00
		Nos. 737-748 (12)	15.95	12.00

Souvenir Sheets

749-760	A84	25nu each	4.00	4.00

Nos. 289-291 Overprinted:
WORLD / AIDS DAY
1988, Dec. 1 Litho. Perf. 14x13½

761	A37	2nu multicolored	.45 .35
762	A37	5nu multicolored	1.10 .90
763	A37	10nu multicolored	2.25 1.75
		Nos. 761-763 (3)	3.80 3.00

Nos. 486-494 Ovptd. in Silver:
ASIA-PACIFIC EXPOSITION FUKUOKA '89
1989, Mar. 17 Perf. 13½

764	A61	5ch multicolored	.15 .15
765	A61	35ch multicolored	.15 .15
766	A61	50ch multicolored	.15 .15
767	A61	2.50nu multicolored	.40 .30
768	A61	3nu multicolored	.50 .35
769	A61	4nu multicolored	.65 .50
770	A61	5nu multicolored	.80 .60
771	A61	5.50nu multicolored	.90 .65
772	A61	6nu multicolored	1.00 .80
		Nos. 764-772 (9)	4.70 3.65

This set exists overprinted in Japanese.

Chhukha Hydroelectric Project — A85

1988, Oct. 21 Litho. Perf. 13½
773 A85 50ch multicolored   .15 .15

Jawaharlal Nehru (1889-1964), Indian Prime Minister — A85a

1989, Nov. 14 Photo. Perf. 14
773A A85a 100ch olive brown   .15 .15

Denomination is shown as 1.00ch in error.

Birds A86

Designs: 50ch, Larger goldenbacked woodpecker. 1nu, Black-naped monarch. 2nu, White-crested laughing thrush. 3nu, Blood-pheasant. 4nu, Blossom-headed parakeet. 5nu, Rosy minivet. 6nu, Chestnut-headed tit babbler. 7nu, Blue pitta. 10nu, Black-naped oriole. 15nu, Green magpie. 20nu, Indian three-toed kingfisher. No. 785, Ibisbill. No. 786, Great pied hornbill. No. 787, Himalayan redbreasted falconet. No. 788, Lammergeier. No. 789, Large racket-tailed drongo. No. 790, Fire-tailed sunbird. No. 791, Indian crested swift. No. 792, White-eared pheasant. No. 793, Satyr tragopan. No. 794, Wallcreeper. No. 795, Fairy bluebird. No. 796, Little spiderhunter. No. 797, Spotted forktail. Nos. 774-779 vert.

1989, Nov. 22 Litho. Perf. 14

774	A86	50ch multicolored	.15 .15
775	A86	1nu multicolored	.15 .15
776	A86	2nu multicolored	.30 .25
777	A86	3nu multicolored	.50 .35
778	A86	4nu multicolored	.65 .50
779	A86	5nu multicolored	.80 .60
780	A86	6nu multicolored	.95 .70
781	A86	7nu multicolored	1.10 .80
782	A86	10nu multicolored	1.60 1.25
783	A86	15nu multicolored	2.50 1.75
784	A86	20nu multicolored	3.25 2.50
785	A86	25nu multicolored	4.00 3.00
		Nos. 774-785 (12)	15.95 12.00

Souvenir Sheets
786-797 A86 25nu each   4.00 4.00

Steam Locomotives A87

Designs: 50ch, Best Friend of Charleston, 1830, US 1nu, Class U, 1949, France. 2nu, Consolidation, 1866, US. 3nu, Luggage Engine, 1843, Great Britain. 4nu, Class 60-3 Shay, 1913, US. 5nu, John Bull, 1831, US. 6nu, Hercules, 1837, US. 7nu, Eight-wheel tank engine, 1874, Great Britain. 10nu, The Illinois, 1852, US. 15nu, German State 4-6-4, 1935. 20nu, American Standard, 1865. No. 809, Class Ps-4, 1926, US. No. 810, Puffing Billy, 1814, Great Britain. No. 811, Stephenson's Rocket, 1829, Great Britain. No. 812, Cumberland, 1845, US, vert. No. 813, John Stevens, 1849, US, vert. No. 814, No. 22 Baldwin Locomotive Works, 1873, US. No. 815, Ariel, 1877, US. No. 816, 1899 No. 1301 Webb Compound Engine, Great Britain. No. 817, 1893 No. 999 Empire State Express, US. No. 818, 1923 Class K-36, US. No. 819, 1935 Class A4, Great Britain. No. 820, 1935 Class A, US. No. 821, 1943 Class P-1, US.

1990, Jan. 30

798	A87	50ch multi	.15 .15
799	A87	1nu multi	.15 .15
800	A87	2nu multi	.30 .25
801	A87	3nu multi	.50 .35
802	A87	4nu multi	.65 .50
803	A87	6nu multi	.80 .60
804	A87	6nu multi	.95 .70
805	A87	7nu multi	1.10 .80
806	A87	10nu multi	1.60 1.25
807	A87	15nu multi	2.50 1.75
808	A87	20nu multi	3.25 2.50
809	A87	25nu multi	4.00 3.00
		Nos. 798-809 (12)	15.95 12.00

Souvenir Sheets
810-821 A87 25nu each   4.00 4.00

Butterflies A88

1990, Jan. 30 Litho. Perf. 14

822	A88	50ch Charaxes harmodius	.15 .15
823	A88	1nu Prioneris thestylis	.15 .15
824	A88	2nu Sephisa chandra	.30 .25
825	A88	3nu Penthema usarda	.50 .35
826	A88	4nu Troides aecus	.65 .50
827	A88	5nu Polyura eudamippus	.80 .60
828	A88	6nu Polyura dolon	.95 .70
829	A88	7nu Neope bhadra	1.10 .80
830	A88	10nu Delias descombesi	1.60 1.25
831	A88	15nu Childreni childrena	2.50 1.75
832	A88	20nu Kallima inachus	3.25 2.50
833	A88	25nu Elymnias malelas	4.00 3.00
		Nos. 822-833 (12)	15.95 12.00

Souvenir Sheets

834	A88	25nu Red lacewing	4.00 4.00
835	A88	25nu Bhutan glory	4.00 4.00
836	A88	25nu Great eggfly	4.00 4.00
837	A88	25nu Kaiser-I-Hind	4.00 4.00
838	A88	25nu Chestnut tiger	4.00 4.00
839	A88	25nu Common map	4.00 4.00
840	A88	25nu Swallowtail	4.00 4.00
841	A88	25nu Jungle glory	4.00 4.00
842	A88	25nu Checkered swallowtail	4.00 4.00
843	A88	25nu Common birdwing	4.00 4.00
844	A88	25nu Blue banded peacock	4.00 4.00
845	A88	25nu Camberwell beauty	4.00 4.00

Nos. 822-824, 826-827, 830-831, 834-835, 844-845 are vert.

Paintings by Hiroshige A89

Designs: 10ch, Plum Estate, Kameido. 20ch, Yatsumi Bridge. 50ch, Ayase River and Kanegafuchi. 75ch, View of Shiba Coast. 1nu, Grandpa's Teahouse, Meguro. 2nu, Kameido Tenjin Shrine. 6nu, Yoroi Ferry, Koami-cho. 7nu, Sakasai Ferry. 10nu, Fukagawa Lumberyards. 15nu, Suido Bridge and Surugadai. 20nu, Meguro Drum Bridge and Sunset Hill. No. 857, Atagoshita and Yabu Lane. No. 858, Towboats Along the Yotsugi-dori Canal. No. 859, Minowa, Kanasugi, Mikawashima. No. 860, Horikiri Iris Garden. No. 861, Fukagawa Susaki and Jumantsubo. No. 862, Suijin Shrine and Massaki on the Sumida River. No. 863, New Year's Eve Foxfires at the Changing Tree, Oji. No. 864, Nihonbashi, Clearing After Snow. No. 865, View to the North from Asukayama. No. 866, Komakata Hall and Azuma Bridge. No. 867, The City Flourishing, Tanabata Festival. No. 868, Suruga-cho. No. 869, Sudden Shower over Shin-Ohashi Bridge and Atake.

1990, May 21 Litho. Perf. 13½

846	A89	10ch multicolored	.15 .15
847	A89	20ch multicolored	.15 .15
848	A89	50ch multicolored	.15 .15
849	A89	75ch multicolored	.15 .15
850	A89	1nu multicolored	.15 .15
851	A89	2nu multicolored	.30 .25
852	A89	6nu multicolored	.95 .70
853	A89	7nu multicolored	1.10 .85
854	A89	10nu multicolored	1.60 1.25
855	A89	15nu multicolored	2.50 1.75
856	A89	20nu multicolored	3.25 2.50
857	A89	25nu multicolored	4.00 3.00
		Nos. 846-857 (12)	14.45 11.05

Souvenir Sheets
858-869 A89 25nu each   4.00 3.00

Hirohito (1901-1989) and enthronement of Akihito as emperor of Japan.

Orchids — A90

1990, Apr. 6 Litho. Perf. 14

870	A90	10ch Renanthera monachica	.15 .15
871	A90	50ch Vanda coerulea	.15 .15
872	A90	1nu Phalaenopsis violacea	.15 .15
873	A90	5nu Dendrobium nobile	.30 .25
874	A90	5nu Vandopsis lissochiloides	.80 .60
875	A90	6nu Paphiopedilum rothschildianum	.95 .70
876	A90	7nu Phalaenopsis schilleriana	1.10 .80
877	A90	9nu Paphiopedilum insigne	1.50 1.10
878	A90	10nu Paphiopedilum bellatulum	1.60 1.25
879	A90	20nu Doritis pulcherrima	3.25 2.50
880	A90	25nu Cymbidium giganteum	4.00 3.00
881	A90	35nu Phalaenopsis mariae	5.50 4.25
		Nos. 870-881 (12)	19.45 14.90

Souvenir Sheets

882	A90	30nu Vanda coerulescens	4.75 4.75
883	A90	30nu Vandopsis parishi	4.75 4.75
884	A90	30nu Dendrobium aphyllum	4.75 4.75
885	A90	30nu Phalaenopsis amabilis	4.75 4.75
886	A90	30nu Paphiopedilum haynaldianum	4.75 4.75
887	A90	30nu Dendrobium lodigesii	4.75 4.75
888	A90	10nu Vanda alpina	4.75 4.75
889	A90	30nu Phalaenopsis equestris	4.75 4.75
890	A90	30nu Vanda cristata	4.75 4.75
891	A90	30nu Phalaenopsis cornu cervi	4.75 4.75
892	A90	30nu Paphiopedilum niveum	4.75 4.75
893	A90	30nu Dendrobium margaritaceum	4.75 4.75

EXPO '90 Intl. Garden and Greenery Exposition, Osaka, Apr. 1-Dec. 31.

G.P.O., Thimphu — A90a

1990, May 29 Photo. Perf. 14
893A A90a 1nu multicolored   .15 .15

Penny Black, 150th Anniv. A90b

Penny Black and: 50ch, Bhutan #1. 1nu, Oldenburg #1. 2nu, Bergedorf #3. 4nu, German Democratic Republic #48. 5nu, Brunswick #1. 6nu, Basel #3L1. 8nu, Geneva #2L1. 10nu, Zurich #1L1. No. 902, France #3. 20nu, Vatican City #1. 25nu, Israel #1. No. 905, Japan #1.

Penny Black and: No. 906a, Mecklenburg-Schwerin #1. b, Mecklenburg-Strelitz #1. No. 907a, Germany #5. 9b, Prussia #2. No. 908a, Hamburg #1. b, North German Confederation #1, #7. No. 909a, Baden #1. b, Wurttemberg #1. No. 910a, Heligoland #1. b, Hanover #1. No. 911a, Thurn & Taxis #3. b, Thurn & Taxis #42. No. 912a, Schleswig-Holstein #1. b, Lubeck #5. No. 913, Saxony #1. No. 914, Berlin #9N1. No. 915, No other stamp. No. 916, US #1. No. 917, Bavaria #1.

1990, Oct. 9 Perf. 14

894	A90b	50ch multicolored	.15 .15
895	A90b	1nu multicolored	.15 .15
896	A90b	2nu multicolored	.30 .25
897	A90b	4nu multicolored	.65 .50
898	A90b	5nu multicolored	.80 .60
899	A90b	6nu multicolored	1.00 .75
900	A90b	8nu multicolored	1.25 1.00
901	A90b	10nu multicolored	1.60 1.25
902	A90b	15nu multicolored	2.50 1.75
903	A90b	20nu multicolored	3.25 2.50
904	A90b	25nu multicolored	4.00 3.00
905	A90b	30nu multicolored	.15 .15
		Nos. 894-905 (12)	20.40 15.40

Souvenir Sheets
Sheets of 2 (#906-912) or 1
906-912 A90b 15nu each   4.75 4.75
913-917 A90b 30nu each   4.75 4.75

Stamp World London '90.

Giant Pandas A91

Tiger A92

Endangered wildlife of Asia.

1990 Perf. 14

918	A91	50ch multi, diff.	.15 .15
919	A91	1nu multi, diff.	.15 .15
920	A91	2nu multi, diff.	.30 .25
921	A91	3nu shown	.50 .35
922	A91	4nu multi, diff.	.65 .50
923	A92	5nu shown	.80 .60
924	A91	6nu multi, diff.	.95 .70
925	A91	7nu multi, diff.	1.10 .80
926	A92	10nu Elephant	1.60 1.25
927	A91	15nu multi, diff.	2.50 1.75
928	A92	20nu Barking deer	3.25 2.50
929	A92	25nu Snow leopard	4.00 3.00
		Nos. 918-929 (12)	15.95 12.00

Souvenir Sheets

930	A92	25nu Rhinoceros	4.00 4.00
931	A92	25nu Clouded leopard	4.00 4.00
932	A92	25nu Asiatic wild dog	4.00 4.00
933	A92	25nu Himalayan shou	4.00 4.00
934	A92	25nu Golden cat	4.00 4.00
935	A92	25nu Himalayan musk deer	4.00 4.00
936	A91	25nu multi, diff.	4.00 4.00
937	A92	25nu Asiatic black bear	4.00 4.00
938	A92	25nu Gaur	4.00 4.00

939	A92	25nu	Pygmy hog	4.00	4.00
940	A92	25nu	Wolf	4.00	4.00
941	A92	25nu	Sloth bear	4.00	4.00

Nos. 919-920 and 927 vert.

Buddhist Musical Instruments — A93

1990, Sept. 29   Litho.   Perf. 13½x13

942	A93	10ch	Dungchen	.15	.15
943	A93	20ch	Dungkar	.15	.15
944	A93	30ch	Roim	.15	.15
945	A93	50ch	Tinchag	.15	.15
946	A93	1nu	Dradu & drilbu	.15	.15
947	A93	2nu	Gya-ling	.30	.25
948	A93	2.50nu	Nga	.40	.30
a.			Souv. sheet of 4, #943, 945, 947-948	.85	.65
949	A93	3.50nu	Kang-dung	.55	.40
a.			Souv. sheet of 4, #942, 944, 946, 949	.85	.65
			Set value	1.65	1.25

Year of the Girl
BHUTAN 50ch Child — A94

1990, Dec. 8

| 950 | A94 | 50ch | shown | .15 | .15 |
| 951 | A94 | 20nu | Young girl | 3.25 | 2.50 |

Wonders of
the World
A95

Walt Disney characters viewing: 1ch, Temple of Artemis, Ephesus. 2ch, Statue of Zeus, Olympia. 3ch, Egyptian pyramids. 4ch, Lighthouse, Alexandria. 5ch, Mausoleum at Halicarnassus. 10ch, Colossus of Rhodes. 50ch, Hanging gardens of Babylon. 5nu, Mauna Loa volcano, Hawaii. 6nu, Carlsbad Caverns, New Mexico. 10nu, Rainbow Bridge, Utah. 15nu, Grand Canyon of the Colorado, Arizona. 20nu, Old Faithful geyser, Wyoming. 25nu, Giant sequoias, California. 30nu, Crater Lake and Wizard Island, Oregon. 5nu, 6nu, 10nu, 15nu, 20nu, 25nu, 30nu are horiz.

Walt Disney characters viewing: No. 966, Great Wall of China, horiz. No. 967, Mosque of St. Sophia, Istanbul, Turkey. No. 968, The Leaning Tower of Pisa, Italy. No. 969, Colosseum, Rome. No. 970, Stonehenge, England. No. 971, Catacombs of Alexandria, Egypt. No. 972, Porcelain Tower, Nanking, China, horiz. No. 973, The Panama Canal, horiz. No. 974, Golden Gate Bridge, San Francisco, horiz. No. 975, Sears Tower, Chicago, horiz. No. 976, Gateway Arch, St. Louis. No. 977, Alcan Highway, Alaska and Canada, horiz. No. 978, Hoover Dam, Nevada, horiz. No. 979, Empire State Building, New York.

1991, Feb. 2   Litho.   Perf. 14

952	A95	1ch	multicolored	.15	.15
953	A95	2ch	multicolored	.15	.15
954	A95	3ch	multicolored	.15	.15
955	A95	4ch	multicolored	.15	.15
956	A95	5ch	multicolored	.15	.15
957	A95	10ch	multicolored	.15	.15
958	A95	50ch	multicolored	.15	.15
959	A95	5nu	multicolored	.80	.60
960	A95	6nu	multicolored	.95	.70
961	A95	10nu	multicolored	1.60	1.25
962	A95	15nu	multicolored	2.50	1.75
963	A95	20nu	multicolored	3.25	2.50
964	A95	25nu	multicolored	4.00	3.00
965	A95	30nu	multicolored	4.75	3.50
			Nos. 952-965 (14)	18.90	14.35

Souvenir Sheets
Perf. 14x13½, 13½x14

| 966-979 | A95 | 25nu each | 4.00 | 4.00 |

Peter Paul
Rubens (1577-
1640),
Painter — A96

Entire paintings or different details from: 10ch, 5nu, 6nu, 10nu, No. 992, Atalanta and Meleager. 50ch, Fall of Phaethon. 1nu, No. 993, Feast of Venus Verticordia. 2nu, Achilles Slaying Hector. 3nu, No. 994, Arachne Punished by Minerva. 4nu, No. 995, Jupiter Receives Psyche on Olympus. 7nu, Venus in Vulcan's Furnace. 20nu, No. 996, Briseis Returned to Achilles. 30nu, No. 997, Mars and Rhea Sylvia. No. 998, Venus Shivering. No. 999, Ganymede and the Eagle. No. 1000, Origin of the Milky Way. No. 1001, Adonis and Venus. No. 1002, Hero and Leander. No. 1003, Fall of the Titans.

Nos. 994, 996-997, 1000-1003 are horiz.

1991, Feb. 2

980	A96	10ch	multicolored	.15	.15
981	A96	50ch	multicolored	.15	.15
982	A96	1nu	multicolored	.15	.15
983	A96	2nu	multicolored	.30	.15
984	A96	3nu	multicolored	.50	.15
985	A96	4nu	multicolored	.65	.15
986	A96	5nu	multicolored	.80	.60
987	A96	6nu	multicolored	.95	.70
988	A96	7nu	multicolored	1.10	.85
989	A96	10nu	multicolored	1.60	1.25
990	A96	20nu	multicolored	3.25	2.50
991	A96	30nu	multicolored	4.75	3.50
			Nos. 980-991 (12)	14.35	10.30

Souvenir Sheets

| 992-1003 | A96 | 25nu each | 4.00 | 4.00 |

Vincent Van
Gogh (1853-
1890),
Painter — A97

Paintings: 10ch, Cottages, Reminiscence of the North. 50ch, Head of a Peasant Woman with Dark Cap. 1nu, Portrait of a Woman in Blue. 2nu, The Midwife. 8nu, Vase with Hollyhocks. 10nu, Portrait of a Man with a Skull Cap. 12nu, Agostina Segatori Sitting in the Cafe du Tambourin. 15nu, Vase with Daisies and Anemones. 18nu, Fritillaries in a Copper Vase. 20nu, Woman Sitting in the Grass. 25nu, On the Outskirts of Paris, horiz. 30nu, Chrysanthemums and Wild Flowers in a Vase.

No. 1016, Le Moulin de la Galette. No. 1017, Bowl with Sunflowers, Roses and Other Flowers, horiz. No. 1018, Poppies and Butterflies. No. 1019, Trees in the Garden of Saint-Paul Hospital. No. 1020, Le Moulin de Blute Fin. No. 1021, Le Moulin de la Galette, diff. No. 1022, Vase with Peonies. No. 1023, Vase with Zinnias. No. 1024, Fishing in the Spring, Pont de Clichy, horiz. No. 1025, Village Street in Auvers, horiz. No. 1026, Vase with Zinnias and Other Flowers, horiz. No. 2027, Vase with Red Poppies.

1991, July 22   Litho.   Perf. 13½

1004	A97	10ch	multicolored	.15	.15
1005	A97	50ch	multicolored	.15	.15
1006	A97	1nu	multicolored	.15	.15
1007	A97	2nu	multicolored	.30	.15
1008	A97	8nu	multicolored	1.25	1.00
1009	A97	10nu	multicolored	1.65	1.25
1010	A97	12nu	multicolored	2.00	1.50
1011	A97	15nu	multicolored	2.50	1.75
1012	A97	18nu	multicolored	3.00	2.25
1013	A97	20nu	multicolored	3.25	2.50
1014	A97	25nu	multicolored	4.00	3.00
1015	A97	30nu	multicolored	4.75	3.50
			Nos. 1004-1015 (12)	23.15	17.35

Size: 76x102mm, 102x76mm
Imperf

| 1016-1027 | A97 | 30nu each | 4.75 | 4.75 |

History of World Cup Soccer — A98

Winning team pictures, plays or possible future site: 50ch, Uruguay, 1930. 1nu, Italy, 1934. 2nu, Italy, 1938. 3nu, Uruguay, 1950. 5nu, West Germany, 1954. 10nu, Brazil, 1958. 20nu, Brazil, 1962. 25nu, England, 1966. 29nu, Brazil, 1970. 30nu, West Germany, 1974. 31nu, Argentina, 1978. 32nu, Italy, 1982. 33nu, Argentina, 1986. 34nu, West Germany, 1990. 35nu, Los Angeles Coliseum, 1994.

Players: No. 1043, Claudio Caniggia, Argentina, vert. No. 1044, Salvatore Schillaci, Italy, vert. No. 1045, Roberto Baggio, Italy, vert. No. 1046, Peter Shilton, England, vert. No. 1047, Lothar Matthaus, West Germany, vert. No. 1048, Paul Gascoigne, England, vert.

1991, Aug. 1   Litho.   Perf. 13½

1028	A98	50ch	multicolored	.15	.15
1029	A98	1nu	multicolored	.15	.15
1030	A98	2nu	multicolored	.30	.15
1031	A98	3nu	multicolored	.50	.15
1032	A98	5nu	multicolored	.80	.60
1033	A98	10nu	multicolored	1.65	1.25
1034	A98	20nu	multicolored	3.25	2.50
1035	A98	25nu	multicolored	4.00	3.00
1036	A98	29nu	multicolored	4.75	3.50
1037	A98	30nu	multicolored	4.75	3.50
1038	A98	31nu	multicolored	5.00	3.75
1039	A98	32nu	multicolored	5.25	4.00
1040	A98	33nu	multicolored	5.50	4.00
1041	A98	34nu	multicolored	5.50	4.25
1042	A98	35nu	multicolored	5.75	4.25
			Nos. 1028-1042 (15)	47.30	35.20

Souvenir Sheets

| 1043-1048 | A98 | 30nu each | 4.75 | 4.75 |

Phila Nippon
'91 — A99

1991, Nov. 16   Perf. 13

| 1049 | A99 | 15nu | multicolored | 2.50 | 1.50 |

Education in
Bhutan
A100

1992, Mar. 5   Photo.   Perf. 13½

| 1050 | A100 | 1nu | multicolored | .20 | .15 |

A101

1992 Summer Olympics,
Barcelona — A102

1992, July 24   Litho.   Perf. 12

| 1051 | A101 | 25nu | Pair, #a.-b. | 8.25 | 8.25 |

Souvenir Sheet

| 1052 | A102 | 25nu | Archer | 4.00 | 4.00 |

German Reunification — A103

1992, Oct. 3   Litho.   Perf. 12

| 1053 | A103 | 25nu | multicolored | 2.00 | 2.00 |

Souvenir Sheet

| 1054 | A103 | 25nu | multicolored | 2.00 | 2.00 |

Stamp from No. 1054 does not have white inscription or border.

Bhutan
Postal
Service,
30th Anniv.
A104

Designs: 1nu, Mail truck, plane. 3nu, Letter carrier approaching village. 5nu, Letter carrier emptying mail box.

1992, Oct. 9

1055	A104	1nu	multicolored	.15	.15
1056	A104	3nu	multicolored	.25	.25
1057	A104	5nu	multicolored	.40	.40
			Nos. 1055-1057 (3)	.80	.80

This miniature sheet of four was never officially issued.

A106

A107

1992, Sept. 18   Perf. 12

| 1059 | A106 | 15nu | Ship | 1.25 | 1.25 |
| 1060 | A106 | 20nu | Portrait | 1.60 | 1.60 |

Souvenir Sheet

| 1061 | A106 | 25nu | like #1060 | 2.00 | 2.00 |

Discovery of America, 500th anniv.
Stamp from No. 1061 does not have silver inscription or white border.

1992, Nov. 11   Litho.   Perf. 12

Reign of King Jigme Singye Wangchuk, 20th Anniv.: a, 1nu, Man tilling field, factory. b, 5nu, Airplane. c, 10nu, House, well. d, 15nu, King.

20nu, People, flag, King, horiz.
1062 A107 Block of 4, #a.-d. 2.50 2.50

Souvenir Sheet
1063 A107 20nu multicolored 1.75 1.75

Intl.
Volunteer
Day
A108

Designs: a, 1.50nu, White inscription. b, 9nu, Green inscription. c, 15nu, Red inscription.

1992, Dec. 5   Litho.   Perf. 14
1067 A108 Block of 4, #a.-c. + label 2.00 2.00

Medicinal
Plants — A109

1993, Jan. 1   Litho.   Perf. 12
1068 A109 1.50nu Meconopsis
　　　　　　　grandis prain .15 .15
1069 A109 7nu Meconopsis sp. .60 .60
1070 A109 10nu Meconopsis wal-
　　　　　　　lichii .80 .80
1071 A109 12nu Meconopsis hor-
　　　　　　　ridula 1.00 1.00
1072 A109 20nu Meconopsis dis-
　　　　　　　cigera 1.75 1.75
　　　　Nos. 1068-1072 (5) 4.30 4.30

Souvenir Sheet
1073 A109 25nu Meconopsis hor-
　　　　　　　ridula, diff. 2.00 2.00

Miniature Sheet

Lunar New Year — A110

1993, Feb. 22   Litho.   Perf. 14
1074 A110 25nu multicolored 2.00 2.00

No. 1074 Surcharged "TAIPEI '93" in
Silver and Black

1993, Aug. 14   Litho.   Perf. 14
1075 A110 30nu on 25nu 2.50 2.50

Door
Gods — A112   Flowers — A113

1993, Dec. 17   Litho.   Perf. 12
1091 A112 1.50nu Namtheo-Say .15 .15
1092 A112 5nu Pha-Ke-Po .50 .50
1093 A112 10nu Chen-Mi-Jang 1.00 1.00
1094 A112 15nu Yul-Khor-Sung 1.50 1.50
　　　　Nos. 1091-1094 (4) 3.15 3.15

1993, Jan. 1   Perf. 13
Designs: No. 1095a, 1nu, Rhododendron mucronatum. b, 1.5nu. Anemone rupicola. c, 2nu, Polemonium coeruleum. d, 2.5nu, Rosa marophylla. e, 4nu, Paraquilegia microphylla. f, 5nu, Aquilegia nivalis. g, 6nu, Geranium wallichianum. h, 7nu, Rhododendron campanulatum. i, 9nu, Viola suavis. j, 10nu, Cyananthus lobatus.
13nu, Red flower, horiz.
1095 A113 Strip of 10, #a.-j. 4.75 4.75

Souvenir Sheet
1096 A113 13nu multicolored 1.40 1.40

New Year 1994
(Year of the
Dog) — A114

1994, Feb. 11   Litho.   Perf. 14
1097 A114 11.50nu multicolored .80 .80

Souvenir Sheet
1098 A114 20nu like #1097 1.40 1.40

Hong Kong '94.

Stamp Cards — A115

Designs: 16nu, Tagtshang Monastery. 20nu, Map of Bhutan. Illustration reduced.

Rouletted 26 on 2 or 3 Sides
1994, Aug. 15   Litho.
Self-Adhesive
Cards of 6 + 6 labels
1099 A115 16nu #a.-f. 6.25 6.25
1100 A115 20nu #a.-f. 7.75 7.75

Individual stamps measure 70x9mm and have a card backing. Se-tenant labels inscribed "AIR MAIL."

Souvenir Sheet

First Manned Moon Landing, 25th
Anniv. — A116

Designs: a, 30nu, Astronaut on moon. b, 36nu, Space shuttle, earth, moon. Illustration reduced.

1994, Nov. 11   Litho.   Perf. 14x14¹/₂
1101 A116 Sheet of 2, #a.-b. 4.25 4.25

Nos. 1101a, 1101b have holographic images. Soaking in water may affect the holograms.

Souvenir Sheet

Victory Over
Tibet-Mongol
Army, 350th
Anniv. — A117

Battle scene: a, Mounted officer. b, Hand to hand combat, soldiers in yellow or blue armor. c, Soldier on gray horse. d, Soldiers in red, drummer, horn player.

1994, Dec. 17   Litho.   Perf. 12¹/₂
Granite Paper
1102 A117 15nu Sheet of 4, #a.-d. 4.00 4.00

Souvenir Sheet

Bridges
A118

Designs: a, 15nu, Tower Bridge, London, cent. b, 16nu, Wangdue Bridge, Bhutan, 250th anniv.

1994, Nov. 11   Perf. 12
1103 A118 Sheet of 2, #a.-b. 2.00 2.00

1994 World Cup Soccer Championships,
US — A119

1994, July 17   Litho.   Perf. 12
1104 A119 15nu multicolored 1.00 1.00

Souvenir Sheet

World
Tourism
Year
A120

Scenes of Bhutan: a, 1.50nu, Paro Valley. b, 5nu, Chorten Kora. c, 10nu, Thimphu Tshechu. d, 15nu, Wangdue Tshechu.

1995, Apr. 2   Litho.   Perf. 12
1105 A120 Sheet of 4, #a.-d. 2.00 2.00

Miniature Sheet of 12

New Year
1995 (Year
of the
Boar)
A121

Symbols of Chinese Lunar New Year: a, 10ch, Rat. b, 20ch, Ox. c, 30ch, Tiger. d, 40ch, Rabbit. e, 1nu, Dragon. f, 2nu, Snake. g, 3nu, Horse. h, 4nu, Sheep. i, 5nu, Monkey. j, 7nu, Rooster. k, 8nu, Dog. l, 9nu, Boar.
10nu, Wood Hog.

1995, Mar. 2
1106 A121 #a.-l. 2.50 2.50

Souvenir Sheet
1107 A121 10nu multicolored .65 .65

No. 1107 is a continuous design.

A122   A123

Flowers: 9nu, Pleione praecox. 10nu, Primula calderina. 16nu, Primula whitei. 18nu, Notholirion macrophyllum.

1995, May 2   Litho.   Perf. 12
1108-1111 A122 Set of 4 3.50 3.50

1995, June 26   Perf. 14
UN, 50th Anniv.: a, 1.5nu, Human resources development. b, 9nu, Health & population. c, 10nu, Water & sanitation. d, 5nu, Transport & communications. e, 16nu, Forestry & environment. f, 18nu, Peace & security. g, 11.5nu, UN in Bhutan.
1112 A123 Strip of 7 4.75 4.75

Miniature Sheet of 6

Singapore '95 — A124

Birds: No. 1113a, 1nu, Himalayan pied kingfisher. b, 2nu, Blyth's tragopan. c, 3nu, Long-tailed minivet. d, 10nu, Red junglefowl. e, 15nu, Black-capped sibia. f, 20nu, Red-billed chough.
No. 1114, Black-neck crane.

1995, June 2   Litho.   Perf. 12
1113 A124 #a.-f. + 3 labels 3.50 3.50

Souvenir Sheet
1114 A124 20nu multicolored 1.40 1.40

Traditional
Crafts — A125

Designs: 1nu, Drying parchment. 2nu, Making tapestry. 3nu, Restoring archaeological finds. 10nu, Weaving textiles. 15nu, Sewing garments. No. 1120, 20nu, Carving wooden vessels.
No. 1121, Mosaic.

1995, Aug. 15   Litho.   Perf. 14
1115-1120 A125 Set of 6 2.50 2.50

Souvenir Sheet
1121 A125 20nu multicolored 1.40 1.40

New Year 1996
(Year of the
Rat) — A126

Designs: a, Monkey. b, Rat, fire. c, Dragon.

1996, Jan. 1   Litho.   Perf. 14
1122 A126 10nu Sheet of 3, #a.-c. 2.00 2.00

Butterflies
A127

Designs: a, 2nu, Blue pansy. b, 3nu, Blue peacock. c, 5nu, Great Mormon. d, 10nu, Fritillary. e, 15nu, Blue duke. f, 25nu, Brown Gorgon.
No. 1124, Xanthomelas. No. 1124A, Fivebar swordtail.

1996	Litho.		Perf. 14
1123	A127	Sheet of 6, #a.-f.	4.00 4.00
Souvenir Sheets			
1124-1124A	A127	30nu each	2.00 2.00

1996 Summer
Olympic Games,
Atlanta — A128

5nu, Silver 300n coin, soccer. 7nu, Silver 300n coin, basketball. 10nu, Gold 5s coin, judo. 15nu, Archery.

1996	Litho.		Perf. 14
1125-1127	A128	Set of 3	1.50 1.50
Souvenir Sheet			
1128	A128	15nu multicolored	1.00 1.00

Olymphilex '96.

Folktales — A129

Designs: a, 1nu, The White Bird. b, 2nu, Sing Sing Lhamo and the Moon. c, 3nu, The Hoopoe. d, 5nu, The Cloud Fairies. e, 10nu, The Three Wishes. f, 20nu, The Abominable Snowman.

1996			Perf. 12
1129	A129	Sheet of 6, #a.-f.	3.00 3.00
Souvenir Sheet			
1130	A129	25nu like #1129d	1.75 1.75

Locomotives — A130

No. 1131: a, 0-6-4 Tank engine (Chile). b, First Pacific locomotive in Europe (France). c, 4-6-0 Passenger engine (Norway). d, Atlantic type express (Germany). e, 4-Cylinder 4-6-0 express (Belgium). f, Standard type "4" diesel-electric (England).
No. 1132: a, Standard 0-6-0 Goods engine (India). b, Main-line 1,900 horsepower diesel-electric (Finland). c, 0-8-0 Shunting tank engine (Russia). d, Alco "PA-1" diesel-electric (US). e, "C11" Class 2-6-4 branch passenger tank engine (Japan). f, "Settebello" deluxe high-speed electric train (Italy).
No. 1133, Class "KD" 0-6-0 Goods locomotive, 1900 (Sweden). No. 1134, Shinkansen "New Railway" series 200 (Japan).

1996, Nov. 25	Litho.		Perf. 14
1131-1132	A130	20nu Sheets of 6, #a.-f., each	8.00 8.00
Souvenir Sheets			
1133-1134	A130	70nu each	4.75 4.75

Penny
Black — A131

Litho. & Embossed			
1996, Dec. 17			Perf. 13½
1135	A131	140nu black & gold	9.50 9.50

A132   A133

Winter Olympic Medalists: 10nu, Vegard Ulvang, cross-country skiing, 1992. 15nu, Kristi Yamaguchi, figure skating, 1992. 25nu, Markus Wasmeier, giant slalom, 1994. 30nu, Georg Hackl, luge, 1992.
No. 1140: a, Andreas Ostler, 2-man bobsled, 1952. b, Wolfgang Hoppe, 4-man bobsled, 1984. c, Stein Eriksen, giant slalom, 1952. d, Alberto Tomba, giant slalom, 1988.
No. 1141, Henri Oreiller, downhill, 1948. No. 1142, Eduard Scherrer, 4-man bobsled, 1924.

1997			Perf. 14
1136-1139	A132	Set of 4	5.50 5.50
1140	A132	15nu Strip of 4, #a.-d.	4.00 4.00
Souvenir Sheets			
1141-1142	A132	70nu each	4.50 4.50

No. 1140 was issued in sheets of 8 stamps.

1997, Jan. 15   Perf. 13

Insects and Arachnids: a, 1ch, Apis laboriosa smith. b, 2ch, Neptunides polychromus. c, 3ch, Conocephalus maculctus. d, 4ch, Blattidae. e, 5ch, Dytiscus marginalis. f, 10ch, Dynastes hercules. g, 15ch, Hippodamia. h, 20ch, Sarcophaga haemorrhoidalis. i, 25ch, Lucanus cervus. j, 30ch, Caterpillar. k, 35ch, Lycia hirtaria. l, 40ch, Clytarlus pennatus. m, 45ch, Ephemera denica. n, 50ch, Gryllus campestris. o, 60ch, Deilephila elpenor. p, 65ch, Gerris. q, 70ch, Agrion splendens. r, 80ch, Tachyta nana. s, 90ch, Eurydema pulchra. t, 1nu, Hadrurus hirsutus. u, 1.50nu, Vespa germanica. v, 2nu, Pyrops. w, 2.50nu, Mantis religiosa. x, 3nu, Araneus diadematus. y, 3.50nu, Atrophaneura. 15nu, Melolontha.

1143	A133	Sheet of 25, #a.-y.	1.35 1.35
Souvenir Sheet			
1144	A133	15nu multicolored	1.00 1.00

Hong Kong
'97 — A134

Wildlife: a, Thalarctos maritimus. b, Phascolarctos cinereus. c, Selenarcios thibetanus. d, Ailurus fulgens.
No. 1146, Ailuropoda melanoleuca.

1997	Litho.		Perf. 14
1145	A134	10nu Sheet of 4, #a.-d.	2.75 2.75
Souvenir Sheet			
1146	A134	20nu multicolored	1.35 1.35

Signs of the
Chinese
Zodiac — A135

No. 1147: a, 1ch, Mouse. b, 2ch, Ox. c, 3ch, Tiger. d, 4ch, Rabbit. e, 5nu, Dragon. f, 6nu, Snake. g, 7nu, Horse. h, 8nu, Sheep. i, 90ch, Monkey. j, 10nu, Rooster. k, 11nu, Dog. l, 12nu, Pig. 20nu, Ox, diff.

1997, Feb. 8	Litho.		Perf. 14
1147	A135	Sheet of 12, #a.-l. + label	4.00 4.00
Souvenir Sheet			
1148	A135	20nu multicolored	1.35 1.35

Fauna
A136

Cuon alpinus: No. 1149: a, Adult, hind legs off ground. b, Adult walking right. c, Mother nursing young. d, Two seated.
Endangered species: No. 1150: a, Lynx. b, Red panda. c, Takin. d, Musk deer. e, Snow leopard. f, Golden langur. g, Tiger. h, Muntjac. i, Marmot.
No. 1151, Pseudois nayaur. No. 1152, Ursus thibetanus.

1997, Apr. 24			
1149	A136	10nu Block or strip of 4, #a.-d.	2.75 2.75
1150	A136	10nu Sheet of 9, #a.-i.	6.00 6.00
Souvenir Sheets			
1151-1152	A136	70nu each	4.75 4.75

World Wildlife Fund (No. 1149).
No. 1149 issued in sheets of 12 stamps.

UNESCO,
50th Anniv.
A137

No. 1153: a, Mount Hungshan, China. b, Mausoleum of first Qin Emperor, China. c, Imperial Bronze Dragon, China. d, Tikal Natl. Park, Guatemala. e, Evora, Portugal. f, Shirakami-Sanchi, Japan. g, Paris, France. h, Valley Below the Falls, Plitvice Lakes Natl. Park, Croatia.
Sites in Germany: No. 1154: a, Cathedral, Bamberg. b, Bamberg. c, St. Michael's Church, Hildesheim. d, Potsdam Palace. e, Potsdam Church. f, Lubeck. g, Quedlinberg. h, Benedictine Church, Lorsch.
No. 1155, Goslar, Germany, horiz. No. 1156, Cathedral, Comenzada, Portugal, horiz.

1997, May 15			
Sheets of 8 + Label			
1153	A137	10nu #a.-h.	5.50 5.50
1154	A137	15nu #a.-h.	8.00 8.00
Souvenir Sheets			
1155-1156	A137	60nu each	4.00 4.00

Chernobyl
Disaster, 10th
Anniv. — A138

1997, May 2	Litho.	Perf. 13½x14
1157	A138	35nu UNESCO	2.40 2.40

Dogs — A139   Cats — A140

Designs: 10nu, Dalmatian. 15nu, Siberian husky. 20nu, Saluki. 25nu, Shar pei.
No. 1162: a, Dandie Dinmont terrier. b, Chinese crested. c, Norwich terrier. d, Basset hound. e, Cardigan welsh corgi. f, French bulldog. 60nu, Hovawart.

1997, July 15			Perf. 14
1158-1161	A139	Set of 4	4.75 4.75
1162	A139	20nu Sheet of 6, #a.-f.	8.00 8.00
Souvenir Sheet			
1163	A139	60nu multicolored	4.00 4.00

1997, July 15

Designs: 10nu, Turkish angora. 15nu, Oriental shorthair. 20nu, British shorthair. 25nu, Burmese.
No. 1168: a, Japanese bobtail. b, Ceylon. c, Exotic. d, Rex. e, Ragdoll. f, Russian blue. 60nu, Tonkinese.

1164-1167	A140	Set of 4	4.75 4.75
1168	A140	15nu Sheet of 6, #a.-f.	6.00 6.00
Souvenir Sheet			
1169	A140	60nu multicolored	4.25 4.25

1998 World
Cup Soccer,
France — A141

English players: 5nu, Pearce. 10nu, Gascoigne. 15nu, Beckham. 20nu, McManaman. 25nu, Adams. 30nu, Ince.
World Cup captains, horiz.: No. 1176: a, Maradona, Argentina, 1986. b, Alberto, Brazil, 1970. c, Dunga, Brazil, 1994. d, Moore, England, 1966. e, Fritzwalter, Germany, 1954. f, Matthaus, Germany, 1990. g, Beckenbauer, Germany, 1974. h, Passarella, Argentina, 1978.
Winning teams, horiz.: No. 1177: a, Italy, 1938. b, W. Germany, 1954. c, Uruguay, 1958. d, England, 1966. e, Argentina, 1978. f, Brazil, 1962. g, Italy, 1934. h, Brazil, 1970. i, Uruguay, 1930.
No. 1178, Philippe Albert, Belgium. No. 1179, Salvatore (Toto) Schillaci, Italy, horiz.

Perf. 13½x14, 14x13½			
1997, Oct. 9			Litho.
1170-1175	A141	Set of 6	7.00 7.00
Sheets of 8 or 9			
1176	A141	10nu #a.-h. + label	5.50 5.50
1177	A141	10nu #a.-i.	6.00 6.00
Souvenir Sheets			
1178-1179	A141	35nu each	3.75 3.75

SEMI-POSTAL STAMPS

Nos. 10-12
Surcharged

+ 50 ch

Perf. 14x14½

1964, Mar.   **Litho.**   **Unwmk.**
B1	A3	33ch + 50ch multi	2.00 2.00
B2	A3	70ch + 50ch multi	2.00 2.00
B3	A3	1.30nu + 50ch multi	2.00 2.00
		Nos. B1-B3 (3)	6.00 6.00

9th Winter Olympic Games, Innsbruck, Jan. 29-Feb. 9, 1964.

Olympic Games Type of Regular Issue, 1964

Souvenir Sheet

1964, Oct. 10   **Perf. 13½, Imperf.**
B4	A6	Sheet of 2	7.50 7.50
a.		1nu + 50ch Archery	.90 .90
b.		2nu + 50ch Soccer	.90 .90

18th Olympic Games, Tokyo, Oct. 10-25.

FLOOD RELIEF

+ 5Ch

1968, Dec. 7   **Photo.**   **Perf. 13½**
B5	A14n	5ch +5ch	.15 .15
B6	A14n	80ch +25ch	.35 .35
B7	A14n	2nu +50ch	.85 .85
		Nos. B5-B7 (3)	1.35 1.35

AIR POST STAMPS

Nos. 19-21, 38-39, 63-67 Ovptd.

a   b

1967, Jan. 10   **Litho.**   **Perfs. as Before**
Overprint "a"
C1	A5	33ch on #19	.15 .15
C2	A5	70ch on #20	.30 .30
C3	A5	1nu on #21	.40 .40
C4	A8	50ch on #38	.20 .20
C5	A8	75ch on #39	.30 .30
C6	A11	1.50nu on #63	.65 .65
C7	A11	2nu on #64	.85 .85
C8	A11	3nu on #65	1.25 1.25
C9	A11	4nu on #66	1.75 1.75
C10	A11	5nu on #67	2.25 2.25

Overprint "b"
C11	A5	33ch on #19	.15 .15
C12	A5	70ch on #20	.30 .30
C13	A5	1nu on #21	.40 .40
C14	A8	50ch on #38	.20 .20
C15	A8	75ch on #39	.30 .30
C16	A11	1.50nu on #63	.65 .65
C17	A11	2nu on #64	.85 .85
C18	A11	3nu on #65	1.25 1.25
C19	A11	4nu on #66	1.75 1.75
C20	A11	5nu on #67	2.25 2.25
		Nos. C1-C20 (20)	16.20 16.20

UN Type of Regular Issue

Bhutan Flag and: 2.50nu, UN Headquarters, NYC. 5nu, Security Council Chamber and mural by Per Krohg. 6nu, General Assembly Hall.

1971, Sept. 21   **Photo.**   **Perf. 13½**
C21	A16	2.50nu silver & multi	.50 .50
C22	A16	5nu silver & multi	.95 .95
C23	A16	6nu silver & multi	1.10 1.10
		Nos. C21-C23 (3)	2.55 2.55

Bhutan's admission to the United Nations. Exist imperf.

Nos. C21-C23 Overprinted in Gold: "UNHCR / UNRWA / 1971" like Nos. 145-145C

1971, Dec. 23   **Litho.**   **Perf. 13½**
C24	A16	2.50nu silver & multi	.70 .70
C25	A16	5nu silver & multi	1.40 1.40
C26	A16	6nu silver & multi	1.90 1.90
		Nos. C24-C26 (3)	4.00 4.00

World Refugee Year. Exist imperf.

UPU Types of 1974

UPU Emblem, Carrier Pigeon and: 1nu, Mail runner and jeep. 1.40nu, 10nu, Old and new locomotives. 2nu, Old biplane and jet.

1974, Oct. 9   **Litho.**   **Perf. 14½**
C27	A19	1nu salmon & multi	.25 .25
C28	A20	1.40nu lilac & multi	.40 .40
C29	A20	2nu multicolored	.50 .50
		Nos. C27-C29 (3)	1.15 1.15

Souvenir Sheet
Perf. 13

C30	A20	10nu lilac & multi	2.75 2.75

Cent. of the UPU. Nos. C27-C29 were issued in sheets of 50 and sheets of 5 plus label with multicolored margin. Exist imperf.

Issues of 1968-1974 Surcharged 25ch and Bars

1978   **Perf. & Printing as Before**
C31	A16	25ch on 5nu, #C22	1.25 1.25
C32	A16	25ch on 6nu, #C23	1.25 1.25
C33	A20	25ch on 1.40nu, #C28	1.25 1.25
C34	A20	25ch on 2nu, #C29	1.25 1.25
C35	A14j	25ch on 4nu, #94L	1.25 1.25
C36	A14j	25ch on 10nu, #94N	1.25 1.25
C37	A17k	25ch on 5nu, #154F	1.25 1.25
C38	A17k	25ch on 6nu, #154G	1.25 1.25
		Nos. C31-C38 (8)	10.00 10.00

BOLIVIA

bə-'li–vē–ə

LOCATION — Central South America, separated from the Pacific Ocean by Chile and Peru.
GOVT. — Republic
AREA — 424,165 sq. mi.
POP. — 6,252,250 (est. 1984)
CAPITAL — Sucre (La Paz is the actual seat of government).

100 Centavos = 1 Boliviano
100 Centavos = 1 Peso Boliviano (1963)
100 Centavos = 1 Boliviano (1987)

Catalogue values for unused stamps in this country are for Never Hinged items, beginning with Scott 308 in the regular postage section, Scott C112 in the airpost section, Scott RA5 in the postal tax section, and Scott RAC1 in airpost postal tax section.

On Feb. 21, 1863, the Bolivian Government decreed contracts for carrying the mails should be let to the highest bidder, the service to commence on the day the bid was accepted, and stamps used for the payment of postage. On Mar. 18, the contract was awarded to Sr. Justiniano Garcia and was in effect until Apr. 29, 1863, when it was rescinded. Stamps in the form illustrated above were prepared in denominations of ½, 1, 2 and 4 reales. All values exist in black and in blue. The blue are twice as scarce as the black. Value, black, $75 each.

It is said that used copies exist on covers, but the authenticity of these covers remains to be established.

Condor — A1   A2

A3

72 varieties of each of the 5c, 78 varieties of the 10c, 30 varieties of each of the 50c and 100c.

The plate of the 5c stamps was entirely reengraved 4 times and retouched at least 6 times. Various states of the plate have distinguishing characteristics, each of which is typical of most, though not all the stamps in a sheet. These characteristics (usually termed types) are found in the shading lines at the right side of the globe. a, vertical and diagonal lines. b, diagonal lines only. c, diagonal and horizontal lines with traces of vertical lines. d, diagonal and horizontal lines. e, horizontal lines only. f, no lines except the curved ones forming the outlines of the globe.

1867-68   **Unwmk.**   **Engr.**   **Imperf.**
1	A1	5c yel grn, thin paper (a, b)	3.50 4.50
a.		5c blue green (a)	4.50 14.00
b.		5c deep green (a)	4.50 14.00
c.		5c ol grn, thick paper (a)	35.00 25.00
d.		5c yel grn, thick paper (a)	80.00 80.00
e.		5c yel grn, thick paper (b)	80.00 80.00
f.		5c blue green (b)	4.50 14.00
2	A1	5c green (d)	4.00 7.00
a.		5c green (c)	4.00 7.00
b.		5c green (e)	4.00 7.00
c.		5c green (f)	4.00 7.00
3	A1	5c vio ('68)	185.00 140.00
a.		5c rose lilac ('68)	185.00 140.00
		Revenue cancel	28.00
4	A3	10c brown	225.00 140.00
5	A2	50c orange	20.00
6	A2	50c blue ('68)	325.00
a.		50c dark blue ('68)	325.00
		Revenue cancel	28.00
7	A3	100c blue	60.00
		Revenue cancel	15.00
8	A3	100c green ('68)	140.00
a.		100c pale blue grn ('68)	140.00
		Revenue cancel	28.00

Used values are for postally canceled copies. Pen cancellations usually indicate that the stamps have been used fiscally and such stamps sell for about one-fifth as much as those with postal cancellations. The 500c is an essay.

Reprints of Nos. 3,4, 6 and 8 are common. Value, $10 each. Reprints of Nos. 2 and 5 are scarcer. Value, $25 each.

Coat of Arms
A4   A5

1868-69   **Perf. 12**
Nine Stars
10	A4	5c green	17.50 8.75
11	A4	10c vermilion	25.00 8.75
12	A4	50c blue	45.00 25.00
13	A4	100c orange	45.00 27.50
14	A4	500c black	475.00 375.00

Eleven Stars
15	A5	5c green	10.00 6.25
16	A5	10c vermilion	14.00 10.00
a.		Half used as 5c on cover	400.00
17	A5	50c blue	37.50 17.50
18	A5	100c dp orange	35.00 17.50
19	A5	500c black	1,750. 1,750.

See Nos. 26-27, 31-34.

Arms and "The Law" — A6

1878   **Various Frames**   **Perf. 12**
20	A6	5c ultra	9.25 4.25
21	A6	10c orange	7.50 4.00
a.		Half used as 5c on cover	50.00

22	A6	20c green	22.50 4.25
a.		Half used as 10c on cover	160.00
23	A6	50c dull carmine	110.00 12.00
		Nos. 20-23 (4)	149.25 23.75

Numerals Upright
(11 Stars)-A7   (9 Stars)-A8

1887   **Rouletted**
24	A7	1c rose	2.25 2.00
25	A7	2c violet	2.25 2.00
26	A5	5c blue	7.25 3.50
27	A5	10c rose	7.25 3.50
		Nos. 24-27 (4)	19.00 11.00

See No. 37.

1890   **Perf. 12**
28	A8	1c rose	1.65 .80
29	A8	2c violet	4.25 2.00
30	A4	5c blue	3.00 .80
31	A4	10c orange	6.25 .95
32	A4	20c dk green	12.50 1.65
33	A4	50c red	6.25 1.65
34	A4	100c yellow	12.50 3.25
		Nos. 28-34 (7)	46.40 11.10

See Nos. 35-36, 38-39.

1893   **Litho.**   **Perf. 11**
35	A8	1c rose	3.50 2.50
a.		Imperf. pair	35.00
b.		Horiz. pair, imperf. vert.	20.00
c.		Horiz. pair, imperf. btwn.	35.00
36	A8	2c violet	3.50 2.50
a.		Block of 4 imperf. vert. and horiz. through center	50.00
b.		Horiz. pair, imperf. btwn.	27.50
37	A7	5c blue	6.00 2.50
a.		Vert. pair, imperf. horiz.	27.50
b.		Horiz. pair, imperf. btwn.	35.00
38	A8	10c orange	17.00 4.00
a.		Horiz. pair, imperf. btwn.	50.00
39	A8	20c dark green	40.00 18.00
a.		Imperf. pair, vert. or horiz.	140.00
b.		Pair, imperf. btwn., vert. or horiz.	140.00
		Nos. 35-39 (5)	70.00 29.50

Coat of Arms — A9

1894   **Unwmk.**   **Engr.**   **Perf. 14, 14½**
Thin Paper
40	A9	1c bister	1.00 .60
41	A9	2c red orange	1.00 .60
42	A9	5c green	1.00 .60
43	A9	10c yellow brn	1.00 .60
44	A9	20c dark blue	3.00 1.25
45	A9	50c claret	7.50 1.75
46	A9	100c brown rose	17.50 6.25
		Nos. 40-46 (7)	32.00 11.65

Stamps of type A9 on thick paper were surreptitiously printed in Paris on the order of an official and without government authorization. Some of these stamps were substituted for part of a shipment of stamps on thin paper, which had been printed in London on government order. When the thick paper stamps reached Bolivia they were at first repudiated but afterwards were allowed to do postal duty. A large quantity of the thick paper stamps were fraudulently canceled in Paris with a cancellation of heavy bars forming an oval.

To be legitimate, copies of the thick paper stamps must have genuine cancellations of Bolivia. Value, on cover, each $125.

The 10c blue on thick paper is not known to have been issued.

Some copies of Nos. 40-46 show part of a papermakers' watermark "1011."

For overprints see Nos. 55-59.

President Tomas Frias — A10

President Jose M. Linares — A11

Pedro Domingo
Murillo
A12

Bernardo
Monteagudo
A13

Gen. Jose
Ballivian — A14

Gen. Antonio
Jose de
Sucre — A15

Simon
Bolivar — A16

Coat of
Arms — A17

1897   Litho.   Perf. 12

47	A10	1c pale yellow grn	1.25	.80
a.		Vert. pair, imperf. horiz.	50.00	
b.		Vert. pair, imperf. btwn.	50.00	
48	A11	2c red	1.75	1.40
49	A12	5c dk green	2.50	.80
a.		Horiz. pair, imperf. btwn.	50.00	
50	A13	10c brown vio	2.50	.80
a.		Vert. pair, imperf. btwn.	50.00	
51	A14	20c lake & blk	4.75	.95
a.		Imperf., pair		150.00
52	A15	50c orange	4.75	2.50
53	A16	1b Prus blue	4.75	5.50
54	A17	2b red, yel, grn & blk	37.50	50.00
		Nos. 47-54 (8)	59.75	62.75

Excellent forgeries of No. 54, perf and imperf, exist, some postally used.
Reprint of No. 53 has dot in numeral. Same value.

Nos. 40-44 Handstamped
in Violet or Blue

E.F.
1899

1899   Perf. 14½

55	A9	1c yellow bis	13.00	13.00
56	A9	2c red orange	16.00	16.00
57	A9	5c green	10.50	10.50
58	A9	10c yellow brn	13.00	10.50
59	A9	20c dark blue	21.00	21.00
		Nos. 55-59 (5)	73.50	71.00

The handstamp is found inverted, double, etc. Values twice the listed amounts. Forgeries of this handstamp are plentiful. "E.F." stands for Estado Federal.

The 50c and 100c (Nos. 45-46) were overprinted at a later date in Brazil.

Antonio José de
Sucre — A18

Perf. 11½, 12

1899		Engr.	Thin Paper	
62	A18	1c gray blue	2.50	.75
63	A18	2c brnsh red	1.75	.75
64	A18	5c dk green	6.00	1.50
65	A18	10c yellow org	2.50	1.25
66	A18	20c rose pink	3.00	.80
67	A18	50c bister brn	6.00	2.50
68	A18	1b gray violet	1.75	1.75
		Nos. 62-68 (7)	23.50	9.30

1901

69	A18	5c dark red	1.90	.60

Col. Adolfo
Ballivian
A19

Eliodoro
Camacho
A20

President
Narciso
Campero
A21

Jose Ballivian
A22

Gen. Andres
Santa
Cruz — A23

Coat of
Arms — A24

1901-02   Engr.

70	A19	1c claret	.55	.15
71	A20	2c green	.55	.20
73	A21	5c scarlet	.55	.20
74	A22	10c blue	1.40	.15
75	A23	20c violet & blk	.80	.15
76	A24	2b brown	3.75	2.75
		Nos. 70-71,73-76 (6)	7.60	3.60

Nos. 73, 74 exist imperf. Value, pairs, each $50.
For surcharges see #95-96, 193.

1904   Litho.

77	A19	1c claret	2.25	.55

In No. 70 the panel above "CENTAVO" is shaded with continuous lines. In No. 77 the shading is of dots.
See Nos. 103-105, 107, 110.

Coat of Arms of Dept.
of La Paz — A25

Murillo — A26

Jose Miguel
Lanza — A27

Ismael
Montes — A28

1909   Litho.   Perf. 11

78	A25	5c blue & blk	9.00	5.00
79	A26	10c green & blk	9.00	5.00
80	A27	20c orange & blk	9.00	5.00
81	A28	2b red & black	9.00	5.00
		Nos. 78-81 (4)	36.00	20.00

Centenary of Revolution of July, 1809.
Nos. 78-81 exist imperf. and tête bêche. Nos. 79-81 exist with center inverted.

Miguel
Betanzos
A29

Col. Ignacio
Warnes
A30

Murillo
A31

Monteagudo
A32

Esteban
Arce — A33

Antonio Jose
de
Sucre — A34

Simon Bolivar
A35

Manuel
Belgrano
A36

Coat of
Arms — A24

1909   Dated 1809-1825   Perf. 11½

82	A29	1c lt brown & blk	.55	.35
83	A30	2c green & blk	.55	.40
84	A31	5c red & blk	.55	.30
85	A32	10c dull bl & blk	.55	.30
86	A33	20c violet & blk	.65	.40
87	A34	50c olive bister & blk	1.00	.55
88	A35	1b gray brn & blk	1.00	.80
89	A36	2b chocolate & blk	1.65	1.10
		Nos. 82-89 (8)	6.50	4.20

War of Independence, 1809-1825.
Exist imperf. For surcharge see #97.

Warnes
A37

Betanzos
A38

Arce — A39

Dated 1910-1825

1910   Perf. 13x13½

92	A37	5c green & black	.40	.15
a.		Imperf., pair	5.00	
93	A38	10c claret & indigo	.40	.15
a.		Imperf., pair	5.00	
94	A39	20c dull blue & indigo	.65	.40
a.		Imperf., pair	5.00	
		Nos. 92-94 (3)	1.45	.70

War of Independence.
Nos. 92-94 may be found with parts of a papermaker's watermark: "A I & Co/EXTRA STRONG/9303."
Both perf and imperf exist with inverted centers.

Nos. 71 and 75
Surcharged in Black

5 Centavos
1911

1911   Perf. 11½, 12

95	A20	5c on 2c green	.45	.20
a.		Inverted surcharge	5.00	5.00
b.		Double surcharge	15.00	
c.		Period after "1911"	3.50	.80
d.		Blue surcharge	75.00	60.00
e.		Double dsurch., one invtd.	15.00	
96	A23	5c on 20c vio & blk	16.00	16.00
a.		Inverted surcharge	30.00	30.00
b.		Double surch., one invtd.	60.00	

No. 83 Handstamp
Surcharged in Green

20 CENTS
1911

97	A30	20c on 2c grn & blk	1,100.

This provisional was issued by local authorities at Villa Bella, a town on the Brazilian border. The 20c surcharge was applied after the stamp had been affixed to the cover. Excellent forgeries of No. 96-97 exist.

"Justice"
A40   A41

1912
Black or Dark Blue Overprint On Revenue Stamps

98	A40	2c green (Bk)	.35	.25
a.		Inverted overprint	5.00	
99	A41	10c ver (Bl)	1.10	.40
a.		Inverted overprint	5.00	

A42

A43

Red or Black Overprint
Engr.

100	A42	5c orange (R)	.55	.40
a.		Inverted overprint	5.00	
b.		Pair, one without overprint	12.50	
c.		Black overprint	50.00	

Red or Black Surcharge

101	A43	10c on 1c bl (R)	.55	.20
a.		Inverted surcharge	6.00	
b.		Double surcharge	6.00	
c.		Dbl. surcharge, one invtd.	7.50	
d.		Black surcharge	100.00	100.00
e.		As "d," inverted		
f.		As "d," double surcharge		
g.		Pair, one without black surch.	400.00	

Fakes of No. 101d are plentiful.

Revenue Stamp Surcharged "CORREOS /
10 Cts. / · 1917 ·" in Red

1917   Litho.

102	10c on 1c blue	6,000.	1,750.

Design similar to type A43.
Excellent forgeries exist.

Types of 1901 and

Frias-A45

Sucre-A46

Bolivar-A47

1913   Engr.   Perf. 12

103	A19	1c car rose	.40	.25
104	A20	2c vermilion	.40	.15
105	A21	5c green	.45	.15
106	A45	8c yellow	.80	.50
107	A22	10c gray	.80	.25
108	A46	50c dull violet	1.50	.55
109	A47	1b slate blue	2.25	1.40
110	A24	2b black	4.50	2.75
		Nos. 103-110 (8)	11.10	6.00

No. 107, litho., was not regularly issued.

Nine values commemorating the Guiqui-La Paz railroad were printed in 1915 but never issued. Typographed forgeries exist.

Monolith of
Tiahuanacu
A48

Mt. Potosí
A49

Lake
Titicaca — A50

Mt.
Illimani — A51

Legislature
Building — A53

FIVE CENTAVOS.

Type I · Numerals have background of vertical
lines. Clouds formed of dots.

Type II · Numerals on white background.
Clouds near the mountain formed of wavy lines.

1916-17		**Litho.**	**Perf. 11½**	
111	A48	½c brown	.15	.15
a.		Horiz. pair, imperf. vert.	5.00	
112	A49	1c gray green	.15	.15
a.		Imperf., pair	2.00	
113	A50	2c car & blk	.25	.15
a.		Imperf., pair	2.00	
b.		Vert. pair, imperf. horiz.		
c.		Center inverted	12.50	11.25
d.		Imperf., center inverted	17.50	
114	A51	5c dk blue (I)	.50	.18
a.		Imperf., pair	2.00	
b.		Vert. pair, imperf. horiz.	3.50	
c.		Horiz. pair, imperf. vert.	3.50	
115	A51	5c dk blue (II)	.50	.15
a.		Imperf., pair	2.50	
116	A53	10c org & bl	1.00	.15
a.		Imperf., pair	3.50	
b.		No period after "Legislativo"	1.00	.15
c.		Center inverted	40.00	40.00
d.		Vertical pair, imperf. between	5.00	
		Nos. 111-116 (6)	2.55	
		Set value		.69

For surcharges see Nos. 194-196.

Coat of Arms
A54   A55

Printed by the American Bank Note Co.

1919-20		**Engr.**	**Perf. 12**	
118	A54	1c carmine	.25	.20
119	A54	2c dk violet	4.75	3.00
120	A54	5c dk green	.50	.15
121	A54	10c vermilion	.50	.15
122	A54	20c dk blue	1.50	.30
123	A54	22c lt blue	.90	.75
124	A54	24c purple	.60	.50
125	A54	50c orange	4.75	.60
126	A55	1b red brown	6.00	1.75
127	A55	2b black brn	9.00	4.50
		Nos. 118-127 (10)	28.75	11.90

Printed by Perkins, Bacon & Co., Ltd.

1923-27		**Re-engraved**	**Perf. 13½**	
128	A54	1c carmine ('27)	.15	.15
129	A54	2c dk violet	.25	.15
130	A54	5c dp green	.80	.15
131	A54	10c vermilion	14.00	12.00
132	A54	20c slate blue	1.75	.20
135	A54	50c orange	2.75	.60
136	A55	1b red brown	.70	.30
137	A55	2b black brown	.50	.30
		Nos. 128-137 (8)	20.90	13.85

There are many differences in the designs of the
two issues but they are too minute to be illustrated
or described.

Nos. 128-137 exist imperf.

See Nos. 144-146, 173-177. For surcharges see
Nos. 138-143, 160, 162, 181-186, 236-237.

Stamps of 1919-20
Surcharged in Blue,
Black or Red

**Habilitada
15 cts.**

1924			**Perf. 12**	
138	A54	5c on 1c car (Bl)	.40	.20
a.		Inverted surcharge	5.00	5.00
b.		Double surcharge	5.00	5.00
139	A54	5c on 10c ver (Bk)	.70	.50
a.		Inverted surcharge	6.00	6.00
140	A54	15c on 22c lt bl (Bk)	.70	.30
a.		Inverted surcharge	5.25	5.25
b.		Double surcharge, one inverted		

No. 140 surcharged in red or blue probably are
trial impressions. They appear jointly, and with
black in blocks.

Same Surcharge on No. 131
Perf. 13½

142	A54	15c on 10c ver (Bk)	.70	.25
a.		Inverted surcharge	6.00	6.00

No. 121 Surcharged

**Habilitada
15 cts.**

Perf. 12

143	A54	15c on 10c ver (Bk)	.90	.30
a.		Inverted surcharge	6.00	6.00
b.		Double surcharge	5.00	5.00
		Nos. 138-143 (5)	3.40	1.55

Type of 1919-20 Issue
Printed by Waterlow & Sons
Second Re-engraving

1925		**Unwmk.**	**Perf. 12½**	
144	A54	5c deep green	.80	.25
145	A54	5c ultra	.80	.15
146	A54	20c dark blue	.35	.15
		Nos. 144-146 (3)	1.95	.55

These stamps may be identified by the
perforation.

Miner — A56

Condor
Looking
Toward the
Sea — A57

Designs: 2c, Sower. 5c, Torch of Eternal Freedom. 10c, National flower (kantuta). 15c, Pres.
Bautista Saavedra. 50c, Liberty head. 1b, Archer on
horse. 2b, Mercury. 5b, Gen. A. J. de Sucre.

1925		**Engr.**	**Perf. 14**	
150	A56	1c dark green	.75	
151	A56	2c rose	.75	
152	A56	5c red, grn	.75	.35
153	A56	10c car, yel	1.25	.75
154	A56	15c red brown	.50	.25
155	A57	25c ultra	.50	.50
156	A56	50c dp violet	.50	.50
157	A56	1b red	1.25	1.25
158	A57	2b orange	1.75	1.75
159	A56	5b black brn	2.00	2.00
		Nos. 150-159 (10)	10.00	

Cent. of the Republic. The 1c and 2c were not
released for general use.
Nos. 150-159 exist imperf. Value, $60 each pair.
For surcharges see Nos. C59-C62.

1927

Stamps of 1919-27
Surcharged in Blue, Black
or Red

**5
CENTAVOS**

1927				
160	A54	5c on 1c car (Bl)	2.50	.90
a.		Inverted surcharge	6.00	6.00
b.		Black surcharge	22.50	22.50
			Perf. 12	
162	A54	10c on 24c pur (Bk)	2.50	1.50
a.		Inverted surcharge	30.00	30.00
b.		Red surcharge	22.50	22.50

Coat of Arms — A66

Printed by Waterlow & Sons

1927		**Litho.**	**Perf. 13½**	
165	A66	2c yellow	.40	.20
166	A66	3c pink	.50	.20
167	A66	4c red brown	.40	.40
168	A66	20c lt ol grn	.65	.20
169	A66	25c deep blue	.65	.30
170	A66	30c violet	.80	.80
171	A66	40c orange	1.50	1.25
172	A66	50c dp brown	1.50	.50
173	A55	1b red	1.75	1.25
174	A55	2b plum	2.50	2.50
175	A55	3b olive grn	2.50	2.50
176	A55	4b claret	4.00	3.50
177	A55	5b bister brn	4.75	4.00
		Nos. 165-177 (13)	21.90	17.90

For overprints and surcharges see Nos. 178-180,
208, 211-212.

Type of 1927 Issue
Overprinted

1927				
178	A66	5c dark green	.20	.15
179	A66	10c slate	.45	.15
180	A66	15c carmine	.65	.25
		Nos. 178-180 (3)	1.30	.55

Exist with inverted overprint. Value $20 each.

Stamps of 1919-27
Surcharged

**15 cts.
1928**

1928			**Perf. 12, 12½, 13½**	
		Red Surcharge		
181	A54	15c on 20c #122	9.00	9.00
182	A54	15c on 20c #132	9.00	9.00
a.		Black surcharge	30.00	
183	A54	15c on 20c #146	165.00	165.00
		Black Surcharge		
184	A54	15c on 24c #124	1.65	.90
a.		Inverted surcharge	5.00	5.00
b.		Blue surcharge	50.00	
185	A54	15c on 50c #125	50.00	42.50
186	A54	15c on 50c #135	1.25	.70
		Nos. 181-186 (6)	235.90	227.10

Condor — A67

Hernando
Siles — A68

Map of Bolivia — A69

Printed by Perkins, Bacon & Co., Ltd.

1928		**Engr.**	**Perf. 13½**	
189	A67	5c green	1.50	.15
190	A68	10c slate	.30	.15
191	A69	15c carmine lake	.60	.15
		Nos. 189-191 (3)	2.40	
		Set value		.15

Nos. 104, 111, 113,
Surcharged in Various
Colors

**0.03
Centavos
R. S. 21-4
1930**

1930			**Perf. 12, 11½**	
193	A20	1c on 2c (Bl)	.80	.80
a.		"0.10" for "0.01"	12.50	12.50

194	A50	3c on 2c (Br)	.80	.80
195	A48	25c on ½c (Bk)	.80	.80
196	A50	25c on 2c (V)	.80	.80
		Nos. 193-196 (4)	3.20	3.20

The lines of the surcharges were spaced to fit the
various shapes of the stamps. The surcharges exist
inverted, double, etc.

Trial printings were made of the surcharges on
#193 and 194 in black and on #196 in brown.

Mt.
Potosi — A70

Mt.
Illimani — A71

Eduardo
Abaroa — A72

Map of
Bolivia — A73

Sucre — A74   Bolivar — A75

1931		**Engr.**	**Perf. 14**	
197	A70	2c green	1.40	.50
198	A71	5c light blue	1.40	.20
199	A72	10c red orange	1.40	.20
200	A73	15c violet	1.40	.20
201	A73	35c carmine	2.00	.85
202	A73	45c orange	2.00	.75
203	A74	50c gray	.55	.55
204	A75	1b brown	.55	.55
		Nos. 197-204 (8)	10.70	3.80

No. 198 exists imperf.
See #207, 241. For surcharges see #209-210.

Symbols of 1930 Revolution — A76

1931		**Litho.**	**Perf. 11**	
205	A76	15c scarlet	2.25	.40
a.		Pair, imperf. between		
206	A76	50c brt violet	.70	.70
a.		Pair, imperf. between	7.50	

Revolution of June 25, 1930.
For surcharges see Nos. 239-240.

Map Type of 1931
Without Imprint

1932			**Litho.**	
207	A73	15c violet	1.50	.35

Stamps of 1927-31
Surcharged

**Habilitada
A 15 Cts.**
D. S. 13-7. 1933

1933			**Perf. 13½, 14**	
208	A66	5c on 1b red	.60	.35
a.		Without period after "Cts"	1.25	1.25
209	A73	15c on 35c car	.35	.35
a.		Inverted surcharge	20.00	
210	A73	15c on 45c orange	.35	.35
a.		Inverted surcharge	3.00	3.00
211	A66	15c on 50c dp brn	1.50	.30
212	A66	25c on 40c orange	.60	.25
		Nos. 208-212 (5)	3.40	1.60

The hyphens in "13-7-33" occur in three
positions.

Coat of Arms — A77

1933 **Engr.** *Perf. 12*
213 A77 2c blue green .25 .15
214 A77 5c blue .25 .15
215 A77 10c red .45 .30
216 A77 15c deep violet .35 .15
217 A77 25c dark blue .65 .55
Nos. 213-217 (5) 1.95 1.30

For surcharges see Nos. 233-235, 238.

Mariano Baptista — A78   Map of Bolivia — A79

1935
218 A78 15c dull violet .45 .20

1935
219 A79 2c dark blue .15 .15
220 A79 3c yellow .15 .15
221 A79 5c vermilion .15 .15
222 A79 5c blue grn .35 .15
223 A79 10c black brn .35 .15
224 A79 15c deep rose .35 .15
225 A79 15c ultra .35 .15
226 A79 20c yellow grn .40 .15
227 A79 25c lt blue .40 .15
228 A79 30c deep rose .80 .55
229 A79 40c orange .80 .55
230 A79 50c gray violet .80 .25
231 A79 1b yellow .55 .35
232 A79 2b olive brown .80 .70
Nos. 219-232 (14) 6.40 3.75

Comunicaciones D. S. 25-2-37 0.05

Regular Stamps of 1925-33 Surcharged in Black

1937 *Perf. 11, 12, 13½*
233 A77 5c on 2c bl grn .25 .25
234 A77 15c on 25c dk bl .30 .30
235 A77 30c on 25c dk bl .50 .50
236 A55 45c on 1b red brn .60 .60
237 A55 1b on 2b plum .75 .75
a. "1" missing 7.50 7.50
238 A77 2b on 25c dk bl .75 .75

"Comunicaciones" on one line
239 A76 3b on 50c brt vio 1.25 1.25
a. "3" of value missing 6.00 6.00
240 A76 5b on 50c brt vio 1.25 1.25
Nos. 233-240 (8) 5.65 5.65

Exist inverted, double, etc.

President Siles — A80

1937 **Unwmk.** *Perf. 14*
241 A80 1c yellow brown .30 .30

Native School — A81   Oil Wells — A82

Modern Factories A83   Torch of Knowledge A84

Map of the Sucre-Camiri R. R. — A85   Allegory of Free Education — A86

Allegorical Figure of Learning A87   Symbols of Industry A88

Modern Agriculture — A89

1938 **Litho.** *Perf. 10½, 11*
242 A81 2c dull red .40 .40
243 A82 10c pink .45 .25
244 A83 15c yellow grn .60 .30
245 A84 30c yellow .75 .35
246 A85 45c rose red 1.40 .75
247 A86 60c dk violet 1.10 .35
248 A87 75c dull blue 1.50 .35
249 A88 1b lt brown 2.25 .35
250 A89 2b bister 2.00 .75
Nos. 242-250 (9) 10.45 3.85

For surcharge see No. 314.

Llamas — A90   Vicuna — A91

Coat of Arms — A92   Cocoi Herons — A93

Chinchilla — A94   Toco Toucan — A95

Condor — A96   Jaguar — A97

1939, Jan. 21 *Perf. 10½, 11½x10½*
251 A90 2c green .40 .30
252 A90 4c fawn .40 .30
253 A90 5c red violet .40 .25
254 A91 10c black .60 .30
255 A91 15c emerald .60 .35
256 A91 20c dk slate grn .60 .25
257 A92 25c lemon .60 .25
258 A92 30c dark blue .60 .30
259 A93 40c vermilion 1.40 .30
260 A93 45c gray 1.40 .30
261 A94 60c rose red 1.40 .55
262 A94 75c slate blue 2.75 .55
263 A95 90c orange 2.00 .55
264 A95 1b blue 2.00 .55
265 A96 2b rose lake 2.75 .55
266 A96 3b dark violet 3.50 .80
267 A97 4b brown org 4.00 1.10
268 A97 5b gray brown 5.00 1.40
Nos. 251-268 (18) 30.40 8.95

All but 20c exist imperf.
Imperf. counterfeits with altered designs exist of some values.
For surcharges see Nos. 315-317.

Flags of 21 American Republics A98

1940, Apr. **Litho.** *Perf. 10½*
269 A98 9b multicolored 1.10 1.10
Pan American Union, 150th anniversary.

Statue of Murillo — A99   Urns of Murillo and Sagarnaga — A100

Dream of Murillo A101   Murillo A102

1941, Apr. 15
270 A99 10c dull vio brn .15 .15
271 A100 15c lt green .20 .15
a. Imperf., pair 3.50
b. Double impression 6.00
272 A101 45c carmine rose .20 .15
a. Double impression 6.00
273 A102 1.05b dk ultra .45 .15
Nos. 270-273 (4) 1.00
Set value .50

130th anniv. of the execution of Pedro Domingo Murillo (1759-1810), patriot.
For surcharge see No. 333.

First Stamp of Bolivia and 1941 Airmail Stamp — A103

1942, Oct. **Litho.** *Perf. 13½*
274 A103 5c pink .50 .50
275 A103 10c orange .50 .40
276 A103 20c yellow grn 1.00 .65
277 A103 40c carmine rose 1.25 .80
278 A103 90c ultra 2.50 1.00
279 A103 1b violet 3.00 1.65
280 A103 10b olive bister 10.00 8.25
Nos. 274-280 (7) 18.75 13.25

1st School Phil. Exposition held in La Paz, Oct., 1941.

Gen. Ballivian Leading Cavalry Charge, Battle of Ingavi — A104

1943 **Photo.** *Perf. 12½*
281 A104 2c lt blue grn .15 .15
282 A104 3c orange .15 .15
283 A104 25c deep plum .15 .15
284 A104 45c ultra .18 .15
285 A104 3b scarlet .38 .35
286 A104 4b brt rose lilac .55 .45
287 A104 5b black brown .80 .55
Nos. 281-287 (7) 2.36 1.95

Souvenir Sheets
Perf. 13, Imperf.
288 A104 Sheet of 4 1.50 1.50
289 A104 Sheet of 3 4.50 4.50

Centenary of the Battle of Ingavi, 1841. No. 288 contains 4 stamps similar to Nos. 281-284, No. 289 three stamps similar to Nos. 285-287.

Potosi A107   Quechisla A108

Miner — A109

Dam A110

Mine Interior A111

Chaquiri Dam A112

Entrance to Pulacayo Mine A113

1943 **Engr.** *Perf. 12½*
290 A107 15c red brown .20 .15
291 A108 45c vio blue .20 .15
292 A109 1.25b brt rose vio .25 .30
293 A110 1.50b emerald .25 .30
294 A111 2b brown blk .30 .35
295 A112 2.10b lt blue .40 .45
296 A113 3b red orange .50 .55
Nos. 290-296 (7) 2.10 2.25

General José Ballivián and Cathedral at Trinidad A114

1943, Nov. 18
297 A114 5c dk green & brn .15 .15
298 A114 10c dull pur & brn .15 .15
299 A114 30c rose red & brn .15 .15
300 A114 45c brt ultra & brn .20 .25
301 A114 2.10b dp org & brn .30 .35
Nos. 297-301,C91-C95 (10) 2.05 1.98

Department of Beni centenary.

"Honor, Work, Law" A115

"United for the Country" A116

1944 Litho. Perf. 13½
302 A115 20c orange .15 .15
303 A115 90c ultra .15 .15
304 A116 1b brt red vio .15 .15
305 A116 2.40b dull brown .20 .15

1945
306 A115 20c green .15 .15
307 A115 90c dp rose .15 .15
Set value, #302-307, C96-C99 1.50 1.00
Nos. 302-307 were issued to commemorate the Revolution of Dec. 20, 1943.

Catalogue values for unused stamps in this section, from this point to the end of the section, are for Never Hinged items.

Leopold Benedetto Vincenti, Joseph Ignacio de Sanjines and Bars of Anthem A117

1946, Aug. 21 Litho. Perf. 10½
308 A117 5c rose vio & blk .15 .15
309 A117 10c ultra & blk .15 .15
310 A117 15c blue grn & blk .15 .15
311 A117 30c vermilion & brn .15 .15
  a. Souv. sheet of 1, imperf. .65 .65
312 A117 90c dk blue & brn .15 .15
313 A117 2b black & brn .30 .15
  a. Souv. sheet of 1, imperf. 1.25 1.25
Set value .85 .60
Cent. of the adoption of Bolivia's natl. anthem.
Nos. 311a and 313a sold for 4b over face.

1947
Nos. 248 and 262 Surcharged in Carmine, Black or Orange

1947, Mar. 12 Perf. 10½, 11
314 A87 1.40b on 75c (C) .15 .15
315 A94 1.40b on 75c (Bk) .15 .15
316 A94 1.40b on 75c (C) .15 .15
317 A94 1.40b on 75c (O) .15 .15
Set value, #314-317, C112 .65 .65

People Attacking Presidential Palace — A118

Arms of Bolivia and Argentina — A119

1947, Sept. Litho. Perf. 13½
318 A118 20c blue grn .15 .15
319 A118 50c lilac rose .15 .15
320 A118 1.40b grnsh bl .15 .15
321 A118 3.70b dull org .15 .15
322 A118 4b violet .18 .14
323 A118 10b olive .40 .25
Set value, #318-323, C113-C117 1.50 1.10
1st anniv. of the Revolution of July 21, 1946. Exist imperf.

1947, Oct. 23
324 A119 1.40b deep orange .20 .15
Meeting of Presidents Enrique Hertzog of Bolivia and Juan D. Peron of Argentina at Yacuiba on Oct. 23, 1947. Exist imperf. See No. C118.

Statue of Christ above La Paz — A120

2b, Child kneeling before cross of Golgotha. 3b, St. John Bosco. #328, Virgin of Copacabana. #329, Pope Pius XII blessing University of La Paz.

1948, Sept. 26 Unwmk. Perf. 11½
325 A120 1.40b blue & yel .30 .15
326 A120 2b yel grn & sal .40 .15
327 A120 3b green & gray .65 .20
328 A120 5b violet & sal .80 .25
329 A120 5b red brn & lt grn 1.10 .25
Nos. 325-329,C119-C123 (10) 6.05 2.51
3rd Inter-American Cong. of Catholic Education.

Map and Emblem of Bolivia Auto Club — A125

Pres. Gregorio Pacheco, Map and Post Horn — A126

1948, Oct. 20
330 A125 5b indigo & salmon 1.50 .15
Intl. Automobile Races of South America, Sept.-Oct. 1948. See No. C124.

1950, Jan. 2 Litho. Perf. 11½
331 A126 1.40b violet blue .15 .15
332 A126 4.20b red .15 .15
Set value, #331-332, C125-C127 .60 .60
75th anniv. of the UPU.

No. 273 Surcharged in Black

1950 Perf. 10½
333 A102 2b on 1.05b dk ultra .16 .15

Crucifix and View of Potosi — A127

Symbols of United Nations — A128

Perf. 11½
1950, Sept. 14 Litho. Unwmk.
334 A127 20c violet .15 .15
335 A127 30c dp orange .15 .15
336 A127 50c lilac rose .15 .15
337 A127 1b carmine .15 .15
338 A127 2b blue .30 .15
339 A127 6b chocolate .25 .15
Set value .85 .35
400th anniv. of the appearance of a crucifix at Potosi. Exist imperf.

1950, Oct. 24
340 A128 60c ultra 1.00 .15
341 A128 2b green 1.40 .22
5th anniv. of the UN, Oct. 24, 1945. See Nos. C138-C139.

Gate of the Sun and Llama A129

Church of San Francisco A130

Designs: 40c, Avenue Camacho. 50c, Consistorial Palace. 1b, Legislative Palace. 1.40b, Communications Bldg. 2b, Arms. 3b, La Gasca ordering Mendoza to found La Paz. 5b, Capt. Alonso de Mendoza founding La Paz. 10b, Arms; portrait of Mendoza.

1951, Mar. Engr. Perf. 12½
Center in Black
342 A129 20c green .15 .15
343 A130 30c dp orange .15 .15
344 A129 40c bister brn .15 .15
345 A129 50c dk red .15 .15
346 A129 1b dp purple .15 .15
347 A129 1.40b dk vio blue .15 .15
348 A129 2b dp purple .15 .15
349 A129 3b red lilac .20 .15
  a. Sheet, Nos. 345, 346, 348, 349 1.10 1.10
  b. As "a," imperf. 1.10 1.10
350 A129 5b dk red .22 .16
  a. Sheet, Nos. 344, 347, 350 1.10 1.10
  b. As "a," imperf. 1.10 1.10
351 A129 10b legend .50 .22
  a. Sheet, Nos. 342, 343, 351 1.10 1.10
  b. As "a," imperf. 1.10 1.10
Nos. 342-351,C140-C149 (20) 4.97 4.58
400th anniv. of the founding of La Paz.
For surcharges see Nos. 393-402.

Boxing — A131

Perf. 12½
1951, July 1 Unwmk. Engr.
352 A131 20c shown .16 .15
353 A131 50c Tennis .16 .15
354 A131 1b Diving .20 .15
355 A131 1.40b Soccer .20 .15
356 A131 2b Skiing .38 .30
357 A131 3b Handball .80 .80
  a. Sheet, Nos. 352, 353, 356, 357 2.25 1.75
  b. As "a," imperf. 2.25 1.75
358 A131 4b Cycling 1.00 1.00
  a. Sheet, Nos. 354, 355, 358 2.00 1.50
  b. As "a," imperf. 2.00 1.50
Nos. 352-358,C150-C156 (14) 8.15 5.85
The stamps were intended to commemorate the 5th athletic championship matches held at La Paz, October 1948.

Eagle and Flag of Bolivia — A132

1951, Nov. 5 Litho. Perf. 11½
Flag in Red, Yellow and Green.
359 A132 2b aqua .15 .15
360 A132 3.50b ultra .15 .15
361 A132 5b purple .15 .15
362 A132 7.50b gray .20 .15
363 A132 15b dp car .25 .22
364 A132 30b sepia .50 .50
Nos. 359-364 (6) 1.40 1.32
Cent. of the adoption of Bolivia's natl. flag.

Eduardo Abaroa A133

Queen Isabella I A134

1952, Mar. Perf. 11
365 A133 80c dk carmine .15 .15
366 A133 1b red orange .15 .15
367 A133 2b emerald .20 .15
368 A133 5b ultra .25 .15

369 A133 10b lilac rose .50 .16
370 A133 20b dk brown .75 .65
Nos. 365-370,C157-C162 (12) 5.00 4.11
73rd anniversary of the death of Eduardo Abaroa.

1952, July 16 Unwmk. Perf. 13½
371 A134 2b vio bl .15 .15
372 A134 6.30b carmine .20 .20
Set value .30 .30
500th anniv. of the birth of Isabella I of Spain. See Nos. C163-C164.

Columbus Lighthouse A135

1952, July 16 Litho.
373 A135 2b vio bl, bl .15 .15
374 A135 5b car, sal .50 .40
375 A135 9b emer, grn .85 .60
Nos. 373-375,C165-C168 (7) 2.50 1.90

Miner — A136

1953, Apr. 9
376 A136 2.50b vermilion .15 .15
377 A136 8b violet .15 .15
Set value .25 .20
Nationalization of the mines.

Gualberto Villarroel, Victor Paz Estenssoro and Hernan Siles Zuazo — A137

1953, Apr. 9 Perf. 11½
378 A137 50c rose lil .15 .15
379 A137 1b brt rose .15 .15
380 A137 2b vio bl .15 .15
381 A137 3b lt grn .15 .15
382 A137 4b yel org .15 .15
383 A137 5b dl vio .16 .15
Set value, #378-383, C169-C175 1.90 1.50
Revolution of Apr. 9, 1952, 1st anniv.

Map of Bolivia and Cow's Head — A138

Designs: 17b, Same as 5b. 25b, 85b, Map and ear of wheat.

1954, Aug. 2 Perf. 12x11½
384 A138 5b car rose .15 .15
385 A138 17b aqua .15 .15
386 A138 25b chalky blue .15 .15
387 A138 85b blk brn .25 .20
Set value, #384-387, C176-C181 2.35 1.15
Nos. 384-385 for the agrarian reform laws of 1953-54. Nos. 386-387 for the 1st National Congress of Agronomy. Exist imperf.

Oil Refinery A139

1955, Oct. 9 Unwmk. Perf. 12x11½
388 A139 10b ultra & lt ultra .15 .15
389 A139 35b rose car & rose .15 .15
390 A139 40b dk & lt yel grn .15 .15

391 A139	50b red vio & lil rose	.15	.15
392 A139	80b brn & bis brn	.18	.15
Nos. 388-392,C182-C186 (10)		3.28	
Set value		2.25	

Exist imperf.

Nos. 342-351, Surcharged with New Values and Bars in Ultramarine

1957, Feb. 14   Engr.   Perf. 12½
Center in Black

393 A129	50b on 3b red lilac	.15	.15
394 A129	100b on 2b dp pur	.15	.15
395 A129	200b on 1b dp pur	.15	.15
396 A129	300b on 1.40b dk vio bl	.16	.15
397 A129	350b on 20c green	.22	.15
398 A129	400b on 40c bis brn	.22	.15
399 A130	600b on 30c dp org	.35	.15
400 A129	800b on 50c dk red	.40	.15
401 A129	1000b on 10b sepia	.40	.15
402 A129	2000b on 5b dk red	.65	.20
Nos. 393-402 (10)		2.85	
Set value		.75	

See Nos. C187-C196.

CEPAL Building, Santiago de Chile, and Meeting Hall in La Paz — A140

1957, May 15   Litho.   Perf. 13

403 A140	150b gray & ultra	.15	.15
404 A140	350b bis brn & gray	.18	.18
405 A140	550b chlky bl & brn	.20	.20
406 A140	750b dp rose & grn	.30	.20
407 A140	900b grn & brn blk	.40	.15
Nos. 403-407,C197-C201 (10)		5.03	3.48

7th session of the C. E. P. A. L. (Comision Economica para la America Latina de las Naciones Unidas), La Paz. Exist imperf.
For surcharges see Nos. 482-484.

Presidents Siles Zuazo and Aramburu A141

1957, Dec. 15   Unwmk.   Perf. 11½

408 A141	50b red org	.15	.15
409 A141	350b blue	.25	.15
410 A141	1000b redsh brn	.50	.15
Nos. 408-410,C202-C204 (6)		1.97	
Set value		.48	

Opening of the Santa Cruz-Yacuiba Railroad and the meeting of the Presidents of Bolivia and Argentina. Exist imperf.
For surcharge see No. 699.

Flags of Bolivia and Mexico and Presidents Hernan Siles Zuazo and Adolfo Lopez Mateos A142

1960, Jan. 30   Litho.   Perf. 11½

411 A142	350b olive	.16	.16
412 A142	600b red brn	.22	.22
413 A142	1500b blk brn	.50	.50
Nos. 411-413,C205-C207 (6)		3.03	2.18

Issued for an expected visit of Mexico's President Adolfo Lopez Mateos. On sale Jan. 30-Feb. 1, 1960.

Indians and Mt. Illimani A143

Refugee Children A144

1960, Mar. 26   Unwmk.

414 A143	500b ol bis	.50	.15
415 A143	1000b blue	.90	.30
416 A143	2000b brown	2.00	.50
417 A143	4000b green	3.75	2.50
Nos. 414-417,C208-C211 (8)		23.90	12.90

1960, Apr. 7   Perf. 11½

418 A144	50b brown	.15	.15
419 A144	350b claret	.15	.15
420 A144	400b steel blue	.16	.16
421 A144	1000b gray brn	.50	.50
422 A144	3000b slate grn	1.00	1.00
Nos. 418-422,C212-C216 (10)		4.26	4.21

Issued to publicize World Refugee Year, July 1, 1959-June 30, 1960.
For surcharges see Nos. 454-458, 529.

Jaime Laredo A145

Rotary Emblem and Nurse with Children A146

1960, Aug. 15   Litho.   Perf. 11½

423 A145	100b olive	.20	.15
424 A145	350b dp rose	.30	.25
425 A145	500b Prus grn	.38	.20
426 A145	1000b brown	.50	.50
427 A145	1500b vio bl	.90	.90
428 A145	5000b gray	3.00	3.00
Nos. 423-428,C217-C222 (12)		13.03	8.70

Issued to honor violinist Jaime Laredo.
For surcharge see No. 485.

1960, Nov. 19   Perf. 11½

429 A146	350b multi	.16	.15
430 A146	500b multi	.22	.15
431 A146	600b multi	.35	.35
432 A146	1000b multi	.40	.20
Nos. 429-432,C223-C226 (8)		6.13	3.49

Issued for the Children's Hospital, sponsored by the Rotary Club of La Paz.
For surcharges see Nos. 486-487.

Designs from Gate of the Sun
A147   A148

Designs: Various prehistoric gods and ornaments from Tiahuanacu excavations.

1960, Dec. 16   Perf. 13x12, 12x13
Gold Background
Surcharge in Black or Dark Red
Sizes: 21x23mm, 23x21mm

433 A147	50b on ½c red	.45	.30
434 A147	100b on 1c red	.35	.15
435 A147	200b on 2c blk	.75	.35
436 A147	300b on 5c grn (DR)	.25	.20
437 A147	350b on 10c grn	.25	.75
438 A148	400b on 15c ind	.35	.15
439 A148	500b on 20c red	.35	.30
440 A148	500b on 50c red	.40	.15
441 A148	600b on 22½c grn	.45	.45
442 A148	600b on 60c vio	.60	.50
443 A148	700b on 25c vio	.75	.15
444 A148	700b on 1b grn	1.00	1.00
445 A148	800b on 30c red	.60	.15
446 A148	900b on 40c grn	.45	.20
447 A148	1000b on 2b bl	.60	.50
448 A148	1800b on 3b gray	5.00	3.50

Perf. 11
Size: 49½x23mm

449 A148	4000b on 4b gray	30.00	25.00

Perf. 11x13½
Size: 49x53mm

450 A147	5000b on 5b gray	7.50	7.00
Nos. 433-450 (18)		50.10	40.80

Nos. 433-450 were not regularly issued without surcharge. Value, set $20.
The decree for Nos. 433-450 stipulated that 7 were for air mail (500b on 50c, 600b on 60c, 700b on 1b, 1000b, 1800b, 4000b and 5000b), but the overprinting failed to include "Aereo."
The 800b surcharge also exists on the 1c red and gold. This was not listed in the decree.
For surcharges see Nos. 528, 614.

Miguel de Cervantes A149

Nuflo de Chaves A150

1961, Nov.   Photo.   Perf. 13x12½
451 A149 600b ocher & dl vio   .38 .15

Cervantes' appointment as Chief Magistrate of La Paz. See No. C230.

1961, Nov.   Unwmk.
452 A150 1500b dk bl, *buff*   .75 .30

Founding of Santa Cruz de la Sierra, 400th anniv. See #468, C246. For surcharge see #533.

People below Eucharist Symbol — A151

Flowers — A152

1962, Mar. 19   Litho.   Perf. 10½
453 A151 1000b gray grn, red & yel   .65 .35

4th Natl. Eucharistic Congress, Santa Cruz, 1961. See No. C231.

Nos. 418-422 Surcharged Horizontally with New Value and Bars or Greek Key Border Segment

1962, June   Perf. 11½

454 A144	600b on 50b brown	.18	.18
455 A144	900b on 350b claret	.22	.15
456 A144	1000b on 400b steel blue	.32	.15
457 A144	2000b on 1000b gray brn	.38	.15
458 A144	3500b on 3000b slate grn	.65	.65
Nos. 454-458,C232-C236 (10)		5.15	4.45

Old value obliterated with two short bars on No. 454; four short bars on Nos. 455-456 and Greek key border on Nos. 457-458. The Greek key obliteration comes in two positions: two full "keys" on top, and one full and two half keys on top.

1962, June 28   Litho.   Perf. 10½

459 A152	200b Hibiscus	.30	.15
460 A152	400b Bicolored vanda	.45	.15
461 A152	600b Lily	.75	.15
462 A152	1000b Orchid	1.00	.18
Nos. 459-462,C237-C240 (8)		7.50	3.18

Bolivia's Armed Forces A153

Anti-Malaria Emblem A154

1962, Sept. 5   Perf. 11½

463 A153	400b Infantry	.15	.15
464 A153	500b Cavalry	.15	.15
465 A153	600b Artillery	.16	.15
466 A153	2000b Engineers	.50	.35
Nos. 463-466,C241-C244 (8)		3.96	2.15

1962, Oct. 4
467 A154 600b dk & lt vio & yel   .25 .25

WHO drive to eradicate malaria. See #C245.

Portrait Type of 1961
Design: 600b, Alonso de Mendoza.

1962   Photo.   Perf. 13x12½
468 A150 600b rose vio, *bluish*   .25 .15

Soccer and Flags — A155

Design: 1b, Goalkeeper catching ball, vert.

1963, Mar. 21   Litho.   Perf. 11½
Flags in National Colors

469 A155	60c gray	.40	.40
470 A155	1b gray	.60	.20

21st South American Soccer Championships. See Nos. C247-C248.

Globe and Wheat Emblem — A156

1963, Aug. 1   Unwmk.   Perf. 11½
471 A156 60c dk bl, bl & yel   .25 .25

"Freedom from Hunger" campaign of the FAO. See No. C249.

Oil Derrick and Chart — A157

Designs: 60c, Map of Bolivia. 1b, Students.

1963, Dec. 21   Litho.   Perf. 11½

472 A157	10c grn & dk brn	.15	.15
473 A157	60c ocher & dk brn	.22	.15
474 A157	1b dk bl, grn & yel	.28	.15
Nos. 472-474,C251-C253 (6)		2.55	1.80

Revolution of Apr. 9, 1952, 10th anniv.

Flags of Bolivia and Peru — A158

1966, Aug. 10   Wmk. 90   Perf. 13½
Flags in National Colors

475 A158	10c blk & tan	.15	.15
476 A158	60c blk & lt grn	.20	.20
477 A158	1b blk & gray	.35	.35
478 A158	2b blk & rose	.50	.50
Nos. 475-478,C254-C257 (8)		2.85	2.85

Marshal Andrés Santa Cruz (1792-1865), president of Bolivia and of Peru-Bolivian Confederation.

Children — A159

Perf. 13½

1966, Dec. 16   Unwmk.   Litho.
479 A159 30c ocher & sepia   .15 .15

Issued to help poor children. See No. C258.

Map and Flag of Bolivia and Generals Ovando and Barrientos A160

1966, Dec. 16 Litho. Perf. 13½
Flag in Red, Yellow and Green
480 A160 60c vio brn & tan .30 .20
481 A160 1b dl grn & tan .45 .15

Issued to honor Generals Rene Barrientos Ortuno and Alfredo Ovando C., co-Presidents, 1965-66. See Nos. C259-C260.

Various Issues 1957-60 and Type A161
Surcharged with New Values and Bars

A161

1966, Dec. 21
On No. 403: "Centenario de la / Cruz Roja / Internacional"
482 A140 20c on 150b gray & ultra .20 .15

On Nos. 405-406: "Homenaje a la / Generala / J. Azurduy de / Padilla"
483 A140 30c on 550b chlky bl & brn .30 .15
484 A140 2.80b on 750b dp rose .75 .50

On No. 424: "CL Aniversario / Heroinas Coronilla"
485 A145 60c on 350b dp rose .50 .15

Nos. 429-430 Surcharged
486 A146 1.60b on 350b multi .75 .50
487 A146 2.40b on 500b multi 1.00 .75

Revenue Stamps of 1946 surcharged with New Value, "X" and: "XXV Aniversario / Gobierno Busch"
488 A161 20c on 5b red .20 .15

Overprinted: "XX Aniversario / Gob. Villaroel"
489 A161 60c on 2b grn .30 .15

Overprinted: "Centenario do / Rurrenabaque"
490 A161 1b on 10b brn .50 .15

Overprinted: "XXV Aniversario / Dpto. Pando"
491 A161 1.60b on 50c vio .50 .16
Nos. 482-491,C261-C272 (22) 14.50 8.86

For surcharge see No. C272.

Sower A162

"Macheteros" A163

1967, Sept. 20 Litho. Perf. 13½x13
492 A162 70c multi .35 .15

50th anniv. of Lions Intl. See #C273-C273a.

1968, June 24 Perf. 13½x13
Designs (Folklore characters): 60c, Chunchos. 1b, Wiphala. 2b, Diablada.
493 A163 30c gray & multi .15 .15
494 A163 60c sky bl & multi .25 .25
495 A163 1b gray & multi .40 .15
496 A163 2b gray ol & multi .60 .20
Nos. 493-496,C274-C277 (8) 3.90 1.65

Issued to publicize the 9th Congress of the Postal Union of the Americas and Spain.
A souvenir sheet exists containing 4 imperf. stamps similar to #493-496. Size: 131x81½mm.

Arms of Tarija — A164

Pres. Gualberto Villaroel — A165

1968, Oct. 29 Litho. Perf. 13½x13
497 A164 20c pale sal & multi .15 .15
498 A164 30c gray & multi .15 .15
499 A164 40c dl yel & multi .15 .15
500 A164 60c lt yel grn & multi .20 .20
Nos. 497-500,C278-C281 (8) 3.15 2.40

Battle of Tablada sesquicentennial.

1968, Nov. 6 Unwmk.
501 A165 20c sep & org .30 .15
502 A165 30c sep & dl bl grn .30 .15
503 A165 40c sep & dl rose .30 .20
504 A165 50c sep & yel grn .30 .15
505 A165 1b sep & ol bis .30 .15
Nos. 501-505 (5) 1.50
Set value .45

4th centenary of the founding of Cochabamba. See Nos. C282-C286.

ITU Emblem — A166

1968, Dec. 3 Litho. Perf. 13½x13
506 A166 10c gray, blk & yel .20 .20
507 A166 60c org, blk & ol .40 .40

Cent. (in 1965) of the ITU. See Nos. C287-C288.

Polychrome Painted Clay Cup, Inca Period — A167

1968, Nov. 14 Perf. 13½x13
508 A167 20c dk bl grn & multi .15 .15
509 A167 60c vio bl & multi .35 .35

20th anniv. (in 1966) of UNESCO. See Nos. C289-C290.

John F. Kennedy — A168
Tennis Player — A169

1968, Nov. 22 Perf. 13½x13
510 A168 10c vio grn & blk .15 .15
511 A168 4b vio & blk 1.40 1.40

A souvenir sheet contains one imperf. stamp similar to No. 511. Green marginal inscription. Size: 131x81½mm.
See Nos. C291-C292.

1968, Dec. 10 Perf. 13½x13
512 A169 10c gray, blk & lt brn .25 .25
513 A169 20c yel, blk & lt brn .25 .25
514 A169 30c ultra, blk & lt brn .25 .25
Nos. 512-514 (3) .75 .75

32nd South American Tennis Championships, La Paz, 1965. See Nos. C293-C294.
A souvenir sheet exists containing 3 imperf. stamps similar to Nos. 512-514. Size: 131x81½mm.

Issue of 1863 — A170

1968, Dec. 23 Litho. Perf. 13½x13
515 A170 10c yel grn, brn & blk .35 .20
516 A170 30c lt bl, brn & blk .35 .35
517 A170 2b gray, brn & blk .35 .35
Nos. 515-517,C295-C297 (6) 3.55 3.40

Cent. of Bolivian postage stamps. See Nos. C295-C297.

A souvenir sheet exists containing 3 imperf. stamps similar to Nos. 515-517. Yellow green marginal inscription. Size: 131x81½mm.

Rifle Shooting — A171

Sports: 50c, Equestrian. 60c, Canoeing.

1969, Oct. 29 Litho. Perf. 13x13½
518 A171 40c red brn, org & blk .40 .40
519 A171 50c emer, red & blk .40 .40
520 A171 60c bl, emer & blk .40 .40
Nos. 518-520,C299-C301 (6) 4.20 3.85

Issued to commemorate the 19th Olympic Games, Mexico City, Oct. 12-27, 1968.
A souvenir sheet exists containing 3 imperf. stamps similar to Nos. 518-520. Size: 130½x81mm.

Temenis Laothoe Violetta A172

Butterflies: 10c, Papilio crassus. 20c, Catagramma cynosura. 30c, Eunica eurota flora. 80c, Ituna phenarete.

1970, Apr. 24 Litho. Perf. 13x13½
521 A172 5c pale lil & multi .70 .70
522 A172 10c pink & multi 1.40 1.40
523 A172 20c gray & multi 1.40 1.40
524 A172 30c yel & multi 1.40 1.40
525 A172 80c multicolored 1.40 1.40
Nos. 521-525,C302-C306 (10) 20.20 20.20

A souvenir sheet exists similar to Nos. 521-523. Black marginal inscription. Size: 129½x80mm.

Boy Scout — A173

Design: 10c, Girl Scout planting rose bush.

1970, June 17 Perf. 13½x13
526 A173 5c multicolored .20 .15
527 A173 10c multicolored .20 .15

Issued to honor the Bolivian Scout movement. See Nos. C307-C308.

No. 437 Surcharged "EXFILCA 70 / $b. 0.30" and Two Bars in Red
1970, Dec. 6 Litho. Perf. 13x12
528 A147 30c on 350b on 10c .25 .25

EXFILCA 70, 2nd Interamerican Philatelic Exhib., Caracas, Venezuela, Nov. 27-Dec. 6.

Nos. 455 and 452 Surcharged in Black or Red
1970, Dec. Photo. Perf. 11½
529 A144 60c on 900b on 350b .25 .20
533 A150 1.20b on 1500b (R) .50 .15

Amaryllis Yungacensis A174

Sica Sica Church, EXFILIMA Emblem A175

Bolivian Flowers: 30c, Amaryllis escobar uriae, horiz. 40c, Amaryllis evansae, horiz. 2b, Gymnocalycium chiquitanum.

Perf. 13x13½, 13½x13
1971, Aug. 9 Litho. Unwmk.
534 A174 30c gray & multi .30 .30
535 A174 40c multi .30 .30
536 A174 50c multi .35 .35
537 A174 2b multi 1.00 .60
Nos. 534-537,C310-C313 (8) 6.95 4.45

1971, Nov. 6 Perf. 14x13½
538 A175 20c red & multi .20 .15

EXFILIMA '71, 3rd Inter-American Philatelic Exhibition, Lima, Peru, Nov. 6-14.

A176

A177

Design: Pres. Hugo Banzer Suarez.

1972, Jan. 24 Litho. Perf. 13½
539 A176 1.20b blk & multi .50 .15

Bolivia's development, Aug. 19, 1971, to Jan. 24, 1972.

1972, Mar. 23 Litho. Perf. 13½x13
Folk Dances: 20c, Chiriwano de Achocalla. 40c, Rueda Chapaca. 60c, Kena-kena. 1b, Waca Thokori.
540 A177 20c red & multi .15 .15
541 A177 40c rose lil & multi .30 .25
542 A177 60c cream & multi .45 .20
543 A177 1b citron & multi .55 .22
Nos. 540-543,C314-C315 (6) 2.60 1.14

Madonna and Child by B. Bitti — A178

Tarija Cathedral, EXFILBRA Emblem — A179

Bolivian paintings: 10c, Nativity, by Melchor Perez de Holguin. 50c, Coronation of the Virgin, by G. M. Berrio. 70c, Harquebusier, anonymous. 80c, St. Peter of Alcantara, by Holguin.

1972 Litho. Perf. 14x13½
544 A178 10c gray & multi .15 .15
545 A178 50c sal & multi .25 .15
546 A178 70c lt grn & multi .35 .15
547 A178 80c buff & multi .40 .15
548 A178 1b multi .50 .15
Nos. 544-548,C316-C319 (9) 3.40
Set value 1.10

Issue dates: 1b, Aug. 17; others, Dec. 4.

1972, Aug. 26
549 A179 30c multi .16 .15

4th Inter-American Philatelic Exhibition, EXFILBRA, Rio de Janeiro, Brazil, Aug. 26-Sept. 2.

Echinocactus Notocactus — A180

Designs: Various cacti.

1973, Aug. 6 Litho. Perf. 13½
550 A180 20c crim & multi .30 .25
551 A180 40c multi .30 .25
552 A180 50c multi .30 .15
553 A180 70c multi .30 .20
Nos. 550-553,C321-C323 (7) 2.70 1.45

Power
Station,
Santa Isabel
A181

Designs: 20c, Tin industry. 90c, Bismuth industry. 1b, Natural gas plant.

1973, Nov. 26   Litho.   Perf. 13½
554 A181 10c gray & multi   .15   .15
555 A181 20c tan & multi   .15   .15
556 A181 90c lt grn & multi   .25   .20
557 A181 1b yel & multi   .25   .15
  Nos. 554-557,C324-C325 (6)   1.80
    Set value   .75

Bolivia's development.

Cattleya
Nobilior — A182

Orchids: 50c, Zygopetalum bolivianum. 1b,
Huntleya melagris.

1974, May 15   Perf. 13½
558 A182 20c gray & multi   .40   .15
559 A182 50c lt bl & multi   .40   .15
560 A182 1b cit & multi   .40   .15
  Nos. 558-560,C327-C330 (7)   7.70 1.97

For surcharge see No. 704.

UPU and
Philatelic
Exposition
Emblems
A183

1974, Oct. 9
561 A183 3.50b grn, blk & bl   1.00 .40

Centenary of Universal Postal Union: PRENFIL-
UPU Philatelic Exhibition, Buenos Aires, Oct. 1-12;
EXPO-UPU Philatelic Exhibition, Montevideo, Oct.
20-27.

Gen. Sucre, by I.
Wallpher — A184

1974, Dec. 9   Litho.   Perf. 13½
562 A184 5b multicolored   1.10 .50

Sesquicentennial of the Battle of Ayacucho.

Lions
Emblem and
Steles
A185

1975, Mar.   Litho.   Perf. 13½
563 A185 30c red & multi   .35   .35

Lions Intl. in Bolivia, 25th anniv.

España 75
Emblem
A186

1975, Mar.
564 A186 4.50b yel, red & blk   .80   .35

España 75 International Philatelic Exhibition,
Madrid, Apr. 4-13.

Emblem
A187

1975   Litho.   Perf. 13½
565 A187 2.50b lil, blk & sil   .65   .25

First meeting of Postal Ministers, Quito, Ecuador,
March 1974, and for the Cartagena Agreement.

Pando Coat of
Arms — A188

Designs: Departmental coats of arms.

1975, July 16   Litho.   Perf. 13½
566 A188 20c shown   .15   .15
567 A188 2b Chuquisaca   .40   .40
568 A188 3b Cochabamba   .50   .50
  Nos. 566-568,C336-C341 (9)   4.10 4.10

Sesquicentennial of Republic of Bolivia.

Simón
Bolívar — A189

Presidents and Statesmen of Bolivia: 30c, Victor
Paz Estenssoro. 60c, Tomas Frias. 1b, Ismael Montes. 2.50b, Aniceto Arce. 7b, Bautista Saavedra.
10b, Jose Manuel Pando. 15b, Jose Maria Linares.
50b, Simon Bolivar.

1975   Litho.   Perf. 13½
       Size: 24x32mm
569 A189 30c multi   .15   .15
569A A189 60c multi   .20   .20
570 A189 1b multi   .30   .30
571 A189 2.50b multi   .50   .50
572 A189 7b multi   1.40 .50
573 A189 10b multi   2.00 .75
574 A189 15b multi   2.50 2.50
       Size: 28x39mm
575 A189 50b multi   10.00 10.00
  Nos. 569-575,C346-C353 (16)   36.05 31.15

Sesquicentennial of Republic of Bolivia.

"EXFIVIA
75"
A190

1975, Dec. 1   Litho.   Perf. 13½
576 A190 3b multicolored   .75   .60
  a.   Souvenir sheet   1.50 1.50

EXFIVIA 75, first Bolivian Philatelic Exposition.
No. 576a contains one stamp similar to No. 576
with simulated perforations. Sold for 5b.

A191   A192

Chiang Kai-shek, flags of Bolivia and China.

1976, Apr. 4   Litho.   Perf. 13½
577 A191 2.50b multi, red circle   1.00 1.00
578 A191 2.50b multi, bl circle   1.00 1.00

Pres. Chiang Kai-shek of China (1887-1975).
Erroneous red of sun's circle on Chinese flag of
No. 577 was corrected on No. 578 with a dark blue
overlay.

1976, Apr.   Litho.   Perf. 13½
579 A192 50c Naval insignia   .40   .35

Navy anniversary.

Geological
Map, Pickax
and Lamp
A193

1976, May
580 A193 4b multicolored   .80   .60

Bolivian Geological Institute.

Lufthansa
Jet, Bolivian
and German
Colors
A194

1976, May
581 A194 3b multicolored   .80   .35

Lufthansa, 50th anniversary.

Boy Scout and Scout
Emblem — A195

1976, May   Litho.   Perf. 13½
582 A195 1b multicolored   .50   .50

Bolivian Boy Scouts, 60th anniversary.

Battle Scene,
US
Bicentennial
Emblem
A196

1976, May 25
583 A196 4.50b bis & multi   1.40 .65

American Bicentennial.
A souvenir sheet contains one stamp similar to
No. 583 with simulated perforations. Size:
130x80mm.

Family, Map of   Vicente
Bolivia — A197   Bernedo — A198

1976   Perf. 13½
584 A197 2.50b multicolored   .50   .40

National Census 1976.

1976, Oct.
585 A198 1.50b multicolored   .35   .30

Brother Vicente Bernedo de Potosi (1544-1619),
missionary to the Indians.

Policeman with
Dog, Rainbow
over La
Paz — A199

1976, Oct.
586 A199 2.50b multicolored   .60   .60

Bolivian Police, 150 years of service.

Emblem,
Bolivar and
Sucre
A200

1976, Nov. 18   Litho.   Perf. 13½
587 A200 1.50b multicolored   .60   .60

Intl. Congress of Bolivarian Societies.

Pedro Poveda,
View of La
Paz — A201

1976, Dec.
588 A201 1.50b multicolored   .35   .25

Pedro Poveda (1874-1936), educator.

A202   Boy and
                  Girl — A203

1976, Dec. 17   Perf. 10½
594 A202 20c brown   .30   .15
595 A202 1b ultra   .45   .15
596 A202 1.50b green   .75   .50
  Nos. 594-596 (3)   1.50
    Set value   .62

1977, Feb. 4   Litho.   Perf. 13½
599 A203 50c multicolored   .15   .15

Christmas 1976, and for 50th anniversary of the
Inter-American Children's Institute.

Staff of
Aesculapius
A204

Supreme Court,
La Paz
A205

1977, Mar. 18   Litho.   Perf. 13¹/₂x13
600 A204 3b multicolored   .75 .30
National Seminar on Chagas' disease, Cochabamba, Feb. 21-26.

1977, May 3
Designs: 4b, Manuel Maria Urcullu, first President of Supreme Court. 4.50b, Pantaleon Dalence,
President 1883-1889.
601 A205 2.50b multi   .30 .30
602 A205 4b multi   .42 .15
603 A205 4.50b multi   .50 .20
    Nos. 601-603 (3)   1.22 .65
Sesquicentennial of Bolivian Supreme Court.

Newspaper
Mastheads
A206

Map of Bolivia,
Tower and Flag
A207

Designs: 2.50b, Alfredo Alexander and Hoy,
horiz. 3b, Jose Carrasco and El Diario, horiz. 4b,
Demetrio Canelas and Los Tiempos. 5.50b,
Frontpage of Presencia.

1977, June   Litho.   Perf. 13¹/₂
604 A206 1.50b multi   .22 .15
605 A206 2.50b multi   .35 .30
606 A206 3b multi   .42 .25
607 A206 4b multi   .50 .35
608 A206 5.50b multi   .65 .20
    Nos. 604-608 (5)   2.14 1.25
Bolivian newspapers and their founders.

1977, June
609 A207 3b multi   .50 .16
90th anniversary of Oruro Club.

Games'
Poster — A208

Tin Miner and
Emblem — A209

1977, Oct. 20   Litho.   Perf. 13¹/₂
610 A208 5b blue & multi   .75 .20
8th Bolivian Games, La Paz, Oct. 1977.

1977, Oct. 31   Litho.   Perf. 13
611 A209 3b multicolored   .60 .40
Bolivian Mining Corp., 25th anniv.

Miners, Globe,
Tin
Symbol — A210

Map of Bolivia,
Radio
Masts — A211

1977, Nov. 3
612 A210 6b silver & multi   .80 .25
Intl. Tin Symposium, La Paz, Nov. 14-21.

1977, Nov. 11
613 A211 2.50b blue & multi   .50 .35
Radio Bolivia, ASBORA, 50th anniversary.

No. 450 Surcharged with New Value, 3
Bars and "EXFIVIA-77"

1977, Nov. 25   Litho.   Perf. 11x13¹/₂
614 A147 5b on 5000b on 5b   1.00 1.25
EXFIVIA '77 Philatelic Exhibition, Cochabamba.

Eye, Compass, Book of
Law — A212

1978, May 3   Litho.   Perf. 13¹/₂x13
615 A212 5b multi   .65 .16
Audit Department, 50th anniversary.

Mt.
Illimani — A213

Pre-Columbian
Monolith — A214

Design: 1.50b, Mt. Cerro de Potosi.

Perf. 11x10¹/₂, 10¹/₂x11
1978, June 1   Litho.
616 A213 50c bl & Prus bl   .15 .15
617 A214 1b brn & lemon   .20 .15
618 A213 1.50b red & bl gray   .35 .25
    Nos. 616-618 (3)   .70
    Set value   .35

Andean Countries,
Staff of
Aesculapius — A215

Map of Americas
with
Bolivia — A216

1978, June 1   Perf. 10¹/₂x11
626 A215 2b org & blk   .35 .15
Health Ministers of Andean Countries, 5th
meeting.

1978, June 1
627 A216 2.50b dp ultra & red   .35 .15
World Rheumatism Year.
For surcharges see Nos. 697, 972.

Central Bank
Building — A217

Jesus and
Children — A218

1978, July 26   Litho.   Perf. 13¹/₂
628 A217 7b multi   1.00 .25
50th anniversary of Bank of Bolivia.

1979, Feb. 20   Litho.   Perf. 13¹/₂
629 A218 8b multicolored   .90 .16
International Year of the Child.

Antofagasta
Cancel — A219

Eduardo Abaroa,
Chain — A220

Designs: 1b, La Chimba cancel. 1.50b, Mejil-
lones cancel. 5.50b, View of Antofagasta, horiz.
6.50b, Woman in chains, symbolizing captive province. 8b, Map of Antofagasta Province, 1876. 10b,
Arms of province.

1979, Mar. 23   Litho.   Perf. 10¹/₂
630 A219 50e buff & blk   .30 .20
631 A219 1b pink & blk   .50 .25
632 A219 1.50b pale grn & blk   .50 .25
    Perf. 13¹/₂
633 A220 5.50b multi   .60 .25
634 A220 6.50b multi   .80 .30
635 A220 7b multi   .80 .30
636 A220 8b multi   .90 .35
637 A220 10b multi   1.10 .35
    Nos. 630-637 (8)   5.50 2.25
Loss of Antofagasta coastal area to Chile, cent.
For surcharge see No. 696.

Emblem and Map
of Bolivia
A221

Gymnast
A222

1979, Mar. 26   Perf. 13¹/₂x13
638 A221 3b multicolored   .75 .50
Radio Club of Bolivia.

Perf. 13x13¹/₂, 13¹/₂x13
1979, Mar. 27
6.50b, Runner and Games emblem, horiz.
639 A222 6.50b multi   .80 .50
640 A222 10b multi   1.10 .25
Southern Cross Sports Games, Bolivia, Nov. 3-
12, 1978.
A souvenir sheet contains 1 stamp similar to No.
640 with simulated perforations. Sold for 20b. Size:
80x130mm.
For surcharge see No. 965.

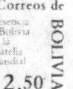
Bulgaria
No. 1 — A223

EXFILMAR
Emblem — A224

1979, Mar. 30   Perf. 10¹/₂
641 A223 2.50b multi   .35 .25
PHILASERDICA '79 International Philatelic Exhibition, Sofia, Bulgaria, May 18-27.

For surcharge see No. 694.

1979, Apr. 2
642 A224 2b multi   .20 .20
Bolivian Maritime Philatelic Exhibition, La Paz,
Nov. 18-28.
For surcharge see No. 698.

OAS Emblem, Map
of Bolivia — A226

1979, Oct. 22   Litho.   Perf. 14x13¹/₂
644 A226 6b multi   .75 .25
Organization of American States, 9th Congress,
La Paz, Oct.-Nov.

Franz
Tamayo — A227

Bolivian and
Japanese Flags,
Hospital — A228

UN Emblem and
Meeting — A229

Radio Tower and
Waves — A230

1979, Dec.
645 A227 2.80b blk & gray   .35 .25
646 A228 5b multi   .50 .35
648 A229 5b multi   .50 .35
649 A230 6b multi   .65 .25
    Nos. 645-649 (4)   2.00 1.20
Franz Tamayo, lawyer, birth centenary; Japanese-
Bolivian health care cooperation; CEPAL, 18th Congress, La Paz, Sept. 18-26; Bolivian National Radio,
50th anniversary.
For surcharge see No. 695.

Puerto
Suarez Iron
Ore Deposits
A231

1979   Litho.   Perf. 13¹/₂x14
650 A231 9.50b multi   1.10 .50

Bolivia No.
19,
EXFILMAR
Emblem,
Bolivian
Flag — A232

1980   Litho.   Perf. 13¹/₂
651 A232 4b multi   .55 .30
EXFILMAR, Bolivian Maritime Philatelic Exhibition, La Paz, Nov. 18-28, 1979.

Juana Azurduy on Horseback — A233

1980   Litho.   Perf. 14x13½
652 A233 4b multi   .55 .30

Juana Azurduy de Padilla, independence fighter, birth bicentenary.

La Salle and World Map A234

1980   Perf. 13½x14
653 A234 9b multi   1.10 .60

St. Jean Baptiste de la Salle (1651-1719), educator.
For surcharge see No. 966.

"Victory" in Chariot, Madrid, Exhibition Emblem, Flags of Bolivia and Spain A235

1980, Oct.   Litho.   Perf. 13½x14
654 A235 14b multi   1.60 .75

ESPAMER '80 Stamp Exhibition, Madrid.

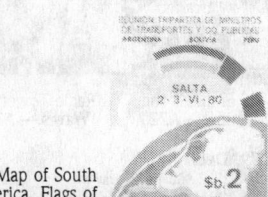

Map of South America, Flags of Argentina, Bolivia and Peru — A236

1980, Oct.   Perf. 14x13½
655 A236 2b multi   .25 .20

Ministers of Public Works and Transport of Argentina, Bolivia and Peru meeting.

Santa Cruz-Trinidad Railroad, Inauguration of Third Section — A237

1980, Oct.
656 A237 3b multi   .35 .20

15-Cent Minimum Value
The minimum catalogue value is 15 cents. Separating se-tenant pieces into individual stamps does not increase the value of the stamps since demand for the separated stamps may be small.

Flag on Provincial Map — A238   Parrots — A239

Perf. 14x13½, 13½x14
1981, May 11   Litho.
657 A238 1b Soldier, flag, map   .15 .15
658 A238 3b Flag, map   .35 .15
659 A238 40b shown   5.00 1.25
660 A238 50b Soldier, civilians, horiz. 6.00 1.25
      Nos. 657-660 (4)   11.50 2.80

July 17 Revolution memorial.

1981, May 11   Perf. 14x13½
661 A239 4b Ara macao   .50 .30
662 A239 7b Ara chloroptera   .80 .50
663 A239 8b Ara ararauna   1.00 .60
664 A239 9b Ara rubrogenys   1.10 .65
665 A239 10b Ara auricollis   1.10 .65
666 A239 12b Anodorynchus hyacinthinus 1.50 .75
667 A239 15b Ara militaris   1.75 1.00
668 A239 20b Ara severa   2.25 1.25
      Nos. 661-668 (8)   10.00 5.70

Christmas 1981 — A240

1981, Dec. 7   Litho.   Perf. 10½
669 A240 1b Virgin and Child, vert. .15 .15
670 A240 2b Child, star   .25 .15

American Airforces Commanders' 22nd Conference, Buenos Aires — A241

1982, Apr. 12   Litho.   Perf. 13½
671 A241 14b multi   1.60 .50

75th Anniv. of Cobija — A242   Simon Bolivar Birth Bicentenary (1983) — A243

1982, July 8   Litho.   Perf. 13½
672 A242 28b multi   .40 .25

1982, July 12
673 A243 18b multi   .25 .20

1983 World Telecommunications Day — A244   1982 World Cup — A245

1982, July 15
674 A244 26b Receiving station   .40 .25

1982, July 21   Perf. 11
675 A245 4b shown   .15 .15
676 A245 100b Final Act, by Picasso 1.75 .95
For surcharge see No. 701.

Girl Playing Piano — A246

1982, July 25   Perf. 13½
677 A246 16b Boy playing soccer, vert. .25 .15
678 A246 20b shown   .35 .20

Bolivian-Chinese Agricultural Cooperation, 1972-1982 — A247

1982, Aug. 12
679 A247 30b multi   .50 .25

First Bolivian-Japanese Gastroenterology Conference, La Paz, Jan. — A248

1982, Aug. 26
680 A248 22b multi   .35 .25

A249   A250

1982, Aug. 31 Litho. Perf. 14x13½
681 A249 19b Stamps   .35 .20

10th Anniv. of Bolivian Philatelic Federation.

1982, Sept. 1
682 A250 20b tan & dk brown   .30 .20
Pres. Hernando Siles, birth centenary.

Scouting Year — A251   Cochabamba Philatelic Center, 25th Anniv. — A252

1982, Sept. 3   Perf. 11
683 A251 5b Baden-Powell   .15 .15
For surcharge see No. 703.

1982, Sept. 14
684 A252 3b multicolored   .15 .15
For surcharge see No. 700.

Cochabamba Superior Court of Justice Sesquicentennial A253

1982   Litho.   Perf. 13½
685 A253 10b multicolored   .20 .15
For surcharge see No. 970.

Enthronement of Virgin of Copacabana, 400th Anniv. — A254   Navy Day — A255

1982, Nov. 15   Litho.   Perf. 13½
686 A254 13b multicolored   .25 .15
For surcharge see No. 971.

1982, Nov. 17
687 A255 14b Port Busch Naval Base   .25 .15

A256   A257

1982, Nov. 19   Perf. 11
688 A256 10b grn & gray   .20 .15
Christmas. For surcharge see No. 702.

1983, Feb. 13   Litho.   Perf. 13½
689 A257 50b multicolored   .80 .40
10th Youth Soccer Championship, Jan. 22-Feb. 13.

EXFIVIA '83 Philatelic Exhibition A258

1983, Nov. 5   Litho.   Perf. 13½
690 A258 150b brn car   1.00 .50

Visit of Brazilian Pres. Joao Figueiredo, Feb. A259

1984, Feb. 7   Litho.   Perf. 13½x14
691 A259 150b multicolored   .40 .20

Simon Bolivar Entering La Paz, by Carmen Baptista A260

Paintings of Bolivar: 50b, Riding Horse, by Mulato Gil de Quesada, vert.

Perf. 14x13½, 13½x14
1984, Mar. 30
692 A260 50b multi .15 .15
693 A260 200b multi .55 .22
Set value .28

Types of 1957-79 Surcharged

$b. 60.-

No. 697

1984, Mar.
694 A223 40b on 2.50b #641 .15 .15
695 A227 40b on 2.80b #645 .15 .15
696 A219 60b on 1.50b #632 .18 .15
697 A216 60b on 2.50b #627 .18 .15
698 A224 100b on 2b #642 .30 .15
699 A141 200b on 350b #409 .60 .25
Nos. 694-699 (6) 1.56
Set value .80

See No. 972 for surcharge similar to No. 697.

Nos. 675, 683-684, 688, C328 Surcharged
1984, June 27 Litho. Perf. 11
700 A252 500b on 3b #684 .75 .35
701 A245 1000b on 4b #675 1.50 .75
702 A256 2000b on 10b #688 3.00 1.25
703 A251 5000b on 5b #683 7.50 3.00

Perf. 13½
704 A182 10,000b on 3.80b #C328 10.00 6.00
Nos. 700-704 (5) 22.75 11.35

Road Safety
Education
A261

Jose Eustaquio
Mendez, 200th Birth
Anniv.
A262

Cartoons.

1984, Sept. 7 Litho. Perf. 11
705 A261 80b Jaywalker .15 .15
706 A261 120b Motorcycle policeman, ambulance .15 .15
Set value .15 .15

Perf. 14x13½, 13½x14
1984, Sept. 19
Paintings: 300b, Birthplace, by Jorge Campos.
500b, Mendez Leading the Battle of La Tablada, by
M. Villegas, horiz.
707 A262 300b multi .15 .15
708 A262 500b multi .15 .15
Set value .15

1983 World Cup
Soccer
Championships,
Mexico — A263
Chasqui, Postal
Runner — A264

Sponsoring shoe-manufacturers' trademarks and:
100b, 200b, Outline map of Bolivia, national colors.
600b, World map and soccer ball, horiz.

1984, Oct. 26 Perf. 11
709 A263 100b multi .15 .15
710 A263 200b multi .15 .15
711 A263 600b multi .15 .15
Set value .25 .16

1985
712 A264 11000b vio bl .25 .15
For surcharge see No. 962.

Intl. Year of
Professional
Education
A265
Intl. Anti-Polio
Campaign
A266

1985, Apr. 25
713 A265 2000b Natl. Manual Crafts
emblem .15 .15
For surcharges see Nos. 721-722, 959.

1985, May 22
714 A266 20000b lt bl & vio .25 .15

Endangered
Wildlife — A267

1985, May 22
715 A267 23000b Altiplano boliviano .20 .15
716 A267 25000b Sarcorhamphus
gryphus .22 .15
717 A267 30000b Blastocaros
dichotomus .30 .15
Nos. 715-717 (3) .72
Set value .30

Nos. 716-717 vert.
For surcharge see No. 963.

Dona Vicenta
Juaristi Eguino (b.
1785),
Independence
Heroine — A268
UN, 40th
Anniv. — A269

1985, Oct. Litho. Perf. 13½
718 A268 300000b multi .20 .15

1985, Oct. 24 Perf. 11
719 A269 1000000b bl & gold .65 .30
For surcharge see No. 964.

A270
A271

1985, Nov.
720 A270 200000b multi .15 .15
Soccer Team named "The Strongest," 75th anniv.

No. 713 Surcharged
1986 Litho. Perf. 11
721 A265 200000b on 2000b .22 .15
722 A265 5000000b on 2000b 5.25 2.50

1986
723 A271 300000 Emblems, vert. .32 .15
724 A271 550000 Pique trademark,
vert. .58 .24
725 A271 1000000 Azteca Stadium 1.05 .50
726 A271 2500000 World cup, vert. 2.65 1.25
Nos. 723-726 (4) 4.60 2.14
1986 World Cup Soccer Championships.
For surcharge see No. 961.

Intl. Youth Year
A272 A273

1986
727 A272 150000 brt car rose .16 .15
728 A272 500000 bl grn .55 .35
729 A273 3000000 multi 3.15 1.50
Nos. 727-729 (3) 3.86 2.00
Inscribed 1985.
For surcharge see No. 958.

Alfonso Sobieta
Viaduct, Carretera
Quillacollo,
Confital — A274

1986 Perf. 13½
730 A274 400000 int bl & gray .42 .20
Inter-American Development Bank, 25th anniv.

Admission of Bolivia
to the UPU,
Cent. — A275
Postal Workers
Soc., 50th
Anniv. — A276

1986, Apr. 3 Perf. 11
731 A275 800000 multi .85 .40

1986, Sept. 5
732 A276 2000000 brn & pale brn 2.10 1.00
For surcharge see No. 967.

Founding of
Trinidad,
300th
Anniv.
A277

1986, May 25 Perf. 13½x14
733 A277 1400000 Bull and Rider,
by Vaca 1.50 .75
For surcharge see No. 960.

Bolivian
Philatelic
Federation,
15th Anniv.
A278

1986, Nov. 28
734 A278 600000b No. 19 .62 .30

Death of a Priest,
by Jose Antonio
Zampa — A279
Intl. Peace
Year — A280

1986, Nov. 21 Perf. 14x13½
735 A279 400000b multi .42 .20

1986, Sept. 16 Perf. 11
736 A280 200000 yel grn & pale grn .22 .15

Natl. Oil Corp.
(YPBF), 50th
Anniv. — A281

1986, Dec. 22 Litho. Perf. 11
737 A281 1000000b multi 1.50 .50

A282 A283

Photograph of a Devil-mask Dancer, by Jimenez
Cordero.

1987, Feb. 13 Litho. Perf. 14x13½
738 A282 20c multi .30 .15
February 10th Society, cent. (in 1985).

1987, Mar. 20 Litho. Perf. 14x13½
739 A283 30c Crossed flags .45 .25
State Visit of Richard von Weizsacker, Pres. of
Germany, Mar. 20.

State Visit of
King Juan
Carlos of
Spain, May
20 — A284

1987, May 20 Perf. 13½x14
740 A284 60c Natl. arms .90 .40

EXFIVIA '87 — A285

Mount Potosi, 18th cent. engraving.

1987, Oct. Litho. Perf. 13½
741 A285 50c multi .72 .35
See No. 750.

Wildlife
Conservation
A286

1987, Oct.
742 A286 20c Condor .30 .15
743 A286 20c Tapir .30 .15
744 A286 30c Vicuna .45 .25
745 A286 30c Armadillo .45 .25
746 A286 40c Spectacled bears .58 .30
747 A286 60c Toucans .88 .40
Nos. 742-747 (6) 2.96 1.50
Wildlife in danger of extinction.

ESPAMER '87,
La Coruna
A287

1987, Oct.   Litho.   *Perf. 14x13½*
748 A287 20c Nina, stern of Santa
           Maria   .30 .15
749 A287 20c Bow of Santa Maria,
           Pinta   .30 .15
a.   Pair, #748-749   .60 .25
   No. 749a has a continuous design.

EXFIVIA Type of 1987
Photograph of Mt. Potosi by Jimenez Cordero.

1987, Aug. 5   Litho.   *Perf. 13½*
750 A285 40c multi   .58 .30

Musical
Instruments
A288

1987, Dec. 3   *Perf. 13½x14, 14x13½*
751 A288 50c Zampona and quena
           (wind instruments)   .72 .35
752 A288 1b Charango, vert.   1.45 .70

A289 CORREOS DE BOLIVIA

State Visit of Pope
John Paul II
A290

Pontiff, religious architecture and art: No. 753,
Cathedral of Kings, Beni. No. 754, Carabuco
Church. No. 755, Tihuanacu Church. No. 756, St.
Francis's Church, Sucre. No. 757, St. Joseph's of
Chiquitos Church. 40c, Cobija Chapel, vert. No.
759, Jayu Kcota Church. No. 760, Cochabamba
Cathedral, vert. 60c, St. Francis's Basilica, La Paz,
vert. No. 762, Christ of Machaca Church. No. 763,
St. Lawrence's Church, Potosi, vert. No. 764, *The
Holy Family*, by Rubens, vert. No. 765, *The Virgin
of Copacabana*, statue, vert. No. 766, Vallegrande
Church. No. 767, Tarija Cathedral, vert. No. 768,
Concepcion Church.

1988   Litho.   *Perf. 13½x14, 14x13½*
753 A289 20c multi   .25 .15
754 A289 20c multi   .25 .15
755 A289 20c multi   .25 .15
756 A289 30c multi   .38 .20
757 A289 30c multi   .38 .20
758 A289 40c multi   .50 .25
759 A289 50c multi   .65 .30
760 A289 50c multi   .65 .30
761 A289 60c multi   .75 .35
762 A289 70c multi   .90 .35
763 A289 70c multi   .90 .35
764 A289 80c multi   1.00 .45
765 A289 80c multi   1.00 .45
766 A289 80c multi   1.00 .45
767 A289 1.30b multi   1.65 .75
768 A289 1.30b multi   1.65 .75
769 A290 1.50b shown   1.90 .90
       Nos. 753-769 (17)   14.06 6.50
   Issue dates: 1.50b, May 9. Others, Mar. 3.

Visit of
Pres. Jose
Sarney of
Brazil
A291

1988, Aug. 2   Litho.   *Perf. 13½x14*
770 A291 50c multi   .60 .30

St. John Bosco (1815-
1888) — A292

1988, Aug. 16   *Perf. 13½*
771 A292 30c multi   .42 .20

Bolivian
Railways,
Cent. — A293

Design: 1b, Steam locomotive from the La Paz-
Beni line, made by Marca Shy Ohio, Natl. Railway
Museum, Sucre.

1988, Aug. 29
772 A293 1b multi   1.20 .60

Nataniel Aguirre
(b. 1888),
Author — A294

Department of
Pando, 50th
Anniv. — A295

1988, Sept. 14   Litho.   *Perf. 13½*
773 A294 1b blk & beige   1.20 .60

1988, Sept. 26   *Perf. 13½*
Designs: 40c, *Columna Porvenir*, memorial to
the Battle of Bahio. 60c, Siringuero rubber production (worker sapping latex from *Hevea brasiliensis*).
774 A295 40c multi   .48 .25
775 A295 60c multi   .72 .35

A296

A297

1988, Sept. 27
776 A296 1.50b multi   1.85 .90
   1988 Summer Olympics, Seoul.

1988
Designs: 70c, Archbishop Bernardino de Carde-
nas (1579-1668). 80c, Mother Rosa Gattorno
(1831-1900), founder of the Sisters of Santa Ana.
777 A297 70c multi   .90 .45
778 A297 80c multi   1.05 .50
   Issue dates: 70c, Oct. 20, 80c, Oct. 14.

Ministry of
Transportation &
Communications
A298

1988, Oct. 24   Litho.   *Perf. 14x13½*
779 A298 2b deep car, blk & pale ol-
           ive grn   2.35 1.00

Army
Communications,
50th Anniv. (in
1987) — A299

1988, Nov. 29   Litho.   *Perf. 13½*
780 A299 70c multi   .95 .45

Bolivian
Automobile Club,
50th
Anniv. — A300

1988, Dec. 29   Litho.   *Perf. 13½*
781 A300 1.50b multi   1.45 .70

Flowering Plants
and Emblems
A301

Designs: 50c, Orchid, BULGARIA '89 emblem,
vert. 60c, Kantuta blossoms, ITALIA '90 emblem.
70c, *Heliconia humilis*, Albertville '86 emblem,
vert. 1b, Hoffmanseggia, Barcelona '92 Games
emblem, vert. 2b, Puya raymondi, Seoul '88 Games
and five-ring emblems, vert.

1989, Feb. 17   Litho.   *Perf. 13½*
782 A301 50c multi   .58 .24
783 A301 60c multi   .70 .28
784 A301 70c multi   .80 .32
785 A301 1b multi   1.15 .45
786 A301 2b multi   2.30 .92
       Nos. 782-786 (5)   5.53 2.21

Radio FIDES,
50th
Anniv. — A302

1989, Feb. 2
787 A302 80c multi   .92 .38

Gold
Quarto of
1852
A303

1989, Feb. 9   *Perf. 13½x14*
788 A303 1b multi   1.20 .48

French Revolution,
Bicent. — A304

1989, June 23   Litho.   *Perf. 14x13½*
789 A304 70c red, blk & blue   .90 .35

Uyuni Township,
Cent. — A305

1989, July 9   Litho.   *Perf. 14x13½*
790 A305 30c blue, black & gray   .38 .15

Noel Kempff
Mercado Natl.
Park, Santa
Cruz — A306

Designs: 1.50b, Federico Ahlfeld Falls, Pauserna
River. 3b, *Ozotoceros bezcarticus* (deer).

1989, Sept. 24   Litho.   *Perf. 13½x14*
791 A306 1.50b multicolored   2.00 .75
792 A306   3b multicolored   4.00 1.50

UPAEP — A306a

1989, Oct. 12   Litho.   *Perf. 13½*
792A A306a 50c Metalworking   .52 .20
792B A306a 1b Temple of
            Kalasasaya   1.05 .42
        See Nos. 808-809.

State Visit by
Dr. Carlos
Andres Perez,
Pres. of
Venezuela
A306b

1989, Oct. 14
792C A306b 2b multi   2.05 .82
        See Nos. 825-826, 832.

City of
Potosi — A306c

1989, Nov. 10   Litho.   *Perf. 13½*
792D A306c 60c Cobija Arch   .75 .30
792E A306c 80c Mint   .85 .40
f.   Pair, #792D-792E   1.60 .70

Christmas
A307

Paintings: 40c, *Andean Stillwaters*, by Arturo Borda. 60c, *The Virgin of the Roses*, anonymous. 80c, *The Conquistador*, by Jorge de la Reza. 1b, *Native Harmony*, by Juan Rimsa. 1.50b, *Woman with Jug*, by Cecilio Guzman de Rojas. 2b, *Bloom of Tenderness*, by Gil Imana. Nos. 794-798 vert.

Perf. 13¹/₂x14, 14x13¹/₂

1989, Dec. 18
793	A307	40c multicolored	.42	.17
794	A307	60c multicolored	.62	.25
795	A307	80c multicolored	.82	.32
796	A307	1b multicolored	1.05	.42
797	A307	1.50b multicolored	1.55	.62
798	A307	2b multicolored	2.05	.82
		Nos. 793-798 (6)	6.51	2.60

A308   A309

1990, Jan. 23   Litho.   *Perf. 13¹/₂*
799 A308 80c multicolored   .85 .35

Fight against drug abuse.

1990, May 13   *Perf. 14x13¹/₂*

Design: Great Britain No. 1, Sir Rowland Hill and Bolivia No. 1

800 A309 4b multicolored   4.10 1.70

Penny Black, 150th anniv.

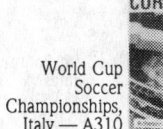

World Cup Soccer Championships, Italy — A310

1990, June 16   *Perf. 13¹/₂*
801 A310 2b Stadium, Milan   2.00 .80
802 A310 6b Game   6.00 2.40

Organization of American States, Cent. — A311

1990, Apr. 14
803 A311 80c dark bl & brt bl   .82 .32

A312   A313

1990, Apr. 16
804 A312 1.20b multi   1.22 .62

1990   Litho.   *Perf. 14x13¹/₂*
805 A313 70c Telecommunications   .72 .55

National Chamber of Commerce, Cent. — A314

1990, June
806 A314 50c gold, blk & bl   .58 .42

Cochabamba Social Club, Cent. — A315

1990, Sept. 14   Litho.   *Perf. 13¹/₂*
807 A315 40c multicolored   .42 .32

UPAEP Type of 1989
Perf. 13¹/₂x14, 14x13¹/₂

1990, Oct. 12   Litho.
808 A306a 80c Huts   .75 .30
809 A306a 1b Mountains, lake, vert.   .95 .38

A317   A318

1990, Oct. 19   *Perf. 14x13¹/₂*
810 A317 1.20b multicolored   1.05 .42

Magistrate's District of Larecaja, 400th Anniv.

1990, Oct. 12   *Perf. 14x13¹/₂*
811 A318 2b multicolored   1.75 .70

Discovery of America, 500th anniv. (in 1992).

German Reunification A319

1990, Nov. 19   Litho.   *Perf. 14x13¹/₂*
812 A319 2b multicolored   1.70 .70

Visit of Carlos Salinas de Gortari, Pres. of Mexico — A320

Design: 80c, Visit of Rodrigo Borja Cevallos, Pres. of Ecuador.

1990, Dec. 13   Litho.   *Perf. 13¹/₂*
813 A320 60c multicolored   .75 .30
814 A320 80c multicolored   .85 .40

4th Congress of the Andean Presidents A321

1990, Nov. 29   *Perf. 13¹/₂x14*
815 A321 1.50b multicolored   1.35 .55

Exfivia '90   Christmas
A322   A323

1990, Dec. 9   *Perf. 13¹/₂*
816 A322 40c dk blue   .40 .15

1990, Nov. 20   *Perf. 11*
817 A323 50c multicolored   .45 .18

Express Mail Service A324

1990, Dec. 14   *Perf. 13¹/₂x14*
818 A324 1b multicolored   .90 .35

Bolivian Radio Club, 50th Anniv. — A325

1991, Mar. 1   Litho.   *Perf. 14x13¹/₂*
819 A325 2.40b multicolored   2.00 .80

End of Chaco War, 56th Anniv. — A326   National Museums — A327

Map of Heroes of Chaco Highway.

1991, June 14   Litho.   *Perf. 14x13¹/₂*
820 A326 60c multicolored   .55 .22

1991, June 13   *Perf. 13¹/₂*
821 A327 50c Archaeology   .42 .18
822 A327 50c Art   .42 .18
823 A327 1b Ethnology, Folklore   .85 .35
a.   Strip of 3, #821-823   1.70 .70

Espamer '91.

A328   A329

Our Lady of Peace, Metropolitan Cathedral.

1991, July 15   Litho.   *Perf. 14x13¹/₂*
824 A328 1.20b multicolored   1.15 .45

Presidential State Visit Type of 1989

Jaime Paz Zamora, Pres. of Bolivia and: No. 825, Dr. Carlos Saul Menem, Pres. of Argentina. No. 826, Dr. Luis Alberto Lacalle, Pres. of Uruguay.

1991   *Perf. 13¹/₂x14*
825 A306b 1b multicolored   .85 .35
826 A306b 1b multicolored   .85 .35

Issue dates: #825, Aug. 5; #826, Aug. 12.

1991, May 31   *Perf. 13¹/₂*

Tremarctos ornatus.
827 A329 30c Adult, 2 cubs   1.10 .15
828 A329 30c Adult's head   1.10 .15
829 A329 30c Adult on tree limb   1.10 .15
830 A329 30c Adult, cubs on tree limb   1.10 .15
Nos. 827-830 (4)   4.40 .60

World Wildlife Fund.

A330   A331

1991, Aug. 21   Litho.   *Perf. 14x13¹/₂*
831 A330 70c multicolored   .68 .28

Bolivian Philatelic Federation, 20th anniv.

Presidential State Visit Type of 1989

Design: 50c, Jaime Paz Zamora, Pres. of Bolivia and Alberto Fujimori, Pres. of Peru.

1991, Aug. 29   Litho.   *Perf. 13¹/₂x14*
832 A306b 50c multicolored   .45 .18

1991, Nov. 19   Litho.   *Perf. 14x13¹/₂*
833 A331 50c multicolored   .45 .18

National census.

America Issue — A332

UPAEP emblem and: 60c, First Discovery of Chuquiago, 1535, by Arturo Reque M. 1.20c, Founding of the City of La Paz, 1548, by J. Rimsa, vert.

Perf. 13¹/₂x14, 14x13¹/₂

1991, Oct. 12
834 A332 60c multicolored   .58 .25
835 A332 1.20b multicolored   1.15 .45

First National Grand Prix Auto and Motorcycle Race — A332a

1991, Sept. 5 Litho. Perf. 14x13½
835A A332a 50c multicolored .45 .18

ECOBOL, Postal Security System A333

1991, Sept. 9 Perf. 13½x14
836 A333 1.40b multicolored 1.35 .52

Simon Bolivar — A334

1992, Feb. 15 Litho. Perf. 13½
837 A334 1.20b buff, brn & org brn 1.15 .45
Exfilbo '92.

Scouting in Bolivia, 75th Anniv. (in 1990) and 1992 Andes Jamboree A335

1992, Jan. 13 Perf. 13½x14
838 A335 1.20b multicolored 1.15 .45
Dated 1991.

Christmas A336

Paintings: 2b, Landscape, by Daniel Pena y Sarmiento. 5b, Woman with Fruit, by Cecilio Guzman de Rojas. 15b, Native Mother, by Crespo Gastelu.

1991, Dec.19 Litho. Perf. 13½
839 A336 2b multicolored 1.50 .60
840 A336 5b multicolored 3.75 1.50
841 A336 15b multicolored 11.20 4.50
Nos. 839-841 (3) 16.45 6.60

Pacific Ocean Access Pact Between Bolivia and Peru A337

Designs: 1.20b, Pres. Zamora raising flag, vert. 1.50b, Pres. Jaime Paz Zamora of Bolivia and Pres. Alberto Fujimori, Peru. 1.80b, Shoreline of access zone near Ilo, Peru.

Perf. 14x13½, 13½x14
1992, Mar. 23
842 A337 1.20b multicolored .95 .40
843 A337 1.50b multicolored 1.15 .48
844 A337 1.80b multicolored 1.40 .55
Nos. 842-844 (3) 3.50 1.43

Expo '92, Seville A338

1992, Apr. 15 Perf. 13½x14
845 A338 30c multicolored .28 .15
846 A338 50c Columbus' ships .45 .18

Miraflores Rotary Club, District 4690, Mt. Illimani — A339

1992, Apr. 30 Litho. Perf. 13½
847 A339 90c multicolored .70 .45

Prof. Elizardo Perez, Founder of Ayllu of Warisata School, Birth Cent. — A340

1992, June 6 Litho. Perf. 13½
848 A340 60c multicolored .52 .22

Government Palace, Sucre A341

1992, July 10 Litho. Perf. 13½x14
849 A341 50c multicolored .42 .16

A342 A343

1992, Sept. 11 Perf. 14x13½
850 A342 50c multicolored .42 .16
Los Tiempos Newpaper, 25th anniv.

1992, Aug. 9 Perf. 13½
1.50b, Mario Martinez Guzman, tennis player.
851 A343 1.50b multicolored 1.15 .48
1992 Summer Olympics, Barcelona.

First Intl. Whitewater Canoe Regatta, Bermejo River — A343a

1992, Sept. 17 Litho. Perf. 13½
851A A343a 1.20b multicolored 1.10 .48

1994 World Cup Soccer Championships, US — A344

1992, Oct. 2 Litho. Perf. 13½
852 A344 1.20b multicolored 1.85 .75

Oruro Technical University, Cent. — A345

1992, Oct. 15 Perf. 13½x14
853 A345 50c multicolored .38 .15

Interamerican Institute for Agricultural Cooperation, 50th Anniv. — A346

1992, Oct. 7 Perf. 13½
854 A346 1.20b Chenopodium quinoa 1.15 .48

Discovery of America, 500th Anniv. A347

Paintings: 60c, Columbus departing from Palos, vert. 2b, Columbus with Caribbean natives.

1992, Oct. 1 Perf. 14x13½, 13½x14
855 A347 60c multicolored .42 .18
856 A347 2b multicolored 1.40 .58

Battle of Ingavi, 150th Anniv. (in 1991) A348

1992, Nov. 18 Litho. Perf. 13½x14
857 A348 1.20b sepia & black .95 .38

12th Bolivian Games, Cochabamba and Santa Cruz — A349

1992, Nov. 13
858 A349 2b multicolored 1.50 .60

Fauna, Events — A350

Event emblem and fauna: 20c, Beni Dept., sesquicentennial, caiman. 50c, Polska '93, paca. 1b, Bangkok '93, chinchilla. 2b, 1994 Winter Olympics, Lillehammer, Norway, anteater. 3b, Brandenburg Gate, jaguar. 4b, Brasiliana '93, hummingbird, vert. 5b, 1994 World Cup Soccer Championships, US, piranhas.

1992, Nov. 18 Litho. Perf. 13½
859 A350 20c multicolored .15 .15
860 A350 50c multicolored .35 .15
861 A350 1b multicolored .75 .30
862 A350 2b multicolored 1.50 .60
863 A350 3b multicolored 2.25 .90
864 A350 4b multicolored 3.00 1.25
865 A350 5b multicolored 3.75 1.50
Nos. 859-865 (7) 11.75 4.85

Christmas A350a

Designs: 1.20b, Man in canoe, star. 2.50b, Star over churches. 6b, Flowers, church, infant on hay.

1992, Dec. 1 Litho. Perf. 13½
865A A350a 1.20b multicolored .90 .35
865B A350a 2.50b multicolored 1.90 .75
865C A350a 6b multicolored 4.50 1.75
Nos. 865A-865C (3) 7.30 2.85

A351 A352

Nicolaus Copernicus (1473-1543), Polish Astronomer: 50c, Santa Ana Intl. astrometrical observatory, Tarija, horiz.

Perf. 13x13½, 13½x13
1993, Feb. 18 Litho.
866 A351 50c multicolored .38 .15
867 A351 2b black 1.50 .60

1993, Apr. 14 Litho. Perf. 13½
868 A352 60c multicolored .58 .24
Beatification of Mother Nazaria.

12th Bolivar Games A353

1993, Apr. 24 Perf. 13½x14
869 A353 2.30b multicolored 1.65 .65

Bolivia #C240, Brazil #3 — A354

1993, May 31
870 A354 2.30b multicolored 1.65 .65
First Brazilian Stamp, 150th anniv.

A355 A356

Eternal Father, by Gaspar de la Cueva.

1993, June 9 Litho. Perf. 13½
871 A355 1.80b multicolored 1.25 .50

1993, July 31 Litho. Perf. 14x13½
872 A356 50c Virgin of Urkupina .35 .15

City of Quillacollo, 400th anniv.

Pedro Domingo Murillo Industrial School — A357

1993, Aug. 4 Perf. 13½
873 A357 60c multicolored .40 .15

Butterflies
A358

1993, June 4 Perf. 13½x14
874 A358 60c Archaeoprepona demophon .55 .20
875 A358 60c Morpho sp. .55 .20
876 A358 80c Papilio sp. .70 .25
877 A358 80c Historis odius .70 .25
878 A358 80c Euptoieta hegesia .70 .25
879 A358 1.80b Morpho deidamia 1.75 .55
880 A358 1.80b Papilio thoas 1.75 .55
881 A358 1.80b Danaus plexippus 1.75 .55
882 A358 2.30b Caligo sp. 2.00 .60
883 A358 2.30b Anaea marthesia 2.00 .60
884 A358 2.30b Rothschildia sp. 2.00 .60
885 A358 2.70b Heliconius sp. 2.25 .75
886 A358 2.70b Marpesia corinna 2.25 .75
887 A358 2.70b Prepona chromus 2.25 .75
888 A358 3.50b Heliconius sp., diff. 3.00 .95
889 A358 3.50b Siproeta epaphus 3.00 .95
a. Sheet of 16, #874-889 30.00 30.00
Nos. 874-889 (16) 27.20 8.75

Pan-American Health Organization, 90th Anniv. — A359

1993, Oct. 13 Litho. Perf. 13½
890 A359 80c multicolored .55 .20

Archaeological Finds — A360

Location of cave paintings: No. 891, Oruro. No. 892, Santa Cruz, vert. No. 893, Beni, vert. No. 894, Chuquisaca, vert. No. 895, Chuquisaca. No. 896, Potosi. No. 897, La Paz, vert. No. 898, Tarija, vert. No. 899, Cochabamba.

1993, Sept. 28
891 A360 80c multicolored .55 .20
892 A360 80c multicolored .55 .20
893 A360 80c multicolored .55 .20
894 A360 80c multicolored .55 .20
895 A360 80c multicolored .55 .20
896 A360 80c multicolored .55 .20
897 A360 80c multicolored .55 .20
898 A360 80c multicolored .55 .20
899 A360 80c multicolored .55 .20
Nos. 891-899 (9) 4.95 1.80

America Issue — A361

1993, Oct. 9 Litho. Perf. 13½
900 A361 80c Saimiri sciereus .55 .20
901 A361 2.30b Felis pordalis 1.50 .60

Famous People — A361a Christmas — A361b

Designs: 50c, Yolanda Bedregal, poet. 70c, Simon Martinic, President of Cochabamba Philatelic Center. 90c, Eugenio von Boeck, politician, President of Bolivian Philatelic Federation. 1b, Marina Nunez del Prado, sculptor.

1993, Nov. 17 Litho. Perf. 11
901A A361a 50c sepia .32 .15
901B A361a 70c sepia .45 .18
901C A361a 90c sepia .55 .22
901D A361a 1b sepia .60 .25
Nos. 901A-901D (4) 1.92 .80

1993, Dec. 8 Perf. 14x13½
Paintings: 2.30b, Adoration of the Shepherds, by Leonardo Flores. 3.50b, Virgin with Child and Saints, by unknown artist. 6b, Virgin of the Milk, by Melchor Perez de Holguin.
901E A361b 2.30b multicolored 1.40 .55
901F A361b 3.50b multicolored 2.25 .85
901G A361b 6b multicolored 3.75 1.50
Nos. 901E-901G (3) 7.40 2.90

Town of Riberalta, Cent. — A362

1994, Feb. 3 Litho. Perf. 13½
902 A362 2b multicolored 1.25 .60

World Population Day A363

1994, Feb. 17 Litho. Perf. 13½
903 A363 2.30b multicolored 1.50 .60

A364 A365

1994, Feb. 21 Perf. 13½
904 A364 2b buff & multi 1.25 .60
905 A364 2.30b multi 1.50 .60
Inauguration of Pres. Gonzalo Sanchez de Lozada.

1994, Mar. 22
1994 World Cup Soccer Championships, US: 80c, Mascot. 1.80b, Bolivia, Uruguay. 2.30b, Bolivia, Venezuela. No. 909, Part of Bolivian team, goalies in black. No. 910, Part of Bolivian team, diff. 2.70b, Bolivia, Ecuador. 3.50b, Bolivia, Brazil.
906 A365 80c multicolored .48 .20
907 A365 1.80b multicolored 1.10 .45
908 A365 2.30b multicolored 1.40 .55
909 A365 2.50b multicolored 1.50 .60
910 A365 2.50b multicolored 1.50 .60
a. Pair, #909-910 3.00 1.25
911 A365 2.70b multicolored 1.65 .65
912 A365 3.50b multicolored 2.25 .85
Nos. 906-912 (7) 9.88 3.90

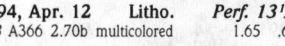

SOS Children's Village, Bolivia — A366

1994, Apr. 12 Litho. Perf. 13½
913 A366 2.70b multicolored 1.65 .65

Catholic Archdiocese La Paz, 50th Anniv. — A367

Churches, priests: 1.80b, Church of San Pedro, Msgr. Jorge Manrique Hurtado. 2b, Archbishop Abel I. Antezana y Rojas, Church of the Sacred Heart of Mary, vert. 3.50b, Msgr. Luis Sainz Hinojosa, Church of Santo Domingo, vert.

1994, July 12 Litho. Perf. 13½
914 A367 1.80b multicolored 1.10 .45
915 A367 2b multicolored 1.25 .60
916 A367 3.50b multicolored 2.25 .85
Nos. 914-916 (3) 4.60 1.90

A368 A369

Design: 2b, Pres. Victor Paz Estenssoro.

1994, Oct. 2 Litho. Perf. 13½
917 A368 2b multicolored 1.25 .50

1994, Oct. 9
918 A369 1.80b No. 46 1.10 .45

Battle of Ft. Boqueron A370

Col. Manuel Marzana Oroza, battle scene.

1994, Oct. 6
919 A370 80c multicolored .50 .20

San Borja, 300th Anniv. — A371

1994, Oct. 14
920 A371 1.60b Erythrina fusca 1.00 .40

America Issue — A372

Old, new methods of postal transport: 1b, Streetcar, van. 5b, Airplane, ox cart.

1994, Oct. 12
921 A372 1b multicolored .65 .25
922 A372 5b multicolored 3.25 1.25

1994 Solar Eclipse — A373 Environmental Protection — A374

1994 Oct. 21
923 A373 3.50b multicolored 2.25 .85

1994, Sept. 21
Trees: 60c, Buddleja coriacea. 1.80b, Bertholletia exelsa. 2b, Schinus molle, horiz. 2.70b, Polylepis racemosa. 3, Tabebuia chrysantha. 3.50b, Erythrina falcata, horiz.
924 A374 60c multicolored .38 .15
925 A374 1.80b multicolored 1.10 .45
926 A374 2b multicolored 1.25 .50
927 A374 2.70b multicolored 1.65 .65
928 A374 3b multicolored 1.90 .75
929 A374 3.50b multicolored 2.25 .85
Nos. 924-929 (6) 8.53 3.35

Gen. Antonio Jose de Sucre (1795-1830) A375

1995, Jan. 25 Litho. Perf. 13½
930 A375 1.80b shown .75 .30
931 A375 3.50b diff. background 1.50 .60

A377 A378

1994, Nov. 25 Litho. Perf. 13½
933 A377 2b Tarija girl 1.10 .45
934 A377 5b High plateau child 2.75 .45
935 A377 20b Eastern girl 11.00 3.75
Nos. 933-935 (3) 14.85 4.65

Christmas.

1994, Nov. 28 Litho. Perf. 13½
936 A378 1.80b multicolored .90 .35

Pan-American Scout Jamboree, Cochabamba

Yacuma-Beni Province, Cent. — A379

Design: 1.90b, 2.90b, Cathedral of St. Anne.

1995, Apr. 21 Litho. Perf. 13½
937 A379 1.90b black & multi 1.25 .60
938 A379 2.90b blue & multi 1.75 .90

Franciscans at Copacabana Natl. Sanctuary,
Cent. — A380

1995, May 2
939 A380 60c gray & multi .40 .15
940 A380 80c bister & multi .55 .20

A381　　　　　A382

1995　　**Litho.**　　*Perf. 13¹/₂*
941 A381 2b multicolored 1.00 .40
Peace Between Bolivia and Paraguay. Dated 1994.

1995, July 25
942 A382 2.40b multicolored 1.25 .50
Andes Development Corporation (CAF), 25th
anniv.

50th Anniv. of
Publication of
"Nationalism and
the Colonial Age,"
by Carlos
Montenegro (1904-
53) — A383

1995, Aug. 8
943 A383 1.20b pink & black .60 .25

A384　　　　　A385

1995, Sept. 26
944 A384 1b multicolored .50 .20
FAO, 50th anniv.

1995, Oct. 24　　*Perf. 14¹/₂*
945 A385 2.90b multicolored 1.50 .60
UN, 50th anniv.

America Issue — A386

1995, Nov. 21　　*Perf. 14*
946 A386 5b Condor 2.50 1.00
947 A386 5b Llamas 2.50 1.00
　　a.　Pair, #946-947 5.00 2.00

ICAO, 50th
Anniv. — A387

1995, Dec. 4　　*Perf. 13¹/₂x13*
948 A387 50c multicolored .25 .15

Temple of
Samaipata
A388

Archaeological finds and: a, 1.90b, Top of ruins.
b, 1b, Top of ruins, diff. c, 2.40b, Lower excava-
tion. d, 2b, Floor, tiers.

1995, Dec. 4　　*Perf. 13x13¹/₂*
949 A388 Block of 4, #a.-d. 3.75 1.50
No. 949 is a continuous design.

Taquiña Brewery,
Cent. — A389

1995, Dec. 8　　*Perf. 14*
950 A389 1b multicolored .50 .20

Christmas — A390

Paintings: 1.20b, The Annunciation, by Cima da
Conegliano. 3b, The Nativity, by Hans Baldung.
3.50b, Adoration of the Magi, by Rogier van der
Weyden.

1995, Dec. 15　　*Perf. 14x13¹/₂*
951 A390 1.20b multicolored .60 .25
952 A390 3b multicolored 1.50 .60
953 A390 3.50b multicolored 1.75 .70
　　Nos. 951-953 (3) 3.85 1.55

Natl. Anthem,
150th
Anniv. — A391

Designs: 1b, J.I. de Sanjines, lyricist. 2b, B.
Vincenti, composer.

1995, Dec. 18　　**Litho.**　　*Perf. 13¹/₂*
954 A391 1b multicolored .40 .15
955 A391 2b multicolored .80 .30
　　a.　Pair, #954-955 1.20 .45

Decree to
Abolish Abuse of
Indian Labor,
50th
Anniv. — A392

Designs: 1.90b, Modern representations of industry, Gov. Gualberto Villarroel. 2.90, Addressing
labor policies, silhouettes of people rejoicing.

1996, Jan. 26　　*Perf. 14*
956 A392 1.90b multicolored .75 .30
957 A392 2.90b multicolored 1.15 .45
　　a.　Pair, #956-957 1.90 .75

Nos. 639, 653, 685-686, 712-713, 715,
719, 726, 729, 732-733, C332, C348
Surcharged

Bs. 0.50

Perfs. and Printing Methods as Before

1996
958 A273 50c on 3,000,000b
　　　　 #729 .20 .15
959 A265 60c on 2000b #713 .25 .15
960 A277 60c on 1,400,000b
　　　　 #733 .25 .15
961 A271 1b on 2,500,000b
　　　　 #726 .40 .15
962 A264 1.50b on 11,000b #712 .60 .25
963 A267 2.50b on 23,000b #715 1.00 .40
964 A269 3b on 1,000,000b
　　　　 #719 1.15 .45
965 A222 3.50b on 6.50b #639 1.40 .55
966 A234 3.50b on 9b #653 1.40 .55
967 A276 3.50b on 2,000,000b
　　　　 #732 1.40 .55
968 AP67 3.80b on 3.80b #C332 1.50 .60
969 A189 20b on 3.80b #C348 8.00 3.20
970 A253 20b on 10b #685 8.00 3.20
971 A254 20b on 13b #686 8.00 3.20
　　Nos. 958-971 (14) 33.55 13.55

Size and location of surcharge varies.

Bs 0.60

No. 627 Surcharged

1996　　**Litho.**　　*Perf. 10¹/₂*
972 A216(b) 60c multicolored .40 .15
See No. 697 for similar surcharge.

10th Summit of the
Chiefs of State and
Government (Rio
Group),
Cochabamba
A393

Designs: 2.50b, Stylized person. 3.50b, Stylized
globe surrounded by lines.

1996, Sept. 4　　*Perf. 14*
973 A393 2.50b multicolored 1.00 .40
974 A393 3.50b multicolored 1.35 .55

Anniversaries
A394

50c, Natl. Bank of Bolivia, 125th anniv. 1b, Jose
Joaquin de Lemoine (1776-1851), first postal
administrator, vert.

1996, Dec. 8　　**Litho.**　　*Perf. 13¹/₂*
975 A394 50c multicolored .20 .15
976 A394 1b multicolored .20 .15

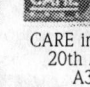

Summit of the
Americas to Sustain
Development
A395

CARE in Bolivia,
20th Anniv.
A396

1996, Dec. 8　　*Perf. 14x13¹/₂*
977 A395 2.50b brown & multi .95 .40
978 A395 5b black & multi 1.90 .75

1996, Dec. 19　　*Perf. 13¹/₂*
979 A396 60c Family, horiz. .25 .15
980 A396 70c shown .25 .15

Natl. Symphony
Orchestra, 50th
Anniv. — A397

1996, Dec. 24
981 A397 1.50b shown .60 .25
982 A397 2b String instruments .75 .30
　　a.　Pair, #981-982 1.35 .55
No. 982a is a continuous design.

Tourism
in Oruro
A398

Designs: 50c, Miners' Monument, vert. 60c,
Folklore costume, vert. 1b, Virgin of Socavon, vert.
1.50b, Sajama mountains. 2.50b, Chipaya child,
building, vert. 3b, Raul Shaw, "Moreno."

1997, Feb. 3　　**Litho.**　　*Perf. 14¹/₂*
983 A398 50c multicolored .20 .15
984 A398 60c multicolored .25 .15
985 A398 1b multicolored .40 .15
986 A398 1.50b multicolored .60 .25
987 A398 2.50b multicolored .95 .40
988 A398 3b multicolored 1.10 .45
　　Nos. 983-988 (6) 3.50 1.55
Dated 1996.

Tourism in
Chuquisaca
A399

Designs: 60c, La Glorieta. 1b, Governor's Palace,
vert. No. 991, Dinosaur tracks. No. 992, House of
Liberty. 2b, Tarabaqueno, vert. 3b, Statue of Juana
Azurduy of Padilla, vert.

Perf. 13¹/₂x14, 14x13¹/₂
1997, Jan. 30
989 A399 60c multicolored .25 .15
990 A399 1b multicolored .40 .15
991 A399 1.50b multicolored .60 .25
992 A399 1.50b multicolored .60 .25

993	A399	2b multicolored	.75	.30
994	A399	3b multicolored	1.10	.45
		Nos. 989-994 (6)	3.70	1.55

Dated 1996.

Tourism in Tarija
A400

Designs: 50c, House of Culture, Dorada, vert. 60c, Church of Entre Rios, vert. 80c, San Luis Falls. 1b, Monument to the Chaco War. 3b, Temple, Statue of the Virgin Mary, Chaguay. 20b, Eustaquio Mendez house, monument.

Perf. 14x13½, 13½x14

1997, Jan. 24

995	A400	50c multicolored	.20	.15
996	A400	60c multicolored	.25	.15
997	A400	80c multicolored	.30	.15
998	A400	1b multicolored	.40	.15
999	A400	3b multicolored	1.10	.45
1000	A400	20b multicolored	7.75	3.00
		Nos. 995-1000 (6)	10.00	4.05

Dated 1996.

Visit of French Pres. Jacques Chirac
A401

Design: Bolivian Pres. Gonzalo Sanchez de Lozada, Chirac.

1997, Mar. 15 *Perf. 14*

1001	A401	4b multicolored	1.50	.60

Salesian Order in Bolivia, Cent. — A402

Designs: 1.50b, St. John Bosco (1815-88), church. 2b, Statue of St. John Bosco talking with boy, church.

1997, Apr. 29 Litho. *Perf. 13½*

1002	A402	1.50b multicolored	.60	.25
1003	A402	2b multicolored	.75	.30

UNICEF, 50th Anniv. — A403

Children's drawings: 50c, Houses, children on playground. 90c, Child running, cactus, rock, lake. 1b, Boys, girls arm in arm across globe. 2.50b, Girl on swing, others in background.

1997

1004	A403	50c multicolored	.20	.15
1005	A403	90c multicolored	.35	.15
1006	A403	1b multicolored	.40	.15
1007	A403	2.50b multicolored	.95	.40
		Nos. 1004-1007 (4)	1.90	.85

Department of La Paz
A404

Tourism: 50c, Mt. Chulumani, Las Yungas, vert. 80c, Inca monolith, vert. 1.50b, City, Mt. Illimani,

vert. 2b, Gate of the Sun, Tiwanacu. 2.50b, Traditional dancers, vert. 10b, Virgin of Copacabana, reed boat.

1997, May 28 Litho. *Perf. 13½*

1008	A404	50c multicolored	.20	.15
1009	A404	80c multicolored	.30	.15
1010	A404	1.50b multicolored	.60	.25
1011	A404	2b multicolored	.75	.30
1012	A404	2.50b multicolored	.95	.40
1013	A404	10b multicolored	3.75	1.50
		Nos. 1008-1013 (6)	6.55	2.75

1997 America Cup Soccer Championships, Bolivia — A405

1998 World Cup Soccer Championships, France — A406

1997, June 13

1014	A405	3b multicolored	1.20	.50
1015	A406	5b multicolored	1.90	.75

America Issue — A408

Women in traditional costumes: 5b, From valley region. 15b, From eastern Bolivia.

1997, July 14 Litho. *Perf. 13½*

1017	A408	5b multicolored	1.90	.75
1018	A408	15b multicolored	5.75	2.25

Mercosur (Common Market of Latin America) — A409

1997

1019	A409	3b multicolored	1.10	.45

AIR POST STAMPS

Aviation School
AP1   AP2

1924, Dec. Unwmk. Engr. *Perf. 14*

C1	AP1	10c ver & blk	.25	.30
a.		Inverted center	800.00	
C2	AP1	15c carmine & blk	1.50	.50
C3	AP1	25c dk bl & blk	.60	.60
C4	AP1	50c orange & blk	1.50	1.25
C5	AP2	1b red brn & blk	.95	.95
C6	AP2	2b blk brn & blk	1.75	1.75
C7	AP2	5b dk vio & blk	5.50	5.50
		Nos. C1-C7 (7)	12.05	10.85

Natl. Aviation School establishment.
These stamps were available for ordinary postage. Nos. C1, C3, C5 and C6 exist imperforate. Proofs of the 2b with inverted center exist imperforate and privately perforated.
For overprints and surcharges see Nos. C11-C23, C56-C58.

Emblem of Lloyd Aéreo Boliviano — AP3

1928 Litho. *Perf. 11*

C8	AP3	15c green	1.00	1.00
a.		Imperf., pair	50.00	
C9	AP3	20c dark blue	.25	.25
C10	AP3	35c red brown	.60	.60
		Nos. C8-C10 (3)	1.85	1.85

No. C8 exists imperf. between.
For surcharges see #C24-C26, C53-C55.

Graf Zeppelin Issues
Nos. C1-C5 Surcharged or Overprinted in Various Colors:

CORREO AEREO
R. S. 6-V-1930

5 Cts.
Nos. C11, C19

CORREO AEREO
R. S.
6-V- 1930
Nos. C12-C18, C20-C23

1930, May 6 *Perf. 14*

C11	AP1	5c on 10c ver & blk (G)	9.50	9.50
C12	AP1	10c ver & blk (Bl)	9.50	9.50
C13	AP1	10c ver & blk (Br)	600.00	875.00
C14	AP1	15c car & blk (V)	9.50	9.50
C15	AP1	25c dk bl & blk (R)	9.50	9.50
C16	AP1	50c org & blk (Br)	9.50	9.50
C17	AP1	50c org & blk (R)	475.00	600.00
C18	AP2	1b red brn & blk (gold)	150.00	150.00

Experts consider the 50c with gold or silver overprint and 5c with black to be trial color proofs.
Nos. C11-C18 exist with the surcharges inverted, double, or double with one inverted, but the regularity of these varieties is questioned.
See notes following No. C23.

Surcharged or Overprinted in Bronze Inks of Various Colors

C19	AP1	5c on 10c ver & blk (G)	77.50	80.00
C20	AP1	10c ver & blk (Bl)	67.50	67.50
C21	AP1	15c car & blk (V)	77.50	80.00
C22	AP1	25c dk bl & blk (cop)	77.50	80.00
C23	AP2	1b red brn & blk (gold)	190.00	200.00
		Nos. C19-C23 (5)	490.00	507.50

Flight of the airship Graf Zeppelin from Europe to Brazil and return via Lakehurst, NJ.
Nos. C19 to C23 were intended for use on postal matter forwarded by the Graf Zeppelin.
No. C18 was overprinted with light gold or gilt bronze ink. No. C23 was overprinted with deep gold bronze ink. Nos. C13 and C17 were overprinted with trial colors but were sold with the regular printings. The 5c on 10c is known surcharged in black and in blue.

Z 1930
No. C8-C10 Surcharged
Bs. 3.—

1930, May 6 *Perf. 11*

C24	AP3	1.50b on 15c	25.00	25.00
a.		Inverted surcharge	57.50	57.50
b.		Comma instead of period after "1"	35.00	35.00
C25	AP3	3b on 20c	25.00	25.00
a.		Inverted surcharge	62.50	62.50
b.		Comma instead of period after "3"	40.00	40.00
C26	AP3	6b on 35c	37.50	40.00
a.		Inverted surcharge	110.00	110.00
b.		Comma instead of period after "6"	62.50	62.50
		Nos. C24-C26 (3)	87.50	90.00

Airplane and Bullock Cart — AP6

Airplane and River Boat — AP7

1930, July 24 Litho. *Perf. 14*

C27	AP6	5c dp violet	1.25	1.00
C28	AP7	15c red	1.25	1.00
C29	AP7	20c yellow	.50	.50
C30	AP7	35c yellow grn	.40	.25
C31	AP7	50c deep blue	.40	.25
C32	AP6	1b lt brown	.40	.25
C33	AP7	2b deep rose	.40	.25
C34	AP6	3b slate	1.40	1.40
		Nos. C27-C34 (8)	6.00	5.05

Nos. C27 to C34 exist imperforate.
For surcharge see No. C52.

Air Service Emblem
AP8

1932, Sept. 16 *Perf. 11*

C35	AP8	5c ultra	.70	.55
C36	AP8	10c gray	.45	.35
C37	AP8	15c dark rose	.70	.55
C38	AP8	25c orange	.70	.55
C39	AP8	30c green	.60	.30
C40	AP8	50c violet	.60	.35
C41	AP8	1b dk brown	.60	.35
		Nos. C35-C41 (7)	4.35	3.00

Map of Bolivia — AP9

1935, Feb. 1 Engr. *Perf. 12*

C42	AP9	5c brown red	.15	.15
C43	AP9	10c dk green	.15	.15
C44	AP9	20c dk violet	.15	.15
C45	AP9	30c ultra	.25	.15
C46	AP9	50c orange	.30	.15
C47	AP9	1b bister brn	.30	.15
C48	AP9	1½b violet	.60	.15
C49	AP9	2b carmine	.60	.30
C50	AP9	5b green	1.10	.40
C51	AP9	10b dk brown	1.75	.75
		Nos. C42-C51 (10)	5.35	2.60

Nos. C1, C4, C10, C30 Surcharged in Red (#C52-C56) or Green (#C57-C58) — c

Correo Aéreo
D. S. 25-2-37
0.05

1937, Oct. 6 *Perf. 11, 14*

C52	AP6	5c on 35c yel grn	.40	.30
a.		"Carreo"	12.50	
b.		Inverted surcharge		
C53	AP3	20c on 35c red brn	.50	.40
a.		Inverted surcharge		
C54	AP3	50c on 35c red brn	1.50	1.25
a.		Inverted surcharge	17.50	
C55	AP3	1b on 35c red brn	1.10	.65
a.		Inverted surcharge		
C56	AP1	2b on 50c org & blk	1.65	1.00
a.		Inverted surcharge		
C57	AP1	12b on 10c ver & blk	5.75	4.75
a.		Inverted surcharge	22.50	
C58	AP1	15b on 10c ver & blk	5.75	2.75
a.		Inverted surcharge		

Regular Postage Stamps of 1925 Surcharged in Green or Red — d

Correo Aéreo
D. S.
25-2-37
Bs. 4.—

Perf. 14

C59	A56 (d)	3b on 50c dp vio (G)	1.10	1.00
C60	A56 (d)	4b on 1b red (G)	1.40	1.40
C61	A57 (c)	5b on 2b org (G)	1.90	1.65
a.		Double surcharge	90.00	
C62	A56 (d)	10b on 5b blk brn	4.50	3.25
a.		Double surcharge	35.00	
		Nos. C52-C62 (11)	25.55	18.40

No. C59-C62 exist with inverted surcharge, No. C62a with black and black and red surcharges.

Courtyard of
Potosí
Mint — AP10

Miner — AP11

Virgin of
Copacabana
AP20

Jesus Christ
AP21

1943, Nov. 18   Engr.   Perf. 12½
C91	AP27	10c rose vio & brn	.15	.15
C92	AP27	20c emerald & brn	.15	.15
C93	AP27	30c rose car & brn	.18	.15
C94	AP27	3b blue & brn	.22	.18
C95	AP27	5b black & brn	.40	.30
		Nos. C91-C95 (5)	1.10	.93

Department of Beni centenary.

C116	AP32	3b dp orange	.18	.15
C117	AP32	4b rose lilac	.20	.15
		Set value	.64	.46

1st anniv. of the Revolution of July 21, 1946.
1.40b, 2.50b exist imperf.
For surcharge see No. C137.

1947, Oct. 23   Perf. 13½
C118	AP33	2.90b ultra	.25	.15
a.		Imperf., pair	20.00	
b.		Perf. 10½	5.00	4.00

Meeting of Presidents Enrique Hertzog of Bolivia
and Juan D. Perón of Argentina at Yacuiba, Oct. 23,
1947.

Types of Regular Issue of 1948

Designs: 2.50b, Statue of Christ above La Paz.
3.70b, Child kneeling before cross. No. C121, St.
John Bosco. No. C122, Virgin of Copacabana.
13.60b, Pope Plus XII blessing University of La Paz.

1948, Sept. 26   Perf. 11½
C119	A120	2.50b ver & yel	.45	.35
C120	A120	3.70b rose & cream	.55	.35
C121	A120	4b rose lil & gray	.55	.25
C122	A120	4b lt ultra & sal	.55	.16
C123	A120	13.60b ultra & lt grn	.70	.40
		Nos. C119-C123 (5)	2.80	1.51

Type of Regular Issue of 1948

1948, Oct.
C124	A125	10b emerald & salmon	1.60	.18

Emancipated
Woman — AP12

Pincers, Torch and
Good Will
Principles — AP15

Church of San
Francisco, La
Paz — AP22

Condor and Sun
Rising — AP28

Plane — AP29

1944, Sept. 19   Litho.   Perf. 13½
C96	AP28	40c red violet	.15	.15
C97	AP28	1b blue violet	.15	.15
C98	AP29	1.50b yellow green	.18	.15
C99	AP29	2.50b dk gray blue	.38	.18
		Nos. C96-C99 (4)	.86	
		Set value		.42

Revolution of Dec. 20, 1943.

Pres. Gregorio Pacheco,
Map and Post
Horn — AP34

L. A. B.
Plane — AP35

1950, Jan. 2   Unwmk.
C125	AP34	1.40b orange brown	.15	.15
C126	AP34	2.50b orange	.15	.15
C127	AP34	3.30b rose violet	.15	.15
		Nos. C125-C127 (3)	.45	.45

75th anniv. of the UPU.

Airplane over
Field — AP13

Airplanes and
Liberty
Monument
AP14

St. Anthony of
Padua — AP23

Perf. 13½, 10½

1939, July 19   Litho.
C72	AP19	5c dull violet	.35	.35
a.		Pair, imperf. between	30.00	
C73	AP20	30c lt bl grn	.30	.20
C74	AP21	45c violet bl	.60	.20
a.		Vertical pair, imperf. between	42.50	
C75	AP22	60c carmine	.40	.35
C76	AP23	75c vermilion	.65	.60
C77	AP23	90c deep blue	.45	.25
C78	AP22	2b dull brown	.75	.25
C79	AP21	4b deep plum	1.00	.40
C80	AP20	5b lt blue	2.50	.25
C81	AP19	10b yellow	5.00	.25
		Nos. C72-C81 (10)	12.00	3.10

2nd National Eucharistic Congress.
For surcharge see No. C112.

Map of Natl.
Airways — AP30

Map of Bolivian Air
Lines — AP31

1945, May 31   Perf. 11
C100	AP30	10c red	.15	.15
a.		Imperf., pair	9.00	
C101	AP30	50c yellow	.15	.15
a.		Imperf., pair	27.50	
C102	AP30	90c lt green	.20	.15
a.		Imperf., pair	30.00	
C103	AP30	5b lt ultra	.35	.15
C104	AP30	20b deep brown	1.00	.45
		Nos. C100-C104 (5)	1.85	
		Set value		.84

10th anniversary of first flight, La Paz to Tacha,
Peru, by Panagra Airways.
For surcharges see Nos. C128-C129.

Nos. C100 and
C104 Surcharged
in Black

1950, May 31   Perf. 11
C128	AP30	4b on 10c red	.15	.15
a.		Inverted surcharge	17.50	17.50
C129	AP30	10b on 20b dp brn	.30	.22
a.		Inverted surcharge	17.50	17.50

Panagra air services in Bolivia, 15th anniv.

Emblem of
New
Government
AP17

Transport Planes over
Map of Bolivia
AP18

1938, May   Litho.   Perf. 10½
C63	AP10	20c deep rose	.25	.25
C64	AP11	30c gray	.25	.25
C65	AP12	40c yellow	.25	.25
C66	AP13	50c yellow grn	.50	.25
C67	AP14	60c dull blue	.50	.25
C68	AP15	1b dull red	.75	.25
C69	AP16	2b bister	1.25	.25
C70	AP17	3b lt brown	1.25	.25
C71	AP18	5b dk violet	1.90	.25
		Nos. C63-C71 (9)	6.90	2.25

40c, 1b, 2b exist imperf.

Plane over Lake
Titicaca — AP24

Mt. Illimani and
Condor — AP25

1941, Aug. 21   Perf. 13½
C82	AP24	10b dull green	3.25	.38
C83	AP24	20b light ultra	3.75	.65
C84	AP25	50b rose lilac	6.50	1.00
C85	AP25	100b olive bister	16.00	6.00
		Nos. C82-C85 (4)	29.50	8.03

Counterfeits exist.

1945, Sept. 15   Perf. 13½
Centers in Red and Blue
C105	AP31	20c violet	.15	.15
C106	AP31	30c orange brn	.15	.15
C107	AP31	50c brt blue grn	.15	.15
C108	AP31	90c brt violet	.15	.15
C109	AP31	2b blue	.15	.15
C110	AP31	3b magenta	.20	.15
C111	AP31	4b olive bister	.35	.16
		Set value	1.00	.68

Founding of Lloyd Aéreo Boliviano, 20th anniv.

Catalogue values for unused
stamps in this section, from this
point to the end of the section, are
for Never Hinged items.

No. C116
Surcharged in
Black

1950, Sept. 24   Perf. 11½
C137	AP32	1.40b on 3b dp orange	.25	.25

1st anniv. of the ending of the Civil War of Aug.
24-Sept. 24, 1949.
Exists with inverted and double surcharge.

Chalice — AP19

Liberty and Clasped
Hands — AP26

1942, Nov. 12
C86	AP26	40c rose lake	.25	.25
C87	AP26	50c ultra	.25	.25
C88	AP26	1b orange brn	1.25	.75
C89	AP26	5b magenta	.75	.25
a.		Double impression		
C90	AP26	10b dull brn vio	2.50	1.25
		Nos. C86-C90 (5)	5.00	2.75

Conference of Chancellors, Jan. 15, 1942.

No. C76 Surcharged

in Blue

1947, Mar. 23
C112	AP23	1.40b on 75c ver	.18	.18

Mt.
Illimani — AP32

Arms of Bolivia
and
Argentina — AP33

1947, Sept. 15   Litho.   Perf. 11½
C113	AP32	1b rose car	.15	.15
C114	AP32	1.40b emerald	.15	.15
C115	AP32	2.50b blue	.15	.15

1950, Sept. 15   Litho.   Perf. 13½
C130	AP35	20c red orange	.15	.15
C131	AP35	30c purple	.15	.15
C132	AP35	50c green	.15	.15
C133	AP35	1b orange	.15	.15
C134	AP35	3b ultra	.25	.15
C135	AP35	15b carmine	.50	.15
C136	AP35	50b chocolate	1.00	.35
		Nos. C130-C136 (7)	2.35	
		Set value		1.00

25th anniv. of the founding of Lloyd Aero Boliviano. 30c, 50c, 15b exist imperforate.
No. C132 exists without imprint at bottom of
stamp.

General José Ballivián; Old and Modern
Transportation — AP27

Symbols of United
Nations — AP36

1950, Oct. 24   Unwmk.
C138 AP36 3.60b crimson rose   .50 .16
C139 AP36 4.70b black brown   .65 .16
    5th anniv. of the UN.

Gate of the Sun and   Church of San
Llama   Francisco
AP37   AP38

Designs: 40c, Avenue Camacho. 50c, Consistorial Palace. 1b, Legislative Palace. 2b, Communications Bldg. 3b, Arms. 4b, La Gasca ordering Mendoza to found La Paz. 5b, Capt. Alonso de
Mendoza founding La Paz. 10b, Arms; portrait of
Mendoza.

1951, Mar. 1   Engr.   Perf. 12½
        Center in Black
C140 AP37 20c carmine   .15 .15
C141 AP38 30c dk vio bl   .15 .15
C142 AP37 40c dark blue   .15 .15
C143 AP37 50c blue green   .15 .15
C144 AP37 1b red   .20 .20
C145 AP37 2b red orange   .35 .35
C146 AP37 3b deep blue   .35 .35
C147 AP37 4b vermilion   .45 .45
   a.   Souvenir sheet of 4   1.00 1.00
C148 AP37 5b dark green   .40 .40
   a.   Souvenir sheet of 3   1.00 1.00
C149 AP37 10b red brown   .65 .65
   a.   Souvenir sheet of 3   1.00 1.00
    Nos. C140-C149 (10)   3.00 3.00

    400th anniv. of the founding of La Paz.
No. C147a contains C143-C145, C147; No.
C148a contains C142, C146, C148; No. C149a
contains C140, C141, C149. Perf. and imperf.,
size: 150x100mm.
    For surcharges see Nos. C187-C196.

Horsemanship
AP39

Designs: 30c, Basketball. 50c, Fencing. 1b, Hurdling. 2.50b, Javelin throwing. 3b, Relay race. 5b,
La Paz stadium.

1951, Aug. 23   Unwmk.
        Center in Black
C150 AP39 20c purple   .20 .15
C151 AP39 30c rose vio   .30 .15
C152 AP39 50c dp red org   .50 .15
C153 AP39 1b chocolate   .50 .15
C154 AP39 2.50b orange   .75 .30
C155 AP39 3b black brn   1.00 .75
   a.   Souvenir sheet of 3, #C153-C155   4.00 3.50
C156 AP39 5b red   2.00 1.50
   a.   Souvenir sheet of 4, C150-C152,   C156   4.50 4.00
    Nos. C150-C156 (7)   5.25 3.15

    The stamps were intended to commemorate the
5th South American Games and the 2nd National
Sports Congress held at La Paz, October 1948.
    Nos. C155a, C156a exist perf. and imperf.

Eduardo   Queen
Abaroa — AP40   Isabella
                 I — AP41

1952, Mar. 24   Litho.   Perf. 11
C157 AP40 70c rose red   .15 .15
C158 AP40 2b orange yel   .25 .25
C159 AP40 3b yellow green   .25 .15
C160 AP40 5b blue   .25 .15
C161 AP40 50b rose lilac   1.00 .90
C162 AP40 100b gray black   1.10 1.10
   a.   Perf. 14   10.00
    Nos. C157-C162 (6)   3.00 2.70
    73rd anniv. of the death of Abaroa.

1952, July 16   Perf. 13½
C163 AP41 50b emerald   .35 .25
C164 AP41 100b brown   .65 .35
    500th anniversary of the birth of Queen Isabella I
of Spain. Exist imperforate.

Columbus
Lighthouse
AP42

1952, July 16
C165 AP42 2b rose lilac, salmon   .20 .20
C166 AP42 3.70b blue grn, bl   .20 .20
C167 AP42 4.40b orange, salmon   .20 .20
C168 AP42 20b dk brn, cream   .40 .15
    Nos. C165-C168 (4)   1.00 .75
    No. C168 exists imperforate.

Soldiers — AP43

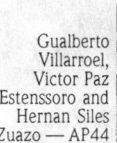

Gualberto
Villarroel,
Victor Paz
Estenssoro and
Hernan Siles
Zuazo — AP44

Perf. 13½ (AP43), 11½ (AP44)
1953, Apr. 9   Litho.
C169 AP44 3.70b chocolate   .15 .15
C170 AP43 6b red violet   .15 .15
C171 AP44 9b brown rose   .15 .15
C172 AP44 10b aqua   .15 .15
C173 AP44 16b vermilion   .15 .15
C174 AP43 22.50b dk brown   .25 .20
C175 AP44 40b gray   .40 .15
    Nos. C169-C175 (7)   1.40 1.10

    1st anniv. of the Revolution of Apr. 9, 1952.
Nos. C169-C170 and C174 exist imperf.

Pres. Victor Paz   Map and
Estenssoro   Peasant — AP46
Embracing
Indian — AP45

1954, Aug. 2   Perf. 12x11½
C176 AP45 20b orange brn   .15 .15
C177 AP46 27b brt pink   .15 .16
C178 AP46 30b red org   .15 .15
C179 AP46 45b violet brn   .20 .15
C180 AP45 100b blue grn   .38 .15
C181 AP46 300b yellow grn   1.00 .28
    Nos. C176-C181 (6)   2.03
        Set value   .77

    Nos. C176, C180 for 3rd Inter-American Indian
Congress. Nos. C177-C179, C181 agrarian reform
laws of 1953-1954.
    Nos. C176-C180 exist imperf.
    For surcharge see No. C261.

Oil   Map of South
Derricks — AP47   America and La
               Paz
              Arms — AP48

1955, Oct. 9   Perf. 10½
C182 AP47 55b dk & lt grnsh bl   .20 .15
C183 AP47 70b dk gray & gray   .20 .15
C184 AP47 90b dk & lt grn   .20 .15
          Perf. 13
C185 AP47 500b red lilac   .65 .40
C186 AP47 1000b blk brn & fawn   1.25 1.25
    Nos. C182-C186 (5)   2.50 2.10
    For surcharge see No. C262.

   Nos. C140-C149 Surcharged with New
    Values and Bars in Black or Carmine
1957   Engr.   Perf. 12½
      Center in Black
C187 AP37 100b on 3b (C)   .15 .15
C188 AP37 200b on 20b   .15 .15
C189 AP37 500b on 4b   .16 .15
C190 AP37 600b on 1b   .16 .15
C191 AP37 700b on 20c   .25 .15
C192 AP37 800b on 40c (C)   .35 .15
C193 AP38 900b on 30c (C)   .40 .15
C194 AP37 1800b on 50c (C)   .65 .25
C195 AP37 3000b on 50b   1.00 .45
C196 AP37 5000b on 10b (C)   1.60 .75
    Nos. C187-C196 (10)   4.87
        Set value   2.15

            Unwmk.
1957, May 25   Litho.   Perf. 12
C197 AP48 700b lilac & vio   .35 .35
C198 AP48 1200b pale brn   .40 .35
C199 AP48 1350b rose car   .55 .50
C200 AP48 2700b blue grn   1.10 .65
C201 AP48 4000b violet bl   1.40 .75
    Nos. C197-C201 (5)   3.80 2.60

    7th session of the C. E. P. A. L. (Comision
Economica para la America Latina de las Naciones
Unidas), La Paz.
    Exist imperf.
    For surcharges see Nos. C263-C265.

    Type of Regular Issue, 1957
1957, Dec. 19   Perf. 11½
C202 A141 600b magenta   .22 .15
C203 A141 700b violet bl   .35 .15
C204 A141 900b pale vio   .50 .15
    Nos. C202-C204 (3)   1.07
        Set value   .27

    Type of Regular Issue, 1960
1960, Jan. 30
C205 A142 400b rose claret   .50 .30
C206 A142 800b slate blue   .65 .40
C207 A142 2000b slate   1.00 .60
    Nos. C205-C207 (3)   2.15 1.30

Gate of the Sun,   Uprooted Oak
Tiahuanacu   Emblem
AP49   AP50

1960, Mar. 26   Litho.   Perf. 11½
C208 AP49 3000b gray   2.00 1.10
C209 AP49 5000b gray   3.00 1.10
C210 AP49 10,000b rose claret   4.75 2.75
C211 AP49 15,000b blue violet   7.00 4.50
    Nos. C208-C211 (4)   16.75 9.45

1960, Apr. 7   Perf. 11½
C212 AP50 600b ultra   .35 .35
C213 AP50 700b lt red brn   .35 .35
C214 AP50 900b dk bl grn   .35 .35
C215 AP50 1800b violet   .60 .60
C216 AP50 2000b gray   .60 .60
    Nos. C212-C216 (5)   2.30 2.25

    WRY, July 1, 1959-June 30, 1960.
    No. C215 exists with "1961" overprint in dark
carmine, but was not regularly issued in this form.

Jaime
Laredo — AP51

        Perf. 11½
1960, Aug. 15   Unwmk.   Litho.
C217 AP51 600b rose vio   .75 .45
C218 AP51 700b ol gray   .75 .25
C219 AP51 800b vio brn   .75 .25
C220 AP51 900b dk bl   1.00 .25
C221 AP51 1800b green   1.50 1.50
C222 AP51 4000b dk gray   3.00 1.00
    Nos. C217-C222 (6)   7.75 3.70

    Issued to honor the violinist Jaime Laredo.
    For surcharges see Nos. C266-C267.

    Children's Hospital Type of 1960
1960, Nov. 21   Perf. 11½
C223 A146 600b multi   .40 .22
C224 A146 1000b multi   .60 .22
C225 A146 1800b multi   1.00 1.00
C226 A146 5000b multi   3.00 1.20
    Nos. C223-C226 (4)   5.00 2.64
    For surcharges see No. C268-C269.

Pres. Paz
Estenssoro
and Pres.
Getulio Vargas
of Brazil
AP52

1960, Dec. 14   Litho.   Perf. 11½
C227 AP52 1200b on 10b org & blk   .70 .70
    Exists with surcharge inverted.
    No. C227 without surcharge was not regularly
issued, although a decree authorizing its circulation
was published. Value, $2.
    Postally-used counterfeits of surcharge exist.

Pres. Paz
Estenssoro and
Pres. Frondizi of
Argentina
AP53

    Design: 4000b, Flags of Bolivia and Argentina.

1961, May 23   Perf. 10½
C228 AP53 4000b brn, red, yel, grn
                  & bl   .75 .75
C229 AP53 6000b dk grn & blk   1.50 1.50

    Visit of the President of Argentina, Dr. Arturo
Frondizi, to Bolivia.
    For surcharge see No. C309.

Miguel de Cervantes — AP54

1961, Oct.   Photo.   Perf. 13
C230 AP54 1400b pale grn & dk ol
                grn   .58 .22
    Cervantes' appointment as Chief Magistrate of La
Paz.

    *Market value for a particular scarce
stamp may remain relatively low if
few collectors want it.*

Virgin of Cotoca
and Symbol of
Eucharist
AP55

Planes and
Parachutes
AP56

1962, Mar. 19   Litho.   Perf. 10¹/₂
C231 AP55 1400b brn, pink & yel   .65   .35
4th Natl. Eucharistic Cong., Santa Cruz, 1961.

Nos. C212-C216 Surcharged Vertically
with New Value and Greek Key Border

1962, June   Unwmk.   Perf. 11¹/₂
C232 AP50 1200b on 600b   .55   .55
C233 AP50 1300b on 700b   .50   .50
C234 AP50 1400b on 900b   .55   .55
C235 AP50 2800b on 1,800b   .90   .75
C236 AP50 3000b on 2,000b   .90   .75
Nos. C232-C236 (5)   3.40 3.10

The overprinted segment of Greek key border on
Nos. C232-C236 comes in two positions: two full
"keys" on top, and one full and two half keys on
top.

Flower Type of 1962

Flowers: 100b, 1800b, Cantua buxifolia. 800b,
10,000b, Cantua bicolor.

1962, June 28   Litho.   Perf. 10¹/₂
Flowers in Natural Colors
C237 A152   100b dk bl   .25   .15
C238 A152   800b green   .50   .15
C239 A152   1800b violet   1.00   .50
a.   Souvenir sheet of 3   7.50 6.00
C240 A152   10,000b dk bl   3.25 1.75
Nos. C237-C240 (4)   5.00 2.55

No. C239a contains 3 imperf. stamps similar to
Nos. C237-C239, but with the 1,800b background
color changed to dark violet blue.
For surcharges see Nos. C270-C271.

1962, Sept. 5   Litho.   Perf. 11¹/₂
1200b, 5000b, Plane and oxcart. 2000b, Aerial
photography (plane over South America).
Emblem in Red, Yellow & Green
C241 AP56   600b blk & bl   .25   .15
C242 AP56   1200b multi   .50   .20
C243 AP56   1200b multi   .75   .35
C244 AP56   5000b multi   1.50   .65
Nos. C241-C244 (4)   3.00 1.35

Armed Forces of Bolivia.

Malaria Type of 1962

Design: Inscription around mosquito, laurel
around globe.

1962, Oct. 4
C245 A154 2000b ind, grn & yel   .80   .50

Type of Regular Issue, 1961

Design: Pedro de la Gasca (1485-1567).

1962 Unwmk. Photo.   Perf. 13x12¹/₂
C246 A150 1200b brn, yel   .35   .20

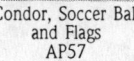

Condor, Soccer Ball
and Flags
AP57

Alliance for
Progress
Emblem
AP58

1.80b, Map of Bolivia, soccer ball, goal and flags.

1963, Mar. 21   Litho.   Perf. 11¹/₂
C247 AP57 1.40b multi   1.00   .65
C248 AP57 1.80b multi   1.00   .65
21st South American Soccer Championships.

Freedom from Hunger Type

Design: Wheat, globe and wheat emblem.

1963, Aug. 1   Unwmk.   Perf. 11¹/₂
C249 A156 1.20b dk grn, bl & yel   .75   .75

1963, Nov. 15   Perf. 11¹/₂
C250 AP58 1.20b dl yel, ultra & grn   .80   .75
2nd anniv. of the Alliance for Progress, which
aims to stimulate economic growth and raise living
standards in Latin America.

Type of Regular Issue, 1963

Designs: 1.20b, Ballot box and voters. 1.40b,
Map and farmer breaking chain. 2.80b, Miners.

1963, Dec. 21   Perf. 11¹/₂
C251 A157 1.20b gray, dk brn &
rose   .40   .20
C252 A157 1.40b bister & grn   .50   .25
C253 A157 2.80b slate & buff   1.00   .90
Nos. C251-C253 (3)   1.90 1.35

Andrés Santa
Cruz — AP59

Perf. 13¹/₂
1966, Aug. 10   Wmk. 90   Litho.
C254 AP59   20c dp bl   .15   .15
C255 AP59   60c dp grn   .20   .20
C256 AP59   1.20b red brn   .50   .50
C257 AP59   2.80b black   .80   .80
Nos. C254-C257 (4)   1.65 1.65

Cent. (in 1965) of the death of Marshal Andrés
Santa Cruz (1792-1865), pres. of Bolivia and of
Peru-Bolivia Confederation.

Children Type of 1966

Design: 1.40b, Mother and children.

1966, Dec. 16   Unwmk.   Perf. 13¹/₂
C258 A159 1.40b gray bl & blk   1.00   .42

Co-Presidents Type of Regular Issue

1966, Dec. 16   Litho.   Perf. 12¹/₂
Flag in Red, Yellow and Green
C259 A160 2.80b gray & tan   1.40 1.00
C260 A160 10b sep & tan   1.60   .50
a.   Souvenir sheet of 4   6.50 6.50

No. C260a contains 4 imperf. stamps similar to
Nos. 480-481 and C259-C260. Dark green marginal inscription. Size: 135x82mm.

Various Issues 1954-62 Surcharged with
New Values and Bars

1966, Dec. 21
**On No. C177: "XII Aniversario /
Reforma / Agraria"**
C261 AP46   10c on 27b   .20   .15
a.   Agraria/Agraria   10.00
**On No. C182: "XXV / Aniversario /
Paz / del Chaco"**
C262 AP47   10c on 55b   .20   .15
**On No. C199: "Centenario de /
Tupiza"**
C263 AP48   60c on 1350b   .50   .20
**On No. C200: "XXV / Aniversario /
Automovil Club / Boliviano"**
C264 AP48 2.80b on 2700b   2.00 1.60
**On No. C201: "Centenario de la /
Cruz Roja / Internacional"**
C265 AP48   4b on 4000b   1.40 1.00
**On No. C219: "CL Aniversario /
Heroinas Coronilla"**
C266 AP51 1.20b on 800b   .75   .20
**On No. C222: "Centenario Himno /
Paceño"**
C267 AP51 1.40b on 4,000b   .75   .50
Nos. C224-C225 Surcharged
C268 A146 1.40b on 1,000b   .60   .60
C269 A146 1.40b on 1,800b   .60   .60
**On No. C238-C239: "Aniversario /
Centro Filatelico / Cochabamba"**
C270 A152 1.20b on 800b   1.00   .25
C271 A152 1.20b on 1,800b   1.00   .25

Revenue Stamp of 1946 Surcharged
with New Value "X" and:
"XXV Aniversario / Dpto. Pando /
Aéreo"

C272 A161 1.20b on 1b dk bl   .50   .25
Nos. C261-C272 (12)   9.50 6.05

Lions Emblem
and Pre-historic
Sculptures
AP60

1967, Sept. 20   Litho.   Perf. 13x13¹/₂
C273 AP60 2b red & multi   .80   .65
a.   Souvenir sheet of 2   3.75 3.75

50th anniv. of Lions Intl. No. C273a contains 2
imperf. stamps similar to Nos. 492 and C273.

Folklore Type of Regular Issue

Designs (Folklore characters): 1.20p, Pujllay.
1.40p, Ujusiris. 2p, Morenada. 3p, Auki-aukis.

1968, June 24   Perf. 13x12¹/₂x13
C274 A163 1.20b lt yel grn & multi   .35   .20
C275 A163 1.40b gray & multi   .40   .20
C276 A163   2b dk ol bis & multi   .75   .25
C277 A163   3b sky bl & multi   1.00   .25
Nos. C274-C277 (4)   2.50   .90

A souvenir sheet exists containing 4 imperf.
stamps similar to Nos. C274-C277. Size:
131x81¹/₂mm.

Moto Mendez — AP61

1968, Oct. 29   Litho.   Perf. 13¹/₂x13
C278 AP61   1b multi   .35   .15
C279 AP61   1.40b multi   .40   .35
C280 AP61   2b multi   .75   .50
C281 AP61   4b multi   1.00   .75
Nos. C278-C281 (4)   2.50 1.75

Battle of Tablada sesquicentennial.

Pres. Gualberto
Villaroel — AP62

1968, Nov. 6   Perf. 13x13¹/₂
C282 AP62 1.40b org & blk   .30   .22
C283 AP62   3b lt bl & blk   .55   .32
C284 AP62   4b rose & blk   .70   .40
C285 AP62   5b gray grn & blk   .90   .55
C286 AP62   10b pale pur & blk   1.60 1.10
Nos. C282-C286 (5)   4.05 2.59

4th centenary of Cochabamba.

ITU Type of Regular Issue

1968, Dec. 3   Litho.   Perf. 13x13¹/₂
C287 A166 1.20b gray, blk & yel   .60   .30
C288 A166 1.40b bl, blk & gray ol   .60   .20

UNESCO
Emblem — AP63

1968, Nov. 14   Perf. 13¹/₂x13
C289 AP63 1.20b pale vio & blk   .35   .35
C290 AP63 2.80b yel grn & blk   .65   .65

20th anniv. (in 1966) of UNESCO.

Kennedy Type of Regular Issue

1968, Nov. 22   Unwmk.
C291 A168 1b grn & blk   .25   .15
C292 A168 10b scar & blk   2.75 2.75

A souvenir sheet contains one imperf. stamp similar to No. C291. Dark violet marginal inscription.
Size: 131x81¹/₂mm.

Tennis Type of Regular Issue

1968, Dec. 10   Perf. 13x13¹/₂
C293 A169 1.40b org, blk & lt brn   .35   .35
C294 A169 2.80b sky bl, blk & lt brn   .65   .65

A souvenir sheet exists containing one imperf.
stamp similar to No. C293. Size: 131x81¹/₂mm.

Stamp Centenary Type of Regular Issue

Design: 1.40b, 2.80b, 3b, Bolivia No. 1.

1968, Dec. 23   Litho.   Perf. 13x13¹/₂
C295 A170 1.40b org, grn & blk   .50   .50
C296 A170 2.80b pale rose, grn &
blk   1.00 1.00
C297 A170   3b lt vio, grn & blk   1.00 1.00
Nos. C295-C297 (3)   2.50 2.50

A souvenir sheet exists containing 3 imperf.
stamps similar to Nos. C295-C297. Size:
131x81¹/₂mm.

Franklin D.
Roosevelt — AP64

1969, Oct. 29   Litho.   Perf. 13¹/₂x13
C298 AP64 5b brn, blk & buff   1.75 1.10

Olympic Type of Regular Issue

Sports: 1.20b, Woman runner, vert. 2.80b, Discus thrower, vert. 5b, Hurdler.

Perf. 13¹/₂x13, 13x13¹/₂
1969, Oct. 29   Litho.
C299 A171 1.20b yel grn, bis & blk   .50   .40
C300 A171 2.80b red, org & blk   1.00   .75
C301 A171   5b bl, lt bl, red & blk   1.50 1.50
Nos. C299-C301 (3)   3.00 2.65

A souvenir sheet exists containing 3 imperf.
stamps similar to Nos. C299-C301. Size:
130¹/₂x81mm.

Butterfly Type of Regular Issue

Butterflies: 1b, Metamorpha dido wernichei.
1.80b, Heliconius felix. 2.80b, Morpho casica. 3b,
Papilio yuracares. 4b, Heliconius melitus.

1970, Apr. 24   Litho.   Perf. 13x13¹/₂
C302 A172   1b sal & multi   1.40 1.40
C303 A172 1.80b lt bl & multi   2.00 2.00
C304 A172 2.80b multi   3.25 3.25
C305 A172   3b multi   3.25 3.25
C306 A172   4b multi   4.00 4.00
Nos. C302-C306 (5)   13.90 13.90

A souvenir sheet exists containing 3 imperf.
stamps similar to Nos. C302-C304. Black marginal
inscription. Size: 129¹/₂x80mm.

Scout Type of Regular Issue

Designs: 50c, Boy Scout building brick wall.
1.20b, Bolivian Boy Scout emblem.

1970, June 17   Litho.   Perf. 13¹/₂x13
C307 A173   50c yel & multi   .15   .15
C308 A173 1.20b multi   .40   .40

No. C228 Surcharged

1970, Dec.   Litho.   Perf. 10¹/₂
C309 AP53 1.20b on 4000b multi   .25   .15

Flower Type of Regular Issue

Bolivian Flowers: 1.20b, Amaryllis
pseudopardina, horiz. 1.40b, Rebutia kruegeri.
2.80b, Lobivia pentlandii, horiz. 4b, Rebutia
tunariensis.

Perf. 13x13¹/₂, 13¹/₂x13
1971, Aug. 9   Litho.   Unwmk.
C310 A174 1.20b multi   .70   .40
C311 A174 1.40b multi   .80   .50
C312 A174 2.80b multi   1.50   .75
C313 A174   4b multi   2.00 1.25
Nos. C310-C313 (4)   5.00 2.90

Two souvenir sheets of 4 exist. One contains
imperf. stamps similar to Nos. 534-535 and C310,
C312. The other contains imperf. stamps similar to
Nos. 536-537, C311, C313. Size: 130x80mm.

Folk Dance Type of Regular Issue

1972, Mar. 23   Litho.   *Perf. 13¹/₂x13*
C314 A177 1.20b Kusillo   .50   .16
C315 A177 1.40b Taquirari   .65   .16

Two souvenir sheets of 3 exist. One contains imperf. stamps similar to Nos. 542-543, C314. The other contains imperf. stamps similar to Nos. 540-541, C315. Size: 80x129mm.

Painting Type of Regular Issue

Bolivian Paintings: 1.40b, Portrait of Chola Paceña, by Cecilio Guzman de Rojas. 1.50b, Adoration of the Kings, by G. Gamarra. 1.60b, Adoration of Pachamama (mountain), by A. Borda. 2b, The Kiss of the Idol, by Guzman de Rojas.

1972   Litho.   *Perf. 13¹/₂*
C316 A178 1.40b multi   .40   .15
C317 A178 1.50b multi   .40   .15
C318 A178 1.60b multi   .40   .20
C319 A178 2b multi   .55   .20
        Nos. C316-C319 (4)   1.75   .70

Two souvenir sheets of 2 exist. One contains imperf. stamps similar to Nos. 548 and C318. The other contains imperf. stamps similar to Nos. C317 and C319. Size: 129x80mm.

Issue dates: 1.40b, Dec. 4. Others, Aug. 17.

Bolivian
Coat of
Arms
AP65

1972, Dec. 4   *Perf. 13¹/₂x14*
C320 AP65 4b lt bl & multi   1.40   .50

Cactus Type of Regular Issue

Designs: Various cacti.

1973, Aug. 6   Litho.   *Perf. 13¹/₂*
C321 A180 1.20b tan & multi   .35   .15
C322 A180 1.90b org & multi   .50   .20
C323 A180 2b multi   .65   .25
        Nos. C321-C323 (3)   1.50   .60

Development Type of Regular Issue

1.40b, Highway 1Y4. 2b, Rail car on bridge.

1973, Nov. 26   Litho.   *Perf. 13¹/₂*
C324 A181 1.40b salmon & multi   .40   .15
C325 A181 2b multi   .60   .20

Santos-Dumont and 14-Bis Plane — AP66

1973, July 20
C326 AP66 1.40b yel & blk   .65   .35

Centenary of the birth of Alberto Santos-Dumont (1873-1932), Brazilian aviation pioneer.

Orchid Type of 1974

Orchids: 2.50b, Cattleya luteola, horiz. 3.80b, Stanhopaea. 4b, Catasetum, horiz. 5b, Maxillaria.

1974   Litho.   *Perf. 13¹/₂*
C327 A182 2.50b multi   1.00   .22
C328 A182 3.80b rose & multi   1.50   .45
C329 A182 4b multi   1.50   .40
C330 A182 5b sal & multi   2.50   .45
        Nos. C327-C330 (4)   6.50 1.52

Air Force
Emblem, Plane
over Map of
Bolivia — AP67

Designs: 3.80b, Plane over Andes. 4.50b, Triple decker and jet. 8b, Rafael Pabon and double decker. 15b, Jet and "50".

1974   Litho.   *Perf. 13x13¹/₂*
C331 AP67 3b multi   .65   .25
C332 AP67 3.80b multi   1.00   .25
C333 AP67 4.50b multi   1.00   .25

C334 AP67 8b multi   1.60   .40
C335 AP67 15b multi   3.50   .50
        Nos. C331-C335 (5)   7.75 1.65

Bolivian Air Force, 50th anniv. Exist imperf.
For surcharge see No. 968.

Coat of Arms Type of 1975

Designs: Departmental coats of arms.

1975, July 16   Litho.   *Perf. 13¹/₂*
C336 A188 20c Beni   .15   .15
C337 A188 30c Tarija   .15   .15
C338 A188 50c Potosi   .25   .25
C339 A188 1b Oruro   .50   .50
C340 A188 2.50b Santa Cruz   1.00 1.00
C341 A188 3b La Paz   1.00 1.00
        Nos. C336-C341 (6)   3.05 3.05

LAB
Emblem — AP68

Bolivia on Map of
Americas — AP69

Map of Bolivia,
Plane and
Kyllmann
AP70

1975   Litho.   *Perf. 13¹/₂*
C342 AP68 1b gold, bl & blk   .40   .40
C343 AP69 1.50b multi   .60   .60
C344 AP70 2b multi   .75   .75
        Nos. C342-C344 (3)   1.75 1.75

Lloyd Aereo Boliviano, 50th anniversary, founded by Guillermo Kyllmann.

Bolivar,
Presidents
Perez and
Banzer, and
Flags
AP71

1975, Aug. 4   Litho.   *Perf. 13¹/₂*
C345 AP71 3b gold & multi   .75   .65

Visit of Pres. Carlos A. Perez of Venezuela.

Bolivar Type of 1975

Presidents and Statesmen of Bolivia: 50c, Rene Barrientes O. 2b, Francisco B. O'Connor. 3.80b, Gualberto Villarroel. 4.20b, German Busch. 4.50b, Hugo Banzer Suarez. 20b, José Ballivian. 30b, Andres de Santa Cruz. 40b, Antonio Jose de Sucre.

1975   *Perf. 13¹/₂*
        Size: 24x33mm
C346 A189 50c multi   .25   .25
C347 A189 2b multi   .50   .50
C348 A189 3.80b multi   .75   .75
C349 A189 4.20b multi   1.00   .75
        Size: 28x39mm
C350 A189 4.50b multi   1.00 1.00
        Size: 24x33mm
C351 A189 20b multi   4.00 2.00
C352 A189 30b multi   5.00 5.00
C353 A189 40b multi   6.50 6.50
        Nos. C346-C353 (8)   19.00 16.25

For surcharge see No. 969.

UPU Emblem
AP72

1975, Dec. 7   Litho.   *Perf. 13¹/₂*
C358 AP72 25b bl & multi   3.00 3.00

Cent. of UPU (in 1974).

POSTAGE DUE STAMPS

  D1

1931   Unwmk.   Engr.   *Perf. 14, 14¹/₂*
J1 D1 5c ultra   1.10 1.25
J2 D1 10c red   1.10 1.25
J3 D1 15c yellow   1.75 1.90
J4 D1 30c deep green   1.75 1.90
J5 D1 40c deep violet   2.75 3.00
J6 D1 50c black brown   4.00 4.25
        Nos. J1-J6 (6)   12.45 13.55

Symbol of
Youth — D2

Torch of
Knowledge — D3

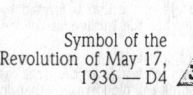

Symbol of the
Revolution of May 17,
1936 — D4

1938   Litho.   *Perf. 11*
J7 D2 5c deep rose   .50   .45
a.   Pair, imperf. between
J8 D3 10c green   .50   .45
J9 D4 30c gray blue   .50   .45
        Nos. J7-J9 (3)   1.50 1.35

POSTAL TAX STAMPS

Worker — PT1

Imprint: "LITO. UNIDAS LA PAZ."

Perf. 13¹/₂x10¹/₂, 10¹/₂, 13¹/₂
1939   Unwmk.
RA1 PT1 5c dull violet   .70   .15
a.   Double impression

Redrawn
Imprint: "TALL. OFFSET LA PAZ."

1940   *Perf. 12x11, 11*
RA2 PT1 5c violet   .60   .15
a.   Horizontal pair, imperf. between 2.00
b.   Imperf. horiz., pair

Tax of Nos. RA1-RA2 was for the Workers' Home Building Fund.

Communications
Symbols — PT2

Condor, Envelope
and Post
Horn — PT3

Communication
Symbols — PT4

Postman Blowing
Horn — PT5

1944-45   Litho.   *Perf. 10¹/₂*
RA3 PT2 10c salmon   .40   .15
RA4 PT2 10c blue ('45)   .40   .15

A 30c orange inscribed "Centenario de la Creacion del Departamento del Beni" was issued in 1946 and required to be affixed to all air and surface mail to and from the Department of Beni in addition to regular postage. Five higher denominations in the same scenic design were used for local revenue purposes.

Type of 1944 Redrawn

1947-48   Unwmk.   *Perf. 10¹/₂*
RA5 PT2 10c carmine   .40   .15
RA6 PT2 10c org yel ('48)   .35   .15
RA7 PT2 10c yel brn ('48)   .35   .15
RA8 PT2 10c emerald ('48)   .35   .15
        Nos. RA5-RA8 (4)   1.45
        Set value   .30

Post horn and envelope reduced in size.

1951-52
RA9 PT3 20c deep orange   .40   .20
a.   Imperf., pair   20.00
RA10 PT3 20c green ('52)   .50   .20
a.   Imperf., pair   20.00
RA11 PT3 20c blue ('52)   .50   .20
a.   Imperf., pair   20.00
        Nos. RA9-RA11 (3)   1.40   .60

For surcharges see Nos. RA17-RA18.

1952-54   *Perf. 13¹/₂, 10¹/₂, 10¹/₂x12*
RA12 PT4 50c green   .50   .15
RA13 PT4 50c carmine   .50   .15
RA14 PT4 3b green   .50   .15
RA15 PT4 3b olive bister   .50   .50
RA16 PT4 5b violet ('54)   .50   .15
        Nos. RA12-RA16 (5)   2.50 1.45

For surcharges see Nos. RA21-RA22.

No. RA10 and Type of 1951-52
Surcharged with New Value in Black

1953   *Perf. 10¹/₂*
RA17 PT3 50c on 20c green   .25   .15
RA18 PT3 50c on 20c red vio   .25   .15

1954-55   Unwmk.   *Perf. 10¹/₂*
RA19 PT5 1b brown   .20   .15
RA20 PT5 1b car rose ('55)   .20   .15
        Set value   .20

Exist imperf.

Nos. RA15 and RA14 Surcharged in Black
"Bs. 5.-/D. S./21-IV-55"

1955   *Perf. 10¹/₂, 10¹/₂x12*
RA21 PT4 5b on 3b olive bister   .25   .15
RA22 PT4 5b on 3b green   .25   .15

Tax of Nos. RA3-RA22 was for the Communications Employees Fund.

No. RA21 is known with surcharge in thin type of different font and with comma added after "55."

Plane over
Airport — PT6

Planes — PT7

Perf. 10¹/₂, 12, 13¹/₂
1955   Unwmk.   Litho.
RA23 PT6 5b dp ultra   .25   .15
a.   Vertical pair imperf. between

Perf. 11¹/₂
RA24 PT7 10b light green   .20   .15

PT8   PT9

1955 Litho. Perf. 10½
RA25 PT8 5b red — 7.50 7.50
a. Imperf., pair — 35.00

Perf. 12
RA26 PT9 20b dark brown — .25 .15

Tax of Nos. RA23-RA26 was for the building of new airports.

General Alfredo Ovando and Three Men — PT10

1970, Sept. 26 Litho. Perf. 13x13½
RA27 PT10 20c black & red — .50 .15
See No. RAC1.

Pres. German Busch — PT11

1971, May 13 Litho. Perf. 13x13½
RA28 PT11 20c lilac & black — .50 .15

AIR POST POSTAL TAX STAMPS

Catalogue values for unused stamps in this section are for Never Hinged items.

Type of Postal Tax Issue
Design: 30c, General Ovando and oil well.

1970, Sept. 26 Litho. Perf. 13x13½
RAC1 PT10 30c blk & grn — .50 .15

Pres. Gualberto Villarroel, Refinery PTAP1

1971, May 25 Litho. Perf. 13x13½
RAC2 PTAP1 30c lt bl & blk — .50 .15

Type of 1971 Inscribed: "XXV ANIVERSARIO DE SU GOBIERNO"

1975 Litho. Perf. 13x13½
RAC3 PTAP1 30c lt bl & blk — 3.00 3.00

BOSNIA AND HERZEGOVINA

'bäz–nē–ə and ˌhert–sə–gō–'vē–nə

LOCATION — Dalmatia and Serbia
GOVT. — Provinces of Turkey under Austro-Hungarian occupation, 1879-1908; provinces of Austria-Hungary 1908-1918
AREA — 19,768 sq. mi.
POP. — 2,000,000 (approx. 1918)
CAPITAL — Sarajevo

Following World War I Bosnia and Herzegovina united with the kingdoms of Montenegro and Serbia, and Croatia, Dalmatia and Slovenia, to form the Kingdom of Yugoslavia (See Yugoslavia.)

100 Novcica (Neukreuzer) = 1 Florin (Gulden)

100 Heller = 1 Krone (1900)

Bosnia and Herzegovina stamps can be mounted in the Scott Austria album.

Watermark

Wmk. 91- BRIEF-MARKEN or (from 1890) ZEITUNGS-MARKEN in Double-lined Capitals, Across the Sheet

 Coat of Arms — A1

Type I - The heraldic eaglets on the right side of the escutcheon are entirely blank. The eye of the lion is indicated by a very small dot, which sometimes fails to print.
Type II - There is a colored line across the lowest eaglet. A similar line sometimes appears on the middle eaglet. The eye of the lion is formed by a large dot which touches the outline of the head above it.
Type III - The eaglets and eye of the lion are similar to type I. Each tail feather of the large eagle has two lines of shading and the lowest feather does not touch the curved line below it. In types I and II there are several shading lines in these feathers, and the lowest feather touches the curved line.

Varieties of the Numerals
2 NOVCICA:
A - The "2" has curved tail. All are type I.
B - The "2" has straight tail. All are type II.

15 NOVCICA:
C - The serif of the "1" is short and forms a wide angle with the vertical stroke.
D - The serif of the "1" forms an acute angle with the vertical stroke.
The numerals of the 5n were retouched several times and show minor differences, especially in the flag.

Other Varieties
½ NOVCICA:
There is a black dot between the curved ends of the ornaments near the lower spandrels.
G - This dot touches the curve at its right. Stamps of this (1st) printing are litho.
H - This dot stands clear of the curved lines. Stamps of this (2nd) printing are typo.

10 NOVCICA:
Ten stamps in each sheet of type II show a small cross in the upper section of the right side of the escutcheon.

Perf. 9 to 13½ and Compound
1879-94 Litho. Wmk. 91
Type I
1	A1	½n blk (type II) ('94)	7.25	15.00
2	A1	1n gray	4.75	1.50
c.	In gray lilac		1.50
4	A1	2n yellow	9.00	.90
5	A1	3n green	6.00	1.75
6	A1	5n rose red	10.00	.40
7	A1	10n blue	30.00	.75
8	A1	15n brown	32.50	4.50
9	A1	20n gray green ('93)	150.00	6.75
10	A1	25n violet	27.50	6.75

No. 2c was never issued. It is usually canceled by blue pencil marks and "mint" copies generally have been cleaned.

Perf. 10½ to 13 and Compound
1894-98 Typo.
Type II
1a	A1	½n black	10.00	15.00
2a	A1	1n gray	4.00	1.00
4a	A1	2n yellow	3.00	.55
5a	A1	3n green	4.00	1.25
6a	A1	5n rose red	55.00	.35
7a	A1	10n blue	5.50	.70
8a	A1	15n brown	4.75	3.25
9a	A1	20n gray green	6.75	3.50
10a	A1	25n violet	7.25	5.75

Type III
6b	A1	5n rose red ('98)	1.50	.35

All the preceding stamps exist in various shades.
Nos. 1a to 10a were reprinted in 1911 in lighter colors, on very white paper and perf. 12½. Value, set $25.

A2 A3

Perf. 10½, 12½ and Compound
1900 Typo.
11	A2	1h gray black	.30	.15
12	A2	2h gray	.30	.15
13	A2	3h yellow	.30	.15
14	A2	5h green	.30	.15
15	A2	6h brown	.60	.15
16	A2	10h red	.25	.15
17	A2	20h rose	100.00	4.00
18	A2	25h blue	.85	.15
19	A2	30h bister brown	110.00	4.75
20	A2	40h orange	150.00	8.00
21	A2	50h red lilac	1.00	.85
22	A3	1k dark rose	1.25	.50
23	A3	2k ultra	1.50	1.25
24	A3	5k dull blue grn	3.75	3.75
Nos. 11-24 (14)		370.40	23.65

All values of this issue except the 3h exist on ribbed paper.
Nos. 17, 19 and 20 were reprinted in 1911. The reprints are in lighter colors and on whiter paper than the originals. Reprints of Nos. 17 and 19 are perf. 10½ and those of No. 20 are perf. 12½. Value each $1.50.

Numerals in Black
1901-04 Perf. 12½
25	A2	20h pink ('02)	.55	.30
26	A2	30h bister brn ('03)	.55	.30
27	A2	35h blue	.75	.30
a.	35h ultramarine		80.00	4.75
28	A2	40h orange ('03)	1.00	.60
29	A2	45h grnsh blue ('04)	.65	.35
Nos. 25-29 (5)		3.50	1.85

Nos. 11-16, 18, 21-29 exist imperf. Most of Nos. 11-29 exist perf. 6½; compound with 12½; part perf.; in pairs imperf. between. These were supplied only to some high-ranking officials and never sold at any P.O.

View of Deboj — A4

 The Carsija at Sarajevo — A5

Designs: 2h, View of Mostar. 3h, Pliva Gate, Jajce. 5h, Narenta Pass and Prenj River. 6h, Rama Valley. 10h, Vrbas Valley. 20h, Old Bridge, Mostar. 25h, Bey's Mosque, Sarajevo. 30h, Donkey post. 35h, Jezero and tourists' pavilion. 40h, Mail wagon. 45h, Bazaar at Sarajevo. 50h, Postal car. 2k, St. Luke's Campanile, Jajce. 5k, Emperor Franz Josef.

Perf. 6½, 9½, 10½ and 12½, also Compounds
1906 Engr. Unwmk.
30	A4	1h black	.15	.15
31	A4	2h violet	.15	.15
32	A4	3h olive	.15	.15
33	A4	5h dark green	.15	.15
34	A4	6h brown	.15	.15
a.	Perf. 13½		15.00	18.00
35	A4	10h carmine	.15	.15
36	A4	20h dark brown	.35	.20
a.	Perf. 13½		37.50	37.50
37	A4	25h deep blue	1.00	.75
38	A4	30h green	1.10	.30
39	A4	35h myrtle grn	1.25	.30
40	A4	40h orange red	1.25	.30
41	A4	45h brown red	1.25	.90
42	A4	50h dull violet	1.40	.60
43	A5	1k maroon	3.50	1.25
44	A5	2k gray green	4.25	6.00
45	A5	5k dull blue	3.75	4.50
Nos. 30-45 (16)		25.00	22.45

Nos. 30-45 exist imperf. Value, set $50 unused, $37.50 canceled.
For overprint and surcharges see #126, B1-B4.

Birthday Jubilee Issue
Designs of 1906 Issue, with "1830-1910" in Label at Bottom
1910 Perf. 12½
46	A4	1h black	.35	.15
47	A4	2h violet	.40	.15
48	A4	3h olive	.40	.20
49	A4	5h dark green	.45	.15
50	A4	6h orange brn	.45	.20
51	A4	10h carmine	.45	.15
52	A4	20h dark brown	1.00	1.10
53	A4	25h deep blue	2.00	2.25
54	A4	30h green	1.50	1.90
55	A4	35h myrtle grn	2.00	2.00
56	A4	40h orange red	2.00	2.50
57	A4	45h brown red	3.50	4.25
58	A4	50h dull violet	3.50	4.50
59	A5	1k maroon	3.50	4.50
60	A5	2k gray green	13.00	13.00
61	A5	5k dull blue	2.50	3.00
Nos. 46-61 (16)		37.00	40.00

80th birthday of Emperor Franz Josef.

Scenic Type of 1906
Views: 12h, Jajce. 60h, Konjica. 72h, Vishegrad.
1912
62	A4	12h ultra	3.25	4.00
63	A4	60h dull blue	2.00	3.50
64	A4	72h carmine	10.00	13.00
Nos. 62-64 (3)		15.25	20.50

Value, imperf. set, $75.

See Austria for similar designs inscribed "FELDPOST" instead of "MILITARPOST."

Emperor Franz Josef
A23 A24

A25 A26

1912-14
Various Frames
65	A23	1h olive green	.35	.15
66	A23	2h brt blue	.35	.15
67	A23	3h claret	.35	.15
68	A23	5h green	.35	.15
69	A23	6h dark gray	.40	.15
70	A23	10h rose car	.40	.15
71	A23	12h dp olive grn	1.10	.30
72	A23	20h orange brn	4.50	.15
73	A23	25h ultra	2.25	.15
74	A23	30h orange red	2.25	.15
75	A23	35h myrtle grn	2.25	.15
76	A24	40h dk violet	6.75	.15
77	A24	45h olive brn	3.00	.15
78	A24	50h slate blue	3.00	.15
79	A24	60h brown vio	2.75	.15
80	A24	72h dark blue	3.25	3.00
81	A25	1k brn vio, straw	12.50	.35
82	A25	2k dk gray, bl	7.25	.25
83	A26	3k carmine, grn	12.00	9.00
84	A26	5k dk vio, gray	22.50	20.00
85	A25	10k dk ultra, gray ('14)	82.50	70.00
Nos. 65-85 (21)		170.00	105.00

Value, imperf. set, $450.
For overprint and surcharges see #127, B5-B8.

A27 A28

1916-17 Perf. 12½
86	A27	3h dark gray	.15	.20
87	A27	5h olive green	.25	.35
88	A27	6h violet	.30	.35
89	A27	10h bister	1.25	1.65
90	A27	12h blue gray	.40	.45
91	A27	15h car rose	.15	.15
92	A27	20h brown	.35	.45
93	A27	25h blue	.25	.15

94	A27	30h dark green	.25	.35
95	A27	40h vermilion	.25	.35
96	A27	50h green	.25	.35
97	A27	60h lake	.25	.35
98	A27	80h orange brn	1.10	.40
a.		Perf. 11½	3.25	3.00
99	A27	90h dark violet	.65	.50
			450.00	675.00
101	A28	2k claret, *straw*	.65	.75
102	A28	3k green, *bl*	1.75	3.25
103	A28	4k carmine, *grn*	5.25	7.25
104	A28	10k dp vio, *gray*	14.00	20.00
		Nos. 86-104 (18)	27.50	37.50

Value, imperf. set, $175.
For overprints see Nos. B11-B12.

Emperor Karl I
A29   A30

1917			*Perf. 12½*	
105	A29	3h olive gray	.15	.20
a.		Perf. 11½	75.00	75.00
b.		Perf. 12½x11½	13.00	21.00
106	A29	5h olive green	.15	.15
107	A29	6h violet	.30	.55
108	A29	10h orange brn	.15	.15
a.		Perf. 11½x12½	62.50	95.00
109	A29	12h blue	.50	.75
110	A29	15h brt rose	.15	.15
111	A29	20h red brown	.15	.15
112	A29	25h ultra	1.00	.50
113	A29	30h gray green	.25	.20
114	A29	40h olive bis	.25	.15
115	A29	50h dp green	.85	.50
116	A29	60h car rose	.85	.45
a.		Perf. 11½	15.00	21.00
117	A29	80h steel blue	.25	.25
118	A29	90h dull violet	1.00	1.40
119	A30	2k carmine, *straw*	.50	.45
120	A30	3k green, *bl*	13.00	16.00
121	A30	4k carmine, *grn*	5.25	7.25
122	A30	10k dp violet, *gray*	3.25	5.75
		Nos. 105-122 (18)	28.00	35.00

Value, imperf. set, $85.

Nos. 47 and 66 Overprinted in **1918** Red

1918				
126	A4	2h violet	.45	.50
b.		Inverted overprint	15.00	
d.		Double overprint	35.00	
f.		Double overprint, one inverted		
127	A23	2h bright blue	.50	.60
a.		Pair, one without overprint		
b.		Inverted overprint	15.00	
c.		Double overprint	13.00	
d.		Double overprint, one inverted		

Emperor Karl I — A31

1918	**Typo.**	*Perf. 12½, Imperf.*	
128	A31	2h orange	9.00
129	A31	3h dark green	9.00
130	A31	5h lt green	9.00
131	A31	6h blue green	9.00
132	A31	10h brown	9.00
133	A31	20h brick red	9.00
134	A31	25h ultra	9.00
135	A31	45h dk slate	9.00
136	A31	50h lt bluish grn	9.00
137	A31	60h blue violet	9.00
138	A31	70h ocher	9.00
139	A31	80h rose	9.00
140	A31	90h violet brn	9.00

		Engr.	
141	A30	1k ol grn, *grnsh*	*2,250.*
		Nos. 128-140 (13)	117.00

Nos. 128-141 were prepared for use in Bosnia and Herzegovina, but were not issued there. They were sold after the Armistice at the Vienna post office for a few days.

SEMI-POSTAL STAMPS

Nos. 33 and 35 Surcharged in Red
1914. 7 Heller

1914	**Unwmk.**		*Perf. 12½*	
B1	A4	7h on 5h dk grn	.40	.40
B2	A4	12h on 10h car	.40	.40

Various minor varieties of the surcharge include "4" with open top, narrow "4" and wide "4." Nos. B1-B2 exist with double and inverted surcharges. Value about $20 each.

Nos. 33 and 35 Surcharged in Red or Blue
❖ **1915.** ❖
7 Heller

1915			*Perf. 12½*	
B3	A4	7h on 5h (R)	8.75	8.75
a.		Perf. 9½	140.00	140.00
B4	A4	12h on 10h (Bl)	.30	.30

Nos. B3-B4 exist with double and inverted surcharges. Value about $18.50 each.

❖ **1915** ❖

Nos. 68 and 70 Surcharged in Red or Blue

7 Heller.

1915				
B5	A23	7h on 5h (R)	.75	.75
a.		"1915" at top and bottom	35.00	37.50
B6	A23	12h on 10h (Bl)	1.25	1.50
a.		Surcharged "7 Heller."	35.00	37.50

Nos. B5-B6 are found in three types differing in length of surcharge lines:
I- date 18mm, denomination 14mm.
II- date 16mm, denomination 14mm.
III- date 18mm, denomination 16mm.
Nos. B5-B6 exist with double and inverted surcharges. Value $25 each.
Nos. B5a and B6a exist double and inverted.

❖ **1916.** ❖

Nos. 68 and 70 Surcharged in Red or Blue

7 Heller.

1916				
B7	A23	7h on 5h (R)	.50	.65
B8	A23	12h on 10h (Bl)	.50	.65

Nos. B7-B8 exist with double and inverted surcharges. Value $12.50 each.

Wounded Soldier — SP1
Blind Soldier — SP2

1916			**Engr.**	
B9	SP1	5h (+ 2h) green	.60	.60
B10	SP2	10h (+ 2h) magenta	.90	.90

Nos. B9-B10 exist imperf. Value, set $27.50.

Nos. 89, 91 Overprinted WITWEN- UND WAISENWOCHE 1917

1917				
B11	A27	10h bister	.15	.15
B12	A27	15h carmine rose	.15	.15
		Set value	.20	.20

Nos. B11-B12 exist imperf. Value set, $16.
Nos. B11-B12 exist with double and inverted overprint. Value $9 each.

Design for Memorial Church at Sarajevo SP3

Archduke Francis Ferdinand — SP4

Duchess Sophia and Archduke Francis Ferdinand SP5

1917	**Typo.**		*Perf. 11½, 12½*	
B13	SP3	10h violet black	.15	.25
B14	SP4	15h claret	.15	.25
B15	SP5	40h deep blue	.15	.25
		Set value		.35

Assassination of Archduke Ferdinand and Archduchess Sophia. Sold at a premium of 2h each which helped build a memorial church at Sarajevo. Exist imperf. Value, set $2.50.

Blind Soldier — SP6
Emperor Karl I — SP8

Design: 15h, Wounded soldier.

1918		**Engr.**	*Perf. 12½*	
B16	SP6	10h (+ 10h) grnsh bl	.45	.55
B17	SP6	15h (+ 10h) red brn	.45	.55

#B16-B17 exist imperf. Value, set $18.50.

1918	**Typo.**		*Perf. 12½x13*	

Design: 15h, Empress Zita.

B18	SP8	10h gray green	.30	.45
B19	SP8	15h brown red	.30	.45
B20	SP8	40h violet	.30	.45
		Nos. B18-B20 (3)	.90	1.35

Sold at a premium of 10h each which went to the "Karl's Fund."
#B18-B20 exist imperf. Value, set $22.50.

POSTAGE DUE STAMPS

D1   D2

Perf. 9½, 10½, 12½ and Compound				
1904			**Unwmk.**	
J1	D1	1h black, red & yel	.35	.15
J2	D1	2h black, red & yel	.35	.20
J3	D1	3h black, red & yel	.40	.15
J4	D1	4h black, red & yel	.40	.15
J5	D1	5h black, red & yel	.40	.15
J6	D1	6h black, red & yel	.15	.15
J7	D1	7h black, red & yel	2.25	2.50
J8	D1	8h black, red & yel	.45	.50
J9	D1	10h black, red & yel	.55	.15
J10	D1	15h black, red & yel	.50	.15
J11	D1	20h black, red & yel	2.75	.45
J12	D1	50h black, red & yel	1.90	.15
J13	D1	200h black, red & grn	7.75	.70
		Nos. J1-J13 (13)	20.00	5.30

Value, imperf. set, $150.
For overprints see Western Ukraine Nos. 61-72.

1916-18			*Perf. 12½*	
J14	D2	2h red ('18)	.40	.40
J15	D2	4h red ('18)	.30	.30
J16	D2	5h red	.40	.40
J17	D2	6h red ('18)	.30	.30
J18	D2	10h red	.40	.40
J19	D2	15h red	3.00	3.00
J20	D2	20h red	.45	.45
J21	D2	25h red	1.25	1.25
J22	D2	30h red	1.00	1.00
J23	D2	40h red	7.50	7.50
J24	D2	50h red	24.00	24.00
J25	D2	1k dark blue	3.00	3.00
J26	D2	3k dark blue	13.00	13.00
		Nos. J14-J26 (13)	55.00	55.00

Nos. J25-J26 have colored numerals on a white tablet.
Value, imperf. set, $110.

NEWSPAPER STAMPS

Bosnian Girl — N1

1913	**Unwmk.**		*Imperf.*	
P1	N1	2h ultra	.40	.40
P2	N1	6h violet	1.50	1.50
P3	N1	10h rose	1.50	1.50
P4	N1	20h green	1.90	1.90
		Nos. P1-P4 (4)	5.30	5.30

After Bosnia and Herzegovina became part of Yugoslavia stamps of type N1 perf., and imperf. copies surcharged with new values, were used as regular postage stamps. See Yugoslavia Nos. 1L21-1L22, 1L43-1L45.

SPECIAL HANDLING STAMPS

"Lightning" — SH1

1916	**Unwmk.**	**Engr.**	*Perf. 12½*	
QE1	SH1	2h vermilion	.20	.20
a.		Perf. 11½x12½	250.00	250.00
QE2	SH1	5h deep green	.35	.35
a.		Perf. 11½	13.00	13.00

BOTSWANA
bä-'swä-nə

LOCATION — In central South Africa, north of the Republic of South Africa, east of South-West Africa and bounded on the north and east by Angola and Zimbabwe.
GOVT. — Independent republic
AREA — 222,000 sq. mi.
POP. — 941,027 (1981)
CAPITAL — Gaborone

The former Bechuanaland Protectorate became an independent republic, September 30, 1966, taking the name Botswana.

100 Cents = 1 Rand
100 Thebe = 1 Pula (1976)

Catalogue values for all unused stamps in this country are for Never Hinged items.

National Assembly Building A1

Designs: 5c, Abattoir, Lobatsi. 15c, Dakota plane. 35c, State House, Gaborone.

Unwmk.

1966, Sept. 30   Photo.   Perf. 14

1	A1	2½c multicolored	.15	.15
a.		Imperf. pair	200.00	
2	A1	5c multicolored	.15	.15
3	A1	15c multicolored	.35	.35
4	A1	35c multicolored	.75	.75
		Nos. 1-4 (4)	1.40	1.40

Establishment of Republic of Botswana.

Bechuanaland Protectorate Nos. 180-193 Overprinted **REPUBLIC OF BOTSWANA**

Perf. 14x14½, 14½x14

1966, Sept. 30   Wmk. 314

5	A15	1c multicolored	.15	.15
6	A15	2c multicolored	.15	.15
7	A15	2½c multicolored	.15	.15
8	A15	3½c multicolored	.15	.15
9	A15	5c multicolored	.15	.15
10	A15	7½c multicolored	.18	.18
11	A15	10c multicolored	.22	.22
12	A15	12½c multicolored	1.25	.28
13	A15	20c gray & brown	1.25	.40
14	A15	25c yel & dk brn	.55	.55
15	A15	35c dp org & ultra	.70	.70
16	A15	50c lt grn & sep	1.75	1.25
17	A15	1r ocher & black	3.25	2.50
18	A15	2r blue & brown	7.00	8.00
		Nos. 5-18 (14)	16.90	14.83

European Golden Oriole — A2

Birds: 2c, African hoopoe. 3c, Groundscraper thrush. 4c, Blue waxbill. 5c, Secretary bird. 7c, Yellow-billed hornbill. 10c, Crimson-breasted shrike. 15c, Malachite kingfisher. 20c, Fish eagle. 25c, Gray lourie. 35c, Scimitar bill. 50c, Knob-billed duck. 1r, Crested barbet. 2r, Didrio cuckoo.

Perf. 14x14½

1967, Jan. 3   Photo.   Unwmk.

19	A2	1c gray & multi	.20	.15
20	A2	2c lt blue & multi	.20	.15
21	A2	3c yel green & multi	.30	.15
22	A2	4c salmon & multi	.50	.25
23	A2	5c pink & multi	.50	.28
24	A2	7c slate & multi	.75	.40
25	A2	10c emerald & multi	1.00	.50
26	A2	15c lt green & multi	2.00	1.00
27	A2	20c ultra & multi	2.25	1.25
28	A2	25c green & multi	3.00	1.60
29	A2	35c multicolored	3.50	2.00
30	A2	50c dl yel & multi	5.00	3.00
31	A2	1r dl grn & multi	11.00	6.00
32	A2	2r org brn & multi	21.00	10.00
		Nos. 19-32 (14)	51.20	26.73

University Buildings and Graduates — A3

1967, Apr. 7   Perf. 14x14½

33	A3	3c yel, sepia & dp blue	.15	.15
34	A3	7c blue, sepia & dp bl	.15	.15
35	A3	15c dull rose, sepia & dp bl	.16	.16
36	A3	35c lt vio, sepia & dp bl	.38	.38
		Nos. 33-36 (4)	.84	.84

1st conferment of degrees by the University of Botswana, Lesotho and Swaziland at Roma, Lesotho.

Chobe Bush Bucks — A4

Designs: 7c, Sable antelopes. 35c, Fishing on the Chobe River.

1967, Oct. 2   Photo.   Perf. 14

37	A4	3c multicolored	.15	.15
38	A4	7c multicolored	.22	.22
39	A4	35c multicolored	1.10	1.10
		Nos. 37-39 (3)	1.47	1.47

Publicity for Chobe Game Reserve.

Human Rights Flame and Arms of Botswana — A5

Design elements rearranged on 15c, 25c.

1968, Apr. 8   Litho.   Perf. 13½x13

40	A5	3c brown red & multi	.15	.15
41	A5	15c emerald & multi	.25	.20
42	A5	25c yellow & multi	.40	.30
		Nos. 40-42 (3)	.80	.65

International Human Rights Year.

Rock Painting — A6

Girl Wearing Ceremonial Beads — A7

Designs: 10c, Baobab Trees, by Thomas Baines (34x25mm). 15c, National Museum and Art Gallery (71½x19mm).

Perf. 13x13½ (3c, 10c); Perf. 12½ (7c); Perf. 12½x13 (15c)

1968, Sept. 30   Litho.

43	A6	3c multicolored	.15	.15
44	A7	7c multicolored	.18	.18
45	A6	10c multicolored	.32	.32
46	A6	15c multicolored	.60	.60
a.		Souv. sheet of 4, #43-46, perf. 13½	2.25	2.25
		Nos. 43-46 (4)	1.25	1.25

Opening of the National Museum and Art Gallery, Gaborone, Sept. 30, 1968.

African Nativity Scene — A8

1968, Nov. 11   Unwmk.   Perf. 13x14

47	A8	1c car & multi	.15	.15
48	A8	2c brown & multi	.15	.15
49	A8	5c green & multi	.15	.15
50	A8	25c dp violet & multi	.55	.50
		Set value	.75	.65

Christmas.

Boy Scout, Botswana Scout Emblem and Lion — A9

Botswana Boy Scout Emblem, Lion and: 15c, Boy Scouts cooking, vert. 25c, Boy Scouts around campfire.

1969, Aug. 21   Litho.   Perf. 13½

51	A9	3c emerald & multi	.15	.15
52	A9	15c lt brown & multi	.75	.75
53	A9	25c dk brown & multi	1.40	1.40
		Nos. 51-53 (3)	2.30	2.30

22nd World Scouting Conf., Helsinki, Finland, Aug. 21-27.

Mother, Child and Star of Bethlehem — A10

Diamond Treatment Plant, Orapa — A11

1969, Nov. 6   Perf. 14½x14

54	A10	1c dk brn & lt blue	.15	.15
55	A10	2c dk brn & apple grn	.15	.15
56	A10	4c dk brn & dull red	.15	.15
57	A10	35c dk brn & vio blue	.80	.80
a.		Souv. sheet of 4, #54-57, perf. 14½	1.40	1.00
		Set value	1.00	1.00

Christmas.

Perf. 14½x14, 14x14½

1970, Mar. 23

Designs: 7c, Copper and nickel mining, Selebi-Pikwe. 10c, Copper and nickel mining and metal bars, Selebi-Pikwe, horiz. 35c, Orapa diamond mine and diamonds, horiz.

58	A11	3c multicolored	.15	.15
59	A11	7c multicolored	.26	.26
60	A11	10c multicolored	.52	.52
61	A11	35c multicolored	.85	.85
		Nos. 58-61 (4)	1.78	1.78

Botswana development program.

Mr. Micawber and Charles Dickens — A12

Charles Dickens (1812-70), English novelist and: 7c, Scrooge. 15c, Fagin. 25c, Bill Sykes.

1970, July 7   Litho.   Perf. 11

62	A12	3c gray green & multi	.15	.15
63	A12	7c multicolored	.26	.26
64	A12	15c brown & multi	.52	.52
65	A12	25c dp violet & multi	.85	.85
a.		Souvenir sheet of 4, #62-65	3.00	3.00
		Nos. 62-65 (4)	1.78	1.78

UN Headquarters, Emblem — A13

1970, Oct. 24   Litho.   Perf. 11

66	A13	15c ultra, red & silver	.60	.60

United Nations' 25th anniversary.

Toys — A14

1970, Nov. 3   Litho.   Perf. 14

67	A14	1c Crocodile	.15	.15
68	A14	2c Giraffe	.15	.15
69	A14	7c Elephant	.25	.25
70	A14	25c Rhinoceros	1.00	1.00
a.		Souvenir sheet of 4, #67-70		
		Nos. 67-70 (4)	1.55	1.55

Christmas.

Sorghum — A15

1971, Apr. 6   Litho.   Perf. 14

71	A15	3c shown	.15	.15
72	A15	7c Millet	.16	.16
73	A15	10c Corn	.20	.20
74	A15	35c Peanuts	.80	.80
		Nos. 71-74 (4)	1.31	1.31

Ox Head and Botswana Map — A16

King Bringing Gift — A17

Map of Botswana and: 4c, Cogwheels and waves. 7c, Zebra rampant. 10c, Tusk and corn. 20c, Coat of arms of Botswana.

1971, Sept. 30   Perf. 14½x14

75	A16	3c yel grn, blk & brn	.15	.15
76	A16	4c lt blue, blk & bl	.15	.15
77	A16	7c orange & blk	.16	.16
78	A16	10c yellow & multi	.28	.28
79	A16	20c blue & multi	.60	.60
		Nos. 75-79 (5)	1.34	1.34

5th anniversary of independence.

1971, Nov. 11   Perf. 14

Christmas: 2c, King bringing gift. 7c, Kneeling King with gift. 20c, Three Kings and star.

80	A17	2c brt rose & multi	.15	.15
81	A17	3c lt blue & multi	.15	.15
82	A17	7c brt pink & multi	.20	.20
83	A17	20c vio blue & multi	.80	.80
a.		Souvenir sheet of 4, #80-83	1.65	1.65
		Nos. 80-83 (4)	1.30	1.30

Constellation Orion — A18

Night Sky over Botswana: 7c, Scorpio. 10c, Centaur. 20c, Southern Cross.

1972, Apr. 24   Litho.   Perf. 14

84	A18	3c dp org, bl grn & blk	.25	.25
85	A18	7c org, blue & blk	.50	.50
86	A18	10c org, green & blk	.75	.75
87	A18	20c emer, vio bl & blk	1.50	1.50
		Nos. 84-87 (4)	3.00	3.00

Gubulawayo Cancel and Map of Trail — A19

Cross, Map of Botswana, Bells — A20

Sections of Mafeking-Gubulawayo Trail and: 4c, Bechuanaland Protectorate No. 65. 7c, Mail runners. 20c, Mafeking 638 killer cancellation.

1972, Aug. 21   Perf. 13½x13

88	A19	3c cream & multi	.15	.15
89	A19	4c cream & multi	.18	.18
90	A19	7c cream & multi	.45	.45

91 A19 20c cream & multi 1.50 1.50
a. Souvenir sheet of 4 6.75 6.75
Nos. 88-91 (4) 2.28 2.28

84th anniv. of Mafeking to Gubulawayo runner post. No. 91a contains one each of Nos. 88-91, arranged vertically to show map of trail. Compare with design A89.

1972, Nov. 6 Litho. Perf. 14

Cross, Map of Botswana and: 3c, Candle. 7c, Christmas tree. 20c, Star and holly.

92 A20 2c yellow & multi .15 .15
93 A20 3c pale lilac & multi .15 .15
94 A20 7c yel green & multi .24 .24
95 A20 20c pink & multi .60 .60
a. Souvenir sheet of 4, #92-95 2.00 2.00
Nos. 92-95 (4) 1.14 1.14

Christmas.

Chariot of the Sun, Trundholm, Denmark A21

WMO Emblem and: 3c, Thor, Norse thunder god, vert. 7c, Ymir, Icelandic frost giant, vert. 20c, Odin on 8-legged horse Sleipnir.

1973, Mar. 23 Litho. Perf. 14

96 A21 3c orange & multi .15 .15
97 A21 4c yellow & multi .16 .16
98 A21 7c ultra & multi .30 .30
99 A21 20c gold & multi .90 .90
Nos. 96-99 (4) 1.51 1.51

Intl. meteorological cooperation, cent.

Livingstone and Boat on Lake Ngwami — A22

Design: 20c, Livingstone and his meeting with Henry Stanley.

1973, Sept. 10 Litho. Perf. 13½x14

100 A22 3c gray & multi .15 .15
101 A22 20c yel green & multi .95 .95

Dr. David Livingstone (1813-1873), medical missionary and explorer.

Shepherd and Flock A23

Christmas: 3c, Ass and foal, African huts, vert. 7c, African mother, child and star, vert. 20c, Tribal meeting (kgotla), symbolic of Wise Men.

1973, Nov. 12 Litho. Perf. 14½

102 A23 3c multicolored .15 .15
103 A23 4c multicolored .15 .15
104 A23 7c multicolored .24 .24
105 A23 20c multicolored .70 .70
Nos. 102-105 (4) 1.24 1.24

Gaborone Campus, Botswana A24

Designs: 7c, Kwaluseni Campus, Swaziland. 20c, Roma Campus, Lesotho. 35c, Map and flags of Botswana, Swaziland and Lesotho.

1974, May 8 Litho. Perf. 14

106 A24 3c lt blue & multi .15 .15
107 A24 7c yel green & multi .15 .15
108 A24 20c yel green & multi .32 .32
109 A24 35c brt blue & multi .48 .48
Nos. 106-109 (4) 1.10 1.10

10th anniversary of the University of Botswana, Lesotho and Swaziland.

UPU Emblem, Mail Vehicles — A25

UPU Cent.: 3c, Post Office, Palapye, c. 1889. 7c, Bechuanaland police camel post, 1900. 20c, 1920 and 1974 planes.

1974, May 22 Litho. Perf. 13½x14

110 A25 2c car & multi .15 .15
111 A25 3c green & multi .25 .20
112 A25 7c brown & multi .65 .50
113 A25 20c blue & multi 2.00 1.50
Nos. 110-113 (4) 3.05 2.35

Amethyst A26

Minerals, precious and semiprecious stones.

1974, July 1 Photo. Perf. 14x13

114 A26 1c shown .15 .15
115 A26 2c Agate .20 .15
116 A26 3c Quartz .25 .20
117 A26 4c Niccolite .45 .35
118 A26 5c Moss agate .55 .40
119 A26 7c Agate .85 .60
120 A26 10c Stilbite 1.25 .85
121 A26 15c Moshaneng banded marble 1.90 1.25
122 A26 20c Gem diamonds 2.25 1.65
123 A26 25c Chrysotile 2.75 2.00
124 A26 35c Jasper 4.00 2.75
125 A26 50c Moss quartz 5.50 3.75
126 A26 1r Citrine 11.00 8.00
127 A26 2r Chalcopyrite 25.00 17.00
Nos. 114-127 (14) 56.10 39.10

For surcharges see Nos. 155-168.

Stapelia Variegata — A27 / Pres. Sir Seretse Khama — A28

Flowers of Botswana: 7c, Hibiscus lunarifolius. 15c, Ceratotheca triloba. 20c, Nerine laticoma.

1974, Nov. 4 Litho. Perf. 14

128 A27 2c multicolored .15 .15
129 A27 7c multicolored .40 .40
130 A27 15c multicolored .90 .90
131 A27 20c multicolored 1.25 1.25
a. Souvenir sheet of 4, #128-131 2.50 2.50
Nos. 128-131 (4) 2.70 2.70

1975, Mar. 24 Photo. Perf. 13½x13

132 A28 4c olive & multi .15 .15
133 A28 10c yellow & multi .15 .15
134 A28 20c ultra & multi .30 .30
135 A28 35c brown & multi .50 .50
a. Souvenir sheet of 4, #132-135 1.40 1.40
Nos. 132-135 (4) 1.10 1.10

10th anniv. of self-government.

Ostrich and Rock Painting — A29

Paintings and Animals: 10c, Rhinoceros. 25c, Hyena. 35c, Scorpion.

1975, June 23 Litho. Perf. 14x14½

136 A29 4c yel green & multi .25 .25
137 A29 10c buff & multi .75 .75
138 A29 25c blue & multi 1.65 1.65
139 A29 35c lilac & multi 2.50 2.50
a. Souvenir sheet of 4, #136-139 8.00 8.00
Nos. 136-139 (4) 5.15 5.15

Rock paintings from Tsodilo Hills.

Map of British Bechuanaland A30

Chiefs Sebele, Bathoen and Khama A31

Design: 10c, Khama the Great and antelope.

Perf. 14½x14, 14x14½

1975, Oct. 31 Litho.

140 A30 6c buff & multi .28 .28
141 A30 10c rose & multi .48 .48
142 A31 25c lt green & multi 1.25 1.25
Nos. 140-142 (3) 2.01 2.01

Establishment of Protectorate, 90th anniv. (6c); Khama the Great (1828-1923), centenary of his accession as chief (10c); visit of the chiefs of the Bakwena, Bangwaketse and Bamangwato tribes to London, 80th anniv. (25c).

Aloe Marlothii — A32

Christmas: 10c, Aloe lutescens. 15c, Aloe zebrina. 25c, Aloe littoralis.

1975, Nov. 3 Litho. Perf. 14½x14

143 A32 3c multicolored .25 .20
144 A32 10c multicolored .60 .55
145 A32 15c multicolored .85 .80
146 A32 25c multicolored 1.75 1.65
Nos. 143-146 (4) 3.45 3.20

Drum A33

Traditional Musical Instruments: 10c, Hand piano. 15c, Segankuru (violin). 25c, Kudu signal horn.

1976, Mar. 1 Litho. Perf. 14

147 A33 4c yellow & multi .15 .15
148 A33 10c lilac & multi .35 .35
149 A33 15c dull yel & multi .60 .60
150 A33 25c lt blue & multi .90 .90
Nos. 147-150 (4) 2.00 2.00

1-pula Bank Note with Seretse Khama A34

Reverse of Bank Notes: 10c, Farm workers. 15c, Antelopes. 25c, National Assembly building.

1976, June 28 Litho. Perf. 14

151 A34 4c rose & multi .15 .15
152 A34 10c brt green & multi .25 .25
153 A34 15c yel green & multi .35 .35
154 A34 25c blue & multi .65 .65
a. Souvenir sheet of 4, #151-154 2.25 2.25
Nos. 151-154 (4) 1.40 1.40

First national currency.

Nos. 114-127 Surcharged in Black or Gold

1976, Aug. 23 Photo. Perf. 14x13

155 A26 1t on 1c multi .25 .15
156 A26 2t on 2c multi .25 .15
157 A26 3t on 3c multi (G) .25 .15
158 A26 4t on 4c multi .50 .30
159 A26 5t on 5c multi .60 .35
160 A26 7t on 7c multi .85 .45
161 A26 10t on 10c multi 1.00 .60
162 A26 15t on 15c multi (G) 1.75 1.00
163 A26 20t on 20c multi 2.25 1.40
164 A26 25t on 25c multi 3.00 1.75
165 A26 35t on 35c multi 3.75 2.00
166 A26 50t on 50c multi 5.25 2.50
167 A26 1p on 1r multi 11.00 6.50
168 A26 2p on 2r multi (G) 20.00 12.50
Nos. 155-168 (14) 50.70 29.80

Cattle Industry A35

Designs: 10t, Antelope, tourism, vert. 15t, Schoolhouse and children, education. 25t, Rural weaving, vert. 35t, Mining industry, vert.

**1976, Sept. 30 Litho. Perf. 14x14½
Textured Paper**

169 A35 4t multicolored .15 .15
170 A35 10t multicolored .25 .25
171 A35 15t multicolored .30 .30
172 A35 25t multicolored .50 .50
173 A35 35t multicolored .75 .75
Nos. 169-173 (5) 1.95 1.95

10th anniversary of independence.

Colophospermum Mopane — A36

Trees: 4t, Baikiaea plurijuga. 10t, Sterculia rogersii. 25t, Acacia nilotica. 40t, Kigelia africana.

1976, Nov. 1 Litho. Perf. 13

174 A36 3t multicolored .15 .15
175 A36 4t multicolored .15 .15
176 A36 10t multicolored .35 .35
177 A36 25t multicolored .75 .75
178 A36 40t multicolored 1.25 1.25
Nos. 174-178 (5) 2.65 2.65

Christmas.

Pres. Seretse Khama and Elizabeth II — A37

Designs: 25t, Coronation coach in procession. 40t, Recognition scene.

1977, Feb. 7 Litho. Perf. 12

179 A37 4t multicolored .15 .15
180 A37 25t multicolored .45 .45
181 A37 40t multicolored .75 .75
Nos. 179-181 (3) 1.35 1.35

Reign of Queen Elizabeth II, 25th anniv.

Clawless Otter A38

Wildlife Fund Emblem and: 4t, Serval. 10t, Bat-eared foxes. 25t, Pangolins. 40t, Brown hyena.

1977, June 6 Litho. Perf. 14

182 A38 3t multicolored 1.00 .30
183 A38 4t multicolored 1.25 .60
184 A38 10t multicolored 2.50 1.25

185	A38	25t multicolored	6.75	3.00
186	A38	40t multicolored	13.00	6.00
		Nos. 182-186 (5)	24.50	11.15

Endangered wildlife.

Khama Memorial
A39 5t

Designs: 4t, Cwihaba Caves. 15t, Green's (expedition) tree. 20t, Mmajojo ruins. 25t, Ancient morabaraba board. 35t, Matsieng's footprints.

1977, Aug. 22   Litho.   Perf. 14

187	A39	4t multicolored	.15	.15
188	A39	5t multicolored	.18	.18
189	A39	15t multicolored	.45	.45
190	A39	20t multicolored	.55	.55
191	A39	25t multicolored	.80	.80
192	A39	35t multicolored	1.10	1.10
a.		Souvenir sheet of 6, #187-192	3.50	3.50
		Nos. 187-192 (6)	3.23	3.23

Historical sites and national monuments.

Hypoxis itida — A40   Black Korhaan — A41

Lilies: 5t, Haemanthus magnificus. 10t, Boophane disticha. 25t, Vellozia retinervis. 40t, Ammocharis coranica.

1977, Oct. 31   Litho.   Perf. 14

193	A40	3t sepia & multi	.15	.15
194	A40	5t gray & multi	.18	.18
195	A40	10t multicolored	.35	.35
196	A40	25t multicolored	1.00	1.00
197	A40	40t multicolored	1.75	1.75
		Nos. 193-197 (5)	3.43	3.43

Christmas.

1978, July 3   Photo.   Perf. 14

Designs: Birds.

198	A41	1t shown	.15	.15
199	A41	2t Marabou storks	.15	.15
200	A41	3t Red-billed hoopoe	.15	.15
201	A41	4t Carmine bee-eaters	.20	.15
202	A41	5t African jacana	.20	.15
203	A41	7t Paradise flycatcher	.25	.16
204	A41	10t Bennett's woodpecker	.35	.25
205	A41	15t Red bishop	.50	.38
206	A41	20t Crowned plovers	.70	.50
207	A41	25t Giant kingfishers	.85	.62
208	A41	30t White-faced ducks	1.00	.75
209	A41	35t Green-backed heron	1.25	.88
210	A41	45t Black-headed herons	1.50	1.12
211	A41	50t Spotted eagle owl	1.75	1.25
212	A41	1p Gabar goshawk	3.50	2.50
213	A41	2p Martial eagle	7.00	5.00
214	A41	5p Saddlebill storks	14.00	10.00
		Nos. 198-214 (17)	33.50	24.16

For surcharges see Nos. 289-290.

 Tawana Making Kaross (garment) A42

Designs: 5t, Map of Okavango Delta. 15t, Bushman collecting roots. 20t, Herero woman milking cow. 25t, Yei pulling mokoro (boat). 35t, Mbukushu fishing.

1978, Sept. 11   Litho.   Perf. 14
Textured Paper

215	A42	4t multicolored	.15	.15
216	A42	5t multicolored	.15	.15
217	A42	15t multicolored	.20	.20
218	A42	20t multicolored	.32	.32
219	A42	25t multicolored	.40	.40
220	A42	35t multicolored	.52	.52
a.		Souvenir sheet of 6, #215-220	2.50	3.00
		Nos. 215-220 (6)	1.74	1.74

People of the Okavango Delta.

Caralluma Lutea — A43   Boy at Sip Well — A44

Flowers: 10t, Hoodia lugardii. 15t, Ipomoea transvaalensis. 25t, Ansellia gigantea.

1978, Nov. 6

221	A43	5t multicolored	.16	.16
222	A43	10t multicolored	.32	.32
223	A43	15t multicolored	.48	.48
224	A43	25t multicolored	.80	.80
		Nos. 221-224 (4)	1.76	1.76

Christmas.

1979, Feb. 12   Litho.   Perf. 14

Water Development: 5t, Watering pit. 10t, Hand-dug well and goats. 25t, Windmill, well and cattle. 40t, Modern drilling rig.

225	A44	3t multicolored	.15	.15
226	A44	3t multicolored	.15	.15
227	A44	10t multicolored	.15	.15
228	A44	25t multicolored	.40	.40
229	A44	40t multicolored	.65	.65
		Nos. 225-229 (5)	1.50	1.50

Botswana Pot — A45

Handicrafts: 10t, Clay buffalo. 25t, Woven covered basket. 40t, Beaded bag.

1979, June 4   Litho.   Perf. 14

230	A45	5t multicolored	.15	.15
231	A45	10t multicolored	.16	.16
232	A45	25t multicolored	.42	.42
233	A45	40t multicolored	.65	.65
a.		Souvenir sheet of 4, #230-233	1.65	1.65
		Nos. 230-233 (4)	1.38	1.38

Bechuanaland No. 6, Rowland Hill — A46

Sir Rowland Hill (1795-1879), originator of penny postage, and: 25t, Bechuanaland Protectorate No. 107. 45t, Botswana No. 20.

1979, Aug. 27   Litho.   Perf. 13½

234	A46	5t rose & black	.15	.15
235	A46	25t multicolored	.35	.35
236	A46	45t multicolored	.60	.60
		Nos. 234-236 (3)	1.10	1.10

Children Playing — A47

Design: 10t, Child playing with rag doll, and IYC emblem, vert.

1979, Sept. 24   Perf. 14

237	A47	5t multicolored	.15	.15
238	A47	10t multicolored	.25	.25

International Year of the Child.

Ximenia Caffra — A48

Christmas: 10t, Sclerocarya caffra. 15t, Hexalobus monopetalus. 25t, Ficus soldanella.

1979, Nov. 12   Litho.   Perf. 14

239	A48	5t multicolored	.15	.15
240	A48	10t multicolored	.20	.20
241	A48	15t multicolored	.30	.30
242	A48	25t multicolored	.50	.50
		Nos. 239-242 (4)	1.15	1.15

Flap-Necked Chameleon A49

1980, Mar. 3   Litho.   Perf. 14

243	A49	5t shown	.15	.15
244	A49	10t Leopard tortoise	.18	.18
245	A49	25t Puff adder	.45	.45
246	A49	40t White-throated monitor	.75	.75
		Nos. 243-246 (4)	1.53	1.53

Rock Breaking (Early Mining) — A50

1980, July 7   Litho.   Perf. 13½x14

247	A50	5t shown	.15	.15
248	A50	10t Ore hoisting	.18	.18
249	A50	15t Ore transport	.25	.25
250	A50	20t Ore crushing	.35	.35
251	A50	25t Smelting	.40	.40
252	A50	35t Tools, products	.60	.60
		Nos. 247-252 (6)	1.93	1.93

Chiwele and the Giant — A51

Folktales: 10t, Kgori Is Not Deceived. 30t, Nyambi's Wife and Crocodile. 45t, Clever Hare, horiz.

Perf. 14, 14½ (10t, 30t)
1980, Sept. 8

253	A51	5t multicolored	.15	.15

Size: 28x36mm

254	A51	10t multicolored	.18	.18
255	A51	30t multicolored	.52	.52

Size: 44x26mm

256	A51	45t multicolored	.80	.80
		Nos. 253-256 (4)	1.65	1.65

Game Watching — A52

1980, Oct. 6   Litho.   Perf. 14

257	A52	5t multicolored	.20	.20

World Tourism Conf., Manila, Sept. 27.

Acacia Gerrardii — A53

Christmas: Flowering Trees.

1980, Nov. 3   Litho.   Perf. 14

258	A53	5t shown	.15	.15
259	A53	10t Acacia nilotica	.15	.15
260	A53	25t Acacia erubescens	.32	.32
261	A53	40t Dichrostachys cinerea	.45	.45
		Nos. 258-261 (4)	1.07	1.07

Heinrich von Stephan, Bechuanaland Protectorate No. 150, Botswana No. 111 — A55

Design: 20t, Von Stephan, Bechuanaland Protectorate No. 151, Botswana No. 112.

1981, Jan. 7   Wmk. 373   Perf. 14

266	A55	6t multicolored	.15	.15
267	A55	20t multicolored	.45	.45

Von Stephan (1831-1897), founder of UPU.

Emperor Dragonfly — A56

1981, Feb. 23   Litho.   Perf. 14

268	A56	6t shown	.15	.15
269	A56	7t Praying mantis	.15	.15
270	A56	10t Elegant grasshopper	.15	.15
271	A56	20t Dung beetle	.25	.25
272	A56	30t Citrus swallowtail butterfly	.40	.40
273	A56	45t Mopane worm	.60	.60
a.		Souv. sheet of 6, #268-273	2.00	2.00
		Nos. 268-273 (6)	1.70	1.70

Blind Basket Weaver A57

1981, Apr. 4   Litho.   Perf. 14

274	A57	6t Seamstress	.15	.15
275	A57	20t shown	.30	.30
276	A57	30t Carpenter	.40	.40
		Nos. 274-276 (3)	.85	.85

International Year of the Disabled.

Woman Reading Letter (Literacy Campaign) — A58

1981, June 8

277	A58	6t shown	.15	.15
278	A58	7t Man sending telegram	.15	.15
279	A58	20t Boy, newspaper	.25	.25
280	A58	30t Father and daughter reading	.40	.40
		Nos. 277-280 (4)	.95	.95

Pres. Seretse Khama and Flag — A59

First death anniv. of Pres. Khama: Portrait and local buildings.

1981, July 13

281	A59	6t multicolored	.15	.15
282	A59	10t multicolored	.15	.15
283	A59	30t multicolored	.40	.40
284	A59	45t multicolored	.60	.60
		Nos. 281-284 (4)	1.30	1.30

Cattle in Agricultural Show — A60

1981, Sept. 21   Litho.   Perf. 14½
285	A60	6t Plowing	.15	.15
286	A60	20t shown	.20	.20
287	A60	30t Meat Commission	.35	.35
288	A60	50t Vaccine Institute	.50	.50
		Nos. 285-288 (4)	1.20	1.20

Nos. 209, 204 Surcharged in Black
1981, Sept.   Photo.   Perf. 14
289	A41	25t on 35t multicolored	.30	.30
290	A41	30t on 10t multicolored	.40	.40

Christmas — A61

Designs: Water lilies.

1981, Nov. 2   Litho.
291	A61	6t Nymphaea caerulea	.15	.15
292	A61	10t Nymphoides indica	.15	.15
293	A61	25t Nymphaea lotus	.30	.30
294	A61	40t Ottelia kunenensis	.50	.50
		Nos. 291-294 (4)	1.10	1.10

Children's Drawings — A62

1982, Feb. 15   Litho.   Perf. 14½x14
295	A62	6t Cattle	.15	.15
296	A62	10t Kgotla meeting	.15	.15
297	A62	30t Village	.40	.40
298	A62	45t Huts	.60	.60
		Nos. 295-298 (4)	1.30	1.30

Traditional Houses — A63

1982, May 3   Litho.   Perf. 14
299	A63	6t Common type	.15	.15
300	A63	10t Kgatleng	.15	.15
301	A63	30t Northeastern	.40	.40
302	A63	45t Sarwa	.60	.60
		Nos. 299-302 (4)	1.30	1.30

Red-billed Teals — A64

Perf. 14x14½, 14½x14
1982, July 1   Photo.
303	A64	1t Masked weaver	.15	.15
304	A64	2t Lesser double-collared sunbirds	.15	.15
305	A64	3t White-fronted bee-eaters	.15	.15
306	A64	4t Ostriches	.15	.15
307	A64	5t Grey-headed gulls	.30	.20
308	A64	6t Pygmy geese	.40	.20
309	A64	7t Cattle egrets	.50	.40
310	A64	8t Lanner falcon	.60	.45
311	A64	10t Yellow-billed storks	.75	.65
312	A64	15t shown	1.25	1.00
313	A64	20t Barn owls	1.50	1.25
314	A64	25t Hamerkops	2.00	1.40
315	A64	30t Stilts	2.25	1.65
316	A64	35t Blacksmith plovers	2.75	2.00
317	A64	45t Wattled plover	3.50	2.25

318	A64	50t Crowned guinea-fowl	3.75	2.75
319	A64	1p Cape vultures	8.00	5.50
320	A64	2p Augur bustards	15.00	11.00
		Nos. 303-320 (18)	43.15	31.40

Nos. 303-311 vert.
For surcharges see Nos. 401-403.

Christmas — A65   Endangered Species — A67

A66

Designs: Mushrooms.

1982, Nov. 2   Litho.   Perf. 14½
321	A65	7t Shaggy mane	.70	.70
322	A65	15t Orange milk	1.50	1.50
323	A65	35t Panther	3.50	3.50
324	A65	50t King boletus	4.75	4.75
		Nos. 321-324 (4)	10.45	10.45

1983, Mar. 14   Litho.   Perf. 14
325	A66	7t Pres. Quett Masire	.15	.15
326	A66	15t Dancers	.20	.20
327	A66	35t Melbourne Conference Center	.50	.50
328	A66	45t Heads of State meeting	.60	.60
		Nos. 325-328 (4)	1.45	1.45

Commonwealth Day.

1983, Apr. 19   Litho.   Perf. 14x14½
329	A67	7t Wattle crane	.40	.20
330	A67	15t Aloe lutescens	1.10	.70
331	A67	35t Roan antelope	2.75	1.65
332	A67	50t Hyphaene ventricosa	3.50	2.00
		Nos. 329-332 (4)	7.75	4.55

Wooden Spoons — A68   Christmas — A69

1983, July 20   Litho.   Perf. 14
333	A68	7t shown	.25	.15
334	A68	15t Jewelry	.45	.35
335	A68	35t Ox-hide milk bag	1.10	.85
336	A68	50t Decorated knives	1.25	1.00
a.		Souvenir sheet of 4, #333-336	6.00	5.00
		Nos. 333-336 (4)	3.05	2.35

1983, Nov. 7   Litho.   Perf. 14½x14
Designs: Dragonflies.
337	A69	6t Pantala flavescens	.15	.15
338	A69	15t Anax imperator	.30	.30
339	A69	25t Trithemis arteriosa	.50	.50
340	A69	45t Chlorolestes elegans	.90	.90
		Nos. 337-340 (4)	1.85	1.85

Mining Industry — A70

1984, Mar. 19   Litho.   Perf. 14½
341	A70	7t Diamonds	.40	.20
342	A70	15t Lime	1.10	.65
343	A70	35t Copper, nickel, vert.	3.00	2.00
344	A70	50t Coal, vert.	3.50	2.50
		Nos. 341-344 (4)	8.00	5.35

Traditional Transport — A71

1984, June 16   Litho.   Perf. 14½x14
345	A71	7t Man riding ox	.15	.15
346	A71	25t Sled	.42	.42
347	A71	35t Wagon	.65	.65
348	A71	50t Cart	.90	.90
		Nos. 345-348 (4)	2.12	2.12

Intl. Civil Aviation Org., 40th Anniv. — A72

1984, Oct. 8   Litho.   Perf. 14x13½
349	A72	7t Avro 504	.15	.15
350	A72	10t Westland Wessex	.15	.15
351	A72	15t Junkers 52-3M	.25	.25
352	A72	25t Dragon Rapide	.40	.40
353	A72	35t DC-3	.60	.60
354	A72	50t F27 Fokker Friendship	.80	.80
		Nos. 349-354 (6)	2.35	2.35

Christmas — A73

Butterflies.

1984, Nov. 5   Litho.   Perf. 14½x14
355	A73	7t Papilio demodocus	.40	.30
356	A73	25t Byblia acheloia	1.75	1.50
357	A73	35t Hypolimnas missipus	2.75	1.50
358	A73	50t Graphium taboranus	3.50	2.00
		Nos. 355-358 (4)	8.40	4.80

Traditional & Exotic Foods — A74   Bechuanaland No. 4 — A75

1985, Mar. 18   Litho.   Perf. 14½
359	A74	7t Man preparing seswaa	.15	.15
360	A74	15t Woman preparing bogobe	.20	.20
361	A74	25t Girl eating madilla	.32	.32
362	A74	50t Woman collecting caterpillars	.65	.65
a.		Souvenir sheet of 4, #359-362	1.40	1.40
		Nos. 359-362 (4)	1.32	1.32

Southern African Development Coordination Conference, 5th anniv.

1985, June 24
Postage stamp cent.: 15t, Bechuanaland Protectorate No. 72. 25t, Bechuanaland Protectorate No. 106. 35t, Bechuanaland No. 199, 50t, Botswana No. 1, horiz.
363	A75	7t multicolored	.15	.15
364	A75	15t multicolored	.18	.18
365	A75	25t multicolored	.30	.30
366	A75	35t multicolored	.42	.42
367	A75	50t multicolored	.62	.62
		Nos. 363-367 (5)	1.67	1.67

Police Centenary — A76

Designs: 7t, Bechuanaland Border Police, 1885-1895. 10t, Bechuanaland Mounted Police, 1894-1902. 25t, Bechuanaland Protectorate Police, 1903-1966. 50t, Botswana Motorcycle Police, 1966-1985.

1985, Aug. 5   Perf. 14½x14
368	A76	7t multicolored	.15	.15
369	A76	10t multicolored	.15	.15
370	A76	25t multicolored	.30	.30
371	A76	50t multicolored	.62	.62
		Nos. 368-371 (4)	1.22	1.22

Edible Wild Cucumbers A77

1985, Nov. 4
372	A77	7t Cucumis metuliferus	.15	.15
373	A77	15t Acanthosicyos naudinianus	.18	.18
374	A77	25t Coccinia sessifolia	.30	.30
375	A77	50t Momordica balsamina	.62	.62
		Nos. 372-375 (4)	1.25	1.25

Christmas.

Declaration of Protectorate, Cent. — A78

1985, Dec. 30   Litho.   Perf. 14x14½
376	A78	7t Heads of state meet	.15	.15
377	A78	15t Declaration reading, 1885	.18	.18
378	A78	25t Mackenzie and Khama	.30	.30
379	A78	50t Map	.62	.62
a.		Souvenir sheet of 4, #376-379	1.20	1.20
		Nos. 376-379 (4)	1.25	1.25

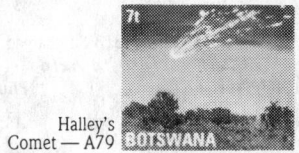

Halley's Comet — A79

1986, Mar. 24   Perf. 14½x14
380	A79	7t Comet over Serowe	.15	.15
381	A79	15t Over Bobonong	.18	.18
382	A79	35t Over Gomare swamps	.42	.42
383	A79	50t Over Thamaga, Letlhakeng	.62	.62
		Nos. 380-383 (4)	1.37	1.37

Milk Containers — A80

1986, June 23   Perf. 14½
384	A80	8t Leather bag	.15	.15
385	A80	15t Ceramic pots	.18	.18
386	A80	35t Wood pot	.42	.42
387	A80	50t Woman, pots	.62	.62
		Nos. 384-387 (4)	1.37	1.37

Souvenir Sheet

Natl. Independence, 20th Anniv. — A81

Designs: a, Map of natl. parks and reserves. b, Morupule Power Station. c, Cattle, Kgalagadi. d, Natl. Assembly.

1986, Sept. 30 Litho. Perf. 14½x14
388 Sheet of 4 .90 .90
a.-d. A81 20t any single .22 .22

Flowers of the Okavango Swamps — A82

1986, Nov. 3 Litho. Perf. 14x14½
389 A82 8t Ludwigia stogonifera .15 .15
390 A82 15t Sopubia mannii .16 .16
391 A82 35t Commelina diffusa .38 .38
392 A82 50t Hibiscus diversifolius .55 .55
　Nos. 389-392 (4) 1.24 1.24

Christmas.

Traditional Medicine A83

UN Child Survival Campaign A84

1987, Mar. 2 Litho. Perf. 14½x14
393 A83 8t Professional diviners .15 .15
394 A83 15t Lightning prevention .18 .18
395 A83 35t Rainmaker .45 .45
396 A83 50t Bloodletting .65 .65
　Nos. 393-396 (4) 1.43 1.43

1987, June 1
397 A84 8t Oral rehydration therapy .15 .15
398 A84 15t Growth monitoring .18 .18
399 A84 35t Immunization .45 .45
400 A84 50t Breast-feeding .65 .65
　Nos. 397-400 (4) 1.43 1.43

Nos. 308, 311 and 318 Surcharged
Perf. 14x14½, 14½x14½

1987, Apr. 1 Photo.
401 A64 3t on 6t No. 308 .15 .15
402 A64 5t on 10t No. 311 .15 .15
403 A64 20t on 50t No. 318 .30 .30
　Set value .40 .40

Wildlife Conservation A85

1987, Aug. 3 Perf. 14
404 A85 1t Cape fox .15 .15
405 A85 2t Lechwe .15 .15
406 A85 3t Zebra .15 .15
407 A85 4t Duiker .15 .15
408 A85 5t Banded mongoose .15 .15
409 A85 6t Rusty-spotted genet .15 .15
410 A85 8t Hedgehog .15 .15
411 A85 10t Scrub hare .15 .15
412 A85 12t Hippopotamus .15 .15
413 A85 15t Suricate .20 .15
414 A85 20t Caracal .25 .20
415 A85 25t Steenbok .35 .30
416 A85 30t Gemsbok .45 .35
417 A85 35t Square-lipped rhino .50 .45
418 A85 40t Mountain reedbuck .60 .50
419 A85 50t Rock dassie .75 .60
420 A85 1p Giraffe 1.50 1.25
421 A85 2p Tsessebe 3.00 2.50
422 A85 3p Side-striped jackal 4.75 3.75
423 A85 5p Hartebeest 8.00 6.50
　Nos. 404-423 (20) 21.70 17.90

For surcharges see Nos. 480-482, 506-509.

Wetland Grasses — A86

1987, Oct. 26 Perf. 14x14½
424 A86 8t Cyperus articulatus .15 .15
425 A86 15t Miscanthus junceus .15 .15
426 A86 30t Cyperus alopecuroides .36 .36
427 A86 1p Typha latifolia 1.20 1.20
a. Souvenir sheet of 4, #424-427 1.85 1.85
　Nos. 424-427 (4) 1.86 1.86

Christmas, preservation of the Okavango and Kuando-Chobe River wetlands.

Early Cultivation Techniques A87

1988, Mar. 14 Litho. Perf. 14½x14
428 A87 8t Digging stick .15 .15
429 A87 15t Iron hoe .18 .18
430 A87 35t Wooden plow .42 .42
431 A87 50t Communal planting, Lesotla .60 .60
　Nos. 428-431 (4) 1.35 1.35

World Wildlife Fund — A88

Designs: WWF emblem and various red lechwe, Kobus leche.

1988, June 6 Litho. Perf. 14½x14
432 A88 10t Adult wading .35 .35
433 A88 15t Adult, sun .50 .50
434 A88 35t Cow, calf 1.10 1.10
435 A88 75t Herd 2.50 1.75
　Nos. 432-435 (4) 4.45 3.70

Runner Post, Cent. — A89

Routes and: 10t, Gubulawayo, Bechuanaland, cancellation dated Aug. 21 '88. 15t, Bechuanaland Protectorate No. 65. 30t, Pack traders. 60t, Mafeking killer cancel No. 638.

1988, Aug. 22 Litho. Perf. 14½
436 A89 10t multicolored .15 .15
437 A89 15t multicolored .18 .18
438 A89 30t multicolored .35 .35
439 A89 60t multicolored .65 .65
a. Souvenir sheet of 4, #436-439 1.30 1.30
　Nos. 436-439 (4) 1.33 1.33

Printed in a continuous design picturing the Mafeking-Gubulawayo route and part of the Shoshong runner post route.

State Visit of Pope John Paul II, Sept. 13 — A90

Natl. Museum and Art Gallery, Gaborone, 20th Anniv. — A91

1988, Sept. 13 Litho. Perf. 14x14½
440 A90 10t Map, portrait .15 .15
441 A90 15t Portrait .15 .15
442 A90 30t Map, portrait, diff. .35 .35
443 A90 80t Portrait, diff. .85 .85
　Nos. 440-443 (4) 1.50 1.50

1988, Sept. 30 Perf. 14½
444 A91 8t Museum .15 .15
445 A91 15t Pottery, c. 400-1300 .18 .18
446 A91 30t Buffalo bellows .35 .35
447 A91 60t Children, mobile museum .68 .68
　Nos. 444-447 (4) 1.36 1.36

A92

A93

Flowering plants of southeastern Botswana.

1988, Oct. 11 Litho. Perf. 14x14½
448 A92 8t Grewia flava .15 .15
449 A92 15t Cienfuegosia digitata .15 .15
450 A92 40t Solanum seaforthianum .42 .42
451 A92 75t Carissa bispinosa .78 .78
　Nos. 448-451 (4) 1.50 1.50

Christmas.

1989, Mar. 13 Litho. Perf. 14x14½

Traditional grain storage.

452 A93 8t Sesigo basket granary .15 .15
453 A93 15t Letlole daga granary .15 .15
454 A93 30t Sefalana bisque granary .30 .30
455 A93 60t Serala granaries .60 .60
　Nos. 452-455 (4) 1.20 1.20

Slaty Egrets — A94

1989, July 5 Perf. 15x14
456 A94 8t Nesting .15 .15
457 A94 15t Young .45 .30
458 A94 30t Adult in flight .75 .60
459 A94 60t Two adults 1.65 1.40
a. Souvenir sheet of 4, #456-459 3.00 2.50
　Nos. 456-459 (4) 3.00 2.45

Children's Drawings A95

Perf. 14½x14, 14x14½
1989, Sept. 4
460 A95 10t Ephraim Seeletso .15 .15
461 A95 15t Neelma Bhatia, vert. .15 .15
462 A95 30t Thabo Habana .30 .30
463 A95 1p Thabo Olesitse 1.00 1.00
　Nos. 460-463 (4) 1.60 1.60

Star and Orchids — A96

1989, Oct. 30 Litho. Perf. 14x14½
464 A96 8t Eulophia angolensis .15 .15
465 A96 15t Eulophia hereroensis .26 .26
466 A96 30t Eulophia speciosa .52 .52
467 A96 60t Eulophia petersii 1.10 1.10
　Nos. 464-467 (4) 2.03 2.03

Christmas.

Anniversaries — A97

8t, Bechuanaland Protectorate #201. 15t, Voter at ballot box. 30t, Map & flags of nations at SADCC conference. 60t, Great Britain #1.

1990, Mar. 5 Litho. Perf. 14½
468 A97 8t multicolored .15 .15
469 A97 15t multicolored .15 .15
470 A97 30t multicolored .30 .30
471 A97 60t multicolored .60 .60
　Nos. 468-471 (4) 1.20 1.20

25th anniv. of self government (8t); 1st elections, 25th anniv. (15t); Southern African Development Coordination Conference (SADCC), 10th anniv. (30t); and Penny Black, 150th anniv. (60t).

Stamp World London '90 — A98

Traditional Dress — A99

Aspects of the telecommunications industry.

1990, May 3
472 A98 8t Training .15 .15
473 A98 15t Transmission .15 .15
474 A98 30t Public telephone .30 .30
475 A98 2p Testing circuitry 2.00 2.00
　Nos. 472-475 (4) 2.60 2.60

1990, Aug. 1 Litho. Perf. 14
476 A99 8t Children .15 .15
477 A99 15t Young woman .15 .15
478 A99 30t Man .26 .26
479 A99 2p Adult woman 1.75 1.75
a. Souvenir sheet of 4, #476-479 2.50 2.50
　Nos. 476-479 (4) 2.31 2.31

Nos. 404 and 412 Surcharged **10t**

No. 409 Surcharged **20t**

1990
480 A85 10t on 1t No. 404 .15 .15
481 A85 20t on 6t No. 409 .20 .20
482 A85 50t on 12t No. 412 .50 .50
　Nos. 480-482 (3) .85 .85

Flowering Trees — A100

1990, Oct. 30 Litho. Perf. 14
483 A100 8t Acacia nigrescens .15 .15
484 A100 15t Peltophorum africanum .15 .15
485 A100 30t Burkea africana .26 .26
486 A100 2p Pterocarpus angolensis 1.75 1.75
　Nos. 483-486 (4) 2.31 2.31

Christmas.

Natl. Road Safety Day — A101

1990, Dec. 7 Litho. Perf. 14½
487 A101 8t Children playing on road .15 .15
488 A101 15t Accident .18 .18
489 A101 30t Livestock on road .36 .36
　Nos. 487-489 (3) .69 .69

Petroglyphs A102

Various petroglyphs.

1991, Mar. 4   Litho.   Perf. 14x14½
Textured Paper

490	A102	8t multicolored	.15	.15
491	A102	15t multicolored	.15	.15
492	A102	30t multicolored	.30	.30
493	A102	2p multicolored	2.00	2.00
		Nos. 490-493 (4)	2.60	2.60

Natl. Census — A103

1991, June 3   Perf. 14
494	A103	8t Children playing	.15	.15

Perf. 14½
495	A103	15t Houses	.18	.18

Perf. 14x14½
496	A103	30t Children in schoolyard	.36	.36
497	A103	2p Children, hospital	2.40	2.40
		Nos. 494-497 (4)	3.09	3.09

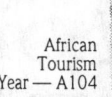

African Tourism Year — A104

1991, Sept. 30   Litho.   Perf. 14
498	A104	8t Tourists, elephants	.15	.15
499	A104	15t Birds, crocodiles	.18	.18
500	A104	35t Airplane, fish eagles	.40	.40

Size 26x43mm
501	A104	2p Okavango Delta	2.40	2.40
		Nos. 498-501 (4)	3.13	3.13

No. 501 incorporates designs of #498-500.

Christmas — A105

Seed pods: 8t, Harpagophytum procumbens. 15t, Tylosema esculentum. 30t, Abrus precatorius. 2p, Kigelia africana.

1991, Nov. 4   Litho.   Perf. 14
502	A105	8t multicolored	.15	.15
503	A105	15t multicolored	.16	.16
504	A105	30t multicolored	.32	.32
505	A105	2p multicolored	2.25	2.25
		Nos. 502-505 (4)	2.88	2.88

Nos. 406, 409, & 412 Surcharged **8t**

1992, Mar. 9   Litho.   Perf. 14
506	A85	8t on 12t No. 412	.15	.15
507	A85	10t on 12t No. 412	.15	.15
508	A85	25t on 6t No. 409	.25	.25
509	A85	40t on 3t No. 406	.38	.38
		Nos. 506-509 (4)	.93	.93

Climbing Frogs — A106

Designs: 8t, Cacosternum boettgeri, horiz. 10t, Hyperolius marmoratus angolensis. 40t, Bufo fenoulheti, horiz. 1p, Hyperolius.

Perf. 14½x14, 14x14½
1992, Mar. 23
510	A106	8t multicolored	.15	.15
511	A106	10t multicolored	.15	.15
512	A106	40t multicolored	.40	.40
513	A106	1p multicolored	.95	.95
		Nos. 510-513 (4)	1.65	1.65

Botswana Railways A107

Designs: 10t, Deluxe air-conditioned coaches. 25t, BD1 locomotive, vert. 40t, Deluxe coach interior, vert. 2p, Locomotive pulling air-conditioned coaches.

1992, June 29   Litho.   Perf. 14
514	A107	10t multicolored	.15	.15
515	A107	25t multicolored	.15	.15
516	A107	40t multicolored	.20	.20
517	A107	2p multicolored	1.00	1.00
a.		Souv. sheet of 4, #514-517 + label	1.40	1.40
		Nos. 514-517 (4)	1.50	1.50

Wild Animals A108

1992, Aug. 3   Litho.   Perf. 14½
518	A108	1t Cheetah	.15	.15
519	A108	2t Spring hares	.15	.15
520	A108	4t Blackfooted cat	.15	.15
521	A108	5t Striped mouse	.15	.15
522	A108	10t Oribi	.15	.15
523	A108	12t Pangolin	.15	.15
524	A108	15t Aardwolf	.15	.15
525	A108	20t Warthog	.20	.20
526	A108	25t Ground squirrels	.25	.25
527	A108	35t Honey badger	.30	.30
528	A108	40t Common mole rat	.35	.35
529	A108	45t Wild dogs	.40	.40
530	A108	50t Water mongoose	.45	.45
531	A108	80t Klipspringer	.70	.70
532	A108	1p Lesser bushbaby	.90	.90
533	A108	2p Bushveld elephant shrew	1.80	1.80
534	A108	5p Zorilla	4.50	4.50
535	A108	10p Vervet monkey	9.00	9.00
		Nos. 518-535 (18)	19.90	19.90

For surcharges see Nos. 518-520.

A109   Ferns — A110

1992, Aug. 7   Perf. 14x15
536	A109	10t Boxer	.15	.15
537	A109	50t Four sprinters	.45	.45
538	A109	1p Two boxers	.95	.95
539	A109	2p Three runners	1.85	1.85
a.		Souvenir sheet of 4, #536-539	3.40	3.40
		Nos. 536-539 (4)	3.40	3.40

1992 Summer Olympics, Barcelona.

1992, Nov. 23   Litho.   Perf. 14½
540	A110	10t Adiantum incisum	.15	.15
541	A110	25t Actiniopteris radiata	.25	.25
542	A110	40t Ceratopteris cornuta	.40	.40
543	A110	1.50p Pellaea calomelanos	1.40	1.40
		Nos. 540-543 (4)	2.20	2.20

Christmas.

Organizations A111

Designs: 10t, Lions Intl., conquering blindness, vert. 15t, Red Cross Society. 25t, Ecumenical Decade, churches in solidarity with women, vert. 35t, Round Table supporting the deaf. 40t, Rotary Intl., vert. 50t, Botswana Christian Council.

1993, Mar. 29   Litho.   Perf. 14
544	A111	10t multicolored	.15	.15
545	A111	15t multicolored	.15	.15
546	A111	25t multicolored	.20	.20
547	A111	35t multicolored	.30	.30
548	A111	40t multicolored	.40	.40
549	A111	50t multicolored	.45	.45
		Nos. 544-549 (6)	1.65	1.65

Botswana Railway, Cent. A112

Designs: 10t, Engine No. 1, 6th class 4-6-0, Bechuanaland Railways. 40t, Engine No. 317, 19th class 4-8-2. 50t, Engine No. 256, 12th class 4-8-2. 1.50p, Engine No. 71, 7th class 4-8-0, Rhodesia Railways.

1993, May 24   Litho.   Perf. 15x14
550	A112	10t multicolored	.15	.15
551	A112	40t multicolored	.40	.40
552	A112	50t multicolored	.50	.50
553	A112	1.50p multicolored	1.45	1.45
a.		Souvenir sheet of 4, #550-553	2.50	2.50
		Nos. 550-553 (4)	2.50	2.50

Eagles — A113   Christmas — A114

1993, Aug. 30   Litho.   Perf. 14½
554	A113	10t Long crested eagle	.20	.20
555	A113	25t Snake eagle	.50	.50
556	A113	50t Bateleur eagle	1.00	1.00
557	A113	1.50p Secretary bird	3.00	3.00
		Nos. 554-557 (4)	4.70	4.70

1993, Oct. 25   Litho.   Perf. 14x14½
558	A114	12t Aloe zebrina	.15	.15
559	A114	25t Croton megalobotrys	.20	.20
560	A114	50t Boophane disticha	.45	.45
561	A114	1p Euphorbia davyi	.90	.90
		Nos. 558-561 (4)	1.70	1.70

Traditional Children's Toys A115

1994, Mar. 28   Litho.   Perf. 14½
562	A115	10t Mantadile	.15	.15
563	A115	40t Dikgomo tsa mimopa	.30	.30
564	A115	50t Sefuu-fuu	.40	.40
565	A115	1p Mantlwane	.75	.75
		Nos. 562-565 (4)	1.60	1.60

ICAO, 50th Anniv. A116

Perf. 14½x14, 14x14½
1994, June 30   Litho.
566	A116	10t Inside control tower	.15	.15
567	A116	25t Fire engine	.25	.25
568	A116	40t Baggage carts, vert.	.40	.40
569	A116	50t Control tower, vert.	.50	.50
		Nos. 566-569 (4)	1.30	1.30

A117   A118

Environmental Protection: 10t, Flamingos, Sua Pan, vert. 35t, Makgadikgadi Pan trees. 50t, Zebra,

Makgadikgadi Palm trees, vert. 2p, Map of Makgadikgadi Pans.

1994, Aug. 30   Litho.   Perf. 14
570	A117	10t multicolored	.15	.15
571	A117	35t multicolored	.45	.45
572	A117	50t multicolored	.65	.65
573	A117	2p multicolored	2.50	2.50
		Nos. 570-573 (4)	3.75	3.75

1994, Oct. 24

Edible fruits: 10t, Ziziphus mucronata. 25t, Strychnos cocculoides. 40t, Bauhinia petersiana. 50t, Schinziphyton rautaneli.

574	A118	10t multicolored	.15	.15
575	A118	25t multicolored	.20	.20
576	A118	40t multicolored	.30	.30
577	A118	50t multicolored	.35	.35
		Nos. 574-577 (4)	1.00	1.00

Christmas.
See Nos. 587-590.

Traditional Fishing A119

1995, Apr. 3   Litho.   Perf. 14
578	A119	15t Spear	.15	.15
579	A119	40t Hook	.30	.30
580	A119	65t Net	.50	.50
581	A119	80t Basket	.60	.60
		Nos. 578-581 (4)	1.55	1.55

UN, 50th Anniv. — A120

1995, Oct. 16   Litho.   Perf. 14
582	A120	20t FAO	.15	.15
583	A120	50t World Food Program	.35	.35
584	A120	80t Development Plan	.60	.60
585	A120	1p UNICEF	.70	.70
		Nos. 582-585 (4)	1.80	1.80

World Wildlife Fund — A121

Hyaena brunnea: a, 20t, Adult walking right. b, 50t, Two young. c, 80t, Adult finding eggs. d, 1p, Two young, adult resting.

1995, Nov. 6
586	A121	Strip of 4, #a.-d.	1.75	1.75

No. 586 was issued in miniature sheets of 4 each.

Christmas Type of 1994
1995, Nov. 27   Litho.   Perf. 14
587	A118	20t Adenia glauca	.15	.15
588	A118	50t Pterodiscus ngamicus	.35	.35
589	A118	80t Sesamothamnus lugardii	.60	.60
590	A118	1p Fockea multiflora	.70	.70
		Nos. 587-590 (4)	1.80	1.80

Traditional Weapons — A122

1996, Mar. 25   Litho.   Perf. 14
591	A122	20t Spears	.15	.15
592	A122	50t Axes	.30	.30
593	A122	80t Shield, knob-kerries	.50	.50
594	A122	1p Knives, cases	.60	.60
		Nos. 591-594 (4)	1.55	1.55

Nos. 518-520 Surcharged 20t

1996   Litho.   Perf. 14½

595	A108	20t on 2t No. 519	.15	.15
596	A108	30t on 1t No. 518	.20	.20
597	A108	70t on 4t No. 520	.40	.40
		Nos. 595-597 (3)	.75	.75

A123   A124

Radio, Cent.: 20t, Child listening to early radio. 50t, Mobile unit, transmitter. 80t, Local police. 1p, Radio Botswana at the Kgotila.

1996, June 3   Litho.   Perf. 14

598	A123	20t multicolored	.15	.15
599	A123	50t multicolored	.35	.35
600	A123	80t multicolored	.60	.60
601	A123	1p multicolored	.75	.75
		Nos. 598-601 (4)	1.85	1.85

1996, July 19   Litho.   Perf. 14

Modern Olympic Games, Cent.: 20t, Hand holding torch, laurel wreath, Olympic rings. 50t, Pierre de Coubertin. 80t, Map, flag of Botswana, athletes. 1p, Ruins of original Olympic Stadium, Olympia.

602	A124	20t multicolored	.15	.15
603	A124	50t multicolored	.35	.35
604	A124	80t multicolored	.60	.60
605	A124	1p multicolored	.75	.75
		Nos. 602-605 (4)	1.85	1.85

A125   A126

Worthy Causes: 20t, Family planning education, Welfare Association. 30t, Skills for the blind, Pudulogong Rehabilitation Center. 50t, Collection of seeds, Forestry Association. 70t, Secretarial class, YWCA. 80t, Day care center, Council of Women. 1p, SOS Children's Village, Tlokweng.

1996, Sept. 23   Litho.   Perf. 14

606	A125	20t multicolored	.15	.15
607	A125	30t multicolored	.25	.25
608	A125	50t multicolored	.35	.35
609	A125	70t multicolored	.55	.55
610	A125	80t multicolored	.60	.60
611	A125	1p multicolored	.75	.75
		Nos. 606-611 (6)	2.65	2.65

1996, Nov. 4   Litho.   Perf. 14

Adansonia Digitata

612	A126	20t Leaf, flower	.15	.15
613	A126	50t Fruit	.35	.35
614	A126	80t Tree in leaf	.60	.60
615	A126	1p Tree without leaves	.75	.75
		Nos. 612-615 (4)	1.85	1.85

Christmas.

Francistown, Cent. — A127

20t, Tati Hotel. 50t, Railway station. 80t, Company manager's house. 1p, Monarch Mine.

1997, Apr. 21   Litho.   Perf. 14

616	A127	20t multicolored	.15	.15
617	A127	50t multicolored	.30	.30
618	A127	80t multicolored	.45	.45
619	A127	1p multicolored	.55	.55
		Nos. 616-619 (4)	1.45	1.45

Birds — A128

5t, Pel's fishing owl, vert. 10t, Gymnogene. 15t, Meyers parrot, vert. 20t, Harlequin quail. 25t, Marico sunbird. 30t, Kurrichane thrush. 40t, Redheaded finch, vert. 50t, Buffalo weaver, vert. 60t, Sacred ibis. 70t, Cape shoveller. 80t, Greater honeyguide. 1p, Woodland kingfisher. 1.25p, Purple heron, vert. 1.50p, Yellowbilled oxpecker. 2p, Shafttailed whydah, vert. 2.50p, White stork, vert. 5p, Ovambo sparrowhawk, vert. 10p, Spotted crake, vert.

1997, Aug. 4   Litho.   Perf. 13½

620	A128	5t multicolored	.15	.15
621	A128	10t multicolored	.15	.15
622	A128	15t multicolored	.15	.15
623	A128	20t multicolored	.15	.15
624	A128	25t multicolored	.15	.15
625	A128	30t multicolored	.20	.20
626	A128	40t multicolored	.25	.25
627	A128	50t multicolored	.30	.30
628	A128	60t multicolored	.35	.35
629	A128	70t multicolored	.40	.40
630	A128	80t multicolored	.45	.45
631	A128	1p multicolored	.55	.55
632	A128	1.25p multicolored	.70	.70
633	A128	1.50p multicolored	.85	.85
634	A128	2p multicolored	1.10	1.10
635	A128	2.50p multicolored	1.40	1.40
636	A128	5p multicolored	2.75	2.75
637	A128	10p multicolored	5.50	5.50
		Nos. 620-637 (18)	15.55	15.55

Botswana Railway, Cent. — A129

Designs: 35t, Bechuanaland Rail, 1897. 50t, Elephants on the tracks. 80t, First locomotives in Bechuanaland, Cape of Good Hope 4-6-0. 1p, 4-6-4+4-6-4 Beyer Garratt. 2p, New BD3 locomotive. 2.50p, Fantuzzi Container Stacker.

1997, July 12   Litho.   Perf. 14x14½

638	A129	35t multicolored	.20	.20
639	A129	50t multicolored	.30	.30
640	A129	80t multicolored	.50	.50
641	A129	1p multicolored	.60	.60
642	A129	2p multicolored	1.20	1.20
643	A129	2.50p multicolored	1.50	1.50
		Nos. 638-643 (6)	4.30	4.30

A130   A131

Queen Elizabeth II and Prince Philip, 50th Wedding Anniv.: No. 644, Prince in casual attire. No. 645, Queen wearing white & blue hat. No. 646, Queen with horse. No. 647, Prince with horse. No. 648, Prince, Queen. No. 649, Princess Ann in riding attire.

10p, Queen, Prince riding in open carriage.

Wmk. 373

1997, Sept. 22   Litho.   Perf. 13

644	A130	35t multicolored	.20	.20
645	A130	35t multicolored	.20	.20
a.		Pair, #644-645	.40	.40
646	A130	2p multicolored	1.20	1.20
647	A130	2p multicolored	1.20	1.20
a.		Pair, #646-647	2.40	2.40
648	A130	2.50p multicolored	1.50	1.50
649	A130	2.50p multicolored	1.50	1.50
a.		Pair, #648-649	3.00	3.00
		Nos. 644-649 (6)	5.80	5.80

Souvenir Sheet

650	A130	10p multicolored	6.00	6.00

1997, Nov. 10   Litho.   Perf. 14

Christmas (Combretum):, 35t, Zeyheri. 1p, Apiculatum. 2p, Molle. 2.50p, Imberbe.

651	A131	35t multicolored	.20	.20
652	A131	1p multicolored	.60	.60
653	A131	2p multicolored	1.20	1.20
654	A131	2.50p multicolored	1.50	1.50
		Nos. 651-654 (4)	3.50	3.50

POSTAGE DUE STAMPS

Bechuanaland Protectorate Nos. J10-J12 Overprinted: "REPUBLIC OF / BOTSWANA"

Wmk. 4

1967, Mar. 1   Typo.   Perf. 14

J1	D2	1c carmine rose	.15	1.00
J2	D2	2c dull violet	.25	1.00
J3	D2	5c olive green	.60	2.00
		Nos. J1-J3 (3)	1.00	4.50

Elephant   Zebra
D1   D2

Perf. 13½

1971, June 9   Litho.   Unwmk.

J4	D1	1c carmine rose	.80	2.25
J5	D1	2c violet blue	1.00	3.00
J6	D1	6c sepia	1.65	5.00
J7	D1	14c green	3.00	7.00
		Nos. J4-J7 (4)	6.45	17.25

1978   Perf. 12½

J8	D2	1t red orange & black	.50	.50
J9	D2	2t emerald & black	.50	.50
J10	D2	4t red & black	.50	.50
J11	D2	10t dark blue & black	.50	.50
J12	D2	16t brown & black	.50	.50
		Nos. J8-J12 (5)	2.50	2.50

1984   Perf. 14½x14

J8a	D2	1t	.50	.50
J9a	D2	2t	.50	.50
J10a	D2	4t	.50	.50
J11a	D2	10t	.50	.50
J12a	D2	16t	.50	.50
		Nos. J8a-J12a (5)	2.50	2.50

1989, Apr. 1   Litho.   Perf. 14½

J8b	D2	1t	.15	.15
J9b	D2	2t	.15	.15
J10b	D2	4t	.15	.15
J11b	D2	10t	.20	.20
J12b	D2	16t	.35	.35
		Set value	.85	.85

The design is the same size on the 1984 and 1989 issues, but the paper is wider on the 1989 issue.

BRAZIL

brə-'zil

Brasil (after 1918)

LOCATION — On the north and east coasts of South America, bordering on the Atlantic Ocean.
GOVT. — Republic
AREA — 3,286,000 sq. mi.
POP. — 132,580,000 (est. 1984)
CAPITAL — Brasilia

Brazil was an independent empire from 1822 to 1889, when a constitution was adopted and the country became officially known as The United States of Brazil.

1000 Reis = 1 Milreis
100 Centavos = 1 Cruzeiro (1942)
100 Centavos = 1 Cruzado (1986)
100 Centavos = 1 Cruzeiro (1990)
100 Centavos = 1 Cruzeiro Real (Aug. 2, 1993)

Catalogue values for unused stamps in this country are for Never Hinged items, beginning with Scott 680 in the regular postage section, Scott C66 in the airpost section, Scott RA2 in the postal tax section, and Scott RAB1 in the postal tax semi-postal section.

Values for unused stamps are for examples with original gum as defined in the catalogue introduction except for Nos. 1-38 and 42-52 which are valued without gum.

Watermarks

Wmk. 97-   Wmk. 98-
"CORREIO   "IMPOSTO DE
FEDERAL   CONSUMO
REPUBLICA DOS   REPUBLICA DOS
ESTADOS UNIDOS   ESTADOS UNIDOS
DO BRAZIL" in   DO BRAZIL" in
Sheet   Sheet

Wmk. 99- "CORREIO"

Wmk. 100- "CASA DA MOEDA" in Sheet

Because of the spacing of this watermark, a few stamps in each sheet may show no watermark.

Wmk. 101- Stars and CASA DA MOEDA

Wmk. 193- ESTADOS UNIDOS DO BRASIL

Wmk. 206- Star-framed CM, Multiple

Wmk. 218- E U BRASIL Multiple, Letters 8mm High

Wmk. 221- ESTADOS UNIDOS DO BRASIL, Multiple, Letters 6mm High

Wmk. 222- CORREIO BRASIL and 5 Stars in Squared Circle

Wmk. 236- Coat of Arms in Sheet

Watermark (reduced illustration) covers 22 stamps in sheet.

Wmk. 245- Multiple "CASA DA MOEDA DO BRASIL" and Small Formee Cross

Wmk. 249- "CORREIO BRASIL" multiple

Wmk. 256- "CASA+DA+MOEDA+DO+BRAZIL" in 8mm Letters

Wmk. 264- "*CORREIO*BRASIL*" Multiple, Letters 7mm High

Wmk. 267- "*CORREIO*BRASIL*" Multiple in Small Letters 5mm High

Wmk. 268- "CASA+DA+MOEDA+DO+BRASIL" in 6mm Letters

Wmk. 270- Wavy Lines and Seal

Wmk. 271- Wavy Lines

Wmk. 281- Wavy Lines

Issues of the Empire

A1

Grayish or Yellowish Paper
Fine Impressions

1843, Aug. 1 Unwmk. Engr. *Imperf.*

1	A1	30r black	2,250.	550.
c.	In pair with No. 2			300,000.
2	A1	60r black	600.	225.
3	A1	90r black	2,750.	1,150.

Nos. 1-3 were issued with gum, but very few unused examples retain even a trace of their original gum. Copies with original gum command substantial premiums.

Fine impressions are true black and have background lathework complete. Intermediate impressions are grayish black and have weaker lathework in the background. These sell for somewhat less than fine impressions. Worn impressions have white areas in the background surrounding the numerals due to plate wear affecting especially the lathework. These examples sell for somewhat less than intermediate impressions.

Most examples of Nos. 1-3 also exist on white paper, usually thin and somewhat translucent. Such examples are scarce and command premiums.

A2

A3

Grayish or Yellowish Paper

1844-46

7	A2	10r black	100.00	20.00
8	A2	30r black	125.00	30.00
9	A2	60r black	100.00	22.50
10	A2	90r black	750.00	100.00
11	A2	180r black	3,500.	1,300.
12	A2	300r black	5,250.	1,800.
13	A2	600r black	5,000.	2,000.

Nos. 8, 9 and 10 exist on thick paper and are considerably scarcer.

Grayish or Yellowish Paper

1850, Jan. 1

21	A3	10r black	25.00	35.00
22	A3	30r black	75.00	100.00
23	A3	30r black	10.00	3.00
24	A3	60r black	10.00	2.25
25	A3	90r black	80.00	11.50

26	A3	180r black	80.00	52.50
27	A3	300r black	325.00	60.00
28	A3	600r black	375.00	90.00

No. 22 used is generally found precanceled with a single horizontal line in pen or blue crayon. Value precanceled without gum, $75.

All values except the 90r were reprinted in 1910 on very thick paper.

1854

37	A3	10r blue	12.00	11.50
38	A3	30r blue	32.50	50.00

A4

1861

39	A4	280r red	140.00	100.00
40	A4	430r yellow	225.00	140.00

Nos. 39 and 40 have been reprinted on thick white paper with white gum. They are printed in aniline inks and the colors are brighter than those of the originals.

1866   *Perf. 13½*

42	A3	10r blue	120.00	150.00
43	A3	20r black	900.00	400.00
44	A3	30r black	300.00	150.00
45	A3	30r blue	675.00	750.00
46	A3	60r black	120.00	25.00
47	A3	90r black	575.00	275.00
48	A3	180r black	600.00	275.00
49	A4	280r red	650.00	675.00
50	A3	300r black	750.00	400.00
51	A4	430r yellow	600.00	350.00
52	A3	600r black	575.00	240.00

Fraudulent perforations abound. Purchases should be accompanied by certificates of authenticity.

A 10r black is questioned.

A8a

A9

Emperor Dom
Pedro — A9a

Thick or Thin White Wove Paper

1866, July 1				Perf. 12	
53	A5	10r vermilion		12.00	5.00
54	A6	20r red lilac		20.00	3.00
a.		20r dull violet		65.00	25.00
56	A7	50r blue		30.00	2.50
57	A8	80r slate violet		75.00	5.00
58	A8a	100r blue green		30.00	1.50
a.		100r yellow green		30.00	1.50
59	A9	200r black		100.00	3.00
a.		Half used as 100r on cover			1,500.
60	A9a	500r orange		200.00	35.00
		Nos. 53-60 (7)		467.00	

The 10r and 20r exist imperf. on both white and
bluish paper. Some authorities consider them
proofs.
Nos. 58 and 65 are found in three types.

Bluish Paper

53a	A5	10r	500.00	425.00
54b	A6	20r	160.00	24.00
56a	A7	50r	200.00	25.00
57a	A8	80r	240.00	27.50
58b	A8a	100r	800.00	115.00

1876-77				Rouletted	
61	A5	10r vermilion ('77)		60.00	35.00
62	A6	20r red lilac ('77)		70.00	27.50
63	A7	50r blue ('77)		70.00	10.00
64	A8	80r violet ('77)		175.00	20.00
65	A8a	100r green		40.00	1.25
66	A9	200r black ('77)		80.00	7.50
a.		Half used as 100r on cover			1,000.
67	A9a	500r orange		190.00	40.00
		Nos. 61-67 (7)		685.00	141.25

A10

 A11

A12

A13

A14

A15

A16

A17

A18

A19

A20

1878-79				Rouletted	
68	A10	10r vermilion		12.00	3.00
69	A11	20r violet		15.00	2.50
70	A12	50r blue		24.00	2.00
71	A13	80r lake		27.50	10.00
72	A14	100r green		27.50	1.25
73	A15	200r black		140.00	17.50
a.		Half used as 100r on cover			1,200.
74	A16	260r dk brown		80.00	22.00
75	A18	300r bister		80.00	6.00
a.		One-third used as 100r on cover			10,000.
76	A19	700r red brown		160.00	85.00
77	A20	1000r gray lilac		190.00	37.50
a.		Half used as 500r on cover			10,000.
		Nos. 68-77 (10)		756.00	186.75

1878, Aug. 21			Perf. 12	
78	A17	300r orange & grn	85.00	20.00

Nos. 68-78 exist imperforate.

A21   A22   A23

**Small Heads
Laid Paper**

Perf. 13, 13½ and Compound

1881, July 15					
79	A21	50r blue		120.00	18.00
80	A22	100r olive green		500.00	30.00
81	A23	200r pale red brn		475.00	110.00
a.		Half used as 100r on cover			1,750.

On Nos. 79 and 80 the hair above the ear curves
forward. On Nos. 83 and 88 it is drawn backward.
On the stamps of the 1881 issue the beard is
smaller than in the 1882-85 issues and fills less of
the space between the neck and the frame at the
left.
See No. 88.

A24   A25

A26   A27

Two types each of the 100 and 200 reis.

100 REIS:
Type I - Groundwork formed of diagonal crossed
lines and horizontal lines.
Type II - Groundwork formed of diagonal crossed
lines and vertical lines.

200 REIS:
Type I - Groundwork formed of diagonal and
horizontal lines.
Type II - Groundwork formed of diagonal crossed
lines.

**Larger Heads
Laid Paper**

Perf. 12½ to 14 and Compound

1882-84					
82	A24	10r black		10.00	20.00
83	A25	100r ol grn, type I		35.00	3.00
a.		100r dark green, type I		37.50	3.00
b.		100r dark green, type II		200.00	12.00
84	A26	200r pale red brn, type I		85.00	22.50
a.		Half used as 100r on cover			1,100.
85	A27	200r pale rose, type II		45.00	4.50
a.		Diag. half used as 100r on cover			800.00
		Nos. 82-85 (4)		175.00	50.00

See No. 86.

A28   A29   A30

Three types of A29

Type I - Groundwork of horizontal lines.
Type II - Groundwork of diagonal crossed lines.
Type III - Groundwork solid.

Perf. 13, 13½, 14 and Compound

1884-85					
86	A24	10r orange		2.50	2.00
87	A28	20r slate green		30.00	3.00
a.		20r olive green		30.00	3.00
b.		Half used as 10r on newspaper			3,000.
88	A21	50r bl, head larger		30.00	3.00
90	A29	100r lilac, type I		120.00	2.50
a.		100r lilac, type II		450.00	75.00
b.		100r lilac, type III		325.00	55.00
91	A30	100r lilac		180.00	4.00

A31

A32

Southern
Cross
A33

Crown
A34

Perf. 13, 13½, 14 and Compound

1885				
92	A31	100r lilac	100.00	2.50

Compare design A31 with A35.

1887				
93	A32	50r chalky blue	27.50	4.00
94	A33	300r gray blue	200.00	25.00
95	A34	500r olive	110.00	12.00

A35   A36

Entrance to Bay of Rio de
Janeiro — A37

1888				
96	A35	100r lilac	60.00	1.50
a.		Imperf., pair	120.00	100.00
97	A36	700r violet	65.00	100.00
98	A37	1000r dull blue	250.00	100.00

Issues of the Republic

Southern Cross — A38

Wove Paper, Thin to Thick

*Perf. 12½ to 14, 11 to 11½, and
12½ to 14x11 to 11½, Rough or
Clean-Cut*

Engraved; Typographed (#102)

1890-91					
99	A38	20r gray green		2.00	1.50
a.		20r blue green		2.00	1.50
b.		20r emerald		16.00	6.00
100	A38	50r gray green		5.00	1.50
a.		50r olive green		12.00	6.00
b.		50r yellow green		12.00	6.00
c.		50r dark slate green		7.00	3.50
d.		Horiz. pair, imperf. btwn.			
101	A38	100r lilac rose		360.00	4.50
102	A38	100r red lil, redrawn		25.00	1.50
a.		Tete beche pair		15,000.	16,500.
103	A38	200r purple		8.00	1.50
a.		200r violet		10.00	2.00
b.		200r violet blue		22.50	3.00
104	A38	300r slate vio		150.00	25.00
a.		300r gray		75.00	8.50
b.		300r gray blue		85.00	8.50
c.		300r dark violet		75.00	5.00
105	A38	500r olive bister		17.50	8.00
a.		500r olive gray		17.50	10.00
106	A38	500r slate		17.50	12.00
107	A38	700r chocolate		20.00	22.50
a.		700r fawn		16.00	16.00
108	A38	1000r bister		15.00	3.00
a.		1000r yellow buff		30.00	7.50
		Nos. 99-108 (10)		620.00	81.00

The redrawn 100r may be distinguished by the
absence of the curved lines of shading in the left
side of the central oval. The pearls in the oval are
not well aligned and there is less shading at right
and left of "CORREIO" and "100 REIS."
A 100 reis stamp of type A38 but inscribed
"BRAZIL" instead of "E. U. DO BRAZIL" was not
placed in issue but postmarked copies are known. A
reprint on thick paper was made in 1910.
No. 101 exists imperf., not regularly issued.
For surcharges see Nos. 151-158.

Liberty Head
A39   A40

*Perf. 12½ to 14, 11 to 11½ and
12½ to 14x11 to 11½*

1891, May 1				Typo.	
109	A39	100r blue & red		32.50	1.50
a.		Head inverted		100.00	90.00
b.		Tete beche pair		675.00	750.00
c.		100r ultra & red		32.50	1.50

*Perf. 11, 11½, 13, 13½, 14 and
Compound*

1893, Jan. 18				Litho.	
111	A40	100r rose		75.00	1.75

Sugarloaf Mountain
A41   A41a

Liberty Head
A42   A42a

Hermes — A43

*Perf. 11 to 11½, 12½ to 14 and
12½ to 14x11 to 11½*

1894-97				Unwmk.	
112	A41	10r rose & blue		2.00	.75
113	A41a	10r rose & blue		2.00	.75
114	A41a	20r orange & bl		1.10	.35
115	A41a	50r dk blue & blue		8.00	1.25
116	A42	100r carmine & blk		4.00	.40
a.		Vert. pair, imperf. btwn.		100.00	
118	A42a	200r orange & blk		1.00	.40
a.		Imperf. horiz., pair		80.00	
b.		Vert. pair, imperf. btwn.		80.00	

119 A42a 300r green & blk 15.00 .60
120 A42a 500r blue & blk 25.00 1.75
121 A42a 700r lilac & blk 16.00 2.00
122 A43 1000r green & vio 55.00 1.75
124 A43 2000r blk & gray lil 65.00 15.00
Nos. 112-124 (11) 194.10 25.00

The head of No. 116 exists in five types. See Nos. 140-150A, 159-161, 166-171d.

Newspaper Stamps Surcharged:

a b

c

Surcharged on 1889 Issue of type N1

1898 *Rouletted*

Green Surcharge
125 (b) 700r on 500r yel 6.75 10.00
126 (c) 1000r on 700r yel 32.50 27.50
a. Surcharged "700r" 675.00 775.00
127 (c) 2000r on 1000r yel 27.50 15.00
128 (c) 2000r on 1000r brn 20.00 6.00

Violet Surcharge
129 (a) 100r on 50r brn yel 2.00 45.00
130 (c) 100r on 50r brn yel 65.00 45.00
131 (c) 300r on 200r blk 3.50 1.25
a. Double surcharge 160.00 275.00

The surcharge on No. 130 is handstamped. The impression is blurred and lighter in color than on No. 129. The two surcharges differ most in the shapes and serifs of the figures "1." Counterfeits exist of No. 126a.

Black Surcharge
132 (b) 200r on 100r violet 3.50 1.25
a. Double surcharge 80.00 175.00
b. Inverted surcharge 80.00 175.00
132C (b) 500r on 300r car 5.50 3.00
133 (b) 700r on 500r green 8.00 2.00

Blue Surcharge
134 (b) 500r on 300r car 6.50 5.50

Red Surcharge
135 (c) 1000r on 700r ultra 22.50 15.00
a. Inverted surcharge 200.00 200.00

Surcharged on 1890-94 Issues:

d e

Perf. 11 to 14 and Compound
Black Surcharge
136 N3(e) 20r on 10r blue 3.00 6.00
137 N2(d) 200r on 100r red lilac 20.00 15.00
a. Double surcharge 225.00 250.00
Surcharge on No. 137 comes blue to deep black.

Blue Surcharge
138 N3(e) 50r on 20r green 8.00 10.00

Red Surcharge
139 N3(e) 100r on 50r green 18.00 20.00
a. Blue surcharge 12.50
The surcharge on Nos. 139 and 139a exists double, inverted, one missing, etc.

Types of 1894-97
1899
Perf. 5½-7 and 11-11½x5½-7
140 A41a 10r rose & bl 4.50 12.00
141 A41a 20r orange & bl 7.50 7.50
142 A41a 50r dk bl & lt bl 9.00 30.00
143 A42 100r carmine & blk 16.00 4.50
144 A42a 200r orange & blk 9.00 3.00
145 A42a 300r green & blk 60.00 7.50

Perf. 8½-9½, 8½-9½x11-11½
146 A41a 10r rose & bl 4.50 3.00
147 A41a 20r orange & bl 15.00 3.00
147A A41a 50r dk bl & bl 125.00 30.00
148 A42 100r carmine & blk 30.00 1.50
149 A42a 200r orange & blk 15.00 1.00
150 A42a 300r green & blk 60.00 3.00
150A A43 1000r green & vio 125.00 12.50
Nos. 140-150A are valued with perfs just cut into the design on one or two sides. Expect some irregularity of the perforations.

1899
Issue of 1890-93
Surcharged in Violet or Magenta

1899
50 RÉIS

Perf. 11 to 11½, 12½ to 14 and Compound

1899, June 25
151 A38 50r on 20r gray grn 2.00 3.00
a. Double surcharge 125.00 125.00
152 A38 100r on 50r gray grn 2.00 3.00
b. Double surcharge 100.00 100.00
153 A38 300r on 200r pur 7.50 12.00
a. Double surcharge 250.00 250.00
b. Pair, one without surcharge 425.00
154 A38 500r on 300r ultra,
perf. 13 18.00 7.50
a. 500r on 300r gray lilac 30.00 9.00
b. Pair, one without surcharge 425.00 500.00
c. 500r on 300r slate violet 37.50 15.00
155 A38 700r on 500r ol bis 24.00 6.00
a. Pair, one without surcharge 425.00
156 A38 1000r on 700r choc 17.50 6.00
157 A38 1000r on 700r fawn 17.50 6.00
a. Pair, one without surcharge 425.00 500.00
158 A38 2000r on 1000r yel
buff 60.00 4.50
a. 2000r on 1000r bister 30.00 4.50
b. Pair, one without surcharge 425.00 500.00
Nos. 151-158 (8) 148.50 48.00

Types of 1894-97
Perf. 11, 11½, 13 and Compound
1900
159 A41a 50r green 10.00 .60
160 A42 100r rose 20.00 .30
a. Frame around inner oval 100.00 4.00
161 A42a 200r blue 12.00 .35
Nos. 159-161 (3) 42.00 1.25
Three types exist of No. 161, all of which have the frame around inner oval.

Cabral Arrives at Brazil — A44

Independence Proclaimed A45

"Emancipation of Slaves" — A46   Allegory, Republic of Brazil — A47

1900, Jan. 1 Litho. *Perf. 12½*
162 A44 100r red 5.50 4.50
a. Imperf., pair 400.00 500.00
163 A45 200r green & yel 5.50 4.50
164 A46 500r blue 5.50 4.50
165 A47 700r emerald 5.50 4.50
Nos. 162-165 (4) 22.00 18.00
Discovery of Brazil, 400th anniversary.

Types of 1894-97
Wmk. (97? or 98?)
1905 *Perf. 11, 11½*
166 A41a 10r rose & bl 5.75 4.00
167 A41a 20r orange & bl 10.00 2.00
168 A41a 50r green 20.00 3.00
169 A42 100r rose 27.50 1.00
170 A42a 200r dark blue 16.00 1.00
171 A42a 300r green & blk 55.00 2.00
Nos. 166-171 (6) 134.25 13.00
Positive identification of Wmk. 97 or 98 places stamp in specific watermark groups below.

Wmk. 97
166b A41a 10r rose & blue 30.00 16.00
167b A41a 20r orange & blue 30.00 8.00
168b A41a 50r green 55.00 8.00
169b A42 100r rose 200.00 30.00
170b A42a 200r dark blue 120.00 4.00
171b A42a 300r green & blk 375.00 30.00
171A A43 1000r green & vio 290.00 30.00
Nos. 166b-171A (7) 1,100. 126.00

Wmk. 98
166c A41a 10r rose & blue 40.00 40.00
167c A41a 20r orange & blue 80.00 20.00
168c A41a 50r green 160.00 30.00
169c A42 100r rose 80.00 4.00
170c A42a 200r dark blue 120.00 4.00
171d A42a 300r green & blk 290.00 30.00
Nos. 166c-171d (6) 770.00 128.00

Allegory, Pan-American Congress A48

1906, July 23 Litho. Unwmk.
172 A48 100r carmine rose 30.00 30.00
173 A48 200r blue 75.00 10.00
Third Pan-American Congress.

Aristides Lobo — A48a   Benjamin Constant — A49

Pedro Alvares Cabral — A50   Eduardo Wandenkolk — A51

Manuel Deodoro da Fonseca — A52   Floriano Peixoto — A53

Prudente de Moraes — A54   Manuel Ferraz de Campos Salles — A55

Francisco de Paula Rodrigues Alves — A56   Liberty Head — A57

A58   A59

1906-16 Engr. *Perf. 12*
174 A48a 10r bluish slate .90 .20
175 A49 20r aniline vio .90 .20
176 A50 50r green .90 .20
a. Booklet pane of 6 ('08) 40.00 120.00
177 A51 100r anil rose 2.00 .20
a. Imperf. vert., coil ('16) 4.00 .35
b. Booklet pane of 6 ('08) 80.00 120.00
178 A52 200r blue 2.00 .20
a. Booklet pane of 6 ('08) 60.00 120.00
179 A52 200r ultra ('15) 2.00 .35
a. Imperf. vert., coil ('16) 2.00 .35
180 A53 300r gray blk 3.00 .65
181 A54 400r olive grn 30.00 2.00
182 A54 500r dk violet 6.00 .65
183 A54 600r olive grn ('10) 3.00 1.00
184 A56 700r red brown 6.00 3.00
185 A57 1000r vermilion 32.50 1.00
186 A58 2000r yellow grn 20.00 .65
187 A58 2000r Prus blue ('15) 10.00 1.00
188 A59 5000r carmine rose 8.00 2.00
Nos. 174-188 (15) 127.20 13.30

Allegorical Emblems: Liberty, Peace, Industry, etc. — A60

1908, July 14
189 A60 100r carmine 20.00 1.75
National Exhibition, Rio de Janeiro.

Emblems of Peace Between Brazil and Portugal A61

1908, July 14
190 A61 100r red 8.00 1.25
Opening of Brazilian ports to foreign commerce, cent. Medallions picture King Carlos I of Portugal and Pres. Affonso Penna of Brazil.

Bonifacio, Bolivar, Hidalgo, O'Higgins, San Martin, Washington — A62

1909
191 A62 200r deep blue 7.50 1.00
For surcharge see No. E1.

Nilo Peçanha — A63   Baron of Rio Branco — A64

1910, Nov. 15
192 A63 10,000r brown 8.00 2.00

1913-16
193 A64 1000r deep green 3.75 .35
194 A64 1000r slate ('16) 21.00 .65

Cabo Frio — A65

Perf. 11½
1915, Nov. 13 Litho. Wmk. 99
195 A65 100r dk grn, *yelsh* 4.00 3.50
Founding of the town of Cabo Frio, 300th anniversary.

Bay of Guajara — A66

1916, Jan. 5
196 A66 100r carmine 7.50 4.00
City of Belem, 300th anniversary.

The values of stamps in extremely fine to superb condition are greater than catalogue value.

Revolutionary Flag — A67

1917, Mar. 6
197 A67 100r deep blue   15.00 7.50

Revolution of Pernambuco, Mar. 6, 1817.

Rodrigues Alves — A68

Unwmk.
1917, Aug. 31   Engr.   Perf. 12
198 A68 5000r red brown   60.00 10.00

Liberty Head
A69   A70

Perf. 12½, 13, 13x13½.

		1918-20	**Typo.**	**Unwmk.**
200	A69	10r orange brn	.50	.25
201	A69	20r slate	.50	.25
202	A69	25r ol gray ('20)	.50	.25
203	A69	50r green	27.50	3.25
204	A70	100r rose	1.75	.25
a.		Imperf., pair		
205	A70	300r red orange	19.00	3.25
206	A70	500r dull violet	19.00	3.25
		Nos. 200-206 (7)	68.75	10.75

		1918-20		**Wmk. 100**
207	A69	10r red brown	6.00	1.75
a.		Imperf., pair		
207B	A69	20r slate	1.50	1.50
c.		Imperf., pair		
208	A69	25r ol gray ('20)	.75	.50
209	A69	50r green	1.50	.50
210	A70	100r rose	47.50	.50
a.		Imperf., pair		
211	A70	200r dull blue	6.00	.50
212	A70	300r orange	47.50	3.50
213	A70	500r dull violet	47.50	7.50
214	A70	600r orange	2.50	7.50
		Nos. 207-214 (9)	160.75	23.75

Because of the spacing of this watermark, a few stamps in each sheet may show no watermark.

"Education" — A72

1918		**Engr.**		**Perf. 11½**
215	A72	1000r blue	6.00	.25
216	A72	2000r red brown	27.50	6.00
217	A72	5000r dark violet	7.50	6.00
		Nos. 215-217 (3)	41.00	12.25

Watermark note below No. 257 also applies to Nos. 215-217.

See Nos. 233-234, 283-285, 404, 406, 458, 460. For surcharge see No. C30.

Railroad
A73

"Industry"
A74

"Aviation"
A75

Mercury
A76

"Navigation" — A77

Perf. 13½x13, 13x13½

		1920-22	**Typo.**	**Unwmk.**
218	A73	10r red violet	.75	.40
219	A73	20r olive green	.75	.40
220	A74	25r brown violet	.50	.40
221	A74	50r blue green	.85	.40
222	A74	50r orange brn ('22)	1.40	.40
223	A75	100r rose red	2.75	.40
224	A75	100r orange ('22)	7.50	.40
225	A75	150r violet ('21)	1.40	.40
226	A75	200r blue	4.50	.40
227	A75	200r rose red ('22)	8.00	.40
228	A76	300r olive gray	12.50	.50
229	A76	400r dull blue ('22)	22.50	3.50
230	A76	500r red brown	17.50	.50
		Nos. 218-230 (13)	80.90	8.50

See Nos. 236-257, 265-266, 268-271, 273-274, 276-281, 302-311, 316-322, 326-340, 357-358, 431-434, 436-441, 461-463B, 467-470, 472-474, 488-490, 492-494. For surcharges see Nos. 356-358, 376-377.

Perf. 11, 11½

			Engr.	**Wmk. 100**
231	A77	600r red orange	2.00	.35
232	A77	1000r claret	5.00	.25
a.		Perf. 8½	37.50	7.50
233	A72	2000r dull violet	20.00	.75
234	A72	5000r brown	16.00	9.00
		Nos. 231-234 (4)	43.00	10.35

Nos. 233 and 234 are inscribed "BRASIL CORREIO." Watermark note below No. 257 also applies to Nos. 231-234.
See No. 282.

King Albert of Belgium and President Epitacio Pessoa A78

1920, Sept. 19   Engr.   Perf. 11½x11
235 A78 100r dull red   .65 .65

Visit of the King and Queen of Belgium.

Types of 1920-22 Issue
Perf. 13x13½, 13x12½

		1922-29	**Typo.**	**Wmk. 100**
236	A73	10r red violet	.30	.15
237	A73	20r olive green	.30	.15
238	A73	20r gray violet ('29)	.30	.15
239	A74	25r brown violet	.35	.15
240	A74	50r blue grn	3.25	35.00
241	A74	50r org brn ('23)	.45	.35
a.		Booklet pane of 6		
242	A75	100r rose red	22.50	.40
243	A75	100r orange ('26)	.50	.15
a.		Booklet pane of 6		
244	A75	100r turq grn ('28)	.35	.15
245	A75	150r violet	2.50	.15
246	A75	200r blue	300.00	12.50
247	A75	200r rose red	.40	.15
a.		Booklet pane of 6		
248	A75	200r ol grn ('28)	2.50	3.00
249	A76	300r olive gray	1.90	.25
a.		Booklet pane of 6		
250	A76	300r rose red ('29)	.35	.25
251	A76	400r blue	1.90	.15
252	A76	400r orange ('29)	.75	.60
253	A76	500r red brown	7.50	.50
a.		Booklet pane of 6		
254	A76	500r ultra ('29)	8.50	.15
255	A76	600r brn org ('29)	7.50	3.00
256	A76	700r dull vio ('29)	7.50	1.75
257	A76	1000r turq bl ('29)	9.50	.70
		Nos. 236-257 (22)	379.10	59.80

Because of the spacing of the watermark, a few stamps in each sheet show no watermark.

"Agriculture" — A79

1922		**Unwmk.**		**Perf. 13x13½**
258	A79	40r orange brown	.50	.35
259	A79	80r grnsh blue	.35	2.50

See Nos. 263, 267, 275.

Declaration of Ypiranga — A80

Dom Pedro I and Jose Bonifacio — A81

National Exposition and President Pessoa — A82

Unwmk.

1922, Sept. 7		**Engr.**		**Perf. 14**
260	A80	100r ultra	5.00	.45
261	A81	200r red	6.00	.30
262	A82	300r green	6.00	.30
		Nos. 260-262 (3)	17.00	1.05

Cent. of independence and Natl. Exposition of 1922.

Agriculture Type of 1922
Perf. 13½x12

1923		**Wmk. 100**		**Typo.**
263	A79	40r orange brown	.60	.60

Brazilian Army Entering Bahia — A83

Unwmk.

1923, July 12		**Litho.**		**Perf. 13**
264	A83	200r rose	7.50	5.00

Centenary of the taking of Bahia from the Portuguese.

Types of 1920-22 Issues
Perf. 13x13½

		1924	**Typo.**	**Wmk. 193**
265	A73	10r red violet	5.50	3.75
266	A73	20r olive green	6.00	3.75
267	A79	40r orange brown	4.25	.60
268	A74	50r orange brown	3.75	18.00
269	A75	100r orange	4.25	.35
270	A75	200r rose	6.00	.25
271	A76	400r blue	3.75	3.75
		Nos. 265-271 (7)	33.50	30.45

Arms of Equatorial Confederation, 1824 — A84

Unwmk.

1924, July 2		**Litho.**		**Perf. 11**
272	A84	200r bl, blk, yel, & red	3.00	2.25
a.		Red omitted	275.00	275.00

Centenary of the Equatorial Confederation.

Types of 1920-22 Issues
Perf. 9½ to 13½ and Compound

		1924-28	**Typo.**	**Wmk. 101**
273	A73	10r red violet	.45	.30
274	A73	20r olive gray	.45	.30
275	A79	40r orange brn	.45	.30
276	A74	50r orange brn	.75	.30
277	A75	100r red orange	1.50	.30
278	A75	200r rose	.75	.30
279	A76	300r ol gray ('25)	7.00	1.00
280	A76	400r blue	4.00	.35
281	A76	500r red brown	9.00	.45
			Engr.	
282	A77	600r red orange ('26)	1.00	.30
283	A72	2000r dull vio ('26)	5.00	.30
284	A72	5000r brown ('26)	15.00	.70
285	A72	10,000r rose ('28)	17.50	.90
		Nos. 273-285 (13)	62.85	5.80

Nos. 283-285 are inscribed "BRASIL CORREIO."

Ruy Barbosa — A85

1925   Wmk. 100   Perf. 11½
286 A85 1000r claret   4.25 1.50

1926   Wmk. 101
287 A85 1000r claret   1.75 .35

"Justice" — A86

Scales of Justice and Map of Brazil — A87

Perf. 13½x13

1927, Aug. 11		**Typo.**		**Wmk. 206**
288	A86	100r deep blue	.90	.35
289	A87	200r rose	.80	.35

Founding of the law courses, cent.

Liberty Holding Coffee Leaves — A88

1928, Mar. 5

290	A88	100r blue green	1.00	.60
291	A88	200r carmine	.65	.50
292	A88	300r olive black	5.00	.40
		Nos. 290-292 (3)	6.65	1.50

Introduction of the coffee tree in Brazil, bicent.

Official Stamps of 1919 Surcharged in Red or Black   **700 Réis**

Perf. 11, 11½

1928		**Wmk. 100**		**Engr.**
293	O3	700r on 500r orange	2.25	1.50
a.		Inverted surcharge	175.00	175.00
294	O3	1000r on 100r rose red (Bk)	1.50	.30
295	O3	2000r on 200r dull bl	2.25	.45
296	O3	5000r on 50r green	2.25	.55
297	O3	10,000r on 10r ol grn	11.00	.90
		Nos. 293-297 (5)	19.25	3.70

#293-297 were used for ordinary postage. Stamps in the outer rows of the sheets are often without watermark.

Ruy Barbosa — A89

Perf. 9, 9½x11, 11, and Compound
1929   Wmk. 101
300 A89 5000r blue violet   12.50 .75

See #405, 459. For surcharge see #C29.

Types of 1920-21 Issue
Perf. 13½x12½

		1929	**Typo.**	**Wmk. 218**
302	A75	20r gray violet	.25	.20
303	A75	50r red brown	.25	.20
304	A75	100r turq green	.30	.20
305	A75	200r olive green	12.50	2.25
306	A76	300r rose red	.60	.20
307	A76	400r orange	.70	.25
308	A76	500r ultra	7.00	.45
309	A76	600r brown org	8.50	.60
310	A76	700r dp violet	2.25	.20
311	A76	1000r turq blue	4.00	.20
		Nos. 302-311 (10)	36.35	4.75

Wmk. 218 exists both in vertical alignment and in echelon.

Wmk. in echelon

302a	A75	20r		.25	.35
303a	A75	50r		80.00	27.50
306a	A76	300r		.65	.30
308a	A76	500r		110.00	15.00
311a	A76	1000r		6.50	9.00

Architectural Fantasies
A90   A91

Architectural
Fantasy — A92

Perf. 13x13½

1930, June 20		Wmk. 206	
312 A90	100r turq blue	1.25	.80
313 A91	200r olive gray	2.00	.70
314 A92	300r rose red	3.50	.80
	Nos. 312-314 (3)	6.75	2.30

Fourth Pan-American Congress of Architects and Exposition of Architecture.

Types of 1920-21 Issues

1930		Wmk. 221	Perf. 13x12½	
316 A75	20r gray violet		.20	.15
317 A75	50r red brown		.20	.15
318 A75	100r turq blue		.25	.15
319 A75	200r olive green		3.00	.25
320 A76	300r rose red		.60	.25
321 A76	500r ultra		1.50	.25
322 A76	1000r turq blue		25.00	.70
	Nos. 316-322 (7)		30.75	1.90

Imperforates

Since 1930, imperforate or partly perforated sheets of nearly all commemorative and some definitive issues have become obtainable.

Types of 1920-29 Issue

Perf. 11, 13½x13, 13x12½

1931-34		Typo.	Wmk. 222	
326 A75	10r deep brown		.15	.15
327 A75	20r gray violet		.15	.15
328 A74	25r brn vio ('34)		.15	.60
330 A75	50r blue green		.15	.15
331 A75	50r red brown		.15	.15
332 A75	100r orange		.30	.15
334 A75	200r dp carmine		.45	.15
335 A76	300r olive green		.60	.15
336 A76	400r ultra		.85	.15
337 A76	500r red brown		3.50	.15
338 A76	600r brown org		3.50	.15
339 A76	700r deep violet		3.50	.15
340 A76	1000r turq blue		12.50	.15
	Nos. 326-340 (13)		25.95	
	Set value			1.75

Getulio Vargas
and Joao
Pessoa — A93

Vargas and
Pessoa — A94

Oswaldo Aranha
A95   A96

Antonio Carlos   Pessoa
A97   A98

Vargas — A99

Unwmk.

1931, Apr. 29		Litho.	Perf. 14	
342 A93	10r + 10r lt bl		.15	4.50
343 A93	20r + 20r yel brn		.15	3.25
344 A95	50r + 50r bl grn, red & yel		.15	.15
a.	Red missing at left		.90	.90
345 A93	100r + 50r orange		.30	.30
346 A93	200r + 100r green		.30	.30
347 A94	300r + 150r multi		.30	.30
348 A93	400r + 200r dp rose		1.00	.65
349 A93	500r + 250r dk blue		.70	.55
350 A93	600r + 300r brn vio		.50	6.50
351 A94	700r + 350r multi		.90	.55
352 A96	1000r + 500r brt grn, red & yel		2.00	.25
353 A97	2000r + 1000r gray blk & red		4.00	.55
354 A98	5000r + 2500r blk & red		17.50	4.50
355 A99	10000r + 5000r brt grn & yel		42.50	10.00
	Nos. 342-355 (14)		70.45	32.35

Revolution of Oct. 3, 1930. Prepared as semipostal stamps, Nos. 342-355 were sold as ordinary postage stamps with stated surtax ignored.

1931

Nos. 306, 320 and 250
Surcharged

200 Réis

Wmk. E U BRASIL Multiple (218)

1931, July 20		Perf. 13½x12½	
356 A76	200r on 300r rose red	.90	.90
a.	Wmk. in echelon	17.50	17.50
b.	Inverted surcharge	40.00	

Perf. 13x12½
Wmk. 221

357 A76	200r on 300r rose red	.30	.20
a.	Inverted surcharge	45.00	45.00

Perf. 13½x12½
Wmk. 100

358 A76	200r on 300r rose red	60.00	60.00

Map of South America Showing Meridian
of Tordesillas
A100

Joao
Ramalho
and Tibiriça
A101

Martim
Affonso de
Souza
A102

King John III
of Portugal
A103

Disembarkation of M. A. de Souza at Sao
Vicente — A104

Wmk. 222

1932, June 3		Typo.	Perf. 13	
359 A100	20r dk violet		.20	.20
360 A101	100r black		.35	.35
361 A102	200r purple		1.00	.25

362 A103	600r red brown	1.65	1.25

Engr.
Wmk. 101
Perf. 9½, 11, 9½x11

363 A104	700r ultra	2.50	1.75
	Nos. 359-363 (5)	5.70	3.80

1st colonization of Brazil at Sao Vicente, in 1532, under the hereditary captaincy of Martim Affonso de Souza.

Revolutionary Issue

Map of   Soldier and
Brazil — A105   Flag — A106

Allegory: Freedom,   Soldier's
Justice,   Head — A108
Equality — A107

"LEX" and
Sword
A109

Symbolical
of Law and
Order
A110

Symbolical of
Justice
A111

Perf. 11½

1932, Sept. 13		Litho.	Unwmk.	
364 A105	100r brown org		.40	2.00
365 A106	200r dk carmine		.35	.70
366 A107	300r gray green		2.00	3.50
367 A108	400r dark blue		7.25	7.25
368 A105	500r black brown		7.25	7.25
369 A103	600r red		7.25	7.25
370 A106	700r violet		3.50	7.25
371 A108	1000r orange		1.75	7.25
372 A109	2000r dark brown		14.00	20.00
373 A110	5000r yellow grn		17.50	32.50
374 A111	10000r plum		20.00	37.50
	Nos. 364-374 (11)		81.25	132.45

Issued by the revolutionary forces in the state of Sao Paulo during the revolt of September, 1932. Subsequenty the stamps were recognized by the Federal Government and placed in general use. Excellent counterfeits of Nos. 373 and 374 exist. Counterfeit cancellations abound.

City of Vassouras and Illuminated
Memorial — A112

Wmk. 222

1933, Jan. 15		Typo.	Perf. 12	
375 A112	200r rose red		1.00	.90

City of Vassouras founding, cent.

Nos. 306, 320 Surcharged

200 RÉIS

Perf. 13½x12½

1933, July 28			Wmk. 218	
376 A76	200r on 300r rose red		.60	.60
a.	Wmk. 218 in echelon (No. 306a)		12.50	12.50
b.	Wmk. 100 (No. 250)		87.50	87.50

Perf. 13x12½
Wmk. 221

377 A76	200r on 300r rose red	.45	.45
a.	Inverted surcharge	35.00	
b.	Double surcharge	35.00	

Religious Symbols and
Inscriptions — A113

Wmk. 222

1933, Sept. 3		Typo.	Perf. 13	
378 A113	200r dark red		.90	.75

1st Natl. Eucharistic Congress in Brazil.

"Flag of the
Race"
A114

1933, Aug. 18				
379 A114	200r deep red		.90	.75

The raising of the "Flag of the Race" and the 441st anniv. of the sailing of Columbus from Palos, Spain, Aug. 3, 1492.

Republic Figure, Flags of
Brazil and
Argentina — A115

Perf. 11½

1933, Oct. 7		Wmk. 101	Engr.	
380 A115	200r blue		.35	.25

Thick Laid Paper
Perf. 11, 11½
Wmk. 236

381 A115	400r green	.90	.80
382 A115	600r brt rose	3.00	3.25
383 A115	1000r lt violet	4.50	3.75
	Nos. 380-383 (4)	8.75	8.05

Visit of President Justo of the Argentina to Brazil, Oct. 2-7, 1933.

Allegory: "Faith   Allegory of
and   Flight — A117
Energy" — A116

1933		Typo.	Wmk. 222	
384 A116	200r dark red		.25	.15
385 A116	200r dark violet		.30	.15
	Set value			.20

See Nos. 435, 471 and 491.

Wmk. 236

1934, Apr. 15		Engr.	Perf. 12	
386 A117	200r blue		.50	.50

1st Natl. Aviation Congress at Sao Paulo.

A118

Wmk. 222

1934, May 12   Typo.   *Perf. 11*
387 A118 200r dark olive .30 .30
388 A118 400r carmine 1.50 1.50
389 A118 700r ultra 1.50 .90
390 A118 1000r orange 3.75 .60
Nos. 387-390 (4) 7.05 3.30

7th Intl. Fair at Rio de Janeiro.

Christ of Corcovado — A119

1934, Oct. 20
392 A119 300r dark red 1.90 1.90
a. Tete beche pair 6.00 7.25
393 A119 700r ultra 8.00 5.00
a. Tete beche pair 19.00 22.50

Visit of Eugenio Cardinal Pacelli, later Pope Pius XII, to Brazil.
The three printings of Nos. 392-393, distinguishable by shades, sell for different prices.

José de Anchieta A120

Thick Laid Paper
1934, Nov. 8 Wmk. 236 *Perf. 11, 12*
394 A120 200r yellow brown .55 .15
395 A120 300r violet .45 .25
396 A120 700r blue 1.75 1.40
397 A120 1000r lt green 3.50 .55
Nos. 394-397 (4) 6.25 2.35

Jose de Anchieta, S.J. (1534-1597), Portuguese missionary and "father of Brazilian literature."

"Brazil" and "Uruguay" A121 A122

Wmk. 222
1935, Jan. 8   Typo.   *Perf. 11*
398 A121 200r orange .65 .40
399 A122 300r yellow .80 .50
400 A122 700r ultra 3.25 3.25
401 A121 1000r dk violet 8.00 4.00
Nos. 398-401 (4) 12.70 8.15

Visit of President Terra of Uruguay.

View of Town of Igarassu A123

1935, July 1
402 A123 200r maroon & brn .85 .45
403 A123 300r vio & olive brn .85 .35

Captaincy of Pernambuco founding, 400th anniv.

Types of 1918-29
Thick Laid Paper
Perf. 9½, 11, 12, 12x11
1934-36   Engr.   Wmk. 236
404 A72 2000r violet 3.75 .40
405 A89 5000r blue vio ('36) 11.00 1.50
406 A72 10000r claret ('36) 8.75 .75
Nos. 404-406 (3) 23.50 1.65

No. 404 is inscribed "BRASIL CORREIO."

Revolutionist — A124

Bento Gonçalves da Silva — A125

Duke of Caxias A126

1935, Sept. 20   *Perf. 11, 12*
407 A124 200r black .55 .45
408 A124 300r rose lake .55 .35
409 A125 700r dull blue 2.25 2.25
410 A126 1000r light violet 2.50 1.40
Nos. 407-410 (4) 5.85 4.45

Centenary of the "Ragged" Revolution.

Federal District Coat of Arms A127

Wmk. 222
1935, Oct. 19   Typo.   *Perf. 11*
411 A127 200r blue 2.25 2.25

8th Intl. Sample Fair held at Rio de Janeiro.

Coutinho's Ship A128

Arms of Fernandes Coutinho — A129

1935, Oct. 25
412 A128 300r maroon 2.25 1.00
413 A129 700r turq blue 3.25 2.00

400th anniversary of the establishment of the first Portuguese colony at Espirito Santo by Vasco Fernandes Coutinho.

Gavea, Rock near Rio de Janeiro A130

1935, Oct. 12 Wmk. 245   *Perf. 11*
414 A130 300r brown & vio 1.75 1.50
415 A130 300r blk & turq bl 1.75 1.50
416 A130 300r Prus bl & ultra 1.75 1.50
417 A130 300r crimson & blk 1.75 1.50
Nos. 414-417 (4) 7.00 6.00

"Child's Day," Oct. 12.

Viscount of Cairu — A131

Perf. 11, 12x11
1936, Jan. 20 Engr.   Wmk. 236
418 A131 1200r violet 6.00 2.75

Jose da Silva Lisboa, Viscount of Cairu (1756-1835).

View of Cametá A132

1936, Feb. 26   *Perf. 11, 12*
419 A132 200r brown orange 1.25 1.00
420 A132 300r green 1.25 .80

300th anniversary of the founding of the city of Cameta, Dec. 24, 1635.

Coining Press A133

Thick Laid Paper
1936, Mar. 24   *Perf. 11*
421 A133 300r pur brn, cr 1.25 .90

1st Numismatic Cong. at Sao Paulo, Mar., 1936.

Carlos Gomes A134

"Il Guarany" A135

Thick Laid Paper
1936, July 11   *Perf. 11, 11x12*
422 A134 300r dull rose .50 .35
423 A134 300r black brown .50 .35
424 A135 700r ocher 2.00 .90
425 A135 700r blue 1.75 .90
Nos. 422-425 (4) 4.75 2.50

100th anniversary of the birth of Antonio Carlos Gomes, who composed the opera "Il Guarany."

Scales of Justice — A136

Wmk. 222
1936, July 4   Typo.   *Perf. 11*
426 A136 300r rose 1.25 .45

First National Judicial Congress.

Federal District Coat of Arms A137

1936, Nov. 13   Typo.   Wmk. 249
427 A137 200r rose red .75 .45

Ninth International Sample Fair held at Rio de Janeiro.

Eucharistic Congress Seal — A138

1936, Dec. 17 Wmk. 245   *Perf. 11½*
428 A138 300r grn, yel, bl & blk .70 .45

2nd Natl. Eucharistic Congress in Brazil.

Botafogo Bay — A139

Thick Laid Paper
Wmk. 236
1937, Jan. 2   Engr.   *Perf. 11*
429 A139 700r blue .75 .45
430 A139 700r black .75 .45

Birth cent. of Francisco Pereira Passos, engineer who planned the modern city of Rio de Janeiro.

Types of 1920-21, 1933
Perf. 11, 11½ and Compound
1936-37   Typo.   Wmk. 249
431 A75 10r deep brown .15 .15
432 A75 20r dull violet .15 .15
433 A75 50r blue green .15 .15
434 A75 100r orange .25 .15
435 A116 200r dk violet .45 .15
436 A76 300r olive green .25 .15
437 A76 400r ultra .45 .15
438 A76 500r lt brown .70 .15
439 A76 600r brn org ('37) 1.50 .15
440 A76 700r deep violet 2.75 .15
441 A76 1000r turq blue 3.00 .15
Nos. 431-441 (11) 9.80
Set value 1.00

Massed Flags and Star of Esperanto A140

1937, Jan. 19
442 A140 300r green 1.00 .50

Ninth Brazilian Esperanto Congress.

Bay of Rio de Janeiro A141

1937, June 9 Unwmk.   *Perf. 12½*
443 A141 300r orange red & blk .50 .50
444 A141 700r blue & dk brn 1.25 .50

2nd South American Radio Communication Conf. held in Rio, June 7-19.

Globe — A142

1937, Sept. 4 Wmk. 249 *Perf. 11, 12*
445 A142 300r green .85 .50

50th anniversary of Esperanto.

Monroe Palace, Rio de Janeiro — A143

Botanical Garden, Rio de Janeiro — A144

1937, Sept. 30   Unwmk.   Perf. 12½
446	A143	200r lt brn & bl	.50	.35
447	A144	300r org & ol grn	.50	.35
448	A143	2000r grn & cerise	3.75	5.50
449	A144	10000r lake & indigo	32.50	27.50
		Nos. 446-449 (4)	37.25	33.70

Brig. Gen. Jose da Silva Paes — A145

Eagle and Shield — A146

1937, Oct. 11   Wmk. 249   Perf. 11½
450 A145 300r blue   .75 .30

Bicentenary of Rio Grande do Sul.

1937, Dec. 2   Typo.   Perf. 11
451 A146 400r dark blue   .75 .30

150th anniversary of the US Constitution.

Bags of Brazilian Coffee — A147

Frame Engraved, Center Typographed
1938, Jan. 17   Unwmk.   Perf. 12½
452 A147 1200r multicolored   3.00 .40

Arms of Olinda A148

Perf. 11, 11x11½
1938, Jan. 24   Engr.   Wmk. 249
453 A148 400r violet   .50 .25

4th cent. of the founding of the city of Olinda.

Independence Memorial, Ypiranga — A149

1938, Jan. 24   Typo.   Perf. 11
454 A149 400r brown olive   .60 .25

Proclamation of Brazil's independence by Dom Pedro, Sept. 7, 1822.

Iguaçu Falls — A150

Perf. 12½
1938, Jan. 10   Unwmk.   Engr.
455	A150	1000r sepia & yel brn	1.50	.75
456	A150	5000r ol blk & grn	17.00	7.50

Couto de Magalhaes — A151

Perf. 11, 11x11½
1938, Mar. 17   Wmk. 249
457 A151 400r dull green   .50 .25

General Couto de Magalhaes (1837-1898), statesman, soldier, explorer, writer, developer.

Types of 1918-38
Perf. 11, 12x11, 12x11½, 12
1938   Engr.   Wmk. 249
458	A72	2000r blue violet	6.50	.15
459	A89	5000r violet blue	24.00	.50
a.		5000r deep blue	20.00	.50
460	A72	10000r rose lake	27.50	1.00
		Nos. 458-460 (3)	58.00	1.65

No. 458 is inscribed "BRASIL CORREIO."

Types of 1920-22
1938   Wmk. 245   Typo.   Perf. 11
461	A75	50r blue green	.50	.75
462	A75	100r orange	.50	.75
463	A75	300r olive green	.50	.15
463A	A76	400r ultra	100.00	35.00
463B	A76	500r red brown	.50	10.00
		Nos. 461-463B (5)	102.00	46.65

National Archives Building A152

1938, May 20   Wmk. 249
464 A152 400r brown   .40 .25

Centenary of National Archives.

Souvenir Sheets

Sir Rowland Hill A153

1938, Oct. 22   Imperf.
465 A153 Sheet of 10   12.50 12.50
a.   400r dull green, single stamp   .75 .75

Brazilian Intl. Philatelic Exposition (Brapex). Issued in sheets measuring 106x118mm. A few perforated sheets exist.

President Vargas A154

1938, Nov. 10   Perf. 11
Without Gum
466 A154 Sheet of 10   5.00 8.50
a.   400r slate blue, single stamp   .40 .40

Constitution of Brazil, set up by President Vargas, Nov. 10, 1937. Size: 113x135½mm.

Types of 1920-33
1939   Typo.   Wmk. 256   Perf. 11
467	A75	10r red brown	.30	.25
468	A75	20r dull violet	.30	.15
469	A75	50r blue green	.30	.15
470	A75	100r yellow org	.45	.15
471	A116	200r dk violet	.55	.15

472	A76	400r ultra	1.00	.15
473	A76	600r dull orange	1.00	.15
474	A76	1000r turq blue	7.00	.15
		Nos. 467-474 (8)	10.90	
		Set value		.75

View of Rio de Janeiro — A155

View of Santos — A156

1939, June 14   Engr.   Wmk. 249
475 A155 1200r dull violet   1.25 .25

1939, Aug. 23
476 A156 400r dull blue   .40 .20

Centenary of founding of Santos.

Chalice Vine and Blossoms — A157

Eucharistic Congress Seal — A158

1939, Aug. 23
477 A157 400r green   1.00 .25

1st South American Botanical Congress held in January, 1938.

1939, Sept. 3
478 A158 400r rose red   .40 .20

Third National Eucharistic Congress.

Duke of Caxias, Army Patron — A159

1939, Sept. 12   Photo.   Rouletted
479 A159 400r deep ultra   .40 .25

Issued for Soldiers' Day.

A159a

A159b   A159d

A159c

Designs: 400r, George Washington. 800r, Emperor Pedro II. 1200r, Grover Cleveland. 1600r, Statue of Friendship, given by US.

1939, Oct. 7   Unwmk.   Engr.   Perf. 12
480	A159a	400r yellow orange	.40	.25
481	A159b	800r dark green	.25	.15
482	A159c	1200r rose car	.50	.15
483	A159d	1600r dark blue	.50	.25
		Nos. 480-483 (4)	1.65	.80

New York World's Fair.

Benjamin Constant A160

Fonseca on Horseback A161

Manuel Deodoro da Fonseca and President Vargas — A162

Wmk. 249
1939, Nov. 15   Photo.   Rouletted
484 A160 400r deep green   .30 .20
485 A162 1200r chocolate   .75 .30

Engr.   Perf. 11
486 A161 800r gray black   .45 .30
| | | Nos. 484-486 (3) | 1.50 | .80 |

50th anniv. of the Proclamation of the Republic.

President Roosevelt, President Vargas and Map of the Americas A163

1940, Apr. 14
487 A163 400r slate blue   .70 .40

Pan American Union, 50th anniversary.

Types of 1920-33
1940-41   Typo.   Wmk. 264   Perf. 11
488	A75	10r red brown	.15	.25
489	A75	20r dull violet	.25	.25
489A	A75	50r blue grn ('41)	.85	1.25
490	A75	100r yellow org	1.00	.15
491	A116	200r violet	.75	.15
492	A76	400r ultra	4.50	.15
493	A76	600r dull orange	4.50	.15
494	A76	1000r turq blue	11.00	.15
		Nos. 488-494 (8)	23.00	
		Set value		2.00

Map of Brazil — A164

1940, Sept. 7   Engr.
495 A164 400r carmine   .40 .20
a.   Unwmkd.   50.00 30.00

9th Brazilian Congress of Geography held at Florianopolis.

Victoria Regia Water Lily — A165

President Vargas — A166

Relief Map of Brazil — A167

1940, Oct. 30   **Wmk. 249**   *Perf. 11*
Without Gum

496	A165	1000r dull violet	.85	.85
a.		Sheet of 10	8.50	25.00
497	A166	5000r red	6.75	5.00
a.		Sheet of 10	72.50	110.00
498	A167	10,000r slate blue	7.50	2.50
a.		Sheet of 10	100.00	110.00
		Nos. 496-498 (3)	15.10	8.35

New York World's Fair.
All three sheets exist unwatermarked and also with papermaker's watermark of large globe and "AMERICA BANK" in sheet. A few imperforate sheets also exist.

Joaquim Machado de Assis — A168

Pioneers and Buildings of Porto Alegre — A169

1940, Nov. 1
499 A168   400r black   .50   .20
Birth centenary of Joaquim Maria Machado de Assis, poet and novelist.

1940, Nov. 2   **Wmk. 264**
500 A169   400r green   .40   .15
Colonization of Porto Alegre, bicent.

Proclamation of King John IV of Portugal A173

1940, Dec. 1   **Wmk. 249**
501 A173   1200r blue black   1.00   .25
800th anniv. of Portuguese independence and 300th anniv. of the restoration of the monarchy.
No. 501 was also printed on paper with papermaker's watermark of large globe and "AMERICA BANK." Unwatermarked copies are from these sheets.

Brazilian Flags and Head of Liberty — A175

Wmk. 256
1940, Dec. 18   **Engr.**   *Perf. 11*
502   A175   400r dull violet   .50   .20
b.   Unwmkd.   40.00   40.00

Wmk. 245
502A A175   400r dull violet   40.00   40.00
10th anniv. of the inauguration of President Vargas.

Calendar Sheet and Inscription "Day of the Fifth General Census of Brazil" — A176

Wmk. 256
1941, Jan. 14   **Typo.**   *Perf. 11*
503 A176   400r blue & red   .40   .20

Wmk. 245
504 A176   400r blue & red   3.00   .80
Fifth general census of Brazil.

King Alfonso Henriques A177

Father Antonio Vieira A178

Salvador Corrêia de Sa e Benevides — A179

President Carmona of Portugal and President Vargas A180

Wmk. 264
1940-41   **Photo.**   *Rouletted*
504A	A177	200r pink	.15	.15
505	A178	400r ultra	.20	.15
506	A179	800r brt violet	.25	.15
506A	A180	5400r slate grn	1.65	.70

Wmk. 249
507	A177	200r pink	5.25	3.25
507A	A178	400r ultra	25.00	8.50
508	A180	5400r slate grn	2.50	1.25
		Nos. 504A-508 (7)	35.00	14.15

Portuguese Independence, 800th anniv.
For surcharge and overprint see Nos. C45, C47.

Jose de Anchieta A181

Amador Bueno A182

Wmk. 264
1941, Aug. 1   **Engr.**   *Perf. 11*
509 A181   1000r gray vio   1.00   .50
Society of Jesus, 400th anniversary.

1941, Oct. 20   *Perf. 11½*
510 A182   400r black   .50   .30
300th anniv. of the acclamation of Amador Bueno (1572-1648) as king of Sao Paulo.

Air Force Emblem A183

1941, Oct. 20   *Perf. 11*
511 A183   5400r slate grn   3.00   2.00
Issued in connection with Aviation Week, as propaganda for the Brazilian Air Force.

Petroleum — A184   Agriculture — A185

Steel Industry — A186   Commerce — A187

Marshal Peixoto — A188   Count of Porto Alegre — A189

Admiral J. A. C. Maurity — A190   "Armed Forces" — A191

Vargas — A192

1941-42   **Wmk. 264**   **Typo.**   *Perf. 11*
512	A184	10r yellow brn	.20	.20
513	A184	20r olive grn	.15	.15
514	A184	50r olive bis	.15	.15
515	A184	100r blue grn	.20	.15
516	A185	200r brown org	.45	.15
517	A185	300r lilac rose	.25	.15
518	A185	400r grnsh blue	.65	.15
519	A185	500r salmon	.30	.15
520	A186	600r violet	.65	.15
521	A186	700r brt rose	.30	.15
522	A186	1000r gray	1.75	.15
523	A186	1200r dl blue	3.00	.15
524	A187	2000r gray vio	2.50	.15

Engr.
525	A188	5000r blue	5.50	.15
526	A189	10,000r rose red	7.00	.20
527	A190	20,000r dp brown	7.00	.35
528	A191	50,000r red ('42)	27.50	21.00
529	A192	100,000r blue ('42)	.60	9.00
		Nos. 512-529 (18)	58.15	32.70

Nos. 512 to 527 and later issues come on thick or thin paper. The stamps on both papers also exist with three vertical green lines printed on the back, a control mark.
See Nos. 541-587, 592-593, 656-670.

Bernardino de Campos A193

Prudente de Morais A194

1942, May 25
533 A193   1000r red   1.25   .40
534 A194   1200r blue   3.00   .25
100th anniversary of the birth of Bernardino de Campos and Prudente de Morais, lawyers and statesmen of Brazil.

Head of Indo-Brazilian Bull — A195

1942, May 1   **Wmk. 264**   *Perf. 11½*
535 A195   200r blue   .45   .25
536 A195   400r orange brn   .45   .25
a.   Wmk. 267   45.00   45.00
2nd Agriculture and Livestock Show of Central Brazil held at Uberaba.

Outline of Brazil and Torch of Knowledge A196

Map of Brazil Showing Goiania A197

Wmk. 264
1942, July 5   **Typo.**   *Perf. 11*
537 A196   400r orange brn   .30   .25
8th Brazilian Congress of Education.

1942, July 5
538 A197   400r lt violet   .40   .30
Founding of Goiania city.

Seal of Congress — A198

1942, Sept. 20   **Wmk. 264**
539 A198   400r olive bister   .25   .20
a.   Wmk. 267   25.00   12.50
4th Natl. Eucharistic Cong. at Sao Paulo.

Types of 1941-42
1942-47   **Wmk. 245**   *Perf. 11*
541	A184	20r olive green	.15	.40
542	A184	50r olive bister	.15	.15
543	A184	100r blue grn	.40	.40
544	A185	200r brown org	.65	.50
545	A185	400r grnsh blue	.40	.15
546	A186	600r lt violet	3.00	.15
547	A186	700r brt rose	.35	.80
548	A186	1200r dl blue	1.25	.15
549	A187	2000r gray vio ('47)	9.00	9.00

Engr.
550	A188	5000r blue	10.00	.40
551	A189	10,000r rose red	6.00	1.50
552	A190	20,000r dp brn ('47)	4.50	.45
553	A192	100,000r blue	3.50	8.00
		Nos. 541-553 (13)	39.35	22.75

Types of 1941-42
1941-47   **Typo.**   **Wmk. 268**   *Perf. 11*
554	A184	20r olive grn	.20	.15
555	A184	50r ol bis ('47)	.55	.55
556	A184	100r bl grn ('43)	.20	.15
557	A185	200r brn org ('43)	.20	.15
558	A185	300r lilac rose ('43)	.15	.15
559	A185	400r grnsh bl ('42)	.30	.15
560	A185	500r salmon ('43)	.20	.15
561	A186	600r violet	.60	.15
562	A186	700r brt rose ('45)	.35	1.75
563	A186	1000r gray	.65	.15
564	A186	1200r dp blue ('44)	.85	.15
565	A187	2000r gray vio ('43)	1.25	.15

Engr.
566	A188	5000r blue ('43)	4.25	.15
567	A189	10,000r rose red ('43)	8.50	.40
568	A190	20,000r dp brn ('42)	19.00	.45
569	A191	50,000r red ('42)	21.00	3.00
a.		50,000r dark brown red ('47)	15.00	8.50
570	A192	100,000r blue	.55	.55
		Nos. 554-570 (17)	60.55	8.35

Types of 1941-42

1942-47 Typo. Wmk. 267

573	A184	20r ol grn ('43)	.15 .15
574	A184	50r ol bis ('43)	.15 .15
575	A184	100r bl grn ('43)	.20 .15
576	A185	200r brn org ('43)	.25 .25
577	A185	400r grnsh blue	.25 .15
578	A185	500r sal ('43)	70.00 10.00
579	A186	600r violet ('43)	.45 .30
580	A186	700r brt rose ('47)	.35 3.50
581	A186	1000r gray ('44)	2.10 .15
582	A186	1200r dl bl	2.50 .15
583	A187	2000r gray vio	2.50 .15

Engr.

584	A188	5000r blue	4.25 .15
585	A189	10,000r rose red ('44)	7.00 .60
586	A190	20,000r dp brn ('45)	8.50 .15
587	A191	50,000r red ('43)	25.00 5.25
		Nos. 573-587 (15)	123.65 21.55

1942 Typo. Wmk. 249

592	A184	100r bl grn	4.00 2.50
593	A186	600r violet	4.00 .80

Map Showing Amazon River — A199

1943, Mar. 19 Wmk. 267 Perf. 11
607 A199 40c orange brown .35 .35
Discovery of the Amazon River, 400th anniv.

Reproduction of Brazil Stamp of 1866—A200

1943, Mar. 28 Wmk. 267
608 A200 40c violet .50 .25
 a. Wmk. 268 650.00
Centenary of city of Petropolis.

Adaptation of 1843 "Bull's-eye" A201

1943, Aug. 1 Engr. Imperf.
609 A201 30c black .45 .25
610 A201 60c black .55 .25
611 A201 90c black .45 .25
 Nos. 609-611 (3) 1.45 .75
Cent. of the 1st postage stamp of Brazil. The 30c and 90c exist unwatermarked; values $25 and $65.

Souvenir Sheet

A202

Wmk. 281 Horizontally or Vertically
1943 Engr. Imperf.
Without Gum
612 A202 Sheet of 3 7.50 6.75
 a. 30c black 1.90 1.90
 b. 60c black 1.90 1.90
 c. 90c black 1.90 1.90

Ubaldino do Amaral A203   "Justice" A204

Perf. 11, 12
1943, Aug. 27 Typo. Wmk. 264
613 A203 40c dull slate green .40 .20
 a. Wmk. 267 20.00 15.00
Birth centenary of Ubaldino do Amaral, banker and statesman.

1943, Aug. 30 Wmk. 267
614 A204 2cr bright rose .70 .40
Centenary of Institute of Brazilian Lawyers.

Indo-Brazilian Bull — A205

1943, Aug. 30 Engr.
615 A205 40c dk red brn .70 .40
9th Livestock Show at Bahia.

José Barbosa Rodrigues A206

1943, Nov. 13 Typo.
616 A206 40c bluish grn .40 .20
Birth cent. of Jose Barbosa Rodrigues, botanist.

Charity Hospital, Santos A207

1943, Nov. 7 Engr.
617 A207 1cr blue .40 .30
400th anniv. of Charity Hospital, Santos.

Pedro Americo de Figueirido e Melo (1843-1905), Artist-hero and Statesman — A208

1943, Dec. 16 Typo. Perf. 11
618 A208 40c brown orange .20 .20

Gen. A. E. Gomes Carneiro A209

1944, Feb. 9 Engr.
619 A209 1.20cr rose .50 .35
50th anniversary of the Lapa siege.

Statue of Baron of Rio Branco — A210

1944, May 13 Typo.
620 A210 1cr blue .40 .25
Statue of the Baron of Rio Branco unveiling.

Duke of Caxias A211

1944, May 13 Unwmk. Perf. 12
Granite Paper
621 A211 1.20cr bl grn & pale org .50 .30
Centenary of pacification of Sao Paulo and Minas Gerais in an independence movement in 1842.

YMCA Seal — A212

1944, June 7 Litho. Perf. 11
Granite Paper
622 A212 40c dp bl, car & yel .30 .20
Centenary of Young Men's Christian Assn.

Chamber of Commerce Rio Grande — A213

Wmk. 268
1944, Sept. 25 Engr. Perf. 12
623 A213 40c lt yellow brn .30 .25
Centenary of the Chamber of Commerce of Rio Grande.

Martim F. R. de Andrada A214

1945, Jan. 30 Perf. 11
624 A214 40c blue .30 .25
Ccentenary of the death of Martim F. R. de Andrada, statesman.

Meeting of Duke of Caxias and David Canabarro A215

1945, Mar. 19 Photo.
625 A215 40c ultra .30 .20
Pacification of Rio Grande do Sul, cent.

Globe and "Esperanto" A216

1945, Apr. 16
626 A216 40c lt blue grn .50 .25
10th Esperanto Congress, Rio, Apr. 14-22.

Baron of Rio Branco's Bookplate — A217

1945, Apr. 20 Wmk. 268 Perf. 11
627 A217 40c violet .50 .25
Cent. of the birth of Jose Maria da Silva Paranhos, Baron of Rio Branco.

Tranquility — A218   Glory — A219

Victory A220

Peace A221

Cooperation A222

Rouletted 7
1945, May 8 Engr. Wmk. 268
628 A218 20c dk rose vio .15 .15
629 A219 40c dk carmine .15 .15
630 A220 1cr dull orange .35 .30
631 A221 2cr steel blue .85 .45
632 A222 5cr green 1.65 .55
 Nos. 628-632 (5) 3.15 1.60
Victory of the Allied Nations in Europe. Nos. 628-632 exist on thin card, imperf. and unwatermarked.

Francisco Manoel da Silva (1795-1865), Composer (in 1831) of the National Anthem — A223

Wmk. 245
1945, May 30   Typo.   Perf. 12
633 A223 40c brt rose   .45   .30
  a.   Wmk. 268   6.75 6.75

Bahia Institute of Geography and History
A224

1945, May 30   Wmk. 268   Perf. 11
634 A224 40c lt ultra   .25   .20
  50th anniv. of the founding of the Institute of Geography and History at Bahia.

Emblems of 5th Army and B.E.F.
A225   A226

US Flag and Shoulder Patches A227

Brazilian Flag and Shoulder Patches A228

Victory Symbol and Shoulder Patches — A229

1945, July 18   Litho.
635 A225 20c multicolored   .15   .15
636 A226 40c multicolored   .15   .15
637 A227 1cr multicolored   .70   .40
638 A228 2cr multicolored   1.00   .60
639 A229 5cr multicolored   3.00   .70
       Nos. 635-639 (5)   5.00 2.00
  Honoring the Brazilian Expeditionary Force and the US 5th Army Battle against the Axis in Italy.

Radio Tower and Map — A230

1945, Sept. 3   Engr.
640 A230 1.20cr gray   .45   .25
  Third Inter-American Conference on Radio Communications.
  No. 640 was reproduced on a souvenir card with blue background and inscriptions. Size: 145x161mm.

A 40c lilac stamp, picturing the International Bridge between Argentina and Brazil and portraits of Presidents Justo and Vargas, was prepared late in 1945. It was not issued, but later was sold, without postal value, to collectors. Value, 15 cents.

Admiral Luiz Felipe Saldanha da Gama (1846-1895) A231

1946, Apr. 7
641 A231 40c gray black   .25   .25

Princess Isabel d'Orleans-Braganca Birth Cent. — A232

1946, July 29   Unwmk.
642 A232 40c black   .25   .25

Post Horn, V and Envelope — A233

Post Office, Rio de Janeiro — A234

Bay of Rio de Janeiro and Plane A235

Wmk. 268
1946, Sept. 2   Litho.   Perf. 11
643 A233 40c blk & pale org   .15   .15

Perf. 12½
Engr.   Unwmk.
Center in Ultramarine
644 A234 2cr slate   .50   .15
645 A234 5cr orange brn   2.50   .85
646 A234 10cr dk violet   2.75   .50

Center in Brown Orange
647 A235 1.30cr dk green   .30   .35
648 A235 1.70cr car rose   .30   .35
649 A235 2.20cr dp ultra   .50   .50
       Nos. 643-649 (7)   7.00 2.85
  5th Postal Union Congress of the Americas and Spain.
  No. 643 was reproduced on a souvenir card. Size: 188x239mm. Sold for 10cr.

Liberty — A236

Perf. 11x11½
1946, Sept. 18   Wmk. 268
650 A236 40c blk & gray   .25   .15
  a.   Unwmkd.   150.00
  Adoption of the Constitution of 1946.

Columbus Lighthouse, Dominican Republic A237

1946, Sept. 14   Litho.   Perf. 11
651 A237 5cr Prus grn   4.00 1.50

Orchid — A238   Gen. A. E. Gomes Carneiro — A239

1946, Nov. 8   Wmk. 268
652 A238 40c ultra, red & yel   .40   .30
  a.   Unwmkd.   55.00
  4th National Exhibition of Orchids, Rio de Janeiro, November, 1946.

Perf. 10½x12
1946, Dec. 6   Engr.   Unwmk.
653 A239 40c deep green   .20   .20
  Centenary of the birth of Gen. Antonio Ernesto Gomes Carneiro.

Brazilian Academy of Letters A240

1946, Dec. 14   Perf. 11
654 A240 40c blue   .25   .20
  50th anniv. of the foundation of the Brazilian Academy of Letters, Rio de Janeiro.

Antonio de Castro Alves (1847-1871), Poet — A241

1947, Mar. 14   Litho.   Wmk. 267
655 A241 40c bluish green   .20   .20

Types of 1941-42, Values in Centavos or Cruzeiros

1947-54   Wmk. 267   Typo.   Perf. 11
656 A184 2c olive   .15   .15
657 A184 5c yellow brn   .15   .15
658 A184 10c green   .15   .15
659 A185 20c brown org   .15   .15
660 A185 30c dk lilac rose   .60   .15
661 A185 40c blue   .30   .15
  b.   Wmk. 268   800.00 60.00
661A A185 50c salmon   .60   .15
662 A186 60c lt violet   1.00   .15
663 A186 70c brt rose ('54)   .40   .15
664 A186 1cr gray   1.00   .15
665 A186 1.20cr dull blue   2.50   .15
  a.   Wmk. 268   11.00   9.00
666 A187 2cr gray violet   4.00   .15
Engr.
667 A188 5cr blue   7.50   .15
668 A189 10cr rose red   7.50   .15
Perf. 11, 13
669 A190 20cr deep brown   15.00   .75
670 A191 50cr red   30.00   .50
       Nos. 656-670 (16)   71.00
         Set value   2.50
  The 5, 20, 50cr also exist with perf. 12-13.

Pres. Gonzalez Videla of Chile — A242

1947, June 26   Unwmk.   Perf. 12x11
671 A242 40c dk brown orange   .20   .15
  Visit of President Gabriel Gonzalez Videla of Chile, June 1947.
  A souvenir folder contains four impressions of No. 671, and measures 6½x8¼ inches.

"Peace" and Western Hemisphere — A243

1947, Aug. 15   Perf. 11x12
672 A243 1.20cr blue   .20   .15
  Inter-American Defense Conference at Rio de Janeiro, August-September, 1947.

Pres. Harry S Truman, Map and Statue of Liberty A244

1947, Sept. 1   Typo.   Perf. 12x11
673 A244 40c ultra   .20   .15
  Visit of US President Harry S Truman to Brazil, Sept. 1947.

Pres. Eurico Gaspar Dutra — A245   Mother and Child — A246

Wmk. 268
1947, Sept. 7   Engr.   Perf. 11
674 A245 20c green   .15   .15
675 A245 40c rose carmine   .15   .15
676 A245 1.20cr deep blue   .25   .15
       Nos. 674-676 (3)   .55
         Set value   .30
  The souvenir sheet containing Nos. 674-676 is listed as No. C73A. See No. 679.

1947, Oct. 10   Typo.   Unwmk.
677 A246 40c brt ultra   .20   .15
  Issued to mark Child Care Week, 1947.

Arms of Belo Horizonte A247   Globe A248

1947, Dec. 12   Engr.   Wmk. 267
678 A247 1.20cr rose carmine   .30   .15
  50th anniversary of the founding of the city of Belo Horizonte.

Dutra Type of 1947

1948   **Engr.**   **Wmk. 267**
679 A245 20c green   1.50 1.50

> Catalogue values for unused stamps in this section, from this point to the end of the section, are for Never Hinged items.

1948, July 10   **Litho.**
680 A248 40c dl grn & pale lil   .35 .15
International Exposition of Industry and Commerce, Petropolis, 1948.

Arms of Paranagua A249   Child Reading Book A250

1948, July 29
681 A249 5cr bister brown   1.75 .50
300th anniversary of the founding of the city of Paranagua, July 29, 1648.

1948, Aug. 1
682 A250 40c green   .25 .20
National Education Campaign.
No. 682 was reproduced on a souvenir card. Size: 124x157mm.

Tiradentes A251   Symbolical of Cancer Eradication A252

1948, Nov. 12
683 A251 40c brown orange   .25 .20
200th anniversary of the birth of Joaquim José da Silva Xavier (Tiradentes).

1948, Dec. 14
684 A252 40c claret   .25 .25
Anti-cancer publicity.

Adult Student A253

1949, Jan. 3   **Wmk. 267**   *Perf. 12x11*
685 A253 60c red vio & pink   .25 .15
Campaign for adult education.

"Battle of Guararapes," by Vitor Meireles — A254

1949, Feb. 15   *Perf. 11½x12*
686 A254 60c lt blue   .95 .60
2nd Battle of Guararapes, 300th anniv.

Church of Sao Francisco de Paula — A255   Manuel de Nobrega — A256

Perf. 11x12
1949, Mar. 8   **Unwmk.**   **Engr.**
687 A255 60c dark brown   .20 .15
   a.   Souvenir sheet   30.00 30.00
Bicentenary of city of Ouro Fino, state of Minas Gerais.
No. 687a contains one imperf. stamp similar to No. 687, with dates in lower margin. Size: 70x89mm.

1949, Mar. 29   *Imperf.*
688 A256 60c violet   .25 .25
Founding of the City of Salvador, 400th anniv.

Emblem of Brazilian Air Force and Plane — A257

1949, June 18
689 A257 60c blue violet   .25 .25
Issued to honor the Brazilian Air Force.

Star and Angel — A258

1949 Wmk. 267 Litho.   *Perf. 11x12*
690 A258 60c pink   .20 .15
1st Ecclesiastical Cong., Salvador, Bahia.

Globe — A259

1949, Oct. 31   **Typo.**   *Perf. 12x11*
691 A259 1.50c blue   .25 .15
75th anniv. of the UPU.

Ruy Barbosa A260

Unwmk.
1949, Dec. 14   **Engr.**   *Perf. 12*
692 A260 1.20cr rose carmine   .65 .30
Centenary of birth of Ruy Barbosa.

Joaquim Cardinal Arcoverde A. Cavalcanti, Birth Centenary — A261

Perf. 11x12
1950, Feb. 27   **Litho.**   **Wmk. 267**
693 A261 60c rose   .25 .20

Grapes and Factory A262

1950, Mar. 15   *Perf. 12x11*
694 A262 60c rose lake   .25 .20
75th anniversary of Italian immigration to the state of Rio Grande do Sul.

Virgin of the Globe — A263   Globe and Soccer Players — A264

1950, May 31   *Perf. 11x12*
695 A263 60c blk & lt bl   .25 .20
Establishment in Brazil of the Daughters of Charity of St. Vincent de Paul, cent.

1950, June 24
696 A264 60c ultra, bl & gray   .85 .50
4th World Soccer Championship.

Symbolical of Brazilian Population Growth A265

1950, July 10   **Typo.**   *Perf. 12x11*
697 A265 60c rose lake   .25 .20
Issued to publicize the 6th Brazilian census.

Dr. Oswaldo Cruz — A266

1950, Aug. 23   **Litho.**   *Perf. 11x12*
698 A266 60c orange brown   .25 .20
5th International Congress of Microbiology.

View of Blumenau and Itajai River — A267

1950, Sept. 9   **Wmk. 267**   *Perf. 12x11*
699 A267 60c bright pink   .25 .20
Centenary of the founding of Blumenau.

Amazonas Theater, Manaus A268

1950, Sept. 27
700 A268 60c light brn red   .20 .15
Centenary of Amazonas Province.

Arms of Juiz de Fora — A269

1950, Oct. 24   *Perf. 11x12*
701 A269 60c carmine   .25 .25
Centenary of the founding of Juiz de Fora.

Post Office at Recife — A270

1951, Jan. 10   **Typo.**   *Perf. 12x11*
702 A270   60c carmine   .20 .20
703 A270 1.20c carmine   .30 .20
Opening of the new building of the Pernambuco Post Office.

Arms of Joinville — A271   Jean-Baptiste de La Salle — A272

1951, Mar. 9   *Perf. 11x12*
704 A271 60c orange brown   .25 .20
Centenary of the founding of Joinville.

1951, Apr. 30   **Litho.**
705 A272 60c blue   .25 .20
Birth of Jean-Baptiste de La Salle, 300th anniv.

Heart and Flowers — A273   Sylvio Romero — A274

1951, May 13   **Engr.**
706 A273 60c deep plum   .25 .20
Mother's Day, May 14, 1951.

1951, Apr. 21   **Litho.**
707 A274 60c dl vio brn   .20 .20
Romero (1851-1914), poet and author.

Joao Caetano, Stage and Masks — A275

1951, July 9   *Perf. 12x11*
708 A275 60c lt gray bl   .25   .20
1st Brazilian Theater Cong., Rio, July 9-13, 1951.

Orville A. Derby — A276

First Mass Celebrated in Brazil — A277

1951, July 23   *Perf. 11x12*
709 A276 2cr slate   .35   .35
Centenary of the birth (in New York State) of Orville A. Derby, geologist.

1951, July 25
710 A277 60c dl brn & buff   .20   .16
4th Inter-American Congress on Catholic Education, Rio de Janeiro, 1951.

Euclides Pinto Martins A278

1951, Aug. 16   *Perf. 12x11*
711 A278 3.80cr brn & citron   1.50   .35
1st flight from NYC to Rio, 29th anniv.

Monastery of the Rock — A279

1951, Sept. 8
712 A279 60c dl brn & cream   .20   .20
Founding of Vitoria, 4th centenary.

Santos-Dumont and Model Plane Contest — A280

Dirigible and Eiffel Tower — A281

1951, Oct. 19   Wmk. 267   Litho.
713 A280 60c salmon & dk brn   .42   .35

Unwmk.   Engr.
714 A281 3.80cr dk pur   1.25   .40
Week of the Wing and 50th anniv. of Santos-Dumont's flight around the Eiffel Tower.
In December 1951, Nos. 713 and 714 were privately overprinted: "Exposicao Filatelica Regional Distrito Federal 15-XII-1951 23-XII-1951." These were attached to souvenir sheets bearing engraved facsimiles of Nos. 38, 49 and 51, which were sold by Clube Filatelico do Brasil to mark its 20th anniversary. The overprinted stamps on the sheets were canceled, but 530 "unused" sets were sold by the club.

Farmers and Ear of Wheat — A282

1951, Nov. 10   Litho.   Wmk. 267
715 A282 60c dp grn & gray   .25   .25
Festival of Grain at Bage, 1951.

Map and Open Bible — A283

1951, Dec. 9   *Perf. 12x11*
716 A283 1.20cr brn org   .50   .35
Issued to publicize the Day of the Bible.

Queen Isabella — A284

Henrique Oswald — A285

1952, Mar. 10   *Perf. 11x12*
717 A284 3.80cr lt bl   .60   .30
500th anniversary of the birth of Queen Isabella I of Spain.

1952, Apr. 22
718 A285 60c brown   .25   .20
Oswald (1852-1931), composer.

Vicente Licinio Cardoso A286

Map and Symbol of Labor A287

1952, May 2
719 A286 60c gray bl   .25   .20
4th Brazilian Homeopathic Congress.

1952, Apr. 30
720 A287 1.50cr brnsh pink   .25   .20
5th International Labor Organization Conference for American Countries.

Gen. Polidoro da Fonseca — A288

Luiz de Albuquerque M. P. Caceres — A289

Portraits: 5cr, Baron de Capanema. 10cr, Minister Eusebio de Queiros.

Unwmk.
1952, May 11   Engr.   *Perf. 11*
721 A288 2.40cr lt car   .35   .20
722 A288 5cr blue   2.25   .28
723 A288 10cr dk bl grn   2.25   .28
     Nos. 721-723 (3)   4.85   .76
Centenary of telegraph in Brazil.

Perf. 11x12
1952, June 8   Litho.   Wmk. 267
724 A289 1.20cr vio bl   .25   .20
200th anniversary of the founding of the city of Mato Grosso.

Symbolizing the Glory of Sports — A290

1952, July 21   *Perf. 12x11*
725 A290 1.20cr dp bl & bl   .60   .40
Fluminense Soccer Club, 50th anniversary.

José Antonio Saraiva — A291

Emperor Dom Pedro — A292

1952, Aug. 16   *Perf. 11x12*
726 A291 60c lil rose   .25   .20
Centenary of the founding of Terezina, capital of Piaui State.

1952, Sept. 3   **Wmk. 267**
727 A292 60c lt bl & blk   .25   .20
Issued for Stamp Day and the 2nd Philatelic Exhibition of Sao Paulo.

Flag-encircled Globe — A293

1952, Oct. 24   *Perf. 13½*
728 A293 3.80cr blue   .85   .50
Issued to publicize United Nations Day.

View of Sao Paulo, Sun and Compasses A294

1952, Nov. 8   Litho.   *Perf. 12x11*
729 A294 60c dl bl, yel & gray grn   .25   .20
City Planning Day.

Father Diogo Antonio Feijo — A295

1952, Nov. 9   *Perf. 11x12*
730 A295 60c fawn   .25   .20

Rodolpho Bernardelli and His "Christ and the Adultress" A297

1952, Dec. 18   *Perf. 12x11*
732 A297 60c gray bl   .25   .20
Bernardelli, sculptor and painter, birth cent.

Map of Western Hemisphere and View of Rio de Janeiro A298

1952, Sept. 20
733 A298 3.80cr vio brn & lt grn   .80   .30
2nd Congress of American Industrial Medicine, Rio de Janeiro, 1952.

Arms and Head of Pioneer A299

Coffee, Cotton and Sugar Cane — A300

Designs: 2.80cr, Jesuit monk planting tree. 3.80cr and 5.80cr, Spiral, symbolizing progress.

1953, Jan. 25   Litho.   *Perf. 11*
734 A299 1.20cr ol brn & blk brn   .52   .35
735 A300 2cr olive grn & yel   1.75   .35
736 A300 2.80cr red brn & dp org   1.20   .20
737 A300 3.80cr dk brn & yel grn   1.00   .20
738 A300 5.80cr int bl & yel grn   .70   .20
     Nos. 734-738 (5)   5.17 1.30
400th anniversary of Sao Paulo.
Used copies of No. 734 exist with design inverted.

Ledger and Winged Cap — A301

1953, Feb. 22   *Perf. 12x11*
739 A301 1.20cr dl brn & fawn   .25   .20
6th Brazilian Accounting Congress.

Joao Ramalho — A302

1953, Apr. 8   Wmk. 264   Engr.
740 A302 60c blue   .25   .20
Founding of the city of Santo Andre, 4th cent.

Aarao Reis and Plan of Belo Horizonte A303

1953, May 6   **Photo.**
741 A303 1.20cr red brn   .25   .20

Aarao Leal de Carvalho Reis (1853-1936), civil engineer.

A304   A305

1953, May 16
742 A304 1.50cr Almirante Saldanha   .40   .25

4th globe-circling voyage of the training ship Almirante Saldanha.

1953, July 5   **Photo.**

Joaquim Jose Rodrigues Torres, Viscount of Itaboraí.

743 A305 1.20cr violet   .20   .16

Centenary of the Bank of Brazil.

Lamp and Rio-Petropolis Highway A306

1953, July 14
744 A306 1.20cr gray   .25   .20

10th Intl. Congress of Nursing, Petropolis, 1953.

Bay of Rio de Janeiro A307

1953, July 15
745 A307 3.80cr dk bl grn   .40   .20

Issued to publicize the fourth World Congress of Baptist Youth, July 1953.

Arms of Jau and Map — A308

1953, Aug. 15   **Engr.**
746 A308 1.20cr purple   .25   .20

Centenary of the city of Jau.

Ministry of Health and Education Building, Rio — A309   Maria Quiteria de Jesus Medeiros — A310

1953, Aug. 1
747 A309 1.20cr dp grn   .25   .20

Day of the Stamp and the first Philatelic Exhibition of National Education.

1953, Aug. 21   **Photo.**
748 A310 60c vio bl   .25   .20

Centenary of the death of Maria Quiteria de Jesus Medeiros (1792-1848), independence heroine.

Pres. Odria of Peru — A311   Duke of Caxias Leading his Troops — A312

1953, Aug. 25
749 A311 1.40cr rose brn   .25   .20

Issued to publicize the visit of Gen. Manuel A. Odria, President of Peru, Aug. 25, 1953.

Engr. (60c, 5.80cr); Photo.
1953, Aug. 25

Designs: 1.20cr, Caxias' tomb. 1.70cr, 5.80cr, Portrait of Caxias. 3.80cr, Arms of Caxias.

750 A312	60c dp grn	.32	.16
751 A312	1.20cr dp claret	.40	.16
752 A312	1.70cr slate grn	.40	.16
753 A312	3.80cr rose brn	.65	.16
754 A312	5.80cr gray vio	.65	.16
	Nos. 750-754 (5)	2.42	.80

150th anniversary of the birth of Luis Alves de Lima e Silva, Duke of Caxias.

Quill Pen, Map and Tree — A313   Horacio Hora — A314

1953, Sept. 12   **Photo.**
755 A313 60c ultra   .25   .20

5th National Congress of Journalism.

1953, Sept. 17   **Litho.**   **Wmk. 267**
756 A314 60c org & dp plum   .25   .20

Horacio Pinto de Hora (1853-1890), painter.

Pres. Somoza of Nicaragua A315   Auguste de Saint-Hilaire A316

1953, Sept. 24   **Photo.**   **Wmk. 264**
757 A315 1.40cr dk vio brn   .25   .20

Issued to publicize the visit of Gen. Anastasio Somoza, president of Nicaragua.

1953, Sept. 30
758 A316 1.20cr dk brn car   .25   .25

Centenary of the death of Auguste de Saint-Hilaire, explorer and botanist.

Jose Carlos do Patrocinio A317   Clock Tower, Crato A318

1953, Oct. 9   **Photo.**
759 A317 60c dk slate gray   .25   .20

Jose Carlos do Patrocinio, (1853-1905), journalist and abolitionist.

1953, Oct. 17
760 A318 60c blue green   .25   .20

Centenary of the city of Crato.

Joao Capistrano de Abreu — A319   Allegory: "Justice" — A320

1953, Oct. 23
761 A319 60c dull blue   .20   .20
762 A319 5cr purple   .85   .85

Joao Capistrano de Abreu (1853-1927), historian.

1953, Nov. 17
763 A320   60c indigo   .25   .20
764 A320   1.20cr dp magenta   .25   .20

50th anniv. of the Treaty of Petropolis.

Farm Worker in Wheat Field — A321   Teacher and Pupils — A322

1953, Nov. 29   **Photo.**   *Perf. 11½*
766 A321 60c dk green   .25   .20

3rd Natl. Wheat Festival, Erechim, 1953.

1953, Dec. 14
767 A322 60c red   .25   .25

First National Conference of Primary School Teachers, Salvador, 1953.

Zacarias de Gois e Vasconcellos A323   Alexandre de Gusmao A324

Design: 5cr, Porters with Trays of Coffee Beans.

1953-54   **Photo.**
768 A323 2cr org brn & blk, *buff*   .65   .40
     ('54)
  a.   White paper   1.75   .40
769 A323 5cr dp org & blk   1.25   .40

Centenary of the state of Parana.

1954, Jan. 13
770 A324 1.20cr brn vio   .25   .20

Gusmao (1695-1753), statesman, diplomat and writer.

Symbolical of Sao Paulo's Growth — A325

Arms and View of Sao Paulo A326

Designs: 2cr, Priest, settler and Indian. 2.80cr, José de Anchieta.

1954, Jan. 25   *Perf. 11½x11*
771 A325 1.20cr dk vio brn   .75   .50
  a.   Buff paper   1.75   1.00

Engr.
772 A325   2cr lilac rose   1.05   .60
773 A325   2.80cr pur gray   1.05   1.00

Perf. 11x11½
774 A326 3.80cr dl grn   1.25   .50
  a.   Buff paper   2.25   2.00
775 A326 5.80cr dl red   1.25   .60
  a.   Buff paper   5.00   .75
     Nos. 771-775 (5)   5.35   3.20

400th anniversary of Sao Paulo.

J. Fernandes Vieira, A. Vidal de Negreiros, A. F. Camarao and H. Dias — A327

Perf. 11x11½
1954, Feb. 18 Photo. Unwmk.
776 A327 1.20cr ultra .25 .25
300th anniversary of the recovery of Pernambuco from the Dutch.

Sao Paulo and Minerva
A328

1954, Feb. 24
777 A328 1.50cr dp plum .25 .25
10th International Congress of Scientific Organizations, Sao Paulo, 1954.

Stylized Grapes, Jug and Map
A329

Monument of the Immigrants
A330

1954, Feb. 27 Photo. *Perf. 11½x11*
778 A329 40c dp claret .25 .20
Grape Festival, Rio Grande do Sul.

1954, Feb. 28
779 A330 60c dp vio bl .25 .20
Unveiling of the Monument to the Immigrants of Caxias do Sul.

First Brazilian Locomotive
A331

Perf. 11x11½
1954, Apr. 30 Unwmk.
781 A331 40c carmine .25 .20
Centenary of the first railroad engine built in Brazil.

Pres. Chamoun of Lebanon — A332

1954, May 12 Photo. *Perf. 11½x11*
782 A332 1.50cr maroon .25 .25
Visit of Pres. Camille Chamoun of Lebanon.

J. B. Champagnat Marcelin
A334

Apolonia Pinto
A335

1954, June 6 *Perf. 11x11½, 11½x11*
783 A333 60c purple .20 .15
784 A334 120cr vio blue .22 .20
50th anniversary of the founding of the Marist Brothers in Brazil.

1954, June 21 Photo.
785 A335 1.20cr bright green .15 .15
Apolonia Pinto (1854-1937), actress.

Adm. Margues Tamandare — A336

Portraits: 2c, 5c, 10c, Admiral Margues Tamandare. 20c, 30c, 40c, Oswaldo Cruz. 50c, 60c, 90c, Joaquim Murtinho. 1cr, 1.50cr, 2cr, Duke of Caxias. 5cr, 10cr, Ruy Barbosa. 20cr, 50cr, Jose Bonifacio.

1954-60 **Wmk. 267** *Perf. 11x11½*
786 A336 2c vio blue .20 .15
787 A336 5c org red .20 .15
788 A336 10c brt green .20 .15
789 A336 20c magenta .20 .15
790 A336 30c dk gray grn .20 .15
791 A336 40c rose red .35 .15
792 A336 50c violet .25 .15
793 A336 60c gray grn .20 .15
794 A336 90c orange ('55) .35 .15
795 A336 1cr brown .20 .15
796 A336 1.50cr blue .20 .15
 a. Wmk. 264 16.00 8.00
797 A336 2cr dk bl grn ('56) .45 .15
798 A336 5cr rose lil ('56) .35 .15
799 A336 10cr lt grn ('60) .90 .15
800 A336 20cr crim rose ('59) .90 .15
801 A336 50cr ultra ('59) 5.50 .20
 Nos. 786-801 (16) 10.65
 Set value 1.25
See Nos. 890, 930-933.

Boy Scout Waving Flag (Statue)
A337

Baltasar Fernandes, Explorer
A338

1954, Aug. 2 Unwmk. *Perf. 11½x11*
802 A337 1.20cr vio bl .40 .25
Intl. Boy Scout Encampment, Sao Paulo.

1954, Aug. 15
803 A338 60c dk red .25 .25
300th anniversary of city of Sorocaba.

Adeodato Giovanni Cardinal Piazza — A339

Our Lady of Aparecida, Map of Brazil — A340

1954, Sept. 2
804 A339 4.20cr red org .50 .35
Visit of Adeodato Cardinal Piazza, papal legate to Brazil.

1954
Design: 1.20cr, Virgin standing on globe.
805 A340 60c claret .30 .30
806 A340 1.20cr vio bl .40 .30
No. 805 was issued for the 1st Cong. of Brazil's Patron Saint (Our Lady of Aparecida); No. 806, the cent. of the proclamation of the dogma of the Immaculate Conception. Both stamps also for the Marian Year.
Issue dates: 60c, Sept. 6; 1.20cr, Sept. 8.

Benjamin Constant and Hand Reading Braille
A341

1954, Sept. 27 Photo. Unwmk.
807 A341 60c dk grn .25 .20
Centenary of the founding of the Benjamin Constant Institute.

River Battle of Riachuelo
A342

Admiral F. M. Barroso
A343

Dr. Christian F. S. Hahnemann
A344

1954, Oct. 6 *Perf. 11x11½, 11½x11*
808 A342 40c redsh brown .30 .20
809 A343 60c purple .20 .20
Admiral Francisco Manoel Barroso da Silva (1804-82).

1954, Oct. 8 *Perf. 11½x11*
810 A344 2.70cr dk green .30 .25
1st World Cong. of Homeopathic Medicine.

Nizia Floresta
A345

Ears of Wheat
A346

1954, Oct. 12
811 A345 60c lilac rose .25 .20
Reburial of the remains of Nizia Floresta (Dio Nizia Pinto Lisboa), writer and educator.

1954, Oct. 22
812 A346 60c olive green .20 .16
4th National Wheat Festival, Carazinho.

Basketball Player and Ball-Globe
A347

Allegory of the Spring Games
A348

1954, Oct. 23 Photo.
813 A347 1.40cr orange red .30 .30
Issued to publicize the second World Basketball Championship Matches, 1954.

Perf. 11½x11
1954, Nov. 6 **Wmk. 267**
814 A348 60c red brown .25 .25
Issued to publicize the 6th Spring Games.

San Francisco Hydroelectric Plant — A349

1955, Jan. 15 *Perf. 11x11½*
815 A349 60c brown org .20 .15
Issued to publicize the inauguration of the San Francisco Hydroelectric Plant.

Itutinga Hydroelectric Plant — A350

1955, Feb. 3
816 A350 40c blue .20 .15
Issued to publicize the inauguration of the Itutinga Hydroelectric Plant at Lavras.

Rotary Emblem and Bay of Rio de Janeiro — A351

1955, Feb. 23 *Perf. 12x11½*
817 A351 2.70cr slate gray & blk .85 .25
Rotary International, 50th anniversary.

Fausto Cardoso Palace A352

1955, Mar. 17 *Perf. 11x11½*
818 A352 40c henna brown .25 .25
Centenary of Aracaju.

Aviation Symbols A353

1955, Mar. 13 Photo. *Perf. 11½*
819 A353 60c dark gray green .16 .15
Issued to publicize the third National Aviation Congress at Sao Paulo, Mar. 6-13.

Arms of Botucatu A354

1955, Apr. 14
820 A354 60c orange brn .15 .15
821 A354 1.20cr brt green .25 .15
Centenary of Botucatu.

Young Racers at Starting Line — A355

Perf. 11½
1955, Apr. 30 Photo. Unwmk.
823 A355 60c orange brn .25 .20
5th Children's Games.

Marshal Hermes da Fonseca — A356 | Congress Altar, Sail and Sugarloaf Mountain — A357

1955, May 12 Wmk. 267
824 A356 60c purple .20 .16
Marshal Hermes da Fonseca, birth cent.

Engraved; Photogravure (2.70cr)
1955, July 17 Unwmk. *Perf. 11½*
Designs: 2.70cr, St. Pascoal. 4.20cr, Aloisi Benedetto Cardinal Masella.
825 A357 1.40cr green .15 .15
826 A357 2.70cr deep claret .25 .20
827 A357 4.20cr blue .30 .15
Nos. 825-827 (3) .70 .50
36th World Eucharistic Cong. in Rio de Janeiro.

Girl Gymnasts A358

1955, Nov. 12 Engr.
Granite Paper
828 A358 60c rose lilac .20 .20
Issued to publicize the 7th Spring Games.

José B. Monteiro Lobato, Author A359

1955, Dec. 8
Granite Paper
829 A359 40c dark green .20 .15

Adolfo Lutz — A360 | Lt. Col. Vilagran Cabrita — A361

1955, Dec. 18
Granite Paper
830 A360 60c dk green .20 .15
Centenary of the birth of Adolfo Lutz, public health pioneer.

1955, Dec. 22 Photo. Wmk. 267
831 A361 60c violet blue .20 .15
First Battalion of Engineers, cent.

Salto Grande Hydroelectric Dam — A362

1956, Jan. 15 Unwmk. *Perf. 11½*
Granite Paper
832 A362 60c brick red .20 .15

Arms of Mococa — A363 | "G" and Globe — A364

Perf. 11½
1956, Apr. 17 Wmk. 256 Photo.
833 A363 60c brick red .16 .15
Centenary of Mococa, Sao Paulo.

1956, Apr. 14 Unwmk.
Granite Paper
834 A364 1.20cr violet blue .16 .20
18th Intl. Geographic Cong., Rio, Aug. 1956.

Girls' Foot Race — A365

1956, Apr. 28 Photo.
Granite Paper
835 A365 2.50cr brt blue .30 .20
6th Children's Games.

Plane over Map of Brazil — A366

1956, June 12 Wmk. 267 *Perf. 11½*
836 A366 3.30cr brt vio bl .40 .20
National Airmail Service, 25th anniv.

Fireman Rescuing Child — A367

1956, July 2 Wmk. 264
837 A367 2.50cr crimson .40 .25
a. Buff paper 2.25 2.00
Centenary of the Fire Brigade.

Map of Brazil and Open Book — A368

1956, Sept. 8 Wmk. 267
838 A368 2.50cr brt vio bl .30 .20
50th anniversary of the arrival of the Marist Brothers in Northern Brazil.

Church and Monument, Franca — A369

1956, Sept. 7 Engr.
839 A369 2.50cr dk blue .30 .20
Centenary of city of Franca, Sao Paulo.

Woman Hurdler A370

1956, Sept. 22 Photo. Unwmk.
Granite Paper
840 A370 2.50cr dk car .40 .20
Issued to publicize the 8th Spring Games.

Forest and Map of Brazil — A371

1956, Sept. 30 Wmk. 267 *Perf. 11½*
841 A371 2.50cr dk green .25 .20
Issued to publicize education in forestry.

Baron da Bocaina A372

1956, Oct. 8 Engr. Wmk. 268
842 A372 2.50cr reddish brown .25 .20
Centenary of the birth of Baron da Bocaina, who introduced the special delivery mail system to Brazil.

Marbleized Paper
Paper with a distinct wavy-line or marbleized watermark (which Brazilians call *marmorizado* paper) has been found on many stamps of Brazil, 1956-68, including Nos. 843-845, 847, 851-854, 858-858A, 864, 878, 880, 882, 884, 886-887, 896, 909, 918, 920-921, 925-928, 936-939, 949, 955-958, 960, 962-964, 978-979, 983, 985-987, 997-998, 1002-1003, 1005, 1009-1012, 1017, 1024, 1026, 1055, 1075, 1078, 1082, C82, C82a, C83-C87, C96, C99, C109. Quantities are much less than those of stamps on regular paper.

Panama Stamp Showing Pres. Juscelino Kubitschek — A373

1956, Oct. 12 Photo. Wmk. 267
843 A373 3.30cr green & blk .40 .20
Issued on America Day, Oct. 12, to commemorate the meeting of the Presidents and the Pan-American Conference at Panama City, July 21-22.

Symbolical of Steel Production A374

Perf. 11½
1957, Jan. 31 Wmk. 267 Photo.
844 A374 2.50cr chocolate .25 .15
2nd expansion of the National Steel Company at Volta Redonda.

Joaquim E. Gomes da Silva — A375

1957, Mar. 1 Photo. Unwmk.
Granite Paper
845 A375 2.50cr dk bl grn .25 .15
Centenary of the birth (in 1856) of Joaquim E. Gomes da Silva.

Allan Kardec A376

Perf. 11½

1957, Apr. 18　Wmk. 268　Engr.
846 A376 2.50cr dk brown　　.25 .15

Issued in honor of Allan Kardec, pen name of Leon Hippolyto Denizard Rivail, and for the centenary of the publication of his "Codification of Spiritism."

Boy Gymnast
A377

1957, Apr. 27　Photo.　Unwmk.
Granite Paper
847 A377 2.50cr lake　　.48 .25

7th Children's Games.

Pres. Craveiro
Lopes — A378　　Stamp of
1932 — A379

1957, June 7　Engr.　Wmk. 267
848 A378 6.50cr blue　　.40 .20

Visit of Gen. Francisco Higino Craveiro Lopes, President of Portugal.

1957, July 9　　Photo.
849 A379 2.50cr rose　　.25 .15

25th anniv. of the movement for a constitution.

St. Antonio
Monastery,
Pernambuco
A380

1957, Aug. 24　Engr.　Wmk. 267
850 A380 2.50cr dp magenta　　.25 .15

300th anniv. of the emancipation of the Franciscan province of St. Antonio in Pernambuco State.

Volleyball　　Basketball
A381　　A382

1957, Sept. 28　Photo.　Perf. 11½
851 A381 2.50cr dull org red　　.45 .25

Issued for the 9th Spring Games.

1957, Oct. 12
852 A382 3.30cr org & brt grn　　.45 .25

2nd Women's International Basketball Championship, Rio de Janeiro.

Count of
Pinhal and
Sao Carlos
A383

1957, Nov. 4　Wmk. 267　Perf. 11½
853 A383 2.50cr rose　　.28 .25

Centenary of the city of Sao Carlos and honoring the Count of Pinhal, its founder.

Auguste Comte — A384

1957, Nov. 15
854 A384 2.50cr dk red brn　　.25 .20

Centenary of the death of Auguste Comte, French mathematician and philosopher.

Radio Station
A385

1957, Dec. 10　　Wmk. 268
855 A385 2.50cr dk green　　.20 .15

Opening of Sarapui Central Radio Station.

Admiral
Tamandare and
Warship
A386

Design: 3.30cr, Aircraft carrier.

1957-58　　Photo.
856 A386 2.50cr light blue　　.25 .20
Engr.
857 A386 3.30cr green ('58)　　.28 .20

150th anniversary of the birth of Admiral Joaquin Marques de Tamandare, founder of the Brazilian navy.

Coffee Plant and
Symbolic "R" — A387

Perf. 11½
1957-58　Wmk. 267　Photo.
858 A387 2.50cr magenta　　.52 .35
Unwmk.
Granite Paper
858A A387 2.50cr magenta ('58)　　.45 .35

Centenary (in 1956) of the city of Ribeirao Preto in Sao Paulo state.

Dom John
VI — A388

1958, Jan. 28　Engr.　Wmk. 268
859 A388 2.50cr magenta　　.35 .25

150th anniversary of the opening of the ports of Brazil to foreign trade.

Bugler
A389

1958, Mar. 18　　Wmk. 267
860 A389 2.50cr red　　.35 .25

Brazilian Marine Corps, 150th anniv.

Station at Rio and
Locomotive of
1858 — A390　　Court
House — A391

Perf. 11½
1958, Mar. 29　Wmk. 267　Photo.
861 A390 2.50cr red brn　　.35 .25

Central Railroad of Brazil, cent.

1958, Apr. 1　Engr.　Wmk. 256
862 A391 2.50cr green　　.25 .15

150th anniv. of the Military Superior Court.

Emblem and
Brazilian
Pavilion
A392

1958, Apr. 17　　Wmk. 267
863 A392 2.50cr dk blue　　.25 .25

World's Fair, Brussels, Apr. 17-Oct. 19.

High Jump — A393

1958, Apr. 20　Photo.　Unwmk.
Granite Paper
864 A393 2.50cr crimson rose　　.25 .15

8th Children's Games.

Marshal
Mariano da
Silva Rondon
A394

1958, Apr. 19　Engr.　Wmk. 267
865 A394 2.50cr magenta　　.25 .15

Issued to honor Marshal Mariano da Silva Rondon and the "Day of the Indian."

Hydroelectric
Station
A395

1958, Apr. 28　Wmk. 267　Perf. 11½
866 A395 2.50cr magenta　　.25 .15

Opening of Sao Paulo State power plant.

National
Printing
Plant — A396

1958, May 22　　Photo.
867 A396 2.50cr redsh brn　　.20 .15

150th anniversary of the founding of the National Printing Plant.

Marshal
Osorio — A397

1958, May 24
868 A397 2.50cr brt violet　　.20 .15

150th anniversary of the birth of Marshal Manoel Luiz Osorio.

Pres. Ramon
Villeda
Morales — A398　　Fountain — A399

1958, June 7　Engr.　Perf. 11½
869 A398 6.50cr dk green　　1.25 .75
　a.　Wmk. 268　　5.00 2.00

Visit of Pres. Ramon Villeda Morales of Honduras.

1958, June 13
870 A399 2.50cr dk green　　.25 .15

Botanical Garden, Rio de Janeiro, 150th anniv.

Symbols of
Agriculture
A400　　Prophet Joel
A401

1958, June 18　　Photo.
871 A400 2.50cr rose carmine　　.25 .15

50th anniv. of Japanese immigration to Brazil.

1958, June 21　　Engr.
872 A401 2.50cr dk blue　　.25 .15

Bicentenary of the Cathedral of Bom Jesus at Matosinhos.

Stylized
Globe — A402

1958, July 10　　Photo.
873 A402 2.50cr dk brown　　.20 .15

Intl. Investment Conference, Belo Horizonte.

Julio Bueno
Brandao — A403

1958, Aug. 1　Wmk. 268　Perf. 11½
874 A403 2.50cr red brown　　.25 .15

Centenary of the birth of Julio Bueno Brandao, President of Minas Gerais.

Palacio Tiradentes (House of Congress) A404

1958, July 24 **Engr.**
875 A404 2.50cr sepia .25 .15
47th Interparliamentary Conference, Rio de Janeiro, July 24-Aug. 1.

Presidential Palace, Brasilia A405

1958, Aug. 8 **Photo.** **Wmk. 267**
876 A405 2.50cr ultra .20 .15
Issued to publicize the construction of Brazil's new capital, Brasilia.

Freighters A406

1958, Aug. 22
877 A406 2.50cr blue .25 .15
Brazilian merchant marine.

Joaquim Caetano da Silva — A407

1958, Sept. 2 **Unwmk.**
Granite Paper
878 A407 2.50cr redsh brn .25 .15
Joaquim Caetano da Silva, scientist & historian.

Giovanni Gronchi — A408   Archers — A409

1958, Sept. 4 **Engr.** **Wmk. 268**
879 A408 7cr dk blue .50 .15
Visit of Italy's President Giovanni Gronchi to Brazil.

Perf. 11½
1958, Sept. 21 **Photo.** **Unwmk.**
Granite Paper
880 A409 2.50cr red org .35 .20
Issued to publicize the 10th Spring Games.

Elderly Couple — A410   Machado de Assis — A411

1958, Sept. 27 **Wmk. 267**
881 A410 2.50cr magenta .25 .15
Day of the Old People, Sept. 27.

1958, Sept. 28 **Unwmk.**
882 A411 2.50cr red brn .25 .15
50th anniversary of the death of Joaquim Maria Machado de Assis, writer.

Pres. Vargas and Oil Derrick A412

1958, Oct. 6 **Wmk. 268**
883 A412 2.50cr blue .25 .15
5th anniv. of Pres. Getulio D. Vargas' oil law.

Globe — A413   Gen. Lauro Sodré — A414

Perf. 11½
1958, Nov. 14 **Photo.** **Wmk. 267**
884 A413 2.50cr blue .30 .15
7th Inter-American Congress of Municipalities.

1958, Nov. 15 **Engr.**
885 A414 3.30cr green .25 .15
Cent. of the birth of Gen. Lauro Sodré.

UN Emblem — A415   Soccer Player — A416

1958, Dec. 26 **Photo.** **Perf. 11½**
886 A415 2.50cr brt blue .20 .15
10th anniv. of the signing of the Universal Declaration of Human Rights.

1959, Jan. 20
887 A416 3.30cr emer & red brn .40 .20
World Soccer Championships of 1958.

Railroad Track and Map A417   Pres. Sukarno of Indonesia A418

1959, Apr. **Wmk. 267** **Perf. 11½**
888 A417 2.50cr dp orange .25 .20
Centenary of the linking of Patos and Campina Grande by railroad.

1959, May 20
889 A418 2.50cr blue .25 .15
Visit of President Sukarno of Indonesia.

Dom John VI — A419   Boy Polo Players — A420

Perf. 10½x11½
1959, June 12 **Wmk. 267**
890 A419 2.50cr crimson .25 .15

1959, June 13 **Perf. 11½**
891 A420 2.50cr orange brn .25 .15
9th Children's Games.

Loading Freighter A421   Organ and Emblem A422

1959, July 10
892 A421 2.50cr dk green .25 .15
Issued to honor the merchant marine.

1959, July 16 **Photo.**
893 A422 3.30cr magenta .25 .15
Bicentenary of the Carmelite Order in Brazil.

Joachim Silverio de Souza — A423   Symbolic Road — A424

1959, July 20 **Perf. 11½**
894 A423 2.50cr red brown .25 .15
Birth centenary of Joachim Silverio de Souza, first bishop of Diamantina, Minas Gerais.

1959, Sept. 27 **Wmk. 267**
895 A424 3.30cr bl grn & ultra .25 .15
11th International Roadbuilding Congress.

Woman Athlete — A425

1959, Oct. 4
896 A425 2.50cr lilac rose .25 .15
11th Spring Games.

Map of Parana A426

1959, Sept. 27
897 A426 2.50cr dk green .25 .15
Founding of Londrina, Parana, 25th anniv.

Giobe and Snipes A427   Cross of Lusitania A428

1959, Oct. 22 **Perf. 11½**
898 A427 6.50cr dull grn .20 .15
World Championship of Snipe Class Sailboats, Porto Alegre, won by Brazilian yachtsmen.

1959, Oct. 24 **Engr.**
899 A428 6.50cr dull blue .20 .15
4th Intl. Conf. on Brazilian-Portuguese Studies, University of Bahia, Aug. 10-20.

Factory Entrance and Order of Southern Cross — A429   Corcovado Christ, Globe and Southern Cross — A430

1959, Nov. 19 **Photo.**
900 A429 3.30cr orange red .20 .15
Pres. Vargas Gunpowder Factory, 50th anniv.

1959, Nov. 26 **Perf. 11½**
901 A430 2.50cr blue .20 .15
Universal Thanksgiving Day.

Burning Bush — A431

1959, Dec. 24 **Wmk. 267**
902 A431 3.30cr lt grn .20 .15
Centenary of Presbyterian work in Brazil.

Piraja da Silva and Schistosoma Mansoni A432

1959, Dec. 28
903 A432 2.50cr rose violet   .20 .15

25th anniv. of the discovery and identification of schistosoma mansoni, a parasite of the fluke family, by Dr. Piraja da Silva.

Luiz de Matos — A433

1960, Jan. 3   **Photo.**
904 A433 3.30cr red brown   .15 .15

Birth centenary of Luiz de Matos.

Zamenhof A434   Adél Pinto A435

1960, Mar. 10 Wmk. 267 Perf. 11½
905 A434 6.50cr emerald   .20 .15

Lazarus Ludwig Zamenhof (1859-1917), Polish oculist who invented Esperanto in 1887.

1960, Mar. 19   Engr.   Wmk. 268
906 A435 11.50cr rose red   .20 .15

Centenary of the birth of Adél Pinto, civil engineer and railroad expert.

Presidential Palace, Colonnade A436

Design: 27cr, Plan of Brasilia (like #C98).

Perf. 11x11½
1960   Photo.   Wmk. 267
907 A436 2.50cr brt green   .20 .15

Size: 105x46½mm
908 A436   27cr salmon   .60 .60
   Nos. 907-908,C95-C98 (6)   2.00 1.35

No. 907 for the inauguration of Brazil's new capital, Brasilia, Apr. 21, 1960.
No. 908 for the birthday of Pres. Juscelino Kubitschek and has a 27cr in design of No. C98, flanked by the chief design features of Nos. 907, C95-C97, with Kubitschek signature below. Issued in sheets of 4 with wide horizontal gutter.
Issued: 2.50cr, 4/21; 27cr, 9/12.

Grain, Coffee, Cotton and Cacao — A437   Paulo de Frontin — A438

Perf. 11½x11
1960, July 28   **Wmk. 267**
909 A437 2.50cr brown   .20 .15

Centenary of Ministry of Agriculture.

1960, Oct. 12   **Wmk. 268**
910 A438 2.50cr orange red   .20 .15

Cent. of the birth of Paulo de Frontin, engineer.

Woman Athlete Holding Torch — A439

1960, Oct. 18   **Perf. 11½x11**
911 A439 2.50cr blue grn   .20 .15

12th Spring Games.

Volleyball and Net A440   Locomotive Wheels A441

Perf. 11½x11
1960, Nov. 12   **Wmk. 268**
912 A440 11cr blue   .20 .15

International Volleyball Championships.

1960, Oct. 15   **Perf. 11½x11**
913 A441 2.50cr ultra   .20 .15

10th Pan-American Railroad Congress.

Symbols of Flight A442

1960, Dec. 16   Photo.   Perf. 11½
914 A442 2.50cr brn & yel   .15 .15

Intl. Fair of Industry and Commerce, Rio.

Emperor Haile Selassie — A443

1961, Jan. 31   **Perf. 11½x11**
915 A443 2.50cr dk brown   .16 .15

Visit of Emperor Haile Selassie of Ethiopia to Brazil, Dec. 1960.

Map of Brazil, Open Book and Sacred Heart Emblem A444

Perf. 11x11½
1961, Mar. 13   **Wmk. 268**
916 A444 2.50cr blue   .20 .15

50th anniv. of the operation in Brazil of the Order of the Blessed Heart of Mary.

Map of Guanabara A445

1961, Mar. 27   **Wmk. 267**
917 A445 7.50cr org brn   .20 .15

Promulgation of the constitution of the state of Guanabara.

Arms of Agulhas Negras A446   Brazil and Senegal Linked on Map A447

Design: 3.30cr, Dress helmet and sword.

Perf. 11½x11
1961, Apr. 23   **Wmk. 267**
918 A446 2.50cr green   .20 .15
919 A446 3.30cr rose car   .15 .15

Sesquicentennial of the Agulhas Negras Military Academy.

1961, Apr. 28   **Photo.**
920 A447 27cr ultra   .25 .20

Issued to commemorate the visit of Afonso Arinos, Brazilian foreign minister, to Senegal to attend its independence ceremonies.

View of Ouro Preto, 1711 A448

1961, June 6   **Perf. 11x11½**
921 A448 1cr orange   .20 .20

250th anniversary of Ouro Preto.

War Arsenal A449

1961, June 20   **Wmk. 256**
924 A449 5cr dk red brn   .25 .15

150th anniv. of the War Arsenal, Rio de Janeiro.

Coffee Bean and Branch A450   Rabindranath Tagore A451

Perf. 11½x11
1961, June 26   **Wmk. 267**
925 A450 20cr redsh brn   .80 .25

8th Directorial Committee meeting of the Intl. Coffee Convention, Rio, June 26.

1961, July 28   Photo.   Wmk. 267
926 A451 10cr rose car   .20 .15

Rabindranath Tagore, Indian poet, birth cent.

Stamp of 1861 and Map of English Channel A452

Design: 20cr, 430r stamp of 1861 and map of Netherlands.

1961, Aug. 1   **Perf. 11x11½**
927 A452 10cr rose   .75 .20
928 A452 20cr salmon pink   2.00 .30

Centenary of 1861 stamp issue.

Portrait Type of 1954-60
Designs as Before
1961   Wmk. 268   Perf. 11x11½
930 A336 1cr brown   .80 .20
931 A336 2cr dk bl grn   1.25 .50
932 A336 5cr red lilac   3.75 .30
933 A336 10cr emerald   7.25 .30
   Nos. 930-933 (4)   13.05 1.60

1cr, 5cr and 10cr have patterned background.

Sun, Clouds, Rain and Weather Symbols — A453   Dedo de Deus Peak — A454

1962, Mar. 23   **Perf. 11½x11**
936 A453 10cr red brown   .75 .30

World Meteorological Day, Mar. 23.

1962, Apr. 14   Photo.   Wmk. 267
937 A454 8cr emerald   .20 .25

50th anniversary of the climbing of Dedo de Deus (Finger of God) peak.

Dr. Gaspar Vianna and Leishmania Protozoa A455

1962, Apr. 24   **Perf. 11x11½**
938 A455 8cr blue   .25 .15

Discovery by Gaspar Oliveira Vianna (1885-1914) of a cure for leishmaniasis, 50th anniv.

Henrique Dias A456

1962, June 18   **Wmk. 267**
939 A456 10cr dk vio brn   .32 .15

300th anniversary of the death of Henrique Dias, Negro military leader who fought against the Dutch and Spaniards.

Millimeter
Gauge — A457

1962, June 26   *Perf. 11¹/₂x11*
940 A457 100cr car rose   .35 .20
Centenary of the introduction of the metric system in Brazil.

Sailboats, Snipe
Class — A458

1962, July 21   **Photo.**   **Wmk. 267**
941 A458 8cr Prus grn   .20 .15
Issued to commemorate the 13th Brazilian championships for Snipe Class sailing.

Julio
Mesquita
A459

1962, Aug. 18   *Perf. 11x11¹/₂*
942 A459 8cr dull brown   .20 .15
Centenary of the birth of Julio Mesquita, journalist and founder of Sao Paulo.

Empress
Leopoldina — A460

1962, Sept. 7   *Perf. 11¹/₂x11*
943 A460 8cr rose claret   .20 .15
140th anniversary of independence.

Buildings,
Brasilia
A461

Perf. 11x11¹/₂
1962, Oct. 24   **Wmk. 267**
944 A461 10cr orange   .30 .15
51st Interparliamentary Conf., Brasilia.

Pouring Ladle — A462

1962, Oct. 26   *Perf. 11¹/₂x11*
945 A462 8cr orange   .20 .15
Inauguration of the Usiminas State Iron and Steel Foundry at Belo Horizonte, Minas Gerais.

UPAE
Emblem
A463

1962, Nov. 19   *Perf. 11x11¹/₂*
946 A463 8cr bright magenta   .20 .15
Founding of the Postal Union of the Americas and Spain, UPAE, 50th anniv.

Chimney and Cogwheel
Forming "10" — A464

1962, Nov. 26   *Perf. 11¹/₂x11*
947 A464 10cr lt blue grn   .20 .15
Natl. Economic and Development Bank, 10th anniv.

Quintino
Bocaiuva
A465

Soccer Player
and Globe
A466

Perf. 11¹/₂x11
1962, Dec. 27   **Photo.**   **Wmk. 267**
948 A465 8cr brown org   .20 .15
Bocaiuva, journalist, 50th death anniv.

1963, Jan. 14
949 A466 10cr blue grn   .40 .15
World Soccer Championship of 1962.

Carrier
Pigeon
A467

1963, Jan.   **Unwmk.**   **Litho.**   *Perf. 14*
950 A467 8cr yel, dk bl, red & grn   .20 .15
Souvenir Sheet
Imperf
951 A467 100cr yel, dk bl, red & grn   1.25 3.00
300 years of Brazilian postal service. Issue dates: 8cr, Jan. 25; 100cr, Jan. 31.

Severino Neiva — A468

Perf. 10¹/₂x11¹/₂
1963, Jan. 31   **Photo.**   **Wmk. 267**
952 A468 8cr brt vio   .20 .15

Radar Tracking Station
and Rockets — A469

"Cross of
Unity" — A470

Perf. 11¹/₂x11
1963, Mar. 15   **Wmk. 268**
953 A469 21cr lt ultra   .20 .15
Issued to publicize the International Aeronautics and Space Exhibition, Sao Paulo.

1963   **Wmk. 267**   *Perf. 11¹/₂x11*
954 A470 8cr red lilac   .20 .15
Vatican II, the 21st Ecumenical Council of the Roman Catholic Church.

"ABC" in
Geometric
Form — A471

Basketball
Player — A472

1963, Apr. 22   **Photo.**   **Wmk. 267**
955 A471 8cr brt bl & lt bl   .16 .15
Education Week, Apr. 22-27, 3-year alphabetization program.

1963, May 15
956 A472 8cr dp lilac rose   .20 .15
4th International Basketball Championships, Rio de Janeiro, May 10-25, 1963.

Games
Emblem
A473

"OEA" and
Map of the
Americas
A474

1963, May 22   *Perf. 11¹/₂x11*
957 A473 10cr car rose   .30 .15
4th Pan American Games, Sao Paulo.

1963, June 6
958 A474 10cr org & dp org   .30 .15
15th anniversary of the charter of the Organization of American States.

José Bonifacio de
Andrada — A475

1963, June 13
959 A475 8cr dk brown   .15 .15
Bicentenary of the birth of José Bonifacio de Andrada de Silva, statesman.

Wheat
A476

Perf. 11x11¹/₂
1963, June 19   **Photo.**   **Wmk. 267**
960 A476 10cr blue   .30 .15
FAO "Freedom from Hunger" campaign.

Centenary
Emblem
A477

Joao Caetano
A478

1963, Aug. 19   *Perf. 11¹/₂x11*
961 A477 8cr yel org & red   .25 .15
Centenary of International Red Cross.

1963, Aug. 24   *Perf. 11¹/₂x11*
962 A478 8cr slate   .20 .15
Death centenary of Joao Caetano, actor.

Symbols of Agriculture,
Industry and Atomic
Energy
A479

Hammer
Thrower
A480

1963, Aug. 28
963 A479 10cr car rose   .25 .15
Atomic Development Law, 1st anniv.

1963, Sept. 13
964 A480 10cr gray   .42 .15
Intl. College Students' Games, Porto Alegre.

Marshal Tito — A481 | Compass Rose, Map of Brazil and View of Rio — A482

1963, Sept. 19
965 A481 80cr sepia   .35 .30
Visit of Marshal Tito of Yugoslavia.

1963, Sept. 20
966 A482 8cr lt blue grn   .16 .15
8th International Leprology Congress.

Oil Derrick and Storage Tank A483

1963, Oct. 3   *Perf. 11x11½*
967 A483 8cr dk slate grn   .16 .15
10th anniv. of Petrobras, the natl. oil company.

"Spring Games" A484

1963, Nov. 5   Photo.   Wmk. 267
968 A484 8cr yel & org   .20 .20
1963 Spring Games.

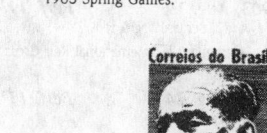

Dr. Borges de Medeiros (1863-1962), Governor of Rio Grande do Sul — A485

1963, Nov. 29   *Perf. 11½x11*
969 A485 8cr red brown   .16 .15

Sao Joao del Rei — A486

1963, Dec. 8   *Perf. 11x11½*
970 A486 8cr violet blue   .16 .15
250th anniversary of Sao Joao del Rei.

Dr. Alvaro Alvim A487

1963, Dec. 19
971 A487 8cr dk gray   .16 .15
Alvaro Alvim (1863-1928), X-ray specialist and martyr of science.

Viscount de Mauá A488 | Mandacaru Cactus and Emblem A489

1963, Dec. 28   *Perf. 11½x11*
972 A488 8cr rose car   .16 .15
Sesquicentennial of the birth of Viscount de Mauá, founder of first Brazilian railroad.

1964, Jan. 23   Photo.   Wmk. 267
973 A489 8cr dull green   .16 .15
Bank of Northeast Brazil, 10th anniv.

Coelho Netto — A490 | Lauro Müller — A491

1964, Feb. 21   *Perf. 11½x11*
974 A490 8cr brt violet   .16 .15
Birth centenary of Coelho Netto, writer.

1964, Mar. 8   Wmk. 267
975 A491 8cr dp orange   .16 .15
Lauro Siverino Müller, politician and member of the Brazilian Academy of Letters, birth cent.

Child Holding Spoon A492

1964, Mar. 25   *Perf. 11x11½*
976 A492 8cr yel brn & yel   .16 .15
Issued for "School Meals Week."

Chalice Rock — A493 | Allan Kardec — A494

1964, Apr. 9   Engr.   *Perf. 11½x11*
977 A493 80cr red orange   .20 .15
Issued for tourist publicity.

1964, Apr. 18   Photo.
978 A494 30cr slate green   .45 .15
Cent. of "O Evangelho" (Gospel) of the codification of Spiritism.

Heinrich Lübke — A495 | Pope John XXIII — A496

Perf. 11½x11
1964, May 8   Photo.   Wmk. 267
979 A495 100cr red brown   .60 .18
Visit of President Heinrich Lübke of Germany.

1964, June 29   Wmk. 267
980 A496 20cr dk car rose   .20 .18
a.   Unwmkd.   .20 .18
Issued in memory of Pope John XXIII.

Pres. Senghor of Senegal — A497

1964, Sept. 19   Wmk. 267
981 A497 20cr dk brown   .25 .15
Visit of Leopold Sedar Senghor, President of Senegal.

Botafogo Bay and Sugarloaf Mountain A498

Designs: 100cr, Church of Our Lady of the Rock, vert. 200cr, Copacabana beach.

Perf. 11x11½, 11½x11
1964-65   Photo.
983 A498 15cr org & bl   .30 .22
984 A498 100cr brt grn & red brn,
           yel   .18 .16
985 A498 200cr black & red   1.75 .30
a.   Souvenir sheet of 3 ('65)   4.75 4.00
      Nos. 983-985 (3)   2.23 .68
4th cent. of Rio de Janeiro.
No. 985a contains three imperf. stamps similar to Nos. 983-985, but printed in brown. Sold for 320cr. Issued Dec. 30, 1965.
A souvenir card containing one lithographed facsimile of No. 984, imperf., exists, but has no franking value. Size: 100x125mm. Sold by P.O. for 250cr.

Pres. Charles de Gaulle A499 | Pres. John F. Kennedy A500

1964, Oct. 13   *Perf. 11½x11*
986 A499 100cr orange brn   .35 .15
Visit of Charles de Gaulle, President of France, Oct. 13-15.

1964, Oct. 24   Photo.   Wmk. 267
987 A500 100cr slate   .20 .15

"Prophet" by A. F. Lisbao — A501

1964, Nov. 18   *Perf. 11½x11*
988 A501 10cr slate   .16 .15
150th death anniv. of the sculptor Antonio Francisco Lisbao, "O Aleijadinho" (The Cripple).

Antonio Goncalves Dias — A502

Designs: 30cr, Euclides da Cunha. 50cr, Prof. Angelo Moreira da Costa Lima. 200cr, Tiradentes. 500cr, Dom Pedro I. 1000cr, Dom Pedro II.

1965-66   Wmk. 267   *Perf. 11x11½*
989 A502 30cr brt bluish grn
             ('66)   2.00 .25
989A A502 50cr dull brn ('66)   1.50 .15
990 A502 100cr blue   .60 .15
991 A502 200cr brown org   1.75 .30
992 A502 500cr red brown   6.00 .50
992A A502 1000cr sl bl ('66)   10.00 .50
      Nos. 989-992A (6)   22.10 1.70

Statue of St. Sebastian, Guanataro Bay — A503

The Arches A504

Design: 35cr, Estacio de Sa (1520-67), founder of Rio de Janeiro.

1965   Photo.   *Perf. 11½*
           Size: 24x37mm
993 A503 30cr bl & rose red   .30 .15

Lithographed and Engraved
        Perf. 11x11½
994 A504 30cr lt bl & blk   .30 .15

**   Photo.   *Perf. 11½***
           Size: 21x39mm
995 A503 35cr blk & org   .18 .25
a.   Souvenir sheet of 3   3.25 4.00
      Nos. 993-995 (3)   .78 .55
4th cent. of Rio de Janeiro. Issue dates: No. 993, Mar. 5. No. 994, Nov. 30. No. 995, July 28. No. 995a, Dec. 30.
No. 995a contains three imperf. stamps similar to Nos. 993-995, but printed in deep orange. Size: 130x79mm. Sold for 100cr.

Sword and Cross — A505

1965, Apr. 15 Wmk. 267 *Perf. 11½*
996 A505 120cr gray   .30 .15
1st anniv. of the democratic revolution.

Vital
Brazil — A506

Shah of
Iran — A507

1965, Apr. 28   Wmk. 267   Perf. 11½
997 A506 120cr dp orange .30 .15

Centenary of birth of Vital Brazil, M.D.
A souvenir card containing one impression similar to No. 997, imperf., exists, printed in dull plum. Sold by P.O. for 250cr. Size: 114x180mm.

1965, May 5   Photo.
998 A507 120cr rose claret .25 .15

Issued to commemorate the visit of Shah Mohammed Riza Pahlavi of Iran.

Marshal Mariano
da Silva Rondon
A508

Lions' Emblem
A509

1965, May 7   Engr.
999 A508 30cr claret .25 .15

Marshal Mariano da Silva Rondon (1865-1958), explorer and expert on Indians.

1965, May 14   Photo.
1000 A509 35cr pale vio & blk .20 .15

12th convention of the Lions Clubs of Brazil, Rio de Janeiro, May 11-16.

ITU Emblem, Old and New
Communication Equipment — A510

1965, May 21   Perf. 11½
1001 A510 120cr yellow & grn .30 .20

Centenary of the ITU.

Epitácio
Pessoa — A511

Statue of Admiral
Barroso — A512

1965, May 23   Photo.
1002 A511 35cr blue gray .20 .15

Epitácio da Silva Pessoa (1865-1942), jurist, president of Brazil, 1919-22.

1965, June 11
1003 A512 30cr blue .25 .15

Cent. of the naval battle of Riachuelo.
A souvenir card containing one lithographed facsimile of No. 1003, imperf., exists. Size: 100x139½mm.

José de Alencar and
Indian Princess — A513

1965, June 24   Perf. 11½x11
1004 A513 30cr deep plum .25 .15

Centenary of the publication of "Iracema" by Joséde Alencar.
A souvenir card containing one lithographed facsimile of No. 1004, printed in rose red and imperf., exists. Size: 100x141½mm.

Winston
Churchill
A514

1965, June 25   Perf. 11x11½
1005 A514 200cr slate .50 .25

A souvenir card containing one lithographed facsimile of No. 1004, printed in rose red and imperf., exists. Size: 100x141½mm.

Scout Jamboree
Emblem — A515

1965, July 17   Photo.
1006 A515 30cr dull bl grn .30 .15

1st Pan-American Boy Scout Jamboree, Fundao Island, Rio de Janeiro, July 15-25.

ICY Emblem
A516

1965, Aug. 25   Wmk. 267   Perf. 11½
1007 A516 120cr dl bl & blk .25 .15

International Cooperation Year, 1965.

Leoncio
Correias
A517

Emblem
A518

1965, Sept. 1   Perf. 11½x11
1008 A517 35cr slate grn .25 .15

Leoncio Correias, poet, birth cent.

1965, Sept. 4
1009 A518 30cr brt rose .20 .15

Issued to publicize the Eighth Biennial Fine Arts Exhibition, Sao Paulo, Nov.-Dec., 1965.

Pres. Saragat of
Italy — A519

1965, Sept. 11   Photo.   Wmk. 267
1010 A519 100cr slate grn, *pink* .25 .15

Visit of Pres. Giuseppe Saragat of Italy.

Grand Duke and Duchess of
Luxembourg — A520

1965, Sept. 17   Perf. 11x11½
1011 A520 100cr brn olive .25 .15

Visit of Grand Duke Jean and Grand Duchess Josephine Charlotte of Luxembourg.

Biplane — A521

1965, Oct. 8   Photo.   Perf. 11½x11
1012 A521 35cr ultra .20 .15

3rd Aviation Week Philatelic Exhibition, Rio.
A souvenir card carries one impression of this 35cr, imperf. Size: 102x140mm. Sold for 100cr.

Flags of OAS
Members
A522

1965, Nov. 17   Perf. 11x11½
1013 A522 100cr brt bl & blk .25 .20

2nd meeting of OAS Foreign Ministers, Rio.

King
Baudouin
and Queen
Fabiola of
Belgium
A523

1965, Nov. 18
1014 A523 100cr gray .25 .20

Visit of King and Queen of Belgium.

...

"Coffee Beans" — A524

Perf. 11½x11
1965, Dec. 21   Photo.   Wmk. 267
1015 A524 30cr brown .30 .15

Brazilian coffee publicity.

Conveyor
and Loading
Crane
A525

1966, Apr. 1   Perf. 11x11½
1016 A525 110cr tan & dk sl grn .25 .20

Opening of the new terminal of the Rio Doce Iron Ore Company at Tubarao.

Pouring Ladle
and Steel
Beam — A526

Prof. de Rocha
Dissecting
Cadaver — A527

Perf. 11½x11
1966, Apr. 16   Photo.   Wmk. 267
1017 A526 30cr blk, *dp org* .25 .15

25th anniv. of the National Steel Company (nationalization of the steel industry).

1966, Apr. 26
1018 A527 30cr brt bluish grn .40 .15

50th anniv. of the discovery and description of Rickettsia prowazeki, the cause of typhus fever, by Prof. Henrique de Rocha Lima.

Battle of
Tuiuti
A528

Perf. 11x11½
1966, May 24   Photo.   Wmk. 267
1019 A528 30cr gray grn .30 .15

Centenary of the Battle of Tuiuti.

Symbolic Water
Cycle — A529

Pres. Shazar of
Israel — A530

1966, July 1   Perf. 11½x11
1020 A529 100cr lt brn & bl .25 .20

Hydrological Decade (UNESCO), 1965-74.

1966, July 18   Photo.   Wmk. 267
1021 A530 100cr ultra .30 .20

Visit of Pres. Zalman Shazar of Israel.

Imperial
Academy
of Fine
Arts
A531

Perf. 11x11½
1966, Aug. 12   Engr.   Wmk. 267
1022 A531 100cr red brown .60 .20

150th anniversary of French art mission.

Military
Service
Emblem
A532

1966, Sept. 6   Photo.   *Perf. 11x11½*
1023 A532 30cr yel, ultra & grn   .25   .15
  a. With commemorative border   3.50 3.00
New Military Service Law.
No. 1023a issued in sheets of 4. It carries at left a
30cr, design A532, in deeper tones of yellow and
ultramarine, Wmk. 264. Without gum. Sold for
100cr.

Ruben Dario — A533

Perf. 11½x11
1966, Sept. 20   Photo.   Wmk. 267
1024 A533 100cr brt rose lilac   .25   .15
Ruben Dario (pen name of Felix Ruben Garcia
Sarmiento (1867-1916), Nicaraguan poet, newspaper correspondent and diplomat.

Ceramic
Candlestick
from
Santarém
A534

1966, Oct. 6   *Perf. 11x11½*
1025 A534 30cr dk brn, *sal*   .25   .15
Centenary of Goeldi Museum at Belem.

Arms of Santa
Cruz — A535

Perf. 11½x11
1966, Oct. 15   Photo.   Wmk. 267
1026 A535 30cr slate grn   .25   .15
1st Natl. Tobacco Exposition, Santa Cruz.

UNESCO
Emblem — A536

1966, Oct. 24   Engr.   *Perf. 11½*
1027 A536 120cr black   .75   .25
  a. With commemorative border   6.00 6.00
20th anniv. of UNESCO. No. 1027a issued in
sheets of 4. It carries at right a design similar to No.
1027. Unwatermarked granite paper, without gum.
Sold for 150cr.

Captain Antonio
Correia Pinto and
Map of
Lages — A537

Cross of Lusitania
and Southern
Cross — A538

Perf. 11½x11
1966, Nov. 22   Photo.   Wmk. 267
1028 A537 30cr salmon pink   .25   .15
Arrival of Capt. Antonio Correia Pinto, cent.

1966, Dec. 4   *Perf. 11½*
1029 A538 100cr blue green   .30   .15
LUBRAPEX 1966 philatelic exhibition at the
National Museum of Fine Arts, Rio.

Madonna and
Child — A539

A540

Perf. 11½x11
1966, Dec.   Photo.   Wmk. 267
1030 A539 30cr blue green   .25   .15
Perf. 11½
1031 A540 35cr salmon & ultra   .20   .20
  a. 150cr salmon & ultra   2.50 3.00
Christmas 1966.
No. 1031a measures 46x103mm and is printed
in sheets of 4. It is inscribed "Pax Hominibus" (but
not "Brasil Correio") and carries the Madonna
shown on No. 1031. Issued without gum.
Issued: 30cr, 12/8; 35cr, 12/22; 150cr, 12/28.

Arms of
Laguna
A541

1967, Jan. 4   Engr.   *Perf. 11x11½*
1032 A541 60cr sepia   .20   .15
Centenary of the Post and Telegraph Agency of
Laguna, Santa Catarina.

Railroad
Bridge
A542

1967, Feb. 16   Photo.   Wmk. 267
1033 A542 50cr deep orange   .45   .20
Centenary of the Santos-Jundiai railroad.

Black Madonna of Czestochowa, Polish
Eagle and Cross — A543

1967, Mar. 12   *Perf. 11x11½*
1034 A543 50cr yel, bl & rose red   .35   .20
Adoption of Christianity in Poland, 1,000th anniv.

Research Rocket
A544

Anita
Garibaldi
A545

1967, Mar. 23   *Perf. 11½x11*
1035 A544 50cr blk & brt bl   .60   .30
World Meteorological Day, March 23.

Perf. 11x11½
1967-69   Photo.   Wmk. 267
Portraits: 1c, Mother Joana Angelica. 2c, Marilia
de Dirceu. 3c, Dr. Rita Lobato. 6c, Ana Neri. 10c,
Darcy Vargas.
1036 A545 1c dp ultra   .15   .15
1037 A545 2c red brn   .15   .15
1038 A545 3c brt grn   .18   .15
1039 A545 5c black   .35   .15
1040 A545 6c brown   .35   .15
1041 A545 10c dk slate grn   1.10   .30
  Nos. 1036-1041 (6)   2.28
    Set value   .64
Issued: 1c, May 3; 2c, Aug. 14; 3c, June 7; 5c,
Apr. 14; 6c, May 14, 1967; 10c, June 18, 1969.

VARIG Airlines
A546

Madonna and Child, by
Robert Feruzzi
A548

1967, May 8   *Perf. 11½x11*
1046 A546 6c brt bl & blk   .30   .25
40th anniversary of VARIG Airlines.

Lions
Emblem
and Globes
A547

1967, May 9   Engr.   *Perf. 11x11½*
1047 A547 6c green   .30   .25
  a. Souvenir sheet   2.50 3.00
50th anniv. of Lions Intl. No. 1047a contains one
imperf. stamp similar to No. 1047. Sold for 15c.

1967, May 14   Photo.   *Perf. 11½x11*
1048 A548 5c violet   .25   .20
  a. 15c Souvenir sheet   2.25 2.25
Mother's Day. No. 1048a contains one 15c
imperf. stamp in design of No. 1048.

Prince
Akihito
and
Princess
Michiko
A549

1967, May 25   *Perf. 11x11½*
1049 A549 10c black & pink   .30   .20
Visit to Brazil of Crown Prince Akihito and Princess Michiko of Japan.

Carrier Pigeon
and Radar
Screen
A550

Brother Vicente
do Salvador
A551

Perf. 11½x11
1967, June 20   Photo.   Wmk. 267
1050 A550 10c sl & brt pink   .25   .15
Issued to commemorate the opening of the Communications Ministry in Brasilia.

1967, June 28   Engr.
1051 A551 5c brown   .25   .15
400th birth anniv. of Brother Vicente do Salvador
(1564-1636), founder of Franciscan convent in Rio
de Janeiro, and historian.

Boy, Girl and
4-S Emblem
A552

1967, July 12   Photo.   *Perf. 11½*
1052 A552 5c green & blk   .25   .20
National 4-S (4-H) Day.

Möbius
Strip
A553

1967, July 21   *Perf. 11x11½*
1053 A553 5c brt bl & blk   .25   .20
6th Brazilian Mathematical Congress.

Fish — A554

1967, Aug. 1   *Perf. 11½*
1054 A554 5c slate   .30   .20
Bicentenary of city of Piracicaba.

Golden Rose and Papal Arms — A555

1967, Aug. 15
1055 A555 20c mag & yel   1.00 .40

Offering of a golden rose by Pope Paul VI to the Virgin Mary of Fatima (Our Lady of Peace), Patroness of Brazil.

General Sampaio A556

King Olaf of Norway A557

1967, Aug. 25   Engr.   Perf. 11½x11
1056 A556 5c blue   .25 .20

Issued to honor General Antonio de Sampaio, hero of the Battle of Tutui.

1967, Sept. 8   Photo.
1057 A557 10c brown org   .25 .20

Visit of King Olaf of Norway.

Sun over Sugar Loaf, Botafogo Bay A558

Nilo Peçanha A559

Photogravure and Embossed
1967, Sept. 25   Wmk. 267   Perf. 11½
1058 A558 10c blk & dp org   .25 .20

22nd meeting of the Intl. Monetary Fund, Intl. Bank for Reconstruction and Development, Intl. Financial Corporation and Intl. Development Assoc.

Perf. 11½x11
1967, Oct. 1   Photo.   Wmk. 267
1059 A559 5c brown violet   .25 .20

Peçanha (1867-1924), Pres. of Brazil 1909-10.

Virgin of the Apparition and Basilica of Aparecida A560

Cockerel, Festival Emblem A561

1967, Oct. 11   Perf. 11½
1060 A560 5c ultra & dl yel   .30 .20
  a.   Souvenir sheet of 2   3.25 3.25

250th anniv. of the discovery of the statue of Our Lady of the Apparition, now in the National Basilica of the Apparition at Aparecida do Norte.
No. 1060a contains imperf. 5c and 10c stamps similar to No. 1060. Issued Dec. 27, 1967, for Christmas.

Engraved and Photogravure
1967, Oct. 16   Perf. 11½x11
1061 A561 20c black & multi   .50 .40

Second International Folksong Festival.

Balloon, Plane and Rocket A562

Perf. 11x11½
1967, Oct. 18   Photo.   Unwmk.
1062 A562 10c blue   .50 .30
  a.   15c souvenir sheet   4.50 4.50

Week of the Wing, Oct. 18-23. No. 1062a contains one imperf. 15c stamp similar to No. 1062 and was issued Oct. 23.

Pres. Arthur Bernardes — A563

Portraits of Brazilian Presidents: 20c, Campos Salles. 50c, Wenceslau Pereira Gomes Braz. 1cr, Washington Pereira de Souza Luiz. 2cr, Castello Branco.

Perf. 11x11½
1967-68   Photo.   Wmk. 267
1063 A563 10c blue   .24 .20
1064 A563 20c dk red brn   .75 .20
Engr.
1065 A563 50c black ('68)   3.75 .30
1066 A563 1cr lil rose ('68)   6.00 .30
1067 A563 2cr emerald ('68)   1.10 .30
Nos. 1063-1067 (5)   11.84 1.30

Carnival of Rio — A564

Ships, Anchor and Sailor — A565

1967, Nov. 22   Perf. 11½x11
1070 A564 10c lem, ultra & pink   .30 .20
  a.   15c souvenir sheet   3.50 4.50

Issued for International Tourist Year, 1967. No. 1070a contains a 15c imperf. stamp in design of No. 1070. Issued Nov. 24.

1967, Dec. 6
1071 A565 10c ultra   .30 .25

Issued for Navy Week.

Christmas Decorations A566

1967, Dec. 8   Perf. 11½
1072 A566 5c car, yel & bl   .25 .20

Christmas 1967.

Olavo Bilac, Planes, Tank and Aircraft Carrier A567

Perf. 11x11½
1967, Dec. 16   Photo.   Wmk. 267
1073 A567 5c brt blue & yel   .30 .20

Issued for Reservists' Day and to honor Olavo Bilac, sponsor of compulsory military service.

Rodrigues de Carvalho — A568

1967, Dec. 18   Engr.   Perf. 11½x11
1074 A568 10c green   .25 .20

Cent. of the birth of Rodrigues de Carvalho, poet and lawyer.

Orlando Rangel A569

1968, Feb. 29   Photo.   Perf. 11x11½
1075 A569 5c lt grnsh bl & blk   .35 .25

Orlando de Fonseca Rangel, pioneer of pharmaceutical industry in Brazil, birth cent.

Virgin of Paranagua and Diver A570

Map of Brazil Showing Manaus A571

1968, Mar. 9   Perf. 11½x11
1076 A570 10c dk sl grn & brt yel grn   .35 .25

250th anniversary of the first underwater explorations at Paranagua.

1968, Mar. 13   Photo.   Wmk. 267
1077 A571 10c yel, grn & red   .35 .25

Free port of Manaus on the Amazon River.

Human Rights Flame A572

Paul Harris and Rotary Emblem A573

1968, Mar. 21   Perf. 11½x11
1078 A572 10c blue & salmon   .35 .25

International Human Rights Year.

1968, Apr. 19   Litho.   Unwmk.
Without Gum
1079 A573 20c grn & org brn   1.25 .70

Paul Percy Harris (1868-1947), founder of Rotary International.

Pedro Alvares Cabral and his Fleet — A574

Design: 20c, First Mass celebrated in Brazil.

1968   Without Gum   Perf. 11½
1080 A574 10c multicolored   .55 .45
1081 A574 20c multicolored   .80 .60

500th anniversary of the birth of Pedro Alvares Cabral, navigator, who took possession of Brazil for Portugal.
Issue dates: 10c, Apr. 22; 20c, July 11.

College Arms — A575

1968, Apr. 22   Photo.   Wmk. 267
1082 A575 10c vio bl, red & gold   .55 .35

Centenary of St. Luiz College, Sao Paulo.

Motherhood, by Henrique Bernardeli A576

1968, May 12   Litho.   Unwmk.
Without Gum
1083 A576 5c multicolored   .35 .25

Issued for Mother's Day.

Harpy Eagle — A577

Photogravure and Engraved
1968, May 28   Wmk. 267
1084 A577 20c brt bl & blk   1.50 .50

Sesquicentennial of National Museum.

Brazilian and Japanese Women — A578

1968, June 28   Litho.   Unwmk.
Without Gum
1085 A578 10c yellow & multi   .60 .40
Issued to commemorate the inauguration of Varig's direct Brazil-Japan airline.

Horse Race
A579

Perf. 11x11¹/₂
1968, July 16   Litho.   Unwmk.
Without Gum
1086 A579 10c multicolored   .35 .25
Centenary of the Jockey Club of Brazil.

Musician Wren
A580

Designs: 10c, Red-crested cardinal, vert. 50c, Royal flycatcher, vert.
Perf. 11¹/₂x11, 11x11¹/₂
1968-69   Engr.   Wmk. in Sheet
Without Gum
1087 A580 10c multi ('69)   .45 .28
1088 A580 20c multicolored   .75 .28
1089 A580 50c multicolored   1.00 .55
       Nos. 1087-1089 (3)   2.20 1.11
Some stamps in each sheet of Nos. 1087-1089 show parts of a two-line papermaker's watermark: "WESTERPOST / INDUSTRIA BRASILEIRA" with diamond-shaped emblem between last two words. Entire watermark appears in one sheet margin.
Issue dates: 10c, Aug. 20, 1969. 20c, July 19, 1968. 50c, Aug. 2, 1968.

Mailbox and Envelope
A581

Photogravure and Engraved
1968, Aug. 1   Wmk. 267   Perf. 11
1091 A581 5c citron, blk & grn   .20 .20
Stamp Day, 1968 and for 125th anniv. of the 1st Brazilian postage stamps.

Emilio Luiz Mallet
A582

Map of South America
A583

Perf. 11¹/₂x11
1968, Aug. 25   Engr.   Wmk. 267
1092 A582 10c pale purple   .20 .20
Issued to honor Marshal Emilio Luiz Mallet, Baron of Itapevi, patron of the marines.

1968, Sept. 5   Photo.
1093 A583 10c deep orange   .20 .20
Visit of President Eduardo Frei of Chile.

Seal of Portuguese Literary School — A584

Photogravure and Engraved
1968, Sept. 10   Perf. 11¹/₂
1094 A584 5c pink & grn   .20 .20
Centenary of Portuguese Literary School.

Map of Brazil and Telex Tape
A585

1968, Sept.   Photo.   Perf. 11x11¹/₂
1095 A585 20c citron & brt grn   .50 .25
Linking of 25 Brazilian cities by teletype.

Soldiers' Heads on Medal — A586

Perf. 11¹/₂x11
1968, Sept. 24   Litho.   Unwmk.
Without Gum
1096 A586 5c blue & gray   .20 .25
8th American Armed Forces Conference.

Clef, Notes and Sugarloaf Mountain
A587

1968, Sept. 30   Perf. 11¹/₂
Without Gum
1097 A587 6c blk, yel & red   .50 .30
Third International Folksong Festival.

Catalytic Cracking Plant — A588

1968, Oct. 4
Without Gum
1098 A588 6c blue & multi   .50 .40
Petrobras, the natl. oil company, 15th anniv.

Child Protection
A589

Whimsical Girl — A590

Design: 5c, School boy walking toward the sun.
Perf. 11¹/₂x11, 11x11¹/₂
1968, Oct. 16   Litho.   Unwmk.
Without Gum
1099 A590 5c gray & lt bl   .32 .30
1100 A589 10c brt bl, dk red & blk   .40 .25
1101 A590 20c multicolored   .50 .25
       Nos. 1099-1101 (3)   1.22 .80
22nd anniv. of UNICEF.

Children with Books
A591

1968, Oct. 23   Perf. 11x11¹/₂
Without Gum
1102 A591 5c multicolored   .25 .25
Issued to publicize Book Week.

UN Emblem and Flags — A592

1968, Oct. 24   Perf. 11¹/₂x11
Without Gum
1103 A592 20c black & multi   .45 .25
20th anniv. of WHO.

Jean Baptiste Debret, Self-portrait — A593

Perf. 11x11¹/₂
1968, Oct. 30   Litho.   Unwmk.
Without Gum
1104 A593 10c dk gray & pale yel   .35 .25
Jean Baptiste Debret, (1768-1848), French painter who worked in Brazil (1816-31). Design includes his "Burden Bearer."

Visita de S. M. Elizabeth II
Rainha da Inglaterra
ao Brasil 1968
Queen Elizabeth II
A594

1968, Nov. 4   Perf. 11¹/₂
Without Gum
1105 A594 70c lt bl & multi   1.75 1.00
Visit of Queen Elizabeth II of Great Britain.

Francisco Braga — A595

Perf. 11¹/₂x11
1968, Nov. 19   Wmk. 267
1106 A595 5c dull red brn   .40 .25
Cent. of the birth of Antonio Francisco Braga, composer of the Hymn of the Flag.

Brazilian Flag — A596

1968, Nov. 19   Unwmk.   Perf. 11¹/₂
Without Gum
1107 A596 10c multicolored   .40 .30
Issued for Flag Day.

Clasped Hands and Globe
A597

Perf. 11x11¹/₂
1968, Nov. 25   Typo.   Unwmk.
Without Gum
1108 A597 5c multicolored   .25 .25
Issued for Voluntary Blood Donor's Day.

Old Locomotive — A598

1968, Nov. 28   Litho.   Perf. 11¹/₂
Without Gum
1109 A598 5c multicolored   1.00 .50
Centenary of the Sao Paulo Railroad.

Bell — A599

Francisco Caldas, Jr. — A600

Design: 6c, Santa Claus and boy.

1968   Without Gum   Perf. 11¹/₂x11
1110 A599 5c multicolored   .30 .25
1111 A599 6c multicolored   .30 .25
Christmas 1968.
Issue dates: 5c, Dec. 12; 6c, Dec. 20.

1968, Dec. 13   Without Gum
1112 A600 10c crimson & blk   .20 .20
Cent. of the birth of Francisco Caldas, Jr., journalist and founder of Correio de Povo, newspaper.

Map of Brazil, War Memorial and Reservists' Emblem
A601

Perf. 11x11¹/₂
1968, Dec. 16   Photo.   Wmk. 267
1113 A601 5c bl grn & org brn   .30 .20
Issued for Reservists' Day.

Radar Antenna
A602

Viscount of Rio Branco
A603

Perf. 11¹/₂x11
1969, Feb. 28   Litho.   Unwmk.
Without Gum
1114 A602 30c ultra, lt bl & blk   .70 .55
Inauguration of EMBRATEL, satellite communications ground station bringing US television to Brazil via Telstar.

1969, Mar. 16
Without Gum
1115 A603 5c black & buff   .25 .25
José Maria da Silva Paranhos, Viscount of Rio Branco (1819-1880), statesman.

St. Gabriel — A604

1969, Mar. 24
Without Gum
1116 A604 5c multicolored   .40 .25
Issued to honor St. Gabriel as patron saint of telecommunications.

Shoemaker's Last and Globe — A605

Perf. 11x11¹/₂
1969, Mar. 29   Litho.   Unwmk.
Without Gum
1117 A605 5c multicolored   .25 .25
4th Intl. Shoe Fair, Novo Hamburgo.

Allan Kardec
A606

1969, Mar. 31   Photo.   Wmk. 267
1118 A606 5c brt grn & org brn   .25 .25
Allan Kardec (pen name of Leon Hippolyto Denizard Rivail, 1803-1869), French physician and spiritist.

Men of 3 Races and Arms of Cuiabá
A607

1969, Apr. 8   Litho.   Unwmk.
Without Gum
1119 A607 5c black & multi   .25 .25
250th anniversary of the founding of Cuiabá, capital of Matto Grosso.

State Mint — A608

1969, Apr. 11   Perf. 11¹/₂
Without Gum
1120 A608 5c olive bister & org   .45 .35
Opening of the state money printing plant.

Brazilian Stamps and Emblem
A609

Perf. 11x11¹/₂
1969, Apr. 30   Litho.   Unwmk.
Without Gum
1121 A609 5c multicolored   .25 .25
Sao Paulo Philatelic Society, 50th anniv.

St. Anne, Baroque Statue — A610

1969, May 8   Perf. 11¹/₂
Without Gum
1122 A610 5c lemon & multi   .50 .40
Issued for Mother's Day.

ILO Emblem
A611

Perf. 11x11¹/₂
1969, May 13   Photo.   Wmk. 267
1123 A611 5c dp rose red & gold   .25 .20
50th anniv. of the ILO.

Diving Platform and Swimming Pool — A612

Mother and Child at Window — A613

Lithographed and Photogravure
Perf. 11¹/₂x11
1969, June 13   Unwmk.
Without Gum
1124 A612 20c bis brn, blk & bl grn   .55 .40
40th anniversary of the Cearense Water Sports Club, Fortaleza.

1969   Litho.   Perf. 11¹/₂
Designs: 20c, Modern sculpture by Felicia Leirner. 50c, "The Sun Sets in Brasilia," by Danilo di Prete. 1cr, Angelfish, painting by Aldemir Martins.

Size: 24x36mm
1125 A613 10c orange & multi   .55 .25
Size: 33x34mm
1126 A613 20c red & multi   .55 .50
Size: 33x53mm
1127 A613 50c yellow & multi   1.90 1.25
Without Gum
1128 A613 1cr gray & multi   2.50 1.25
   Nos. 1125-1128 (4)   5.50 3.25
Issued to publicize the 10th Biennial Art Exhibition, Sao Paulo, Sept.-Dec. 1969.

Angelfish
A614

Fish — A615

Fish: 10c, Tetra. 15c, Piranha. No. 1130c, Megalamphodus megalopterus. 30c, Black tetra.

Perf. 11¹/₂
1969, July 21   Litho.   Wmk. 267
1129 A614 20c multicolored   .70 .40

Souvenir Sheet
1969, July 24   Unwmk.   Imperf.
1130 A615 Sheet of 4   5.00 5.00
   a. 10c yellow & multi   .90 .90
   b. 15c bright blue & multi   .90 .90
   c. 20c green & multi   .90 .90
   d. 30c orange & multi   .90 .90
Issued to publicize the work of ACAPI, an organization devoted to the preservation and development of fish in Brazil.
No. 1130 contains 4 stamps, size: 38¹/₂x21mm.

L. O. Teles de Menezes
A616

Mailman
A617

Perf. 11¹/₂x11
1969, July 26   Photo.   Wmk. 267
1131 A616 50c dp org & bl grn   1.25 1.00
Centenary of Spiritism press in Brazil.

1969, Aug. 1
1132 A617 30c blue   1.10 .90
Issued for Stamp Day.

Map of Brazil
A618

Gen. Tasso Fragoso
A620

Railroad Bridge
A619

Perf. 11¹/₂
1969, Aug. 25   Unwmk.   Litho.
Without Gum
1133 A618 10c lt ultra, grn & yel   .25 .20
Perf. 11x11¹/₂
1134 A619 20c multicolored   .80 .40

Perf. 11¹/₂x11
Engr.   Wmk. 267
With Gum
1135 A620 20c green   .80 .50
   Nos. 1133-1135 (3)   1.85 1.10
No. 1133 honors the Army as guardian of security; No. 1134, as promoter of development. No. 1135 the birth centenary of Gen. Tasso Fragoso.

Jupia Dam, Parana River — A621

Perf. 11½
1969, Sept. 10   Litho.   Unwmk.
Without Gum
1136 A621 20c lt blue & multi   .35 .35
Inauguration of the Jupia Dam, part of the Urubupunga hydroelectric system serving Sao Paulo.

Gandhi and Spinning Wheel A622

1969, Oct. 2   Perf. 11x11½
1137 A622 20c yellow & blk   .40 .30
Mohandas K. Gandhi (1869-1948), leader in India's fight for independence.

Santos Dumont, Eiffel Tower and Module Landing on Moon — A623

1969, Oct. 17   Perf. 11½
Without Gum
1138 A623 50c dk bl & multi   1.75 1.25
Man's first landing on the moon, July 20, 1969. See note after US No. C76.

Smelting Plant — A624

1969, Oct. 26   Unwmk.   Perf. 11½
Without Gum
1139 A624 20c multicolored   .45 .40
Expansion of Brazil's steel industry.

Steel Furnace A625

1969, Oct. 31   Litho.
Without Gum
1140 A625 10c yellow & multi   .45 .40
25th anniversary of Acesita Steel Works.

Water Vendor, by J. B. Debret — A626

Design: 30c, Street Scene, by Debret.

1969-70
Without Gum
1141 A626 20c multicolored   1.25 .50
1141A A626 30c multicolored   1.25 1.00
Jean Baptiste Debret (1768-1848), painter.
Issued: 20c, Nov. 5, 1969; 30c, May 19, 1970.

Exhibition Emblem — A627

1969, Nov. 15   Perf. 11½x11
Without Gum
1142 A627 10c multicolored   .35 .20
Issued to publicize the ABUEXPO 69 Philatelic Exposition, Sao Paulo, Nov. 15-23.

Plane — A628

1969, Nov. 23
Without Gum
1143 A628 50c multicolored   2.75 1.40
Issued to publicize the year of the expansion of the national aviation industry.

Pelé Scoring — A629

1969-70
Without Gum
1144 A629 10c multicolored   .40 .30
Souvenir Sheet
Imperf
1145 A629 75c multi ('70)   4.50 3.50
Issued to commemorate the 1,000th goal scored by Pele, Brazilian soccer player.
No. 1145 contains one imperf. stamp with simulated perforations.
Issued: 10c, Nov. 28, 1969; 75c, Jan. 23, 1970.

Madonna and Child from Villa Velha Monastery A630

Perf. 11½
1969, Dec.   Unwmk.   Litho.
Without Gum
1146 A630 10c gold & multi   .35 .20
Souvenir Sheet
Imperf
1147 A630 75c gold & multi   12.00 15.00
Christmas 1969.
No. 1147 has simulated perforations.
Issue dates: 10c, Dec. 8; 75c, Dec. 18.

Destroyer and Submarine A631

Perf. 11x11½
1969, Dec. 9   Engr.   Wmk. 267
1148 A631 5c bluish gray   .40 .25
Issued for Navy Day.

Dr. Herman Blumenau A632

1969, Dec. 26   Perf. 11½
1149 A632 20c gray grn   .85 .40
Dr. Herman Blumenau (1819-1899), founder of Blumenau, Santa Catarina State.

Carnival Scene — A633

Sugarloaf Mountain, Mask, Confetti and Streamers A634

Designs: 5c, Jumping boy and 2 women, vert. 20c, Clowns. 50c, Drummer.

1969-70   Litho.   Unwmk.
Without Gum
1150 A633 5c multicolored   .40 .30
1151 A633 10c multicolored   .40 .30
1152 A633 20c multicolored   .50 .40
1153 A634 30c multicolored   3.00 3.00
1154 A634 50c multicolored   2.75 2.50
Nos. 1150-1154 (5)   7.05 6.50
Carico Carnival, Rio de Janeiro.
Issue dates: Nos. 1150-1152, Dec. 29, 1969.
Nos. 1153-1154, Feb. 5, 1970.

Opening Bars of "Il Guarani" with Antonio Carlos Gomes Conducting A635

1970, Mar. 19   Litho.   Perf. 11½
Without Gum
1155 A635 20c blk, yel, gray & brn   .60 .40
Centenary of the opera Il Guarani, by Antonio Carlos Gomes.

Church of Penha — A636

1970, Apr. 6   Unwmk.   Perf. 11½
Without Gum
1156 A636 20c black & multi   .30 .20
400th anniversary of the Church of Penha, State of Esperito Santo.

Assembly Building A637

10th anniv. of Brasilia: 50c, Reflecting Pool. 1cr, Presidential Palace.

1970, Apr. 21
Without Gum
1157 A637 20c multicolored   .90 .70
1158 A637 50c multicolored   2.25 1.75
1159 A637 1cr multicolored   2.25 1.75
Nos. 1157-1159 (3)   5.40 4.20

Symbolic Water Design — A638

1970, May 5   Unwmk.   Perf. 11½
Without Gum
1161 A638 50c multicolored   2.50 3.00
Issued to publicize the Rondon Project for the development of the Amazon River basin.

Marshal Manoel Luiz Osorio and Osorio Arms — A639

1970, May 8
Without Gum
1162 A639 20c multicolored   1.50 1.00
Issued to commemorate the inauguration of the Marshal Osorio Historical Park.

Madonna, from San Antonio Monastery, Rio de Janeiro A640

Detail from Brasilia Cathedral A641

1970, May 10
Without Gum
1163 A640 20c multicolored   .40 .40
Issued for Mother's Day.

1970, May 27   Engr.   Wmk. 267
1164 A641 20c lt yellow grn   .25 .25
8th National Eucharistic Congress, Brasilia.

Census Symbol — A642

Perf. 11½
1970, June 22   Unwmk.   Litho.
Without Gum
1165 A642 20c green & yel   .60 .60
Issued to publicize the 8th general census.

Soccer Cup, Maps of Brazil and Mexico A643

Swedish Flag and Player Holding Rimet Cup — A644

Designs: 2cr, Chilean flag and soccer. 3cr, Mexican flag and soccer.

1970
Without Gum
1166 A643 50c blk, lt bl & gold   .90 .90
1167 A644 1cr pink & multi   2.75 1.50
1168 A644 2cr gray & multi   5.25 1.50
1169 A644 3cr multicolored   4.50 1.00
    Nos. 1166-1169 (4)   13.40 4.90
9th World Soccer Championships for the Jules Rimet Cup, Mexico City, May 30-June 21. No. 1166 honors Brazil's victory.
Issued: #1166, June 24; #1167-1169, Aug. 4.

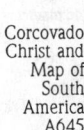

Corcovado Christ and Map of South America A645

1970, July 18
Without Gum
1170 A645 50c brn, dk red & bl   2.50 2.50
6th World Cong. of Marist Brothers' Alumni.

Pandia Calogeras, Minister of War — A646

Perf. 11½x11
1970, Aug. 25   Photo.   Unwmk.
1171 A646 20c blue green   .50 .50

Brazilian Military Emblems and Map A647

Perf. 11x11½
1970, Sept. 8   Litho.   Unwmk.
Without Gum
1172 A647 20c gray & multi   .50 .50
25th anniv. of victory in World War II.

Annunciation (Brazilian Primitive Painting) A648

1970, Sept. 29   Perf. 11½
Without Gum
1173 A648 20c multicolored   1.25 1.00
Issued for St. Gabriel's (patron saint of communications) Day.

Boy in Library — A649

UN Emblem — A650

1970, Oct. 23
Without Gum
1174 A649 20c multicolored   1.25 1.00
Issued to publicize Book Week.

1970, Oct. 24
Without Gum
1175 A650 50c dk bl, lt bl & sil   1.25 1.25
25th anniversary of the United Nations.

Rio de Janeiro, 1820 — A651

Designs: 50c, LUBRAPEX 70 emblem. 1cr, Rio de Janeiro with Sugar Loaf Mountain, 1970. No. 1179, like 20c.

1970, Oct.
Without Gum
1176 A651 20c multicolored   1.75 1.00
1177 A651 50c yel brn & blk   3.50 2.00
1178 A651 1cr multicolored   3.50 3.75
    Nos. 1176-1178 (3)   8.75 6.75
Souvenir Sheet
Imperf
1179 A651 1cr multicolored   11.00 17.00
LUBRAPEX 70, 3rd Portuguese-Brazilian Phil. Exhib., Rio de Janeiro, Oct. 24-31.
Issued: #1176-1178, Oct. 27; #1179, Oct. 31.

Holy Family by Candido Portinari A652

1970, Dec.   Litho.   Perf. 11½
Without Gum
1180 A652 50c multicolored   1.50 1.50
Souvenir Sheet
Imperf
1181 A652 1cr multicolored   15.00 24.00
Christmas 1970. No. 1181 contains one stamp with simulated perforations.
Issue dates: 50c, Dec. 1; 1cr, Dec. 8.

Battleship A653

CIH Emblem A654

1970, Dec. 11   Litho.   Perf. 11½
Without Gum
1182 A653 20c multicolored   1.25 .75
Navy Day.

1971, Mar. 28   Litho.   Perf. 11½
Without Gum
1183 A654 50c black & red   1.50 1.75
3rd Inter-American Housing Congress, Mar. 27-Apr. 3.

Links Around Globe — A655

1971, Mar. 31   Litho.   Perf. 12½x11
Without Gum
1184 A655 20c grn, yel, blk & red   .65 .50
Intl. year against racial discrimination.

Morpho Melacheilus — A656

Design: 1cr, Papilio thoas brasiliensis.

Perf. 11x11½
1971, Apr. 28   Litho.   Unwmk.
Without Gum
1185 A656 20c multicolored   1.25 .60
1186 A656 1cr multicolored   5.50 3.25

Madonna and Child — A657

1971, May 9   Litho.   Perf. 11½
Without Gum
1187 A657 20c multicolored   .85 .40
Mother's Day, 1971.

Basketball A658

1971, May 19
Without Gum
1188 A658 70c multicolored   1.50 1.00
6th World Women's Basketball Championship.

Map of Trans-Amazon Highway A660   A659

Perf. 11½
1971, July 1   Unwmk.   Litho.
Without Gum
1189 A659 40c multicolored   5.50 2.75
1190 A660 1cr multicolored   5.50 5.50
   a.   Pair, #1189-1190   11.00 11.00
Trans-Amazon Highway. No. 1190a printed in sheets of 28 (4x7). Horizontal rows contain 2 No. 1190a with a label between. Each label carries different inscription.

Man's Head, by Victor Mairelles de Lima — A661

Stamp Day: 1cr, Arab Violinist, by Pedro Américo.

1971, Aug. 1
Without Gum
1191 A661 40c pink & multi   1.25 .80
1192 A661 1cr gray & multi   3.25 1.65

Duke of Caxias and Map of Brazil — A662

1971, Aug. 23   **Photo.**
1193 A662 20c yel grn & red brn   .50 .60
Army Day.

Anita Garibaldi — A663

1971, Aug. 30   **Litho.**
Without Gum
1194 A663 20c multicolored   .40 .40
Anita Garibaldi (1821-1849), heroine in liberation of Brazil.

Xavante Jet and Santos Dumont's Plane, 1910 — A664

1971, Sept. 6
Without Gum
1195 A664 40c yellow & multi   1.40 .75
First flight of Xavante jet plane.

Flags and Map of Central American Nations — A665

"71" in French Flag Colors — A666

1971, Sept. 15
Without Gum
1196 A665 40c ocher & multi   1.25 .60
Sesquicentennial of the independence of Central American nations.

1971, Sept. 16
Without Gum
1197 A666 1.30cr ultra & multi   1.25 1.10
French Exhibition.

Black Mother, by Lucilio de Albuquerque A667

Archangel Gabriel A668

1971, Sept. 28
Without Gum
1198 A667 40c multicolored   .60 .50
Centenary of law guaranteeing personal freedom starting at birth.

1971, Sept. 29   **Perf. 11½x11**
Without Gum
1199 A668 40c multicolored   .75 .65
St. Gabriel's Day.

Bridge over River — A669

Children's Drawings: 35c, People crossing bridge. 60c, Woman with hat.

1971, Oct. 25   **Perf. 11½**
Without Gum
1200 A669 35c pink, bl & blk   .55 .45
1201 A669 45c black & multi   1.40 .45
1202 A669 60c olive & multi   .55 .45
   Nos. 1200-1202 (3)   2.50 1.35
Children's Day.

Werkhäuserii Superba A670

1971, Nov. 16
Without Gum
1203 A670 40c blue & multi   2.00 1.00
In memory of Carlos Werkhauser, botanist.

Greek Key Pattern "25" — A671

Design: 40c, like 20c but inscribed "sesc / servicio social / do comercio."

1971, Dec. 3
Without Gum
1204 A671 20c black & blue   1.25 1.00
1205 A671 40c black & org   1.25 1.00
   a.   Pair, #1204-1205   2.50 2.50
25th anniversary of SENAC (national apprenticeship system) and SESC (commercial social service).

Gunboat A672

1971, Dec. 8   **Perf. 11**
Without Gum
1206 A672 20c blue & multi   .85 .50
Navy Day.

Cross and Circles — A673

Washing of Bonfim Church, Salvador, Bahia — A674

1971, Dec. 11
1207 A673 20c car & blue   .40 .40
1208 A673 75c silver & gray   .80 3.00
1209 A673 1.30cr blk, yel, grn & bl 4.75 2.50
   Nos. 1207-1209 (3)   5.95 5.90
Christmas 1971.

1972, Feb. 18   Litho.   Perf. 11½x11
Designs: 40c, Grape Festival, Rio Grande do Sul. 75c, Festival of the Virgin of Nazareth, Belém. 1.30cr, Winter Arts Festival, Ouro Preto.
Without Gum
1210 A674 20c silver & multi   1.50 .75
1211 A674 40c silver & multi   2.75 .75
1212 A674 75c silver & multi   2.75 3.00
1213 A674 1.30cr silver & multi   6.00 3.00
   Nos. 1210-1213 (4)   13.00 7.50

Pres. Lanusse and Flag of Argentina A675

1972, Mar. 13   **Perf. 11x11½**
Without Gum
1214 A675 40c blue & multi   2.00 2.50
Visit of Lt. Gen. Alejandro Agustin Lanusse, president of Argentina.

Presidents Castello Branco, Costa e Silva and Garrastazu Medici A676

1972, Mar. 29
Without Gum
1215 A676 20c emerald & multi   1.25 .60
Anniversary of 1964 revolution.

Post Office Emblem — A677

Perf. 11½x11
1972, Apr. 10   Photo.   Unwmk.
1216 A677 20c red brown   2.00 .20
No. 1216 is luminescent.

Pres. Thomas and Portuguese Flag A678

1972, Apr. 22   Litho.   Perf. 11
Without Gum
1217 A678 75c ol brn & multi   1.75 1.75
Visit of Pres. Americo Thomas of Portugal to Brazil, Apr. 22-27.

Soil Research (CPRM) A679

1972, May 3   **Perf. 11½**
Without Gum
1218 A679 20c shown   1.50 .50
1219 A679 40c Offshore oil rig   3.50 .85
1220 A679 75c Hydroelectric
             dam   1.50 1.75
1221 A679 1.30cr Iron ore produc-
             tion   3.50 1.40
   Nos. 1218-1221 (4)   10.00 4.50
Industrial development. Stamps are inscribed with names of industrial firms. See Nos. 1228-1229.

Souvenir Sheet

Poster for Modern Art Week 1922 — A680

1972, May 5
1222 A680 1cr black & car   26.00 26.00
50th anniversary of Modern Art Week.

Mailman, Map of Brazil and Letters A681

Designs: 45c, "Telecommunications", vert. 60c, Tropospheric scatter system. 70c, Road map of Brazil and worker.

1972, May 26
Without Gum
1223 A681 35c blue & multi   1.25 .40
1224 A681 45c silver & multi   1.50 1.50
1225 A681 60c black & multi   1.50 1.25
1226 A681 70c multicolored   1.75 1.25
   Nos. 1223-1226 (4)   6.00 4.40
Unification of communications in Brazil.

Development Type and

Automobiles — A682

Perf. 11x11½, 11½x11
1972, June 21   **Photo.**
1227 A682 35c shown   1.00 .50
Litho.
1228 A679 45c Ships   1.00 .60
1229 A679 70c Ingots   1.00 .40
   Nos. 1227-1229 (3)   3.00 1.50
Industrial development. The 35c is luminescent.

Soccer — A683

Designs: 75c, Folk music. 1.30cr, Plastic arts.

Perf. 11¹/₂x11

1972, July 7   **Photo.**   **Unwmk.**
1230	A683	20c black & yel	1.00	.50
1231	A683	75c black & ver	2.00	3.50
1232	A683	1.30cr black & ultra	4.00	3.50
	Nos. 1230-1232 (3)		7.00	7.50

150th anniversary of independence. No. 1230 publicizes the 1972 sports tournament, a part of independence celebrations. Luminescent.

Souvenir Sheet

Shout of Independence, by Pedro Americo de Figueiredo e Melo — A684

1972, July 19   **Litho.**   **Perf. 11¹/₂**
Without Gum
1233	A684	1cr multicolored	4.00	9.00

4th Interamerican Philatelic Exhibition, EXFIL-BRA, Rio de Janeiro, Aug 26-Sept. 2.

Figurehead
A685

Brazilian folklore: 60c, Gauchos dancing fandango. 75c, Acrobats (capoeira). 1.15cr, Karajá (ceramic) doll. 1.30cr, Mock bullfight (bumba meu boi).

1972, Aug. 6
Without Gum
1234	A685	45c multicolored	.85	.35
1235	A685	60c orange & multi	1.65	1.50
1236	A685	75c gray & multi	.30	.30
1237	A685	1.15cr multicolored	.55	.55
1238	A685	1.30cr yellow & multi	5.00	2.00
	Nos. 1234-1238 (5)		8.35	4.70

Map of Brazil, by Diego Homem, 1568 — A686

Designs: 1cr, Map of Americas, by Nicholas Visscher, 1652. 2cr, Map of Americas, by Lopo Homem, 1519.

1972, Aug. 26   **Litho.**   **Perf. 11¹/₂**
Without Gum
1239	A686	70c multicolored	.50	.50
1240	A686	1cr multicolored	9.00	1.00
1241	A686	2cr multicolored	4.50	1.50
	Nos. 1239-1241 (3)		14.00	3.00

4th Inter-American Philatelic Exhibition, EXFIL-BRA, Rio de Janeiro, Aug. 26-Sept. 2.

Dom Pedro Proclaimed Emperor, by Jean Baptiste Debret
A687

Designs: 30c, Founding of Brazil (people with imperial flag), vert. 1cr, Coronation of Emperor Dom Pedro, vert. 2cr, Dom Pedro commemorative medal. 3.50cr, Independence Monument, Ipiranga.

1972, Sept. 4   **Litho.**   **Perf. 11¹/₂x11**
1242	A687	30c yellow & grn	1.25	1.25
1243	A687	70c pink & rose lil	1.25	.80
1244	A687	1cr buff & red brn	8.00	1.25
1245	A687	2cr pale yel & blk	4.00	1.25
1246	A687	3.50cr gray & blk	7.25	4.00
	Nos. 1242-1246 (5)		21.75	8.55

Sesquicentennial of independence.

Souvenir Sheet

"Automobile Race" — A688

1972, Nov. 14   **Perf. 11¹/₂**
1247	A688	2cr multicolored	10.00	15.00

Emerson Fittipaldi, Brazilian world racing champion.

Numeral and Post Office Emblem — A689

Möbius Strip — A689a

Perf. 11¹/₂x11
1972-75   **Unwmk.**   **Photo.**
1248	A689	5c orange	.35	.15
a.	Wmk. 267		.20	.15
1249	A689	10c brown ('73)	.20	.15
a.	Wmk. 267		4.00	.15
1250	A689	15c brt blue ('75)	.15	.15
1251	A689	20c ultra	.35	.15
1252	A689	25c sepia ('75)	.25	.15
1253	A689	30c dp carmine	.40	.15
1254	A689	40c dk grn ('73)	.20	.15
1255	A689	50c olive	.30	.15
1256	A689	70c red lilac ('75)	.30	.15

    Engr.   **Perf. 11¹/₂**
1257	A689a	1cr lilac ('74)	.45	.15
1258	A689a	2cr grnsh bl ('74)	.65	.15
1259	A689a	4cr org & vio ('75)	1.40	.20
1260	A689a	5cr brn, car & buff ('74)	2.00	.20
1261	A689a	10cr grn, blk & buff ('74)	4.50	.30
	Nos. 1248-1261 (14)		11.50	
	Set value			1.55

The 5cr and 10cr have beige lithographed multiple Post Office emblem underprint.
Nos. 1248-1261 are luminescent. Nos. 1248a and 1249a are not.

Hand Writing "Mobral" A690

20c, Multiracial group and population growth curve. 1cr, People and hands holding house. 2cr, People, industrial scene and upward arrow.

1972, Nov. 28   **Litho.**   **Perf. 11¹/₂**
Without Gum
1262	A690	10c black & multi	.20	.50
1263	A690	20c black & multi	1.00	.75
1264	A690	1cr black & multi	8.75	.30
1265	A690	2cr black & multi	2.00	.75
	Nos. 1262-1265 (4)		11.95	2.30

Publicity for: "Mobral" literacy campaign (10c); Centenary of census (20c); Housing and retirement fund (1cr); Growth of gross national product (2cr).

Congress Building, Brasilia, by Oscar Niemeyer, and "Os Guerreiros," by Bruno Giorgi
A691

1972, Dec. 4
Without Gum
1266	A691	1cr blue, blk & org	10.00	6.00

Meeting of Natl. Cong., Brasilia, Dec. 4-8.

Holy Family (Clay Figurines) A692

Retirement Plan A693

1972, Dec. 13   **Photo.**   **Perf. 11¹/₂x11**
1267	A692	20c ocher & blk	.85	.50

Christmas 1972. Luminescent.

Perf. 11¹/₂x11, 11x11¹/₂
1972, Dec. 20   **Litho.**

#1269, School children and traffic lights, horiz. 70c, Dr. Oswaldo Cruz with Red Cross, caricature. 2cr, Produce, fish and cattle, horiz.

Without Gum
1268	A693	10c blk, bl & dl org	.50	.50
1269	A693	10c orange & multi	1.00	1.00
1270	A693	70c blk, red & brn	9.00	3.75
1271	A693	2cr green & multi	15.00	6.50
	Nos. 1268-1271 (4)		25.50	11.75

Publicity for: Agricultural workers' assistance program (No. 1268); highway and transportation development (No. 1269); centenary of the birth of Dr. Oswaldo Cruz (1872-1917), Director of Public Health Institute (70c); agricultural and cattle export (2cr). Nos. 1268-1271 are luminescent.

Sailing Ship, Navy A694

Designs: 10c, Monument, Brazilian Expeditionary Force. No. 1274, Plumed helmet, Army. No. 1275, Rocket, Air Force.

Lithographed and Engraved
1972, Dec. 28   **Perf. 11x11¹/₂**
Without Gum
1272	A694	10c brn, dk brn & blk	1.50	1.10
1273	A694	30c lt ultra, grn & blk	1.50	1.10
1274	A694	30c yel grn, brn & blk	1.50	1.10
1275	A694	30c lilac, mar & blk	1.50	1.10
a.	Block of 4, #1272-1275		6.00	5.00

Armed Forces Day.

Rotary Emblem and Cogwheels A695

Perf. 11¹/₂
1973, Mar. 21   **Litho.**   **Unwmk.**
1276	A695	1cr ultra, grnsh bl & yel	1.75	1.50

Rotary International serving Brazil 50 years.

Swimming A696

#1278, Gymnastics. #1279, Volleyball, vert.

1973   **Photo.**   **Perf. 11x11¹/₂, 11¹/₂x11**
1277	A696	40c brt bl & red brn	.35	.35
1278	A696	40c green & org brn	2.75	.70
1279	A696	40c violet & org brn	.70	.70
	Nos. 1277-1279 (3)		3.80	1.75

Issue dates: No. 1277, Apr. 19; No. 1278, May 22; No. 1279, Oct. 15.

Flag of Paraguay A697

1973, Apr. 27   **Litho.**   **Unwmk.**
1280	A697	70c multicolored	1.75	1.25

Visit of Pres. Alfredo Stroessner of Paraguay, Apr. 25-27.

"Communications" — A698

1cr, Neptune, map of South America and Africa.

1973, May 5   **Perf. 11x11¹/₂**
1281	A698	70c multicolored	.80	.70
1282	A698	1cr multicolored	4.25	3.00

Inauguration of the Ministry of Communications Building, Brasilia (70c); and of the first underwater telephone cable between South America and Europe, Bracan 1 (1cr).

Congress Emblem — A699

1973, May 19   **Perf. 11¹/₂x11**
1283	A699	1cr orange & pur	4.00	3.00

24th Congress of the International Chamber of Commerce, Rio de Janeiro, May 19-26.

694

Swallowtailed Manakin — A700

Birds: No. 1285, Orange-backed oriole. No. 1286, Brazilian ruby (hummingbird).

1973   **Litho.**   *Perf. 11x11 1/2*
1284 A700 20c multicolored   .50 .20
1285 A700 20c multicolored   .50 .20
1286 A700 20c multicolored   .50 .20
   Nos. 1284-1286 (3)   1.50 .60

Issue dates: No. 1284, May 26; No. 1285, June 6; No. 1286, June 19.

Tourists A701

1973, June 28   **Litho.**   *Perf. 11x11 1/2*
1287 A701 70c multicolored   .90 .85
National Tourism Year.

Conference at Itu — A702   Satellite and Multi-spectral Image — A703

1973   *Perf. 11 1/2x11*
1288 A702 20c shown   .52 .35
1289 A702 20c Decorated wagon   .52 .35
1290 A702 20c Indian   .52 .35
1291 A702 20c Graciosa Road   .52 .35
   Nos. 1288-1291 (4)   2.08 1.40

Centenary of the Itu Convention (1288); sesqui-centennial of the July 2 episode (1289); 400th anniversary of the founding of Niteroi (1290); centenary of Graciosa Road (1291).
Issue dates: #1291, July 29; others July 2.

1973, July 11   *Perf. 11 1/2*
Designs: 70c, Official opening of Engineering School, 1913. 1cr, Möbius strips and "IMPA."
1292 A703 20c black & multi   .25 .40
1293 A703 70c dk blue & multi   2.25 1.00
1294 A703 1cr lilac & multi   3.00 1.00
   Nos. 1292-1294 (3)   5.50 2.40

Institute for Space Research (20c); School of Engineering, Itajubá, 60th anniversary (70c); Institute for Pure and Applied Mathematics (1cr).

Santos-Dumont and 14-Bis Plane — A704

Designs (Santos-Dumont and): 70c, No. 6 Balloon and Eiffel Tower. 2cr Demoiselle plane.

Lithographed and Engraved
1973, July 20   *Perf. 11x11 1/2*
1295 A704 20c lt grn, brt grn & brn   .75 .25
1296 A704 70c yel, rose red & brn   1.75 1.25
1297 A704 2cr bl, vio bl & brn   1.75 1.25
   Nos. 1295-1297 (3)   4.25 2.75

Centenary of the birth of Alberto Santos-Dumont (1873-1932), aviation pioneer.

Mercator Map A705

No. 1299, Same, red border on top and at left.
Photogravure and Engraved
1973, Aug. 1   **Wmk. 267**
1298 A705 40c red & black   2.50 1.50
1299 A705 40c red & black   2.10 2.10
  a.   Block of 4   21.00 15.00

Stamp Day. Nos. 1298-1299 are printed se-tenant horizontally and tête bêche vertically in sheets of 55. Blocks of 4 have red border all around.

Gonçalves Dias (1823-1864), Poet — A706

Perf. 11 1/2x11
1973, Aug. 10   **Wmk. 267**
1300 A706 40c violet & blk   .70 .42

Souvenir Sheet

Copernicus and Sun — A707

Perf. 11x11 1/2
1973, Aug. 15   **Litho.**   **Unwmk.**
1301 A707 1cr multicolored   4.00 5.00

500th anniversary of the birth of Nicolaus Copernicus (1473-1543), Polish astronomer.

Folklore Festival Banner — A708

1973, Aug. 22   *Perf. 11 1/2*
1302 A708 40c ultra & multi   .75 .52
Folklore Day, Aug. 22.

Masonic Emblem A709

1973, Aug. 24   **Photo.**   *Perf. 11x11 1/2*
1303 A709 1cr Prus blue   3.00 2.00
Free Masons of Brazil, 1822-1973.

Nature Protection A710

#1305, Fire protection. #1306, Aviation safety. #1307, Safeguarding cultural heritage.

1973, Sept. 20   **Litho.**   *Perf. 11x11 1/2*
1304 A710 40c brt grn & multi   .75 .40
1305 A710 40c dk grn & multi   .75 .40
1306 A710 40c lt blue & multi   .75 .40
1307 A710 40c pink & multi   .75 .40
   Nos. 1304-1307 (4)   3.00 1.60

Souvenir Sheet

St. Gabriel and Proclamation of Pope Paul VI — A711

Lithographed and Engraved
1973, Sept. 29   **Unwmk.**   *Perf. 11 1/2*
1308 A711 1cr bister & blk   7.50 10.00

1st National Exhibition of Religious Philately, Rio de Janeiro, Sept. 29-Oct. 6.

St. Teresa — A712

Photogravure and Engraved
Perf. 11 1/2x11
1973, Sept. 30   **Wmk. 267**
1309 A712 2cr dk org & brn   3.50 2.50

St. Teresa of Lisieux, the Little Flower (1873-1897), Carmelite nun.

Monteiro Lobato and Emily A713

Perf. 11 1/2
1973, Oct. 12   **Litho.**   **Unwmk.**
1310 A713 40c shown   .80 .50
1311 A713 40c Aunt Nastacia   .80 .50
1312 A713 40c Snubnose, Peter and Rhino   .80 .50
1313 A713 40c Viscount de Sabugosa   .80 .50
1314 A713 40c Dona Benta   .80 .50
  a.   Block of 5 + label   4.00 4.00

Monteiro Lobato, author of children's books.

Soapstone Sculpture of Isaiah (detail) — A714

Baroque Art in Brazil: No. 1316, Arabesque, gilded wood carving, horiz. 70c, Father José Mauricio Nuñes Garcia and music score. 1cr, Church door, Salvador, Bahia. 2cr, Angels, church ceiling painting by Manoel da Costa Athayde, horiz.

1973, Nov. 5
1315 A714 40c multicolored   .30 .30
1316 A714 40c multicolored   .30 .30
1317 A714 70c multicolored   1.50 1.40
1318 A714 1cr multicolored   9.00 3.00
1319 A714 2cr multicolored   4.00 3.00
   Nos. 1315-1319 (5)   15.10 8.00

Old and New Telephones A715

1973, Nov. 28   *Perf. 11x11 1/2*
1320 A715 40c multicolored   .35 .30
50th anniv. of Brazilian Telephone Co.

Brasil 73 Natal

Symbolic Angel — A716

1973, Nov. 30   *Perf. 11 1/2*
1321 A716 40c ver & multi   .35 .30
Christmas 1973.

River Boats A717

1973, Nov. 30   **Litho.**   *Perf. 11x11 1/2*
1322 A717 40c "Gaiola"   .35 .35
1323 A717 70c "Regatao"   1.05 1.05
1324 A717 1cr "Jangada"   4.50 3.00
1325 A717 2cr "Saveiro"   4.25 3.00
   Nos. 1322-1325 (4)   10.15 7.40

Nos. 1322-1325 are luminescent.

Scales of Justice — A718

1973, Dec. 5   *Perf. 11 1/2*
1326 A718 40c magenta & vio   .50 .32

To honor the High Federal Court, created in 1891. Luminescent.

José Placido de Castro — A719   Scarlet Ibis and Victoria Regia — A720

Lithographed and Engraved
Perf. 11 1/2x11
1973, Dec. 12   **Wmk. 267**
1327 A719 40c lilac rose & blk   .60 .35

Centenary of the birth of Jose Placido de Castro, liberator of the State of Acre.

Perf. 11 1/2x11
1973, Dec. 28   **Litho.**   **Unwmk.**
Designs: 70c, Jaguar and spathodea campanulata. 1cr, Scarlet macaw and carnauba palm. 2cr, Rhea and coral tree.
1328 A720 40c brown & multi   .80 .50
1329 A720 70c brown & multi   2.25 1.50
1330 A720 1cr bister & multi   3.50 .40
1331 A720 2cr bister & multi   6.25 3.50
   Nos. 1328-1331 (4)   12.80 5.90

Nos. 1328-1331 are luminescent.

0,40 Brasil 74

Saci Perere, Mocking Goblin — A721

Characters from Brazilian Legends: 80c, Zumbi, last chief of rebellious slaves. 1cr, Chico Rei, African king. 1.30cr, Little Black Boy of the Pasture. 2.50cr, Iara, Queen of the Waters.

1974, Feb. 28   Litho.   Unwmk.
Perf. 11¹/₂x11
Size: 21x39mm

1332	A721	40c multicolored	.35	.25
1333	A721	80c multicolored	.70	.60
1334	A721	1cr multicolored	1.65	.45

Perf. 11¹/₂
Size: 32¹/₂x33mm

1335	A721	1.30cr multicolored	2.50	.85
1336	A721	2.50cr multicolored	10.50	2.50
		Nos. 1332-1336 (5)	15.70	4.65

Nos. 1332-1336 are luminescent.

Pres. Costa e Silva Bridge A722

1974, Mar. 11
1337 A722 40c multicolored   .60 .30
Inauguration of the Pres. Costa e Silva Bridge, Rio Niteroi, connecting Rio de Janeiro and Guanabara State.

"The Press" — A723

1974, Mar. 25   Perf. 11¹/₂
1338	A723	40c shown	.50	.30
1339	A723	40c "Radio"	.25	.25
1340	A723	40c "Television"	.40	.30
		Nos. 1338-1340 (3)	1.15	.85

Communications Commemorations: No. 1338, bicentenary of first Brazilian newspaper, published in London by Hipolito da Costa; No. 1339, founding of the Radio Sociedade do Rio de Janeiro by Roquette Pinto; No. 1340, installation of first Brazilian television station by Assis Chateaubriand. Luminescent.

"Reconstruction" A724

1974, Mar. 31
1341 A724 40c multicolored   .70 .45
10 years of progress. Luminescent.

Corcovado Christ, Marconi, Colors of Brazil and Italy — A725

1974, Apr. 25   Litho.   Perf. 11¹/₂
1342 A725 2.50cr multi   6.00 3.00
Guglielmo Marconi (1874-1937), Italian physicist and inventor. Luminescent.

Stamp Printing Press, Stamp Designing A726

1974, May 6
1343 A726 80c multicolored   1.00 .50
Brazilian mint.

World Map, Indian, Caucasian and Black Men — A727

World Map and: #1345, Brazilians. #1346, Cabin & German horseback rider. #1347, Italian farm wagon. #1348, Japanese woman & torii.

1974, May 3   Unwmk.
1344	A727	40c multicolored	.30	.30
1345	A727	40c multicolored	.20	.20
1346	A727	2.50cr multicolored	3.25	1.50
1347	A727	2.50cr multicolored	4.75	1.50
1348	A727	2.50cr multicolored	1.25	.85
		Nos. 1344-1348 (5)	9.75	4.35

Ethnic and migration influences in Brazil.

Sandstone Cliffs, Sete Cidades National Park A728

Tourist publicity: 80c, Ruins of Cathedral of Sao Miguel das Missões.

Lithographed and Engraved
1974, June 8   Perf. 11x11¹/₂
1349	A728	40c multicolored	.75	.50
1350	A728	80c multicolored	.75	.50

Souvenir Sheet

Soccer — A729

1974, June 20   Litho.   Perf. 11¹/₂
1351 A729 2.50cr multi   3.50 6.00
World Cup Soccer Championship, Munich, June 13-July 7.

Church and College, Caraça A730

1974, July 6   Litho.   Perf. 11x11¹/₂
1352 A730 40c multicolored   .45 .30
College (Seminary) of Caraça, bicent.

Wave on Television Screen A731

1974, July 15   Perf. 11¹/₂
1353 A731 40c black & blue   .30 .40
TELEBRAS, Third Brazilian Congress of Telecommunications, Brasilia, July 15-20.

Fernao Dias Paes — A732

1974, July 21   Perf. 11¹/₂
1354 A732 20c green & multi   .30 .30
3rd centenary of the expedition led by Fernao Dias Paes exploring Minas Gerais and the passage from South to North in Brazil.

Mexican Flag — A733

1974, July 24   Litho.   Perf. 11¹/₂
1355 A733 80c multicolored   2.25 1.10
Visit of Pres. Luis Echeverria Alvares of Mexico, July 24-29.

Flags of Brazil and Germany A734

1974, Aug. 5   Perf. 11x11¹/₂
1356 A734 40c multicolored   .50 .50
World Cup Soccer Championship, 1974, victory of German Federal Republic.

Souvenir Sheet

Congress Emblem — A735

1974, Aug. 7   Perf. 11¹/₂
1357 A735 1.30cr multi   .85 1.75
5th World Assembly of the World Council for the Welfare of the Blind, Sao Paulo, Aug. 7-16. Stamp and margin inscribed in Braille with name of Assembly.

Raul Pederneiras (1874-1953), Journalist, Professor of Law and Fine Arts), Caricature by J. Carlos — A736

Lithographed and Engraved
1974, Aug. 15   Perf. 11¹/₂x11
1358 A736 40c buff, blk & ocher   .30 .40

Society Emblem and Landscape A737

1974, Aug. 19   Litho.   Perf. 11x11¹/₂
1359 A737 1.30cr multi   1.25 .90
13th Congress of the International Union of Building and Savings Societies.

Souvenir Sheet

Five Women, by Di Cavalcanti — A738

1974, Aug. 26   Litho.   Perf. 11¹/₂
1360 A738 2cr multicolored   2.50 6.00
LUBRAPEX 74, 5th Portuguese-Brazilian Phil. Exhib., Sao Paulo, Nov. 26-Dec. 4.

"UPU" and World Map — A739

1974, Oct. 9   Litho.   Perf. 11¹/₂
1361 A739 2.50cr blk & brt bl   4.50 1.75
Centenary of Universal Postal Union.

Hammock (Antillean Arawak Culture) — A740

Bilro Lace — A741

Singer of "Cord" Verses — A742

Ceramic Figure by Master Vitalino — A743

1974, Oct. 16   Litho.   Perf. 11½
1362 A740 50c deep rose lilac   2.00   .40
1363 A741 50c lt & dk blue   2.50   .40
1364 A742 50c yel & red brn   .60   .40
1365 A743 50c brt yel & dk brn   .75   .40
  Nos. 1362-1365 (4)   5.85 1.60
  Popular Brazilian crafts.

Branch of Coffee A744

1974, Oct. 27   Unwmk.   Perf. 11
1366 A744 50c multicolored   1.00   .60
  Centenary of city of Campinas.

Hornless Tabapua A745

Animals of Brazil: 1.30cr, Creole horse. 2.50cr, Brazilian mastiff.

1974, Nov. 10   Perf. 11½
1367 A745 80c multi   1.10   .75
1368 A745 1.30cr multi   1.10   .75
1369 A745 2.50cr multi   7.75 2.50
  Nos. 1367-1369 (3)   9.95 4.00

Christmas — A746

1974, Nov. 18   Perf. 11½x11
1370 A746 50c Angel   .70   .30

Solteira Island Hydroelectric Dam A747

1974, Nov. 11   Perf. 11½
1371 A747 50c black & yellow   1.40   .50
  Inauguration of the Solteira Island Hydroelectric Dam over Parana River.

The Girls, by Carlos Reis — A748

1974, Nov. 26
1372 A748 1.30cr multi   .70   .50
  LUBRAPEX 74, 5th Portuguese-Brazilian Phil. Exhib., Sao Paulo, Nov. 26-Dec. 4.

Youths, Judge, Scales A749

1974, Dec. 20   Litho.   Perf. 11½
1373 A749 90c yel, red & bl   .30   .35
  Juvenile Court of Brazil, 50th anniversary.

Long Distance Runner — A750

1974, Dec. 23
1374 A750 3.30cr multi   .75   .75
  Sao Silvestre long distance running, 50th anniversary.

News Vendor, 1875, Masthead 1975 — A751

1975, Jan. 4
1375 A751 50c multicolored   1.25   .75
  Newspaper "O Estado de S. Paulo," cent.

Sao Paulo Industrial Park A752

Designs: 1.40cr, Natural rubber industry, Acre. 4.50cr, Manganese mining, Amapá.

1975, Jan. 24   Litho.   Perf. 11x11½
1376 A752 50c vio bl & yel   1.25   .40
1377 A752 1.40cr yellow & brn   .60   .40
1378 A752 4.50cr yellow & blk   6.00   .40
  Nos. 1376-1378 (3)   7.85 1.20
  Economic development.

Fort of the Holy Cross A753

Colonial forts: No. 1380, Fort of the Three Kings. No. 1381, Fort of Monteserrat. 90c, Fort of Our Lady of Help.

Litho. & Engr.
1975, Mar. 14   Perf. 11½
1379 A753 50c yel & red brn   .24   .16
1380 A753 50c yel & red brn   .40   .16
1381 A753 50c yel & red brn   .80   .16
1382 A753 90c yel & red brn   .24   .16
  Nos. 1379-1382 (4)   1.68   .64

House on Stilts, Amazon Region A754

Designs: 50c, Modern houses and plan of Brasilia. 1.40cr, Indian hut, Rondonia. 3.30cr, German-style cottage (Enxaimel), Santa Catarina.

1975, Apr. 18   Litho.   Perf. 11½
1383 A754 50c yel & multi   1.25 2.25
1384 A754 50c yel & multi   8.50 6.25
  a. Pair, #1383-1384   10.00 8.50
1385 A754 1cr yel & multi   .85   .22
1386 A754 1.40cr yel & multi   1.75 2.50
1387 A754 1.40cr yel & multi   .50   .85
  a. Pair, #1386-1387   2.25 3.50
1388 A754 3.30cr yel & multi   .75 1.25
1389 A754 3.30cr yel & multi   3.50 4.00
  a. Pair, #1388-1380   4.25 5.25
  Nos. 1383-1389 (7)   17.10 17.32
  Brazilian architecture. Nos. 1383, 1386, 1388 have yellow strip at right side, others at left.

Astronotus Ocellatus A755

Designs: Brazilian fresh-water fish.

1975, May 2   Litho.   Perf. 11½
1390 A755 50c shown   1.40   .40
1391 A755 50c Colomesus psitacus .25   .25
1392 A755 50c Phallocerus
            caudimaculatus   .25   .40
1393 A755 50c Symphysodon discus .48   .50
  Nos. 1390-1393 (4)   2.38 1.55

Soldier's Head in Brazil's Colors, Plane, Rifle and Ship — A756

Brazilian Otter — A757

1975, May 8   Perf. 11½x11
1394 A756 50c vio bl & multi   .35   .30
  In honor of the veterans of World War II, on the 30th anniversary of victory.

1975, June 17   Litho.   Perf. 11½
  Nature protection: 70c, Brazilian pines, horiz. 3.30cr, Marsh cayman, horiz.
1395 A757 70c bl, grn & blk   1.05   .50
1396 A757 1cr multi   1.05 1.00
1397 A757 3.30cr multi   .90   .75
  Nos. 1395-1397 (3)   3.00 2.25

Petroglyphs, Stone of Ingá — A758

Marjoara Vase, Pará — A759

Vinctifer Comptoni, Petrified Fish — A760

1975, July 8   Litho.   Perf. 11½
1398 A758 70c multicolored   .55   .40
1399 A759 1cr multicolored   .35   .40
1400 A760 1cr multicolored   .35   .40
  Nos. 1398-1400 (3)   1.25 1.20
  Archaeological discoveries.

Immaculate Conception, Franciscan Monastery, Vitoria — A761

Post and Telegraph Ministry — A762

1975, July 15
1401 A761 3.30cr blue & multi   .95   .95
  Holy Year 1975 and 300th anniv. of establishment of the Franciscan Province in Southern Brazil.

1975, Aug. 8   Engr.   Perf. 11½
1402 A762 70c dk carmine   .70   .30
  Stamp Day 1975.

Sword Dance, Minas Gerais — A763

Folk Dances: No. 1404, Umbrella Dance, Pernambuco. No. 1405, Warrior's Dance, Alagoas.

1975, Aug. 22   Litho.   Perf. 11½
1403 A763 70c gray & multi   .35   .35
1404 A763 70c pink & multi   .35   .35
1405 A763 70c yellow & multi   .35   .35
  Nos. 1403-1405 (3)   1.05 1.05

Trees A764

1975, Sept. 15   Perf. 11x11½
1406 A764 70c multicolored   .30   .25
  Annual Tree Festival.

Globe, Radar and Satellite — A765

1975, Sept. 16   Perf. 11½
1407 A765 3.30cr multi   .70   .75
  Inauguration of 2nd antenna of Tangua Earth Station, Rio de Janeiro State.

Woman Holding Flowers and Globe A766

1975, Sept. 23
1408 A766 3.30cr multi   1.00 1.00
International Women's Year 1975.

Tile, Railing and Column, Alcantara A767

Cross and Monastery, Sao Cristovao — A768

Historic cities: No. 1411, Jug and Clock Tower, Goiás, vert.

1975, Sept. 27   Litho.   Perf. 11½
1409 A767 70c multicolored   .32 .45
1410 A768 70c multicolored   .60 .45
1411 A768 70c multicolored   .60 .45
    Nos. 1409-1411 (3)   1.52 1.35

"Books teach how to live" — A769

1975, Oct. 23   Litho.   Perf. 11½
1412 A769 70c multicolored   .25 .30
Day of the Book.

ASTA Congress Emblem A770

1975, Oct. 27   Perf. 11x11½
1413 A770 70c multicolored   .25 .30
American Society of Travel Agents, 45th World Congress, Rio, Oct. 27-Nov. 1.

Angels — A771

1975, Nov. 11
1414 A771 70c red & brown   .25 .20
Christmas 1975.

Map of Americas, Waves — A772

Dom Pedro II — A773

1975, Nov. 19   Perf. 11½x12
1415 A772 5.20cr gray & multi   2.75 2.00
2nd Interamerican Conference of Telecommunications (CITEL), Rio, Nov. 19-27.

1975, Dec. 2   Engr.   Perf. 12
1416 A773 70c violet brown   .75 .45
Dom Pedro II (1825-1891), emperor of Brazil, birth sesquicentennial.

People and Cross A774

1975, Nov. 27   Litho.   Perf. 11x11½
1417 A774 70c lt bl & dp bl   .50 .65
National Day of Thanksgiving.

Guarapari Beach, Espirito Santo A775

Tourist Publicity: #1419, Salt Stone beach, Piaui. #1420, Cliffs, Rio Grande Do Sul.

1975, Dec. 19   Litho.   Perf. 11½
1418 A775 70c multicolored   .28 .28
1419 A775 70c multicolored   .28 .28
1420 A775 70c multicolored   .28 .28
    Nos. 1418-1420 (3)   .84 .84

Triple Jump, Games Emblem A776

1975, Dec. 22   Perf. 11x11½
1421 A776 1.60cr bl grn & blk   .25 .35
Triple jump world record by Joao Carlos de Oliveira in 7th Pan-American Games, Mexico City, Oct. 12-26.

UN Emblem and Headquarters A777

1975, Dec. 29   Perf. 11½
1422 A777 1.30cr dp bl & vio bl .25 .30
United Nations, 30th anniversary.

Light Bulbs, House and Sun A778

Energy conservation: No. 1424, Gasoline drops, car and sun.

1976, Jan. 16
1423 A778 70c multicolored   .30 .20
1424 A778 70c multicolored   .30 .15

Concorde A779

1976, Jan. 21   Litho.   Perf. 11x11½
1425 A779 5.20cr bluish blk   .50 .35
First commercial flight of supersonic jet Concorde from Paris to Rio, Jan. 21.

Souvenir Sheet

Nautical Map of South Atlantic, 1776 A780

1976, Feb. 2   Perf. 11½
1426 A780 70c salmon & multi   .85 1.50
Centenary of the Naval Hydrographic and Navigation Institute.

Telephone Lines, 1876 Telephone A781

1976, Mar. 10   Litho.   Perf. 11x11½
1427 A781 5.20cr orange & bl   .65 .48
Centenary of first telephone call by Alexander Graham Bell, March 10, 1876.

Eye and Exclamation Point — A782

Kaiapo Body Painting — A783

1976, Apr. 7   Litho.   Perf. 11½x11
1428 A782 1cr vio red brn & brn .50 .75
World Health Day: "Foresight prevents blindness."

1976, Apr. 19   Litho.   Perf. 11½
Designs: No. 1430, Bakairi ceremonial mask. No. 1431, Karajá feather headdress.
1429 A783 1cr lt violet & multi .16 .16
1430 A783 1cr lt violet & multi .16 .16
1431 A783 1cr lt violet & multi .16 .16
    Nos. 1429-1431 (3)   .48 .48
Preservation of indigenous culture.

Itamaraty Palace, Brasilia A784

1976, Apr. 20
1432 A784 1cr multicolored   .60 .60
Diplomats' Day. Itamaraty Palace, designed by Oscar Niemeyer, houses the Ministry of Foreign Affairs.

Watering Can over Stones, by José Tarcisio A785

Fingers and Ribbons, by Pietrina Checcacci A786

1976, May 14   Litho.   Perf. 11½
1433 A785 1cr multi   .22 .20
1434 A786 1.60cr multi   .28 .20
Modern Brazilian art.

Basketball — A787

Orchid — A788

Designs (Olympic Rings and): 1.40cr, Yachting. 5.20cr, Judo.

1976, May 21   Litho.   Perf. 11½
1435 A787 1cr emerald & blk   .16 .15
1436 A787 1.40cr dk blue & blk .20 .15
1437 A787 5.20cr orange & blk   .65 .50
    Nos. 1435-1437 (3)   1.01 .80
21st Olympic Games, Montreal, Canada, July 17-Aug. 1.

1976, June 4   Perf. 11½x11
Nature protection: No. 1439, Golden-faced lion monkey.
1438 A788 1cr multicolored   .22 .20
1439 A788 1cr multicolored   .22 .20

Film Camera, Brazilian Colors — A789

1976, June 19
1440 A789 1cr vio bl, brt grn & yel .20 .25
Brazilian film industry.

Bahia Woman — A790

Designs: 10c, Oxcart driver, horiz. 20c, Raft fishermen, horiz. 30c, Rubber plantation worker. 40c, Cowboy, horiz. 50c, Gaucho. 80c, Gold panner. 1cr, Banana plantation worker. 1.10cr, Grape harvester. 1.30cr, Coffee picker. 1.80cr, Farmer gathering wax palms. 2cr, Potter. 5cr, Sugar cane cutter. 7cr, Salt mine worker. 10cr, Fisherman. 15cr, Coconut seller. 20cr, Lacemaker.

Perf. 11½x11, 11x11½
1976-78   **Photo.**
1441 A790 10c red brn ('77)   .15 .15
1442 A790 15c brown   .24 .32
1443 A790 20c vio blue   .15 .15
1444 A790 30c lilac rose   .15 .15
1445 A790 40c org ('77)   .15 .15
1446 A790 50c citron   .15 .15
1447 A790 80c slate grn   .38 .15
1448 A790 1cr black   .16 .15

1449	A790	1.10cr magenta ('77)	.16 .15
1450	A790	1.30cr red ('77)	.16 .15
1451	A790	1.80cr dk vio bl ('78)	.18 .15

Engr.

1452	A790	2cr brown ('77)	.22 .15
1453	A790	5cr dk pur ('77)	.50 .15
1454	A790	7cr violet	1.50 .15
1455	A790	10cr yel grn ('77)	.55 .15
1456	A790	15cr gray grn ('78)	1.40 .15
1457	A790	20cr blue	1.40 .15
		Nos. 1441-1457 (17)	7.60
		Set value	1.10

See Nos. 1653-1657.

Hyphessobrycon Innesi — A791

Designs: Brazilian fresh-water fish.

1976, July 12   Litho.   Perf. 11x11½

1460	A791	1cr shown	.42 .40
1461	A791	1cr Copeina arnoldi	.42 .40
1462	A791	1cr Prochilodus insignis	.42 .40
1463	A791	1cr Crenicichla lepidota	.42 .40
1464	A791	1cr Ageneiosus	.42 .40
1465	A791	1cr Corydoras reticulatus	.42 .40
a.		Block of 6, #1460-1465	2.50 2.50

Santa Marta Lighthouse — A792

1976, July 29   Engr.   Perf. 12x11½

1466	A792	1cr blue	.20 .30

300th anniversary of the city of Laguna.

Children on Magic Carpet A793

1976, Aug. 1   Litho.   Perf. 11½x12

1467	A793	1cr multicolored	.20 .20

Stamp Day.

Nurse's Lamp and Head A794

1976, Aug. 12   Litho.   Perf. 11½

1468	A794	1cr multicolored	.20 .20

Brazilian Nurses' Assoc., 50th anniv.

Puppet, Soldier — A795

Winner's Medal — A796

Designs: 1.30cr, Girl's head. 1.60cr, Hand with puppet head on each finger, horiz.

1976, Aug. 20

1469	A795	1cr multi	.20 .20
1470	A795	1.30cr multi	.20 .20
1471	A795	1.60cr multi	.20 .20
		Nos. 1469-1471 (3)	.60 .60

Mamulengo puppet show.

1976, Aug. 21

1472	A796	5.20cr multi	.70 .50

27th International Military Athletic Championships, Rio de Janeiro, Aug. 21-28.

Family Protection — A797

1976, Sept. 12

1473	A797	1cr lt & dk blue	.20 .20

National organizations SENAC and SESC helping commercial employees to improve their living standard, both commercially and socially.

Dying Tree — A798

1976, Sept. 20   Litho.   Perf. 11½

1474	A798	1cr gray & multi	.20 .20

Protection of the environment.

Atom Symbol, Electron Orbits A799

1976, Sept. 21

1475	A799	5.20cr multi	.70 .50

20th General Conference of the International Atomic Energy Agency, Rio de Janeiro, Sept. 21-29.

Train in Tunnel — A800

1976, Sept. 26

1476	A800	1.60cr multi	.25 .25

Sao Paulo subway, 1st in Brazil.

St. Francis and Birds A801

1976, Oct. 4

1477	A801	5.20cr multi	.60 .42

St. Francis of Assisi, 750th death anniv.

Brasil 76   1,00   Ouro Preto School of Mining — A802

1976, Oct. 12   Engr.   Perf. 12x11½

1478	A802	1cr dk vio	.40 .50

Ouro Preto School of Mining, centenary.

Three Kings — A803

Brasil 76   NATAL   0.80

Designs: Children's drawings.

1976, Nov. 4   Litho.   Perf. 11½

1479	A803	80c shown	.28 .28
1480	A803	80c Santa Claus on donkey	.28 .28
1481	A803	80c Virgin and Child and Angels	.28 .28
1482	A803	80c Angels with candle	.28 .28
1483	A803	80c Nativity	.28 .28
a.		Strip of 5, #1479-1483	1.40 1.40

Christmas 1976.

Souvenir Sheet

30,000 Reis Banknote — A804

1976, Nov. 5   Litho.   Perf. 11½

1484	A804	80c multicolored	.40 1.50

Opening of 1000th branch of Bank of Brazil, Barra do Bugres, Mato Grosso.

Virgin of Monte Serrat, by Friar Agostinho A805

St. Joseph, 18th Century Wood Sculpture — A806

Designs: 5.60cr, The Dance, by Rodolfo Bernadelli, 19th century. 6.50cr, The Caravel, by Bruno Giorgi, 20th century abstract sculpture.

1976, Nov. 5

1485	A805	80c multi	.15 .15
1486	A806	5cr multi	.65 .40
1487	A805	5.60cr multi	.65 .40
1488	A806	6.50cr multi	.65 .40
		Nos. 1485-1488 (4)	2.10 1.35

Development of Brazilian sculpture.

Praying Hands A807

1976, Nov. 25

1489	A807	80c multicolored	.25 .25

National Day of Thanksgiving.

Sailor, 1840 — A808

Design: 2cr, Marine's uniform, 1808.

1976, Dec. 13   Litho.   Perf. 11½x11

1490	A808	80c multicolored	.22 .22
1491	A808	2cr multicolored	.32 .22

Brazilian Navy.

"Natural Resources and Development" — A809

1976, Dec. 17   Perf. 11½

1492	A809	80c multicolored	.20 .16

Brazilian Bureau of Standards, founded 1940.

Wheel of Life — A810

Designs: 5.60cr, Beggar, sculpture by Agnaldo dos Santos. 6.50cr, Benin mask.

1977, Jan. 14

1493	A810	5cr multi	.55 .35
1494	A810	5.60cr multi	.55 .35
1495	A810	6.50cr multi	1.10 .35
		Nos. 1493-1495 (3)	2.20 1.05

FESTAC '77, 2nd World Black and African Festival, Lagos, Nigeria, Jan. 15-Feb. 12.

A811

1977, Jan. 20   Litho.   Perf. 11½

1496	A811	6.50cr bl & yel grn	.85 .65

Rio de Janeiro International Airport.

Brasil 77 1,10

Brasil 77 1,10

Seminar Emblem
with Map of
Americas
A812

Salicylate,
Microphoto
A813

1977, Feb. 6
1497 A812 1.10cr gray, vio bl & bl   .35 .18
6th Inter-American Budget Seminar.

1977, Apr. 10   Litho.   *Perf. 11½*
1498 A813 1.10cr multi   .20 .15
International Rheumatism Year.

Lions
International
Emblem
A814

1977, Apr. 16
1499 A814 1.10cr multi   .20 .20
25th anniv. of Brazilian Lions Intl.

Heitor Villa
Lobos
A815

1977, Apr. 26   *Perf. 11x11½*
1500 A815 1.10cr shown   .15 .20
1501 A815 1.10cr Chiquinha Gonzaga   .15 .20
1502 A815 1.10cr Noel Rosa   .15 .20
Nos. 1500-1502 (3)   .45 .60
Brazilian composers.

Brasil 77 1,10

Brasil 77 1,10

Farmer and
Worker — A816

Medicine Bottles
and
Flask — A817

1977, May 8   Litho.   *Perf. 11½*
1503 A816 1.10cr grn & multi   .15 .20
1504 A817 1.10cr lt & dk grn   .15 .20
Support and security for rural and urban workers
(No. 1503) and establishment in 1971 of Medicine
Distribution Center (CEME) for low-cost medicines
(No. 1504).

Churchyard
Cross, Porto
Seguro
A818

Views, Porto Seguro: 5cr, Beach and boats.
5.60cr, Our Lady of Pena Chapel. 6.50cr, Town
Hall.

1977, May 25   Litho.   *Perf. 11½*
1505 A818 1.10cr multi   .15 .15
1506 A818   5cr multi   1.40 .35
1507 A818 5.60cr multi   .55 .45
1508 A818 6.50cr multi   .80 .55
Nos. 1505-1508 (4)   2.90 1.50
Cent. of Brazil's membership in UPU.

Diario de
Porto Alegre
A819

1977, June 1
1509 A819 1.10cr multi   .20 .20
Diario de Porto Alegre, newspaper, 150th anniv.

Blue Whale
A820

1977, June 3
1510 A820 1.30cr multi   .20 .20
Protection of marine life.

"Life and
Development" — A821

1977, June 20
1511 A821 1.30cr multi   .20 .20
National Development Bank, 25th anniversary.

Train Leaving
Tunnel — A822

1977, July 8   Engr.   *Perf. 11½*
1512 A822 1.30cr black   .20 .20
Centenary of Sao Paulo-Rio de Janeiro railroad.

Vasum Cassiforme
A823

Caduceus, Formulas
for Water and
Fluoride
A824

Sea Shells: No. 1514, Strombus goliath. No.
1515, Murex tenuivaricosus.

1977, July 14   Litho.
1513 A823 1.30cr blue & multi   .20 .20
1514 A823 1.30cr brown & multi   .20 .20
1515 A823 1.30cr green & multi   .20 .20
Nos. 1513-1515 (3)   .60 .60

1977, July 15   *Perf. 11½x11*
1516 A824 1.30cr multi   .20 .20
3rd Intl. Odontology Congress, Rio, July 15-21.

Masonic
Emblem, Map of
Brazil — A825

"Stamps Don't
Sink or Lose their
Way" — A826

1977, July 18   *Perf. 11½*
1517 A825 1.30cr bl, lt bl & blk   .20 .20
50th anniversary of the founding of the Brazilian
Grand Masonic Lodge.

1977, Aug. 1
1518 A826 1.30cr multi   .20 .20
Stamp Day 1977.

Dom Pedro's
Proclamation — A827

Horses and
Bulls — A828

1977, Aug. 11   Litho.   *Perf. 11½*
1519 A827 1.30cr multi   .20 .20
150th anniversary of Brazilian Law School.

Perf. 11½x11, 11x11½
1977, Aug. 20   Litho.
Brazilian folklore: No. 1521, King on horseback.
No. 1522, Joust, horiz.
1520 A828 1.30cr ocher & multi   .20 .20
1521 A828 1.30cr blue & multi   .20 .20
1522 A828 1.30cr yel & multi   .20 .20
Nos. 1520-1522 (3)   .60 .60

2000-reis
Doubloon
A829

Brazilian Colonial Coins: No. 1524, 640r pataca.
No. 1525, 20r copper "vintem."

1977, Aug. 31   *Perf. 11½*
1523 A829 1.30cr vio bl & multi   .20 .15
1524 A829 1.30cr dk red & multi   .20 .15
1525 A829 1.30cr yel & multi   .20 .15
Nos. 1523-1525 (3)   .60 .45

Pinwheel
A830

Neoregelia
Carolinae
A831

1977, Sept. 1
1526 A830 1.30cr multi   .20 .15
National Week.

1977, Sept. 21   Litho.   *Perf. 11½*
1527 A831 1.30cr multi   .20 .15
Nature preservation.

Pen, Pencil,
Letters — A832

1977, Oct. 15   Litho.   *Perf. 11½*
1528 A832 1.30cr multi   .20 .15
Primary education, sesquicentennial.

Dome and
Telescope
A833

1977, Oct. 15
1529 A833 1.30cr multi   .20 .15
National Astrophysics Observatory, Brasópolis,
sesquicentennial.

"Jahu"
Hydroplane
(Savoia
Marchetti S-
55) — A834

Design: No. 1531, PAX, dirigible.

1977, Oct. 17
1530 A834 1.30cr multi   .25 .25
1531 A834 1.30cr multi   .25 .25
50th anniv. of crossing of South Atlantic by Joao
Ribeiro de Barros, Genoa-Sao Paulo (#1530) and
75th anniv. of the PAX airship (#1531).

A835

A836

1977, Oct. 24
1532 A835 1.30cr Il'Guarani   .20 .15
Book Day and to honor Jose Martiniano de Alencar, writer, jurist.

1977, Nov. 5   Litho.   *Perf. 11½*
1533 A836 1.30cr Waves   .20 .15
Amateur Radio Operators' Day.

Nativity — A837

Christmas (folk art): 2cr, Annunciation. 5cr,
Nativity.

1977, Nov. 10
1534 A837 1.30cr bister & multi   .22 .15
1535 A837   2cr bister & multi   .32 .15
1536 A837   5cr bister & multi   .65 .25
Nos. 1534-1536 (3)   1.19 .55

A838

A839

1977, Nov. 19
1537 A838 1.30cr Emerald .20 .20
1538 A838 1.30cr Topaz .20 .20
1539 A838 1.30cr Aquamarine .20 .20
Nos. 1537-1539 (3) .60 .60
PORTUCALE 77, 2nd International Topical Exhibition, Porto, Nov. 19-20.

1977, Nov. 24 Litho. Perf. 11½
1540 A839 1.30cr Angel, cornucopia .20 .20
National Thanksgiving Day.

Army's Railroad Construction Battalion A840

Civilian services of armed forces: No. 1542, Navy's Amazon flotilla. No. 1543, Air Force's postal service (plane).

1977, Dec. 5
1541 A840 1.30cr multi .20 .20
1542 A840 1.30cr multi .20 .20
1543 A840 1.30cr multi .20 .20
Nos. 1541-1543 (3) .60 .60

Varig Emblem, Jet A841

1977, Dec. Perf. 11x11½
1544 A841 1.30cr bl & blk .20 .20
50th anniversary of Varig Airline.

Sts. Cosme and Damiao Church, Igaracu — A842

Woman Holding Sheaf — A843

Brazilian Architecture: 7.50cr, St. Bento Monastery Church, Rio de Janeiro. 8.50cr, Church of St. Francis of Assisi, Ouro Preto. 9.50cr, St. Anthony Convent Church, Joao Pessoa.

1977, Dec. 8
1545 A842 2.70cr multi .30 .15
1546 A842 7.50cr multi .90 .35
1547 A842 8.50cr multi .90 .40
1548 A842 9.50cr multi 1.25 .45
Nos. 1545-1548 (4) 3.35 1.35

1977, Dec. 19 Perf. 11½
1549 A843 1.30cr multi .20 .20
Brazilian diplomacy.

Soccer Ball and Foot — A844

Designs: No. 1551, Soccer ball in net. No. 1552, Symbolic soccer player.

1978, Mar. 1 Litho. Perf. 11½
1550 A844 1.80cr multi .28 .20
1551 A844 1.80cr multi .28 .20
1552 A844 1.80cr multi .28 .20
Nos. 1550-1552 (3) .84 .60
11th World Cup Soccer Championship, Argentina, June 1-25.

"La Fosca" on La Scala Stage and Carlos Gomes A845

1978, Feb. 9
1553 A845 1.80cr multi .20 .20
Bicentenary of La Scala in Milan, and to honor Carlos Gomes (1836-1893), Brazilian composer.

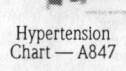
Symbols of Postal Mechanization — A846

1978, Mar. 15 Litho. Perf. 11½
1554 A846 1.80cr multi .20 .20
Opening of Postal Staff College.

Hypertension Chart — A847

Waves from Antenna Uniting World — A848

1978, Apr. 4
1555 A847 1.80cr multi .20 .20
World Health Day, fight against hypertension.

1978, May 17 Litho. Perf. 12x11½
1556 A848 1.80cr multi .20 .20
10th World Telecommunications Day.

Brazilian Canary A849

Birds: 8.50cr, Cotinga. 9.50cr, Tanager fastuosa.

1978, June 5 Perf. 11½x12
1557 A849 7.50cr multi 1.00 .75
1558 A849 8.50cr multi 1.00 .80
1559 A849 9.50cr multi 1.00 1.00
Nos. 1557-1559 (3) 3.00 2.55

Inocencio Serzedelo Correa and Manuel Francisco Correa, 1893 A850

1978, June 20 Litho. Perf. 11x11½
1560 A850 1.80cr multi .20 .20
85th anniversary of Union Court of Audit.

Post and Telegraph Building A851

1978, June 22 Perf. 11½
1561 A851 1.80cr multi .20 .25
Souvenir Sheet
Imperf
1562 A851 7.50cr multi .75 1.50
Inauguration of Post and Telegraph Building (ECT), Brasilia, and for BRAPEX, 3rd Brazilian Philatelic Exhibition, Brasilia, June 23-28 (No. 1562).

Ernesto Geisel, President of Brazil — A852

1978, June 22 Engr. Perf. 11½
1563 A852 1.80cr dl grn .20 .15

Savoia-Marchetti S-64, Map of South Atlantic A853

1978, July 3 Litho.
1564 A853 1.80cr multi .20 .20
50th anniv. of 1st crossing of South Atlantic by Carlos del Prete and Arturo Ferrarin.

Symbolic of Smallpox Eradication A854

Brazil No. 68 A855

1978, July 25
1565 A854 1.80cr multi .20 .20
Eradication of smallpox.

1978, Aug. 1
1566 A855 1.80cr multi .20 .20
Stamp Day, centenary of the "Barba Branca" (white beard) issue.

Stormy Sea, by Seelinger A856

1978, Aug. 4
1567 A856 1.80cr multi .20 .20
Helios Seelinger, painter, birth centenary.

Guitar Players — A857

Musicians and Instruments: No. 1569, Flutes. No. 1570, Percussion instruments.

1978, Aug. 22 Litho. Perf. 11½
1568 A857 1.80cr multi .20 .15
1569 A857 1.80cr multi .20 .15
1570 A857 1.80cr multi .20 .15
Nos. 1568-1570 (3) .60 .50

Children at Play A858

1978, Sept. 1 Litho. Perf. 11½
1571 A858 1.80cr multi .20 .20
National Week.

Collegiate Church A859

1978, Sept. 6 Engr.
1572 A859 1.80cr red brn .20 .20
Restoration of patio of Collegiate Church, Sao Paulo.

Justice by A. Geschiatti A860

1978, Sept. 18 Litho.
1573 A860 1.80cr blk & olive .20 .20
Federal Supreme Court, sesquicentennial.

Iguacu Falls — A861

Design: No. 1575, Yellow ipecac.

1978, Sept. 21
1574 A861 1.80cr multi .20 .20
1575 A861 1.80cr multi .20 .20
Iguacu National Park.

Stages of Intelsat Satellite — A862

1978, Oct. 9 Litho. Perf. 11½
1576 A862 1.80cr multi .20 .20

Flag of Order
of Christ
A863

Brazilian Flags: No. 1578, Principality of Brazil.
No. 1579, United Kingdom. No. 1580, Imperial
Brazil. No. 1581, National flag (current).

1978, Oct. 13
1577	A863	1.80cr multi	.65	.55
1578	A863	1.80cr multi	.65	.55
1579	A863	1.80cr multi	.65	.55
1580	A863	8.50cr multi	.65	.55
1581	A863	8.50cr multi	.65	.55
a.		Block of 5, #1577-1581 + label	4.00	6.50
		Nos. 1577-1581 (5)	3.25	2.75

7th LUBRAPEX Philatelic Exhibition, Porto
Alegre.

Mail Street
Car
A864

Mail Transportation: No. 1583, Overland mail
truck. No. 1584, Mail delivery truck. 7.50cr. Railroad mail car. 8.50cr, Mail coach. 9.50cr, Post
riders.

1978, Oct. 21   *Perf. 11x11½*
1582	A864	1.80cr multi	.50	.40
1583	A864	1.80cr multi	.50	.40
1584	A864	1.80cr multi	.50	.40
1585	A864	7.50cr multi	.50	.40
1586	A864	8.50cr multi	.50	.40
1587	A864	9.50cr multi	.50	.50
a.		Block of 6, #1582-1587	3.00	3.00

18th UPU Congress, Rio de Janeiro, 1979.

Gaucho Herding Cattle,
and Cactus — A865

1978, Oct. 23   *Perf. 11½x11*
1588	A865	1.80cr multi	.20	.20

Joao Guimaraes Rosa, poet and diplomat, 70th
birthday.

St. Anthony's
Hill, by
Nicholas A.
Taunay
A866

Landscape Paintings: No. 1590, Castle Hill, by
Victor Meirelles. No. 1591, View of Sabara, by
Alberto da Veiga Guignard. No. 1592, View of Per-
nambuco, by Frans Post.

1978, Nov. 6   *Litho.*   *Perf. 11½*
1589	A866	1.80cr multi	.20	.20
1590	A866	1.80cr multi	.20	.20
1591	A866	1.80cr multi	.20	.20
1592	A866	1.80cr multi	.20	.20
		Nos. 1589-1592 (4)	.80	.80

Angel with
Harp — A867

Christmas: No. 1594, Angel with lute. No. 1595,
Angel with oboe.

1978, Nov. 10
1593	A867	1.80cr multi	.20	.20
1594	A867	1.80cr multi	.20	.20
1595	A867	1.80cr multi	.20	.20
		Nos. 1593-1595 (3)	.60	.60

Symbolic
Candles — A868

1978, Nov. 23
1596	A868	1.80cr blk, gold & car	.20	.20

National Thanksgiving Day.

Red Crosses
and
Activities
A869

1978, Dec. 5   *Litho.*   *Perf. 11x11½*
1597	A869	1.80cr blk & red	.20	.20

70th anniversary of Brazilian Red Cross.

Paz Theater,
Belem — A870

12cr, José de Alencar Theater, Portaleza.
12.50cr, Municipal Theater, Rio de Janeiro.

1978, Dec. 6   *Perf. 11½*
1598	A870	10.50cr multi	.70	.25
1599	A870	12cr multi	.70	.25
1600	A870	12.50cr multi	.70	.25
		Nos. 1598-1600 (3)	2.10	.75

Subway
Trains — A871

1979, Mar. 5   *Litho.*   *Perf. 11½*
1601	A871	2.50cr multi	.20	.20

Inauguration of Rio subway system.

Old and
New Post
Offices
A872

Designs: No. 1603, Old and new mail boxes. No.
1604, Manual and automatic mail sorting. No.
1605, Old and new planes. No. 1606, Telegraph
and telex machine. No. 1607, Mailmen's uniforms.

1979, Mar. 20   *Litho.*   *Perf. 11x11½*
1602	A872	2.50cr multi	.25	.20
1603	A872	2.50cr multi	.25	.20
1604	A872	2.50cr multi	.25	.20
1605	A872	2.50cr multi	.25	.20
1606	A872	2.50cr multi	.25	.20
1607	A872	2.50cr multi	.25	.20
a.		Block of 6, #1602-1607	1.50	1.50

10th anniv. of the new Post and Telegraph Dept.,
and 18th Universal Postal Union Cong., Rio de
Janeiro, Sept.-Oct., 1979.

O'Day 23
Class Yacht
A873

Yachts and Stamp Outlines: 10.50cr, Penguin
Class. 12cr, Hobie Cat Class. 12.50cr, Snipe Class.

1979, Apr. 18   *Litho.*   *Perf. 11x11½*
1608	A873	2.50cr multi	.30	.25
1609	A873	10.50cr multi	.55	.45
1610	A873	12cr multi	.55	.35
1611	A873	12.50cr multi	.75	.35
		Nos. 1608-1611 (4)	2.15	1.40

Brasiliana '79, 3rd World Thematic Stamp Exhibition, Sao Conrado, Sept. 15-23.

Children, IYC
Emblem — A874

1979, May 30   *Litho.*   *Perf. 11½*
1612	A874	2.50cr multi	.25	.20

Intl. Year of the Child & Children's Book Day.

Giant Water
Lily — A875

12cr, Amazon manatee. 12.50cr, Arrau (turtle).

1979, June 5   *Litho.*   *Perf. 11½*
1613	A875	10.50cr multi	.70	.50
1614	A875	12cr multi	.90	.60
1615	A875	12.50cr multi	.90	.60
		Nos. 1613-1615 (3)	2.50	1.70

Amazon National Park, nature conservation.

Bank
Emblem — A876

1979, June 7
1616	A876	2.50cr multi	.20	.15

Northwest Bank of Brazil, 25th anniversary.

Physician
Tending
Patient 15th
Cent.
Woodcut
A877

1979, June 30
1617	A877	2.50cr multi	.20	.15

Natl. Academy of Medicine, 50th anniv.

Flower made of
Hearts — A878

1979, July 8   *Litho.*   *Perf. 11½*
1618	A878	2.50cr multi	.20	.15

35th Brazilian Cardiology Congress.

Souvenir Sheet

Hotel
Nacional, Rio
de Janeiro
A879

1979, July 16
1619	A879	12.50cr multi	.75	1.50

Brasiliana '79 comprising 1st Inter-American
Exhibition of Classical Philately and 3rd World Topical Exhibition, Rio de Janeiro, Sept. 15-23.

Cithaerias
Aurora — A880

Moths: 10.50cr, Evenus regalis. 12cr, Caligo
eurilochus. 12.50cr, Diaethria clymena janeira.

1979, Aug. 1
1620	A880	2.50cr multi	.18	.15
1621	A880	10.50cr multi	.60	.40
1622	A880	12cr multi	.70	.52
1623	A880	12.50cr multi	.70	.52
		Nos. 1620-1623 (4)	2.18	1.59

Stamp Day 1979.

EMB-121
Xingo
A881

1979, Aug. 19   *Litho.*   *Perf. 11½*
1624	A881	2.50cr vio blue	.20	.20

Embraer, Brazilian aircraft comp., 10th anniv.

A882   A883

Natl. emblem over landscape.

1979, Sept. 12
1625 A882 3.20cr multi   .20 .20
National Week.

1979, Sept. 8   Litho.   Perf. 11½
1626 A883 2.50cr multi   .20 .20
Statue of Our Lady of the Apparition, 75th anniversary of coronation.

"UPU,"
Envelope
and Mail
Transport
A884

"UPU" and: No. 1628, Post Office emblems. 10.50cr, Globe. 12cr, Flags of Brazil and UN. 12.50cr, UPU emblem.

1979, Sept. 12   Perf. 11x11½
1627 A884 2.50cr multi   .16 .16
1628 A884 2.50cr multi   .16 .16
1629 A884 10.50cr multi   .52 .52
1630 A884 12cr multi   .70 .70
1631 A884 12.50cr multi   .70 .70
    Nos. 1627-1631 (5)   2.24 2.24
18th UPU Cong., Rio, Sept.-Oct. 1979.

Pyramid Fountain, Rio
de Janeiro — A885

Fountains: 10.50cr, Facade, Marilia, Ouro Preto, horiz. 12cr, Boa Vista, Recife.

Perf. 12x11½, 11½x12
1979, Sept. 15
1632 A885 2.50cr multi   .16 .16
1633 A885 10.50cr multi   .50 .50
1634 A885 12cr multi   .60 .60
    Nos. 1632-1634 (3)   1.26 1.26
Brasiliana '79, 1st Interamerican Exhibition of Classical Philately.

Church of the
Glory — A886

Landscapes by Leandro Joaquim: 12cr, Fishing on Guanabara Bay. 12.50cr, Boqueirao Lake and Carioca Arches.

1979, Sept. 15   Perf. 11½
1635 A886 2.50cr multi   .16 .16
1636 A886 12cr multi   .60 .60
1637 A886 12.50cr multi   .60 .60
    Nos. 1635-1637 (3)   1.36 1.36
Brasiliana '79, 3rd World Topical Exhibition, Sao Conrado, Sept. 15-23.

World
Map — A887

1979, Sept. 20
1638 A887 2.50cr multi   .20 .20
3rd World Telecommunications Exhibition, Geneva, Sept. 20-26.

"UPU" and UPU
Emblem — A888

1979, Oct. 9   Litho.   Perf. 11½x11
1639 A888 2.50cr multi   .18 .18
1640 A888 10.50cr multi   .55 .55
1641 A888 12cr multi   .65 .65
1642 A888 12.50cr multi   .65 .65
    Nos. 1639-1642 (4)   2.03 2.03
Universal Postal Union Day.

IYC
Emblem,
Feather Toy
A889

IYC Emblem and Toys: No. 1644, Bumble bee, ragdoll. No. 1645, Flower, top. No. 1646, Wooden acrobat.

1979, Oct. 12   Perf. 11½
1643 A889 2.50cr multi   .25 .20
1644 A889 3.20cr multi   .25 .25
1645 A889 3.20cr multi   .25 .25
1646 A889 3.20cr multi   .25 .25
    Nos. 1643-1646 (4)   1.00 .95
International Year of the Child.

Adoration of the
Kings — A890

Christmas 1979: No. 1648, Nativity. No. 1649 Jesus and the Elders in the Temple.

1979, Nov. 12   Litho.   Perf. 11½
1647 A890 3.20cr multi   .20 .18
1648 A890 3.20cr multi   .20 .18
1649 A890 3.20cr multi   .20 .18
    Nos. 1647-1649 (3)   .60 .54

Souvenir Sheet

Hands Reading Braille — A891

Lithographed and Embossed
1979, Nov. 20.   Perf. 11½
1650 A891 3.20cr multi   .50 1.25
Publication of Braille script, 150th anniversary. Margin shows extension of stamp design with Braille printed and embossed.

Wheat
Harvester — A892   Steel
    Mill — A893

1979, Nov. 22
1651 A892 3.20cr multi   .20 .15
Thanksgiving 1979.

1979, Nov. 23
1652 A893 3.20cr multi   .20 .15
COSIPA Steelworks, Sao Paulo, 25th anniversary.

Type of 1976

Designs: 70c, Women grinding coconuts. 2.50cr, Basket weaver. 3.20cr, River boatman. 21cr, Harvesting ramie (China grass). 27cr, Man leading pack mule. 3.20cr, 27cr, horiz.

Photogravure, Engraved (21cr)
1979   Perf. 11x11½, 11½x11
1653 A790 70c gray grn   .15 .15
1654 A790 2.50cr sepia   .15 .15
1655 A790 3.20cr blue   .15 .15
1656 A790 21cr purple   .38 .15
1657 A790 27cr sepia   .45 .15
    Nos. 1653-1657 (5)   1.28
    Set value   .40

A894

Designs: 2cr, Coconuts. 3cr, Mangoes. 4cr, Corn. 5cr, Onions. 7cr, Oranges. 10cr, Maracuja. 12cr, Pineapple. 15cr, Bananas. 17cr, Guarana. 20cr, Sugar cane. 24cr, Beekeeping. 30cr, Silkworm. 34cr, Cacao. 38cr, Coffee. 42cr, Soybeans. 45cr, Mandioca. 50cr, Wheat. 57cr, Peanuts. 66cr, Grapes. 100cr, Cashews. 140cr, Tomatoes. 200cr, Mamona. 500cr, Cotton.

1980-83   Photo.   Perf. 11½x11
1658 A894 2cr yel brn ('82)   .15 .15
1659 A894 3cr red ('82)   .15 .15
1660 A894 4cr orange   .15 .15
1661 A894 5cr dk pur ('82)   .15 .15
1662 A894 7cr org ('81)   .15 .15
1663 A894 10cr bl grn ('82)   .15 .15
1664 A894 12cr dk grn ('81)   .22 .15
1665 A894 15cr gldn brn ('83)   .15 .15
1666 A894 17cr brn org ('82)   .24 .15
1667 A894 20cr olive ('82)   .22 .15
1668 A894 24cr bis ('82)   .15 .15
1669 A894 30cr blk ('82)   .15 .15
1670 A894 34cr brown   .35 .15
1671 A894 38cr red ('83)   .15 .15
1672 A894 42cr green   5.75 .50
1673 A894 45cr sepia ('83)   .55 .15
1674 A894 50cr yel org ('82)   .16 .15
1675 A894 57cr brn ('83)   .16 .15
1676 A894 66cr pur ('81)   3.75 .15
1677 A894 100cr dk red brn ('81)   2.25 .15
1678 A894 140cr red ('82)   2.75 .15

Engr.
1678A A894 200cr grn ('82)   2.75 .15
1679 A894 500cr brn ('82)   5.75 .15
    Nos. 1658-1679 (23)   26.40
    Set value   2.25
See Nos. 1934-1941.

Plant Inside
Raindrop — A896

Light Bulb Containing: 17cr+7cr, Sun. 20cr+8cr, Windmill. 21cr+9cr, Dam.

1980, Jan. 2   Litho.   Perf. 12
1680 A896 3.20cr multi   .15 .15
1681 A896 24cr (17 + 7)   1.25 .65
1682 A896 28cr (20 + 8)   1.50 .75
1683 A896 30cr (21 + 9)   2.25 .85
    Nos. 1680-1683 (4)   5.15 2.40

Anthracite
Industry — A897

1980, Mar. 19   Litho.   Perf. 11½
1684 A897 4cr multi   .20 .15

Map of Americas, Symbols of
Development — A898

1980, Apr. 14   Litho.   Perf. 11x11½
1685 A898 4cr multi   .20 .15
21st Assembly of Inter-American Development Bank Governors, Rio, Apr. 14-16.

Tapirape
Mask, Mato
Grosso
A899

1980, Apr. 18   Perf. 11½
1686 A899 4cr shown   .20 .15
1687 A899 4cr Tukuna mask, Amazonas, vert.   .20 .15
1688 A899 4cr Kanela mask, Maranhao, vert.   .20 .15
    Nos. 1686-1688 (3)   .60 .45

Brazilian
Television, 30th
Anniversary
A900

1980, May 5   Litho.   Perf. 11½
1689 A900 4cr multicolored   .18 .15

Duke of Caixas, by
Miranda — A901   The Worker, by
    Candido
    Partinari — A902

1980, May 7
1690 A901 4cr multicolored   .18 .15
Duke of Caixas, death centenary.

1980, May 18
Paintings: 28cr, Mademoiselle Pogany, by Constantin Brancusi. 30cr, The Glass of Water, by Francisco Aurelio de Figueiredo.

1691 A902 24cr multi   1.10 .55
1692 A902 28cr multi   1.10 .55
1693 A902 30cr multi   1.65 .55
    Nos. 1691-1693 (3)   3.85 1.65

Graf Zeppelin, 50th Anniversary of Atlantic Crossing
A903

1980, June   Litho.   Perf. 11x11½
1694 A903 4cr multicolored   .20 .15

Pope John Paul II, St. Peter's, Rome, Congress Emblem
A904

Pope, Emblem and Brazilian Churches: No. 1696, Fortaleza, vert. 24cr, Apericida 28cr, Rio de Janeiro. 30cr, Brasilia.

1980, June 24   Perf. 12
1695 A904 4cr multi   .18 .15
1696 A904 4cr multi   .18 .15
1697 A904 24cr multi   .90 .40
1698 A904 28cr multi   .90 .40
1699 A904 30cr multi   1.75 .40
    Nos. 1695-1699 (5)   3.91 1.50

Visit of Pope John Paul II to Brazil, June 30-July 12; 10th National Eucharistic Congress, Fortaleza, July 9-16.

First Transatlantic Flight, 50th Anniversary — A905

1980, June   Litho.   Perf. 11x11½
1700 A905 4cr multicolored   .20 .15

Souvenir Sheet

Yacht Sail, Exhibition Emblem — A906

1980, June   Perf. 11½
1701 A906 30cr multi   1.00 1.50

Brapex IV Stamp Exhib., Fortaleza, June 13-21.

Rowing, Moscow '80 Emblem
A907

1980, June 30
1702 A907 4cr shown   .20 .15
1703 A907 4cr Target shooting   .20 .15
1704 A907 4cr Bicycling   .20 .15
    Nos. 1702-1704 (3)   .60 .45

22nd Summer Olympic Games, Moscow, July 19-Aug. 3.

Rondon Community Works Project
A908

1980, July 11
1705 A908 4cr multicolored   .20 .15

Helen Keller and Anne Sullivan
A909

1980, July 28
1706 A909 4cr multicolored   .20 .15

Helen Keller (1880-1968), blind deaf writer and lecturer taught by Anne Sullivan (1867-1936).

Souvenir Sheet

São Francisco River Canoe — A910

1980, Aug. 1   Litho.   Perf. 11½
1707 A910 24cr multi   1.00 1.50

Stamp Day.

Microscope, Red Cross, Insects, Brick and Tile Houses — A911

1980, Aug. 5   Perf. 11½x11
1708 A911 4cr multi   .25 .15

National Health Day.

Brazilian Postal Administration, 15th Anniversary — A912

1980, Sept. 16   Litho.   Perf. 12
1709 A912 5cr multi   .25 .20

Souvenir Sheet

St. Gabriel World Union, 6th Congress
A913

1980, Sept. 29   Perf. 11½x12
1710 A913 30cr multi   1.00 1.50

Cattleya Amethystoglossa
A914

1980, Oct. 3   Perf. 11½
1711 A914 5cr shown   .18 .15
1712 A914 5cr Laelia cinnabarina   .18 .15
1713 A914 24cr Zygopetalum crinitum 1.10 .60
1714 A914 28cr Laelia tenebrosa   1.10 .60
    Nos. 1711-1714 (4)   2.56 1.50

Espamer 80, American-European Philatelic Exhibition, Madrid, Oct. 3-12.

Red-tailed Amazon Parrot — A915   Capitao Rodrigo, Hero of Erico Verissimo's "O Continento" — A916

Parrots: No. 1716, Vinaceous Amazon. No. 1717, Brown-backed. No. 1718, Red-spectacled.

1980, Oct. 18   Litho.   Perf. 12
1715 A915 5cr multi   .18 .15
1716 A915 5cr multi   .18 .15
1717 A915 28cr multi   1.10 .60
1718 A915 28cr multi   1.10 .60
    Nos. 1715-1718 (4)   2.56 1.50

Lubrapex '80 Stamp Exhib., Lisbon, Oct. 18-26.

1980, Oct. 23
1719 A916 5cr multi   .25 .20

Book Day.

Flight into Egypt — A917

1980, Nov. 5
1720 A917 5cr multi   .25 .20

Christmas 1980.

Sound Waves and Oscillator Screen
A918

1980, Nov. 7
1721 A918 5cr multi   .25 .20

Telebras Research Center inauguration.

Carvalho Viaduct, Paranagua-Curitiba Railroad — A919

1980, Nov. 10
1722 A919 5cr multi   .25 .20

Engineering Club centenary.

A920   A921

1980, Nov. 18   Litho.   Perf. 11½
1723 A920 5cr Portable chess board   .25 .50

Postal chess contest.

1980, Nov. 27   Perf. 11½x11
1724 A921 5cr Sun, wheat   .25 .40

Thanksgiving 1980

Father Anchieta Writing "Virgin Mary, Mother of God" on Sand of Iperoig Beach — A922

1980, Dec. 8   Perf. 12
1725 A922 5cr multi   .25 .20

Christ Carrying Cross, By O Aleijadinho
A923

Antonio Francisco Lisboa (O Aleijadinho), 250th Birth Anniv.: Paintings of the life of Christ: a, Mount of Olives. b, Arrest in the Garden. c, Flagellation. d, Crown of Thorns. f, Crucifixion.

1980, Dec. 29
1726   Block of 6   1.65 1.65
a.-f. A923 5cr any single   .24 .16

Agricultural Productivity
A924

1981, Jan. 2   Litho.   Perf. 11x11½
1727 A924 30cr shown   1.25 .35
1728 A924 35cr Domestic markets 1.10 .35
1729 A924 40cr Exports   1.10 .35
    Nos. 1727-1729 (3)   3.45 1.05

Boy Scout and Campfire
A925

1981, Jan. 22   Litho.   Perf. 11x11½
1730 A925 5cr shown   .25 .20
1731 A925 5cr Scouts cooking   .25 .20
1732 A925 5cr Scout, tents   .25 .20
    Nos. 1730-1732 (3)   .75 .60

4th Pan-American Scout Jamboree.

Souvenir Sheet

Mailman, 1930 — A926

1981, Mar. 11   Litho.   *Perf. 11*
1733   Sheet of 3   4.00   4.00
  a.   A926 30cr shown   1.00   1.00
  b.   A926 35cr Mailman, 1981   1.00   1.00
  c.   A926 40cr Telegram messenger, 1930 1.00   1.00
Dept. of Posts & Telegraphs, 50th anniv.

Souvenir Sheet

The Hunter and
the Jaguar, by
Felix Taunay
(1795-1881)
A927

1981, Apr. 10   Litho.   *Perf. 11*
1734 A927 30cr multi   1.00   2.00

Lima Barreto
and Rio de
Janeiro,
1900
A928

1981, May 13   Litho.   *Perf. 11½*
1735 A928 7cr multi   .25   .20
Lima Barreto, writer, birth centenary.

Maraca Indian
Funerary
Urn — A929

1981, May 18
1736 A929 7cr shown   .25   .20
1737 A929 7cr Marajoara triangular jug   .25   .20
1738 A929 7cr Tupi-Guarani bowl   .25   .20
  Nos. 1736-1738 (3)   .75   .60

Lophornis
Magnifica
A930

Designs: Hummingbirds.

1981, May 22   *Perf. 11½*
1739 A930 7cr shown   .30   .20
1740 A930 7cr Phaethornis pretrei   .30   .20
1741 A930 7cr Chrysolampis mos-
    quitus   .30   .20
1742 A930 7cr Heliactin cornuta   .30   .20
  Nos. 1739-1742 (4)   1.20   .80

Rotary Emblem
and
Faces — A931

1981, May 31
1743 A931 7cr Emblem, hands   .20   .15
1744 A931 35cr shown   1.00   .80
72nd Convention of Rotary Intl., Sao Paulo.

Environmental
Protection
A932

1981, June 5   *Perf. 12*
1745 A932 7cr shown   .25   .20
1746 A932 7cr Forest   .25   .20
1747 A932 7cr Clouds (air)   .25   .20
1748 A932 7cr Village (soil)   .25   .20
  a.   Block of 4, #1745-1748   1.00   1.00

Biplane, 1931
(Airmail
Service, 50th
Anniv.) A933

1981, June 10   *Perf. 11½*
1749 A933 7cr multi   .25   .20

Madeira-Mamore Railroad, 50th Anniv. of
Nationalization — A934

1981, July 10   Litho.   *Perf. 11x11½*
1750 A934 7cr multi   .25   .20

66th Intl.
Esperanto
Congress,
Brasilia
A935

1981, July 26   *Perf. 12*
1751 A935 7cr green & blk   .25   .20

No. 79
A936

1981, Aug. 1
1752 A936 50cr shown   1.40   .30
1753 A936 55cr No. 80   1.40   .30
1754 A936 60cr No. 81   1.40   .30
  Nos. 1752-1754 (3)   4.20   .90

Stamp Day; cent. of "small head" stamps.

Institute of
Military
Engineering,
50th
Anniv. — A937

1981, Aug. 11   Litho.   *Perf. 11½*
1755 A937 12cr multi   .25   .20

Reisado
Dancers — A938

1981, Aug. 22
1756 A938 50cr Dancers, diff.   .80   .22
1757 A938 55cr Sailors   .80   .25
1758 A938 60cr shown   .80   .20
  Nos. 1756-1758 (3)   2.40   .67

Intl. Year of the
Disabled
A939

1981, Sept. 17   Litho.   *Perf. 11½*
1759 A939 12cr multi   .25   .20

Flowers of the
Central Plateau
A940

1981, Sept. 21   Litho.   *Perf. 12*
1760 A940 12cr Palicourea rigida   .25   .20
1761 A940 12cr Dalechampia caper-
    onioides   .25   .20
1762 A940 12cr Cassia clausseni, vert.   .25   .20
1763 A940 12cr Eremanthus sphaer-
    ocephalus,   vert.   .25   .20
  Nos. 1760-1763 (4)   1.00   .80

Virgin of Nazareth
Statue — A941

Christ the
Redeemer Statue,
Rio de Janeiro,
50th
Anniv. — A942

1981, Oct. 10   Litho.   *Perf. 12*
1764 A941 12cr multi   .25   .20
Candle Festival of Nazareth, Belem.

1981, Oct. 12
1765 A942 12cr multi   .25   .20

World Food
Day — A943

1981, Oct. 16
1766 A943 12c multi   .25   .20

75th Anniv. of Santos-Dumont's First
Flight — A944

1981, Oct. 23   Litho.   *Perf. 12*
1767 A944 60cr multi   1.00   .35

Father José de Santa Rita Durao, Titlepage
of his Epic Poem Caramuru, Diego Alvares
Correia (Character)
A945

1981, Oct. 29
1768 A945 12cr multi   .25   .20
Caramuru publication cent.; World Book Day.

Christmas
1981 — A946

Designs: Creches and figurines.

1981, Nov. 10   Litho.   *Perf. 12*
1769 A946 12cr multi   .15   .15
1770 A946 50cr multi   1.25   .25
1771 A946 55cr multi, vert.   1.25   .28
1772 A946 60cr multi, vert.   1.25   .30
  Nos. 1769-1772 (4)   3.90   .98

State
Flags — A947

Designs: a, Alagoas. b, Bahia. c, Federal District.
d, Pernambuco. e, Sergipe.

1981, Nov. 19
1773   Block of 5 + label   1.25   1.25
  a.-e.   A947 12cr, any single   .20   .20
Label shows arms of Brazil.

Thanksgiving
1981 — A948

1981, Nov. 26   Litho.   *Perf. 11½*
1776 A948 12cr multi   .25   .15

Ministry of
Labor, 50th
Anniv.
A949

1981, Nov. 26
1777 A949 12cr multi   .20   .15

School of
Engineering,
Itajuba
A950

1981, Nov. 30   *Perf. 11x11½*
1778 A950 15cr lt grn & pur   .35   .15
Theodomiro C. Santiago, founder, birth centenary.

Sao Paulo State Police
Sesquicentennial
A951

1981, Dec. 15   Litho.   *Perf. 12*
1779 A951 12cr Policeman with saxo-
    phone   .20   .15
1780 A951 12cr Mounted policemen   .20   .15

Army Library
Centenary
A952

1981, Dec. 17
1781 A952 12cr multi   .20 .15

Souvenir Sheet

Philatelic
Club of
Brazil,
50th
Anniv.
A953

1981, Dec. 18   *Perf. 11*
1782 A953 180cr multi   4.50 4.50

Brigadier
Eduardo
Gomes
A954

1982, Jan. 20   Litho.   *Perf. 11x11½*
1783 A954 12cr blue & blk   .30 .15

Birth
Centenary of
Henrique
Lage,
Industrialist
A956

1982, Mar. 14   Litho.   *Perf. 11½*
1785 A956 17cr multi   .50 .16

1982 World Cup   TB Bacillus
Soccer — A957   Cent. — A958

Designs: Various soccer players.

1982, Mar. 19
1786 A957 75cr multi   .75 .25
1787 A957 80cr multi   .75 .28
1788 A957 85cr multi   .75 .28
   Nos. 1786-1788 (3)   2.25 .81

Souvenir Sheet
Imperf
1789   Sheet of 3   3.00 6.00
   a.   A957 100cr like #1786   1.00
   b.   A957 100cr like #1787   1.00
   c.   A957 100cr like #1788   1.00

1982, Mar. 24   *Perf. 12*
1790 A958 90cr Microscope, lung   1.25 .80
1791 A958 100cr Lung, pills   1.25 .90
   a.   Pair, #1790-1791   2.50 2.00

Souvenir Sheet

A959

1982, Apr. 17   Litho.   *Perf. 11*
1792   Sheet of 3   3.50 3.25
   a.   A959 75cr Laelia Purpurata   1.00 .50
   b.   A959 80cr Oncidium flexuosum   1.00 .50
   c.   A959 85cr Cleistes revoluta   1.25 .55
BRAPEX V Stamp Exhibition, Blumenau.

Oil Drilling
Centenary
A960

1982, Apr. 18   *Perf. 11½*
1793 A960 17cr multi   .25 .15

400th Birth
Anniv. of St.
Vincent de
Paul — A961

1982, Apr. 24   Litho.   *Perf. 11½*
1794 A961 17cr multi   .25 .15

Seven Steps of
Guaira
(Waterfalls)
A962

1982, Apr. 29
1795 A962 17cr Fifth Fall   .20 .15
1796 A962 21cr Seventh Fall   .30 .20

Ministry of Communications, 15th
Anniv. — A963

1982, May 15
1797 A963 21cr multi   .25 .20

Museology
Course, Natl.
Historical
Museum, 50th
Anniv.
A964

1982, May 18
1798 A964 17cr blk & sal pink   .20 .15

Vale de Rio
Doce Mining
Co. — A965

1982, June 1
1799 A965 17cr Gears   .25 .15

Martin Afonso
de Souza
Reading
Charter to
Settlers
A966

1982, June 3   Litho.   *Perf. 11½*
1800 A966 17cr multi   .25 .15
Town of Sao Vincente, 450th anniv.

Armadillo
A967

1982, June 4
1801 A967 17cr shown   .55 .15
1802 A967 21cr Wolves   .55 .18
1803 A967 30cr Deer   1.65 .22
   Nos. 1801-1803 (3)   2.75 .55

Film Strip
and Award
A968

1982, June 19
1804 A968 17cr multi   .25 .15
20th anniv. of Golden Palm award for The Promise Keeper, Cannes Film Festival.

Souvenir Sheet

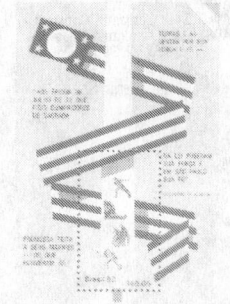

50th Anniv. of Constitutionalist
Revolution — A969

1982, July 9   Litho.   *Perf. 11*
1805 A969 140cr multi   1.75 1.75

Church of Our Lady   St. Francis of Assisi,
of O'Sabara — A970   800th Birth
                        Anniv. — A971

Baroque Architecture, Minas Gerais State: No.
1807, Church of Our Lady of the Rosary, Diamantina, horiz.   No. 1808, Town Square, Mariana,
horiz.

1982, July 16   *Perf. 11½*
1806 A970 17cr multi   .25 .15
1807 A970 17cr multi   .25 .15
1808 A970 17cr multi   .25 .15
   Nos. 1806-1808 (3)   .75 .45

1982, July 24
1809 A971 21cr multi   .20 .16

Stamp Day and
Centenary of
Pedro II "Large
Head" Stamps
A972

1982, Aug. 1
1810 A972 21cr No. 82   .25 .20

Port of
Manaus
Free Trade
Zone
A973

1982, Aug. 15   *Perf. 11x11½*
1811 A973 75cr multi   .65 .35

Scouting Year — A974

1982, Aug. 21   Litho.   *Perf. 11*
1812   Sheet of 2   2.75 3.75
   a.   A974 85cr Baden-Powell   1.00 1.10
   b.   A974 185cr Scout   1.65 2.00

Orixas Folk
Costumes of
African
Origin — A975

1982, Aug. 21   *Perf. 11½*
1813 A975 20cr Iemanja   .20 .16
1814 A975 20cr Xango   .20 .16
1815 A975 20cr Oxumare   .20 .16
   Nos. 1813-1815 (3)   .60 .48

10th Anniv. of
Central Bank
of Brazil
Currency
Museum
A976

1982, Aug. 31
1816 A976 25cr 12-florin coin, 1645,
            obverse and reverse   .25 .20
1817 A976 25cr Emperor Pedro's 6.40-
            reis coronation coin,
            1822   .25 .20

National
Week — A977

1982, Sept. 1
1818 A977 25cr Don Pedro proclaiming
            independence   .38 .25

A978   A979

1982, Oct. 4
1819 A978 85cr Portrait   1.00 .60
St. Theresa of Avila (1515-1582).

1982, Oct. 15   Litho.   Perf. 11½x11
1820 A979 75cr Instruments   .65 .38
1821 A979 80cr Dancers   .65 .38
1822 A979 85cr Musicians   .70 .40
  a.   Souvenir sheet of 3, #1820-1822,
        perf. 11   2.75 2.75
    Nos. 1820-1822 (3)   2.00 1.16
Lubrapex '82, 4th Portuguese-Brazilian Stamp
Exhibition. Stamps in No. 1822a are without
"LUBRAPEX 82."

Aviation
Industry
Day — A980

1982, Oct. 17   Perf. 12
1823 A980 24cr Embraer EMB-312
    trainer plane   .25 .20

Bastos Tigre,
Poet, Birth
Centenary,
and
"Saudade"
Text — A981

1982, Oct. 29
1824 A981 24cr multi   .25 .20
Book Day.

10th Anniv. of Brazilian
Telecommunications Co. — A982

1982, Nov. 9   Litho.   Perf. 11½
1825 A982 24cr multi   .25 .20

Christmas
1982 — A983
Children's Drawings.

1982, Nov. 10
1826 A983 24cr Nativity   .25 .20
1827 A983 24cr Angels   .25 .20
1828 A983 30cr Nativity, diff.   .32 .45
1829 A983 30cr Flight into Egypt   .32 .45
    Nos. 1826-1829 (4)   1.14 1.30

State
Flags — A984
Designs: a, Ceara. b, Espirito Santo. c, Paraiba. d,
Grande de Norte. e, Rondonia.

1982, Nov. 19
1830   Block of 5 + label   5.25 5.25
a.-e.   A984 24cr any single   1.00 .20

Thanksgiving
1982 — A985

1982, Nov. 25
1835 A985 24cr multi   .25 .20

Homage to the
Deaf — A986

1982, Dec. 1
1836 A986 24cr multi   .25 .20

Naval Academy
Bicentenary
A987
Training Ships.

1982, Dec. 14
1837 A987 24cr Brazil   .35 .20
1838 A987 24cr Benjamin Constant   .35 .20
1839 A987 24cr Almirante Saldanha   .35 .20
    Nos. 1837-1839 (3)   1.05 .60

Souvenir Sheet

No. 12 — A988

1982, Dec. 18   Litho.   Perf. 11
1840 A988 200cr multi   4.00 5.00
BRASILIANA '83 Intl. Stamp Exhibition, Rio de
Janeiro, July 29-Aug. 7.

Brasiliana '83
Carnival
A989

1983, Feb. 9   Litho.   Perf. 11½
1841 A989 24cr Samba drummers   .20 .15
1842 A989 130cr Street parade   1.40 .50
1843 A989 140cr Dancer   1.40 .52
1844 A989 150cr Male dancer   1.40 .55
    Nos. 1841-1844 (4)   4.40 1.72

Antarctic
Expedition
A990

1983, Feb. 20   Litho.   Perf. 11½
1845 A990 150cr Support ship Barano
    de Teffe   2.00 .55

50th Anniv. of
Women's
Rights — A991

1983, Mar. 8
1846 A991 130cr multi   1.25 .50

Itaipu
Hydroelectric
Power Station
Opening
A992

1983, Mar.   Litho.   Perf. 12
1847 A992 140cr multi   1.90 .42

Cancer Prevention   Martin Luther
A993   (1483-1546)
    A994
30cr, Microscope. 38cr, Antonio Prudente, Paulista Cancer Assoc. founder, Camargo Hospital.

1983, Apr. 18
1848 A993 30cr multi   .30 .15
1849 A993 38cr multi   .32 .15
  a.   Pair, #1848-1849   .65 .35
    Set value   .22

1983, Apr. 18
1850 A994 150cr pale grn & blk   1.25 .50

Agricultural
Research
A995

1983, Apr. 26   Litho.   Perf. 11½
1851 A995 30cr Chestnut tree   .20 .15
1852 A995 30cr Genetic research   .20 .15
1853 A995 38cr Tropical soy beans   .25 .15
    Nos. 1851-1853 (3)   .65
    Set value   .20

Father Rogerio Neuhaus
(1863-1934), Centenary
of Ordination — A996

1983, May 3   Perf. 11½x11
1854 A996 30cr multi   .25 .15

30th Anniv.
of Customs
Cooperation
Council
A997

1983, May 5   Perf. 11x11½
1855 A997 30cr multi   .25 .15

World Communications Year — A998

1983, May 17   Litho.   Perf. 11½
1856 A998 250cr multi   1.50 .45

Toucans
A999

1983, May 21
1857 A999 30cr Tucanucu   .15 .15
1858 A999 185cr White-breasted   1.25 .38
1859 A999 205cr Green-beaked   1.25 .40
1860 A999 215cr Black-beaked   1.25 .45
    Nos. 1857-1860 (4)   3.90 1.38

Souvenir Sheet

Resurrection, by Raphael (1483-
1517) — A1000

1983, May 25   Perf. 11
1861 A1000 250cr multi   2.50 3.00

Hohenzollern
980
Locomotive,
1875
A1001
Various locomotives.

1983, June 12   Litho.   Perf. 11½
1862 A1001 30cr shown   .25 .15
1863 A1001 30cr Baldwin #1, 1881   .25 .15
1864 A1001 38cr Fowler #1, 1872   .30 .15
    Nos. 1862-1864 (3)   .80
    Set value   .20

9th Women's Basketball
World
Championship — A1002

1983, July 24   Litho.   Perf. 11½x11
1865 A1002 30cr Players, front view   .20 .15
1866 A1002 30cr Players, rear view   .20 .15
    Set value   .15

Simon Bolivar
(1783-1830)
A1003

1983, July 24   Perf. 12
1867 A1003 30cr multi   .20 .15

Children's
Polio and
Measles
Vaccination
Campaign
A1004

1983, July 25
1868 A1004 30cr Girl, measles   .20 .15
1869 A1004 30cr Boy, polio   .20 .15
    Set value   .15

A1005   A1006

1983, July 28   **Perf. 11¹/₂x11**
1870 A1005 30cr Minerva (goddess of
         wisdom), computer
         tape   .20 .15
20th Anniv. of Master's program in engineering.

1983, July 29   **Engr.**
Guanabara Bay.
1871 A1006 185cr No. 1   1.50 .38
1872 A1006 205cr No. 2   1.50 .40
1873 A1006 215cr No. 3   1.50 .45
    Nos. 1871-1873 (3)   4.50 1.23
Souvenir Sheet
      Perf. 11
1874   Sheet of 3   8.00 10.00
  a.   A1006 185cr No. 1   2.00 3.00
  b.   A1006 205cr No. 2   2.00 3.00
  c.   A1006 215cr No. 3   2.00 3.00
BRASILIANA '83 Intl. Stamp Show, Rio de
Janeiro, July 29-Aug. 7.

Souvenir Sheet

The First Mass in
Brazil, by Vitor Meireles
(1833-1903) — A1007

1983, Aug. 18   **Perf. 11**
1875 A1007 250cr multi   3.00 1.50

EMB-120
Brasilia
Passenger
Plane
A1008

1983, Aug. 19   **Perf. 12**
1876 A1008 30cr multi   .25 .15

Vision of Don
Bosco
Centenary
A1009

1983, Aug. 30
1877 A1009 130cr multi   .75 .25

Independence
Week
A1010

1983, Sept. 1   **Litho.**   **Perf. 11¹/₂**
1878 A1010 50cr multi
                         .25 .15

National Steel
Corp., 10th
Anniv. — A1011

1983, Sept. 17   **Litho.**   **Perf. 11¹/₂**
1879 A1011 45cr multi   .25 .15

Cactus — A1012

1983, Sept. 12   **Litho.**   **Perf. 11¹/₂**
1880 A1012 45cr Pilosocereus gounel-
         lei   .32 .15
1881 A1012 45cr Melocactus bahien-
         sis   .32 .15
1882 A1012 57cr Cereus jamacaru   .40 .15
    Nos. 1880-1882 (3)   1.04
    Set value   .32

1st National
Eucharistic
Congress — A1013

1983, Oct. 12   **Litho.**   **Perf. 11¹/₂**
1883 A1013 45cr multi   .25 .15

World Food
Program
A1014

1983, Oct. 14   **Litho.**   **Perf. 11¹/₂**
1884 A1014 45cr Mouth, grain   .30 .15
1885 A1014 57cr Fish, sailboat   .40 .15
    Set value   .22

Souvenir Sheet

Louis
Breguet,
Death
Centenary
A1015

1983, Oct. 27   **Litho.**   **Perf. 11**
1886 A1015 376cr Telegraph trans-
         mitter   4.25 1.50

Christmas
1983 — A1016

17th-18th Cent. Statues: 45cr, Our Lady of the
Angels. 315cr, Our Lady of the Parturition. 335cr,
Our Lady of Joy. 345cr, Our Lady of the
Presentation.

1983, Nov. 10   **Litho.**   **Perf. 11¹/₂**
1887 A1016 45cr multi   .25 .15
1888 A1016 315cr multi   1.65 .60
1889 A1016 335cr multi   1.65 .65
1890 A1016 345cr multi   1.65 .70
    Nos. 1887-1890 (4)   5.20 2.10

Marshal
Mascarenhas
Birth Centenary
A1017

1983, Nov. 13   **Litho.**   **Perf. 11¹/₂**
1891 A1017 45cr Battle sites   .20 .15
Commander of Brazilian Expeditionary Force in
Italy.

State Flags
A1018

Designs: a, Amazonas. b, Goias. c, Rio. d, Mato
Grosso Do Sol. e, Parana.

1983, Nov. 17   **Litho.**   **Perf. 11¹/₂**
1892   Block of 5 + label   3.00 3.00
  a.-e. A1018 45cr any single   .50 .20

Thanksgiving
A1018a

1983, Nov. 24   **Litho.**   **Perf. 12**
1896 A1018a 45cr Madonna, wheat   .35 .15

Manned Flight
Bicentenary — A1019

1983, Dec. 15   **Litho.**   **Perf. 12**
1897 A1019 345cr Montgolfiere bal-
         loon, 1783   5.00 .50

Ethnic Groups
A1020

1984, Jan. 20   **Litho.**   **Perf. 12**
1898 A1020 45cr multi   .20 .15
50th anniv. of publication of Masters and Slaves,
sociological study by Gilberto Freyre.

Centenary of
Crystal Palace,
Petropolis
A1021

1984, Feb. 2
1899 A1021 45cr multi   .18 .15

Souvenir Sheet

Flags (Sculpture with 40 Figures), by
Victor Brecheret (b. 1894)
A1022

1984, Feb. 22   **Litho.**   **Perf. 11**
1900 A1022 805cr multi   1.50 1.00

Naval Museum
Centenary
A1023

1984, Mar. 23   **Litho.**   **Perf. 11¹/₂**
1901 A1023 620cr Figurehead, frigate,
         1847   .85 .52

Slavery
Abolition
Centenary
A1024

1984, Mar. 25
1902 A1024 585cr Broken chain, raft   .85 .55
1903 A1024 610cr Freed slave   .90 .60

Souvenir Sheet

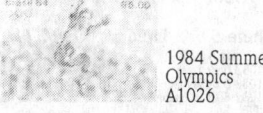

Visit of
King Carl
XVI
Gustaf of
Sweden
A1025

1984, Apr. 2   **Perf. 11**
1904 A1025 2105cr multi   3.50 2.50

1984 Summer
Olympics
A1026

1984, Apr. 13   **Perf. 11¹/₂**
1905 A1026 65cr Long jump   .15 .15
1906 A1026 65cr 100-meter race   .15 .15
1907 A1026 65cr Relay race   .15 .15
1908 A1026 585cr Pole vault   .80 .65
1909 A1026 610cr High jump   .85 .70
1910 A1026 620cr Hurdles   .90 .80
  a.   Block of 6, #1905-1910   3.00 3.00

Voters Casting
Ballots,
Symbols of
Labor
A1027

Pres. Getulio Vargas Birth Centenary: Symbols of
Development.

1984, Apr. 19   **Litho.**   **Perf. 11¹/₂**
1911 A1027 65cr shown   .15 .15
1912 A1027 65cr Oil rig, blast furnace   .15 .15
1913 A1027 65cr High-tension towers   .15 .15
    Nos. 1911-1913 (3)   .45
    Set value   .25

Columbus, Espana '84
Emblem — A1028

1984, Apr. 27
1914 A1028 65cr Pedro Cabral .15 .15
1915 A1028 610cr shown 1.25 .70

Map of Americas,
Heads — A1029

Lubrapex
'84 — A1030

1984, May 7   Litho.   Perf. 11½
1916 A1029 65cr multi .15 .15
Pan-American Association of Finance and Guarantees, 8th Assembly.

1984, May 8   Perf. 11½x11
18th Century Paintings, Mariana Cathedral.
1917 A1030 65cr Hunting scene .15 .15
1918 A1030 585cr Pastoral scene .75 .42
1919 A1030 610cr People under umbrellas .80 .50
1920 A1030 620cr Elephants .85 .50
Nos. 1917-1920 (4) 2.55 1.57

Souvenir Sheet

Intl. Fedn. of Soccer Associations, 80th
Anniv. — A1031

1984, May 21   Perf. 11
1921 A1031 2115cr Globe 3.50 1.75

Matto Grosso
Lowland
Fauna
A1032

1984, June 5   Litho.   Perf. 11½
1922   Strip of 3 .60 .30
a. A1032 65cr Deer .20 .15
b. A1032 65cr Jaguar .20 .15
c. A1032 80cr Alligator .20 .15

First Letter Mailed in
Brazil, by Guido
Mondin — A1033

1984, June 8   Perf. 12x11½
1923 A1033 65cr multi .15 .15
Postal Union of Americas and Spain, first anniv.
of new headquarters.

Brazil-Germany Air Service, 50th
Anniv.
A1034   A1035

1984, June 19
1924 A1034 610cr Dornier-Wal seaplane 1.00 .70
1925 A1035 620cr Steamer Westfalen 1.05 .72
a.   Pair, #1924-1925 2.05 1.50

Woolly Spider Monkey,
World Wildlife Fund
Emblem — A1036

1984, July 6   Perf. 11½
1926 A1036 65cr Mother, baby .48 .15
1927 A1036 80cr Monkey .32 .15
Set value .18

Agriculture Type of 1980
Designs: 65cr, Rubber tree. 80cr, Brazil nuts.
120cr, Rice. 150cr, Eucalyptus. 300cr, Pinha da
Parana. 800cr, Carnauba. 1000cr, Babacu.
2000cr, Sunflower.

**Photogravure (65, 80, 120, 150cr),
Engraved**
1984-85   Perf. 11x11½
1934 A894 65cr lilac .20 .15
1935 A894 80cr brn red .25 .15
1936 A894 120cr dk sl bl .35 .15
1937 A894 150cr green .15 .15
1938 A894 300cr rose mag .50 .15
1939 A894 800cr grnsh bl 1.40 .15
1940 A894 1000cr lemon 1.40 .15
1941 A894 2000cr yel org ('85) .75 .25
Nos. 1934-1941 (8) 5.00
Set value 1.00

Marajo Isld.
Buffalo
A1037

1984, July 9   Litho.   Perf. 12
1942   Strip of 3 .50 .28
a. A1037 65cr Approaching stream .15 .15
b. A1037 65cr Standing on bank .15 .15
c. A1037 80cr Drinking .18 .15
Continuous design.

Banco Economico
Sesquicentenary — A1038

1984, July 13   Perf. 11½
1943 A1038 65cr Bank, coins .15 .15

Historic
Railway
Stations
A1039

1984, July 23   Litho.   Perf. 11½
1944 A1039 65cr Japeri .15 .15
1945 A1039 65cr Luz, vert. .15 .15
1946 A1039 80cr Sao Joao del Rei .16 .15
Nos. 1944-1946 (3) .46
Set value .25

A1040   A1041

1984, Aug. 13   Perf. 11
Souvenir Sheet
1947 A1040 585cr Girl scout 1.40 1.00
Girl Scouts in Brazil, 65th anniv.

1984, Aug. 21   Litho.   Perf. 11½
1948 A1041 65cr Couple sheltered
from rain .15 .15
Housing project bank, 20th anniv.

Independence
Week
A1042

Children's Drawings.

1984, Sept. 3
1949 A1042 100cr Explorer & ship .15 .15
1950 A1042 100cr Sailing ships .15 .15
1951 A1042 100cr "BRASIL" mural .15 .15
1952 A1042 100cr Children under rainbow .15 .15
Nos. 1949-1952 (4) .60
Set value .50

Rio de Janeiro Chamber of Commerce
Sesquicentenary — A1043

1984, Sept. 10
1953 A1043 100cr Monument, worker
silhouette .15 .15

Death Sesquicentenary of Don Pedro I (IV
of Portugal) — A1044

1984, Sept. 23   Perf. 12x11½
1954 A1044 1000cr Portrait 1.50 1.10

Local
Mushrooms — A1045

Book
Day — A1046

1984, Oct. 22   Perf. 11½
1955 A1045 120cr Pycnoporus
sanguineus .15 .15
1956 A1045 1050cr Calvatia sp 1.10 1.25

1957 A1045 1080cr Pleurotus sp,
horiz. 1.20 1.30
Nos. 1955-1957 (3) 2.45 2.70

1984, Oct. 23   Perf. 11½
1958 A1046 120cr Girl in open book .15 .15

New State Mint
Opening — A1047

1984, Nov. 1
1959 A1047 120cr multi .15 .15

Informatics
Fair &
Congress
A1048

1984, Nov. 5   Litho.   Perf. 12
1960 A1048 120cr Eye, computer terminal .15 .15

Org. of American
States, 14th
Assembly — A1049

1984, Nov. 14
1961 A1049 120cr Emblem, flags .15 .15

State Flags
A1050

Designs: a, Maranhaio. b, Mato Grosso. c,
Minas Gerais. d, Piaui. e, Santa Catarina.

1984, Nov. 19   Perf. 11½
1962   Block of 5 + label 1.00 1.00
a.-e. A1050 120cr, any single .20 .15
See Nos. 2037, 2249.

Thanksgiving
1984 — A1051

1984, Nov. 22
1963 A1051 120cr Bell tower, Brasilia .15 .15

Christmas
1984
A1052

Paintings: No. 1964, Nativity, by Djanira. No.
1965, Virgin and Child, by Glauco Rodrigues. No.
1966, Flight into Egypt, by Paul Garfunkel. No.
1967, Nativity, by Di Cavalcanti.

1984, Dec. 3   Litho.   Perf. 12
1964	A1052	120cr multi	.15	.15
1965	A1052	120cr multi	.15	.15
1966	A1052	1050cr multi	.85	.40
1967	A1052	1080cr multi	.85	.40
		Nos. 1964-1967 (4)	2.00	
		Set value		.90

40th Anniv., International Civil Aviation Organization A1053

1984, Dec. 7   Litho.   Perf. 12
1968 A1053 120cr Aircraft, Earth globe .15 .15

25th Anniv., North-Eastern Development A1054

1984, Dec. 14   Litho.   Perf. 12
1969 A1054 120cr Farmer, field   .15 .15

Emilio Rouede A1055

Painting: Church of the Virgin of Safe Travels, by Rouede.

1985, Jan. 22   Litho.   Perf. 12
1970 A1055 120cr multi   .15 .15

BRASILSAT — A1056

1985, Feb. 8   Litho.   Perf. 11½x12
1971 A1056 150cr Satellite, Brazil   .15 .15

Metropolitan Railways — A1057

1985, Mar. 2   Litho.   Perf. 11x11½
1972 A1057 200cr Passenger trains   .15 .15

Brasilia Botanical Gardens A1058

1985, Mar. 8   Litho.   Perf. 11½x12
1973 A1058 200cr Caryocar brasiliense .15 .15

40th Anniv., Brazilian Paratroops — A1059

1985, Mar. 8   Litho.   Perf. 11½x12
1974 A1059 200cr Parachute drop   .15 .15

Natl. Climate Awareness Program — A1060

1985, Mar. 18   Litho.   Perf. 11½x12
1975 A1060 500cr multi   .20 .15

Thoroughbred Horses A1061

1985, Mar. 19   Litho.   Perf. 12
1976	A1061	1000cr Campolina	.38	.22
1977	A1061	1500cr Marajoara	.70	.35
1978	A1061	1500cr Mangalarga marchador	.70	.35
		Nos. 1976-1978 (3)	1.78	.92

Ouro Preto — A1062

1985, Apr. 18   Litho.   Perf. 11½x12
1979	A1062	220cr shown	.15	.15
1980	A1062	220cr St. Miguel des Missoes	.15	.15
1981	A1062	220cr Olinda	.15	.15
		Set value	.30	.20

Polivolume, by Mary Vieira — A1063

1985, Apr. 20   Litho.
1982 A1063 220cr multi   .15 .15

Rio Branco Inst., 40th anniv.

Natl. Capital, Brasilia, 25th Anniv. — A1064

1985, Apr. 22   Litho.
1983	A1064	220cr Natl. Theater, acoustic shell	.15	.15
1984	A1064	220cr Catetinho Palace, JK Memorial	.15	.15
		Set value	.20	.15

A1065   A1065a

1985-86   Photo.   Perf. 11½
1985	A1065	50cr lake	.15	.15
1986	A1065	100cr dp vio	.15	.15
1987	A1065	150cr violet	.15	.15
1988	A1065	200cr ultra	.15	.15
1989	A1065	220cr green	.15	.15
1990	A1065	300cr royal bl	.18	.15
1991	A1065	500cr olive blk	.30	.22
1992	A1065a	1000cr brn ol ('86)	.18	.15
1993	A1065a	2000cr brt grn ('86)	.35	.22
1994	A1065a	3000cr dl vio	.42	.32
1995	A1065a	5000cr brn	.58	.42
		Set value	2.35	1.65

Marshal Rondon, 120th Birth Anniv. A1066

1985, May 5   Perf. 11x11½
1996 A1066 220cr multi   .15 .15

Educator, protector of the Indians, building superintendent of telegraph lines.

Candido Fontoura (1885-1974) A1067

Brapex VI A1068

1985, May 14   Perf. 12x11½
1997 A1067 220cr multi   .15 .15

Pioneer of the Brazilian pharmaceutical industry.

1985, May 18   Perf. 11½x11
Cave paintings: No. 1998, Deer, Cerca Grande. No. 1999, Lizards, Lapa do Caboclo. No. 2000, Running deer, Grande Abrigo de Santana do Riacho.
1998	A1068	300cr multi	.15	.15
1999	A1068	300cr multi	.15	.15
2000	A1068	2000cr multi	.75	.50
a.		Souvenir sheet of 3, #1998-2000, perf. 10½x11	1.00	1.00
		Nos. 1998-2000 (3)	1.05	
		Set value		.65

Wildlife Conservation A1069

Birds in Marinho dos Abrolhos National Park.

1985, June 5   Perf. 11½x12
2001	A1069	220cr Fregata magnificens	.15	.15
2002	A1069	220cr Sula dactylatra	.15	.15
2003	A1069	220cr Anous stolidus	.15	.15
2004	A1069	2000cr Pluvialis squatarola	.60	.25
		Nos. 2001-2004 (4)	1.05	
		Set value		.40

A1070   A1071

1985, June 11   Perf. 12x11½
2005	A1070	220cr Mother breastfeeding infant	.15	.15
2006	A1070	220cr Hand, eyedropper, children	.15	.15
a.		Pair, #2005-2006	.25	.15

UN infant survival campaign.

1985, June 22   Litho.   Perf. 11½x11
Helicopter rescue, search ship, diver.
2007 A1071 220cr multi   .15 .15

Sea Search & Rescue.

World Cup Soccer, Mexico, 1986 A1072

1985, June 23   Perf. 11
2008 A1072 2000cr Player dribbling, World Cup   4.00 .85

Intl. Youth Year — A1073   11th Natl. Eucharistic Congress — A1074

1985, June 28   Perf. 12
2009 A1073 220cr Circle of children   .15 .15

1985, July 16   Perf. 12x11½
2010 A1074 2000cr Mosaic, Priest raising host   .55 .38

Director Humberto Mauro, Scene from Sangue Mineiro, 1929 A1075

1985, July 27
2011 A1075 300cr multi   .15 .15

Cataguases Studios, 60th anniv.

Escola e Sacro Museum, Convent St. Anthony, Joao Pessoa, Paraiba A1076

1985, Aug. 5   Perf. 11½x12
2012 A1076 330cr multi   .15 .15

Paraiba State 400th anniv.

Inconfidencia Museum — A1077   Cabanagem Insurrection, 150th Anniv. — A1078

1985, Aug. 11   Perf. 12x11½
2013	A1077	300cr shown	.15	.15
2014	A1077	300cr Museum of History & Diplomacy	.15	.15
		Set value	.20	.16

1985, Aug. 14
Design: Revolutionary, detail from an oil painting by Guido Mondin.
2015 A1078 330cr multi   .15 .15

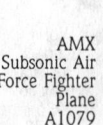

AMX
Subsonic Air
Force Fighter
Plane
A1079

1985, Aug. 19   *Perf. 11¹/₂x12*
2016 A1079 330cr multi   .15 .15
AMX Project, joint program with Italy.

16th-17th Century
Military
Uniforms — A1080

1985, Aug. 26   *Perf. 12x11¹/₂*
2017 A1080 300cr Captain, crossbow-
            man   .16 .15
2018 A1080 300cr Harquebusier, ser-
            geant   .16 .15
2019 A1080 300cr Musketeer, pikeman .16 .15
2020 A1080 300cr Fusilier, pikeman   .16 .15
      Nos. 2017-2020 (4)   .64
      Set value   .50

Farrouphilha
Insurrection,
150th Anniv.
A1081

Design: Bento Goncalves and insurrectionist cavalry on Southern battlefields, detail of an oil painting by Guido Mondin.

1985, Sept. 20   *Perf. 11¹/₂x12*
2021 A1081 330cr multi   .15 .15

Aparados da
Serra National
Park
A1082

1985, Sept. 23
2022 A1082 3100cr Ravine   .65 .52
2023 A1082 3320cr Mountains   .70 .55
2024 A1082 3480cr Forest, waterfall .75 .60
      Nos. 2022-2024 (3)   2.10 1.67

President-elect Tancredo Neves — A1083

Design: Portrait, Natl. Congress, Alvorada Palace, Federal Supreme Court.

1985, Oct. 10   Litho.   *Perf. 11x11¹/₂*
2025 A1083 330cr multi   .15 .15

FEB,
Postmark
A1084

1985, Oct. 10   *Perf. 11¹/₂x12*
2026 A1084 500cr multi   .15 .15
Brazilian Expeditionary Force Postal Service, 41st
anniv.

Rio de Janeiro-Niteroi Ferry Service, 150th
Anniv. — A1085

1985, Oct. 14   *Perf. 11¹/₂x12*
2027 A1085 500cr Segunda   .20 .15
2028 A1085 500cr Terceira   .20 .15
2029 A1085 500cr Especuladora   .20 .15
2030 A1085 500cr Urca   .20 .15
      Nos. 2027-2030 (4)   .80 .60

Muniz M-7 Inaugural Flight, 50th
Anniv. — A1086

1985, Oct. 22
2031 A1086 500cr multi   .15 .15

UN 40th   Natl. Press
Anniv. — A1087   System — A1088

1985, Oct. 24   *Perf. 11¹/₂x11*
2032 A1087 500cr multi   .15 .15

1985, Nov. 7
2033 A1088 500cr Newspaper mast-
            head, reader   .15 .15
Diario de Pernambuco, newspaper, 160th anniv.

Christmas
1985
A1089

1985, Nov. 11   *Perf. 11¹/₂x12*
2034 A1089 500cr Christ in Manger   .20 .15
2035 A1089 500cr Adoration of the
            Magi   .20 .15
2036 A1089 500cr Flight to Egypt   .20 .15
      Nos. 2034-2036 (3)   .60 .45

State Flag Type

State Flags: a, Para. b, Rio Grande do Sul. c,
Acre. d, Sao Paulo.

1985, Nov. 19   *Perf. 12*
2037   Block of 4   .80 .60
a.-d. A1050 500cr, any single   .20 .15

Thanksgiving
Day — A1091

1985, Nov. 28   *Perf. 12x11¹/₂*
2038 A1091 500cr Child gathering
            wheat   .20 .15

Economic
Development
of Serra dos
Carajas Region
A1092

1985, Dec. 11   Litho.   *Perf. 11¹/₂x12*
2039 A1092 500cr multi   .15 .15

Fr. Bartholomeu Lourenco de Gusmao
(1685-1724), Inventor, the Aerostat
A1093

1985, Dec. 19   Litho.   *Perf. 11x11¹/₂*
2040 A1093 500cr multi   .15 .15

A1094   A1095

The Trees, by Da Costa E Silva (b. 1885), poet.

1985, Dec. 20   Litho.   *Perf. 12x11¹/₂*
2041 A1094 500cr multi   .15 .15

1986, Mar. 3   Litho.   *Perf. 11*
            Souvenir Sheet
2042 A1095 10000cr multi   2.25 2.00
1986 World Cup Soccer Championships, Mexico. LUBRAPEX '86, philatelic exhibition.

Halley's Comet — A1096

1986, Apr. 11   Litho.   *Perf. 11¹/₂x12*
2043 A1096 50c multi   .15 .15

Commander
Ferraz Antarctic
Station, 2nd
Anniv.
A1097

1986, Apr. 25
2044 A1097 50c multi   .15 .15

Labor Day   Maternity, by
A1098   Henrique
                     Bernardelli (1858-
                     1936)
                     A1099

1986, May 1   Litho.   *Perf. 12x11¹/₂*
2045 A1098 50c multi   .15 .15

1986, May 8
2046 A1099 50c multi   .15 .15

Amnesty Intl.,
25th Anniv.
A1100

1986, May 28   Litho.   *Perf. 11¹/₂x12*
2047 A1100 50c multi   .15 .15

Butterflies — A1101

1985, June 5   *Perf. 12x11¹/₂*
2048 A1101 50c Pyrrhopyge ruficauda .15 .15
2049 A1101 50c Prepona eugenes
            diluta   .15 .15
2050 A1101 50c Pierriballia mandel
            molione   .15 .15
      Nos. 2048-2050 (3)   .45
      Set value   .15

Score from
Opera "Il
Guarani" and
Antonio
Carlos Gomes
(1836-1896),
Composer
A1102

1986, July 11   *Perf. 11¹/₂x12*
2051 A1102 50c multi   .18 .15

Natl. Accident   Stamp
Prevention   Day — A1104
Campaign — A1103

1986, July 30   Litho.   *Perf. 11¹/₂x11*
2052 A1103 50c Lineman   .15 .15

            Souvenir Sheet

1986, Aug. 1   *Perf. 11*
2053 A1104 5cz No. 53   .85 .35
Brazilian Phil. Soc., 75th anniv., and Dom Pedro
II issue, Nos. 53-60, 120th anniv.

Architecture   Famous Men
A1105   A1106

Designs: 10c, House of Garcia D'Avila, Nazare
de Mata, Bahia. 20c, Church of Our Lady of the
Assumption, Anchieta Village. 50c, Fort Reis
Magos, Natal. 1cz, Pilgrim's Column, Alcantara Vil-
lage, 1648. 2cz, Cloisters, St. Francis Convent,
Olinda. 5cz, St. Anthony's Chapel, Sao Roque.
10cz, St. Lawrence of the Indians Church, Niteroi.
20cz, Principe da Beiro Fort, Mato Dentro. 50cz,
Jesus of Matozinhos Church, vert. 100cz, Church
of our Lady of Sorrow, Campanha. 200cz, Casa dos
Contos, Ouro Preto. 500cz, Antiga Alfandega,
Belem, Para.

Perf. 11¹/₂x11, 11x11¹/₂

			Photo.	
2055	A1105	10c sage grn	.15	.15
2057	A1105	20c brt blue	.15	.15
2059	A1105	50c orange	.15	.15
2064	A1105	1cz golden brn	.15	.15
2065	A1105	2cz dull rose	.25	.18
a.		Litho., perf. 13 ('88)	.15	.15
2067	A1105	5cz lt olive grn	.60	.45
a.		Litho., perf. 13 ('88)	.15	.15
2068	A1105	10cz slate blue	.50	.35
2069	A1105	20cz lt red brn	.75	.58
2070	A1105	50cz brn org	2.25	1.75
2071	A1105	100cz dull grn	2.70	2.00
2072	A1105	200cz deep blue	2.50	1.85
2073	A1105	500cz dull red brn	1.30	1.00
		Nos. 2055-2073 (12)	11.45	8.76

Issued: 10c, Aug. 11; 20c, Dec. 8; 50c, Aug. 19; 1cz, Nov. 19; 2cz, Nov. 9; 5cz, Dec. 30; 10cz, June 2, 1987; 20cz, Sept. 18, 1987; 100cz, Dec. 21, 1987; 200cz, May 9, 1988; 500cz, Nov. 22, 1988.

This is an expanding set. Numbers will change if necessary.

1986   *Perf. 12x11¹/₂, 11¹/₂x12*

Designs: No. 2074, Juscelino Kubitschek de Oliveira, president 1956-61, and Alvorado Palace, Brasilia. No. 2075, Octavio Mangabeira, statesman, and Itamaraty Palace, Rio de Janeiro, horiz.

2074	A1106	50c multi	.15	.15
2075	A1106	50c multi	.15	.15
		Set value	.15	.15

Issue dates: #2074, Aug. 21. #2075, Aug. 27.

World Gastroenterology Congress, Sao Paulo — A1107

1986, Sept. 7   *Perf. 11¹/₂x12*
2076 A1107 50c multi   .15 .15

Federal Broadcasting System, 50th Anniv. — A1108

Intl. Peace Year — A1109

1986, Sept. 15   *Perf. 12x11¹/₂*
2077 A1108 50c multi   .15 .15

1986, Sept. 16

Painting (detail): War and Peace, by Candido Portinari.

2078 A1109 50c multi   .15 .15

Ernesto Simoes Filho (b. 1886), Publisher of A Tarde A1110

1986, Oct. 4   Litho.   *Perf. 11¹/₂x12*
2079 A1110 50c multi   .15 .15

Famous Men — A1111

Federal Savings Bank, 125th Anniv. — A1112

Designs: No. 2080, Title page from manuscript, c. 1683-94, by Gregorio Mattose e Guerra (b. 1636), author. No. 2081, Manuel Bandeira (1886-1968), poet, text from I'll Go Back to Pasargada.

1986, Oct. 29   *Perf. 11¹/₂x11*
2080	A1111	50c lake & beige	.15	.15
2081	A1111	50c lake & dl grn	.15	.15
		Set value	.20	.15

1986, Nov. 4   *Perf. 12x11¹/₂*
2082 A1112 50c multi   .15 .15

Flowering Plants A1113

Glauber Rocha, Film Industry Pioneer A1114

Perf. 12x11¹/₂, 11¹/₂x12

1986, Sept. 23
2083	A1113	50c Urera mitis	.15	.15
2084	A1113	6.50cz Couroupita guyanensis	.52	.40
2085	A1113	6.90cz Bauhinia variegata, horiz.	.55	.42
		Nos. 2083-2085 (3)	1.22	.97

1986, Nov. 20   *Perf. 12x11¹/₂*
2086 A1114 50c multi   .15 .15

LUBRAPEX '86 — A1115

Cordel Folk Tales: No. 2087, Romance of the Mysterious Peacock. No. 2088, History of the Empress Porcina.

1986, Nov. 21   *Perf. 11x12*
2087	A1115	6.90cz multi	.45	.35
2088	A1115	6.90cz multi	.45	.35
a.		Souvenir sheet of 2, #2087-2088, perf. 11	1.10	.85

Christmas A1116

Birds: 50c, And Christ child. 6.50cz, And tree. 7.30cz, Eating fruit.

1986, Nov. 10   *Perf. 11¹/₂x12*
2089	A1116	50c multi	.15	.15
2090	A1116	6.50cz multi	.65	.48
2091	A1116	7.30cz multi	.75	.58
		Nos. 2089-2091 (3)	1.55	1.21

Military Uniforms, c. 1930 — A1117

Bartolomeu de Gusmao Airport, 50th Anniv. — A1118

Designs: No. 2092, Navy lieutenant commander, dreadnought Minas Gerais. No. 2093, Army flight lieutenant, WACO S.C.O. biplane, Fortaleza Airport.

1986, Dec. 15   *Perf. 12x11¹/₂*
2092	A1117	50c multi	.15	.15
2093	A1117	50c multi	.15	.15
		Set value	.15	.15

Fortaleza Air Base, 50th anniv. (No. 2093).

1986, Dec. 26
2094 A1118 1cz multi   .15 .15

Heitor Villa Lobos (1887-1959), Conductor — A1119

1987, Mar. 5   Litho.   *Perf. 12x11¹/₂*
2095 A1119 1.50cz multi   .15 .15

Natl. Air Force C-130 Transport Plane, Flag, the Antarctic A1120

1987, Mar. 9   *Perf. 11x11¹/₂*
2096 A1120 1cz multi   .15 .15

Antarctic Project.

Special Mail Services — A1121

1987, Mar. 20   *Perf. 12x11¹/₂*
2097	A1121	1cz Rural delivery	.15	.15
2098	A1121	1cz Intl. express	.15	.15
		Set value	.20	.16

TELECOM '87, Geneva A1122

1987, May 5   *Perf. 11¹/₂x12*
2099 A1122 2cz Brazilsat, wave, globe   .20 .15

10th Pan American Games, Indianapolis, Aug. 7-25 — A1123

1987, May 20   *Perf. 12x11¹/₂*
2100 A1123 18cz multi   1.00 .75

Natl. Fine Arts Museum, 150th Anniv A1124

1987, Jan. 13   *Perf. 11¹/₂x12*
2101 A1124 1cz multi   .15 .15

Marine Conservation — A1125

1987, June 5
2102	A1125	2cz Eubalaena australis	.15	.15
2103	A1125	2cz Eretmochelys imbricata	.15	.15
		Set value		.20

Federal Court of Appeal, 40th Anniv. A1126

1987, June 15
2104 A1126 2cz multi   .15 .15

Military Club, Cent. — A1127

1987, June 26   *Perf. 12x11¹/₂*
2105 A1127 3cz multi   .18 .15

Agriculture Institute of Campinas, Cent. A1128

1987, June 27   *Perf. 11¹/₂x12*
2106 A1128 2cz multi   .15 .15

Entomological Society, 50th Anniv. A1129

1987, July 17
2107 A1129 3cz Zoolea lopiceps .15 .15
2108 A1129 3cz Fulgora servillei .15 .15
Set value .20

Natl. Tourism
Year
A1130

Designs: No. 2109, Monuments and Sugarloaf Mountain, Rio de Janeiro. No. 2110, Colonial church, sailboats, parrot, cashews.

1987, Aug. 4
2109 A1130 3cz multi .15 .15
2110 A1130 3cz multi .15 .15

Royal Portuguese
Cabinet of Literature,
150th Anniv. — A1131

1987, Aug. 27 *Perf. 12x11½*
2111 A1131 30cz ver & brt grn 1.10 .85

Sport Club
Intl. — A1132

Championship soccer clubs, Brazil's Gold Cup: b, Sao Paulo. c, Guarani. d, Regatas do Flamengo.

1987, Aug. 29 *Perf. 11½x12*
2112 Block of 4 .60 .40
a.-d. A1132 3cz any single .15 .15

St. Francis
Convent,
400th Anniv.
A1133

1987, Oct. 4
2113 A1133 4cz multi .20 .15

Jose
Americo de
Almeida,
Author
A1134

Design: Characters from romance novel, "A Bagaceira," 1928, and portrait of author.

1987, Oct. 23 *Litho. Perf. 11x11½*
2114 A1134 4cz multi .18 .15

Spanish
Galleons
Anchored in
Recife Port,
1537
A1135

1987, Nov. 12 *Litho. Perf. 11½x12*
2115 A1135 5cz Harbor entrance .18 .15
Recife City, 450th anniv.

Thanksgiving
A1136

1987, Nov. 26 *Perf. 12x11½*
2116 A1136 5cz multi .18 .15

Christmas
1987
A1137

1987, Nov. 30 *Perf. 11½x12*
2117 A1137 6cz Shepherd and flock .20 .15
2118 A1137 6cz Christmas pageant .20 .15
2119 A1137 6cz Six angels .20 .15
Nos. 2117-2119 (3) .60 .45

Pedro II College, 150th Anniv. — A1138

Gold pen Emperor Pedro II used to sign edict establishing the school, and Senator Bernardo Pereira de Vasconcellos, founder.

1987, Dec. 2
2120 A1138 6cz multi .18 .15

Natl. Orchid
Growers' Soc.,
50th Anniv.
A1139

1987, Dec. 3
2121 A1139 6cz Laelia lobata veitch .20 .15
2122 A1139 6cz Cattleya guttata lindley .20 .15

Marian Year — A1140

Statue of Our Lady and Basilica at Fatima, Portugal.

1987, Dec. 20 *Perf. 12x11½*
2123 A1140 50cz multi 1.10 .85
Exhibit of the Statue of Our Lady of Fatima in Brazil.

Descriptive Treatise of Brazil, by Gabriel
S. de Sousa, 400th Anniv.
A1141

1987, Dec. 21 *Litho. Perf. 11x11½*
2124 A1141 7cz multi .20 .16

Natl.
Archives,
150th Anniv.
A1142

Design: Text from illuminated Gregorian canticle and computer terminal.

1988, Jan. 5 *Perf. 11½x12*
2125 A1142 7cz multi .20 .16

Opening of Brazilian Ports to Ships of
Friendly Nations, 180th Anniv.
A1143

1988, Jan. 28 *Perf. 11x11½*
2126 A1143 7cz multi .24 .18

Souvenir Sheet

Antarctic Research — A1144

1988, Feb. 9 *Litho. Perf. 11*
2127 A1144 80cz multi 2.00 2.00

Energy
Resources — A1145

1988, Mar. 15 *Litho. Perf. 12x11½*
2128 A1145 14cz Electricity .22 .16
2129 A1145 14cz Fossil fuels .22 .16

Souvenir Sheet

Brazilians as Formula 1 World Champions
in 1981, 1983, 1987 — A1146

1988, Mar. 30 *Perf. 11*
2130 A1146 300cz multi 4.50 4.50

Jose Bonifacio,
Armorial and Masonic
Emblems — A1147

1988, Apr. 6 *Perf. 12x11½*
2131 A1147 20cz multi .30 .24

Jose Bonifacio de Andrada e Silva (c. 1763-1838), geologist and prime minister under Pedro I who supported the movement for independence

from Portugal and was exiled for opposing the emperor's advisors.

Abolition of   Telecom
Slavery,   '88 — A1149
Cent. — A1148

Designs: 20cz, Declaration and quill pen. 50cz, Slave ship and maps of African coastline and slave trade route between Africa and South America.

1988, May 12 *Litho. Perf. 12x11½*
2132 A1148 20cz multi .25 .18
2133 A1148 50cz multi .65 .50

1988, May 16 *Perf. 11½x11*
2134 A1149 50cz multi .60 .45

Jesus of
Matosinhos
Sanctuary
A1150

1988, May 16 *Perf. 11½x12*
2135 A1150 20cz shown .22 .15
2136 A1150 50cz Pilot plan of Brasilia .58 .45
2137 A1150 100cz Salvador historic district 1.20 .90
Nos. 2135-2137 (3) 2.00 1.50
LUBRAPEX '88. World heritage list.

Japanese Immigrants in
Brazil, 80th
Anniv. — A1151

1988, June 18 *Litho. Perf. 11½x11*
2138 A1151 100cz multi .75 .55

A1152   A1153

1988, July 1 *Photo. Perf. 13*
2139 A1152 (A) brt blue .22 .16
No. 2139 met the first class domestic letter postage rate (28cz).
See Nos. 2201, 2218.

1988, July 14 *Litho. Perf. 12x11½*
2140 A1153 20cz Judo .22 .16
1988 Summer Olympics, Seoul.

Wildlife
Conservation
A1154

1988, July 24 — Perf. 11½x12

2141	A1154	20cz Myrmecophaga tridactyla	.15	.15
2142	A1154	50cz Chaetomys sub- spinosus	.32	.25
2143	A1154	100cz Speothos venaticus	.65	.50
		Nos. 2141-2143 (3)	1.12	.90

Souvenir Sheet

The Motherland, 1919 by Pedro Bruno — A1155

1988, Aug. 1 — Litho. Perf. 11

2144	A1155	250cz multi	1.50 1.50

Stamp Day, BRASILIANA '89.

Natl. Confederation of Industries, 50th Anniv. — A1156

1988, Aug. 12 — Perf. 11½x12

2145	A1156	50cz multi	.26 .20

Soccer Clubs A1157

No. 2146, Recife, Pernambuco. No. 2147, Coritiba, Parana. 100cz, Gremio, Porto Alegre, Rio Grando do Sul. 200cz, Fluminense, Rio de Janeiro.

1988, Sept. 29 — Perf. 11½x12

2146	A1157	50cz multi	.16	.15
2147	A1157	50cz multi	.16	.15
2148	A1157	100cz multi	.32	.22
2149	A1157	200cz multi	.60	.48
a.		Block of 4, #2146-2149	1.25	.95

Poems, 1888 A1158

Portraits and text: 50cz, O Ateneu, by Raul Pompeia. 100cz, Poesias, by Olavo Bilac.

1988, Oct. 28 — Perf. 11x11½

2150	A1158	50cz multi	.15	.15
2151	A1158	100cz multi	.26	.20

Souvenir Sheet

1988 Democratic Constitution for the Union of the People and the State — A1159

1988, Oct. 5 — Litho. Perf. 11

2152	A1159	550cz Government building	2.40 2.40

Origami Art — A1160

1988, Nov. 11 — Litho. Perf. 11½x12

2153	A1160	50cz Abbey, nuns	.15	.15
2154	A1160	100cz Nativity	.25	.20
2155	A1160	200cz Santa Claus, presents	.52	.40
		Nos. 2153-2155 (3)	.92	.75

Christmas.

ARBRAFEX Philatelic Exhibition of Argentina and Brazil A1161

1988, Nov. 26

2156	A1161	400cz multi	.85 .65

Fresh-water Fish — A1162

Designs: a, Gasteropelecus. b, Osteoglossum ferreirai. c, Moenkhausia. d, Xavantei. e, Ancistrus hoplogenys. f, Brochis splendens. Se-tenant in a continuous design.
Illustration reduced.

1988, Nov. 29 — Litho. Perf. 11½x12

2157		Block of 6	.90 .72
a.-f.	A1162	55cz any single	.15 .15

Souvenir Sheet

BRAPEX '88, Ecological Preservation — A1163

1988, Dec. 10 — Perf. 11

2158		Sheet of 3	1.80	1.80
a.	A1163	100cz Parrot	.25	.25
b.	A1163	250cz Plant	.60	.60
c.	A1163	400cz Pelican	.95	.95

Satellite Dishes A1164

Performing Arts A1165

1988, Dec. 20 — Perf. 12x11½

2159	A1164	70cz multi	.18 .15

Ansat 10-Earth satellite station communication.

1988, Dec. 21

2160	A1165	70cz multi	.18 .15

Court of Justice, Bahia, 380th Anniv. A1166

1989, Mar. 10 — Litho. Perf. 11½x12

2161	A1166	25c multi	.42 .32

Public Library Year — A1167

1989, Mar. 13 — Perf. 11½

2162	A1167	25c Library, Bahia, 1811	.42 .32

Brazilian Post & Telegraph Enterprise, 20th Anniv. A1168

Intl. and domestic postal services: a, Facsimile transmission (Post-Grama). b, Express mail (EMS). c, Parcel post (Sedex). d, Postal savings (CEFPostal).

1989, Mar. 20 — Perf. 11½x12

2163		Block of 4	1.65 1.25
a.-d.	A1168	25c any single	.40 .30

Souvenir Sheet

Ayrton Senna, 1988 Formula 1 World Champion — A1169

1989, Mar. 23

2164	A1169	2cz multi	4.00 4.00

Environmental Conservation A1170

1989, Apr. 6 — Litho. Perf. 12x11½

2165	A1170	25c multi	.35 .25

Mineira Inconfidencia Independence Movement, Bicent. — A1171

Designs: a, Pyramid, hand. b, Figure of a man, houses. c, Destruction of houses.

1989, Apr. 21 — Perf. 11½x12

2166		Strip of 3	1.30	.95
a.-b.	A1171	30c any single	.38	.28
c.	A1171	40c multi	.52	.38

First rebellion against Portuguese dominion.

Military School, Rio de Janeiro, Cent. A1172

1989, May 6 — Litho. Perf. 11½x12

2167	A1172	50c multi	.50 .38

Flowering Plants A1173

1989, June 5 — Perf. 11½x12, 12x11½

2168	A1173	50c Pavonia alnifolia	.60	.45
2169	A1173	1cz Worsleya rayneri	1.25	.90
2170	A1173	1.50cz Heliconia farinosa	1.75	1.40
		Nos. 2168-2170 (3)	3.60	2.75

Nos. 2169-2170 vert.

Barreto and Recife Law School, Pedro II Square A1174

1989, June 7 — Perf. 11x11½

2171	A1174	50c multi	.65 .48

Tobias Barreto (b. 1839), advocate of Germanization of Brazil.

Cultura Broadcasting System, 20th Anniv. — A1175

1989, June 27 — Litho. Perf. 11½x12

2172	A1175	50c multi	.60 .45

Aviation A1176

1989, July 7

2173	A1176	50c Ultra-light aircraft	.52 .40
2174	A1176	1.50cz Eiffel Tower, Demoiselle	1.65 1.10

Flight of Santos-Dumont's Demoiselle, 80th anniv (1.50cz).

Indigenous Flora — A1177

1989 — Photo. Perf. 11x11½, 11½x11

2176	A1177	10c Dichorisandra, vert.	.15	.15
2177	A1177	20c Quiabentia zehnteri	.22	.16
2178	A1177	50c Bougainvillea glabra	.52	.42
2179	A1177	1cz Impatiens specie	1.00	.80
2180	A1177	2cz Chorisia crispiflora	.25	.18
2181	A1177	5cz Hibiscus trilineatus	.60	.45
		Nos. 2176-2181 (6)	2.74	2.16

Issued: 10c, July 4; 20c, June 21; 50c, June 26; 1cz, June 19; 2cz, 5cz, Dec. 4.
No. 2181 vert.
See Nos. 2259-2273.

Souvenir Sheet

Largo da Carioca, by Nicolas Antoine
Taunay — A1179

1989, July 7   Litho.   Perf. 11
2197 A1179 3cz multi   3.00 3.00
PHILEXFRANCE '89, French revolution bicent.

Cut and Uncut
Gemstones — A1180

1989, July 12   Litho.   Perf. 12x11 1/2
2198 A1180   50c Tourmaline   .40   .30
2199 A1180 1.50cz Amethyst   1.20   .90

Souvenir Sheet

Paco Imperial, Rio de Janeiro, and
Map — A1181

1989, July 28   Perf. 11
2200 A1181 5cz multi   3.75 3.75
BRASILANA '89.

Type of 1988 Redrawn
1989, July 26   Photo.   Perf. 13
Size: 17x21mm
2201 A1152 (A) org & brt blue   .18 .15
Size of type and postal emblem are smaller on
No. 2201; "1e PORTE" is at lower left.
No. 2201 met the first class domestic letter post-
age rate (cz).

Pernambuco
Commercial
Assoc., 150th
Anniv.
A1182

1989, Aug. 1   Litho.   Perf. 11 1/2x12
2202 A1182 50c multi   .40   .30

Photography, 150th Anniv. — A1183

1989, Aug. 14
2203 A1183 1.50cz multi   1.10   .85

1st Hydroelecric Power Station in South
America, Marmelos-o, Cent.
A1184

1989, Sept. 5   Litho.   Perf. 11 1/2x12
2204 A1184 50c multi   .35   .25

Conchs
Endemic to
the Brazilian
Coast
A1185

1989, Sept. 8
2205 A1185   50c *Voluta ebraea*   .32 .22
2206 A1185   1cz *Morum*
                      matthewsi   .60 .45
2207 A1185 1.50cz *Agaronia travas-*
                      sosi   .90 .65
    Nos. 2205-2207 (3)   1.82 1.32
Wildlife conservation.

America Issue
A1186

UPAE emblem and pre-Columbian stone carvings: 1cz, Muiraquita ritual statue, vert. 4cz,
Ceramic brazier under three-footed votive urn.

Perf. 12x11 1/2, 11 1/2x12
1989, Oct. 12   Litho.
2208 A1186 1cz multicolored   .48 .35
2209 A1186 4cz shown   1.85 1.40
Discovery of America 500th anniv. (in 1992).

A1187   A1188

Hologram and: a. *Lemons,* by Danilo di Prete. b.
O Indio E A Suacuapara, by sculptor Victor
Brecheret. c. Francisco Matarazzo.

1989, Oct. 14   Perf. 11
Souvenir Sheet
2210   Sheet of 3   3.75 3.75
  a. A1187 2cz multicolored   .72 .72
  b. A1187 3cz multicolored   1.10 1.10
  c. A1187 5cz multicolored   1.75 1.75
Sao Paulo 20th intl. art biennial.

1989, Oct. 26   Perf. 11 1/2x11
Writers, residences and quotes: No. 2211,
Casimiro de Abreu (b. 1839). No. 2212, Cora
Coralina (b. 1889). No. 2213, Joaquim Machado de
Assis (b. 1839).

2211 A1188 1cz shown   .57 .42
2212 A1188 1cz multicolored   .57 .42
2213 A1188 1cz multicolored   .57 .42
    Nos. 2211-2213 (3)   1.71 1.26

Federal Police
Department,
25th Anniv.
A1189

1989, Nov. 9   Perf. 11 1/2x12
2214 A1189 1cz multicolored   .27 .20

Christmas — A1190   Thanksgiving
                          Day — A1191

1989, Nov. 10   Perf. 12x11 1/2
2215 A1190 70c Heralding angel   .18 .15
2216 A1190 1cz Holy family   .24 .18

1989, Nov. 23
2217 A1191 1cz multicolored   .24 .18

Type of 1988 Redrawn
1989, Nov. 6   Photo.   Perf. 13x13 1/2
Size: 22x26mm
2218 A1152 (B) org & dark red   2.00 1.50
Size of type and postal emblem are smaller on
No. 2218; "1e PORTE" is at lower left.
No. 2218 met the first class intl. letter postage
rate, initially at 9cz.

Souvenir Sheet

Proclamation of the Republic,
Cent. — A1192

1989, Nov. 19   Litho.   Perf. 11
2225 A1192 15cz multicolored   4.50 4.50

Bahia Sports
Club, 58th
Anniv.
A1193

1989, Nov. 30   Perf. 11 1/2x12
2226 A1193 50c Soccer   .15 .15

Yellow Man, by Anita
Malfatti
(b. 1889) — A1194

1989, Dec. 2   Perf. 12x11 1/2
2227 A1194 1cz multicolored   .26 .20

Bahia State Public Archives,
Cent. — A1195

1990, Jan. 16   Litho.   Perf. 11 1/2x12
2228 A1195 2cz multicolored   .28 .20

Brazilian
Botanical
Soc., 40th
Anniv.
A1196

1990, Jan. 21
2229 A1196   2cz Sabia, Caatinga   .22 .16
2230 A1196 13cz Pau, Brazil   1.40 1.10

Churches
A1197

Designs: 2cz, St. John the Baptist Cathedral,
Santa Cruz do Sul, vert. 3cz, Our Lady of Victory
Church, Oeiras. 5cz, Our Lady of the Rosary
Church, Ouro Preto, vert.

1990, Feb. 5   Perf. 12x11 1/2, 11 1/2x12
2231 A1197 2cz multicolored   .16 .15
2232 A1197 3cz multicolored   .25 .20
2233 A1197 5cz multicolored   .42 .32
    Nos. 2231-2233 (3)   .83 .67

Lloyd's of
London in
Brazil, Cent.
A1198

1990, Feb. 19   Litho.   Perf. 11 1/2x12
2234 A1198 3cz multicolored   .15 .15

Souvenir Sheet

Antarctic Research Program — A1199

1990, Feb. 22   Litho.   Perf. 11
2235 A1199 20cz Fauna, map   1.55 1.55

Vasco da
Gama Soccer
Club
A1200

1990, Mar. 5
2236 A1200 10cz multicolored   .48 .38

Lindolfo Collor (b. 1890), Syndicated Columnist, and Labor Monument A1201

1990, Mar. 7
2237 A1201 20cz multicolored .95 .70

A1202 A1203

Pres. Jose Sarney.

1990, Mar. 8 *Perf. 12x11½*
2238 A1202 20cz chalky blue .95 .70

1990, Apr. 6 *Perf. 12x11½*
2239 A1203 20cz multicolored .70 .52
AIDS prevention.

Souvenir Sheet

Penny Black, 150th Anniv. — A1204

Designs: 20cr, Dom Pedro, Brazil No. 1. 100cr, Queen Victoria, Great Britain No. 1.

1990, May 3 *Litho.* *Perf. 11*
2240 A1204 Sheet of 2 2.35 1.75
a. 20cr multicolored
b. 100cr multicolored

Central Bank, 25th Anniv. A1205

1990, Mar. 30 *Litho.* *Perf. 11½x12*
2241 A1205 20cr multicolored .70 .52

Amazon River Postal Network, 21st Anniv. A1207

1990, Apr. 20 *Perf. 11x11½*
2243 A1207 20cr multicolored .70 .52

Souvenir Sheet

World Cup Soccer Championships, Italy — A1208

1990, May 12 *Litho.* *Perf. 12x11½*
2244 A1208 120cr multicolored 3.00 3.00

22nd Congress of the Intl. Union of Highway Transportation — A1209

1990. May 14 *Perf. 11½x12*
2245 A1209 20cr multicolored .65 .48
2246 A1209 80cr multicolored 3.00 2.25
a. Pair, #2245-2246 3.75 2.75

No. 2246a has a continuous design.

Imperial Crown, 18th Cent. — A1210

Designs: No. 2248, Our Lady of Immaculate Conception, 18th cent.

1990, May 18 *Perf. 12x11½*
2247 A1210 20cr shown .68 .52
2248 A1210 20cr multicolored .68 .52

Imperial Museum, 50th anniv.(No. 2247). Mission Museum, 50th anniv. (No. 2248).

State Flags Type

1990, May 20 *Perf. 11½x12*
2249 A1050 20cr Tocantins .68 .52

Army Geographical Service, Cent. — A1212

1990, May 30 *Perf. 11x11½*
2250 A1212 20cr multicolored .68 .52

Film Personalities A1213

1990, June 19 *Perf. 11½x12*
2251 A1213 25cr Adhemar Gonzaga .80 .60
2252 A1213 25cr Carmen Miranda .80 .60
2253 A1213 25cr Carmen Santos .80 .60
2254 A1213 25cr Oscarito .80 .60
a. Block of 4, #2251-2254 3.20 2.40

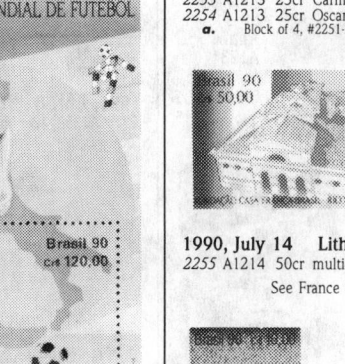

France-Brazil House, Rio de Janeiro A1214

1990, July 14 *Litho.* *Perf. 11½x11*
2255 A1214 50cr multicolored 1.50 1.10
See France No. 2226.

World Men's Volleyball Chmpships. A1215

Intl. Literacy Year A1217

CBA 123 — A1216

1990, July 28 *Litho.* *Perf. 12x11½*
2256 A1215 10cr multicolored .30 .24

1990, July 30 *Perf. 11½x12*
2257 A1216 10cr multicolored .30 .24

1990, Aug. 22 *Perf. 12x11½*
2258 A1217 10cr multicolored .30 .24

Flora Type of 1989
Perf. 11x11½, 11½x11

1989-93			Photo.
	Design A1177		
2259	1cr like #2179	.15	.15
2260	2cr like #2180	.15	.15
2261	5cr like #2181	.15	.15
2262	10cr Tibouchina granulosa	.15	.15
2263	20cr Cassia macranthera	.15	.15
2264	50cr Clitoria fairchildiana	.28	.15
2265	50cr Tibouchina mutabilis	.35	.35
2266	100cr Erythrina crista-galli, perf. 13	.55	.28
2267	200cr Jacaranda mimosifolia	1.10	.55
2268	500cr Caesalpinia peltophoroides	2.75	1.40
2269	1000cr Pachira aquatica	.15	.15
2270	2000cr Hibiscus pernambucensis	.15	.15
2271	5000cr Triplaris surinamensis	.85	.85
2272	10,000cr Tabebuia heptaphylla	1.65	1.65
2273	20,000cr Erythrina speciosa	2.25	2.25
	Nos. 2259-2273 (15)	10.83	8.53

Issued: 1cr, 11/8/90; 2cr, 11/12/90; 5cr, 11/16/90; #2264, 6/1/89; 10cr, 4/18/90; 20cr, 5/4/90; 100cr, 8/24/90; 200cr, 6/16/91; 500cr, 5/14/91; 1000cr, 9/2/92; 2000cr, 9/8/92; 5000cr, 10/16/92; 10,000cr, 11/16/92; 20,000cr, 4/25/93; #2265, 10/20/93.

Granbery Instutute, Cent. A1218

1990, Sept. 8 *Litho.* *Perf. 11½x12*
2279 A1218 13cr multicolored .40 .28

18th Panamerican Railroad Congress A1219

1990, Sept. 9
2280 A1219 95cr multicolored 2.00 1.50

Embratel, 25th Anniv. — A1220

1990, Sept. 21
2281 A1220 13cr multicolored .40 .30

LUBRAPEX '90 — A1221

Statues by Ceschiatti and Giorgi (No. 2283).

1990, Sept. 22
2282 A1221 25cr As Banhistas .62 .45
2283 A1221 25cr Os Candangos .62 .45
2284 A1221 100cr Evangelista Sao Joao 1.25 .90
2285 A1221 100cr A Justica 1.25 .90
a. Block of 4, #2282-2285 4.00 3.00
b. Souv. sheet of 4, #2282-2285 6.00 6.00

Praia Do Sul Wildlife Reserve A1222

1990, Oct. 12
2286 A1222 15cr Flowers .45 .32
2287 A1222 105cr Shoreline 2.60 1.80
a. Pair, #2286-2287 3.05 2.12

Discovery of America, 500th anniv. (in 1992).

Natl. Library, 180th Anniv. A1223

Writers: No. 2289, Guilherme de Almeida (1890-1969). No. 2290, Oswald de Andrade (1890-1954).

1990, Oct. 29 *Litho.* *Perf. 11x11½*
2288 A1223 15cr multicolored .40 .30
2289 A1223 15cr multicolored .40 .30
2290 A1223 15cr multicolored .40 .30
Nos. 2288-2290 (3) 1.20 .90

The only foreign revenue stamps listed in this catalogue are those also authorized for prepayment of postage.

Natl. Tax
Court, Cent.
A1224

1990, Nov. 7 Litho. *Perf. 11¹/₂x12*
2291 A1224 15cr multicolored .40 .30

Christmas
A1225

Architecture of Brasilia: No. 2292, National Congress. No. 2293, Television tower.

1990, Nov. 20
2292 A1225 15cr multicolored .40 .30
2293 A1225 15cr multicolored .40 .30

A1226 A1227

1990, Dec. 13 Litho. *Perf. 12x11¹/₂*
2294 A1226 15cr multicolored .18 .15
Organization of American States, cent.

1990, Dec. 14
2295 A1227 15cr multicolored .18 .15
First Flight of Nike Apache Missile, 25th anniv.

Colonization
of Sergipe,
Founding of
Sao
Cristovao,
400th Anniv.
A1228

1990, Dec. 18 Litho. *Perf. 11¹/₂x12*
2296 A1228 15cr multicolored .18 .15

World
Congress of
Physical
Education
A1229

1991, Jan. 7 *Perf. 11¹/₂x12*
2297 A1229 17cr multicolored .18 .15

Rock in Rio
II — A1230

1991, Jan. 9 *Perf. 12x11¹/₂*
2298 A1230 25cr Cazuza .20 .15
2299 A1230 185cr Raul Seixas 1.65 1.00
  a. Pair, #2298-2299 2.00 1.10
Printed in sheets of 12.

Ministry of
Aviation,
50th
Anniv.
A1231

1991, Jan. 20 *Perf. 11x11¹/₂*
2300 A1231 17cr multicolored .20 .15

A1232 A1233

Carnivals.

1991, Feb. 8 Litho. *Perf. 12x11¹/₂*
2301 A1232 25cr Olinda .24 .16
2302 A1232 30cr Salvador .28 .20
2303 A1232 280cr Rio de Janeiro 2.50 2.00
  Nos. 2301-2303 (3) 3.02 2.36

1991, Feb. 20
2304 A1233 300cr multicolored 3.00 2.25
Visit by Pres. Collor to Antarctica.

Hang Gliding World
Championships — A1234

1991, Feb. 24 *Perf. 11¹/₂x12*
2305 A1234 36cr multicolored .36 .28

11th Pan
American
Games, 25th
Summer
Olympics
A1235

1991, Mar. 30 Litho. *Perf. 11¹/₂x12*
2306 A1235 36cr Sailing .32 .24
2307 A1235 36cr Rowing .32 .24
2308 A1235 300cr Swimming 2.50 1.90
  a. Block of 3, #2306-2308 + label 3.25 2.50

Fight Against Drugs   Yanomami Indian
A1236   Culture
                       A1237

1991, Apr. 7 Litho. *Perf. 12x11¹/₂*
2309 A1236 40cr Drugs .35 .30
2310 A1236 40cr Alcohol .35 .30
2311 A1236 40cr Smoking .35 .30
  Nos. 2309-2311 (3) 1.05 .90

Perf. 11¹/₂x11, 11x11¹/₂
1991, Apr. 19
2312 A1237 40cr shown .35 .28
2313 A1237 400cr Indian, horiz. 3.50 2.75

Journal of
Brazil,
Cent.
A1238

1991, Apr. 8 Litho. *Perf. 11x11¹/₂*
2314 A1238 40cr multicolored .35 .28

Neochen Jubata
(Orinoco
Goose) — A1239

1991, June 5 Litho. *Perf. 12x11¹/₂*
2315 A1239 45cr multi .30 .22
UN Conference on Development.

Snakes &
Dinosaurs
A1240

1991, June 6 *Perf. 11¹/₂x12*
2316 A1240 45cr Bothrops jararaca .30 .22
2317 A1240 45cr Corallus caninus .30 .22
  a. Pair, #2316-2317 .60 .45
2318 A1240 45cr Teropods .30 .22
2319 A1240 350cr Sauropods 2.10 1.60
  a. Pair, #2318-2319 2.40 1.85
  Nos. 2316-2319 (4) 3.00 2.26

Flag of
Brazil — A1241

1991, June 10 Photo. *Perf. 13x13¹/₂*
2320 A1241 A multicolored .25 .20
Valued at domestic letter rate (cr) on day of issue.
Exists with inscription at lower right. Same value.

Fire Pumper
A1242

1991, July 2 Litho. *Perf. 11¹/₂x12*
2321 A1242 45cr multicolored .30 .22

Tourism
A1243

Map location and: 45cr, Painted stones, Roraima. 350cr, Dedo de Deus Mountain, Rio De Janeiro.

1991, July 6 *Perf. 11x11¹/₂*
2322 A1243 45cr multicolored .28 .20
2323 A1243 350cr multicolored 2.00 1.50

Labor Laws,
50th Anniv.
A1244

1991, Aug. 11 *Perf. 11¹/₂x12*
2324 A1244 45cr multicolored .30 .22

Leonardo
Mota, Birth
Cent.
A1245

1991, Aug. 22
2325 A1245 45cr buff, blk & red .30 .22
Folklore Festival.

Jose Basilio da
Gama (1741-
1795), Poet
A1246

Designs: No. 2327, Fagundes Varela (b. 1841), poet. No. 2328, Jackson de Figueiredo (b. 1891), writer.

1991, Aug. 29
2326 A1246 45cr multicolored .26 .18
2327 A1246 50cr multicolored .30 .22
2328 A1246 50cr multicolored .30 .22
  Nos. 2326-2328 (3) .86 .62

12th Natl. Eucharistic
Congress — A1247

1991, Oct. 6 Litho. *Perf. 12x11¹/₂*
2329 A1247 50cr Pope John Paul II .18 .15
2330 A1247 400cr Map, crosses 1.40 1.05
  a. Pair, #2329-2330 1.60 1.20
Visit by Pope John Paul II.

First Brazilian
Constitution,
Cent.
A1248

1991, Oct. 7 *Perf. 11¹/₂x12*
2331 A1248 50cr multicolored .18 .15

Telecom
'91 — A1249

1991, Oct. 8 *Perf. 12x11¹/₂*
2332 A1249 50cr multicolored .18 .15
Sixth World Forum and Exposition on Telecommunications, Geneva, Switzerland.

America Issue
A1250

UPAEP emblem and explorers: 50cr, Ferdinand Magellan (c. 1480-1521). 400cr, Francisco de Orellana (c. 1490-c. 1546).

1991, Oct. 12   *Perf. 11¹/₂x12*
2333 A1250 50cr multicolored .18 .15
2334 A1250 400cr multicolored 1.40 1.05
Discovery of America, 500th anniv. (in 1992).

A1251   A1252

BRAPEX VIII (Orchids and Hummingbirds): 50cr, Colibri serrirostris, cattleya warneri. No. 2336, Chlorostilbon aureoventris, rodriguezia venusta. No. 2337, Clytolaema rubricauda, zygopetalum intermedium. No. 2338a, 50cr, Colibri serrirostris. b, 50cr, Chlorostilbon aureoventris. c, 500cr, Clytolaema rubricauda.

1991, Oct. 29   Litho.   *Perf. 12x11¹/₂*
2335 A1251 50cr multicolored .15 .15
2336 A1251 65cr multicolored .18 .15
2337 A1251 65cr multicolored .18 .15
    Nos. 2335-2337 (3) .51 .45

Souvenir Sheet
2338 A1251 Sheet of 3, #a.-c. 2.20 1.65

1991, Oct. 29   Litho.   *Perf. 11¹/₂x11*
2339 A1252 400cr multicolored .90 .65
Lasar Segall, artist, birth cent.

Bureau of Agriculture and Provision of Sao Paulo, Cent. — A1253

1991, Nov. 11   *Perf. 12x11¹/₂*
2340 A1253 70cr multicolored .20 .15

First Civilian Presidents, Birth Sesquicentennials — A1254

1991, Nov. 14   *Perf. 11¹/₂x12*
2341 A1254 70cr Manuel de Campos Salles .20 .15
2342 A1254 90cr Prudente de Moraes Barros .25 .18
  a.   Pair, #2341-2342 .45 .35

Christmas   Thanksgiving
A1255   A1256

1991, Nov. 20   *Perf. 12x11¹/₂*
2343 A1255 70cr multicolored .20 .15

1991, Nov. 28
2344 A1256 70cr multicolored .20 .15

Military Police
A1257

1991, Dec. 1   *Perf. 11¹/₂x12*
2345 A1257 80cr multicolored .22 .16

Souvenir Sheet

Emperor Dom Pedro (1825-1891) — A1258

Designs: No. 2346a, 80cr, Older age. b, 800cr, Wearing crown.

Litho. & Engr.
1991, Nov. 29   *Perf. 11*
2346 A1258 Sheet of 2, #a.-b. 2.50 2.50
BRASILIANA 93.

Churches — A1259

Designs: No. 2347, Presbyterian Church, Rio de Janeiro. No. 2348, First Baptist Church, Niteroi.

1992, Jan. 12   Litho.   *Perf. 12x11¹/₂*
2347 A1259 250cr multicolored .30 .22
2348 A1259 250cr multicolored .30 .22

1992 Summer Olympics, Barcelona A1260

Medalists in shooting, Antwerp, 1920: 300cr, Afranio Costa, silver. 2500cr, Guilherme Paraense, gold.

1992, Jan. 28   *Perf. 11¹/₂x12*
2349 A1260 300cr multicolored .32 .24
2350 A1260 2500cr multicolored 2.75 2.00

Port of Santos, Cent. — A1261

1992, Feb. 3   Litho.   *Perf. 11¹/₂*
2351 A1261 300cr multicolored .45 .35

Fauna of Fernando de Noronha Island A1262

1992, Feb. 25   Litho.   *Perf. 11¹/₂x12*
2352 A1262 400cr White-tailed tropicbirds .40 .30
2353 A1262 2500cr Dolphins 2.50 1.75
Earth Summit, Rio de Janeiro.

Yellow Amaryllis — A1263

1992, Feb. 27   Photo.   *Perf. 13¹/₂*
2354 A1263 (A) multicolored .25 .20
No. 2354 met the second class domestic letter postage rate of 265cr on date of issue.

ARBRAFEX '92, Argentina-Brazil Philatelic Exhibition — A1264

Designs: No. 2355, Gaucho throwing bola at rhea. No. 2356, Man playing accordion, couple dancing. No. 2357, Couple in horse-drawn cart, woman. 1000cr, Gaucho throwing lasso at steer. No. 2358c, 250cr, like #2356. d, 500cr, like #2355. e, 1500cr, like #2358.

1992, Mar. 20   Litho.   *Perf. 11¹/₂x12*
2355 A1264 250cr multicolored .15 .15
2356 A1264 250cr multicolored .15 .15
2357 A1264 250cr multicolored .15 .15
2358 A1264 1000cr multicolored .60 .60
  a.   Block of 4, Nos. 2355-2358 1.05 1.05

Souvenir Sheet
2358B A1264 Sheet of 4, #2357, 2358c-2358e 1.05 1.05

1992 Summer Olympics, Barcelona — A1265

1992, Apr. 3   *Perf. 12x11¹/₂*
2359 A1265 300cr multicolored .18 .18

Discovery of America, 500th Anniv. A1266

1992, Apr. 24   *Perf. 11¹/₂x12*
2360 A1266 500cr Columbus' fleet .30 .30
2361 A1266 3500cr Columbus, map 2.10 2.10
  a.   Pair, #2360-2361 2.40 2.40

Telebras Telecommunications System — A1267

1992, May 5   *Perf. 11x11¹/₂*
2362 A1267 350cr multicolored .20 .20
Installation of 10 million telephones.

Langsdorff Expedition to Brazil, 170th Anniv. A1268

Designs: No. 2363, Aime-Adrien Taunay, natives. No. 2364, Johann Moritz Rugendas, monkey. No. 2365, Hercule Florence, flowering plant. 3000cr, Gregory Ivanovitch Langsdorff, map.

1992, June 2   *Perf. 11¹/₂x12*
2363 A1268 500cr multicolored .25 .25
2364 A1268 500cr multicolored .25 .25
2365 A1268 500cr multicolored .25 .25
2366 A1268 3000cr multicolored 1.50 1.50
   Nos. 2363-2366 (4) 2.25 2.25
UN Conf. on Environmental Development, Rio.

UN Conference on Environmental Development, Rio de Janeiro — A1269

Globe and: No. 2367, Flags of Sweden and Brazil. No. 2368, City, grain, mountain and tree. 3000cr, Map of Brazil, parrot, orchid.

1992, June 3   Litho.   *Perf. 11x11¹/₂*
2367 A1269 450cr multicolored .20 .20
2368 A1269 450cr multicolored .20 .20
2369 A1269 3000cr multicolored 1.50 1.50
   Nos. 2367-2369 (3) 1.90 1.90

Ecology A1270

Designs: No. 2370, Flowers, waterfall, and butterflies. No. 2371, Butterflies, canoe, and hummingbirds. No. 2372, Boy taking pictures of tropical birds. No. 2373, Armadillo, girl picking fruit.

1992, June 4   *Perf. 11¹/₂x12*
2370 A1270 500cr multicolored .25 .25
2371 A1270 500cr multicolored .25 .25
2372 A1270 500cr multicolored .25 .25
2373 A1270 500cr multicolored .25 .25
  a.   Strip of 4, 2370-2373 1.00 1.00
UN Conf. on Environmental Development, Rio.

Floral Paintings by Margaret Mee — A1271

1992, June 5   *Perf. 12x11¹/₂*
2374 A1271 600cr Nidularium innocentii .35 .35
2375 A1271 600cr Canistrum exiguum .35 .35

2376 A1271 700cr Canistrum cy-
        athiforme   .42 .42
2377 A1271 700cr Nidularium ru-
        bens   .42 .42
    Nos. 2374-2377 (4)   1.54 1.54
UN Conf. on Environmental Development, Rio.

Souvenir Sheet

Joaquim Jose da Silva Xavier (1748-1792),
Patriot — A1272

1992, Apr. 21 Litho. & Engr. Perf. 11
2378 A1272 3500cr multicolored   2.10 2.10

Souvenir Sheet

Expedition
of
Alexandre
Rodrigues
Ferreira,
Bicent.
A1273

Designs: a, 500cr, Sailing ships, gray and green
hulls. b, 1000cr, Sailing ships, red hulls. c, 2500cr,
Sailing ship at shore.

1992, May 9 Litho. Perf. 11½x12
2379 A1273 Sheet of 3, #a.-c.   2.40 2.40
Lubrapex '92.

A1274   A1275

1992, June 5 Litho. Perf. 12x11½
2380 A1274 600cr Hummingbird   .25 .25
Diabetes Day.

1992, July 13 Litho. Perf. 11½x11
2381 A1275 550cr multicolored   .25 .25
Volunteer firemen of Joinville.

A1276   A1277

Serra da Capivara National Park: No. 2382,
Leopard, animals, map of park. No. 2383, Canyon,
map of Brazil.

1992, July 17 Perf. 12x11½
2382 A1276 550cr multicolored   .22 .22
2383 A1276 550cr multicolored   .22 .22
  a.   Pair, #2382-2383   .45 .45

1992, July 24
2384 A1277 550cr multicolored   .25 .25
Financing for studies and projects.

Natl. Service for Industrial Training, 50th
Anniv. — A1278

1992, Aug. 5 Perf. 11½x12
2385 A1278 650cr multicolored   .35 .35

Fortresses
A1279

1992, Aug. 19 Litho. Perf. 11½x12
2386 A1279 650cr Santa Cruz   .28 .28
2387 A1279 3000cr Santo Antonio   1.25 1.25

Masonic
Square,
Compass and
Lodge
A1280

1992, Aug. 20
2388 A1280 650cr multicolored   .28 .28

Brazilian Assistance   Hospital of
Legion, 50th Anniv.   Medicine and
A1281   Orthopedics
                            A1282

1992, Aug. 28 Perf. 12x11½
2389 A1281 650cr multicolored   .28 .28

1992, Sept. 11
2390 A1282 800cr multicolored   .30 .30

Merry
Christmas
A1283

1992, Nov. 20 Perf. 11½
2391 A1283 (1) multicolored   .25 .25
No. 2391 met the first class domestic letter postage rate of 1090cr on day of issue.

Writers
A1284

#2392, Graciliano Ramos (1892-1953), vert.
#2393, Menotti del Picchia (1892-1988), vert.
1000cr, Assis Chateaubriand (1892-1968).

Perf. 12x11½, 11½x12
1992, Oct. 29   Litho.
2392 A1284 900cr multicolored   .22 .22
2393 A1284 900cr multicolored   .22 .22
2394 A1284 1000cr multicolored   .28 .28

Expedition of
Luis Cruls,
Cent.
A1285

1992, Nov. 11 Perf. 11½x12
2395 A1285 900cr multicolored   .22 22

Brazillian
Program for
Quality and
Productivity
A1286

1992, Nov. 12
2396 A1286 1200cr multicolored   .28 .28

Souvenir Sheet

Tourism Year in the Americas — A1287

Designs: a, 1200cr, Mountains, coastline. b,
9000cr, Sugarloaf Mt., aerial tram, Rio de Janeiro.

1992, Nov. 18 Litho. Perf. 11½x12
2397 A1287 Sheet of 2, #a.-b.   2.00 2.00
Brasiliana '93.

Sister Irma
Dulce
A1288

1993, Mar. 13 Litho. Perf. 11½x12
2398 A1288 3500cr multicolored   .35 .35

Souvenir Sheet

Water Sports Championships of South
America — A1289

Designs: a, 3500cr, Diver. b, 3500cr, Synchronized swimmers. c, 25,000cr, Water polo.

1993, Mar. 21 Litho. Perf. 11
2399 A1289 Sheet of 3, #a.-c.   2.75 2.75

Curitiba,
300th Anniv.
A1290

1993, Mar. 29
2400 A1290 4500cr multicolored   .40 .40

Health and   Pedro Americo,
Preservation of   150th Birth
Life — A1291   Anniv. — A1292

Red Cross emblem and: No. 2401, Bleeding
heart, flowers. No. 2402, Cancer symbol, breast.
No. 2403, Brain waves, rainbow emerging from
head.

1993, Apr. 7 Litho. Perf. 12x11½
2401 A1291 4500cr multicolored   .30 .30
2402 A1291 4500cr multicolored   .30 .30
2403 A1291 4500cr multicolored   .30 .30
  a.   Strip of 3, #2401-2403   .90 .90

Perf. 12x11½, 11½x12
1993, Apr. 29
Paintings: 5500cr, A Study of Love, 1883. No.
2405, David and Abizag, 1879, horiz. No. 2406,
Seated Nude, 1882.
2404 A1292 5500cr multi   .25 .25
2405 A1292 36,000cr multi   1.65 1.65
2406 A1292 36,000cr multi   1.65 1.65
    Nos. 2404-2406 (3)   3.55 3.55

Natl.
Flag — A1292a

1993, May 26 Litho. Die Cut
Self-adhesive
2407 A1292a A multicolored   .35 .35
No. 2407 valued at first class domestic letter rate
of 9570cr on day of issue.

Beetles
A1293

1993, June 5 Litho. Perf. 11½x12
2408 A1293 8000cr Dynastes her-
        cules   .35 .35
2409 A1293 55,000cr Batus
        barbicornis   2.25 2.25

3rd Iberian-American Conference of Chiefs of State and Heads of Government, Salvador — A1294

1993, July 15 Litho.   Perf. 11x11¹/₂
2410 A1294 12,000cr multi   .15 .15

1st Brazilian Postage Stamps, 150th Anniv. — A1295

Perf. 12x11¹/₂
1993, July 30   Litho. & Engr.
2411 A1295 30,000cr No. 1   .30 .30
2412 A1295 60,000cr No. 2   .60 .60
2413 A1295 90,000cr No. 3   .90 .90
a.   Souvenir sheet of 3, #2411-2413,
     wmk. 268   2.00 2.00
     Nos. 2411-2413 (3)   1.80 1.80
No. 2413a sold for 200,000cr.

Union of Portuguese Speaking Capitals A1296

a, 15,000cr, Brasilia. b, 71,000cr, Rio de Janeiro.

1993, July 30 Litho.   Perf. 11¹/₂x12
2414 A1296 Pair, #a.-b.   .90 .90
No. 2414 printed in continuous design.

Monica & Friends, by Mauricio de Sousa A1297

Monica, Cebolinha, Cascao, Magali, and Bidu: a, Engraving die. b, Reading proclamation, king, No. 1. c, Writing and sending letter, No. 2. d, Receiving letter, No. 3.
1993, Aug. 1
2415 A1297 (1) Strip of 4, #a.-d.   .85 .85
First Brazilian postage stamps, 150th anniv. Nos. 2415a-2415d paid the first class rate in the new currency on day of issue.

Brazilian Post, 330th Anniv. A1298

Postal buildings: a, Imperial Post Office, Rio de Janeiro. b, Petropolis. c, Central office, Rio de Janeiro. d, Niteroi.

1993, Aug. 3 Litho.   Perf. 11¹/₂x12
2416 A1298 20,000cr Block of 4,
          #a.-d.   .45 .45

Brazilian Engineering Schools A1299

Designs: No. 2417, School of Engineering, Federal University, Rio de Janeiro. No. 2418, Polytechnical School, University of Sao Paulo.

1993, Aug. 24 Litho.   Perf. 11x11¹/₂
2417 A1299 17cr multicolored   .30 .30
2418 A1299 17cr multicolored   .30 .30

Preservation of Sambaquis Archaelogical Sites — A1300

1993, Sept. 19   Perf. 12x11¹/₂
2419 A1300 17cr Two artifacts .22 .22
2420 A1300 17cr Six artifacts .22 .22

Ulysses Guimaraes, Natl. Congress — A1301

1993, Oct. 6 Litho.   Perf. 11x11¹/₂
2421 A1301 22cr multicolored   .28 .28

A1302   A1303

1993, Oct. 8 Litho.   Perf. 12x11¹/₂
2422 A1302 22cr multicolored   .28 .28
Virgin of Nazare Religious Festival, bicent.

1993, Oct. 13 Litho.   Perf. 11¹/₂x11
Endangered birds (America Issue): 22cr, Anodorhynchus hyacinthinus, anodorhynchus glaucus, anodorhynchus leari. 130cr, Cyanopsitta spixii.

2423 A1303 22cr multicolored .25 .25
2424 A1303 130cr multicolored 1.40 1.40

Composers — A1304   A1307

1993, Oct. 19 Litho.   Perf. 12x11¹/₂
2425 A1304 22cr Vinicius de Moraes .18 .18
2426 A1304 22cr Pixinguinha   .18 .18

1993, Oct. 29 Litho.   Perf. 12x11¹/₂
Poets: No. 2427, Mario de Andrade (1893-1945). No. 2428, Alceu Amoroso Lima (Tristao de Athayde) (1893-1983). No. 2429, Gilka Machado (1893-1980).

2427 A1307 30cr multicolored   .28 .28
2428 A1307 30cr multicolored   .28 .28
2429 A1307 30cr multicolored   .28 .28
     Nos. 2427-2429 (3)   .84 .84
Natl. Book Day.

Brazil-Portugal Treaty of Consultation and Friendship, 40th Anniv. — A1308

1993, Nov. 3 Litho.   Perf. 11¹/₂x12
2430 A1308 30cr multicolored   .28 .28
See Portugal No. 1980.

Image of the Republic — A1309

1993, Nov. 3 Photo. & Engr.   Perf. 13
2431 A1309 (B) multicolored   2.50 2.50
Valued at first class international letter rate (cr) on day of issue.

2nd Intl. Biennial of Comic Strips A1310

Cartoon drawings: No. 2432, Nho-Quim. No. 2433, Benjamin. No. 2434, Lamparina. No. 2435, Reco-Reco, Bolao, Azeitona.

1993, Nov. 11 Litho.   Perf. 11¹/₂x12
2432 A1310 (1) multicolored   .42 .42
2433 A1310 (1) multicolored   .42 .42
2434 A1310 (1) multicolored   .42 .42
2435 A1310 (1) multicolored   .42 .42
a.   Block of 4, #2432-2435   1.75 1.75
Valued at first class domestic letter rate (cr) on day of issue.

Launching of First Brazilian-Built Submarine — A1311

1993, Nov. 18   Perf. 11¹/₂
2436 A1311 240cr multicolored 1.75 1.75

Christmas A1312

1993, Nov. 20
2437 A1312 (1) multicolored   .45 .45
Valued at first class domestic letter rate (cr) on day of issue.

First Fighter Group, 50th Anniv. A1313

1993, Dec. 18 Litho.   Perf. 11¹/₂
2438 A1313 42cr multicolored   .35 .35

Convent of Merces, 340th Anniv. A1314

1994, Jan. 31 Litho.   Perf. 11¹/₂x12
2439 A1314 58cr multicolored   .32 .32

Mae Menininha of Gantois, Birth Cent. A1315

1994, Feb. 10 Litho.   Perf. 11x11¹/₂
2440 A1315 80cr multicolored   .40 .40

Intl. Olympic Committee, Cent. A1316

1994, Feb. 17   Perf. 11¹/₂x12
2441 A1316 (1) multicolored   2.25 2.25
No. 2441 valued at first class international letter rate (cr) on day of issue.

Natl. Flag — A1317

1994, Jan. 31 Litho.   Die Cut
                         Self-Adhesive
2442 A1317 (1) multicolored   .40 .40
No. 2442 valued at first class domestic letter rate (cr) on day of issue.

Birds — A1318

1994   Photo.   Perf. 11x11¹/₂
2443 A1318 10cr Notiochelidon cy-
               anoleuca   .15 .15
2444 A1318 20cr Buteo magniros-
               tris   .15 .15
2445 A1318 50cr Turdus rufiventris .15 .15
2446 A1318 100cr Columbina
               talpacoti   .15 .15
2447 A1318 200cr Vanellus chilensis .20 .20
2448 A1318 500cr Zonotrichia
               capensis   .50 .50
               Set value   .90 .90
Issued: 10cr, 3/17/94. 20cr, 3/9/94. 50cr, 3/1/94. 100cr, 200cr, 4/4/94. 500cr, 4/13/94. See Nos. 2484-2494.

Image of the
Republic — A1318a

1994, May 10   Litho.   *Perf. 12x11¹/₂*
Self-Adhesive
Die Cut

2449	A1318a	(1)	blue	.22	.22
2450	A1318a	(3)	claret	.40	.40

Size: 25x35mm

2451	A1318a	(4)	green	.80	.80
2452	A1318a	(5)	henna brown	1.50	1.50
		Nos. 2449-2452 (4)		2.92	2.92

Nos. 2449, 2450, 2451 valued (cr) on day of
issue. No. 2452 valued at (cr) on day of issue.

Prince Henry the Navigator (1394-
1460) — A1319

1994, Mar. 4   Litho.   *Perf. 11¹/₂x12*
2463 A1319 635cr multicolored   2.25 2.25

See Macao No. 719, Portugal No. 1987.

America Issue
A1320

Postal vehicles: 110cr, Bicycle, country scene.
635cr, Motorcycle, city scene.

1994, Mar. 18
2464 A1320 110cr multicolored   .20 .20
2465 A1320 635cr multicolored   1.10 1.10

Father
Cicero
Romao
Batista,
150th Birth
Anniv.
A1321

1994, Mar. 24   *Perf. 11x11¹/₂*
2466 A1321 (1) multicolored   .35 .35

No. 2466 valued at first class domestic letter rate
(cr) on day of issue.

Albert Sabin,
Campaign
Against Polio
A1322

1994, Apr. 7   *Perf. 11¹/₂x12*
2467 A1322 160cr multicolored   .30 .30

Carlos
Castello
Branco,
Journalist
A1323

1994, Apr. 14
2468 A1323 160cr multicolored   .30 .30

Karl Friedrich Phillip
von Martius,
Naturalist — A1324

Flowers: No. 2469, Euterpe oleracea. No. 2470,
Jacaranda paucifoliolata. No. 2471, Barbacernia
tomentosa.

1994, Apr. 24   *Perf. 12x11¹/₂*
2469 A1324 (1) multicolored   .35 .35
2470 A1324 (1) multicolored   .35 .35
2471 A1324 (1) multicolored   2.00 2.00
| | | *Nos. 2469-2471 (3)* | 2.70 2.70 |

Nos. 2469-2470 were valued at first class domestic letter rate (cr) on day of issue. No. 2471 valued
at first class intl. letter rate (cr) on day of issue.

Monkeys — A1326

No. 2474, Leontopithecus rosalia. No. 2475,
Saguinus imperator. No. 2476, Saguinus bicolor.

1994, May 24
2474 A1326 (1) multicolored   .35 .35
2475 A1326 (1) multicolored   .35 .35
2476 A1326 (1) multicolored   .35 .35
| | | *Nos. 2474-2476 (3)* | 1.05 1.05 |

Nos. 2474-2476 were valued at first class domestic letter rate (cr) on day of issue.

1994 World Cup Soccer Championships,
US — A1327

1994, May 19   *Perf. 11¹/₂x12*
2477 A1327 (1) multicolored   2.00 2.00

No. 2477 was valued at first class intl. rate (cr)
on day of issue.
Soccer in Brazil, cent.

Souvenir Sheet

46th Frankfurt Intl. Book Fair — A1328

Illustration reduced.

1994, May 27
2478 A1328 (1) multicolored   2.00 2.00

No. 2478 was valued at first class intl. rate (cr)
on day of issue.

Natl. Literacy
Program — A1329

Designs: No. 2479, Pencil, buildings. No. 2480,
Pencil, people on television, people watching. No.
2481, Classroom, pencil. No. 2482, Pencils crossed
over fingerprint, map of Brazil.

1994, June 3   Litho.   *Perf. 12x11¹/₂*
2479 A1329 (1) multicolored   .32 .32
2480 A1329 (1) multicolored   .32 .32
2481 A1329 (1) multicolored   .32 .32
2482 A1329 (1) multicolored   .32 .32
| | | *Nos. 2479-2482 (4)* | 1.28 1.28 |

Nos. 2479-2482 were valued at first class domestic letter rate (cr) on day of issue.

Souvenir Sheet

*500 Anos da Assinatura
do Tratado de Tordesilhas*

Treaty of Tordesillas, 500th
Anniv. — A1330

1994, June 7
2483 A1330 (1) multicolored   2.25 2.25

No. 2483 was valued at first class intl. letter rate
(cr) on day of issue.

Bird Type of 1994 and

A1330a

Perf. 11x11¹/₂, 13 (15c)
1994-95   Photo.
2484 A1318 1c like No. 2443   .15 .15
2485 A1318 2c like No. 2444   .15 .15
2486 A1318 5c like No. 2445   .15 .15
2487 A1318 10c like No. 2446   .20 .20
2488 A1330a 15c Canário da terra   .35 .35
2489 A1318 20c like No. 2447   .42 .42
2491 A1318 50c like No. 2448   1.00 1.00
2494 A1318 1r Furnarius rufus   2.25 2.25
| | | *Nos. 2484-2494 (8)* | 4.67 4.67 |

Issued: 1c, 2c, 5c, 20c, 20c, 50c, 1r, 7/1/94;
11/16/95.
This is an expanding set. Numbers may change.

Prominent
Brazilians
A1331

Designs: No. 2504, Edgard Santos (1894-1962),
surgeon, educator. No. 2505, Oswaldo Aranha
(1894-1960), politician. No. 2507, Otto Lara
Resende (1922-92), writer, educator.

1994, July 5   Litho.   *Perf. 11¹/₂x12*
2504 A1331 (1) multicolored   .28 .28
2505 A1331 (1) multicolored   .28 .28
2506 A1331 (1) multicolored   .28 .28
| | | *Nos. 2504-2506 (3)* | .84 .84 |

Nos. 2504-2506 were valued at first class domestic letter rate (12c) on day of issue.

A1332   A1333

1994, July 15   *Perf. 12x11¹/₂*
2507 A1332 12c multicolored   .28 .28

Petrobras, 40th anniv.

Litho. & Engr.
1994, July 26   *Perf. 11¹/₂*
2508 A1333 12c multicolored   .28 .28

Brazilian State Mint, 300th anniv.

Campaign
Against
Famine &
Misery
A1334

1994, July 27   Litho.   *Perf. 11¹/₂x12*
2509 A1334 (1) Fish   .28 .28
2510 A1334 (1) Bread   .28 .28

Nos. 2509-2510 were valued at first class domestic letter rate (12c) on day of issue.

Institute of
Brazilian
Lawyers,
150th Anniv.
A1335

1994, Aug. 11
2511 A1335 12c multicolored   .28 .28

Intl. Year of the
Family
A1336

1994, Aug. 16   *Perf. 11¹/₂*
2512 A1336 84c multicolored   2.00 2.00

Maternity
Hospital of
Sao Paulo,
Cent.
A1337

1994, Aug. 26   *Perf. 11¹/₂x12*
2513 A1337 12c multicolored   .28 .28

Vincente
Celestino
(1894-1968),
Singer
A1338

1994, Sept. 12
2514 A1338 12c multicolored   .28 .28

"Contos da Carochinha," First Brazilian Children's Book, Cent. A1339

Fairy tales: a, Joao e Maria (Hansel & Gretel). b, Dona Baratinha. c, Puss 'n Boots. d, Tom Thumb.

1994, Oct. 5   Litho.   Perf. 11 1/2x12
2515	Block of 4	4.75	4.75
a.-b.	A1339 12c any single	.28	.28
c.-d.	A1339 84c any single	2.00	2.00

Brazilian Literature A1340

Portraits: No. 2516, Tomas Antonio Gonzaga (1744-1809?), poet. No. 2517, Fernando de Azevedo (1894-1974), author.

1994, Oct. 5   Perf. 11 1/2
| 2516 | A1340 12c multicolored | .28 | .28 |
| 2517 | A1340 12c multicolored | .28 | .28 |

St. Clare of Assisi (1194-1253) A1341

1994, Oct. 19   Perf. 12x11 1/2
| 2518 | A1341 12c multicolored | .28 | .28 |

Ayrton Senna (1960-1994), Race Car Driver A1342

Designs: a, McClaren Formula 1 race car, Brazilian flag. b, Fans, Senna. c, Flags, race cars, Senna.

1994, Oct. 24   Perf. 11 1/2x12
2519	Triptych	2.75	2.75
a.-b.	A1342 12c any single	.28	.28
c.	A1342 84c multicolored	2.00	2.00

Institute of History & Geography of Sao Paulo, Cent. A1343

1994, Nov. 1
| 2520 | A1343 12c multicolored | .28 | .28 |

Popular Music A1344

Designs: No. 2521, Music from "The Sea," by Dorival Caymmi. No. 2522, Adoniran Barbosa (1910-82), samba composer.

1994, Nov. 5   Perf. 11 1/2
| 2521 | A1344 12c multicolored | .28 | .28 |
| 2522 | A1344 12c multicolored | .28 | .28 |

Christmas A1345

Folk characters: No. 2523: a, Boy wearing Santa coat, pot on head. b, Worm in apple. c, Man, animals singing. d, Shoe on tree stump, man with pipe holding pen.

1994, Dec. 1   Litho.   Perf. 11 1/2
2523	Block of 4	2.75	2.75
a.	A1345 84c multicolored	1.90	1.90
b.-d.	A1345 12c any single	.28	.28
e.	Booklet pane, #2523 + 4 labels	5.50	
	Complete booklet, #2523a	5.50	

Souvenir Sheet

Brazil, 1994 World Cup Soccer Champions — A1346

Illustration reduced.

1994, Dec. 5   Perf. 12x11 1/2
| 2524 | A1346 2.14r multicolored | 5.00 | 5.00 |

Louis Pasteur (1822-95) A1347

1995, Feb. 19   Litho.   Perf. 11 1/2x12
| 2525 | A1347 84c multicolored | 2.00 | 2.00 |

Historical Events A1348

Designs: No. 2526, Capture of Monte Castello, 50th anniv. No. 2527, End of the Farroupilha Revolution, 150th anniv.

1995, Feb. 21
| 2526 | A1348 12c multicolored | .28 | .28 |
| 2527 | A1348 12c multicolored | .28 | .28 |

Pres. Itamar Franco — A1349   FAO, 50th Anniv. — A1350

1995, Mar. 22   Litho.   Perf. 12x11 1/2
| 2528 | A1349 12c multicolored | .28 | .28 |

1995, Apr. 3   Perf. 11 1/2x11
| 2529 | A1350 84c multicolored | 2.00 | 2.00 |

Famous Men A1351

#2530, Alexandre de Gusmao (1695-1753), diplomat. #2531, Francisco Brandao, Viscount of Jequitinhonha (1794-1870), lawyer, abolitionist. 15c, Jose da Silva Paranhos, Jr., Baron of Rio Branco (1845-1912), politician, diplomat.

1995, Apr. 28   Perf. 11 1/2x12
2530	A1351 12c multicolored	.28	.28
2531	A1351 12c multicolored	.28	.28
2532	A1351 15c multicolored	.35	.35
	Nos. 2530-2532 (3)	.91	.91

Radio, Cent. A1352

Design: Guglielmo Marconi (1874-1937), transmitting equipment.

1995, May 5   Litho.   Perf. 11 1/2x12
| 2533 | A1352 84c multicolored | 2.00 | 2.00 |

Friendship Between Brazil & Japan — A1353

1995, May 29
| 2534 | A1353 84c multicolored | 2.00 | 2.00 |

Endangered Birds — A1354

1995, June 5   Perf. 12x11 1/2
| 2535 | A1354 12c Tinamus solitarius | .30 | .30 |
| 2536 | A1354 12c Mitu mitu | .30 | .30 |

June Festivals — A1355

Designs: No. 2537, Couples dancing at Campina Grande, "Greatest St. John's Party of the World." No. 2538, Bride, bridegroom, festivities, Caruaru.

1995, June 11   Perf. 11 1/2x12
| 2537 | A1355 12c multicolored | .30 | .30 |
| 2538 | A1355 12c multicolored | .30 | .30 |

St. Anthony of Padua (1195-1231) — A1356

1995, June 13
| 2539 | A1356 84c multicolored | 2.00 | 2.00 |
| | See Portugal No. 2054. | | |

Souvenir Sheet

Motion Picture, Cent. — A1357

Design: Louis and Auguste Lumiere, camera.

1995, June 21
| 2540 | A1357 2.14r multicolored | 4.75 | 4.75 |

New Currency, The Real, 1st Anniv. — A1358   Volleyball, Cent. — A1359

1995, July 1   Litho.   Perf. 12x11 1/2
| 2541 | A1358 12c multicolored | .30 | .30 |

1995, July 8
| 2542 | A1359 15c multicolored | .35 | .35 |

Dinosaurs A1360

1995, July 23   Perf. 11 1/2x12
| 2543 | A1360 15c Angaturama limai | .35 | .35 |
| 2544 | A1360 1.50r Titanosaurus | 3.25 | 3.25 |

Traffic Safety Program A1361

Designs: 12c, Test dummy without seat belt hitting windshield. 71c, Auto hitting alcoholic beverage glass.

1995, July 25
| 2545 | A1361 12c multicolored | .30 | .30 |
| 2546 | A1361 71c multicolored | 1.65 | 1.65 |

Souvenir Sheet

Roberto Burle Marx, Botanist — A1362

Designs: a, 15c, Calathea burle-marxii. b, 15c, Vellozia burle-marxii. c, 1.50r, Heliconia aemygdiana. Illustration reduced.

1995, Aug. 4   Litho.   Perf. 12x11 1/2
| 2547 | A1362 Sheet of 3, #a.-c. | 4.50 | 4.50 |
| | Singapore '95. | | |

Parachute Infantry Brigade, 50th Anniv. — A1363

1995, Aug. 23
2548 A1363 15c multicolored .35 .35

Paulista Museum, Cent. — A1364

1995, Sept. 5 *Perf. 11¹/₂*
2549 A1364 15c multicolored .35 .35

Lighthouses A1365

1995, Sept. 28
2550 A1365 15c Olinda .35 .35
2551 A1365 15c Sao Joao .35 .35
2552 A1365 15c Santo Antonio da Barra .35 .35
Nos. 2550-2552 (3) 1.05 1.05

Wilhelm Röntgen (1845-1923), Discovery of the X-Ray, Cent. — A1366

1995, Sept. 30
2553 A1366 84c multicolored 2.00 2.00

Lubrapex '95, 15th Brazilian-Portuguese Philatelic Exhibition — A1367

Wildlife scene along Tiete River: 15c, #2556a, Bird, otter with fish. 84c, #2556b, Birds, river boat.

1995, Sept. 30 *Perf. 12x11¹/₂*
2554 A1367 15c multicolored .35 .35
2555 A1367 84c multicolored 2.00 2.00

Souvenir Sheet
2556 A1367 1.50r Sheet of 2, #a.-b. 6.50 6.50
No. 2556 is a continuous design.

Flamengo Regatta Soccer Club A1368

1995, Oct. 6 *Perf. 11x11¹/₂*
2557 A1368 15c multicolored .35 .35

America Issue A1369

Outdoor scenes: 15c, Trees, mushrooms, alligator, lake. 84c, Black-neck swans on lake, false swans in air.

1995, Oct. 12 Litho. *Perf. 11¹/₂x12*
2558 A1369 15c multicolored .35 .35
2559 A1369 84c multicolored 2.00 2.00
a. Pair, #2558-2559 2.35 2.25

UN, 50th Anniv.
A1370 A1371

1995, Oct. 24 *Perf. 12x11¹/₂*
2560 A1370 1.05r multicolored 2.25 2.25
2561 A1371 1.05r multicolored 2.25 2.25
a. Pair, No. 2560-2561 4.50 4.50

Writers — A1372

Designs: No. 2562, Eca de Queiroz (1845-90), village. No. 2563, Rubem Braga (1913-90), beach, Rio de Janeiro. 23c, Carlos Drummond de Andrade (1902-87), letters.

1995, Oct. 27 *Perf. 12x11*
2562 A1372 15c multicolored .35 .35
2563 A1372 15c multicolored .35 .35
2564 A1372 23c multicolored .50 .50
Nos. 2562-2564 (3) 1.20 1.20

Souvenir Sheet

Death of Zumbi Dos Palmares, Slave Resistance Leader, 300th Anniv. — A1373

Illustration reduced.

1995, Nov. 20 *Perf. 12x11¹/₂*
2565 A1373 1.05r multicolored 2.25 2.25

2nd World Short Course Swimming Championships — A1374

Four swimmers performing different strokes: a, Freestyle. b, Backstroke. c, Butterfly. d, Breaststroke.

1995, Nov. 30 *Perf. 11¹/₂x12*
2566 A1374 23c Block of 4, #a.-d. 2.00 2.00

Christmas A1375

Designs: a, 23c, Cherub looking right, stars. b, 15c, Cherub looking left, stars.

1995, Dec. 1 *Perf. 11¹/₂*
2567 A1375 Pair, #a.-b.+2 labels .85 .85

Botafogo Soccer and Regatta Club A1376

1995, Dec. 8 *Perf. 11x11¹/₂*
2568 A1376 15c multicolored .35 .35

Diário de Pernambuco Newspaper, 170th Anniv. — A1377

1995, Dec. 14 Litho. *Perf. 12x11¹/₂*
2569 A1377 23c multicolored .50 .50

Souvenir Sheet

Amazon Theatre, Cent. — A1378

Illustration reduced.

1996, Feb. 27
2570 A1378 1.23r multicolored 2.50 2.50

Francisco Prestes Maia, Politician, Birth Cent. A1379

1996, Mar. 19 *Perf. 11¹/₂x12*
2571 A1379 18c multicolored .40 .40

Irineu Bornhausen, Governor of Santa Catarina, Birth Cent. — A1380

1996, Mar. 25 *Perf. 11x11¹/₂*
2572 A1380 27c multicolored .55 .55

Paintings — A1381

Designs: No. 2573, Boat with Little Flags and Birds, by Alfredo Volpi. No. 2574, Ouro Preto Landscape, by Alberto da Veiga Guignard.

1996, Apr. 15 *Perf. 12x11¹/₂*
2573 A1381 15c multicolored .30 .30
2574 A1381 15c multicolored .30 .30

UNICEF, 50th Anniv. A1382

1996, Apr. 16 *Perf. 11¹/₂*
2575 A1382 23c multicolored .50 .50

Portuguese Discovery of Brazil, 500th Anniv. (in 2000) — A1383

1996, Apr. 22 *Perf. 12x11¹/₂*
2576 A1383 1.05r multicolored 2.10 2.10
See No. 2626.

Israel Pinheiro da Silva, Politician, Business Entrepeneur, Birth Cent. A1384

1996, Apr. 23 *Perf. 11¹/₂x12*
2577 A1384 18c multicolored .40 .40

Tourism — A1385

#2578, Amazon River. #2579, Swampland area. #2580, Sail boat, northeastern states. #2581, Sugarloaf, Guanabara Bay. #2582, Iguacu Falls.

1996, Apr. 24 *Die Cut*
Self-Adhesive
2578 A1385 23c multicolored .50 .50
2579 A1385 23c multicolored .50 .50
2580 A1385 23c multicolored .50 .50
2581 A1385 23c multicolored .50 .50
2582 A1385 23c multicolored .50 .50
a. Strip of 5, #2578-2582 2.50

Hummingbirds A1386

Espamer '96: 15c, Topaza pella. 1.05r, Stephanoxis lalandi. 1.15r, Eupetomena macroura.

1996, May 4 — Litho. — Perf. 11½
2583 A1386 15c multicolored .35 .35
2584 A1386 1.05r multicolored 2.40 2.40
2585 A1386 1.15r multicolored 2.60 2.60
Nos. 2583-2585 (3) 5.35 5.35

1996 Summer Olympic Games, Atlanta A1387

1996, May 21
2586 A1387 18c Marathon .40 .40
2587 A1387 23c Gymnastics .50 .50
2588 A1387 1.05r Swimming 2.40 2.40
2589 A1387 1.05r Beach volleyball 2.40 2.40
Nos. 2586-2589 (4) 5.70 5.70

Souvenir Sheet

Brazilian Caverns — A1388

Illustration reduced.

1996, June 5 — Perf. 11½x12
2590 A1388 2.68r multicolored 6.25 6.25

Americas Telecom '96 — A1389

1996, June 10 — Perf. 11½
2591 A1389 1.05r multicolored 2.40 2.40

Souvenir Sheet

World Day to Fight Desertification — A1390

Illustration reduced.

1996, June 17 — Perf. 12x11½
2592 A1390 1.23r multicolored 2.80 2.80

Fight Against Drug Abuse A1391

1996, June 26 — Perf. 11½x12
2593 A1391 27c multicolored .65 .65

Year of Education — A1392

1996, July 10 — Perf. 12x11½
2594 A1392 23c multicolored .55 .55

Princess Isabel, 150th Birth Anniv. A1393

1996, July 29 — Perf. 11½x12
2595 A1393 18c multicolored .40 .40

Carlos Gomes (1836-96), Composer A1394

1996, Sept. 16 — Perf. 11½
2596 A1394 50c multicolored 1.25 1.25

15th World Orchid Conference A1395

#2597, Promenaea stapelioides. #2598, Cattleya eldorado. #2599, Cattleya loddigesii.

1996, Sept. 17
2597 A1395 15c multicolored .35 .35
2598 A1395 15c multicolored .35 .35
2599 A1395 15c multicolored .35 .35
Nos. 2597-2599 (3) 1.05 1.05

Apparition of Virgin Mary at La Salette, 150th Anniv. A1396

1996, Sept. 19
2600 A1396 1r multicolored 2.30 2.30

Souvenir Sheet

Popular Legends A1397

Designs: a, 23c, "Cuca" walking from house. b, 1.05r, "Boitatá," snake of life. c, 1.15r, "Caipora," defender of ecology.

1996, Sept. 28 — Perf. 11x10½
2601 A1397 Sheet of 3, #a.-c. 5.60 5.60

BRAPEX '96.

23rd Sao Paulo Intl. Biennial Exhibition A1398

Designs: a, Marilyn Monroe by Andy Warhol, vert. b, The Scream, by Edvard Munch, vert. c, Abstract, by Louise Bourgeois, vert. d, Woman Drawing, by Pablo Picasso.

1996, Oct. 5 — Perf. 12x11½
2602 A1398 55c Block of 4, #a.-d. 5.00 5.00

Traditional Costumes A1400

America issue: 50c, Man dressed as cowboy. 1r, Woman dressed in baiana clothes.

1996, Oct. 12 — Litho. — Perf. 11½
2604 A1400 50c multicolored 1.15 1.15
2605 A1400 1r multicolored 2.30 2.30

Christmas A1401

José Carlos (1884-1950), Caricaturist A1402

1996, Nov. 4 — Litho. — Perf. 12x11½
2606 A1401 1st multicolored .60 .60

No. 2606 was valued at 23c on day of issue.

1996, Nov. 22
2607 A1402 1st multicolored .60 .60

No. 2607 was valued at 23c on day of issue.

Rio de Janeiro, Candidate for 2004 Summer Olympic Games A1404

1997, Jan. 17 — Litho. — Perf. 11½
2613 A1404 1st multicolored 2.20 2.20

No. 2613 is inscribed "1o PORTE INTERNACIONAL" and was valued at on day of issue.

The Postman A1405

1997, Jan. 25
2614 A1405 1st multicolored .85 .85

America issue. No. 2614 is inscribed "1o PORTE NACIONAL" and was valued at on day of issue.

Antonio de Castro Alves (1847-71), Poet — A1406

1997, Mar. 14
2615 A1406 15c multicolored .35 .35

Marquis of Tamandaré, Naval Officer, Death Cent. — A1407

1997, Mar. 19 — Perf. 11x11½
2616 A1407 23c multicolored .50 .50

Stamp Design Contest Winner A1408

1997, Mar. 20 — Perf. 11½x12
2617 A1408 15c "Joy Joy" .35 .35

World Day of Water — A1409

1997, Mar. 22 — Perf. 12x11½
2618 A1409 1.05r multicolored 2.10 2.10

Campaign Against AIDS — A1411

1997, Apr. 7 — Litho. — Perf. 12x11½
2624 A1411 23c multicolored .50 .50

Souvenir Sheet

Cultura Indígena Armas

Indian Culture — A1412

Weapons of the Xingu Indians. Illustration reduced.

1997, Apr. 16   Perf. 11x11½
2625 A1412 1.15r multicolored   2.30 2.30

Portuguese Discovery of Brazil, 500th Anniv. Type of 1996

1997, Apr. 22   Perf. 12x11½
2626 A1383 1.05r like #2576   2.10 2.20

No. 2576 has green background and blue in lower right corner. No. 2626 has those colors reversed and is inscribed "BRASIL 97" at top.

Pixinguinha (1897-1973), Composer, Musician — A1413

1997, Apr. 23
2627 A1413 15c multicolored   .35 .35

Souvenir Sheet

Brazilian Claim to Trindade Island, Cent. — A1414

Illustration reduced.

1997, May 7   Perf. 11½x11
2628 A1414 1.23r multicolored   2.50 2.50

Human Rights — A1415

1997, May 13   Perf. 12x11½
2629 A1415 18c multicolored   .45 .45

Souvenir Sheet

Brazilian Antarctic Program — A1416

1997, May 13
2630 A1416 2.68r multicolored   5.50 5.50

 A1418

A1419

Amazon Flora and Fauna — A1419

Designs: No. 2637, Swietenia macropylla. No. 2638, Arapaima gigas.

1997, June 5   Litho.   Perf. 11½x12
2637 A1418 27c multicolored   .55 .55
2638 A1419 27c multicolored   .55 .55

Fr. José de Anchieta (1534-97), Missionary in Brazil — A1420

Design: No. 2640, Fr. António Vieira (1608-97), missionary in Brazil, diplomat.

1997, June 9   Perf. 12
2639 A1420 1.05r multicolored   2.10 2.10
2640 A1420 1.05r multicolored   2.10 2.10
      See Portugal Nos. 2168-2169.

Tourism A1421

Designs: No. 2641, Parnaíba River Delta. No. 2642, Lençóis Maranhenses Park.

1997, June 20   Perf. 11½x12
2641 A1421 1st multicolored   2.10 2.10
2642 A1421 1st multicolored   2.10 2.10

Nos. 2641-2642 are inscribed "1o PORTE INTERNACIONAL TAXE PERCUE" and were each valued at on day of issue.

Brazilian Academy of Literature, Cent. A1422

1997, July 20
2643 A1422 22c multicolored   .50 .50

SEMI-POSTAL STAMPS

National Philatelic Exhibition Issue

SP1

Wmk. Coat of Arms in Sheet (236)
1934, Sept. 16   Engr.   Imperf.
Thick Paper

B1 SP1 200r + 100r dp claret   1.00 2.00
B2 SP1 300r + 100r ver   1.00 2.00
B3 SP1 700r + 100r brt bl   6.00 17.50
B4 SP1 1000r + 100r blk   6.00 17.50
     Nos. B1-B4 (4)   14.00 39.00

The surtax was to help defray the expenses of the exhibition. Issued in sheets of 60, inscribed "EXPOSICAO FILATELICA NACIONAL."

Red Cross Nurse and Soldier SP2

Wmk. 222
1935, Sept. 19   Typo.   Perf. 11
B5 SP2 200r + 100r pur & red   1.25 1.25
B6 SP2 300r + 100r ol brn & red   1.25 .90
B7 SP2 700r + 100r turq bl & red   8.00 7.00
     Nos. B5-B7 (3)   10.50 9.15

3rd Pan-American Red Cross Conf. Exist imperf.

Three Wise Men and Star of Bethlehem — SP3

Angel and Child — SP4

Southern Cross and Child — SP5

Mother and Child — SP6

Perf. 10½
1939, Dec. 20   Litho.   Wmk. 249
B8 SP3 100r + 100r chlky bl & bl blk   .75 .75
a. Horiz. or vert. pair, imperf. between   35.00
B9 SP4 200r + 100r brt grnsh bl   1.00 1.00
a. Horizontal pair, imperf. between   35.00
B10 SP5 400r + 200r ol grn & ol   .80 .50
B11 SP6 1200r + 400r crim & brn red   3.25 1.50
a. Vertical pair, imperf. between   35.00
     Nos. B8-B11 (4)   5.80 3.75

Surtax for charitable institutions. For surcharges see Nos. C55-C59.

AIR POST STAMPS

SERVIÇO AEREO

Nos. O14-O29 Surcharged

200 Rs.

1927, Dec. 28   Unwmk.   Perf. 12

C1	O2	50r on 10r	.35	.35
a.		Inverted surcharge	325.00	
b.		Top ornaments missing	75.00	
C2	O2	200r on 1000r	2.25	2.75
a.		Double surcharge	325.00	
C3	O2	200r on 2000r	1.40	4.75
a.		Double surcharge	750.00	
b.		Double surcharge, one inverted	750.00	
C4	O2	200r on 5000r	1.50	1.00
a.		Double surcharge	325.00	
b.		Double surcharge, one inverted	350.00	
c.		Triple surcharge	450.00	
C5	O2	300r on 500r	1.50	2.00
C6	O2	300r on 600r	.75	.90
b.		Pair, one without surch.	—	
C6A	O2	500r on 10r	325.00	375.00
C7	O2	500r on 50r	1.50	.65
a.		Double surcharge	300.00	
C8	O2	1000r on 20r	1.00	.35
a.		Double surcharge	300.00	
C9	O2	2000r on 100r	2.25	1.40
a.		Pair, one without surcharge	—	
b.		Double surcharge	300.00	
C10	O2	2000r on 200r	2.75	1.40
C11	O2	2000r on 10,000r	2.25	.50
C12	O2	5000r on 20,000r	7.50	3.00
C13	O2	5000r on 50,000r	7.50	3.00
C14	O2	5000r on 100,000r	25.00	30.00
C15	O2	10,000r on 500,000r	27.50	22.50
C16	O2	10,000r on 1,000,000r	25.00	25.00
		Nos. C1-C6,C7-C16 (16)	110.00	99.55

Nos. C1, C1b, C7, C8 and C9 have small diamonds printed over the numerals in the upper corners.

Monument to de Gusmao — AP1

Santos-Dumont's Airship — AP2

Augusto Severo's Airship — AP3

Santos-Dumont's Biplane "14 Bis" — AP4

Ribeiro de Barros's Seaplane "Jahu" — AP5

Perf. 11, 12½x13, 13x13½
1929   Typo.   Wmk. 206
C17 AP1 50r blue grn   .35 .20
C18 AP2 200r red   1.40 .20
C19 AP3 300r brt blue   1.75 .20
C20 AP4 500r red violet   2.50 .20
C21 AP5 1000r orange brn   9.00 .40
     Nos. C17-C21 (5)   15.00 1.20

See #C32-C36. For surcharges see #C26-C27.

Bartholomeu de Gusmao AP6

Augusto Severo AP7

Alberto Santos-Dumont — AP8

Perf. 9, 11 and Compound

1929-30	Engr.	Wmk. 101		
C22	AP6	2000r lt green ('30)	7.50	.35
C23	AP7	5000r carmine	7.50	1.25
C24	AP8	10,000r olive grn	7.50	1.40
	Nos. C22-C24 (3)		22.50	3.00

Nos. C23-C24 exist imperf.
See Nos. C37, C40.

Allegory: Airmail Service between Brazil and the US — AP9

1929	Typo.	Wmk. 206		
C25	AP9	3000r violet	10.00	1.75

Exists imperf. See Nos. C38, C41. For surcharge see No. C28.

ZEPPELIN

Nos. C18-C19 Surcharged in Blue or Red **2$500**

1931, Aug. 16	Perf. 12¹/₂x13¹/₂		
C26	AP2	2500r on 200r (Bl)	25.00	25.00
C27	AP3	5000r on 300r (R)	30.00	30.00

No. C25 Surcharged **2.500 REIS**

1931, Sept. 2		Perf. 11		
C28	AP2	2500r on 3000r vio	27.50	27.50
a.	Inverted surcharge		160.00	
b.	Surch. on front and back		160.00	

Regular Issues of 1928-29 Surcharged **ZEPPELIN 3$500**

1932, May	Wmk. 101	Perf. 11, 11¹/₂		
C29	A89	3500r on 5000r gray lil	20.00	20.00
C30	A72	7000r on 10,000r rose	20.00	20.00
b.	Horiz. pair, imperf. between		750.00	

Imperforates

Since 1933, imperforate or partly perforated sheets of nearly all of the airmail issues have become available.

Flag and Airplane — AP10

	Wmk. 222			
1933, June 7	Typo.	Perf. 11		
C31	AP10	3500r grn, yel & dk bl	5.00	2.00

See Nos. C39, C42.

1934		Wmk. 222		
C32	AP1	50r blue grn	1.75	1.75
C33	AP2	200r red	2.25	.65
C34	AP3	300r brt blue	5.50	1.90
C35	AP4	500r red violet	2.25	.65
C36	AP5	1000r orange brn	7.50	.65
	Nos. C32-C36 (5)		19.25	5.60

1934	Wmk. 236	Engr.	Perf. 12x11	
	Thick Laid Paper			
C37	AP6	2000r lt green	4.50	1.50

Types of 1929, 1933
Perf. 11, 11¹/₂, 12

1937-40	Typo.	Wmk. 249		
C38	AP9	3000r violet	17.50	1.75
C39	AP10	3500r grn, yel & dk bl	3.00	1.50
	Engr.			
C40	AP7	5000r ver ('40)	4.00	.75
	Nos. C38-C40 (3)		24.50	4.00

Watermark note after #501 also applies to #C40.

Types of 1929-33
Perf. 11, 11¹/₂x12

1939-40	Typo.	Wmk. 256		
C41	AP9	3000r violet	1.25	.60
C42	AP10	3500r bl, dl grn & yel ('40)	.90	.50

Map of the Western Hemisphere Showing Brazil AP11

1941, Jan. 14	Engr.	Perf. 11		
C43	AP11	1200r dark brown	2.50	.65

5th general census of Brazil.

No. 506A Overprinted in Carmine **AÉREO "10 Nov." 937-941**

1941, Nov. 10	Wmk. 264	Rouletted		
C45	A180	5400r slate grn	2.50	1.25
a.	Overprint inverted		140.00	

President Varges' new constitution, 4th anniv.

Nos. 506A and 508 Surcharged in Black **AÉREO "10 Nov." 937-942 Cr.$ 5,40**

1942, Nov. 10		Wmk. 264		
C47	A180	5.40cr on 5400r sl grn	2.50	1.90
a.	Wmk. 249		80.00	80.00
b.	Surcharge inverted		60.00	75.00

President Vargas' new constitution, 5th anniv. The status of No. C47a is questioned.

Southern Cross and Arms of Paraguay AP12

	Perf. 12¹/₂			
1943, May 11	Engr.	Wmk. 270		
C48	AP12	1.20cr lt gray blue	1.75	1.00

Issued in commemoration of the visit of President Higinio Morinigo of Paraguay.

Map of South America — AP13

1943, June 30	Wmk. 271	Perf. 12¹/₂		
C49	AP13	1.20cr multi	1.75	.75

Visit of President Penaranda of Bolivia.

Numeral of Value — AP14

1943, Aug. 7				
C50	AP14	1cr blk & dull yel	2.00	1.50
a.	Double impression		30.00	
C51	AP14	2cr blk & pale grn	2.75	1.50
a.	Double impression		40.00	
C52	AP14	4cr blk & pink	3.25	2.00
	Nos. C50-C52 (3)		8.00	5.00

Centenary of Brazil's first postage stamps.

Souvenir Sheet

AP15

	Without Gum	Imperf.		
C53	AP15	Sheet of 3	35.00	35.00
a.	1cr black & dull yellow		10.00	10.00
b.	2cr black & pale green		10.00	10.00
c.	5cr black & pink		10.00	10.00

100th anniv. of the 1st postage stamps of Brazil and the 2nd Phil. Exposition (Brapex). Printed in panes of 6 sheets, perforated 12¹/₂ between. Each sheet is perforated on two or three sides. Size approximately 155x155mm.

Law Book — AP16

1943, Aug. 13		Perf. 12¹/₂		
C54	AP16	1.20cr rose & lil rose	.50	.30

2nd Inter-American Conf. of Lawyers.

AÉREO 20 Cts.

No. B10 Surcharged in Red, Carmine or Black

1944, Jan. 3	Wmk. 249	Perf. 10¹/₂		
C55	SP5	20c on 400r+200r (R)	.85	.65
C56	SP5	40c on 400r+200r (Bk)	1.25	.65
C57	SP5	60c on 400r+200r (C)	1.25	.45
C58	SP5	1cr on 400r+200r (Bk)	1.75	.65
C59	SP5	1.20cr on 400r+200r (C)	2.25	.45
	Nos. C55-C59 (5)		7.35	2.85

No. C59 is known with surcharge in black but its status is questioned.

Bartholomeu de Gusmao and the "Aerostat" — AP17

	Wmk. 268			
1944, Oct. 23	Engr.	Perf. 12		
C60	AP17	1.20cr rose carmine	.35	.15

Week of the Wing.

L. L. Zamenhof AP18

1945, Apr. 16	Litho.	Perf. 11		
C61	AP18	1.20cr dull brown	.35	.25

Esperanto Congress held in Rio, Apr. 14-22.

Map of South America — AP19 · Baron of Rio Branco — AP20

1945, Apr. 20				
C62	AP19	1.20cr gray brown	.35	.25
C63	AP20	5cr rose lilac	.95	.40

Centenary of the birth of José Maria de Silva Paranhos, Baron of Rio Branco.

Dove and Flags of American Republics AP21

	Perf. 12x11			
1947, Aug. 15	Engr.	Unwmk.		
C64	AP21	2.20cr dk blue green	.30	.25

Inter-American Defense Conference at Rio de Janeiro August-September, 1947.

Santos-Dumont Monument, St. Cloud, France — AP22 · Bay of Rio de Janeiro and Rotary Emblem — AP23

1947, Nov. 15	Typo.	Perf. 11x12		
C65	AP22	1.20cr org brn & ol	.30	.25

Issued to commemorate the Week of the Wing and to honor the Santos-Dumont monument which was destroyed in World War II.

Catalogue values for unused stamps in this section, from this point to the end of the section, are for Never Hinged items.

1948, May 16	Engr.	Perf. 11		
C66	AP23	1.20cr deep claret	.50	.40
C67	AP23	3.80cr dull violet	1.00	.40

39th convention of Rotary Intl., Rio.

Hotel Quitandinha, Petropolis AP24

1948, July 10	Litho.	Wmk. 267		
C68	AP24	1.20cr org brn	.25	.25
C69	AP24	3.80cr violet	.50	.30

International Exposition of Industry and Commerce, Petropolis, 1948.

Musician and Singers AP25

1948, Aug. 13	Engr.	Unwmk.		
C70	AP25	1.20cr blue	.30	.20

National School of Music, cent.

Luis Batlle Berres AP26

1948, Sept. 2   Typo.
C71 AP26 1.70cr blue .20 .20

Visit of President Luis Batlle Berres of Uruguay, September, 1948.

Merino Ram — AP27

1948, Oct. 10 Wmk. 267 Perf. 12x11
C72 AP27 1.20cr dp orange .50 .30

Intl. Livestock Exposition at Bagé.

Eucharistic Congress Seal — AP28

Unwmk.
1948, Oct. 23 Engr. Perf. 11
C73 AP28 1.20cr dk car rose .30 .30

5th Natl. Eucharistic Cong., Porto Alegre, Oct. 24-31.

Souvenir Sheet

AP28a

1948, Dec. 14 Engr. Imperf.
Without Gum
C73A AP28a Sheet of 3 50.00 65.00

No. C73A contains one each of Nos. 674-676. Issued in honor of President Eurico Gasper Dutra and the armed forces. Exists both with and without number on back. Measures 130x75mm.

Church of Prazeres, Guararapes — AP29

Perf. 11¹/₂x12
1949, Feb. 15 Litho. Wmk. 267
C74 AP29 1.20cr pink 1.50 .75

Second Battle of Guararapes, 300th anniv.

Thomé de Souza Meeting Indians — AP30

Perf. 11x12
1949, Mar. 29 Engr. Unwmk.
C75 AP30 1.20cr blue .20 .20

Founding of the City of Salvador, 400th anniv. A souvenir folder, issued with No. C75, has an engraved 20cr red brown postage stamp portraying

John III printed on it, and a copy of No. C75 affixed to it and postmarked. Paper is laid, and size of folder front is 100x150mm. Value, $5.

Franklin D. Roosevelt AP31

1949, May 20 Unwmk. Imperf.
C76 AP31 3.80cr deep blue .60 .60
a. Souvenir sheet 12.00 15.00

No. C76a measures 85x110mm, with deep blue inscriptions in upper and lower margins. It also exists with papermaker's watermark.

Joaquim Nabuco (1849-1910), Lawyer and Writer — AP32

1949, Aug. 30 Perf. 12
C77 AP32 3.80cr rose lilac .40 .32
a. Wmk. 256, imperf. 25.00

Maracaná Stadium AP33

Soccer Player and Flag — AP34

Perf. 11x12, 12x11
1950, June 24 Litho. Wmk. 267
C78 AP33 1.20cr ultra & salmon .95 .40
C79 AP34 5.80cr bl, yel grn & yel 2.75 .50

4th World Soccer Championship, Rio.

AP35

AP36

Symbolical of Brazilian population growth.

1950, July 10 Perf. 12x11
C80 AP35 1.20cr red brown .30 .15

Issued to publicize the 6th Brazilian census.

1956, Sept. 8 Engr. Perf. 11¹/₂
Design: J. B. Marcelino Champagnat.
C81 AP36 3.30cr rose lilac .30 .15

50th anniversary of the arrival of the Marist Brothers in Northern Brazil.

Santos-Dumont's 1906 Plane — AP37

1956, Oct. 16 Photo.
C82 AP37 3cr dk blue grn .85 .30
a. Souv. sheet of 4, #C82b 6.00 6.00
b. 3cr dark carmine 1.50 .90
C83 AP37 3.30cr brt ultra .20 .15
C84 AP37 4cr dp claret .40 .15
C85 AP37 6.50cr red brown .15 .15
C86 AP37 11.50cr orange red .85 .35
Nos. C82-C86 (5) 2.45 1.10

1st flight by Santos-Dumont, 50th anniv. No. C82b issued Oct. 14, 1956.

Lord Baden-Powell — AP38

1957, Aug. 1 Unwmk.
Granite Paper
C87 AP38 3.30cr deep red lilac .25 .15

Centenary of the birth of Lord Baden-Powell, founder of the Boy Scouts.

UN Emblem, Soldier and Map of Suez Canal Area — AP39

Perf. 11¹/₂
1957, Oct. 24 Wmk. 267 Engr.
C88 AP39 3.30cr dark blue .25 .18

Brazilian contingent of the UN Emergency Force.

Basketball Player — AP40

1959, May 30 Photo. Perf. 11¹/₂
C89 AP40 3.30cr brt red brn & bl .25 .15

Brazil's victory in the World Basketball Championships of 1959.

Symbol of Flight — AP41

1959, Oct. 21 Wmk. 267
C90 AP41 3.30cr deep ultra .16 .15

Issued to publicize Week of the Wing.

Caravelle AP42

1959, Dec. 18 Perf. 11¹/₂
C91 AP42 6.50cr ultra .16 .15

Inauguration of Brazilian jet flights.

Pres. Adolfo Lopez Mateos AP43

Pres. Dwight D. Eisenhower AP44

1960, Jan. 19 Photo. Wmk. 267
C92 AP43 6.50cr brown .16 .15

Issued to commemorate the visit of President Adolfo Lopez Mateos of Mexico.

1960, Feb. 23 Perf. 11¹/₂
C93 AP44 6.50cr deep orange .16 .15

Visit of Pres. Dwight D. Eisenhower.

World Refugee Year Emblem — AP45

Tower at Brasilia — AP46

1960, Apr. 7 Wmk. 268
C94 AP45 6.50cr blue .16 .15

WRY, July 1, 1959-June 30, 1960.

Type of Regular Issue and AP46

Designs: 3.30cr, Square of the Three Entities. 4cr, Cathedral. 11.50cr, Plan of Brasilia.

Perf. 11x11¹/₂, 11¹/₂x11
1960, Apr. 21 Photo. Wmk. 267
C95 A436 3.30cr violet .15 .15
C96 A436 4cr blue .75 .15
C97 AP46 6.50cr rose carmine .15 .15
C98 A436 11.50cr brown .15 .15
Nos. C95-C98 (4) 1.20
Set value .40

Inauguration of Brazil's new capital, Brasilia, Apr. 21, 1960.

Chrismon and Oil Lamp AP47

1960, May 16 Perf. 11x11¹/₂
C99 AP47 3.30cr lilac rose .15 .15

7th Natl. Eucharistic Congress at Curitiba.

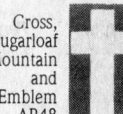

Cross, Sugarloaf Mountain and Emblem AP48

1960, July 1 Wmk. 267
C100 AP48 6.50cr brt blue .15 .15

10th Cong. of the World Baptist Alliance, Rio.

Boy
Scout — AP49

Caravel — AP50

1960, July 23   Perf. 11¹/₂x11
C101 AP49 3.30cr orange ver   .15 .15
   Boy Scouts of Brazil, 50th anniversary.

1960, Aug. 5   Engr.   Wmk. 268
C102 AP50 6.50cr black   .15 .15
   Prince Henry the Navigator, 500th birth anniv.

Maria E.
Bueno
AP51

1960, Dec. 15   Photo.   Perf. 11x11¹/₂
C103 AP51 60cr pale brown   .15 .15
   Victory at Wimbledon of Maria E. Bueno, women's singles tennis champion.

War Memorial, Sugarloaf Mountain and
Allied Flags
AP52

1960, Dec. 22   Wmk. 268
C104 AP52 3.30cr lilac rose   .15 .15
   Reburial of Brazilian servicemen of WW II.

Power Line
and Map
AP53

Malaria
Eradication
Emblem
AP54

1961, Jan. 20   Perf. 11¹/₂x11
C105 AP53 3.30cr lilac rose   .15 .15
   Inauguration of Three Marias Dam and hydroelectric station in Minas Gerais.

1962, May 24   Wmk. 267   Engr.
C106 AP54 21cr blue   .15 .15
   WHO drive to eradicate malaria.

F. A. de
Varnhagen — AP55

1966, Feb. 17   Photo.   Wmk. 267
C107 AP55 45cr red brown   .18 .15
   Francisco Adolfo de Varnhagen, Viscount of Porto Seguro (1816-1878), historian and diplomat.

Map of the
Americas
and Alliance
for Progress
Emblem
AP56

1966, Mar. 14   Perf. 11x11¹/₂
C108 AP56 120cr grnsh bl & vio bl   .40 .15
   5th anniv. of the Alliance for Progress.
   A souvenir card contains one impression of No. C108, imperf. Size: 113x160mm.

Nun and
Globe — AP57

Face of Jesus
from Shroud of
Turin — AP58

1966, Mar. 25   Photo.   Perf. 11¹/₂x11
C109 AP57 35cr violet   .18 .15
   Centenary of the arrival of the teaching Sisters of St. Dorothea.

1966, June 3   Photo.   Wmk. 267
C110 AP58 45cr brown org   .20 .15
   Issued to commemorate Vatican II, the 21st Ecumenical Council of the Roman Catholic Church, Oct. 11, 1962-Dec. 8, 1965.
   A souvenir card contains one impression of No. C110, imperf. Size: 100x39mm.

Admiral Mariz e
Barros
AP59

"Youth" by
Eliseu Visconti
AP60

1966, June 13   Photo.   Wmk. 267
C111 AP59 35cr red brown   .16 .15
   Death centenary of Admiral Antonio Carlos Mariz e Barros, who died in the Battle of Itaperu.

1966, July 31   Perf. 11¹/₂x11
C112 AP60 120cr red brown   .40 .20
   Birth centenary of Eliseu Visconti, painter.

SPECIAL DELIVERY STAMPS

No. 191 Surcharged   **1000 REIS EXPRESSO**

1930   Unwmk.   Perf. 12
E1 A62 1000r on 200r dp blue   4.00 1.75
   a.   Inverted surcharge   500.00

POSTAGE DUE STAMPS

D1   D2

1889   Unwmk.   Typo.   Rouletted
J1	D1	10r carmine	2.00	1.40
J2	D1	20r carmine	2.75	2.00
J3	D1	50r carmine	5.00	4.00
J4	D1	100r carmine	2.00	1.40
J5	D1	200r carmine	55.00	15.00
J6	D1	300r carmine	6.00	8.00
J7	D1	500r carmine	6.00	8.00
J8	D1	700r carmine	10.00	14.00
J9	D1	1000r carmine	10.00	10.00
		Nos. J1-J9 (9)	98.75	63.80

   Counterfeits are common.

1890
J10	D1	10r orange	.60	.30
J11	D1	20r ultra	.60	.30
J12	D1	50r olive	1.25	.30
J13	D1	200r magenta	6.00	.60
J14	D1	300r blue green	3.00	1.50
J15	D1	500r slate	4.00	3.00
J16	D1	700r purple	4.50	7.50
J17	D1	1000r dk violet	5.50	5.00
		Nos. J10-J17 (8)	25.45	18.50

Perf. 11 to 11¹/₂, 12¹/₂ to 14 and Compound

1895-1901
J18	D2	10r dk blue ('01)	2.00	1.25
J19	D2	20r yellow grn	8.00	3.00
J20	D2	50r yellow grn ('01)	10.00	5.50
J21	D2	100r brick red	6.25	1.25
J22	D2	200r violet	6.00	.60
a.		200r gray lilac ('98)	12.00	2.00
J23	D2	300r dull blue	3.50	2.25
J24	D2	2000r brown	12.00	12.00
		Nos. J18-J24 (7)	47.75	25.85

1906   Wmk. 97
J25	D2	100r brick red	8.00	3.00

Wmk. (97? or 98?)
J26	D2	200r violet	7.50	1.25
a.		Wmk. 97	275.00	85.00
b.		Wmk. 98	12.50	50.00

D3   D4

1906-10   Unwmk.   Engr.   Perf. 12
J28	D3	10r slate	.15	.15
J29	D3	20r brt violet	.15	.15
J30	D3	50r dk green	.25	.15
J31	D3	100r carmine	1.75	.60
J32	D3	200r dp blue	1.00	.30
J33	D3	300r gray blk	.40	.60
J34	D3	400r olive grn	1.00	.90
J35	D3	500r dk violet	35.00	35.00
J36	D3	600r violet ('10)	1.25	3.00
J37	D3	700r red brown	30.00	30.00
J38	D3	1000r red	1.50	3.00
J39	D3	2000r green	4.75	5.50
J40	D3	5000r choc ('10)	1.50	14.00
		Nos. J28-J40 (13)	78.70	93.35

Perf. 12¹/₂, 11, 11x10¹/₂
1919-23   Typo.
J41	D4	5r red brown	.15	.25
J42	D4	10r violet	.25	.25
J43	D4	20r olive gray	.20	.15
J44	D4	50r green ('23)	.20	.20
J45	D4	100r red	1.10	1.00
J46	D4	200r blue	5.25	1.50
J47	D4	400r brown ('23)	1.40	1.25
		Nos. J41-J47 (7)	8.55	4.60

Perf. 12¹/₂, 12¹/₂x13¹/₂
1924-35   Wmk. 100
J48	D4	5r red brown	.25	.20
J49	D4	100r red	.75	.30
J50	D4	200r slate bl ('29)	1.00	.50
J51	D4	400r dp brn ('29)	1.50	1.00
J52	D4	600r dk vio ('29)	1.75	1.10
J53	D4	600r orange ('35)	.75	.50
		Nos. J48-J53 (6)	6.00	3.60

1924   Wmk. 193   Perf. 11x10¹/₂
J54	D4	100r red	45.00	45.00
J55	D4	200r slate blue	5.50	5.50

Perf. 11x10¹/₂, 13x13¹/₂
1925-27   Wmk. 101
J56	D4	20r olive gray	.20	.15
J57	D4	100r red	1.05	.30
J58	D4	200r slate blue	3.25	.35
J59	D4	400r brown	1.75	1.25
J60	D4	600r dk violet	4.25	2.50
		Nos. J56-J60 (5)	10.50	4.55

Wmk. E U BRASIL Multiple (218)
1929-30   Perf. 12¹/₂x13¹/₂
J61	D4	100r light red	.25	.20
J62	D4	200r blue black	.40	.25
J63	D4	400r brown	.40	.25
J64	D4	1000r myrtle green	.75	.50
		Nos. J61-J64 (4)	1.80	1.20

Perf. 11, 12¹/₂x13, 13
1931-36   Wmk. 222
J65	D4	10r lt violet ('35)	.15	.15
J66	D4	20r black ('33)	.20	.15
J67	D4	50r blue grn ('35)	.25	.20
J68	D4	100r rose red ('35)	.25	.20
J69	D4	200r sl blue ('35)	.40	.30
J70	D4	400r blk brn ('35)	2.00	2.00
J71	D4	600r dk violet	.35	.20
J72	D4	1000r myrtle grn	.50	.35
J73	D4	2000r brown ('36)	.80	.80
J74	D4	5000r indigo ('36)	1.25	1.00
		Nos. J65-J74 (10)	6.15	5.35

1938   Wmk. 249   Perf. 11
J75	D4	200r slate blue	2.00	.75

1940   Typo.   Wmk. 256
J76	D4	10r light violet	.50	.50
J77	D4	20r black	.50	.50
J79	D4	100r rose red	.50	.50
J80	D4	200r myrtle green	.50	.50
		Nos. J76-J80 (4)	2.00	2.00

1942   Wmk. 264
J81	D4	10r lt violet	.15	.15
J82	D4	20r olive blk	.15	.15
J83	D4	50r lt blue grn	.15	.15
J84	D4	100r vermilion	.40	.30
J85	D4	200r gray blue	.40	.30
J86	D4	400r claret	.40	.30
J87	D4	600r rose vio	.30	.20
J88	D4	1000r dk bl grn	.30	.20
J89	D4	2000r dp yel brn	.75	.50
J90	D4	5000r indigo	.40	.30
		Nos. J81-J90 (10)	3.40	2.55

1949   Wmk. 268
J91	D4	10c pale rose lilac	4.00	3.25
J92	D4	20r black	25.00	25.00

   No. J92 exists in shades of gray ranging to gray olive.

OFFICIAL STAMPS

Pres. Affonso
Penna — O1

Pres. Hermes da
Fonseca — O2

Unwmk.
1906, Nov. 15   Engr.   Perf. 12
O1	O1	10r org & grn	.75	.30
O2	O1	20r org & grn	.90	.30
O3	O1	50r org & grn	1.50	.30
O4	O1	100r org & grn	.75	.30
O5	O1	200r org & grn	.90	.30
O6	O1	300r org & grn	2.75	.60
O7	O1	400r org & grn	6.00	1.75
O8	O1	500r org & grn	3.00	1.25
O9	O1	700r org & grn	4.50	3.00
O10	O1	1000r org & grn	4.50	1.25
O11	O1	2000r org & grn	5.00	2.25
O12	O1	5000r org & grn	10.00	.50
O13	O1	10,000r org & grn	10.00	1.25
		Nos. O1-O13 (13)	50.55	13.35

   The portrait is the same but the frame differs for each denomination of this issue.

1913, Nov. 15
Center in Black
O14	O2	10r gray	.35	.50
O15	O2	20r ol grn	.35	.50
O16	O2	50r gray	.35	.50
O17	O2	100r ver	1.00	.35
O18	O2	200r blue	1.75	.35
O19	O2	500r orange	3.00	.65
O20	O2	600r violet	3.50	2.75
O21	O2	1000r blk brn	4.25	1.25
O22	O2	2000r red brn	6.50	1.25
O23	O2	5000r brown	7.50	3.00
O24	O2	10,000r black	15.00	7.50
O25	O2	20,000r blue	27.50	27.50
O26	O2	50,000r green	50.00	55.00
O27	O2	100,000r org red	175.00	200.00
O28	O2	500,000r black	300.00	325.00
O29	O2	1,000,000r dk brn	325.00	350.00
		Nos. O14-O29 (16)	921.05	976.10

   The portrait is the same on all denominations of this series but there are eight types of the frame.

Pres. Wenceslau Braz — O3

Perf. 11, 11¹/₂

1919, Apr. 11   **Wmk. 100**
O30	O3	10r olive green	.40	2.00
O31	O3	50r green	1.00	1.25
O32	O3	100r rose red	2.00	.85
O33	O3	200r dull blue	2.75	.85
O34	O3	500r orange	7.50	14.00
		Nos. O30-O34 (5)	13.65	18.95

The official decree called for eleven stamps in this series but only five were issued.
For surcharges see Nos. 293-297.

NEWSPAPER STAMPS

N1

Rouletted

1889, Feb. 1   **Unwmk.**   **Litho.**
P1	N1	10r yellow	3.00	3.00
a.		Pair, imperf. between	125.00	145.00
P2	N1	50r yellow	6.00	7.50
P3	N1	70r yellow	10.00	6.00
P4	N1	100r yellow	3.75	3.00
P5	N1	200r yellow	3.00	1.50
P6	N1	300r yellow	3.00	1.50
P7	N1	500r yellow	20.00	8.00
P8	N1	700r yellow	3.00	10.00
P9	N1	1000r yellow	3.00	10.00
		Nos. P1-P9 (9)	54.75	50.50

For surcharges see Nos. 125-127.

1889, May 1
P10	N1	10r olive	2.00	.50
P11	N1	20r green	2.00	.50
P12	N1	50r brn yel	2.75	1.00
P13	N1	100r violet	3.00	2.00
a.		100r deep violet	6.50	15.00
b.		100r lilac	12.00	10.00
P14	N1	200r black	3.00	10.00
P15	N1	300r carmine	12.00	10.00
P16	N1	500r green	50.00	50.00
P17	N1	700r pale blue	25.00	30.00
a.		100r ultramarine	65.00	75.00
b.		100r cobalt	400.00	425.00
P18	N1	1000r brown	12.00	15.00
		Nos. P10-P18 (9)	111.75	111.00

For surcharges see Nos. 128-135.

N2   N3

White Wove Paper Thin to Thick
Perf. 11 to 11¹/₂, 12¹/₂ to 14 and 12¹/₂ to 14x11 to 11¹/₂

1890   **Typo.**
P19	N2	10r blue	14.00	10.00
a.		10r ultramarine	14.00	10.00
P20	N2	20r emerald	40.00	15.00
P21	N2	100r violet	16.00	14.00
		Nos. P19-P21 (3)	70.00	39.00

For surcharge see No. 137.

1890-93
P22	N3	10r ultramarine	3.00	3.00
a.		10r blue	7.50	4.00
P23	N3	10r ultra, *buff*	3.00	3.00
P24	N3	20r green	10.00	3.00
a.		20r emerald	10.00	3.00
P25	N3	50r yel grn ('93)	17.50	10.00
		Nos. P22-P25 (4)	33.50	19.00

For surcharges see Nos. 136, 138-139.

POSTAL TAX STAMPS

Icarus from the Santos-Dumont Monument at St. Cloud, France — PT1

Perf. 13¹/₂x12¹/₂, 11

1933, Oct. 1   **Typo.**   **Wmk. 222**
RA1	PT1	100r deep brown	.65 .25

Honoring the Brazilian aviator, Santos-Dumont. Its use was obligatory as a tax on all correspondence sent to countries in South America, the US and Spain. Its use on correspondence to other countries was optional. The funds obtained were used for the construction of airports throughout Brazil.

> Catalogue values for unused stamps in this section, from this point to the end of the section, are for Never Hinged items.

Father Joseph Damien and Children PT2

Perf. 12x11

1952, Nov. 24   **Litho.**   **Wmk. 267**
RA2	PT2	10c yellow brown	.25 .15

1953, Nov. 30
RA3	PT2	10c yellow green	.25 .15

Father Bento Dias Pacheco PT3   Eunice Weaver PT4

1954, Nov. 22   **Photo.**   *Perf. 11¹/₂*
RA4	PT3	10c violet blue	.20 .15

1955-66, Nov. 24
RA5	PT3	10c dk car rose	.20 .15
RA6	PT3	10c org red ('57)	.20 .15
RA7	PT3	10c dp emer ('58)	.15 .15
RA8	PT3	10c red lilac ('61)	.15 .15
RA9	PT3	10c choc ('62)	.15 .15
RA10	PT3	10c slate ('63)	.15 .15
RA11	PT3	2cr dp mag ('64)	.15 .15
RA12	PT3	2cr violet ('65)	.15 .15
RA13	PT3	2cr orange ('66)	.15 .15
		Set value	.95

1968, Nov. 25
RA14	PT3	5c brt yel grn	1.25 .75

1969, Nov. 28
RA15	PT3	5c deep plum	.50 .25

1971, Nov. 24
RA16	PT4	10c slate green	1.00 .40

1973, Nov. 24
RA17	PT4	10c brt rose lil ('73)	.20 .15

Father Nicodemos PT5   Father Vicente Borgard (1888-1977) PT6

1975, Nov. 24   **Litho.**   **Unwmk.**
RA18	PT5	10c sepia	.20 .15

1983, Nov. 24   **Photo.**   *Perf. 11¹/₂*
RA19	PT6	10cr brown	.60 .60

Father Bento Dias Pacheco — PT7   Father Santiago Uchoa — PT8

1984, Nov. 24   **Photo.**   *Perf. 11¹/₂*
RA20	PT7	30cr deep blue	.15 .15

1985, Nov. 24   **Litho.**
RA21	PT7	100cr lake	.15 .15

1986, Nov. 24   **Litho.**
RA22	PT7	10c gray brown	.15 .15

1987, Nov. 24   **Photo.**
RA23	PT7	30cr sage green	.15 .15

1988, Nov. 24   **Litho.**
RA24	PT8	1.30cz dull red brn	.15 .15

See Nos. RA29-RA30.

Fr. Joseph Damien — PT9

1989-92   **Photo.**   *Perf. 11¹/₂*
RA25	PT9	2c deep lilac rose	.15 .15
RA26	PT9	50c blue	.15 .15

Perf. 12¹/₂
RA27	PT9	3cr green	.15 .15
RA28	PT9	30cr brown	.15 .15
		Set value	.20 .20

Issued: 2c, Nov. 24; 50c, Nov. 24, 1990; 3cr, Nov. 24, 1991; 30cr, Nov. 24, 1992.

Father Santiago Uchoa Type of 1988

1993, Nov. 24   **Photo.**   *Perf. 12¹/₂*
RA29	PT8	50c blue	.15 .15

1994, Nov. 24
RA30	PT8	1c dull lake	.15 .15

The tax was for the care and treatment of lepers. Use of #RA2-RA30 was required for one week.

POSTAL TAX SEMI-POSTAL STAMP

> Catalogue values for unused stamps in this section are for Never Hinged items.

Icarus — PTSP1

Wmk. 267

1947, Nov. 15   **Typo.**   *Perf. 11*
RAB1	PTSP1	40c + 10c brt red	.35 .20
a.		Pair, imperf. between	350.00

Aviation Week, November 15-22, 1947, and compulsory on all domestic correspondence during that week.

BRITISH ANTARCTIC TERRITORY

'bri-tish (₁)ant-'ärk-tik 'ter-ə-₁tōr-ē

LOCATION — South Atlantic Ocean between 20-80 degrees longitude and south of 60 degrees latitude
GOVT. — British territory
POP. — About 100 scientific staff at research stations.

This territory includes Graham Land (Palmer Peninsula), South Shetland Islands

and South Orkney Islands. Formerly part of Falkland Islands Dependency.

12 Pence = 1 Shilling
20 Shillings = 1 Pound
100 Pence = 1 Pound (1971)

> Catalogue values for all unused stamps in this country are for Never Hinged items.

M. V. Kista Dan — A1

Designs: 1p, Skiers hauling load. 1¹/₂p, Muskeg (tractor). 2p, Skiers. 2¹/₂p, Beaver seaplane. 3p, R.R.S. John Biscoe. 4p, Camp scene. 6p, H.M.S. Protector. 9p, Dog sled. 1sh, Otter ski-plane. 2sh, Huskies and aurora australis. 2sh6p, Helicopter. 5sh, Snocat (truck). 10sh, R.R.S. Shackleton. £1, Map of Antarctica.

Perf. 11x11¹/₂

1963, Feb. 1   **Engr.**   **Wmk. 314**
1	A1	¹/₂p dark blue	.20	.15
2	A1	1p brown	.15	.15
3	A1	1¹/₂p plum & red	.20	.15
4	A1	2p rose violet	.30	.20
5	A1	2¹/₂p dull green	.35	.25
6	A1	3p Prus blue	.40	.35
7	A1	4p sepia	.50	.40
8	A1	6p dk blue & ol	.80	.70
9	A1	9p olive	1.00	.80
10	A1	1sh steel blue	1.35	1.10
11	A1	2sh dl vio & bis	6.75	5.50
12	A1	2sh6p blue	7.50	6.25
13	A1	5sh rose red & org	14.50	14.00
14	A1	10sh grn & vio bl	35.00	32.50
15	A1	£1 black & blue	85.00	67.50
		Nos. 1-15 (15)	154.00	130.00

See No. 24. For surcharges see Nos. 25-38.

> Common Design Types pictured following the introduction.

Churchill Memorial Issue
Common Design Type

1966, Jan. 24   **Photo.**   *Perf. 14*
16	CD319	¹/₂p bright blue	.50	.30
17	CD319	1p green	2.00	.70
18	CD319	1sh brown	20.00	15.00
19	CD319	2sh violet	25.00	16.00
		Nos. 16-19 (4)	47.50	32.00

Lemaire Channel, Iceberg and Adelie Penguins A2

Designs: 6p, Weather sonde and operator. 1sh, Muskeg (tractor) pulling tent equipment. 2sh, Surveyors with theodolite.

1969, Feb. 1   **Litho.**
20	A2	3¹/₂p blue, vio bl & blk	1.00	.95
21	A2	6p emer, blk & dp org	1.75	1.65
22	A2	1sh ultra, blk & ver	3.00	3.00
23	A2	2sh grnsh bl, blk & ocher	6.00	6.00
		Nos. 20-23 (4)	11.75	11.60

25 years of continuous scientific work in the Antarctic.

Type of 1963
Design: £1, H.M.S. Endurance and helicopter.

1969, Dec. 1   **Engr.**   *Perf. 11x11¹/₂*
24	A1	£1 black & rose red	125.00	125.00

Nos. 1-14 Surcharged in Decimal Currency; Three Bars Overprinted

1971, Feb. 15   **Wmk. 314**
25	A1	¹/₂p on ¹/₂p dk blue	.15	.15
26	A1	1p on 1p brown	.20	.20
27	A1	1¹/₂p on 1¹/₂p plum & red	.30	.25
28	A1	2p on 2p rose vio	.30	.30
29	A1	2¹/₂p on 2¹/₂p dl grn	.35	.40
30	A1	3p on 3p Prus bl	.70	.60
31	A1	4p on 4p sepia	1.00	.95
32	A1	5p on 6p dk bl & ol	1.40	1.25
33	A1	6p on 9p olive	1.75	1.50
34	A1	7¹/₂p on 1sh steel bl	2.25	2.00
35	A1	10p on 2sh dl vio & bis	5.00	4.25

36	A1	15p on 2sh6p blue	15.00	13.00
37	A1	25p on 5sh rose red & org	30.00	25.00
38	A1	50p on 10sh grn & vio blue	65.00	62.50
		Nos. 25-38 (14)	123.40	112.35

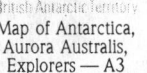
Map of Antarctica, Aurora Australis, Explorers — A3

Capt. Cook and "Resolution" — A4

Map of Antarctica, Aurora Australis and: 4p, Sea gulls. 5p, Seals. 10p, Penguins.

Litho. & Engr.

1971, June 23			**Perf. 14x13**	
39	A3	1½p multicolored	3.25	1.25
40	A3	4p multicolored	6.00	4.00
41	A3	8p multicolored	8.00	6.00
42	A3	10p multicolored	13.00	10.00
		Nos. 39-42 (4)	30.25	21.25

10th anniv. of the Antarctic Treaty pledging peaceful uses of and scientific cooperation in Antarctica.

Silver Wedding Issue, 1972
Common Design Type

Design: Queen Elizabeth II, Prince Philip, seals and emperor penguins.

1972, Dec. 13	**Photo.**		**Perf. 14x14½**	
43	CD324	5p rose brn & multi	2.00	2.00
44	CD324	10p olive & multi	4.00	4.00

Perf. 14½

1975-80	**Litho.**		**Wmk. 373**	

Polar Explorers and their Crafts: 1p, Thaddeus von Bellingshausen and "Vostok." 1½p, James Weddell and "Jane." 2p, John Biscoe and "Tula." 2½p, J. S. C. Dumont d'Urville and "Astrolabe." 3p, James Clark Ross and "Erebus." 4p, C. A. Larsen and "Jason." 5p, Adrien de Gerlache and "Belgica." 6p, Otto Nordenskjöld and "Antarctic." 7½p, W. S. Bruce and "Scotia." 10p, Jean-Baptiste Charcot and "Pourquoi Pas?" 15p, Ernest Shackleton and "Endurance." 25p, Hubert Wilkins and airplane "San Francisco." 50p, Lincoln Ellsworth and airplane "Polar Star." £1, John Rymill and "Penola."

45	A4	½p multi	.15	.15
46	A4	1p multi ('78)	.15	.15
47	A4	1½p multi ('78)	.15	.15
48	A4	2p multi ('79)	.15	.15
49	A4	2½p multi ('79)	.20	.20
50	A4	3p multi ('79)	.20	.20
52	A4	5p multi ('79)	.30	.30
55	A4	10p multi ('79)	.65	.65
56	A4	15p multi ('79)	1.00	1.00
57	A4	25p multi ('79)	1.60	1.60
58	A4	50p multi ('79)	3.25	3.25
59	A4	£1 multi ('78)	5.25	5.25
		Nos. 45-59 (12)	13.05	13.05

1973, Feb. 14			**Wmk. 314**	
45a	A4	½p multi	1.75	1.75
46a	A4	1p multi	2.00	2.10
47a	A4	1½p multi	3.50	3.50
48a	A4	2p multi	.25	.15
49a	A4	2½p multi	.30	.20
50a	A4	3p multi	.30	.20
51a	A4	4p multi	.30	.20
52a	A4	5p multi	.40	.30
53a	A4	6p multi	.40	.30
54a	A4	7½p multi	.55	.50
55a	A4	10p multi	1.05	.55
56a	A4	15p multi	1.75	1.00
57a	A4	25p multi	2.00	1.50
58a	A4	50p multi	4.00	3.00
59a	A4	£1 multi	12.00	11.00
		Nos. 45a-59a (15)	30.55	26.25

1980		**Wmk. 373**	**Perf. 12**	
51	A4	4p multi	.30	.30
53	A4	6p multi	.40	.40
54	A4	7½p multi	.50	.50
55b	A4	10p multi	.65	.65
56b	A4	15p multi	.70	.70
57b	A4	25p multi	1.25	1.25
58b	A4	50p multi	2.50	2.50
59b	A4	£1 multi	5.00	5.00
		Nos. 51-59b (8)	11.30	11.30

Princess Anne's Wedding Issue
Common Design Type

1973, Nov. 14	**Wmk. 314**		**Perf. 14**	
60	CD325	5p ocher & multi	.55	.55
61	CD325	15p blue grn & multi	1.40	1.40

Wedding of Princess Anne and Capt. Mark Phillips, Nov. 14, 1973.

Churchill and Map of Churchill Peninsula A5

Design: 15p, Churchill and "Trepassey" of Operation Tabarin, 1943.

1974, Nov. 30	**Litho.**		**Perf. 14**	
62	A5	5p multicolored	1.50	.95
63	A5	15p multicolored	3.00	3.00
a.		Souvenir sheet of 2, #62-63	6.75	4.50

Sir Winston Churchill (1874-1965).

Humpback Whale — A6

		Wmk. 373		
1977, Jan. 4	**Litho.**		**Perf. 14**	
64	A6	2p Sperm whale	2.25	1.00
65	A6	8p Fin whale	2.75	1.50
66	A6	11p shown	5.50	3.00
67	A6	25p Blue whale	6.50	4.50
		Nos. 64-67 (4)	17.00	10.00

Conservation of whales.

Prince Philip in Antarctica, 1956-57 — A7

Designs: 11p, Coronation oath. 33p, Queen before taking oath.

1977, Feb. 7			**Perf. 13½x14**	
68	A7	6p multicolored	.40	.40
69	A7	11p multicolored	.65	.65
70	A7	33p multicolored	2.25	2.25
		Nos. 68-70 (3)	3.30	3.30

25th anniv. of the reign of Elizabeth II.

Elizabeth II Coronation Anniversary Issue
Common Design Types
Souvenir Sheet
Unwmk.

1978, June 2	**Litho.**		**Perf. 15**	
71		Sheet of 6	5.50	5.50
a.	CD326	25p Black bull of Clarence	.80	.80
b.	CD327	25p Elizabeth II	.80	.80
c.	CD328	25p Emperor penguin	.80	.80

No. 71 contains 2 se-tenant strips of Nos. 71a-71c, separated by horizontal gutter with commemorative and descriptive inscriptions and showing central part of coronation procession with coach.

Macaroni Penguins — A8

		Perf. 13½x14		
1979, Jan. 14	**Litho.**		**Wmk. 373**	
72	A8	3p shown	6.25	2.00
73	A8	8p Gentoo	1.65	1.00
74	A8	11p Adelie	1.40	1.25
75	A8	25p Emperor	3.50	1.50
		Nos. 72-75 (4)	12.80	5.75

John Barrow, Tula, Society Emblem A9

Royal Geographical Society Sesquicentennial (Past Presidents and Expedition Scenes): 7p, Clement Markham 11p, Lord Curzon. 15p, William Goodenough. 22p, James Wordie. 30p, Raymond Priestley.

Perf. 13½

1980, Dec. 1	**Litho.**		**Wmk. 373**	
76	A9	3p multicolored	.15	.15
77	A9	7p multicolored	.20	.20
78	A9	11p multicolored	.35	.35
79	A9	15p multicolored	.60	.60
80	A9	22p multicolored	.90	.90
81	A9	30p multicolored	1.10	1.10
		Nos. 76-81 (6)	3.30	3.30

20th Anniv. of Antarctic Treaty — A10

1981, Dec. 1			**Perf. 13½x14**	
82	A10	10p Map	.30	.30
83	A10	13p Conservation research	.45	.45
84	A10	17p Satellite image mapping	.80	.80
85	A10	26p Global geophysics	.85	.85
		Nos. 82-85 (4)	2.40	2.40

Continental Drift and Climatic Change — A11

1982, Mar. 8	**Litho.**		**Perf. 13½x14**	
86	A11	3p Land, water	.15	.15
87	A11	6p Shrubs	.20	.20
88	A11	10p Dinosaur	.40	.40
89	A11	13p Volcano	.50	.50
90	A11	17p Trees	.90	.90
91	A11	26p Penguins	1.00	1.00
		Nos. 86-91 (6)	3.15	3.15

Princess Diana Issue
Common Design Type

1982, July 1	**Litho.**		**Perf. 14½x14**	
92	CD333	5p Arms	.15	.15
93	CD333	17p Diana, by Bryan Organ	.55	.55
94	CD333	37p Wedding	1.25	1.25
95	CD333	50p Portrait	1.65	1.65
		Nos. 92-95 (4)	3.60	3.60

10th Anniv. of Convention for Conservation of Antarctic Seals — A12

1982, Nov.			**Litho.**	
96	A12	5p shown	.15	.15
97	A12	10p Weddell seals	.30	.30
98	A12	13p Elephant seals	.40	.40
99	A12	17p Fur seals	.55	.55
100	A12	25p Ross seal	.55	.55
101	A12	34p Crabeater seals	1.10	1.10
		Nos. 96-101 (6)	3.05	3.05

Corethron Criophilum A13

1984, Mar. 15		**Litho.**	**Perf. 14**	
102	A13	1p shown	.15	.15
103	A13	2p Desmonema gaudichaudi	.15	.15
104	A13	3p Tomopteris carpenteri	.15	.15
105	A13	4p Pareuchaeta antarctica	.15	.15
106	A13	5p Anarctomysis maxima	.15	.15
107	A13	6p Antarcturus signiensis	.20	.20
108	A13	7p Serolis cornuta	.20	.20
109	A13	8p Parathemisto gaudichaudii	.25	.25
110	A13	9p Bovallia gigantea	.30	.30
110A	A13	10p Euphausia superba	.35	.35
111	A13	15p Colossendeis australis	.50	.50
112	A13	20p Todarodes sagittatus	.65	.65
113	A13	25p Notothenia neglecta	.85	.85
114	A13	50p Chaenocephalus aceratus	1.65	1.65
115	A13	£1 Lobodon carcinophagus	3.25	3.25
116	A13	£3 Antarctic marine food chain	8.25	11.50
		Nos. 102-116 (16)	17.20	20.45

Manned Flight Bicentenary A14

1983, Dec. 17			**Wmk. 373**	
117	A14	5p De Havilland Twin Otter	.15	.15
118	A14	13p De Havilland Single Otter	.30	.30
119	A14	17p Consolidated Canso	.50	.50
120	A14	50p Lockheed Vega	1.50	1.50
		Nos. 117-120 (4)	2.45	2.45

British-Graham Land Expedition, 1934-1937 — A15

Designs: 7p, M. Y. Penola in Stella Creek. 22p, Northern base, Winter Island. 27p, D. H. Fox Moth at southern base, Barry Island. 54p, Dog team near Ablation Point, George VI Sound.

1985, Mar. 23		**Litho.**	**Perf. 14½**	
121	A15	7p multicolored	.20	.20
122	A15	22p multicolored	.55	.55
123	A15	27p multicolored	.65	.65
124	A15	54p multicolored	1.30	1.30
		Nos. 121-124 (4)	2.70	2.70

A16   A17

Naturalists, fauna and flora: 7p, Robert McCormick (1800-1890), Catharacta Skua Maccormicki. 22p, Sir Joseph Dalton Hooker (1817-1911), Deschampsea antarctica. 27p, Jean Rene C. Quoy (1790-1869), Lagenorhynchus cruciger. 54p, James Weddell (1787-1834), Leptonychotes weddelli.

1985, Nov. 4		**Litho.**	**Perf. 14½**	
125	A16	7p multicolored	.25	.25
126	A16	22p multicolored	.80	.80
127	A16	27p multicolored	.95	.95
128	A16	54p multicolored	1.90	1.90
		Nos. 125-128 (4)	3.90	3.90

1986, Jan. 6		**Wmk. 373**	**Perf. 14**	

Halley's comet.

129	A17	7p Edmond Halley	.30	.30
130	A17	22p Halley Station	1.00	1.00
131	A17	27p Trajectory, 1531	1.25	1.25
132	A17	54p Giotto space probe	2.50	2.50
		Nos. 129-132 (4)	5.05	5.05

Intl. Glaciological
Society, 50th
Anniv.— A18

Different snowflakes.

1986, Dec. 6　Wmk. 384　Perf. 14½
133 A18 10p dp blue & lt bl　.30　.30
134 A18 24p blue grn & lt bl grn　.70　.70
135 A18 29p dp rose lil & lt lil　.85　.85
136 A18 58p dp vio & pale vio blue　1.70　1.70
　　Nos. 133-136 (4)　3.55　3.55

Capt. Robert
Falcon Scott,
CVO RN
(1868-1912)
A19

Designs: 24p, The Discovery at Hut Point, 1902-1904. 29p, Cape Evans Hut, 1911-1913. 58p, South Pole, 1912.

1987, Mar. 19　Litho.　Wmk. 373
137 A19 10p multicolored　.30　.30
138 A19 24p multicolored　.70　.70
139 A19 29p multicolored　.85　.85
140 A19 58p multicolored　1.70　1.70
　　Nos. 137-140 (4)　3.55　3.55

Intl. Geophysical
Year, 30th
Anniv.— A20

Commonwealth
Trans-Antarctic
Expedition — A21

1987, Dec. 25　Wmk. 384
141 A20 10p Emblem　.40　.40
142 A20 24p Port Lockroy　.90　.90
143 A20 29p Argentine Islands　1.10　1.10
144 A20 58p Halley Bay　2.25　2.25
　　Nos. 141-144 (4)　4.65　4.65

1988, Mar. 19　Perf. 14
145 A21 10p Aurora over South Ice　.35　.35
146 A21 24p Otter aircraft　.80　.80
147 A21 29p Seismic ice-depth
　　sounding　.95　.95
148 A21 58p Sno-cat over crevasse　1.90　1.90
　　Nos. 145-148 (4)　4.00　4.00

Lichens
A22

1989, Mar. 25　Wmk. 373
149 A22 10p Xanthoria elegans　.40　.40
150 A22 24p Usnea aurantiaco-atra　1.00　1.00
151 A22 29p Cladonia chlorophaea　1.25　1.25
152 A22 58p Umbilicaria antarctica　2.50　2.50
　　Nos. 149-152 (4)　5.15　5.15

Fossils
A23

1990, Apr. 2　Litho.　Wmk. 384
153 A23 1p Archaeocyath　.15　.15
154 A23 2p Brachiopod　.15　.15
155 A23 3p Trilobite (Triplagnostus)　.15　.15
156 A23 4p Trilobite (Lyriaspis)　.15　.15
157 A23 5p Gymnosperm　.15　.15

158 A23 6p Fern　.20　.20
159 A23 7p Belemnite　.25　.25
160 A23 8p Ammonite (Sanmartinoceras)　.25　.25
161 A23 9p Bivalve (Pinna)　.30　.30
162 A23 10p Bivalve (Aucellina)　.35　.35
163 A23 20p Bivalve (Trigonia)　.65　.65
164 A23 25p Gastropod　.80　.80
165 A23 50p Ammonite (Ainoceras)　1.50　1.50
166 A23 £1 Ammonite (Gunnarites)　3.00　3.00
167 A23 £3 Crayfish　9.00　9.00
　　Nos. 153-167 (15)　17.05　17.05

Queen Mother, 90th Birthday
Common Design Types
1990, Aug. 4　Wmk. 384　Perf. 14x15
170 CD343 26p Wedding portrait,
　　1923　.90　.90

Perf. 14½
171 CD344 £1 Family portrait,
　　1940　3.40　3.40

Age of
Dinosaurs
A24

1991, Mar. 27　Wmk. 373　Perf. 14
172 A24 12p Late Cretaceous forest　.75　.75
173 A24 26p Hypsilophodont dinosaur　1.50　1.50
174 A24 31p Frilled shark　1.90　1.90
175 A24 62p Mosasaur, plesiosaur　3.50　3.50
　　Nos. 172-175 (4)　7.65　7.65

Antarctic
Ozone
Hole — A25

1991, Mar. 30　Perf. 14½x14
176 A25 12p Launching weather balloon　.45　.45
177 A25 26p Measuring ozone　1.00　1.00
178 A25 31p Ozone hole over Antarctica　1.20　1.20
179 A25 62p Airplane, chemical studies　2.40　2.40
　　Nos. 176-179 (4)　5.05　5.05

Antarctic Treaty,
30th Anniv.— A26

1991, June 24　Perf. 14½
180 A26 12p Dry valley　.45　.45
181 A26 26p Mapping ice sheet　1.00　1.00
182 A26 31p BIOMASS emblem　1.20　1.20
183 A26 62p Ross seal　2.40　2.40
　　Nos. 180-183 (4)　5.05　5.05

Royal Research
Ship James
Clark
Ross — A27

Designs: 12p, HMS Erebus and Terror in Antarctic by John W. Carmichael. 26p, Launch of RRS James Clark Ross. 62p, Scientific research.

1991, Dec. 10　Perf. 14x14½
184 A27 12p multicolored　.45　.45
185 A27 26p multicolored　1.00　1.00
186 A27 31p shown　1.20　1.20
187 A27 62p multicolored　2.40　2.40
　　Nos. 184-187 (4)　5.05　5.05

Inscribed in Blue

200th Anniversary M. Faraday 1791-1867

1991, Dec. 24
188 A27 12p like #184　.45　.45
189 A27 26p like #185　1.00　1.00
190 A27 31p like #186　1.20　1.20
191 A27 62p like #187　2.40　2.40
　　Nos. 188-191 (4)　5.05　5.05

Seals and
Penguins
A28

1992, Oct. 20　Perf. 13½
192 A28 4p Ross seal　.15　.15
193 A28 5p Adelie penguin　.20　.20
194 A28 7p Weddell seal　.30　.30
195 A28 29p Emperor penguin　1.25　1.25
196 A28 34p Crabeater seal　1.50　1.50
197 A28 68p Chinstrap penguin　3.00　3.00
　　Nos. 192-197 (6)　6.40　6.40

World Wildlife Fund.

Lower
Atmospheric
Phenomena
A29

Perf. 14x14½
1992, Dec. 22　Litho.　Wmk. 373
198 A29 14p Sun pillar at Faraday　.50　.50
199 A29 29p Halo with iceberg　1.10　1.10
200 A29 34p Lee wave cloud　1.30　1.30
201 A29 68p Nacreous clouds　2.60　2.60
　　Nos. 198-201 (4)　5.50　5.50

Research
Ships
A30

Wmk. 373
1993, Dec. 1　Litho.　Perf. 14
202 A30 1p SS Fitzroy　.15　.15
203 A30 2p HMS William
　　Scoresby　.15　.15
204 A30 3p SS Eagle　.15　.15
205 A30 4p MV Trepassey　.15　.15
206 A30 5p RRS John Biscoe (I)　.15　.15
207 A30 10p MV Norsel　.30　.30
208 A30 20p HMS Protector　.55　.55
209 A30 30p MV Oluf Sven　.85　.85
210 A30 50p RRS John Biscoe (II),
　　RRS Shackleton　1.40　1.40
a.　　Souvenir sheet of 1　1.75　1.75
211 A30 £1 MV Tottan　2.75　2.75
a.　　Souvenir sheet of 1　3.50　3.50
212 A30 £3 MV Perla Dan　8.50　8.50
213 A30 £5 HMS Endurance (I)　14.00　14.00
　　Nos. 202-213 (12)　29.10　29.10

No. 210a for Hong Kong '97. Issued 2/3/97.
No. 211a for return of Hong Kong to China. Issued 7/1/97.

Operation
Taberin, 50th
Anniv.— A31

Designs: 15p, Bransfield House and Post Office, Port Lockroy. 31p, Survey team, Hope Bay. 36p, Dog team, Hope Bay. 72p, SS Fitzroy, HMS William Scoresby at sea.

Wmk. 373
1994, Mar. 19　Litho.　Perf. 14
214 A31 15p multicolored　.45　.45
215 A31 31p multicolored　.90　.90
216 A31 36p multicolored　1.10　1.10
217 A31 72p multicolored　2.25　2.25
　　Nos. 214-217 (4)　4.70　4.70

Old and New Transportation — A32

Designs: 15p, Huskies. 24p, DeHavilland DHC-2 Turbo Beaver, British Antarctic Survey. 31p, Dogs, cargo being taken from aircraft. 36p, DHC-6 Twin Otter, sled team. 62p, DHC-6 in flight. 72p, DHC-6 taxiing down runway.

1994, Mar. 21
218 A32 15p multicolored　.45　.45
219 A32 24p multicolored　.70　.70
220 A32 31p multicolored　.90　.90
221 A32 36p multicolored　1.10　1.10
222 A32 62p multicolored　1.75　1.75
223 A32 72p multicolored　2.25　2.25
　　Nos. 218-223 (6)　7.15　7.15

Ovptd. with Hong Kong '94 Emblem
1994, Feb. 18
224 A32 15p on #218　.45　.45
225 A32 24p on #219　.70　.70
226 A32 31p on #220　.90　.90
227 A32 36p on #221　1.10　1.10
228 A32 62p on #222　1.75　1.75
229 A32 72p on #223　2.25　2.25
　　Nos. 224-229 (6)　7.15　7.15

Antarctic
Food Chain
A33

a, Crabeater seals. b, Blue whale. c, Wandering albatross. d, Mackeral icefish. e, Krill. f, Squid.

1994, Nov. 29
230 A33 35p Sheet of 6　6.50　6.50

Geological
Structures
A34

Designs: 17p, Hauberg Mountains, folded sedimentary rocks. 35p, Arrowsmith Peninsula, dikes cross-cutting granite. 40p, Colbert Mountains, columnar jointing in volcanic rocks. 76p, Succession Cliffs, flat-lying sedimentary rocks.

Perf. 14x14½
1995, Nov. 28　Litho.　Wmk. 373
231 A34 17p multicolored　.55　.55
232 A34 35p multicolored　1.10　1.10
233 A34 40p multicolored　1.25　1.25
234 A34 76p multicolored　2.50　2.50
　　Nos. 231-234 (4)　5.40　5.40

Scientific
Committee
on
Antarctic
Research
(SCAR)
A35

Designs: 17p, World map showing SCAR member countries. 35p, Earth sciences. 40p, Atmospheric sciences. 76p, Life sciences. £1, Cambridge, August 1996.

Wmk. 384
1996, Mar. 23　Litho.　Perf. 14
235 A35 17p multicolored　.55　.55
236 A35 35p multicolored　1.10　1.10
237 A35 40p multicolored　1.25　1.25
238 A35 76p multicolored　2.50　2.50
　　Nos. 235-238 (4)　5.40　5.40

Souvenir Sheet
239 A35 £1 multicolored　3.25　3.25

Queen Elizabeth II, 70th Birthday
Common Design Type
Various portraits of Queen: 17p, Pink outfit. 35p, In formal dress, tiara. 40p, Blue outfit. 76p, Red coat.

Perf. 14½
1996, Nov. 25   Litho.   Wmk. 384
240	CD354	17p multicolored	.60 .60
241	CD354	35p multicolored	1.20 1.20
242	CD354	40p multicolored	1.35 1.35
243	CD354	76p multicolored	2.50 2.50
		Nos. 240-243 (4)	5.65 5.65

Whales
A36

Wmk. 373
1996, Nov. 25   Litho.   Perf. 14
244	A36	17p Killer whale	.60 .60
245	A36	35p Sperm whale	1.20 1.20
246	A36	40p Minke whale	1.35 1.35
247	A36	76p Blue whale	2.50 2.50
		Nos. 244-247 (4)	5.65 5.65

Souvenir Sheet
248	A36	£1 Humpback whale	3.50 3.50

SEMI-POSTAL STAMPS

Antarctic
Heritage
SP1

17p+3p

Designs: 17p+3p, Capt. James Cook, HMS Resolution. 35p+15p, Sir James Clark Ross, HMS Erebus, HMS Terror. 40p+10p, Capt. Robert Falcon Scott. 76p+4p, Sir Ernest Shackleton, HMS Endurance trapped in ice.

Perf. 14½
1994, Nov. 23   Litho.   Wmk. 384
B1	SP1	17p + 3p multi	.65 .65
B2	SP1	35p + 15p multi	1.50 1.50
B3	SP1	40p + 10p multi	1.50 1.50
B4	SP1	76p + 4p multi	2.50 2.50
		Nos. B1-B4 (4)	6.15 6.15

Surtax for United Kingdom Antarctic Heritage Trust.

BRITISH CENTRAL AFRICA

'bri-tish 'sen-trəl 'a-fri-kə

LOCATION — Central Africa, on the west shore of Lake Nyassa
GOVT. — Former British territory, under charter to the British South Africa Company
AREA — 37,800 sq. mi.
POP. — 1,639,329
CAPITAL — Zomba

In 1907 the name was changed to Nyasaland Protectorate, and stamps so inscribed replaced those of British Central Africa.

12 Pence = 1 Shilling
20 Shillings = 1 Pound

Rhodesia Nos. 2, 4-19 **B.C.A.**
Overprinted in Black

1891-95   Unwmk.   Perf. 14
1	A1	1p black	2.50 2.50
2	A2	2p gray green & ver	2.50 2.50
3	A2	4p red brn & blk	2.00 3.00
4	A1	6p ultramarine	45.00 24.00
5	A1	6p dark blue	5.00 7.50
6	A2	8p rose & blue	12.00 25.00
7	A1	1sh bis brown	11.00 10.00
8	A1	2sh vermilion	20.00 40.00
9	A1	2sh6p gray lilac	45.00 55.00
10	A2	3sh brn & grn ('95)	45.00 50.00
11	A2	4sh gray & ver ('93)	45.00 65.00
12	A1	5sh yellow	45.00 55.00
13	A1	10sh green	85.00 120.00
14	A3	£1 blue	600.00 650.00
15	A3	£2 rose red	800.00 800.00
16	A3	£5 yel green	1,600. 1,700.
17	A3	£10 red brown	3,000. 3,000.
		Nos. 1-13 (13)	365.00 459.50

High values with fiscal cancellation are fairly common and can be purchased at a small fraction of

the above values. This applies to subsequent issues also.
For surcharge see No. 20.

Rhodesia Nos. 13-14 **B.C.A.**
Surcharged in Black **THREE SHILLINGS.**

1892-93
18	A2	3sh on 4sh gray & ver ('93)	275.00 275.00
19	A1	4sh on 5sh yellow	65.00 75.00

No. 2 Surcharged in **ONE PENNY.**
Black, with Bar

1895
20	A2	1p on 2p	7.50 20.00
a.		Double surcharge	2,000. 2,000.

A double surcharge, without period after "Penny," and measuring 16mm instead of 18mm, is from a trial printing.

Coat of Arms of the
Protectorate
A4   A5

1895   Unwmk.   Typo.   Perf. 14
21	A4	1p black	7.50 5.00
22	A4	2p green & black	12.50 10.00
23	A4	4p org & black	22.50 22.50
24	A4	6p ultra & black	35.00 7.50
25	A4	1sh rose & black	40.00 17.50
26	A5	2sh6p vio & black	100.00 125.00
27	A5	3sh yel & black	65.00 40.00
28	A5	5sh olive & blk	85.00 90.00
29	A5	£1 org & black	650.00 375.00
30	A5	£10 ver & black	3,250. 2,750.
31	A5	£25 bl grn & blk	5,750. 6,000.
		Nos. 21-28 (8)	367.50 317.50

1896   Wmk. 2
32	A4	1p black	4.50 4.50
33	A4	2p green & black	12.00 5.75
34	A4	4p org brown & blk	14.00 16.00
35	A4	6p ultra & black	15.00 8.00
36	A4	1sh rose & black	16.00 9.00

Wmk. 1 Sideways
37	A5	2sh6p vio rose & blk	75.00 90.00
38	A5	3sh yel & black	55.00 40.00
39	A5	5sh olive & blk	80.00 95.00
40	A5	£1 blue & blk	675.00 475.00
41	A5	£10 ver & blk	3,750. 2,250.
42	A5	£25 bl grn & blk	9,500. 9,500.
		Nos. 32-39 (8)	271.50 268.25

A6   A7

1897-1901   Wmk. 2
43	A6	1p ultra & black	1.00 .60
44	A6	1p rose & violet ('01)	1.25 .90
45	A6	2p yel & black	1.50 .70
46	A6	4p car rose & blk	4.50 2.50
47	A6	4p ol green & violet ('01)	5.00 6.00
48	A6	6p green & black	27.50 4.00
49	A6	6p red brown & violet ('01)	4.00 3.75
50	A6	1sh gray lilac & blk	7.50 6.25

Wmk. 1
51	A7	2sh6p ultra & blk	32.50 35.00
52	A7	3sh gray grn & blk	150.00 175.00
53	A7	4sh car rose & blk	45.00 60.00
54	A7	10sh ol & black	75.00 90.00
55	A7	£1 dp vio & blk	225.00 150.00
56	A7	£10 org & black	3,500. 1,600.
		Nos. 43-54 (12)	354.75 384.70

No. 52 Surcharged in Red **ONE**

PENNY

1897
57	A7	1p on 3s	5.00 7.50
a.		"PNNEY"	1,500.
b.		"PENN"	900.00
c.		Double surcharge	750.00 600.00

A8

1898, Mar. 11   Unwmk.   Imperf.
58	A8	1p ver & ultra	1,500. 50.00
a.		Center inverted	10,000.
b.		Double oval	
c.		Pair, one without oval	6,500.
d.		Pair with three ovals	
e.		Initials of P.M. General on back	450.00

Perf. 12
59	A8	1p ver & blue	1,750. 15.00

There are two settings of Nos. 58-59, with 30 types of each.
No. 58 issued without gum.

King Edward VII
A9   A10

1903-04   Wmk. 2
60	A9	1p car & black	3.75 .75
61	A9	2p vio & dull vio	3.00 2.50
62	A9	4p blk & gray green	2.25 5.75
63	A9	6p org brn & blk	2.25 4.50
64	A9	1sh pale blue & blk ('04)	2.25 4.00

Wmk. 1
65	A10	2sh6p gray green	27.50 35.00
66	A10	4sh vio & dl vio	47.50 70.00
67	A10	10sh blk & gray green	62.50 125.00
68	A10	£1 scar & blk	175.00 135.00
69	A10	£10 ultra & blk	3,500. 2,750.
		Nos. 60-68 (9)	326.00 382.50

1907   Wmk. 3
70	A9	1p car & black	2.00 .90
71	A9	2p vio & dull vio	7,250.
72	A9	4p blk & gray grn	7,250.
73	A9	6p org brn & blk	25.00 32.50

Nos. 71-72 were not issued.
British Central Africa stamps were replaced by those of Nyasaland Protectorate in 1908.

BRITISH EAST AFRICA

'bri-tish 'ēst 'a-fri-kə

LOCATION — Formerly included all of the territory in East Africa under British control.

Postage stamps were issued by the British East Africa Company in 1896. Later the territory administered by this company was incorporated in the East Africa and Uganda Protectorate which, together with Kenya, became officially designated Kenya Colony.

16 Annas = 1 Rupee

Queen Victoria
A1   A2   A3

1890   Wmk. 30   Perf. 14
1	A1	½a on 1p lilac	300.00 200.00
2	A2	1a on 2p grn & car rose	400.00 250.00
3	A3	4a on 5p lilac & bl	450.00 275.00

Sun and Crown Symbolical of
"Light and Liberty"
A4   A5

1890-94   Unwmk.   Litho.   Perf. 14
14	A4	½a bister brown	1.00 2.75
b.		½a deep brown	1.00 2.50
c.		As "b," horiz. pair, imperf. btwn.	1,500. 750.00
d.		As "b," vert. pair, imperf. btwn.	750.00 475.00
15	A4	1a blue green	1.00 1.00
16	A4	2a vermilion	2.50 1.50
17	A4	2½a black, yel ('91)	3.50 3.00
b.		Horiz. pair, imperf. btwn.	600.00 400.00
c.		Horiz. pair, imperf. btwn.	800.00 500.00
18	A4	3a black, red ('91)	1.25 1.40
b.		Horiz. pair, imperf. btwn.	600.00 400.00
c.		Vert. pair, imperf. btwn.	400.00 350.00
19	A4	4a yellow brown	2.50 2.25
20	A4	4½a brown vio ('91)	2.50 3.25
b.		4½a gray violet ('91)	25.00 7.25
c.		Horiz. pair, imperf. btwn.	1,250. 1,250.
d.		Vert. pair, imperf. btwn.	675.00 450.00
21	A4	5a black, blue ('94)	1.10 1.75
22	A4	7½a black ('94)	1.10 1.75
23	A4	8a blue	5.50 7.50
24	A4	8a gray	250.00 325.00
25	A4	1r rose	6.00 7.50
26	A4	1r gray	225.00 225.00
27	A5	2r brick red	10.00 8.00
28	A5	3r gray violet	7.50 6.25
29	A5	4r ultra	12.00 12.50
30	A5	5r gray green	30.00 25.00
		Nos. 14-30 (17)	562.45 635.40

Some of the paper used for this issue had a papermaker's watermark and parts of it often can be seen on the stamps.
Values for Nos. 14c, 14d, 17b, 17c, 18b, 18c, 20c, 20d, unused, are for copies with little or no original gum.
For surcharges and overprints see Nos. 31-53.

1890-91   Imperf.
Values for Pairs except No. 19b.
14a	A4	½a bister brown	600. 350.
14e	A4	½a deep brown	650. 400.
15a	A4	1a blue green	800. 475.
16a	A4	2a vermilion	1,200. 550.
17a	A4	2½a black, yellow	750. 400.
18a	A4	3a black, red	725. 600.
19a	A4	4a yel brown	1,400. 600.
19b	A4	4a gray	1,400. 1,400.
20a	A4	4½a dull violet	1,100. 525.
23a	A4	8a blue	1,800. 600.
25a	A4	1r rose	2,400. 625.

A6   A7

Handstamped Surcharges

1891   Perf. 14
31	A6	½a on 2a ver ("A.D.")	2,750. 900.00
a.		Double surcharge	3,250.
32	A6	1a on 4a yel brn ("A.B.")	6,000. 1,300.

Nos. 31-32 are initialed in manuscript "A.D." or "A.B." See note below No. 35.

Manuscript Surcharges

1891-95
33	A6	½a on 2a ver ("A.B.")	3,000. 675.00
a.		"½ Annas" ("A.B.")	1,200.
b.		Initialed "A.D."	1,000.
c.		"½ Annas" ("A.D.")	1,600.
34	A6	½a on 3a blk, red ("T.E.C.R.")	200.00 50.00
b.		Initialed "A.B."	2,400. 1,100.
34A	A6	1a on 3a blk, red ("V.H.M.")	3,000. 1,200.
c.		Initialed "T.E.C.R."	3,000. 1,500.
35	A6	1a on 4a yel brn ("A.B.")	2,750. 950.00

The manuscript initials on Nos. 31-35, given in parentheses, stand for Andrew Dick, Archibald Brown, Victor H. Mackenzie (1891) and T. E. C. Remington (1895).

Printed Surcharges

1894
36	A7	5a on 8a blue	52.50 72.50
37	A7	7½a on 1r rose	52.50 72.50

BRITISH EAST AFRICA

Stamps of 1890-94
Handstamped in Black

1895

38	A4	½a deep brown	60.00	20.00
39	A4	1a blue green	70.00	65.00
40	A4	2a vermilion	125.00	90.00
41	A4	2½a black, *yellow*	110.00	45.00
42	A4	3a black, *red*	42.50	37.50
43	A4	4a yel brown	37.50	37.50
44	A4	4½a gray violet	125.00	85.00
a.		4½a brown violet	750.00	650.00
45	A4	5a black, *blue*	140.00	87.50
b.		Inverted overprint		2,000.
46	A4	7½a black	95.00	80.00
47	A4	8a blue	80.00	75.00
b.		Inverted overprint	2,000.	
48	A4	1r rose	45.00	47.50
49	A5	2r brick red	250.00	175.00
50	A5	3r gray violet	140.00	120.00
b.		Inverted overprint		
51	A5	4r ultra	125.00	125.00
52	A5	5r gray green	325.00	350.00
		Nos. 38-52 (15)	1,770.	1,445.

Double Overprints

38a	A4	½a	350.	350.
39a	A4	1a	350.	350.
40a	A4	2a	400.	400.
41a	A4	2½a	400.	350.
43a	A4	4a	375.	375.
44b	A4	4½a gray violet	475.	450.
44c	A4	4½a brown violet	1,500.	1,400.
45a	A4	5a	700.	650.
46a	A4	7½a	450.	450.
47a	A4	8a	475.	475.
48a	A4	1r	425.	425.
50a	A5	3r	750.	750.
51a	A5	4r	750.	750.
52a	A5	5r	1,100.	1,100.

Surcharged in Red

1895

53	A4	2½a on 4½a gray vio	90.00	55.00
a.		Double overprint (#44b)	700.00	700.00

Stamps of India 1874-95 Overprinted or
Surcharged

**British
East
Africa**

1895   Wmk. Star (39)

54	A17	½a green	3.50	4.00
55	A19	1a maroon	3.50	3.50
56	A20	1a6p bister brn	3.50	3.00
57	A21	2a ultra	3.50	2.25
58	A28	2a6p green	5.00	2.75
59	A20(a)	2½a on 1a6p bis brown	40.00	27.50
a.		"½" without fraction line	70.00	
d.		As "a," "1" of "½" invtd.	750.00	600.00
62	A22	3a orange	7.00	7.50
63	A23	4a olive green	25.00	16.00
64	A25	8a red violet	25.00	32.50
a.		8a red lilac	45.00	
65	A26	12a vio, *red*	18.00	22.50
66	A27	1r gray	55.00	47.50
67	A29	1r car & grn	32.50	55.00
a.		Dbl. ovpt., one sideways	350.00	550.00
68	A30	2r bis & rose	45.00	75.00
69	A30	3r grn & brn	55.00	85.00
70	A30	5r vio & ultra	80.00	120.00
a.		Double overprint	1,800.	

Wmk. Elephant's Head (38)

71	A14	6a bister	21.00	30.00
		Nos. 54-59,62-71 (16)	422.50	534.00

Varieties of the overprint include: "Britlsh," "Brl-tish," "Bpitish" and "Biitish" for "British," "Afrlca" for "Africa"; "Eas" and "Easa" for "East."

No. 59 is surcharged in bright red; surcharges in brown red were prepared for the UPU, but not regularly issued as stamps. See note following No. 93.

Queen Victoria and British
Lions — A8

1896-1903   Engr.   Wmk. 2   *Perf. 14*

72	A8	½a yel green	.80	.70
73	A8	1a carmine	2.50	.40
a.		1a red	2.50	.40
74	A8	1a dp rose ('03)	27.50	3.25
75	A8	2a chocolate	3.75	3.25
76	A8	2½a dark blue	4.75	1.00
77	A8	3a gray	2.50	*4.50*
78	A8	4a deep green	5.00	2.50
79	A8	4½a orange	4.00	*8.00*
80	A8	5a dk ocher	6.00	3.50
81	A8	7½a lilac	4.50	16.00
82	A8	8a olive gray	2.25	4.00
83	A8	1r ultra	25.00	17.00
a.		1r pale blue	25.00	17.50
84	A8	2r red orange	42.50	22.50
85	A8	3r deep violet	42.50	22.50
86	A8	4r lake	42.50	42.50
87	A8	5r dark brown	42.50	35.00
		Nos. 72-87 (16)	258.55	186.60

**British
East
Africa**

Zanzibar Nos. 38-40, 44-46
Overprinted in Black

1897   Wmk. Rosette (71)

88	A2	½a yel grn & red	37.50	37.50
89	A2	1a indigo & red	75.00	75.00
90	A2	2a red brn & red	27.50	18.00
91	A2	4½a org & red	37.50	22.50
92	A2	5a bister & red	37.50	27.50
93	A2	7½a lilac & red	42.50	30.00
a.		Ovptd. on front and back		
		Nos. 88-93 (6)	257.50	210.50

The 1a with red overprint, which includes a period after "Africa", was sent to the UPU, but never placed in use. Nos. 88, 90-93 and 95-100 also exist with period (in black) in sets sent to the UPU. Some experts consider these essays.

Black Ovpt. on Zanzibar #39, 42
New Value Surcharged in Red

1897

95	A2(a)	2½a on 1a	75.00	50.00
a.		Black overprint double	6,500.	
b.		"2" over "1" for "½"	1,200.	
96	A2(b)	2½a on 1a	140.00	90.00
97	A2(c)	2½a on 1a	85.00	55.00
98	A2(a)	2½a on 3a	65.00	45.00
a.		"2" over "1" for "½"	1,200.	
99	A2(b)	2½a on 3a	125.00	85.00
100	A2(c)	2½a on 3a	75.00	50.00
		Nos. 95-100 (6)	565.00	375.00

A10

1898   Wmk. 1   Engr.

102	A10	1r ultra	125.00	100.00
a.		1r gray blue	27.50	17.50
103	A10	2r orange	42.50	45.00
104	A10	3r dk violet	42.50	60.00
105	A10	4r carmine	125.00	*150.00*
106	A10	5r black brown	110.00	150.00
107	A10	10r bister	160.00	225.00
108	A10	20r yel green	575.00	1,000.
109	A10	50r lilac	1,900.	2,750.
		Nos. 102-107 (6)	605.00	730.00

The stamps of this country were superseded in 1904 by the stamps of East Africa and Uganda Protectorate.

BRITISH GUIANA

'bri-tish gē-'a-nə, -'ä-nə

LOCATION — On the northeast coast of South America
GOVT. — Former British Crown Colony
AREA — 83,000 sq. mi.
POP. — 628,000 (estimated 1964)
CAPITAL — Georgetown

British Guiana stamps can be mounted in the Scott British East Caribbean album.

British Guiana became the independent state of Guyana May 26, 1966.

100 Cents = 1 Dollar

Catalogue values for unused stamps in this country are for Never Hinged items, beginning with Scott 242 in the regular postage section and Scott J1 in the postage due section.

Values for unused stamps are for copies with original gum except for Nos. 6-12 and 35-53, which are valued without gum. Very fine examples of all stamps from No. 6 on will have four clear margins. Inferior copies sell at much reduced prices, depending on the condition of the individual specimen.

Ship and Motto of
Colony — A2

Seal of the
Colony — A3

A1

1850-51   Typeset   Unwmk.   *Imperf.*

1	A1	2c blk, *pale rose*, cut to shape ('51)		70,000.
2	A1	4c black, *orange*		20,000.
		Cut to shape		3,500.
a.		4c black, *yellow*		27,500.
		Cut to shape		4,000.
3	A1	4c blk, *yellow* (pelure)		37,500.
		Cut to shape		4,000.
4	A1	8c black, *green*		13,000.
		Cut to shape		2,500.
5	A1	12c black, *blue*		5,250.
		Cut to shape		1,900.
a.		12c black, *pale blue*		11,000.
		Cut to shape		3,000.
b.		12c black, *indigo*		13,000.
		Cut to shape		3,000.
c.		"1" of "12" omitted		3,000.

These stamps were initialed before use by the Deputy Postmaster General or by one of the clerks of the Colonial Postoffice at Georgetown. The following initials are found:—E. T. E. D(alton); E. D. W(ight); G. B. S(mith); H. A. K(illikelley); W. H. L(ortimer). As these stamps are type-set there are several types of each value.

1852   Litho.

6	A2	1c black, *magenta*	10,000.	5,250.
7	A2	4c black, *blue*	15,000.	5,750.

Both 1c and 4c are found in two types. Copies with paper cracked or rubbed sell for much less. Some copies are initialed E. D. W(ight).
The reprints are on thicker paper and the colors are brighter. They are perforated 12½ and imperforate. Value $15 each.

1853-59   *Imperf.*

Without Line above Value

8	A3	1c vermilion	4,500.	1,150.

Copies in reddish brown probably are proofs.

Full or Partial White Line Above Value

9	A3	1c red	2,750.	950.
10	A3	4c blue	1,100.	450.
a.		4c dark blue	1,375.	525.
b.		4c pale blue	950.	375.

On No. 9, "ONE CENT" varies from 11 to 13mm in width.

No. 10 Retouched; White Line above Value Removed

11	A3	4c blue	1,650.	600.
a.		4c dark blue	2,000.	650.
b.		4c pale blue	1,600.	650.

Reprints of Nos. 8 and 10 are on thin paper, perf. 12½ or imperf. The 1c is orange red, the 4c sky blue.

1860

Numerals in Corners Framed

12	A3	4c blue	3,250.	450.

A4

1856   Typeset   *Imperf.*

13	A4	1c black, *magenta*		
14	A4	4c black, *magenta*		7,500.
a.		4c black, *rose carmine*		10,500.
15	A4	4c black, *blue*		45,000.
16	A4	4c black, *blue*, paper colored through		60,000.

These stamps were initialed before being issued and the following initials are found:—E. T. E. D.; E. D. W.; W. H. L.; C. A. W. No. 13 is unique.

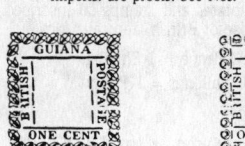

A5

Wide space between value and "Cents"

1860-61   Thick Paper Litho.   *Perf. 12*

17	A5	1c brown red ('61)	350.00	80.00
18	A5	1c pink	1,100.	165.00
19	A5	2c orange	150.00	37.50
20	A5	8c rose	300.00	45.00
21	A5	12c gray	350.00	30.00
a.		12c lilac	450.00	40.00
22	A5	24c green	950.00	75.00

All denominations of type A5 above four cents are expressed in Roman numerals.
Bisects and trisects are found on covers. These were not officially authorized.
The reprints of the 1c pink are perforated 12½; the other values have not been reprinted.

Thin Paper

1862-65

23	A5	1c brown	400.00	175.00
24	A5	1c black	100.00	45.00
25	A5	2c orange	80.00	30.00
26	A5	8c rose	110.00	45.00
27	A5	12c lilac	125.00	25.00
28	A5	24c green	750.00	85.00

Perf. 12½ and 13

29	A5	1c black	55.00	25.00
30	A5	2c orange	75.00	22.50
31	A5	8c rose	225.00	75.00
32	A5	12c lilac	475.00	110.00
33	A5	24c green	550.00	75.00

Medium Paper

33A	A5	1c black	50.00	25.00
33B	A5	2c orange	70.00	20.00
33C	A5	8c pink	145.00	50.00
33D	A5	12c lilac ('65)	425.00	90.00
33E	A5	24c green	160.00	60.00
f.		24c deep green	325.00	80.00

Perf. 10

34	A5	12c gray lilac	400.00	65.00

Imperfs. are proofs. See Nos. 44-62.

A6   A7

A8   A9

A10   A11

1862 Typeset Rouletted

35	A6	1c black, *rose*	1,650.	350.
		Unsigned		200.
36	A7	1c black, *rose*	2,000.	450.
		Unsigned		200.
37	A8	1c black, *rose*	3,500.	575.
		Unsigned		400.
38	A6	2c black, *yellow*	1,600.	275.
		Unsigned		350.
39	A7	2c black, *yellow*	2,250.	350.
		Unsigned		400.
40	A8	2c black, *yellow*	3,250.	575.
		Unsigned		600.
41	A9	4c black, *blue*	2,000.	475.
		Unsigned		375.
42	A10	4c black, *blue*	3,500.	1,450.
		Unsigned		600.
a.		Without inner lines	2,000.	475.
		As "a," unsigned		350.
43	A11	4c black, *blue*	1,750.	400.
		Unsigned		350.

Nos. 35-43 were typeset, there being 24 types of each value. They were initialed before use "R. M. Ac. R. G", being the initials of Robert Mather, Acting Receiver General.

The initials are in black on the 1c and in red on the 2c. An alkali was used on the 4c stamps, which, destroying the color of the paper, caused the initials to appear to be written in white.

Uninitialed stamps are remainders, few sheets having been found.

Specimens with roulette on all sides are valued higher.

Narrow space between value and "Cents"

1860 Thick Paper Litho. Perf. 12

44	A5	4c blue	275.00	50.00
c.		4c deep blue	375.00	75.00

Thin Paper

44A	A5	4c blue	75.00	20.00

Perf. 12½ and 13

44B	A5	4c blue	75.00	22.50

Medium Paper

1863-68 Perf. 12½ and 13

45	A5	1c black ('66)	30.00	16.00
46	A5	2c orange	30.00	5.00
47	A5	4c blue ('64)	65.00	12.50
48	A5	8c rose ('68)	135.00	17.50
49	A5	12c lilac ('67)	375.00	22.50

1866 Perf. 10

50	A5	1c black	8.00	4.00
51	A5	2c orange	17.50	2.50
52	A5	4c blue	75.00	7.00
a.		Half used as 2c on cover		4,000.
53	A5	8c rose	110.00	13.00
a.		Diagonal half used as 4c on cover		—
54	A5	12c lilac	125.00	12.00
a.		Third used as 4c on cover		—

1875 Perf. 15

58	A5	1c black	35.00	7.50
59	A5	2c orange	150.00	8.50
60	A5	4c blue	225.00	70.00
61	A5	8c rose	250.00	75.00
62	A5	12c lilac	525.00	47.50

Seal of Colony
A12 A13

1863 Perf. 12

63	A12	24c yellow green	125.00	12.50
a.		24c green	250.00	22.50

Perf. 12½ to 13

64	A12	6c blue	100.00	40.00
65	A12	24c green	125.00	10.00
66	A12	48c deep red	150.00	45.00
a.		48c rose	250.00	45.00
		Nos. 63-66 (4)	500.00	107.50

1866 Perf. 10

67	A12	6c blue	100.00	22.50
		6c ultramarine	125.00	32.50
68	A12	24c yellow green	150.00	8.00
		24c green	190.00	10.00
69	A12	48c rose red	225.00	25.00
		Nos. 67-69 (3)	475.00	55.50

For surcharges see Nos. 83-92.

1875 Perf. 15

70	A12	6c ultra	375.00	80.00
71	A12	24c yellow green	525.00	35.00
		24c deep green	650.00	55.00

1876 Typo. Wmk. 1 Perf. 14

72	A13	1c slate	2.50	1.50
a.		Perf. 14x12½		190.00
73	A13	2c orange	30.00	2.00
74	A13	4c ultra	110.00	7.00
a.		Perf. 12½	1,300.	200.00

75	A13	6c chocolate	70.00	7.50
76	A13	8c rose	90.00	1.90
77	A13	12c lilac	50.00	3.50
78	A13	24c green	60.00	5.00
79	A13	48c red brown	75.00	17.50
80	A13	96c bister	475.00	250.00
		Nos. 72-80 (9)	962.50	295.90

See Nos. 107-111. For surcharges see Nos. 93-95, 98-101.

Stamps Surcharged by Brush-like Pen Lines

Surcharge Types:
Type a - Two horiz. lines.
Type b - Two lines, one horiz., one vert.
Type c - Three lines, two horiz., one vert.
Type d - One horiz. line.

On Nos. 75 and 67

1878 **Perf. 10, 14**

82	A13(a)	(1c) on 6c choc	37.50	32.50
83	A12(b)	(1c) on 6c blue	140.00	65.00
84	A13(b)	(1c) on 6c choc	175.00	85.00

On Nos. O3, O8-O10

85	A13(c)	(1c) on 4c ultra	175.00	85.00
a.		Type b		2,500.
86	A13(c)	(1c) on 6c choc	200.00	80.00
87	A5(c)	(2c) on 8c rose	750.00	175.00
88A	A13(b)	(2c) on 8c rose	250.00	90.00

On Nos. O1, O3, O6-O7

89	A5(d)	(1c) on 1c blk	150.00	75.00
89A	A5(d)	(2c) on 8c rose		—
90	A13(d)	(1c) on 1c sl	125.00	50.00
91	A13(d)	(2c) on 2c org	250.00	60.00

The provisional values of Nos. 82 to 91 were established by various official decrees. The horizontal lines crossed out the old value, "OFFICIAL," or both.

Nos. 69 and 80 Surcharged with New Values in Black

No. 92 No. 93
No. 94 No. 95

1881

92	A12	1c on 48c red	32.50	5.00
93	A13	1c on 96c bister	4.25	5.00
94	A13	2c on 96c bister	4.25	8.50
95	A13	2c on 96c bister	45.00	50.00
		Nos. 92-95 (4)	86.00	68.50

Unissued Official Stamps Surcharged with New Values

A24 No. 96

No. 97 Nos. 99, 101

No. 102

1881

96	A13	1c on 12c lilac	100.00	65.00
97	A13	1c on 48c red brn	110.00	90.00
98	A24	2c on 12c lilac	275.00	200.00
99	A13	2c on 12c lilac	60.00	25.00
a.		"2" inverted	700.00	475.00
b.		"2" double		
100	A24	2c on 24c green	575.00	575.00
101	A13	2c on 24c green	70.00	35.00
c.		"2" inverted		—
d.		Double surcharge		750.00
102	A13	2c on 24c green	200.00	125.00

A27

Typeset

ONE AND TWO CENTS.
Type I - Ship with three masts.
Type II - Brig with two masts.

"SPECIMEN"
Perforated Diagonally across Stamp

1882 Unwmk. Perf. 12

103	A27	1c black, *lil rose*, I	35.00	30.00
a.		Without "Specimen"	325.00	275.00
104	A27	1c black, *lil rose*, II	35.00	30.00
a.		Without "Specimen"	325.00	275.00
105	A27	2c black, *yel*, I	50.00	40.00
a.		Without "Specimen"	325.00	325.00
b.		Diagonal half used as 1c on cover		
106	A27	2c black, *yel*, II	50.00	42.50
a.		Without "Specimen"	325.00	325.00

Nos. 103-106 were typeset, 12 to a sheet, and, to prevent fraud on the government, the word "*Specimen*" was perforated across them before they were issued. There were 2 settings of the 1c and 3 settings of the 2c, thus there are 24 types of the former and 36 of the latter.

Type of 1876

1882 Typo. Wmk. 2 Perf. 14

107	A13	1c slate	7.00	.35
108	A13	2c orange	20.00	.45
a.		"2 CENTS" double		
109	A13	4c ultra	80.00	7.00
110	A13	6c brown	6.00	8.00
111	A13	8c rose	80.00	1.40
		Nos. 107-111 (5)	193.00	17.20

A28 A29

4 CENTS and $4
Type I - Figure "4" is 3mm high.
Type II - Figure "4" is 3½mm high.
6 CENTS
Type I - Top of "6" is flat.
Type II - Top of "6" turns downward.

"INLAND REVENUE" Overprint and Surcharged in Black

1889

112	A28	1c lilac	1.65	.70
113	A28	2c lilac	1.40	.45
114	A28	3c lilac	1.00	.45
115	A28	4c lilac, I	3.00	.45
116	A28	4c lilac, II	21.00	14.00
117	A28	4c lilac, II	20.00	5.00
118	A28	6c lilac, II	3.00	3.00
119	A28	8c lilac	1.75	.80
120	A28	10c lilac	6.00	2.00
121	A28	20c lilac	16.00	10.00
122	A28	40c lilac	20.00	15.00
123	A28	72c lilac	32.50	32.50
124	A28	$1 green	400.00	400.00
125	A28	$2 green	150.00	175.00
126	A28	$3 green	110.00	110.00
127	A28	$4 green, I	300.00	300.00
127A	A28	$4 green, II	900.00	900.00
128	A28	$5 green	225.00	200.00
		Nos. 112-128 (18)	2,212.	2,169.

For surcharges see Nos. 129, 148-151B.

No. 113 Surcharged "2" in Red

1889

129	A29	2c on 2c lilac	.80	.40

Inverted and double surcharges of "2" were privately made.

A30 A31

1889-1903 Typo.

130	A30	1c lilac & gray	1.75	1.00
131	A30	1c green ('90)	.50	.20
131A	A30	1c gray grn ('00)	3.25	1.75
132	A30	2c lilac & org	1.50	.15
133	A30	2c lil & rose ('00)	3.25	.25
134	A30	2c vio & blk, *red* ('01)	1.10	.90

135	A30	4c lilac & ultra	4.00	1.25
a.		4c lilac & blue	12.00	2.00
136	A30	5c ultra ('91)	2.75	.25
137	A30	6c lilac & mar	6.00	6.00
a.		6c lilac & brown	30.00	8.50
138	A30	6c gray blk & ultra ('02)	6.00	10.00
139	A30	6c lilac & rose	8.00	.75
140	A30	8c lil & blk ('90)	3.00	2.25
141	A30	12c lilac & vio	8.00	1.75
142	A30	24c lilac & grn	7.00	2.25
143	A30	48c lilac & ver	15.00	8.50
144	A30	48c dk gray & lil brn ('01)	27.50	27.50
a.		48c gray & purple brown	50.00	35.00
145	A30	60c gray grn & car ('03)	60.00	65.00
146	A30	72c lil & org brn	25.00	30.00
a.		72c lilac & yellow brown	70.00	75.00
147	A30	96c lilac & carmine	70.00	75.00
a.		96c lilac & rose	75.00	80.00
		Nos. 130-147 (19)	253.60	234.75

Stamps of the 1889-1903 issue with pen or revenue cancellation sell for a small fraction of the above quotations.
See Nos. 160-177.

Red Surcharge

1890

148	A31	1c on $1 grn & blk	1.00	.40
a.		Double surcharge	80.00	80.00
149	A31	1c on $2 grn & blk	.55	.55
a.		Double surcharge	80.00	80.00
150	A31	1c on $3 grn & blk	1.50	1.25
a.		Double surcharge	90.00	90.00
151	A31	1c on $4 grn & blk, type I	2.00	5.00
a.		Double surcharge		80.00
151B	A31	1c on $4 grn & blk, type II	10.00	22.50
c.		Double surcharge		
		Nos. 148-151B (5)	15.05	29.70

Mt. Roraima — A32

Kaieteur (Old Man's) Falls — A33

1898 Wmk. 1 Engr.

152	A32	1c car & gray blk	2.75	.90
153	A33	2c indigo & brn	6.00	1.00
a.		Horiz. pair, imperf. between		4,500.
b.		2c blue & brown	15.00	1.50
154	A32	5c brown & grn	25.00	5.00
155	A33	10c red & blue blk	14.00	20.00
156	A32	15c blue & red brn	22.50	15.00
		Nos. 152-156 (5)	70.25	41.90

60th anniv. of Queen Victoria's accession to the throne.

Nos. 154-156 Surcharged in Black TWO CENTS.

1899

157	A32	2c on 5c brn & grn	2.00	1.65
a.		Without period	60.00	60.00
158	A33	2c on 10c red & bl black	1.00	1.50
a.		"GENTS"	55.00	75.00
b.		Inverted surcharge	300.00	350.00
c.		Without period	22.50	45.00
159	A32	2c on 15c bl & red brown	1.50	1.50
a.		Without period	50.00	50.00
b.		Double surcharge	425.00	525.00
c.		Inverted surcharge	300.00	350.00
		Nos. 157-159 (3)	4.50	4.65

There are many slight errors in the setting of this surcharge, such as: small "E" in "CENTS"; no period and narrow "C"; comma between "T" and "S"; dash between "TWO" and "CENTS"; comma between "N" and "T."

Ship Type of 1889-1903

1905-10 Wmk. 3

Chalky Paper

160	A30	1c gray green	1.50	.30
a.		1c blue green, ordinary paper ('10)	3.50	1.50
b.		Booklet pane of 6		
161	A30	2c vio & blk, *red*	2.50	.20
162	A30	4c lilac & ultra	12.00	8.50
163	A30	5c lil & blue, *bl*	7.75	3.75
164	A30	6c gray black & ultra	14.00	20.00
165	A30	12c lilac & vio	17.50	27.50
166	A30	24c gray & brn ('06)	3.50	4.25
167	A30	48c gray & vio brn	11.00	17.50

168	A30	60c gray grn & car rose	12.50	55.00
169	A30	72c lil & org brn ('07)	32.50	60.00
170	A30	96c blk & red, yel ('06)	35.00	42.50
		Nos. 160-170 (11)	149.75	239.50

The 2c-60c exist on ordinary paper.

A34

George V — A35

Black Overprint

171	A34	$2.40 grn & vio	190.00	190.00

Ship Type of 1889-1903
Ordinary Paper

TWO CENTS

Type I - Only the upper right corner of the flag touches the mast.

Type II - The entire right side of the flag touches the mast.

1907

172	A30	2c red, type I	3.75	.30
b.		2c red, type II	1.00	.25
174	A30	4c brown & vio	3.25	1.65
175	A30	5c blue	5.00	.70
176	A30	6c gray & black	12.50	5.00
177	A30	12c orange & vio	5.50	5.00
		Nos. 172-177 (5)	30.00	12.65

1913-16   **Perf. 14**

178	A35	1c green	1.75	.20
179	A35	2c scarlet	.85	.20
a.		2c carmine	.65	.20
180	A35	4c brn & red vio	1.10	.40
181	A35	5c ultra	1.10	.45
182	A35	6c gray & black	1.10	.95
183	A35	12c org & vio	1.50	1.50

Chalky Paper

184	A35	24c dl vio & grn	2.50	2.50
185	A35	48c blk & vio brn	6.00	6.00
186	A35	60c grn & car	13.00	19.00
187	A35	72c dl vio & org brn	24.00	30.00

Surface Colored Paper

188	A35	96c blk & red, yel	24.00	30.00

Paper Colored Through

189	A35	96c blk & red, yel ('16)	17.00	21.00
		Nos. 178-189 (12)	93.90	112.20

The 72c and late printings of the 2c and 5c are from redrawn dies. The ruled lines behind the value are thin and faint, making the tablet appear lighter than before. The shading lines in other parts of the stamps are also lighter.

1921-27   **Wmk. 4**

191	A35	1c green	1.75	.25
192	A35	2c rose red	1.50	.20
193	A35	2c dp vio ('23)	.90	.15
194	A35	4c brn & vio	2.00	.15
195	A35	6c ultra	1.60	.25
196	A35	12c org & vio	1.65	1.40

Chalky Paper

197	A35	24c dl vio & grn	2.75	2.75
198	A35	48c blk & vio brn ('26)	7.50	2.75
199	A35	60c grn & car ('26)	7.50	25.00
200	A35	72c dl vio & brn org	9.00	22.50
201	A35	96c blk & red, yel ('27)	12.50	20.00
		Nos. 191-201 (11)	48.65	75.40

Plowing a Rice Field — A36   Indian Shooting Fish — A37

Kaieteur Falls — A38   Georgetown, Public Buildings — A39

1931, July 21   **Engr.**   **Perf. 12½**

205	A36	1c blue green	1.25	.50
206	A37	2c dk brown	1.25	.45
207	A38	4c car rose	2.75	1.75
208	A39	6c ultra	2.25	2.50
209	A38	$1 violet	24.00	30.00
		Nos. 205-209 (5)	31.50	35.20

Cent. of the union of Berbice, Demerara and Essequibo to form the Colony of British Guiana.

A40

A41

Gold Mining — A42

Shooting Logs over Falls — A44

Kaieteur Falls — A43

Stabroek Market — A45

Sugar Cane in Punts — A46

Forest Road — A47

Victoria Regia Lilies — A48

Mt. Roraima — A49   Sir Walter Raleigh and Son — A50

Botanical Gardens — A51

1934, Oct. 1   **Perf. 12½**

210	A40	1c green	.40	.25
211	A41	2c brown	.75	.20
212	A42	3c carmine	.30	.15
b.		Perf. 12½x13½ ('43)	.30	.15
c.		Perf. 13x13½ ('49)	.30	.15
213	A43	4c vio black	1.50	.50
a.		Vert. pair, imperf. horiz.	—	8,000.
214	A44	6c dp ultra	2.00	1.75
215	A45	12c orange	.15	.20
a.		Perf. 13½x13 ('51)	.20	.40
216	A46	24c rose violet	3.00	1.75
217	A47	48c black	10.50	9.25

218	A43	50c green	12.00	15.00
219	A48	60c brown	21.00	24.00
220	A49	72c rose violet	1.25	1.00
221	A50	96c black	20.00	25.00
222	A51	$1 violet	25.00	22.50
		Nos. 210-222 (13)	97.85	101.55

See Nos. 236, 238, 240.

Common Design Types pictured following the introduction.

Silver Jubilee Issue
Common Design Type

1935, May 6   **Perf. 13½x14**

223	CD301	2c gray blk & ultra	.20	.20
224	CD301	6c blue & brown	.85	.40
225	CD301	12c indigo & grn	1.40	1.00
226	CD301	24c brt vio & ind	3.25	3.25
		Nos. 223-226 (4)	5.70	4.85

Coronation Issue
Common Design Type

1937, May 12   **Perf. 13½x14**

227	CD302	2c brown	.15	.15
228	CD302	4c gray black	.15	.15
229	CD302	6c bright ultra	.20	.20
		Nos. 227-229 (3)	.50	.50

A52

A53

A54

A56

A55

A57

A58

Victoria Regia Lilies and Jacanas — A59

1938-52   **Engr.**   **Wmk. 4**   **Perf. 12½**

230	A52	1c green	.20	.15
b.		Perf. 14x13 ('49)	.20	.45
231	A53	2c violet blk, perf. 13x14 ('49)	.20	.15
b.		Perf. 12½	.45	.15
232	A54	4c black & rose, perf. 13x14 ('52)	.35	.15
a.		Perf. 12½	.55	.15
c.		Vert. pair, imperf. between	6,500.	6,000.
233	A55	6c deep ultra, perf. 13x14 ('49)	.20	.15
a.		Perf. 12½	.30	.15
234	A56	24c deep green	.95	.15
a.		Wmk. upright	20.00	8.75
235	A53	36c purple	1.40	.15
a.		Perf. 13x14 ('51)	1.90	.25
236	A47	48c orange yel	.45	.35
a.		Perf. 14x13 ('51)	1.10	1.10
237	A57	60c brown	8.50	3.00
238	A50	96c brown vio	1.90	2.25
a.		Perf. 12½x13½ ('44)	3.00	3.50
239	A58	$1 deep violet	7.75	.30
a.		Perf. 14x13 ('51)	200.00	300.00
240	A49	$2 rose vio ('45)	3.25	11.00
a.		Perf. 14x13 ('50)	6.00	11.00

241	A59	$3 orange brn ('45)	19.00	21.00
a.		Perf. 14x13 ('52)	17.50	37.50
		Nos. 230-241 (12)	44.15	38.80

The watermark on No. 234 is sideways.

Catalogue values for unused stamps in this section, from this point to the end of the section, are for Never Hinged items.

Peace Issue
Common Design Type

1946, Oct. 21   **Perf. 13½x14**

242	CD303	3c carmine	.15	.15
243	CD303	6c deep blue	.15	.15
		Set value	.25	.25

Silver Wedding Issue
Common Design Types

1948, Dec. 20   **Photo.**   **Perf. 14x14½**

244	CD304	3c scarlet	.15	.15

Engr.

Perf. 11½x11

245	CD305	$3 orange brown	11.00	17.00

UPU Issue
Common Design Types
Engr.; Name Typo. on 6c and 12c
Perf. 13½, 11x11½

1949, Oct. 10   **Wmk. 4**

246	CD306	4c rose carmine	.35	.15
247	CD307	6c indigo	.55	.55
248	CD308	12c orange	.70	.70
249	CD309	24c blue green	1.40	1.40
		Nos. 246-249 (4)	3.00	2.80

University Issue
Common Design Types

1951, Feb. 16   **Engr.**   **Perf. 14x14½**

250	CD310	3c carmine & black	.30	.20
251	CD311	6c dp ultra & black	.40	.40

Coronation Issue
Common Design Type

1953, June 2   **Perf. 13½x13**

252	CD312	4c carmine & black	.20	.15

G. P. O., Georgetown — A60   Indian Shooting Fish — A61

Designs: 2c, Botanical gardens. 3c, Victoria regia lilies and jacanas. 5c, Map. 6c, Rice combine. 8c, Sugar cane entering factory. 12c, Felling greenheart tree. 24c, Bauxite mining. 36c, Mt. Roraima. 48c, Kaieteur Falls. 72c, Arapaima (fish). $1, Toucan. $2, Dredging gold. $5, Coat of Arms.

Engr., Center Litho. on $1
Perf. 12½x13, 13

1954, Dec. 1   **Wmk. 4**

253	A60	1c black	.15	.15
254	A60	2c dark green	.15	.15
255	A60	3c red brn & ol	2.50	.15
256	A61	4c violet	.15	.15
257	A60	5c black & red	.25	.15
258	A60	6c yellow green	.15	.15
259	A60	8c ultramarine	.15	.15
260	A61	12c brown & black	.50	.30
261	A60	24c orange & black	3.50	.45
262	A60	36c black & rose	1.25	.45
263	A61	48c red brn & ultra	.60	.35
264	A61	72c emerald & rose	9.50	2.00
265	A60	$1 blk, yel, grn & sal	10.00	1.90
266	A60	$2 magenta	10.00	3.25
267	A61	$5 black & ultra	10.50	12.00
		Nos. 253-267 (15)	49.35	21.45

See Nos. 279-287.

Clasped Hands — A62

Perf. 14½x14

1961, Oct. 23	**Photo.**	**Wmk. 314**
268 A62	5c sal pink & brown	.15 .15
269 A62	6c lt blue grn & brown	.15 .15
270 A62	30c lt orange & brown	.40 .40
	Nos. 268-270 (3)	.70 .70

Fourth annual History and Culture Week.

Freedom from Hunger Issue
Common Design Type

1963, June 4		**Perf. 14x14½**
271 CD314	20c lilac	.45 .45

Red Cross Centenary Issue
Common Design Type

	Wmk. 314		
1963, Sept. 2	**Litho.**		**Perf. 13**
272 CD315	5c black & red		.15 .15
273 CD315	20c ultra & red		.65 .65

Queen Types of 1954
Engr.; Center Litho. on $1
Perf. 12½x13, 13

1963-65		**Wmk. 314**	
279 A60	3c red brn & ol ('65)	4.75	4.75
280 A60	5c black & red ('64)	.15	.15
281 A61	12c brown & blk ('64)	.15	.15
282 A60	24c orange & black	1.50	.15
283 A60	36c black & rose	.50	.15
284 A61	48c red brn & ultra	1.00	2.00
285 A61	72c emerald & rose	3.25	16.00
286 A60	$1 blk, yel, grn & sal	5.75	.75
287 A60	$2 magenta	6.25	12.50
	Nos. 279-287 (9)	23.30	36.60

Weight Lifter
A63

1964, Oct. 1	**Photo.**	**Perf. 13x13½**
290 A63	5c orange	.15 .15
291 A63	8c blue	.15 .15
292 A63	25c carmine rose	.40 .40
	Nos. 290-292 (3)	.70 .70

18th Olympic Games, Tokyo, Oct. 10-25.

ITU Issue
Common Design Type
Perf. 11x11½

1965, May 17	**Litho.**	**Wmk. 314**
293 CD317	5c emerald & olive	.15 .15
294 CD317	25c lt blue & brt pink	.45 .45

Intl. Cooperation Year Issue
Common Design Type

1965, Oct. 25	**Wmk. 314**	**Perf. 14½**
295 CD318	5c blue grn & claret	.15 .15
296 CD318	25c lt vio & green	.50 .50

Winston Churchill and St. George's Cathedral, Georgetown
A64

1966, Jan. 24	**Photo.**	**Perf. 14x14½**
297 A64	5c multicolored	.15 .15
298 A64	25c dp blue, blk & gold	.60 .50

Sir Winston Leonard Spencer Churchill (1874-1965), statesman and WWII leader.

Royal Visit Issue
Common Design Type

1966, Feb. 4	**Litho.**	**Perf. 11x12**
299 CD320	3c violet blue	.25 .20
300 CD320	25c dark car rose	1.40 1.10

POSTAGE DUE STAMPS

Catalogue values for unused stamps in this section are for Never Hinged items.

D1

Perf. 13½x14

1940-52	**Typo.**		**Wmk. 4**
J1	D1 1c green	1.25	1.25
a.	Wmk. 4a (error)	40.00	
J2	D1 2c black	1.25	1.25
a.	Wmk. 4a (error)	35.00	
J3	D1 4c ultra ('52)	.80	1.50
a.	Wmk. 4a (error)	35.00	
J4	D1 12c carmine	3.50	7.50
	Nos. J1-J4 (4)	6.80	11.50

The 2c and 12c are on chalky paper as well as ordinary paper.

WAR TAX STAMP

War Tax

Regular Issue No. 179 Overprinted

1918, Jan. 4	**Wmk. 3**	**Perf. 14**
MR1 A35	2c scarlet	.15 .15

OFFICIAL STAMPS

Counterfeit overprints exist.

No. 50 Overprinted in Red **OFFICIAL**

1875	**Unwmk.**	**Perf. 10**
O1 A5	1c black	40.00 16.00
a.	Horiz. pair, imperf btwn.	

Nos. 51, 53-54, 68 Overprinted in Black **OFFICIAL**

O2 A5	2c orange	140.00	16.00
O3 A5	3c blue	375.00	125.00
O4 A5	12c lilac	1,400.	550.00
O5 A12	24c green	850.00	275.00

For surcharges see Nos. 87, 89, 89A, 96, 102.

Nos. 72-76 Overprinted "OFFICIAL" Similar to #O2-O5

1877	**Wmk. 1**		**Perf. 14**
O6 A13	1c slate	225.00	95.00
a.	Vert. pair, imperf btwn.		
O7 A13	2c orange	90.00	16.00
O8 A13	4c ultramarine	100.00	35.00
O9 A13	6c chocolate	2,750.	625.00
O10 A13	8c rose	2,250.	500.00

The type A13 12c lilac, 24c green and 48c red brown overprinted "OFFICIAL" were never placed in use. A few copies of the 12c and 24c have been seen but the 48c is only known surcharged with new value for provisional use in 1881. See Nos. 97-101.

For surcharges see Nos. 85-86, 88A, 90-91.

BRITISH HONDURAS

ˈbri-tish hän-ˈdúr-əs

LOCATION — Central America bordering on Caribbean on east, Mexico on north and Guatemala on west.
GOVT. — British Crown Colony
AREA — 8,867 sq. mi.
POP. — 130,000 (est. 1972)
CAPITAL — Belmopan

Before British Honduras became a colony (subordinate to Jamaica) in 1862, it was a settlement under British influence. In 1884

British Honduras stamps can be mounted in the Scott British North and West Caribbean album.

it became an independent colony. In 1973 the colony changed its name to Belize.

12 Pence = 1 Shilling
100 Cents = 1 Dollar (1888)

Catalogue values for unused stamps in this country are for Never Hinged items, beginning with Scott 127 in the regular postage section, Scott J1 in the postage due section.

Values for unused stamps are for examples with original gum as defined in the catalogue introduction. Very fine examples of Nos. 1-37 will have perforations touching the design on at least one side due to the narrow spacing of the stamps on the plates. Stamps with perfs clear of the design on all four sides are extremely scarce and will command higher prices.

Queen Victoria — A1

1866	**Unwmk.**	**Typo.**	**Perf. 14**
1 A1	1p blue	50.00	50.00
a.	Horiz. pair, imperf. btwn.		
2 A1	6p rose	250.00	100.00
3 A1	1sh green	225.00	100.00

The 6p and 1sh were printed only in a sheet with the 1p. The 1sh is known in se-tenant gutter pairs with the 1p and the 6p.

1872	**Wmk. 1**		**Perf. 12½**
4 A1	1p blue	60.00	18.00
5 A1	3p brown	100.00	70.00
6 A1	6p rose	190.00	30.00
7 A1	1sh green	225.00	22.50
a.	Horiz. pair, imperf. btwn.		12,500.

For surcharges see Nos. 18-19.
No. 7a is unique and has faults.

1877-79			**Perf. 14**
8 A1	1p blue	50.00	14.00
a.	Horiz. strip of 3, imperf. btwn.		4,500.
9 A1	3p brown	85.00	17.50
10 A1	4p violet ('79)	125.00	12.50
11 A1	6p rose ('78)	300.00	175.00
12 A1	1sh green	225.00	12.50

For surcharges see Nos. 20-21, 29.

1882-87			**Wmk. 2**
13 A1	1p blue ('84)	40.00	18.00
14 A1	1p rose ('84)	20.00	12.50
a.	Diagonal half used as ½p on cover		
15 A1	4p violet	70.00	4.00
16 A1	6p yellow ('85)	250.00	175.00
17 A1	1sh gray ('87)	225.00	135.00

For surcharges see Nos. 22-26, 28-35.

Stamps of 1872-87 Surcharged in Black **2 CENTS**

1888	**Wmk. 1**		**Perf. 12½**
18 A1	2c on 6p rose	120.00	100.00
19 A1	3c on 3p brown	10,000.	5,250.
	Perf. 14		
20 A1	2c on 6p rose	70.00	65.00
a.	Diagonal half used as 1c on cover		225.00
b.	Double surcharge	1,300.	1,300.
c.	"2" with curved tail	850.00	850.00
21 A1	3c on 3p brown	60.00	55.00
	Wmk. 2		
22 A1	2c on 1p rose	9.00	17.50
a.	Diagonal half used as 1c on cover		250.00
b.	Double surcharge	1,000.	950.00
c.	Inverted surcharge	1,300.	1,250.
23 A1	10c on 4p violet	35.00	15.00
a.	Inverted surcharge		250.00
24 A1	20c on 6p yellow	27.50	30.00
25 A1	50c on 1sh gray	350.00	500.00

No. 25 with Additional Surcharge in Red or Black **TWO**

26 A1	2c (R) on 50c on 1sh gray	40.00	75.00
a.	"TWO" in black	8,750.	8,500.
b.	"TWO" double (Blk + R)	8,750.	8,000.
c.	Diagonal half used as 1c on cover		325.00

Stamps of 1872-87 Surcharged in Black **2 CENTS**

c

1888-89			
28 A1	2c on 1p rose	.50	1.25
a.	Diagonal half used as 1c on cover		110.00
29 A1	3c on 3p brown	1.25	1.50
30 A1	10c on 4p violet	2.50	1.75
31 A1	20c on 6p yel ('89)	10.00	15.00
32 A1	50c on 1sh gray	20.00	50.00
	Nos. 28-32 (5)	34.25	68.00

For other examples of this surcharge see Nos. 36, 47. For overprint see No. 51.

No. 30 with Additional Surcharge in Black or Red **6**

1891			
33 A1	6c (Blk) on 10c on 4p	1.00	3.75
a.	"6" and bar inverted	3,000.	900.
b.	"6" only inverted		3,000.
34 A1	6c (R) on 10c on 4p	.75	2.50
a.	"6" and bar inverted	500.00	500.
b.	"6" only inverted		3,000.

Stamps similar to No. 33 but with "SIX" instead of "6," both with and without bar, were prepared but not regularly issued.
See No. 37.

No. 29 with Additional Surcharge in Black **FIVE**

1891			
35 A1	5c on 3c on 3p brown	1.50	3.25
a.	Double surcharge of "Five" and bar	200.00	250.00

Black Surcharge, Type "c"

36 A1	6c on 3p blue	1.50	7.50

No. 36 with Additional Surcharge like Nos. 33-34 in Red

1891			
37 A1	15c (R) on 6c on 3p blue	7.50	20.00
a.	Double surcharge		

A8   A9

1891-98	**Wmk. 2**		**Perf. 14**
38 A8	1c green	1.00	1.00
39 A8	2c carmine rose	1.00	.20
40 A8	3c brown	3.75	1.50
41 A8	5c ultra ('95)	12.50	.90
42 A8	6c ultramarine	3.50	1.00
43 A8	10c vio & grn ('95)	8.50	8.50
44 A8	12c vio & green	3.50	2.50
45 A8	24c yellow & blue	6.00	12.50
46 A8	25c red brn & grn ('98)	30.00	60.00
	Nos. 38-46 (9)	69.75	88.15

Numeral tablet on Nos. 43-46 has lined background with colorless value and "c." For overprints see Nos. 48-50.

Type of 1866 Surcharged Type "c"

1892			
47 A1	1c on 1p green	.30 .80	

Regular Issue Overprinted **REVENUE** in Black

1899			
48 A8	5c ultramarine	4.50	2.25
a.	"BEVENUE"	70.00	80.00
49 A8	10c lilac & green	3.50	11.00
a.	"BEVENUE"	190.00	225.00
50 A8	25c red brn & grn	3.00	25.00
a.	"BEVENUE"	135.00	135.00
51 A1	50c on 1sh gray (No. 32)	135.00	275.00
a.	"BEVENUE"	2,750.	2,750.
	Nos. 48-51 (4)	146.00	313.25

The overprint is found in two lengths: 12mm (43 to the pane) and 11mm (17 to the pane). The "U" is found in both a tall, narrow type and the more common small type.

1899-1901			
52 A9	5c gray blk & ultra, bl ('00)	7.50	1.50
53 A9	10c vio & grn ('01)	6.50	6.50
54 A9	50c grn & car rose	16.00	37.50
55 A9	$1 grn & car rose	35.00	60.00

56	A9	$2 green & ultra	55.00	75.00
57	A9	$5 green & black	240.00	275.00
		Nos. 52-57 (6)	360.00	455.50

Numeral tablet on Nos. 53-54 has lined background with colorless value and "c."

King Edward VII — A10

1902-04 Typo. Wmk. 2

58	A10	1c gray grn & grn ('04)	4.00	12.50
59	A10	2c vio & blk, red	2.00	.35
60	A10	5c gray blk & ultra, blue	3.00	.80
61	A10	20c dl vio & vio ('04)	5.00	12.00
		Nos. 58-61 (4)	14.00	25.65

1904-06 Chalky Paper Wmk. 3

62	A10	1c green	.30	.50
63	A10	2c vio & blk, red	1.25	.15
64	A10	5c blk & ultra, bl ('05)	1.75	.30
65	A10	10c vio & grn ('06)	4.00	9.00
66	A10	25c vio & org ('06)	6.00	25.00
67	A10	50c grn & car rose ('06)	10.00	35.00
68	A10	$1 grn & car rose ('06)	25.00	50.00
69	A10	$2 grn & ultra ('06)	55.00	100.00
70	A10	$5 grn & blk ('06)	190.00	225.00
71	A10	Nos. 62-71 (9)	293.30	444.95

The 1c and 2c exist also on ordinary paper.

1909 Ordinary Paper

72	A10	2c carmine	3.00	.25
73	A10	5c ultramarine	3.00	.25

1911

74	A10	25c black, green	6.00	27.50

Numeral tablet on #61, 65-68, 74 has lined background with colorless value and "c."

King George V
A11   A12

1913-17 Wmk. 3 Perf. 14

75	A11	1c green	1.00	.40
76	A11	2c scarlet	1.10	.30
a.		2c carmine	.90	.95
77	A11	3c orange ('17)	.45	.20
78	A11	5c ultra	2.25	1.25

Chalky Paper

79	A12	10c dl vio & ol grn	2.50	5.00
80	A12	25c blk, gray grn	3.75	3.75
a.		25c black, emerald	2.50	12.50
b.		25c blk, bl grn, olive bara	3.25	6.00
81	A12	50c vio & ultra, bl	4.50	9.00
82	A11	$1 black & scar	8.00	17.50
83	A11	$2 grn & dull vio	32.50	37.50
84	A11	$5 vio & blk, red	225.00	250.00
		Nos. 75-84 (10)	281.05	328.65

See No. 91. For overprints see Nos. MR2-MR5.

With Moire Overprint in Violet

1915

85	A11	1c green	1.50	7.50
86	A11	2c carmine	1.10	2.00
87	A11	5c ultramarine	.75	3.25
		Nos. 85-87 (3)	3.35	12.75

For overprint see No. MR1.

Peace Commemorative Issue

Seal of Colony and
George V — A13

1921, Apr. 28 Engr.

89	A13	2c carmine	2.50 1.00

Similar to A13 but without "Peace Peace"

1922 Wmk. 4

90	A13	4c dark gray	2.75 .95

Type of 1913-17

1921 Typo. Wmk. 4

91	A11	1c green	2.00 5.00

A14

1922-33 Typo. Wmk. 4

92	A14	1c green ('29)	.80	1.10
93	A14	2c dark brown	.35	.20
94	A14	2c rose red ('27)	.85	.70
95	A14	3c orange ('33)	3.50	1.00
96	A14	4c gray ('29)	1.25	.25
97	A14	5c ultramarine	.20	.20

Chalky Paper

98	A14	10c olive grn & lil	1.25	.35
99	A14	25c black, emerald	1.50	4.00
100	A14	50c ultra & vio, bl	4.00	9.00
101	A14	$1 scarlet & blk	6.50	12.50
102	A14	$2 red vio & grn	22.50	50.00

Wmk. 3

103	A14	25c black, emerald	4.25	17.50
104	A14	$5 blk & vio, red	200.00	190.00
		Nos. 92-104 (13)	247.75	286.80

For surcharges see Nos. B1-B5.

Silver Jubilee Issue
Common Design Type
Perf. 11x12

1935, May 6 Engr. Wmk. 4

108	CD301	3c black & ultra	.65	.65
109	CD301	4c indigo & grn	1.10	1.40
110	CD301	5c ultra & brn	2.00	2.00
111	CD301	25c brn vio & ind	4.00	6.00
		Nos. 108-111 (4)	7.75	10.05
		Set, never hinged	12.00	

Coronation Issue
Common Design Type

1937, May 12 Perf. 13½x14

112	CD302	3c deep orange	.15	.20
113	CD302	4c gray black	.25	.20
114	CD302	5c bright ultra	.25	.35
		Nos. 112-114 (3)	.65	.75
		Set, never hinged	1.75	

Mayan
Figures — A15

Mayan
Figures — A15

Chicle Tapping — A16   Cohune Palm — A17

Local Products
A18

Grapefruit
Industry
A19

Mahogany Logs
in River — A20   Sergeant's Cay — A21

Dory — A22

Chicle Industry
A23

Court House,
Belize — A24

Mahogany
Cutting — A25

Seal of Colony — A26

1938 Perf. 11x11½, 11½x11

115	A15	1c green & violet	.15	.70
116	A16	2c car & black	.15	.70
a.		Perf. 12 ('47)	1.10	.75
117	A17	3c brown & dk vio	.20	.50
118	A18	4c green & black	.20	.50
119	A19	5c slate bl & red vio	.35	.50
120	A20	10c brown & yel grn	.45	.50
121	A21	15c blue & brown	.65	.50
122	A22	25c green & ultra	1.10	.85
123	A23	50c dk vio & blk	7.00	2.50
124	A24	$1 ol green & car	12.50	5.25
125	A25	$2 rose lake & ind	14.00	13.00
126	A26	$5 brn & carmine	13.00	19.00
		Nos. 115-126 (12)	49.75	44.30
		Set, never hinged	70.00	

Issued: 3c-5c, 1/10; 1c, 2c, 10c-50c, 2/14; $1-$5, 2/28.

> Catalogue values for unused stamps in this section, from this point to the end of the section, are for Never Hinged items.

Peace Issue
Common Design Type
Perf. 13½x14

1946, Sept. 9 Engr. Wmk. 4

127	CD303	3c brown	.15	.15
128	CD303	5c deep blue	.15	.15
		Set value	.25	.25

Silver Wedding Issue
Common Design Types

1948, Oct. 1 Photo. Perf. 14x14½

129	CD304	4c dark green	.20	.20

Engraved; Name Typographed
Perf. 11½x11

130	CD305	$5 light brown	22.50	25.00

St. George's
Cay — A27

H.M.S.
Merlin — A28

1949, Jan. 10 Engr. Perf. 12½

131	A27	1c green & ultra	.15	.15
132	A27	3c yel brn & dp blue	.20	.20
133	A27	4c purple & brn ol	.30	.30

134	A28	5c dk blue & brown	.30	.30
135	A28	10c vio brn & blue grn	.50	.50
136	A28	15c ultra & emerald	.90	.90
		Nos. 131-136 (6)	2.35	2.35

Battle of St. George's Cay, 150th anniv.

UPU Issue
Common Design Types
Perf. 13½, 11x11½

1949, Oct. 10 Engr. Wmk. 4

137	CD306	4c blue green	.35	.35
138	CD307	5c indigo	.55	.55
139	CD308	10c chocolate	.90	.90
140	CD309	25c blue	1.50	1.50
		Nos. 137-140 (4)	3.30	3.30

University Issue
Common Design Types

1951, Feb. 16 Engr. Perf. 14x14½

141	CD310	3c choc & purple	.35	.35
142	CD311	10c choc & green	.65	.65

Coronation Issue
Common Design Type

1953, June 2 Perf. 13½x13½

143	CD312	4c dk green & black	.40	.40

Arms — A29

Maya — A30

Designs: 2c, Tapir. 3c, Legislative Council Chamber and mace. 4c, Pine industry. 5c, Spiny lobster. 10c, Stanley Field Airport. 15c, Mayan frieze. 25c, Blue butterfly. $1, Armadillo. $2, Hawkesworth Bridge. $5, Pine Ridge orchid.

1953-57 Engr. Perf. 13½

144	A29	1c gray blk & green	.15	.15
145	A29	2c gray blk & brn, perf. 14 ('57)	.15	.15
a.		Perf. 13½	.30	.30
146	A29	3c mag & rose lil, perf. 14 ('57)	.15	.15
a.		Perf. 13½	.15	.15
147	A29	4c grn & dk brn	.15	.15
148	A29	5c car & ol brn, perf. 14 ('57)	.20	.20
a.		Perf. 13½	.45	.45
149	A29	10c ultra & bl gray	.20	.20
150	A29	15c vio & yel grn	.35	.35
151	A29	25c brown & ultra	3.50	1.75
152	A30	50c purple & brown	4.00	1.65
153	A29	$1 red brn & sl bl	4.00	3.50
154	A29	$2 gray & car	5.50	4.00
155	A30	$5 blue gray & pur	25.00	15.00
		Nos. 144-155 (12)	43.35	27.25

Issue dates: No. 148, May 15, Nos. 145-146, Sept. 18, perf. 13½, Sept. 2.
For overprints see Nos. 159-166.

View of Belize,
1842 — A31

Designs: 10c, Public seals, 1860 and 1960. 15c, Tamarind Tree, Newtown Barracks.

Perf. 11½x11

1960, July 1 Wmk. 314

156	A31	2c green	.15	.15
157	A31	10c carmine	.25	.25
158	A31	15c blue	.45	.45
		Nos. 156-158 (3)	.85	.85

Cent. of the establishment of a local PO.

Nos. 145-146 and 149-150 Overprinted:
"NEW CONSTITUTION/1960"

1961, Mar. 1 Wmk. 4 Perf. 14, 13

159	A29	2c gray black & brn	.15	.15
160	A29	3c mag & rose lilac	.15	.15
161	A29	10c ultra & blue gray	.35	.25
162	A29	15c violet & yel green	.50	.30
		Nos. 159-162 (4)	1.15	.85

Nos. 144, 149, 151 and 152 Overprinted: "HURRICANE/HATTIE"

1962, Jan. 15		Perf. 13	
163 A29	1c gray black & green	.15	.15
164 A29	10c ultra & blue gray	.15	.15
165 A29	25c brown & ultra	.30	.30
166 A30	50c purple & brown	.70	.70
	Nos. 163-166 (4)	1.30	1.30

Hurricane Hattie struck Belize, Oct. 31, 1961.

Great Curassow A32

Birds: 2c, Red-legged honeycreeper. 3c, American jacana. 4c, Great kiskadee. 5c, Scarlet-rumped tanager. 10c, Scarlet macaw. 15c, Massena trogon. 25c, Redfooted booby. 50c, Keel-billed toucan. $1, Magnificent frigate bird. $2, Rufoustailed jacamar. $5, Montezuma oropendola.

Perf. 14x14½

1962, Apr. 2		Photo.	Wmk. 314	
Birds in Natural Colors; Black Inscriptions				
167 A32	1c yellow		.90	.70
168 A32	2c gray		1.40	.15
a.	Green omitted		175.00	
169 A32	3c lt yel green		1.40	.85
a.	Dark grn (legs) omitted		250.00	
170 A32	4c lt gray		2.75	1.25
171 A32	5c buff		1.65	.15
172 A32	10c beige		1.90	.20
a.	Blue omitted		225.00	
173 A32	15c pale lemon		.90	.30
174 A32	25c bluish gray & pink		3.50	.25
175 A32	50c pale blue		5.00	.35
b.	Blue (beak & claw) omitted			
176 A32	$1 gray		7.75	.70
177 A32	$2 pale gray		8.25	2.50
178 A32	$5 light blue		24.00	12.50
	Nos. 167-178 (12)		59.40	19.90

For overprints see Nos. 182-186, 195-199.

1967		Wmk. 314 Sideways		
Colors as 1962 Issue				
167a A32	1c		.15	.15
168b A32	2c		.15	.15
170a A32	4c		.30	.25
171a A32	5c		.55	.30
172b A32	10c		.80	.65
173a A32	15c		1.10	.95
175a A32	50c		4.25	3.50
	Nos. 167a-175a (7)		7.30	5.95

Issued: 1c, 4c, 5c, 50c, 2/16; 2c, 10c, 15c, 11/28.

Freedom from Hunger Issue
Common Design Type

1963, June 4		Perf. 14x14½	
179 CD314	22c green	.85	.85

Red Cross Centenary Issue
Common Design Type
Wmk. 314

1963, Sept. 2		Litho.	Perf. 13	
180 CD315	4c black & red		.15	.15
181 CD315	22c ultra & red		1.40	1.40

Nos. 167, 169, 170, 172 and 174 Overprinted: "SELF GOVERNMENT / 1964"

1964		Photo.	Perf. 14x14½	
182 A32	1c multicolored		.15	.15
a.	Yellow omitted		125.00	
183 A32	3c multicolored		.15	.15
184 A32	4c multicolored		.15	.15
185 A32	10c multicolored		.30	.30
186 A32	25c multicolored		.55	.55
	Set value		1.10	1.10

Attainment of self-government.

ITU Issue
Common Design Type
Perf. 11x11½

1965, May 17		Litho.	Wmk. 314	
187 CD317	2c ver & green		.15	.15
188 CD317	50c yel & red lilac		1.00	1.00

Intl. Cooperation Year Issue
Common Design Type

1965, Oct. 25		Perf. 14½	
189 CD318	1c bl grn & claret	.15	.15
190 CD318	22c lt violet & green	.75	.75

Churchill Memorial Issue
Common Design Type

1966, Jan. 24		Photo.	Perf. 14	
Design in Black, Gold and Carmine Rose				
191 CD319	1c bright blue		.15	.15
192 CD319	4c green		.15	.15
193 CD319	22c brown		.65	.65
194 CD319	25c violet		.90	.90
	Nos. 191-194 (4)		1.85	1.85

Bird Type of 1962 Overprinted:
"DEDICATION OF SITE / NEW CAPITAL / 9th OCTOBER 1965"
Wmk. 314 Sideways

1966, July 1		Perf. 14x14½	
195 A32	1c multicolored	.15	.15
196 A32	3c multicolored	.25	.25
197 A32	4c multicolored	.25	.15
198 A32	10c multicolored	.30	.25
199 A32	25c multicolored	.50	.50
	Nos. 195-199 (5)	1.45	
	Set value		.95

Citrus Grove — A33

10c, Half Moon Cay & Lighthouse Reef. 22c, Hidden Valley Falls & Mountain Pine Ridge. 25c, Xunantunich Mayan ruins in Cayo district.

Perf. 14x14½

1966, Oct. 1		Photo.	Wmk. 314	
200 A33	5c multicolored		.15	.15
201 A33	10c multicolored		.20	.20
202 A33	22c multicolored		.25	.25
203 A33	25c multicolored		.40	.40
	Nos. 200-203 (4)		1.00	1.00

1st British Honduras stamp issue, cent.

International Tourist Year — A34

1967, Dec. 4		Perf. 12½	
204 A34	5c Sailfish	.15	.15
205 A34	10c Deer	.15	.15
206 A34	22c Jaguar	.35	.35
207 A34	25c Tarpon	.45	.45
	Nos. 204-207 (4)	1.10	1.10

Schomburgkia Tibicinis — A35

Belizean Patriots' Memorial, Belize City, and Human Rights Flame — A36

Orchids: 10c, Maxillaria tenuifolia. 22c, Bletia purpurea. 25c, Sobralia macrantha.

Inscribed: "20th Anniversary of E.C.L.A."

Perf. 14½x14

1968, Apr. 16		Photo.	Wmk. 314	
208 A35	5c violet & multi		.15	.15
209 A35	10c green & multi		.20	.20
210 A35	22c multicolored		.35	.35
211 A35	25c olive & multi		.50	.50
	Nos. 208-211 (4)		1.20	1.20

20th anniv. of the Economic Commission for Latin America. See #226-229, 255-258.

Perf. 13x13½

1968, July 15		Litho.	Wmk. 314	

Design: 50c, Mayan motif stele, monument at new capital site and Human Rights flame.

212 A36	22c multicolored	.30	.30
213 A36	50c multicolored	.70	.70

International Human Rights Year.

BRITISH HONDURAS Jewfish — A37

Designs: 2c, White-lipped peccary. 3c, Grouper (sea bass). 4c, Collared anteater. 5c, Bonefish. 10c, Paca. 15c, Dolphinfish. 25c, Kinkajou. 50c, Yellow-and-green-banded muttonfish. $1, Tayra. $2, Great barracudas. $5, Mountain lion.

Perf. 13x12½

1968, Oct. 15		Litho.	Unwmk.	
214 A37	1c yellow & multi		.15	.15
215 A37	2c brt yel & multi		.15	.15
216 A37	3c pink & multi		.15	.15
217 A37	4c brt grn & multi		.15	.15
218 A37	5c brick red & multi		.15	.15
219 A37	10c lilac & multi		.20	.15
220 A37	15c org yel & multi		.25	.20
221 A37	25c multicolored		.45	.40
222 A37	50c bl grn & multi		.95	.95
223 A37	$1 ocher & multi		1.90	1.75
224 A37	$2 violet & multi		3.75	3.50
225 A37	$5 ultra & multi		8.25	7.50
	Nos. 214-225 (12)		16.50	15.10

See Nos. 234-240, 327-339.
For overprints see Nos. 251-254, 281-282.

Orchid Type of 1968
Inscribed "Orchids of Belize"

Designs: 5c, Rhyncholaetia digbyana. 10c, Cattleya bowringiana. 22c, Lycaste cochleatum. 25c, Coryanthes speciosum.

Perf. 14½x14

1969, Apr. 9		Photo.	Wmk. 314	
226 A35	5c Prus blue & multi		.15	.15
227 A35	10c olive bis & multi		.30	.30
228 A35	22c yellow grn & multi		.70	.70
229 A35	25c violet blue & multi		.85	.85
	Nos. 226-229 (4)		2.00	2.00

Hardwood Trees — A38

Virgin and Child, by Giovanni Bellini — A39

1969, Sept. 1		Litho.	Perf. 14	
230 A38	5c Ziricote		.15	.15
231 A38	10c Rosewood		.15	.15
232 A38	22c Mayflower		.30	.30
233 A38	25c Mahogany		.40	.40
	Nos. 230-233 (4)		1.00	1.00

Timber industry of British Honduras. Issued in sheets of 9 (3x3) on simulated wood background.

Fish-Animal Type of 1968
Designs: ½c, Crana (fish). Others as before.

Wmk. 314 Sideways (½c, 2c, $5), Upright (3c, 5c, 10c)				
1969-72		Litho.	Perf. 13x12½	
234 A37	½c vio bl, yel & blk		.15	.15
235 A37	½c citron, blk & bl ('71)		.70	1.00
236 A37	2c brt yel, blk & grn ('72)		3.00	3.00
237 A37	3c pink & multi ('72)		1.00	1.65
a.	Wmk. sideways ('72)		3.00	3.00
238 A37	5c brick red & multi ('72)		1.00	1.65
239 A37	10c lilac & multi ('72)		1.00	1.65
a.	Wmk. sideways ('72)		3.50	3.50
240 A37	$5 ultra & multi ('70)		9.00	9.00
	Nos. 234-240 (7)		15.85	18.10

For overprints see Nos. 251-252.

1969, Oct. 1		Litho.	Perf. 14	

Christmas: 22c, 25c, Adoration of the Kings, by Veronese.

247 A39	5c multicolored	.15	.15
248 A39	15c dp orange & multi	.20	.20
249 A39	22c lilac rose & multi	.40	.40
250 A39	25c emerald & multi	.50	.50
	Nos. 247-250 (4)	1.25	1.25

Nos. 238-239 and Type of 1968 Overprinted "POPULATION/ CENSUS 1970"
Wmk. 314 Sideways

1970, Feb. 2		Photo.	Perf. 13x12½	
251 A37	5c brick red & multi		.15	.15
252 A37	10c lilac & multi		.15	.15
253 A37	15c org yel & multi		.25	.25
254 A37	25c multicolored		.40	.40
	Nos. 251-254 (4)		.95	.95

Orchid Type of 1968
Inscribed: "Orchids of Belize"
Wmk. 314

1970, Apr. 2		Litho.	Perf. 14	
255 A35	5c Black		.15	.15
256 A35	15c White butterfly		.35	.35
257 A35	22c Swan		.50	.50
258 A35	25c Butterfly		.60	.60
	Nos. 255-258 (4)		1.60	1.60

Santa Maria Tree and Wood (Calophyllum Brasiliense) — A40

Nativity, by Arthur Hughes — A41

Hardwood Trees and Woods: 15c, Nargusta (terminalia amazonia). 22c, Cedar (cedrela mexicana). 25c, Sapodilla (achras sapota).

1970, Sept. 7		Perf. 14	
259 A40	5c multicolored	.15	.15
260 A40	15c multicolored	.30	.30
261 A40	22c multicolored	.45	.45
262 A40	25c multicolored	.45	.45
	Nos. 259-262 (4)	1.35	1.35

1970, Nov. 2		Perf. 14	

Christmas: 5c, 15c, 50c, Mystic Nativity, by Botticelli.

263 A41	½c black & multi	.15	.15
264 A41	5c brown & multi	.15	.15
265 A41	10c multicolored	.15	.15
266 A41	15c slate bl & multi	.25	.25
267 A41	22c dk green & multi	.40	.40
268 A41	50c black & multi	.85	.85
	Nos. 263-268 (6)	1.95	1.95

Legislative Assembly House A42

Designs: 5c, View of South Side of Belize. 10c, Government Plaza, Belmopan. 22c, Magistrates' Court. 25c, Police Headquarters. 50c, New General Post Office.

1971, Jan. 30		Litho.	Perf. 13½x14	
Size: 59x22mm				
269 A42	5c multicolored		.15	.15
270 A42	10c multicolored		.15	.15
Size: 37x21½mm				
271 A42	15c multicolored		.20	.20
272 A42	22c multicolored		.30	.30
273 A42	25c multicolored		.40	.40
274 A42	50c multicolored		.70	.70
	Nos. 269-274 (6)		1.90	1.90

New capital at Belmopan.

Tabebuia Chrysantha — A43

Flowers: 5c, 22c, Hymenocallis littoralis. 10c, 25c, Hippeastrum equestre. 15c, like ½c.

1971, Mar. 27   Litho.   Perf. 14

275	A43	½c vio blue & multi	.15	.15
276	A43	5c olive & multi	.15	.15
277	A43	10c violet & multi	.20	.20
278	A43	15c multicolored	.30	.30
279	A43	22c multicolored	.45	.45
280	A43	25c lt brown & multi	.55	.55
		Nos. 275-280 (6)	1.80	1.80

Easter.

Type of 1968 Overprinted: "RACIAL
EQUALITY / YEAR—1971"

Perf. 13x12½

1971, June 14   Litho.   Wmk. 314

281	A37	10c lilac & multi	.15	.15
282	A37	50c blue green & multi	.70	.70

Intl. year against racial discrimination.

Tubroos
(Enterolobium
Cyclocarpum)
A44

Hardwood Trees of Belize: 15c, Yemeri (Vochysia hondurensis). 26c, Billyweb (Sweetia panamensis). 50c, Logwood (Haematoxylum campechiaum).

1971, Aug. 16   Perf. 14

Queen's Head in Silver

283	A44	5c green, brn & blk	.15	.15
284	A44	15c multicolored	.50	.50
285	A44	26c multicolored	.85	.85
286	A44	50c multicolored	1.50	1.50
a.		Souvenir sheet of 4, #283-286	5.25	5.25
		Nos. 283-286 (4)	3.00	3.00

Verrazano-Narrows Bridge, New York, and
Quebec Bridge, Canada — A45

Bridges of the World: ½c, Hawksworth Bridge connecting San Ignacio and Santa Helena and Belcan Bridge, Belize, Br. Honduras. 26c, London Bridge in 1871, and at Lake Havasu City, Ariz., in 1971. 50c, Belize-Mexico Bridge and Belize Swing Bridge.

1971, Sept. 23   Litho.

287	A45	½c multicolored	.15	.15
288	A45	5c multicolored	.15	.15
289	A45	26c multicolored	.55	.55
290	A45	50c multicolored	1.10	1.10
		Nos. 287-290 (4)	1.95	1.95

Petrae
Volubis — A46

Seated Jade
Figure — A47

Wild Flowers: 15c, Vochysia hondurensis. 26c, Tabebuia pentaphylla. 50c, Erythrina americana.

1972, Feb. 28

**Flowers in Natural Colors; Black
Inscriptions**

292	A46	6c lilac & yellow	.15	.15
293	A46	15c lt blue & pale grn	.35	.35
294	A46	26c pink & lt blue	.65	.65
295	A46	50c orange & lt grn	1.25	1.25
		Nos. 292-295 (4)	2.40	2.40

Easter.

Perf. 14x13½, 13½x14

1972, May 22   Unwmk.

Mayan Carved Jade, 4th-8th centuries: 6c, Dancing priest. 16c, Sun god's head, horiz. 26c, Priest on throne and sun god's head. 50c, Figure and mask.

296	A47	3c rose red & multi	.15	.15
297	A47	6c vio bl & multi	.15	.15
298	A47	16c brown & multi	.25	.25
299	A47	26c ol grn & multi	.40	.40
300	A47	50c purple & multi	.85	.85
		Nos. 296-300 (5)	1.80	1.80

Black inscription with details of designs on back of stamps.

Banak (Virola
Koschnyi) — A48

Hardwood Trees of Belize: 5c, Quamwood (Schizolobium parahybum). 16c, Waika chewstick (Symphonia globulifera). 26c, Mammee-apple (Mammea americana). 50c, My lady (Aspidosperma megalocarpon).

1972, Aug. 21   Wmk. 314   Perf. 14

Queen's Head in Gold

301	A48	3c brt pink & multi	.15	.15
302	A48	5c gray & multi	.15	.15
303	A48	16c green & multi	.30	.30
304	A48	26c lemon & multi	.50	.50
305	A48	50c lt violet & multi	.90	.90
		Nos. 301-305 (5)	2.00	2.00

Silver Wedding Issue, 1972

Common Design Type

Design: Queen Elizabeth II, Prince Philip and Belize orchids.

1972, Nov. 20   Photo.   Perf. 14x14½

306	CD324	26c slate grn & multi	.40	.40
307	CD324	50c violet & multi	.75	.75

Baron Bliss
Day
A49

Festivals of Belize: 10c, Labor Day boat race. 26c, Carib Settlement Day dance. 50c, Pan American Day parade.

1973, Mar. 9   Litho.   Perf. 14½

308	A49	3c dull blue & black	.15	.15
309	A49	10c red & multi	.15	.15
310	A49	26c ver & multi	.40	.40
311	A49	50c black & multi	.75	.75
		Nos. 308-311 (4)	1.45	1.45

SEMI-POSTAL STAMPS

Regular Issue of 1921-
29 Surcharged in Black
or Red

BELIZE
RELIEF FUND
PLUS
3 CENTS

1932   Wmk. 4   Perf. 14

B1	A14	1c + 1c green	1.50	4.75
B2	A14	2c + 2c rose red	1.50	4.75
B3	A14	3c + 3c orange	2.50	6.25
B4	A14	4c + 4c gray (R)	3.25	9.50
B5	A14	5c + 5c ultra	5.00	16.00
		Nos. B1-B5 (5)	13.75	41.25

The surtax was for a fund to aid sufferers from the destruction of the city of Belize by a hurricane in Sept. 1931.

POSTAGE DUE STAMPS

Catalogue values for unused
stamps in this section are for Never
Hinged items.

D1

1923   Typo.   Wmk. 4   Perf. 14

J1	D1	1c black	.90	5.00
J2	D1	2c black	1.10	4.00
J3	D1	4c black	3.00	10.00
		Nos. J1-J3 (3)	5.00	19.00

Nos. J1-J3 were re-issued on chalky paper in 1956.

Perf. 13½x13, 13½x14

1965-72   Wmk. 314

J4	D1	2c black ('72)	1.50	3.00
J5	D1	4c black	1.00	3.50

WAR TAX STAMPS

Nos. 85, 75 and 77
Overprinted   **WAR**

1916-17   Wmk. 3   Perf. 14

With Moire Overprint

MR1	A11	1c green	.15	.35
a.		"WAR" inverted	250.00	250.00

Without Moire Overprint

MR2	A11	1c green ('17)	.25	.75
MR3	A11	3c orange ('17)	.75	.75
a.		Double overprint	450.00	450.00
		Nos. MR1-MR3 (3)	1.15	1.85

Nos. 75 and 77
Overprinted   **WAR**

1918

MR4	A11	1c green	.15	.25
MR5	A11	3c orange	.20	.50

BRITISH INDIAN OCEAN TERRITORY

'bri-tish 'in-dēən 'ō-chən
'ter-ə-,tōr-ē

LOCATION — Indian Ocean
GOVT. — British Dependency
POP. — 558 (1972)

B.I.O.T. was established Nov. 8, 1965. This island group lies 1,180 miles north of Mauritius. It consisted of Chagos Archipelago (chief island: Diego Garcia), Aldabra, Farquhar and Des Roches Islands until June 23, 1976, when the last three named islands were returned to Seychelles.

100 Cents = 1 Rupee
100 Pence = 1 Pound (1990)

Catalogue values for all unused
stamps in this country are for Never
Hinged items.

Seychelles Nos. 198-202,
204-212 Overprinted   **B.I.O.T.**

Perf. 14½x14, 14x14½

1968, Jan. 17   Photo.   Wmk. 314

Size: 24x31, 31x24mm

1	A17	5c multicolored	.15	.15
2	A17	10c multicolored	.15	.15
3	A17	15c multicolored	.15	.15
4	A17	20c multicolored	.15	.15
5	A17	25c multicolored	.15	.15
6	A18	40c multicolored	.25	.30
7	A18	45c multicolored	.35	.35
8	A17	50c multicolored	.35	.40
9	A17	75c multicolored	.45	.45
10	A18	1r multicolored	1.10	1.25
11	A18	1.50r multicolored	2.00	2.25
12	A18	2.25r multicolored	3.50	3.50

13	A18	3.50r multicolored	5.50	5.50
14	A18	5r multicolored	12.00	12.50

Perf. 13x14

Size: 22½x39mm

15	A17	10r multicolored	24.00	25.00
		Nos. 1-15 (15)	50.25	52.25

Lascar — A1

Marine Fauna: 10c, Hammerhead shark, vert. 15c, Tiger shark. 20c, Sooty eagle ray. 25c, Butterflyfish, vert. 30c, Robber crab. 40c, Green carangue. 45c, Needlefish, vert. 50c, Barracuda. 60c, Spotted pebble crab. 75c, Parrotfish. 85c, Rainbow runner (fish). 1r, Giant hermit crab. 1.50r, Humphead. 2.25r, Rock cod. 3.50r, Black marlin. 5r, Whale shark, vert. 10r, Lionfish.

Perf. 14x13½, 13½x14; 14 (30c, 60c, 85c)

1968-73   Litho.   Wmk. 314

16	A1	5c multicolored	.40	.40
a.		Wmk. upright ('73)	.55	.55
17	A1	10c multicolored	.15	.15
18	A1	15c multicolored	.15	.15
19	A1	20c multicolored	.15	.15
20	A1	25c multicolored	.35	.35
21	A1	30c multi ('70)	.40	.40
22	A1	40c multicolored	.35	.35
23	A1	45c multicolored	2.75	2.75
24	A1	50c multicolored	.35	.35
25	A1	60c multi ('70)	.80	.80
26	A1	75c multicolored	4.00	4.00
27	A1	85c multi ('70)	1.75	1.75
28	A1	1r multicolored	1.40	1.40
29	A1	1.50r multicolored	1.75	1.75
30	A1	2.25r multicolored	14.00	14.00
31	A1	3.50r multicolored	4.00	4.00
32	A1	5r multicolored	6.00	6.00
33	A1	10r multicolored	17.00	17.00
		Nos. 16-33 (18)	55.75	55.75

No. 16 has watermark sideways.

Aldabra
Atoll
and
Sacred
Ibis
A2

1969, July 10   Litho.   Perf. 13½x13

34	A2	2.25r vio blue & multi	3.50	2.50

Outrigger Canoe — A3

Designs: 75c, Beaching canoe. 1r, Merchant ship Nordvaer. 1.50r, Yacht, Isle of Farquhar.

Perf. 13½x14

1969, Dec. 15   Litho.   Wmk. 314

35	A3	45c multicolored	.50	.50
36	A3	75c multicolored	1.00	.90
37	A3	1r multicolored	1.50	1.40
38	A3	1.50r multicolored	2.50	2.00
		Nos. 35-38 (4)	5.50	4.80

Giant
Land
Tortoise
A4

Designs: 75c, Aldabra lily. 1r, Aldabra tree snail. 1.50r, Dimorphic egrets.

1971, Feb. 1 Litho. Wmk. 314

39 A4	45c multicolored	1.90	1.10
40 A4	75c multicolored	2.50	1.65
41 A4	1r multicolored	5.00	3.25
42 A4	1.50r multicolored	6.50	4.25
	Nos. 39-42 (4)	15.90	10.25

Aldabra Nature Reserve.

Society Coat of Arms and Flightless
Rail — A5

1971, June 30 Litho. Perf. 13½

43 A5	3.50r multicolored	10.00	7.00

Opening of Royal Society Research Station at
Aldabra.

Acropora
Formosa
A6

Corals: 60c, Goniastrea pectinata. 1r, Fungia
fungites. 1.75r, Tubipora musica.

1972, Mar. 1

44 A6	40c blue & multi	.95	.95
45 A6	60c brt pink & multi	1.65	1.65
46 A6	1r blue & multi	3.25	3.25
47 A6	1.75r brt pink & multi	7.25	7.25
	Nos. 44-47 (4)	13.10	13.10

Common Design Types
pictured following the introduction.

Silver Wedding Issue, 1972
Common Design Type

Design: Queen Elizabeth II, Prince Philip, flightless rail and sacred ibis.

1972, Nov. 20 Photo. Perf. 14x14½

48 CD324	95c multicolored	1.10	.50
49 CD324	1.50r violet & multi	1.50	.75

Crucifixion, 17th
Century — A7

Upsidedown
Jellyfish — A8

Paintings, Ethiopian Manuscripts, 17th Century:
75c, 1.50r, Joseph and Nicodemus burying Jesus.
1r, Like 45c.

1973, Apr. 9 Litho. Perf. 14

50 A7	45c buff & multi	.45	.30
51 A7	75c buff & multi	.65	.50
52 A7	1r buff & multi	.90	.60
53 A7	1.50r buff & multi	1.50	1.00
a.	Souvenir sheet of 4, #50-53	4.50	3.50
	Nos. 50-53 (4)	3.50	2.40

Easter.

1973, Nov. 12 Litho. Wmk. 314

54 A8	50c shown	1.40	1.00
55 A8	1r Butterflies	2.25	1.50
56 A8	1.50r Spider	3.75	2.50
	Nos. 54-56 (3)	7.40	5.00

Nordvaer and July 14,
1969 Cancel — A9

Design: 2.50r, Nordvaer offshore and cancel.

1974, July 14

57 A9	85c multicolored	.70	.50
58 A9	2.50r multicolored	1.90	1.25

Nordvaer traveling post office, 5th anniv.

Terebra Maculata and Terebra
Subulata — A10

Sea Shells: 75c, Turbo marmoratus. 1r, Drupa
rubusidaeus. 1.50r, Cassis rufa.

1974, Nov. 12 Litho. Perf. 13½x14

59 A10	45c multicolored	.90	.70
60 A10	75c multicolored	1.40	1.25
61 A10	1r multicolored	2.25	1.75
62 A10	1.50r multicolored	4.00	3.00
	Nos. 59-62 (4)	8.55	6.70

Aldabra
Drongo — A11

Grewia
Salicifolia — A12

Birds: 10c, Malagasy coucal. 20c, Red-headed
forest fody. 25c, Fairy tern. 30c, Crested tern. 40c,
Brown booby. 50c, Noddy tern. 60c, Gray heron.
65c, Blue-faced booby. 95c, Malagasy white-eye.
1r, Green-backed heron. 1.75r, Lesser frigate bird.
3.50r, White-tailed tropic bird. 5r, Souimanga sunbird. 10r, Malagasy turtledove. Nos. 69, 71-77
horiz.

1975, Feb. 28 Wmk. 314 Perf. 14

63 A11	5c buff & multi	.15	.15
64 A11	10c lt ultra & multi	.15	.15
65 A11	20c dp yel & multi	.15	.15
66 A11	25c ultra & multi	.20	.15
67 A11	30c dl yel & multi	.30	.30
68 A11	40c bis & multi	.40	.40
69 A11	50c lt blue & multi	.45	.45
70 A11	60c yel & multi	.50	.50
71 A11	65c yel grn & multi	.60	.60
72 A11	95c cit & multi	.75	.75
73 A11	1r bis & multi	.95	.95
74 A11	1.75r yel & multi	1.90	1.90
75 A11	3.50r blue & multi	3.75	3.75
76 A11	5r pale sal & multi	6.25	6.25
77 A11	10r brt yel & multi	9.50	9.50
	Nos. 63-77 (15)	26.00	25.95

1975, July 10 Litho. Wmk. 314

Native Plants: 65c, Cassia aldabrensis. 1r,
Hypoestes aldabrensis. 1.60r, Euphorbia pyrifolia.

78 A12	50c multicolored	.35	.35
79 A12	65c multicolored	.50	.50
80 A12	1r multicolored	.75	.75
81 A12	1.60r multicolored	1.25	1.25
	Nos. 78-81 (4)	2.85	2.85

Nature protection.

Aldabra and Compass Rose — A13

Maps of Islands: 1r, Desroches. 1.50r, Farquhar.
2r, Diego Garcia.

1975, Nov. 8 Litho. Perf. 13½x14

82 A13	50c blk, blue & grn	.30	.25
83 A13	1r green & multi	.65	.50
84 A13	1.50r blk, ultra & grn	1.00	.70
85 A13	2r blk, lilac & grn	1.40	1.00
a.	Souvenir sheet of 4, #82-85	4.00	3.25
	Nos. 82-85 (4)	3.35	2.45

British Indian Ocean Territory, 10th anniv.

Crimson
Speckled
Moth
A14

Insects: 1.20r, Dysdercus fasciatus. 1.50r, Sphex
torridus. 2r, Oryctes rhinoceros.

1976, Mar. 22 Litho. Wmk. 373

86 A14	65c multicolored	.40	.40
87 A14	1.20r multicolored	.65	.65
88 A14	1.50r multicolored	.90	.90
89 A14	2r multicolored	1.40	1.40
	Nos. 86-89 (4)	3.35	3.35

Exhibition Emblem and No. 37 — A15

1990, May 3 Wmk. 373 Perf. 14

90 A15	15p No. 62	.50	.50
91 A15	20p No. 89	.70	.70
92 A15	34p No. 85	1.10	1.10
93 A15	54p shown	1.90	1.90
	Nos. 90-93 (4)	4.20	4.20

Stamp World London '90.

Birds — A16

1990, May 3 Wmk. 384 Perf. 14

94 A16	15p White-tailed tropic birds	.40	.40
95 A16	20p Turtle doves	.60	.60
96 A16	24p Greater frigate birds	.70	.70
97 A16	30p Little green herons	.90	.90
98 A16	34p Greater sand plovers	1.00	1.00
99 A16	41p Crab plovers	1.25	1.25
100 A16	45p Crested terns	1.40	1.40
101 A16	54p Lesser crested terns	1.65	1.65
102 A16	62p Fairy terns	1.75	1.75
103 A16	71p Red-footed boobies	2.00	2.00
104 A16	80p Indian mynahs	2.50	2.50
105 A16	£1 Madagascar fodies	3.00	3.00
	Nos. 94-105 (12)	17.15	17.15

For overprints see Nos. 145-146.

Queen Mother, 90th Birthday
Common Design Types

Designs: 24p, Lady Elizabeth Bowes-Lyon, 1923.
£1, Queen, Princesses Elizabeth & Margaret, 1940.

1990, Aug. 4 Wmk. 384 Perf. 14x15

106 CD343	24p multicolored	1.00	1.00

Perf. 14½

107 CD344	£1 brown & black	4.00	4.00

British Indian
Ocean Territory,
25th
Anniv. — A17

1990, Nov. 8 Litho. Perf. 14

108 A17	20p Flag	.75	.75
109 A17	24p Coat of arms	.95	.95

Souvenir Sheet

110 A17	£1 Map	4.00	4.00

Govt.
Services
A18

Wmk. 373

1991, June 3 Perf. 14

111 A18	20p Postal service	.70	.70
112 A18	24p Royal Marines	.85	.85
113 A18	34p Police station, officers	1.25	1.25
114 A18	54p Customs service	1.90	1.90
	Nos. 111-114 (4)	4.70	4.70

Visiting
Ships
A19

1991, Nov. 8

115 A19	20p Survey ship Experiment, 1786	.70	.70
116 A19	24p US Brig Pickering, 1819	.85	.85
117 A19	34p SMS Emden, 1914	1.25	1.25
118 A19	54p HMS Edinburgh, 1988	1.90	1.90
	Nos. 115-118 (4)	4.70	4.70

Queen Elizabeth II's Accession to the Throne, 40th Anniv.
Common Design Type

Wmk. 373

1992, Feb. 6 Litho. Perf. 14

119 CD349	15p multicolored	.50	.50
120 CD349	20p multicolored	.70	.70
121 CD349	24p multicolored	.85	.85
122 CD349	34p multicolored	1.25	1.25
123 CD349	54p multicolored	1.90	1.90
	Nos. 119-123 (5)	5.20	5.20

Aircraft
A20

Wmk. 384

1992, Oct. 23 Litho. Perf. 14

124 A20	20p Catalina	.75	.75
125 A20	24p Nimrod	.95	.95
126 A20	34p P-3 Orion	1.25	1.25
127 A20	54p B-52	2.00	2.00
	Nos. 124-127 (4)	4.95	4.95

Christmas — A21

Paintings: 5p, The Mystical Marriage of St.
Cathrin, by Correggio. 24p, Madonna and Child by
unknown artist. 34p, Madonna and Child, diff. 54p, The Birth of Jesus, by
Kaspar Jele.

1992, Nov. 27   *Perf. 14¹⁄₂*
128	A21	5p multicolored	.20	.20
129	A21	24p multicolored	.80	.80
130	A21	34p multicolored	1.10	1.10
131	A21	54p multicolored	1.90	1.90
		Nos. 128-131 (4)	4.00	4.00

Coconut
Crab
A22

Wmk. 384
1993, Mar. 3   Litho.   *Perf. 14*
132	A22	10p Crab, coconut	.30	.30
133	A22	10p Large crab	.30	.30
134	A22	10p Two crabs	.30	.30
135	A22	15p Crab on tree trunk	.45	.45
		Nos. 132-135 (4)	1.35	1.35

World Wildlife Fund.

Royal Air Force, 75th Anniv.
Common Design Type
#136, Vickers Virginia. 24p, Bristol Bulldog. 34p, Short Sunderland. 54p, Bristol Blenheim IV.
#140: a, Douglas Dakota. b, Gloster Javelin. c, Blackburn Beverley. d, Vickers VC10.

1993, Apr. 1   **Wmk. 373**
136	CD350	20p multicolored	.60	.60
137	CD350	24p multicolored	.70	.70
138	CD350	34p multicolored	1.00	1.00
139	CD350	54p multicolored	1.50	1.50
		Nos. 136-139 (4)	3.80	3.80

Souvenir Sheet
140	CD350	20p Sheet of 4, #a.-d.	2.30	2.30

Flowers — A23

Christmas: 20p, Stachytarpheta urticifolia. 24p, Ipomea pes-caprae. 34p, Sida pusilla. 54p, Catharanthus roseus.

Perf. 14¹⁄₂
1993, Nov. 22   Litho.   **Wmk. 373**
141-144	A23	Set of 4	3.75 3.75

Nos. 96, 105 Ovptd. with Hong Kong '94 Emblem
Wmk. 384
1994, Feb. 18   Litho.   *Perf. 14*
145	A16	24p multicolored	.65	.65
146	A16	£1 multicolored	2.75	2.75

A24   Butterflies — A25

18th Cent. Maps and Charts: a, 20p, Sketch of Diego Garcia. b, 24p, Plan of harbor, Chagos Island or Diego Garcia, by Lt. Archibald Blair. c, 34p, Chart of Chagos Archipelago, by Lt. Blair. d, 44p, Plan of part of Chagos Island or Diego Garcia, from survey made by the Drake. e, 54p, Plan of Chagos Island or Diego Garcia, by M. Aa Fontaine.

1994, June 1   **Wmk. 373**
147	A24	Strip of 5, #a.-e.	5.25 5.25

1994, Aug. 16   **Wmk. 384**
148	A25	24p Junonia villida	.80	.80
149	A25	30p Petrelaea dana	1.00	1.00
150	A25	56p Hypolimnas misippus	1.75	1.75
		Nos. 148-150 (3)	3.55	3.55

Sharks A26

1994, Nov. 1   **Wmk. 373**
151	A26	15p Nurse	.45	.45
152	A26	20p Silver tip	.60	.60
153	A26	24p Black tip reef	.75	.75
154	A26	30p Oceanic white tip	.95	.95
155	A26	35p Black tip	1.10	1.10
156	A26	41p Smooth hammer- head	1.25	1.25
157	A26	46p Lemon	1.40	1.40
158	A26	55p White tip reef	1.75	1.75
159	A26	65p Tiger	2.00	2.00
a.		Souvenir sheet of 1	2.00	2.00
160	A26	74p Indian sand tiger	2.25	2.25
a.		Souvenir sheet of 1	2.25	2.25
161	A26	80p Great hammerhead	2.50	2.50
162	A26	£1 Great white	3.00	3.00
		Nos. 151-162 (12)	18.00	18.00

No. 159a for Hong Kong '97. Issued 2/3/97.
No. 160a for return of Hong Kong to China. Issued 7/1/97.

End of World War II, 50th Anniv.
Common Design Types
20p, War graves, memorial cross, Diego Garcia. 24p, 6-inch naval gun, Cannon Point. 30p, Sunderland flying boat, 230 Squadron. 56p, HMIS Clive. £1, Reverse of War Medal 1939-45.

Wmk. 373
1995, May 8   Litho.   *Perf. 14*
163	CD351	20p multicolored	.50	.50
164	CD351	24p multicolored	.65	.65
165	CD351	30p multicolored	.80	.80
166	CD351	56p multicolored	1.50	1.50
		Nos. 163-166 (4)	3.45	3.45

Souvenir Sheet
167	CD352	£1 multicolored	2.75	2.75

Game Fish A27

1995, Oct. 6   **Wmk. 384**
168	A27	20p Dolphinfish	.60	.60
169	A27	24p Sailfish	.75	.75
170	A27	30p Wahoo	.95	.95
171	A27	56p Striped marlin	1.75	1.75
		Nos. 168-171 (4)	4.05	4.05

Sea Shells — A28

20p, Terebra crenulata. 24p, Bursa bufonia. 30p, Nassarius papillosus. 56p, Lopha cristagalli.

1996, Jan. 8   **Wmk. 373**   *Perf. 14*
172	A28	20p multicolored	.60	.60
173	A28	24p multicolored	.75	.75
174	A28	30p multicolored	.95	.95
175	A28	56p multicolored	1.75	1.75
		Nos. 172-175 (4)	4.05	4.05

Queen Elizabeth II, 70th Birthday
Common Design Type
Various portraits of Queen, scenes of British Indian Ocean Territory: 20p, View to north from south end of lagoon. 24p, Manager's House, Peros Banhos. 30p, Wireless station, Peros Banhos. 56p, Sunset scene.
£1, Wearing crown, formal dress.

Perf. 14x14¹⁄₂
1996, Apr. 22   **Wmk. 384**
176	CD354	20p multicolored	.65	.65
177	CD354	24p multicolored	.80	.80
178	CD354	30p multicolored	1.00	1.00
179	CD354	56p multicolored	1.75	1.75
		Nos. 176-179 (4)	4.20	4.20

Souvenir Sheet
180	CD354	£1 multicolored	3.25	3.25

Turtles — A29

1996, Sept. 2   **Wmk. 373**
181	A29	20p Loggerhead	.60	.60
182	A29	24p Leatherback	.75	.75
183	A29	30p Hawksbill	.95	.95
184	A29	56p Green	1.75	1.75
		Nos. 181-184 (4)	4.05	4.05

Uniforms — A30

Designs: 20p, British representative. 24p, Royal Marine officer. 30p, Royal Marine in camouflage. 56p, Police dog handler, female police officer.

1996, Dec.   *Perf. 14*
185	A30	20p multicolored	.65	.65
186	A30	24p multicolored	.80	.80
187	A30	30p multicolored	1.00	1.00
188	A30	56p multicolored	1.85	1.85
		Nos. 185-188 (4)	4.30	4.30

Queen Elizabeth
II and Prince
Philip, 50th
Wedding
Anniv. — A31

#189, Queen up close. #190, 4-horse team fording river. #191, Queen riding in open carriage. Prince Philip up close. #192, Prince driving 4-horse team, Prince, Queen near jeep. #193, Queen on horseback, castle in distance.
£1.50, Queen, Prince riding in open carriage.

1997   *Perf. 14¹⁄₂x14*
189	A31	20p multicolored	.65	.65
190	A31	20p multicolored	.65	.65
a.		Pair, #189-190	1.30	1.30
191	A31	24p multicolored	.80	.80
192	A31	24p multicolored	.80	.80
a.		Pair, #191-192	1.60	1.60
193	A31	30p multicolored	1.00	1.00
194	A31	30p multicolored	1.00	1.00
a.		Pair, #193-194	2.00	2.00
		Nos. 189-194 (6)	4.90	4.90

Souvenir Sheet
195	A31	£1.50 multicolored	5.00	5.00

BRUNEI
'brü-,nī

LOCATION — On the northwest coast of Borneo
GOVT. — Independent state
AREA — 2,226 sq. mi.
POP. — 191,770 (1981)
CAPITAL — Bandar Seri Begawan

Brunei became a British protectorate in 1688. A treaty between the sultan and the British Government in 1979 provided for independence in 1983.

100 Cents (Sen) = 1 Dollar

Catalogue values for unused stamps in this country are for Never Hinged items, beginning with Scott 62.

Watermark

Wmk. 385 -
CARTOR

Labuan Stamps of 1902-03 Overprinted or Surcharged in Red:
BRUNEI.

BRUNEI.   **TWO CENTS.**

1906   Unwmk.   *Perf. 12 to 15*
1	A38	1c violet & blk	14.00	32.50
a.		Black overprint	2,000.	2,750.
2	A38	2c on 3c brn & blk	1.50	5.00
a.		"BRUNEI." double	4,250.	4,250.
3	A38	2c on 8c org & blk	16.00	55.00
a.		"TWO CENTS." double	5,750.	
b.		"TWO CENTS." omitted, in pair with normal	6,000.	
4	A38	3c brown & blk	16.00	55.00
5	A38	4c on 12c yel & blk	1.75	4.75
6	A38	5c on 16c org brn & green	20.00	42.50
7	A38	8c orange & blk	7.00	17.00
8	A38	10c on 16c org brn & green	7.00	15.00
9	A38	25c on 16c org brn & green	72.50	110.00
10	A38	30c on 16c org brn & green	72.50	100.00
11	A38	50c on 16c org brn & green	72.50	100.00
12	A38	$1 on 8c org & blk	72.50	100.00
		Nos. 1-12 (12)	373.25	636.75

The 25c surcharge reads: "25 CENTS."

Scene on Brunei
River — A1

Two Types of 1908 1c, 3c:
Type I - Dots form bottom line of water shading. (Double plate.)
Type II - Dots removed. (Single plate.)

1907-21   Engr.   Wmk. 3   *Perf. 14*
13	A1	1c yel green & blk	1.50	2.75
14	A1	1c green (II) ('08)	.40	.40
a.		Type I ('19)	.60	1.50
15	A1	2c red & black	1.50	3.00
16	A1	2c brn & blk ('11)	.60	1.40
17	A1	3c red brn & blk	12.50	15.00
18	A1	3c car (I) ('08)	.85	1.50
a.		Type II ('17)	12.50	17.50
19	A1	4c lilac & blk	5.00	9.00
20	A1	4c claret ('12)	4.00	.50
21	A1	5c ultra & blk	37.50	50.00
22	A1	5c org & blk ('08)	3.50	4.00
23	A1	5c orange ('16)	1.75	2.25
24	A1	8c orange & blk	5.50	20.00
25	A1	8c blue ('08)	4.25	6.25
26	A1	8c ultra ('16)	2.00	2.25
27	A1	10c dk green & blk	9.00	15.00
28	A1	10c violet, yel ('12)	1.00	1.25
29	A1	25c yel brn & blue	19.00	30.00
30	A1	25c violet ('12)	1.90	4.00
31	A1	30c black & pur	19.00	30.00
32	A1	30c org & red vio ('12)	6.50	12.50
33	A1	50c brown & grn	19.00	30.00
34	A1	50c blk, grn ('12)	19.00	30.00
35	A1	50c blk, grnsh bl ('21)	5.50	13.50
36	A1	$1 slate & red	62.50	75.00
37	A1	$1 red & blk, bl ('12)	25.00	50.00
38	A1	$5 lake, grn ('08)	67.50	125.00
39	A1	$25 blk, red ('08)	450.00	450.00
		Nos. 13-38 (26)	335.75	534.55

Used value for No. 39 is for CTO. CTOs dated before Dec. 1941 cost more.

Stamps of 1908-21 Overprinted in Black: "MALAYA-BORNEO EXHIBITION, 1922" in Four Lines

1922

14b	A1	1c green		2.25	17.00
16a	A1	2c brown & black		5.00	21.00
18b	A1	3c carmine		6.75	30.00
20a	A1	4c claret		5.25	35.00
23a	A1	5c orange		10.00	45.00
28a	A1	10c violet, yellow		8.75	45.00
30a	A1	25c violet		19.00	67.50
35a	A1	50c greenish blue		60.00	125.00
37a	A1	$1 red & black, blue		92.50	165.00
		Nos. 14b-37a (9)		209.50	550.50

Industrial fair, Singapore, Mar. 31-Apr. 15.

Type of 1907 Issue

1924-37   **Wmk. 4**

43	A1	1c black ('26)		.20	.30
44	A1	2c deep brown		.70	2.75
45	A1	2c green ('33)		.25	.50
46	A1	3c green		.70	3.75
47	A1	4c claret brown		1.90	.65
48	A1	4c orange ('29)		.50	.40
49	A1	5c orange		.65	.75
50	A1	5c lt gray ('31)		3.50	5.75
51	A1	5c brown ('33)		1.75	.15
52	A1	8c ultra ('27)		2.50	4.25
53	A1	8c gray ('33)		2.75	.45
54	A1	10c violet, yel ('37)		6.25	15.00
55	A1	25c dk violet ('31)		4.00	9.00
56	A1	30c org & red vio ('31)		4.75	12.50
57	A1	50c black, grn ('31)		6.00	10.50
58	A1	$1 red & blk, bl ('31)		25.00	55.00
		Nos. 43-58 (16)		61.40	121.45

For overprints see Nos. N1-N20.

Dwellings in Town of Brunei — A2

1924-31

59	A2	6c black	3.50	8.25
60	A2	6c red ('31)	2.75	9.00
61	A2	12c blue	5.00	7.50
		Nos. 59-61 (3)	11.25	24.75

See note after Nos. N1-N19.

Catalogue values for unused stamps in this section, from this point to the end of the section, are for Never Hinged items.

Types of 1907-24

1947-51   **Engr.**   **Perf. 14**

62	A1	1c brown	.15	.15
63	A1	2c gray	.15	.15
a.		Perf. 14½x13½ ('50)	1.75	2.50
64	A2	3c dark green	.35	.35
65	A1	5c deep orange	.15	.15
a.		Perf. 14½x13½ ('50)	7.25	9.00
66	A2	6c gray black	1.75	1.75
67	A2	8c scarlet	.20	.20
a.		Perf. 13 ('51)	.20	.20
68	A1	10c violet	.20	.20
a.		Perf. 14½x13½ ('50)	1.75	3.00
69	A1	15c brt ultra	3.75	3.75
70	A1	25c red violet	.35	.35
a.		Perf. 14½x13½ ('51)	.60	1.25
71	A1	30c dp org & gray blk	.45	.45
a.		Perf. 14½x13½ ('51)	.55	1.25
72	A1	50c black	.45	.45
a.		Perf. 13 ('50)	3.50	12.00
73	A1	$1 scar & gray blk	1.25	1.25
74	A1	$5 red org & grn ('48)	15.00	15.00
75	A1	$10 dp claret & gray blk ('48)	30.00	42.50
		Nos. 62-75 (14)	54.20	66.70

Sultan Ahmed and Pile Dwellings A3

1949, Sept. 22   Wmk. 4   Perf. 13

76	A3	8c car & black	1.60	1.60
77	A3	25c red orange & pur	1.60	1.60
78	A3	50c blue & black	2.00	2.00
		Nos. 76-78 (3)	5.20	5.20

25th anniv. of the reign of Sultan Ahmed Tajudin Akhazul Khair Wad-din.

UPU Issue
Common Design Types
Engr.; Name Typo. on 15c and 25c

1949, Oct. 10   Perf. 13½, 11x11½

79	CD306	8c rose car	.50	.50
80	CD307	15c indigo	.75	.75
81	CD308	25c red lilac	1.25	1.25
82	CD309	50c slate	2.50	2.50
		Nos. 79-82 (4)	5.00	5.00

Sultan Omar Ali Saifuddin — A4

River Kampong A5

1952, Mar. 1   Engr.   Wmk. 4
Center in Black   Perf. 13½x13

83	A4	1c black	.15	.15
84	A4	2c red orange	.15	.15
85	A4	3c red brown	.15	.15
86	A4	4c green	.15	.15
87	A4	6c gray	.25	.15
88	A4	8c carmine	.30	.15
89	A4	10c olive brown	.30	.15
90	A4	12c violet	.35	.15
91	A4	15c blue	.50	.15
92	A4	25c purple	.75	.25
93	A4	50c ultramarine	1.10	.30

Perf. 13

94	A5	$1 dull green	3.00	.60
95	A5	$2 red	4.50	1.50
96	A5	$5 deep plum	15.00	5.00
		Nos. 83-96 (14)	26.65	9.00

See Nos. 101-114.

Mosque and Sultan Omar — A6

1958, Sept. 24   Wmk. 314   Perf. 13
Center in Black

97	A6	8c dull green	.25	.30
98	A6	15c carmine rose	.30	.25
99	A6	35c rose violet	.50	.75
		Nos. 97-99 (3)	1.05	1.30

Opening of the Brunei Mosque.

Freedom from Hunger Issue
Common Design Type with Portrait of Sultan Omar

1963, June 4   Photo.   Perf. 14x14½

100	CD314	12c sepia	1.50	1.50

Types of 1952
Wmk. 314 Upright

1964-70   Engr.   Perf. 13½x13
Center in Black

101	A4	1c black	.15	.15
102	A4	2c red orange	.15	.15
103	A4	3c red brown	.15	.15
104	A4	4c green	.15	.15
105	A4	6c black	.25	.15
106	A4	8c dk carmine	.45	.15
107	A4	10c olive brown	.35	.30
108	A4	12c violet	.60	.30
109	A4	15c blue	.60	.35
110	A4	25c purple	1.25	.40
111	A4	50c ultramarine	2.50	1.50

Perf. 13

112	A5	$1 dull green ('68)	4.75	3.00
113	A5	$2 red ('70)	16.00	10.00
114	A5	$5 deep plum ('70)	32.50	25.00
		Nos. 101-114 (14)	59.85	41.75

Nos. 101-112 were reissued in 1968-70 on whiter, glazed paper; the $2 and $5 are only on this paper.

Wmk. 314 Sideways
1972-73   Perf. 13½x13
Center in Black

102a	A4	2c red orange	.35	.35
103a	A4	3c red brown	.40	.40
104a	A4	4c green	.50	.50
105a	A4	6c black	.85	.85
106a	A4	8c dark carmine	1.10	1.10
107a	A4	10c olive brown	1.50	1.50
108a	A4	12c violet	1.75	1.75
109a	A4	15c blue	3.00	3.00
		Nos. 102a-109a (8)	9.45	9.45

The stamps with watermark sideways are on the whiter, glazed paper. Issue dates: 2c, 8c, May 9, 1973, others, Nov. 17, 1972.

The following six sets are Common Design Types but with the portrait of Sultan Omar.

ITU Issue
1965, May 17   Perf. 11x11½
Litho.   Wmk. 314

116	CD317	4c red lil & org brn	.15	.15
117	CD317	75c orange & emer	1.40	1.40

Intl. Cooperation Year Issue
1965, Oct. 25   Perf. 14½

118	CD318	4c blue grn & claret	.15	.15
119	CD318	15c lt violet & grn	.70	.70

Churchill Memorial Issue
1966, Jan. 24   Photo.   Perf. 14

120	CD319	3c multicolored	.25	.15
121	CD319	10c multicolored	.65	.35
122	CD319	25c multicolored	1.00	.60
123	CD319	75c multicolored	3.50	2.50
		Nos. 120-123 (4)	5.40	3.60

World Cup Soccer Issue
1966, July 4   Litho.   Perf. 14

124	CD321	4c multicolored	.15	.15
125	CD321	75c multicolored	1.25	1.25

WHO Headquarters Issue
1966, Sept. 20   Litho.   Perf. 14

126	CD322	12c multicolored	.25	.20
127	CD322	25c multicolored	.75	.75

UNESCO Anniversary Issue
1966, Dec. 1   Litho.   Wmk. 314

128	CD323	4c "Education"	.15	.15
129	CD323	15c "Science"	.45	.45
130	CD323	75c "Culture"	2.25	2.25
		Nos. 128-130 (3)	2.85	2.85

State Religious Building and Sultan Hassanal Bolkiah — A7

1967, Dec. 19   Photo.   Perf. 12½

131	A7	4c violet & multi	.15	.15
132	A7	10c red & multi	.15	.15
133	A7	25c orange & multi	.35	.35
134	A7	50c lt violet & multi	.65	.65
		Nos. 131-134 (4)	1.30	1.30

A three-stamp set (12c, 25c, 50c) showing views of the new Language and Communications Headquarters was prepared and announced for release in April, 1968. The Crown Agents distributed sample sets, but the stamps were not issued. Later, Nos. 144-146 were issued instead.

Sultan Hassanal Bolkiah, Brunei Mosque and Flags — A8

Sultan Hassanal Bolkiah Installation: 12c, Sultan, Mosque and flags, horiz.

Perf. 13x14, 14x13

1968, July 9   Photo.   Unwmk.

135	A8	4c green & multi	.15	.15
136	A8	12c dp bister & multi	.30	.30
137	A8	25c violet & multi	.75	.75
		Nos. 135-137 (3)	1.20	1.20

Sultan Hassanal Bolkiah — A9

1968, July 15   Wmk. 314   Perf. 12
Litho.

138	A9	4c multicolored	.15	.15
139	A9	12c multicolored	.20	.20
140	A9	25c multicolored	.40	.50
		Nos. 138-140 (3)	.75	.85

Sultan Hassanal Bolkiah's birthday.

Coronation of Sultan Hassanal Bolkiah, Aug. 1, 1968 — A10

1968, Aug. 1   Photo.   Perf. 14½x14

141	A10	4c Prus blue & multi	.15	.15
142	A10	12c rose lilac & multi	.25	.25
143	A10	25c multicolored	.50	.50
		Nos. 141-143 (3)	.90	.90

A11

Hall of Language and Culture — A12

Perf. 13½, 12½x13½ (A12)

1968, Sept. 29   Photo.   Wmk. 314

144	A11	10c blue grn & multi	.15	.25
145	A11	15c ocher & multi	.20	.30
146	A12	30c ultra & multi	.45	.75
		Nos. 144-146 (3)	.80	1.30

Opening of the Hall of Language and Culture and of the Broadcasting and Information Department Building. Nos. 144-146 are overprinted "1968" and 4 bars over the 1967 date. They were not issued without this overprint.

Human Rights Flame and Struggling Man — A13

Unwmk.

1968, Dec. 16   Litho.   Perf. 14

147	A13	12c green, yel & blk	.15	.15
148	A13	25c ultra, yel & blk	.35	.35
149	A13	75c dk plum, yel & blk	.90	.90
		Nos. 147-149 (3)	1.40	1.40

International Human Rights Year.

Sultan and
WHO
Emblem
A14

1968, Dec. 19   Litho.   Perf. 14
150 A14 4c lt blue, org & blk   .15 .15
151 A14 15c brt purple, org & blk   .22 .22
152 A14 25c olive, org & blk   .38 .38
　　Nos. 150-152 (3)   .75 .75
20th anniv. of the WHO.

Sultan Hassanal Bolkiah, Pengiran
Shahbandar and Oil Rig — A15

Perf. 14x13
1969, July 10   Photo.   Wmk. 314
153 A15 12c green & multi   .20 .20
154 A15 40c dk rose brn & multi   .60 .60
155 A15 50c violet & multi   .75 .75
　　Nos. 153-155 (3)   1.55 1.55
Installation of Pengiran Shahbandar as Second
Minister (Di-Galong Sahibol Mal).

Royal Assembly Hall and Council
Chamber — A16

Design: 50c, Front view of buildings.

Unwmk.
1969, Sept. 23   Litho.   Perf. 15
156 A16 12c multicolored   .15 .15
157 A16 25c multicolored   .35 .35
158 A16 50c violet & pink   .65 .65
　　Nos. 156-158 (3)   1.15 1.15
Opening of the Royal Assembly Hall and Council
Chamber.

Youth Center — A17

1969, Dec. 20   Litho.   Wmk. 314
159 A17 6c lt org, blk & dull vio   .15 .15
160 A17 10c cit, blk & dl Prus grn   .15 .15
161 A17 30c yel green, blk & brn   .45 .45
　　Nos. 159-161 (3)   .75 .75
Opening of Youth Center, Mar. 15, 1969.

Helicopter
and
Emblem
A18

Designs: 10c, Soldier and emblem, vert. 75c,
Patrol boat and emblem.

1971, May 31   Litho.   Perf. 14
162 A18 10c green & multi   .38 .15
163 A18 15c Prus blue & multi   .45 .25
164 A18 75c lt ultra & multi   2.75 1.75
　　Nos. 162-164 (3)   3.58 2.15
10th anniv. of Royal Brunei Malay Reg.

50th Anniv. of the
Royal Brunei Police
Force — A19

1971, Aug. 14   Perf. 14½
165 A19 10c Superintendent   .40 .25
166 A19 15c Constable   .50 .32
167 A19 50c Traffic policeman   2.25 1.60
　　Nos. 165-167 (3)   3.15 2.17

Sultan, Heir Apparent and View of
Brunei — A20

Portraits and: 25c, View of Brunei with Mosque.
50c, Mosque and banner.

1971, Aug. 27   Litho.   Wmk. 314
168 A20 15c multicolored   .38 .22
169 A20 25c multicolored   .75 .55
170 A20 50c multicolored   1.40 1.10
　　Nos. 168-170 (3)   2.53 1.87
Installation of Sultan Hassanal Bolkiah's brother
Muda Omar Ali Saifuddin as heir apparent (Perdana
Wazir).

Brass and
Copper Goods
A21

Designs: 12c, Basketware. 15c, Leather goods.
25c, Silverware. 50c, Brunei Museum.

1972, Feb. 29   Perf. 13½x14
Size: 37x21mm
Portrait in Black
171 A21 10c brn, sal & yel grn   .15 .15
172 A21 12c org, yel & green   .18 .15
173 A21 15c dk grn, emer & org   .25 .22
174 A21 25c brown, org & sl   .70 .60
Size: 58x21mm
175 A21 50c dull blue & multi   1.50 1.10
　　Nos. 171-175 (5)   2.78 2.22
Opening of Brunei Museum.

Queen Elizabeth II, Sultan and
View — A22

Queen Elizabeth II, Sultan Hassanal Bolkiah and:
15c, View of Brunei. 25c, Mosque and barge. 50c,
Royal Assembly Hall.

1972, Feb. 29   Photo.   Perf. 13x13½
176 A22 10c lt brown & multi   .24 .20
177 A22 15c lt blue & multi   .35 .30
178 A22 25c lt green & multi   .70 .60
179 A22 50c dull purple & multi   2.00 2.00
　　Nos. 176-179 (4)   3.29 3.10
Visit of Queen Elizabeth II, Feb. 29.

Bangunan Secretariat (Government
Buildings) — A23

Sultans Omar Ali Saifuddin and Hassanal
Bolkiah: 15c, Istana Darul Hana (Sultan's resi-
dence). 25c, View of capital. 50c, View of new
Mosque.

1972, Oct. 4   Litho.   Perf. 13½
180 A23 10c org, blk & green   .15 .15
181 A23 15c green & multi   .25 .25
182 A23 25c ultra & multi   .50 .50
183 A23 50c rose red & multi   1.00 1.00
　　Nos. 180-183 (4)   1.90 1.90
Change of capital's name from Brunei to Bandar
Seri Begawan, Oct. 4, 1970.

Beverley Plane Landing — A24

Design: 25c, Blackburn Beverley plane dropping
supplies by parachute, vert.

Perf. 14x13½, 13½x14
1972, Nov. 15   Litho.
184 A24 25c blue & multi   1.65 1.65
185 A24 75c ultra & multi   4.00 4.00
Opening of Royal Air Force Museum, Hendon,
London.

Silver Wedding Issue, 1972
Common Design Type
Design: Queen Elizabeth II, Prince Philip; girl
and boy with traditional gifts.

1972, Nov. 20   Photo.   Perf. 14x14½
186 CD324 12c multi   .40 .15
187 CD324 75c multi   1.25 1.25

INTERPOL Emblem and Headquarters,
Paris — A25

Design: 50c, similar to 25c.

1973, Sept. 7   Litho.   Perf. 14x14½
188 A25 25c emerald & multi   .75 .75
189 A25 50c multicolored   1.50 1.50
50th anniv. of Intl. Criminal Police Org.
(INTERPOL).

Princess Anne and Mark Phillips — A26

1973, Nov. 14   Litho.   Perf. 13½
190 A26 25c vio blue & multi   .20 .20
191 A26 50c red lilac & multi   .40 .40
Wedding of Princess Anne and Capt. Mark Phillips, Nov. 14, 1973.

Churchill
Painting
Outdoors
A27

Sultan Hassanal
Bolkiah
A28

Design: 50c, Churchill making "V" sign.

Perf. 14x13½
1973, Dec. 31   Litho.   Wmk. 314
192 A27 12c car rose & multi   .15 .15
193 A27 50c dk green & multi   .55 .55
Winston Churchill Memorial Exhibition.

Wmk. 314 Sideways
1974, July 15   Photo.   Perf. 13x15
194 A28 4c blue grn & multi   .15 .15
195 A28 5c dull blue & multi   .15 .15
196 A28 6c olive grn & multi   .15 .15
197 A28 10c lt violet & multi   .15 .15
　b. Watermark upright ('76)   .15 .15
198 A28 15c brown & multi   .15 .15
199 A28 20c buff & multi   .16 .16
　b. Watermark upright ('76)   .16 .16
200 A28 25c olive & multi   .18 .18
　b. Watermark upright ('76)   .20 .18
201 A28 30c multicolored   .22 .22
202 A28 35c gray & multi   .25 .22
203 A28 40c multicolored   .32 .32
204 A28 50c yel brn & multi   .38 .32
205 A28 75c multicolored   .60 .50
206 A28 $1 dull org & multi   .75 .75
207 A28 $2 multicolored   1.65 1.40
208 A28 $5 silver & multi   3.50 3.50
209 A28 $10 gold & multi   8.25 8.25
　　Nos. 194-209 (16)   17.01 16.13
Issue date: Nos. 197b-200b, Apr. 12.

1975, Aug. 13   Wmk. 373
194a A28 4c   .15 .15
195a A28 5c   .15 .15
196a A28 6c   .15 .15
197a A28 10c   .15 .15
198a A28 15c   .15 .15
199a A28 20c   .16 .16
200a A28 25c   .20 .20
201a A28 30c   .24 .24
202a A28 35c   .28 .28
203a A28 40c   .32 .32
204a A28 50c   .40 .40
205a A28 75c   .60 .60
206a A28 $1   .80 .80
207a A28 $2   1.60 1.60
208a A28 $5   4.00 4.00
209a A28 $10   8.00 8.00
　　Nos. 194a-209a (16)   17.35 17.35
For surcharge see No. 225.

Brunei
Airport
A29

Design: 75c, Sultan Hassanal Bolkiah in uniform
and jet over airport.

Perf. 14x14½, 12½x13 (75c)
1974, July 18   Litho.   Wmk. 314
Size: 44x28mm
215 A29 50c multicolored   1.00 1.00
Size: 47x36mm
216 A29 75c multicolored   1.35 1.35
Opening of Brunei Airport.

UPU
Emblem
A30

1974, Oct. 28   Perf. 14½
217 A30 12c orange & multi   .15 .15
218 A30 50c blue & multi   .50 .50
219 A30 75c emerald & multi   .75 .75
　　Nos. 217-219 (3)   1.40 1.40
Centenary of Universal Postal Union.

Winston
Churchill
A31

Design: 75c, Churchill smoking cigar.

1974, Nov. 30   Wmk. 373   Perf. 14
220 A31 12c vio blue, blue & gold   .15 .15
221 A31 75c dk green, black & gold .90 .90
Sir Winston Churchill (1874-1965).

Boeing 737
Planes at
Airport
A32

Designs: 35c, Boeing 737 over Bandar Seri
Begawan Mosque. 75c, Boeing 737 in flight. All
planes with crest of Royal Brunei Airlines.

Perf. 12¹/₂x12

1975, May 14   Unwmk.
222 A32 12c multicolored   .30   .25
223 A32 35c multicolored   1.00   .75
224 A32 75c multicolored   2.00   2.00
    Nos. 222-224 (3)   3.30   3.00

Inauguration of Royal Brunei Airlines.

10 sen

No. 196a Surcharged in
Silver

Perf. 13x15
1976, Aug. 16   Photo.   Wmk. 373
225 A28 10c on 6c multicolored   .25   .25

British Royal Coat
of Arms — A33

20c, Imperial State Crown. 75c, Elizabeth II.

Wmk. 373
1977, June 7   Litho.   Perf. 14
226 A33 10c dk blue & multi   .15   .15
227 A33 20c purple & multi   .20   .20
228 A33 75c yellow & multi   .65   .65
    Nos. 226-228 (3)   1.00   1.00

25th anniv. of the reign of Elizabeth II.

Coronation of
Elizabeth II — A34

20c, Elizabeth II with coronation regalia. 75c,
Departure from Westminster Abbey (coach).

1978, June 2   Litho.   Perf. 13¹/₂x13
229 A34 10c multicolored   .15   .15
230 A34 20c multicolored   .20   .20
231 A34 75c multicolored   .65   .65
    Nos. 229-231 (3)   1.00   1.00

25th anniv. of coronation of Elizabeth II.

Sultan's Coat of
Arms — A35

Struggling Man,
Human Rights
Flame — A36

Coronation of Sultan Hassanal Bolkiah, 10th
Anniv.: 20c, Ceremony. 75c, Royal crown.

1978, Aug. 1   Wmk. 373   Perf. 12
232 A35 10c multicolored   .15   .15
233 A35 20c multicolored   .22   .18
234 A35 75c multicolored   .90   .75
    a. Souvenir sheet of 3, #232-234 8.50   6.00
    Nos. 232-234 (3)   1.27   1.08

1978, Dec. 10   Litho.   Perf. 14
235 A36 10c red, black & yel   .15   .15
236 A36 20c violet, black & yel   .18   .18
237 A36 75c olive, black & yel   .65   .65
    Nos. 235-237 (3)   .98   .98

Universal Declaration of Human Rights, 30th
anniversary.

Children
and IYC
Emblem
A37   International Year of the Child 1979

1979, June 30   Wmk. 373   Perf. 14
238 A37 10c shown   .15   .15
239 A37 $1 IYC emblem   .90   .90

Telisai
Earth
Satellite
Station
A38

Designs: 20c, Radar screen and satellite. 75c,
Cameraman, telex operator, telephone.

1979, Sept. 23   Litho.   Perf. 14¹/₂x14
240 A38 10c multicolored   .15   .15
241 A38 20c multicolored   .18   .15
242 A38 75c multicolored   .75   .75
    Nos. 240-242 (3)   1.08   1.05

Hajeer
Emblem — A39

1979, Nov. 21
243 A39 10c multicolored   .15   .15
244 A39 20c multicolored   .20   .20
245 A39 75c multicolored   .75   .75
    a. Souvenir sheet of 3, #243-245 2.50   2.50
    Nos. 243-245 (3)   1.10   1.10

Hegira, 1400th anniversary.

A40   A41

1980   Litho.   Perf. 14
246 A40 10c Installation ceremony   .15   .15
247 A40 10c Ceremony, diff.   .15   .15
248 A40 75c Jefri Bolkiah   .60   .60
249 A40 75c Sufri Bolkiah   .60   .60
    Nos. 246-249 (4)   1.50   1.50

Installation of Jefri Bolkiah and Sufri Bolkiah as
Wizars (Ministers of State for Royalty) 1st anniv.
Issue dates: Nos. 246, 248, Nov. 8; others, Dec. 6.

1981, Jan. 19   Litho.   Perf. 12x11¹/₂
255 A41 10c Umbrella   .15   .15
256 A41 15c Dagger, shield   .18   .18
257 A41 20c Spears   .25   .25
258 A41 30c Gold pouch   .35   .35

Size: 22¹/₂x40mm
Perf. 14x13¹/₂
259 A41 50c Headdress   .60   .60
    a. Souvenir sheet of 5, #255-259 2.25   2.25
    Nos. 255-259 (5)   1.53   1.53

A42   A43

1981, May 17   Litho.   Perf. 13x13¹/₂
260 A42 10c car rose & black   .15   .15
261 A42 75c dp violet & black   .75   .75

13th World Telecommunications Day.

Perf. 12¹/₂x12, 12 (75c)
1981, July 15   Litho.
Deep Rose Lilac Background
262 A43 10c Dagger, case   .15   .15
263 A43 15c Rifle, powder pouch   .15   .15
264 A43 20c Spears   .18   .18
265 A43 30c Sword, tunic, shield   .30   .30
266 A43 50c Horns   .50   .50

Size: 28¹/₂x45mm
267 A43 75c Gold bowl, table   .75   .75
    Nos. 262-267 (6)   2.03   2.03

See Nos. 278-289.

Royal Wedding Issue
Common Design Type

1981, July 29   Perf. 14
268 CD331 10c Bouquet   .15   .15
269 CD331 $1 Charles   .65   .65
270 CD331 $2 Couple   1.25   1.25
    Nos. 268-270 (3)   2.05   2.05

World Food
Day — A44   Intl. Year of the
                   Disabled — A45

1981, Oct. 16   Litho.   Perf. 12
271 A44 10c Fishermen   .15   .15
272 A44 $1 Produce   .80   .80

1981, Dec. 16   Wmk. 373   Perf. 12
273 A45 10c Blind man   .15   .15
274 A45 20c Sign language   .16   .16
275 A45 75c Man in wheelchair   .60   .60
    Nos. 273-275 (3)   .91   .91

TB Bacillus
Centenary
A46

1982, Mar. 24   Perf. 12, 13¹/₂ (75c)
276 A46 10c Lungs   .15   .15
277 A46 75c Bacillus, microscope   .60   .60

Type of 1981
1982, May 31   Litho.   Perf. 12¹/₂x12
Deep Magenta Background
278 A43 10c shown   .15   .15
279 A43 15c Pedestal urn   .15   .15
280 A43 20c Silver bowl   .20   .20
281 A43 30c Candle   .30   .30
282 A43 50c Gold pipe   .50   .50

Size: 28x44mm
Perf. 13¹/₂
283 A43 75c Silver pointer   .75   .75
    Nos. 278-283 (6)   2.05   2.05

1982, July 15   Litho.   Perf. 12¹/₂x12
Violet Background
284 A43 10c Urn   .15   .15
285 A43 15c Crossed banners   .15   .15
286 A43 20c Golden fan   .20   .20
287 A43 30c Lid   .30   .30
288 A43 50c Sword, sheath   .50   .50

Size: 28x44mm
Perf. 12
289 A43 75c Golden chalice pole   .75   .75
    Nos. 284-289 (6)   2.05   2.05

A47

1983, Mar. 14   Litho.   Perf. 13¹/₂
290 A47 10c Flag   .15   .15
291 A47 20c Natl. palace   .20   .20
292 A47 75c Oil drilling   .75   .75
293 A47 $2 Sultan Bolkiah   2.00   2.00
    a. Block of 4, #290-293   3.05   3.05

Commonwealth Day.

World Communications Year — A48

1983, July 15   Litho.   Perf. 13¹/₂
294 A48 10c Mail delivery   .15   .15
295 A48 75c Typewriter, phone   .80   .80
296 A48 $2 Dish antenna, satellite,
            TV   2.00   2.00
    Nos. 294-296 (3)   2.95   2.95

Opening
of
Hassanal
Bolkiah
National
Stadium
$1   A49

1983, Sept. 23   Litho.   Perf. 12
297 A49 10c Soccer, vert.   .15   .15
298 A49 75c Runners, vert.   1.00   1.00
299 A49 $1 shown   1.25   1.25
    Nos. 297-299 (3)   2.40   2.40

Size, Nos. 297-298: 26x33mm.

Fishing Industry — A50

1983, Sept. 23   Litho.   Perf. 13½
300 A50	10c Shrimp, lobster	.15	.15
301 A50	50c Pacific jacks	.60	.60
302 A50	75c Parrotfish, flatfish	.90	.90
303 A50	$1 Tuna	1.25	1.25
	Nos. 300-303 (4)	2.90	2.90

State Assembly Building — A51

Map of Southeast Asia, Flag — A52

Sultan Hassanal Bolkiah — A53

1984, Jan. 1   Litho.   Perf. 13
304 A51	10c shown	.15	.15
305 A51	20c State Secretariat building	.25	.25
306 A51	35c New Law Court	.40	.40
307 A51	50c Liquid natural gas well	.60	.60
308 A51	75c Omar Ali Saifuddin Mosque	.90	.90
309 A51	$1 Sultan's Palace	1.20	1.20
310 A52	$3 shown	3.60	3.60
a.	Souvenir sheet of 7, #304-310	7.25	7.25
	Nos. 304-310 (7)	7.10	7.10

Souvenir Sheets
311	Sheet of 4, Constitution signing, 1959	1.25	1.25
a.-d.	A53 25c any single	.25	.25
312	Sheet of 4, Brunei U.K. Friendship Agreement, 1979	1.25	1.25
a.-d.	A53 25c any single	.25	.25

Forestry Resources — A54

1984, Apr. 21   Litho.   Perf. 13½
313 A54	10c Forests, enrichment planting	.15	.15
314 A54	50c Irrigation canal	.60	.60
315 A54	75c Recreation forest	.90	.90
316 A54	$1 Wildlife	1.20	1.20
	Nos. 313-316 (4)	2.85	2.85

Philakorea 1984 — A55

Litho. & Engr.

1984, Oct. 22   Perf. 13
317 A55	10c No. 93	.15	.15
a.	Souvenir sheet of 1	.15	.15
318 A55	75c No. 27	.90	.90
a.	Souvenir sheet of 1	.90	.90
319 A55	$2 1895 local stamp	2.50	2.50
a.	Souvenir sheet of 1	2.50	2.50
	Nos. 317-319 (3)	3.55	3.55

Brunei Admission to Intl. Organizations A56

1985, Sept. 23   Litho.   Perf. 13
320 A56	50c UN	.45	.45
321 A56	50c Commonwealth	.45	.45
322 A56	50c ASEAN	.45	.45
323 A56	50c OIC	.45	.45
a.	Souv. sheet of 4, #320-323 + label	2.00	2.00
	Nos. 320-323 (4)	1.80	1.80

Intl. Youth Year — A57

1985, Oct. 17   Perf. 12
324 A57	10c shown	.15	.15
325 A57	75c Industry, education	.55	.55
326 A57	$1 Public Service	.70	.70
	Nos. 324-326 (3)	1.40	1.40

Intl. Day of Solidarity with the Palestinian People — A58

1985, Nov. 29   Perf. 12x12½
327 A58	10c lt blue & multi	.15	.15
328 A58	50c pink & multi	.55	.55
329 A58	$1 lt green & multi	1.10	1.10
	Nos. 327-329 (3)	1.80	1.80

Natl. Scout Jamboree, Dec. 14-20 — A59   Sultan Hassanal Bolkiah — A60

1985, Dec. 14   Perf. 13½
330 A59	10c Scout handshake	.15	.15
331 A59	20c Semaphore	.18	.18
332 A59	$2 Jamboree emblem	1.75	1.75
	Nos. 330-332 (3)	2.08	2.08

1985-86   Wmk. 233   Perf. 13½x14½
333 A60	10c multi	.15	.15
334 A60	15c multi	.15	.15
335 A60	20c multi	.18	.18
336 A60	25c multi	.22	.22
337 A60	35c multi ('86)	.32	.32
338 A60	40c multi ('86)	.36	.36
339 A60	50c multi ('86)	.45	.45
340 A60	75c multi ('86)	.68	.68

Size: 35x42mm
Perf. 14
341 A60	$1 multi ('86)	.90	.90
342 A60	$2 multi ('86)	1.75	1.75
343 A60	$5 multi ('86)	4.50	4.50
344 A60	$10 multi ('86)	9.00	9.00
	Nos. 333-344 (12)	18.66	18.66

Issued: #333-336, Dec. 23; #337-340, Jan. 15; #341-343, Feb. 23; #344, Mar. 29.

Admission to Intl. Organizations A61

Wmk. Cartor (385)

1986, Apr. 30   Litho.   Perf. 13
345 A61	50c WMO	.45	.45
346 A61	50c ITU	.45	.45
347 A61	50c UPU	.45	.45
348 A61	50c ICAO	.45	.45
a.	Souv. sheet of 4, #345-348 + label	1.80	1.80
	Nos. 345-348 (4)	1.80	1.80

Royal Brunei Armed Forces, 25th Anniv. A62

1986, May 31   Unwmk.   Perf. 13½
349	Strip of 4	1.40	1.40
a.	A62 10c In combat	.15	.15
b.	A62 20c Communications	.18	.18
c.	A62 50c Air and sea defense	.45	.45
d.	A62 75c On parade, Royal Palace	.68	.68

Royal Ensigns — A63

Designs: No. 350, Tunggul charok buritan, Pisang-pisang, Alam bernaga, Sandaran. No. 351, Dadap, Tunggul kawan, Ambal, Payong ubor-ubor, Sapu-sapu ayeng and Rawai lidah. No. 352, Ula-ula besar, Payong haram, Sumbu layang. No. 353, Payong ubor-ubor tiga ringkat and Payong tinggi. No. 354, Panji-panji, Chogan istiadat, Chogan ugama. No. 355, Lambang duli yang maha mulia and Mahligai.

1986   Litho.   Perf. 12½
350 A63	10c multicolored	.15	.15
351 A63	10c multicolored	.15	.15
352 A63	75c multicolored	.68	.68
353 A63	75c multicolored	.68	.68
354 A63	$2 multicolored	1.75	1.75
355 A63	$2 multicolored	1.75	1.75
	Nos. 350-355 (6)	5.16	5.16

Intl. Peace Year — A64

1986, Oct. 24   Litho.   Perf. 12
356 A64	50c Peace doves	.48	.48
357 A64	75c Hands	.68	.68
358 A64	$1 Peace symbols	.88	.88
	Nos. 356-358 (3)	2.04	2.04

Natl. Anti-Drug Campaign Posters — A65   Brass Artifacts — A66

1987, Mar. 15   Litho.   Perf. 12
359 A65	10c Jail	.15	.15
360 A65	75c Noose	.65	.65
361 A65	$1 Execution	.88	.88
	Nos. 359-361 (3)	1.68	1.68

1987, July 15
362 A66	50c Kiri (kettle)	.45	.45
363 A66	50c Langguai (bowl)	.45	.45
364 A66	50c Badil (cannon)	.45	.45
365 A66	50c Pelita (lamp)	.45	.45
	Nos. 362-365 (4)	1.80	1.80

See Nos. 388-391.

Dewan Bahasa Dan Pustaka, 25th Anniv. — A67

Illustration reduced.

1987, Sept. 29   Perf. 13½x13
366 A67	Strip of 3	1.75	1.75
a.	10c multicolored	.15	.15
b.	50c multicolored	.30	.30
c.	$2 multicolored	1.25	1.25

Language and Literature Bureau.

ASEAN, 20th Anniv. — A68

1987, Aug. 8   Litho.   Perf. 14x13½
367 A68	20c Map	.18	.18
368 A68	50c Year dates	.45	.45
369 A68	$1 Flags, emblem	.90	.90
	Nos. 367-369 (3)	1.53	1.53

World Food Day A70

Fruit: a, Artocarpus odoratissima. b, Canarium odontophyllum mig. c, Litsea garciae. d, Mangifera foetida lour.

1987, Oct. 31   Perf. 12½
370	Strip of 4	1.80	1.80
a.-d.	A70 50c any single	.45	.45

See Nos. 374, 405, 423, 457-460.

Intl. Year of Shelter for the Homeless A71

Various houses.

1987, Nov. 28   Litho.   Perf. 13
371 A71	50c multi	.48	.48
372 A71	75c multi, diff.	.70	.70
373 A71	$1 multi, diff.	.95	.95
	Nos. 371-373 (3)	2.13	2.13

Fruit Type of 1987
Without FAO Emblem, Dated 1988

Fruit: a, Durio. b, Durio oxleyanus. c, Durio graveolens (cross section at L). d, Durio graveolens (cross section at R).

1988, Jan. 30   Litho.   Perf. 12
374	Strip of 4	2.00	2.00
a.-d.	A70 50c, any single	.50	.50

Opening of Malay Technology Museum — A72

1988, Feb. 29   Perf. 12½x12
375 A72	10c Wooden lathe	.15	.15
376 A72	75c Water wheel, buffalo	.75	.75
377 A72	$1 Bird caller in blind	1.00	1.00
	Nos. 375-377 (3)	1.90	1.90

Handwoven Cloth — A73

Designs: 10c, Kain Beragi Bunga Sakah-Sakah Dan Bunga Cengkih. 20c, Kain Jong Sarat. 25c, Kain Si Pugut. 40c, Kain Si Pugut Bunga Berlapis. 75c, Kain Si Lobang Bangsi Bunga Belitang Kipas.

1988, Apr. 30   Litho.   Perf. 12
378 A73 10c multicolored .15 .15
379 A73 20c org brown & blk .20 .20
380 A73 25c multicolored .25 .25
381 A73 40c multicolored .40 .40
382 A73 75c multicolored .75 .75
a. Souvenir sheet of 5, #378-382 + label 1.70 1.70
Nos. 378-382 (5) 1.75 1.75

1988, Sept. 29   Litho.   Perf. 12

Designs: 10c, Kain Beragi. 20c, Kain Bertabur. 25c, Kain Sukma Indra. 40c, Kain Si Pugut Bunga Bersusup. 75c, Kain Beragi Si Lobang Bangsi Bunga Cendera Kesuma.

383 A73 10c multicolored .15 .15
384 A73 20c multicolored .20 .20
385 A73 25c multicolored .25 .25
386 A73 40c multicolored .40 .40
387 A73 75c multicolored .75 .75
a. Souvenir sheet of 5, #383-387 1.70 1.70
Nos. 383-387 (5) 1.75 1.75

Brass Artifacts Type of 1987

1988, June 30   Litho.   Perf. 12
388 A66 50c Celapa (repousse box) .50 .50
389 A66 50c Gangsa (footed plate) .50 .50
390 A66 50c Periok (lidded pot) .50 .50
391 A66 50c Lampong (candlestick) .50 .50
Nos. 388-391 (4) 2.00 2.00

Coronation of Sultan Hassanal Bolkiah, 20th Anniv. — A74

1988, Aug. 1   Litho.   Perf. 14
392 A74 20c shown .20 .20
393 A74 75c Reading from the Koran .75 .75
Size: 26x62mm
Perf. 12½x13
394 A74 $2 In full regalia 2.00 2.00
a. Souvenir sheet of 3, #392-394 3.00 3.00
Nos. 392-394 (3) 2.95 2.95

Eradicate Malaria, WHO 40th Anniv. A75

1988, Dec. 17   Litho.   Perf. 14x13½
395 A75 25c Mosquito .25 .25
396 A75 35c Extermination .35 .35
397 A75 $2 Microscope, infected blood cells 2.10 2.10
Nos. 395-397 (3) 2.70 2.70

Natl. Day — A76

1989, Feb. 23   Litho.   Perf. 12
Size of 60c: 22x54½mm
398 A76 20c Sultan Bolkiah, officials .20 .20
399 A76 30c Honor guard .30 .30
400 A76 60c Fireworks, palace, vert. .60 .60
401 A76 $2 Religious ceremony 2.00 2.00
a. Souvenir sheet of 4, #398-401 3.20 3.20
Nos. 398-401 (4) 3.10 3.10

Independence from Britain, 5th anniv.

Solidarity with the Palestinians A77

1989, Apr. 1   Litho.   Perf. 13½
402 A77 20c shown .20 .20
403 A77 75c Map, flag .75 .75
404 A77 $1 Dome of the Rock 1.00 1.00
Nos. 402-404 (3) 1.95 1.95

Fruit Type of 1987
Without FAO Emblem, Dated 1989

Designs: a, Daemonorops fissa. b, Eleiodoxa conferia. c, Salacca zalacca. d, Calamus ornatus.

1989, Oct. 31   Litho.   Perf. 12
405 Strip of 4 2.50 2.50
a.-d. A70 60c any single .82 .82

Oil and Gas Industry, 60th Anniv. A79

1989, Dec. 28   Perf. 13½
406 A79 20c Drill .22 .22
407 A79 60c Tanker .65 .65
408 A79 90c Refinery 1.00 1.00
409 A79 $1 Rail transport 1.10 1.10
410 A79 $2 Offshore rig 2.20 2.20
Nos. 406-410 (5) 5.17 5.17

Brunei Museum, 25th Anniv. A80

1990, Jan. 1   Litho.   Perf. 12x12½
411 A80 30c Exhibits .30 .30
412 A80 60c Official opening, 1965 .60 .60
413 A80 $1 Museum exterior 1.00 1.00
Nos. 411-413 (3) 1.90 1.90

Intl. Literacy Year — A81

1990, July 15   Litho.   Perf. 12x12½
414 A81 15c multicolored .16 .16
415 A81 90c multicolored .95 .95
416 A81 $1 multicolored 1.10 1.10
Nos. 414-416 (3) 2.21 2.21

Tarsier — A82   **Fight Against AIDS — A83**

1990, Sept. 29   Litho.   Perf. 12
417 A82 20c shown .22 .22
418 A82 60c Eating leaves .68 .68
419 A82 90c Climbing tree 1.00 1.00
Nos. 417-419 (3) 1.90 1.90

1990, Dec. 1   Litho.   Perf. 13
420 A83 20c shown .22 .22
421 A83 35c AIDS transmission .35 .35
422 A83 90c Tombstone, skulls 1.00 1.00
Nos. 420-422 (3) 1.57 1.57

Fruit Type of 1987
Without FAO Emblem, Dated 1990

Fruit: a, Willoughbea (uncut core). b, Willoughbea (core cut in half). c, Willoughbea angustifolia.

1990, Dec. 31   Perf. 12½
423 Strip of 3 2.05 2.05
a.-c. A70 60c any single .68 .68

Proboscis Monkey — A84

1991, Mar. 30   Litho.   Perf. 13½x14
424 A84 15c shown .18 .18
425 A84 20c Head, facing .22 .22
426 A84 50c Sitting on branch .60 .60
427 A84 60c Adult with young .70 .70
Nos. 424-427 (4) 1.70 1.70

Teacher's Day A85

Design: 90c, Teacher at blackboard.

1991, Sept. 23   Litho.   Perf. 13½x14
428 A85 60c multicolored .70 .70
429 A85 90c multicolored 1.05 1.05

Brunei Beauty A86

1991, Oct. 1   Litho.   Perf. 13
430 A86 30c Three immature .35 .35
431 A86 60c Female .70 .70
432 A86 $1 Adult male 1.20 1.20
Nos. 430-432 (3) 2.25 2.25

Happy Family Campaign — A87

1991, Nov. 30   Litho.   Perf. 13
433 A87 25c Family, graduating son .25 .25
434 A87 60c Mothers, children .70 .70
435 A87 90c Adults, children, heart 1.05 1.05
Nos. 433-435 (3) 2.00 2.00

World Health Day — A88

1992, Apr. 7   Litho.   Perf. 13
436 A88 20c multicolored .25 .25
437 A88 50c multi, diff. .58 .58
Size: 48x28mm
438 A88 75c multi, diff. .90 .90
Nos. 436-438 (3) 1.73 1.73

Brunei-Singapore and Brunei-Malaysia-Philippines Fiber Optic Submarine Cables — A89

1992, Apr. 28   Litho.   Perf. 12
439 A89 20c Map .25 .25
440 A89 30c Diagram .35 .35
441 A89 90c Submarine cable 1.05 1.05
Nos. 439-441 (3) 1.65 1.65

Visit ASEAN Year A90

Designs: a, 20c, Sculptures. b, 60c, Judo exhibition. c, $1, Sculptures, diff.

1992, June 30   Litho.   Perf. 13½x14
442 A90 Strip of 3, #a.-c. 2.00 2.00

ASEAN, 25th Anniv. — A91   **A92**

1992, Aug. 8   Litho.   Perf. 14
443 A91 20c shown .25 .25
444 A91 60c Building .70 .70
445 A91 90c Views of member states 1.05 1.05
Nos. 443-445 (3) 2.00 2.00

1992, Oct. 5   Perf. 14x13½

Sultan in various forms of dress and: No. 446a, Coronation procession. b, Airport. c, New Law Court, Sultan's Palace. d, Ship and Brunei University. e, Mosque, buildings.

446 A92 25c Strip of 5, #a.-e. 1.50 1.50

Sultan Hassanal Bolkiah's Accession to the Throne, 25th Anniv.

Birds — A93

Designs: No. 447, Crested wood partridge, vert. No. 448, Long-tailed parakeet, vert. No. 449, Chestnut-breasted malkoha. No. 450, Asian paradise flycatcher, vert. No. 451, Magpie robin, vert. No. 452, White-rumped shama. No. 453, Great argus pheasant, vert. No. 454, Malay lorikeet, vert. No. 455, Black and red broadbill, vert.

Perf. 14x13½, 13½x14
1992-93   Litho.
447 A93 30c multicolored .38 .38
448 A93 30c multicolored .38 .38
449 A93 30c multicolored .38 .38
450 A93 60c multicolored .75 .75
451 A93 60c multicolored .75 .75
452 A93 60c multicolored .75 .75
453 A93 $1 multicolored 1.20 1.20
454 A93 $1 multicolored 1.20 1.20
455 A93 $1 multicolored 1.20 1.20
Nos. 447-455 (9) 6.99 6.99

Issued: #447, 450, 453, 12/30/92; #448, 451, 454, 1/27/93; others, 5/3/93.

Natl. Day, 10th
Anniv. — A94

10th anniv. emblem and: a, 10c, Natl. flag. b, 20c, Hands supporting inscription. c, 30c, Natl. day emblems, 1985-93. d, 60c, Emblem with star, crossed swords.

1994, June 16   Litho.   Perf. 13
456   A94   Strip of 4, #a.-d.   1.50   1.50

Fruit Type of 1987
Without FAO Emblem, Dated 1994

Designs: No. 457, Nephelium mutabile. No. 458, Nephelium xerospermoides. No. 459, Nephelium spp. No. 460, Nephelium macrophyllum.

1994, Aug. 8   Litho.   Perf. 13½x13
457   A70   60c multicolored   .75   .75
458   A70   60c multicolored   .75   .75
459   A70   60c multicolored   .75   .75
460   A70   60c multicolored   .75   .75
     Nos. 457-460 (4)   3.00   3.00

A95   A96

World Stop Smoking Day: 10c, Cigarette, lung, fetus over human figure. 15c, People throwing away tobacco, cigarettes, pipe. $2, Arms around world crushing out cigarettes.

1994, Sept. 1   Litho.   Perf. 13½x13
461   A95   10c multicolored   .15   .15
462   A95   15c multicolored   .20   .20
463   A95 $2 multicolored   2.50   2.50
     Nos. 461-463 (3)   2.85   2.85

1994, Oct. 7   Perf. 13½

Girl Guides in Brunei, 40th anniv.: a, Leader. b, Girl receiving award. c, Girl reading. d, Girls in various costumes. e, Girls camping out.

464   A96   40c Strip of 5, #a.-e.   2.50   2.50

Royal Brunei
Airlines, 20th
Anniv. — A97

Airplanes: 10c, Twin-engine propeller. 20c, Passenger jet attached to tow bar. $1, Passenger jet in air.

1994, Nov. 18   Litho.   Perf. 13½
465   A97   10c multicolored   .15   .15
466   A97   20c multicolored   .28   .28
467   A97 $1 multicolored   1.25   1.25
     Nos. 465-467 (3)   1.68   1.68

Values quoted in this catalogue are for stamps graded Very Fine and with no faults. An illustrated guide to grade is provided in the "Catalogue Information" section of the Introduction.

Intl. Day Against
Drug Abuse — A98

Healthy people wearing traditional costumes: 20c, 60c, $1.

1994, Dec. 30   Litho.   Perf. 13½
468   A98   Strip of 3, #a.-c.   2.25   2.25
     No. 468 is a continuous design.

City of Badar
Seri Begawan,
25th Anniv.
A100

Aerial view of city: 30c, In 1970. 50c, In 1980, with details of significant buildings. $1, In 1990.

1995, Oct. 4   Litho.   Perf. 13½
481   A100   30c multicolored   .40   .40
482   A100   50c multicolored   .70   .70
483   A100 $1 multicolored   1.40   1.40
     Nos. 481-483 (3)   2.50   2.50

A101   A102

UN headquarters: 20c, Delegates in General Assembly. 60c, Security Council. 90c, Exterior.

1995, Oct. 24   Perf. 14½x14
484   A101   20c multicolored   .30   .30
485   A101   60c multicolored   .85   .85

Size: 27x44mm
486   A101   90c multicolored   1.30   1.30
     Nos. 484-486 (3)   2.45   2.45
     UN, 50th anniv.

1995, Oct. 28   Perf. 13x13½

University of Brunei, 10th Anniv.: 30c, Students in classroom. 50c, Campus buildings. 90c, Sultan in procession.

487   A102   30c multicolored   .40   .40
488   A102   50c multicolored   .70   .70
489   A102   90c multicolored   1.30   1.30
     Nos. 487-489 (3)   2.40   2.40

A103   A104

Royal Brunei Police, 25th Anniv.: 25c, Policemen in various uniforms. 50c, Various tasks performed by police. 75c, Sultan reviewing police.

1996, Feb. 10   Litho.   Perf. 13½x13
490   A103   25c multicolored   .35   .35
491   A103   50c multicolored   .75   .75
492   A103   75c multicolored   1.10   1.10
     Nos. 490-492 (3)   2.20   2.20

1996, May 17   Litho.   Perf. 13½

World Telecommunications Day: 20c, Cartoon telephone, cordless telephone. 35c, Globe, telephone dial surrounded by communication devices. $1, Signals transmitting from earth, people communicating.

493   A104   20c multicolored   .30   .30
494   A104   35c multicolored   .50   .50
495   A104 $1 multicolored   1.45   1.45
     Nos. 493-495 (3)   2.25   2.25

A105   A106

Sultan: No. 496, Among people, in black attire. No. 497, Waving, in yellow attire. No. 498, In blue shirt. No. 499, Among people, wearing cream-colored robe.
$1, Hand raised in yellow attire.

1996, July 15   Litho.   Perf. 13
496   A105   50c multicolored   .75   .75
497   A105   50c multicolored   .75   .75
498   A105   50c multicolored   .75   .75
499   A105   50c multicolored   .75   .75
     Nos. 496-499 (4)   3.00   3.00

Souvenir Sheet

500   A105 $1 multicolored   1.40   1.40

Sultan Paduka Seri Baginda, 50th birthday.
A souvenir sheet of five $50 stamps exists.

1996, Nov. 11   Litho.   Perf. 13½

Terns.

501   A106   20c Black-naped tern   .30   .30
502   A106   30c Roseate tern   .45   .45
503   A106 $1 Bridle tern   1.45   1.45
     Nos. 501-503 (3)   2.20   2.20

No. 502 is spelled "Roslate" on stamp.

Sultan Hassanal Bolkiah
A107   A108

Perf. 14x13½

1996, Oct. 9   Wmk. 387
Background Color
504   A107   10c yellow green   .15   .15
505   A107   15c pale pink   .20   .20
506   A107   20c lilac pink   .30   .30
507   A107   30c salmon   .45   .45
508   A107   50c yellow   .75   .75
509   A107   60c pale green   .85   .85
510   A107   75c blue   1.10   1.10
511   A107   90c lilac   1.30   1.30
512   A108 $1 pink   1.45   1.45
513   A108 $2 orange yellow   2.90   2.90
514   A108 $5 light blue   7.25   7.20
515   A108 $10 bright yellow   14.50   14.50
     Nos. 504-515 (12)   31.20   31.15

Flowers
A109

1997   Litho.   Perf. 12
516   A109   20c Acanthus ebracteatus   .30   .30
517   A109   30c Lumnitzera littorea   .45   .45
518   A109 $1 Nypa fruticans   1.45   1.45
     Nos. 516-518 (3)   2.20   2.20

OCCUPATION STAMPS

Issued under Japanese Occupation
Stamps and Types of 1908-37
Handstamped in Violet, Red Violet, Blue or Red

府政国帝本日大

Perf. 14, 14x11½ (#N7)

1942-44   Wmk. 4
N1   A1   1c black   6.50   11.00
N2   A1   2c green   65.00   100.00
N3   A1   2c dull orange   3.50   6.00
N4   A1   3c green   27.50   65.00
N5   A1   4c orange   5.00   14.00
N6   A1   5c brown   5.50   14.00
N7   A2   6c slate gray   65.00   140.00
N8   A2   6c red   650.00   500.00
N9   A1   8c gray (RV)   650.00   825.00
N10   A2   8c carmine   5.00   10.00
N11   A1   10c violet, *yel*   10.00   17.50
N12   A2   12c blue   10.00   17.50
N13   A2   15c ultra   10.00   17.50
N14   A1   25c dk violet   22.50   65.00
N15   A1   30c org & red vio   110.00   275.00
N16   A1   50c blk, *green*   35.00   80.00
N17   A1 $1 red & blk, *bl*   60.00   100.00

                     Wmk. 3
N18   A1 $5 lake, *green*   800.   750.
N19   A1 $25 black, *red*   1,400.   1,250.

Overprints vary in shade. Nos. N3, N7, N10 and N13 without overprint are not believed to have been regularly issued.

大日本

郵務

No. 43 Surcharged in
Red

帝国郵便

1944   Wmk. 4   Perf. 14
N20   A1 $3 on 1c black   3,250.   3,250.
   a.   On No. N1   3,250.   3,250.

BULGARIA

ˌbəl-ˈgar-ē-ə

LOCATION — Southeastern Europe bordering on the Black Sea on the east and the Danube River on the north
GOVT. — Republic
AREA — 42,823 sq. mi.
POP. — 8,929,332 (1983)
CAPITAL — Sofia

In 1885 Bulgaria, then a principality under the suzerainty of the Sultan of Turkey, was joined by Eastern Rumelia. Independence from Turkey was obtained in 1908.

100 Centimes = 1 Franc
100 Stotinki = 1 Lev (1881)

Catalogue values for unused stamps in this country are for Never Hinged items, beginning with Scott 293 in the regular postage section, Scott B1 in the semi-postal section, Scott C15 in the airpost section, Scott CB1 in the airpost semi-postal section, Scott E1 in the special delivery section, Scott J47 in the postage due section, Scott O1 in the officials section, and Scott Q1 in the parcel post section.

Watermarks

Wmk.
145-
Wavy
Lines

Wmk. 168- Wavy Lines and EZGV in Cyrillic

Wmk. 275-
Entwined Curved Lines

Lion of Bulgaria
A1   A2   A3

Perf. 14½x15

1879, June 1   Wmk. 168   Typo.
Laid Paper

1	A1	5c black & yel	65.00	18.00
2	A1	10c black & grn	250.00	60.00
3	A1	25c black & vio	175.00	15.00
a.		Imperf.		
4	A1	50c black & blue	250.00	50.00
5	A2	1fr black & red	50.00	17.50

1881, June 10
6	A3	1s red & silver	12.50	2.50
7	A3	5s black & org	15.00	2.50
a.		Background inverted		1,750.
8	A3	10s black & grn	65.00	6.50
9	A3	15s red & grn	60.00	6.50
10	A3	25s black & vio	250.00	30.00
11	A3	30s blue & fawn	17.50	6.50

1882, Dec. 4
12	A3	3s orange & yel	1.00	.50
13	A3	5s green & pale green	6.00	.50
a.		5s rose, pale rose (error)	1,600.	1,300.
14	A3	10s rose & pale rose	8.00	.75
15	A3	15s red vio & pale lil	6.00	.40
16	A3	25s blue & pale blue	6.00	.50
17	A3	30s violet & grn	6.00	.75
18	A3	50s blue & pink	6.00	.75
		Nos. 12-18 (7)	39.00	4.15

See Nos. 207-210, 286.

A4   A5

Surcharged in Black, Carmine or Vermilion
1884, May 1
Typo. Surcharge
19	A4	3s on 10s rose (Bk)	95.00	30.00
20	A4	5s on 30s blue & fawn (C)	95.00	45.00
20A	A4	5s on 30s bl & fawn (Bk)	1,750.	1,750.
21	A5	15s on 25s blue (C)	140.00	40.00

On some values the surcharge may be found inverted or double.

1885, June
Litho. Surcharge
21B	A4	3s on 30s rose (Bk)	45.00	27.50
21C	A4	5s on 30s bl & fawn (V)	50.00	35.00

21D	A5	15s on 25s blue (V)	70.00	45.00
22	A5	50s on 1fr blk & red (Bk)	190.00	125.00

Forgeries of Nos. 19-22 are plentiful.

Word below left star in oval has 5 letters — A6   Third letter below left star is "A" — A7

1885, May 25
23	A6	1s gray vio & pale gray	12.00	5.00
24	A7	2s sl grn & pale gray	12.00	4.00

Word below left star has 4 letters — A8

Third letter below left star is "b" with cross-bar in upper half — A9   A10

1886-87
25	A8	1s gray vio & pale gray	1.00	.20
26	A9	2s sl grn & pale gray	1.00	.20
27	A10	1 1 black & red ('87)	27.50	3.00
		Nos. 25-27 (3)	29.50	3.40

For surcharge see No. 40.

A11

Perf. 10½, 11, 11½, 13, 13½
1889   Wove Paper   Unwmk.
28	A11	1s lilac	.16	.15
29	A11	2s gray	.60	.15
30	A11	3s bister brown	.40	.15
31	A11	5s yellow green	.25	.15
a.		Vert. pair, imperf. btwn.		
32	A11	10s rose	1.10	.15
33	A11	15s orange	.65	.15
34	A11	25s blue	1.00	.15
35	A11	30s dk brown	8.75	.15
36	A11	50s green	.60	.32
37	A11	1 1 orange red	.52	.38
		Nos. 28-37 (10)	14.03	
		Set value		1.50

The 10s orange is a proof.
Nos. 28-34 exist imperforate. Value, set $225.
See Nos. 39, 41-42. For overprints and surcharges see Nos. 38, 55-56, 77-81, 113.

No. 35 Surcharged in Black   15

1892, Jan. 26
38	A11	15s on 30s brn	10.00	1.00
a.		Inverted surcharge	70.00	52.50

1894   *Perf. 10½, 11, 11½*
Pelure Paper
39	A11	10s red	7.00	.50
a.		Imperf.	57.50	

No. 26 Surcharged in Red   01

Wmk. Wavy Lines (168)
1895, Oct. 25   *Perf. 14½x15*
Laid Paper
40	A9	1s on 2s	.75	.20
a.		Inverted surcharge		
b.		Double surcharge	62.50	62.50
c.		Pair, one without surcharge	125.00	125.00

This surcharge on No. 24 is a proof.

Wmk. Coat of Arms in the Sheet
1896, Apr. 30   *Perf. 11½, 13*
Wove Paper
41	A11	2 1 rose & pale rose	2.00	1.50
42	A11	3 1 black & buff	3.50	3.00

Coat of Arms — A14   Cherry Wood Cannon — A15

1896, Feb. 2   *Perf. 13*
43	A14	1s blue green	.32	.15
44	A14	5s dark blue	.32	.15
45	A14	15s purple	.50	.15
46	A14	25s red	4.75	.85
		Nos. 43-46 (4)	5.89	1.33

Baptism of Prince Boris.
Examples of Nos. 41-46 from sheet edges show no watermark.
Nos. 43, 45-46 were also printed on rough unwatermarked paper.

1901, Apr. 20   Litho.   Unwmk.
53	A15	5s carmine	1.25	.90
54	A15	15s yellow green	1.25	.90

Insurrection of Independence in April, 1876, 25th anniversary.
Exist imperf. Forgeries exist.

Nos. 30 and 36 Surcharged in Black   5   —

1901, Mar. 24   Typo.
55	A11	5s on 3s bister brn	1.75	.75
a.		Inverted surcharge	42.50	42.50
b.		Pair, one without surcharge	70.00	70.00
56	A11	10s on 50s green	2.25	.75
a.		Inverted surcharge	50.00	50.00
b.		Pair, one without surcharge	70.00	70.00

Tsar Ferdinand
A17   Fighting at Shipka Pass
A18

ONE LEV:
Type I - The numerals in the upper corners have, at the top, a sloping serif on the left side and a short straight serif on the right.
Type II - The numerals in the upper corners are of ordinary shape without the serif at the right.

1901-05   Typo.   *Perf. 12½*
57	A17	1s vio & gray blk	.15	.15
58	A17	2s brnz grn & ind	.15	.15
a.		Imperf.		
59	A17	3s orange & ind	.15	.15
60	A17	5s emerald & brn	2.25	.15
61	A17	10s rose & blk	1.50	.15
62	A17	15s claret & gray blk	.65	.15
63	A17	25s blue & blk	.65	.15
64	A17	30s bis & gray blk	15.00	.15
65	A17	50s dk blue & brn	.80	.15
66	A17	1 1 red org & brnz grn, type I	2.00	.15
67	A17	1 1 brn red & brnz grn, II ('05)	45.00	1.75
68	A17	2 1 carmine & blk	4.00	.85
69	A17	3 1 slate & red brn	5.00	1.90
		Nos. 57-69 (13)	77.30	
		Set value		4.50

For surcharges see Nos. 73, 83-85, 87-88.

1902, Aug. 29   Litho.   *Perf. 11½*
70	A18	5s lake	1.00	.35
71	A18	10s blue green	1.00	.35
72	A18	15s blue	5.25	1.65
		Nos. 70-72 (3)	7.25	2.35

Battle of Shipka Pass, 1877.
Imperf. copies are proofs.
Excellent forgeries of Nos. 70 to 72 exist.

No. 62 Surcharged in Black   10

1903, Oct. 1   *Perf. 12½*
73	A17	10s on 15s	5.00	.35
a.		Inverted surcharge	57.50	50.00
b.		Double surcharge	57.50	50.00
c.		Pair, one without surcharge	100.00	100.00
d.		10s on 10s rose & black	275.00	275.00

Ferdinand in 1887 and 1907 — A19

1907, Aug. 12   Litho.   *Perf. 11½*
74	A19	5s deep green	9.00	.90
75	A19	10s red brown	16.00	.90
76	A19	25s deep blue	24.00	1.75
		Nos. 74-76 (3)	49.00	3.55

Accession to the throne of Ferdinand I, 20th anniversary.
Nos. 74-76 imperf. are proofs. Nos. 74-76 exist in pairs imperforate between.

Stamps of 1889 Overprinted   1909

1909
77	A11	1s lilac	1.00	.50
a.		Inverted overprint	21.00	17.50
b.		Double overprint, one inverted	25.00	25.00
78	A11	5s yellow green	1.00	.50
a.		Inverted overprint	25.00	25.00
b.		Double overprint	25.00	25.00

With Additional Surcharge   5   or   10

79	A11	5s on 30s brown (Bk)	1.50	.18
a.		"5" double	700.00	550.00
b.		"1990" for "1909"		
80	A11	10s on 15s org (Bk)	1.50	.40
a.		Inverted surcharge	17.50	17.50
b.		"1909" omitted	27.50	27.50
81	A11	10s on 50s dk grn (R)	1.50	.40
a.		"1990" for "1909"	100.00	100.00
b.		Black surcharge	52.50	52.50

Nos. 62 & 64 Surcharged with Value Only
83	A17	5s on 15s (Bl)	1.75	.60
a.		Inverted surcharge	21.00	21.00
84	A17	10s on 15s (Bl)	4.50	.40
a.		Inverted surcharge	21.00	21.00
85	A17	25s on 30s (R)	5.75	.90
a.		Double surcharge	70.00	70.00
b.		"2" of "25" omitted	87.50	87.50
c.		Blue surcharge	275.00	175.00

1910

Nos. 59 and 62 Surcharged in Blue   5

1910, Oct.
87	A17	1s on 3s	3.50	.75
a.		"1910" omitted	21.00	
88	A17	5s on 15s	1.50	.50

Tsar Assen's Tower (Crown over lion)
A20   Tsar Ferdinand
A21

City of Trnovo
A22   Tsar Ferdinand
A23

Ferdinand
A24

Isker River
A25

Ferdinand
A26

Rila Monastery
(Crown at UR)
A27

Tsar and
Princes — A28

Ferdinand in
Robes of Ancient
Tsars — A29

Monastery of Holy
Trinity — A30

View of
Varna — A31

1911, Feb. 14   **Engr.**   **Perf. 12**

89	A20	1s myrtle green	.16	.15
90	A21	2s car & blk	.16	.15
91	A22	3s lake & blk	.40	.15
92	A23	5s green & blk	1.00	.15
93	A24	10s dp red & blk	1.40	.15
94	A25	15s brown bister	2.50	.15
95	A26	25s ultra & blk	.50	.15
96	A27	30s blue & blk	6.75	.16
97	A28	50s ocher & blk	16.00	.22
a.		Center inverted		2,250.
98	A29	1 l chocolate	6.00	.28
99	A30	2 l dull pur & blk	1.65	.90
100	A31	3 l blue vio & blk	6.75	3.00
		Nos. 89-100 (12)	43.27	5.61

See Nos. 114-120, 161-162. For overprints and surcharges see Nos. 104-112, 188, B8, Greece N167-N178, N182-N187, Thrace 16-21, Romania 2N1-2N4.

Tsar
Ferdinand — A32

1912, Aug. 2   **Typo.**   **Perf. 12½**

101	A32	5s olive green	2.25	.70
a.		5s pale green	275.00	125.00
102	A32	10s claret	3.50	1.50
103	A32	25s slate	5.00	1.75
		Nos. 101-103 (3)	10.75	3.95

25th year of reign of Tsar Ferdinand.

ОСВОБ. ВОЙНА

Nos. 89-95
Overprinted in Various
Colors

1912-1913

1913, Aug. 6   **Engr.**

104	A20	1s myrtle grn (C)	.15	.15
105	A21	2s car & blk (Bl)	.15	.15
107	A22	3s lake & blk (Bl Bk)	.18	.15
108	A23	5s grn & blk (R)	.15	.15
109	A24	10s dp red & blk (Bk)	.28	.15

110	A25	15s brown bis (G)	.55	.26
111	A26	25s ultra & blk (R)	2.75	.38
		Nos. 104-111 (7)	4.21	
		Set value		1.00

Victory over the Turks in Balkan War of 1912-1913.

10 ст.

No. 95 Surcharged in Red

——

1915, July 6

112	A26	10s on 25s	.50	.15

No. 28 Surcharged in Green

3 СТОТИНКИ

113	A11	3s on 1s lilac	3.50	4.50

Types of 1911 Re-engraved

1915, Nov. 7   **Perf. 11½, 14**

114	A20	1s dk bl grn	.15	.15
115	A23	5s grn & brn vio	1.40	.15
116	A24	10s red brn & brnsh blk	.22	.15
117	A25	15s olive green	.22	.15
118	A26	25s indigo & blk	.22	.15
119	A27	30s ol grn & red brn	.22	.15
120	A29	1 l dark brown	.32	.28
		Nos. 114-120 (7)	2.75	
		Set value		.55

Widths: No. 114 is 19½mm; No. 89, 18½mm. No. 118 is 19¼mm; No. 95, 18¼mm. No. 120 is 20mm; No. 98, 19mm. The re-engraved stamps also differ from the 1911 issue in many details of design. Nos. 114-120 exist imperforate.
The 5s and 10s exist perf. 14x11½.
For Nos. 114-116 and 118 overprinted with Cyrillic characters and "1916-1917," see Romania Nos. 2N1-2N4.

Coat of
Arms — A33

Peasant and
Bullock — A34

Soldier and Mt.
Sonichka — A35

View of Nish — A36

Town and Lake
Okhrida — A37

Demir-Kapiya (Iron
Gate) — A37a

View of
Gevgeli — A38

Perf. 11½, 12½x13, 13x12½
1917-19   **Typo.**

122	A33	5s green	.28	.15
123	A34	15s slate	.15	.15
124	A35	25s blue	.15	.15
125	A36	30s orange	.15	.15
126	A37	50s violet	.52	.28
126A	A37a	2 l brn org ('19)	.52	.35
127	A38	3 l claret	.80	.75
		Nos. 122-127 (7)	2.57	1.98

Liberation of Macedonia. A 1 l dark green was prepared but not issued. Value $1.65.
For surcharges see Nos. B9-B10, B12.

View of
Veles — A39

Monastery of St.
Clement at
Okhrida — A40

1918   **Perf. 13x14**

128	A39	1s gray	.15	.15
129	A40	5s green	.15	.15
		Set value	.15	.15

Tsar Ferdinand
A41

Plowing with Oxen
A42

1918, July 1   **Perf. 12½x13**

130	A41	1s dark green	.15	.15
131	A41	2s dark brown	.15	.15
132	A41	3s indigo	.30	.16
133	A41	10s brown red	.30	.16
		Set value	.75	.50

Ferdinand's accession to the throne, 30th anniv.

1919   **Perf. 13½x13**

134	A42	1s gray	.15	.15

Sobranye
Palace — A43   Tsar Boris
III — A44

1919   **Perf. 11½x12, 12x11½**

135	A43	1s black	.15	.15
137	A43	2s olive green	.15	.15
		Set value	.15	.15

For surcharges see Nos. 186, B1.

1919, Oct. 3

138	A44	3s orange brn	.15	.15
139	A44	5s green	.15	.15
140	A44	10s rose red	.15	.15
141	A44	15s violet	.15	.15
142	A44	25s deep blue	.15	.15
143	A44	30s chocolate	.18	.15
144	A44	50s yellow brn	.18	.15
		Set value	.65	.35

1st anniv. of enthronement of Tsar Boris III.
Nos. 135-144 exist imperforate.
For surcharges see Nos. 187, B2-B7.

Birthplace of
Vazov at Sopot
and
Cherrywood
Cannon — A47

"The Bear Fighter"-a
Character from "Under
the Yoke" — A48

Ivan Vazov in
1870 and
1920 — A49

Vazov — A50

The Monk
Paisii — A52

Homes of
Vazov at
Plovdiv and
Sofia — A51

1920, Oct. 20   **Photo.**   **Perf. 11½**

147	A47	30s brown red	.15	.15
148	A48	50s dark green	.15	.15
149	A49	1 l drab	.22	.28
150	A50	2 l light brown	.60	.60
151	A51	3 l black violet	.95	.65
152	A52	5 l deep blue	1.10	.80
		Nos. 147-152 (6)	3.17	2.63

70th birthday of Ivan Vazov (1850-1921), Bulgarian poet and novelist.
Several values of this series exist imperforate and in pairs imperforate between.

Tsar Ferdinand
A53   A54

Mt.
Shar — A55

Bridge over Vardar
River — A56

View of
Ohrid — A57

Perf. 13x14, 14x13
1921, June 11   **Typo.**

153	A53	10s claret	.15	.15
154	A54	10s claret	.15	.15
155	A55	10s claret	.15	.15
156	A56	10s rose lil	.15	.15
157	A57	20s blue	.28	.16
		Set value	.55	.36

Nos. 153-157 were intended to be issued in 1915 to commemorate the liberation of Macedonia. They were not put in use until 1921. A 50s violet was prepared but never placed in use. Value $1.75.

View of
Sofia — A58

"The Liberator,"
Monument to
Alexander II
A59

Monastery at Shipka Pass — A62

Tsar Boris III — A63

Harvesting Grain — A64

Tsar Assen's Tower (No crown over lion) — A65

Rila Monastery (Rosette at upper right) — A66

1921-23   Engr.   Perf. 12

158 A58	10s blue gray	.15	.15
159 A59	20s deep green	.15	.15
160 A63	25s blue grn ('22)	.15	.15
161 A22	50s orange	.15	.15
162 A22	50s dk blue ('23)	2.50	2.50
163 A22	75s dull vio	.15	.15
164 A62	75s dp blue ('23)	.30	.15
165 A63	1 l carmine	.30	.16
166 A63	1 l dp blue ('22)	.30	.15
167 A64	2 l brown	.32	.15
168 A65	3 l brown vio	.38	.15
169 A66	5 l lt blue	2.50	.32
170 A63	10 l violet brn	6.75	1.10
	Nos. 158-170 (13)	14.10	5.43

For surcharge see No. 189.

Bourchier in Bulgarian Costume A67

James David Bourchier A68

View of Rila Monastery A69

1921, Dec. 31

171 A67	10s red orange	.15	.15
172 A67	20s orange	.15	.15
173 A68	30s dp gray	.15	.15
174 A68	50s bluish gray	.15	.15
175 A68	1 l dull vio	.18	.15
176 A69	1½ l olive grn	.18	.15
177 A69	2 l deep green	.18	.15
178 A69	3 l Prus blue	.45	.20
179 A69	5 l red brown	.85	.35
	Set value	2.00	1.00

Death of James D. Bourchier, Balkan correspondent of the London Times.
For surcharges see Nos. B13-B16.

Postage Due Stamps of 1919-22 Surcharged

a

10
СТОТИНКИ

1924

182 D6	10s on 20s yellow	.15	.15
183 D6	20s on 5s gray grn	.15	.15
a.	20s on 5s emerald	7.00	7.00
184 D6	20s on 10s violet	.15	.15
185 D6	20s on 30s orange	.15	.15
	Set value	.35	.35

Nos. 182 to 185 were used for ordinary postage.

Regular Issues of 1919-23 Surcharged in Blue or Red:

1 ЛЕВЪ
b

3 ЛЕВА
c

186 A43 (a)	10s on 1s black (R)	.15	.15
187 A44 (b)	1 l on 5s emer (Bl)	.15	.15
188 A22 (c)	3 l on 50s dk bl (R)	.20	.15
189 A63 (b)	6 l on 1 l car (Bl)	.60	.20
	Set value	1.10	.60

The surcharge of No. 188 comes in three types: normal, thick and thin.
#182, 184-189 exist with inverted surcharge.

Lion of Bulgaria
A70   A71

Tsar Boris III — A72

New Sofia Cathedral — A73

Harvesting — A74

1925   Typo.   Perf. 13, 11½

191 A70	10s red & bl, pink	.15	.15
192 A70	15s car & org, blue	.15	.15
193 A70	30s blk & buff	.15	.15
a.	Cliche of 15s in plate of 30s		
194 A71	50s choc, green	.15	.15
195 A72	1 l dull green	.48	.15
196 A73	2 l dk grn & buff	1.10	.15
197 A74	4 l lake & yellow	1.10	.15
	Set value	2.90	.50

Several values of this series exist imperforate and in pairs imperforate between.
See #199, 201. For overprint see #C2.

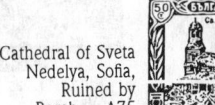
Cathedral of Sveta Nedelya, Sofia, Ruined by Bomb — A75

1926   Perf. 11½

198 A75	50s gray black	.15	.15

A76

A77

Type A72 Re-engraved. (Shoulder at left does not touch frame)

1926

199 A76	1 l gray	.45	.15
a.	1 l green	.45	.15
201 A76	2 l olive brown	.52	.15

Center Embossed

202 A77	6 l dp bl & pale lemon	1.10	.15
203 A77	10 l brn blk & brn org	4.00	.75
	Nos. 199-203 (4)	6.07	
	Set value		1.00

For overprints see Nos. C1, C3-C4.

Christo Botev — A78

Tsar Boris III — A79

1926, June 2

204 A78	1 l olive green	.32	.15
205 A78	2 l slate violet	.90	.15
206 A78	4 l red brown	.90	.35
	Nos. 204-206 (3)	2.12	
	Set value		.49

Botev (1847-76), Bulgarian revolutionary, poet.

Lion Type of 1881

1927-29   Perf. 13

207 A3	10s dk red & drab	.15	.15
208 A3	15s blk & org ('29)	.15	.15
209 A3	30s dk bl & bis brn ('28)	.15	.15
a.	30s indigo & buff	.15	.15
210 A3	50s blk & rose red ('28)	.15	.15
	Set value	.35	.25

1928, Oct. 3   Perf. 11½

211 A79	1 l olive green	.90	.15
212 A79	2 l deep brown	1.00	.15
	Set value		.15

St. Clement — A80

Konstantin Miladinov — A81

George S. Rakovski A82

Drenovo Monastery A83

Paisii — A84

Tsar Simeon — A85

Lyuben Karavelov A86

Vassil Levski A87

Georgi Benkovski A88

Tsar Alexander II A89

1929, May 12

213 A80	10s dk violet	.15	.15
214 A81	15s violet brn	.15	.15
215 A82	30s red	.15	.15
216 A83	50s olive grn	.25	.15
217 A84	1 l orange brn	.60	.15
218 A85	2 l dk blue	.70	.15
219 A86	3 l dull green	1.50	.45
220 A87	4 l olive brown	2.50	.22
221 A88	5 l brown	1.50	.35
222 A89	6 l Prus green	2.25	.90
	Nos. 213-222 (10)	9.75	2.82

Millenary of Tsar Simeon and 50th anniv. of the liberation of Bulgaria from the Turks.

Royal Wedding Issue

Tsar Boris and Fiancee, Princess Giovanna A90

Queen Ioanna and Tsar Boris — A91

1930, Nov. 12   Perf. 11½

223 A90	1 l green	.25	.24
224 A91	2 l dull violet	.22	.32
225 A90	4 l rose red	.22	.32
226 A91	6 l dark blue	.25	.38
	Nos. 223-226 (4)	.94	1.26

Fifty-five copies of a miniature sheet incorporating one each of Nos. 223-226 were printed and given to royal, governmental and diplomatic personages.

Tsar Boris III
A92   A93

Perf. 11½, 12x11½, 13

1931-37   Unwmk.

227 A92	1 l blue green	.25	.15
228 A92	2 l carmine	.40	.15
229 A92	4 l red org ('34)	.75	.15
230 A92	4 l yel org ('37)	.20	.15
231 A92	6 l dull green	.70	.15
232 A92	7 l dp bl ('37)	.20	.15
233 A92	10 l slate blk	8.75	.70
234 A92	12 l lt brown	.40	.18
235 A92	14 l lt brn ('37)	.28	.22
236 A93	20 l claret & org brn	1.00	.45
	Nos. 227-236 (10)	12.93	
	Set value		2.00

Nos. 230-233 and 235 have outer bars at top and bottom as shown on cut A92; Nos. 227-229 and 234 are without outer bars.
See Nos. 251, 279-280, 287. For surcharge see No. 252.

Balkan Games Issues

Gymnast — A95

Soccer — A96

Riding — A97

Swimmer
A100

"Victory"
A101

Designs: 6 l, Fencing. 10 l, Bicycle race.

1931, Sept. 18   *Perf. 11½*

237	A95	1 l lt green	.85	.50
238	A96	2 l garnet	.85	.50
239	A97	4 l carmine	1.90	.75
240	A95	6 l Prus blue	4.00	1.25
241	A95	10 l red org	9.50	3.75
242	A100	12 l dk blue	32.50	7.50
243	A101	50 l olive brn	30.00	22.50
		Nos. 237-243 (7)	79.60	36.75

1933, Jan. 5

244	A95	1 l blue grn	1.10	.95
245	A96	2 l blue	1.90	.95
246	A97	4 l brn vio	2.50	1.10
247	A95	6 l brt rose	4.75	1.65
248	A95	10 l olive brn	26.00	9.00
249	A100	12 l orange	55.00	18.00
250	A101	50 l red brown	100.00	82.50
		Nos. 244-250 (7)	191.25	114.15

Nos. 244-250 were sold only at the philatelic agency.

Boris Type of 1931
Outer Bars at Top and Bottom Removed

1933   *Perf. 13*

251	A92	6 l deep blue	.80	.15

Type of 1931 Surcharged in Blue **2**

1934

252	A92	2 (l) on 3 l ol brn	4.00	.25

Soldier
Defending
Shipka Pass
A102

Shipka Battle
Memorial
A103

Color-Bearer
A104

Veteran of the War of
Liberation, 1878
A105

Widow and
Orphans — A106

Perf. 10½, 11½

1934, Aug. 26   **Wmk. 145**

253	A102	1 l green	.45	.38
254	A103	2 l pale red	.45	.24
255	A104	3 l yellow	1.40	1.25
256	A105	4 l dk carmine	1.25	.60
257	A104	7 l dk blue	2.25	2.00
258	A106	14 l plum	6.00	5.75
		Nos. 253-258 (6)	11.80	10.22

Shipka Pass Battle memorial unveiling.
An unwatermarked miniature sheet incorporating one each of Nos. 253-258 was put on sale in 1938 in five cities at a price of 8,000 leva. Printing: 100 sheets.

1934, Sept. 21

259	A102	1 l bright green	.45	.38
260	A103	2 l dull orange	.45	.24
261	A104	3 l brn	1.40	1.25
262	A105	4 l rose	1.25	.60
263	A104	7 l blue	2.25	2.00
264	A106	14 l olive bister	6.00	5.75
		Nos. 259-264 (6)	11.80	10.22

An unwatermarked miniature sheet incorporating one each of Nos. 259-263 was issued.

Velcho A.
Djamjiyata
A108

Capt. G. S.
Mamarchev
A109

1935, May 5   *Perf. 11½*

265	A108	1 l deep blue	.95	.25
266	A109	2 l maroon	.95	.28

Bulgarian uprising against the Turks, cent.

Soccer Game — A110

Cathedral of
Alexander
Nevski — A111

Soccer Team — A112

Symbolical of
Victory — A113

Player and
Trophy — A114

The
Trophy — A115

1935, June 14

267	A110	1 l green	1.10	.90
268	A111	2 l blue gray	2.50	1.40
269	A112	4 l crimson	4.00	2.00
270	A113	7 l brt blue	7.75	2.50
271	A114	14 l orange	7.75	3.25
272	A115	50 l lilac brn	60.00	52.50
		Nos. 267-272 (6)	83.10	62.55

5th Balkan Soccer Tournament.

Gymnast on
Parallel
Bars — A116

Youth in "Yunak"
Costume — A117

Girl in "Yunak"
Costume
A118

Pole Vaulting
A119

Stadium,
Sofia — A120

Yunak
Emblem — A121

1935, July 10

273	A116	1 l green	1.90	1.10
274	A117	2 l lt blue	2.50	1.10
275	A118	4 l carmine	5.00	2.25
276	A119	7 l blue	5.00	3.00
277	A120	14 l dk brown	5.00	3.00
278	A121	50 l red	55.00	42.50
		Nos. 273-278 (6)	74.40	52.95

8th tournament of the Yunak Gymnastic Organization at Sofia, July 12-14.

Boris Type of 1931

1935   **Wmk. 145**   *Perf. 12½, 13*

279	A92	1 l green	.30	.15
280	A92	2 l carmine	20.00	.15
		Set value		.15

Janos Hunyadi
A122

King Ladislas
Varnenchik
A123

Varna Memorial — A124

King Ladislas
III — A125

Battle of Varna,
1444 — A126

1935, Aug. 4   *Perf. 10½, 11½*

281	A122	1 l brown org	1.10	.75
282	A123	2 l maroon	1.10	.75
283	A124	4 l vermilion	5.50	3.75
284	A125	7 l dull blue	2.50	1.25
285	A126	14 l green	2.50	1.25
		Nos. 281-285 (5)	12.70	7.75

Battle of Varna, and the death of the Polish King, Ladislas Varnenchik (1424-44).

Lion Type of 1881

1935   **Wmk. 145**   *Perf. 13*

286	A3	10s dk red & drab	.70	.15

Boris Type of 1933
Outer Bars at Top and Bottom Removed

1935

287	A92	6 l gray blue	.60	.15

Dimitr Monument
A127

Haji Dimitr
A128

Haji Dimitr and
Stefan
Karaja — A129

Taking the
Oath — A130

Birthplace of
Dimitr — A131

1935, Oct. 1   **Unwmk.**   *Perf. 11½*

288	A127	1 l green	1.25	.35
289	A128	2 l brown	1.75	.70
290	A129	4 l car rose	3.50	2.50
291	A130	7 l blue	4.50	3.50
292	A131	14 l orange	4.50	3.50
		Nos. 288-292 (5)	15.50	10.55

67th anniv. of the death of the Bulgarian patriots, Haji Dimitr and Stefan Karaja.

> Catalogue values for unused stamps in this section, from this point to the end of the section, are for Never Hinged items.

A132

A133

1936-39   *Perf. 13x12½, 13*

293	A132	10s red org ('37)	.15	.15
294	A132	15s emerald	.15	.15
295	A133	30s maroon	.15	.15
296	A133	30s yel brn ('37)	.15	.15
297	A133	30s Prus bl ('37)	.15	.15
298	A133	50s ultra	.15	.15
299	A133	50s dk car ('37)	.20	.15
300	A133	50s sl grn ('39)	.15	.15
		Set value	1.00	.50

Meteorological
Station, Mt.
Moussalla — A134

Peasant
Girl — A135

Town of
Nessebr
A136

1936, Aug. 16   Photo.   Perf. 11½
301 A134   1 l purple   1.40   .65
302 A135   2 l ultra   1.40   .60
303 A136   7 l dark blue   3.75 1.50
        Nos. 301-303 (3)   6.55 2.75

4th Geographical & Ethnographical Cong., Sofia, Aug. 1936.

Sts. Cyril and
Methodius
A137

Displaying the Bible to
the People
A138

1937, June 2
304 A137   1 l dk green   .22   .15
305 A137   2 l dk plum   .22   .15
306 A138   4 l vermilion   .45   .22
307 A137   7 l dk blue   1.75 1.10
308 A138 14 l rose red   1.75 1.10
        Nos. 304-308 (5)   4.39 2.72

Millennium of Cyrillic alphabet.

Princess Marie
Louise — A139

Tsar Boris
III — A140

1937, Oct. 3
310 A139   1 l yellow green   .35   .15
311 A139   2 l brown red   .26   .15
312 A139   7 l scarlet   .35   .15
        Nos. 310-312 (3)   .96
        Set value   .30

Issued in honor of Princess Marie Louise.

1937, Oct. 3
313 A140   2 l brown red   .35   .15

19th anniv. of the accession of Tsar Boris III to the throne. See No. B11.

National Products Issue

Peasants Bundling
Wheat
A141

Sunflower
A142

Wheat — A143

Chickens and
Eggs — A144

Cluster of
Grapes — A145

Rose and Perfume
Flask — A146

Strawberries
A147

Girl Carrying
Grape Clusters
A148

Rose — A149

Tobacco
Leaves — A150

1938   Perf. 13
316 A141 10s orange   .15   .15
317 A141 10s red org   .15   .15
318 A142 15s brt rose   .30   .15
319 A142 15s deep plum   .30   .15
320 A143 30s golden brn   .15   .15
321 A143 30s copper brn   .15   .15
322 A144 50s black   .15   .15
323 A144 50s indigo   .15   .15
324 A145   1 l yel grn   .65   .15
325 A145   1 l green   .65   .15
326 A146   2 l rose pink   .60   .15
327 A146   2 l rose brn   .60   .15
328 A147   3 l dp red lil   1.25   .15
329 A147   3 l brn lake   1.25   .15
330 A148   4 l plum   .80   .15
331 A148   4 l golden brn   .80   .15
332 A149   7 l vio blue   1.50   .55
333 A149   7 l dp blue   1.50   .55
334 A150 14 l dk brown   2.25   .90
335 A150 14 l red brn   2.25   .90
        Nos. 316-335 (20)   15.60
        Set value   4.00

Several values of this series exist imperforate.

Crown Prince Simeon
A151   A153

Designs: 2 l, Same portrait as 1 l, value at lower left. 14 l, similar to 4 l, but no wreath.

1938, June 16
336 A151   1 l brt green   .15   .15
337 A151   2 l rose pink   .15   .15
338 A153   4 l dp orange   .16   .16
339 A151   7 l ultra   .80   .38
340 A153 14 l dp brown   .80   .38
        Nos. 336-340 (5)   2.06
        Set value   .90

First birthday of Prince Simeon.

Tsar Boris III
A155   A156

Various Portraits of Tsar.

1938, Oct. 3
341 A155   1 l lt green   .15   .15
342 A156   2 l rose brown   .60   .15
343 A156   4 l golden brn   .15   .15
344 A156   7 l brt ultra   .30   .22
345 A156 14 l deep red lilac   .35   .26
        Nos. 341-345 (5)   1.55
        Set value   .65

Reign of Tsar Boris III, 20th anniv.

Early
Locomotive
A160

Designs: 2 l, Modern locomotive. 4 l, Train crossing bridge. 7 l, Tsar Boris in cab.

1939, Apr. 26
346 A160   1 l yel green   .20   .15
347 A160   2 l copper brn   .20   .15
348 A160   4 l red orange   1.40   .16
349 A160   7 l dark blue   3.25   .85
        Nos. 346-349 (4)   5.05 1.31

50th anniv. of Bulgarian State Railways.

Post Horns and
Arrows — A164

Central Post
Office,
Sofia — A165

1939, May 14   Typo.
350 A164   1 l yellow grn   .16   .15
351 A165   2 l brt carmine   .24   .15
        Set value   .15

Establishment of the postal system, 60th anniv.

Gymnast on
Bar — A166

Yunak
Emblem — A167

Discus
Thrower — A168

Athletic
Dancer — A169

Weight Lifter — A170

1939, July 7   Photo.
352 A166   1 l yel grn & pale grn   .35   .15
353 A167   2 l brt rose   .35   .15
354 A168   4 l brn & gldn brn   .52   .22
355 A169   7 l dk bl & bl   1.25   .65
356 A170 14 l plum & rose vio   5.50 2.75
        Nos. 352-356 (5)   7.97 3.92

9th tournament of the Yunak Gymnastic Organization at Sofia, July 4-8.

Tsar Boris
III — A171

Bulgaria's First
Stamp — A172

1940-41   Typo.
356A A171   1 l dl grn ('41)   .80   .15
357 A171   2 l brt crimson   .20   .15
        Set value   .15

1940, May 19   Photo.   Perf. 13
20 l, Similar design, scroll dated "1840-1940."
358 A172 10 l olive black   1.25   .85
359 A172 20 l indigo   1.25   .85

Cent. of 1st postage stamp. Exist imperf.

Peasant Couple
and Tsar
Boris — A174

Flags over Wheat
Field and Tsar
Boris — A175

Tsar Boris and
Map of
Dobrudja
A176

1940, Sept. 20
360 A174   1 l slate green   .15   .15
361 A175   2 l rose red   .15   .15
362 A176   4 l dark brown   .15   .15
363 A176   7 l dark blue   .60   .32
        Nos. 360-363 (4)   1.05
        Set value   .50

Return of Dobrudja from Romania.

Fruit
A177

Bees and Flowers
A178

Plowing
A179

Shepherd and Sheep
A180

Tsar Boris III — A181

Perf. 10, 10½x11½, 11½, 13
1940-44   Typo.   Unwmk.
364 A177 10s red orange   .15   .15
365 A178 15s blue   .15   .15
366 A179 30s olive brn ('41)   .15   .15
367 A180 50s violet   .15   .15
368 A181   1 l brt green   .15   .15
369 A181   2 l rose car   .15   .15
370 A181   4 l red orange   .15   .15
371 A181   6 l red vio ('44)   .28   .15
372 A181   7 l blue   .28   .15
373 A181 10 l blue grn ('41)   .30   .15
        Set value   1.50   .55

See Nos. 373A-377, 440. For overprints see Nos. 455-463, C31-C32.

1940-41   Wmk. 145   *Perf. 13*

373A	A180	50s violet ('41)	.15 .15
374	A181	1 l brt grn	.15 .15
375	A181	2 l rose car	.18 .15
376	A181	7 l dull blue	.45 .15
377	A181	10 l blue green	.65 .15
		Nos. 373A-377 (5)	1.58
		Set value	.35

Watermarked vertically or horizontally.

P. R. Slaveikov
A182

Sofronii, Bishop of
Vratza
A183

Saint Ivan
Rilski — A184

Martin S.
Drinov — A185

Monk
Khrabr — A186

Kolio
Ficheto — A187

1940, Sept. 23   Photo.   Unwmk.

378	A182	1 l brt bl grn	.15 .15
379	A183	2 l brt carmine	.15 .15
380	A184	3 l dp red brn	.15 .15
381	A185	4 l red orange	.15 .15
382	A186	7 l deep blue	1.00 .60
383	A187	10 l dp red brn	1.50 .85
		Nos. 378-383 (6)	3.10
		Set value	1.65

Liberation of Bulgaria from the Turks in 1878.

Johannes
Gutenberg
A188

N. Karastoyanov, 1st
Bulgarian Printer
A189

1940, Dec. 16

384	A188	1 l slate green	.15 .15
385	A189	2 l orange brown	.15 .15
		Set value	.25 .15

500th anniv. of the invention of the printing press and 100th anniv. of the 1st Bulgarian printing press.

Christo
Botev — A190

Monument to
Botev — A192

Botev with his
Insurgent
Band — A191

1941, May 3

386	A190	1 l dark blue green	.15 .15
387	A191	2 l crimson rose	.20 .15
388	A192	7 l dark brown	.65 .32
		Nos. 386-388 (3)	1.00
		Set value	.42

Christo Botev, patriot and poet.

Palace of Justice,
Sofia — A193

20 l, Workers' hospital. 50 l, National Bank.

1941-43   Engr.   *Perf. 11½*

389	A193	14 l lt gray brn ('43)	.20 .15
390	A193	20 l gray grn ('43)	.38 .16
391	A193	50 l lt bl gray	1.90 1.25
		Nos. 389-391 (3)	2.48 1.56

Macedonian
Woman — A196

City of
Okhrida — A200

Outline of
Macedonia and
Tsar Boris III
A197

View of Aegean
Sea — A198

Poganovski
Monastery
A199

1941, Oct. 3   Photo.   *Perf. 13*

392	A196	1 l slate grn	.15 .15
393	A197	2 l crimson	.15 .15
394	A198	2 l red org	.15 .15
395	A199	4 l org brn	.15 .15
396	A200	7 l dp gray bl	.38 .28
		Set value	.65 .50

Issued to commemorate the acquisition of Macedonian territory from neighboring countries.

Peasant Working
in a
Field — A201

Designs: 15s, Plowing. 30s, Apiary. 50s, Women harvesting fruit. 3 l, Shepherd and sheep. 5 l, Inspecting cattle.

1941-44

397	A201	10s dk violet	.15 .15
398	A201	10s dk blue	.15 .15
399	A201	15s Prus blue	.15 .15
400	A201	15s dk ol brn	.15 .15
401	A201	30s red orange	.15 .15
402	A201	30s dk slate grn	.15 .15
403	A201	50s blue vio	.15 .15
404	A201	50s red lilac	.15 .15
405	A201	3 l henna brn	.42 .25
406	A201	3 l dk brn ('44)	1.40 1.10
407	A201	5 l sepia	.52 .48
408	A201	5 l vio bl ('44)	1.40 1.10
		Set value	4.00 3.25

Girls
Singing — A207

Boys in
Camp — A208

Raising
Flag — A209

Folk
Dancers — A211

Camp
Scene — A210

1942, June 1   Photo.

409	A207	1 l dk bl grn	.15 .15
410	A208	2 l scarlet	.15 .15
411	A209	4 l olive gray	.15 .15
412	A210	7 l deep blue	.16 .15
413	A211	14 l fawn	.32 .22
		Nos. 409-413 (5)	.93
		Set value	.45

National "Work and Joy" movement.

Wounded
Soldier — A212

Soldier's
Farewell — A213

4 l, Aiding wounded soldier. 7 l, Widow & orphans at grave. 14 l, Tomb of Unknown Soldier. 20 l, Queen Ioanna visiting wounded.

1942, Sept. 7

414	A212	1 l slate grn	.15 .15
415	A213	2 l brt rose	.15 .15
416	A213	4 l yel org	.15 .15
417	A213	7 l dark blue	.15 .15
418	A213	14 l brown	.15 .15
419	A213	20 l olive blk	.22 .15
		Set value	.75 .36

Issued to aid war victims. No. 419 was printed in sheets of 50, alternating with 50 labels.

Legend of
Kubrat — A218

Cavalry
Charge — A219

Designs: 30s, Rider of Madara. 50s, Christening of Boris I. 1 l, School, St. Naum. 2 l, Crowning of Tsar Simeon by Boris I. 3 l, Golden era of Bulgarian literature. 4 l, Sentencing of the Bogomil Basil. 5 l, Proclamation of 2nd Bulgarian Empire. 7 l, Ivan Assen II at Trebizond. 10 l, Deporting the Patriarch Jeftimi. 14 l, Wandering minstrel. 20 l, Monk Paisii. 30 l, Monument, Shipka Pass.

1942, Oct. 12

420	A218	1 l bluish blk	.15 .15
421	A219	15s Prus grn	.15 .15
422	A219	30s dk rose vio	.15 .15
423	A219	50s indigo	.15 .15
424	A219	1 l slate grn	.15 .15
425	A219	2 l crimson	.15 .15
426	A219	3 l brown	.15 .15
427	A219	4 l orange	.15 .15
428	A219	5 l grnsh blk	.15 .15
429	A219	7 l dk blue	.15 .15
430	A219	10 l brown blk	.15 .15
431	A219	14 l olive blk	.15 .15
432	A219	20 l henna brn	.42 .15
433	A219	30 l black	.70 .42
		Set value	2.00 1.25

Tsar
Boris III — A234

Designs: Various portraits of Tsar.

1944, Feb. 28   Photo.   Wmk. 275   *Perf. 13, Imperf.*
Frames in Black

434	A234	1 l olive grn	.15 .15
435	A234	2 l red brown	.16 .15
436	A234	4 l brown	.20 .15
437	A234	5 l gray vio	.28 .16
438	A234	7 l slate blue	.28 .15
		Nos. 434-438 (5)	1.07
		Set value	.52

Tsar Boris III (1894-1943).

Tsar Simeon II — A239

1944, June 12   Typo.   Unwmk.   *Perf. 11½, 13*

439	A239	3 l red orange	.25 .15

Shepherd Type of 1940

1944

440	A180	50s yellow green	.20 .15

Parcel Post Stamps of
1944 Overprinted in Black
or Orange

ВСИЧКО
ЗА
ФРОНТА

1945, Jan. 25   *Perf. 11½*

448	PP5	1 l dk carmine	.15 .15
449	PP5	7 l rose lilac	.15 .15
450	PP5	20 l dk brn	.15 .15
451	PP5	30 l dk brn car	.15 .15
452	PP5	50 l red orange	.25 .15
453	PP5	100 l blue (O)	.60 .16

Overprint reads: "Everything for the Front."

No. 448 with Additional Surcharge of
New Value in Black

454	PP5	4 l on 1 l dk car	.15 .15
		Nos. 448-454 (7)	1.60
		Set value	.45

Nos. 368 to 370
Overprinted in Black

СЪБИРАЙТЕ
СТАРО
ЖЕЛЬЗО

1945, Mar. 15   *Perf. 11½, 13*

455	A181	1 l brt green	.25 .15
456	A181	2 l rose carmine	.40 .15
457	A181	4 l red orange	.60 .15

Overprint reads: "Collect old iron."

Overprinted in Black

СЪБИРАЙТЕ
ХАРТИЕНИ
ОТПАДЬЦИ

458	A181	1 l brt green	.25 .15
459	A181	2 l rose carmine	.40 .15
460	A181	4 l red orange	.60 .15

Overprint reads: "Collect discarded paper."

Overprinted in Black — **СЪБИРАЙТЕ ВСЪКАКВИ ПАРЦАЛИ**

461	A181	1 1 brt green	.25	.15
462	A181	2 1 rose carmine	.40	.15
463	A181	4 1 red orange	.60	.15

Nos. 455-463 (9)   3.75
Set value   .40

Overprint reads: "Collect all kinds of rags."

Oak Tree — A245

Imperf., Perf. 11½.

1945   Litho.   Unwmk.

464	A245	4 1 vermilion	.15	.15
465	A245	10 1 blue	.15	.15

Imperf

466	A245	50 1 brown lake	.15	.15

Set value   .25 .25

Slav Congress, Sofia, March, 1945.

A246   A247

A248   A249

A251   A252

A253   A254

2 1 and 4 1:
Type I. Large crown close to coat of arms.
Type II. Smaller crown standing high.

1945-46   Photo.   *Perf. 13*

469	A246	30s yellow grn	.15	.15
470	A247	50s peacock grn	.15	.15
471	A248	1 1 dk green	.15	.15
472	A249	2 1 choc (I)	.15	.15
a.		Type II	.15	.15
473	A249	4 1 dk blue (I)	.15	.15
a.		Type II	.15	.15
475	A251	5 1 red violet	.15	.15
476	A251	9 1 slate gray	.15	.15
477	A252	10 1 Prus blue	.15	.15
478	A253	15 1 brown	.15	.15
479	A254	20 1 carmine	.20	.15
480	A254	20 1 gray blk	.20	.15

Set value   1.00 .55

Breaking Chain — A255   1 Lev Coin — A256

Water Wheel — A257   Coin and Symbols of Agriculture and Industry — A258

Unwmk.

1945, June 4   Litho.   *Imperf.*
Laid Paper

481	A255	50 1 brn red, *pink*	.15	.15
482	A255	50 1 org, *pink*	.15	.15
483	A256	100 1 gray bl, *pink*	.20	.15
484	A256	100 1 brn, *pink*	.20	.15
485	A257	150 1 dk ol gray, *pink*	.35	.18
486	A257	150 1 dl car, *pink*	.35	.18
487	A258	200 1 dp bl, *pink*	.50	.30
488	A258	200 1 ol grn, *pink*	.50	.30

Nos. 481-488 (8)   2.40
Set value   1.25

Souvenir Sheets

489		Sheet of 4	3.00	1.75
a.	A255	50 1 violet blue	.30	.18
b.	A256	100 1 violet blue	.30	.18
c.	A257	150 1 violet blue	.30	.18
d.	A258	200 1 violet blue	.30	.18
490		Sheet of 4	3.00	1.75
a.	A255	50 1 brown orange	.30	.18
b.	A256	100 1 brown orange	.30	.18
c.	A257	150 1 brown orange	.30	.18
d.	A258	200 1 brown orange	.30	.18

Publicizing Bulgaria's Liberty Loan.

Olive Branch — A260

1945, Sept. 1   Typo.   *Perf. 13*

491	A260	10 1 org brn & yel grn	.15	.15
492	A260	50 1 dull red & dp grn	.25	.15

Set value   .31 .20

Victory of Allied Nations, World War II.

September 9, 1944 — A261   Numeral, Broken Chain — A262

1945, Sept. 7

493	A261	1 1 gray green	.15	.15
494	A261	4 1 deep blue	.15	.15
495	A261	5 1 rose lilac	.15	.15
496	A262	10 1 lt blue	.15	.15
497	A262	20 1 brt car	.18	.15
498	A261	50 1 brt bl grn	.42	.20
499	A261	100 1 orange brn	.48	.35

Set value   1.25 .80

1st anniv. of Bulgaria's liberation.

Old Postal Savings Emblem — A263   Child Putting Coin in Bank — A265

First Bulgarian Postal Savings Stamp — A264   Postal Savings Building, Sofia — A266

1946, Apr. 12

500	A263	4 1 brown org	.15	.15
501	A264	10 1 dk olive	.15	.15
502	A265	20 1 ultra	.15	.15
503	A266	50 1 slate gray	.52	.52

Set value   .75 .66

50th anniv. of Bulgarian Postal Savings.

Refugee Children — A267   Nurse Assisting Wounded Soldier — A269

Wounded Soldier — A268

Design: 35 1, 100 1, Red Cross hospital train.

1946, Apr. 4
Cross in Carmine

504	A267	2 1 dk olive	.15	.15
505	A268	4 1 violet	.15	.15
506	A268	10 1 plum	.15	.15
507	A268	20 1 ultra	.15	.15
508	A269	30 1 brown org	.15	.15
509	A268	35 1 gray blk	.15	.15
510	A269	50 1 violet brn	.22	.18
511	A268	100 1 gray brn	.70	.60

Set value   1.50 1.15

See Nos. 553 to 560.

Advancing Troops A271   Grenade Thrower A272

Attacking Planes — A274

Designs: 5 1, Horse-drawn cannon. 9 1, Engineers building pontoon bridge. 10 1, 30 1, Cavalry charge.

40 1, Horse-drawn supply column. 50 1, Motor transport column. 60 1, Infantry, tanks and planes.

1946, Aug. 9   Typo.   Unwmk.

512	A271	2 1 dk red vio	.15	.15
513	A272	4 1 dk gray	.15	.15
514	A271	5 1 dk org red	.15	.15
515	A274	6 1 black brn	.15	.15
516	A271	9 1 rose lilac	.15	.15
517	A271	10 1 dp violet	.15	.15
518	A271	20 1 dp blue	.24	.15
519	A271	30 1 red org	.24	.15
520	A271	40 1 dk ol bis	.30	.16
521	A271	50 1 dk green	.30	.16
522	A271	60 1 red brown	.42	.28

Set value   1.85 1.10

Bulgaria's participation in World War II.

Arms of Russia and Bulgaria A279   Lion Rampant A280

1946, May 23

523	A279	4 1 red orange	.15	.15
525	A279	20 1 turq green	.22	.15

Set value   .30 .21

Congress of the Bulgarian-Soviet Association, May 1946. The 4 1 exists in dk car rose and 20 1 in blue, value, set $7.

1946, May 25   *Imperf.*

526	A280	20 1 blue	.30	.22

Day of the Postage Stamp, May 26, 1946.

Alekandr Stamboliski A281   Flags of Albania, Romania, Bulgaria and Yugoslavia A282

1946, June 13   *Perf. 12*

527	A281	100 1 red orange	4.00	1.90

23rd anniversary of the death of Alekandr Stamboliski, agrarian leader.

1946, July 6   *Perf. 11½*

528	A282	100 1 black brown	.75	.50

1946 Balkan Games.
Sheet of 100 arranged so that all stamps are tete beche vert. and horiz., except 2 center rows in left pane which provide 10 vert. pairs that are not tete beche vert.

St. Ivan Rilski — A283   A286

A284

A285

754

Views of Rila
Monastery
A287

1946, Aug. 26

529	A283	1 l	red brown	.15	.15
530	A284	4 l	black brn	.15	.15
531	A285	10 l	dk green	.15	.15
532	A286	20 l	dp blue	.18	.15
533	A287	50 l	dk red	.80	.50
			Set value	1.25	.70

Millenary of Rila Monastery.

People's Republic

A288

1946, Sept. 15   Typo.

534	A288	4 l	brown lake	.15	.15
535	A288	20 l	dull blue	.15	.15
536	A288	50 l	olive bister	.18	.16
			Set value	.30	.26

No. 535 is inscribed "BULGARIA" in Latin
characters.
Referendum of Sept. 8, 1946, resulting in the
establishment of the Bulgarian People's Republic.

Partisan Army — A289   Snipers — A290

Soldiers: Past and
Present — A291

Design: 30 l, Partisans advancing.

1946, Dec. 2

537	A289	1 l	violet brn	.15	.15
538	A290	4 l	dull grn	.15	.15
539	A291	5 l	chocolate	.15	.15
540	A290	10 l	crimson	.15	.15
541	A289	20 l	ultra	.24	.15
542	A290	30 l	olive bister	.24	.15
543	A291	50 l	black	.28	.22
			Set value	1.00	.66

Relief Worker
and
Children — A294   Child with Gift
Parcels — A295

Waiting for Food
Distribution
A296   Mother and
Child
A297

1946, Dec. 30

545	A294	1 l	dk vio brn	.15	.15
546	A295	4 l	brt red	.15	.15
547	A295	9 l	olive bis	.15	.15
548	A294	10 l	slate gray	.15	.15
549	A296	20 l	ultra	.15	.15
550	A297	30 l	dp brn org	.15	.15
551	A296	40 l	maroon	.18	.15
552	A294	50 l	peacock grn	.32	.28
			Set value	.90	.72

"Bulgaria" is in Latin characters on No. 548.

Red Cross Types of 1946

1947, Jan. 31
Cross in Carmine

553	A267	2 l	olive bister	.15	.15
554	A268	4 l	olive black	.15	.15
555	A267	10 l	blue grn	.15	.15
556	A268	20 l	brt blue	.15	.15
557	A269	30 l	yellow grn	.30	.22
558	A268	35 l	grnsh gray	.32	.24
559	A269	50 l	henna brn	.48	.35
560	A268	100 l	dark blue	.70	.50
			Nos. 553-560 (8)	2.40	1.91

Laurel Branch, Allied
and Bulgarian
Emblems — A298   Dove of
Peace — A299

1947, Feb. 28

561	A298	4 l	olive	.15	.15
562	A299	10 l	brown red	.15	.15
563	A299	20 l	deep blue	.18	.16
			Set value	.30	.26

Return to peace at the close of World War II.
"Bulgaria" in Latin characters on No. 563.

A302

Guerrilla Fighters
A303   A304

1947, Jan. 21   Perf. 11½

567	A302	10 l	choc & brn org	.32	.16
568	A303	20 l	dk bl & bl	.32	.16
569	A304	70 l	dp claret & rose	18.00	8.00
			Nos. 567-569 (3)	18.64	8.32

Issued to honor the anti-fascists.

Hydroelectric
Station — A305

Miner
A306   Symbols of
Industry
A307

Tractor — A308

1947, Aug. 6

570	A305	4 l	olive green	.15	.15
571	A306	9 l	red brown	.15	.15
572	A307	20 l	deep blue	.18	.18
573	A308	40 l	olive brown	.42	.28
			Nos. 570-573 (4)	.90	
			Set value		.50

Exhibition Building
A309   Former Home of
Alphonse de
Lamartine
A310

Symbols of Agriculture
and
Horticulture — A311

1947, Aug. 31   Litho.   Unwmk.

574	A309	4 l	scarlet	.15	.15
575	A310	9 l	brown lake	.15	.15
576	A311	20 l	brt ultra	.20	.15
			Set value	.31	.18

Plovdiv Intl. Fair, 1947. See No. C54.

Perf. 11x11½, 11½x11

Basil Evstatiev
Aprilov — A312

1947, Oct. 19   Photo.   Perf. 11
| 577 | A312 | 40 l | brt ultra | .35 | .18 |

Cent. of the death of Basil Evstatiev Aprilov, educator and historian. See No. 603.

Bicycle
Race — A313

Basketball
A314   Chess
A315

Balkan Games: 20 l, Soccer players. 60 l, Four
flags of participating nations.

1947, Sept. 29   Typo.   Perf. 11½

578	A313	2 l	plum	.18	.15
579	A314	4 l	dk olive grn	.18	.15
580	A315	9 l	orange brn	.42	.15
581	A315	20 l	brt ultra	.80	.18
582	A315	60 l	violet brn	1.65	.75
			Nos. 578-582 (5)	3.23	1.38

People's Theater,
Sofia
A316   National
Assembly
A317

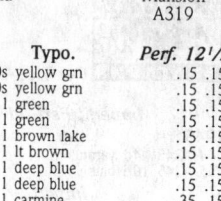

Central Post
Office, Sofia
A318   Presidential
Mansion
A319

1947-48   Typo.   Perf. 12½

583	A316	50s	yellow grn	.15	.15
584	A317	50s	yellow grn	.15	.15
585	A318	1 l	green	.15	.15
586	A319	1 l	green	.15	.15
587	A316	2 l	brown lake	.15	.15
588	A317	2 l	lt brown	.15	.15
589	A316	4 l	deep blue	.15	.15
590	A317	4 l	deep blue	.15	.15
591	A316	9 l	carmine	.35	.15
592	A317	20 l	deep blue	.75	.30
			Set value	1.50	.75

On Nos. 583-592 inscription reads "Bulgarian
Republic." No. 592 is inscribed in Latin characters.

Redrawn
НАРОДНА
added to inscription

593	A318	1 l	green	.15	.15
594	A318	2 l	brown lake	.15	.15
595	A318	4 l	deep blue	.15	.15
			Set value	.25	.15

Cyrillic inscription beneath design on Nos. 593-
595 reads "Bulgarian People's Republic."

Geno Kirov — A320

Actors' Portraits: 1 l, Zlatina Nedeva. 2 l, Ivan
Popov. 3 l, Athanas Kirchev. 4 l, Elena Snejina. 5 l,
Stoyan Bachvarov.

Perf. 10½

1947, Dec. 8   Unwmk.   Litho.

596	A320	50s	bister brn	.15	.15
597	A320	1 l	lt blue grn	.15	.15
598	A320	2 l	slate green	.15	.15
599	A320	3 l	dp blue	.15	.15
600	A320	4 l	scarlet	.15	.15
601	A320	5 l	red brown	.15	.15
			Set value, #596-601, B22-B26	1.60	1.00

National Theater, 50th anniversary.

Merchant Ship "Fatherland" — A321

1947, Dec. 19
| 602 | A321 | 50 l | Prus bl, *cream* | .45 | .15 |

B. E.
Aprilov — A322

Worker — A323

1948, Feb. 19 *Perf. 11*
603 A322 4 l brn car, *cream* .15 .15
Centenary of the death of Basil Evstatiev Aprilov, educator and historian.

1948, Feb. 29 Photo. *Perf. 11½x12*
604 A323 4 l dp blue, *cream* .15 .15
2nd Bulgarian Workers' Congress.

Self-education — A324

Accordion
Player — A325

Factory Recess
A326

Girl Throwing
Basketball
A327

1948, Mar. 31 **Photo.**
605 A324 4 l red .15 .15
606 A325 20 l deep blue .15 .15
607 A326 40 l dull green .20 .15
608 A327 60 l brown .60 .35
 Nos. 605-608 (4) 1.10
 Set value .60

Nicholas
Vaptzarov — A328

Portraits: 9 l, P. K. Iavorov. 15 l, Christo Smirnenski. 20 l, Ivan Vazov. 45 l, P. R. Slaveikov.

1948, May 18 *Perf. 11*
Cream Paper
611 A328 4 l brt ver .15 .15
612 A328 9 l lt brown .15 .15
613 A328 15 l claret .15 .15
614 A328 20 l deep blue .15 .15
615 A328 45 l green .32 .32
 Set value .60 .56

Soviet
Soldier — A329

Civilians Offering Gifts
to Soldiers — A330

Designs: 20 l, Soldiers, 1878 and 1944. 60 l, Stalin and Spasski Tower.

1948, July 5 **Photo.**
Cream Paper
616 A329 4 l brown org .15 .15
617 A330 10 l olive grn .15 .15
618 A330 20 l dp blue .15 .15
619 A329 60 l olive brn .42 .35
 Set value .62 .52
The Soviet Army.

Demeter
Blagoev — A331

Monument to Bishop
Andrey — A332

9 l, Gabriel Genov. 60 l, Marching youths.

1948, Sept. 6 **Litho.**
Cream Paper
620 A331 4 l dk brown .15 .15
621 A331 9 l brown org .15 .15
622 A332 20 l dp blue .15 .15
623 A332 60 l brown .52 .42
 Set value .69 .58
No. 623 is inscribed in Cyrillic characters.
Natl. Insurrection of 1923, 25th anniv.

Christo
Smirnenski
A333

Battle of
Grivitza, 1877
A334

1948, Oct. 2 Photo. *Perf. 11½*
Cream Paper
624 A333 4 l blue .15 .15
625 A333 16 l red brown .16 .15
 Set value .25 .15
Christo Smirnenski, poet, 1898-1923.

1948, Nov. 1
626 A334 20 l blue .15 .15
Romanian-Bulgarian friendship. See #C56-C57.

Bath, Gorna
Banya — A335

Bath,
Bankya — A336

Mineral Bath,
Sofia
A337

Maliovitza
A338

1948-49 **Typo.** *Perf. 12½*
627 A335 2 l red brown .15 .15
628 A335 3 l red orange .15 .15
629 A337 4 l deep blue .15 .15
630 A338 5 l violet brown .15 .15
631 A336 10 l red violet .15 .15
632 A338 15 l olive grn ('49) .20 .15
633 A335 20 l deep blue .75 .16
 Nos. 627-633 (7) 1.70
 Set value .50
Latin characters on No. 633. See No. 653.

Emblem of the
Republic — A339

1948-50
634 A339 50s red orange .15 .15
634A A339 50s org brn ('50) .15 .15
635 A339 1 l green .15 .15
636 A339 9 l black .15 .15
 Set value .30 .20

Botev's Birthplace,
Kalofer — A340

Christo
Botev — A341

Designs: 9 l, Steamer "Radetzky." 15 l, Kalofer village. 20 l, Botev in uniform. 40 l, Botev's mother. 50 l, Pen, pistol and wreath.

Perf. 11x11½, 11½

1948, Dec. 21 **Photo.**
Cream Paper
638 A340 1 l dk green .15 .15
639 A341 4 l violet brn .15 .15
640 A340 9 l violet .15 .15
641 A340 15 l brown .15 .15
642 A341 20 l blue .16 .15
643 A340 40 l red brown .25 .16
644 A341 50 l olive blk .35 .22
 Set value 1.00 .65
Botev, Bulgarian natl. poet, birth cent.

Lenin — A342

Lenin
Speaking — A343

1949, Jan. 24 Unwmk. *Perf. 11½*
Cream Paper
645 A342 4 l brown .15 .15
646 A343 20 l brown red .30 .18
 Set value .23
25th anniversary of the death of Lenin.

Road Construction
A344

Designs: 5 l, Tunnel construction. 9 l, Locomotive. 10 l, Textile worker. 20 l, Female tractor driver. 40 l, Workers in truck.

1949, Apr. 6 *Perf. 10½*
Inscribed: "CHM"
Cream Paper
647 A344 4 l dark red .15 .15
648 A344 5 l dark brown .15 .15
649 A344 9 l dk slate grn .22 .15
650 A344 10 l violet .25 .15
651 A344 20 l dull blue .60 .38
652 A344 40 l brown .95 .55
 Nos. 647-652 (6) 2.32
 Set value 1.28
Issued to honor the Workers' Cultural Brigade.

Type of 1948
Redrawn
Country Name and "POSTA" in Latin
Characters

1949 **Typo.** *Perf. 12½*
653 A337 20 l deep blue .55 .15

Miner — A345

1949 *Perf. 11x11½*
654 A345 4 l dark blue .20 .15

Prime Minister
George Dimitrov,
1882-1949 — A348

1949, July 10 **Photo.**
656 A347 4 l red brown .22 .15
657 A348 20 l dark blue .52 .16
 Set value .21

Power
Station — A349

Grain
Towers — A350

Farm Machinery
A351

Tractor Parade
A352

Agriculture and
Industry — A353

1949, Aug. 5 *Perf. 11½x11, 11x11½*
658 A349 4 l olive green .15 .15
659 A350 9 l dark red .15 .15
660 A351 15 l purple .18 .15
661 A352 20 l blue .55 .38
662 A353 50 l orange brn 1.75 .85
 Nos. 658-662 (5) 2.78 1.68
Bulgaria's Five Year Plan.

Grenade and
Javelin Throwers
A354

Hurdlers
A355

Motorcycle and Tractor — A356   Boy and Girl Athletes — A357

1949, Sept. 5
663	A354	4 l brown orange	.30	.15
664	A355	9 l olive green	.60	.22
665	A356	20 l violet blue	1.25	.65
666	A357	50 l red brown	3.00	1.25
		Nos. 663-666 (4)	5.15	2.27

Frontier Guards
A358   A359

1949, Oct. 31
667	A358	4 l chestnut brn	.15	.15
668	A359	20 l gray blue	.60	.26
		Set value		.31

See No. C60.

George Dimitrov A360   Allegory of Labor A361

Laborers of Both Sexes — A362   Workers and Flags of Bulgaria and Russia — A363

Perf. 11½

1949, Dec. 13   Photo.   Unwmk.
669	A360	4 l orange brn	.15	.15
670	A361	9 l purple	.18	.15
671	A362	20 l dull blue	.32	.22
672	A363	50 l red	.65	.45
		Nos. 669-672 (4)	1.30	
		Set value		.77

Joseph V. Stalin — A364   Stalin and Dove — A365

1949, Dec. 21
673	A364	4 l deep orange	.20	.15
674	A365	40 l rose brown	.60	.32
		Set value		.37

70th anniv. of the birth of Joseph V. Stalin.

Kharalamby Stoyanov — A366   Communications Strikers — A368

Railway Strikers — A367

1950, Feb. 15
675	A366	4 l yellow brown	.15	.15
676	A367	20 l violet blue	.22	.15
677	A368	60 l brown olive	.60	.38
		Nos. 675-677 (3)	.97	
		Set value		.50

30th anniv. (in 1949) of the General Railway and Postal Employees' Strike of 1919.

Miner — A369   Locomotive — A370

Shipbuilding A371   Tractor A372

Stalin Central Heating Plant — A374   Textile Worker — A375

Farm Machinery A373

1950-51   *Perf. 11½, 13*
678	A369	1 l olive	.15	.15
679	A370	2 l gray blk	.15	.15
680	A371	3 l gray blue	.20	.15
681	A372	4 l dk blue grn	1.75	.52
682	A373	4 l henna brn	.40	.15
682A	A373	9 l gray blk ('51)	.20	.15
683	A374	10 l dp plum ('51)	.28	.15
684	A375	15 l dk car ('51)	.40	.15
685	A375	20 l dk blue ('51)	.70	.40
		Nos. 678-685 (9)	4.23	
		Set value		1.30

No. 685 is inscribed in Latin characters. See Nos. 750-751A.

Vassil Kolarov (1877-1950) — A377

1950, Mar. 6   *Perf. 11½*
Size: 21½x31½mm
686	A377	4 l red brown	.15	.15

Size: 27x39½mm
687	A377	20 l violet blue	.26	.22
		Set value	.31	.27

No. 687 has altered frame and is inscribed in Latin characters.

Stanislav Dospevski, Self-portrait A378   King Kaloyan and Desislava A379

Plowman Resting, by Christo Stanchev A380

Statue of Dimtcho Debelianov, by Ivan Lazarov A381   "Harvest," by V. Dimitrov A382

Design: 9 l, Nikolai Pavlovich, self-portrait.

1950, Apr. 15   *Perf. 11½*
688	A378	1 l dk olive grn	.32	.15
689	A379	4 l dk red	.90	.22
690	A378	9 l chocolate	.90	.22
691	A380	15 l brown	1.50	.25
692	A380	20 l deep blue	2.00	.80
693	A381	40 l red brown	2.75	1.25
694	A382	60 l deep orange	4.00	1.65
		Nos. 688-694 (7)	12.37	4.54

Latin characters on No. 692.

Ivan Vazov (1850-1921), Poet and Birthplace A383

1950, June 26
695	A383	4 l olive green	.15	.15

Road Building — A384   Men of Three Races and "Stalin" Flag — A385

Perf. 11½x11, 11x11½

1950, Sept. 19
696	A384	4 l brown red	.15	.15
697	A385	20 l violet blue	.32	.16
		Set value	.40	.21

2nd National Peace Conference.

Molotov, Kolarov, Stalin and Dimitrov — A386   Spasski Tower and Flags — A387

Russian and Bulgarian Women — A388   Loading Russian Ship — A389

Perf. 11½

1950, Oct. 10   Unwmk.   Photo.
698	A386	4 l brown	.15	.15
699	A387	9 l rose carmine	.15	.15
700	A388	20 l gray blue	.20	.15
701	A389	50 l dk grnsh blue	1.10	.45
		Nos. 698-701 (4)	1.60	
		Set value		.67

2nd anniversary of the Soviet-Bulgarian treaty of mutual assistance.

St. Constantine Sanatorium — A390

2 l, 10 l, Children at seashore. 5 l, Rest home.

1950   Typo.
702	A390	1 l dark green	.15	.15
703	A390	2 l carmine	.15	.15
704	A390	5 l deep orange	.16	.15
705	A390	10 l deep blue	.42	.42
		Set value	.75	.42

Originally prepared in 1945 as "Sunday Delivery Stamps," this issue was released for ordinary postage in 1950.

Runners — A393

1950, Aug. 21   Photo.   *Perf. 11*
706	A393	4 l shown	.15	.15
707	A393	9 l Cycling	.15	.15
708	A393	20 l Shot put	.20	.20
709	A393	40 l Volleyball	.42	.42
		Nos. 706-709 (4)	.92	.92

Marshal Fedor I. Tolbukhin A394   Natives Greeting Tolbukhin A395

Perf. 11½x11, 11x11½

1950, Dec. 10   Photo.   Unwmk.
710	A394	4 l claret	.15	.15
711	A395	20 l dk blue	.35	.18
		Set value		.24

The return of Dobrich and part of the province of Dobruja from Romania to Bulgaria.

Dimitrov's
Birthplace
A396

George Dimitrov
A397   A398
Various Portraits, Inscribed:

Г.ДИМИТРОВ

Design: 2 l, Dimitrov Museum, Sofia.

1950, July 2   **Perf. 10½**
712 A396 50s olive grn   .15   .15
713 A397 50s brown   .15   .15
714 A397   1 l redsh brn   .22   .15
715 A396   2 l gray   .22   .15
716 A397   4 l claret   .40   .15
717 A397   9 l red brown   .60   .25
718 A398 10 l brown red   .65   .35
719 A396 15 l olive gray   .65   .35
720 A396 20 l dark blue   1.75   .55
    Nos. 712-720,C61 (10)   7.79
       Set value   2.90

1st anniversary of the death of George Dimitrov,
statesman. No. 720 is inscribed in Latin characters.

A. S. Popov — A400

1951, Feb. 10
722 A400   4 l red brown   .20   .15
723 A400 20 l dark blue   .55   .15
       Set value   .24

No. 723 is inscribed in Latin characters.

Arms of Bulgaria
A401   A402

1950   **Unwmk.**   **Typo.**   **Perf. 13**
724 A401   2 l dk brown   .15   .15
725 A401   3 l rose   .15   .15
726 A402   5 l carmine   .15   .15
727 A402   9 l aqua   .15   .15
                              .31   .20

Nos. 724-727 were prepared in 1947 for official
use but were issued as regular postage stamps Oct.
1, 1950.

Heroes Chankova,
Antonov-Malchik,
Dimitrov and
Dimitrova — A403

Stanke Dimitrov-
Marek
A404

George Kirkov
A405

George Dimitrov at
Leipzig — A406

Natcho Ivanov and
Avr.
Stoyanov — A407

9 l, Anton Ivanov. 15 l, Christo Michailov.

1951, Mar. 25   **Photo.**   **Perf. 11½**
728 A403   1 l red violet   .15   .15
729 A404   2 l dk red brn   .15   .15
730 A405   4 l car rose   .15   .15
731 A405   9 l orange brn   .45   .15
732 A405 15 l olive brn   .80   .22
733 A406 20 l dark brown   1.10   .15
734 A407 50 l olive gray   2.50   .90
    Nos. 728-734 (7)   5.30 2.27

First Bulgarian
Tractor
A408

First Steam
Roller — A409

First
Truck — A410

Bulgarian
Embroidery — A411

15 l, Carpet. 20 l, Tobacco & roses. 40 l, Fruits.

Perf. 11x10½
1951, Mar. 30   **Photo.**   **Unwmk.**
735 A408   1 l olive brn   .18   .15
736 A409   2 l violet   .28   .15
737 A410   4 l red brown   .50   .15
738 A411   9 l purple   .70   .15
739 A409 15 l deep plum   1.00   .28
740 A411 20 l violet blue   1.50   .32
741 A410 40 l deep green   2.50   .65

Perf. 13
Size: 23x18½mm
742 A408   1 l purple   .15   .15
743 A409   2 l Prus green   .28   .15
744 A410   4 l red brown   .28   .15
    Nos. 735-744 (10)   7.37
       Set value   1.70

See Nos. 894, 973. For surcharge see No. 973.

Turkish
Attack
on Mt.
Zlee Dol
A412

Designs: 4 l, Georgi Benkovski speaking to
rebels. 9 l, Cherrywood cannon of 1876 and Russian cavalry, 1945. 20 l, Rebel, 1876 and partisan,
1944. 40 l, Benkovski and Dimitrov.

1951, May 3   **Perf. 10½**
Cream Paper
745 A412   1 l redsh brown   .16   .15
746 A412   4 l dark green   .16   .15
747 A412   9 l violet brown   .50   .28
748 A412 20 l deep blue   .65   .48
749 A412 40 l dark red   1.00   .70
    Nos. 745-749 (5)   2.47 1.76

75th anniv. of the "April" revolution.

Industrial Types of 1950

1951   **Perf. 13**
750 A369   1 l violet   .15   .15
751 A370   2 l dk brown   .15   .15
751A A372   4 l dk yel grn   1.05
    Nos. 750-751A (3)   .17

Demeter Blagoev Addressing 1891
Congress at Busludja — A413

1951   **Photo.**   **Perf. 11**
752 A413   1 l purple   .24   .15
753 A413   4 l dark green   .35   .15
754 A413   9 l deep claret   .60   .32
    Nos. 752-754 (3)   1.19
       Set value   .50

60th anniversary of the first Congress of the Bulgarian Social-Democratic Party.
See Nos. 1174-1176.

Day
Nursery — A414

Designs: 4 l, Model building construction. 9 l,
Playground. 20 l, Children's town.

1951, Oct. 10   **Unwmk.**
755 A414   1 l brown   .15   .15
756 A414   4 l deep plum   .20   .15
757 A414   9 l blue green   .60   .22
758 A414 20 l deep blue   1.00   .55
    Nos. 755-758 (4)   1.95 1.07

Children's Day, Sept. 25, 1951.

Order of Labor
A415   A416

1952, Feb. 1   **Perf. 13**
Reverse of Medal
759 A415   1 l red brown   .15   .15
760 A415   4 l blue green   .15   .15
761 A415   9 l dark blue   .28   .15

Obverse of Medal
762 A416   1 l carmine   .15   .15
763 A416   4 l green   .15   .15
764 A416   9 l purple   .28   .15
       Set value   .85   .32

No. 764 has numeral at lower left and different
background.

Workers and Symbols of
Industry — A417

Design: 4 l, Flags, Dimitrov, Chervenkov.

1951, Dec. 29   **Perf. 11**
Inscribed: "16 XII 1951"
765 A417   1 l olive black   .15   .15
766 A417   4 l chocolate   .16   .15
       Set value   .25   .15

Third Congress of Bulgarian General Workers'
Professional Union.

Dimitrov and
Chemical
Works — A418

George
Dimitrov
and V.
Chervenkov
A419

Portrait: 80s, Dimitrov.

Unwmk.
1952, June 18   **Photo.**   **Perf. 11**
767 A418 16s brown   .35   .22
768 A419 44s brown carmine   .52   .25
769 A418 80s brt blue   1.10   .52
    Nos. 767-769 (3)   1.97   .99

70th anniv. of the birth of George Dimitrov.

Vassil Kolarov   Republika Power
Dam — A420   Station — A421

1952, May 16   **. Perf. 13**
770 A420   4s dark green   .15   .15
771 A420 12s purple   .15   .15
772 A420 16s red brown   .15   .15
773 A420 44s rose brown   .50   .15
774 A420 80s brt blue   1.65   .18
    Nos. 770-774 (5)   2.60
       Set value   .40

No. 774 is inscribed in Latin characters.

1952, June 30   **Perf. 13, Pin Perf.**
775 A421 16s dark brown   .20   .15
776 A421 44s magenta   .75   .15
       Set value   .20

Nikolai I.
Vapzarov — A422

Designs: Various portraits.

1952, July 23   **Perf. 10½**
777 A422 16s rose brown   .16   .15
778 A422 44s dk red brn   .65   .16
779 A422 80s dk olive brn   1.40   .52
    Nos. 777-779 (3)   2.21   .83

10th anniversary of the death of Nikolai I.
Vapzarov, poet and revolutionary.

Dimitrov and Youth Conference — A423

Designs: 16s, Resistance movement incident. 44s, Frontier guards and industrial scene. 80s, George Dimitrov and young workers.

1952, Sept. 1   *Perf. 11x11¹/₂*
780	A423	2s brown carmine	.15	.15
781	A423	16s purple	.20	.15
782	A423	44s dark green	.52	.28
783	A423	80s dark brown	1.10	.60
		Nos. 780-783 (4)	1.97	1.18

40th anniv. of the founding conference of the Union of Social Democratic Youth.

Assault on the Winter Palace — A424

Designs: 8s, Volga-Don Canal. 16s, Symbols of world peace. 44s, Lenin and Stalin. 80s, Himlay hydroelectric station.

          Perf. 11¹/₂
1952, Nov. 6   Unwmk.   Photo.
      Dated: "1917-1952"
784	A424	4s red brown	.15	.15
785	A424	8s dark green	.15	.15
786	A424	16s dark blue	.15	.15
787	A424	44s brown	.32	.18
788	A424	80s olive brown	.75	.35
		Nos. 784-788 (5)	1.52	
		Set value		.70

35th anniv. of the Russian revolution.

Vassil Levski — A425

Design: 44s, Levski and comrades.

1953, Feb. 19   Cream Paper   *Perf. 11*
789	A425	16s brown	.15	.15
790	A425	44s brown blk	.25	.15
		Set value		.15

80th anniv. of the death of Levski, patriot.

Ferrying Artillery and Troops into Battle A426

Soldier A427   Mother and Children A428

Designs: 44s, Victorious soldiers. 80s, Soldier welcomed. 1 l, Monuments.

1953, Mar. 3   *Perf. 10¹/₂*
791	A426	8s Prus green	.16	.15
792	A427	16s dp brown	.22	.15
793	A426	44s dk slate grn	.42	.15
794	A426	80s dull red brn	.85	.20
795	A426	1 l black	1.10	.32
		Nos. 791-795 (5)	2.75	
		Set value		.70

Bulgaria's independence from Turkey, 75th anniv.

1953, Mar. 9
796	A428	16s slate green	.15	.15
797	A428	16s bright blue	.15	.15
		Set value	.25	.15

Women's Day.

Woodcarvings at Rila Monastery
A429   A430

Designs: 12s, 16s, 28s, Woodcarvings, Rila Monastery. 44s, Carved Ceilings, Trnovo. 80s, 1 l, 4 l, Carvings, Pasardjik.

1953   Unwmk.   Photo.   *Perf. 13*
798	A429	2s gray brown	.15	.15
799	A430	8s dk slate grn	.15	.15
800	A430	12s brown	.15	.15
801	A430	16s rose lake	.24	.15
802	A429	28s dk olive grn	.32	.15
803	A430	44s dk brown	.50	.15
804	A430	80s ultra	.85	.15
805	A430	1 l violet blue	1.75	.22
806	A430	4 l rose lake	3.50	.90
		Nos. 798-806 (9)	7.61	
		Set value		1.55

For surcharge see No. 1204.

Karl Marx   "Das Kapital"
A431   A432

1953, Apr. 30   *Perf. 10¹/₂*
807	A431	16s bright blue	.15	.15
808	A432	44s deep brown	.32	.18
		Set value		.25

70th anniversary of the death of Karl Marx.

Labor Day Parade — A433   Joseph V. Stalin — A434

1953, Apr. 30   *Perf. 13*
809	A433	16s brown red	.15	.15

Labor Day, May 1, 1953.

1953, May 23   *Perf. 13x13¹/₂*
810	A434	16s dark gray	.20	.15
811	A434	16s dark brown	.20	.15
		Set value		.15

Death of Joseph V. Stalin, Mar. 5, 1953.

Georgi Delchev — A435   Battle Scene — A436

Peasants Attacking Turkish Troops — A437

1953, Aug. 8   *Perf. 13*
812	A435	16s dark brown	.15	.15
813	A436	44s purple	.30	.15
814	A437	1 l deep claret	.45	.16
		Nos. 812-814 (3)	.90	
		Set value		.35

50th anniv. of the Ilinden Revolt (#812, 814) and the Preobrazhene Revolt (#813).

Soldier and Rebels — A438

44s, Soldier guarding industrial construction.

1953, Sept. 18
815	A438	16s deep claret	.15	.15
816	A438	44s greenish blue	.35	.15
		Set value		.17

Army Day.

George Dimitrov and Vassil Kolarov — A439   Demeter Blagoev — A440

Designs: 16s, Citizens in revolt. 44s, Attack.

1953, Sept. 22
817	A439	8s olive gray	.15	.15
818	A439	16s dk red brn	.18	.15
819	A439	44s cerise	.45	.18
		Nos. 817-819 (3)	.78	
		Set value		.28

September Revolution, 30th anniversary.

1953, Sept. 21

Portraits: 44s, G. Dimitrov and D. Blagoev.
820	A440	16s brown	.25	.15
821	A440	44s red brown	.38	.15
		Set value		.17

50th anniversary of the formation of the Social Democratic Party.

Railway Viaduct — A441   Pouring Molten Metal — A442

Designs: 16s, Welder and storage tanks. 80s, Harvesting machine.

1953, Oct. 17
826	A441	8s brt blue	.15	.15
827	A441	16s grnsh blk	.15	.15
828	A442	44s brown red	.28	.15
829	A441	80s orange	.45	.28
		Nos. 826-829 (4)	1.03	
		Set value		.50

Month of Bulgarian-Russian friendship.

Belladonna A443   Kolarov Library, Sofia A444

Medicinal Flowers: 4s, Jimson weed. 8s, Sage. 12s, Dog rose. 16s, Gentian. 20s, Poppy. 28s, Peppermint. 40s, Bear grass. 44s, Coltsfoot. 80s, Cowslip. 1 l, Dandelion. 2 l, Foxglove.

1953   Unwmk.   Photo.   *Perf. 13*
     White or Cream Paper
830	A443	2s dull blue	.15	.15
831	A443	4s brown org	.15	.15
832	A443	8s blue grn	.15	.15
833	A443	12s brown org	.15	.15
834	A443	16s blue grn	.15	.15
835	A443	16s violet blue	.15	.15
836	A443	16s dp red brn	.15	.15
837	A443	20s car rose	.15	.15
838	A443	28s dk gray grn	.30	.15
839	A443	40s dark blue	.35	.18
840	A443	44s brown	.35	.18
841	A443	80s yellow brn	.60	.35
842	A443	1 l henna brn	2.25	.48
843	A443	2 l purple	3.75	1.25
a.		Souvenir sheet	27.50	20.00
		Nos. 830-843 (14)	8.80	
		Set value		2.95

No. 843a contains 12 stamps, one of each denomination above, printed in dark green. Size: 161x172mm. Sold for 6 leva.

1953, Dec. 16
854	A444	44s brown	.25	.15

75th anniversary of the founding of the Kolarov Library, Sofia.

Singer and Accordionist A445   Lenin and Stalin A446

1953, Dec. 26
855	A445	16s shown	.15	.15
856	A445	44s Dancers	.18	.15
		Set value	.25	.17

1954, Mar. 13

Designs: 44s, Lenin statue. 80s, Lenin mausoleum, Moscow. 1 l, Lenin.
     Cream Paper
857	A446	16s brown	.20	.15
858	A446	44s rose brown	.26	.15
859	A446	80s blue	.42	.15
860	A446	1 l dp olive grn	.60	.26
		Nos. 857-860 (4)	1.48	
		Set value		.50

30th anniversary of the death of Lenin.

Demeter Blagoev and Followers A447

Design: 44s, Blagoev at desk.

1954, Apr. 28
     Cream Paper
861	A447	16s dp red brn	.15	.15
862	A447	44s black brn	.32	.15
		Set value		.15

30th anniv. of the death of Demeter Blagoev.

George Dimitrov A448   Dimitrov and Refinery A449

1954, June 11
863	A448	44s lake, *cream*	.22	.15
864	A449	80s brown, *cream*	.65	.15
		Set value		.15

5th anniv. of the death of George Dimitrov.

Train Leaving
Tunnel — A450

1954, July 30

865	A450	44s dk grn, *cream*	.60	.15
866	A450	44s blk brn, *cream*	.60	.15
		Set value		.20

Day of the Railroads, Aug. 1, 1954.

Miner at
Work — A451

1954, Aug. 19

867	A451	44s grnsh blk, *cream*	.20	.15

Miners' Day.

Academy of
Science — A452

1954, Oct. 27

868	A452	80s black, *cream*	.55	.18

85th anniversary of the foundation of the Bulgarian Academy of Science.

Horsemanship
A454

16s, 44s, 2 l, vert.

1954, Dec. 21

869	A454	16s Gymnastics	.52	.16
870	A454	44s Wrestling	.60	.20
871	A454	80s shown	1.25	.55
872	A454	2 l Skiing	3.00	1.65
		Nos. 869-872 (4)	5.37	2.56

Welcoming
Liberators — A455 | Soldier's
Return — A456

Designs: 28s, Refinery. 44s, Dimitrov and Workers. 80s, Girl and boy. 1 l, George Dimitrov.

1954, Oct. 4
Cream Paper

873	A455	12s brown car	.15	.15
874	A456	16s dp carmine	.15	.15
875	A455	28s indigo	.15	.15
876	A455	44s redsh brn	.15	.15
877	A456	80s deep blue	.55	.25
878	A456	1 l dark green	.55	.25
		Set value	1.40	.70

10th anniversary of Bulgaria's liberation.

Recreation at Workers'
Rest Home — A457 | Metal Worker
and
Furnace — A458

Portraits: 80s, Dimitrov, Blagoev, and Kirkov.

Unwmk.
1954, Dec. 28   Photo.   Perf. 13
Cream Paper

879	A457	16s dark green	.16	.15
880	A458	44s brown orange	.16	.15
881	A457	80s dp violet blue	.42	.20
		Nos. 879-881 (3)	.74	
		Set value		.30

50th anniversary of Bulgaria's trade union movement.

Geese — A459

Designs: 4s, Chickens. 12s, Hogs. 16s, Sheep. 28s, Telephone building. 44s, Communist party headquarters. 80s, Apartment buildings. 1 l, St. Kiradgieff Mills.

1955-56

882	A459	2s dk blue grn	.16	.15
883	A459	4s olive green	.28	.15
884	A459	12s dk red brn	.42	.15
885	A459	16s brown orange	.65	.15
886	A459	28s violet blue	.32	.15
887	A459	44s lil red, *cream*	.60	.15
a.		44s brown red	4.50	
888	A459	80s dk red brown	.75	.15
889	A459	1 l dk blue green	1.50	.16
		Nos. 882-889 (8)	4.68	
		Set value		.56

Issued: #887, 4/20/56; others, 2/19/55.

Textile Worker — A460 | Mother and
Child — A461

Design: 16s, Woman feeding calf.

1955, Mar. 5

890	A460	12s dark brown	.15	.15
891	A460	16s dark green	.15	.15
892	A461	44s dk car rose	.50	.15
893	A461	44s blue	.50	.15
		Nos. 890-893 (4)	1.30	
		Set value		.26

Women's Day, Mar. 8, 1955.

No. 744 Surcharged in Blue

1955, Mar. 8   Perf. 13

894	A410	16s on 4 l red brown	.45	.15

May Day
Demonstration
of Workers
A462 | Sts. Cyril and
Methodius
A463

Design: 44s, Three workers and globe.

1955, Apr. 23   Photo.

895	A462	16s car rose	.15	.15
896	A462	44s blue	.30	.15
		Set value		.15

Labor Day, May 1, 1955.

1955, May 21

Designs: 8s, Paisii Hilendarski. 16s, Nicolas Karastoyanov's printing press. 28s, Christo Botev. 44s, Ivan Vazov. 80s, Demeter Blagoev and socialist papers. 2 l, Blagoev printing plant, Sofia.

Cream Paper

897	A463	4s deep blue	.15	.15
898	A463	8s olive	.15	.15
899	A463	16s black	.15	.15
900	A463	28s henna brn	.16	.15
901	A463	44s brown	.32	.15

902	A463	80s rose red	.50	.16
903	A463	2 l black	1.50	.42
		Nos. 897-903 (7)	2.93	
		Set value		.80

Creation of the Cyrillic alphabet, 1100th anniv. Latin lettering at bottom on #901-903.

Sergei
Rumyantzev
A464 | Mother and
Children
A465

Portraits: 16s, Christo Jassenov. 44s, Geo Milev.

1955, June 30   Unwmk.   Perf. 13
Cream Paper

904	A464	12s orange brn	.16	.15
905	A464	16s lt brown	.16	.15
906	A464	44s grnsh blk	.42	.15
		Nos. 904-906 (3)	.74	
		Set value		.24

30th anniv. of the deaths of Sergei Rumyanchev, Christo Jassenov and Geo Milev. Latin lettering at bottom of No. 906.

1955, July 30

907	A465	44s brn car, *cream*	.30	.15

World Congress of Mothers in Lausanne, 1955.

Young People of
Three
Races — A466 | Friedrich Engels and
Book — A467

1955, July 30

908	A466	44s blue, *cream*	.30	.15

5th World Festival of Youth in Warsaw, July 31-Aug. 14.

1955, July 30

909	A467	44s brown	.30	.15

60th anniv. of the death of Friedrich Engels.

Entrance to Fair,
1892 — A468 | Statuary Group
at Fair,
1955 — A469

Designs: 44s, "Fruit of our Land." 80s, Woman holding Fair emblem.

1955, Aug. 31
Cream Paper

910	A468	4s deep brown	.15	.15
911	A469	16s dk car rose	.15	.15
912	A468	44s olive blk	.20	.15
913	A469	80s deep blue	.45	.15
		Set value	.80	.32

16th International Plovdiv Fair. Latin lettering on Nos. 912-913.

 Friedrich von
Schiller — A470

Portraits: 44s, Adam Mickiewicz. 60s, Hans Christian Andersen. 80s, Baron de Montesquieu. 1 l, Miguel de Cervantes. 2 l, Walt Whitman.

1955, Oct. 31
Cream Paper

914	A470	16s brown	.15	.15
915	A470	44s brown red	.38	.15
916	A470	60s Prus blue	.60	.15
917	A470	80s black	.60	.15
918	A470	1 l rose violet	1.40	.32
919	A470	2 l olive green	1.90	.50
		Nos. 914-919 (6)	5.03	
		Set value		1.05

Various anniversaries of famous writers. Nos. 918 and 919 are issued in sheets alternating with labels without franking value. The labels show title pages for Leaves of Grass and Don Quixote in English and Spanish, respectively. Latin lettering on #915-919.

Karl Marx Industrial Plant — A471

Friendship
Monument — A472 | I. V.
Michurin — A473

Designs: 4s, Alekandr Stamboliski Dam. 16s, Bridge over Danube. 1 l, Vladimir V. Mayakovsky.

1955, Dec. 1   Unwmk.

920	A471	2s slate blk	.15	.15
921	A471	4s deep blue	.15	.15
922	A471	16s dk blue grn	.15	.15
923	A473	44s red brown	.15	.15
924	A473	80s dark green	.25	.15
925	A473	1 l gray blk	.90	.45

Russian-Bulgarian friendship.

Library
Seal — A474 | Krusto
Pishurka — A475

Portrait: 44s, Bacho Kiro.

1956, Feb. 10   Perf. 11x10½

926	A474	12s car lake, *cream*	.15	.15
927	A475	16s dp brn, *cream*	.15	.15
928	A475	44s slate blk, *cream*	.22	.15
		Set value	.33	.17

100th anniversary of the National Library. Latin lettering at bottom of No. 928.

Canceled to Order

Beginning about 1956, some issues were sold in sheets canceled to order. Values in second column when much less than unused are for "CTO" copies. Postally used stamps are valued at slightly less than, or the same as, unused.

Quinces — A476 | Cherrywood
Cannon — A477

Designs: 8s, Pears. 16s, Apples. 44s, Grapes.

1956 Photo. Perf. 13
929 A476 4s carmine .75 .15
930 A476 8s blue green .32 .15
931 A476 16s lilac rose .80 .15
932 A476 44s deep violet .80 .16
Nos. 929-932 (4) 2.67
Set value .32

Latin lettering on #932. See #964-967. For surcharge see #1364.

1956, Apr. 28 Perf. 11x10½
933 A477 16s shown .15 .15
934 A477 44s Cavalry attack .22 .15
Set value .15

April Uprising against Turkish rule, 80th anniv.

Demeter Blagoev (1856-1924), Writer, Birthplace A478

Cherries A479

1956, May 30 Perf. 11
935 A478 44s Prus blue .25 .15

1956 Unwmk. Perf. 13
936 A479 2s shown .15 .15
937 A479 12s Plums .15 .15
938 A479 28s Peaches .18 .15
939 A479 80s Strawberries .55 .20
Nos. 936-939 (4) 1.03
Set value .35

Latin lettering on No. 939.

Gymnastics A480

Pole Vaulting A481

Designs: 12s, Discus throw. 44s, Soccer. 80s, Basketball. 1 l, Boxing.

Perf. 11x10½, 10½x11
1956, Aug. 29
940 A480 4s brt ultra .15 .15
941 A480 12s brick red .15 .15
942 A481 16s yellow brn .32 .16
943 A480 44s dark green .48 .25
944 A480 80s dark red brn 1.00 .50
945 A481 1 l deep magenta 1.65 .65
Nos. 940-945 (6) 3.75 1.86

Latin lettering on Nos. 943-945.
16th Olympic Games at Melbourne, Nov. 22-Dec. 8, 1956.

Tobacco, Rose and Distillery A482

People's Theater A483

1956, Sept. 1 Perf. 13
946 A482 44s deep carmine .38 .16
947 A482 44s olive green .38 .16

17th International Plovdiv Fair.

1956, Nov. 16 Unwmk.
Design: 44s, Dobri Woinikoff and Sawa Dobroplodni, dramatists.
948 A483 16s dull red brown .15 .15
949 A483 44s dark blue green .22 .15
Set value .15

Bulgarian Theater centenary.

Benjamin Franklin A484

Cyclists, Palms and Pyramids A485

Portraits: 20s, Rembrandt. 40s, Mozart. 44s, Heinrich Heine. 60s, Shaw. 80s, Dostoevski. 1 l, Ibsen. 2 l, Pierre Curie.

1956, Dec. 29
950 A484 16s dark olive grn .15 .15
951 A484 20s brown .18 .15
952 A484 40s dark car rose .18 .15
953 A484 44s dark violet brn .22 .15
954 A484 60s dark slate .32 .15
955 A484 80s dark brown .45 .15
956 A484 1 l bluish grn .80 .30
957 A484 2 l Prus green 1.75 .52
Nos. 950-957 (8) 4.05
Set value 1.20

Great personalities of the world.

1957, Mar. 6 Photo. Perf. 10½
958 A485 80s henna brown .50 .25
959 A485 80s Prus green .50 .25

Fourth Egyptian bicycle race.

Woman Technician — A486

"New Times" Review — A487

Designs: 16s, Woman and children. 44s, Woman feeding chickens.

1957, Mar. 8 Photo.
960 A486 12s deep blue .15 .15
961 A486 16s henna brown .15 .15
962 A486 44s slate green .30 .15
Set value .40 .17

Women's Day. Latin lettering on 44s.

1957, Mar. 8 Unwmk.
963 A487 16s deep carmine .20 .15

60th anniversary of the founding of the "New Times" review.

Fruit Type of 1956.
4s, Quinces. 8s, Pears. 16s, Apples. 44s, Grapes.

1957 Photo. Perf. 13
964 A476 4s yellow green .15 .15
965 A476 8s brown orange .15 .15
966 A476 16s rose red .15 .15
967 A476 44s orange yellow .40 .15
Set value .62 .35

Latin lettering on #967. For surcharge see #1364.

Sts. Cyril and Methodius A488

Basketball A489

1957, May 22 Perf. 11
968 A488 44s olive grn & buff .50 .15
Centenary of the first public veneration of Sts. Cyril and Methodius, inventors of the Cyrillic alphabet.

1957, June 20 Photo. Perf. 10½x11
969 A489 44s dark green .95 .30
10th European Basketball Championship at Sofia.

Dancer and Spasski Tower, Moscow — A490

1957, July 18 Perf. 13
970 A490 44s blue .30 .15
Sixth World Youth Festival in Moscow.

George Dimitrov (1882-1949) — A491

1957, July 18
971 A491 44s deep carmine .50 .15

Vassil Levski — A492

1957, July 18 Perf. 11
972 A492 44s grnsh black .30 .15
120th anniversary of the birth of Vassil Levski, patriot and national hero.

No. 742 Surcharged in Carmine
1957 Unwmk. Perf. 13
973 A408 16s on 1 l purple .15 .15

Trnovo and Lazarus L. Zamenhof A493

1957, July 27
974 A493 44s slate green .50 .15
50th anniv. of the Bulgarian Esperanto Society and the 70th anniv. of Esperanto.
For surcharge see No. 1235.

Bulgarian Veteran of 1877 War and Russian Soldier — A494

Design: 44s, Battle of Shipka Pass.

1957, Aug. 13
975 A494 16s dk blue grn .15 .15
976 A494 44s brown .32 .15
80th anniversary of Bulgaria's liberation from the Turks. Latin lettering on No. 976.

Woman Planting Tree — A495

Red Deer in Forest — A496

Designs: 16s, Dam, lake and forest. 44s, Plane over forest. 80s, Fields on edge of forest.

1957, Sept. 16 Photo. Perf. 13
977 A495 2s deep green .15 .15
978 A496 12s dark brown .15 .15
979 A496 16s Prus blue .15 .15
980 A496 44s Prus green .22 .15
981 A496 80s yellow green .42 .15
Set value .90 .15

Latin lettering on Nos. 980 and 981.

Lenin — A497

Designs: 16s, Cruiser "Aurora." 44s, Dove over map of communist area. 60s, Revolutionaries and banners. 80s, Oil refinery.

1957, Oct. 29 Perf. 11
982 A497 12s chocolate .16 .15
983 A497 16s Prus green .32 .15
984 A497 44s deep blue .65 .15
985 A497 60s dk car rose .75 .15
986 A497 80s dark green 1.25 .22
Nos. 982-986 (5) 3.13
Set value .54

40th anniv. of the Communist Revolution. Latin lettering on Nos. 984-985.

Globes A498

1957, Oct. 4 Perf. 13
987 A498 44s Prus blue .30 .15
4th Intl. Trade Union Cong., Leipzig, Oct. 4-15.

Vassil Kolarov Hotel A499

Bulgarian Health Resorts: 4s, Skis and Pirin Mountains. 8s, Old house at Koprivspitsa. 12s, Rest home at Velingrad. 44s, Momin-Prochod Hotel. 60s, Nesebr Hotel, shoreline and peninsula. 80s, Varna beach scene. 1 l, Hotel at Varna.

1958 Photo. Perf. 13
988 A499 4s blue .15 .15
989 A499 8s orange brn .15 .15
990 A499 12s dk green .15 .15
991 A499 16s green .15 .15
992 A499 44s dk blue grn .15 .15
993 A499 60s deep blue .18 .15
994 A499 80s fawn .28 .15
995 A499 1 l dk red brn .35 .18
Set value 1.14 .62

Latin lettering on 44s, 60s, 80s, and 1 l.
Issue dates: #991-994, Jan. 20. Others, July 5.
For surcharges see Nos. 1200, 1436.

Mikhail I. Glinka — A500

Portraits: 16s, Jan A. Komensky (Comenius). 40s, Carl von Linné. 44s, William Blake. 60s, Carlo Goldoni. 80s, Auguste Comte.

1957, Dec. 30

996	A500	12s dark brown	.20	.15
997	A500	16s dark green	.20	.15
998	A500	40s Prus blue	.20	.15
999	A500	44s maroon	.20	.15
1000	A500	60s orange brown	.75	.15
1001	A500	80s deep plum	2.50	.90
		Nos. 996-1001 (6)	4.05	
		Set value		1.25

Famous men of other countries. Latin lettering on Nos. 999-1001.

Young Couple, Flag, Dimitrov A501

People's Front Salute A502

1957, Dec. 28   *Perf. 11*

1002	A501	16s carmine rose	.15	.15

10th anniversary of Dimitrov's Union of the People's Youth.

1957, Dec. 28

1003	A502	16s dk violet brn	.15	.15

15th anniversary of the People's Front.

Hare — A503

12s, Red deer (doe), vert. 16s, Red deer (stag). 44s, Chamois. 80s, Brown bear. 1 l, Wild boar.

Perf. 10½

1958, Apr. 5   Unwmk.   Photo.

1004	A503	2s lt & dk ol grn	.15	.15
1005	A503	12s sl grn & red brn	.18	.15
1006	A503	16s bluish grn & dk red brn	.20	.15
1007	A503	44s blue & brown	.24	.15
1008	A503	80s bis & dk brn	.75	.25
1009	A503	1 l stl bl & dk brn	1.00	.22
		Nos. 1004-1009 (6)	2.52	
		Set value		.55

Value, imperf. set $4.

Marx and Lenin A504

Designs: 16s, Marchers and flags. 44s, Lenin blast furnaces.

1958, July 2   *Perf. 11*

1010	A504	12s dark brown	.16	.15
1011	A504	16s dark carmine	.20	.15
1012	A504	44s dark blue	.85	.15
		Nos. 1010-1012 (3)	1.21	
		Set value		.20

Bulgarian Communist Party, 7th Congress.

Wrestlers — A505

1958, June 20   *Perf. 10½*

1013	A505	60s dk carmine rose	.65	.35
1014	A505	80s deep brown	1.10	.55

World Wrestling Championship, Sofia.

Chessmen and Globe A506

Perf. 10½

1958, July 18   Unwmk.   Photo.

1015	A506	80s grn & yel grn	2.50	.80

5th World Students' Chess Games, Varna.

Conference Emblem A507

1958, Sept. 24

1016	A507	44s blue	.40	.15

World Trade Union Conference of Working Youth, Prague, July 14-20.

Swimmer A508

1958 Students' Games: 28s, Dancer, vert. 44s, Volleyball, vert.

1958, Sept. 19   *Perf. 11x10½*

1017	A508	16s brt blue	.15	.15
1018	A508	28s brown orange	.22	.15
1019	A508	44s brt green	.30	.15
		Nos. 1017-1019 (3)	.67	
		Set value		.35

Onions — A509

Vegetables: 12s, Garlic. 16s, Peppers. 44s, Tomatoes. 80s, Cucumbers. 1 l, Eggplant.

1958, Sept. 20   *Perf. 13*

1020	A509	2s orange brown	.15	.15
1021	A509	12s Prus blue	.15	.15
1022	A509	16s dark green	.15	.15
1023	A509	44s deep carmine	.16	.15
1024	A509	80s deep green	.40	.15
1025	A509	1 l brt purple	.60	.15
		Nos. 1020-1025 (6)	1.61	
		Set value		.38

Value, imperf. set $4.
See No. 1072. For surcharge see No. 1201.

Plovdiv Fair Building A510

1958, Sept. 14   Unwmk.   *Perf. 11*

1026	A510	44s deep carmine	.40	.15

18th International Plovdiv Fair.

Attack — A511

Design: 44s, Fighter dragging wounded man.

1958, Sept. 23   Photo.   *Perf. 11*

1027	A511	16s orange ver	.15	.15
1028	A511	44s lake	.35	.15
		Set value		.15

35th anniv. of the September Revolution.

Emblem, Brussels Fair — A512

1958, Oct. 13   *Perf. 11*

1029	A512	1 l blk & brt blue	5.00	1.25

Brussels World's Fair, Apr. 17-Oct. 19. Exists imperf.

Runner at Finish Line — A513

Woman Throwing Javelin A514

60s, High jumper. 80s, Hurdler. 4 l, Shot putter.

1958, Nov. 30

1030	A513	16s red brn, *pnksh*	.40	.15
1031	A514	44s olive, *yelsh*	.40	.15
1032	A514	60s dk bl, *bluish*	.75	.20
1033	A514	80s dp grn, *grnsh*	1.00	.20
1034	A513	4 l dp rose cl, *pnksh*	6.25	1.40
		Nos. 1030-1034 (5)	8.80	2.10

1958 Balkan Games.
Latin lettering on Nos. 1032-1033.

Christo Smirnenski — A515

1958, Dec. 22

1035	A515	16s dark carmine	.15	.15

Christo Smirnenski (1898-1923), poet.

Girls Harvesting — A516

Girl Tending Calves A517

Designs: 16s, Boy and girl laborers. 40s, Boy pushing wheelbarrow. 44s, Headquarters building.

1959, Nov. 29   Photo.

1036	A516	8s dk olive green	.15	.15
1037	A517	12s redsh brown	.15	.15
1038	A517	16s violet brown	.15	.15
1039	A517	40s Prus blue	.15	.15
1040	A516	44s deep carmine	.60	.15
		Set value	.95	.34

4th Congress of Dimitrov's Union of People's Youth.

UNESCO Building, Paris A518

1959, Mar. 28   Unwmk.   *Perf. 11*

1041	A518	2 l dp red lilac, *cream*	1.25	1.00

Opening of UNESCO Headquarters, Paris, Nov. 3, 1958. Value imperf. $2.50.

Skier — A519

Soccer Players — A520

1959, Mar. 28   *Perf. 11*

1042	A519	1 l blue, *cream*	.90	.50

Forty years of skiing in Bulgaria.

1959, Mar. 25

1043	A520	2 l chestnut, *cream*	1.25	.65

1959 European Youth Soccer Championship.

Russian Soldiers Installing Telegraph Wires — A521

First Bulgarian Postal Coach A522

Designs: 60s, Stamp of 1879. 80s, First Bulgarian automobile. 1 l, Television tower. 2 l, Strike of railroad and postal workers, 1919.

1959, May 4

1044	A521	12s dk grn & cit	.15	.15
1045	A514	16s deep plum	.15	.15
1046	A521	60s dk brn & yel	.32	.15
1047	A522	80s hn brn & sal	.45	.15

1048	A521	1 l blue	.60	.16
1049	A522	2 l dk red brown	1.65	.80
		Nos. 1044-1049 (6)	3.32	
		Set value		1.25

80th anniv. of the Bulgarian post. Latin lettering on Nos. 1046-1049.

Two imperf. souvenir sheets exist with olive borders and inscriptions. One contains one copy of No. 1046 in black & ocher, and measures 92x121mm. The other sheet contains one copy each of Nos. 1044-1045 and 1047-1048 in changed colors: 12s, olive green & ocher; 16s, deep claret & ocher; 80s, dark red & ocher; 1 l, olive & ocher. Each sheet sold for 5 leva. Value, each $22.50.

Great Tits
A523

Birds: 8s, Hoopoe. 16s, Great spotted woodpecker, vert. 45s, Gray partridge, vert. 60s, Rock partridge. 80s, European cuckoo.

1959, June 30   **Photo.**

1050	A523	2s olive & sl grn	.15	.15
1051	A523	8s dp orange & blk	.15	.15
1052	A523	16s chestnut & dk brn	.22	.15
1053	A523	45s brown & blk	.28	.15
1054	A523	60s dp blue & gray	.65	.15
1055	A523	80s dp bl grn & gray	1.10	.18
		Nos. 1050-1055 (6)	2.55	
		Set value		.55

Bagpiper — A524

Designs: 12s, Acrobats. 16s, Girls exercising with hoops. 20s, Male dancers. 80s, Ballet dancers. 1 l, Ceramic pitcher. 16s, 20s, 80s are horizontal.

1959, Aug. 29   **Unwmk.**   **Perf. 11**
Surface-colored Paper

1056	A524	4s dk olive	.15	.15
1057	A524	12s scarlet	.15	.15
1058	A524	16s maroon	.15	.15
1059	A524	20s dk blue	.25	.15
1060	A524	80s brt green	.52	.26
1061	A524	1 l brown org	.95	.42
		Nos. 1056-1061 (6)	2.17	
		Set value		1.00

7th International Youth Festival, Vienna. Latin inscriptions on Nos. 1060-1061.

Partisans in Truck
A525

Designs: 16s, Partisans and soldiers shaking hands. 45s, Refinery. 60s, Tanks. 80s, Harvester. 1.25 l, Children with flag, vert.

1959, Sept. 8

1062	A525	12s red & Prus grn	.15	.15
1063	A525	16s red & dk pur	.15	.15
1064	A525	45s red & int bl	.15	.15
1065	A525	60s red & ol grn	.15	.15
1066	A525	80s red & brn	.26	.15
1067	A525	1.25 l red & dp brn	.65	.38
		Set value	1.20	.75

15th anniversary of Bulgarian liberation.

Soccer
A526

1959, Oct. 10   **Unwmk.**   **Perf. 11**

1068	A526	1.25 l dp green, yel	3.50	2.00

50 years of Bulgarian soccer.
Set exists imperf. in changed colors. Value $7.50 unused, $4 canceled.

Batak Defenders
A527

1959, Aug. 8

1069	A527	16s deep claret	.20	.15

300th anniv. of the settlement of Batak.

Post Horn and Letter — A528   Bird-shaped Lyre — A529

Design: 1.25 l, Dove and letter.

1959, Nov. 23

1070	A528	45s emerald & blk	.30	.15
1071	A528	1.25 l lt blue, red & blk	.50	.20
		Set value		.27

Intl. Letter Writing Week Oct. 5-11.

Type of 1958 Surcharged "45 CT." in Dark Blue

Design: Tomatoes.

1959   **Photo.**   **Perf. 13**

1072	A509	45s on 44s scarlet	.55	.15

1960, Feb. 23   **Unwmk.**   **Perf. 10½**

1073	A529	80s shown	.40	.15
1074	A529	1.25 l Lyre	.70	.18
		Set value		.27

50th anniv. of Bulgaria's State Opera.

N. I. Vapzarov — A530   Parachute and Radio Tower — A531

1959, Dec. 14   **Perf. 11**

1075	A530	80s yel grn & red brn	.35	.15

Vapzarov, poet and patriot, 50th birth anniv.

1959, Dec. 3   **Photo.**

1076	A531	1.25 l dp grnsh bl & yel	1.25	.45

3rd Cong. of Voluntary Participants in Defense.

Cotton Picker — A532   Harvester Combine — A533

Designs: 2s, Kindergarten. 4s, Woman doctor and child. 10s, Woman milking cow. 12s, Woman holding tobacco leaves. 15s, Woman working loom. 16s, Stalin textile mill, Dimitrovgrad. 25s, Rural electrification. 28s, Woman picking sunflowers. 40s, "Cold-well" hydroelectric dam. 45s, Miner. 60s, Foundry worker. 80s. Woman harvesting grapes. 1 l, Worker and peasant with cogwheel. 1.25 l, Industrial worker. 2 l, Party leader.

1959-61   **Photo.**   **Perf. 13**

1077	A533	2s brown org ('60)	.15	.15
1077A	A532	4s gldn brn ('61)	.15	.15
1078	A532	5s dk green	.15	.15
1079	A533	10s red brn ('61)	.15	.15
1080	A533	12s red brown	.15	.15
1081	A532	15s red lil ('60)	.15	.15

1082	A533	16s dp vio ('60)	.15	.15
1083	A533	20s orange	.15	.15
1084	A532	25s brt blue ('60)	.15	.15
1085	A532	28s brt green	.18	.15
1086	A533	40s brt grnsh bl	.30	.15
1087	A533	45s choc ('60)	.22	.15
1088	A533	60s scarlet	.42	.15
1089	A532	80s ol ('60)	.50	.15
1090	A532	1 l maroon	.50	.15
1090A	A533	1.25 l dull bl ('61)	1.75	.30
1091	A532	2 l dp car ('60)	1.10	.22
		Nos. 1077-1091 (17)	6.32	
		Set value		1.25

Early completion of the 5-year plan (in 1959). For surcharges see Nos. 1192-1199, 1202-1203.

L. L. Zamenhof — A534   Path of Lunik 3 — A535

1959, Dec. 5   **Unwmk.**   **Perf. 11**

1092	A534	1.25 l dk grn & yel grn	.75	.38

Lazarus Ludwig Zamenhof (1859-1917), inventor of Esperanto.

1960, Mar. 28   **Perf. 11**

1093	A535	1.25 l Prus bl & brt yel	3.50	1.90

Flight of Lunik 3 around moon. Value, imperf. $5

Skier
A536

1960, Apr. 15   **Litho.**

1094	A536	2 l ultra, blk & brn	.95	.35

8th Winter Olympics, Squaw Valley, CA, Feb. 18-29. Value, imperf. $2 unused, $1 canceled.

Vela Blagoeva — A537

Portraits: 28s, Anna Maimunkova. 45s, Vela Piskova. 60s, Rosa Luxemburg. 80s, Klara Zetkin. 1.25 l, N. K. Krupskaya.

1960, Apr. 27   **Photo.**   **Perf. 11**

1095	A537	16s rose & red brn	.15	.15
1096	A537	28s citron & olive	.15	.15
1097	A537	45s ol grn & sl grn	.20	.15
1098	A537	60s lt bl & Prus bl	.20	.15
1099	A537	80s red org & dp brn	.35	.15
1100	A537	1.25 l dull yel & olive	.60	.18
		Nos. 1095-1100 (6)	1.65	
		Set value		.50

International Women's Day, Mar. 8, 1960.

Lenin — A538

1960, May 12

1101	A538	16s shown	.50	.15
1102	A538	45s Lenin sitting	1.10	.16

90th anniversary of the birth of Lenin.

A539   A541

1960, June 3   **Perf. 11**

1103	A539	1.25 l yel & slate grn	.85	.35

Seventh European Women's Basketball championships.

1960, June 29   **Litho.**

1105	A541	16s Parachutist	.55	.50
1106	A541	1.25 l Parachutes	1.50	.45

5th International Parachute Championships.

Yellow Gentian — A542

Flowers: 5s, Tulips. 25s, Turk's-cap lily. 45s, Rhododendron. 60s, Lady's-slipper. 80s, Violets.

1960, July 27   **Photo.**   **Perf. 11**

1107	A542	2s beige, grn & yel	.15	.15
1108	A542	5s yel grn, grn & car rose	.15	.15
1109	A542	25s pink, grn & org	.20	.15
1110	A542	45s pale lil, grn & rose lil	.35	.15
1111	A542	60s yel, grn & org	.75	.15
1112	A542	80s gray, grn & vio bl	.90	.15
		Nos. 1107-1112 (6)	2.50	
		Set value		.55

Soccer
A543

Sports: 12s, Wrestling. 16s, Weight lifting. 45s, Woman gymnast. 80s, Canoeing. 2 l, Runner.

1960, Aug. 29   **Unwmk.**   **Perf. 11**
Athletes' Figures in Pink

1113	A543	8s brown	.15	.15
1114	A543	12s violet	.15	.15
1115	A543	16s Prus blue	.15	.15
1116	A543	45s deep plum	.18	.15
1117	A543	80s blue	.30	.15
1118	A543	2 l deep green	1.25	.18
		Set value	2.00	.75

17th Olympic Games, Rome, Aug. 25-Sept. 11. Value, set imperf. in changed colors, $3.50.

Globes
A544

Unwmk.
1960, Oct. 12   **Photo.**   **Perf. 11**

1125	A544	1.25 l blue & ultra	.50	.20

15th anniversary of the World Federation of Trade Unions.

Alexander Popov — A545

1960, Oct. 12
1126 A545 90s blue & blk .75 .15
Centenary of the birth of Alexander Popov, radio pioneer.

Bicyclists A546

1960, Sept. 22
1127 A546 1 l yel, red org & blk .90 .45
The 10th Tour of Bulgaria Bicycle Race.

Jaroslav Vésin — A547

1960, Nov. 22   Unwmk.   *Perf. 11*
1128 A547 1 l brt citron & ol grn 2.75 .65
Birth centenary of Jaroslav Vesin, painter.

UN Headquarters A548

Costume of Kyustendil A549

1961, Jan. 14   Photo.   *Perf. 11*
1129 A548 1 l brown & yel 1.00 .45
  a. Souvenir sheet 4.00 2.75
15th anniv. of the UN. #1129 sold for 2 l. Value, imperf. $3.50.
No. 1129a sold for 2.50 l and contains one copy of No. 1129, imperf, in dark olive and pink.

1961, Jan. 28
Designs (Regional Costumes): 16s, Pleven. 28s, Sliven. 45s, Sofia. 60s, Rhodope. 80s, Karnobat.
1130 A549 12s salmon, sl grn & yel .15 .15
1131 A549 16s pale lil, brn vio & buff .15 .15
1132 A549 28s pale grn, sl grn & rose .15 .15
1133 A549 45s blue & red .30 .15
1134 A549 60s grnsh bl, Prus bl & yel .48 .15
1135 A549 80s yel, sl grn & pink .60 .26
  Nos. 1130-1135 (6) 1.83
  Set value .60

Theodor Tiro (Fresco) A550

Designs: 60s, Boyana Church. 1.25 l, Duchess of Dessislava (fresco).

1961, Jan. 28   Photo.
1136 A550 60s yel grn, blk & grn .50 .15
1137 A550 80s yel, sl grn & org .50 .15
1138 A550 1.25 l yel grn, hn brn & buff 1.00 .22
  Nos. 1136-1138 (3) 2.00
  Set value .40
700th anniv. of murals in Boyana Church.

Clock Tower, Vratsa — A551

Wooden Jug — A552

Designs: 12s, Clock tower, Bansko. 20s, Anguchev House, Mogilitsa. 28s, Oslekov House, Koprivshtsa, horiz. 40s, Pasha's house. Melnik, horiz. 45s, Lion sculpture. 60s, Man on horseback, Madara. 80s, Fresco, Bratchkovo monastery. 1 l, Tsar Assen coin.

1961, Feb. 25   Unwmk.   *Perf. 11*
Denomination and Stars in Vermilion
1139 A551 8s olive grn .15 .15
1140 A551 12s lt violet .15 .15
1141 A552 16s dk red brn .15 .15
1142 A551 20s brt blue .15 .15
1143 A551 28s grnsh blue .15 .15
1144 A551 40s red brown .15 .15
1145 A552 45s olive gray .16 .15
1146 A552 60s slate .32 .15
1147 A552 80s dk olive gray .55 .15
1148 A552 1 l green .70 .16
  Set value 2.25 .65

Capercaillie — A553

Birds: 4s, Dalmatian pelican. 16s, Ringnecked pheasant. 80s, Great bustard. 1 l, Lammergeier. 2 l, Hazel hen.

1961, Mar. 31
1149 A553 2s blk, sal & Prus grn .15 .15
1150 A553 4s blk, yel grn & org .15 .15
1151 A553 16s brn, lt grn & org .15 .15
1152 A553 80s brn, bluish grn & yel .35 .15
1153 A553 1 l blk, lt bl & yel .65 .15
1154 A553 2 l brn, bl & yel 1.65 .55
  Nos. 1149-1153 (5) 1.45
  Set value 1.00

Radio Tower and Winged Anchor — A554

1961, Apr. 1   Unwmk.   *Perf. 11*
1155 A554 80s brt green & blk .45 .20
50th anniv. of the Transport Workers' Union.

T. G. Shevchenko — A555

Water Polo — A556

1961, Apr. 27
1156 A555 1 l olive & blk 2.50 .65
Centenary of the death of Taras G. Shevchenko, Ukrainian poet.

1961, May 15
Designs: 5s, Tennis. 16s, Fencing. 45s, Throwing the discus. 1.25 l, Sports Palace. 2 l, Basketball. 5 l, Sports Palace, different view. 5s, 16s, 45s and 1.25 l, are horizontal.

Black Inscriptions
1157 A556 4s lt ultra .15 .15
1158 A556 5s orange ver .15 .15
1159 A556 16s olive grn .15 .15
1160 A556 45s dull blue .15 .15

1161 A556 1.25 l yellow brn .60 .18
1162 A556 2 l lilac .85 .40
  Nos. 1157-1162 (6) 2.05
  Set value .75

Souvenir Sheet
Imperf
1163 A556 5 l yel grn, dl bl & yel 7.50 6.50
1961 World University Games, Sofia, Aug. 26-Sept. 3.
Value, Nos. 1157-1162 in changed colors, imperf. $4.50.

Monk Seal A557

Black Sea Fauna: 12s, Jellyfish. 16s, Dolphin. 45s, Black Sea sea horse, vert. 1 l, Starred sturgeon. 1.25 l, Thornback ray.

1961, June 19   *Perf. 11*
1164 A557 2s green & blk .15 .15
1165 A557 12s Prus grn & pink .15 .15
1166 A557 16s ultra & vio bl .15 .15
1167 A557 45s lt blue & brn .28 .15
1168 A557 1 l yel grn & Prus grn .65 .20
1169 A557 1.25 l lt vio bl & red brn 1.10 .35
  Nos. 1164-1169 (6) 2.48
  Set value .90

Hikers — A558

Designs: 4s, "Sredetz" hostel, horiz. 16s, Tents. 1.25 l, Mountain climber.

1961, Aug. 25   Litho.   *Perf. 11*
1170 A558 4s yel grn, yel & blk .15 .15
1171 A558 12s lt bl, cr & blk .15 .15
1172 A558 16s green, cr & blk .15 .15
1173 A558 1.25 l bister, cr & blk .45 .15
  Set value .65 .30
"Know Your Country" campaign.

Demeter Blagoev Addressing 1891 Congress at Busludja — A559

1961, Aug. 5   Photo.
1174 A559 45s dk red & buff .20 .15
1175 A559 80s blue & pink .30 .15
1176 A559 2 l dk brn & pale citron .75 .25
  Nos. 1174-1176 (3) 1.25 .55
70th anniversary of the first Congress of the Bulgarian Social-Democratic Party.

The Golden Girl — A560

Fairy Tales: 8s, The Living Water. 12s, The Golden Apple. 16s, Krali-Marko, hero. 45s, Samovila-Vila, Witch. 80s, Tom Thumb.

1961, Oct. 10   Unwmk.   *Perf. 11*
1177 A560 2s blue, blk & org .18 .15
1178 A560 8s rose lil, blk & gray .24 .15
1179 A560 12s bl grn, blk & pink .24 .15
1180 A560 16s red, blk, bl & gray .38 .15
1181 A560 45s ol grn, blk & pink .75 .22
1182 A560 80s ocher, blk & dk car 1.10 .28
  Nos. 1177-1182 (6) 2.89
  Set value .80

Caesar's Mushroom A561

Miladinov Brothers and Title Page A562

Designs: Various mushrooms.

1961, Dec. 20   Photo.   *Perf. 11*
Denominations in Black
1183 A561 2s lemon & red .15 .15
1184 A561 4s ol grn & red brn .15 .15
1185 A561 12s bister & red brn .15 .15
1186 A561 16s lilac & red brn .15 .15
1187 A561 45s car rose & yel .15 .15
1188 A561 80s brn org & sep .18 .15
1189 A561 1.25 l vio & dk brn .40 .18
1190 A561 2 l org brn & brn .70 .40
  Set value 1.55 1.00
Value, denomination in dark grn, imperf. set $5 unused, $1.75 canceled.

1961, Dec. 21   Unwmk.   *Perf. 10½*
1191 A562 1.25 l olive & blk .60 .20
Publication of "Collected Folksongs" by the Brothers Miladinov, Dimitri and Konstantin, cent.

Nos. 1079-1085, 1087, 992, 1023, 1090-1091 and 806 Surcharged with New Value in Black, Red or Violet

1962, Jan. 1
1192 A533 1s on 10s red brown .15 .15
1193 A532 1s on 12s red brown .15 .15
1194 A532 2s on 15s red lilac .15 .15
1195 A533 2s on 16s dp vio (R) .15 .15
1196 A533 2s on 20s orange .15 .15
  a. "2 CT." on 2 lines .15 .15
1197 A532 3s on 25s brt bl (R) .15 .15
  a. Black surcharge 7.00 4.00
1198 A532 3s on 28s brt grn (R) .15 .15
1199 A532 5s on 45s chocolate .15 .15
1200 A499 5s on 44s dk bl grn (R) .15 .15
1201 A509 5s on 44s dp car (V) .15 .15
1202 A532 10s on 1 l maroon .25 .15
1203 A532 20s on 2 l dp car .70 .22
1204 A430 40s on 4 l rose lake (V) 1.50 .48
  Nos. 1192-1204 (13) 3.95
  Set value 1.30

Freighter "Varna" A563

Designs: 5s, Tanker "Komsomoletz." 20s, Liner "G. Dimitrov."

1962, Mar. 1   Photo.   *Perf. 10½*
1205 A563 1s lt grn & brt bl .15 .15
1206 A563 5s lt blue & gn .18 .15
1207 A563 20s gray bl & grnsh bl .70 .16
  Nos. 1205-1207 (3) 1.03
  Set value .26

Dimitrov Working as Printer — A564

Roses — A565

13s, Griffin, emblem of state printing works.

1962, Mar. 19   Unwmk.
1208 A564 2s ver, blk & yel .15 .15
1209 A564 13s red org, blk & yel .42 .15
  Set value .50 .15
80th anniversary (in 1961) of the George Dimitrov state printing works.

1962, Mar. 28
Various Roses in Natural Colors
1210 A565 1s deep violet .15 .15
1211 A565 2s salmon & dk car .15 .15
1212 A565 3s gray & car .15 .15

1213	A565	4s	dark green	.16	.15
1214	A565	5s	ultra	.22	.15
1215	A565	6s	bluish grn & dk car	.48	.15
1216	A565	8s	citron & car	1.10	.18
1217	A565	13s	blue	2.25	.60
		Nos. 1210-1217 (8)		4.66	
		Set value			1.15

For overprint and surcharges see Nos. 1281-1283.

Malaria
Eradication
Emblem and
Mosquito
A566

Design: 20s, Malaria eradication emblem.

1962, Apr. 19
| 1218 | A566 | 5s | org brn, yel & blk | .40 | .15 |
| 1219 | A566 | 20s | emerald, yel & blk | .85 | .35 |

WHO drive to eradicate malaria.
Value, imperf. $2.50 unused, $1.50 canceled.

Lenin and
First Issue
of Pravda
A567

1962, May 4   Unwmk.   Perf. 10
| 1220 | A567 | 5s | deep rose & slate | .50 | .15 |

50th anniversary of Pravda, Russian newspaper
founded by Lenin.

Blackboard and
Book — A568

1962, May 21   Photo.
| 1221 | A568 | 5s | Prus bl, blk & yel | .25 | .15 |

The 1962 Teachers' Congress.

Soccer Player
and
Globe — A569

1962, May 26   Perf. 10½
| 1222 | A569 | 13s | brt grn, blk & lt brn | .65 | .25 |

World Soccer Championship, Chile, May 30-June
17. Value, imperf. in changed colors, $2.50 unused,
$1.65 canceled.

George Dimitrov
A570

1962, June 18   Photo.
1223	A570	2s	dark green	.20	.15
1224	A570	5s	turq blue	.40	.15
		Set value			.15

80th anniv. of the birth of George Dimitrov
(1882-1949), communist leader and premier of the
Bulgarian Peoples' Republic.

Bishop — A571

1962, July 7   Unwmk.   Perf. 10½
1225	A571	1s	shown	.15	.15
1226	A571	2s	Rook	.15	.15
1227	A571	3s	Queen	.15	.15
1228	A571	13s	Knight	.65	.22
1229	A571	20s	Pawn	1.10	.42
		Nos. 1225-1229 (5)		2.20	
		Set value			.95

15th Chess Olympics, Varna. Nos. 1225-1229
were also issued imperf. in changed colors.
An imperf. souvenir sheet contains one 20s horizontal stamp showing five chessmen. Size:
75x66mm.

Rila Mountain
A572

Designs: 2s, Pirin mountain. 6s, Nesebr, Black
Sea. 8s, Danube. 13s, Vidin Castle. 1 l, Rhodope
mountain.

1962-63   Perf. 13
1230	A572	1s	dk blue grn	.15	.15
1231	A572	2s	blue	.15	.15
1232	A572	6s	grnsh blue	.15	.15
1233	A572	8c	lilac	.16	.15
1234	A572	13s	yellow grn	.38	.15
1234A	A572	1 1	dp green ('63)	3.25	.30
		Nos. 1230-1234A (6)		4.24	
		Set value			.58

No. 974 Surcharged in Red

**XXXV КОНГРЕС
1962**

 **13** =

1962, July 14   Perf. 13
| 1235 | A493 | 13s on 44s | slate grn | 2.25 | .80 |

25th Bulgarian Esperanto Congress, Burgas, July
14-16.

Girl and
Festival
Emblem
A573

Design: 5s, Festival emblem.

1962, Aug. 18   Photo.   Perf. 10½
1236	A573	5s	green, lt bl & pink	.20	.15
1237	A573	13s	lilac, lt bl & gray	.35	.15
		Set value			.15

8th Youth Festival for Peace and Friendship, Helsinki, July 28-Aug. 6, 1962.

Parnassius
Apollo
A574

1962, Sept. 13
Various Butterflies in Natural Colors
1238	A574	1s	pale cit & dk grn	.15	.15
1239	A574	2s	rose & brown	.15	.15
1240	A574	3s	buff & red brn	.15	.15
1241	A574	4s	gray & brown	.15	.15
1242	A574	5s	lt gray & brn	.16	.15
1243	A574	6s	gray & black	.18	.15

1244	A574	10s	pale grn & blk	1.25	.25
1245	A574	13s	buff & red brn	1.90	.40
		Nos. 1238-1245 (8)		4.09	
		Set value			1.00

Planting
Machine
A575

2s, Electric locomotive. 3s, Blast furnace. 13s,
Blagoev and Dimitrov and Communist flag.

1962, Nov. 1   Perf. 11½
1246	A575	1s	bl grn & dk ol grn	.15	.15
1247	A575	2s	bl & Prus bl	.15	.15
1248	A575	3s	carmine & brn	.18	.15
1249	A575	13s	plum, red & blk	.55	.20
		Nos. 1246-1249 (4)		1.03	
		Set value			.45

Bulgarian Communist Party, 8th Congress.

Title Page of "Slav-
Bulgarian
History" — A576

Paisii Hilendarski
Writing
History — A577

1962, Dec. 8   Unwmk.   Perf. 10½
1250	A576	2s	olive grn & blk	.15	.15
1251	A577	5s	brown org & blk	.15	.15
		Set value		.25	.20

200th anniv. of "Slav-Bulgarian History."

Aleco Konstantinov
(1863-1897),
Writer — A578

1963, Mar. 5   Photo.   Perf. 11½
| 1252 | A578 | 5s | red, grn & blk | .25 | .15 |

Printed with alternating red brown and black
label showing Bai Ganu, hero from Konstantinov's
books.

A579   Sofia University — A580

Designs: No. 1255, Levski Stadium, Sofia. No.
1256, Arch, Nissaria. No. 1257, Parachutist.

1963, Feb. 20   Unwmk.   Perf. 10
1253	A579	1s	brown red	.15	.15
1254	A580	1s	red brown	.15	.15
1255	A580	1s	blue green	.15	.15
1256	A580	1s	dark green	.15	.15
1257	A580	1s	brt blue	.15	.15
		Set value		.25	.25

Vassil Levski — A581   Boy, Girl and
Dimitrov — A582

1963, Apr. 11   Photo.
| 1258 | A581 | 13s | grnsh blue & buff | .75 | .25 |

90th anniversary of the death of Vassil Levski,
revolutionary leader in the fight for liberation from
the Turks.

1963, Apr. 25   Unwmk.   Perf. 11½

13s, Girl with book & boy with hammer.
1259	A582	2s	org, ver, red brn & blk	.15	.15
1260	A582	13s	bluish grn, brn & blk	.42	.15
		Set value			.20

10th Congress of Dimitrov's Union of the People's Youth.

Red   Sun Coast
Squirrel — A583   Promenade — A584

2s, Hedgehog. 3s, European polecat. 5s, Pine
marten. 13s, Badger. 20s, Otter. 2s, 3s, 13s, horiz.

1963, Apr. 30
Red Numerals
1261	A583	1s	grn & brn, *grnsh*	.15	.15
1262	A583	2s	grn & blk, *yel*	.15	.15
1263	A583	3s	grn & brn, *bis*	.15	.15
1264	A583	5s	vio & red brn, *lil*	.20	.15
1265	A583	13s	red brn & blk, *pink*	.80	.15
1266	A583	20s	blk & brn, *blue*	1.25	.20
		Nos. 1261-1266 (6)		2.70	
		Set value			.60

1963, Mar. 12   Unwmk.   Perf. 13

Black Sea Resorts: 2s, 3s, 13s, Views of Gold
Sand. 5s, 20s, Sun Coast.
1267	A584	1s	blue	.15	.15
1268	A584	2s	vermilion	.26	.15
1269	A584	2s	car rose	.38	.15
1270	A584	3s	ocher	.18	.15
1271	A584	5s	lilac	.18	.15
1272	A584	13s	blue green	.52	.15
1273	A584	20s	green	.95	.20
		Nos. 1267-1273 (7)		2.62	
		Set value			.53

Freestyle
Wrestling — A585

Design: 20s, Freestyle wrestling, horiz.

1963, May 31   Perf. 11½
1274	A585	5s	yel bister & blk	.16	.15
1275	A585	20s	org brn & blk	.80	.18
		Set value			.24

15th International Freestyle Wrestling Competi-
tions, Sofia.

"Women
for Peace"
A586

1963, June 24   Unwmk.   Perf. 11½
| 1276 | A586 | 20s | blue & blk | .60 | .15 |

World Congress of Women, Moscow, June 24-29.

Esperanto Emblem and Arms of Sofia — A587

Moon, Earth and Lunik 4 — A588

1963, June 29   Photo.
1277 A587 13s multicolored   .60 .15
48th World Esperanto Congress, Sofia, Aug. 3-10.

1963, July 22
2s, Radar equipment. 3s, Satellites and moon.
1278 A588 1s ultra   .15 .15
1279 A588 2s red lilac   .15 .15
1280 A588 3s greenish blue   .15 .15
    Set value   .25 .15
Russia's rocket to the moon, Apr. 2, 1963.

Nos. 1211-1212 and 1215 Overprinted or Surcharged in Green, Ultramarine or Black

1963, Aug. 31   Perf. 10½
1281 A565 2s (G)   .25 .15
1282 A565 5s on 3s (U)   .38 .15
1283 A565 13s on 6s   .70 .22
    Nos. 1281-1283 (3)   1.33
    Set value   .40
Intl. Stamp Fair, Riccione, Aug. 31.

Women's Relay Race A589

Designs: 2s, Hammer thrower. 3s, Women's long jump. 5s, Men's high jump. 13s, Discus thrower.

Perf. 11½
1963, Sept. 13   Photo.   Unwmk.
Flags in National Colors
1284 A589 1s slate green   .15 .15
1285 A589 2s purple   .15 .15
1286 A589 3s Prus blue   .16 .15
1287 A589 5s maroon   .45 .30
1288 A589 13s chestnut brn   1.65 1.25
    Nos. 1284-1288 (5)   2.56 2.00
Balkan Games. A multicolored, 50s, imperf. souvenir sheet shows design of women's relay race. Size: 74x70mm.

"Slav-Bulgarian History" — A590

1963, Sept. 19   Perf. 10½
1289 A590 5s salmon pink, slate & yel   .20 .15
5th International Slavic Congress.

Revolutionists A591

Christo Smirnenski A592

1963, Sept. 22   Perf. 11½
1290 A591 2s brt red & blk   .15 .15
40th anniversary of the September Revolution.

1963, Oct. 28   Perf. 10½
1291 A592 13s pale lilac & indigo   .45 .15
Christo Smirnenski, poet, 65th birth anniv.

Columbine A593

Horses A594

1963, Oct. 9   Photo.   Perf. 11½
1292 A593 1s shown   .15 .15
1293 A593 2s Edelweiss   .15 .15
1294 A593 3s Primrose   .15 .15
1295 A593 5s Water lily   .15 .15
1296 A593 6s Tulips   .16 .15
1297 A593 8s Larkspur   .30 .15
1298 A593 10s Alpine clematis   .70 .16
1299 A593 13s Anemone   1.25 .25
    Nos. 1292-1299 (8)   3.01
    Set value   .90

1963, Dec. 28   Unwmk.   Perf. 10½
Designs: 2s, Charioteer and chariot. 3s, Trumpeters. 5s, Woman carrying tray with food. 13s, Man holding bowl. 20s, Woman in armchair. Designs are from a Thracian tomb at Kazanlik.
1300 A594 1s gray, org & dk red   .15 .15
1301 A594 2s gray, ocher & pur   .15 .15
1302 A594 3s gray, dl yel & sl grn   .15 .15
1303 A594 5s pale grn, ocher & brn   .15 .15
1304 A594 13s pale grn, bis & blk   .42 .15
1305 A594 20s pale grn, org & dk car   .75 .30
    Set value   1.50 .75

World Map and Emblem A595

Designs: 2s, Blood transfusion. 3s, Nurse bandaging injured wrist. 5s, Red Cross nurse. 13s, Henri Dunant.

1964, Jan. 27   Perf. 10½
1306 A595 1s lem, blk & red   .15 .15
1307 A595 2s ultra, blk & red   .15 .15
1308 A595 3s gray, sl, blk & red   .15 .15
1309 A595 5s brt bl, blk & red   .15 .15
1310 A595 13s org yel, blk & red   .42 .15
    Set value   .80 .32
Centenary of International Red Cross.

Speed Skating A596

Sports: 2s, 50s, Women's figure skating. 3s, Cross-country skiing. 5s, Ski jump. 10s, Ice hockey goalkeeper. 13s, Ice hockey players.

1964, Feb. 21   Unwmk.   Perf. 10½
1311 A596 1s grnsh bl, ind & ocher   .15 .15
1312 A596 2s brt pink, ol grn & dk sl grn   .15 .15
1313 A596 3s dl grn, dk grn & brn   .15 .15
1314 A596 5s bl, blk & yel brn   .18 .15

1315 A596 10s gray, org & blk   .40 .18
1316 A596 13s lil, blk & lil rose   .70 .28
    Nos. 1311-1316 (6)   1.73
    Set value   .60

Miniature Sheet
Imperf
1317 A596 50s gray, Prus grn & pink   3.75 3.00
9th Winter Olympic Games, Innsbruck, Jan. 29-Feb. 9, 1964.

Mask of Nobleman, 2nd Century — A597

Designs: 2s, Thracian horseman. 3s, Ceramic jug. 5s, Clasp and belt. 6s, Copper kettle. 8s, Angel. 10s, Lioness. 13s, Scrub woman, contemporary sculpture.

1964, Mar. 14   Photo.   Perf. 10½
Gray Frame
1318 A597 1s dp green & red   .15 .15
1319 A597 2s ol gray & red   .15 .15
1320 A597 3s bister & red   .15 .15
1321 A597 5s indigo & red   .16 .15
1322 A597 6s org brn & red   .22 .15
1323 A597 8s brn red & red   .38 .15
1324 A597 10s olive & red   .42 .15
1325 A597 13s gray ol & red   .65 .22
    Nos. 1318-1325 (8)   2.28
    Set value   .75
2,500 years of Bulgarian art.

"The Unborn Maid" A598

Fairy Tales: 2s, Grandfather's Glove. 3s, The Big Turnip. 5s, The Wolf and the Seven Kids. 8s, Cunning Peter. 13s, The Wheat Cake.

1964, Apr. 17   Unwmk.   Perf. 10½
1326 A598 1s bl grn, red & org brn   .15 .15
1327 A598 2s ultra, ocher & blk   .15 .15
1328 A598 3s cit, red & blk   .15 .15
1329 A598 5s dp rose, brn & blk   .15 .15
1330 A598 8s yel grn, red & blk   .20 .15
1331 A598 13s lt vio bl, grn & blk   .70 .18
    Set value   1.25 .46

Ascalaphus Otomanus A599

Insects: 2s, Nemoptera coa., vert. 3s, Saga natalia (grasshopper). 5s, Rosalia alpina, vert. 13s, Anisoplia austriaca, vert. 20s, Scolia flavitrons.

1964, May 16   Photo.   Perf. 11½
1332 A599 1s brn org, red & blk   .15 .15
1333 A599 2s dl bl grn, bis & blk   .15 .15
1334 A599 3s gray, grn & blk   .15 .15
1335 A599 5s lt ol grn, blk & vio   .15 .15
1336 A599 13s vio, bis & blk   .55 .16
1337 A599 20s gray bl, yel & blk   .85 .28
    Nos. 1332-1337 (6)   2.00
    Set value   .75

Soccer — A600

Designs: 13s, Women's volleyball. 60s, Map of Europe and European Women's Volleyball Championship Cup (rectangular, size: 60x69mm).

1964, June 8   Unwmk.   Perf. 11½
1338 A600 2s bl, dk bl, ocher & red   .15 .15
1339 A600 13s bl, dk bl, ocher & red   .52 .22
    Set value   .30

Miniature Sheet
Imperf
1340 A600 60s ultra, ocher, red & gray   3.00 2.25
Levski Physical Culture Assoc., 50th anniv.

Peter Beron and Title Page of Primer A601

1964, June 22   Perf. 11½
1341 A601 20s red brn & dk brn, grysh   1.00 .60
140th anniversary of the publication of the first Bulgarian primer.

Robert Stephenson's "Rocket" Locomotive, 1825 — A602

Designs: 2s, Modern steam locomotive. 3s, Diesel locomotive. 5s, Electric locomotive. 8s, Freight train on bridge. 13s, Diesel locomotive and tunnel.

1964, July 1   Photo.   Perf. 11½
1342 A602 1s multicolored   .15 .15
1343 A602 2s multicolored   .15 .15
1344 A602 3s multicolored   .15 .15
1345 A602 5s multicolored   .15 .15
1346 A602 8s multicolored   .32 .15
1347 A602 13s multicolored   .80 .20
    Nos. 1342-1347 (6)   1.72
    Set value   .50

German Shepherd A603

1964, Aug. 22   Photo.
1348 A603 1s shown   .15 .15
1349 A603 2s Setter   .15 .15
1350 A603 3s Poodle   .15 .15
1351 A603 4s Pomeranian   .16 .15
1352 A603 5s St. Bernard   .20 .15
1353 A603 6s Terrier   .26 .15
1354 A603 10s Pointer   1.40 .15
1355 A603 13s Dachshund   2.75 .42
    Nos. 1348-1355 (8)   5.22
    Set value   .90

Partisans — A604

Designs: 2s, People welcoming Soviet army. 3s, Russian aid to Bulgaria. 4s, Blast furnace, Kremikovski. 5s, Combine. 6s, Peace demonstration. 8s, Sentry. 13s, Demeter Blagoev and George Dimitrov.

1964, Sept. 9   Unwmk.   Perf. 11½
Flag in Red
1356 A604 1s lt & dp ultra   .15 .15
1357 A604 2s ol bis & dp ol   .15 .15
1358 A604 3s rose lil & mar   .15 .15
1359 A604 4s lt vio & vio   .15 .15
1360 A604 5s org & red brn   .15 .15
1361 A604 6s bl & dp bl   .15 .15
1362 A604 8s lt grn & grn   .20 .15
1363 A604 13s fawn & red brn   .42 .15
    Set value   1.00 .50
20th anniv. of People's Government of Bulgaria.

No. 967
Surcharged

1964, Sept. 13 *Perf. 13*
1364 A476 20s on 44s org yel 1.00 .35
International Plovdiv Fair.

Gymnast on Parallel Bars
A606

Vratcata
Mountain
Road
A607

Sports: 2s, Long jump. 3s, Woman diver. 5s, Soccer. 13s, Women's volleyball. 20s, Wrestling.

1964, Oct. 10 *Perf. 11½*
1366 A606 1s pale grn, grn & red .15 .15
1367 A606 2s pale vio, vio bl & red .15 .15
1368 A606 3s bl grn, brn & red .15 .15
1369 A606 5s pink, pur & red .16 .15
1370 A606 13s bl, Prus grn & red .52 .15
1371 A606 20s yel, grn & red .90 .22
    Set value 1.75 .60

18th Olympic Games, Tokyo. Oct. 10-25. See No. B27.

1964, Oct. 26 Photo. *Perf. 12½x13*
Bulgarian Views: 2s, Ritlite mountain road. 3s, Pines, Malovica peak. 4s, Pobitite rocks. 5s, Erkupria. 6s, Rhodope mountain road.

1372 A607 1s dk slate grn .15 .15
1373 A607 2s brown .15 .15
1374 A607 3s grnsh blue .15 .15
1375 A607 4s dk red brn .15 .15
1376 A607 5s deep green .20 .15
1377 A607 6s blue violet .30 .15
    Set value .80 .35

Mail Coach,
Plane and
Rocket
A608

1964, Oct. 3 Unwmk. *Perf. 11½*
1378 A608 20s greenish blue 1.25 .48

First national stamp exhibition, Sofia, Oct. 3-18. Issued in sheets of 12 stamps and 12 labels (woman's head and inscription, 5x5) arranged around one central label showing stylized bird design.

Students Holding
Book — A609

1964, Dec. 30 *Photo.*
1379 A609 13s lt blue & blk .45 .15
8th Intl. Students' Congress, Sofia.

500-Year-Old
Walnut Tree at
Golemo
Drenovo
A610

Designs: Various old trees.

1964, Dec. 28
1380 A610 1s blk, buff & cl brn .15 .15
1381 A610 2s blk, pink & dp cl .15 .15
1382 A610 3s blk, yel & dk brn .15 .15
1383 A610 4s blk, lt bl & Prus bl .15 .15
1384 A610 10s blk, pale grn & grn .22 .15
1385 A610 13s blk, pale bis & dk ol grn .42 .15
    Set value .84 .42

Soldiers'
Monument — A611

1965, Jan. 1 **Unwmk.**
1386 A611 2s red & black .20 .15
Bulgarian-Soviet friendship.

Olympic Medal
Inscribed
"Olympic
Glory" — A612

1965, Jan. 27 Photo. *Perf. 11½*
1387 A612 20s org brn, gold & blk .60 .16
Bulgarian victories in the 1964 Olympic Games.

"Victory Over
Fascism"
A613

Design: 13s, "Fight for Peace" (dove and globe).

1965, Apr. 16 *Perf. 11½*
1388 A613 5s gray, blk & ol bis .15 .15
1389 A613 13s gray, blk & blue .26 .16
    Set value .21

20th anniv. of victory over Fascism, May 9, 1945.

Vladimir M. Komarov and Section of
Globe — A614

Designs: 2s, Konstantin Feoktistov. 5s, Boris B. Yegorov. 13s, Komarov, Feoktistov and Yegorov. 20s, Spaceship Voskhod.

1965, Feb. 15 **Photo.**
1390 A614 1s pale lil & dk bl .15 .15
1391 A614 2s lt bl, ind & dl vio .15 .15
1392 A614 5s pale grn, grn & ol grn .15 .15
1393 A614 13s pale pink, dp rose & mar .42 .15
1394 A614 20s lt bl, vio bl, grnsh bl & yel .75 .16
    Nos. 1390-1394 (5) 1.62
    Set value .42

Russian 3-man space flight, Oct. 12-13, 1964. Imperfs. in changed colors. Four low values setenant. Value, set $2 unused, $1 canceled.

Bullfinch — A615

Birds: 2s, European golden oriole. 3s, Common rock thrush. 5s, Barn swallow. 8s, European roller. 10s, European goldfinch. 13s, Rosy pastor starling. 20s, Nightingale.

1965, Apr. 20 Unwmk. *Perf. 11½*
Birds in Natural Colors
1395 A615 1s blue green .15 .15
1396 A615 2s rose lilac .15 .15
1397 A615 3s rose .15 .15
1398 A615 5s brt blue .15 .15
1399 A615 8s citron .32 .15
1400 A615 10s gray 1.10 .15
1401 A615 13s lt vio blue 1.10 .18
1402 A615 20s emerald 2.25 .35
    Nos. 1395-1402 (8) 5.37
    Set value .88

Black Sea
Fish — A616

1965, June 10 Photo. *Perf. 11½*
Gray Frames
1403 A616 1s Sting ray .15 .15
1404 A616 2s Belted bonito .15 .15
1405 A616 3s Hogfish .15 .15
1406 A616 5s Gurnard .18 .15
1407 A616 10s Scad .75 .16
1408 A616 13s Turbot 1.10 .26
    Nos. 1403-1408 (6) 2.48
    Set value .64

Plane, Bus,
Train, Ship and
Whale — A617

1965, Apr. 30
1409 A617 13s multicolored .45 .15
4th Intl. Conf. of Transport, Dock and Fishery Workers, Sofia, May 10-14.

ITU Emblem and
Communications
Symbols — A618

1965, May 17
1410 A618 20s multicolored .65 .30
Centenary of the ITU.

Col. Pavel Belyayev and Lt. Col. Alexei
Leonov
A619

Design: 20s, Leonov floating in space.

1965, May 20 **Unwmk.**
1411 A619 2s gray, dull bl & dk brn .15 .20
1412 A619 20s multicolored 1.00 .45

Space flight of Voskhod 2 and the first man floating in space, Lt. Col. Alexei Leonov.

ICY
Emblem — A620

1965, May 15 **Photo.**
1413 A620 20s orange, olive & blk .65 .15
International Cooperation Year, 1965.

Corn
A621

Marx and Lenin
A622

1965, Apr. 1 *Perf. 12½x13*
1414 A621 1s shown .15 .15
1415 A621 2s Wheat .15 .15
1416 A621 3s Sunflowers .15 .15
1417 A621 4s Sugar beet .15 .15
1418 A621 5s Clover .15 .15
1419 A621 10s Cotton .42 .15
1420 A621 13s Tobacco .60 .15
    Set value 1.40 .42

1965, June *Perf. 10½*
1421 A622 13s red & dk brn .65 .15
6th Conference of Postal Ministers of Communist Countries, Peking, June 21-July 15.

Film and
UNESCO
Emblem
A623

1965, June 30
1422 A623 13s dp bl, blk & lt gray .50 .15
Balkan Film Festival, Varna.

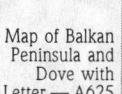

Ballerina — A624

1965, July 10 **Photo.**
1423 A624 5s dp lil rose & blk .60 .25
2nd Intl. Ballet Competition, Varna.

Map of Balkan
Peninsula and
Dove with
Letter — A625

Col. Pavel Belyayev and Lt. Col. Alexei Leonov — A626

2s, Sailboat and modern buildings. 3s, Fish and plants. 13s, Symbolic sun and rocket. 40s, Map of Balkan Peninsula and dove with letter (like 1s).

1965 Perf. 10½
1424	A625	1s sil, dp ultra & yel	.15 .15
1425	A625	2s sil, pur & yel	.15 .15
1426	A625	3s gold, grn & yel	.15 .15
1427	A625	13s gold, hn brn & yel	.55 .50
1428	A626	20s sil, bl & brn	.70 .55
	Nos. 1424-1428 (5)		1.70
	Set value		1.25

Miniature Sheet
Imperf
1429	A625	40s gold & brt bl	1.75 1.00

Balkanphila 1965 Philatelic Exhibition, Varna, Aug. 7-15, and visit of Russian astronauts Belyayev and Leonov.
Value, No. 1428 imperf. in changed colors, 90 cents.
Issued: 20s, 40s, 8/7; others, 7/23.

Woman Gymnast — A627

Designs: 2s, Woman gymnast on parallel bars. 5s, Weight lifter. 5s, Automobile and chart. 10s, Women basketball players. 13s, Automobile and map of rally.

1965, Aug. 14 Perf. 10½
1430	A627	1s crim, brn & blk	.15 .15
1431	A627	2s rose vio, dp cl & blk	.15 .15
1432	A627	3s dp car, brn & blk	.15 .15
1433	A627	5s fawn, red brn & blk	.15 .15
1434	A627	10s dp lil rose, dp cl & blk	.52 .15
1435	A627	13s lilac, claret & blk	.65 .16
	Set value		1.45 .48

Sports events in Bulgaria during May-June, 1965.

No. 989 Surcharged

1965, Aug. 12 Perf. 13
1436	A499	2s on 8s orange brn	.75 .26

1st Natl. Folklore Competition, Aug. 12-15.

Escaping Prisoners A628

Fruit A629

1965, July 23 Perf. 10½
1437	A628	2s slate	.20 .15

40th anniversary of the escape of political prisoners from Bolshevik Island.

1965, July 1 Perf. 13
1438	A629	1s Apples	.15 .15
1439	A629	2s Grapes	.15 .15
1440	A629	3s Pears	.15 .15
1441	A629	4s Peaches	.15 .15
1442	A629	5s Strawberries	.20 .15
1443	A629	6s Walnuts	.32 .15
	Set value		.75 .34

Horsemanship — A630

1965, Sept. 30 Unwmk. Perf. 10½
1444	A630	1s Dressage	.15 .15
1445	A630	2s Three-day test	.15 .15
1446	A630	3s Jumping	.15 .15
1447	A630	5s Race	.15 .15
1448	A630	10s Steeplechase	.75 .20
1449	A630	13s Hurdle race	1.40 .28
	Nos. 1444-1449 (6)		2.75
	Set value		.75

See No. B28.

Smiling Children — A631

Designs: 2s, Two girl Pioneers. 3s, Bugler. 5s, Pioneer with model plane. 8s, Two singing girls in national costume. 13s, Running boy.

1965, Oct. 24 Photo.
1450	A631	1s dk bl grn & yel grn	.15 .15
1451	A631	2s vio & deep rose	.15 .15
1452	A631	3s olive & lemon	.15 .15
1453	A631	5s dp blue & bister	.15 .15
1454	A631	8s olive bister & org	.28 .15
1455	A631	13s rose car & vio	.65 .24
	Set value		1.25 .60

Dimitrov Pioneer Organization.

U-52 Plane over Trnovo A632

Designs: 2c, 1L-14 over Plovdiv. 3s, Mi-4 Helicopter over Dimitrovgrad. 5s, Tu-104 over Ruse. 13s, IL-18 over Varna. 20s, Tu-114 over Sofia.

1965, Nov. 25 Perf. 10½
1456	A632	1s gray, blue & red	.15 .15
1457	A632	2s gray, lilac & red	.15 .15
1458	A632	3s gray, grnsh bl & red	.15 .15
1459	A632	5s gray, orange & red	.15 .15
1460	A632	13s gray, bister & red	.70 .15
1461	A632	20s gray, lt grn & red	1.00 .28
	Set value		2.00 .60

Development of Bulgarian Civil Air Transport.

IQSY Emblem, and Earth Radiation Zones A633

Designs (IQSY Emblem and): 2s, Sun with corona. 13s, Solar eclipse.

1965, Dec. 15 Photo. Perf. 10½
1462	A633	1s grn, yel & ultra	.15 .15
1463	A633	2s yel, red lil & red	.15 .15
1464	A633	13s bl, yel & blk	.32 .15
	Set value		.42 .24

International Quiet Sun Year, 1964-65.

"North and South Bulgaria" A634

"Martenitsa" Emblem A635

1965, Dec. 6
1465	A634	13s brt yel grn & blk	.50 .25

Union of North and South Bulgaria, cent.

1966, Jan. 10 Photo. Perf. 10½
"Spring" in Folklore: 2s, Drummer. 3s, Bird ornaments. 5s, Dancer "Lazarka." 8s, Vase with flowers. 13s, Bagpiper.
1466	A635	1s rose lil, vio bl & gray	.15 .15
1467	A635	2s gray, blk & crim	.15 .15
1468	A635	3s red, vio & gray	.15 .15
1469	A635	5s lil, blk & crim	.15 .15
1470	A635	8s rose lil, brn & pur	.22 .15
1471	A635	13s bl, blk & rose lil	.50 .20
	Set value		1.00 .50

Church of St. John the Baptist, Nessebr A636

Designs: 1s, Christ, fresco from Bojana Church. 2s, Ikon "Destruction of Idols," horiz. 3s, Bratchkovo Monastery. 4s, Zemen Monastery, horiz. 13s, Nativity, ikon from Arbanassi. 20s, Ikon "Virgin and Child," 1342.

1966, Feb. 25 Litho. Perf. 11½
1472	A636	1s gray & multi	3.50 1.25
1473	A636	2s gray & multi	.25 .15
1474	A636	3s multicolored	.25 .15
1475	A636	4s multicolored	.25 .15
1476	A636	5s multicolored	.25 .15
1477	A636	13s gray & multi	.50 .15
1478	A636	20s multicolored	.95 .35
	Nos. 1472-1478 (7)		5.95 2.35

2,500 years of art in Bulgaria.

Georgi Benkovski and T. Kableshkov A637

Designs: 1s, Proclamation of April Uprising, Koprivstitsa. 3s, Dedication of flag, Panaguriste. 5s, V. Petleshkov and Z. Dyustabanov. 10s, Botev landing at Kozlodui. 13s, P. Volov and Ilarion Dragostinov.

1966, Mar. 3 Photo. Perf. 10½
Center in Black
1479	A637	1s red brn & gold	.15 .15
1480	A637	2s brt red & gold	.15 .15
1481	A637	3s ol grn & gold	.15 .15
1482	A637	5s steel bl & gold	.15 .15
1483	A637	10s brt rose lil & gold	.20 .15
1484	A637	13s lt vio & gold	.48 .15
	Set value		.95 .34

April Uprising against the Turks, 90th anniv.

Sofia Zoo Animals A638

1966, May 23 Litho.
1485	A638	1s Elephant	.15 .15
1486	A638	2s Tiger	.15 .15
1487	A638	3s Chimpanzee	.15 .15
1488	A638	4s Siberian ibex	.18 .15
1489	A638	5s Polar bear	.25 .15
1490	A638	8s Lion	.25 .15
1491	A638	13s Bison	.80 .20
1492	A638	20s Kangaroo	1.50 .30
	Nos. 1485-1492 (8)		3.43
	Set value		.85

WHO Headquarters, Geneva — A639

1966, May 3 Photo.
1493	A639	13s deep blue & silver	.60 .25

Inauguration of the WHO Headquarters, Geneva.

Worker A640

1966, May 9 Photo. Perf. 10½
1494	A640	20s gray & rose	.65 .15

Sixth Trade Union Congress.

Yantra River Bridge, Biela — A641

Designs: No. 1496, Maritsa River Bridge, Svilengrad. No. 1497, Fountain, Samokov. No. 1498, Ruins of Fort, Kaskovo. 8s, Old Fort, Ruse. 13s, House, Gabrovo.

1966, Feb. 10 Photo. Perf. 13
1495	A641	1s Prus blue	.15 .15
1496	A641	1s brt green	.15 .15
1497	A641	2s olive green	.15 .15
1498	A641	3s dk red brown	.15 .15
1499	A641	8s red brown	.25 .15
1500	A641	13s dark blue	.42 .15
	Set value		.95 .36

Souvenir Sheet

Moon Allegory — A642

1966, Apr. 29 Imperf.
1501	A642	60s blk, plum & sil	2.50 1.25

1st Russian soft landing on the moon by Luna 9, Feb. 3, 1966.

Steamer Radetzky and Bugler A643

1966, May 28 Perf. 10½
1502	A643	2s multicolored	.15 .15

90th anniv. of the participation of the Danube steamer Radetzky in the uprising against the Turks.

Standard Bearer
Nicola Simov-Kuruto
A644

1966, May 30
1503 A644 5s bister, green & olive .25 .15
Hero of the Turkish War.

UNESCO
Emblem — A645

1966, June 8
1504 A645 20s gold, blk & ver .60 .16
20th anniv. of UNESCO.

Youth Federation Badge — A646

1966, June 6 Photo. Perf. 10¹/₂
1505 A646 13s silver, bl & blk .40 .15
7th Assembly of the Intl. Youth Federation.

Soccer — A647

Various soccer scenes. 50s, Jules Rimet Cup.

1966, June 27
1506 A647 1s gray, yel brn & blk .15 .15
1507 A647 2s gray, crim & blk .15 .15
1508 A647 5s gray, ol bis & blk .15 .15
1509 A647 13s gray, ultra & blk .35 .15
1510 A647 20s gray, Prus bl & blk .60 .20
Nos. 1506-1510 (5) 1.40
Set value .45

Miniature Sheet
Imperf
1511 A647 50s gray, dp lil rose & gold 2.25 1.50
World Soccer Cup Championship, Wembley, England, July 11-30. Size of No. 1511: 60x64mm.

Woman Javelin Thrower — A648

Designs: No. 1513, Runner. No. 1514, Young man and woman carrying banners, vert.

1966 Photo. Perf. 10¹/₂
1512 A648 2s grn, yel & ver .15 .15
1513 A648 13s dp grn, yel & sal pink .40 .15
1514 A648 13s bl, lt bl & salmon .40 .15
Nos. 1512-1514 (3) .95
Set value .26

Nos. 1512-1513: 3rd Spartacist Games; issued Aug. 10. No. 1514: 3rd congress of the Bulgarian Youth Federation; issued May 25.

Wrestlers Nicolas Petrov and Dan Kolov — A649

1966, July 29
1515 A649 13s bis brn, dk brn & lt ol grn .40 .20
3rd International Wrestling Championships.

Map of Balkan Countries, Globe and UNESCO Emblem — A650

1966, Aug. 26 Perf. 10¹/₂x11¹/₂
1516 A650 13s ultra, lt grn & pink .40 .15
First Congress of Balkanologists.

Children with Building Blocks — A651

Designs: 2s, Bunny and teddy bear with book. 3s, Children as astronauts. 13s, Children with pails and shovel.

1966, Sept. 1 Perf. 10¹/₂
1517 A651 1s dk car, org & blk .15 .15
1518 A651 2s emerald, blk & red brn .15 .15
1519 A651 3s ultra, org & blk .15 .15
1520 A651 13s blue, rose & blk .60 .15
Set value .80 .29
Children's Day.

Yuri A. Gagarin and Vostok 1 — A652

Designs: 2s, Gherman S. Titov, Vostok 2. 3s, Andrian G. Nikolayev, Pavel R. Popovich, Vostoks 3 & 4. 5s, Valentina Tereshkova, Valeri Bykovski, Vostoks 5 & 6. 8s, Vladimir M. Komarov, Boris B. Yegorov, Konstantin Feoktistov, Voskhod 1. 13s, Pavel Belyayev, Alexei Leonov, Voskhod 2.

1966, Sept. 29 Photo. Perf. 11¹/₂x11
1521 A652 1s slate & gray .15 .15
1522 A652 2s plum & gray .15 .15
1523 A652 3s yel brn & gray .15 .15
1524 A652 5s brn red & gray .15 .15
1525 A652 8s ultra & gray .15 .15
1526 A652 13s Prus bl & gray .48 .15
Set value, #1521-1526, B29 1.90 .72
Russian space explorations.

St. Clement, 14th Century Wood Sculpture — A653

1966, Oct. 27 Photo. Perf. 11¹/₂x11
1527 A653 5s red, buff & brn .20 .15
1050th anniversary of the birth of St. Clement of Ochrida.

Metodi Shatorov A654

Portraits: 3s, Vladimir Trichkov. 5s, Valcho Ivanov. 10s, Raiko Daskalov. 13s, General Vladimir Zaimov.

1966, Nov. 8 Perf. 11x11¹/₂
Gold Frame, Black Denomination
1528 A654 2s crimson & bl vio .15 .15
1529 A654 3s magenta & blk .15 .15
1530 A654 5s car rose & dk bl .15 .15
1531 A654 10s orange & olive .28 .15
1532 A654 13s red & brown .40 .15
Set value .90 .32
Fighters against fascism.

George Dimitrov — A655

Steel Worker — A656

1966, Nov. 14 Photo. Perf. 11¹/₂x11
1533 A655 2s magenta & blk .15 .15
1534 A656 20s fawn, gray & blk .70 .15
Set value .17
Bulgarian Communist Party, 9th Congress.

Deer's Head Drinking Cup A667

Gold Treasure: 2s, 6s, 10s, Various Amazon's head jugs. 3s, Ram's head cup. 5s, Circular plate. 8s, Deer's head cup. 13s, Amphora. 20s, Ram drinking horn.

1966, Nov. 28 Perf. 12x11¹/₂
Vessels in Gold and Brown; Black Inscriptions
1535 A667 1s gray & violet .15 .15
1536 A667 2s gray & green .15 .15
1537 A667 3s gray & dk bl .15 .15
1538 A667 5s gray & red brn .15 .15
1539 A667 6s gray & Prus bl .15 .15
1540 A667 8s gray & brn ol .85 .15
1541 A667 10s gray & sepia .85 .18
1542 A667 13s gray & dk vio bl .85 .28
1543 A667 20s gray & vio brn .95 .32
Nos. 1535-1543 (9) 4.25
Set value 1.25
The gold treasure from the 4th century B.C. was found near Panagyurishte in 1949.

Tourist House, Bansko — A668

Tourist Houses: No. 1545, Belogradchik. No. 1546, Triavna. 20s, Rila.

1966, Nov. 29 Photo. Perf. 11x11¹/₂
1544 A668 1s dark blue .15 .15
1545 A668 2s dark green .15 .15
1546 A668 2s brown red .15 .15
1547 A668 20s lilac .42 .15
Set value .65 .25

Decorated Tree — A669

Design: 13s, Jug with bird design.

1966, Dec. 12 Perf. 11
1548 A669 2s grn, pink & gold .18 .15
1549 A669 13s brn lake, rose, emer & gold .38 .15
Set value .15
New Year, 1967.

Pencho Slavikov, Author — A670

Dahlia — A671

Portraits: 2s, Dimcho Debeljanov, author. 3s, P. H. Todorov, author. 5s, Dimitri Dobrovich, painter. 8s, Ivan Markvichka, painter. 13s, Ilya Bezhkov, painter.

1966, Dec. 15 Perf. 10¹/₂x11
1550 A670 1s blue, olive & org .15 .15
1551 A670 2s orange, brn & gray .15 .15
1552 A670 3s olive, bl & org .15 .15
1553 A670 5s gray, red brn & org .15 .15
1554 A670 8s lilac, dk gray & bl .30 .15
1555 A670 13s blue, vio & lil .38 .15
Set value .95 .34

1966, Dec. 29
Flowers: No. 1557, Clematis. No. 1558, Foxglove. No. 1559, Narcissus. 3s, Snowdrop. 5s, Petunia. 13s, Tiger lily. 20s, Bellflower.

Flowers in Natural Colors
1556 A671 1s gray & lt brn .15 .15
1557 A671 1s gray & dull bl .15 .15
1558 A671 2s gray & dull lil .15 .15
1559 A671 2s gray & brown .15 .15
1560 A671 3s gray & dk org .16 .15
1561 A671 5s gray & dp ultra .22 .15
1562 A671 5s gray & brown .60 .15
1563 A671 20s gray & ultra .95 .15
Nos. 1556-1563 (8) 2.53
Set value .55

Ringnecked Pheasant A672

Game: 2s, Rock partridge. 3s, Gray partridge. 5s, Hare. 8s, Roe deer. 13s, Red deer.

1967, Jan. 28 Perf. 11x10¹/₂
1564 A672 1s lt ultra, dk brn & ocher .15 .15
1565 A672 2s pale yel grn & dk grn .15 .15
1566 A672 3s lt bl, blk & cr .16 .15
1567 A672 5s lt grn & blk .16 .15
1568 A672 8s pale bl, dk brn & ocher .70 .15
1569 A672 13s bl & dk brn 1.25 .25
Nos. 1564-1569 (6) 2.57
Set value .60

Bulgaria No. 1, 1879 — A673

Thracian Coin, 6th Century, B.C. — A674

1967, Feb. 4 Photo. Perf. 10¹/₂
1570 A673 10s emerald, blk & yel .75 .22
Bulgarian Philatelic Union, 10th Congress.

1967, Mar. 30 Perf. 11¹/₂x11
Coins: 2s, Macedonian tetradrachma, 2nd cent. B.C. 3s, Tetradrachma of Odessus, 2nd cent. B.C. 5s, Philip II of Macedonia, 4th cent. B.C. 13s, Thracian King Seuthus VII, 4th cent., B.C., obverse and reverse. 20s, Apollonian coin, 5th cent., B.C., obverse and reverse.

Size: 25x25mm

1571	A674	1s brn, blk & sil	.15 .15
1572	A674	2s red lil, blk & sil	.15 .15
1573	A674	3s grn, blk & sil	.15 .15
1574	A674	5s brn org, blk & sil	.16 .15

Size: 37½x25mm

1575	A674	13s brt bl, blk & brnz	.70 .24
1576	A674	20s vio, blk & sil	1.25 .45
		Nos. 1571-1576 (6)	2.56
		Set value	.88

Partisans Listening to Radio — A675

Design: 20s, George Dimitrov addressing crowd and Bulgarian flag.

1967, Apr. 20   Perf. 11x11½

1577	A675	1s red, gold, buff & sl grn	.15 .15
1578	A675	20s red, gold, dl red, grn & blk	.55 .15
		Set value	.17

25th anniversary of the Union of Patriotic Front Organizations.

Nikolas Kofardjiev A676

Portraits: 2s, Petko Napetov. 5s, Petko D. Petkov. 10s, Emil Markov. 13s, Traitcho Kostov.

1967, Apr. 24   Perf. 11½x11

1579	A676	1s brn red, gray & blk	.15 .15
1580	A676	2s ol grn, gray & blk	.15 .15
1581	A676	5s brn, gray & blk	.15 .15
1582	A676	10s dp bl, gray & blk	.20 .15
1583	A676	13s mag, gray & blk	.42 .15
		Set value	.85 .30

Fighters against fascism.

Symbolic Flower and Flame — A677

1967, May 18   Photo.   Perf. 11x11½

1584	A677	13s gold, yel & lt grn	.45 .15

First Cultural Congress, May 18-19.

Gold Sand Beach and ITY Emblem A678

20s, Hotel, Pamporovo. 40s, Nessebr Church.

1967, June 12   Photo.   Perf. 11x11½

1585	A678	13s ultra, yel & blk	.28 .15
1586	A678	20s Prus bl, blk & buff	.42 .15
1587	A678	40s brt grn, blk & ocher	1.00 .28
		Nos. 1585-1587 (3)	1.70 .58

International Tourist Year, 1967.

Angora Cat — A679

Cats: 2s, Siamese, horiz. 3s, Abyssinian. 5s, Black European. 13s, Persian, horiz. 20s, Striped domestic.

Perf. 11½x11, 11x11½

1967, June 19

1588	A679	1s dl vio, dk brn & buff	.15 .15
1589	A679	2s ol, sl & brt bl	.15 .15
1590	A679	3s dull blue & brn	.15 .15
1591	A679	5s grn, blk & yel	.20 .15
1592	A679	13s dl red brn, sl & org	.90 .15
1593	A679	20s gray grn, brn & buff	1.65 .25
		Nos. 1588-1593 (6)	3.20
		Set value	.56

Scene from Opera "The Master of Boyana" by K. Iliev — A680

Songbird on Keyboard — A681

1967, June 19

1594	A680	5s gray, vio bl & dp car	.38 .15
1595	A681	13s gray, dp car & dk bl	1.10 .15
		Set value	.15

3rd Intl. Competition for Young Opera Singers.

George Kirkov (1867-1919), Revolutionist A682

1967, June 24   Perf. 11x11½

1596	A682	2s rose red & dk brn	.15 .15

Symbolic Tree and Stars — A683

1967, July 28   Photo.   Perf. 11½x11

1597	A683	13s dp bl, car & blk	.30 .15

11th Congress of Dimitrov's Union of the People's Youth.

Roses and Distillery A684

Designs: No. 1599, Chick and incubator. No. 1600, Cucumbers and hothouse. No. 1601, Lamb and sheep farm. 3s, Sunflower and oil mill. 4s, Pigs and pig farm. 5s, Hops and hop farm. 6s, Corn and irrigation system. 8s, Grapes and Bolgar tractor. 10s, Apples and cultivated tree. 13s, Bees and honey. 20s, Bee, blossoms and beehives.

1967   Perf. 11x11½

1598	A684	1s multicolored	.15 .15
1599	A684	1s dk car, yel & blk	.15 .15
1600	A684	2s vio, lt grn & blk	.15 .15
1601	A684	2s brt grn, gray & blk	.15 .15
1602	A684	3s yel grn, yel & blk	.15 .15
1603	A684	4s brt pur, yel & blk	.15 .15
1604	A684	5s ol bis, yel & blk	.15 .15
1605	A684	6s ol, brt grn & blk	.15 .15
1606	A684	8s grn, bis & blk	.15 .15
1607	A684	10s multicolored	.25 .15
1608	A684	13s grn, bis brn & blk	.42 .15

1609	A684	20s grnsh bl, brt pink & blk	.55 .15
		Set value	2.00 .80

Issue dates: Nos. 1598-1601, 1607, 1609, July 15; Nos. 1602-1606, 1608, July 24.

Map of Communist Countries, Spasski Tower A685

2s, Lenin speaking to soldiers. 3s, Fighting at Wlodaja, 1918. 5s, Marx, Engels & Lenin. 13s, Oil refinery. 20s, Molniya communication satellite.

1967, Aug. 25   Perf. 11

1610	A685	1s multicolored	.15 .15
1611	A685	2s magenta & olive	.15 .15
1612	A685	3s magenta & dull vio	.15 .15
1613	A685	5s magenta & red	.15 .15
1614	A685	13s magenta & ultra	.25 .15
1615	A685	20s magenta & blue	.45 .15
		Set value	1.10 .50

50th anniv. of the Russian October Revolution.

Rod, "Fish" and Varna — A686

1967, Aug. 29   Photo.   Perf. 11

1616	A686	10s multicolored	.35 .15

7th World Angling Championships, Varna.

Skiers and Winter Olympics' Emblem — A687

Sports and Emblem: 2s, Ski jump. 3s, Biathlon. 5s, Ice hockey. 13s, Figure skating couple.

1967, Sept. 20   Photo.   Perf. 11

1617	A687	1s dk bl grn, red & blk	.15 .15
1618	A687	2s ultra, blk & ol	.15 .15
1619	A687	3s vio brn, bl & blk	.15 .15
1620	A687	5s green, yel & blk	.15 .15
1621	A687	13s vio bl, blk & buff	.35 .15
		Nos. 1617-1621,B31 (6)	2.05
		Set value	.50

10th Winter Olympic Games, Grenoble, France, Feb. 6-18, 1968.

Mountain Peaks — A688

1967, Sept. 25   Engr.   Perf. 11½

1622	A688	1s Bogdan	.15 .15
1623	A688	2s Czerny	.15 .15
1624	A688	3s Ruen, vert.	.15 .15
1625	A688	5s Persenk	.15 .15
1626	A688	10s Botev	.15 .15
1627	A688	13s Rila, vert.	.25 .15
1628	A688	20s Vihren	.55 .15
		Set value	1.25 .50

George Rakovski A689

1967, Oct. 20   Photo.   Perf. 11

1629	A689	13s yellow grn & blk	.40 .15

Centenary of the death of George Rakovski, revolutionary against Turkish rule.

Yuri A. Gagarin, Valentina Tereshkova and Alexei Leonov — A690

Designs: 2s, Lt. Col. John H. Glenn, Jr., and Maj. Edward H. White. 5s, Earth and Molniya 1. 10s, Gemini 6 and 7. 13s, Luna 13 moon probe. 20s, Gemini 10 and Agena rocket.

1967, Nov. 25

1630	A690	1s Prus bl, blk & yel	.15 .15
1631	A690	2s dl bl, blk & dl yel	.15 .15
1632	A690	5s vio bl, grnsh bl & blk	.15 .15
1633	A690	10s dk bl, blk & red	.35 .15
1634	A690	13s grnsh bl, brt yel & blk	.55 .15
1635	A690	20s dl bl, blk & red	.75 .20
		Nos. 1630-1635 (6)	2.10
		Set value	.50

Achievements in space exploration.

Various Views of Trnovo — A691

1967, Dec. 5   Photo.   Perf. 11

1636	A691	1s multicolored	.15 .15
1637	A691	2s multicolored	.15 .15
1638	A691	3s multicolored	.15 .15
1639	A691	5s multicolored	.16 .15
1640	A691	13s multicolored	.32 .15
1641	A691	20s multicolored	.50 .15
		Nos. 1636-1641 (6)	1.43
		Set value	.46

Restoration of the ancient capital Veliko Trnovo.

Ratchenitza Folk Dance, by Ivan Markvichka — A692

1967, Dec. 9

1642	A692	20s gold & gray green	1.00 .80

Belgo-Bulgarian Philatelic Exposition, Brussels, Dec. 9-10. Printed in sheets of 8 stamps and 8 labels.

Cosmos 186 and 188 Docking — A693

40s, Venus 4 and orbits around Venus, horiz.

1968, Jan.

1643	A693	20s	vio, gray & pink	.55 .15
1644	A693	40s	multicolored	1.00 .24

Docking maneuvers of the Russian spaceships Cosmos 186 and Cosmos 188, Nov. 1, 1967, and the flight to Venus of Venus 4, June 12-Nov. 18, 1967.

Crossing the Danube, by Orenburgski A694

Paintings: 2s, Flag of Samara, by J. Veschin, vert. 3s, Partisans' Song, by Ilya Petrov. 5s, Portrait of Anna Penchovich, by Nikolai Pavlovski, vert. 13s, Battle of Orlovo Gnezdo, by N. Popov, vert. 20s, Welcome for Russian Soldiers, by D. Gudienov.

1968, Jan. 25   Photo.   Perf. 11

1645	A694	1s	gold & dk green	.15 .15
1646	A694	2s	gold & dk blue	.15 .15
1647	A694	3s	gold & chocolate	.15 .15
1648	A694	3s	gold & dk vio	.32 .15
1649	A694	20s	gold & Prus grn	.48 .18
			Set value	.95 .45

90th anniv. of the liberation from Turkey.

Shepherds, by Zlatyn Boyadjiev — A695

Paintings: 2s, Wedding dance, by V. Dimitrov, vert. 3s, Partisans' Song, by Ilya Petrov. 5s, Portrait of Anna Penchovich, by Nikolai Zograf, vert. 13s, Self-portrait, by Zachary Zograf, vert. 20s, View of Old Plovdiv, by T. Lavrenov. 60s, St. Clement of Ochrida, by A. Mitov.

1967, Dec.   Litho.   Perf. 11½

Size: 45x38mm, 38x45mm

1650	A695	1s	gray & multi	.15 .15
1651	A695	2s	gray & multi	.15 .15

Size: 55x35mm

1652	A695	3s	gray & multi	.22 .15

Size: 38x45mm, 45x38mm

1653	A695	5s	gray & multi	.40 .15
1654	A695	13s	gray & multi	.90 .22
1655	A695	20s	gray & multi	1.25 .40
			Nos. 1650-1655 (6)	3.07
			Set value	.88

Miniature Sheet

Size: 65x84mm

Imperf

1656	A695	60s	multicolored	3.25 1.90

Marx Statue, Sofia — A696

Maxim Gorky — A697

1968, Feb. 20   Photo.   Perf. 11

1657	A696	13s	black & red	.35 .15

150th anniversary of birth of Karl Marx.

1968, Feb. 20

1658	A697	13s	ver & grnsh blk	.40 .15

Maxim Gorky (1868-1936), Russian writer.

Folk Dancers — A698

Designs: 5s, Runners. 13s, Doves. 20s, Festival poster, (head, flowers and birds). 40s, Globe and Bulgaria No. 1 under magnifying glass.

1968, Mar. 20

1659	A698	2s	multicolored	.15 .15
1660	A698	5s	multicolored	.15 .15
1661	A698	13s	multicolored	.22 .15
1662	A698	20s	multicolored	.48 .20
1663	A698	40s	multicolored	1.10 .40
			Nos. 1659-1663 (5)	2.10
			Set value	.80

9th Youth Festival for Peace and Friendship, Sofia, July 28-Aug. 6.

Bellflower — A699

1968, Apr. 25   Perf. 11

1664	A699	1s	shown	.15 .15
1665	A699	2s	Gentian	.15 .15
1666	A699	3s	Crocus	.15 .15
1667	A699	5s	Iris	.16 .15
1668	A699	10s	Dog-tooth violet	.20 .15
1669	A699	13s	Sempervivum	.70 .15
1670	A699	20s	Dictamnus	.95 .22
			Nos. 1664-1670 (7)	2.46
			Set value	.60

"The Unknown Hero," Tale by Ran Bosilek A700

Design: 20s, The Witch and the Young Man (Hans Christian Andersen fairy tale.)

1968, Apr. 25   Photo.   Perf. 10½

1671	A700	13s	black & multi	.35 .15
1672	A700	20s	black & multi	.52 .20

Bulgarian-Danish Philatelic Exhibition.

Memorial Church, Shipka — A701

Steeplechase — A702

1968, May 3

1673	A701	13s	multicolored	.60 .20

Bulgarian Stamp Exhibition in Berlin.

1968, June 24   Photo.   Perf. 10½

Olympic Rings and: 1s, Gymnast on bar. 3s, Fencer. 10s, Boxer. 13s, Woman discus thrower.

1674	A702	1s	red & black	.15 .15
1675	A702	2s	gray, blk & rose brn	.15 .15
1676	A702	3s	magenta, gray & blk	.15 .15
1677	A702	10s	grnsh bl, blk & lem	.15 .15
1678	A702	13s	vio bl, gray & pink	.55 .18
			Nos. 1674-1678,B33 (6)	2.15
			Set value	.75

19th Olympic Games, Mexico City, Oct. 12-27.

Battle of Buzluja A703

Design: 13s, Haji Dimitr and Stefan Karaja.

1968, July 1

1679	A703	2s	silver & red brn	.15 .15
1680	A703	13s	gold & sl grn	.32 .15
			Set value	.40 .17

Centenary of the death of the patriots Haji Dimitr and Stefan Karaja.

Lakes of Smolian — A704

Sofia Zoo, Cent. — A705

Bulgarian Scenes: 2s, Ropotamo Lake. 3s, Erma-Idreloto mountain pass. 8s, Isker River dam. 10s, Slanchev Breg (sailing ship). 13s, Cape Caliacra. 40s, Old houses, Sozopol. 2 l, Chudnite Skali ("Strange Mountains").

1968   Photo.   Perf. 13

1681	A704	1s	Prus green	.15 .15
1682	A704	2s	dark green	.15 .15
1683	A704	3s	dark brown	.15 .15
1684	A704	8s	olive green	.15 .15
1685	A704	10s	redsh brown	.15 .15
1686	A704	13s	dk olive grn	.22 .15
1687	A704	40s	Prus blue	.60 .24
1688	A704	2 l	sepia	3.75 .85
			Nos. 1681-1688 (8)	5.32
			Set value	1.40

1968, July 29   Perf. 10½

1689	A705	1s	Cinereous vulture	.15 .15
1690	A705	2s	Crowned crane	.15 .15
1691	A705	3s	Zebra	.22 .15
1692	A705	5s	Cheetah	.38 .15
1693	A705	13s	Indian python	.70 .15
1694	A705	20s	African crocodile	1.25 .30
			Nos. 1689-1694 (6)	2.85
			Set value	.75

Human Rights Flame — A706

1968, July 8

1695	A706	20s	dp blue & gold	.60 .15

International Human Rights Year, 1968.

Congress Hall, Varna, and Emblem A707

1968, Sept. 17   Photo.   Perf. 10½

1696	A707	20s	bister, grn & red	.50 .15

56th International Dental Congress, Varna.

Flying Swans — A708

Rose A709

Stag Beetle A710

Designs: 2s, Jug. 20s, Five Viking ships.

1968   Photo.   Perf. 10½

1697	A709	2s	green & ocher	.75 .50
1698	A708	5s	dp blue & gray	.75 .50
1699	A709	13s	dp plum & lil rose	.75 .50
a.			Pair, #1698, 1699 + label	1.50 1.00
1700	A708	20s	dp vio & gray	.75 .50
a.			Pair, #1697, 1700 + label	1.50 1.00
			Nos. 1697-1700 (4)	3.00 2.00

Cooperation with the Scandinavian countries. Issued: 5s, 13s, Sept. 12; 2s, 20s, Nov. 22.

Perf. 12½x13, 13x12½

1968, Aug. 26

#1702, Ground beetle (Procerus scabrosus). #1703, Ground beetle (Calosoma sycophania). #1704, Scarab beetle, horiz. #1705, Saturnid moth, horiz.

1701	A710	1s	brown olive	.15 .15
1702	A710	1s	dark blue	.15 .15
1703	A710	1s	dark green	.15 .15
1704	A710	1s	orange brown	.15 .15
1705	A710	1s	magenta	.15 .15
			Set value	.30 .25

Turks Fighting Insurgents, 1688 A711

1968, Aug. 22   Perf. 10½

1706	A711	13s	multicolored	.45 .15

280th anniversary of the Tchiprovtzi insurrection.

Christo Smirnenski (1898-1923),
Poet — A712

1968, Sept. 28   Litho.   Perf. 10½
1707 A712 13s gold, red org & blk   .40 .15

Dalmatian
Pelican
A713

Birds: 2s, Little egret. 3s, Crested grebe. 5s, Common tern. 13s, European spoonbill. 20s, Glossy ibis.

1968, Oct. 28   Photo.
1708 A713 1s silver & multi   .15 .15
1709 A713 2s silver & multi   .15 .15
1710 A713 3s silver & multi   .15 .15
1711 A713 5s silver & multi   .15 .15
1712 A713 13s silver & multi   .52 .15
1713 A713 20s silver & multi   1.10 .32
　　Nos. 1708-1713 (6)   2.22
　　　Set value   .65

Srebirna wild life reservation.

Carrier Pigeon
A714

1968, Oct. 19
1714 A714 20s emerald   .70 .25
　a.　Sheet of 4 + labels   5.00 1.65
2nd Natl. Stamp Exhib. in Sofia, Oct. 25-Nov. 15. No. 1714a contains 4 No. 1714 and 5 labels.

Man and Woman
from
Lovetch — A715

Regional Costumes: 1s, Silistra. 3s, Jambol. 13s, Chirpan. 20s, Razgrad. 40s, Ihtiman.

1968, Nov. 20   Litho.   Perf. 13½
1715 A715 1s dp org & multi   .15 .15
1716 A715 2s Prus bl & multi   .15 .15
1717 A715 3s multicolored   .16 .15
1718 A715 13s multicolored   .28 .15
1719 A715 20s multicolored   .55 .25
1720 A715 40s green & multi   1.40 .45
　　Nos. 1715-1720 (6)   2.69
　　　Set value   1.00

St. Arsenius
A716

Designs (10th century Murals and Icons): 2s, Procession with relics of St. Ivan Rilsky, horiz. 3s, St. Michael Torturing the Soul of the Rich Man. 13s, St. Ivan Rilski. 20s, St. John. 40s, St. George.

1 l, Procession meeting relics of St. Ivan Rilsky, horiz.

Perf. 11½x12½, 12½x11½
1968, Nov. 25   Photo.
1721 A716 1s gold & multi   .15 .15
1722 A716 2s gold & multi   .15 .15
1723 A716 3s gold & multi   .15 .15
1724 A716 13s gold & multi   .42 .16
1725 A716 20s gold & multi   .95 .28
1726 A716 40s gold & multi   1.40 .60
　　Nos. 1721-1726 (6)   3.22
　　　Set value   1.25

Souvenir Sheet
Imperf
1727 A716 1 l gold & multi   3.75 2.75
Millenium of Rila Monastery. No. 1727 also: Sofia 1969 Intl. Phil. Exhib., May 31-June 8, 1969. No. 1727 contains one stamp, size: 57x51mm.

Medlar
A717

Herbs: No. 1729, Camomile. 2s, Lily-of-the-valley. 3s, Belladonna. 5s, Mallow. 10s, Buttercup. 13s, Poppies. 20s, Thyme.

1969, Jan. 2   Litho.   Perf. 10½
1728 A717 1s black, grn & org red   .15 .15
1729 A717 1s black, grn & yel   .15 .15
1730 A717 2s black, emer & grn   .15 .15
1731 A717 3s black & multi   .15 .15
1732 A717 5s black & multi   .15 .15
1733 A717 10s black, grn & yel   .16 .15
1734 A717 13s black & multi   .30 .15
1735 A717 20s black, lil & grn   .65 .15
　　　Set value   1.50 .60

Silkworms and
Spindles
A718

Designs: 2s, Silkworm, cocoons and pattern. 3s, Cocoons and spinning wheel. 5s, Cocoons, woof-and-warp diagram. 13s, Silk moth, Cocoon and spinning frame. 20s, Silk moth, eggs and shuttle.

1969, Jan. 30   Photo.   Perf. 10½
1736 A718 1s bl, grn, sl & blk   .15 .15
1737 A718 2s dp car, sil & blk   .15 .15
1738 A718 3s Prus bl, sil & blk   .15 .15
1739 A718 5s pur, ver, sil & blk   .15 .15
1740 A718 13s red lil, ocher, sil & blk   .25 .15
1741 A718 20s grn, org, sil & blk   .45 .15
　　　Set value   .95 .45

Bulgarian silk industry.

Attack and Capture
of Emperor
Nicephorus — A719

Sts. Cyril and
Methodius, Mural,
Troian
Monastery — A720

Designs (Manasses Chronicle): No. 1742, Death of Ivan Asen. 3s, Khan Kroum feasting after victory. No. 1748, Invasion of Bulgaria by Prince Sviatoslav of Kiev. No. 1750, Russian invasion and campaigns of Emperor John I Zimisces, c. 972 A.D. 40s, Tsar Ivan Alexander, Jesus and Constantine Manasses.
Horizontal designs: No. 1743, Kings Nebuchadnezzar, Balthazar, Darius and Cyrus. No. 1745, Kings Cambyses, Gyges and Darius. 5s, King David and Tsar Ivan Alexander. No. 1749, Persecution of Byzantine army after battle of July 26, 811. No. 1751, Christening of Bulgarian Tsar Boris, 865. 60s, Arrival of Tsar Simeon in Constantinople and his succeeding surprise attack on that city.

1969   Photo.   Perf. 14x13½, 13½x14
1742 A719 1s multicolored   .15 .15
1743 A719 1s multicolored   .15 .15
1744 A719 2s multicolored   .15 .15
1745 A719 2s multicolored   .15 .15
1746 A719 3s multicolored   .15 .15
1747 A719 5s multicolored   .15 .15
1748 A719 13s multicolored   .38 .15
1749 A719 13s multicolored   .38 .15
1750 A719 20s multicolored   .80 .15
1751 A719 20s multicolored   .80 .15
1752 A719 40s multicolored   1.25 .38
1753 A719 60s multicolored   2.25 .42
　　Nos. 1742-1753 (12)   6.76
　　　Set value   1.50

1969, Mar. 23
1754 A720 28s gold & multi   .75 .45

Post Horn — A721

Designs: 13s, Bulgaria Nos. 1 and 534. 20s, Street fighting at Stackata, 1919.

1969, Apr. 15   Photo.   Perf. 10½
1755 A721 2s green & yel   .15 .15
1756 A721 13s multicolored   .40 .15
1757 A721 20s dk bl & lt bl   .48 .18
　　Nos. 1755-1757 (3)   1.03
　　　Set value   .35

Bulgarian postal administration, 90th anniv.

The Fox and
the Rabbit
A722

Children's Drawings: 2s, Boy reading to wolf and fox. 13s, Two birds and cat singing together.

1969, Apr. 21
1758 A722 1s emer, org & blk   .15 .15
1759 A722 2s org, lt bl & blk   .15 .15
1760 A722 13s lt bl, ol & blk   .38 .15
　　　Set value   .50 .25

Issued for Children's Week.

ILO Emblem — A723

1969, Apr. 28
1761 A723 13s dull grn & blk   .30 .15
50th anniv. of the ILO.

St. George and
SOFIA 69
Emblem — A724

Designs: 2s, Virgin Mary and St. John Bogoslov. 3s, Archangel Michael. 5s, Three Saints. 8s, Jesus Christ. 13s, Sts. George and Dimitrie. 20s, Christ, the Almighty. 40s, St. Dimitrie. 60s, The 40 Martyrs. 80s, The Transfiguration.

1969, Apr. 30   Perf. 11x12
1762 A724 1s gold & multi   .15 .15
1763 A724 2s gold & multi   .15 .15
1764 A724 3s gold & multi   .15 .15
1765 A724 5s gold & multi   .15 .15
1766 A724 8s gold & multi   .16 .15
1767 A724 13s gold & multi   .32 .15
1768 A724 20s gold & multi   .65 .22

1769 A724 40s gold & multi   1.40 .42
　a.　Sheet of 4   5.75 5.00
1770 A724 60s gold & multi   1.75 .85
1771 A724 80s gold & multi   2.75 1.00
　　Nos. 1762-1771 (10)   7.63
　　　Set value   3.00

Old Bulgarian art from the National Art Gallery. No. 1769a contains 4 of No. 1769 with center gutter showing Alexander Nevski Shrine. See note on SOFIA 69 after Nos. C112-C120.

St. Cyril
Preaching — A725

Design: 28s, St. Cyril and followers.

1969, June 20   Litho.   Perf. 10½
1772 A725 2s sil, grn & red   .16 .15
1773 A725 28s sil, dk bl & red   .75 .22
　　　Set value   .27

St. Cyril (827-869), apostle to the Slavs, inventor of Cyrillic alphabet. Issued in sheets of 25 with se-tenant labels; Cyrillic inscription on label of 2s, Glagolitic inscription on label of 28s.

St. Sophia
Church — A726

Sofia Through the Ages: 1s, Roman coin with inscription "Ulpia Serdica." 2s, Roman coin with Aesculapius Temple. 4s, Bojana Church. 5s, Sobranic Parliament. 13s, Vasov National Theater. 20s, Alexander Nevski Shrine. 40s, Clement Ochrida University. 1 l, Coat of arms.

1969, May 25   Perf. 13x12½
1774 A726 1s gold & blue   .15 .15
1775 A726 2s gold & ol grn   .15 .15
1776 A726 3s gold & red brn   .15 .15
1777 A726 4s gold & purple   .15 .15
1778 A726 5s gold & plum   .15 .15
1779 A726 13s gold & brt grn   .28 .15
1780 A726 20s gold & vio bl   .45 .15
1781 A726 40s gold & dp car   1.10 .25
　　Nos. 1774-1781 (8)   2.58
　　　Set value   .75

Souvenir Sheet
Imperf
1782 A726 1 l grn, gold & red   2.25 2.00
Historic Sofia in connection with the International Philatelic Exhibition, Sofia, May 31-June 8. #1782 contains one 43½x43½mm stamp. Emblems of 8 preceding philatelic exhibitions in metallic ink in margin; gold inscription.
No. 1782 was overprinted in green "IBRA 73" and various symbols, and released May 4, 1973, for the Munich Philatelic Exhibition. The overprint also exists in gray.

St.
George — A727

1969, June 9   Litho.   Perf. 11½
1783 A727 40s sil, blk & pale rose   1.25 .50

38th FIP Congress, June 9-11.

Hand Planting
Sapling
A728

1969, Apr. 28　Photo.　Perf. 11
1784 A728 2s ol grn, blk & lilac　.15 .15
25 years of the reforestation campaign.

Partisans
A729

Designs: 2s, Combine harvester. 3s, Dam. 5s, Flutist and singers. 13s, Factory. 20s, Lenin, Dimitrov, Russian and Bulgarian flags.

1969, Sept. 9
1785 A729 1s blk, pur & org　.15 .15
1786 A729 2s blk, ol bis & org　.15 .15
1787 A729 3s blk, bl grn & org　.15 .15
1788 A729 5s blk, brn red & org　.15 .15
1789 A729 13s blk, bl & org　.30 .15
1790 A729 20s blk, brn & org　.50 .15
　　　Set value　1.10 .45
25th anniversary of People's Republic.

Women
Gymnasts
A730

1969, Sept.　Photo.　Perf. 11
1791 A730 2s shown　.15 .15
1792 A730 20s Wrestlers　.42 .22
　　　Set value　.30
Third National Spartakiad.

Tchanko Bakalov
Tcherkovski, Poet.
Birth Cent. — A731

1969, Sept.
1793 A731 13s multicolored　.35 .15

Woman
Gymnast
A732

Designs: 2s, Two women with hoops. 3s, Woman with hoop. 5s, Two women with spheres.

1969, Oct.
Gymnasts in Light Gray
1794 A732 1s green & dk blue　.15 .15
1795 A732 2s blue & dk blue　.15 .15
1796 A732 3s emer & sl grn　.15 .15
1797 A732 5s orange & pur　.15 .15
　Set value, #1794-1797,
　B35-B36　1.45 .70
World Championships for Artistic Gymnastics, Varna.

The Priest Rilski,
by Zachary
Zograf — A733

Paintings from the National Art Gallery. 2s, Woman at Window, by Vasil Stoilov. 3s, Workers at Rest, by Nenko Balkanski, horiz. 4s, Woman Dressing (Nude), by Ivan Nenov. 5s, Portrait of a Woman, by N. Pavlovich. 13s, Falstaff, by Duzunov Kr. Sarafov. No. 1804, Portrait of a Woman, by N. Mihajlov, horiz. No. 1805, Workers at Mealtime, by Stojan Sotirov, horiz. 40s, Self-portrait, by Tcheno Togorov.

Perf. 11½x12, 12x11½
1969, Nov. 10
1798 A733 1s gold & multi　.15 .15
1799 A733 2s gold & multi　.15 .15
1800 A733 3s gold & multi　.15 .15
1801 A733 4s gold & multi　.15 .15
1802 A733 5s gold & multi　.15 .15
1803 A733 13s gold & multi　.32 .15
1804 A733 20s gold & multi　.70 .22
1805 A733 20s gold & multi　.70 .22
1806 A733 40s gold & multi　1.40 .60
　　Nos. 1798-1806 (9)　3.87
　　　Set value　1.50

Roman
Bronze
Wolf
A734

Design: 2s, Roman statue of woman, found at Silistra, vert.

1969, Oct.　Photo.　Perf. 11
1807 A734 2s sil, ultra & gray　.15 .15
1808 A734 13s sil, dk grn & gray　.42 .15
　　　Set value　.17
City of Silistra's 1,800th anniversary.

Worker and
Factory — A735

1969　　　Perf. 13
1809 A735 6s ultra & blk　.15 .15
25th anniversary of the factory militia.

European Hake — A736

Designs: No. 1811, Deep-sea fishing trawler. Fish: 2s, Atlantic horse mackerel. 3s, Pilchard. 5s, Dentex macrophthalmus. 10s, Chub mackerel. 13s, Otolithes macrognathus. 20s, Lichia vadigo.

1969　　　Perf. 11
1810 A736 1s ol grn & blk　.15 .15
1811 A736 1s ultra, ind & gray　.15 .15
1812 A736 2s lilac & blk　.15 .15
1813 A736 3s vio bl & blk　.15 .15
1814 A736 5s rose cl, pink & blk　.24 .15
1815 A736 10s gray & blk　.48 .15
1816 A736 13s ver, sal & blk　.70 .15
1817 A736 20s ocher & black　1.25 .18
　　Nos. 1810-1817 (8)　3.27
　　　Set value　.58

Marin
Drinov
A737

1969, Nov. 10　Litho.　Perf. 11
1818 A737 20s black & red org　.35 .15
Centenary of the Bulgarian Academy of Science, founded by Marin Drinov.

Trapeze Artists
A738

Pavel Bania
Sanatorium
A739

Circus Performers: 2s, Jugglers. 3s, Jugglers with loops. 5s, Juggler and bear on bicycle. 13s, Woman and performing horse. 20s, Musical clowns.

1969　　　Photo.　Perf. 11
1819 A738 1s dk blue & multi　.15 .15
1820 A738 2s dk green & multi　.15 .15
1821 A738 3s dk violet & multi　.15 .15
1822 A738 5s multicolored　.15 .15
1823 A738 13s multicolored　.30 .15
1824 A738 20s multicolored　.55 .20
　　　Set value　1.10 .50

1969, Dec.　Photo.　Perf. 10½-14
Health Resorts: 5s, Chisar Sanatorium. 6s, Kotel Children's Sanatorium. 20s, Narechen Polyclinic.
1825 A739 2s blue　.15 .15
1826 A739 5s ultra　.15 .15
1827 A739 6s green　.15 .15
1828 A739 20s emerald　.32 .15
　　　Set value　.65 .22

G. S. Shonin, V. N.
Kubasov and
Spacecraft — A740

Designs: 2s, A. V. Filipchenko, V. N. Volkov, V. V. Gorbatko and spacecraft. 3s, Vladimir A. Shatalov, Alexei S. Yeliseyev and spacecraft. 28s, Three spacecraft in orbit.

1970, Jan.　Photo.　Perf. 11
1829 A740 1s rose car, ol grn & blk　.15 .15
1830 A740 2s bl, dl cl & blk　.15 .15
1831 A740 3s grnsh bl, vio & blk　.15 .15
1832 A740 28s vio bl, lil rose & lt bl　.70 .16
　　　Set value　.90 .31
Russian space flights of Soyuz 6, 7 and 8, Oct. 11-13, 1969.

Khan Krum and Defeat of Emperor
Nicephorus, 811 — A741

Bulgarian History: 1s, Khan Asparuch and Bulgars crossing the Danube (679). 3s, Conversion of Prince Boris to Christianity, 865. 5s, Tsar Simeon

and battle of Akhelo, 917. 8s, Tsar Samuel defeating the Byzantines, 976. 10s, Tsar Kaloyan defeating Emperor Baldwin, 1205. 13s, Tsar Ivan Assen II defeating Greek King Theodore Komnine, 1230. 20s, Coronation of Tsar Ivailo, 1277.

1970, Feb.　　　Perf. 10½
1833 A741 1s gold & multi　.15 .15
1834 A741 2s gold & multi　.15 .15
1835 A741 3s gold & multi　.15 .15
1836 A741 5s gold & multi　.15 .15
1837 A741 8s gold & multi　.18 .15
1838 A741 10s gold & multi　.30 .15
1839 A741 13s gold & multi　.40 .15
1840 A741 20s gold & multi　.70 .15
　　Nos. 1833-1840 (8)　2.18
　　　Set value　.56
See Nos. 2126-2133.

Bulgarian Pavilion, EXPO '70 — A742

1970　　　Perf. 12½
1841 A742 20s brown, sil & org　.75 .50
EXPO '70 International Exposition, Osaka, Japan, Mar. 15-Sept. 13, 1970.

Soccer
A743

Designs: Various views of soccer game.

1970, Mar. 4　Photo.　Perf. 12½
1842 A743 1s blue & multi　.15 .15
1843 A743 2s rose car & multi　.15 .15
1844 A743 3s ultra & multi　.15 .15
1845 A743 5s green & multi　.15 .15
1846 A743 20s emerald & multi　.55 .15
1847 A743 40s red & multi　1.25 .28
　　Nos. 1842-1847 (6)　2.40
　　　Set value　.65
9th World Soccer Championships for the Jules Rimet Cup, Mexico City, May 30-June 21, 1970. See No. B37.

Lenin (1870-
1924)
A744

1970, Apr. 22
1848 A744 2s shown　.15 .15
1849 A744 13s Portrait　.32 .15
1850 A744 20s Writing　.70 .15
　　Nos. 1848-1850 (3)　1.17
　　　Set value　.26

Tephrocactus
Alexanderi V.
Bruchii — A745

Cacti: 2s, Opuntia drummondii. 3s, Hatiora cilindrica. 5s, Gymnocalycium vatteri. 8s, Heliantho cereus grandiflorus. 10s, Neochilenia andreaeana. 13s, Peireskia vargasii v. longispina. 20s, Neobesseya rosiflora.

1970　　　Photo.　Perf. 12½
1851 A745 1s multicolored　.15 .15
1852 A745 2s dk green & multi　.15 .15
1853 A745 3s multicolored　.15 .15
1854 A745 5s blue & multi　.15 .15
1855 A745 8s brown & multi　.28 .15
1856 A745 10s vio bl & multi　1.00 .15

1857 A745 13s brn red & multi   1.00   .16
1858 A745 20s purple & multi   1.40   .32
     Nos. 1851-1858 (8)   4.28
     Set value   1.00

Rose — A746

Designs: Various Roses.

1970, June 8   **Litho.**   *Perf. 13¹/₂*
1859 A746 1s gray & multi   .15   .15
1860 A746 2s gray & multi   .15   .15
1861 A746 3s gray & multi   .15   .15
1862 A746 4s gray & multi   .15   .15
1863 A746 13s gray & multi   .16   .15
1864 A746 13s gray & multi   .16   .15
1865 A746 20s gray & multi   1.10   .25
1866 A746 28s gray & multi   1.90   .42
     Nos. 1859-1866 (8)   3.91
     Set value   1.10

Gold
Bowl — A747

Designs: Various bowls and art objects from Gold
Treasure of Thrace.

1970, June 15   **Photo.**   *Perf. 12¹/₂*
1867 A747 1s blk, bl & gold   .15   .15
1868 A747 2s blk, lt vio & gold   .15   .15
1869 A747 3s blk, ver & gold   .15   .15
1870 A747 5s blk, yel grn & gold   .15   .15
1871 A747 13s blk, org & gold   .70   .15
1872 A747 20s blk, lil & gold   .85   .18
     Nos. 1867-1872 (6)   2.15
     Set value   .50

EXPO Emblem, Rose and Bulgarian
Woman — A748

Designs (EXPO Emblem and): 2s, Three women.
3s, Woman and fruit. 28s, Dancers. 40s, Mt. Fuji
and pavilions.

1970, June 20
1873 A748 1s gold & multi   .15   .15
1874 A748 2s gold & multi   .15   .15
1875 A748 3s gold & multi   .15   .15
1876 A748 28s gold & multi   .70   .22
     Nos. 1873-1876 (4)   1.15
     Set value   .45

Miniature Sheet
Imperf

1877 A748 40s gold & multi   1.00   .60

EXPO '70 International Exposition, Osaka, Japan,
Mar. 15-Sept. 13. No. 1877 contains one stamp
with simulated perforations.

Ivan
Vasov — A749

1970, Aug. 1   **Photo.**   *Perf. 12¹/₂*
1878 A749 13s violet blue   .40   .15

120th anniv. of the birth of Ivan Vasov, author.

UN Emblem — A750

1970, Aug. 1
1879 A750 20s Prus bl & gold   .50   .20

25th anniversary of the United Nations.

George Dimitrov
A751

Retriever
A752

1970, Aug.
1880 A751 20s blk, gold & org   .60   .15

BZNC (Bulgarian Communist Party), 70th anniv.

1970   **Photo.**   *Perf. 12¹/₂*
   Dogs: 1s, Golden retriever, horiz. 3s, Great
Dane. 4s, Boxer. 5s, Cocker spaniel. 13s,
Doberman pinscher. 20s, Scottish terrier. 28s, Rus-
sian greyhound, horiz.

1881 A752 1s multicolored   .15   .15
1882 A752 2s multicolored   .15   .15
1883 A752 3s multicolored   .15   .15
1884 A752 4s multicolored   .15   .15
1885 A752 5s multicolored   .15   .15
1886 A752 13s multicolored   .52   .15
1887 A752 20s multicolored   1.10   .26
1888 A752 28s multicolored   1.65   .32
     Nos. 1881-1888 (8)   4.02
     Set value   .94

Volleyball — A753

Designs: No. 1890, Two women players. No.
1891, Woman player. No. 1892, Man player.

1970, Sept.   **Photo.**   *Perf. 12¹/₂*
1889 A753 2s dk red brn, bl & blk   .15   .15
1890 A753 2s ultra, org & blk   .15   .15
1891 A753 20s Prus bl, yel & blk   .48   .15
1892 A753 20s grn, yel & blk   .48   .15
     Nos. 1889-1892 (4)   1.26
     Set value   .34

World Volleyball Championships.

Enrico Caruso and "I Pagliacci" by
Ruggiero Leoncavallo — A754

Opera Singers and Operas: 2s, Christina Morfova
and "The Bartered Bride" by Bedrich Smetana. 3s,
Peter Reitchev and "Tosca" by Giacomo Puccini.
10s, Svetana Tabakova and "The Flying Dutchman"
by Richard Wagner. 13s, Katia Popova and "The
Masters" by Paroshkev Hadjev. 20s, Feodor Chalia-
pin and "Boris Godunov" by Modest Musorgski.

1970, Oct. 15   **Photo.**   *Perf. 14*
1893 A754 1s black & multi   .15   .15
1894 A754 2s black & multi   .15   .15
1895 A754 3s black & multi   .15   .15
1896 A754 10s black & multi   .20   .15
1897 A754 13s black & multi   .28   .16
1898 A754 20s black & multi   1.00   .25
     Nos. 1893-1898 (6)   1.93
     Set value   .80

Honoring opera singers in their best roles.

Ivan Assen II Coin — A755

   Coins from 14th Century with Ruler's Portrait:
2s, Theodor Svetoslav. 3s, Mikhail Chichman. 13s,
Ivan Alexander and Mikhail Assen. 20s, Ivan Srat-
simir. 28s, Ivan Chichman (initials).

1970, Nov.   *Perf. 12¹/₂*
1899 A755 1s buff & multi   .15   .15
1900 A755 2s gray & multi   .15   .15
1901 A755 3s multicolored   .15   .15
1902 A755 13s multicolored   .22   .15
1903 A755 20s lt blue & multi   .60   .15
1904 A755 28s multicolored   .85   .22
     Nos. 1899-1904 (6)   2.12
     Set value   .65

Fire Protection
A756

1970   **Litho.**   *Perf. 12¹/₂*
1905 A756 1s Fireman   .15   .15
1906 A756 3s Fire engine   .15   .15
     Set value   .20   .15

Bicyclists — A757   Congress
Emblem — A758

1970   **Photo.**
1907 A757 20s grn, yel & pink   .50   .20

20th Bulgarian bicycle race.

1970
1908 A758 13s gold & multi   .35   .15

7th World Congress of Sociology, Varna, Sept.
14-19.

Ludwig van
Beethoven — A759   Friedrich
Engels — A760

1970
1909 A759 28s lil rose & dk bl   .90   .40

Beethoven (1770-1827), composer.

1970   **Photo.**   *Perf. 12¹/₂*
1910 A760 13s ver, tan & brn   .30   .15

Friedrich Engels (1820-1895), German socialist,
collaborator of Karl Marx.

Miniature Sheets

Luna 16
A761

Russian moon mission: 80s, Lunokhod 1,
unmanned vehicle on moon, horiz.

1970   **Photo.**   *Imperf.*
1911 A761 80s plum, sil, blk & bl   2.00   2.00
1912 A761 1 l vio bl, sil & red   4.00   2.75

No. 1911, Lunokhod 1, Nov. 10-17. No. 1912,
Luna 16 mission, Sept. 12-24.
   Issue dates: 80s, Dec. 18; 1 l, Nov. 10.

Snowflake
A762

1970, Dec. 15   **Photo.**   *Perf. 12¹/₂x13*
1913 A762 2s ultra & multi   .15   .15

New Year 1971.

Birds and
Flowers
A763

Folk Art: 2s, Bird and flowers. 3s, Flying birds.
5s, Birds and flowers. 13s, Sun. 20s, Tulips and
pansies.

1971, Jan. 25   *Perf. 12¹/₂x13¹/₂*
1914 A763 1s multicolored   .15   .15
1915 A763 2s multicolored   .15   .15
1916 A763 3s multicolored   .15   .15
1917 A763 5s multicolored   .15   .15
1918 A763 13s multicolored   .16   .15
1919 A763 20s multicolored   .55   .15
     Set value   .95   .40

Spring 1971.

Girl, by Zeko
Spiridonov
A764

Modern Bulgarian Sculpture: 2s, Third Class
(people looking through train window), by Ivan
Funev. 3s, Bust of Elin Pelin, by Marko Markov.
13s, Bust of Nina, by Andrej Nikolov. 20s, Monument to P. K. Yavorov (kneeling woman), by Ivan
Lazarov. 28s, Engineer, by Ivan Funev. 1 l, Refugees, by Sekul Krimov, horiz.

1971, Feb.   *Perf. 12¹/₂*
1920 A764 1s gold & vio   .15   .15
1921 A764 2s gold & dk ol grn   .15   .15
1922 A764 3s gold & rose brn   .15   .15
1923 A764 13s gold & dk grn   .30   .15
1924 A764 20s gold & red brn   .52   .15
1925 A764 28s gold & dk brn   .80   .20
     Nos. 1920-1925 (6)   2.07
     Set value   .65

Souvenir Sheet
Imperf

1926 A764 1 l gold, dk brn & buff   2.00   1.75

Runner
A765

Design: 20s, Woman putting the shot.

1971, Mar. 13 Photo. Perf. 12¹/₂x13
1927 A765 2s brown & multi .15 .15
1928 A765 20s dp grn, org & blk .90 .22
Set value .30

2nd European Indoor Track and Field Championships.

Bulgarian Secondary School,
Bolgrad — A766

Educators: 20s, Dimiter Mitev, Prince Bogoridi and Sava Radoulov.

1971, Mar. 16 Perf. 12¹/₂
1929 A766 2s silver, brn & grn .15 .15
1930 A766 20s silver, brn & vio .52 .15
Set value .20

First Bulgarian secondary school, 1858, in Bolgrad, USSR.

Communards — A767

1971, Mar. 18 Photo. Perf. 12¹/₂x13
1931 A767 20s rose mag & blk .50 .20

Centenary of the Paris Commune.

Dimitrov
Facing
Goering,
Quotation,
FIR
Emblem
A768

1971, Apr. 11 Perf. 12¹/₂
1932 A768 2s grn, gold, blk & red .15 .15
1933 A768 13s plum, gold, blk & red .70 .15

Intl. Fed. of Resistance Fighters (FIR), 20th anniv.

George S. Rakovski
(1821-1867),
Revolutionary Against
Turkish Rule — A769

1971, Apr. 14
1934 A769 13s olive & blk brn .30 .15

Edelweiss Hotel,
Borovets — A770

Designs: 2s, Panorama Hotel, Pamporovo. 4s, Boats at Albena, Black Sea. 8s, Boats at Rousalka. 10s, Shtastlivetsa Hotel, Mt. Vitosha.

1971 Perf. 13
1935 A770 1s brt green .15 .15
1936 A770 2s olive gray .15 .15
1937 A770 4s brt blue .15 .15
1938 A770 8s blue .15 .15
1939 A770 10s bluish green .25 .15
Set value .65 .30

Technological Progress — A771

Designs: 1s, Mason with banner, vert. 13s, Two men and doves, vert.

1971, Apr. 20 Photo. Perf. 12¹/₂
1940 A771 1s gold & multi .15 .15
1941 A771 2s gray blue & multi .15 .15
1942 A771 13s lt green & multi .52 .16
Set value .70 .30

10th Cong. of Bulgarian Communist Party.

Panayot
Pipkov and
Anthem
A772

1971, May 20
1943 A772 13s sil, blk & brt grn .45 .15
Panayot Pipkov, composer, birth cent.

Mammoth
A773

Prehistoric Animals: 2s, Bear, vert. 3s, Hipparion (horse). 13s, Platybelodon. 20s, Dinotherium, vert. 28s, Saber-tooth tiger.

1971, May 29 Perf. 12¹/₂
1944 A773 1s dull bl & multi .15 .15
1945 A773 2s lilac & multi .15 .15
1946 A773 3s multicolored .15 .15
1947 A773 13s multicolored .48 .15
1948 A773 20s dp grn & multi .80 .18
1949 A773 28s multicolored 1.40 .28
Nos. 1944-1949 (6) 3.13
Set value .75

Khan Asparuch Crossing Danube, 679
A.D., by Boris Angelushev — A774

Historical Paintings: 3s, Reception at Trnovo, by Ilya Petrov. 5s, Chevartov's Troops at Benkovski, by P. Morozov. 8s, Russian Gen. Gurko and People in Sofia, 1878, by D. Gudjenko. 28s, People Greeting Red Army, by S. Venov.

1971, Mar. 6 Perf. 13¹/₂x14
1950 A774 2s gold & multi .15 .15
1951 A774 3s gold & multi .15 .15
1952 A774 5s gold & multi .16 .15
1953 A774 8s gold & multi .32 .15
a. Souv. sheet of 4, #1950-1953 1.00 .50
1954 A774 28s gold & multi 2.75 .85
Nos. 1950-1954 (5) 3.53
Set value 1.20

In 1973, No. 1953a was surcharged 1 lev and overprinted "Visitez la Bulgarie," airline initials and emblems, and, on the 5s stamp, "Par Avion."

Freed Black, White
and Yellow
Men — A775

1971, May 20 Photo. Perf. 12¹/₂
1955 A775 13s blue, blk & yel .35 .15

Intl. Year against Racial Discrimination.

Map of Europe,
Championship
Emblem — A776

"XXX" Supporting
Barbell — A777

1971, June 19
1956 A776 2s lt blue & multi .15 .15
1957 A777 13s yellow & multi .60 .18
Set value .65 .25

30th European Weight Lifting Championships, Sofia, June 19-27.

Facade, Old
House,
Koprivnica
A778

Designs: Decorated facades of various old houses in Koprivnica.

1971, July 10 Photo. Perf. 12¹/₂
1958 A778 1s green & multi .15 .15
1959 A778 2s brown & multi .15 .15
1960 A778 6s violet & multi .15 .15
1961 A778 13s dk red & multi .42 .15
Set value .65 .30

Frontier Guard
and German
Shepherd
A779

1971, July 31 Perf. 13
1962 A779 2s green & ol grn .15 .15

25th anniversary of the Frontier Guards.

Congress of Busludja, Bas-relief — A780

1971, July 31 Perf. 12¹/₂
1963 A780 2s dk red & ol grn .15 .15

80th anniversary of the first Congress of the Bulgarian Social Democratic party.

Young Woman, by
Ivan Nenov — A781

Paintings: 2s, Lazarova in Evening Gown, by Stefan Ivanov. 3s, Performer in Dress Suit, by Kyril Zonev. 13s, Portrait of a Woman, by Detchko Uzunov. 20s, Woman from Kalotina, by Vladimir Dimitrov. 40s, Gorjanin (Mountain Man), by Stoyan Venev.

1971, Aug. 2 Perf. 14x13¹/₂
1964 A781 1s green & multi .15 .15
1965 A781 2s green & multi .15 .15
1966 A781 3s green & multi .15 .15
1967 A781 13s green & multi .38 .15
1968 A781 20s green & multi .75 .30
1969 A781 40s green & multi 1.65 .45
Nos. 1964-1969 (6) 3.23
Set value 1.00

National Art Gallery.

Wrestlers
A782

Designs: 13s, Wrestlers.

1971, Aug. 27 Perf. 12¹/₂
1970 A782 2s green, blk & bl .15 .15
1971 A782 13s red org, blk & bl .48 .15
Set value .20

European Wrestling Championships.

Young Workers
A783

Post Horn Emblem
A784

1971 Photo. Perf. 13
1972 A783 2s dark blue .15 .15

25th anniv. of the Young People's Brigade.

1971, Sept. 15 Perf. 12¹/₂
1973 A784 20s dp green & gold .45 .20

8th meeting of postal administrations of socialist countries, Varna.

FEBS Waves Emblem — A785

1971, Sept. 20
1974 A785 13s black, red & mar .50 .20

7th Congress of European Biochemical Association (FEBS), Varna.

Statue of Republic — A786

Design: 13s, Bulgarian flag.

1971, Sept. 20   Perf. 13x12 1/2
1975 A786 2s gold, yel & dk red   .15 .15
1976 A786 13s gold, grn & red   .38 .20
          Set value   .45 .25

Bulgarian People's Republic, 25th anniv.

Cross Country Skiing and Winter Olympics Emblem A787

Sport and Winter Olympics Emblem: 2s, Downhill skiing. 3s, Ski jump and skiing. 4s, Women's figure skating. 13s, Ice hockey. 28s, Slalom skiing. 1 l, Torch and stadium.

1971, Sept. 25   Perf. 12 1/2
1977 A787 1s dk green & multi   .15 .15
1978 A787 2s vio blue & multi   .15 .15
1979 A787 3s ultra & multi   .15 .15
1980 A787 4s dp plum & multi   .15 .15
1981 A787 13s dk blue & multi   .40 .15
1982 A787 28s multicolored   .90 .35
          Set value   1.50 .75
Miniature Sheet
Imperf
1983 A787 1 l multicolored   3.50 1.65

11th Winter Olympic Games, Sapporo, Japan, Feb. 3-13, 1972.

Factory, Botevgrad A788

Industrial Buildings: 2s, Petro-chemical works, Pleven, vert. 10s, Chemical works, Vratsa. 13s, Maritsa-Istok Power Station, Dimitrovgrad. 40s, Electronics works, Sofia.

1971   Photo.   Perf. 13
1984 A788 1s violet   .15 .15
1985 A788 2s orange   .15 .15
1986 A788 10s deep purple   .18 .15
1987 A788 13s lilac rose   .22 .15
1988 A788 40s deep brown   .70 .15
          Nos. 1984-1988 (5)   1.40
          Set value   .32

UNESCO Emblem A789

1971, Nov. 4   Perf. 12 1/2
1989 A789 20s lt bl, blk, gold & red .45 .15
25th anniv. of UNESCO.

Soccer Player, by Kyril Zonev (1896-1971) A790

Paintings by Kyril Zonev: 2s, Landscape, horiz. 3s, Self-portrait. 13s, Lilies. 20s, Landscape, horiz. 40s, Portrait of a Young Woman.

1971, Nov. 10   Perf. 11x12
1990 A790 1s gold & multi   .15 .15
1991 A790 2s gold & multi   .15 .15
1992 A790 3s gold & multi   .15 .15
1993 A790 13s gold & multi   .22 .15
1994 A790 20s gold & multi   .85 .24
1995 A790 40s gold & multi   1.25 .15
          Nos. 1990-1995 (6)   2.77
          Set value   .85

Salyut Space Station — A791

Astronauts Dobrovolsky, Volkov and Patsayev — A792

Designs: 13s, Soyuz 11 space transport. 40s, Salyut and Soyuz 11 joined.

1971, Dec. 20   Perf. 12 1/2
1996 A791 2s dk grn, yel & red   .15 .15
1997 A791 13s multicolored   .22 .16
1998 A791 40s dk blue & multi   1.25 .40
          Nos. 1996-1998 (3)   1.62 .71
Souvenir Sheet
Imperf
1999 A792 80s multicolored   2.00 1.50

Salyut-Soyuz 11 space mission, and in memory of the Russian astronauts Lt. Col. Georgi T. Dobrovolsky, Vladislav N. Volkov and Victor I. Patsayev, who died during the Soyuz 11 space mission, June 6-30, 1971.

Oil Tanker Vihren A793

1972, Jan. 8   Photo.   Perf. 12 1/2
2000 A793 18s lil rose, vio & blk   .75 .25
Bulgarian shipbuilding industry.

Goce Delchev A794

Portraits: 5s, Jan Sandanski. 13s, Damjan Gruev.

1972, Jan. 21   Photo.   Perf. 12 1/2
2001 A794 2s brick red & blk   .15 .15
2002 A794 5s green & blk   .15 .15
2003 A794 13s lemon & blk   .35 .15
          Set value   .50 .22
Centenary of the births of Bulgarian patriots Delchev (1872-1903) and Sandanski, and of Macedonian Gruev (1871-1906).

Gymnast with Ball, Medals — A795

Designs: 18s, Gymnast with hoop, and medals. 70s, Gymnasts with hoops, and medals.

1972, Feb. 10
2004 A795 13s multicolored   .42 .15
2005 A795 18s multicolored   .55 .16
          Set value   .25
Miniature Sheet
Imperf
2006 A795 70s multicolored   2.25 2.00
5th World Women's Gymnastic Championships, Havana, Cuba.

View of Melnik, by Petar Mladenov — A796

Paintings from National Art Gallery: 2s, Plower, by Pencho Georgiev. 3s, Funeral, by Alexander Djendov. 13s, Husband and Wife, by Vladimir Dimitrov. 20s, Nursing Mother, by Nenko Balkanski. 40s, Paisii Hilendarski Writing History, by Koio Denchev.

1972, Feb. 20   Perf. 13 1/2x14
2007 A796 1s green & multi   .15 .15
2008 A796 2s green & multi   .15 .15
2009 A796 3s green & multi   .15 .15
2010 A796 13s green & multi   .42 .15
2011 A796 20s green & multi   .75 .20
2012 A796 40s green & multi   1.25 .35
          Nos. 2007-2012 (6)   2.87
          Set value   .90
Paintings from National Art Gallery.

Worker — A797

1972, Mar. 7   Perf. 12 1/2
2013 A797 13s silver & multi   .20 .15
7th Bulgarian Trade Union Congress.

Singing Harvesters A798

Designs: Paintings by Vladimir Dimitrov.

Perf. 11 1/2x12, 12x11 1/2
1972, Mar. 31
2014 A798 1s shown   .15 .15
2015 A798 2s Harvester   .15 .15
2016 A798 3s Women Diggers   .15 .15
2017 A798 13s Fabric Dyers   .15 .15
2018 A798 20s "My Mother"   .70 .15
2019 A798 40s Self-portrait   1.40 .32
          Nos. 2014-2019 (6)   2.90
          Set value   .80
Vladimir Dimitrov, painter, 90th birth anniv.

"Your Heart is your Health" — A799   St. Mark's Basilica and Wave — A800

1972, Apr. 30   Perf. 12 1/2
2020 A799 13s red, blk & grn   .70 .30
World Health Day.

1972, May 6   Perf. 13x12 1/2
Design: 13s, Ca' D'Oro and wave.
2021 A800 2s ol grn, bl grn & lt bl .15 .15
2022 A800 13s red brn, vio & lt grn .52 .18
          Set value   .60 .25
UNESCO campaign to save Venice.

Dimitrov in Print Shop, 1901 — A801

Designs: Life of George Dimitrov.

1972, May 8   Photo.   Perf. 12 1/2
2023 A801 1s shown   .15 .15
2024 A801 2s Dimitrov as leader of
             1923 uprising   .15 .15
2025 A801 3s Leipzig trial, 1933   .15 .15
2026 A801 5s As Communist func-
             tionary, 1935   .15 .15
2027 A801 13s As leader and teach-
             er, 1948   .15 .15
2028 A801 18s Addressing youth ral-
             ly, 1948   .42 .15
2029 A801 28s With Pioneers, 1948   .65 .16
2030 A801 40s Mausoleum   1.00 .32
2031 A801 80s Portrait   2.75 .45
    a.   Souvenir sheet   4.25 2.50
          Nos. 2023-2031 (9)   5.57 1.83

90th anniversary of the birth of George Dimitrov (1882-1949), communist leader.
No. 2031a contains one imperf. stamp similar to No. 2031, but in different colors.
Value, No. 2031 imperf. in slightly changed colors, $5.

Paisii Hilendarski — A802

Design: 2s, Flame and quotation.

1972, May 12
2032 A802 2s gold, grn & brn   .15 .15
2033 A802 13s gold, grn & brn   .50 .15
          Set value   .15
Paisii Hilendarski (1722-1798), monk, writer of Bulgarian-Slavic history.

Canoeing, Motion and Olympic Emblems — A803

Designs (Motion and Olympic emblems and): 2s, Gymnastics. 3s, Swimming, women's. 13s, Volleyball. 18s, Jumping. 40s, Wrestling. 80s, Stadium and sports.

1972, June 25
Figures of Athletes in Silver & Black
2034	A803	1s lt blue & multi	.15 .15
2035	A803	2s orange & multi	.15 .15
2036	A803	3s multicolored	.15 .15
2037	A803	13s yellow & multi	.15 .15
2038	A803	18s multicolored	.42 .18
2039	A803	40s pink & multi	1.25 .30
		Nos. 2034-2039 (6)	2.27
		Set value	.75

Miniature Sheet
Imperf
Size: 62x60mm
2040	A803	80s gold, ver & yel	1.75 1.00

20th Olympic Games, Munich, Aug. 26-Sept. 11.

Angel
Kunchev
A804

1972, June 30   Photo.   Perf. 12¹/₂
2041	A804	2s magenta, dk pur & gold	.15 .15

Centenary of the death of Angel Kunchev, patriot and revolutionist.

Zlatni
Pyassatsi — A805

1972, Sept. 16
2042	A805	1s shown	.15 .15
2043	A805	2s Drouzhba	.15 .15
2044	A805	3s Slunchev Bryag	.15 .15
2045	A805	13s Primorsko	.15 .15
2046	A805	28s Roussalka	.60 .24
2047	A805	40s Albena	.85 .30
		Nos. 2042-2047 (6)	2.05
		Set value	.80

Bulgarian Black Sea resorts.

Bronze
Medal,
Olympic
Emblems,
Canoeing
A806

Olympic Emblems and: 2s, Silver medal, broad jump. 3s, Gold medal, boxing. 18s, Gold medal, wrestling. 40s, Gold medal, weight lifting.

1972, Sept. 29
2048	A806	1s Prus bl & multi	.15 .15
2049	A806	2s dk green & multi	.15 .15
2050	A806	3s orange brn & multi	.15 .15
2051	A806	18s olive & multi	.50 .16
2052	A806	40s multicolored	1.00 .30
		Nos. 2048-2052 (5)	1.95
		Set value	.65

Bulgarian victories in 20th Olympic Games. For overprint see No. 2066.

Stoj Dimitrov — A807

Resistance Fighters: 2s, Cvetko Radoinov. 3s, Bogdan Stivrodski. 5s, Mirko Laiev. 13s, Nedelyo Nikolov.

1972, Oct. 30   Photo.   Perf. 12¹/₂x13
2053	A807	1s olive & multi	.15 .15
2054	A807	2s multicolored	.15 .15
2055	A807	3s multicolored	.15 .15
2056	A807	5s multicolored	.15 .15
2057	A807	13s multicolored	.28 .15
		Set value	.60 .30

"50 Years
USSR"
A808

1972, Nov. 3   Photo.   Perf. 12¹/₂x13
2058	A808	13s gold, red & yellow	.35 .15

50th anniversary of Soviet Union.

Turk's-cap
Lily — A809

Protected Plants: 2s, Gentian. 3s, Sea daffodil. 4s, Globe flower. 18s, Primrose. 23s, Pulsatilla vernalis. 40s, Snake's-head.

1972, Nov. 25   Perf. 12¹/₂
Flowers in Natural Colors
2059	A809	1s olive bister	.15 .15
2060	A809	2s olive bister	.15 .15
2061	A809	3s olive bister	.15 .15
2062	A809	4s olive bister	.15 .15
2063	A809	18s olive bister	.28 .15
2064	A809	23s olive bister	.75 .20
2065	A809	40s olive bister	1.40 .35
		Nos. 2059-2065 (7)	3.03
		Set value	.90

No. 2052 Overprinted in световен първенец Red

1972, Nov. 27
2066	A806	40s multicolored	.95 .24

Bulgarian weight lifting Olympic gold medalists.

Dobri
Chintulov — A810

1972, Nov. 28   Photo.   Perf. 12¹/₂
2067	A810	2s gray, dk & lt grn	.20 .15

Dobri Chintulov, writer, 150th birth anniversary.

Forehead
Band — A811

Designs (14th-19th Century Jewelry): 2s, Belt buckles. 3s, Amulet. 8s, Pendant. 23s, Earrings. 40s, Necklace.

1972, Dec. 27   Engr.   Perf. 14x13¹/₂
2068	A811	1s red brn & blk	.15 .15
2069	A811	2s emerald & blk	.15 .15
2070	A811	3s Prus bl & blk	.15 .15
2071	A811	8s dk red & blk	.15 .15
2072	A811	23s red org & multi	.50 .20
2073	A811	40s violet & blk	1.10 .42
		Set value	1.90 .90

Skin Divers
A812

Designs: 2s, Shelf-1 underwater house and divers. 18s, Diving bell and diver, vert. 40s, Elevation balloon and divers, vert.

1973, Jan. 24   Photo.   Perf. 12¹/₂
2074	A812	1s lt bl, blk & yel	.15 .15
2075	A812	2s blk, bl & org yel	.15 .15
2076	A812	18s blk, Prus bl & dl org	.42 .15
2077	A812	40s blk, ultra & bister	.95 .30
		Nos. 2074-2077 (4)	1.67
		Set value	.54

Bulgarian deep-sea research in the Black Sea.
A souvenir sheet of four contains imperf. 20s stamps in designs of Nos. 2074-2077 with colors changed. Sold for 1 l. Value $3.50 unused, $3 canceled.

Execution of Levski,
by Boris
Angelushev — A813

Design: 20s, Vassil Levski, by Georgi Danchev.

1973, Feb. 19   Perf. 13x12¹/₂
2078	A813	2s dull rose & Prus grn	.15 .15
2079	A813	20s dull grn & brn	.90 .18
		Set value	.23

Centenary of the death of Vassil Levski (1837-1873), patriot, executed by the Turks.

Kukersky Mask,	Nicolaus
Elhovo Region	Copernicus
A814	A815

Kukersky Masks at pre-Spring Festival: 2s, Breznik. 3s, Hissar. 13s, Radomir. 20s, Karnobat. 40s, Pernik.

1973, Feb. 26   Perf. 12¹/₂
2080	A814	1s dp rose & multi	.15 .15
2081	A814	2s emerald & multi	.15 .15
2082	A814	3s violet & multi	.15 .15
2083	A814	13s multicolored	.35 .15
2084	A814	20s multicolored	.38 .15
2085	A814	40s multicolored	2.25 1.10
		Nos. 2080-2085 (6)	3.43
		Set value	1.45

1973, Mar. 21   Photo.   Perf. 12¹/₂
2086	A815	28s ocher, blk & claret	1.25 .60

500th anniversary of the birth of Nicolaus Copernicus (1473-1543), Polish astronomer.

Vietnamese Worker
and
Rainbow — A816

1973, Apr. 16
2087	A816	18s lt blue & multi	.35 .15

Peace in Viet Nam.

A817   A818

Wild flowers.

1973, May   Photo.   Perf. 13
2088	A817	1s Poppy	.15 .15
2089	A817	2s Daisy	.15 .15
2090	A817	3s Peony	.15 .15
2091	A817	13s Centaury	.25 .15
2092	A817	18s Corn cockle	2.75 1.10
2093	A817	28s Ranunculus	.60 .22
		Nos. 2088-2093 (6)	4.05
		Set value	1.50

1973, June 2
2094	A818	2s pale grn, buff & brn	.15 .15
2095	A818	18s pale brn, gray & grn	.65 .42

Christo Botev (1848-1876), poet.

"Suffering Worker" — A819

Design: 1s, Asen Halachev and revolutionists.

1973, June 6   Photo.   Perf. 13
2096	A819	1s gold, red & blk	.15 .15
2097	A819	2s gold, org & dk brn	.15 .15
		Set value	.15 .15

50th anniversary of Pleven uprising.

Muskrat
A820

Perf. 12¹/₂x13, 13x12¹/₂
1973, June 29   Litho.
2098	A820	1s shown	.15 .15
2099	A820	2s Racoon	.15 .15
2100	A820	3s Mouflon, vert.	.15 .15
2101	A820	12s Fallow deer, vert.	.22 .15
2102	A820	18s European bison	.50 .15
2103	A820	40s Elk	2.50 1.00
		Nos. 2098-2103 (6)	3.67
		Set value	1.35

Aleksandr
Stamboliski
A821

1973, June 14   Photo.   Perf. 12¹/₂
2104	A821	18s dp brown & org	.35 .18
	a.	18s orange	2.50 .75

Aleksandr Stamboliski (1879-1923), leader of Peasants' Party and premier.

Trade Union Emblem — A822

Stylized Sun, Olympic Rings — A823

1973, Aug. 27   Photo.   Perf. 12½
2105 A822 2s yellow & multi   .15 .15
8th Congress of World Federation of Trade Unions, Varna, Oct. 15-22.

1973, Aug. 29   Perf. 13
28s, Emblem of Bulgarian Olympic Committee & Olympic rings. 80s, Soccer, emblems of Innsbruck & Montreal 1976 Games, horiz.
2106 A823 13s multicolored   .70 .32
2107 A823 28s multicolored   1.25 .40

Souvenir Sheet
2108 A823 80s multicolored   3.25 1.75
Olympic Congress, Varna. No. 2108 contains one stamp. It also exists imperf.; also with violet margin, imperf.

Revolutionists with Communist Flag — A824

Designs: 5s, Revolutionists on flatcar blocking train. 13s, Raising Communist flag, vert. 18s, George Dimitrov and Vassil Kolarov.

1973, Sept. 22   Photo.   Perf. 12½
2109 A824 2s magenta & multi   .15 .15
2110 A824 5s magenta & multi   .15 .15
2111 A824 13s magenta & multi   .30 .15
2112 A824 18s magenta & multi   .85 .32
      Nos. 2109-2112 (4)   1.45
         Set value   .50
50th anniv. of the September Revolution.

Warrior Saint — A825

Murals from Boyana Church: 1s, Tsar Kaloyan and 2s, his wife Dessislava. 5s, "St. Wystratti." 10s, Tsar Constantine Assen. 13s, Deacon Laurentius. 18s, Virgin Mary. 20s, St. Ephraim. 28s, Jesus. 80s, Jesus in the Temple, horiz.

1973, Sept. 24
2113 A825 1s gold & multi   .15 .15
2114 A825 2s gold & multi   .15 .15
2115 A825 3s gold & multi   .15 .15
2116 A825 5s gold & multi   .15 .15
2117 A825 10s gold & multi   .35 .15
2118 A825 13s gold & multi   .45 .15
2119 A825 18s gold & multi   .70 .15
2120 A825 20s gold & multi   .95 .18
2121 A825 28s gold & multi   3.50 .35
      Nos. 2113-2121 (9)   6.55
         Set value   1.00

Miniature Sheet
Imperf
2122 A825 80s gold & multi   3.75 2.25
No. 2122 contains one stamp with simulated perforations.

Christo Smirnenski — A826

1973, Sept. 29   Photo.   Perf. 12½
2123 A826 1s multicolored   .15 .15
2124 A826 2s vio blue & multi   .18 .15
         Set value   .25
75th anniversary of the birth of Christo Smirnenski (1898-1923), poet.

Human Rights Flame — A827

1973, Oct. 10
2125 A827 13s dk blue, red & gold .30 .16
25th anniversary of the Universal Declaration of Human Rights.

Type of 1970
History of Bulgaria: 1s, Tsar Theodor Svetoslav receiving Byzantine envoys. 2s, Tsar Mihail Shishman's army in battle with Byzantines. 3s, Tsar Ivan Alexander's victory at Russocastro. 4s, Patriarch Euthimius at the defense of Turnovo. 5s, Tsar Ivan Shishman leading horsemen against the Turks. 13s, Momchil attacking Turks at Umour. 18s, Tsar Ivan Stratsimir meeting King Sigismund's crusaders. 28s, The Boyars Balik, Theodor and Dobrotitsa, meeting ship bringing envoys from Anne of Savoy.

1973, Oct. 23   Perf. 13
Silver and Black Vignettes
2126 A741 1s olive bister   .15 .15
2127 A741 2s Prus blue   .15 .15
2128 A741 3s lilac   .15 .15
2129 A741 4s green   .15 .15
2130 A741 5s violet   .15 .15
2131 A741 13s orange & brn   .22 .15
2132 A741 18s olive green   .40 .18
2133 A741 28s yel brn & brn   1.10 .48
      Nos. 2126-2133 (8)   2.47
         Set value   1.25

Finn Class — A828

Sailboats: 2s, Flying Dutchman. 3s, Soling class. 13s, Tempest class. 20s, Class 470. 40s, Tornado class.

1973, Oct. 29   Litho.   Perf. 13
2134 A828 1s ultra & multi   .15 .15
2135 A828 2s green & multi   .15 .15
2136 A828 3s dk blue & multi   .15 .15
2137 A828 13s dull vio & multi   .28 .15
2138 A828 20s gray bl & multi   .60 .32
2139 A828 40s dk blue & multi   2.50 2.00
      Nos. 2134-2139 (6)   3.83 2.92
Value, set imperf. in changed colors, $10.

Village, by Bencho Obreshkov — A829

Paintings: 2s, Mother and Child, by Stoyan Venev. 3s, Rest (woman), by Tsenko Boyadjiev. 13s, Flowers in Vase, by Sirak Skitnik. 18s, Meri Kuneva (portrait), by Ilya Petrov. 40s, Winter in Plovdiv, by Zlatyu Boyadjiev. 13s, 18s, 40s, vert.

Perf. 12½x12, 12x12½
1973, Nov. 10
2140 A829 1s gold & multi   .15 .15
2141 A829 2s gold & multi   .15 .15
2142 A829 3s gold & multi   .15 .15
2143 A829 13s gold & multi   .22 .15
2144 A829 18s gold & multi   .42 .20
2145 A829 40s gold & multi   2.25 .75
      Nos. 2140-2145 (6)   3.34
         Set value   1.20

Souvenir Sheet
Paintings by Stanislav Dospevski: a, Domnica Lambreva. b, Self-portrait. Both vert.
2146 Sheet of 2   2.75 1.75
   a. A829 50s gold & multi   .70 .52
   b. A829 50s gold & multi   .70 .52
Bulgarian paintings. No. 2146 commemorates the 150th birth anniv. of Stanislav Dospevski.

Souvenir Sheet

Soccer A830

1973, Dec. 10   Photo.   Perf. 13
2147 A830 28s multicolored   4.00 3.50
No. 2147 sold for 1 l. Exists overprinted for Argentina 78.

Angel and Ornaments — A831

Designs: 1s, Attendant facing right. 2s, Passover table and lamb. 3s, Attendant facing left. 8s, Abraham and ornaments. 13s, Adam and Eve. 28s, Expulsion from Garden of Eden.

1974, Jan. 21   Photo.   Perf. 13
2148 A831 1s fawn, yel & brn   .15 .15
2149 A831 2s fawn, yel & brn   .15 .15
2150 A831 3s fawn, yel & brn   .15 .15
   a. Strip of 3, #2148-2150   .25 .20
2151 A831 8s slate grn & yel   .15 .15
2152 A831 8s slate grn & yel   .20 .15
   a. Pair, #2151-2152   .30 .25
2153 A831 13s lt brown, yel & ol .28 .24
2154 A831 28s lt brown, yel & ol .52 .32
   a. Pair, #2153-2154   .80 .35
         Set value   1.28 1.00
Woodcarvings from Rozhen Monastery, 19th century.

Lenin, by N. Mirtchev — A832

18s, Lenin visiting Workers, by W. A. Serov.

1974, Jan. 28   Litho.   Perf. 12½x12
2155 A832 2s ocher & multi   .15 .15
2156 A832 18s ocher & multi   .48 .22
         Set value   .30
50th anniversary of the death of Lenin.

1974, Jan. 28
Demeter Blagoev at Rally, by G. Kowachev.
2157 A832 2s multicolored   .15 .15
50th anniversary of the death of Demeter Blagoev, founder of Bulgarian Communist Party.

Domestic Animals A833

1974, Feb. 1   Photo.   Perf. 13
2158 A833 1s Sheep   .15 .15
2159 A833 2s Goat   .15 .15
2160 A833 3s Pig   .15 .15
2161 A833 5s Cow   .16 .15
2162 A833 13s Buffalo cow   .30 .15
2163 A833 20s Horse   .80 .28
      Nos. 2158-2163 (6)   1.71
         Set value   .75

Comecon Emblem A834

1974, Feb. 11   Photo.   Perf. 13
2164 A834 13s silver & multi   .40 .15
25th anniversary of the Council of Mutual Economic Assistance.

Soccer — A835

Designs: Various soccer action scenes.

1974, Mar.   Photo.   Perf. 13
2165 A835 1s dull green & multi   .15 .15
2166 A835 2s brt green & multi   .15 .15
2167 A835 3s slate grn & multi   .15 .15
2168 A835 13s olive & multi   .15 .20
2169 A835 23s blue grn & multi   .65 .42
2170 A835 40s emerald & multi   1.50 .70
      Nos. 2165-2170 (6)   2.75 1.77

Souvenir Sheet
2171 A835 1 l green & multi   3.00 1.65
World Soccer Championship, Munich, June 13-July 7. No. 2171 exists imperf.

Salt Production A836

Children's Paintings: 1s, Cosmic Research for Peaceful Purposes. 3s, Fire Dancers. 28s, Russian-

Bulgarian Friendship (train and children). 60s, Spring (birds).

1974, Apr. 15   Photo.   *Perf.* 13

2172	A836	1s lilac & multi	.15 .15
2173	A836	2s lt green & multi	.15 .15
2174	A836	3s blue & multi	.15 .15
2175	A836	28s slate & multi	1.75 .95
		Nos. 2172-2175 (4)	2.20 1.40

Souvenir Sheet

Imperf

2176 A836 60s blue & multi   2.25 1.75

Third World Youth Philatelic Exhibition, Sofia, May 23-30. No. 2176 contains one stamp with simulated perforations.

Folk Singers — A837

Designs: 2s, Folk dancers (men). 3s, Bagpiper and drummer. 5s, Wrestlers. 13s, Runners (women). 18s, Gymnast.

1974, Apr. 25   *Perf.* 13

2178	A837	1s vermilion & multi	.15 .15
2179	A837	2s orange brn & multi	.15 .15
2180	A837	3s brn red & multi	.15 .15
2181	A837	5s blue & multi	.15 .15
2182	A837	13s ultra & multi	.75 .24
2183	A837	18s violet bl & multi	.42 .15
		Set value	1.45 .58

4th Amateur Arts and Sports Festival

Flowers A838

1974, May   Photo.   *Perf.* 13

2184	A838	1s Aster	.15 .15
2185	A838	2s Petunia	.15 .15
2186	A838	3s Fuchsia	.15 .15
2187	A838	18s Tulip	.28 .15
2188	A838	20s Carnation	.60 .22
2189	A838	28s Pansy	1.65 .55
		Nos. 2184-2189 (6)	2.98
		Set value	1.10

Souvenir Sheet

2190 A838 80s Sunflower   1.75 .85

Automobiles and Emblems A839

1974, May 15   Photo.   *Perf.* 13

2191 A839 13s multicolored   .30 .15

International Automobile Federation (FIA) Spring Congress, Sofia, May 20-24.

Old and New Buildings, UNESCO Emblem A840

1974, June 15

2192 A840 18s multicolored   .30 .15

UNESCO Executive Council, 94th Session, Varna.

Postrider A841

Designs: 18s, First Bulgarian mail coach. 28s, UPU Monument, Bern.

1974, Aug. 5

2193	A841	2s ocher, blk & vio	.15 .15
2194	A841	18s ocher, blk & grn	.38 .15
		Set value	.45 .19

Souvenir Sheet

2195 A841 28s ocher, blk & bl   2.00 1.50

UPU cent. No. 2195 exists imperf.

Pioneer and Komsomol Girl — A842

Designs: 2s, Pioneer and birds. 60s, Emblem with portrait of George Dimitrov.

1974, Aug. 12

2196	A842	1s green & multi	.15 .15
2197	A842	2s blue & multi	.15 .15
		Set value	.15 .15

Souvenir Sheet

2198 A842 60s red & multi   1.65 1.10

30th anniversary of Dimitrov Pioneer Organization, Septemvrilche.

"Bulgarian Communist Party" — A843

Symbolic Designs: 2s, Russian liberators. 5s, Industrialization. 13s, Advanced agriculture and husbandry. 18s, Scientific and technical progress.

1974, Aug. 20

2199	A843	1s blue gray & multi	.15 .15
2200	A843	2s blue gray & multi	.15 .15
2201	A843	5s gray & multi	.15 .15
2202	A843	13s gray & multi	.26 .15
2203	A843	18s gray & multi	.35 .15
		Set value	.85 .30

30th anniversary of the People's Republic.

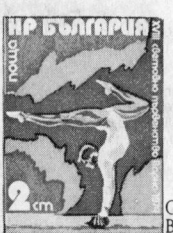

Gymnast on Parallel Bars — A844

Design: 13s, Gymnast on vaulting horse.

1974, Oct. 18   Photo.   *Perf.* 13

2204	A844	2s multicolored	.15 .15
2205	A844	13s multicolored	.28 .20
		Set value	.35 .25

18th Gymnastic Championships, Varna.

Souvenir Sheet

Symbols of Peace — A845

1974, Oct. 29   Photo.   *Perf.* 13

2206	A845	Sheet of 4	2.50 1.10
a.		13s Doves	.18 .15
b.		13s Map of Europe	.18 .15
c.		13s Olive Branch	.18 .15
d.		13s Inscription	.18 .15

1974 European Peace Conference. "Peace" in various languages written on Nos. 2206a-2206c. Sold for 60s. Exists imperf.

Nib and Envelope — A846

1974, Nov. 20

2207 A846 2s yellow, blk & grn   .15 .15

Introduction of postal zone numbers.

Flowers A847

1974, Dec. 5

2208 A847 2s emerald & multi   .15 .15

St. Todor, Ceramic Icon — A848

Fruit Tree Blossoms — A849

Designs: 2s, Medallion, Veliko Turnovo. 3s, Carved capital. 5s, Silver bowl. 8s, Goblet. 13s, Lion's head finial. 18s, Gold plate with Cross. 28s, Breastplate with eagle.

1974, Dec. 18   Photo.   *Perf.* 13

2209	A848	1s orange & multi	.15 .15
2210	A848	2s pink & multi	.15 .15
2211	A848	3s blue & multi	.15 .15
2212	A848	5s lt vio & multi	.15 .15
2213	A848	8s brown & multi	.15 .15
2214	A848	13s multicolored	.22 .15
2215	A848	18s red & multi	.32 .16
2216	A848	28s ultra & multi	1.00 .60
		Set value	1.90 1.25

Art works from 9th-12th centuries.

1975, Jan.   Photo.   *Perf.* 13

2217	A849	1s Apricot	.15 .15
2218	A849	2s Apple	.15 .15
2219	A849	3s Cherry	.15 .15
2220	A849	19s Pear	.28 .15
2221	A849	28s Peach	.70 .25
		Set value	1.10 .50

Tree and Book A850

1975, Mar. 25   Photo.   *Perf.* 13

2222 A850 2s gold & multi   .15 .15

Forestry High School, 50th anniversary.

Souvenir Sheet

Farmers' Activities (Woodcuts) — A851

1975, Mar. 25

2223	A851	Sheet of 4	.80 .48
a.		2s Farmer with ax and flag	
b.		5s Farmers on guard	
c.		13s Dancing couple	
d.		18s Woman picking fruit	

Bulgarian Agrarian Peoples Union, 75th anniv.

Michelangelo, Self-portrait A852

13s, Night, horiz. 18s, Day, horiz. Both designs after sculptures from Medici Tomb, Florence.

1975

2224	A852	2s plum & dk blue	.15 .15
2225	A852	13s vio bl & plum	.24 .15
2226	A852	18s brown & green	.52 .15
		Nos. 2224-2226 (3)	.91
		Set value	.30

Souvenir Sheet

2227 A852 2s olive & red   1.25 1.25

Michelangelo Buonarotti (1475-1564), Italian sculptor, painter and architect. No. 2227 issued to publicize ARPHILA 75 Intl. Phil. Exhib., Paris, June 6-16. Sheet sold for 60s.
Issued: #2224-2226, 3/28; #2227, 3/31.

Souvenir Sheet

Spain No. 1 and España 75 Emblem A853

1975, Apr. 4

2228 A853 40s multicolored   3.75 3.00

Espana 75 International Philatelic Exhibition, Madrid, Apr. 4-13.

Gabrov Costume — A854

Regional Costumes: 3s, Trnsk. 5s, Vidin. 13s, Gocedelchev. 18s, Risen.

1975, Apr.   **Photo.**   *Perf. 13*

2229	A854	2s blue & multi	.15	.15
2230	A854	3s emerald & multi	.15	.15
2231	A854	5s orange & multi	.15	.15
2232	A854	13s olive & multi	.35	.15
2233	A854	18s multicolored	.80	.24
		Nos. 2229-2233 (5)	1.60	
		Set value		.50

Red Star and Arrow — A855

Standard Kilogram and Meter — A856

Design: 13s, Dove and broken sword.

1975, May 9

2234	A855	2s red, blk & gold	.15	.15
2235	A855	13s blue, blk & gold	.32	.15
		Set value	.37	.19

Victory over Fascism, 30th anniversary.

1975, May 9   *Perf. 13x13½*

2236	A856	13s silver, lil & blk	.35	.15

Cent. of Intl, Meter Convention, Paris, 1875.

IWY Emblem, Woman's Head — A857

Ivan Vasov — A858

1975, May 20   **Photo.**   *Perf. 13*

2237	A857	13s multicolored	.35	.15

International Women's Year 1975.

1975, May

Design: 13s, Ivan Vasov, seated.

2238	A858	2s buff & multi	.15	.15
2239	A858	13s gray & multi	.32	.15
		Set value	.40	.15

125th birth anniversary of Ivan Vasov.

Nikolov and Sava Kokarechkov — A859

Designs: 2s, Mitko Palaouzov and Ivan Vassilev. 5s, Nicolas Nakev and Stevtcho Kraychev. 13s, Ivanka Pachkoulova and Detelina Mintcheva.

1975, May 30

2240	A859	1s multicolored	.15	.15
2241	A859	2s multicolored	.15	.15
2242	A859	5s multicolored	.15	.15
2243	A859	13s multicolored	.28	.15
		Set value	.50	.35

Teen-age resistance fighters, killed during World War II.

Mother Feeding Child, by John E. Millais — A861

Etchings: 2s, The Dead Daughter, by Goya. 3s, Reunion, by Beshkov. 13s, Seated Nude, by Renoir. 20s, Man in a Fur Hat, by Rembrandt. 40s, The Dream, by Daumier, horiz. 1 1, Temptation, by Dürer.

Photogravure and Engraved

1975, Aug.   *Perf. 12x11½, 11½x12*

2248	A861	1s yel grn & multi	.15	.15
2249	A861	2s orange & multi	.15	.15
2250	A861	3s lilac & multi	.15	.15
2251	A861	13s lt blue & multi	.26	.15
2252	A861	20s ocher & multi	.40	.18
2253	A861	40s rose & multi	1.10	.28
		Set value	1.95	.70

Souvenir Sheet

2254	A861	1 1 emerald & multi	2.00	1.25

World Graphics Exhibition.

Letter "Z" from 12th Century Manuscript A862

Initials from Illuminated Manuscripts: 2s, "B" from 17th cent. prayerbook. 3s, "V" from 16th cent. Bouhovo Gospel. 8s, "B" from 14th cent. Turnovo collection. 13s, "V" from Dobreisho's Gospel, 13th cent. 18s, "E" from 11th cent. Enina book of the Apostles.

1975, Aug.   **Litho.**   *Perf. 11½*

2255	A862	1s multicolored	.15	.15
2256	A862	2s multicolored	.15	.15
2257	A862	3s multicolored	.15	.15
2258	A862	8s multicolored	.15	.15
2259	A862	13s multicolored	.25	.15
2260	A862	18s multicolored	.65	.16
		Set value	1.25	.50

Bulgarian art.

Whimsical Globe — A863

1975, Aug.   **Photo.**   *Perf. 13*

2261	A863	2s multicolored	.15	.15

Festival of Humor and Satire.

Lifeboat Dju IV and Gibraltar-Cuba Route — A864

1975, Aug. 5   **Photo.**   *Perf. 13*

2262	A864	13s multicolored	.25	.15

Oceanexpo 75, 1st Intl. Ocean Exhib., Okinawa, July 20, 1975-Jan. 18, 1976.

Sts. Cyril and Methodius A865

Sts. Constantine and Helena A866

St. Sophia Church, Sofia, Woodcut by V. Zahriev — A867

1975, Aug. 21

2263	A865	2s ver, yel & brn	.15	.15
2264	A866	13s green, yel & brn	.25	.15
		Set value	.30	.20

Souvenir Sheet

2265	A867	50s orange & multi	1.25	.80

Balkanphila V, philatelic exhibition, Sofia, Sept. 27-Oct. 5.

Peace Dove and Map of Europe — A868

1975, Nov.   **Photo.**   *Perf. 13*

2266	A868	18s ultra, rose & yel	.45	.22

European Security and Cooperation Conference, Helsinki, Finland, July 30-Aug. 1. No. 2266 printed in sheets of 5 stamps and 4 labels, arranged checkerwise.

Acherontia Atropos A869

Designs: Moths.

1975   **Photo.**   *Perf. 13*

2267	A869	1s shown	.15	.15
2268	A869	2s Daphnis nerii	.15	.15
2269	A869	3s Smerinthus ocellata	.15	.15
2270	A869	10s Deilephila nicea	.20	.15

2271	A869	13s Choerocampa elpenor	.24	.15
2272	A869	18s Macroglossum fuciformis	.90	.24
		Set value	1.50	.53

Soccer Player — A870

1975, Sept. 21

2273	A870	2s multicolored	.15	.15

8th Inter-Toto (soccer pool) Soccer Championships, Varna.

Constantine's Rebellion Against the Turks, 1403 — A871

Designs (Woodcuts): 2s, Campaign of Vladislav III, 1443-1444. 3s, Battles of Turnovo, 1598 and 1686. 10s, Battle of Liprovsko, 1688. 13s, Guerrillas, 17th century. 18s, Return of exiled peasants.

1975, Nov. 27   **Photo.**   *Perf. 13*

2274	A871	1s bister, grn & blk	.15	.15
2275	A871	2s blue, car & blk	.15	.15
2276	A871	3s yellow, lil & blk	.15	.15
2277	A871	10s orange, grn & blk	.16	.15
2278	A871	13s green, lil & blk	.22	.15
2279	A871	18s pink, grn & blk	.45	.18
		Set value	1.00	.45

Bulgarian history.

Red Cross and First Aid — A872

Design: 13s, Red Cross and dove.

1975, Dec. 1

2280	A872	2s red brn, red & blk	.15	.15
2281	A872	13s bl grn, red & blk	.22	.15
		Set value	.30	.15

90th anniversary of Bulgarian Red Cross.

Egyptian Galley A873

Historic Ships: 2s, Phoenician galley. 3s, Greek trireme. 5s, Roman galley. 13s, Viking longship. 18s, Venetian galley.

1975, Dec. 15   **Photo.**   *Perf. 13*

2282	A873	1s multicolored	.15	.15
2283	A873	2s multicolored	.15	.15
2284	A873	3s multicolored	.15	.15
2285	A873	5s multicolored	.15	.15
2286	A873	13s multicolored	.32	.15
2287	A873	18s multicolored	.60	.16
		Set value	1.25	.46

See Nos. 2431-2436, 2700-2705.

Souvenir Sheet

Ethnographical Museum, Plovdiv — A874

1975, Dec. 17
2288   Sheet of 3   4.50 2.50
  a. A874 80s green, yellow & dark brown 1.25 .65
European Architectural Heritage Year. No. 2288 contains 3 stamps and 3 labels showing stylized bird.

Dobri Hristov — A875

1975, Dec.   *Perf. 13*
2289 A875 5s brt green, yel & brn   .15 .15
Dobri Hristov, musician, birth centenary.

United Nations Emblem — A876

1975, Dec.
2290 A876 13s gold, blk & mag   .20 .15
United Nations, 30th anniversary.

Glass Ornaments — A877

Design: 13s, Peace dove, decorated ornament.

1975, Dec. 22   **Photo.**   *Perf. 13*
2291 A877 2s brt violet & multi   .15 .15
2292 A877 13s gray & multi   .20 .15
    Set value   .25 .15
New Year 1976.

Downhill Skiing — A878

Designs (Winter Olympic Games Emblem and): 2s, Cross country skier, vert. 3s, Ski jump. 13s, Biathlon, vert. 18s, Ice hockey, vert. 23s, Speed skating, vert. 80s, Figure skating, pair, vert.

1976, Jan. 30   *Perf. 13½*
2293 A878 1s silver & multi   .15 .15
2294 A878 2s silver & multi   .15 .15
2295 A878 3s silver & multi   .15 .15
2296 A878 13s silver & multi   .22 .15
2297 A878 18s silver & multi   .32 .15
2298 A878 23s silver & multi   .80 .30
    Set value   1.50 .68

Souvenir Sheet

2299 A878 80s silver & multi   1.65 1.10
12th Winter Olympic Games, Innsbruck, Austria, Feb. 4-15.

Electric Streetcar, Sofia, 1976 — A879

Design: 13s, Streetcar and trailer, 1901.

1976, Jan. 12   **Photo.**   *Perf. 13½x13*
2300 A879 2s gray & multi   .15 .15
2301 A879 13s gray & multi   .38 .15
    Set value   .15
75th anniversary of Sofia streetcars.

Stylized Bird — A880

Designs: 5s, Dates "1976" and "1956" and star. 13s, Hammer and sickle. 50s, George Dimitrov.

1976, Mar. 1   *Perf. 13*
2302 A880 2s gold & multi   .15 .15
2303 A880 5s gold & multi   .15 .15
2304 A880 13s gold & multi   .25 .15
    Set value   .45 .18

Souvenir Sheet

2305 A880 50s gold & multi   1.00 .45
11th Bulgarian Communist Party Congress.

A. G. Bell and Telephone, 1876 — A881

1976, Mar. 10
2306 A881 18s dk brn, yel & ocher   .25 .15
Centenary of first telephone call by Alexander Graham Bell, Mar. 10, 1876.

Mute Swan — A882

Waterfowl: 2s, Ruddy shelduck. 3s, Common shelduck. 5s, Garganey teal. 13s, Mallard. 18s, Red-crested pochard.

1976, Mar. 27   **Litho.**   *Perf. 11½*
2307 A882 1s vio bl & multi   .15 .15
2308 A882 2s yel grn & multi   .15 .15
2309 A882 3s blue & multi   .15 .15
2310 A882 5s multicolored   .22 .15
2311 A882 13s purple & multi   .65 .15
2312 A882 18s green & multi   .90 .15
    Nos. 2307-2312 (6)   2.22
    Set value   .40

Guerrillas — A883

Designs (Woodcuts by Stoev): 2s, Peasants with rifle and proclamation. 5s, Raina Knaginia with horse and guerrilla. 13s, Insurgents with cherrywood cannon.

1976, Apr. 5   **Photo.**   *Perf. 13*
2313 A883 1s multicolored   .15 .15
2314 A883 2s multicolored   .15 .15
2315 A883 5s multicolored   .15 .15
2316 A883 13s multicolored   .24 .15
    Set value   .45 .23
Centenary of uprising against Turkey.

Guard and Dog A884

13s, Men on horseback, observation tower.

1976, May 15
2317 A884 2s multicolored   .15 .15
2318 A884 13s multicolored   .20 .15
    Set value   .25 .15
30th anniversary of Border Guards.

Construction Worker — A885

1976, May 20
2319 A885 2s multicolored   .15 .15
Young Workers Brigade, 30th anniversary.

Busludja, Bas-relief — A886   AES Complex — A887

Design: 5s, Memorial building.

1976, May 28   **Photo.**   *Perf. 13*
2320 A886 2s green & multi   .15 .15
2321 A886 5s violet bl & multi   .15 .15
    Set value   .20 .15
First Congress of Bulgarian Social Democratic Party, 85th anniversary.

1976, Apr. 7
Designs: 8s, Factory. 10s, Apartment houses. 13s, Refinery. 20s, Hydroelectric station.
2322 A887 5s green   .15 .15
2323 A887 8s maroon   .16 .15
2324 A887 10s green   .20 .15
2325 A887 13s violet   .32 .15
2326 A887 20s brt green   .42 .15
    Nos. 2322-2326 (5)   1.25
    Set value   .32
Five-year plan accomplishments.

Children Playing Around Table — A888

Kindergarten Children: 2s, with doll carriage & hobby horse. 5s, playing ball. 23s, in costume.

1976, June 15
2327 A888 1s green & multi   .15 .15
2328 A888 2s yellow & multi   .15 .15
2329 A888 5s lilac & multi   .15 .15
2330 A888 23s rose & multi   .42 .15
    Set value   .65 .29

Demeter Blagoev — A889   Christo Botev — A890

1976, May 28
2331 A889 13s bluish blk, red & gold   .25 .15
Demeter Blagoev (1856-1924), writer, political leader, 120th birth anniversary.

1976, May 25
2332 A890 13s ocher & slate grn   .25 .15
Christo Botev (1848-1876), poet, death centenary. Printed se-tenant with yellow green and ocher label, inscribed with poem.

Boxing, Montreal Olympic Emblem — A891   Belt Buckle — A892

Designs (Montreal Olympic Emblem): 1s, Wrestling, horiz. 3s, 1 l, Weight lifting. 13s, One-man kayak. 18s, Woman gymnast. 28s, Woman diver. 40s, Woman runner.

1976, June 25
2333 A891 1s orange & multi   .15 .15
2334 A891 2s multicolored   .15 .15
2335 A891 3s lilac & multi   .15 .15
2336 A891 13s multicolored   .18 .15
2337 A891 18s multicolored   .28 .15
2338 A891 28s blue & multi   .38 .16
2339 A891 40s lemon & multi   .75 .30
    Set value   1.75 .75

Souvenir Sheet

2340 A891 1 l orange & multi   1.65 1.10
21st Olympic Games, Montreal, Canada, July 17-Aug. 1.

1976, July 30   **Photo.**   *Perf. 13*
Thracian Art (8th-4th Centuries): 2s, Brooch. 3s, Mirror handle. 5s, Helmet cheek cover. 13s, Gold ornament. 18s, Lion's head (harness decoration). 20s, Knee guard. 28s, Jeweled pendant.
2341 A892 1s brown & multi   .15 .15
2342 A892 2s blue & multi   .15 .15
2343 A892 3s multicolored   .15 .15
2344 A892 5s claret & multi   .15 .15
2345 A892 13s purple & multi   .24 .15
2346 A892 18s multicolored   .32 .15
2347 A892 20s multicolored   .42 .15
2348 A892 28s multicolored   .60 .18
    Set value   1.85 .68

Souvenir Sheet

Composite
of Bulgarian
Stamp
Designs
A893

1976, June 5
2349 A893 50s red & multi 1.65 .65
International Federation of Philately (F.I.P.), 50th
anniversary and 12th Congress.

Partisans at Night, by Ilya Petrov — A894

Paintings: 5s, Old Town, by Tsanko Lavenov.
13s, Seated Woman, by Petrov, vert. 18s, Seated
Boy, by Petrov, vert. 28s, Old Plovdiv,
vert. 80s, Ilya Petrov, self-portrait, vert.

1976, Aug. 11 Photo. Perf. 14
2350 A894 2s multicolored .15 .15
2351 A894 5s multicolored .15 .15
2352 A894 13s ultra & multi .32 .15
2353 A894 18s multicolored .45 .15
2354 A894 28s multicolored .65 .18
Nos. 2350-2354 (5) 1.72
Set value .45

Souvenir Sheet
2354A A894 80s multicolored 1.25 .95

Souvenir Sheet

Olympic Sports and Emblems — A895

1976, Sept. 6 Photo. Perf. 13
2355 A895 Sheet of 4 1.65 1.00
a. 25s Weight Lifting .35 .18
b. 25s Rowing .35 .18
c. 25s Running .35 .18
d. 25s Wrestling .35 .18
Medalists, 21st Olympic Games, Montreal.

Souvenir Sheet

Fresco and UNESCO Emblem — A896

1976, Dec. 3
2356 A896 50s red & multi 1.25 .55
UNESCO, 30th anniv.

"The Pianist" by Fish and
Jendov — A897 Hook — A898

Designs (Caricatures by Jendov): 5s, Imperialist
"Trick or Treat." 13s, The Leader, 1931.

1976, Sept. 30 Photo. Perf. 13
2357 A897 2s green & multi .15 .15
2358 A897 5s purple & multi .15 .15
2359 A897 13s magenta & multi .32 .15
Set value .50 .18
Alex Jendov (1901-1953), caricaturist.

1976, Sept. 21 Photo. Perf. 13
2360 A898 5s multicolored .15 .15
World Sport Fishing Congress, Varna.

St. Theodore
A899

Frescoes: 3s, St. Paul. 5s, St. Joachim. 13s, Mel-
chizedek. 19s, St. Porphyrius. 28s, Queen. 1 l, The
Last Supper.

1976, Oct. 4 Litho. Perf. 12x12½
2361 A899 2s gold & multi .15 .15
2362 A899 3s gold & multi .15 .15
2363 A899 5s gold & multi .15 .15
2364 A899 13s gold & multi .32 .15
2365 A899 19s gold & multi .35 .15
2366 A899 28s gold & multi .65 .20
Set value 1.50 .56

Miniature Sheet
Perf. 12
2367 A899 1 l gold & multi 1.50 .95
Zemen Monastery frescoes, 14th cent.

Document — A900

1976, Oct. 5
2368 A900 5s multicolored .15 .15
State Archives, 25th anniversary.

Cinquefoil — A901

1976, Oct. 14 Photo. Perf. 13
2369 A901 1s Chestnut .15 .15
2370 A901 2s shown .15 .15
2371 A901 5s Holly .15 .15
2372 A901 8s Yew .15 .15
2373 A901 13s Daphne .32 .15
2374 A901 23s Judas tree .60 .18
Set value 1.25 .46

Dimitri Polianov — A902

1976, Nov. 19
2375 A902 2s dk purple & ocher .15 .15
Dimitri Polianov (1876-1953), poet.

Christo Botev,
by Zlatyu
Boyadjiev
A903

Paintings: 2s, Partisan Carrying Cherrywood
Cannon, by Ilya Petrov. 3s, "Necklace of Immortal-
ity" (man's portrait), by Detchko Uzunov. 13s,
"April 1876," by Georgi Popoff. 18s, Partisans, by
Stoyan Venev. 60s, The Oath, by Svetlin Russeff.

1976, Dec. 8
2376 A903 1s bister & multi .15 .15
2377 A903 2s bister & multi .15 .15
2378 A903 3s bister & multi .15 .15
2379 A903 13s bister & multi .24 .15
2380 A903 18s bister & multi .35 .15
Set value .80 .32

Souvenir Sheet
Imperf
2381 A903 60s gold & multi .95 .55
Uprising against Turkish rule, centenary.

"Pollution"
and Tree
A904

Design: 18s, "Pollution" obscuring sun.

1976, Nov. 10 Perf. 13
2382 A904 2s ultra & multi .15 .15
2383 A904 18s blue & multi .30 .15
Set value .35 .15
Protection of the environment.

Congress Flags — A904b
Emblem — A904a

1976, Nov. 28 Photo. Perf. 13
2384 A904a 2s multicolored .15 .15
2384A A904b 13s multicolored .26 .15
Set value .15
33rd BSIS Cong. (Bulgarian Socialist Party).

Tobacco
Workers,
by Stajkov
A905

Paintings by Stajkov: 2s, View of Melnik. 13s,
Shipbuilder.

1976, Dec. 16 Photo. Perf. 13
2385 A905 1s multicolored .15 .15
2386 A905 2s multicolored .15 .15
2387 A905 13s multicolored .28 .15
Set value .38 .20
Veselin Stajkov (1906-1970), painter.

Snowflake
A906

1976, Dec. 20
2388 A906 2s silver & multi .15 .15
New Year 1977.

Zachary Stoyanov
(1851-1889),
Historian — A907

1976, Dec. 30
2389 A907 2s multicolored .15 .15

Bronze Coin of Septimus Severus — A908

Roman Coins: 2s, 13s, 18s, Bronze coins of Cara-
calla, diff. 23s, Copper coin of Diocletian.

1977, Jan. 28 Photo. Perf. 13½x13
2390 A908 1s gold & multi .15 .15
2391 A908 2s gold & multi .15 .15
2392 A908 13s gold & multi .20 .15
2393 A908 18s gold & multi .26 .15
2394 A908 23s gold & multi .45 .20
Set value 1.00 .52
Coins struck in Serdica (modern Sofia).

Skis and
Compass — A909

Tourist Congress
Emblem — A910

1977, Feb. 14   *Perf. 13*
2395 A909 13s ultra, red & lt bl   .25 .15
2nd World Ski Orienteering Championships.

1977, Feb. 24   **Photo.**   *Perf. 13*
2396 A910 2s multicolored   .15 .15
5th Congress of Bulgarian Tourist Organization.

Bellflower — A911

Designs: Various bellflowers.

1977, Mar. 2
2397 A911   1s yellow & multi   .15 .15
2398 A911   2s rose & multi   .15 .15
2399 A911   3s lt blue & multi   .15 .15
2400 A911   13s multicolored   .30 .15
2401 A911   43s green & multi   1.10 .38
        Set value   1.50 .50

Vasil
Kolarov — A912

Union Congress
Emblem — A913

1977, Mar. 21   **Photo.**   *Perf. 13*
2402 A912 2s blue & black   .15 .15
Vasil Kolarov (1877-1950), politician.

1977, Mar. 25
2403 A913 2s multicolored   .15 .15
8th Bulgarian Trade Union Cong., Apr. 4-7.

Wolf
A914

Wild Animals: 2s, Red fox. 10s, Weasel. 13s,
European wildcat. 23s, Jackal.

1977, May 16   **Litho.**   *Perf. 12½x12*
2404 A914   1s multicolored   .15 .15
2405 A914   2s multicolored   .15 .15
2406 A914   10s multicolored   .18 .15
2407 A914   13s multicolored   .35 .15
2408 A914   23s multicolored   .60 .18
    Nos. 2404-2408 (5)   1.43
       Set value   .40

Diseased
Knee — A915

1977, Mar. 31   **Photo.**   *Perf. 13*
2409 A915 23s multicolored   .40 .15
World Rheumatism Year.

Writers'
Congress
Emblem
A916

1977, June 7
2410 A916 23s lt bl & yel grn   .65 .20
International Writers Congress: "Peace, the Hope
of the Planet." No. 2410 printed in sheets of 8
stamps and 4 labels with signatures of participating
writers.

Old Testament
Trinity, Sofia,
16th Century
A917

Icons: 1s, St. Nicholas, Nessebur, 13th cent. 3s,
Annunciation, Royal Gates, Veliko Turnovo, 16th
cent. 5s, Christ Enthroned, Nessebur, 17th cent.
13s, St. Nicholas, Elena, 18th cent. 23s, Presenta-
tion of the Virgin, Rila Monastery, 18th cent. 35s,
Virgin and Child, Tryavna, 19th cent. 40s, St.
Demetrius on Horseback, Provadia, 19th cent. 1 l,
The 12 Holidays, Rila Monastery, 18th cent.

1977, May 10   **Photo.**   *Perf. 13*
2411 A917   1s black & multi   .15 .15
2412 A917   2s green & multi   .15 .15
2413 A917   3s brown & multi   .15 .15
2414 A917   5s blue & multi   .15 .15
2415 A917   13s olive & multi   .30 .15
2416 A917   23s maroon & multi   .50 .15
2417 A917   35s green & multi   .80 .25
2418 A917   40s dp ultra & multi   1.10 .38
    Nos. 2411-2418 (8)   3.30
       Set value   1.00
Miniature Sheet
Imperf
2419 A917   1 l gold & multi   2.25 1.10
Bulgarian icons. See Nos. 2615-2619.

Souvenir Sheet

St. Cyril
A918

1977, June 7   **Photo.**   *Perf. 13*
2420 A918   1 l gold & multi   1.75 .90
1150th anniversary of the birth of St. Cyril (827-
869), reputed inventor of Cyrillic alphabet.

Congress
Emblem — A919

1977, May 9
2421 A919 2s red, gold & grn   .15 .15
13th Komsomol Congress.

Newspaper
Masthead
A920

1977, June 3   **Photo.**   *Perf. 13*
2422 A920 2s multicolored   .15 .15
Cent. of Bulgarian daily press and 50th anniv. of
Rabotnichesko Delo newspaper.

Patriotic Front
Emblem — A921

Weight
Lifting — A922

1977, May 26
2423 A921 2s gold & multi   .15 .15
8th Congress of Patriotic Front.

1977, June 15
2424 A922 13s dp brown & multi   .25 .15
European Youth Weight Lifting Championships,
Sofia, June.

Women Basketball
Players — A923

1977, June 15   *Perf. 13*
2425 A923 23s multicolored   .50 .18
7th European Women's Basketball
Championships.

Wrestling — A924

Designs (Games Emblem and): 13s, Running.
23s, Basketball. 43s, Women's gymnastics.

1977, Apr. 15
2426 A924   2s multicolored   .15 .15
2427 A924   13s multicolored   .20 .15
2428 A924   23s multicolored   .38 .15
2429 A924   43s multicolored   .70 .26
    Nos. 2426-2429 (4)   1.43
       Set value   .50
UNIVERSIADE '77, University Games, Sofia,
Aug. 18-27.

TV Tower,
Berlin — A925

1977, Aug. 12   **Litho.**   *Perf. 13*
2430 A925 25s blue & dk blue   .50 .16
SOZPHILEX 77 Philatelic Exhibition, Berlin,
Aug. 19-28.

Ship Type of 1975

Historic Ships: 1s, Hansa cog. 2s, Santa Maria,
caravelle. 3s, Golden Hind, frigate. 12s, Santa
Catherina, carrack. 13s, La Corone, galleon. 43s,
Mediterranean galleass.

1977, Aug. 29   **Photo.**   *Perf. 13*
2431 A873   1s multicolored   .15 .15
2432 A873   2s multicolored   .15 .15
2433 A873   3s multicolored   .15 .15
2434 A873   12s multicolored   .25 .15
2435 A873   13s multicolored   .25 .15
2436 A873   43s multicolored   1.00 .26
       Set value   1.65 .52

Ivan Vasov
National
Theater — A926

Buildings, Sofia: 13s, Party Headquarters. 23s,
House of the People's Army. 30s, Clement Ochrida
University. 80s, National Gallery. 1 l, National
Assembly.

1977, Aug. 30   **Photo.**   *Perf. 13*
2437 A926   12s red, *gray*   .18 .15
2438 A926   13s red brn, *gray*   .18 .15
2439 A926   23s blue, *gray*   .30 .15
2440 A926   30s olive, *gray*   .40 .15
2441 A926   80s violet, *gray*   1.10 .42
2442 A926   1 l claret, *gray*   1.40 .52
    Nos. 2437-2442 (6)   3.56 1.54

Map of
Europe
A927

1977, June 10
2443 A927 23s brown, bl & grn   .40 .18
21st Congress of the European Organization for
Quality Control, Varna.

Union of Earth and Water, by Rubens
A928

Rubens Paintings: 23s, Venus and Adonis. 40s, Pastoral Scene (man and woman). 1 l, Portrait of a Lady in Waiting.

1977, Sept. 23   Litho.   Perf. 12
2444 A928 13s gold & multi   .45 .15
2445 A928 23s gold & multi   .65 .15
2446 A928 40s gold & multi   1.10 .25
    Nos. 2444-2446 (3)   2.20
    Set value   .44

Souvenir Sheet

2447 A928 1 l gold & multi   2.50 1.65
Peter Paul Rubens (1577-1640).

George Dimitrov
A929

1977, June 17   Photo.   Perf. 13
2448 A929 13s red & deep claret   .35 .15
George Dimitrov (1882-1947).

Flame with Star — A930   Smart Pete on Donkey, by Ilya Beshkov — A931

1977, May 17
2449 A930 13s gold & multi   .25 .15
3rd Bulgarian Culture Congress.

1977, May 19
2450 A931 2s multicolored   .15 .15
11th National Festival of Humor and Satire Gabrovo.

Elin Pelin — A932   Dr. Pirogov — A934

13th Canoe World Championships — A933

Albena, Black Sea
A933a

Writers: 2s, Pelin (Dimitur Ivanov Stojanov, (1877-1949). 5s, Peju K. Jaworov (1878-1914). Artists: 13s, Boris Angelushev (1902-1966), 23s, Ceno Todorov (Ceno Todorov Dikov, 1877-1953). Each printed with label showing scenes from authors' works or illustrations by the artists.

1977, Aug. 26   Photo.   Perf. 13
2451 A932 2s gold & brown   .15 .15
2452 A932 5s gold & gray grn   .15 .15
2453 A932 13s gold & claret   .22 .15
2454 A932 23s gold & blue   .45 .15
    Set value   .80 .28

1977, Sept. 1   Photo.   Perf. 13
2455 A933 2s shown   .15 .15
2456 A933 23s 2-man canoe   .42 .18
    Set value   .25

1977, Oct. 5   Photo.   Perf. 13
2456A A933a 35s shown   .65 .25
2456B A933a 43s Rila Monastery   .80 .30
Sheet contains 4 each plus label.

1977, Oct. 14   Photo.   Perf. 13
2457 A934 13s olive, ocher & brown .25 .15
Centenary of visit by Russian physician N. J. Pirogov during war of liberation from Turkey.

Peace Decree, 1917   Old Soldier with Grandchild
A935   A936

13s, Lenin, 1917. 23s, "1917" as a flame.

1977, Oct. 21
2458 A935 2s black, buff & red   .15 .15
2459 A935 13s multicolored   .24 .15
2460 A935 23s multicolored   .45 .15
    Nos. 2458-2460 (3)   .84
    Set value   .30
60th anniv. of Russian October Revolution.

1977, Sept. 30
Designs (Festival Posters): 13s, "The Bugler." 23s, Liberation Monument, Sofia (detail). 25s, Samara flag.

2461 A936 2s multicolored   .15 .15
2462 A936 13s multicolored   .25 .15
2463 A936 23s multicolored   .42 .15
2464 A936 25s multicolored   .52 .22
    Nos. 2461-2464 (4)   1.34
    Set value   .50
Liberation from Turkish rule, centenary.

Souvenir Sheet

Games' and Sports Emblems — A937

1977, Aug. 10   Photo.   Perf. 13½x13
2465 A937 1 l multicolored   1.50 1.25
University Games '77, Sofia.

Conference Building — A938

1977, Sept. 12   Perf. 13½
2466 A938 23s multicolored   .40 .18
64th Interparliamentary Union Conference, Sofia.

Bulgarian Worker's Newspaper, Anniversaries
A939

1977, Sept. 12   Photo.   Perf. 13
2467 A939 2s yel grn, blk & red   .15 .15

Ornament
A940

New Year 1978: 13s, Different ornament.

1977, Dec. 1
2468 A940 2s gold & multi   .15 .15
2469 A940 13s silver & multi   .26 .15
    Set value   .15

Railroad Bridge — A941

1977, Nov. 9
2470 A941 13s green, yel & gray   .30 .15
Transport Organization, 50th anniversary.

A942   A943

1977, Nov. 15
2471 A942 8s gold & vio brn   .15 .15
Petko Ratchev Slaveikov (1827-95), poet, birth sesquicentennial. No. 2471 printed in sheets of 8 stamps and 8 labels in 4 alternating vertical rows.

1978, Jan. 30   Photo.   Perf. 13
Designs: 23s, Soccer player and Games' emblem. 50s, Soccer players.

2472 A943 13s multicolored   .24 .15
2473 A943 23s multicolored   .45 .15
    Set value   .19

Souvenir Sheet

2474 A943 50s ultra & multi   1.00 .85
11th World Cup Soccer Championship, Argentina, June 1-25.

Todor Zhivkov and Leonid I. Brezhnev — A944   Ostankino Tower, Moscow, Bulgarian Post Emblem — A945

1977, Sept. 7   Photo.   Perf. 13
2475 A944 18s gold, car & brn   .30 .15
Bulgarian-Soviet Friendship. No. 2475 issued in sheets of 3 stamps and 3 labels.

1978, Mar. 1
2476 A945 13s multicolored   .25 .15
20th anniversary of the Comecon Postal Organization (Council of Mutual Economic Assistance).

Leo Tolstoy — A946   Shipka Pass Monument — A947

5s, Fedor Dostoevski. 13s, Ivan Sergeevich Turgenev. 23s, Vasili Vasilievich Vershchagin. 25s, Giuseppe Garibaldi. 35s, Victor Hugo.

1978, Mar. 28   Photo.   Perf. 13
2477 A946 2s yellow & dk grn   .15 .15
2478 A946 5s lemon & brown   .15 .15
2479 A946 13s tan & sl grn   .22 .15
2480 A946 23s gray & vio brn   .35 .15
2481 A946 25s yel grn & blk   .40 .15
2482 A946 35s lt bl & vio bl   .80 .38
    Nos. 2477-2482 (6)   2.07
    Set value   .73

Souvenir Sheet

2483 A947 50s multicolored   .80 .60
Bulgaria's liberation from Ottoman rule, cent.

Bulgarian and Russian Colors
A948

1978, Mar. 18
2484 A948 2s multicolored .15 .15
30th anniv. of Russo-Bulgarian co-operation.

Heart and WHO Emblem
A949

1978, May 12
2485 A949 23s gray, red & org .32 .15
World Health Day, fight against hypertension.

Goddess
A950

Ceramics (2nd-4th Centuries) and Exhibition Emblem: 5s, Mask of bearded man. 13s, Vase. 23s, Vase. 35s, Head of Silenus. 53s, Cock.

1978, Apr. 26
2486 A950 2s green & multi .15 .15
2487 A950 5s multicolored .15 .15
2488 A950 13s multicolored .26 .15
2489 A950 23s multicolored .48 .16
2490 A950 35s multicolored .75 .24
2491 A950 53s carmine & multi 1.25 .32
Nos. 2486-2491 (6) 3.04
Set value .90

Philaserdica Philatelic Exhibition.

Nikolai Roerich, by Svyatoslav Roerich — A951

"Mind and Matter," by Andrei Nikolov — A952

1978, Apr. 5
2492 A951 8s multicolored .16 .15
2493 A952 13s multicolored .28 .15
Set value .15

Nikolai K. Roerich (1874-1947) and Andrei Nikolov (1878-1959), artists.

Bulgarian Flag and Red Star — A953

1978, Apr. 18
2494 A953 2s vio blue & multi .15 .15
Bulgarian Communist Party Congress.

Young Man, by Albrecht Dürer
A954

Paintings: 23s, Bathsheba at Fountain, by Rubens. 25s, Portrait of a Man, by Hans Holbein the Younger. 35s, Rembrandt and Saskia, by Rembrandt. 43s, Lady in Mourning, by Tintoretto. 60s, Old Man with Beard, by Rembrandt. 80s, Knight in Armor, by Van Dyck.

1978, June 19 Photo. Perf. 13
2495 A954 13s multicolored .16 .15
2496 A954 23s multicolored .30 .15
2497 A954 25s multicolored .32 .15
2498 A954 35s multicolored .45 .15
2499 A954 43s multicolored .55 .20
2500 A954 60s multicolored .85 .26
2501 A954 80s multicolored 1.10 .38
Nos. 2495-2501 (7) 3.73
Set value 1.18

Dresden Art Gallery paintings.

Doves and Festival Emblem — A955

1978, May 31
2502 A955 13s multicolored .25 .15
11th World Youth Festival, Havana, 7/28-8/5.

Fritillaria Stribrnyi — A956

Rare Flowers: 2s, Fritillaria drenovskyi. 3s, Lilium rhodopaeum. 13s, Tulipa urumoffii. 23s, Lilium jankae. 43s, Tulipa rhodopaea.

1978, June 27
2503 A956 1s multicolored .15 .15
2504 A956 2s multicolored .15 .15
2505 A956 3s multicolored .15 .15
2506 A956 13s multicolored .26 .15
2507 A956 23s multicolored .45 .15
2508 A956 43s multicolored .90 .30
Nos. 2503-2508 (6) 2.06
Set value .67

Yacht Cor Caroli and Map of Voyage
A957

1978, May 19 Photo. Perf. 13
2509 A957 23s multicolored .50 .18
First Bulgarian around-the-world voyage, Capt. Georgi Georgiev, Dec. 20, 1976-Dec. 20, 1977.

Market, by Naiden Petkov — A958

Views of Sofia: 5s, Street, by Emil Stoichev. 13s, Street, by Boris Ivanov. 23s, Tolbukhin Boulevard, by Nikola Tanev. 35s, National Theater, by Nikola Petrov. 53s, Market, by Anton Mitov.

1978, Aug. 28 Litho. Perf. 12½x12
2510 A958 2s multicolored .15 .15
2511 A958 5s multicolored .15 .15
2512 A958 13s multicolored .18 .15
2513 A958 23s multicolored .30 .15
2514 A958 35s multicolored .52 .18
2515 A958 53s multicolored .85 .28
Nos. 2510-2515 (6) 2.15
Set value .72

Miniature Sheet

Sleeping Venus, by Giorgione — A959

1978, Aug. 7 Photo. Imperf.
2516 A959 1 l multicolored 2.00 .85

View of Varna — A960

1978, July 13 Photo. Perf. 13
2517 A960 13s multicolored .25 .15
63rd Esperanto Cong., Varna, July 29-Aug. 5.

Black Woodpecker — A961

Woodpeckers: 2s, Syrian. 3s, Three-toed. 13s, Middle spotted. 23s, Lesser spotted. 43s, Green.

1978, Sept. 1
2518 A961 1s multicolored .15 .15
2519 A961 2s multicolored .15 .15
2520 A961 3s multicolored .15 .15
2521 A961 13s multicolored .26 .15
2522 A961 23s multicolored .42 .15
2523 A961 43s multicolored 1.10 .24
Set value 1.95 .58

"September 1923"
A962

1978, Sept. 5
2524 A962 2s red & brn .25 .15
55th anniversary of September uprising.

Souvenir Sheet

National Theater, Sofia
A963

Photogravure and Engraved
1978, Sept. 1 Perf. 12x11½
2525 Sheet of 4 2.50 1.00
a. A963 40s shown .60 .16
b. A963 40s Festival Hall, Sofia .60 .16
c. A963 40s Charles Bridge, Prague .60 .16
d. A963 40s Belvedere Palace, Prague .60 .16

PRAGA '78 and PHILASERDICA '79 Philatelic Exhibitions.

Black and White Hands, Human Rights Emblem — A964

1978, Oct. 3 Photo. Perf. 13x13½
2526 A964 13s multicolored .25 .15
Anti-Apartheid Year.

Gotse Deltchev — A965

Bulgarian Calculator — A966

1978, Aug. 1 Photo. Perf. 13
2527 A965 13s multicolored .25 .15
Gotse Deltchev (1872-1903), patriot.

1978, Sept. 3
2528 A966 2s multicolored .15 .15
International Sample Fair, Plovdiv.

Guerrillas — A967

1978, Aug. 1
2529 A967 5s blk & rose red .15 .15
Ilinden and Preobrazhene revolts, 75th anniv.

"Pipe Line" and Flags
A968

1978, Oct. 3
2530 A968 13s multicolored .25 .15
Construction of gas pipe line from Orenburg to Russian border.

A969

A970

1978, Oct. 4   *Perf. 13x13¹/₂*
2531 A969 13s Three acrobats   .25 .15
3rd World Acrobatic Championships, Sofia, Oct. 6-8.

1978, Sept. 18   **Photo.**   *Perf. 13*
2532 A970 2s dp claret & ocher   .15 .15
Christo G. Danov (1828-1911), 1st Bulgarian publisher. No. 2532 printed with se-tenant label showing early printing press.

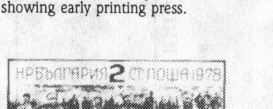

Insurgents, by Todor Panajotov A971

1978, Sept. 20
2533 A971 2s multicolored   .15 .15
Vladaja mutiny, 60th anniversary.

A972

A973

1978, Oct. 11   **Photo.**   *Perf. 13*
2534 A972 13s dk brn & org red   .25 .15
Salvador Allende (1908-1973), president of Chile.

1978, Oct. 18
2535 A973 23s Human Rights flame   .50 .20
Universal Declaration of Human Rights, 30th anniversary.

A974

A975

Burgarian Paintings: 1s, Levski and Matei Mitkaloto, by Kalina Tasseva. 2s, "Strength for my Arm" by Zlatyu Boyadjiev. 3s, Rumena, woman military leader, by Nikola Mirchev, horiz. 13s, Kolju Ficeto, by Elza Goeva. 23s, Family, National Revival Period, by Naiden Petkov.

Perf. 12x12¹/₂, 12¹/₂x12

1978, Oct. 25   **Litho.**
2536 A974 1s multicolored   .15 .15
2537 A974 2s multicolored   .15 .15
2538 A974 3s multicolored   .15 .15
2539 A974 13s multicolored   .24 .15
2540 A974 23s multicolored   .42 .15
      Set value   .85 .30
1300th anniversary of Bulgaria (in 1981).

1978, Nov. 1   **Photo.**   *Perf. 13*
Designs: a, Tourism building, Plovdiv. b, Chrelo Tower, Rila Cloister.

Souvenir Sheet
2541   Sheet of 5 + label   4.00 2.00
   a. A975 43s multicolored   .70 .28
   b. A975 43s multicolored   .70 .28
Conservation of European architectural heritage. No. 2541 contains 3 No. 2541a & 2 No. 2541b.

Ferry, Map of Black Sea with Route A976

1978, Nov. 1   **Photo.**   *Perf. 13*
2542 A976 13s multicolored   .25 .15
Opening of Ilychovsk-Varna Ferry.

Bird, from Marble Floor, St. Sofia Church — A977

1978, Nov. 20
2543 A977 5s multicolored   .15 .15
3rd Bulgaria '78, National Philatelic Exhibition, Sofia. Printed se-tenant with label showing emblems of Bulgaria '78 and Philaserdica '79.

Initial, 13th Century Gospel — A978

Designs: 13s, St. Cyril, miniature, 1567. 23s, Book cover, 16th century. 80s, St. Methodius, miniature, 13th century.

1978, Dec. 15   **Photo.**   *Perf. 13*
2544 A978 2s multicolored   .15 .15
2545 A978 13s multicolored   .20 .15
2546 A978 23s multicolored   .35 .15
   Nos. 2544-2546 (3)   .70
      Set value   .24

Souvenir Sheet
2547 A978 80s multicolored   1.25 1.00
Cent. of the Cyril and Methodius Natl. Library.

Bulgaria No. 53 A979

Bulgarian Stamps: 13s, #534. 23s, #968. 35s, #1176, vert. 53s, #1223, vert. 1 l, #1.

1978, Dec. 30
2548 A979   2s ol grn & red   .15 .15
2549 A979   13s ultra & rose car   .18 .15
2550 A979   23s rose lil & ol grn   .32 .15
2551 A979   35s brt bl & blk   .48 .20
2552 A979   53s ver & sl grn   .90 .32
   Nos. 2548-2552 (5)   2.03
      Set value   .74

Souvenir Sheet
2553 A979   1 l multicolored   1.50 1.25
Philaserdica '79, International Philatelic Exhibition, Sofia, May 18-27, 1979, and centenary of Bulgarian stamps. No. 2553 exists imperf. See Nos. 2560-2564.

St. Clement of Ochrida — A980

1978, Dec. 8
2554 A980 2s multicolored   .15 .15
Clement of Ochrida University, 90th anniv.

Ballet Dancers A981

1978, Dec. 22
2555 A981 13s multicolored   .30 .15
Bulgarian ballet, 50th anniversary.

Nikola Karastojanov A982

1978, Dec. 12
2556 A982 2s multicolored   .15 .15
Nikola Karastojanov (1778-1874), printer. No. 2556 printed se-tenant with label showing printing press.

Christmas Tree Made of Birds A983

1978, Dec. 22
2557 A983   2s shown   .15 .15
2558 A983   13s Post horn   .20 .15
      Set value   .25 .15
     New Year 1979.

COMECON Building, Moscow, Members' Flags — A984

1979, Jan. 25   **Photo.**   *Perf. 13*
2559 A984 13s multicolored   .25 .15
Council for Mutual Economic Aid (COMECON), 30th anniversary.

Philaserdica Type of 1978
Designs as Before

1979, Jan. 30
2560 A979   2s brt bl & red   .15 .15
2561 A979   13s grn & dk car   .18 .15
2562 A979   23s org brn & multi   .32 .15
2563 A979   35s dl red & blk   .50 .22
2564 A979   53s vio & dk ol   .90 .35
   Nos. 2560-2564 (5)   2.05
      Set value   .78
     Philaserdica '79.

Bank Building, Commemorative Coin — A985

1979, Feb. 13
2565 A985 2s yel, gray & sil   .15 .15
Centenary of Bulgarian People's Bank.

Aleksandr Stamboliski A986

1979, Feb. 28
2566 A986 2s orange & dk brn   .15 .15
Aleksandr Stamboliski (1879-1923), leader of peasant's party and premier.

Flower with Child's Face, IYC Emblem — A987

1979, Mar. 8
2568 A987 23s multicolored   .40 .15
International Year of the Child.

Stylized Heads, World Association Emblem — A988

1979, Mar. 20
2569 A988 13s multicolored   .25 .15
8th World Cong. for the Deaf, Varna, June 20-27.

"75" and Trade Union Emblem — A989

1979, Mar. 20
2570 A989 2s slate grn & org   .15 .15
75th anniversary of Bulgarian Trade Unions.

Souvenir Sheet

Sculptures in Sofia — A990

Designs: 2s, Soviet Army Monument (detail). 5s, Mother and Child, Central Railroad Station. 13s, 23s, 25s, Bas-relief from Monument of the Liberators.

1979, Apr. 2   Photo.   Perf. 13
2571 A990   Sheet of 5 + label   1.25   .60
  a.   2s multicolored   .15
  b.   5s multicolored   .15
  c.   13s multicolored   .22
  d.   23s multicolored   .38
  e.   25s multicolored   .48

    Centenary of Sofia as capital.

Rocket Launch,
Space Flight
Emblems — A991

Designs (Intercosmos and Bulgarian-USSR Flight Emblems and): 25s, Link-up, horiz. 35s, Parachute descent. 1 l, Globe, emblems and orbit, horiz.

1979, Apr. 11
2572 A991   12s multicolored   .20   .15
2573 A991   25s multicolored   .45   .15
2574 A991   35s multicolored   .60   .22
    Nos. 2572-2574 (3)   1.25   .52

Souvenir Sheet
2575 A991   1 l multicolored   1.50   .75

1st Bulgarian cosmonaut on Russian space flight. A slightly larger imperf. sheet similar to No. 2575 with control numbers at bottom and rockets at sides exists.

Nicolai Rukavishnikov — A992

Design: 13s, Rukavishnikov and Soviet cosmonaut Georgi Ivanov.

1979, May 14   Photo.   Perf. 13
2576 A992   2s multicolored   .15   .15
2577 A992   13s multicolored   .32   .15
    Set value   .40   .15

    Col. Rukavishnikov, 1st Bulgarian astronaut.

Souvenir Sheet

Thracian Gold-leaf Collar — A993

1979, May 16
2578 A993   1 l multicolored   2.00   1.50
    48th International Philatelic Federation Congress, Sofia, May 16-17.

Post Horn, Carrier Pigeon, Jet, Globes and
UPU Emblem — A994

Designs (Post Horn, Globes and ITU Emblem): 5s, 1st Bulgarian and modern telephones. 13s, Morse key and teleprinter. 23s, Old radio transmitter and radio towers. 35s, Bulgarian TV tower and satellite. 50s, Ground receiving station

1979, May 8   Perf. 13½x13
2579 A994   2s multicolored   .15   .15
2580 A994   5s multicolored   .15   .15
2581 A994   13s multicolored   .20   .15
2582 A994   23s multicolored   .38   .15
2583 A994   35s multicolored   .60   .22
    Nos. 2579-2583 (5)   1.48
    Set value   .48

Souvenir Sheet
Perf. 13
2584 A994   50s vio, blk & gray   1.00   .65

Intl. Telecommunications Day and cent. of Bulgarian Postal & Telegraph Services. Size of stamp in #2584: 39x28mm. #2584 exists imperf.

Hotel Vitosha-New
Otani — A996

1979, May 20
2586 A996   2s ultra & pink   .15   .15
    Philaserdica '79 Day.

Horseman
Receiving
Gifts, by
Karellia
and Boris
Kuklievi
A997

1979, May 23
2587 A997   2s multicolored   .15   .15
    Bulgarian-Russian Friendship Day.

A998   A999

Design: Man on Donkey, by Boris Angeloushev.

1979, May 23   Photo.   Perf. 13½
2588 A998   2s multicolored   .15   .15
    12th National Festival of Humor and Satire, Gabrovo.

Lithographed and Engraved
1979, May 31   Perf. 14x13½
Durer Engravings: 13s, Four Women. 23s, Three Peasants. 25s, The Cook and his Wife. 35s, Portrait of Helius Eobanus Hessus. 80s, Rhinoceros, horiz.
2589 A999   13s multicolored   .24   .15
2590 A999   23s multicolored   .40   .15
2591 A999   25s multicolored   .45   .15
2592 A999   35s multicolored   .65   .18
    Nos. 2589-2592 (4)   1.74
    Set value   .49

Souvenir Sheet
Imperf
2593 A999   80s multicolored   1.50   1.25
    Albrecht Durer (1471-1528), German engraver and painter.

R. Todorov (1879-
1916)
A1000

Bulgarian Writers: No. 2595, Dimitri Dymov (1909-1966). No. 2596, S. A. Kostov (1879-1939).

1979, June 26   Photo.   Perf. 13
2594 A1000   2s multicolored   .15   .15
2595 A1000   2s slate grn & yel grn   .15   .15
2596 A1000   2s dp claret & yel   .15   .15
    Set value   .25   .15

Nos. 2594-2596 each printed se-tenant with label showing title page or character from writer's work.

Moscow '80
Emblem,
Runners — A1001

Moscow '80 Emblem and: 13s, Pole vault, horiz. 25s, Discus. 35s, Hurdles, horiz. 43s, High jump, horiz. 1 l, Long jump.

1979, May 15   Perf. 13
2597 A1001   2s multicolored   .15   .15
2598 A1001   13s multicolored   .20   .15
2599 A1001   25s multicolored   .40   .15
2600 A1001   35s multicolored   .80   .24
2601 A1001   43s multicolored   1.00   .30
2602 A1001   1 l multicolored   2.25   .65
    Nos. 2597-2602 (6)   4.80   1.64

Souvenir Sheet
2602A A1001   2 l multicolored   6.00   3.25
    22nd Summer Olympic Games, Moscow, July 19-Aug. 3, 1980.

Rocket — A1002

5s, Flags of USSR and Bulgaria. 13s, "35."

1979, Sept. 4   Photo.
2603 A1002   2s multicolored   .15   .15
2604 A1002   5s multicolored   .15   .15
2605 A1002   13s multicolored   .18   .15
    Set value   .30   .18
    35th anniversary of liberation.

Moscow '80
Emblem, Gymnast
A1003

Moscow '80 Emblem & gymnasts. 13s horiz.

1979, July 31   Photo.   Perf. 13
2606 A1003   2s multicolored   .15   .15
2607 A1003   13s multicolored   .20   .15
2608 A1003   25s multicolored   .48   .15
2609 A1003   35s multicolored   .75   .22
2610 A1003   43s multicolored   1.00   .15
2611 A1003   1 l multicolored   2.25   .80
    Nos. 2606-2611 (6)   4.83   1.72

Souvenir Sheet
2612 A1003   2 l multicolored   6.00   3.25
    22nd Summer Olympic Games, Moscow, July 19-Aug. 3, 1980.

A1004   A1005

1979, July 8   Photo.   Perf. 13
2613 A1004   13s ultra & blk   .18   .15
    Theater Institute, 18th Congress.

1979, July 17
2614 A1005   8s multicolored   .15   .15
    Journalists' Vacation House, Varna, 20th Anniv.

Icon Type of 1977
Virgin and Child by: 13s, 23s, Nesebar, 16th cent., diff. 35s, 43s, Sozopol, 16th cent., diff. 53s, Samokov, 19th cent. Inscribed 1979.

1979, Aug. 7   Litho.   Perf. 12½
2615 A917   13s multicolored   .20   .15
2616 A917   23s multicolored   .35   .15
2617 A917   35s multicolored   .50   .15
2618 A917   43s multicolored   .60   .16
2619 A917   53s multicolored   .85   .24
    Nos. 2615-2619 (5)   2.50
    Set value   .69

A1006

A1007

1979, Aug. 9   Photo.   *Perf. 13x13½*
2620 A1006 2s Anton Besenschek   .15 .15
Bulgarian stenography centenary.

1979, Aug. 28   *Perf. 13*
2621 A1007 2s multicolored   .15 .15
Bulgarian Alpine Club, 50th anniv.

Public Health Ordinance A1008

1979, Aug. 31   *Perf. 13½*
2622 A1008 2s multicolored   .15 .15
Public Health Service centenary. No. 2622 printed with label showing Dimitar Mollov, founder.

Isotope Measuring Device — A1009

1979, Sept. 8   *Perf. 13½x13*
2623 A1009 2s multicolored   .15 .15
International Sample Fair, Plovdiv.

Games' Emblem — A1010

1979, Sept. 20   *Perf. 13*
2624 A1010 5s multicolored   .15 .15
Universiada '79, World University Games, Mexico City, Sept.

Sofia Locomotive Sports Club, 50th Anniversary — A1011

1979, Oct. 2
2625 A1011 2s blue & org red   .15 .15

Ljuben Karavelov (1837-1879), Poet and Freedom Fighter — A1012

1979, Oct. 4   Photo.   *Perf. 13*
2626 A1012 2s blue & slate grn   .15 .15

A1013

A1014

1979, Oct. 20
2627 A1013   2s Biathlon   .15 .15
2628 A1013 13s Speed skating   .22 .15
2629 A1013 23s Downhill skiing   .38 .15
2630 A1013 43s Luge   .75 .22
   Nos. 2627-2630 (4)   1.50
   Set value   .44

Souvenir Sheet

Imperf

2631 A1013 1 l Slalom   1.75 1.10
13th Winter Olympic Games, Lake Placid, NY, Feb. 12-24.

1979, Oct. 31   *Perf. 14*
Decko Uzunov, 80th Birthday: 12s, Apparition in Red. 13s, Woman from Thrace. 23s, Composition.
2632 A1014 12s multicolored   .24 .15
2633 A1014 13s multicolored   .24 .15
2634 A1014 23s multicolored   .38 .15
   Nos. 2632-2634 (3)   .86
   Set value   .22

Swimming, Moscow '80 Emblem A1016

1979, Nov. 30   Photo.   *Perf. 13*
2636 A1016   2s Two-man kayak, vert.   .15 .15
2637 A1016 13s Swimming, vert.   .18 .15
2638 A1016 25s shown   .40 .15
2639 A1016 35s One-man kayak   .80 .20
2640 A1016 43s Diving, vert.   1.00 .40
2641 A1016 1 l Diving, vert., diff.   2.25 .70
   Nos. 2636-2641 (6)   4.78 1.75

Souvenir Sheet

2642 A1016   2 l Water polo, vert.   6.00 3.25
22nd Summer Olympic Games, Moscow, July 19-Aug. 3, 1980.

Nikola Vapzarov A1017

1979, Dec. 7   Photo.   *Perf. 13*
2643 A1017 2s claret & rose   .15 .15
Vapzarov (1909-1942), poet and freedom fighter. No. 2643 printed with label showing smokestacks.

The First Socialists, by Bojan Petrov — A1018

Paintings: 13s, Demeter Blagoev Reading Newspaper, by Demeter Gjudshenov, 1892. 25s, Workers' Party March, by Sotir Sotirov, 1917. 35s, Dawn in Plovdiv, by Johann Leviev, vert.

Perf. 12½x12, 12x12½

1979, Dec. 10   *Litho.*
2644 A1018   2s multicolored   .15 .15
2645 A1018 13s multicolored   .22 .15
2646 A1018 25s multicolored   .38 .15
2647 A1018 35s multicolored   .55 .15
   Nos. 2644-2647 (4)   1.30
   Set value   .36

Sharpshooting, Moscow '80 Emblem — A1019

1979, Dec. 22   Photo.   *Perf. 13*
2648 A1019   2s shown   .15 .15
2649 A1019 13s Judo, horiz.   .20 .15
2650 A1019 25s Wrestling, horiz.   .40 .16
2651 A1019 35s Archery   .80 .25
2652 A1019 43s Fencing, horiz.   1.00 .50
2653 A1019 1 l Fencing   2.25 .90
   Nos. 2648-2653 (6)   4.80 2.11

Souvenir Sheet

2654 A1019   2 l Boxing   6.00 4.00

Procession with Relics, 11th Century Fresco A1020

Frescoes of Sts. Cyril and Methodius, St. Clement's Basilica, Rome: 13s, Reception by Pope Hadrian II. 23s, Burial of Cyril the Philosopher, 18th century. 25s, St. Cyril. 35s, St. Methodius.

1979, Dec. 25
2655 A1020   2s multicolored   .15 .15
2656 A1020 13s multicolored   .24 .15
2657 A1020 23s multicolored   .42 .15
2658 A1020 25s multicolored   .45 .15
2659 A1020 35s multicolored   .65 .18
   Nos. 2655-2659 (5)   1.91
   Set value   .48

Bulgarian Television Emblem A1021

1979, Dec. 29   *Perf. 13½*
2660 A1021 5s violet bl & lt bl   .15 .15
Bulgarian television, 25th anniversary. No. 2660 printed with label showing Sofia television tower.

Doves in Girl's Hair A1022

Design: 2s, Children's heads, mosaic, vert.

1979   *Perf. 13*
2661 A1022   2s multicolored   .15 .15
2662 A1022 13s multicolored   .16 .15
   Set value   .25 .15
International Year of the Child. Issue dates: 2s, July 17; 13s, Dec. 14.

Puppet on Horseback, IYC Emblem — A1023

Thracian Rider, Votive Tablet, 3rd Century — A1024

1980, Jan. 22   Photo.   *Perf. 13*
2663 A1023 2s multicolored   .15 .15
UNIMA, Intl. Puppet Theater Organization, 50th anniv. (1979); Intl. Year of the Child (1979).

1980, Jan. 29   Photo.   *Perf. 13x13½*
National Archaeological Museum Centenary; 13s, Deines stele, 5th century B.C.
2664 A1024 2s brown & gold   .15 .15
2665 A1024 13s multicolored   .20 .15
   Set value   .25 .15

Dimitrov Meeting Lenin in Moscow, by Alexander Poplilov A1026

1980, Mar. 28   *Perf. 12x12½*
2667 A1026 13s multicolored   .20 .15
Lenin, 110th birth anniversary.

A1027

A1027a

Circulatory system, lungs enveloped in smoke.

1980, Apr. 7   *Perf. 13*
2668 A1027 5s multicolored   .15 .15
World Health Day fight against cigarette smoking.

1980, Apr. 10   Photo.   *Perf. 13*
2669 A1027a   2s Basketball   .15 .15
2670 A1027a 13s Soccer   .18 .15
2671 A1027a 25s Hockey   .40 .15
2672 A1027a 35s Cycling   .80 .20
2673 A1027a 43s Handball   1.00 .40
2674 A1027a 1 l Volleyball   2.25 .70
   Nos. 2669-2674 (6)   4.78 1.75

Souvenir Sheet

2675 A1027a   2 l Weightlifting   6.50 4.25

Souvenir Sheet

Intercosmos Emblem,
Cosmonauts — A1028

1980, Apr. 22   *Perf. 12*
2676 A1028 50s multicolored   1.00 .45
Intercosmos cooperative space program.

Penio Penev
(1930-1959),
Poet — A1029

1980, Apr. 22   Photo.   *Perf. 13*
2677 A1029 5s multicolored   .15 .15
Se-tenant with label showing quote from author's
work.

Penny
Black — A1030

1980, Apr. 24   *Perf. 13*
2678 A1030 25s dark red & sepia   .60 .45
London 1980 International Stamp Exhibition,
May 6-14; printed se-tenant with label showing
Rowland Hill between every two stamps.

Demeter H. Tchorbadjiiski, Self-
portrait — A1031

1980, Apr. 29
2679 A1031 5s shown   .15 .15
2680 A1031 13s "Our People"   .18 .15
        Set value   .25 .15

Nikolai   Raising Red Flag
Giaurov — A1032   Reichstag Building,
                     Berlin — A1033

1980, Apr. 30
2681 A1032 5s multicolored   .15 .15
Nikolai Giaurov (b. 1930), opera singer; printed
se-tenant with label showing Boris Godunov.

1980, May 6   *Perf. 13x13½*
Armistice, 35th Anniversary: 13s, Soviet Army
memorial, Berlin-Treptow.

2682 A1033 5s multicolored   .15 .15
2683 A1033 13s multicolored   .18 .15
        Set value   .25 .15

Numeral — A1034

1979   *Perf. 14*
2684 A1034 2s ultra   .15 .15
2685 A1034 5s rose car   .15 .15
        Set value   .20 .15

A1034a   A1035

1980, May 12   Photo.   *Perf. 13*
2685A A1034a 5s multicolored   .15 .15
75th Anniv. of Teachers' Union.

1980, May 14   Photo.   *Perf. 13*
2686 A1035 13s multicolored   .20 .15
Warsaw Pact, 25th anniv.

A1036   A1037

Statues.

1980, June 10
2687 A1036 2s multicolored   .15 .15
2688 A1036 13s multicolored   .18 .15
2689 A1036 25s multicolored   .40 .15
2690 A1036 35s multicolored   .80 .30
2691 A1036 43s multicolored   1.00 .60
2692 A1036 1 l multicolored   2.25 1.10
        Nos. 2687-2692 (6)   4.78 2.45

Souvenir Sheet
2693 A1036 2 l multicolored   6.00 3.25
22nd Summer Olympic Games, Moscow, July
19-Aug. 3.

1980, Sept.   Photo.   *Perf. 13*
2694 A1037 13s multicolored   .25 .15
10th Intl. Ballet Competition, Varna.

Hotel
Europa,
Sofia
A1038

Hotels: No. 2696, Bulgaria, Burgas, vert. No.
2697, Plovdiv, Plovdiv. No. 2698, Riga, Russe,
vert. No. 2699, Varna, Djuba.

1980, July 11
2695 A1038 23s lt ultra & multi   .30 .15
2696 A1038 23s orange & multi   .30 .15
2697 A1038 23s gray & multi   .30 .15

2698 A1038 23s blue & multi   .30 .15
2699 A1038 23s yellow & multi   .30 .15
        Nos. 2695-2699 (5)   1.50
        Set value   .60
See No. 2766.

Ship Type of 1975
Ships of 16th, 17th Centuries: 5s, Christ of
Lubeck, galleon. 8s, Roman galley. 13s, Eagle, Russian galleon. 23s, Mayflower. 35s, Maltese galley.
53s, Royal Louis, galleon.

1980, July 14
2700 A873 5s multicolored   .15 .15
2701 A873 8s multicolored   .15 .15
2702 A873 13s multicolored   .25 .15
2703 A873 23s multicolored   .45 .18
2704 A873 35s multicolored   .70 .20
2705 A873 53s multicolored   1.10 .35
        Nos. 2700-2705 (6)   2.80
        Set value   .92

НР БЪЛГАРИЯ поща 1980 ст 3
Int'l Year of the Child, 1979 — A1040

Designs: Children's drawings and IYC emblem.
43s, Tower. 5s, 25s, 43s, vert.

1980 Litho.   *Perf. 12½x12, 12x12½*
2708 A1040 3s multicolored   .15 .15
2709 A1040 5s multicolored   .15 .15
2710 A1040 8s multicolored   .15 .15
2711 A1040 13s multicolored   .20 .15
2712 A1040 25s multicolored   .38 .15
2713 A1040 35s multicolored   .52 .15
2714 A1040 43s multicolored   .65 .18
        Nos. 2708-2714 (7)   2.20
        Set value   .64

Helicopter, Missile
Transport,
Tank — A1041

1980, Sept. 23   Photo.   *Perf. 13*
2715 A1041 3s shown   .15 .15
2716 A1041 5s Jet, radar, rocket   .15 .15
2717 A1041 8s Helicopter, ships   .16 .15
        Set value   .35 .15
Bulgarian People's Army, 35th anniversary.

St. Anne, by
Leonardo da
Vinci
A1042

Da Vinci Paintings: 8s, 13s, Annunciation (diff.).
25s, Adoration of the Kings. 35s, Lady with the
Ermine. 50s, Mona Lisa.

1980, Nov.
2718 A1042 5s multicolored   .15 .15
2719 A1042 8s multicolored   .15 .15
2720 A1042 13s multicolored   .20 .15
2721 A1042 25s multicolored   .38 .15
2722 A1042 35s multicolored   .55 .18
        Nos. 2718-2722 (5)   1.43
        Set value   .45

Souvenir Sheet
Imperf
2723 A1042 50s multicolored   1.00 .35

International Peace
Conference,
Sofia — A1043

1980, Sept. 4   Photo.   *Perf. 13*
2724 A1043 25s multicolored   .35 .15

Jordan Jowkov (1880-1937),
Writer — A1044

1980, Sept. 19
2725 A1044 5s multicolored   .15 .15
Se-tenant with label showing scene from
Jowkov's work.

International Samples Fair,
Plovdiv — A1045

1980, Sept. 24   *Perf. 13½x13*
2726 A1045 5s multicolored   .15 .15

Blooming
Cacti — A1045a

1980, Nov. 4   Photo.   *Perf. 13*
2726A A1045a 5s multicolored   .15 .15
2726B A1045a 13s multicolored   .20 .15
2726C A1045a 25s multicolored   .42 .16
2726D A1045a 35s multicolored   .60 .25
2726E A1045a 35s multicolored   1.00 .32
        Nos. 2726A-2726E (5)   2.37 1.03

Souvenir Sheet

25th Anniv. of Bulgarian UN
Membership — A1045b

1980, Nov. 25
2726F A1045b 60s multicolored   2.25 2.00

World Ski Racing Championship,
Velingrad — A1046

1981, Jan. 17   Photo.   Perf. 13
2727 A1046 43s multicolored   .60 .22

Hawthorn — A1047   Slalom — A1048

Designs: Medicinal herbs.

1981, Jan.
2728 A1047 3s shown   .15 .15
2729 A1047 5s St. John's wort   .15 .15
2730 A1047 13s Common elder   .20 .15
2731 A1047 25s Blackberries   .38 .15
2732 A1047 35s Lime   .55 .20
2733 A1047 43s Wild briar   .65 .24
       Nos. 2728-2733 (6)   2.08
       Set value   .75

1981, Feb. 27   Photo.   Perf. 13
2734 A1048 43s multicolored   .60 .25
Evian Alpine World Ski Cup Championship,
Borovets.

Nuclear Traces, Research
Institute — A1049

1981, Mar. 10   Perf. 13½x13
2735 A1049 13s gray & blk   .20 .15
Nuclear Research Institute, Dubna, USSR, 25th
anniversary.

Congress
Emblem
A1050

1981, Mar. 12   Perf. 13½
2736 A1050 5s shown   .15 .15
2737 A1050 13s Stars   .20 .15
2738 A1050 35s Teletape   .35 .15
       Nos. 2736-2738 (3)   .70
       Set value   .24

Souvenir Sheet
2739 A1050 50s Demeter Blagoev,
              George Dimitrov   .80 .48
12th Bulgarian Communist Party Congress. Nos.
2736-2738 each printed se-tenant with label.

Paintings by Zachary Zograf — A1050a

1981, Mar. 23   Photo.   Perf. 12x12½
2739A A1050a 5s multicolored   .15 .15
2739B A1050a 13s multicolored   .22 .15
2739C A1050a 23s multicolored   .42 .15
2739D A1050a 25s multicolored   .48 .15
2739E A1050a 35s multicolored   .70 .18
       Nos. 2739A-2739E (5)   1.97
       Set value   .55
    Nos. 2739A-2739C are vert.

EXPO '81,
Plovdiv
A1050b

1981, Apr. 7
2739F A1050b 5s multicolored   .15 .15
2739G A1050b 8s multicolored   .15 .15
2739H A1050b 13s multicolored   .25 .15
2739J A1050b 25s multicolored   .45 .15
2739K A1050b 53s multicolored   1.00 .24
       Nos. 2739F-2739K (5)   2.00
       Set value   .55

Centenary of Bulgarian
Shipbuilding — A1050c

1981, Apr. 15   Photo.   Perf. 13
2739L A1050c 35s Georgi Dimitrov,
                liner   .55 .20
2739M A1050c 43s 5th from RMS,
                freighter   .65 .25
2739N A1050c 53s Khan Asparuch,
                tanker   .80 .28
       Nos. 2739L-2739N (3)   2.00 .73

Arabian Horse
A1051

1980, Nov. 27   Litho.   Perf. 12½x12
2740 A1051 3s multicolored   .15 .15
2741 A1051 5s multicolored   .15 .15
2742 A1051 13s multicolored   .30 .15
2743 A1051 23s multicolored   .45 .15
2744 A1051 35s multicolored   .75 .20
       Nos. 2740-2744 (5)   1.80
       Set value   .48

Vassil Stoin, Ethnologist, Birth
Centenary — A1052

1980, Dec. 5   Photo.   Perf. 13½x13
2745 A1052 5s multicolored   .15 .15

12th Bulgarian
Communist Party
Congress — A1052a

1980, Dec. 26   Photo.   Perf. 13x13½
2745A A1052a 5s Party symbols   .15 .15

New Year
A1053

1980, Dec. 8   Perf. 13
2746 A1053 5s shown   .15 .15
2747 A1053 13s Cup, date   .18 .15
       Set value   .25 .15

Culture
Palace, Sofia
A1053a

1981, Mar. 13   Photo.   Perf. 13
2747A A1053a 5s multicolored   .15 .15

Vienna
Hofburg
Palace
A1054

1981, May 15   Photo.   Perf. 13
2748 A1054 35s multicolored   .45 .18
WIPA 1981 Intl. Philatelic Exhibition, Vienna,
May 22-31.

34th
Farmers'
Union
Congress
A1055

1981, May 18   Perf. 13½
2749 A1055 5s shown   .15 .15
2750 A1055 8s Flags   .15 .15
2751 A1055 13s Flags, diff.   .20 .15
       Set value   .40 .18

Wild Cat
A1056

1981, May 27
2752 A1056 5s shown   .15 .15
2753 A1056 13s Boar   .22 .15
2754 A1056 23s Mouflon   .40 .15
2755 A1056 25s Mountain goat   .45 .15
2756 A1056 35s Stag   .60 .18
2757 A1056 53s Roe deer   1.00 .26
       Nos. 2752-2757 (6)   2.82
       Set value   .82

Souvenir Sheet
Perf. 13½x13
2758 A1056 1 l Stag, diff.   1.65 .85
    EXPO '81 Intl. Hunting Exhibition, Plovdiv. Nos.
2752-2757 each se-tenant with labels showing various hunting rifles. No. 2758 contains one stamp,
size: 48½x39mm.

25th Anniv. of
UNESCO
Membership
A1057

1981, June 11   Perf. 13
2759 A1057 13s multicolored   .20 .15

Hotel Type of 1980

1981, July 13   Photo.   Perf. 13
2766 A1038 23s Veliko Tirnovo Hotel .35 .15

Flying Figure, Sculpture by Velichko
Minekov — A1059

Bulgarian Social Democratic Party Buzludja Congress, 90th Anniv. (Minkov Sculpture): 13s,
Advancing Female Figure.

1981, July 16   Perf. 13½
2767 A1059 5s multicolored   .15 .15
2768 A1059 13s multicolored   .18 .15
       Set value   .25 .15

Kukeri, by Georg   Statistics Office
Tschapkanov   Centenary
A1060   A1061

1981, May 28   Photo.   Perf. 13
2769 A1060 5s multicolored   .15 .15
13th Natl. Festival of Humor and Satire.

1981, June 9
2770 A1061 5s multicolored   .15 .15

Gold Dish
A1063

Designs: Goldsmiths' works, 7th-9th cent.

1981, July 21
2772 A1063 5s multicolored   .15 .15
2773 A1063 13s multicolored   .20 .15
2774 A1063 23s multicolored   .35 .22
2775 A1063 25s multicolored   .40 .25
2776 A1063 35s multicolored   .55 .35
2777 A1063 53s multicolored   .90 .38
       Nos. 2772-2777 (6)   2.55 1.50

35th Anniv. of Frontier Force — A1064

1981, July 28   Perf. 13½x13
2778 A1064 5s multicolored   .15 .15

1300th Anniv. of First Bulgarian
State — A1065

Designs: No. 2779, Sts. Cyril and Methodius.
No. 2780, 9th cent. bas-relief. 8s, Floor plan,
Round Church, Preslav, 10th cent. 12s, Four Evan-
gelists of King Ivan Alexander, miniature, 1356.
No. 2783, King Ivan Asen II memorial column. No.
2784, Warriors on horseback. 16s, April uprising,
1876. 23s, Russian liberators, Tirnovo. 25s, Social
Democratic Party founding, 1891. 35s, September
uprising, 1923. 41s, Fatherland Front. 43s, Prime
Minister George Dimitrov, 5th Communist Party
Congress, 1948. 50s, Lion, 10th cent. bas-relief.
53s, 10th Communist Party Congress. 55s,
Kremikovski Metalurgical Plant. 1 l, Brezhnev,
Gen. Todor Zhivkov.

1981, Aug. 10
2779	A1065	5s multicolored	.15	.15
2780	A1065	5s multicolored	.15	.15
2781	A1065	8s multicolored	.15	.15
2782	A1065	12s multicolored	.18	.15
2783	A1065	13s multicolored	.18	.15
2784	A1065	13s multicolored	.18	.15
2785	A1065	16s multicolored	.22	.15
2786	A1065	23s multicolored	.30	.15
2787	A1065	25s multicolored	.35	.15
2788	A1065	35s multicolored	.48	.20
2789	A1065	41s multicolored	.55	.22
2790	A1065	43s multicolored	.60	.24
2791	A1065	53s multicolored	.75	.30
2792	A1065	55s multicolored	.75	.30
	Nos. 2779-2792 (14)		4.99	
	Set value			2.00

Souvenir Sheets
2793	A1065	50s multicolored	.90	.55
2794	A1065	1 l multicolored	1.90	1.10

European Volleyball
Championship
A1066

1981, Sept. 16   *Perf. 13*
2795	A1066	13s multicolored	.20	.15

Pegasus, Bronze
Sculpture (Word
Day) — A1067

World Food
Day — A1068

1981, Oct. 2
2796	A1067	5s olive & cream	.15	.15

1981, Oct. 16
2797	A1068	13s multicolored	.16	.15

Professional Theater
Centenary
A1069

1981, Oct. 30
2798	A1069	5s multicolored	.15	.15

Anti-Apartheid Year — A1070

1981, Dec. 2
2799	A1070	5s multicolored	.15	.15

Espana '82 World
Cup
Soccer — A1071

Designs: Various soccer players.

1981, Dec.
2800	A1071	5s multicolored	.15	.15
2801	A1071	13s multicolored	.24	.15
2802	A1071	43s multicolored	.70	.24
2803	A1071	53s multicolored	.95	.35
	Nos. 2800-2803 (4)		2.04	.92

Heritage
Day
A1072

1981, Nov. 21   Photo.   *Perf. 13*
2804	A1072	13s multicolored	.20	.15

Souvenir Sheet
2804A	A1072	60s multicolored	4.25	1.10

Bagpipe — A1073

Public Libraries and
Reading Rooms, 125th
Anniv — A1074

1982, Jan. 14
2805	A1073	13s shown	.20	.15
2806	A1073	25s Flutes	.40	.18
2807	A1073	30s Rebec	.50	.20
2808	A1073	35s Flute, recorder	.55	.24
2809	A1073	44s Mandolin	.75	.30
	Nos. 2805-2809 (5)		2.40	1.07

1982, Jan. 20
2810	A1074	5s dk grn	.15	.15

Souvenir Sheet

Intl. Decade for Women (1975-
1985) — A1075

1982, Mar. 8
2811	A1075	1 l multicolored	1.65	1.00

New Year
1982
A1076

1981, Dec. 22   Photo.   *Perf. 13*
2812	A1076	5s Ornament	.15	.15
2813	A1076	13s Ornament, diff.	.18	.15
	Set value		.25	.15

The Sofia Plains, by Nicolas Petrov (1881-
1916) — A1077

1982, Feb. 10   *Perf. 12 1/2*
2814	A1077	5s shown	.15	.15
2815	A1077	13s Girl Embroidering	.20	.15
2816	A1077	30s Fields of Peshtera	.48	.20
	Nos. 2814-2816 (3)		.83	
	Set value			.33

25th Anniv. of
UNICEF
(1981) — A1078

Mother and Child Paintings.

1982, Feb. 25   *Perf. 14*
2817	A1078	53s Vladimir Dimitrov	.80	.32
2818	A1078	53s Basil Stoilov	.80	.32
2819	A1078	53s Ivan Milev	.80	.32
2820	A1078	53s Liliana Russeva	.80	.32
	Nos. 2817-2820 (4)		3.20	1.28

Figures, by Vladimir Dimitrov (1882-
1961) — A1079

1982, Mar. 8   Litho.
2821	A1079	5s shown	.15	.15
2822	A1079	8s Landscape	.15	.15
2823	A1079	13s View of Istanbul	.22	.15
2824	A1079	25s Harvesters, vert.	.42	.16
2825	A1079	30s Woman in a Land-scape, vert.	.50	.20
2826	A1079	35s Peasant Woman, vert.	.60	.25
	Nos. 2821-2826 (6)		2.04	
	Set value			.78

Souvenir Sheet
2827	A1079	50s Self-portrait	.80	.65

No. 2827 contains one stamp, size: 54x32mm.

Trade Union
Congress
A1080

1982, Apr. 8   Photo.   *Perf. 13 1/2*
2828	A1080	5s Dimitrov reading union paper	.15	.15
2829	A1080	5s Culture Palace	.15	.15
	Set value		.25	.15

#2828-2829 se-tenant with label showing text.

Marsh
Snowdrop — A1081

Designs: Medicinal plants.

1982, Apr. 10   Photo.   *Perf. 13*
2830	A1081	3s shown	.15	.15
2831	A1081	5s Chicory	.15	.15
2832	A1081	8s Chamaenerium angustifolium	.15	.15
2833	A1081	13s Solomon's seal	.25	.15
2834	A1081	25s Violets	.50	.20
2835	A1081	35s Centaury	.70	.26
	Nos. 2830-2835 (6)		1.90	
	Set value			.70

Cosmonauts' Day — A1082

1982, Apr. 12   *Perf. 13 1/2*
2836	A1082	13s Salyut-Soyuz link-up	.20	.15

Se-tenant with label showing K.E. Tsiolkovsky
(space pioneer).

Souvenir Sheet

SOZFILEX Stamp Exhibition — A1083

1982, May 7   *Perf. 13*
2837 A1083 50s Dimitrov, emblems   .80 .45

14th Komsomol Congress (Youth Communists) — A1084

1982, May 25
2838 A1084 5s multicolored   .15 .15

PHILEXFRANCE '82 Intl. Stamp Exhibition, Paris, June 11-21 — A1085

1982, May 28
2839 A1085 42s France #1, Bulgaria #1 .65 .25

19th Cent. Fresco A1086

Designs: Various floral pattern frescoes.

1982, June 8   *Perf. 11½*
2840 A1086 5s red & multi   .15 .15
2841 A1086 13s green & multi   .30 .15
2842 A1086 25s violet & multi   .50 .16
2843 A1086 30s ol grn & multi   .60 .22
2844 A1086 42s blue & multi   .90 .26
2845 A1086 60s brown & multi   1.25 .42
    Nos. 2840-2845 (6)   3.70 1.36

Souvenir Sheet

George Dimitrov (1882-1949), First Prime Minister — A1087

1982, June 15   *Perf. 13*
2846 A1087 50s multicolored   1.00 .45

9th Congress of the National Front — A1088

1982, June 21   Photo.   *Perf. 13*
2847 A1088 5s Dimitrov   .15 .15

35th Anniv. of Balkan Bulgarian Airline A1089

1982, June 28   *Perf. 13½x13*
2848 A1089 42s multicolored   .65 .26

A1090   A1091

1982, July 15   *Perf. 13*
2849 A1090 13s multicolored   .25 .15
   Nuclear disarmament.

1982, July   Photo.   *Perf. 13*
2850 A1091 5s multicolored   .15 .15
2851 A1091 13s multicolored   .18 .15
    Set value   .25 .15

Souvenir Sheet
2852 A1091 1 1 multicolored   1.50 .75
   Ludmila Zhivkova (b. 1942), artist.

5th Congress of Bulgarian Painters — A1092

1982, July 27   *Perf. 13½*
2853 A1092 5s multicolored   .20 .15
   Se-tenant with label showing text.

Flag of Peace Youth Assembly — A1093

Various children's drawings.

1982, Aug. 10   *Perf. 14*
2853A A1093 3s multicolored   .15 .15
2853B A1093 5s multicolored   .15 .15
2853C A1093 8s multicolored   .15 .15
2853D A1093 13s multicolored   .22 .15
    Set value   .46 .23

Souvenir Sheet
Perf. 14, Imperf.
2853E A1093 50s In balloon   3.00 .35
   See Nos. 2864-2870, 3052-3058, 3321-3327.

10th Anniv. of UN Conference on Human Environment, Stockholm — A1093a

1982, Nov. 10   *Perf. 13*
2854 A1093a 13s dk blue & grn   .20 .15

A1094   A1095

Designs: No. 2855, Park Hotel Moskva, Sofia. No. 2856, Tchernomore, Varna.

1982, Oct. 20   Photo.   *Perf. 13*
2855 A1094 32s lt blue & multi   .42 .18
2856 A1094 32s pink & multi   .42 .18

1982, Nov. 4
2857 A1095 13s Cruiser Aurora, Sputnik II   .16 .15

   October Revolution, 65th anniv.

60th Anniv. of Institute of Communications A1096

1982, Dec. 9
2858 A1096 5s ultra   .15 .15

60th Anniv. of USSR A1097

1982, Dec. 9
2859 A1097 13s multicolored   .18 .15

The Piano, by Pablo Picasso (1881-1973) A1098

Perf. 11½x12½
         Litho.
2860 A1098 13s shown   .20 .15
2861 A1098 30s Portrait of Jacqueline   .40 .18
2862 A1098 42s Maternity   .60 .26
    Nos. 2860-2862 (3)   1.20 .59

Souvenir Sheet
2863 A1098 1 1 Self-portrait   2.50 .75

Children's Drawings Type of 1982
Various children's drawings. 8s, 13s, 50s vert.

1982, Dec. 28   *Perf. 14*
2864 A1093 3s multicolored   .15 .15
2865 A1093 5s multicolored   .15 .15
2866 A1093 8s multicolored   .15 .15
2867 A1093 13s multicolored   .20 .15
2868 A1093 25s multicolored   .35 .15
2869 A1093 30s multicolored   .40 .18
    Nos. 2864-2869 (6)   1.40
    Set value   .56

Souvenir Sheet
Perf. 14, Imperf.
2870 A1093 50s Shaking hands   2.50 .35

New Year A1100

1982, Dec. 28   Photo.   *Perf. 13*
2872 A1100 5s multicolored   .15 .15
2873 A1100 13s multicolored   .18 .15
    Set value   .25 .15

A1101   A1102

1982, Dec. 28
2874 A1101 25s Robert Koch   .38 .15
2875 A1101 30s Simon Bolivar   .42 .18
2876 A1101 30s Rabindranath Tagore (1861-1941)   .42 .18
    Nos. 2874-2876 (3)   1.22 .51

No. 2874 also for TB bacillus cent.

1983, Jan. 10   Photo.   *Perf. 13x13½*
2877 A1102 5s olive & brown   .15 .15

   Vassil Levski (1837-73), revolutionary.

Universiade Games — A1103

1983, Feb. 15   *Perf. 13*
2878 A1103 30s Downhill skiing   .35 .18

Fresh-water Fish — A1104

1983, Mar. 24　Photo.　Perf. 13¹/₂x13
2879 A1104	3s Pike	.15	.15
2880 A1104	5s Sturgeon	.15	.15
2881 A1104	13s Chub	.20	.15
2882 A1104	25s Perch	.38	.15
2883 A1104	30s Catfish	.42	.18
2884 A1104	42s Trout	.55	.24
	Nos. 2879-2884 (6)	1.85	
	Set value		.75

Karl Marx (1818-1883)
A1105

1983, Apr. 5　　　Perf. 13x13¹/₂
2885 A1105	13s multicolored	.20	.15

Jaroslav Hasek (1883-1923) — A1106

1983, Apr. 20　Photo.　Perf. 13
2886 A1106	13s multicolored	.20	.15

Martin Luther (1483-1546)
A1107

1983, May 10
2887 A1107	13s multicolored	.20	.15

55th Anniv. of Komsomol Youth Movement — A1108

1983, May 13
2888 A1108	5s "PMC"	.15	.15

A1109　　　　A1111

National costumes.

1983, May 17　Litho.　Perf. 14
2889 A1109	5s Khaskovo	.15	.15
2890 A1109	8s Pernik	.15	.15
2891 A1109	13s Burgas	.20	.15
2892 A1109	25s Tolbukhin	.38	.15

2893 A1109	30s Blagoevgrad	.40	.15
2894 A1109	42s Topolovgrad	.55	.22
	Nos. 2889-2894 (6)	1.83	
	Set value		.68

1983, May 20

6th Intl. Satire and Humor Biennial, Gabrovo: Old Man Feeding Chickens.
2900 A1111	5s multicolored	.15	.15

Christo Smirnensky (1898-1983), Poet — A1112

1983, May 25
2901 A1112	5s multicolored	.15	.15

17th Intl. Geodesists' Congress — A1113

1983, May 27
2902 A1113	30s Emblem	.45	.20

Interarch '83 Architecture Exhibition, Sofia — A1114

1983, June 6
2903 A1114	30s multicolored	.45	.20

8th European Chess Championships, Plovdiv — A1115

1983, June 20　Photo.　Perf. 13
2904 A1115	13s Chess pieces, map of Europe	.20	.15

Souvenir Sheet

BRASILIANA '83 Philatelic Exhibition — A1116

1983, June 24
2905 A1116	11 Brazilian and Bulgarian stamps	1.50	.95

Social Democratic Party Congress of Russia, 80th Anniv. A1118

Design: Lenin addressing congress.

1983, July 29　Photo.　Perf. 13
2907 A1118	5s multicolored	.15	.15

Ilinden-Preobrazhensky Insurrection, 80th Anniv. — A1119

1983, July 29
2908 A1119	5s Gun, dagger, book	.15	.15

Institute of Mining and Geology, Sofia, 30th Anniv. — A1120

1983, Aug. 10
2909 A1120	5s multicolored	.15	.15

60th Anniv. of September 1923 Uprising — A1121

1983, Aug. 19
2910 A1121	5s multicolored	.15	.15
2911 A1121	13s multicolored	.18	.15
	Set value	.25	.15

Angora Cat
A1123

1983, Sept. 26　　　Perf. 13
2917 A1123	5s shown	.15	.15
2918 A1123	13s Siamese	.22	.15
2919 A1123	20s Abyssinian, vert.	.38	.15
2920 A1123	25s Persian	.45	.18
2921 A1123	30s European, vert.	.55	.22
2922 A1123	42s Indochinese	.75	.30
	Nos. 2917-2922 (6)	2.50	1.15

Animated Film Festival — A1124

1983, Sept. 15　Photo.　Perf. 14x13¹/₂
2923 A1124	5s Articulation layout	.15	.15

Trevethick's Engine, 1804 — A1125

Locomotives: 13s, Blenkinsop's Prince Royal, 1810. 42s, Hedley's Puffing Billy, 1812. 60s, Adler (first German locomotive), 1835.

1983, Oct. 20　　　　Perf. 13
2924 A1125	5s multicolored	.15	.15
2925 A1125	13s multicolored	.32	.15
2926 A1125	42s multicolored	.95	.30
2927 A1125	60s multicolored	1.40	.42
	Nos. 2924-2927 (4)	2.82	
	Set value		.84

See Nos. 2983-2987.

Souvenir Sheet

Liberation Monument, Plovdiv — A1126

1983, Nov. 4
2928 A1126	50s multicolored	.80	.60

Philatelic Federation, 90th anniv.

Sofia Opera, 75th Anniv. — A1127　　Composers' Assoc., 50th Anniv. — A1128

1983, Dec. 2　　　　Perf. 13x13¹/₂
2929 A1127	5s Mask, lyre, laurel	.15	.15

1983, Dec. 5

Composers: 5s, Ioan Kukuzel (14th cent.) 8s, Atanasov. 13s, Petko Stainov. 20s, Veselin Stodiov. 25s, Liubomir Pipkov. 30s, Pancho Vladigerov. Se-tenant with labels showing compositions.
2930 A1128	5s multicolored	.15	.15
2931 A1128	8s multicolored	.15	.15
2932 A1128	13s multicolored	.18	.15
2933 A1128	20s multicolored	.30	.15
2934 A1128	25s multicolored	.38	.16
2935 A1128	30s multicolored	.48	.20
	Nos. 2930-2935 (6)	1.64	
	Set value		.65

New Year 1984
A1129

1983, Dec. 10　　　　Perf. 13
2936 A1129	5s multicolored	.15	.15

Angelo Donni, by Raphael — A1130

1983, Dec. 22   **Perf. 14**
2937	A1130	5s shown	.15	.15
2938	A1130	13s Cardinal	.20	.15
2939	A1130	30s Baldassare Castiglioni	.45	.20
2940	A1130	42s Donna Belata	.68	.30
		Nos. 2937-2940 (4)	1.48	
		Set value		.62

Souvenir Sheet
2941	A1130	1 l Sistine Madonna	1.65	1.25

Bat, World Wildlife Emblem A1131

Various bats and rodents.

1983, Dec. 30   **Perf. 13**
2942	A1131	12s multicolored	.16	.15
2943	A1131	13s multicolored	.18	.15
2944	A1131	20s multicolored	.28	.15
2945	A1131	30s multicolored	.45	.22
2946	A1131	42s multicolored	.65	.30
		Nos. 2942-2946 (5)	1.72	
		Set value		.79

Dmitri Mendeleev (1834-1907), Russian Chemist — A1132

1984, Mar. 14
2947	A1132	13s multicolored	.22	.15

Ljuben Karavelov, Poet and Freedom Fighter, Birth Sesquicentenary A1133

1984, Jan. 31   **Perf. 13x13 1/2**
2948	A1133	5s multicolored	.15	.15

Tanker Gen. V.I. Zaimov A1137

1984, Mar. 22   **Perf. 13 1/2**
2959	A1137	5s shown	.15	.15
2960	A1137	13s Mesta	.22	.15
2961	A1137	25s Veleka	.42	.16
2962	A1137	32s Ferry	.52	.22
2963	A1137	42s Cargo ship Rossen	.70	.28
		Nos. 2959-2963 (5)	2.01	
		Set value		.78

Souvenir Sheet

34160

World Cup Soccer Commemorative of 1982, Spain No. 2281 — A1137a

1984, Apr. 18   **Photo.**   **Perf. 13x13 1/2**
2963A	A1137a	2 l multicolored	3.00	2.50

ESPANA '84.

Dove with Letter over Globe — A1138   Berries — A1139

1984, Apr. 24   **Perf. 13**
2964	A1138	5s multicolored	.15	.15

World Youth Stamp Exhibition, Pleven, Oct. 5-11.

1984, May 5
2965	A1139	5s Cherries	.15	.15
2966	A1139	8s Strawberries	.15	.15
2967	A1139	13s Blackberries	.20	.15
2968	A1139	20s Raspberries	.35	.15
2969	A1139	42s Currants	.70	.32
		Nos. 2965-2969 (5)	1.55	
		Set value		.62

A1140   A1142

1984, May 23
2970	A1140	13s Athlete, doves	.20	.15

6th Republican Spartikiade games,

1984, June 12
2972	A1142	5s Folk singer, drum	.15	.15

6th amateur art festival.

Bulgarian-Soviet Relations, 50th Anniv. — A1143

1984, June 27
2973	A1143	13s Initialed seal	.15	.15

Doves and Pigeons — A1144

1984, July 6   **Litho.**   **Perf. 14**
2974	A1144	5s Rock dove	.15	.15
2975	A1144	13s Stock dove	.20	.15
2976	A1144	20s Wood pigeon	.35	.15
2977	A1144	30s Turtle dove	.48	.20
2978	A1144	42s Domestic pigeon	.70	.28
		Nos. 2974-2978 (5)	1.88	
		Set value		.74

1st Natl. Communist Party Congress, 60th Anniv. — A1145

1984, May 18   **Photo.**   **Perf. 13 1/2x13**
2979	A1145	5s multicolored	.15	.15

Souvenir Sheet

59655

Intl. Stamp Exhibition, Essen, May 26-31 — A1146

Europa Conference stamps: No. 2980a, 1980. No. 2980b, 1981.

1984, May 22   **Perf. 13x13 1/2**
2980	A1146	Sheet of 2	12.00	10.00
a.-b.		1.50 1 multi	6.00	5.00

Mount Everest — A1147

1984, May 31   **Perf. 13**
2981	A1147	5s multicolored	.15	.15

1st Bulgarian Everest climbing expedition, Apr. 20-May 9.

Souvenir Sheet

23766

UPU Congress, Hamburg — A1148

1984, June 11   **Perf. 13 1/2x13**
2982	A1148	3 l Sailing ship	12.00	10.00

Locomotives Type of 1983

1984, July 31   **Perf. 13**
2983	A1125	13s Best Friend of Charleston, 1830, US	.24	.15
2984	A1125	25s Saxonia, 1836, Dresden	.42	.25
2985	A1125	30s Lafayette, 1837, US	.52	.30
2986	A1125	42s Borsig, 1841, Germany	.75	.42
2987	A1125	60s Philadelphia, 1843, Austria	1.10	.65
		Nos. 2983-2987 (5)	3.03	1.77

September 9 Revolution, 40th Anniv. — A1149

1984, Aug. 4
2988	A1149	5s K, production quality emblem	.15	.15
2989	A1149	20s Victory Monument, Sofia	.35	.20
2990	A1149	30s Star, "9"	.55	.30
		Nos. 2988-2990 (3)	1.05	
		Set value		.55

Paintings by Nenko Balkanski (1907-1977) — A1150

1984, Sept. 17   **Perf. 14**
2991	A1150	5s Boy Playing Harmonica, vert.	.15	.15
2992	A1150	30s A Paris Window, vert.	.55	.30
2993	A1150	42s Double Portrait	.80	.42
		Nos. 2991-2993 (3)	1.50	.87

Souvenir Sheet
2994	A1150	1 l Self-portrait, vert.	1.75	1.25

MLADPOST '84 International Youth Stamp Exhibition, Pleven — A1151

Buildings in Pleven: 5s, Mausoleum to Russian soldiers, 1877-78 Russo-Turkish War. 13s, Panorama Building.

1984, Sept. 20 — Perf. 13

2995 A1151 5s multicolored .15 .15
2996 A1151 13s multicolored .28 .15
  Set value .19

Septembrist Young Pioneers Org., 40th Anniv. A1152

1984, Sept. 21 — Photo. Perf. 13

2997 A1152 5s multicolored .15 .15

Nikola Vapzarov A1153

1984, Oct. 2

2998 A1153 5s maroon & pale yel .15 .15

Natl. Soccer, 75th Anniv. A1154

1984, Oct. 3

2999 A1154 42s multicolored .75 .42

Souvenir Sheet

MLADPOST '84 — A1155

1984, Oct. 5 — Photo. Perf. 13

3000 A1155 50s multicolored 1.00 .50

Bridges and Maps — A1156

1984, Oct. 5 — Photo. Perf. 13½x13

3001 A1156 5s Devil's Bridge, Arda River .15 .15
3002 A1156 13s Koljo-Fitscheto, Bjala .28 .15
3003 A1156 30s Asparuchow, Warna .65 .32
3004 A1156 42s Bebresch Highway Bridge, Botevgrad .90 .45
  Nos. 3001-3004 (4) 1.98 1.07

Intl. Olympic Committee, 90th Anniv. A1158

1984, Oct. 24 — Photo. Perf. 13

3007 A1158 13s multicolored .25 .15

A1159   A1160

Pelecanus crispus.

1984, Nov. 2

3008 A1159 5s Adult, young .15 .15
3009 A1159 13s Two adults .28 .15
3010 A1159 20s Adult in water .40 .20
3011 A1159 32s In flight .65 .32
  Nos. 3008-3011 (4) 1.48 .82

World Wildlife Fund.

1984, Nov. 2

3012 A1160 5s multicolored .15 .15

Anton Ivanov (1884-1942), labor leader.

Women's Socialist Movement, 70th Anniv. — A1161

1984, Nov. 9

3013 A1161 5s multicolored .15 .15

Telecommunication Towers — A1162

1984, Nov. 23

3014 A1162 5s Snezhanka .15 .15
3015 A1162 1 l Orelek 1.90 1.00

Snowflakes, New Year 1985 — A1163

1984, Dec. 5

3016 A1163 5s Doves, posthorns .15 .15
3017 A1163 13s Doves, blossom .22 .15
  Set value .30 .20

Paintings by Stoyan Venev (b. 1904) — A1164

1984, Dec. 10 — Litho.

3018 A1164 5s September Nights .15 .15
3019 A1164 30s Man with Three Medals .48 .30
3020 A1164 42s The Best .70 .42
  Nos. 3018-3020 (3) 1.33 .87

Butterflies A1165

1984, Dec. 14 — Perf. 11½

3021 A1165 13s Inachis io .25 .15
3022 A1165 25s Papilio machaon .42 .25
3023 A1165 30s Brintesia circe .52 .30
3024 A1165 42s Anthocaris cardamines .75 .42
3025 A1165 60s Vanessa atalanta 1.00 .60
  Nos. 3021-3025 (5) 2.94 1.72

Souvenir Sheet

3026 A1165 1 l Limenitis populi 2.00 1.00

A1166   A1167

1984, Dec. 18 — Photo. Perf. 13x13½

3027 A1166 13s multicolored .25 .15

Cesar Augusto Sandino (1895-1934), Nicaraguan freedom fighter.

1984, Dec. 28 — Litho. Perf. 14

3028 A1167 5s The Three Graces .15 .15
3029 A1167 13s Cupid and the Graces .28 .15
3030 A1167 30s Original Sin .55 .30
3031 A1167 42s La Fornarina .80 .42
  Nos. 3028-3031 (4) 1.78 1.02

Souvenir Sheet

3032 A1167 1 l Galatea 2.00 1.00

Raphael, 500th birth anniv. (1983).

Cruise Ship Sofia, Maiden Voyage — A1168

1984, Dec. 29 — Photo. Perf. 13

3033 A1168 13s blue, dk bl & yel .25 .15

Predators A1170

1985, Jan. 17

3035 A1170 13s Conepatus leuconotus .25 .15
3036 A1170 25s Prionodon linsang .42 .25
3037 A1170 30s Ictonix striatus .52 .30
3038 A1170 42s Hemigalus derbyanus .75 .42
3039 A1170 60s Galidictis fasciata 1.00 .60
  Nos. 3035-3039 (5) 2.94 1.72

Nikolai Liliev (1885-1960), Poet, UNESCO Emblem — A1171

1985, Jan. 25

3040 A1171 30s multicolored .50 .30

Zviatko Radojnov (1895-1942), Labor Leader — A1172

1985, Jan. 29

3041 A1172 5s dk red & dk brn .15 .15

Dr. Assen Zlatarov (1885-1936), Chemist — A1173

1985, Feb. 14

3042 A1173 5s multicolored .15 .15

Souvenir Sheet

Akademik, Research Vessel — A1174

1985, Mar. 1

3043 A1174 80s multicolored 1.25 .80

UNESCO Intl. Oceanographic Commission, 25th anniv.

Souvenir Sheet

Lenin — A1175

1985, Mar. 12
3044 A1175 50s multicolored .85 .50

A1176

A1177

1985, Mar. 19
3045 A1176 13s multicolored .25 .15
Warsaw Treaty Org., 30th anniv.

1985, Mar. 25
Composers.
3046 A1177 42s Bach .75 .42
3047 A1177 42s Mozart .75 .42
3048 A1177 42s Tchaikovsky .75 .42
3049 A1177 42s Mussorgsky .75 .42
3050 A1177 42s Verdi .75 .42
3051 A1177 42s Tenev .75 .42
Nos. 3046-3051 (6) 4.50 2.52

Children's Drawings Type of 1982
Inscribed 1985. Various children's drawings.

1985, Mar. 26 Litho. Perf. 14
3052 A1093 5s multicolored .15 .15
3053 A1093 8s multicolored .15 .15
3054 A1093 13s multicolored .24 .15
3055 A1093 20s multicolored .35 .20
3056 A1093 25s multicolored .42 .25
3057 A1093 30s multicolored .52 .30
Nos. 3052-3057 (6) 1.83 1.20

Souvenir Sheet
3058 A1093 50s Children dancing, vert. 1.00 .50

3rd Flag of Peace Intl. Assembly, Sofia. No. 3058 exists imperf. with blue control number, same value.

St. Methodius, 1100th Death Anniv. — A1179

1985, Apr. 6 Photo. Perf. 13
3059 A1179 13s multicolored .25 .15

Victory Parade, Moscow, 1945 A1180

13s, 11th Infantry on parade, Sofia. 30s, Soviet soldier, orphan. 50s, Soviet flag-raising, Berlin.

1985, Apr. 30 Perf. 13½
3060 A1180 5s multicolored .15 .15
3061 A1180 13s multicolored .24 .15
3062 A1180 30s multicolored .52 .30
Nos. 3060-3062 (3) .91
Set value .50

Souvenir Sheet
Perf. 13
3063 A1180 50s multicolored 1.00 .50

Defeat of Nazi Germany, end of World War II, 40th anniv. Nos. 3060-3062 printed se-tenant with labels picturing Soviet (5s, 30s) and Bulgarian medals of honor.

7th Intl. Humor and Satire Biennial A1181

1985, Apr. 30 Perf. 13½
3064 A1181 13s yel, sage grn & red .25 .15
No. 3064 printed se-tenant with label picturing Gabrovo Cat emblem.

Intl. Youth Year — A1182

1985, May 21 Perf. 13
3065 A1182 13s multicolored .25 .15

Ivan Vasov (1850-1921), Poet — A1183

1985, May 30 Perf. 13½
3066 A1183 5s tan & sepia .15 .15
No. 3066 printed se-tenant with label picturing Vasov's birthplace in Sopot.

Soviet War Memorial, Haskovo City Arms A1184

1985, June 1 Perf. 13
3067 A1184 5s multicolored .15 .15
Haskovo millennium.

12th World Youth Festival, Moscow — A1185

1985, June 25
3068 A1185 13s multicolored .25 .15

Indira Gandhi (1917-1984), Prime Minister of India — A1186

1985, June 26
3069 A1186 30s org yel, sepia & ver .60 .30

Vasil Aprilov, Founder — A1187

1985, June 30
3070 A1187 5s multicolored .15 .15
1st secular school, Gabrovo, 150th anniv.

INTERSTENO '85 — A1188

1985, June 30
3071 A1188 13s multicolored .25 .15
Congress for the Intl. Union of Stenographers and Typists, Sofia.

Alexander Nevski Cathedral A1189

1985, July 9
3072 A1189 42s multicolored .80 .42
World Tourism Org., general assembly, Sofia.

UN, 40th Anniv. A1190

1985, July 16
3073 A1190 13s multicolored .25 .15

A1191

Roses — A1192

1985, July 16
3074 A1191 13s multicolored .25 .15
Admission of Bulgaria to UN, 30th anniv.

1985, July 20 Litho.
3075 A1192 5s Rosa damascena .15 .15
3076 A1192 13s Rosa trakijka .24 .15
3077 A1192 20s Rosa radiman .35 .20
3078 A1192 30s Rosa marista .50 .30
3079 A1192 42s Rosa valentina .75 .42
3080 A1192 60s Rosa maria 1.00 .60
a. Min. sheet of 6, #3075-3080 3.50 2.00
Nos. 3075-3080 (6) 2.99 1.82

Helsinki Conference, 10th Anniv. — A1193

1985, Aug. 1 Photo.
3081 A1193 13s multicolored .25 .15

European Swimming Championships, Sofia — A1194

1985, Aug. 2 Litho. Perf. 12½
3082 A1194 5s Butterfly stroke .15 .15
3083 A1194 13s Water polo, vert. .25 .15
3084 A1194 42s Diving, vert. .80 .42
3085 A1194 60s Synchronized swimming 1.10 .50
Nos. 3082-3085 (4) 2.30 1.22

The 60s exists with central design inverted.

Natl. Tourism Assoc., 90th Anniv. A1195

1985, Aug. 15 Photo. Perf. 13
3086 A1195 5s multicolored .15 .15

1986 World Cup Soccer Championships, Mexico — A1196

Various soccer plays. Nos. 3087-3090 vert.

1985, Aug. 29 Perf. 13
3087 A1196 5s multicolored .15 .15
3088 A1196 13s multicolored .28 .15
3089 A1196 30s multicolored .60 .30
3090 A1196 42s multicolored .85 .42
Nos. 3087-3090 (4) 1.88 1.02

Souvenir Sheet
3091 A1196 1 l multicolored 2.00 1.00

Union of Eastern
Rumelia and Bulgaria,
1885 — A1197

1985, Aug. 29   *Perf. 14x13½*
3092 A1197 5s multicolored   .15 .15

Computer Design Portraits — A1198

1985, Sept. 23   *Perf. 13*
3093 A1198 5s Boy   .15 .15
3094 A1198 13s Youth   .24 .15
3095 A1198 30s Cosmonaut   .52 .30
Nos. 3093-3095 (3)   .91
    Set value   .50

Intl. Exhibition of the Works of Youth Inventors, Plovdiv.

St. John the Baptist
Church,
Nessebar — A1199

Natl. restoration projects: 13s, Tyrant Hreljo Tower, Rila Monastery. 35s, Soldier, fresco, Ivanovo Rock Church. 42s, Archangel Gabriel, fresco, Bojana Church. 60s, Thracian Woman, fresco, Tomb of Kasanlak, 3rd century B.C. 1 l, The Horseman of Madara, bas-relief.

1985, Sept. 25   Litho.   Perf. 12½
3096 A1199   5s multicolored   .15 .15
3097 A1199   13s multicolored   .22 .15
3098 A1199   35s multicolored   .60 .32
3099 A1199   42s multicolored   .75 .40
3100 A1199   60s multicolored   1.10 .60
    Nos. 3096-3100 (5)   2.82 1.62

Souvenir Sheet
Imperf
3101 A1199   1 l multicolored   1.75 1.00

UNESCO, 40th anniv.

Souvenir Sheet

Ludmila Zhishkova Cultural Palace,
Sofia — A1200

1985, Oct. 8   *Perf. 13*
3102 A1200   1 l multicolored   1.75 1.00

UNESCO 23rd General Assembly, Sofia.

Colosseum,
Rome
A1201

1985, Oct. 15   Photo.   Perf. 13½
3103 A1201 42s multicolored   .75 .42

ITALIA '85. No. 3103 printed se-tenant with label picturing the exhibition emblem.

Souvenir Sheet

Cultural Congress, Budapest — A1202

Designs: No. 3104a, St. Cyril, patron saint of Europe. No. 3104b, Map of Europe. No. 3104c, St. Methodius, patron saint of Europe.

Perf. 13, 13 Vert. (#3104b)
1985, Oct. 22   Photo.
3104 A1202   Sheet of 3   2.75 1.50
a.-c.   50s, any single   .90 .50

Helsinki Congress, 10th anniv.

Flowers — A1203

1985, Oct. 22   Photo.   Perf. 13x13½
3105 A1203 5s Gladiolus hybridy   .15 .15
3106 A1203 5s Iris germanica   .15 .15
3107 A1203 5s Convolvulus tricolor   .15 .15
    Set value   .25 .15

See Nos. 3184-3186.

Historic
Sailing Ships
A1204

1985, Oct. 28   Photo.   Perf. 13
3108 A1204 5s Dutch   .15 .15
3109 A1204 12s Sea Sovereign, Britain   .22 .15
3110 A1204 20s Mediterranean   .35 .20
3111 A1204 25s Royal Prince, Britain   .45 .25
3112 A1204 42s Mediterranean   .75 .42
3113 A1204 60s British battleship   1.10 .60
    Nos. 3108-3113 (6)   3.02 1.77

Souvenir Sheet

PHILATELIA '85, Cologne — A1205

Designs: a, Cologne Cathedral. b, Alexander Nevski Cathedral, Sofia.

1985, Nov. 4   *Imperf.*
3114 A1205   Sheet of 2   1.25 .65
a.-b.   30s, any single   .60 .30

Conspiracy to
Liberate Bulgaria
from Turkish Rule,
150th
Anniv. — A1206

Freedom fighters and symbols: #3115, Georgi Stojkov Rakowski (1820-76). #3116, Batscho Kiro (1835-76). #3117, Sword, Bible & hands.

1985, Nov. 6   *Perf. 13*
3115 A1206 5s multicolored   .15 .15
3116 A1206 5s multicolored   .15 .15
3117 A1206 13s multicolored   .22 .15
    Set value   .40 .22

Liberation
from
Byzantine
Rule,
800th
Anniv.
A1207

Paintings: 5s, The Revolt 1185, by G. Bogdanov. 13s, The Revolt 1185, by Alexander Tersiev. 30s, Battle Near Klokotnitza, by B. Grigorov and M. Ganowski. 42s, Velika Tarnovo Town Wall, by Zanko Lawrenov. 1 l, St. Dimitriev Church, 12th cent.

1985, Nov. 15   Litho.
3118 A1207   5s multicolored   .15 .15
3119 A1207   13s multicolored   .22 .15
3120 A1207   30s multicolored   .52 .30
3121 A1207   42s multicolored   .75 .42
    Nos. 3118-3121 (4)   1.64 1.02

Souvenir Sheet
Imperf
3122 A1207   1 l multicolored   2.00 1.00

Souvenir Sheet

BALKANPHILA '85 — A1208

1985, Nov. 29   Photo.   Perf. 13
3123 A1208 40s Dove, posthorn   .75 .40

Intl. Post and Telecommunications
Development Program — A1209

1985, Dec. 2
3124 A1209 13s multicolored   .25 .15

Anton Popov (1915-1942), Freedom
Fighter — A1210

1985, Dec. 11   Photo.   Perf. 13
3125 A1210 5s lake   .15 .15

New Year
1986
A1211

1985, Dec. 11   Photo.   Perf. 1.
3126 A1211 5s Doves, snowflake   .15 .15
3127 A1211 13s Doves   .22 .15
    Set value   .30 .19

Hunting Dogs and Prey — A1212

Designs: 5s, Pointer and partridge. 8s, Irish setter and pochard. 13s, English setter and mallard 20s, Cocker spaniel and woodcock. 25s, German pointer and rabbit. 30s, Balkan hound and boar 42s, Shorthaired dachshund and fox.

1985, Dec. 27   Litho.   Perf. 13x12½
3128 A1212 5s multicolored   .15 .15
3129 A1212 8s multicolored   .16 .15
3130 A1212 13s multicolored   .28 .15
3131 A1212 20s multicolored   .40 .20
3132 A1212 25s multicolored   .50 .25

3133 A1212 30s multicolored .60 .30
3134 A1212 42s multicolored .85 .42
Nos. 3128-3134 (7) 2.94 1.62

Intl. Year of the Handicapped — A1213

1985, Dec. 30 Photo. *Perf. 13*
3135 A1213 5s multicolored .15 .15

George Dimitrov (1882-1949) — A1214

1985, Dec. 30 Photo. *Perf. 13*
3136 A1214 13s brn lake .25 .15
7th Intl. Communist Congress, Moscow.

UN Child Survival Campaign — A1215

1986, Jan. 21 Photo. *Perf. 13*
3137 A1215 13s multicolored .25 .15
UNICEF, 40th anniv.

Demeter Blagoev
(1856-1924) — A1216

1986, Jan. 28 Photo. *Perf. 13*
3138 A1216 5s dk lake, car & dk red .15 .15

Intl. Peace
Year — A1217

1986, Jan. 31 *Perf. 13½*
3139 A1217 5s multicolored .15 .15

Orchids — A1218

1986, Feb. 12 Litho. *Perf. 13x12½*
3140 A1218 5s Dactylorhiza
romana .15 .15
3141 A1218 13s Epipactis palustris .25 .15
3142 A1218 30s Ophrys cornuta .60 .30
3143 A1218 32s Limodorum abor-
tivum .60 .32

3144 A1218 42s Cypripedium calceolus .85 .42
3145 A1218 60s Orchis papilionacea 1.25 .60
a. Min. sheet of 6, #3140-3145 4.00 2.00
Nos. 3140-3145 (6) 3.70 1.94

Hares and
Rabbits
A1219

1986, Feb. 24 *Perf. 12½x12*
3146 A1219 5s multicolored .15 .15
3147 A1219 25s multicolored .45 .25
3148 A1219 30s multicolored .55 .30
3149 A1219 32s multicolored .60 .32
3150 A1219 42s multicolored .75 .42
3151 A1219 60s multicolored 1.00 .60
Nos. 3146-3151 (6) 3.50 2.04

Bulgarian Eagle, Newspaper, 140th
Anniv. — A1220

Design: Front page of first issue and Ivan
Bogorov, journalist.

1986, Feb. 2 Photo. *Perf. 13*
3152 A1220 5s multicolored .15 .15

Souvenir Sheet

Halley's
Comet
A1221

Comet's orbit in the Solar System: a, 1980. b,
1910-86. c, 1916-70. d, 1911.

1986, Mar. 7 *Perf. 13½x13*
3153 Sheet of 4 1.75 1.25
a.-d. A1221 25s, any single .42 .30

A1222

A1223

1986, Mar. 12 *Perf. 13x13½*
3154 A1222 5s dp bl & bl .15 .15
Vladimir Bachev (1935-1967), poet.

1986, Mar. 17 *Perf. 13*
3155 A1223 5s Wavy lines .15 .15
3156 A1223 8s Star .15 .15
3157 A1223 13s Worker .24 .15
Set value .45 .27

Souvenir Sheet
Imperf
3158 A1223 50s Scaffold, flags .90 .50
13th Natl. Communist Party Congress.

Souvenir Sheet

1st Manned Space Flight, 25th
Anniv. — A1224

Designs: a, Vostok I, 1961. b, Yuri Gagarin
(1934-68), Russian cosmonaut.

1986, Mar. 28 *Perf. 13½x13*
3159 Sheet of 2 1.75 1.00
a.-b. A1224 50s, any single 1.00 .50

April Uprising against
the Turks, 110th
Anniv. — A1225

Monuments: 5s, 1876 Uprising monument,
Panagjuriste. 13s, Christo Botev, Vraca.

1986, Mar. 30 *Perf. 13*
3160 A1225 5s multicolored .15 .15
3161 A1225 13s multicolored .26 .15
Set value .20

A1225a

Levsky-Spartak Sports Club, 75th
Anniv. — A1226

1986 *Perf. 13*
3161A A1225a 5s multicolored .15 .15
Souvenir Sheet
Imperf
3162 A1226 50s Rhythmic gymnastics .80 .50
Issue dates: 5s, Dec. 50s, May 12.

A1227

A1228

1986, May 19 *Perf. 13*
3163 A1227 5s Congress emblem .15 .15
3164 A1227 8s Emblem on globe .15 .15
3165 A1227 13s Flags .24 .15
Set value .45 .27
35th Congress of Bulgarian farmers, Sofia.

1986, May 27 *Perf. 13x13½*
3166 A1228 13s multicolored .25 .15
Conference of Transport Ministers from Socialist
Countries.

17th Intl. Book
Fair,
Sofia — A1229

1986, May 28
3167 A1229 13s blk, brt red & grysh
blk .25 .15

1986 World Cup Soccer Championships,
Mexico — A1230

Various soccer plays; attached labels picture Mexican landmarks.

1986, May 30 *Perf. 13½*
3168 A1230 5s multi, vert. .15 .15
3169 A1230 13s multicolored .25 .15
3170 A1230 20s multicolored .35 .20
3171 A1230 30s multicolored .55 .30
3172 A1230 42s multicolored .75 .42
3173 A1230 60s multi, vert. 1.10 .60
Nos. 3168-3173 (6) 3.15 1.82

Souvenir Sheet
Perf. 13
3174 A1230 1 l Azteca Stadium 1.75 1.00

Treasures of Preslav — A1231

Gold artifacts: 5s, Embossed brooch. 13s, Pendant with pearl cross, vert. 20s, Crystal and pearl
pendant. 30s, Embossed shield. 42s, Pearl and
enamel pendant, vert. 60s, Enamel shield.

1986, June 7 *Perf. 13½x13, 13x13½*
3175 A1231 5s multicolored .15 .15
3176 A1231 13s multicolored .25 .15
3177 A1231 20s multicolored .35 .20
3178 A1231 30s multicolored .55 .30
3179 A1231 42s multicolored .75 .42
3180 A1231 60s multicolored 1.00 .60
Nos. 3175-3180 (6) 3.05 1.82

World Fencing Championships, Sofia, July
25-Aug. 3 — A1232

1986, July 25 Photo. *Perf. 13*
3181 A1232 5s Head cut, lunge .15 .15
3182 A1232 13s Touche .25 .15
3183 A1232 25s Lunge, parry .45 .25
Nos. 3181-3183 (3) .85
Set value .44

Flower Type of 1985

1986, July 29 *Perf. 13x13½*
3184 A1203 8s Ipomoea tricolor .15 .15
3185 A1203 13s Anemone coronaria .25 .15
3186 A1203 32s Lilium auratum .55 .32
Nos. 3184-3186 (3) .85
Set value .48

A1233   A1234

1986, Aug. 25
3187 A1233 42s sepia, sal brn & lake   .75 .42
STOCKHOLMIA '86. No. 3187 printed in sheets of 3 + 3 labels picturing folk art.

Miniature Sheet

Environmental Conservation: a, Ciconia ciconia. b, Nuphar lutea. c, Salamandra salamandra. d, Nymphaea alba.

1986, Aug. 25   Litho.   Perf. 14
3188   Sheet of 4 + label   2.00 .90
a.-d. A1234 30s any single   .50 .22
No. 3188 contains center label picturing the oldest oak tree in Bulgaria, Granit Village.

Natl. Arms, Building of the Sobranie — A1235

1986, Sept. 13   Photo.   Perf. 13
3189 A1235 5s Prus grn, yel grn & red   .15 .15
People's Republic of Bulgaria, 40th anniv.

15th Postal Union Congress — A1236

1986, Sept. 24
3190 A1236 13s multicolored   .25 .15

Natl. Youth Brigade Movement, 40th Anniv. A1237 / Intl. Organization of Journalists, 10th Congress A1238

1986, Oct. 4
3191 A1237 5s multicolored   .15 .15

1986, Oct. 13
3192 A1238 13s blue & dark blue   .25 .15

Sts. Cyril and Methodius, Disciples A1239

1986, Oct. 23   Perf. 13½
3193 A1239 13s dark brown & buff   .25 .15
Sts. Cyril and Methodius in Bulgaria, 1100th anniv. No. 3193 se-tenant with inscribed label.

Telephones in Bulgaria, Cent. A1240

1986, Nov. 5   Perf. 13
3194 A1240 5s multicolored   .15 .15

World Weight Lifting Championships — A1241

1986, Nov. 6
3195 A1241 13s multicolored   .25 .15

Ships A1242

1986, Nov. 20
3196 A1242 5s King of Prussia   .15 .15
3197 A1242 13s East Indiaman, 18th cent. .25 .15
3198 A1242 25s Shebek, 18th cent.   .45 .25
3199 A1242 30s St Paul   .55 .30
3200 A1242 32s Topsail schooner, 18th cent. .60 .32
3201 A1242 42s Victory   .80 .42
Nos. 3196-3201 (6)   2.80 1.59

Souvenir Sheet

European Security and Cooperation Congress, Vienna — A1243

Various buildings and emblems: a, Bulgaria. b, Austria. c, Donau Park, UN.

Perf. 13, Imperf. x13 (#3202b)
1986, Nov. 27
3202   Sheet of 3   3.00 1.50
a.-c. A1243 50s any single   1.00 .50
Exists imperf. bearing control number.

Rogozen Thracian Pitchers A1244

1986, Dec. 5   Perf. 13
3203 A1244 10s Facing left   .18 .15
3204 A1244 10s Facing right   .18 .15
Set value   .20
Union of Bulgarian Philatelists, 14th Congress. Nos. 3203-3204 printed se-tenant with labels picturing carved figures on pitchers in blocks of 4.

New Year 1987 A1245

1986, Dec. 9
3205 A1245 5s shown   .15 .15
3206 A1245 13s Snow flakes   .26 .15
Set value   .19

Home Amateur Radio Operators in Bulgaria, 60th Anniv. — A1246

1986, Dec. 10
3207 A1246 13s multicolored   .25 .15

Miniature Sheet

Paintings by Bulgarian Artists — A1247

Designs: a, Red Tree, by Danail Dechev (1891-1962). b, Troopers Confront Two Men, by Ilya Beshkov (1901-58). c, View of Melnik, by Veselin Stajkov (1906-70). d, View of Houses through Trees, by Kyril Zonev (1896-1961).

1986, Dec. 10   Litho.   Perf. 14
3208   Sheet of 4   2.25 1.10
a.-b. A1247 25s any single   .50 .25
c.-d. A1247 30s any single   .60 .30
Sofia Academy of Art, 90th anniv.

Augusto Cesar Sandino (1893-1934), Nicaraguan Revolutionary, and Flag — A1248

1986, Dec. 16   Photo.   Perf. 13
3209 A1248 13s multicolored   .25 .15
Sandinista movement in Nicaragua, 25th anniv.

Smoyan Mihylovsky (b. 1856), Writer — A1249

Ran Bossilek (b. 1886) — A1250 / Title Page from Bulgarian Folk Songs of the Miladinov Brothers — A1251

Annivs. and events: No. 3211, Pentcho Slaveyckov (b. 1861), writer. No. 3212, Nickola Atanassov (b. 1886), musician.

1986, Dec. 17
3210 A1249 5s multicolored   .15 .15
3211 A1249 5s multicolored   .15 .15
3212 A1249 8s multicolored   .16 .15
3213 A1250 8s multicolored   .16 .15
3214 A1251 10s multicolored   .20 .15
Nos. 3210-3214 (5)   .82
Set value   .36

A1252

Paintings by Titian — A1253

Various portraits.

1986, Dec. 23   Litho.   Perf. 14
3215 A1252 5s multicolored   .15 .15
3216 A1252 13s multicolored   .28 .15
3217 A1252 20s multicolored   .40 .20
3218 A1252 30s multicolored   .60 .30
3219 A1252 32s multicolored   .65 .32
3220 A1252 42s multicolored   .85 .42
a.   Min. sheet of 6, #3215-3220   3.00 1.50
Nos. 3215-3220 (6)   2.93 1.54

Souvenir Sheet

3221 A1253 1 l multicolored   2.25 1.00

Rayko Daskalov (b. 1886), Politician A1254

1986, Dec. 23   Photo.   Perf. 13
3222 A1254 5s deep claret   .15 .15

Sports Cars — A1255

1986, Dec. 30   Litho.   Perf. 13½
3223 A1255 5s 1905 Fiat   .15 .15
3224 A1255 10s 1928 Bugatti   .18 .15
3225 A1255 25s 1936 Mercedes   .45 .25
3226 A1255 32s 1952 Ferrari   .55 .32
3227 A1255 40s 1985 Lotus   .70 .40
3228 A1255 42s 1986 McLaren   .75 .42
    Nos. 3223-3228 (6)   2.78 1.69

Varna Railway Inauguration, 120th
Anniv. — A1257

1987, Jan. 19   Photo.
3229 A1257 5s multicolored   .15 .15

Dimcho Debelianov (1887-1916),
Poet — A1258

1987, Jan. 20   Photo.   Perf. 13
3230 A1258 5s blue, dull yel & dp blue .15 .15

L.L.
Zamenhof,
Creator of
Esperanto
A1259

1987, Feb. 12
3231 A1259 13s multicolored   .15 .15

Mushrooms
A1260

10th Natl. Trade
Unions Congress
A1261

1987, Feb. 6   Litho.   Perf. 11½
3232 A1260 5s Amanita rubescens .15 .15
3233 A1260 20s Boletus regius   .50 .30
3234 A1260 30s Leccinum auran-
                tiacum   .70 .45
3235 A1260 32s Coprinus comatus .75 .48
3236 A1260 40s Russula vesca   1.00 .60
3237 A1260 60s Cantharellus cibari-
                us   1.40 .90
  a. Min. sheet of 6, #3232-3237 5.25
    Nos. 3232-3237 (6)   4.50 2.88

1987, Mar. 20   Photo.   Perf. 13
3238 A1261 5s dark red & violet .15 .15

Rogozen
Thracian
Treasure
A1262

Embossed and gilded silver artifacts: 5s, Plate, Priestess Auge approaching Heracles. 8s, Pitcher, lioness attacking stag. 20s, Plate, floral pattern. 30s, Pitcher, warriors on horseback dueling. 32s, Urn, decorative pattern. 42s, Pitcher (not gilded), winged horses.

1987, Mar. 31
3239 A1262 5s multicolored   .15 .15
3240 A1262 8s multicolored   .20 .15
3241 A1262 20s multicolored   .48 .30
3242 A1262 30s multicolored   .70 .45
3243 A1262 32s multicolored   .75 .48
3244 A1262 42s multicolored   1.00 .62
    Nos. 3239-3244 (6)   3.28 2.15

Miniature Sheet

Modern Architecture — A1263

Designs: a, Ludmila Zhivkova conf. center, Varna. b, Ministry of Foreign Affairs, Sofia. c, Interpred Building, Sofia. d, Hotel, Sandanski.

1987, Apr. 7   Perf. 13½x13
3245   Sheet of 4   3.00 1.80
  a.-d. A1263 30s any single .75 .45

Exists imperf. with black control number.

European Freestyle
Wrestling
Championships
A1264

1987, Apr. 22   Perf. 13
3246 A1264 5s multicolored   .15 .15
3247 A1264 13s multi, diff.   .38 .18

CAPEX '87,
Toronto
A1265

1987, Apr. 24
3248 A1265 42s multicolored   1.00 .42

10th Congress of
the Natl. Front — A1266

1987, May 11
3249 A1266 5s multicolored   .15 .15

15th
Communist
Youth
Congress
A1267

1987, May 13
3250 A1267 5s George Dimitrov   .15 .15

8th Intl. Humor and
Satire Biennial,
Gabrovo — A1268

1987, May 15   Perf. 13x13½
3251 A1268 13s multicolored   .35 .15

13th World Rhythmic
Gymnastics
Championships,
Varna — A1269

Gymnasts.

1987, Aug. 5   Photo.   Perf. 13
3252 A1269 5s Maria Gigova   .15 .15
3252A A1269 8s Iliana Raeva   .18 .15
3252B A1269 13s Anelia Ralenkova .28 .16
3252C A1269 25s Pilyana Georgieva .55 .32
3252D A1269 30s Lilia Ignatova   .65 .38
3252E A1269 42s Bianca Panova   .90 .52
    Nos. 3252-3252E (6)   2.71 1.68

Souvenir Sheet
Perf. 13x13½
3252F A1269 1 l Neshka Robeva,
               coach   2.25 1.50

Exists imperf. with black control number.

Vassil Kolarov — A1270

1987, June 3   Perf. 13
3253 A1270 5s dk red, yel & dk bl .15 .15

Stela Blagoeva (b.
1887) — A1271

1987, June 4
3254 A1271 5s pink & sepia   .15 .15

Rabotnichesko Delo Newspaper, 60th
Anniv. — A1272

1987, May 28
3255 A1272 5s black & lake   .15 .15

Deer
A1273

1987, June 23   Litho.
3256 A1273 5s Capreolus capreolus,
              vert.   .15 .15
3257 A1273 10s Alces alces   .25 .15
3258 A1273 32s Dama dama, vert. .75 .25
3259 A1273 40s Cervus nippon, vert. 1.10 .30
3260 A1273 42s Cervus elaphus   1.10 .32
3261 A1273 60s Rangifer tarandus,
              vert.   1.40 .45
  a. Min. sheet of 6, #3256-3261, im-
         perf.   5.50 2.85
    Nos. 3256-3261 (6)   4.75 1.62

Vassil Levski
(1837-73)
A1274

Various portraits.

1987, June 19   Photo.
3262 A1274 5s red brn & dark grn .15 .15
3263 A1274 13s dark grn & red brn .35 .20
    Set value   .26

Namibia
Day
A1275

1987, July 8
3264 A1275 13s org, blk & dark red .30 .20

Georgi Kirkov (1867-
1919), Revolutionary
A1276

1987, July 17   Perf. 13x13½
3265 A1276 5s claret & deep claret .15 .15

Bees and Plants — A1277

1987, July 29   Litho.   Perf. 13

3266	A1277	5s	Phacelia tanacetifolia	.15	.15
3267	A1277	10s	Helianthus annuus	.25	.15
3268	A1277	30s	Robinia pseudoacacia	.75	.45
3269	A1277	32s	Lavandula vera	.80	.48
3270	A1277	42s	Tilia parvifolia	1.10	.62
3271	A1277	60s	Onobrychis sativa	1.50	.90
a.			Min. sheet of 6, #3266-3271	5.00	2.75
			Nos. 3266-3271 (6)	4.55	2.75

BULGARIA '89 — A1278

1987, Sept. 3   Perf. 13½x13
3272	A1278	13s No. 1	.40	.20

HAFNIA '87 — A1279

1987, Sept. 8   Perf. 13
3273	A1279	42s multicolored	1.00	.62

No. 3273 issued in sheets of 3 plus 2 labels picturing emblems of the HAFNIA '87 and BULGARIA '89 exhibitions, and 1 label with background similar to Denmark Type A32 with castle instead of denomination.

Portrait of a Girl, by Stefan Ivanov — A1280

Paintings in the Sofia City Art Galler: 8s, Grapegatherer, by Bencho Obreshkov. 20s, Portrait of a Lady with a Hat, by David Perets. 25s, Listeners of Marimba, by Kiril Tsonev. 32s, Boy with an Harmonica, by Nenko Balkanski. 60s, Rumyana, by Vasil Stoilov.

1987, Sept. 15   Litho.   Perf. 14

3274	A1280	5s shown	.15	.15
3275	A1280	8s multicolored	.22	.15
3276	A1280	20s multicolored	.52	.30
3277	A1280	25s multicolored	.65	.38
3278	A1280	32s multicolored	.85	.48
3279	A1280	60s multicolored	1.50	.90
		Nos. 3274-3279 (6)	3.89	2.36

Intl. Atomic Energy Agency, 30th Anniv. A1281

1987, Sept. 15   Photo.   Perf. 13½x13
3280	A1281	13s red, lt blue & emer	.35	.20

Songbirds A1282

1987, Oct. 12   Litho.   Perf. 12½x12

3281	A1282	5s	Troglodytes troglodytes	.15	.15
3282	A1282	13s	Emberiza citrinella	.35	.16
3283	A1282	20s	Sitta europaea	.55	.25
3284	A1282	30s	Turdus merula	.80	.35
3285	A1282	42s	Coccothraustes coccothraustes	1.10	.50
3286	A1282	60s	Cinclus cinclus	1.50	.75
a.			Min. sheet of 6, #3281-3286	5.00	2.25
			Nos. 3281-3286 (6)	4.45	2.16

Balkan War, 75th Anniv. A1283

1987, Sept. 15   Perf. 13½
3287	A1283	5s buff, blk & brt org	.15	.15

Newspaper Anniversaries — A1283a

1987, Sept. 24   Photo.   Perf. 13
3287A	A1283a	5s multicolored	.15	.15

Rabotnik, 95th anniv., Rabotnicheski Vstnik, 90th anniv. and Rabotnichesko Delo, 60th anniv.

October Revolution, Russia, 70th Anniv. A1284

Lenin and: 5s, Revolutionary. 13s, Cosmonaut.

1987, Oct. 27   Photo.   Perf. 13
3288	A1284	5s rose brn & red org	.15	.15
3289	A1284	13s brt ultra & red org	.35	.20
		Set value		.26

1988 Winter Olympics, Calgary — A1285

1987, Oct. 27   Litho.   Perf. 13x13½
3290	A1285	5s	Biathlon	.15	.15
3291	A1285	13s	Slalom	.38	.20
3292	A1285	30s	Women's figure skating	.85	.45
3293	A1285	42s	4-Man bobsled	1.10	.62
			Nos. 3290-3293 (4)	2.48	1.42

Souvenir Sheet
3294	A1285	1 1 Ice hockey	2.75	1.50

No. 3294 exists imperf.

Souvenir Sheet

Soviet Space Achievements, 1937-87 — A1286

Designs: No. 3295a, Vega probe. No. 3295b, Mir-Soyuz Space Station.

1987, Dec. 24   Photo.   Perf. 13½x13
3295	A1286	Sheet of 2	2.75	1.50
a.-b.		50s any single	1.25	.75

Exists imperf.

New Year 1988 A1287

Sofia stamp exhibition emblem within folklore patterns.

1987, Dec. 25   Perf. 13
3296	A1287	5s multicolored	.15	.15
3297	A1287	13s multi, diff.	.35	.20
		Set value		.26

Souvenir Sheet

European Security Conferences A1288

Conferences held in Helsinki, 1973, and Vienna, 1987: a, Helsinki Conf. Center. b, Map of Europe. c, Vienna Conf. Center.

Perf. 13x13½ on 2 or 4 Sides
1987, Dec. 30
3298	Sheet of 3	4.00	3.00
a.-c.	A1288 50s any single	1.50	.75

Exists imperf.

Christo Kabaktchiev A1289   A1290

1988, Jan. 20
3299	A1289	5s multicolored	.15	.15

Christo Kabaktchiev (b. 1878), party leader.

1988, Jan. 25   Litho.   Perf. 12

Marine flowers.

3300	A1290	5s	Scilla bythynica	.15	.15
3301	A1290	10s	Geum rhodopaeum	.24	.15
3302	A1290	13s	Caltha polypetala	.32	.20
3303	A1290	25s	Nymphoides peltata	.60	.38
3304	A1290	30s	Cortusa matthioli	.75	.45
3305	A1290	42s	Stratiotes aloides	1.00	.62
a.			Min. sheet of 6, #3300-3305	3.50	2.00
			Nos. 3300-3305 (6)	3.06	1.95

Liberation of Bulgaria, 110th Anniv. A1291

1988, Feb. 15   Photo.   Perf. 13
3306	A1291	5s Officer, horse	.15	.15
3307	A1291	13s Soldiers	.35	.20
		Set value		.26

8th Intl. Civil Servants Congress, Sofia A1292

1988, Mar. 22   Photo.   Perf. 13
3308	A1292	13s multicolored	.30	.16

State Railways, Cent. — A1293

Locomotives: 5s, Jantra, 1888. 13s, Christo Botev, 1905. 25s, 0-10-1, 1918. 32s, 4-12-1 heavy duty, 1943. 42s, Diesel, 1964. 60s, Electric, 1979.

1988, Mar. 25   Litho.   Perf. 11
3309	A1293	5s multicolored	.15	.15
3310	A1293	13s multicolored	.28	.16
3311	A1293	25s multicolored	.52	.30
3312	A1293	32s multicolored	.70	.40
3313	A1293	42s multicolored	.95	.52
3314	A1293	60s multicolored	1.25	.72
a.		Min. sheet of 6, #3309-3314	4.00	2.50
		Nos. 3309-3314 (6)	3.85	2.25

Ivan Nedyalkov (1880-1925) A1294

Postal workers, heroes of socialism: 8s, Delcho Spasov (1918-43). 10s, Nikola Ganchev (1915-43). 13s, Ganka Stoyanova Rasheva (1921-44).

1988, Mar. 31   Photo.   Perf. 13½x13
3315	A1294	5s buff & dark rose brn	.15	.15
3316	A1294	8s pale ultra & violet blue	.16	.15
3317	A1294	10s pale olive grn & olive grn	.22	.15
3318	A1294	13s pale pink & lake	.26	.16
		Nos. 3315-3318 (4)		
		Set value		.44

1898-1988
ГЕОРГИ ТРАЙКОВ
Georgi Traikov (b.
1898), Statesman
A1295

Intl. Red Cross and
Red Crescent
Organizations,
125th Anniv.
A1296

1988, Apr. 8   Litho.   Perf. 13x13½
3319 A1295 5s orange & brn   .15 .15

1988, Apr. 26   Photo.   Perf. 13
3320 A1296 13s multicolored   .25 .16

Children's Drawings Type of 1982

Designs: 5s, Girl wearing a folk costume, vert.
8s, Painter at easel, vert. 13s, Children playing.
20s, Ringing bells for peace. 32s, Accordion player,
vert. 42s, Cosmonaut, vert. 50s, Assembly emblem.

1988, Apr. 28   Litho.   Perf. 14
3321 A1093 5s multicolored   .15 .15
3322 A1093 8s multicolored   .18 .15
3323 A1093 13s multicolored   .28 .16
3324 A1093 20s multicolored   .42 .25
3325 A1093 32s multicolored   .65 .40
3326 A1093 42s multicolored   .90 .52
    Nos. 3321-3326 (6)   2.58 1.63

Souvenir Sheet

3327 A1093 50s multicolored   1.00 .62

4th Intl. Children's Assembly, Sofia. No. 3327
exists imperf.

Karl Marx
A1297

1988, May 5   Perf. 13
3328 A1297 13s multicolored   .30 .16

ПОЩА 87   Birds — A1297a

1988, May 6   Litho.   Perf. 13x13½
3328A A1297a 5s Ciconia ciconia   .15 .15
3328B A1297a 5s Larus argentatus .15 .15
3328C A1297a 8s Ardea cinerea   .18 .15
3328D A1297a 8s Corvus corone
                cornix   .18 .15
3328E A1297a 10s Accipiter gentil-
                 lis   .22 .15
3328F A1297a 42s Bubo bubo   .90 .50
     Nos. 3328A-3328F (6)   1.78
     Set value   .94

Dated 1987.

Sofia Zoo,
Cent.
A1298

1988, May 20
3329 A1298 5s Loxodonta africana   .15 .15
3330 A1298 13s Ceratotherium
               simum   .25 .16
3331 A1298 25s Lycaon pictus   .50 .30
3332 A1298 30s Pelecanus onocrota-
               lus   .65 .36
3333 A1298 32s Bucorvus abissinicus .70 .40
3334 A1298 42s Nyctea scandiaca   .90 .52
   a. Min. sheet of 6, #3329-3334 3.60 1.80
     Nos. 3329-3334 (6)   3.15 1.89

FINLANDIA '88 — A1299

1988, June 7
3335 A1299 30s Finland No. 1   .70 .35

No. 3335 printed in miniature sheets of 3 plus 3
labels picturing skyline, SOFIA '89 and FINLANDIA
'88 exhibition emblems.
Exists imperf.

2nd Joint USSR-
Bulgaria Space
Flight — A1300

1988, June 7
3336 A1300 5s shown   .15 .15
3337 A1300 13s Rocket, globe   .30 .16
     Set value   .22

EXPO '91, Plovdiv — A1301

1988, June 7   Perf. 13½x13
3338 A1301 13s multicolored   .30 .16

1988 European Soccer
Championships — A1302

1988, June 10   Perf. 13
3339 A1302 5s Corner kick   .15 .15
3340 A1302 13s Heading the ball   .25 .16
3341 A1302 30s Referee, player   .55 .36
3342 A1302 42s Player holding tro-
               phy   .85 .55
     Nos. 3339-3342 (4)   1.80 1.22

Souvenir Sheet

3343 A1302 1 l Stadium   2.25 1.25

Paintings by
Dechko Usunov
(1899-1986)
A1303

Designs: 5s, Portrait of a Young Girl. 13s, Portrait
of Maria Wassilewa. 30s, Self-portrait.

1988, June 14   Perf. 13x13½
3344 A1303 5s multicolored   .15 .15
3345 A1303 13s multicolored   .32 .16
3346 A1303 30s multicolored   .72 .36
     Nos. 3344-3346 (3)   1.19 .67

Souvenir Sheet

1st Woman in Space, 25th
Anniv. — A1304

1988, June 16   Perf. 13½x13
3347 A1304 1 l multicolored   2.50 1.50
Valentina Tereshkova's flight, June 16-19, 1963.

Kurdzhali Region
Religious
Art — A1305

Designs: 5s, St. John the Baptist, 1592. 8s, St.
George Slaying the Dragon, 1841.

1988, June 27   Perf. 13x13½
3348 A1305 5s multicolored   .15 .15
3349 A1305 8s multicolored   .20 .15
     Set value   .16

1988 Summer
Olympics,
Seoul — A1306

1988, July 25   Litho.   Perf. 13
3350 A1306 5s High jump   .15 .15
3351 A1306 13s Weight lifting   .28 .16
3352 A1306 30s Greco-Roman wres-
               tling   .65 .38
3353 A1306 42s Rhythmic gymnas-
               tics   .90 .52
     Nos. 3350-3353 (4)   1.98 1.21

Souvenir Sheet

3354 A1306 1 l Volleyball   2.50 1.25

No. 3354 exists imperf.

Dimitr and
Karaja
A1307

1988, July 25   Litho.   Perf. 13
3355 A1307 5s blk, dark olive bister
               & grn   .15 .15

120th anniv. of the deaths of Haji Dimitr and
Stefan Karaja, patriots killed during the Balkan
Wars.

Problems of
Peace and
Socialism,
30th Anniv.
A1308

1988, July 26   Photo.
3356 A1308 13s multicolored   .25 .16

Paintings in the
Ludmila Zhivkova
Art
Gallery — A1309

Paintings: No. 3357, Harbor, Algiers, by
Albermarke (1875-1947). No. 3358, Portrait of
Ermin David in the Studio, by Jul Pasken (1885-
1930). No. 3359, Madonna with Child and Sts.
Sebastian and Roko, by Giovanni Rosso (1494-
1540). No. 3360, The Barren Tree, by Roland Udo
(1879-1982).

1988, July 27   Litho.   Perf. 14
3357 A1309 30s multicolored   .65 .38
3358 A1309 30s multicolored   .65 .38
3359 A1309 30s multicolored   .65 .38
3360 A1309 30s multicolored   .65 .38
     Nos. 3357-3360 (4)   2.60 1.52

St. Clement of Ohrid University, Sofia,
100th Anniv.
A1310

1988, Aug. 22   Perf. 13
3361 A1310 5s blk & pale yel   .15 .15

PRAGA '88
A1311

1988, Aug. 22
3362 A1311 25s Czechoslovakia #2 in
               vermilion   .60 .30

Printed in miniature sheets of 3 plus 3 labels
picturing skyline, PRAGA '88 and SOFIA '89 exhibition emblems.
Exists imperf.

OLYMPHILEX '88 — A1312

1988, Sept. 1
3363 A1312 62s Korea No. 1   1.25 .75

Printed in miniature sheets of 3 plus 3 labels
picturing skyline, OLYMPHILEX '88 and SOFIA '89
exhibition emblems.
Exists imperf.

A1313

A1314

1988, Sept. 15
3364 A1313 5s deep blue, lt blue & red　　.15　.15
Kremikovtsi steel mill, 25th anniv.

1988, Sept. 16　　　*Perf. 13¹/₂x13*
3365 A1314 13s dark red & ultra　　.25　.16
80th Interparliamentary Conference.

Transportation Commission 80th Congress — A1315

1988, Oct. 17
3366 A1315 13s deep lil rose & blk　　.25　.16

Kurdzhali Region Artifacts A1316

5s, Earthenware bowl, 13th-14th cent. 8s, Medieval fortification, Gorna Krepost Village, vert.

1988, Sept. 20　　　*Perf. 13*
3367 A1316 5s multicolored　　.15　.15
3368 A1316 8s multicolored　　.20　.15
　　　Set value　　.16

Chiprovo Uprising, 300th Anniv. — A1317

1988, Sept. 23
3369 A1317 5s multicolored　　.15　.15

Bears A1318

1988, Sept. 26　　　*Perf. 12¹/₂*
3370 A1318 5s *Ursus arctos*　　.15　.15
3371 A1318 8s *Thalassarctos maritimus*　　.18　.15
3372 A1318 13s *Melursus ursinus*　　.30　.16
3373 A1318 20s *Helarctos malayanus*　　.45　.25
3374 A1318 30s *Selenarctos thibetanus*　　.70　.40
3375 A1318 42s *Tremarctos ornatus*　　.95　.52
　a.　Min. sheet of 6, #3370-3375　3.00　1.50
　　　Nos. 3370-3375 (6)　2.73　1.63

ECOFORUM for Peace — A1319

1988, Oct. 29　　　*Perf. 13*
3376 A1319 20s multicolored　　.50　.25

PLOVDIV '88 A1320

Design: Amphitheater ruins, PRAGA '88 and PLOVDIV '88 emblems.

1988, Nov. 2
3377 A1320 5s multicolored　　.15　.15
Exists in imperf. sheet of six.

Radio & Television Authority, 25th Anniv. — A1321

1988, Nov. 17　　*Litho.*　*Perf. 13*
3378 A1321 5s multicolored　　.15　.15

BULGARIA '89 A1321a

1988, Nov. 22　　*Litho.*　*Perf. 13*
3379 A1321a 42s No. 1　　1.10　.58
Printed in miniature sheets of 3+3 labels picturing exhib. emblem and conf. center.
Exists imperf.

Souvenir Sheet

Danube Cruise Excursion Industry, 40th Anniv. — A1321b

1988, Nov. 25　　　*Perf. 13¹/₂x13*
3380　Sheet of 2　　4.75　2.75
　a.　A1321b 1 l *Russia*　　2.50　1.35
　b.　A1321b 1 l *Aleksandr Stamboliski*　2.50　1.35

Traffic Safety A1321c

1988, Nov. 28
3381 A1321c 5s multicolored　　.15　.15

New Year 1989 — A1321d

1988, Dec. 20　　　*Perf. 13*
3382 A1321d 5s shown　　.15　.15
3383 A1321d 13s multi, diff.　　.35　.25

Hotels in Winter A1322

1988, Dec. 19　*Litho.*　*Perf. 13¹/₂x13*
3384 A1322 5s shown　　.15　.15
3385 A1322 8s multi, diff.　　.18　.15
3386 A1322 13s multi, diff.　　.28　.16
3387 A1322 30s multi, diff.　　.70　.38
　　Nos. 3384-3387 (4)　1.31
　　Set value　　.70

Souvenir Sheet

Soviet Space Shuttle *Energija-Buran* — A1322a

1988, Dec. 28　　　*Perf. 13¹/₂x13*
3387A A1322a 1 l dark blue　　2.75　1.50

BULGARIA '89 — A1322b

Traditional modes of postal conveyance.

1988, Dec. 29　　　*Perf. 13¹/₂x13*
3387B A1322b 25s Mail coach　　.50　.30
3387C A1322b 25s Biplane　　.50　.30
3387D A1322b 25s Truck　　.50　.30
3387E A1322b 25s Steam packet　　.50　.30
　　Nos. 3387B-3387E (4)　2.00　1.20

Philatelic Exhibitions A1323

1989　　*Litho.*　*Perf. 13*
3388 A1322 42s France No. 1　　1.00　.52
3389 A1322 62s India No. 200　　1.50　.78
BULGARIA '89 and PHILEXFRANCE '89 (42s) or INDIA '89 (62s).
Nos. 3388-3389 each printed in sheets of 3 + 3 labels picturing skylines, BULGARIA '89 and PHILEXFRANCE or INDIA exhibition labels. Exist in sheets of 4 also. Exist imperf.
Issue dates: 42s, Feb. 23; 62s, Jan. 14.

Souvenir Sheet

Universiade Winter Games, Sofia — A1324

Designs: a, Downhill skiing. b, Ice hockey. c, Cross-country skiing. d, Speed skating.

1989, Jan. 30　*Litho.*　*Imperf.*
Simulated Perforations
3390　Sheet of 4　　2.25　1.25
　a.-d.　A1324 25s multicolored　　.55　.30
No. 3390 exists imperf. without simulated perforations and containing black control number.

Humor and Satire Festival, Gabrovo A1325

1989, Feb. 7　　　*Perf. 13¹/₂x13*
3391 A1325 13s Don Quixote　　.30　.16

Endangered Plant Species — A1326

1989, Feb. 22　　　*Perf. 13x13¹/₂*
3392 A1326 5s *Ramonda serbica*　　.15　.15
3393 A1326 10s *Paeonia maskula*　　.20　.15
3394 A1326 25s *Viola perinensis*　　.50　.30
3395 A1326 30s *Dracunculus vulgaris*　　.60　.35
3396 A1326 42s *Tulipa splendens*　　.85　.50
3397 A1326 60s *Rindera umbellata*　1.25　.70
　a.　Min. sheet of 6, #3392-3397　4.00　2.50
　　Nos. 3392-3397 (6)　3.55　2.15

World Wildlife Fund A1327

Bats.

1989, Feb. 27　　　*Perf. 13*
3398 A1327 5s *Nyctalus noctula*　　.15　.15
3399 A1327 13s *Rhinolophus ferrumequinum*　　.30　.15
3400 A1327 30s *Myotis myotis*　　.70　.40
3401 A1327 42s *Vespertilio murinus*　1.00　.50
　a.　Min. sheet of 4, #3398-3401　2.25　1.25
　　Nos. 3398-3401 (4)　2.15　1.15

Aleksandr Stamboliski (1879-1923), Premier — A1328

1989, Mar. 1   *Perf. 13½x13*
3402 A1328 5s brt org & blk   .15   .15

Souvenir Sheet

Soviet-Bulgarian Joint Space Flight, 10th Anniv. — A1329

Designs: a, Liftoff. b, Crew.

1989, Apr. 10   *Perf. 13*
3403 A1329 Sheet of 2   2.25 1.25
a.-b.   50s any single   1.10   .62

Exists imperf.

EXPO '91 Young Inventors Exhibition, Plovdiv — A1330

1989, Apr. 20   *Perf. 13½x13*
3404 A1330 5s multicolored   .15   .15

Petko Enev (b. 1889) A1331

Stanke Dimitrov Marek (b. 1889) — A1332

Perf. 13½x13, 13x13½
1989, Apr. 28
3405 A1331 5s scarlet & black   .15   .15
3406 A1332 5s scarlet & black   .15   .15
Set value   .15

Icons A1333   Photocopier A1334

Paintings by Bulgarian artists: No. 3407, Archangel Michael, by Dimiter Molerov. No. 3408, Mother and Child, by Toma Vishanov. No. 3409, St. John, by Vishanov. No. 3410, St. Dimitri, by Ivan Terziev.

1989, Apr. 28   *Perf. 13x13½*
3407 A1333 30s multicolored   .65   .35
3408 A1333 30s multicolored   .65   .35
3409 A1333 30s multicolored   .65   .35
3410 A1333 30s multicolored   .65   .35
Nos. 3407-3410 (4)   2.60 1.40

Nos. 3408, 3410 exist in sheets of four. Nos. 3407-3410 exist in souvenir sheets of four and together in one sheet of four, imperf.

1989, May 5
3411 A1334 5s shown   .15   .15
3412 A1334 8s Computer   .18   .15
3413 A1334 35s Telephone   .80   .45
3414 A1334 42s Dish receiver   .90   .52
Nos. 3411-3414 (4)   2.03 1.27

Bulgarian Communications, 110th anniv. Nos. 3411-3413 exist in imperf. sheets of six.

Souvenir Sheet

58th FIP Congress — A1335

1989, May 22
3415 A1335 1 l Charioteer   2.00 1.00
Exists imperf.

1st Communist Party Congress in Bulgaria, 70th Anniv. — A1336   Famous Men — A1337

1989, June 15
3416 A1336 5s mar, blk & dk red   .15   .15

1989

Portraits: No. 3417, Ilya Blaskov. No. 3418, Sofronii, Bishop of Vratza. No. 3419, Vassil Aprilov (b. 1789), educator, historian. No. 3420, Christo

Jassenov (1889-1925). 10s, Stoyan Zagorchinov (1889-1969).

3417 A1337 5s black & gray olive   .15   .15
3418 A1337 5s blk, brn blk & pale green   .15   .15
3419 A1337 8s lt blue, blk & vio blk   .28   .15
3420 A1337 8s tan, blk & dark red brown   .22   .15
3421 A1337 10s blk, pale pink & gray blue   .28   .15
Nos. 3417-3421 (5)   1.08
Set value   .50

Issued: #3417-3418, June 15; #3419, Aug. 1; #3420, Sept. 25; 10s, Aug. 5.

French Revolution, Bicent. — A1338

1989, June 26   *Perf. 13½x13*
3422 A1338 13s Anniv. emblem   .26   .15
3423 A1338 30s Jean-Paul Marat   .60   .35
3424 A1338 42s Robespierre   .85   .50
Nos. 3422-3424 (3)   1.71 1.00

7th Army Games A1339

1989, June 30   *Perf. 13*
3425 A1339 5s Gymnast   .15   .15
3426 A1339 13s Equestrian   .28   .16
3427 A1339 30s Running   .65   .38
3428 A1339 42s Shooting   .95   .52
Nos. 3425-3428 (4)   2.03 1.21

22nd World Canoe and Kayak Championships, Plovdiv — A1340

1989, Aug. 11   *Litho.*   *Perf. 13*
3429 A1340 13s Woman paddling   .28   .15
3430 A1340 30s Man rowing   .60   .25

Photography, 150th Anniv. — A1341

1989, Aug. 29   *Perf. 13½x13*
3431 A1341 42s blk, buff & yellow   .85   .45

September 9 Revolution, 45th Anniv. — A1342

1989, Aug. 30   *Perf. 13*
3432 A1342 5s Revolutionaries   .15   .15
3433 A1342 8s Couple embracing   .16   .15
3434 A1342 13s Faces in a crowd   .25   .16
Nos. 3432-3434 (3)   .56
Set value   .32

Natural History Museum, Cent. A1343

1989, Aug. 31
3435 A1343 13s multicolored   .30   .16

Postal Workers Killed in World War II — A1343a

Designs: 5s, L.D. Dardjikov. 8s, I.B. Dobrev. 10s, N.P. Antonov.

1989, Sept. 22   *Litho.*   *Perf. 13*
3436 A1343a 5s multicolored   .15   .15
3437 A1343a 8s multicolored   .18   .15
3438 A1343a 13s multicolored   .32   .18
Nos. 3436-3438 (3)   .65
Set value   .34

12th Shipping Unions Congress (FIATA) A1344

1989, Sept. 25   *Litho.*   *Perf. 13½x13*
3439 A1344 42s light blue & dark blue   .85   .45

Jawaharlal Nehru, 1st Prime Minister of Independent India — A1346

1989, Oct. 10
3440 A1346 13s blk, pale yel & brn   .32   .16

Souvenir Sheet

European Ecology Congress — A1347

1989, Oct. 12   *Perf. 13*
3441 A1347 Sheet of 2   3.50 1.75
a.   50s multicolored   1.20   .60
b.   1 l multicolored   2.25 1.15

Snakes A1368

1989, Oct. 20   *Litho.*   *Perf. 13*
3491 A1368 5s *Eryx jaculus turcicus*   .15   .15
3492 A1368 10s *Elaphe longissima*   .22   .15

3493	A1368	25s Elaphe situla	.55 .30
3494	A1368	30s Elaphe quatuor-lineata	.65 .35
3495	A1368	42s Telescopus fallax	.90 .50
3496	A1368	60s Coluber rubriceps	1.25 .70
a.		Min. sheet of 6, #3491-3496	4.00 2.05
		Nos. 3491-3496 (6)	3.72 2.15

Intl. Youth Science Fair, Plovdiv, 1989 — A1369

1989, Nov. 4
3497 A1369 13s multicolored .25 .15

1990 World Soccer Championships, Italy — A1370

Various athletes: No. 3502a, Athletes facing right. No. 3502b, Athletes facing left.

1989, Dec. 1
3498	A1370	5s shown	.15 .15
3499	A1370	13s multi, diff.	.30 .15
3500	A1370	30s multi, diff.	.70 .35
3501	A1370	42s multi, diff.	.98 .50
		Nos. 3498-3501 (4)	2.13 1.15

Souvenir Sheet
| 3502 | | Sheet of 2 | 2.30 1.15 |
| a.-b. | | A1370 50s any single | 1.15 .57 |

Air Sports A1371

1989, Dec. 8
3503	A1371	5s Glider planes	.15 .15
3504	A1371	13s Hang glider	.30 .15
3505	A1371	30s Sky diving	.70 .35
3506	A1371	42s Three sky divers	.98 .50
		Nos. 3503-3506 (4)	2.13 1.15

82nd General conference of the FAI, Varna.

Traffic Safety A1372

1989, Dec. 12
3507 A1372 5s multicolored .15 .15

New Year 1990 — A1373

1989, Dec. 25 Litho. Perf. 13
| 3508 | A1373 | 5s Santa's sleigh | .15 .15 |
| 3509 | A1373 | 13s Snowman | .32 .16 |

Cats — A1374

Designs: No. 3510, Persian. No. 3511, Tiger. 8s, Tabby. No. 3513, Himalayan. No. 3514, Persian, diff. 13s, Siamese. Nos. 3511 and 3514-3515 vert.

Perf. 13½x13, 13x13½
1989, Dec. 26 Background Color
3510	A1374	5s gray	.15 .15
3511	A1374	5s yellow	.15 .15
3512	A1374	8s orange	.20 .15
3513	A1374	10s blue	.24 .15
3514	A1374	10s brown orange	.24 .15
3515	A1374	13s red	.30 .15
		Nos. 3510-3515 (6)	1.28
		Set value	.61

Explorers and Their Ships A1375

1990, Jan. 17 Perf. 13
3516	A1375	5s Christopher Columbus	.15 .15
3517	A1375	8s Vasco da Gama	.20 .15
3518	A1375	13s Fernando Magellan	.30 .15
3519	A1375	32s Sir Francis Drake	.78 .38
3520	A1375	42s Henry Hudson	1.00 .50
3521	A1375	60s James Cook	1.45 .72
a.		Min. sheet of 6, #3516-3521	3.85 1.90
		Nos. 3516-3521 (6)	3.88 2.05

Natl. Esperanto Movement, Cent. — A1376

1990, Feb. 23 Litho. Perf. 13
3522 A1376 10s multicolored .25 .15

Paintings by Foreign Artists in the Natl. Museum — A1377

Artists: No. 3523, Suzanna Valadon (1867-1938). No. 3524, Maurice Brianchon (1899-1978). No. 3525, Moise Kisling (1891-1953). No. 3526, Giovanni Beltraffio (1467-1516).

1990, Mar. 23 Perf. 14
3523	A1377	30s multicolored	.65 .38
3524	A1377	30s multicolored	.65 .38
3525	A1377	30s multicolored	.65 .38
3526	A1377	30s multicolored	.65 .38
		Nos. 3523-3526 (4)	2.60 1.52

1990 World Soccer Championships, Italy — A1378

Various athletes.

1990, Mar. 26 Perf. 13
3527	A1378	5s multicolored	.15 .15
3528	A1378	13s multi, diff.	.28 .15
3529	A1378	30s multi, diff.	.70 .38
3530	A1378	42s multi, diff.	.95 .50
		Nos. 3527-3530 (4)	2.08 1.18

Souvenir Sheet
3531		Sheet of 2	2.25 1.20
a.		A1378 50s Three players	1.10 .60
b.		A1378 50s Two players	1.10 .60

Bavaria No. 1 A1379

1990, Apr. 6 Litho. Perf. 13
3532 A1379 42s ver & blk 1.00 .50

ESSEN '90, Germany, Apr. 12-22. No. 3532 printed in sheets of 3 + 3 labels.

Souvenir Sheet

Penny Black, 150th Anniv. A1380

1990, Apr. 10
3533		Sheet of 2	2.25 1.20
a.		A1380 50s Great Britain #1	1.10 .60
b.		A1380 50s Sir Rowland Hill	1.10 .60

Cooperative Farming in Bulgaria, Cent. — A1381

1990, Apr. 17
3534 A1381 5s multicolored .15 .15

Dimitar Chorbadjiski-Chudomir (1890-1967) — A1382

1990, Apr. 24
3535 A1382 5s multicolored .15 .15

Labor Day, Cent. — A1383

1990, May 1 Perf. 13x13½
3536 A1383 10s multicolored .25 .15

ITU, 125th Anniv. — A1384

1990, May 13 Litho. Perf. 13½x13
3537 A1384 20s blue, red & black .45 .24

Belgium No. 1 A1385

1990, May 23 Perf. 13
3538 A1385 30s multicolored .75 .38

Belgica '90. No. 3538 printed in sheets of 3 + 3 labels.

Lamartine (1790-1869), French Poet — A1386

1990, June 15 Perf. 13½x13
3539 A1386 20s multicolored .45 .25

Dinosaurs — A1387

1990, June 19 Perf. 12½
3540	A1387	5s Brontosaurus	.15 .15
3541	A1387	8s Stegosaurus	.20 .15
3542	A1387	13s Edaphosaurus	.32 .16
3543	A1387	25s Rhamphorhynchus	.62 .30
3544	A1387	32s Protoceratops	.80 .40
3545	A1387	42s Triceratops	1.05 .55
a.		Min. sheet of 6, #3540-3545	3.25 1.60
		Nos. 3540-3545 (6)	3.14 1.71

1992 Summer Olympic Games, Barcelona — A1388

1990, July 13 Perf. 13½x13
3546	A1388	5s Swimming	.15 .15
3547	A1388	13s Handball	.32 .16
3548	A1388	30s Hurdling	.75 .38
3549	A1388	42s Cycling	1.05 .55
		Nos. 3546-3549 (4)	2.27 1.24

Souvenir Sheet
3550		Sheet of 2	2.50 1.25
a.		A1388 50s Tennis, forehand	1.25 .62
b.		A1388 50s Tennis, backhand	1.25 .62

Butterflies A1389

990, Aug. 8   Litho.   *Perf. 13*
3551	A1389	5s Zerynthia Polyxena	.15	.15
3552	A1389	10s Panaxia		
		quadripunctaria	.22	.15
3553	A1389	20s Proserpinus proser-		
		pina	.45	.24
3554	A1389	30s Hyles lineata	.65	.55
3555	A1389	42s Thecla betulae	.95	.55
3556	A1389	60s Euphydryas cynthia	1.25	.72
a.		Min. sheet of 6, #3551-3556	4.00	2.10
		Nos. 3551-3556 (6)	3.67	2.17

Airplanes — A1390

1990, Aug. 30   Litho.   *Perf. 13¹/₂x13*
3557	A1390	5s Airbus A-300	.15	.15
3558	A1390	10s Tu-204	.18	.15
3559	A1390	20s Concorde	.42	.36
3560	A1390	30s DC-9	.52	.36
3561	A1390	42s Il-86	.75	.55
3562	A1390	60s Boeing 747	1.00	.72
a.		Min. sheet of 6, #3557-3562	3.25	2.15
		Nos. 3557-3562 (6)	3.02	2.23

Exarch Joseph I
(1840-1915),
Religious
Leader — A1391

1990, Sept. 27   *Perf. 13*
3563	A1391	5s blk, pur & grn	.15	.15

Intl. Traffic
Safety Year
A1392

1990, Oct. 9   Litho.   *Perf. 13*
3564	A1392	5s multicolored	.15	.15

Olymphilex '90,
Varna — A1393

1990, Oct. 16   *Perf. 13x13¹/₂*
3565	A1393	5s Shot put	.15	.15
3566	A1393	13s Discus	.25	.15
3567	A1393	42s Hammer throw	.90	.55
3568	A1393	60s Javelin	1.25	.72
a.		Souv. sheet of 4, #3565-3568,		
		imperf.	12.00	1.50
		Nos. 3565-3568 (4)	2.55	1.57

Space Exploration — A1394

Designs: 5s, Sputnik, 1957, USSR. 8s, Vostok, 1961, USSR. 10s, Voshkod 2, 1965, USSR. 20s, Apollo-Soyuz, 1975, US-USSR. 42s, Space Shuttle Columbia, 1981, US. 60s, Galileo, 1989-1996, US. 1 l, Apollo 11 Moon landing, 1969, US.

1990, Oct. 22   *Perf. 13¹/₂x13*
3569	A1394	5s multicolored	.15	.15
3570	A1394	8s multicolored	.16	.15
3571	A1394	10s multicolored	.20	.15

3572	A1394	20s multicolored	.40	.24
3573	A1394	42s multicolored	.90	.55
3574	A1394	60s multicolored	1.25	.72
		Nos. 3569-3574 (6)	3.06	1.96

Souvenir Sheet
3575	A1394	1 l multicolored	2.75	1.50

St. Clement of
Okhrida — A1395   Christmas — A1396

1990, Nov. 29   Litho.   *Perf. 13*
3576	A1395	5s multicolored	.15	.15

1990, Dec. 25   Litho.   *Perf. 13*
3577	A1396	5s Christmas tree	.15	.15
3578	A1396	20s Santa Claus	.40	.24
		Set value		.30

European Figure Skating Championships,
Sofia — A1397

1991, Jan. 18   *Perf. 13¹/₂x13*
3579	A1397	15s multicolored	.35	.18

Farm
Animals — A1398

1991-92   *Perf. 14x13¹/₂*
3581	A1398	20s Sheep	.30	.18
3582	A1398	25s Goose	.35	.22
3583	A1398	30s Hen, chicks	.42	.28
3584	A1398	40s Horse	.55	.35
3585	A1398	62s Goat	.85	.55
3586	A1398	86s Sow	1.25	.75
3587	A1398	95s Goat	.70	.42
3588	A1398	1 l Donkey	1.40	.90
3589	A1398	2 l Bull	2.75	1.75
3590	A1398	5 l Turkey	7.00	4.25
3591	A1398	10 l Cow	14.00	8.50
		Nos. 3581-3591 (11)	29.57	18.15

Issued: 20s, 25s, 40s, 86s, 1 l, Aug. 21; 10 l, Feb. 22; 95s, May 5, 1992; others, Feb. 11, 1991.

Mushrooms
A1399

1991, Mar. 19   *Perf. 12¹/₂x13*
3597	A1399	5s Amanita phalloides	.15	.15
3598	A1399	10s Amanita verna	.16	.15
3599	A1399	20s Amanita pantherina	.32	.18
3600	A1399	32s Amanita muscaria	.55	.30
3601	A1399	42s Gyromitra esculenta	.70	.38
3602	A1399	60s Boletus satanas	.95	.55
a.		Min. sheet of 6, #3597-3602	3.00	1.50
		Nos. 3597-3602 (6)	2.83	1.71

French
Impressionists
A1400

Designs: 20s, Good Morning, by Gauguin. 43s, Madame Dobini, by Degas. 62s, Peasant Woman, by Pissarro. 67s, Woman with Black Hair, by Manet. 80s, Blue Vase, by Cezanne. 2 l, Jeanny Samari, by Renoir. 3 l, Self portrait, by Van Gogh.

1991, Apr. 1   *Perf. 13*
3603	A1400	20s multicolored	.22	.18
3604	A1400	43s multicolored	.50	.38
3605	A1400	62s multicolored	.70	.55
3606	A1400	67s multicolored	.80	.60
3607	A1400	80s multicolored	1.00	.75
3608	A1400	2 l multicolored	2.25	1.75
		Nos. 3603-3608 (6)	5.47	4.21

Miniature Sheet
3609	A1400	3 l multicolored	4.50	2.65

Swiss Confederation, 700th
Anniv. — A1401

1991, Apr. 11
3610	A1401	62s multicolored	.90	.55

Philatelic Review, Cent. — A1402

1991, May 7   Litho.   *Perf. 13*
3611	A1402	30s multicolored	.45	.25

Europa — A1403

1991, May 10   *Perf. 13x13¹/₂*
3612	A1403	43s Meteosat	.70	.38
3613	A1403	62s Ariane rocket	1.00	.55

Horses
A1404

1991, May 21   *Perf. 13x12¹/₂*
3614	A1404	5s Przewalski's horse	.15	.15
3615	A1404	10s Tarpan	.16	.15
3616	A1404	25s Arabian	.40	.22
3617	A1404	35s Arabian	.55	.32
3618	A1404	42s Shetland pony	.65	.38
3619	A1404	60s Draft horse	.90	.55
a.		Min. sheet of 6, #3614-3619	3.00	1.65
		Nos. 3614-3619 (6)	2.81	1.77

EXPO 91, Plovdiv — A1405

1991, June 6   Litho.   *Perf. 13¹/₂x13*
3620	A1405	30s multicolored	.45	.28

Wolfgang
Amadeus
Mozart
A1406

1991, July 2   *Perf. 13*
3621	A1406	62s multicolored	.95	.55

Space
Shuttle
Missions,
10th Anniv.
A1407

1991, July 23   Litho.   *Perf. 13*
3622	A1407	12s Columbia	.16	.15
3623	A1407	32s Challenger	.45	.30
3624	A1407	50s Discovery	.70	.45
3625	A1407	86s Atlantis, vert.	1.25	.75
3626	A1407	1.50 l Buran, vert.	2.25	1.30
3627	A1407	2 l Atlantis, diff.,		
		vert.	2.75	1.75
		Nos. 3622-3627 (6)	7.56	4.70

Souvenir Sheet
3628	A1407	3 l US shuttle, earth	4.50	2.65

1992 Winter
Olympics,
Albertville — A1408

1991, Aug. 7   Litho.   *Perf. 13x13¹/₂*
3629	A1408	30s Luge	.40	.28
3630	A1408	43s Slalom skiing	.52	.38
3631	A1408	67s Ski jumping	.85	.60
3632	A1408	2 l Biathlon	2.50	1.75
		Nos. 3629-3632 (4)	4.27	3.01

Souvenir Sheet
3633	A1408	3 l Two-man bobsled	4.50	2.65

Sheraton
Sofia Hotel
Balkan
A1409

1991, Sept. 6   Litho.   *Perf. 13*
3634	A1409	62s multicolored	1.10	.55

Printed in sheets of 3 + 3 labels.

Dogs — A1410

1991, Oct. 11   *Perf. 13x13½*
3635	A1410	30s Japanese	.52	.26
3636	A1410	43s Chihuahua	.75	.38
3637	A1410	62s Pinscher	1.10	.55
3638	A1410	80s Yorkshire terrier	1.40	.70
3639	A1410	1 l Chinese	1.75	.90
3640	A1410	3 l Pug	5.25	2.65
a.		Min. sheet of 6, #3635-3640	10.80	5.45
		Nos. 3635-3640 (6)	10.77	5.44

Cologne '91, Intl. Philatelic Exhibition A1411

1991, Oct. 21   *Perf. 13*
3641 A1411 86s multicolored   1.50   .75
Printed in sheets of 3 + 3 labels.

Souvenir Sheet

Brandenburg Gate, Bicent. — A1412

1991, Oct. 23
3642 A1412 4 l multicolored   7.00   3.50
Exists imperf.

Phila Nippon '91 A1413

1991, Nov. 11
3643 A1413 62s Japan #1   1.10   .55
Printed in sheets of 3 + 3 labels.

Bulgarian Railroad, 125th Anniv. — A1414

1991, Nov. 30
3644	A1414	30s Locomotive	.55	.28
3645	A1414	30s Passenger car	.55	.28

Medicinal Plants A1415

Designs: 30s, Pulsatilla vernalis. 40s, Pulsatilla pratensis. 55s, Pulsatilla halleri. 60s, Aquilegia nigricans. 1 l, Hippophae rhamnoides. 2 l, Ribes nigrum.

1991, Nov. 20   *Litho.*   *Perf. 13*
3646	A1415	30s +15s label	.78	.38
3647	A1415	40s multicolored	.70	.35
3648	A1415	55s multicolored	.95	.48
3649	A1415	60s multicolored	1.05	.58
3650	A1415	1 l multicolored	1.75	.90
3651	A1415	2 l multicolored	3.50	1.75
a.		Min. sheet of 6, #3646-3651	8.75	4.45
		Nos. 3646-3651 (6)	8.73	4.44

No. 3646 printed se-tenant with label. No. 3651a sold for 5 l, but does not contain the 15s label printed with No. 3646.

Basketball, Cent. A1416

1991, Dec. 6   *Perf. 13½x13*
3652	A1416	43s Ball below rim	.75	.38
3653	A1416	62s Ball at rim	1.10	.55
3654	A1416	90s Ball in cylinder	1.60	.80
3655	A1416	1 l Ball in basket	1.75	.90
		Nos. 3652-3655 (4)	5.20	2.63

El Greco, 450th Birth Anniv. — A1417

Paintings: 43s, Christ Carrying the Cross. 50s, Holy Family with St. Anne. 60s, St. John the Evangelist and St. John the Baptist. 62s, St. Andrew and St. Francis. 1 l, Holy Family with St. Mary Magdalene. 2 l, Cardinal Nino de Guevara. 3 l, Holy Family with St. Anne (detail).

1991, Dec. 13   *Perf. 13*
3656	A1417	43s multicolored	.75	.38
3657	A1417	50s multicolored	.90	.45
3658	A1417	60s multicolored	1.05	.52
3659	A1417	62s multicolored	1.10	.55
3660	A1417	1 l multicolored	1.75	.90
3661	A1417	2 l multicolored	3.50	1.75
		Nos. 3656-3661 (6)	9.05	4.55

Souvenir Sheet
3662 A1417 3 l multicolored   5.25   2.65

No. 3662 contains one 43x53mm stamp.

Christmas A1418

1991, Dec. 18
3663	A1418	30s Snowman, candle, bell, heart	.55	.28
3664	A1418	62s Star, angel, flower, house, tree	1.10	.55

Marine Mammals — A1419

Designs: 30s, Phogophoca graenlandica. 43s, Orcinus orca. 62s, Odobenus rosmarus. 68s, Tursiops truncatus. 1 l, Monachus monachus. 2 l, Phocaena phocaena.

1991, Dec. 24
3665	A1419	30s multicolored	.52	.26
3666	A1419	43s multicolored	.75	.38
3667	A1419	62s multicolored	1.10	.55
3668	A1419	68s multicolored	1.20	.60
3669	A1419	1 l multicolored	1.75	.90
3670	A1419	2 l multicolored	3.50	1.75
a.		Min. sheet of #3665-3670	8.85	4.45
		Nos. 3665-3670 (6)	8.82	4.44

Settlement of Jews in Bulgaria, 500th Anniv. — A1420

1992, Mar. 5   *Litho.*   *Perf. 13*
3671 A1420 1 l multicolored   1.75   .90

Gioacchino Rossini (1792-1868), Composer — A1421

1992, Mar. 11
3672 A1421 50s multicolored   .88   .45

Plovdiv Fair, Cent. A1422

1992, Mar. 25
3673 A1422 1 l buff & black   1.75   .90

Fiat Croma — A1423

Automobiles.

1992, Mar. 26   *Perf. 13½x13*
3674	A1423	30s Volvo 740	.52	.26
3675	A1423	45s Ford Escort	.80	.40
3676	A1423	50s shown	.90	.45
3677	A1423	50s Mercedes 600	.90	.45
3678	A1423	1 l Peugeot 605	1.75	.90
3679	A1423	2 l BMW 316	3.50	1.75
		Nos. 3674-3679 (6)	8.37	4.21

Francisco de Orellana — A1424

Explorers: No. 3681, Vespucci. No. 3682, Magellan. No. 3683, Gonzalo Jimenez de Quesada (1500-1579). 2 l, Drake. 3 l, Pedro de Valdivia (1500-1553). 4 l, Columbus.

1992, Apr. 22   *Litho.*   *Perf. 13*
3680	A1424	50s multicolored	.45	.22
3681	A1424	50s multicolored	.45	.22
3682	A1424	1 l multicolored	.90	.45
3683	A1424	1 l multicolored	.90	.45
3684	A1424	2 l multicolored	1.80	.90
3685	A1424	3 l multicolored	2.70	1.35
		Nos. 3680-3685 (6)	7.20	3.59

Souvenir Sheet
3686 A1424 4 l multicolored   3.50   1.75

Granada '92 A1425

1992, Apr. 23
3687 A1425 62s multicolored   .55   .28
No. 3687 printed in sheets of 3 + 3 labels.

Discovery of America, 500th Anniv. A1426

1992, Apr. 24
3688	A1426	1 l Ships, map	.90	.45
3689	A1426	2 l Columbus, ship	1.80	.90
a.		Pair, #3688-3689	2.60	1.30

Europa.

SOS Children's Village A1427

1992, June 15   *Litho.*   *Perf. 13*
3690 A1427 1 l multicolored   .90   .45

1992 Summer Olympics, Barcelona A1428

1992, July 15   *Perf. 13½x13*
3691	A1428	50s Swimming	.45	.22
3692	A1428	50s Long jump	.45	.22
3693	A1428	1 l High jump	.90	.45
3694	A1428	3 l Gymnastics	2.70	1.35
		Nos. 3691-3694 (4)	4.50	2.24

Souvenir Sheet   *Perf. 13x13½*
3695 A1428 4 l Torch, vert.   3.60   1.80

Motorcycles A1429

Designs: 30s, 1902 Laurin & Klement. No. 3697, 1928 Puch 200 Luxus. No. 3698, 1931 Norton CS1. 70s, 1950 Harley Davidson. 1 l, 1986 Gilera SP 01. 2 l, 1990 BMW K1.

1992, July 30   *Perf. 13*
3696	A1429	30s multicolored	.28	.15
3697	A1429	50s multicolored	.45	.22
3698	A1429	50s multicolored	.45	.22
3699	A1429	70s multicolored	.62	.30
3700	A1429	1 l multicolored	.90	.45
3701	A1429	2 l multicolored	1.80	.90
		Nos. 3696-3701 (6)	4.50	2.24

Genoa '92 Intl. Philatelic Exhibition A1430

1992, Sept. 18   *Perf. 13*
3702 A1430 1 l multicolored   .90 .45

This is a developing set. Numbers may change.

Insects — A1431

1992   *Litho.*   *Perf. 14x13¹/₂*
3710 A1431   1 l Dragonfly   .15
3711 A1431   2 l Mayfly   .22
3712 A1431   3 l Locust   .32
3713 A1431   4 l Stag beetle   .45
3714 A1431   5 l Carrion beetle   .55
3715 A1431   7 l Ant   .75
3718 A1431 20 l Bee   2.25
3718A A1431 50 l Praying mantis   5.75
    Nos. 3710-3718A (8)   10.44

Issued: 7, 20 l, Sept. 25; 3, 50 l, Nov. 30; 1, 2, 4, 5 l, Dec. 15, 1993.
This is a developing set. Numbers may change.

Based on available currency exchange rates the face value of No. 3718A was about $2. It appears that many Bulgarian stamps are appearing in the market at significantly higher prices than face values would indicate.

A1432   A1433

1992, Sept. 30   *Perf. 13*
3719 A1432 1 l blk, pink & rose   .90 .45

Higher Institute of Architecture and Building, 50th anniv.

1992, Oct. 16   *Litho.*   *Perf. 13*
Trees: No. 3720, Quercus mestensis. No. 3721, Aesculus hippocastanum. No. 3722, Quercus thracica. No. 3723, Pinus peuce. 2 l, Acer heldreichii. 3 l, Pyrus bulgarica.

3720 A1433 50s multicolored   .45 .22
3721 A1433 50s multicolored   .45 .22
3722 A1433 1 l multicolored   .90 .45
3723 A1433 1 l multicolored   .90 .45
3724 A1433 2 l multicolored   1.80 .90
3725 A1433 3 l multicolored   2.70 1.35
    Nos. 3720-3725 (6)   7.20 3.59

Ethnographical Museum, Cent. — A1434

1992, Oct. 23
3726 A1434 1 l multicolored   .90 .45

Tanker Bulgaria — A1435

1992, Oct. 30   *Litho.*   *Perf. 13*
3727 A1435 30s Freighter Bulgaria   .28 .15
3728 A1435 50s Castor   .45 .22
3729 A1435   1 l Hero of Sevastopol   .90 .45
3730 A1435   2 l shown   1.80 .90
3731 A1435   2 l Aleko Constantinov   1.80 .90
3732 A1435   3 l Varna   2.70 1.35
    Nos. 3727-3732 (6)   7.93 3.97

Bulgarian Merchant Fleet, Cent.

Bulgaria, Member of the Council of Europe — A1436

1992, Nov. 6   *Litho.*   *Perf. 13*
3733 A1436 7 l multicolored   6.30 3.15

Souvenir Sheet

4th World Congress of Popular Sports, Varna — A1437

1992, Nov. 17   *Litho.*   *Perf. 13*
3734 A1437 4 l multicolored   4.00

Christmas A1438

1992, Dec. 1   *Perf. 13¹/₂x13*
3735 A1438 1 l Santa Claus   .75
3736 A1438 7 l Madonna & Child   5.25

Wild Cats — A1439

1992, Dec. 18   *Litho.*   *Perf. 13*
3737 A1439 50s Panthera pardus   .38
3738 A1439 50s Acinonyx jubatus   .38
3739 A1439   1 l Panthera onca   .75
3740 A1439   2 l Panthera tigris   1.50
3741 A1439   2 l Felis concolor   1.50
3742 A1439   3 l Panthera leo   2.25
    Nos. 3737-3742 (6)   6.76

Sports A1440

1992, Dec. 18
3743 A1440 30s Baseball   .38
3744 A1440 50s Cricket   .38
3745 A1440   1 l Polo   .75
3746 A1440   1 l Harness racing   .75
3747 A1440   2 l Field hockey   1.50
3748 A1440   3 l Football   2.25
    Nos. 3743-3748 (6)   6.01

Owls A1441

1992, Dec. 23
3749 A1441 30s Aegolius funereus   .25
3750 A1441 50s Strix aluco   .38
3751 A1441   1 l Asio otus   .75
3752 A1441   1 l Otus scops   1.50
3753 A1441   2 l Asio flammeus   1.50
3754 A1441   3 l Tyto alba   2.25
    Nos. 3749-3754 (6)   6.63

Nos. 3749, 3751, 3753-3754 are vert.

Paintings Depicting History of Bulgaria A1442

Artists: 50s, Dimiter Gyudzhenov. 1 l, 3 l, Nikolai Pavlovich. 2 l, Dimiter Panchev. 4 l, Mito Ganovski.

1992, Dec. 28
3755 A1442 50s multicolored   .38
3756 A1442   1 l multicolored   .75
3757 A1442   2 l multicolored   1.50
3758 A1442   3 l multicolored   2.25
    Nos. 3755-3758 (4)   4.88

Souvenir Sheet
3759 A1442   4 l multicolored, vert.   3.00

Archeological Museum, Cent. — A1443   1993 World Biathlon Championships, Borovetz — A1444

1993, Jan. 1   *Litho.*   *Perf. 13x13¹/₂*
3760 A1443 1 l multicolored   .75

1993, Feb. 5
3761 A1444 1 l Woman aiming rifle   .75
3762 A1444 7 l Skiing   5.25

Neophit Rilski, Birth Bicent. A1445

1993, Apr. 22   *Litho.*   *Perf. 13¹/₂x13*
3763 A1445 1 l henna brn & ol bis   .75

Contemporary Art — A1446

Europa: 3 l, Sculpture of centaur, by Georgi Chapkinov. 8 l, Painting of geometric forms, by D. Bujukliski.

1993, Apr. 29   *Perf. 13x13¹/₂*
3764 A1446 3 l multicolored   2.25
3765 A1446 8 l multicolored   6.00

Fish A1447

1993, June 29   *Litho.*   *Perf. 13*
3766 A1447 1 l C.a.j. bicaudatus   .75
3767 A1447 2 l Mollienesia velifera   1.50
3768 A1447 3 l Aphyosemion bivittatum   2.25
3769 A1447 3 l Pterophyllum eimekei   2.25
3770 A1447 4 l Symphysodon discus   3.00
3771 A1447 8 l Trichogaster leeri   6.00
    Nos. 3766-3771 (6)   15.75

Fruit — A1448

1993, July 8   *Perf. 13x13¹/₂*
3772 A1448 1 l Malus domestica   .75
3773 A1448 2 l Pyrus sativa   1.50
3774 A1448 2 l Persica vulgaris   1.50
3775 A1448 3 l Cydonia oblonga   2.25
3776 A1448 3 l Punica granatum   3.75
3777 A1448 7 l Ficus carica   5.25
    Nos. 3772-3777 (6)   15.00

Claudio Monteverdi (1567-1643), Composer A1449

1993, July 20   *Litho.*   *Perf. 13¹/₂x13*
3778 A1449 1 l multicolored   .75

17th World Summer Games for the Deaf A1450

1993, July 20   *Perf. 13*
3779 A1450 1 l shown   .75
3780 A1450 2 l Swimming   1.50
3781 A1450 3 l Cycling   2.25
3782 A1450 4 l Tennis   3.00
    Nos. 3779-3782 (4)   7.50

Souvenir Sheet
3783 A1450 5 l Soccer

Miniature Sheet

A1451

Council of Preslav, Cyrillic Alphabet in Bulgaria, 1100th Anniv.: a, Baptism of Christian convert. b, Tsar Boris I (852-889). c, Tsar Simeon (893-927). d, Battle between Bulgarians and Byzantines.

1993, Sept. 16 Litho. Perf. 13¹/₂x13
3784 A1451 5 l Sheet of 4, #a.-d. 3.50

Alexander of Battenberg (1857-93), Prince of Bulgaria — A1452

1993, Sept. 23 Perf. 13x13¹/₂
3785 A1452 3 l multicolored .50

Peter I. Tchaikovsky (1840-93) A1453

1993, Sept. 30 Perf. 13¹/₂x13
3786 A1453 3 l multicolored .50

Small Arms A1454   Isaac Newton (1643-1725) A1455

1993, Oct. 22 Litho. Perf. 13¹/₂x14
3787 A1454 1 l Crossbow, 16th cent. .18
3788 A1454 2 l Pistol, 18th cent. .35
3789 A1454 3 l Luger, 1908 .50
3790 A1454 3 l Pistol, 1873 .50
3791 A1454 5 l Rifle, 1938 .85
3792 A1454 7 l Kalashnikov, 1947 1.25
  Nos. 3787-3792 (6) 3.63

1993, Oct. 29 Perf. 13¹/₂x13
3793 A1455 1 l multicolored .18

Organized Philately in Bulgaria, Cent. A1456

1993, Nov. 16
3794 A1456 1 l multicolored .18

Ecology A1457

1993, Nov. 17
3795 A1457 1 l shown .18
3796 A1457 7 l Ecology 1.25

Game Animals A1458

1993, Nov. 25
3797 A1458 1 l Anas platrhynchos .18
3798 A1458 1 l Phasianus colchicus .18
3799 A1458 2 l Vulpes vulpes .35
3800 A1458 3 l Capreolus capreolus .50
3801 A1458 6 l Lepus europaeus 1.00
3802 A1458 8 l Sus scrofa 1.40
  Nos. 3797-3802 (6) 3.61

Christmas A1459

Signs of Zodiac on sundial: No. 3803a, Taurus, Gemini, Cancer. b, Libra, Virgo, Leo.
No. 3804a, Aquarius, Pisces, Aries. b, Capricorn, Sagittarius, Scorpio.

1993, Dec. 1
3803 A1459 1 l Pair, #a.-b. .35
3804 A1459 7 l Pair, #a.-b. 2.50

When placed together, Nos. 3803-3804 form a complete sundial.

Regional Folk Costumes for Men
A1460   A1461

1993, Dec. 16 Litho. Perf. 13¹/₂x14
3805 A1460 1 l Sofia .15
3806 A1461 1 l Plovdiv .15
3807 A1460 2 l Belogradchik .22
3808 A1460 3 l Shumen .32
3809 A1461 3 l Oryakhovitsa .32
3810 A1461 5 l Kurdzhali .90
  Nos. 3805-3810 (6) 2.06

1994 Winter Olympics, Lillehammer A1462

1994, Feb. 8 Perf. 13
3811 A1462 1 l Freestlye skiing .15
3812 A1462 2 l Speed skating .22
3813 A1462 3 l 2-Man luge .32
3814 A1462 4 l Hockey .45
  Nos. 3811-3814 (4) 1.14

Souvenir Sheet
3815 A1462 5 l Downhill skiing .55

Nikolai Pavlovich (1835-94) A1463

1994, Feb. 16 Perf. 13¹/₂x13
3816 A1463 3 l multicolored .32

Dinosaurs A1464

1994, Apr. 27 Litho. Perf. 13
3817 A1464 2 l Plesiosaurus .15
3818 A1464 3 l Iguanodon .15
3819 A1464 3 l Archaeopteryx .15
3820 A1464 4 l Edmontonia .16
3821 A1464 5 l Styracosaurus .20
3822 A1464 7 l Tyrannosaurus Rex .28
  Nos. 3817-3822 (6) 1.09

1994 World Cup Soccer Championships, US — A1465

Players in championships of : 3 l, Chile, 1962. 6 l, England, 1966. 7 l, Mexico, 1970. 9 l, West Germany, 1974. No. 3827a, Mexico, 1986, vert. b, US, 1994.

1994, Apr. 28
3823 A1465 3 l multicolored .15
3824 A1465 6 l multicolored .22
3825 A1465 7 l multicolored .28
3826 A1465 9 l multicolored .35
  Nos. 3823-3826 (4) 1.00

Souvenir Sheet
3827 A1465 1 l Sheet of 2, #a.-b. .40

For No. 3827 with inscription reading up along the left margin, see No. 3851.

Europa — A1466

European Discoveries: 3 l, Axis of symmetry. 15 l, Electrocardiogram.

1994, Apr. 29 Litho. Perf. 13¹/₂
3828 A1466 3 l multicolored .15
3829 A1466 15 l multicolored .60

Boris Hristov (1914-93) — A1467

1994, May 18 Litho. Perf. 13
3830 A1467 3 l brown & bister .15

Cricetus
Cricetus — A1468

Designs: 3 l, In nest. 7 l, Emerging from burrow. 10 l, Standing on hind legs. 15 l, Finding berry.

1994, Sept. 23 Litho. Perf. 13
3831 A1468 3 l multicolored .15
3832 A1468 7 l multicolored .28
3833 A1468 10 l multicolored .40
3834 A1468 15 l multicolored .60
  Nos. 3831-3834 (4) 1.43

World Wildlife Fund.

Space Program — A1469   Intl. Olympic Committee, Cent. — A1470

1994, Nov. 4 Litho. Perf. 13
3835 A1469 3 l multicolored .15

1994, Nov. 7
3836 A1470 3 l multicolored .15

Icons A1471   Christmas A1472

1994, Nov. 24 Litho. Perf. 13x13¹/₂
3837 A1471 2 l Christ .15
3838 A1471 3 l Christ, the healer .15
3839 A1471 5 l Crucifixion .16
3840 A1471 7 l Archangel Michael .22
3841 A1471 8 l Sts. Cyril, Methodi-us .25
3842 A1471 15 l Madonna & Child .45
  Nos. 3837-3842 (6) 1.38

1994, Dec. 1
3843 A1472 3 l Ancient coin .20
3844 A1472 15 l Coin, diff. 1.00

Roses A1473

1994, Dec. 12 Perf. 13
Color of Rose
3845 A1473 2 l yellow .15
3846 A1473 3 l rose red .15
3847 A1473 5 l white .16
3848 A1473 7 l salmon .22
3849 A1473 10 l carmine .32
3850 A1473 15 l orange & yellow .45
  Nos. 3845-3850 (6) 1.45

Souvenir Sheet
No. 3827 with Additional Inscription in Left Sheet Margin

1994, Dec. 15 Litho. Perf. 13
3851 A1465 5 l Sheet of 2, #a.-b. .40

Trams A1474

1994, Dec. 29
3852 A1474 1 l Model 1912 .15
3853 A1474 2 l Model 1928 .15
3854 A1474 3 l Model 1931 .15
3855 A1474 5 l Model 1942 .16
3856 A1474 8 l Model 1951 .25
3857 A1474 10 l Model 1961 .32
  Set value .88

Vassil
Petleshkov
(1845-76),
Revolutionary
A1475

1995, Feb. 27   Litho.   Perf. 13½x13
3858 A1475 3 l multicolored   .15

End of World War II,
50th
Anniv. — A1476

Europa: 15 l, Dove holding olive branch standing
on gun barrel.

1995, May 3   Litho.   Perf. 13
3859 A1476 3 l multicolored   .15
3860 A1476 15 l multicolored   .45

Souvenir Sheet

Men's
World
Volleyball
League,
Cent.
A1477

Designs: a, 10 l, Player digging ball. b, 15 l,
Player spiking ball, vert.

1995, May 25   Litho.   Perf. 13
3861 A1477 Sheet of 2, #a.-b.   .75

Souvenir Sheet

European Nature Conservation
Year — A1478

Designs: a, 10 l, Pancratium maritimum. b, 15 l,
Aquila heliaca. Illustration reduced.

1995, June 23   Litho.   Perf. 13
3862 A1478 Sheet of 2, #a.-b.   .75

Antarctic Wildlife — A1479

1 l, Euphausia superba. 2 l, Chaenocephalus. 3 l,
Physeter catodon. 5 l, Leptonychotes weddelli. 8 l,
Stercorarius skua. 10 l, Aptenodytes forsteri, vert.

1995, June 29
3863 A1479   1 l multicolored   .15
3864 A1479   2 l multicolored   .15
3865 A1479   3 l multicolored   .15
3866 A1479   5 l multicolored   .15
3867 A1479   8 l multicolored   .25
3868 A1479 10 l multicolored   .30
           Set value   .65

Stephan Stambolov (1854-95),
Revolutionary Leader, Politician — A1480

1995, July 6   Litho.   Perf. 13
3869 A1480 3 l multicolored   .15

1996
Summer
Olympics,
Atlanta
A1481

Designs: 3 l, Pole vault. 7 l, High jump. 10 l,
Women's long jump. 15 l, Track.

1995, July 17
3870 A1481   3 l multicolored   .15
3871 A1481   7 l multicolored   .20
3872 A1481 10 l multicolored   .30
3873 A1481 15 l multicolored   .45
           Nos. 3870-3873 (4)   1.10

Legumes — A1482

1995, July 31
3874 A1482   2 l Pisum sativum   .15
3875 A1482   3 l Glicine   .15
3876 A1482   3 l Cicer arietinum   .15
3877 A1482   4 l Spinacia oleracea   .15
3878 A1482   5 l Arachis hypogaea   .15
3879 A1482 15 l Lens esculenta   .45
           Set value   .95

Organized
Tourism in
Bulgaria,
Cent.
A1483

1995, Aug. 21   Litho.   Perf. 13
3880 A1483 3 l multicolored   .15

Vassil Zahariev (1895-
1971), Graphic
Artist — A1484

Designs: 2 l, Woodcut of a man. 3 l, Woodcut of
building in valley. 5 l, Self-portrait. 10 l, Carving of
two women.

1995, Sept. 4   Litho.   Perf. 13
3881 A1484   2 l multicolored   .15
3882 A1484   3 l multicolored   .15
3883 A1484   5 l multicolored   .15
3884 A1484 10 l multicolored   .30
           Set value   .60

UN, 50th
Anniv.
A1485

1995, Sept. 12
3885 A1485 3 l multicolored   .15

Airplanes — A1486

1995, Sept. 26   Litho.   Perf. 13
3886 A1486   3 l PO-2   .15
3887 A1486   5 l Li-2   .15
3888 A1486   7 l JU52-3M   .20
3889 A1486 10 l FV-58   .30
           Nos. 3886-3889 (4)   .80
           Set value   .75

Motion Pictures,
Cent. — A1487

Designs: 2 l, Charlie Chaplin, Mickey Mouse. 3 l,
Marilyn Monroe, Marlene Dietrich. 5 l, Humphrey
Bogart. 8 l, Sophia Loren, Liza Minnelli. 10 l,
Toshiro Mifune. 15 l, Katya Paskaleva.

1995, Oct. 16
3890 A1487   2 l multicolored   .15
3891 A1487   3 l multicolored   .15
3892 A1487   5 l multicolored   .15
3893 A1487   8 l multicolored   .25
3894 A1487 10 l multicolored   .30
3895 A1487 15 l multicolored   .45
                                               1.25

Minerals
A1488

1995, Nov. 20   Litho.   Perf. 13
3896 A1488   1 l Agate   .15
3897 A1488   2 l Sphalerite   .15
3898 A1488   5 l Calcite   .15
3899 A1488   7 l Quartz   .20
3900 A1488   8 l Pyromorphite   .25
3901 A1488 10 l Almandine   .30
           Nos. 3896-3901 (6)   1.20

Christmas
A1489

1995, Dec. 8   Litho.   Perf. 13
3902 A1489   3 l shown   .15
3903 A1489 15 l Magi   .45

Southern Fruit, by Cyril Tsonev (1896-
1961) — A1490

1996, Jan. 25   Litho.   Perf. 13
3904 A1490 3 l multicolored   .15

Martin Luther (1483-1546) — A1491

1996, Feb. 5
3905 A1491 3 l multicolored   .15

Historic Buildings
A1492

Monasteries: 3 l, Preobragenie. 5 l, Arapovsky.
10 l, Drianovo. 20 l, Bachkovo. 25 l, Troyan. 40 l,
Zografski.

1996, Feb. 28   Perf. 14x13½
3906 A1492   3 l green   .15
3907 A1492   5 l red   .15
3908 A1492 10 l blue   .30
3909 A1492 20 l yellow orange   .60
3910 A1492 25 l brown   .75
3911 A1492 40 l purple   1.20
           Nos. 3906-3911 (6)   3.15

5th Meeting of
European Bank for
Reconstruction and
Development
A1493

1996, Apr. 15   Litho.   Perf. 13
3912 A1493   7 l   shown   .15
3913 A1493 30 l   Building, diff.   .50

Conifers
A1494

Designs: 5 l, Taxus baccata. 8 l, Abies alba. 10 l,
Picea abies. 20 l, Pinus silvestris. 25 l, Pinus heldreichii. 40 l, Juniperus excelsa.

1996, Apr. 23   Perf. 13¹/₂x13
3914 A1494   5 l   multicolored   .15
3915 A1494   8 l   multicolored   .15
3916 A1494 10 l   multicolored   .15
3917 A1494 20 l   multicolored   .30
3918 A1494 25 l   multicolored   .40
3919 A1494 40 l   multicolored   .65
        Nos. 3914-3919 (6)   1.80

A1495   A1496

Designs: 10 l, People in distress. 40 l, Khristo
Botev (1848-1876), poet, patriot, horiz.

1996, May 1   Perf. 13
3920 A1495 10 l   multicolored   .15
3921 A1495 40 l   multicolored   .65

April Uprising, death of Khristo Botev, 120th
anniv.

1996, May 6
Uniforms: 5 l, Light brown dress uniform. 8 l,
Brown combat, helmet. 10 l, Brown uniform, holding gun with fixed bayonet. 20 l, Early red, blue
dress uniform. 25 l, Officer's early green dress uniform. 40 l, Soldier's green uniform.

1996, May 6
3922 A1496   5 l   multicolored   .15
3923 A1496   8 l   multicolored   .15
3924 A1496 10 l   multicolored   .15
3925 A1496 20 l   multicolored   .30
3926 A1496 25 l   multicolored   .40
3927 A1496 40 l   multicolored   .65
        Nos. 3922-3927 (6)   1.80

Republic of Bulgaria,
50th Anniv. — A1497

1996, May 13   Litho.   Perf. 13¹/₂
3928 A1497 10 l   multicolored   .15

Famous
Women
A1498

Europa: 10 l, Elisaveta Bagriana (1893-1990),
poet. 40 l, Katia Popova (1924-66), opera singer.

1996, May 29   Litho.   Perf. 13
3929 A1498 10 l   multicolored   .25
    Complete booklet, 5 #3929   1.25
3930 A1498 40 l   multicolored   .95
    Complete booklet, 5 #3930   4.75

A1499   A1500

10 l, Soccer player. 15 l, Soccer player, diff.

1996, June 4
Souvenir Sheet
3931 A1499   Sheet of 2, #a.-b.   .60
Euro '96, European Soccer Championships,
Great Britain.

1996, July 4
3932 A1500   5 l   Wrestling   .15
3933 A1500   8 l   Boxing   .20
3934 A1500 10 l   Women's shot put   .25
3935 A1500 25 l   2-Man rowing   .60
Souvenir Sheet
3936 A1500 15 l   Pierre de Coubertin .35
1996 Summer Olympic Games, Atlanta.
Olymphilex '96 (#3936).

Crabs
A1501

Designs: 5 l, Gammarus arduus. 10 l, Asellus
aquaticus. 12 l, Astacus astacus. 25 l, Palaemon
serratus. 30 l, Cumella limicola. 40 l, Carcinus
mediterraneus.

1996, July 30
3937 A1501   5 l   multicolored   .15
3938 A1501 10 l   multicolored   .25
3939 A1501 12 l   multicolored   .30
3940 A1501 25 l   multicolored   .60
3941 A1501 30 l   multicolored   .70
3942 A1501 40 l   multicolored   .95
        Nos. 3937-3942 (6)   2.95

Francisco Goya (1746-
1828) — A1502

Entire paintings or details: 8 l, Young Woman
with a Letter. 26 l, The Second of May, 1808. 40 l,
Neighboring Women on a Balcony.
No. 3947: a, 10 l, The Clothed Maja. b, 15 l,
The Naked Maja.

1996, July 9   Litho.   Perf. 13
3943 A1502   5 l   multicolored   .15
3944 A1502   8 l   multicolored   .20
3945 A1502 26 l   multicolored   .65
3946 A1502 40 l   multicolored   1.00
        Nos. 3943-3946 (4)   2.00
Souvenir Sheet
Perf. 13¹/₂x13
3947 A1502   Sheet of 2, #a.-b.   .60
No. 3947 contains two 54x29mm stamps.

Souvenir Sheet

St. John of Rila (876-946), Founder of Rila
Monastery — A1503

1996, Sept. 3
3948 A1503 10 l   multicolored   .25

Bulgarian
Renaissance
Houses — A1504

Various multi-level houses.

1996, Sept. 12   Litho.   Perf. 14x13¹/₂
Background Color
3949 A1504   10 l   buff   .15
3950 A1504   15 l   orange yellow   .15
3951 A1504   30 l   yellow green   .30
3952 A1504   50 l   red lilac   .45
3953 A1504   60 l   apple green   .55
3954 A1504 100 l   green blue   .95
        Nos. 3949-3954 (6)   2.55

Steam
Locomotives
A1505

1996, Sept. 24   Perf. 13
3955 A1505   5 l   1836   .15
3956 A1505 10 l   1847   .15
3957 A1505 12 l   1848   .15
3958 A1505 26 l   1876   .25
        Set value   .50

Natl.
Gallery of
Art, Cent.
A1506

1996, Oct. 14   Litho.   Perf. 13
3959 A1506 15 l   multicolored   .15

Defeat of Byzantine Army by Tsar Simeon,
1100th Anniv. — A1507

Designs: 10 l, Sword hilt, soldiers on horseback.
40 l, Sword blade, dagger, fallen soldiers.

1996, Oct. 21
3960 A1507 10 l   multicolored   .15
3961 A1507 40 l   multicolored   .35
    a.   Pair, #3960-3961   .50
No. 3961 is a continuous design.

UNICEF, 50th Anniv. — A1508

Children's drawings: 7 l, Diver, fish. 15 l, Circus
performers. 20 l, Boy, artist's pallete. 60 l, Women
seated at table.

1996, Nov. 18   Litho.   Perf. 13
3962 A1508   7 l   multicolored   .15
3963 A1508 15 l   multicolored   .30
3964 A1508 20 l   multicolored   .40
3965 A1508 60 l   multicolored   1.25
        Nos. 3962-3965 (4)   2.10

A1509   A1510

1996, Nov. 26
3966 A1509 15 l   Candles on tree   .30
3967 A1509 60 l   Church   1.20
        Christmas.

1996, Dec. 11   Litho.   Perf. 13
Painting of Old Bulgarian Town, by Tsanko
Lavrenov (1896-1978).
3968 A1510 15 l   multicolored   .30

Puppies
A1511   POINTER

1997, Feb. 25   Litho.   Perf. 13
3969 A1511   5 l   Pointer   .15
3970 A1511   7 l   Chow chow   .15
3971 A1511 25 l   Carakachan dog   .30
3972 A1511 50 l   Basset hound   .60
        Nos. 3969-3972 (4)   1.20

Alexander Graham Bell (1847-
1922) — A1512

1997, Mar. 10
3973 A1512 30 l   multicolored   .40

Ivan Milev (1897-
1927),
Painter — A1513

Stories and
Legends — A1514

Paintings: 5 l, Boy drinking from jar. 15 l, Person
with head bowed holding up hand. 30 l, Woman.
60 l, Woman carrying child.

1997, Mar. 20

3974	A1513	5 l	multicolored	.15
3975	A1513	15 l	multicolored	.20
3976	A1513	30 l	multicolored	.40
3977	A1513	60 l	multicolored	.80
	Nos. 3974-3977 (4)			*1.55*

1997, Apr. 14

Europa: 120 l, "March" lady in folk costume, symbol of spring. 600 l, St. George.

3978	A1514	120 l	multicolored	1.60
3979	A1514	600 l	multicolored	7.75

Konstantin Kissimov (1897-1965), Actor — A1515

1997, Apr. 16

3980	A1515	120 l	multicolored	1.60

A1516   A1517

1997, Apr. 21

3981	A1516	60 l	multicolored	.80

Heinrich von Stephan (1831-97).

1997, May 2   *Perf. 13½*

Historical Landmarks: 80 l, Nessebar. 200 l, Ivanovo Rock Churches. 300 l, Boyana Church. 500 l, Madara horseman. 600 l, Tomb of Sveshtari. 1000 l, Tomb of Kazanlak.

3982	A1517	80 l	browm & multi	1.00
3983	A1517	200 l	purple & multi	2.50
3984	A1517	300 l	bister & multi	4.00
3985	A1517	500 l	green & multi	6.50
3986	A1517	600 l	yellow & multi	7.75
3987	A1517	1000 l	orange & multi	13.00
	Nos. 3982-3987 (6)			*34.75*

Composers A1518

Designs: a, Gaetano Donizetti (1797-1848). b, Franz Schubert (1797-1828). c, Felix Mendelssohn (1809-1847). d, Johannes Brahms (1833-1897).

1997, May 29   Litho.   *Perf. 13½x13*

3988	A1518	120 l	Sheet of 4, #a.-d.	6.50

Plants in Bulgaria's Red Book A1519

Designs: 80 l, Trifolium rubens. 100 l, Tulipa hageri. 120 l, Inula spiraeifolia. 200 l, Paeonia tenuifolia.

1997, June 24   *Perf. 13*

3989	A1519	80 l	multicolored	1.00
3990	A1519	100 l	multicolored	1.25
3991	A1519	120 l	multicolored	1.60
3992	A1519	200 l	multicolored	2.50
	Nos. 3989-3992 (4)			*6.35*

A1520   A1521

1997, June 29   Litho.   *Perf. 13*

3993	A1520	120 l	multicolored	1.60

Civil aviation in Bulgaria, 50th anniv.

1997, July 3

3994	A1521	120 l	multicolored	1.60

Evlogy Georgiev (1819-97), banker, philanthopist.

Sofia '97, Modern Pentathlon World Championship — A1522

Designs: 60 l, Equestrian cross-country, running. 80 l, Fencing, swimming. 100 l, Running, women's fencing. 120 l, Men's shooting, diving. 200 l, Equestrian jumping, women's shooting.

1997, July 25

3995	A1522	60 l	multicolored	.75
3996	A1522	80 l	multicolored	1.00
3997	A1522	100 l	multicolored	1.25
3998	A1522	120 l	multicolored	1.60
3999	A1522	200 l	multicolored	2.50
	Nos. 3995-3999 (5)			*7.10*

City of Moscow, 850th Anniv. — A1523

1997, July 30

4000	A1523	120 l	multicolored	1.60

No. 4000 is printed se-tenant with label for Moscow '97 Intl. Philatelic Exhibition.

Diesel Engine, Cent. A1524

1997, Sept. 8   Litho.   *Perf. 13½x13*

4001	A1524	80 l	Boat	.15
4002	A1524	100 l	Tractor	.15
4003	A1524	120 l	Truck	.15
4004	A1524	200 l	Forklift	.30
	Nos. 4001-4004 (4)			*.75*

43rd General Assembly of Atlantic Club of Bulgaria — A1525

Designs: a, Goddess Tyche. b, Eagle on sphere. c, Building, lion statue, denomination UL. d, Building, denomination UR.

1997, Oct. 2   *Perf. 13*

4005	A1525	120 l	Sheet of 4, #a.-d.	.55

Miguel de Cervantes (1547-1616) — A1526

1997, Oct. 15

4006	A1526	120 l	multicolored	.15

Asen Raztsvetnikov (1897-1951), Poet, Writer — A1527

1997, Nov. 5

4007	A1528	120 l	multicolored	.15

Tsar Samuel (d. 1014), Ascension to Throne, 1000th Anniv. A1528

1997, Nov. 18   *Perf. 13½x13*

4008	A1528	120 l	Inscription	.15
4009	A1528	600 l	Tsar, soldiers	.85
a.	Pair, #4008-4009			1.00

Christmas — A1529

Designs: 120 l, Snow-covered houses, stars inside shape of Christmas tree, animals. 600 l, Nativity scene.

1997, Dec. 8   *Perf. 13x13½*

4010	A1529	120 l	multicolored	.15
4011	A1529	600 l	multicolored	.85

1998 Winter Olympic Games, Nagano A1530

Designs: 60 l, Speed skating. 80 l, Skiing. 120 l, Biathlon. 600 l, Pairs figure skating.

1997, Dec. 17   *Perf. 13½x13*

4012	A1530	60 l	multicolored	.15
4013	A1530	80 l	multicolored	.15
4014	A1530	120 l	multicolored	.15
4015	A1530	600 l	multicolored	.85
	Nos. 4012-4015 (4)			*1.30*

SEMI-POSTAL STAMPS

> Catalogue values for unused stamps in this section are for Never Hinged items.

Regular Issues of 1911-20 Surcharged:

a   b

c

50

Perf. 11½x12, 12x11½

1920, June 20   Unwmk.

B1	A43 (a)	2s + 1s ol grn	.15	.15
B2	A44 (b)	5s + 2½s grn	.15	.15
B3	A44 (b)	10s + 5s rose	.15	.15
B4	A44 (b)	15s + 7½s vio	.15	.15
B5	A44 (b)	25s + 12½s dp bl	.15	.15
B6	A44 (b)	30s + 15s choc	.15	.15
B7	A44 (b)	50s + 25s yel brn	.15	.15
B8	A29 (c)	1 l + 50s dk brn	.15	.15
B9	A37a (a)	2 l + 1 l brn org	.24	.24
B10	A38 (a)	3 l + 1 ½ l claret	.55	.42
	Set value		1.50	1.10

Surtax aided ex-prisoners of war. Value, Nos. B1-B7 imperf., $7.75.

Tsar Boris Type of 1937 Souvenir Sheet

1937, Nov. 22   Photo.   *Imperf.*

B11	A140	2 l + 18 l ultra	4.50	2.50

19th anniv. of the accession of Tsar Boris III to the throne.

Наводненнето 1939

Stamps of 1917-21 Surcharged in Black

1+1
лсва

1939, Oct. 22   *Perf. 12½, 12*

B12	A34	1 l + 1 l on 15s slate	.15	.15
B13	A69	2 l + 1 l on 1½ l ol grn	.15	.15
B14	A69	4 l + 2 l on 2 l dp grn	.18	.15
B15	A69	7 l + 4 l on 3 l Prus bl	.50	.28
B16	A69	14 l + 7 l on 5 l red brn	.85	.48
	Nos. B12-B16 (5)			*1.83*
	Set value			1.00

Surtax aided victims of the Sevlievo flood. The surcharge on #B13-B16 omits "leva."

Map of Bulgaria — SP2

1947, June 6   Typo.   *Perf. 11½*

B17	SP2	20 l + 10 l dk brn red & grn	.45	.30

30th Jubilee Esperanto Cong., Sofia, 1947.

Postman — SP3   Radio Towers — SP6

Designs: 10 l+5 l, Lineman. 20 l+10 l, Telephone operators.

1947, Nov. 5

B18	SP3	4 l + 2 l ol brn	.15	.15
B19	SP3	10 l + 5 l brt red	.15	.15
B20	SP3	20 l + 10 l dp ultra	.15	.15
B21	SP6	40 l + 20 l choc	.70	.55
	Nos. B18-B21 (4)			*1.15*
	Set value			.80

БЪЛГАРИЯ Christo Ganchev — SP7

Actors' Portraits: 10 l+6 l, Adriana Budevska. 15 l+7 l, Vasil Kirkov. 20 l+15 l, Sava Ognianov. 30 l+20 l, Krostyu Sarafov.

1947, Dec. 8   Litho.   Perf. 10½
B22	SP7	9 l + 5 l Prus grn	.15	.15
B23	SP7	10 l + 6 l car lake	.20	.15
B24	SP7	15 l + 7 l rose vio	.20	.15
B25	SP7	20 l + 15 l ultra	.20	.15
B26	SP7	30 l + 20 l vio brn	.48	.30
		Nos. B22-B26 (5)	1.23	
		Set value		.73

National Theater, 50th anniversary.

Souvenir Sheet

Olympic Emblem — SP8

1964, Oct. 10   Litho.   Imperf.
B27 SP8 40s + 20s bis, red & bl   2.75 1.40

18th Olympic Games, Tokyo, Oct. 10-25.

Horsemanship Type of 1965
Miniature Sheet

1965, Sept. 30   Photo.   Imperf.
B28 A630 40s + 20s Hurdle race   2.00 1.00

Space Exploration Type of 1966

Designs: 20s+10s, Yuri A. Gagarin, Alexei Leonov and Valentina Tereshkova. 30s+10s, Rocket and globe.

1966, Sept. 29   Photo.   Perf. 11½x11
B29 A652 20s + 10s pur & gray   1.00 .35

Miniature Sheet
B30	A652	30s + 10s gray, fawn & blk	2.00	.95

Winter Olympic Games Type of 1967

Sports and Emblem: 20s+10s, Slalom. 40s+10s, Figure skating couple.

1967, Sept.   Photo.   Perf. 11
B31 A687 20s + 10s multi   1.10 .28

Souvenir Sheet
Imperf
B32 A687 40s + 10s multi   2.00 .85

Type of Olympic Games Issue, 1968

Designs: 20s+10s, Rowing. 50s+10s, Stadium, Mexico City, and communications satellite.

1968, June 24   Photo.   Perf. 10½
B33	A702	20s + 10s vio bl, gray & pink	1.00	.32

Miniature Sheet
Imperf
B34	A702	50s + 10s gray, blk & Prus bl	2.25	1.50

Sports Type of Regular Issue, 1969

Designs: 13s+5s, Woman with ball. 20s+10s, Acrobatic jump.

1969, Oct.   Photo.   Perf. 11
Gymnasts in Light Gray
B35	A732	13s + 5s brt rose & vio	.40	.15
B36	A732	20s + 10s cit & bl grn	.70	.30

Miniature Sheet

Soccer
Ball — SP9

1970, Mar. 4   Photo.   Imperf.
B37 SP9 80s + 20s multi   2.25 1.40

9th World Soccer Championships for the Jules Rimet Cup, Mexico City, May 30-June 21, 1970.

Souvenir Sheet

Yuri A. Gagarin — SP10

1971, Apr. 12   Photo.   Imperf.
B38 SP10 40s + 20s multi   2.00 1.10

10th anniversary of the first man in space.

SP11   SP12

Bulgarian lion, magnifying glass, stamp tongs

1971, July 10   Photo.   Perf. 12½
B39	SP11	20s + 10s brn org, blk & gold	.90	.40

11th Congress of Bulgarian Philatelists, Sofia, July, 1971.

1989, Nov. 10   Litho.   Perf. 13x13½

Toys: a, Skateboarding. b, Doll, ball. c, Rope. d, Train set.

Souvenir Sheet
B40		Sheet of 4	2.75	1.40
a.-d.	SP12	30s +15s any single	.65	.35

For the benefit of the Children's Foundation.

AIR POST STAMPS

Regular Issues of 1925-26 Overprinted in Various Colors

1927-28   Unwmk.   Perf. 11½
C1	A76	2 l ol (R) ('28)	1.10	.70
C2	A74	4 l lake & yel (Bl)	1.10	.70
C3	A77	10 l brn blk & brn org (G) ('28)	17.00	13.00

Overprinted Vertically and Surcharged with New Value

C4	A77	1 l on 6 l dp bl & pale lem (C)	1.10	.70
a.		Inverted surcharge	325.00	275.00
b.		Pair, one without surcharge	425.00	
		Nos. C1-C4 (4)	20.30	15.10

Nos. C2-C4 overprinted in changed colors were not issued, value set $10.50.

Dove Delivering Message — AP1   Junkers Plane, Rila Monastery — AP2

1931, Oct. 28   Typo.
C5	AP1	1 l dk green	.18	.15
C6	AP1	2 l maroon	.18	.15
C7	AP1	6 l dp blue	.28	.20
C8	AP1	12 l carmine	.28	.30
C9	AP1	20 l dk violet	.70	.55
C10	AP1	30 l dp orange	1.10	1.25
C11	AP1	50 l orange brn	2.25	1.40
		Nos. C5-C11 (7)	4.97	4.00

Counterfeits exist. See Nos. C15-C18.

1932, May 9
C12	AP2	18 l blue grn	14.00	11.00
C13	AP2	24 l dp red	14.00	11.00
C14	AP2	28 l ultra	14.00	11.00
		Nos. C12-C14 (3)	42.00	33.00

> Catalogue values for unused stamps in this section, from this point to the end of the section, are for Never Hinged items.

1938, Dec. 27
C15	AP1	1 l violet brown	.24	.15
C16	AP1	2 l green	.18	.15
C17	AP1	6 l deep rose	.70	.28
C18	AP1	12 l peacock blue	.85	.32
		Nos. C15-C18 (4)	1.97	.90

Counterfeits exist.

Mail Plane — AP3   Plane over Tsar Assen's Tower — AP4

Designs: 4 l, Plane over Bachkovski Monastery. 6 l, Bojurishte Airport, Sofia. 10 l, Plane, train and motorcycle. 12 l, Planes over Sofia Palace. 16 l, Plane over Pirin Valley. 19 l, Plane over Rila Monastery. 30 l, Plane and Swallow. 45 l, Plane over Sofia Cathedral. 70 l, Plane over Shipka Monument. 100 l, Plane and Royal Cipher.

1940, Jan. 15   Photo.   Perf. 13
C19	AP3	1 l dk green	.15	.15
C20	AP4	2 l crimson	1.10	.15
C21	AP4	4 l red orange	.15	.15
C22	AP3	6 l dp blue	.20	.15
C23	AP4	10 l dk brown	.30	.15
C24	AP3	12 l dull brown	.52	.18
C25	AP3	16 l brt bl vio	.55	.24
C26	AP3	19 l sapphire	.75	.32
C27	AP4	30 l rose lake	1.10	.48
C28	AP4	45 l gray violet	2.75	.95
C29	AP4	70 l rose pink	2.75	1.25
C30	AP4	100 l dp slate bl	9.00	3.75
		Nos. C19-C30 (12)	19.32	7.92

Nos. 368 and 370 Overprinted in Black

1945, Jan. 26
C31	A181	1 l bright green	.15	.15
C32	A181	4 l red orange	.15	.15
		Set value	.18	.15

A similar overprint on Nos. O4, O5, O7 and O8 was privately applied.

Type of Parcel Post Stamps of 1944 Surcharged or Overprinted in Various Colors

Imperf
C37	PP5	10 l on 100 l dl yel (Bl)	.18	.15
C38	PP5	45 l on 100 l dl yel (C)	.28	.15
C39	PP5	75 l on 100 l dl yel (G)	.38	.25
C40	PP5	100 l dl yel (V)	.70	.35
		Nos. C37-C40 (4)	1.54	.90

Plane and Sun — AP16   Pigeon with Letter — AP17

Plane, Letter — AP18   Wings, Posthorn — AP19

Winged Letter — AP20   Plane, Sun — AP21

Pigeon, Posthorn — AP22   Mail Plane — AP23

Conventionalized Figure Holding Pigeon — AP24

1946, July 15   Litho.   Perf. 13
C41	AP16	1 l dull lilac	.15	.15
C42	AP16	2 l slate gray	.15	.15
C43	AP17	4 l violet blk	.15	.15
C44	AP18	6 l blue	.15	.15
C45	AP19	10 l turq green	.15	.15
C46	AP19	12 l yellow brn	.15	.15
C47	AP20	16 l rose violet	.15	.15
C48	AP19	19 l carmine	.15	.15
C49	AP21	30 l orange	.18	.15
C50	AP22	45 l lt ol grn	.18	.15
C51	AP22	75 l red brown	.24	.15
C52	AP23	100 l slate blk	.65	.24
C53	AP24	100 l red	.65	.24
		Set value	2.50	1.25

No. C47 exists imperf. Value $90.

People's Republic

Plane over
Plovdiv
AP25

1947, Aug. 31   Photo.   *Imperf.*
C54 AP25 40 l dull olive grn   .60 .50
Plovdiv International Fair, 1947.

Baldwin's Tower — AP26

1948, May 23   Litho.   *Perf. 11½*
C55 AP26 50 l ol brn, cr   .75 .60
Stamp Day and the 10th Congress of Bulgarian
Philatelic Societies, June 1948.

Romanian and
Bulgarian
Parliament
Buildings
AP27

Romanian and
Bulgarian Flags,
Bridge over
Danube
AP28

1948, Nov. 3   Photo.
C56 AP27 40 l ol gray, cr   .22 .15
C57 AP28 100 l red vio, cr   .52 .32
Romanian-Bulgarian friendship.

Mausoleum of Pleven — AP29

1949, June 26
C58 AP29 50 l brown   2.00 1.25
7th Congress of Bulgarian Philatelic Associations,
June 26-27, 1949.

Symbols of the
UPU — AP30

Frontier Guard and
Dog — AP31

1949, Oct. 10   *Perf. 11½*
C59 AP30 50 l violet blue   1.50 .75
75th anniv. of the UPU.

1949, Oct. 31
C60 AP31 60 l olive black   1.25 .90

Dimitrov
Mausoleum
AP32

1950, July 3   *Perf. 10½*
C61 AP32 40 l olive brown   3.00 1.10
1st anniv. of the death of George Dimitrov.

Belogradchic
Rocks — AP33

Air View of
Plovdiv
Fair — AP34

Designs: 16s, Beach, Varna. 20s, Harvesting
grain. 28s, Rila monastery. 44s, Studena dam.
60s, View of Dimitrovgrad. 80s, View of Trnovo.
1 l, University building, Sofia. 4 l, Partisans'
Monument.

1954, Apr. 1   Unwmk.   *Perf. 13*
C62 AP33   8s olive black   .15 .15
C63 AP34 12s rose brown   .15 .15
C64 AP33 16s brown   .15 .15
C65 AP33 20s brn red, cream   .15 .15
C66 AP33 28s dp bl, cream   .18 .15
C67 AP33 44s vio brn, cream   .18 .15
C68 AP33 60s red brn, cream   .26 .15
C69 AP34 80s dk grn, cream   .26 .18
C70 AP33   1 l dk bl grn, cream   1.25 .35
C71 AP34   4 l deep blue   3.00 .80
     Nos. C62-C71 (10)   5.73 2.38

Glider on
Mountainside
AP35

60s, Glider over airport. 80s, Three gliders.

1956, Oct. 15   Photo.
C72 AP35 44s brt blue   .16 .15
C73 AP35 60s purple   .30 .15
C74 AP35 80s dk blue grn   .48 .15
     Nos. C72-C74 (3)   .94
     Set value   .31
30th anniv. of glider flights in Bulgaria.

Passenger
Plane
AP36

1957, May 21   Unwmk.   *Perf. 13*
C75 AP36 80s deep blue   .60 .32
10th anniv. of civil aviation in Bulgaria.

Sputnik 3 over
Earth — AP37

1958, Nov. 28   *Perf. 11*
C76 AP37 80s brt grnsh blue   3.00 2.25
International Geophysical Year, 1957-58. Value,
imperf. $7.50.

Lunik 1 Leaving Earth
for Moon — AP38

1959, Feb. 28   *Perf. 10½*
C77 AP38   2 l brt blue & ocher   3.00 2.75
Launching of 1st man-made satellite to orbit
moon. Value, imperf. in slightly different colors,
$7.50 unused, $5.25 canceled.

Statue of
Liberty and
Tu-110
Airliner
AP39

Perf. 10½
1959, Nov. 11   Photo.   Unwmk.
C78 AP39   1 l violet bl & pink   1.75 1.50
Visit of Khrushchev to US. Value, imperf. $5.

Lunik 2 and
Moon — AP40

1960, June 23   Litho.   *Perf. 11*
C79 AP40 1.25 l blue, blk & yel   3.50 1.65
Russian rocket to the Moon, Sept. 12, 1959.

Sputnik 5 and Dogs Belka and Strelka
AP41

1961, Jan. 14   Photo.   *Perf. 11*
C80 AP41 1.25 l brt grnsh bl & org 4.00 2.50
Russian rocket flight of Aug. 19, 1970.

Maj. Yuri
A. Gagarin
and
Vostok 1
AP42

1961, Apr. 26   Unwmk.
C81 AP42   4 l grnsh bl, blk & red 2.50 1.50
First manned space flight, Apr. 12, 1961.

Soviet Space
Dogs — AP43

1961, June 28   *Perf. 11*
C82 AP43   2 l slate & dk car   2.00 1.00

Venus-bound
Rocket — AP44

1961, June 28
C83 AP44   2 l brt bl, yel & org   4.00 2.50
Soviet launching of the Venus space probe,
2/12/61.

Maj. Gherman
Titov — AP45

Design: 1.25 l, Spaceship Vostok 2.

1961, Nov. 20   Photo.   *Perf. 11x10½*
C84 AP45 75s dk ol grn & gray
                   grn   1.75 1.25
C85 AP45 1.25 l vio bl, lt bl & pink 2.25 1.75
1st manned space flight around the world, Maj.
Gherman Titov of Russia, Aug. 6-7, 1961.

Iskar River
Narrows — AP46

Designs: 2s, Varna and sailboat. 3s, Melnik.
10s, Trnovo. 40s, Pirin mountains.

1962, Feb. 3   Unwmk.   *Perf. 13*
C86 AP46   1s bl grn & gray bl   .15 .15
C87 AP46   2s blue & pink   .15 .15
C88 AP46   3s brown & ocher   .22 .15
C89 AP46 10s black & lemon   .45 .15
C90 AP46 40s dk green & green   1.10 .28
     Nos. C86-C90 (5)   2.07
     Set value   .48

Ilyushin
Turboprop
Airliner
AP47

1962, Aug. 18   *Perf. 11*
C91 AP47 13s blue & black   .60 .25
15th anniversary of TABSO airline.

Konstantin
E.
Tsiolkovsky
and Rocket
Launching
AP48

Design: 13s, Earth, moon and rocket on future
flight to the moon.

1962, Sept. 24   *Perf. 11*
C92 AP48   5s dp green & gray   1.90 .85
C93 AP48 13s ultra & yellow   1.10 .35
13th meeting of the International Astronautical
Federation.

Maj. Andrian G. Nikolayev — AP49

Designs: 2s, Lt. Col. Pavel R. Popovich. 40s,
Vostoks 3 and 4 in orbit.

1962, Dec. 9   Photo.   Unwmk.

C94	AP49	1s bl, sl grn & blk	.15	.15
C95	AP49	2s bl grn, grn & blk	.24	.15
C96	AP49	40s dk bl grn, pink & blk	1.65	.85
		Nos. C94-C96 (3)	2.04	1.15

First Russian group space flight of Vostoks 3 and 4, Aug. 12-15, 1962.

Spacecraft "Mars 1" Approaching Mars — AP50

Design: 13s, Rocket launching spacecraft, Earth, Moon and Mars.

1963, Feb. 25   Unwmk.   Perf. 11

C97	AP50	5s multicolored	.50	.28
C98	AP50	13s multicolored	1.00	.45

Launching of the Russian spacecraft "Mars 1," Nov. 1, 1962.

Lt. Col. Valeri F. Bykovski AP51

Designs: 2s, Lt. Valentina Tereshkova. 5s, Globe and trajectories.

1963, Aug. 26   Unwmk.   Perf. 11½

C99	AP51	1s pale vio & Prus bl	.15	.15
C100	AP51	2s citron & red brn	.15	.15
C101	AP51	5s rose & dk red	.15	.15
		Set value	.24	.15

The space flights of Valeri Bykovski, June 14-19, and Valentina Tereshkova, first woman cosmonaut, June 16-19, 1963. An imperf. souvenir sheet contains one 50s stamp showing Spasski tower and globe in lilac and red brown. Light blue border with red brown inscription. Size: 77x67mm. Value $2.50. See No. CB3.

Nos. C99-C100 Surcharged in Magenta or Green

1964, Aug. 22

C102	AP51	10s on 1s (M)	.32	.18
C103	AP51	20s on 2s	.65	.22

International Space Exhibition in Riccione, Italy. Overprint in Italian on No. C103.

St. John's Monastery, Rila — AP52

13s, Notre Dame, Paris; French inscription.

1964, Dec. 22   Photo.   Perf. 11½

C104	AP52	5s pale brn & blk	.18	.15
C105	AP52	13s lt ultra & sl bl	.65	.20
		Set value		.27

The philatelic exhibition at St. Ouen (Seine) organized by the Franco-Russian Philatelic Circle and philatelic organizations in various People's Democracies.

Paper Mill, Bukijovtz AP53

Designs: 10s, Metal works, Plovdiv. 13s, Metal works, Kremikovtsi. 20s, Oil refinery, Stara-Zagora. 40s, Fertilizer plant, Stara-Zagora. 1 l, Rest home, Meded.

1964-68   Unwmk.   Perf. 13

C106	AP53	8s grnsh blue	.15	.15
C107	AP53	10s red lilac	.15	.15
C108	AP53	13s brt violet	.22	.15
C109	AP53	20s slate blue	.70	.15
C110	AP53	40s dk olive grn	1.10	.18
C111	AP53	1 l red ('68)	1.90	.32
		Nos. C106-C111 (6)	4.22	
		Set value		.75

Issue dates: 1 l, May 6. Others, Dec. 7.

Three-master — AP54   Veliko Turnovo — AP55

Means of Communication: 2s, Postal coach. 3s, Old steam locomotive. 5s, Early cars. 10s, Montgolfier balloon. 13s, Early plane. 20s, Jet planes. 40s, Rocket and satellites. 1 l, Postrider.

1969, Mar. 31   Photo.   Perf. 13x12½

C112	AP54	1s gray & multi	.15	.15
C113	AP54	2s gray & multi	.15	.15
C114	AP54	3s gray & multi	.15	.15
C115	AP54	5s gray & multi	.15	.15
C116	AP54	10s gray & multi	.15	.15
C117	AP54	13s gray & multi	.25	.15
C118	AP54	20s gray & multi	.50	.22
C119	AP54	40s gray & multi	.90	.38
		Set value	2.00	1.00

Miniature Sheet

Imperf

C120	AP54	1 l gold & org	2.25	1.50

SOFIA 1969 Philatelic Exhibition, Sofia, May 31-June 8.

1973, July 30   Photo.   Perf. 13

Designs: Historic buildings in various cities.

C121	AP55	2s shown	.15	.15
C122	AP55	13s Roussalka	.25	.15
C123	AP55	20s Plovdiv	1.50	.80
C124	AP55	28s Sofia	.65	.18
		Nos. C121-C124 (4)	2.55	1.28

Aleksei A. Leonov and Soyuz AP56

Designs: 18s, Thomas P. Stafford and Apollo. 28s, Apollo and Soyuz over earth. 1 l, Apollo Soyuz link-up.

1975, July 15

C125	AP56	13s blue & multi	.30	.15
C126	AP56	18s purple & multi	.40	.15
C127	AP56	28s multicolored	1.00	.28
		Nos. C125-C127 (3)	1.70	
		Set value		.38

Souvenir Sheet

C128	AP56	1 l violet & multi	2.00	1.25

Apollo Soyuz space test project (Russo-American cooperation), launching July 15; link-up July 17.

Balloon Over Plovdiv — AP57

1977, Sept. 3

C129	AP57	25s yellow, brn & red	.50	.20

Alexei Leonov Floating in Space — AP58

Designs: 25s, Mariner 6, US spacecraft. 35s, Venera 4, USSR Venus probe.

1977, Oct. 14   Photo.   Perf. 13½

C130	AP58	12s multicolored	.20	.15
C131	AP58	25s multicolored	.42	.15
C132	AP58	35s multicolored	.60	.22
		Nos. C130-C132 (3)	1.22	.52

Space era, 20 years.

TU-154, Balkanair Emblem — AP59

1977   Perf. 13

C133	AP59	35s ultra & multi	.75	.35

30th anniv. of Bulgarian airline, Balkanair. Issued in sheets of 6 stamps + 3 labels (in lilac) with inscription and Balkanair emblem.

Baba Vida Fortress AP60

Design: 35s, Peace Bridge, connecting Rousse, Bulgaria, with Giurgiu, Romania.

1978   Photo.   Perf. 13

C134	AP60	25s multicolored	.40	.40
C135	AP60	35s multicolored	.55	.55

The Danube, European Intercontinental Waterway. Issued in sheets containing 5 each of Nos. C134-C135 and 2 labels, one showing course of Danube, the other hydrofoil and fish.

Red Cross AP61

1978, Mar.   Photo.   Perf. 13

C136	AP61	25s multicolored	.50	.16

Centenary of Bulgarian Red Cross.

AP62   AP63

Clock towers.

1979, June 5   Litho.   Perf. 12x12½

C137	AP62	13s Byalla Cherkva	.16	.15
C138	AP62	23s Botevgrad	.30	.15
C139	AP62	25s Pazardgick	.32	.15
C140	AP62	35s Grabovo	.42	.18
C141	AP62	53s Tryavna	.75	.30
		Nos. C137-C141 (5)	1.95	.93

1980, Oct. 22   Photo.   Perf. 12x12½

C142	AP62	13s Bjala	.20	.15
C143	AP62	23s Rasgrad	.35	.22
C144	AP62	25s Karnabat	.40	.18
C145	AP62	35s Serlievo	.52	.25
C146	AP62	53s Berkovitza	.80	.35
		Nos. C142-C146 (5)	2.27	1.15

1980

C147	AP63	13s shown	.20	.15
C148	AP63	25s Parachutist	.40	.15
		Set value		.21

15th World Parachute Championships, Kazanluk.

DWVY-1 Aircraft — AP64

1981, June 27   Litho.   Perf. 12½

C149	AP64	5s shown	.15	.15
C150	AP64	12s LAS-7	.20	.15
C151	AP64	25s LAS-8	.40	.15
C152	AP64	35s DAR-1	.52	.20
C153	AP64	45s DAR-3	.70	.26
C154	AP64	55s DAR-9	.88	.32
		Nos. C149-C154 (6)	2.85	1.23

AP65   AP66

1983, June 28

C155		Sheet of 2	1.50	1.00
a.	AP65	50s Valentina Tereshkova	.75	.50
b.	AP65	50s Svetlana Savitskaya	.75	.50

Women in space, 20th anniv.

1983, July 20   Photo.   Perf. 13

C156	AP66	5s TV tower, Tolbukhin	.15	.15
C157	AP66	13s Postwoman	.25	.15
C158	AP66	30s TV tower, Mt. Botev	.60	.30
a.		Strip of 3, #C156-C158	.95	.50
		Nos. C156-C158 (3)		
		Set value		.47

World Communications Year. Emblems of World Communications Year, Bulgarian Post, UPU and ITU on attached margins.

Souvenir Sheet

Geophysical Map of the Moon, Russia's Luna I, II and III Satellites — AP67

1984, Oct. 24   Photo.   *Perf. 13*
C159 AP67 1 l multicolored   2.00 1.00
Conquest of Space.

Intl. Civil Aviation Org., 40th Anniv. — AP68

1984, Dec. 21   Photo.   *Perf. 13*
C160 AP68 42s Balkan Airlines jet   .85 .42

Balkan Airlines — AP69

Design: Helicopter MU-8, passenger jet TU-154 and AN-21 transport plane.

1987, Aug. 25   Photo.
C161 AP69 25s multicolored   .75 .35

2nd Joint Soviet-Bulgarian Space Flight — AP70

Cosmonauts: A. Aleksandrov, A. Solovov and V. Savinich.

1989, June 7   Litho.   *Perf. 13½x13*
C162 AP70 13s multicolored   .35 .18

AIR POST SEMI-POSTAL STAMPS

> Catalogue values for unused stamps in this section are for Never Hinged items.

Statue of Liberty, Plane and Bridge — SPAP1

Perf. 11½.
1947, May 24   Unwmk.   Litho.
CB1 SPAP1 70 l + 30 l red brown   .95 .95
5th Philatelic Congress, Trnovo, and CIPEX, NYC, May, 1947.

Bulgarian Worker SPAP2

1948, Feb. 28   Photo.   *Perf. 12x11½.*
CB2 SPAP2 60 l henna brn, *cream*   .45 .35
2nd Bulgarian Workers' Congress, and sold by subscription only, at a premium of 16 l over face value.

Type of Air Post Stamps, 1963
Valeri Bykovski & Valentina Tereshkova.

1963, Aug. 26   Unwmk.   *Perf. 11½*
CB3 AP51 20s + 10s pale bluish grn & dk grn   1.25 .45
See note after No. C101.

SPECIAL DELIVERY STAMPS

> Catalogue values for unused stamps in this section are for Never Hinged items.

Postman on Bicycle — SD1   Mail Car — SD2

Postman on Motorcycle — SD3

1939   Unwmk.   Photo.   *Perf. 13*
E1 SD1 5 l deep blue   .60 .15
E2 SD2 6 l copper brn   .24 .15
E3 SD3 7 l golden brn   .35 .15
E4 SD2 8 l red orange   .60 .15
E5 SD1 20 l bright rose   1.25 .38
    Nos. E1-E5 (5)   3.04 .98

POSTAGE DUE STAMPS

D1   D2

Large Lozenge Perf. 5½ to 6½
1884   Typo.   Unwmk.
J1 D1 5s orange   150.00 15.00
J2 D1 25s lake   75.00 10.00
J3 D1 50s blue   12.00   5.00
    Nos. J1-J3 (3) 237.00 30.00

1886   *Imperf.*
J4 D1 5s orange   75.00   2.50
J5 D1 25s lake   120.00   2.50
J6 D1 50s blue   5.00   2.75
    Nos. J4-J6 (3) 200.00   7.75

1887   *Perf. 11½*
J7 D1 5s orange   9.50   1.00
J8 D1 25s lake   9.50   1.00
J9 D1 50s blue   3.50   1.00
    Nos. J7-J9 (3) 22.50   3.00

Same, Redrawn
24 horizontal lines of shading in upper part instead of 30 lines
1892   *Perf. 10½, 11½.*
J10 D1 5s orange   7.50   1.25
J11 D1 25s lake   7.50   1.25

1893
Pelure Paper
J12 D2 5s orange   10.00   3.50

D3   D4

1895   *Imperf.*
J13 D3 30s on 50s blue   7.00   2.00
Perf. 10½, 11½.
J14 D3 30s on 50s blue   7.00   2.00

Wmk. Coat of Arms in the Sheet
1896   *Perf. 13*
J15 D4 5s orange   3.00   .75
J16 D4 10s purple   2.00   .75
J17 D4 30s green   1.40   .45
    Nos. J15-J17 (3) 6.40   1.95
Nos. J15-J17 are also known on unwatermarked paper from the edges of sheets.
In 1901 a cancellation, "T" in circle, was applied to Nos. 60-65 and used provisionally as postage dues.

D5   D6

1901-04   Unwmk.   *Perf. 11½*
J19 D5 5s dl rose   .20 .15
J20 D5 10s yel grn   .42 .15
J21 D5 20s dl bl ('04)   3.25 .16
J22 D5 30s vio brn   .35 .16
J23 D5 50s org ('02)   5.50 4.00
    Nos. J19-J23 (5)   9.72 4.62
Nos. J19-J23 exist imperf. and in pairs imperf. between. Value, imperf., $250.

1915   Unwmk.   *Perf. 11½*
Thin Semi-Transparent Paper
J24 D6 5s green   .15 .15
J25 D6 10s purple   .20 .15
J26 D6 20s dl rose   .20 .15
J27 D6 30s dp org   1.10 .20
J28 D6 50s dp bl   .35 .17
    Nos. J24-J28 (5)   2.00
    Set value   .52

1919-21   *Perf. 11½, 12x11½*
J29 D6 5s emerald   .15 .15
    a. 5s gray green ('21) .30 .15
J30 D6 10s violet   .15 .15
J31 D6 20s salmon   .15 .15
    a. 20s yellow   .15 .15
J32 D6 30s orange   .15 .15
    a. 30s red orange ('21) .65 .65
J33 D6 50s blue   .15 .15
J34 D6 1 l emerald ('21) .18 .15
J35 D6 2 l rose ('21)   .18 .15
J36 D6 3 l brown org ('21) .15 .15
    Set value   1.16 .42
Stotinki values of the above series surcharged 10s or 20s were used as ordinary postage stamps. See Nos. 182-185.
The 1919 printings are on thicker white paper with clean-cut perforations, the 1921 printings on thicker grayish paper with rough perforations.
Most of this series exist imperforate and in pairs imperforate between.

Heraldic Lion — D7

1932, Aug. 15
Thin Paper
J37 D7 1 l olive bister   .24 .20
J38 D7 2 l rose brown   .24 .20
J39 D7 6 l brown violet   .75 .35
    Nos. J37-J39 (3)   1.23 .75

Lion of Trnovo — D8   National Arms — D9

1933, Apr. 10
J40 D8 20s dk brn   .15 .15
J41 D8 40s dp bl   .15 .15
J42 D8 80s car rose   .15 .15
J43 D9 1 l org brn   .24 .18
J44 D9 2 l olive   .30 .25
J45 D9 6 l dl vio   .15 .15
J46 D9 14 l ultra   .24 .15
    Set value   1.00 .78

> Catalogue values for unused stamps in this section, from this point to the end of the section, are for Never Hinged items.

National Arms — D10

1947, June   Typo.   *Perf. 10½*
J47 D10 1 l chocolate   .15 .15
J48 D10 2 l deep claret   .15 .15
J49 D10 8 l deep orange   .15 .15
J50 D10 20 l blue   .22 .15
    Set value   .42 .25

Arms of the People's Republic — D11

1951   *Perf. 11½x10½*
J51 D11 1 l chocolate   .15 .15
J52 D11 2 l claret   .15 .15
J53 D11 8 l red orange   .22 .15
J54 D11 20 l deep blue   .60 .32
    Set value   .92 .52

OFFICIAL STAMPS

> Catalogue values for unused stamps in this section are for Never Hinged items.

Bulgarian Coat of Arms
O1   O2

1942   Unwmk.   Typo.   *Perf. 13*
O1 O1 10s yel grn   .15 .15
O2 O1 30s red   .15 .15
O3 O1 50s bister   .15 .15
O4 O2 1 l vio bl   .15 .15
O5 O2 2 l dk grn   .15 .15
O6 O2 3 l lilac   .15 .15
O7 O2 4 l rose   .15 .15
O8 O2 5 l carmine   .16 .15
    Set value   .65 .40

1944   *Perf. 10½x11½*
O9 O2 1 l blue   .20 .15
O10 O2 2 l brt red   .20 .15

Lion Rampant
O3   O4

O5

1945   *Imperf.*
O11   O5   1 l pink   .15   .15

Perf. 10¹/₂x11¹/₂, Imperf.
O12   O3   2 l blue green   .15   .15
O13   O4   3 l bister brown   .15   .15
O14   O4   4 l light ultra   .15   .15
O15   O5   5 l brown lake   .15   .15
         Set value   .25   .25

In 1950, four stamps prepared for official use were issued as regular postage stamps. See Nos. 724-727.

PARCEL POST STAMPS

Catalogue values for unused stamps in this section are for Never Hinged items.

Weighing   Parcel Post — PP2
Packages — PP1

Designs: 3 l, 8 l, 20 l, Parcel post truck. 4 l, 6 l, 10 l, Motorcycle.

Perf. 12¹/₂x13¹/₂, 13¹/₂x12¹/₂
1941-42   **Photo.**   **Unwmk.**
Q1   PP1   1 l slate grn   .15   .15
Q2   PP2   2 l crimson   .15   .15
Q3   PP2   3 l dull brn   .15   .15
Q4   PP2   4 l red org   .15   .15
Q5   PP2   5 l deep blue   .15   .15
Q6   PP1   5 l slate grn ('42)   .15   .15
Q7   PP2   6 l red vio   .15   .15
Q8   PP2   6 l henna brn ('42)   .15   .15
Q9   PP1   7 l dark blue   .15   .15
Q10   PP1   7 l dk brn ('42)   .15   .15
Q11   PP2   8 l brt bl grn   .15   .15
Q12   PP2   8 l green ('42)   .15   .15
Q13   PP2   9 l olive gray   .15   .15
Q14   PP2   9 l dp olive ('42)   .15   .15
Q15   PP2   10 l orange   .15   .15
Q16   PP2   20 l gray vio   .42   .15
Q17   PP2   30 l dull blk   .55   .15
Q18   PP2   30 l sepia ('42)   .50   .15
        Set value   2.50   1.00

Arms of Bulgaria — PP5

1944   **Litho.**   *Imperf.*
Q21   PP5   1 l dk carmine   .15   .15
Q22   PP5   3 l blue grn   .15   .15
Q23   PP5   5 l dull bl grn   .15   .15
Q24   PP5   7 l rose lilac   .15   .15
Q25   PP5   10 l deep blue   .15   .15
Q26   PP5   20 l orange brn   .15   .15
Q27   PP5   30 l dk brn car   .15   .15
Q28   PP5   50 l red orange   .30   .16
Q29   PP5   100 l blue   .52   .22
        Set value   1.30   .75

For overprints and surcharges see Nos. 448-454, C37-C40.

POSTAL TAX STAMPS

The use of stamps Nos. RA1 to RA18 was compulsory on letters, etc., to be delivered on Sundays and holidays. The money received from their sale was used toward maintaining a sanatorium for employees of the post, telegraph and telephone services.

View of Sanatorium
PT1

Sanatorium, Peshtera
PT2

1925-29   **Unwmk.**   **Typo.**   *Perf. 11¹/₂*
RA1   PT1   1 l blk, grnsh bl   2.75   .15
RA2   PT1   1 l chocolate ('26)   2.75   .15
RA3   PT1   1 l orange ('27)   3.00   .15
RA4   PT1   1 l pink ('28)   4.50   .15
RA5   PT1   1 l vio, pnksh ('29)   4.25   .15
RA6   PT2   2 l blue green   .35   .15
RA7   PT2   2 l violet ('27)   .35   .16
RA8   PT2   5 l deep blue   3.00   .80
RA9   PT2   5 l rose ('27)   3.75   .40
    Nos. RA1-RA9 (9)   24.70   2.26

St. Constantine Sanatorium
PT3

1930-33
RA10   PT3   1 l red brn & ol grn   4.00   .16
RA11   PT3   1 l ol grn & yel ('31)   .50   .16
RA12   PT3   1 l red vio & ol brn ('33)   .50   .16
    Nos. RA10-RA12 (3)   5.00   .48

Trojan Rest Home — PT4

Sanatorium PT5

1935   **Wmk. 145**   *Perf. 11, 11¹/₂*
RA13   PT4   1 l choc & red org   .32   .15
RA14   PT4   1 l emer & indigo   .32   .15
RA15   PT5   5 l red brn & indigo   1.40   .35
    Nos. RA13-RA15 (3)   2.04
       Set value   .51

St. Constantine Sanatorium
PT6

2 l, Children at seashore. 5 l, Rest home.

1941   **Unwmk.**   **Photo.**   *Perf. 13*
RA16   PT6   1 l dark olive green   .15   .15
RA17   PT6   2 l red orange   .15   .15
RA18   PT6   5 l deep blue   .30   .15
       Set value   .50   .22

See Nos. 702-705 for same designs in smaller size issued as regular postage.

BURKINA FASO

búr-'kē-nə-'fä-sō

Upper Volta

LOCATION — Northwestern Africa, north of Ghana
GOVT. — Republic
AREA — 105,869 sq. mi.
POP. — 6,695,500 (est. 1984)
CAPITAL — Ouagadougou

In 1919 the French territory of Upper Volta was detached from the southern section of Upper Senegal and Niger and made a separate colony. In 1933 the colony was divided among its neighbors: French Sudan, Ivory Coast, and Niger Territory. The Republic of Upper Volta was proclaimed December 11, 1958; the name was changed to Burkina Faso on August 4, 1984.

100 Centimes = 1 Franc

Catalogue values for unused stamps in this country are for Never Hinged items, beginning with Scott 70 in the regular postage section, Scott B1 in the semi-postal section, Scott C1 in the airpost section, Scott J21 in the postage due section, and Scott O1 in the official section.

Stamps and Types of Upper Senegal and Niger, 1914-17, Overprinted in Black or Red   **HAUTE-VOLTA**

1920-28   **Unwmk.**   *Perf. 13¹/₂x14*
1   A4   1c brn vio & vio   .15   .15
2   A4   2c gray & brn vio (R)   .15   .15
3   A4   4c blk & bl   .15   .15
4   A4   5c yel grn & bl grn   .25   .15
5   A4   5c ol brn & dk brn ('22)   .15   .15
6   A4   10c red org & rose   .40   .15
7   A4   10c yel grn & bl grn ('22)   .15   .15
8   A4   10c claret & bl ('25)   .25   .25
   a.   Overprint omitted   80.00
9   A4   15c choc & org   .40   .30
10   A4   20c brn vio & blk (R)   .65   .55
11   A4   25c ultra & bl   .65   .30
12   A4   25c blk & bl grn ('22)   .45   .40
   a.   Overprint omitted   65.00
13   A4   30c ol brn & brn (R)   1.10   .65
14   A4   30c red org & rose ('22)   .40   .35
15   A4   30c vio & brn red ('25)   .40   .35
16   A4   30c dl grn & bl grn ('27)   .70   .45
17   A4   35c car rose & vio   .45   .30
18   A4   40c gray & car rose   .45   .35
19   A4   45c bl & brn (R)   .35   .20
20   A4   50c blk & grn   1.50   1.10
21   A4   50c ultra & bl ('22)   .15   .15
22   A4   50c red org & bl ('25)   .40   .35
23   A4   60c org red ('26)   .15   .15
24   A4   65c bis & pale bl ('28)   .70   .45
25   A4   75c org & brn   .30   .30
26   A4   1fr brn & brn vio   .65   .40
27   A4   2fr grn & bl   1.00   .65
28   A4   5fr vio & blk (R)   2.50   1.75
    Nos. 1-28 (28)   15.00   11.00

No. 9 Surcharged in Various Colors   **0,01 ═ 0,01**

1922
29   A4   0,01c on 15c (Bk)   .40   .40
   a.   Double surcharge   50.00   50.00
30   A4   0,02c on 15c (Bl)   .40   .40
31   A4   0,05c on 15c (R)   .40   .40
    Nos. 29-31 (3)   1.20   1.20

Type of 1920 Surcharged   **60 ═ 60**

1922
32   A4   60c on 75c vio, pnksh   .35   .35

Stamps and Types of 1920 Surcharged with New Value and Bars

1924-27
33   A4   25c on 2fr grn & blk   .45   .45
34   A4   25c on 5fr vio & blk   .45   .45
35   A4   65c on 45c bl & brn ('25)   .50   .50
36   A4   85c on 75c org & brn ('25)   .70   .70
37   A4   90c on 75c brn red & sal pink ('27)   .70   .70
38   A4   1.25fr on 1fr dp bl & lt bl (R) ('26)   .45   .45
39   A4   1.50fr on 1fr dp bl & ultra ('27)   1.25   1.25
40   A4   3fr on 5fr dl red & brn org ('27)   1.65   1.65
41   A4   10fr on 5fr ol grn & lil rose ('27)   7.25   7.25

---

42   A4   20fr on 5fr org brn & vio ('27)   10.00   10.00
    Nos. 33-42 (10)   23.40   23.40

Hausa   Hausa
Chief — A5   Woman — A6

Hausa Warrior
A7

1928   **Typo.**   *Perf. 13¹/₂x14*
43   A5   1c indigo & grn   .15   .15
44   A5   2c brn & lil   .15   .15
45   A5   4c blk & yel   .15   .15
46   A5   5c indigo & gray bl   .20   .20
47   A5   10c indigo & pink   .50   .50
48   A5   15c brn & bl   .90   .90
49   A5   20c brn & grn   .90   .90
50   A6   25c brn & yel   1.10   1.10
51   A6   30c dp grn & grn   1.10   1.10
52   A6   40c blk & pink   1.10   1.10
53   A6   45c brn & blue   1.10   1.10
54   A6   50c blk & grn   1.10   1.10
55   A6   65c indigo & bl   1.65   1.65
56   A6   75c blk & lil   1.10   1.10
57   A6   90c brn red & lil   1.10   1.10

Perf. 14x13¹/₂
58   A7   1fr brn & grn   1.10   1.10
59   A7   1.10fr indigo & bl   1.10   1.10
60   A7   1.50fr ultra & grysh   1.75   1.75
61   A7   2fr blk & bl   2.25   2.25
62   A7   3fr brn & yel   2.25   2.25
63   A7   5fr brn & lil   2.25   2.25
64   A7   10fr blk & grn   9.00   9.00
65   A7   20fr blk & pink   13.00   13.00
    Nos. 43-65 (23)   45.00   45.00

Colonial Exposition Issue
Common Design Types
1931   **Engr.**   *Perf. 12¹/₂*
Country Name Typo. in Black
66   CD70   40c dp grn   1.50   1.50
67   CD71   50c violet   1.50   1.50
68   CD72   90c red org   1.50   1.50
69   CD73   1.50fr dull blue   2.00   2.00
    Nos. 66-69 (4)   6.50   6.50

Common Design Types pictured in section at front of book.

Catalogue values for unused stamps in this section, from this point to the end of the section, are for Never Hinged items.

Republic

President   Deer Mask and
Ouezzin   Deer — A9
Coulibaly — A8

1959   **Unwmk.**   **Engr.**   *Perf. 13*
70   A8   25fr black & magenta   .25   .15

1st anniv. of the proclamation of the Republic; Ouezzin Coulibaly, Council President, who died in December, 1958.

Imperforates
Most Upper Volta stamps from 1959 onward exist imperforate in issued and trial colors, and also in small presentation sheets in issued colors.

1960

Animal Masks: 1fr, 2fr, 4fr, Wart hog. 5fr, 6fr, 8fr, Monkey. 10fr, 15fr, 20fr, Buffalo. 25fr, Coba (antelope). 30fr, 40fr, 50fr, Elephant. 60fr, 85fr, Secretary bird.

71	A9	30c rose & violet	.15	.15
72	A9	40c buff & dp claret	.15	.15
73	A9	50c bl grn & gray ol	.15	.15
74	A9	1fr red, blk & red brn	.15	.15
75	A9	2fr emer, yel grn & dk grn	.15	.15
76	A9	4fr bl, vio & ind	.15	.15
77	A9	5fr ol bis, red & brn	.15	.15
78	A9	6fr grnsh bl & vio brn	.15	.15
79	A9	8fr org & red brn	.15	.15
80	A9	10fr lt yel grn & plum	.15	.15
81	A9	15fr org, ultra & brn	.15	.15
82	A9	20fr green & ultra	.22	.15
83	A9	25fr bl, emer & dp claret	.25	.15
84	A9	30fr dk bl grn, blk & brn	.30	.15
85	A9	40fr ultra, ind & dk car	.38	.15
86	A9	50fr brt pink, brn & grn	.42	.18
87	A9	60fr org brn & bl	.55	.25
88	A9	85fr gray ol & dk bl	.80	.32
		Set value	3.60	1.80

C.C.T.A. Issue
Common Design Type

1960		Engr.	Perf. 13	
89	CD106	25fr vio bl & slate	.35	.35

Emblem of the Entente — A9a

Pres. Maurice Yameogo — A10

1960		Photo.	Perf. 13x13½	
90	A9a	25fr multicolored	.40	.35

Council of the Entente.

1960, May 1		Engr.	Perf. 13	
91	A10	25fr dk vio brn & slate	.25	.16

Flag, Village and Couple — A11

1960, Aug. 5		Unwmk.	Perf. 13	
92	A11	25fr red brn, blk & red	.35	.25

Proclamation of independence, Aug. 5, 1960.

World Meteorological Organization Emblem — A12

1961, May 4				
93	A12	25fr blk, bl & red	.30	.25

First World Meteorological Day.

Arms of Republic — A13

1961, Dec. 8		Photo.	Perf. 12x12½	
94	A13	25fr multicolored	.25	.25

The 1961 independence celebrations.

WMO Emblem, Weather Station and Sorghum Grain — A14

1962, Mar. 23		Unwmk.	Perf. 13	
95	A14	25fr dk bl, emer & brn	.30	.25

UN 2nd World Meteorological Day, Mar. 23.

Hospital and Nurse — A15

1962, June 23			Perf. 13x12	
96	A15	25fr multicolored	.35	.35

Founding of Upper Volta Red Cross.

Buffalos at Water Hole — A16

Designs: 10fr, Lions, horiz. 15fr, Defassa waterbuck. 25fr, Arly reservation, horiz. 50fr, Diapaga reservation, horiz. 85fr, Buffon's kob.

		Perf. 12½x12, 12x12½		
1962, June 30			Engr.	
97	A16	5fr sepia, bl & grn	.15	.15
98	A16	10fr red brn, grn & yel	.16	.15
99	A16	15fr sepia, grn & yel	.25	.16
100	A16	25fr vio brn, bl & grn	.45	.20
101	A16	50fr vio brn, bl & grn	.80	.55
102	A16	85fr red brn, bl & grn	1.20	.80
		Nos. 97-102 (6)	3.01	2.01

Abidjan Games Issue
Common Design Type

Designs: 20fr, Soccer. 25fr, Bicycling. 85fr, Boxing. All horiz.

1962, July 21		Photo.	Perf. 12½x12	
103	CD109	20fr multicolored	.25	.18
104	CD109	25fr multicolored	.30	.25
105	CD109	85fr multicolored	.60	.40
		Nos. 103-105 (3)	1.15	.83

African-Malgache Union Issue
Common Design Type

1962, Sept. 8			Unwmk.	
106	CD110	30fr red, bluish grn & gold	.70	.65

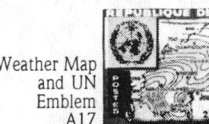

Weather Map and UN Emblem A17

1963, Mar. 23			Perf. 12x12½	
107	A17	70fr multicolored	.60	.45

3rd World Meteorological Day, Mar. 23.

Friendship Games, Dakar, Apr. 11-21 — A18

1963, Apr. 11		Engr.	Perf. 13	
108	A18	20fr Basketball	.22	.15
109	A18	25fr Discus	.25	.15
110	A18	50fr Judo	.55	.25
		Nos. 108-110 (3)	1.02	.55

Amaryllis A19

Flowers: 50c, Hibiscus. 1fr, Oldenlandia grandiflora. 1.50fr, Rose moss (portulaca). 2fr, Tobacco. 4fr, Morning glory. 5fr, Striga senegalensis. 6fr, Cowpea. 8fr, Lepidagathis heudelotiana. 10fr, Spurge. 25fr, Argyreia nervosa. 30fr, Rangoon creeper. 40fr, Water lily. 50fr, White plumeria. 60fr, Crotalaria retusa. 85fr, Hibiscus. Nos. 111-119 are vert.

1963		Photo.		
111	A19	50c multicolored	.15	.15
112	A19	1fr multicolored	.15	.15
113	A19	1.50fr multicolored	.15	.15
114	A19	2fr multicolored	.15	.15
115	A19	4fr multicolored	.15	.15
116	A19	5fr multicolored	.15	.15
117	A19	6fr multicolored	.15	.15
118	A19	8fr multicolored	.15	.15
119	A19	10fr multicolored	.16	.15
120	A19	15fr multicolored	.20	.15
121	A19	25fr multicolored	.30	.16
122	A19	30fr multicolored	.35	.20
123	A19	40fr multicolored	.40	.30
124	A19	50fr multicolored	.55	.35
125	A19	60fr multicolored	.65	.42
126	A19	85fr multicolored	.90	.55
		Set value	4.00	2.75

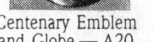

Centenary Emblem and Globe — A20

Scroll — A21

1963, Oct. 21		Unwmk.	Perf. 12	
127	A20	25fr multicolored	.50	.40

Centenary of International Red Cross.

1963, Dec. 10		Photo.	Perf. 13x12½	
128	A21	25fr dp claret, gold & bl	.30	.20

15th anniv. of the Universal Declaration of Human Rights.

Sound Wave Patterns A22

1964, Jan. 16			Perf. 12½x13	
129	A22	25fr multicolored	.25	.20

Upper Volta's admission to the ITU.

Barograph and WMO Emblem A23

1964, Mar. 23		Engr.	Perf. 13	
130	A23	50fr dk car rose, grn & bl	.55	.40

4th World Meteorological Day, Mar. 23.

World Connected by Letters and Carrier Pigeon — A24

60fr, World connected by letters and jet plane.

1964, Mar. 29		Photo.	Perf. 13x12	
131	A24	25fr gray brn & ultra	.25	.20
132	A24	60fr gray brn & org	.60	.42

Upper Volta's admission to the UPU.

IQSY Emblem and Seasonal Allegories — A25

1964, Aug. 17		Engr.	Perf. 13	
133	A25	30fr grn, ocher & car	.35	.25

International Quiet Sun Year.

Cooperation Issue
Common Design Type

1964, Nov. 7			Perf. 13	
134	CD119	70fr dl bl grn, dk brn & car	.65	.42

Hotel Independance, Ouagadougou A26

1964, Dec. 11		Litho.	Perf. 12½x13	
135	A26	25fr multicolored	1.00	.35

Pigmy Long-tailed Sunbird — A27

Comoe Waterfall — A28

1965, Mar. 1		Photo.	Perf. 13x12½	
		Size: 22x36mm		
136	A27	10fr shown	.20	.16
137	A27	15fr Olive-bellied Sunbird	.25	.20
138	A27	20fr Splendid Sunbird	.40	.25
		Nos. 136-138,C20 (4)	6.35	3.11

1965		Engr.	Perf. 13	

Design: 25fr, Great Waterfall of Banfora, horiz.

139	A28	5fr yel grn, bl & red brn	.15	.15
140	A28	25fr dk red, brt bl & grn	.25	.16
		Set value		.23

Soccer — A29

Abraham Lincoln — A30

Designs: 25fr, Boxing gloves and ring. 70fr, Tennis rackets, ball and net.

1965, July 15		Unwmk.	Perf. 13	
141	A29	15fr brn, red & dk grn	.16	.15
142	A29	25fr pale org, bl & brn	.28	.18
143	A29	70fr dk car & brt grn	.60	.32
		Nos. 141-143 (3)	1.04	.65

1st African Games, Brazzaville, July 18-25.

1965, Nov. 3		Photo.	Perf. 13x12½	
144	A30	50fr green & multi	.50	.38

Centenary of death of Abraham Lincoln.

Pres. Maurice Yameogo — A31

1965, Dec. 11 Photo. Perf. 13x12¹/₂
145 A31 25fr multicolored .25 .16

Mantis
A32

Wart Hog
A33

Headress
A34

1966 Perf. 13x12¹/₂, 12¹/₂x13
146 A33 1fr Nemopistha imperatrix .15 .15
147 A33 2fr Ball python .15 .15
148 A32 3fr shown .15 .15
149 A32 4fr Grasshopper .15 .15
150 A33 5fr shown .15 .15
151 A32 6fr Scorpion .15 .15
152 A33 8fr Green monkey .15 .15
153 A32 10fr Dromedary .15 .15
154 A32 15fr Leopard .20 .16
155 A32 20fr Cape buffalo .22 .16
156 A33 25fr Hippopotamus .30 .16
157 A32 30fr Agama lizard .38 .20
158 A33 45fr Common puff adder .55 .22
159 A33 50fr Chameleon .60 .35
160 A33 60fr Ugada limbata .70 .42
161 A33 85fr Elephant .90 .50
Nos. 146-161 (16) 5.05
Set value 2.65

1966, Apr. 9 Photo. Perf. 13x12¹/₂
25fr, Plumed headdress. 60fr, Male dancer.
162 A34 20fr yel grn, choc & red .20 .15
163 A34 25fr multicolored .25 .16
164 A34 60fr org, dk brn & red .60 .35
Nos. 162-164 (3) 1.05 .66
Intl. Negro Arts Festival, Dakar, Senegal, 4/1-24.

Pô Church
A35

Design: No. 166, Bobo-Dioulasso Mosque.

1966, Apr. 15 Perf. 12¹/₂x13
165 A35 25fr multicolored .22 .16
166 A35 25fr bl, cream & red brn .22 .16

The Red Cross Helping
the World — A36

1966, June Photo. Perf. 13x12¹/₂
167 A36 25fr lemon, blk & car .22 .15
Issued to honor the Red Cross.

Boy Scouts in
Camp — A37

15fr, Two Scouts on a cliff exploring the country.

1966, June 15 Perf. 12¹/₂x13
168 A37 10fr multicolored .15 .15
169 A37 15fr blk, bis brn, & dl yel .16 .15
Set value .17
Issued to honor the Boy Scouts.

Cow Receiving
Injection
A38

1966, Aug. 16 Photo. Perf. 12¹/₂x13
170 A38 25fr yel, blk & blue .25 .20
Campaign against cattle plague.

Plowing with
Donkey
A39

Design: 30fr, Crop rotation, Kamboince Experimental Station.

1966, Sept. 15 Photo. Perf. 12¹/₂x13
171 A39 25fr multicolored .22 .15
172 A39 30fr multicolored .25 .16
Natl. and rural education; 3rd anniv. of the Kamboince Experimental Station (No. 172).

UNESCO
Emblem and
Map of
Africa — A40

UNICEF
Emblem and
Children
A41

1966, Dec. 10 Engr. Perf. 13
173 A40 50fr brt bl, blk & red .50 .25
174 A41 50fr dk vio, dp lil & dk red .50 .25
20th anniv. of UNESCO and of UNICEF.

Arms of Upper
Volta — A42

Symbols of
Agriculture,
Industry, Men and
Women — A43

1967, Jan. 2 Photo. Perf. 12¹/₂x13
175 A42 30fr multicolored .22 .15

Europafrica Issue
1967, Feb. 4 Photo. Perf. 12¹/₂
176 A43 60fr multicolored .50 .30

Scout
Handclasp
and Jamboree
Emblem
A44

5fr, Jamboree emblem and Scout holding hat.

1967, June 8 Photo. Perf. 12¹/₂x13
177 A44 5fr multicolored .20 .15
178 A44 20fr multicolored .55 .40
12th Boy Scout World Jamboree, Farragut State Park, Idaho, Aug. 1-9. See No. C41.

Bank Book
and Hands
with
Coins — A45

1967, Aug. 22 Engr. Perf. 13
179 A45 30fr slate grn, ocher & olive .25 .15
National Savings Bank.

Mailman on
Bicycle — A46

1967, Oct. 15 Engr. Perf. 13
180 A46 30fr dk bl, emer & brn .30 .16
Stamp Day.

Monetary Union Issue
Common Design Type
1967, Nov. 4 Engr. Perf. 13
181 CD125 30fr dk vio & dl bl .25 .15

View of
Nizier — A47

Olympic Emblem and: 50fr, Les Deux-Alps, vert. 100fr, Ski lift and view of Villard-de-Lans.

1967, Nov. 28
182 A47 15fr brt bl, grn & brn .16 .15
183 A47 50fr brt bl & slate grn .45 .20
184 A47 100fr brt bl, grn & red .90 .45
Nos. 182-184 (3) 1.51 .80
10th Winter Olympic Games, Grenoble, France, Feb. 6-18, 1968.

White and
Black Men
Holding
Human Rights
Emblem
A48

1968, Jan. 2 Photo. Perf. 12¹/₂x13
185 A48 20fr brt bl, gold & dp car .20 .15
186 A48 30fr grn, gold & dp car .30 .16
International Human Rights Year.

Administration School and Student — A49

1968, Feb. 2 Engr. Perf. 13
187 A49 30fr ol bis, Prus bl & brt grn .25 .15
National School of Administration.

WHO Emblem
and Sick
People — A50

1968, Apr. 7 Engr. Perf. 13
188 A50 30fr ind, brt bl & car rose .30 .16
189 A50 50fr brt bl, sl grn & lt brn .45 .22
WHO, 20th anniversary.

Telephone Office, Bobo-Dioulasso — A51

1968, Sept. 30 Photo. Perf. 12¹/₂x12
190 A51 30fr multicolored .28 .16
Opening of the automatic telephone office in Bobo-Dioulasso.

Weaver
A52

1968, Oct. 30 Engr. Perf. 13
Size: 36x22mm
191 A52 30fr magenta, brn & ocher .30 .16
See No. C58.

Grain Pouring over
World, Plower and FAO
Emblem — A53

1969, Jan. 7 Engr. Perf. 13
192 A53 30fr slate, vio bl & maroon .25 .15
UNFAO world food program.

Automatic
Looms and
ILO Emblem
A54

1969, Mar. 15 Engr. Perf. 13
193 A54 30fr brt grn, mar & ind .25 .15
ILO, 50th anniversary.

Smith — A55

1969, Apr. 3 Engr. Perf. 13
Size: 36x22mm
194 A55 5fr magenta & blk .15 .15
See No. C64.

Blood
Donor — A56

1969, May 15 Engr. Perf. 13
195 A56 30fr blk, bl & car .25 .16
League of Red Cross Societies, 50th anniv.

Nile
Pike — A57

Fish: 20fr, Nannocharax gobioides. 25fr, Hemigrammocharax polli. 55fr, Alestes luteus. 85fr, Micralestes voltae.

1969   Engr.   Perf. 13
Size: 36x22mm

196	A57 20fr brt bl, brn & yel	.32	.20
197	A57 25fr slate, brn & dk brn	.32	.20
198	A57 30fr dk olive & blk	.45	.25
199	A57 55fr dk grn, yel & ol	.60	.42
200	A57 85fr slate brn & pink	1.25	.90
	Nos. 196-200,C66-C67 (7)	5.24	3.01

Development Bank Issue
Common Design Type

1969, Sept. 10   Engr.   Perf. 13
201 CD130 30fr sl grn, grn & ocher   .22   .15

Millet — A58

Design: 30fr, Cotton.

1969, Oct. 30   Photo.   Perf. 12½x13
202 A58 15fr dk brn, grn & yel   .16   .15
203 A58 30fr dp claret & brt bl   .30   .16

See Nos. C73-C74.

ASECNA Issue
Common Design Type

1969, Dec. 12   Engr.   Perf. 13
204 CD132 100fr brown   .80   .50

Niadale Mask — A59

Carvings from National Museum: 30fr, Niaga. 45fr, Man and woman, Iliu Bara. 80fr, Karan Weeba figurine.

1970, Mar. 5   Engr.   Perf. 13
207 A59 10fr dk car rose, org & dk   .15   .15
209 A59 30fr dk brn, brt vio & grnsh bl   .22   .15
211 A59 45fr yel grn, brn & bl   .32   .15
212 A59 80fr pur, rose lil & brn   .60   .25
   Nos. 207-212 (4)   1.29
   Set value   .55

African Huts and European City — A60

1970, Apr. 25   Engr.   Perf. 13
213 A60 30fr dk brn, red & bl   .25   .15

Issued for Linked Cities' Day.

Mask for Nebwa Gnomo Dance — A61

Designs: 8fr, Cauris dancers, vert. 20fr, Gourmantchés dancers, vert. 30fr, Larllé dancers.

1970, May 7   Photo.   Perf. 13
214 A61 5fr lt brn, vio bl & blk   .15   .15
215 A61 8fr org brn, car & blk   .15   .15
216 A61 20fr dk brn, sl grn & ocher   .16   .15
217 A61 30fr dp car, dk gray & brn   .25   .15
   Set value   .58   .36

Education Year Emblem, Open Book and Pupils — A62

Design: 90fr, Education Year emblem, telecommunication and education symbols.

1970, May 14   Perf. 12½x12
218 A62 40fr black & multi   .35   .20
219 A62 90fr olive & multi   .65   .35

International Education Year.

UPU Headquarters Issue

Abraham Lincoln, UPU Headquarters and Emblem — A63

1970, May 20   Engr.   Perf. 13
220 A63 30fr dk car rose, ind & red brn   .30   .16
221 A63 60fr dk bl grn, vio & red brn   .50   .25

See note after CD133, Common Design section.

Ship-building Industry — A64

45fr, Chemical industry. 80fr, Electrical industry.

1970, June 15
222 A64 15fr brt pink, red brn & blk   .15   .15
223 A64 45fr emerald, dp bl & blk   .35   .20
224 A64 80fr red brn, claret & blk   .65   .35
   Nos. 222-224 (3)   1.15   .70

Hanover Fair.

Cattle Vaccination — A65

1970, June 30   Photo.   Perf. 13
225 A65 30fr Prus bl, yel & sepia   .30   .15

National Veterinary College.

Vaccination and Red Cross — A66

1970, Aug. 28   Engr.   Perf. 12½x13
226 A66 30fr choc & car   .25   .16

Issued for the Upper Volta Red Cross. For surcharge see No. 252.

Europafrica Issue

Nurse with Child, by Frans Hals — A67

Paintings: 30fr, Courtyard of a House in Delft, by Pieter de Hooch. 150fr, Christina of Denmark, by Hans Holbein. 250fr, Courtyard of the Royal Palace at Innsbruck, Austria, by Albrecht Dürer.

1970, Sept. 25   Litho.   Perf. 13x14
227 A67 25fr multicolored   .22   .15
228 A67 30fr multicolored   .30   .16
229 A67 150fr multicolored   1.40   .65
230 A67 250fr multicolored   2.00   1.00
   Nos. 227-230 (4)   3.92   1.96

Citroen — A68

Design: 40fr, Old and new Citroen cars.

1970, Oct. 16   Engr.   Perf. 13
231 A68 25fr ol brn, mar & sl grn   .22   .15
232 A68 40fr brt grn, plum & sl   .40   .20

57th Paris Automobile Salon.

Professional Training Center — A69

1970, Dec. 10   Engr.   Perf. 13
233 A69 50fr grn, bis & brn   .38   .16

Opening of Professional Training Center under joint sponsorship of Austria and Upper Volta.

Upper Volta Arms and Soaring Bird — A70

1970, Dec. 10   Photo.
234 A70 30fr lt blue & multi   .22   .15

Tenth anniversary of independence, Dec. 11.

Political Maps of Africa — A71

1970, Dec. 14   Litho.   Perf. 13½
235 A71 50fr multicolored   .40   .20

10th anniv. of the declaration granting independence to colonial territories and countries.

Beingolo Hunting Horn — A72

Musical Instruments: 15fr, Mossi guitar, vert. 20fr, Gourounsi flutes, vert. 25fr, Lunga drums.

1971, Mar. 1   Engr.   Perf. 13
236 A72 5fr blue, brn & car   .15   .15
237 A72 15fr green, crim rose & brn   .15   .15
238 A72 20fr car rose, bl & gray   .15   .15
239 A72 25fr brt grn, red brn & ol gray   .20   .15
   Nos. 236-239 (4)   .66
   Set value   .37

Voltaphilex I, National Phil. Exhibition.

Four Races — A73

1971, Mar. 21   Engr.   Perf. 13
240 A73 50fr rose cl, lt grn & dk brn   .40   .22

Intl. year against racial discrimination.

Telephone and Globes — A74

1971, May 17   Engr.   Perf. 13
241 A74 50fr brn, gray & dk pur   .40   .20

3rd World Telecommunications Day.

Cane Field Worker, Banfora Sugar Mill — A75   Cotton and Voltex Mill Emblem — A76

1971, June 24   Photo.   Perf. 13
242 A75 10fr multicolored   .15   .15
243 A76 35fr multicolored   .25   .15
   Set value   .19

Industrial development.

Gonimbrasia Hecate — A77

Butterflies and Moths: 2fr, Hamanumida daedalus. 3fr, Ophideres materna. 5fr, Danaus chyrsippus. 40fr, Hypolimnas misippus. 45fr, Danaus petiverana.

1971, June 30
244 A77 1fr blue & multi   .15   .15
245 A77 2fr lt lilac & multi   .15   .15
246 A77 3fr multicolored   .15   .15
247 A77 5fr gray & multi   .15   .15
248 A77 40fr ocher & multi   .60   .35
249 A77 45fr multicolored   .80   .50
   Set value   1.65   1.10

Kabuki Actor — A78

Design: 40fr, African mask and Kabuki actor.

1971, Aug. 12   Photo.   Perf. 13
250 A78 25fr multicolored   .20   .15
251 A78 40fr multicolored   .30   .15
   Set value   .24

Philatokyo 71, Philatelic Exposition, Tokyo, Apr. 19-29.

100ᶠ

No. 226
Surcharged

=

1971   Engr.   Perf. 12½x13
252 A66 100fr on 30fr choc & car   .65 .40
10th anniversary of Upper Volta Red Cross.

Seed
Preparation
A79

Designs: 75fr, Old farmer with seed packet, vert.
100fr, Farmer in rice field.

1971, Sept. 30   Photo.   Perf. 13
253 A79 35fr ocher & multi   .22 .15
254 A79 75fr lt blue & multi   .50 .20
255 A79 100fr brown & multi   .65 .35
    Nos. 253-255 (3)   1.37 .70
National campaign for seed protection.

Outdoor
Classroom
A80

Design: 50fr, Mother learning to read.

1971, Oct. 14
256 A80 35fr multicolored   .22 .15
257 A80 50fr multicolored   .38 .16
Women's education.

Joseph Dakiri,
Soldiers Driving
Tractors — A81

Children and
UNICEF
Emblem — A84

Spraying Lake,
Fly, Man
Leading Blind
Women
A82

40fr, Dakiri & soldiers gathering harvest.

1971, Oct. 13   Perf. 12x12½
258 A81 15fr blk, yel & red brn   .15 .15
259 A81 40fr blue & multi   .25 .16
Joseph Dakiri (1938-1971), inaugurator of the
Army-Aid-to-Agriculture Program.

1971, Nov. 26   Photo.   Perf. 13
260 A82 40fr dk brn, yel & bl   .25 .16
Drive against onchocerciasis, roundworm
infestation.
For surcharge see No. 295.

1971, Dec. 11   Perf. 13
262 A84 45fr red, bister & blk   .35 .16
UNICEF, 25th anniv.

Peulh
House — A85

Upper Volta Houses: 20fr, Gourounsi house.
35fr, Mossi houses. 45fr, Bobo house, vert. 50fr,
Dagari house, vert. 90fr, Bango house, interior.

Perf. 13x13½, 13½x13
1971-72   Photo.
263 A85 10fr ver & multi   .15 .15
264 A85 20fr multicolored   .16 .15
265 A85 35fr brt grn & multi   .22 .15
266 A85 45fr multi ('72)   .35 .15
267 A85 50fr multi ('72)   .40 .20
268 A85 90fr multi ('72)   .60 .35
    Nos. 263-268 (6)   1.88 1.16

Town Halls of Bobo-Dioulasso and
Chalons-sur-Marne — A86

1971, Dec. 23   Perf. 13x12½
269 A86 40fr yellow & multi   .25 .15
Kinship between the cities of Bobo-Dioulasso,
Upper Volta, and Chalons-sur-Marne, France.

Louis Armstrong — A87

1972, May 17   Perf. 14x13
270 A87 45fr multicolored   .45 .25
Black musician. See No. C104.

Red Crescent,
Cross and
Lion Emblems
A88

1972, June 23   Perf. 13x14
271 A88 40fr yellow & multi   .35 .16
World Red Cross Day. See No. C105.

Coiffure of Peulh
Woman — A89

Designs: Various hair styles.

1972, July 23   Litho.   Perf. 13
272 A89 25fr blue & multi   .20 .15
273 A89 35fr emerald & multi   .22 .15
274 A89 75fr yellow & multi   .45 .18
    Nos. 272-274 (3)   .87
    Set value   .38

Classroom
A90

Designs: 15fr, Clinic. 20fr, Factory. 35fr, Cattle.
40fr, Plowers. 85fr, Road building machinery.

1972, Oct. 30   Engr.   Perf. 13
275 A90 10fr sl grn, lt grn & choc   .15 .15
276 A90 15fr brt grn, brn org & brn   .15 .15
277 A90 20fr bl, lt brn & grn   .15 .15

278 A90 35fr grn, brn & brt bl   .18 .15
279 A90 40fr choc, pink & sl grn   .22 .16
    Nos. 275-279,C106 (6)   1.30
    Set value   .75
2nd Five-Year Plan.

West African Monetary Union Issue
Common Design Type
1972, Nov. 2
280 CD136 40fr brn, bl & gray   .25 .15

Lottery Office
and
Emblem — A91

1972, Nov. 6   Litho.
281 A91 35fr multicolored   .22 .15
5th anniversary of National Lottery.

Domestic Animals — A92

1972, Dec. 4 Litho. Perf. 13½x12½
282 A92 5fr Donkeys   .15 .15
283 A92 10fr Geese   .15 .15
284 A92 30fr Goats   .20 .15
285 A92 50fr Cow   .35 .15
286 A92 65fr Dromedaries   .42 .20
    Nos. 282-286 (5)   1.27
    Set value   .52

Mossi Woman's Hair Style, and
Village — A93

1973, Jan. 24   Engr.   Perf. 13
287 A93 5fr slate grn, org & choc   .15 .15
288 A93 40fr bl, org & chocolate   .22 .15
    Set value   .27 .19

Eugene A.
Cernan and
Lunar Module
A94

65fr, Ronald E. Evans & splashdown. 100fr, Capsule, in orbit & interior, horiz. 150fr, Harrison H.
Schmitt & lift-off. 200fr, Conference & moon-buggy.
500fr, Moon-buggy & capsule, horiz.

Perf. 12½x13½, 13½x12½
1973, Mar. 29   Litho.
289 A94 50fr multi   .32 .16
290 A94 65fr multi   .38 .18
291 A94 100fr multi   .60 .30
292 A94 150fr multi   .90 .45
293 A94 200fr multi   1.25 .60
    Nos. 289-293 (5)   3.45 1.69
Souvenir Sheet
294 A94 500fr multi   3.50 1.60
Apollo 17 moon mission.

No. 260 Surcharged in Red

O. M. S.
25ᵉ Anniversaire

45ᶠ
=

1973, Apr. 7   Photo.   Perf. 13
295 A82 45fr on 40fr multi   .25 .16
WHO, 25th anniversary.

Scout
Bugler — A95

1973, July 18   Litho.   Perf. 12½x13
296 A95 20fr multicolored   .15 .15
    Nos. 296,C160-C163 (5)   3.30 1.70

African Postal Union Issue
Common Design Type
1973, Sept. 12   Engr.   Perf. 13
297 CD137 100fr brt red, mag & dl
              yel   .65 .25

Pres.
Kennedy,
Saturn 5 on
Assembly
Trailer — A96

Pres. John F. Kennedy (1917-1963) and: 10fr,
Atlas rocket carrying John H. Glenn. 30fr, Titan 2
rocket and Gemini 3 capsule.

1973, Sept. 12   Litho.   Perf. 12½x13
298 A96 5fr multicolored   .15 .15
299 A96 10fr multicolored   .15 .15
300 A96 30fr multicolored   .20 .15
    Nos. 298-300,C167-C168 (5)   3.90 2.10

Cross-examination — A97

Designs: 65fr, "Diamond Ede." 70fr, Forensic
Institute. 150fr, Robbery scene.

1973, Sept. 15   Perf. 13x12½
301 A97 50fr multicolored   .32 .16
302 A97 65fr multicolored   .38 .18
303 A97 70fr multicolored   .40 .20
304 A97 150fr multicolored   .90 .45
    Nos. 301-304 (4)   2.00 .99
Interpol, 50th anniversary. See No. C170.

Market Place, Ouagadougou — A98

40fr, Swimming pool, Hotel Independence.

1973, Sept. 30
305	A98	35fr multicolored	.22	.15
306	A98	40fr multicolored	.25	.15

Tourism. See Nos. C171-C172.

Protestant Church — A99

Design: 40fr, Ouahigouya Mosque.

1973, Sept. 28   *Perf. 13x12½*
307	A99	35fr multicolored	.22	.15
308	A99	40fr multicolored	.25	.15

Houses of worship. See No. C173.

Kiembara
Dancers
A100

Design: 40fr, Dancers.

1973, Nov. 30   Litho.   *Perf. 12½x13*
309	A100	35fr multicolored	.22	.15
310	A100	40fr multicolored	.25	.15

Folklore. See Nos. C174-C175.

Yuri Gagarin and Aries — A101

Famous Men and their Zodiac Signs: 10fr, Lenin and Taurus. 20fr, John F. Kennedy, rocket and Gemini. 25fr, John H. Glenn, orbiting capsule and Cancer. 30fr, Napoleon and Leo. 50fr, Goethe and Virgo. 60fr, Pelé and Libra. 75fr, Charles de Gaulle and Scorpio. 100fr, Beethoven and Sagittarius. 175fr, Conrad Adenauer and Capricorn. 200fr, Edwin E. Aldrin, Jr. (Apollo XI) and Aquarius. 250fr, Lord Baden-Powell and Pisces.

1973, Dec. 15   Litho.   *Perf. 13x14*
311	A101	5fr multicolored	.15	.15
312	A101	10fr multicolored	.15	.15
313	A101	20fr multicolored	.15	.15
314	A101	25fr multicolored	.15	.15
315	A101	30fr multicolored	.16	.15
316	A101	50fr multicolored	.30	.15
317	A101	60fr multicolored	.38	.18
318	A101	75fr multicolored	.42	.20
319	A101	100fr multicolored	.60	.30
320	A101	175fr multicolored	1.10	.55
321	A101	200fr multicolored	1.20	.55
322	A101	250fr multicolored	1.50	.70
		Nos. 311-322 (12)	6.26	3.38

See Nos. C176-C178.

Rivera with Italian Flag and Championship '74 Emblem — A102

40fr, World Cup, soccer ball, World Championship '74 emblem & Pelé with Brazilian flag.

1974, Jan. 15   *Perf. 13x12½*
323	A102	5fr multicolored	.15	.15
324	A102	40fr multicolored	.25	.15
		Nos. 323-324,C179-C181 (5)	3.15	1.70

10th World Cup Soccer Championship, Munich, June 13-July 7.

Charles de
Gaulle
A103

40fr, De Gaulle memorial. 60fr, Pres. de Gaulle.

1974, Feb. 4   Litho.   *Perf. 12½x13*
325	A103	35fr multicolored	.20	.15
326	A103	40fr multicolored	.20	.15
327	A103	60fr multicolored	.35	.16
a.		Strip of 3, Nos. 325-327	.75	.45
		Nos. 325-327,C183 (4)	2.75	1.46

Gen. Charles de Gaulle (1890-1970), president of France. See #C184.

N'Dongo and
Cameroun
Flag — A104

World Cup, Emblems and: 20fr, Kolev and Bulgarian flag. 50fr, Keita and Mali flag.

1974, Mar. 19
328	A104	10fr multicolored	.15	.15
329	A104	20fr multicolored	.15	.15
330	A104	50fr multicolored	.35	.16
		Nos. 328-330,C185-C186 (5)	2.90	1.59

10th World Cup Soccer Championship, Munich, June 13-July 7.

Map and Flags
of Members
A105

1974, May 29   Photo.   *Perf. 13x12½*
331	A105	40fr blue & multi	.22	.15

15th anniversary of the Council of Accord.

UPU Emblem and Mail Coach — A106

1974, July 23   Litho.   *Perf. 13½*
332	A106	35fr shown	.22	.15
333	A106	40fr Steamship	.25	.15
334	A106	85fr Mailman	.55	.28
		Nos. 332-334,C189-C191 (6)	4.02	2.08

Universal Postal Union centenary.
For overprints see #339-341, C197-C200.

Soccer Game, Winner Italy, in France, 1938 — A107

World Cup, Game and Flags: 25fr, Uruguay, in Brazil, 1950. 50fr, East Germany, in Switzerland, 1954.

1974, Sept. 2   Litho.   *Perf. 13½*
335	A107	10fr multicolored	.15	.15
336	A107	25fr multicolored	.16	.15
337	A107	50fr multicolored	.35	.16
		Nos. 335-337,C193-C195 (6)	4.66	2.41

World Cup Soccer winners.

Map and Farm Woman — A108

1974, Oct. 2   Litho.   *Perf. 13x12½*
338	A108	35fr yellow & multi	.20	.15

Kou Valley Development.

Nos. 332-334 Overprinted in Red "100e ANNIVERSAIRE DE L'UNION POSTALE UNIVERSELLE / 9 OCTOBRE 1974"

1974, Oct. 9
339	A106	35fr multicolored	.22	.15
340	A106	40fr multicolored	.25	.15
341	A106	85fr multicolored	.55	.28
		Nos. 339-341,C197-C199 (6)	5.07	2.58

Universal Postal Union centenary.

Flowers, by
Pierre Bonnard
A109

Flower Paintings by: 10fr, Jan Brueghel. 30fr, Jean van Os. 50fr, Van Brussel.

1974, Oct. 31   Litho.   *Perf. 12½x13*
342	A109	5fr multicolored	.15	.15
343	A109	10fr multicolored	.15	.15
344	A109	30fr multicolored	.16	.15
345	A109	50fr multicolored	.25	.15
		Nos. 342-345,C201 (5)	2.71	
		Set value		1.30

Churchill as Officer of India
Hussars — A110

Churchill: 75fr, As Secretary of State for Interior. 100fr, As pilot. 125fr, meeting with Roosevelt, 1941. 300fr, As painter. 450fr, and "HMS Resolution."

1975, Jan. 11   *Perf. 13½*
346	A110	50fr multicolored	.30	.15
347	A110	75fr multicolored	.42	.20
348	A110	100fr multicolored	.55	.28
349	A110	125fr multicolored	.70	.38
350	A110	300fr multicolored	1.60	.80
		Nos. 346-350 (5)	3.57	1.81

Souvenir Sheet
351	A110	450fr multicolored	2.50	1.25

Sir Winston Churchill, birth centenary.

US No. 619 and Minutemen — A111

US Stamps: 40fr, #118 and Proclamation of Independence. 75fr, #798 and Signing the Constitution. 100fr, #703 and Surrender at Yorktown. 200fr, #1003 and George Washington. 300fr, #644 and Surrender of Burgoyne at Saratoga. 500fr, #63, 68, 73, 157, 179, 228 and 1483a.

1975, Feb. 17   Litho.   *Perf. 11*
352	A111	35fr multicolored	.20	.15
353	A111	40fr multicolored	.22	.15
354	A111	75fr multicolored	.42	.20
355	A111	100fr multicolored	.55	.28
356	A111	200fr multicolored	1.20	.55
357	A111	300fr multicolored	1.60	.80
		Nos. 352-357 (6)	4.19	2.13

Souvenir Sheet
Imperf
358	A111	500fr multicolored	3.00	1.50

American Bicentennial.

"Atlantic" No. 2670, 1904-12 — A112

Locomotives from Mulhouse, France, Railroad Museum: 25fr, No. 2029, 1882. 50fr, No. 2129, 1882.

1975, Feb. 28   Litho.   *Perf. 13x12½*
359	A112	15fr multicolored	.15	.15
360	A112	25fr multicolored	.16	.15
361	A112	50fr multicolored	.35	.16
		Nos. 359-361,C203-C204 (5)	2.71	1.46

French Flag and Renault Petit Duc,
1910 — A113

Flags and Old Cars: 30fr, US and Ford Model T, 1909. 35fr, Italy and Alfa Romeo "Le Mans," 1931.

1975, Apr. 6   Perf. 14x13½

362	A113	10fr multicolored	.15	.15
363	A113	30fr multicolored	.20	.15
364	A113	35fr multicolored	.22	.15
		Nos. 362-364,C206-C207 (5)	2.97	1.60

Washington and Lafayette — A114

American Bicentennial: 40fr, Washington reviewing troops at Valley Forge. 50fr, Washington taking oath of office.

1975, May 6   Litho.   Perf. 14

365	A114	30fr multicolored	.20	.15
366	A114	40fr multicolored	.25	.15
367	A114	50fr multicolored	.35	.16
		Nos. 365-367,C209-C210 (5)	4.20	2.11

Souvenir Sheet

367A	A114	500fr multicolored	3.50	1.60

Schweitzer and Pelicans — A115

15fr, Albert Schweitzer and bateleur eagle.

1975, May 25   Litho.   Perf. 13½

368	A115	5fr multicolored	.15	.15
369	A115	15fr multicolored	.15	.15
		Nos. 368-369,C212-C214 (5)	3.90	2.00

Albert Schweitzer, birth centenary.

Apollo and Soyuz Orbiting Earth — A116

Design: 50fr, Apollo and Soyuz near link-up.

1975, July 18

370	A116	40fr multicolored	.25	.15
371	A116	50fr multicolored	.35	.16
		Nos. 370-371,C216-C218 (5)	4.23	2.31

Apollo-Soyuz space test project, Russo-American cooperation, launched July 15, link-up July 17.

Maria Picasso Lopez, Artist's Mother A117

Paintings by Pablo Picasso (1881-1973): 60fr, Self-portrait. 90fr, First Communion.

1975, Aug. 7

372	A117	50fr multicolored	.35	.16
373	A117	60fr multicolored	.40	.20
374	A117	90fr multicolored	.60	.30
		Nos. 372-374,C220-C221 (5)	4.60	2.36

Expo '75 Emblem and Tanker, Idemitsu Maru — A118

Oceanographic Exposition, Okinawa: 25fr, Training ship, Kaio Maru. 45fr, Firefighting ship, Hiryu. 50fr, Battleship, Yamato. 60fr, Container ship, Kamakura Maru.

1975, Sept. 26   Litho.   Perf. 11

375	A118	15fr multicolored	.15	.15
376	A118	25fr multicolored	.16	.15
377	A118	45fr multicolored	.30	.15
377A	A118	50fr multicolored	.35	.16
378	A118	60fr multicolored	.40	.20
		Nos. 375-378,C223 (6)	2.11	1.19

Woman, Globe and IWY Emblem — A119

1975, Nov. 20   Photo.   Perf. 13

379	A119	65fr multicolored	.38	.22

International Women's Year.

Msgr. Joanny Thevenoud and Cathedral — A120

65fr, Father Guillaume Templier & Cathedral.

1975, Nov. 20   Engr.   Perf. 13x12½

380	A120	55fr grn, blk & dl red	.20	.15
381	A120	65fr blk, org & dl red	.26	.16

75th anniv. of the Evangelization of Upper Volta.

Farmer's Hat, Hoe and Emblem A121

1975, Dec. 10   Photo.   Perf. 13x13½

382	A121	15fr buff & multi	.15	.15
383	A121	50fr lt green & multi	.18	.15
		Set value	.24	.16

Development of the Volta valleys.

Sledding and Olympic Emblem — A122

Innsbruck Background, Olympic Emblem and: 45fr, Figure skating. 85fr, Skiing.

1975, Dec. 16   Litho.   Perf. 13½

384	A122	35fr multicolored	.18	.15
385	A122	45fr multicolored	.22	.15
386	A122	85fr multicolored	.45	.22
		Nos. 384-386,C225-C226 (5)	2.90	1.52

12th Winter Olympic Games, Innsbruck, Austria, Feb. 4-15, 1976.

Gymnast and Olympic Emblem — A123

1976, Mar. 17

387	A123	40fr shown	.20	.15
388	A123	50fr Sailing	.25	.15
389	A123	100fr Soccer	.55	.28
		Nos. 387-389,C228-C229 (5)	2.40	1.26

21st Olympic Games, Montreal, Canada, July 17-Aug. 1.

Olympic Emblem and Sprinters A124

Olympic Emblem and: 55fr, Equestrian. 75fr, Hurdles.

1976, Mar. 25   Litho.   Perf. 11

390	A124	30fr multicolored	.16	.15
391	A124	30fr multicolored	.30	.15
392	A124	75fr multicolored	.42	.20
		Nos. 390-392,C231-C232 (5)	2.63	1.38

21st Olympic Games, Montreal. For overprints see #420-422, C245-C247.

Blind Woman and Man — A125

1976, Apr. 7   Engr.   Perf. 13

393	A125	75fr dk brn, grn & org	.40	.25
394	A125	250fr dk brn, ocher & org	1.40	.80

Drive against onchocerciasis, roundworm infestation.

"Deutschland" over Friedrichshafen — A126

Airships: 40fr, "Victoria Louise" over sailing ships. 50fr, "Sachsen" over German countryside.

1976, May 11   Litho.   Perf. 11

395	A126	10fr multicolored	.70	.15
396	A126	40fr multicolored	.25	.15
397	A126	75fr multicolored	.35	.16
		Nos. 395-397,C234-C236 (6)	5.35	2.46

75th anniversary of the Zeppelin.

Viking Lander and Probe on Mars — A127

Viking Mars project: 55fr, Viking orbiter in flight. 75fr, Titan rocket start for Mars, vert.

1976, June 24   Perf. 13½

398	A127	30fr multicolored	.15	.15
399	A127	55fr multicolored	.22	.15
400	A127	75fr multicolored	.32	.16
		Nos. 398-400,C238-C239 (5)	3.19	1.71

World Map, Arms of Upper Volta — A128

Design: 100fr, World map, arms and dove.

1976, Aug. 19   Litho.   Perf. 12½

401	A128	55fr brown & multi	.22	.16
402	A128	100fr blue & multi	.42	.30

5th Summit Conference of Non-aligned Countries, Colombo, Sri Lanka, Aug. 9-19.

Bicentennial, Interphil 76 Emblems and Washington at Battle of Trenton — A129

Design: 90fr, Bicentennial, Interphil 76 emblems and Seat of Government, Pennsylvania.

1976, Sept. 30   Perf. 13½

403	A129	60fr multicolored	.40	.16
404	A129	90fr multicolored	.55	.22
		Nos. 403-404,C241-C243 (5)	5.00	2.38

American Bicentennial, Interphil 76, Philadelphia, Pa., May 29-June 6.

UPU and UN Emblems — A130

1976, Dec. 8   Engr.   Perf. 13

405	A130	200fr red, olive & blue	1.00	.60

UN Postal Administration, 25th anniv.

Arms of Tenkodogo A131

Bronze Statuette A132

Coats of Arms: 20fr, 100fr, Ouagadougou.

1977, May 2   **Litho.**   *Perf. 13*

406	A131	10fr multicolored	.15	.15
407	A131	20fr multicolored	.15	.15
408	A131	65fr multicolored	.35	.25
409	A131	100fr multicolored	.55	.40
		Nos. 406-409 (4)	1.20	
		Set value		.78

1977, June 13   **Photo.**   *Perf. 13*

Design: 65fr, Woman with bowl, bronze.

410	A132	55fr multicolored	.30	.20
411	A132	65fr multicolored	.35	.20

#410-411 issued in sheets and coils with black control number on every 5th stamp.

Granaries — A133   Handbags — A134

1977, June 20   **Photo.**   *Perf. 13¹/₂x13*

412	A133	5fr Samo	.15	.15
413	A133	35fr Boromo	.20	.15
414	A133	45fr Banfora	.22	.15
415	A133	55fr Mossi	.30	.20
		Nos. 412-415 (4)	.87	
		Set value		.50

1977, June 20

416	A134	30fr Gouin	.16	.15
417	A134	40fr Bissa	.20	.15
418	A134	60fr Lobi	.35	.20
419	A134	70fr Mossi	.38	.22
		Nos. 416-419 (4)	1.09	.72

Nos. 390-392 Overprinted in Gold:
a. VAINQUEUR 1976 / LASSE VIREN / FINLANDE
b. VAINQUEUR 1976 / ALWIN SCHOCKEMOHLE / R.F.A.
c. VAINQUEUR 1976 / JOHANNA SCHALLER / R.D.A.

1977, July 4   **Litho.**   *Perf. 11*

420	A124 (a)	30fr multicolored	.16	.15
421	A124 (b)	55fr multicolored	.30	.15
422	A124 (c)	75fr multicolored	.40	.20
		Nos. 420-422,C245-C246 (5)	3.26	1.65

Winners, 21st Olympic Games.

Crinum Ornatum — A135   Haemanthus Multiflorus — A136

Hannoa Undulata — A137

Designs: Flowers, flowering branches and wild fruits. 175fr, 300fr, horiz.

1977   **Litho.**   *Perf. 12¹/₂*

423	A137	2fr Cordia myxa	.15	.15
424	A137	3fr Opilia celtidifolia	.15	.15
425	A135	15fr shown	.15	.15
426	A136	25fr shown	.15	.15
427	A135	50fr shown	.25	.20
428	A135	90fr Cochlospermum planchonii	.45	.35
429	A135	125fr Clitoria ternatea	.65	.50
430	A136	150fr Cassia alata	.80	.60
431	A136	175fr Nauclea latifolia	.90	.45

432	A136	300fr Bombax costatum	1.60	1.20
433	A135	400fr Eulophia cucullata	2.00	1.60
		Nos. 423-433 (11)	7.25	5.70

Issued: 25fr, 150fr, 175fr, 300fr, Aug. 1; 2fr, 3fr, 50fr, Aug. 8; 15fr, 90fr, 125fr, 400fr, Aug. 23.

De Gaulle and Cross of Lorraine A138

Designs: 200fr, King Baudouin of Belgium.

1977, Aug. 16   *Perf. 13¹/₂x14*

434	A138	100fr multicolored	.55	.22
435	A138	200fr multicolored	1.10	.42

Elizabeth II A139

Designs: 300fr, Elizabeth II taking salute. 500fr, Elizabeth II after Coronation.

1977, Aug. 16   **Litho.**   *Perf. 11*

436	A139	200fr multicolored	.80	.32
437	A139	300fr multicolored	1.20	.50

Souvenir Sheet

438	A139	500fr multicolored	2.00	.90

25th anniv. of reign of Queen Elizabeth II. For overprints see Nos. 478-480.

Lottery Tickets, Cars and Map of Upper Volta in Flag Colors — A140

1977, Sept. 16   **Photo.**   *Perf. 13*

439	A140	55fr multicolored	.30	.22

10th anniversary of National Lottery.

Selma Lagerlof, Literature — A141

Nobel Prize Winners: 65fr, Guglielmo Marconi, physics. 125fr, Bertrand Russell, literature. 200fr, Linus C. Pauling, chemistry. 300fr, Robert Koch, medicine. 500fr, Albert Schweitzer, peace.

1977, Sept. 22   **Litho.**   *Perf. 13¹/₂*

440	A141	55fr multicolored	.30	.15
441	A141	65fr multicolored	.38	.16
442	A141	125fr multicolored	.65	.25
443	A141	200fr multicolored	1.10	.42
444	A141	300fr multicolored	1.60	.65
		Nos. 440-444 (5)	4.03	1.63

Souvenir Sheet

445	A141	500fr multicolored	2.50	1.20

The Three Graces, by Rubens A142

Paintings by Peter Paul Rubens (1577-1640): 55fr, Heads of Black Men, horiz. 85fr, Bathsheba at the Fountain. 150fr, The Drunken Silenus. 200fr, 300fr, Life of Maria de Medicis, diff.

1977, Oct. 19   **Litho.**   *Perf. 14*

446	A142	55fr multicolored	.30	.15
447	A142	65fr multicolored	.38	.16
448	A142	85fr multicolored	.45	.22
449	A142	150fr multicolored	.80	.40
450	A142	200fr multicolored	1.10	.45
451	A142	300fr multicolored	1.60	.60
		Nos. 446-451 (6)	4.63	1.98

Lenin in His Office A143

85fr, Lenin Monument, Kremlin. 200fr, Lenin with youth. 500fr, Lenin & Leonid Brezhnev.

1977, Oct. 28   **Litho.**   *Perf. 12*

452	A143	10fr multicolored	.15	.15
453	A143	85fr multicolored	.45	.25
454	A143	200fr multicolored	1.10	.65
455	A143	500fr multicolored	2.50	1.60
		Nos. 452-455 (4)	4.20	2.65

Russian October Revolution, 60th anniv.

Stadium and Brazil No. C79 — A144

Stadium and: 65fr, Brazil #1144. 125fr, Gt. Britain #458. 200fr, Chile #340. 300fr, Switzerland #350. 500fr, Germany #1147.

1977, Dec. 30   **Litho.**   *Perf. 13¹/₂*

456	A144	55fr multicolored	.30	.15
457	A144	65fr multicolored	.38	.16
458	A144	125fr multicolored	.65	.25
459	A144	200fr multicolored	1.10	.42
460	A144	300fr multicolored	1.60	.65
		Nos. 456-460 (5)	4.03	1.63

Souvenir Sheet

461	A144	500fr multicolored	2.50	1.20

11th World Cup Soccer Championship, Argentina. For overprints see Nos. 486-491.

Jean Mermoz and Seaplane — A145

History of Aviation: 75fr, Anthony H. G. Fokker. 85fr, Wiley Post. 90fr, Otto Lilienthal, vert. 100fr, Concorde. 500fr, Charles Lindbergh and "Spirit of St. Louis."

1978, Jan. 2   **Litho.**   *Perf. 13¹/₂*

462	A145	65fr multicolored	.38	.16
463	A145	75fr multicolored	.40	.20
464	A145	85fr multicolored	.45	.20
465	A145	90fr multicolored	.50	.20
466	A145	100fr multicolored	.55	.22
		Nos. 462-466 (5)	2.28	.98

Souvenir Sheet

467	A145	500fr multicolored	2.50	1.25

Crataeva Religiosa — A146

1978, Feb. 28   **Litho.**   *Perf. 12¹/₂*

468	A146	55fr shown	.30	.22
469	A146	75fr Fig tree	.40	.30

Souvenir Sheet

Virgin and Child, by Rubens A147

1978, May 24   **Litho.**   *Perf. 13¹/₂x14*

470	A147	500fr multicolored	2.50	1.20

Peter Paul Rubens (1577-1640).

Antenna and ITU Emblem A148

1978, May 30   *Perf. 13*

471	A148	65fr silver & multi	.38	.16

10th World Telecommunications Day.

Fetish Gate of Bobo — A149

1978, July 10   **Litho.**   *Perf. 13¹/₂*

472	A149	55fr shown	.30	.15
473	A149	65fr Mossi fetish	.38	.16

Capt. Cook and "Endeavour" — A150

Capt. James Cook (1728-1779) and: 85fr, Death on Hawaiian beach. 250fr, Navigational instruments. 350fr, "Resolution."

1978, Sept. 1   **Litho.**   *Perf. 14¹/₂*

474	A150	65fr multicolored	.38	.16
475	A150	85fr multicolored	.45	.20
476	A150	250fr multicolored	1.40	.65
477	A150	350fr multicolored	1.90	.80
		Nos. 474-477 (4)	4.13	1.81

Nos. 436-438 Overprinted Vertically in Silver: "ANNIVERSAIRE DU COURONNEMENT 1953-1978"

1978, Oct. 24   Litho.   Perf. 13½x14
478 A139 200fr multicolored   1.10 .42
479 A139 300fr multicolored   1.60 .65

Souvenir Sheet
480 A139 500fr multicolored   2.50 1.20

25th anniversary of Coronation of Queen Elizabeth II. Overprint in 3 lines on 200fr, in 2 lines on 300fr and 500fr.
#478-480 exist with overprint in metallic red.

Trent Castle, by Dürer — A151

Paintings by Albrecht Durer (1471-1528): 150fr, Virgin and Child with St. Anne, vert. 250fr, Sts. George and Eustachius, vert. 350fr, Hans Holzschuher, vert.

Perf. 14x13½, 13½x14
1978, Nov. 20   Litho.
481 A151 65fr multicolored   .38 .16
482 A151 150fr multicolored   .80 .38
483 A151 250fr multicolored   1.40 .65
484 A151 350fr multicolored   1.90 .65
   Nos. 481-484 (4)   4.48 1.84

Human Rights Emblem — A152

1978, Dec. 10   Litho.   Perf. 12½
485 A152 55fr multicolored   .30 .15

Universal Declaration of Human Rights, 30th anniv.

Nos. 456-461 Overprinted in Silver
a, VAINQUEURS 1950 URUGUAY / 1978 / ARGENTINE
b, VAINQUEURS 1970 BRESIL / 1978 ARGENTINE
c, VAINQUEURS 1966 GRANDE BRETAGNE / 1978 ARGENTINE
d, VAINQUEURS / 1962 BRESIL / 1978 ARGENTINE
e, VAINQUEURS 1954 ALLEMAGNE (RFA) / 1978 ARGENTINE
f, VAINQUEURS 1974 ALLEMAGNE (RFA) / 1978 ARGENTINE

1979, Jan. 4   Litho.   Perf. 13½
486 A144(a) 55fr multicolored   .30 .15
487 A144(b) 65fr multicolored   .38 .16
488 A144(c) 125fr multicolored   .65 .25
489 A144(d) 200fr multicolored   1.10 .40
490 A144(e) 300fr multicolored   1.60 .65
   Nos. 486-490 (5)   4.03 1.61

Souvenir Sheet
491 A144(f) 500fr multicolored   2.50 1.20

Winners, World Soccer Cup Championships 1950-1978.

Radio Station — A153

Design: 65fr, Mail plane at airport.

1979, Mar. 30   Litho.   Perf. 12½
492 A153 55fr multicolored   .30 .15
493 A153 65fr multicolored   .38 .16

Post and Telecommunications Org., 10th anniv.

Teacher and Pupils, IYC Emblem — A154

1979, Apr. 9   Perf. 13½
494 A154 75fr multicolored   .40 .20

International Year of the Child.

Telecommunications — A155

1979, May 17   Litho.   Perf. 13
495 A155 70fr multicolored   .45 .20

11th Telecommunications Day.

Basketmaker and Upper Volta No. 111 — A156

Design: No. 497, May of Upper Volta, Concorde, truck and UPU emblem.

1979, June 8   Photo.
496 A156 100fr multicolored   .65 .35
497 A156 100fr multicolored   .65 .35

Philexafrique II, Libreville, Gabon, June 8-17. Nos. 496, 497 each printed in sheets of 10 and 5 labels showing exhibition emblem.

Synodontis Voltae — A157

Fresh-water Fish: 50fr, Micralestes comoensis. 85fr, Silurus.

1979, June 10   Litho.   Perf. 12½
498 A157 20fr multicolored   .15 .15
499 A157 50fr multicolored   .35 .16
500 A157 85fr multicolored   .55 .30
   Nos. 498-500 (3)   1.05 .61

Rowland Hill, Train and Upper Volta No. 60 — A158

Sir Rowland Hill (1795-1879), originator of penny postage, Trains and Upper Volta Stamps: 165fr, #59. 200fr, #57. 300fr, #56. 500fr, #55.

1979, June   Litho.   Perf. 13½
501 A158 65fr multicolored   .42 .20
502 A158 165fr multicolored   1.10 .55
503 A158 200fr multicolored   1.40 .65
504 A158 300fr multicolored   2.00 1.00
   Nos. 501-504 (4)   4.92 2.40

Souvenir Sheet
505 A158 500fr multicolored   3.50 1.60

Wildlife Fund Emblem and Protected Animals — A159

1979, Aug. 30   Litho.   Perf. 14½
506 A159 30fr Waterbuck   .20 .15
507 A159 40fr Roan antelope   .25 .15
508 A159 60fr Caracal   .40 .20
509 A159 100fr African bush elephant   .65 .35
510 A159 175fr Hartebeest   1.20 .55
511 A159 250fr Leopard   1.60 .80
   Nos. 506-511 (6)   4.30 2.20

Adult Students and Teacher — A160

Design: 55fr, Man reading book, vert.

Perf. 12½x13, 13x12½
1979, Sept. 8
512 A160 55fr multicolored   .38 .18
513 A160 250fr multicolored   1.60 .85

World Literacy Day.

Map of Upper Volta, Telephone Receiver and Lines, Telecom Emblem — A161

1979, Sept. 20   Perf. 13x12½
514 A161 200fr multicolored   1.40 .65

3rd World Telecommunications Exhibition, Geneva, Sept. 20-26.

King Vulture — A162

1979, Oct. 26   Litho.   Perf. 13
515 A162   5fr shown   .15 .15
516 A162 10fr Hoopoe   .15 .15
517 A162 15fr Bald vulture   .15 .15
518 A162 25fr Herons   .16 .15
519 A162 35fr Ostrich   .22 .15
520 A162 45fr Crowned crane   .30 .15
521 A162 125fr Eagle   .80 .40
   Nos. 515-521 (7)   1.93
   Set value   .90

Control Tower, Emblem, Jet — A163

1979, Dec. 12   Photo.   Perf. 13x12½
522 A163 65fr multicolored   .42 .20

ASECNA (Air Safety Board), 20th anniv.

Central Bank of West African States — A164

1979, Dec. 28   Litho.   Perf. 12½
523 A164 55fr multicolored   .38 .18

Eugene Jamot, Map of Upper Volta, Tsetse Fly — A165

1979, Dec. 28   Perf. 13x13½
524 A165 55fr multicolored   .38 .18

Eugene Jamot (1879-1937), discoverer of sleeping sickness cure.

UPU Emblem, Upper Volta Type D4 under Magnifier — A166

1980, Feb. 26   Litho.   Perf. 12½x13
525 A166 55fr multicolored   .38 .18

Stamp Day.

World Locomotive Speed Record, 25th Anniversary — A167

1980, Mar. 30   Litho.   Perf. 12½
526 A167 75fr multicolored   .50 .25
527 A167 100fr multicolored   .65 .35

Pres. Sangoule Lamizana, Pope John Paul II, Cardinal Pau Zoungrana, Map of Upper Volta — A168

1980, May 10   Litho.   Perf. 12½
528 A168 65fr shown .42 .20
Size: 21x36mm
529 A168 100fr Pope John Paul II .65 .35
Visit of Pope John Paul II to Upper Volta.

A169   A170

1980, May 17   Perf. 13x12½
530 A169 50fr multicolored .35 .16
12th World Telecommunications Day.

1980, June 12   Litho.   Perf. 13
531 A170 65fr Sun and earth .42 .20
532 A170 100fr Solar energy .65 .35

Downhill Skiing, Lake Placid '80 Emblem A171

1980, June 26   Perf. 14½
533 A171 65fr shown .35 .16
534 A171 100fr Women's downhill .55 .50
535 A171 200fr Figure skating 1.25 .55
536 A171 350fr Slalom, vert. 1.90 1.00
    Nos. 533-536 (4) 4.05 2.01

Souvenir Sheet
537 A171 500fr Speed skating 3.50 1.60
12th Winter Olympic Game Winners, Lake Placid, NY, Feb. 12-24.

Map of Europe and Africa, Jet — A172   Hand Holding Back Sand Dune — A173

Europafrica Issue
1980, July 14   Litho.   Perf. 13
538 A172 100fr multicolored .65 .35

1980, July 18
Operation Green Sahel: 55fr, Hands holding seedlings.
539 A173 50fr multicolored .35 .16
540 A173 55fr multicolored .38 .20

Gourmantche Chief Initiation — A174

1980, Sept. 12   Litho.   Perf. 14
541 A174 30fr shown .20 .15
542 A174 55fr Moro Naba, Mossi Emperor .38 .18
543 A174 65fr Princess Guimbe Quattara, vert. .42 .20
    Nos. 541-543 (3) 1.00 .53

A175   A176

Gourounsi mask, conference emblem.

1980, Oct. 6   Perf. 13½x13
544 A175 65fr multicolored .42 .20
World Tourism Conf., Manila, Sept. 27.

1980, Nov. 5   Litho.   Perf. 12½
545 A176 55fr Agriculture .38 .18
546 A176 65fr Transportation .42 .20
547 A176 75fr Dam, highway .50 .25
548 A176 100fr Industry .65 .35
    Nos. 545-548 (4) 1.95 .98
West African Economic Council, 5th anniv.

20th Anniv. of Independence — A177

1980, Dec. 11   Perf. 13
549 A177 500fr multicolored 3.50 1.60

Madonna and Child, by Raphael — A178   West African Postal Union, 5th Anniv. — A179

Christmas: Paintings of Madonna and Child, by Raphael.

1980, Dec. 22   Perf. 12½
550 A178 60fr multicolored .40 .20
551 A178 150fr multicolored 1.00 .50
552 A178 250fr multicolored 1.60 .80
    Nos. 550-552 (3) 3.00 1.50

1980, Dec. 24   Photo.   Perf. 13½
553 A179 55fr multicolored .38 .20

Dung Beetle — A180

Perf. 13x13½, 13½x13
1981, Mar. 10   Litho.
554 A180 5fr shown .15 .15
555 A180 10fr Crickets .15 .15
556 A180 15fr Termites .15 .15
557 A180 20fr Praying mantis, vert. .15 .15
558 A180 55fr Emperor moth .38 .25
559 A180 65fr Locust, vert. .42 .20
    Set value 1.15 .65

Antelope Mask, Kouroumba — A181

Designs: Various ceremonial masks.

1981, Mar. 20   Litho.   Perf. 13
560 A181 45fr multicolored .26 .15
561 A181 55fr multicolored .32 .16
562 A181 85fr multicolored .48 .25
563 A181 105fr multicolored .60 .30
    Nos. 560-563 (4) 1.66 .86

Notre Dame of Kologh' Naba College, 25th Anniv. A182

1981, Mar. 30
564 A182 55fr multicolored .32 .18

Heinrich von Stephan, UPU Founder, Birth Sesquicentennial — A183

1981, May 4   Litho.   Perf. 13
565 A183 65fr multicolored .35 .18

13th World Telecommunications Day — A184

1981, May 17   Perf. 13½x13
566 A184 90fr multicolored .52 .25

Diesel Train, Abidjan-Niger Railroad A185

Designs: Trains.

1981, July 6   Litho.   Perf. 13
567 A185 25fr shown .16 .15
568 A185 30fr Gazelle .20 .15
569 A185 40fr Belier .25 .15
    Nos. 567-569 (3) .61
    Set value .32

Tree Planting Month — A186

1981, July 15
570 A186 70fr multicolored .45 .22

Natl. Red Cross, 20th Anniv. A187

1981, July 31   Perf. 12½x13
571 A187 70fr multicolored .45 .22

Intl. Year of the Disabled — A188

1981, Aug. 20   Litho.   Perf. 13x12½
572 A188 70fr multicolored .45 .22

View of Koudougou A189

1981, Sept. 3   Litho.   Perf. 12½
573 A189 35fr shown .22 .15
574 A189 45fr Toma .30 .15
575 A189 85fr Volta Noire .55 .28
    Nos. 573-575 (3) 1.07 .58

World Food Day A190

1981, Oct. 16   Perf. 13
576 A190 90fr multicolored .60 .30

Elephant A191

Designs: Various protected species.

1981, Oct. 21   Photo.   Perf. 14
577 A191 5fr multicolored .15 .15
578 A191 15fr multicolored .15 .15
579 A191 40fr multicolored .25 .15
580 A191 40fr multicolored .40 .20
581 A191 70fr multicolored .45 .22
    Nos. 577-581 (5) 1.40
    Set value .65

Fight Against Apartheid — A192   Mangoes — A193

1981, Dec. 9   Litho.   Perf. 12½
582 A192 90fr red orange .60 .30

Perf. 13x13½, 13½x13
1981, Dec. 15
583 A193 20fr Papayas, horiz. .15 .15
584 A193 35fr Fruits, vegetables, horiz. .22 .15
585 A193 75fr shown .50 .25
586 A193 90fr Melons, horiz. .60 .30
    Nos. 583-586 (4) 1.47 .85

Guinea
Hen — A194

West African Rice
Development
Assoc., 10th
Anniv. — A195

Designs: Breeding animals. 10fr, 25fr, 70fr,
250fr, 300fr horiz.

1981, Dec. 22   *Perf. 13*
587 A194 10fr Donkey   .15 .15
588 A194 25fr Pig   .16 .15
589 A194 70fr Cow   .45 .22
590 A194 90fr shown   .60 .30
591 A194 250fr Rabbit   1.60 .80
    Nos. 587-591 (5)   2.96 1.62

Souvenir Sheet
592 A194 300fr Sheep   2.00 1.00

1981, Dec. 29
593 A195 90fr multicolored   .60 .30

20th Anniv. of World
Food Program — A196

1982, Jan. 18
594 A196 50fr multicolored   .35 .16

Traditional Houses — A197

1982, Apr. 23   Litho.   *Perf. 12½*
595 A197 30fr Morhonaba Palace,
     vert.   .20 .15
596 A197 70fr Bobo   .45 .22
597 A197 100fr Gourounsi   .65 .35
598 A197 200fr Peulh   1.40 .65
599 A197 250fr Dagari   1.60 .80
    Nos. 595-599 (5)   4.30 2.17

14th World Telecommunications
Day — A198

1982, May 17
600 A198 125fr multicolored   .85 .40

Water
Lily — A199

25th Anniv. of
Cultural Aid
Fund — A201

African Postal
Union
A200

1982, Sept. 22   *Perf. 13x12½*
601 A199 25fr shown   .15 .15
602 A199 40fr Kapoks   .20 .15
603 A199 70fr Frangipani   .35 .18
604 A199 90fr Cochlospermum
     planchonii   .60 .22
605 A199 100fr Cotton   .50 .25
    Nos. 601-605 (5)   1.80 .95

1982, Oct. 7
606 A200 70fr multicolored   .45 .22
607 A200 90fr multicolored   .60 .30

1982, Nov. 10   *Perf. 12½x13*
608 A201 70fr multicolored   .45 .22

Map, Hand
Holding
Grain, Steer
Head — A202

1982   *Perf. 12½*
609 A202 90fr multicolored   .60 .30

Traditional
Hairstyle
A203

1983, Jan.   Litho.   *Perf. 12½*
610 A203 90fr lt green & multi   .52 .25
611 A203 120fr lt blue & multi   .70 .35
612 A203 170fr pink & multi   .95 .48
    Nos. 610-612 (3)   2.17 1.08

For overprints see Nos. 884-886.

8th Film Festival, Ouagadougou — A204

1983, Feb. 10   Litho.   *Perf. 13x12½*
613 A204 90fr Scene   .60 .30
614 A204 500fr Filmmaker Dumarou
     Ganda   3.50 1.60

UN Intl. Drinking
Water and Sanitation
Decade, 1981-
90 — A205

1983, Apr. 21   Litho.   *Perf. 13½x13*
615 A205 60fr Water drops   .40 .20
616 A205 70fr Carrying water   .45 .22

Manned Flight
Bicentenary
A206

Portraits and Balloons: 15fr, J.M. Montgolfier,
1783. 25fr, Etienne Montgolfier's balloon, 1783,
Pilatre de Rozier. 70fr, Charles & Roberts flight,
1783, Jacques Charles. 90fr, Flight over English
Channel, John Jeffries. 100fr, Testu-Brissy's horseback flight, Wilhemine Reichardt. 250fr, Andree's
Spitzbergen flight, 1897, S.A. Andree. 300fr, Piccard's stratosphere flight, 1931, August Piccard.

1983, Apr. 15   Litho.   *Perf. 13½*
617 A206 15fr multicolored   .15 .15
618 A206 25fr multicolored   .16 .15
619 A206 70fr multicolored   .45 .22
620 A206 90fr multicolored   .60 .30
621 A206 100fr multicolored   .65 .35
622 A206 250fr multicolored   1.60 .80
    Nos. 617-622 (6)   3.61 1.97

Souvenir Sheet
623 A206 300fr multicolored   2.00 1.00

No. 623 contains one stamp 38x47mm. Nos.
621-623 airmail.

World
Communications
Year — A207

1983, May 26   Litho.   *Perf. 12½*
624 A207 30fr Man reading letter   .16 .15
625 A207 35fr Like No. 624   .18 .15
626 A207 45fr Aircraft over stream   .25 .15
627 A207 90fr Girl on telephone   .50 .25
    Nos. 624-627 (4)   1.09
    Set value   .55

Fishing
Resources
A208

1983, July 28   Litho.   *Perf. 13*
628 A208 20fr Synadontis gambiensis   .15 .15
629 A208 30fr Palmotochromis   .15 .15
630 A208 40fr Boy fishing, vert.   .15 .15
631 A208 50fr Fishing with net   .16 .15
632 A208 75fr Fishing with basket   .25 .15
    Set value   .72 .37

Anti-deforestation — A209

1983, Sept. 13   Litho.   *Perf. 13*
633 A209 10fr Planting saplings   .15 .15
634 A209 50fr Tree nursery   .16 .15
635 A209 100fr Prevent forest fires   .35 .16
636 A209 150fr Woman cooking   .50 .25
637 A209 200fr Prevent felling, vert.   .65 .35
    Nos. 633-637 (5)   1.81
    Set value   .88

Fresco Detail, by Raphael — A210

Paintings: 120fr, Self-portrait, by Pablo Picasso,
1901, vert. 185fr, Self-portrait at the palette, by
Manet, 1878, vert. 350fr, Fresco Detail, diff., by
Raphael. 500fr, Goethe, by George Oswald May,
1779, vert.

1983, Nov.   Litho.   *Perf. 13*
638 A210 120fr multicolored   .40 .20
639 A210 185fr multicolored   .62 .32
640 A210 300fr multicolored   1.00 .50
641 A210 350fr multicolored   1.20 .60
642 A210 500fr multicolored   1.60 .80
    Nos. 638-642 (5)   4.82 2.42

25th
Anniv. of
the
Republic
A211

1983, Dec. 9   Litho.   *Perf. 14*
643 A211 90fr Arms   .30 .15
644 A211 500fr Family, flag   1.60 .80

A212   Scouting — A213

1984, May 29   Litho.   *Perf. 12½*
645 A212 90fr multicolored   .30 .15
646 A212 100fr multicolored   .35 .16

Council of Unity, 25th anniv.

1984, June 15   Litho.   *Perf. 13½*
647 A213 25fr Polystictus leoninus   .15 .15
648 A213 185fr Pterocarpus Lucens   .90 .45
649 A213 200fr Phlebopus colossus
     sudanicus   1.10 .50
650 A213 250fr Cosmos sulphureus   1.25 .62
651 A213 300fr Trametes versicolor   1.50 .80
652 A213 400fr Ganoderma
     lucidum   2.00 1.10
    Nos. 647-652 (6)   6.90 3.62

Souvenir Sheet
653 A213 600fr Leucocoprinus
     cepaestipes   3.25 1.60

Nos. 651-653 are airmail. For overprints see Nos.
669-674.

Wildlife
A214

Wildlife — A215

1984, July 19
654	A214	15fr Cheetah, four cubs	.15	.15
655	A214	35fr Two adults	.15	.15
656	A214	90fr One adult	.35	.16
657	A214	120fr Cheetah, two cubs	.45	.22
658	A214	300fr Baboons	1.20	.55
659	A214	400fr Vultures	1.50	.80
		Nos. 654-659 (6)	3.80	2.03

Souvenir Sheet
660	A215	1000fr Antelopes	4.00	1.90

World Wildlife Fund (Nos. 654-567); Rotary Intl. (Nos. 658, 660); Natl. Boy Scouts (No. 659). Nos. 658-660 are airmail.

Sailing Ships and Locomotives — A216

1984, Aug. 14 Perf. 12½
661	A216	20fr Maiden Queen	.15	.15
662	A216	40fr CC 2400 ch	.16	.15
663	A216	60fr Scawfell	.22	.15
664	A216	100fr PO 1806	.38	.18
665	A216	120fr Harbinger	.45	.22
666	A216	145fr Livingstone	.55	.28
667	A216	400fr True Briton	1.50	.80
668	A216	450fr Pacific C51	1.60	.85
		Nos. 661-668 (8)	5.01	2.78

Burkina Faso

Natl. Defense — A216a

Design: 120fr, Capt. Sankara, crowd, horiz.

1984, Nov. 21 Litho. Perf. 13½
668A	A216a	90fr multicolored	
668B	A216a	120fr multicolored	

Nos. 647-652 Ovptd. with Two Bars and "BURKINA FASO"

1985, Mar. 5 Litho. Perf. 13½
669	A213	25fr multicolored	.15	.15
670	A213	185fr multicolored	.55	.25
671	A213	200fr multicolored	.60	.30
672	A213	250fr multicolored	.75	.38
673	A213	300fr multicolored	.90	.45
674	A213	400fr multicolored	1.20	.60
		Nos. 669-674 (6)	4.15	2.13

A217

Designs: 5fr, 120fr, Flag. 15fr, 150fr, Natl. Arms, vert. 90fr, 185fr, Map.

1985, Mar. 8 Litho. Perf. 12½
675	A217	5fr multicolored	
676	A217	15fr multicolored	
677	A217	90fr multicolored	

678	A217	120fr multicolored	
679	A217	150fr multicolored	
680	A217	185fr multicolored	

Nos. 678-680 are airmail.

1986 World Cup Soccer Championships, Mexico — A218

A219

Various soccer plays and Aztec artifacts.

1985, Apr. 20 Litho. Perf. 13
681	A218	25fr multicolored	.15	.15
682	A218	45fr multicolored	.16	.15
683	A218	90fr multicolored	.35	.16
684	A218	100fr multicolored	.38	.18
685	A218	150fr multicolored	.55	.25
686	A218	200fr multicolored	.70	.38
687	A218	250fr multicolored	.90	.45
		Nos. 681-687 (7)	3.19	1.72

Souvenir Sheet
688	A219	500fr multicolored	1.90	1.20

Nos. 681-685 vert. No. 684-688 are airmail.

Motorcycle, Cent. — A220

1985, May 26
689	A220	50fr Steam tricycle, G.A. Long	.18	.15
690	A220	75fr Pope	.28	.15
691	A220	80fr Manet-90	.30	.15
692	A220	100fr Ducati	.38	.18
693	A220	150fr Jawa	.55	.28
694	A220	200fr Honda	.70	.35
695	A220	250fr B.M.W.	.90	.45
		Nos. 689-695 (7)	3.29	1.74

Nos. 692-695 are airmail.

Reptiles — A221

1985, June 20
696	A221	5fr Chamaeleon dilepis	.15	.15
697	A221	15fr Agama stellio	.15	.15
698	A221	35fr Lacerta Lepida	.15	.15
699	A221	85fr Hiperolius marmoratus	.32	.16
700	A221	100fr Echis leucogaster	.38	.18
701	A221	150fr Kinixys erosa	.55	.28
702	A221	250fr Python regius	.90	.45
		Nos. 696-702 (7)	2.60	
		Set value		1.24

#696-697 vert. #700-702 are airmail.

British Queen Mother, 85th Birthday — A222

1985, June 21 Perf. 13½
703	A222	75fr On pony bobs	.22	.15
704	A222	85fr Wedding, 1923	.25	.15
705	A222	500fr Holding infant Elizabeth, 1926	1.60	.80
706	A222	600fr Coronation of King George VI, 1937	1.90	.90
		Nos. 703-706 (4)	3.97	2.00

Souvenir Sheet
707	A222	1000fr Christening of Prince William, 1982	3.25	1.60

Nos. 705-707 are airmail.

Vintage Autos and Aircraft — A223

1985, June 21
708	A223	5fr Benz Victoria, 1893	.15	.15
709	A223	25fr Peugeot 174, 1927	.15	.15
710	A223	45fr Louis Bleriot	.16	.15
711	A223	50fr Breguet 14	.20	.15
712	A223	500fr Bugatti Coupe Napoleon T41 Royale	1.90	.90
713	A223	500fr Airbus A300-P4	1.90	.90
714	A223	600fr Mercedes-Benz 540K, 1938	2.25	1.20
715	A223	600fr Airbus A300B	2.25	1.20
		Nos. 708-715 (8)	8.96	4.80

Souvenir Sheet
716	A223	1000fr Louis Bleriot, Karl Benz	4.00	1.90

Automobile, cent. Nos. 712-716 are airmail.

Audubon Birth Bicent. — A224

Illustrations of No. American bird species by Audubon and scouting trefoil.

1985, June 21
717	A224	60fr Aix sponsa	.22	.15
718	A224	100fr Mimus polyglotos	.38	.18
719	A224	300fr Icterus galbula	1.20	.60
720	A224	400fr Sitta carolinensis	1.50	.80
721	A224	500fr Asyndesmus lewis	1.50	.90
722	A224	600fr Buteo cagopus	2.25	1.10
		Nos. 717-722 (6)	7.05	3.73

Souvenir Sheet
723	A224	1000fr Columba leucocephala	4.00	1.90

Nos. 721-723 are airmail.

ARGENTINA '85, Buenos Aires — A225

Various equestrians.

1985, July 5 Perf. 13
724	A225	25fr Gaucho, piebald	.15	.15
725	A225	45fr Horse and rider, Andes Mountains	.16	.15
726	A225	90fr Rodeo	.32	.16
727	A225	100fr Hunting gazelle	.38	.18
728	A225	150fr Gauchos, 3 horses	.55	.25
729	A225	200fr Rider beside mount	.70	.35
730	A225	250fr Contest	.90	.42
		Nos. 724-730 (7)	3.16	1.66

Souvenir Sheet
731	A225	500fr Foal	1.90	.70

Nos. 727-731 are airmail.

Locomotives — A226

1985, July 23
732	A226	50fr 105-30 electric, tank wagon	.18	.15
733	A226	75fr Diesel shunting locomotive	.25	.15
734	A226	80fr Diesel locomotive	.28	.15
735	A226	100fr Diesel railcar	.38	.18
736	A226	150fr No. 6093	.55	.25
737	A226	200fr No. 105 diesel railcar	.70	.35
738	A226	250fr Diesel, passenger car	.90	.42
		Nos. 732-738 (7)	3.24	1.65

Nos. 735-738 are airmail.

Artifacts — A227   Fungi — A228

1985, July 27 Perf. 13x12½
739	A227	10fr 4-legged jar, Tikare	.15	.15
740	A227	40fr Lidded pot with bird handles, P. Bazega	.15	.15
741	A227	90fr Mother and child, bronze statue, Ouagadougou	.35	.16
742	A227	120fr Drummer, bronze statue, Ouagadougou	.42	.20
		Nos. 739-742 (4)	1.07	
		Set value		.48

No. 742 is airmail.

1985, Aug. 8 Perf. 13
743	A228	15fr Philiota mutabilis	.15	.15
744	A228	20fr Hypholoma (nematoloma) fasciculare	.15	.15
745	A228	30fr Ixocomus granulatus	.15	.15
746	A228	60fr Agaricus campestris	.22	.15
747	A228	80fr Trachypus scaber	.30	.15
748	A228	150fr Armillaria mellea	.55	.25
749	A228	250fr Marasmius scorodonius	.90	.42
		Nos. 743-749 (7)	2.42	
		Set value		1.05

Nos. 748 is airmail.

ITALIA '85 — A228a

Paintings by Botticelli: 25fr, Virgin and Child. 45fr, Portrait of a Man. 90fr, Mars and Venus.

100fr, Birth of Venus. 150fr, Allegory of the Cal-
umny. 200fr, Pallas and the Centaur. 250fr, Allegory of Spring. 500fr, The Virgin of Melagrana.

1985, Oct. 25   Litho.   Perf. 12½x13
749A A228a 25fr multicolored .15 .15
749B A228a 45fr multicolored .22 .15
749C A228a 90fr multicolored .45 .22
749D A228a 100fr multicolored .50 .25
749E A228a 150fr multicolored .70 .38
749F A228a 200fr multicolored 1.00 .50
749G A228a 250fr multicolored 1.25 .60
    Nos. 749A-749G (7) 4.27 2.25
Souvenir Sheet
749H A228a 500fr multicolored 2.50 1.25
    No. 749D-749H are airmail.

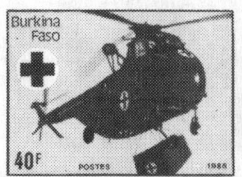

Intl. Red
Cross in
Burkina
Faso, 75th
Anniv.
A229

1985, Nov. 10
750 A229 40f Helicopter .15 .15
751 A229 85fr Ambulance .30 .15
752 A229 150fr Henri Dunant .55 .25
753 A229 250fr Physician, patient .90 .42
    Nos. 750-753 (4) 1.90 .97
    Nos. 752-753 are vert. and airmail.

Child
Survival — A230

1986, Jan. 6
754 A230 90fr Breast-feeding .48 .25
    Dated 1985.

Dodo
Carnival
A231

1986, Jan. 6   Perf. 12½
755 A231 20fr Three children, drum-
        mer .15 .15
756 A231 25fr Lion, 4 dancers .15 .15
757 A231 40fr Two dancers, two
        drummers .22 .15
758 A231 45fr Three dancers .25 .15
759 A231 90fr Zebra, ostrich, danc-
        ers .48 .25
760 A231 90fr Elephant, dancer .48 .25
    Nos. 755-760 (6) 1.73
    Set value .86
    Dated 1985.

Christophe Columbus (1451-
1506) — A232

Columbus: 250fr, At Court of King of Portugal,
the Nina. 300fr, Using astrolabe, the Santa Maria.
400fr, Imprisonment at Hispanola, 1500, the Santa
Maria. 450fr, At San Salvador, 1492, the Pinta.
1000fr, Fleet departing Palos harbor, 1492.

1986, Feb. 10   Perf. 13½
761 A232 250fr multicolored 1.35 .68
762 A232 300fr multicolored 1.65 .82
763 A232 400fr multicolored 2.25 1.15
764 A232 450fr multicolored 2.50 1.25
    Nos. 761-764 (4) 7.75 3.90
Souvenir Sheet
765 A232 1000fr multicolored 5.50 2.75
    Nos. 764-765 are airmail. Dated 1985.

Railroad Construction — A233

1986, Feb. 10
766 A233 90fr Man, woman carry-
        ing rail .50 .25
767 A233 120fr Laying rails .65 .32
768 A233 185fr Diesel train on new
        tracks 1.00 .50
769 A233 500fr Adler locomotive,
        1835 2.75 1.40
    Nos. 766-769 (4) 4.90 2.47
Souvenir Sheet
770 A233 1000fr Electric train, Series
        290 diesel 5.00 2.75
    German Railways, sesquicentennial. Nos. 769-
770 are airmail. Dated 1985.

Intl. Peace   World Health by the
Year — A234   Year 2000 — A235

1986, Oct. 10   Photo.   Perf. 12½x13
771 A234 90fr blue 1.10 .55

1986, Aug. 8   Litho.   Perf. 13
    Designs: 100fr, Primary care medicine. 150fr,
Mass inoculations.
772 A235 90fr multicolored .65 .32
    Size: 26x30mm
    Perf. 12½x13
773 A235 100fr multicolored .72 .35
774 A235 120fr multicolored .85 .42
    Nos. 772-774 (3) 2.22 1.09

Insects — A236   World Post
                    Day — A237

1986, Sept. 10   Litho.   Perf. 12½x13
775 A236 15fr Phryneta aurocinta .15 .15
776 A236 20fr Sternocera interrupta .18 .15
777 A236 40fr Prosoprocera lactator .36 .18
778 A236 45fr Gonimbrasia hecate .42 .20
778A A236 85fr Charaxes epijasius .78 .36
    Nos. 775-778A (5) 1.89 1.04

1986, Oct. 9   Perf. 13
779 A237 120fr multicolored .68 .35

UN Child Survival
Campaign — A238

Designs: 30fr, Mother feeding child. 60fr, Adding
medicines to food. 90fr, Nurse vaccinating child.

1986, Oct. 8   Litho.   Perf. 11½x12
780 A238 30fr multicolored
781 A238 60fr multicolored
782 A238 90fr multicolored
    No. 783 has been reserved for a 120fr stamp.

Mammals
A239

Designs: 50fr, Warthog. 65fr, Hyena. 90fr, Antelope. 100fr, Gazelle. 120fr, Bushbuck. 145fr, Kudu.
500fr, Gazelle, diff.

1986, Nov. 3   Litho.   Perf. 13x12½
784 A239 50fr multicolored
784A A239 65fr multicolored
784B A239 90fr multicolored
784C A239 100fr multicolored
784D A239 120fr multicolored
784E A239 145fr multicolored
784F A239 500fr multicolored

Traditional
Dances — A240

Designs: 10fr, Namende. 25fr, Mouhoun. 90fr,
Houet. 105fr, Seno. 120fr, Ganzourgou.

1986, Nov. 3   Litho.   Perf. 12½x13
785 A240 10fr multicolored
785A A240 25fr multicolored
785B A240 90fr multicolored
785C A240 105fr multicolored
785D A240 120fr multicolored

Hairstyles — A241

1986, Nov. 4   Litho.   Perf. 12½x13
788 A241 35fr Peul .28 .15
789 A241 60fr Dafing .60 .30
790 A241 90fr Peul, diff. .70 .35
791 A241 120fr Mossi .95 .48
792 A241 185fr Peul, diff. 1.50 .75
    Nos. 788-792 (5) 4.03 2.03

10th African Film   Intl Women's
Festival — A242   Day — A243

Flora — A244   Fight Against
                  Leprosy — A245

1987, Feb. 21   Litho.   Perf. 12x12½
793 A242 90fr Maps, cameras
794 A242 120fr Jolson, cameramen
795 A242 185fr Charlie Chaplin
    60th Anniv. of the film The Jazz Singer (120fr);
10th anniv. of the death of Charlie Chaplin (185fr).

1987, Mar. 8   Perf. 13½
796 A243 90fr multicolored

1987, June 6   Litho.   Perf. 12½x13
797 A244 70fr Calotropis procera .48 .24
798 A244 75fr Acacia seyal .52 .25
799 A244 85fr Parkia biglobosa .60 .30
800 A244 90fr Sterospermum kun-
        thianum .62 .30
801 A244 100fr Dichrostachys ciner-
        ea .70 .35
802 A244 300fr Combretum panicu-
        latum 2.10 1.05
    Nos. 797-802 (6) 5.02 2.49

1987, Aug. 6   Perf. 13
    Raoul Follereau (1903-1977) and: 90fr, Doctors
examining African youth. 100fr, Laboratory
research. 120fr, Gerhard Hansen (1841-1912),
microscope, bacillus under magnification. 300fr,
Follereau embracing cured leper.
803 A245 90fr multicolored .62 .30
804 A245 100fr multicolored .70 .35
805 A245 120fr multicolored .85 .42
806 A245 300fr multicolored 2.10 1.05
    Nos. 803-806 (4) 4.27 2.12

World
Environment
Day — A246

1987, Aug. 18   Litho.   Perf. 13x12½
807 A246 90fr shown .68 .35
808 A246 145fr Emblem, huts 1.10 .55

Pre-Olympic Year — A247

1987, Aug. 31   Perf. 12½
809 A247 75fr High jump .55 .28
810 A247 85fr Tennis, vert. .62 .30
811 A247 90fr Ski jumping .68 .35
812 A247 100fr Soccer .75 .38
813 A247 145fr Running 1.10 .55
814 A247 350fr Pierre de Coubertin,
        tennis, vert. 2.60 1.30
    Nos. 809-814 (6) 6.30 3.16
    Pierre de Coubertin (1863-1937).

World Post Day — A248

1987, Oct. 5   Litho.   Perf. 12½x13
815 A248 90fr multicolored

Fight Against Apartheid — A249

1987, Nov. 11   Litho.   Perf. 13
816 A249 90fr shown   1.00 .50
817 A249 100fr Luthuli, book, 1962   1.10 .55

Albert John Luthuli (1898-1967), South African reformer, author and 1960 Nobel Peace Prize winner. No. 817 incorrectly inscribed "1899-1967."

Traditional Costumes — A250

1987, Dec. 4   Litho.   Perf. 11½x12
818 A250 10fr Dagari
819 A250 30fr Peul
820 A250 90fr Mossi
821 A250 200fr Senoufo

No. 822 has been reserved for a 500fr stamp.

Traditional Musical Instruments A251

Perf. 12x11½, 11½x12
1987, Dec. 4   Litho.
823 A251 20fr Xylophone   .18 .15
824 A251 25fr 3-Stringed lute, vert.   .22 .15
825 A251 35fr Zither   .30 .15
826 A251 90fr Conical drum   .78 .40
827 A251 1000fr Calabash drum, vert.   8.50 4.25
     Nos. 823-827 (5)   9.98 5.10

Intl. Year of Shelter for the Homeless — A252

1987, Dec. 4   Litho.   Perf. 13
828 A252 90fr multicolored   .65 .32

Five-year Natl. Development Plan — A253

1987, Dec. 15   Perf. 13½
829 A253 40fr Small businesses   .30 .15
830 A253 55fr Agriculture   .40 .20
831 A253 60fr Constructing schools   .45 .22
832 A253 90fr Transportation and communications   .65 .32

833 A253 100fr Literacy   .72 .35
834 A253 120fr Animal husbandry   .88 .45
     Nos. 829-834 (6)   3.40 1.69

World Health Organization, 40th Anniv. — A254

1988, Mar. 31   Litho.   Perf. 12½x13
835 A254 120fr multicolored   .78 .40

1988 Summer Olympics, Seoul — A255

1988, May 5   Perf. 13x12½
836 A255 30fr shown   .20 .15
837 A255 75fr Torch, vert.   1.05 .52
838 A255 175fr Soccer   1.15 .58
839 A255 235fr Volleyball, vert.   1.50 .75
840 A255 450fr Basketball, vert.   2.90 1.45
     Nos. 836-840 (5)   6.80 3.45

Souvenir Sheet
Perf. 12½x13
841 A255 500fr Runners   3.25 1.65

No. 841 contains one stamp, size: 40x52mm plus two labels.

Ritual Masks A256

1988, May 30   Litho.   Perf. 13
842 A256 10fr Epervier, Houet   .15 .15
843 A256 20fr Jeunes Filles, Oullo   .15 .15
844 A256 30fr Bubale, Houet   .20 .15
845 A256 40fr Forgeron, Mouhoun   .28 .15
846 A256 120fr Nounouma, Ouri   .80 .40
847 A256 175fr Chauve-souris, Ouri   1.20 .60
     Nos. 842-847 (6)   2.78
     Set value   1.35

Nos. 842-846 vert.

Handicrafts A257

1988, Aug. 22   Litho.   Perf. 13½
848 A257 5fr Kieriebe ceramic pitcher, vert.   .15 .15
849 A257 15fr Mossi basket   .15 .15
850 A257 25fr Gurunsi chair   .18 .15
851 A257 30fr Bissa basket   .20 .15
852 A257 45fr Ougadougou leather box   .35 .18
853 A257 85fr Ougadougou bronze statue, vert.   .68 .35
854 A257 120fr Ougadougou leather valise   .80 .40
     Nos. 848-854 (7)   2.51
     Set value   1.20

World Post Day — A258

1988, Oct. 9   Litho.   Perf. 13
855 A258 120fr multicolored   .80 .40

Aquatic Fauna — A259

1988, Oct. 31   Perf. 12
856 A259 70fr Angler martin   .48 .25
857 A259 100fr Mormyrus rume   .68 .35
858 A259 120fr Frog   .80 .40
859 A259 160fr Duck   1.10 .55
     Nos. 856-859 (4)   3.06 1.55

Civil Rights and Political Activists A260

Designs: 80fr, Mohammed Ali Jinnah (1876-1948), 1st Governor General of Pakistan. 120fr, Mahatma Gandhi (1869-1948), India. 160fr, John F. Kennedy. 235fr, Martin Luther King, Jr.

1988, Nov. 22   Litho.   Perf. 14
860 A260 80fr multicolored   .52 .25
861 A260 120fr multicolored   .78 .40
862 A260 160fr multicolored   1.00 .50
863 A260 235fr multicolored   1.50 .75
     Nos. 860-863 (4)   3.80 1.90

A261   A262

Christmas: Stained-glass windows.

1988, Dec. 2   Perf. 12
864 A261 120fr Adoration of the shepherds   .78 .40
865 A261 160fr Adoration of the Magi   1.00 .50
866 A261 450fr Madonna and child   2.90 1.45
867 A261 1000fr Flight into Egypt   6.35 3.15
     Nos. 864-867 (4)   11.03 5.50

1989, Feb. 25   Litho.   Perf. 14
868 A262 75fr shown   .24 .15
869 A262 500fr Ababacar Makharam   1.60 .80
870 A262 500fr Jean Tchissoukou   1.60 .80
871 A262 500fr Paulin Vieyra   1.60 .80
     Nos. 868-871 (4)   5.04 2.55

Souvenir Sheet
872 Sheet of 3   9.00 4.50
a.-c. A262 500fr like #869-871, inscribed in gold   3.00 1.50

Panafrican Film Festival (FESPACO), 20th anniv. Nos. 869-872 are airmail.

World Fight Against AIDS A263

1989, Apr. 7   Litho.   Perf. 13
873 A263 120fr multicolored   .78 .40

Council for Rural Development, 30th Anniv. A264

1989, May 3   Litho.   Perf. 15x14
874 A264 75fr multicolored   .48 .25

Parasitic Plants — A265

Legumes and cereals.

1989, Oct. 9   Litho.   Perf. 11½
Granite Paper
875 A265 20fr Striga generiodes   .15 .15
876 A265 50fr Striga hermonthica   .32 .16
877 A265 235fr Striga aspera   1.50 .78
878 A265 450fr Alectra vogelii   3.00 1.50
     Nos. 875-878 (4)   4.97 2.59

Dogs A266

1989, Oct. 9   Perf. 15x14½
879 A266 35fr Sahel   .24 .15
880 A266 50fr Puppy   .35 .18
881 A266 60fr Hunting dog   .40 .20
882 A266 350fr Guard dog   2.30 1.15
     Nos. 879-882 (4)   3.29 1.68

Solidarity with the Palestinian People — A267

1989, Nov. 15   Perf. 13
883 A267 120fr Monument, Place de la Palestine   .80 .40

Nos. 610-612 Overprinted

1988, Dec. 21   Litho.   Perf. 12½
884	A203	90fr	multicolored	.62	.30
885	A203	120fr	multicolored	.85	.42
886	A203	170fr	multicolored	1.20	.60
		Nos. 884-886 (3)		2.67	1.32

Visit of Pope
John Paul II
A268

1990, Jan. 1   Litho.   Perf. 15x14
887	A268	120fr	Our Lady of Yagma	.85	.42
888	A269	160fr	Pope, crowd	1.20	.60

150th Anniv.
of the
Postage
Stamp
A269

1990, Mar. 20   Litho.   Perf. 15x14
889	A269	120fr	multicolored	1.00	.50

Souvenir Sheet
Perf. 14x15
890	A269	500fr	Penny Black, ship	4.00	2.00

Stamp World London '90.

World Cup Soccer
Championships,
Italy — A270

1990, Apr. 26   Litho.   Perf. 11½
891	A270	30fr	multicolored	.22	.15
892	A270	150fr	multi, diff.	1.10	.55

Souvenir Sheet
893	A270	1000fr	multi, horiz.	7.25	3.65

Intl. Literacy
Year — A271

1990, July 10   Litho.   Perf. 13
894	A271	40fr	multicolored	.28	.15
895	A271	130fr	multicolored	.90	.45

Mushrooms — A272

1990, May 17   Litho.   Perf. 11½
896	A272	10fr	Cantharellus cibarius	.15	.15
897	A272	15fr	Psalliota bispora	.15	.15
898	A272	60fr	Amanita caesarea	.48	.24
899	A272	190fr	Boletus badius	1.50	.75
a.		Souv. sheet of 4, #896-899		2.25	1.10
		Nos. 896-899 (4)		2.28	
		Set value			1.10

Intl. Exposition of Handicrafts — A273

1990, Sept. 25   Litho.   Perf. 13
900	A273	35fr	Masks, fans, vert.	.30	.15
901	A273	45fr	shown	.40	.20
902	A273	270fr	Rattan chair, vert.	2.35	1.20
		Nos. 900-902 (3)		3.05	1.55

Gen. Charles de
Gaulle (1890-1970)
A274

1990, Nov. 22   Litho.   Perf. 13
903	A274	200fr	multicolored	1.75	.90

Minerals
A275

1991, Feb. 4   Litho.   Perf. 15x14
904	A275	20fr	Quartz	.15	.15
905	A275	50fr	Granite	.40	.20
906	A275	280fr	Amphibolite	2.25	1.12
		Nos. 904-906 (3)		2.80	1.47

African Film   Fight Against
Festival — A276   Drugs — A277

1991, Feb. 20   Perf. 11½
907	A276	150fr	multicolored	1.20	.60

Souvenir Sheet
908	A276	1000fr	Award	8.00	4.00

1991, Feb. 20
909	A277	130fr	multicolored	1.05	.55

Samuel F.B. Morse (1791-1872),
Inventor — A278

1991, May 17   Litho.   Perf. 13
910	A278	200fr	multicolored	1.60	.80

Native   Flowers — A280
Girl — A279

1991-93   Litho.   Perf. 14½x15
911	A279	5fr	gray & multi	.15	.15
912	A279	10fr	yellow & multi	.15	.15
913	A279	25fr	lilac rose & multi	.15	.15
914	A279	50fr	red lilac & multi	.28	.15
915	A279	130fr	blue & multi	1.10	.55
916	A279	150fr	multicolored	1.20	.60

920	A279	200fr	multicolored	1.60	.80
922	A279	330fr	orange & multi	2.75	1.40
		Nos. 911-922 (8)		7.38	3.95

Issued: 150fr, 200fr, 6/20/91; 130fr, 330fr,
1/15/93; 5-50fr, 1994.
This is an expanding set. Numbers may change.

1991, July 31   Litho.   Perf. 11½
926	A280	5fr	Grewia tenax	.15	.15
927	A280	15fr	Hymenocardia acide	.15	.15
928	A280	60fr	Cassia sieberiana, vert.	.48	.24
929	A280	100fr	Adenium obesum	.78	.40
930	A280	300fr	Mitragyna inermis	2.40	1.20
		Nos. 926-930 (5)		3.96	2.14

Traditional Dance   World Post
Costumes — A281   Day — A282

1991, Aug. 20   Perf. 12½
931	A281	75fr	Warba	.60	.30
932	A281	130fr	Wiskamba	1.05	.52
933	A281	280fr	Pa-zenin	2.20	1.10
		Nos. 931-933 (3)		3.85	1.92

1991, Oct. 9   Perf. 13½
934	A282	130fr	multicolored	1.05	.52

Cooking
Utensils
A283

1992, Jan. 8   Litho.   Perf. 11½
935	A283	45fr	Pancake fryer	.35	.18
936	A283	130fr	Cooking pot, vert.	1.00	.50
937	A283	310fr	Mortar & pestle, vert.	2.40	1.20
938	A283	500fr	Ladle, calabash	4.00	2.00
		Nos. 935-938 (4)		7.75	3.88

1992 African Soccer
Championships,
Senegal — A284

1992, Jan. 17   Perf. 13½
939	A284	50fr	Yousouf Fofana	.40	.20
940	A284	100fr	Francois-Jules Bo-cande	.78	.40

Souvenir Sheet
Perf. 13x12½
941	A284	500fr	Trophy	4.00	2.00

UN Decade
For the
Handicapped
A285

1992, Mar. 31   Litho.   Perf. 12½
942	A285	100fr	multicolored	.85	.42

World Health
Day — A286

1992, Apr. 7   Perf. 13
943	A286	330fr	multicolored	2.70	1.35

Discovery of
America,
500th Anniv.
A287

1992, Aug. 12   Litho.   Perf. 12½
944	A287	50fr	Columbus, Santa Maria	.42	.22
945	A287	150fr	Ships, natives	1.25	.65

Souvenir Sheet
946	A287	350fr	Map	3.00	1.50

Genoa '92. No. 946 contains one 52x31mm
stamp.

A288   A289

Insects.

1992, Aug. 17   Perf. 15x14
947	A288	20fr	Dysdercus voelkeri	.18	.15
948	A288	40fr	Rhizopertha dominica	.35	.18
949	A288	85fr	Orthetrum microstigma	.75	.35
950	A288	500fr	Apis mellifera	4.25	2.25
		Nos. 947-950 (4)		5.53	2.93

1992, Dec. 21   Litho.   Perf. 11½
Christmas: 10fr, Boy, creche. 130fr, Children
decorating creche. 1000fr, Boy holding painting of
Madonna and Child.
951	A289	10fr	multicolored	.15	.15
952	A289	130fr	multicolored	1.00	.50
953	A289	1000fr	multicolored	8.00	4.00
		Nos. 951-953 (3)		9.15	4.65

Invention of
the Diesel
Engine,
Cent.
A290

1993, Jan. 25   Litho.   Perf. 11½
954	A290	1000fr	multicolored	8.00	4.00

The date of issue is in question.

Paris '94,
Philatelic
Exhibition
A291

1993, July 15
955	A291	400fr	multicolored	3.50	1.75
956	A291	650fr	multi, diff.	5.50	2.75

African Film
Festival — A292

Designs: 250fr, Monument to the cinema. 750fr,
M. Douta (1919-1991), comedian, horiz.

Perf. 11¹/₂x12, 12x11¹/₂

1993, Feb. 16 Litho.
957 A292 250fr multicolored 2.00 1.00
958 A292 750fr multicolored 6.00 3.00

1993, Mar. 31 *Perf. 11¹/₂x12*
100fr, Mycteria ibis. 200fr, Leptoptilos
crumeniferus. 500fr, Ephippiorhynchus
senegalensis.

959 A293 100fr multicolored .80 .40
960 A293 200fr multicolored 1.60 .80
961 A293 500fr multicolored 4.00 2.00
a. Souvenir sheet of 3, #959-961 9.60 4.80
Nos. 959-961 (3) 6.40 3.20

No. 961a sold for 1200fr.

1994 World Cup Soccer Championships,
US — A294

1993, Apr. 8 *Perf. 15*
962 A294 500fr shown 4.00 2.00
963 A294 1000fr Players, US flag 8.00 4.00

Fruit
Trees — A295

150fr, Saba senegalensis, vert. 300fr, Butyros-
permum parkii. 600fr, Adansonia digitata, vert.

1993, June 2 Litho. *Perf. 11¹/₂*
964 A295 150fr multicolored 1.25 .65
965 A295 300fr multicolored 2.50 1.25
966 A295 600fr multicolored 5.00 2.50
Nos. 964-966 (3) 8.75 4.40

Traditional
Jewelry — A296

1993, Sept. 25 Litho. *Perf. 11¹/₂*
967 A296 200fr Ring for hair 1.65 .85
968 A296 250fr Agate necklace, vert. 2.00 1.00
969 A296 500fr Bracelet 4.00 2.00
Nos. 967-969 (3) 7.65 3.85

Gazella
Rufifrons
A297

1993, Dec. 10 Litho. *Perf. 14¹/₂*
970 A297 30fr shown .25 .15
971 A297 40fr Two facing left .32 .16
972 A297 60fr Two standing .50 .25
973 A297 100fr Young gazelle .80 .40
a. Souvenir sheet, #970-973 3.25 1.65
Nos. 970-973 (4) 1.87 .96

World Wildlife Fund (#970-973). No. 973a sold
for 400fr.

Kingfishers — A298

1994, Mar. 8 Litho. *Perf. 11¹/₂*
974 A298 600fr Halcyon senegalensis 2.00 1.00
975 A298 1200fr Halcyon chelicuti 4.25 2.25

Souvenir Sheet

976 A298 2000fr Ceyx picta 7.00 3.50

1994 World Cup Soccer Championships,
US — A299

1994, Mar. 28
977 A299 1000fr Players, US map 3.50 1.75
978 A299 1800fr Soccer ball, players 6.50 3.25
a. Souvenir sheet of 1 7.00 3.50

No. 978a sold for 2000fr.

First Manned Moon
Landing, 25th
Anniv. — A300

1994, July 15 Litho. *Perf. 11¹/₂*
979 A300 750fr Astronaut, flag 3.75 1.90
980 A300 750fr Lunar module, earth 3.75 1.90
a. Pair, #979-980 7.50 3.75

No. 980a is a continuous design.

First Stamp
Exhibition,
Paris, 1994
A301

1994, Apr. 28
981 A301 1500fr Dogs 7.75 3.75
a. Souvenir sheet of 1 7.75 3.75

BURKINA FASO 40ʹ Legumes — A302

Designs: 40fr, Hibiscus sabdariffa. 45fr, Solanum
aethiopicum. 75fr, Solanum melongena. 100fr,
Hibiscus esculentus.

1994 Litho. *Perf. 11¹/₂*
982 A302 40fr multicolored .20 .15
983 A302 45fr multicolored .22 .15
984 A302 75fr multicolored .38 .20
985 A302 100fr multicolored .50 .25
Nos. 982-985 (4) 1.30 .75

Intl. Olympic
Committee,
Cent. — A303

Domestic
Animals — A304

1994, Oct. 10 *Perf. 15*
986 A303 320fr multicolored 1.65 .80

1994, Oct. 10 *Perf. 11¹/₂*
987 A304 150fr Pig, horiz. .75 .35
988 A304 1000fr Capra hircus 4.75 2.50
989 A304 1500fr Ovis aries, horiz. 7.25 3.75
Nos. 987-989 (3) 12.75 6.60

Elvis Presley
(1935-77)
A305

A305a

Portraits in feature films: 300fr, Loving You.
500fr, Jailhouse Rock. 1000fr, Blue Hawaii.
1500fr, Marilyn Monroe, Presley. 0

1995 Litho. *Perf. 13¹/₂*
990-992 A305 Set of 3 7.50 3.75
Souvenir Sheets
993 A305 1500fr multicolored 6.00 3.00
Litho. & Embossed
993A A305a 3000fr gold & multi
Issued: No. 993A, 2/24/95.

Nos. 990-992 exist in souvenir sheets of one.
No. 993 contains one 51x42mm stamp with continuous design. No. 993A, exists in souvenir sheets
of silver & multi with different designs in sheet
margin.
See Nos. 1012-1015A.

Crocodile — A306

1995, Feb. 6 Litho. *Perf. 15x14¹/₂*
994 A306 10fr brown & multi .15 .15
995 A306 20fr lilac & multi .15 .15
996 A306 25fr olive brn & multi .15 .15
997 A306 30fr green & multi .15 .15
998 A306 40fr red brown & multi .20 .15
999 A306 50fr gray & multi .25 .15
1000 A306 75fr gray violet & multi .38 .18
1001 A306 100fr gray brown & multi .50 .25
1002 A306 150fr olive & multi .75 .38
1003 A306 175fr gray blue & multi .90 .45
1004 A306 250fr brown lake & multi 1.25 .65
1005 A306 400fr blue green & multi 2.00 1.00
Nos. 994-1005 (12) 6.83 3.81

World Tourism
Organization,
20th
Anniv. — A307

Designs: 150fr, Man riding donkey, vert. 350fr,
Bobo-Dioulasso railroad station. 450fr, Grand
Mosque, Bani. 650fr, Gazelle, map.

1995, Jan. 26 Litho. *Perf. 11¹/₂*
1006 A307 150fr multicolored .75 .38
1007 A307 350fr multicolored 1.75 .90
1008 A307 450fr multicolored 2.25 1.10
1009 A307 650fr multicolored 3.25 1.65
Nos. 1006-1009 (4) 8.00 4.03

FESPACO
'95 — A308

Motion pictures: 150fr, "Rabi," Gaston Kabore.
250fr, "Tilai," Idrissa Ouedraogo.

1995 *Perf. 13¹/₂*
1010 A308 150fr multicolored .80 .40
1011 A308 250fr multicolored 1.40 .70

Nos. 1010-1011 exist in souvenir sheets of one.
Motion pictures, cent.

Stars of Motion Pictures Type of 1995

Marilyn Monroe in feature films: 400fr, The Joy-
ful Parade. 650fr, The Village Tramp. 750fr,
Niagara.
1500fr, The Seven Year Itch. 3000fr, Marilyn
Monroe (1926-62).

1995 Litho. *Perf. 13¹/₂*
1012-1014 A305 Set of 3 7.50 3.75
Souvenir Sheets
1015 A305 1500fr multicolored 6.00 3.00
Litho. & Embossed
1015A A305a 3000fr gold & multi

Nos. 1012-1014 exist in souvenir sheets of 1.
No. 1015 contains one 42x51mm stamp with continuous design. No. 1015A exists in souvenir sheets
of silver & multi with different designs in sheet
margin.

Issued: No. 993A, 2/24/95.

Birds — A309

Designs: 450fr, Laniarius barbarus. 600fr,
Estrilda bengala. 750fr, Euplectes afer.

1995, Apr. 5 Litho. *Perf. 11¹/₂*
1016 A309 450fr multicolored 2.00 1.00
1017 A309 600fr multicolored 2.75 1.40
1018 A309 750fr multicolored 3.50 1.75
a. Souvenir sheet of 3, #1016-1018 9.00 4.50
Nos. 1016-1018 (3) 8.25 4.15

No. 1018a sold for 2000fr.

Reptiles
A310

Designs: 450fr, Psammophis sibilans. 500fr, Eryx
muelleri. 1500fr, Turtle.

1995
1019 A310 450fr multicolored 2.00 1.00
1020 A310 500fr multicolored 2.25 1.10
1021 A310 1500fr multicolored 6.75 3.50
Nos. 1019-1021 (3) 11.00 5.60

1996 Summer Olympics, Atlanta — A311

Design: 3000fr, Tennis, diff.

1995		**Litho.**	**Perf. 13¹/₂**	
1022	A311	150fr Basketball	.70	.35
1023	A311	250fr Baseball	1.25	.60
1024	A311	650fr Tennis	3.00	1.50
1025	A311	750fr Table tennis	3.50	1.75
a.		Souv. sheet of 4, #1022-1025	8.45	4.20
		Nos. 1022-1025 (4)	8.45	4.20

Souvenir Sheets

1026	A311	1500fr Equestrian event	7.00	7.00

Litho. & Embossed

1026A A311 3000fr gold & multi

No. 1026A also exists as a silver & multi souvenir sheet with different design in sheet margin. Both the gold & silver stamps also exist together in a souvenir sheet of 2.

Sports Figures — A312

Ayrton Senna (1960-94), World Driving Champion A313

Designs: 300fr, Juan Manuel Fangio, race car driver, 1955 Mercedes W 196. 400fr, Andre Agassi, US tennis player. 500fr, Ayrton Senna (1960-94), race car driver, McLaren MP 4/6 Honda. 1000fr, Michael Schumacher, race car driver, 1995 Benetton B 195.
1500fr, Enzo Ferrari, 412 TR, F40.

1995				
1027	A312	300fr multicolored	2.25	1.10
1028	A312	400fr multicolored	3.25	1.65
1029	A312	500fr multicolored	4.00	2.00
1030	A312	1000fr multicolored	8.00	4.00
a.		Souvenir sheet of 3, #1027, 1029-1030	14.50	7.25
		Nos. 1027-1030 (4)	17.50	8.75

Souvenir Sheets

1031	A312	1500fr multicolored	7.00	3.50

Litho. & Embossed

1032 A313 3000fr gold & multi

Nos. 1027-1030 exist in souvenir sheets of 1. No. 1031 contains one 55x48mm stamp.
No. 1032 also exists as a silver & multi souvenir sheet with different design in sheet margin. Both the gold and silver stamps also exist together in a souvenir sheet of 2.
For surcharge see No. 1078.

Souvenir Sheets

John Lennon (1940-1980) — A314

Designs: No. 1033, With guitar, circular pattern with name "LENNON," portrait. No. 1034, With guitar, emblem, portrait.

1995	**Litho. & Embossed**		**Perf. 13¹/₂**	
1033	A314	3000fr gold & multi		
1034	A314	3000fr gold & multi		

Nos. 1033-1034 each exist in souvenir sheets of silver & multi. Souvenir sheets of one gold and one silver exist in same designs and one of each design.

1995 Boy Scout Jamboree, Holland A315

Mushrooms: 150fr, Russula nigricans. 250fr, Lepiota rhacodes. 300fr, Xerocomus subtomentos. 400fr, Boletus erythropus. 500fr, Russula sanguinea. 650fr, Amanita rubescens. 750fr, Amanita vaginata. 1000fr, Geastrum sessil.
No. 1043, Amanita muscaria. No. 1044, Morchella esculenta.

1995		**Litho.**	**Perf. 13¹/₂**	
1035-1042	A315	Set of 8	16.00	8.00
1041a		Sheet of 4, #1035, 1037, 1040-1041	7.30	3.70
1042a		Sheet of 4, #1036, 1038-1039, 1042	8.50	4.25

Souvenir Sheets

1043-1044	A315	1500fr each	6.00	3.00

Mushrooms — A316

Designs: 175fr, Hygrophore perroquet. 250fr, Pleurote en huitre. 300fr, Pezize (oreille d'ane). 450fr, Clavaire jolie.

1996				
1045-1048	A316	Set of 4	4.60	2.30
1048a		Souvenir sheet of 4, #1045-1048	4.60	2.30

#1045-1048 each exist in souvenir sheets of 1.

UN, 50th Anniv. — A317

Designs: 500fr, UN headquarters, New York. 1000fr, UN emblem, people, vert.

1995			**Perf. 11¹/₂**	
1049	A317	500fr multicolored	2.70	1.30
1050	A317	1000fr multicolored	5.30	2.70

Christmas A318

Designs: 150fr, Christmas tree, children pointing to picture of nativity scene. 450fr, Yagma Grotto. 500fr, Flight into Egypt. 1000fr, Adoration of the Magi.

1995				
1051	A318	150fr multicolored	.80	.40
1052	A318	450fr multicolored	2.40	1.20
1053	A318	500fr multicolored	2.70	1.30
1054	A318	1000fr multicolored	5.30	2.70
		Nos. 1051-1054 (4)	11.20	5.60

Butterflies and Insects A320

Designs: 100fr, Epiphora bauhiniae, vert. 150fr, Kraussella amabile, vert. 175fr, Charaxes epijasius, vert. 250fr, Locusta migratoria.

1996		**Litho.**	**Perf. 13¹/₂**	
1065	A320	100fr multicolored	.45	.20
1066	A320	150fr multicolored	.70	.35
1067	A320	175fr multicolored	.80	.40
1068	A320	250fr multicolored	1.15	.60
		Nos. 1065-1068 (4)	3.10	1.55

Two souvenir sheets containing Nos. 1065, 1067 and Nos. 1066, 1068, respectively, exist.

Butterflies A321

Designs: 150fr, Morpho rega. 250fr, Hypolymnas misippus. 450fr, Pseudacraea boisduvali. 600fr, Charaxes castor.
1500fr, Antanartia delius.

1996		**Litho.**	**Perf. 13¹/₂**	
1069	A321	150fr multicolored	.70	.35
1070	A321	250fr multicolored	1.10	.55
1071	A321	450fr multicolored	2.00	1.00
1072	A321	600fr multicolored	2.70	2.70
		Nos. 1069-1072 (4)	6.50	4.60

Souvenir Sheet

1073	A321	1500fr multicolored	6.75	6.75
a.		Ovptd. in sheet margin	6.30	6.30

Overprint in silver in sheet margin of No. 1073a contains Hong Kong '97 Exhibition emblem and two line inscription in Chinese. Issued in 1997.

1998 World Cup Soccer Championships, France — A322

Various soccer plays.

1996		**Litho.**	**Perf. 13**	
1074	A322	50fr multi	.20	.15
1075	A322	150fr multi, vert.	.65	.30
1076	A322	250fr multi, vert.	1.10	.55
1077	A322	450fr multi, vert.	1.90	1.00
		Nos. 1074-1077 (4)	3.85	2.00

MEDAILLE D'OR J.O D'ATLANTA ANDRE AGASSI

No. 1028 Ovptd. in Metallic Red

1996		**Litho.**	**Perf. 13¹/₂**	
1078	A312	400fr multicolored	1.65	.80

No. 1078 exists in souvenir sheet of 1.

Wild Cats — A323

Designs: 100fr, Panthera leo. 150fr, Acinonyx jubatus. 175fr, Lynx caracal. 250fr, Panthera pardus.
Illustration reduced.

1996			**Perf. 12¹/₂x12**	
1079	A323	100fr multicolored	.40	.20
1080	A323	150fr multicolored	.55	.30
1081	A323	175fr multicolored	.65	.35
1082	A323	250fr multicolored	.95	.45
		Nos. 1079-1082 (4)	2.55	1.30

Orchids — A324

Various orchids.

1996		**Litho.**	**Perf. 12¹/₂x13**	
1083	A324	100fr blue & multi	1.10	.55
1084	A324	175fr lilac & multi	1.90	.95
1085	A324	250fr orange & multi	2.75	1.30
1086	A324	300fr olive & multi	3.25	1.60
		Nos. 1083-1086 (4)	9.00	4.40

Birds A325

Designs: 500fr, Falco peregrinus. 750fr, Crossoptilon mantchuricum. 1000fr, Branta canadensis. 1500fr, Pelecanus crispus.

1996			**Perf. 12¹/₂x12**	
1087	A325	500fr multicolored	2.00	1.00
1088	A325	750fr multicolored	2.60	1.30
1089	A325	1000fr multicolored	3.75	1.90
1090	A325	1500fr multicolored	5.75	2.90
		Nos. 1087-1090 (4)	14.10	7.10

#1087-1090 each printed se-tenant with labels.

See French West Africa Nos. 67, 84 for additional stamps inscribed "Haute Volta" and "Afrique Occidentale Francaise."

SEMI-POSTAL STAMPS

Catalogue values for unused stamps in this section are for Never Hinged items.

Anti-Malaria Issue
Common Design Type

			Perf. 12¹/₂x12	
1962, Apr. 7		**Engr.**	**Unwmk.**	
B1	CD108	25fr + 5fr red org	.50	.50

Freedom from Hunger Issue
Common Design Type
1963, Mar. 21   *Perf. 13*
B2 CD112 25fr + 5fr dk grn, bl & brn .50 .50

CAN '96 (African Nations) Soccer
Championships — SP1

Designs: 150fr+25fr, Stallions, soccer ball.
250fr+25fr, Map of Africa, soccer player.
1996   **Litho.**   *Perf. 11½*
B3 SP1 150fr +25fr multi   .95 .45
    a.   Souvenir sheet of 1   2.75 1.40
B4 SP1 250fr +25fr multi   1.50 .75

No. B3a sold for 500fr.

AIR POST STAMPS

Catalogue values for unused
stamps in this section are for Never
Hinged items.

Plane over Map Showing Air
Routes — AP1

Designs: 200fr, Plane at airport, Ouagadougou.
500fr, Champs Elysees, Ouagadougou.
Unwmk.
1961, Mar. 4   **Engr.**   *Perf. 13*
C1 AP1 100fr multicolored   .85 .28
C2 AP1 200fr multicolored   1.65 .55
C3 AP1 500fr multicolored   4.00 1.50
    Nos. C1-C3 (3)   6.50 2.33

Air Afrique Issue
Common Design Type
1962, Feb. 17
C4 CD107 25fr brt pink, dk pur & lt
        grn   .30 .18

UN Emblem and Upper Volta Flag — AP2

Perf. 13½x12½
1962, Sept. 22   **Photo.**
C5 AP2 50fr multicolored   .42 .22
C6 AP2 100fr multicolored   .85 .48
Admission to UN, second anniversary.

Post Office, Ouagadougou — AP3

1962, Dec. 11   *Perf. 13x12*
C7 AP3 100fr multicolored   .75 .42

Jet
Over
Map
AP4

1963, June 24
C8 AP4 200fr multicolored   1.65 .65
First jet flight, Ouagadougou to Paris.
For surcharge see No. C10.

African Postal Union Issue
Common Design Type
1963, Sept. 8   **Unwmk.**   *Perf. 12½*
C9 CD114 85fr dp vio, ocher & red   .70 .48

No. C8 Surcharged in Red

AIR AFRIQUE
19-11-63

50ᶠ

1963, Nov. 19   *Perf. 13x12*
C10 AP4 50fr on 200fr multi   .52 .42
See note after Mauritania No. C26.

Europafrica Issue
Common Design Type
50fr, Sunburst & Europe linked with Africa.
1964, Jan. 6   *Perf. 12x13*
C11 CD116 50fr multicolored   .75 .52

Ramses II, Abu   Greek
Simbel — AP5   Sculptures — AP6

1964, Mar. 8   **Engr.**   *Perf. 13*
C12 AP5 25fr dp green & choc   .35 .30
C13 AP5 100fr brt bl & brn   1.40 1.20
UNESCO world campaign to save historic monuments of Nubia.

1964, July 1   **Unwmk.**   *Perf. 13*
C14 AP6 15fr Greek Portrait Head   .20 .15
C15 AP6 25fr Seated boxer   .25 .20
C16 AP6 85fr Victorious athlete   .80 .60
C17 AP6 100fr Venus of Milo   1.10 .70
    a.   Min. sheet of 4, #C14-C17   3.50 3.50
    Nos. C14-C17 (4)   2.35 1.65
18th Olympic Games, Tokyo, Oct. 10-25.

West African Gray   President John F.
Woodpecker   Kennedy (1917-
AP7   1963)
                   AP8

1964, Oct. 1   **Engr.**   *Perf. 13*
C18 AP7 250fr multicolored   2.75 1.90
1964, Nov. 25   **Photo.**   *Perf. 12½*
C19 AP8 100fr orange, brn & lil   .70 .70
    a.   Souvenir sheet of 4   4.50 4.50

Bird Type of Regular Issue, 1965
1965, Mar. 1   **Photo.**   *Perf. 13*
Size: 27x48mm
C20 A27 500fr Abyssinian roller   5.50 2.50

Earth
and
Sun
AP9

1965, Mar. 23   **Engr.**
C21 AP9 50fr multicolored   .45 .16
5th World Meteorological Day.

Hughes Telegraph, ITU Emblem and Dial
Telephone — AP10

1965, May 17   **Unwmk.**   *Perf. 13*
C22 AP10 100fr red, sl grn & bl grn   .80 .40
ITU, centenary.

Intl. Cooperation Year — AP10a

1965, June 21   **Photo.**   *Perf. 13*
C23 AP10a 25fr multicolored   .20 .15
C24 AP10a 100fr multicolored   .55 .26
    a.   Min. sheet, 2 each #C23-C24   1.90 1.90

Sacred Sabou Crocodile — AP11

1965, Aug. 9   **Engr.**   *Perf. 13*
C25 AP11 60fr shown   .60 .30
C26 AP11 85fr Lion, vert.   .80 .42

Early Bird Satellite   Tiros Satellite and
over Globe — AP12   Weather
                     Map — AP13

1965, Sept. 15   **Unwmk.**   *Perf. 13*
C27 AP12 30fr brt bl, brn & brn red   .28 .16
Space communications.

1966, Mar. 23   **Engr.**   *Perf. 13*
C28 AP13 50fr dk car, brt bl & blk   .40 .28
6th World Meteorological Day.

FR-1 Satellite
over
Ouagadougou
Space Tracking
Station
AP14

1966, Apr. 28   *Perf. 13*
C29 AP14 250fr mag, ind & org brn   2.00 .90

Inauguration of WHO Headquarters,
Geneva — AP15

1966, May 3   **Photo.**
C30 AP15 100fr yel, blk & bl   .80 .45

Air Afrique Issue
Common Design Type
1966, Aug. 31   **Photo.**   *Perf. 13*
C31 CD123 25fr tan, blk & yel grn   .30 .15

Sir Winston Churchill, British Lion and
"V" Sign — AP16

1966, Nov. 5   **Engr.**   *Perf. 13*
C32 AP16 100fr slate grn & car rose   1.00 .55
Sir Winston Spencer Churchill (1874-1965),
statesman and WWII leader.

Pope Paul VI, Peace Dove, UN General
Assembly and Emblem — AP17

1966, Nov. 5
C33 AP17 100fr dk blue & pur   1.00 .55
Pope Paul's appeal for peace before the UN General Assembly, Oct. 4, 1965.

Blind Man and Lions Emblem — AP18

1967, Feb. 28   **Engr.**   *Perf. 13*
C34 AP18 100fr dk vio bl, brt bl & dk
        brn   1.40 .55
50th anniversary of Lions Intl.

UN Emblem and Rain over Landscape — AP19

Diamant Rocket — AP20

1967, Mar. 23   **Engr.**   *Perf. 13*
C35 AP19 50fr ultra, dk grn & bl grn   .50 .22

7th World Meteorological Day.

1967, Apr. 18   **Engr.**   *Perf. 13*
French Spacecraft: 20fr, FR-1 satellite, horiz. 30fr, D1-C satellite. 100fr, D1-D satellite, horiz.

C36	AP20	5fr brt bl, sl grn & org	.15	.15
C37	AP20	20fr lilac & slate blue	.20	.15
C38	AP20	30fr red brn, brt bl & emer	.32	.16
C39	AP20	100fr emer & dp claret	.90	.45
		Nos. C36-C39 (4)	1.57	.91

For overprint see No. C69.

Albert Schweitzer (1875-1965), Medical Missionary and Organ Pipes — AP21

1967, May 12   **Engr.**   *Perf. 13*
C40 AP21 250fr claret & blk   1.75 .95

World Map and 1967 Jamboree Emblem — AP22

1967, June 8   **Photo.**
C41 AP22 100fr multicolored   1.00 .55

12th Boy Scout World Jamboree, Farragut State Park, Idaho, Aug. 1-9.

Madonna and Child, 15th Century AP23

Paintings: 20fr, Still life by Paul Gauguin. 50fr, Pietà, by Dick Bouts. 60fr, Anne of Cleves, by Hans Holbein the Younger. 90fr, The Money Lender and his Wife, by Quentin Massys (38x40mm). 100fr, Blessing of the Risen Christ, by Giovanni Bellini. 200fr, The Handcart, by Louis Le Nain, horiz. 250fr, The Four Evangelists, by Jacob Jordaens.

Perf. 12¹⁄₂x12, 12x12¹⁄₂, 13¹⁄₂ (90fr)
1967-68   **Photo.**

C42	AP23	20fr multi ('68)	.25	.15
C43	AP23	30fr multicolored	.30	.15
C44	AP23	50fr multicolored	.50	.25
C45	AP23	60fr multi ('68)	.60	.25
C46	AP23	90fr multi ('68)	.85	.42
C47	AP23	100fr multicolored	1.00	.38
C48	AP23	200fr multi ('68)	2.00	.70
C49	AP23	250fr multicolored	2.75	1.00
		Nos. C42-C49 (8)	8.25	3.30

See Nos. C70-C72.

African Postal Union Issue, 1967
Common Design Type

1967, Sept. 9   *Perf. 13*
C50 CD124 100fr multicolored   .80 .35

Caravelle "Ouagadougou" — AP24

1968, Feb. 29   **Engr.**   *Perf. 13*
C51 AP24 500fr bl, dp claret & blk   3.75 1.40

WMO Emblem, Sun, Rain, Wheat — AP25

1968, Mar. 23   **Engr.**   *Perf. 13*
C52 AP25 50fr dk red, ultra & gray grn   .45 .22

8th World Meteorological Day.

Europafrica Issue

Clove Hitch — AP25a

1968, July 20   **Photo.**   *Perf. 13*
C53 AP25a 50fr yel bis, blk & dk red   .40 .20

See note after Niger No. C89.

Vessel in Form of Acrobat with Bells, Colima Culture — AP26

Mexican Sculptures: 30fr, Ballplayer, Veracruz, vert. 60fr, Javelin thrower, Colima, vert. 100fr, Seated athlete with cape, Jalisco.

1968, Oct. 14   **Engr.**   *Perf. 13*

C54	AP26	10fr dk red, ocher & choc	.15	.15
C55	AP26	30fr bl grn, brt grn & dk brn	.22	.15
C56	AP26	60fr ultra, ol & mar	.45	.22
C57	AP26	100fr brt grn, bl & mar	.65	.35
		Nos. C54-C57 (4)	1.47	.87

19th Olympic Games, Mexico City, Oct. 12-27.

Artisan Type of Regular Issue
1968, Oct. 30   **Engr.**   *Perf. 13*
Size: 48x27mm
C58 A52 100fr Potter   .70 .32

PHILEXAFRIQUE Issue

Too Late or The Letter, by Armand Cambon AP27

1968, Nov. 22   **Photo.**   *Perf. 12¹⁄₂*
C59 AP27 100fr multicolored   1.00 .75

PHILEXAFRIQUE, Phil. Exhib., Abidjan, Feb. 14-23, 1969. Printed with alternating rose claret label.

Albert John Luthuli — AP28

Design: No. C61, Mahatma Gandhi.

1968, Dec. 16   **Photo.**   *Perf. 12¹⁄₂*

C60	AP28	100fr dk grn, yel grn & blk	.75	.40
C61	AP28	100fr dk grn, yel & blk	.75	.40
a.		Min. sheet, 2 each #C60-C61	3.00	3.00

Exponents of non-violence.

2nd PHILEXAFRIQUE Issue
Common Design Type
50fr, Upper Volta #59, dancers & musicians.

1969, Feb. 14   **Engr.**   *Perf. 13*
C62 CD128 50fr pur, bl car & brn   .55 .55

Weather Sonde, WMO Emblem, Mule and Cattle in Irrigated Field — AP29

1969, Mar. 24   **Engr.**   *Perf. 13*
C63 AP29 100fr dk brn, brt bl & grn   .90 .50

9th World Meteorological Day.

Artisan Type of Regular Issue
Design: 150fr, Basket weaver.

1969, Apr. 3   **Engr.**   *Perf. 13*
Size: 48x27mm
C64 A55 150fr brn, bl & blk   1.20 .60

Lions Emblem, Eye and Blind Man — AP30

1969, Apr. 30   **Photo.**
C65 AP30 250fr red & multi   2.50 1.00

12th Congress of District 403 of Lions Intl., Ouagadougou, May 2-3.

Fish Type of Regular Issue
Designs: 100fr, Phenacogrammus pabrensis. 150fr, Upside-down catfish.

1969   **Engr.**   *Perf. 13*
Size: 48x27mm

C66	A57	100fr slate, pur & yel	.90	.42
C67	A57	150fr org brn, gray & slate	1.40	.62

Earth and Astronaut — AP31

Embossed on Gold Foil
1969   *Die-cut Perf. 10¹⁄₂x10*
C68 AP31 1000fr gold   8.25 8.25

Apollo 8 mission, which put the first man in orbit around the moon, Dec. 21-27, 1968.

No. C39 Overprinted in red with Lunar Landing Module and: "L'HOMME SUR LA LUNE / JUILLET 1969 / APOLLO 11"

1969, July 25   **Engr.**   *Perf. 13*
C69 AP20 100fr emer & dp claret   2.25 1.90

See note after Mali No. C80.

Painting Type of 1967-68
Paintings: 50fr, Napoleon Crossing Great St. Bernard Pass, by Jacques Louis David. 150fr, Napoleon Awarding the First Cross of the Legion of Honor, by Jean-Baptiste Debret. 250fr, Napoleon Before Madrid, by Carle Vernet.

1969, Aug. 18   **Photo.**   *Perf. 12¹⁄₂x12*

C70	AP23	50fr carmine & multi	.45	.35
C71	AP23	150fr violet & multi	1.10	.80
C72	AP23	250fr green & multi	2.25	1.40
		Nos. C70-C72 (3)	3.80	2.55

Napoleon Bonaparte (1769-1821).

Agriculture Type of Regular Issue
1969, Oct. 30   **Photo.**   *Perf. 12¹⁄₂x13*
Size: 47¹⁄₂x27mm

C73	A58	100fr Peanuts	.75	.28
C74	A58	200fr Rice	1.65	.55

AP32   AP33

Tree of Life, symbols of science, agriculture and industry.

1969, Nov. 21   **Photo.**   *Perf. 12x13*
C75 AP32 100fr multicolored   .65 .35

See note after Mauritania No. C28.

1970, Apr. 22   **Photo.**   *Perf. 12¹⁄₂*
Designs: 20fr, Lenin. 100fr, Lenin Addressing Revolutionaries in Petrograd, by V. A. Serov, horiz.

C76	AP33	20fr ocher & brn	.15	.15
C77	AP33	100fr blk, lt grn & red	.65	.38

Lenin (1870-1924), Russian communist leader.

Pres. Roosevelt with Stamp Collection — AP34

Design: 10fr, Franklin Delano Roosevelt, vert.

1970, June 4   Photo.   Perf. 12½
C78 AP34 10fr dk brn, emer & red brn   .15 .15
C79 AP34 200fr vio bl, gray & dk car   1.40 .45
Set value   .50

Soccer Game and Jules Rimet Cup — AP35

100fr, Goalkeeper catching ball, globe.

1970, June 4   Engr.   Perf. 13
C80 AP35 40fr olive, brt grn & brn   .40 .20
C81 AP35 100fr blk, lil, brn & grn   .90 .40

9th World Soccer Championships for the Jules Rimet Cup, Mexico City, May 30-June 21, 1970.

EXPO Emblem, Monorail and "Cranes at the Seashore" — AP36

UN Emblem, Dove and Star — AP37

Design: 150fr, EXPO emblem, rocket, satellites and "Geisha."

1970, Aug. 7   Photo.   Perf. 12½
C82 AP36 50fr multicolored   .35 .16
C83 AP36 150fr green & multi   1.00 .60

Issued to publicize EXPO '70 International Exhibition, Osaka, Japan, Mar. 15-Sept. 13.

1970, Oct. 2   Engr.   Perf. 13
Design: 250fr, UN emblem and doves, horiz.
C84 AP37 60fr dk bl, bl & grn   .40 .20
C85 AP37 250fr dk red brn, vio bl & ol   1.60 .65

25th anniversary of the United Nations.

Holy Family AP38

Silver Embossed
1970, Nov. 27   Die-Cut Perf. 10
C86 AP38 300fr silver   2.50 2.50
Gold Embossed
C87 AP38 1000fr gold   9.00 9.00
Christmas.

Family and Upper Volta Flag — AP39

Gamal Abdel Nasser — AP41

UN "Key to a Free World" — AP40

Litho.; Gold Embossed
1970, Dec. 10   Perf. 12½
C88 AP39 500fr gold, blk & red   2.50 1.50
10th anniversary of independence, Dec. 11.

1970, Dec. 14   Engr.   Perf. 13
C89 AP40 40fr red, bister & blue   .35 .16
UN Declaration of Independence for Colonial Peoples, 10th anniv.

1971, Jan. 30   Photo.   Perf. 12½
C90 AP41 100fr green & multi   .65 .30
Nasser (1918-1970), president of Egypt.

Herons, Egyptian Art, 1354 — AP42

Design: 250fr, Page from Koran, Egypt, 1368-1388, vert.

1971, May 13   Photo.   Perf. 13
C91 AP42 100fr multicolored   .55 .25
C92 AP42 250fr multicolored   1.40 .70

Olympic Rings and Various Sports — AP43

1971, June 10   Engr.   Perf. 13
C93 AP43 150fr vio bl & red   1.00 .60
Pre-Olympic Year.

Boy Scout and Buildings — AP44

1971, Aug. 12   Photo.   Perf. 12½
C94 AP44 45fr multicolored   .35 .16
13th Boy Scout World Jamboree, Asagiri Plain, Japan, Aug. 2-10.

De Gaulle, Map of Upper Volta, Cross of Lorraine — AP45

Charles de Gaulle — AP46

1971, Nov. 9   Photo.   Perf. 13x12
C95 AP45 40fr lt brn, grn & blk   .40 .35
Lithographed; Gold Embossed
Perf. 12½
C96 AP46 500fr gold & grn   4.00 3.75
Gen. Charles de Gaulle (1890-1970), president of France.

African Postal Union Issue, 1971
Common Design Type
Design: 100fr, Mossi dancer and UAMPT building, Brazzaville, Congo.

1971, Nov. 13   Photo.   Perf. 13x13½
C97 CD135 100fr bl & multi   .65 .35

Gen. Sangoule Lamizana — AP47

Kabuki Actor and Ice Hockey — AP48

1971, Dec. 11   Photo.   Perf. 12½
C98 AP47 35fr sep, blk, gold & ultra   .22 .15
Inauguration of 2nd Republic of Upper Volta.

1972, Feb. 15   Engr.   Perf. 13
C99 AP48 150fr red, bl & pur   1.00 .60
11th Winter Olympic Games, Sapporo, Japan, Feb. 3-13.

Music, by Pietro Longhi AP49

Design: 150fr, Gondolas and general view, by Ippolito Caffi, horiz.

1972, Feb. 28   Photo.   Perf. 13
C100 AP49 100fr gold & multi   .65 .35
C101 AP49 150fr gold & multi   1.10 .40
UNESCO campaign to save Venice.

Running and Olympic Rings — AP50

Design: 200fr, Discus and Olympic rings.

1972, May 5   Engr.   Perf. 13
C102 AP50 65fr dp bl, brn & grn   .35 .15
C103 AP50 200fr dp bl & brn   1.10 .35
a.   Min. sheet of 2, #C102-C103   1.65 1.65
20th Olympic Games, Munich, Aug. 26-Sept. 10.

Musician Type of Regular Issue
Design: 500fr, Jimmy Smith and keyboard.

1972, May 17   Photo.   Perf. 14x13
C104 A87 500fr green & multi   4.00 1.90

Red Crescent Type of Regular Issue
1972, June 23   Perf. 13x14
C105 A88 100fr yellow & multi   .65 .25

2nd Plan Type of Regular Issue
Design: 85fr, Road building machinery.

1972, Oct. 30   Engr.   Perf. 13
C106 A90 85fr brick red, bl & blk   .45 .22

Presidents Pompidou and Lamizana — AP51

Design: 250fr, Presidents Pompidou and Lamizana, different design.

1972, Nov. 20   Photo.   Perf. 13
Size: 48x37mm
C107 AP51 40fr gold & multi   .45 .35
Photogravure; Gold Embossed
Size: 56x36mm
C108 AP51 250fr yel grn, dk grn & gold   2.50 2.50
Visit of Pres. Georges Pompidou of France, Nov. 1972.

Skeet-shooting, Scalzone, Italy — AP52

Gold-medal Winners: 40fr, Pentathlon, Peters, Great Britain. 45fr, Dressage, Meade, Great Britain. 50fr, Weight lifting, Talts, USSR. 60fr, Boxing, lightweight, Seales, US. 65fr, Fencing, Ragno-Lonzi, Italy. 75fr, Gymnastics, rings, Nakayama, Japan. 85fr, Gymnastics, Touritcheva, USSR. 90fr, 110m high hurdles, Milburn, US. 150fr, Judo, Kawaguchi, Japan. 200fr, Sailing, Finn class, Maury, France. 250fr, Swimming, Spitz, US (7 gold). 300fr, Women's high jump, Meyfarth, West Germany. 350fr, Field Hockey, West Germany. 400fr, Javelin, Wolfermann, West Germany. No. C124, Women's diving, King, US. No. C125, Cycling, Morelon, France. No. C126, Individual dressage, Linsenhoff, West Germany.

1972-73   Litho.   Perf. 12½
C109 AP52 35fr multi ('73)   .18 .15
C110 AP52 40fr multicolored   .20 .15
C111 AP52 45fr multi ('73)   .22 .15
C112 AP52 50fr multi ('73)   .25 .15
C113 AP52 60fr multi ('73)   .30 .15
C114 AP52 65fr multicolored   .35 .16
C115 AP52 75fr multi ('73)   .40 .20
C116 AP52 85fr multicolored   .42 .20
C117 AP52 90fr multi ('73)   .45 .22
C118 AP52 150fr multi ('73)   .80 .40
C119 AP52 200fr multicolored   1.10 .50
C120 AP52 250fr multi ('73)   1.40 .65
C121 AP52 300fr multicolored   1.60 .80
C122 AP52 350fr multi ('73)   1.90 .90
C123 AP52 400fr multi ('73)   2.00 1.10
Nos. C109-C123 (15)   11.57 5.88
Souvenir Sheets
C124 AP52 500fr multicolored   2.25 1.60
C125 AP52 500fr multi ('73)   2.25 1.60
C126 AP52 500fr multi ('73)   2.25 1.60
20th Olympic Games, Munich.

Nativity, by Della Notte — AP53

Christmas: 200fr, Adoration of the Kings, by Albrecht Dürer.

1972, Dec. 23   Photo.   Perf. 13
C127 AP53 100fr gold & multi   .50   .22
C128 AP53 200fr gold & multi   1.10   .65

Madonna and Child, by Albrecht Dürer — AP54

Christmas: 75fr, Virgin Mary, Child and St. John, by Joseph von Führich. 100fr, The Virgin of Grand Duc, by Raphael. 125fr, Holy Family, by David. 150fr, Madonna and Child, artist unknown. 400fr, Flight into Egypt, by Gentile da Fabriano, horiz.

1973, Mar. 22   Litho.   Perf. 12½x13
C129 AP54 50fr multi   .35   .16
C130 AP54 75fr multi   .50   .25
C131 AP54 100fr multi   .65   .35
C132 AP54 125fr multi   .80   .40
C133 AP54 150fr multi   1.00   .50
    Nos. C129-C133 (5)   3.30   1.66

Souvenir Sheet
C134 AP54 400fr multi   2.50   1.40

Manned Lunar Buggy on Moon — AP55

Moon Exploration: 65fr, Lunakhod, Russian unmanned vehicle on moon. 100fr, Lunar module returning to orbiting Apollo capsule. 150fr, Apollo capsule in moon orbit. 200fr, Space walk. 250fr, Walk in Sea of Tranquillity.

1973, Apr. 30   Litho.   Perf. 13x12½
C135 AP55 50fr multi   .35   .16
C136 AP55 65fr multi   .42   .20
C137 AP55 100fr multi   .65   .35
C138 AP55 150fr multi   1.00   .50
C139 AP55 200fr multi   1.40   .65
    Nos. C135-C139 (5)   3.82   1.86

Souvenir Sheet
C140 AP55 250fr multi   1.60   .80

Giraffes
AP56

African Wild Animals: 150fr, Elephants. 200fr, Leopard, horiz. 250fr, Lion, horiz. 300fr, Rhinoceros, horiz. 500fr, Crocodile, horiz.

Perf. 12½x13, 13x12½
1973, May 3   Litho.
C141 AP56 100fr multi   .65   .35
C142 AP56 150fr multi   1.00   .50
C143 AP56 200fr multi   1.40   .65
C144 AP56 250fr multi   1.60   .80
C145 AP56 500fr multi   3.50   1.60
    Nos. C141-C145 (5)   8.15   3.90

Souvenir Sheet
C146 AP56 300fr multi   2.00   1.00

Europafrica Issue

Girl Reading Letter, by Jan Vermeer
AP57

Paintings: 65fr, Portrait of a Lady, by Roger van der Weyden. 100fr, Young Lady at her Toilette, by Titian. 150fr, Jane Seymour, by Hans Holbein. 200fr, Mrs. Williams, by John Hoppner. 250fr, Milkmaid, by Jean-Baptiste Greuze.

1973, June 7   Litho.   Perf. 12½x13
C147 AP57 50fr multi   .35   .16
C148 AP57 65fr multi   .42   .20
C149 AP57 100fr multi   .65   .35
C150 AP57 150fr multi   1.00   .50
C151 AP57 200fr multi   1.40   .65
    Nos. C147-C151 (5)   3.82   1.86

Souvenir Sheet
C152 AP57 250fr multi   1.60   .80

For overprint see No. C165-C166.

Africa Encircled by OAU Flags — AP58

1973, June 7
C153 AP58 45fr multi   .30   .15

10th anniv. of Org. for African Unity.

Locomotive "Pacific" 4546, 1908 — AP59

Locomotives from Railroad Museum, Mulhouse, France: 40fr, No. 242, 1927. 50fr, No. 2029, 1882. 150fr, No. 701, 1885-92. 250fr, "Coupe-Vent" No. C145, 1900. 300fr, Buddicomb No. 33, Paris to Rouen, 1884.

1973, June 30   Perf. 13x12½
C154 AP59 10fr multi   .15   .15
C155 AP59 40fr multi   .25   .15
C156 AP59 50fr multi   .35   .16
C157 AP59 150fr multi   1.00   .50
C158 AP59 250fr multi   1.60   .80
    Nos. C154-C158 (5)   3.35   1.76

Souvenir Sheet
C159 AP59 350fr multi   2.25   1.20

Boy Scout Type of 1973

40fr, Flag signaling. 75fr, Skiing. 150fr, Cooking. 200fr, Hiking. 250fr, Studying stars.

1973, July 18   Litho.   Perf. 12½x13
C160 A95 40fr multi   .25   .15
C161 A95 75fr multi   .50   .25
C162 A95 150fr multi   1.00   .50
C163 A95 200fr multi   1.40   .65
    Nos. C160-C163 (4)   3.15   1.55

Souvenir Sheet
C164 A95 250fr multi   1.60   .80

Nos. C148 and C150 Surcharged in Silver New Value and "SECHERESSE / SOLIDARITE AFRICAINE / ET INTERNATIONALE"

1973, Aug. 16
C165 AP57 100fr on 65fr multi   .65   .35
C166 AP57 200fr on 150fr multi   1.40   .65

Drought relief.

Kennedy Type, 1973

John F. Kennedy and: 200fr, Firing Saturn 1 rocket, Apollo program. 300fr, First NASA manned space capsule. 400fr, Saturn 5 countdown.

1973, Sept. 12   Litho.   Perf. 12½x13
C167 A96 200fr multi   1.40   .65
C168 A96 300fr multi   2.00   1.00

Souvenir Sheet
C169 A96 400fr multi   2.50   1.40

10th death anniv. of Pres John F. Kennedy.

Interpol Type of 1973
Souvenir Sheet

Design: Victim in city street.

1973, Sept. 15   Perf. 13x12½
C170 A97 300fr multi   2.00   1.00

Tourism Type of 1973

1973, Sept. 30
C171 A98 100fr Waterfalls   .65   .35

Souvenir Sheet
C172 A98 275fr Elephant   1.90   .90

House of Worship Type of 1973
Cathedral of the Immaculate Conception.

1973, Sept. 28
C173 A99 200fr multi   1.40   .65

Folklore Type of 1973
100fr, 225fr, Bobo masked dancers, diff.

1973, Nov. 30   Litho.   Perf. 12½x13
C174 A100 100fr multi   .65   .35
C175 A100 225fr multi   1.50   .70

Zodiac Type of 1973
Souvenir Sheets

Zodiacal Light and: #C176, 1st 4 signs of Zodiac. #C177, 2nd 4 signs. #C178, Last 4 signs.

1973, Dec. 15   Perf. 13x14
C176 A101 250fr multi   1.60   .80
C177 A101 250fr multi   1.60   .80
C178 A101 250fr multi   1.60   .80

Nos. C176-C178 have multicolored margin showing night sky and portraits: No. C176, Louis Armstrong; No. C177, Mahatma Gandhi; No. C178, Martin Luther King.

Soccer Championship Type, 1974

Championship '74 emblem and: 75fr, Gento, Spanish flag. 100fr, Bereta, French flag. 250fr, Best, British flag. 400fr, Beckenbauer, West German flag.

1974, Jan. 15   Litho.   Perf. 13x12½
C179 A102 75fr multi   .50   .25
C180 A102 100fr multi   .65   .35
C181 A102 250fr multi   1.60   .80
    Nos. C179-C181 (3)   2.75   1.40

Souvenir Sheet
C182 A102 400fr multi   2.50   1.40

De Gaulle Type, 1974

Designs: 300fr, De Gaulle and Concorde, horiz. 400fr, De Gaulle and French space shot.

Perf. 13x12½, 12½x13
1974, Feb. 4   Litho.
C183 A103 300fr multi   2.00   1.00

Souvenir Sheet
C184 A103 400fr multi   2.50   1.40

Soccer Cup Championship Type, 1974

World Cup, Emblems and: 150fr, Brindisis, Argentinian flag. No. C186, Kenko, Zaire flag. No. C187, Streich, East German flag. 400fr, Cruyff, Netherlands flag.

1974, Mar. 19   Perf. 12½x13
C185 A104 150fr multi   .75   .38
C186 A104 300fr multi   1.50   .75

Souvenir Sheets
C187 A104 300fr multi   1.50   .75
C188 A104 400fr multi   2.00   1.00

UPU Type, 1974

UPU Emblem and: 100fr, Dove carrying mail. 200fr, Air Afrique 707. 300fr, Dish antenna. 500fr, Telstar satellite.

1974, July 23   Perf. 13½
C189 A106 100fr multi   .50   .25
C190 A106 200fr multi   1.00   .50
C191 A106 300fr multi   1.50   .75
    Nos. C189-C191 (3)   3.00   1.50

Souvenir Sheet
C192 A106 500fr multi   2.50   1.25

For overprint see No. C197-C200.

Soccer Cup Winners Type, 1974

World Cup, Game and Flags: 150fr, Brazil, in Sweden, 1958. 200fr, Brazil, in Chile, 1962. 250fr, Brazil, in Mexico, 1970. 450fr, England, in England, 1966.

1974, Sept. 2
C193 A107 150fr multi   1.00   .50
C194 A107 200fr multi   1.40   .65
C195 A107 250fr multi   1.60   .80
    Nos. C193-C195 (3)   4.00   1.95

Souvenir Sheet
C196 A107 450fr multi   3.00   1.50

Nos. C189-C192 Overprinted in Red "100e ANNIVERSAIRE DE L'UNION POSTALE UNIVERSELLE / 9 OCTOBRE 1974"

1974, Oct. 9
C197 A106 100fr multi   .65   .35
C198 A106 200fr multi   1.40   .65
C199 A106 300fr multi   2.00   1.00
    Nos. C197-C199 (3)   4.05   2.00

C200 A106 500fr multi   3.00   1.40

Universal Postal Union, centenary.

Flower Type of 1974

Flower Paintings by: 300fr, Auguste Renoir. 400fr, Carl Brendt.

1974, Oct. 31   Litho.   Perf. 12½x13
C201 A109 300fr multi   2.00   1.00

Souvenir Sheet
C202 A109 400fr multi   2.50   1.40

Locomotive Type of 1975

Locomotives from Railroad Museum, Mulhouse, France: 100fr, Crampton No. 80, 1852. 200fr, No. 701, 1885-92. 300fr, "Forquenot," 1882.

1975, Feb. 28   Litho.   Perf. 13x12½
C203 A112 100fr multi   .65   .35
C204 A112 200fr multi   1.40   .65

Souvenir Sheet
C205 A112 300fr multi   2.00   1.00

Old Cars Type, 1975

Flags and Old Cars: 150fr, Germany and Mercedes-Benz, 1929. 200fr, Germany and Maybach, 1936. 400fr, Great Britain and Rolls Royce Silver Ghost, 1910.

1975, Apr. 6   Perf. 14x13½
C206 A113 150fr multi   1.00   .50
C207 A113 200fr multi   1.40   .65

Souvenir Sheet
C208 A113 400fr multi   2.50   1.40

American Bicentennial Type of 1975

200fr, Washington crossing Delaware. 300fr, Hessians Captured at Trenton.

1975, May 6   Litho.   Perf. 14
C209 A114 200fr multi   1.40   .65
C210 A114 300fr multi   2.00   1.00

Schweitzer Type of 1975

Albert Schweitzer and: 150fr, Toucan. 175fr, Vulturine guinea fowl. 200fr, King vulture. 450fr, Crested corythornis.

1975, May 25   Litho.   Perf. 13½
C212 A115 150fr multi   1.00   .50
C213 A115 175fr multi   1.20   .55
C214 A115 200fr multi   1.40   .65
    Nos. C212-C214 (3)   3.60   1.70

Souvenir Sheet
C215 A115 450fr multi   3.00   1.50

Apollo Soyuz Type of 1975

Designs: 100fr, Apollo and Soyuz near link-up. 200fr, Cosmonauts Alexei Leonov and Valeri Kubasov. 300fr, Astronauts Donald K. Slayton, Vance Brand and Thomas P. Stafford. 500fr, Apollo Soyuz emblem, US and USSR flags.

1975, July 18   Litho.   Perf. 13½
C216 A116 100fr multi   .65   .35
C217 A116 200fr multi   1.40   .65
C218 A116 300fr multi   2.00   1.00
    Nos. C216-C218 (3)   4.05   2.00
Souvenir Sheet
C219 A116 500fr multi   3.50   1.60

Picasso Type of 1975

Picasso Paintings: 150fr, El Prado, horiz. 350fr, Couple in Patio. 400fr, Science and Charity.

1975, Aug. 7
C220 A117 150fr multi   1.00   .50
C221 A117 350fr multi   2.25   1.20
Souvenir Sheet
C222 A117 400fr multi   2.50   1.40

EXPO '75 Type of 1975

Expo '75 emblem and: 150fr, Passenger liner Asama Maru. 300fr, Future floating city Aquapolis.

1975, Sept. 26   Litho.   Perf. 11
C223 A118 150fr multi   .75   .38
Souvenir Sheet
Perf. 13½
C224 A118 300fr multi   1.50   .75

Winter Olympic Games Type of 1975

Innsbruck Background, Olympic Emblem and: 100fr, Ice hockey. 200fr, Ski jump. 300fr, Speed skating.

1975, Dec. 15   Perf. 13½
C225 A122 100fr multi   .65   .35
C226 A122 200fr multi   1.40   .65
Souvenir Sheet
C227 A122 300fr multi   2.00   1.00

Olympic Games Type of 1976

Olympic Emblem and: 125fr, Heavyweight judo. 150fr, Weight lifting. 500fr, Sprint.

1976, Mar. 17   Litho.   Perf. 13½
C228 A123 125fr multi   .65   .30
C229 A123 150fr multi   .75   .38
Souvenir Sheet
C230 A123 500fr multi   2.50   1.25

Summer Olympic Games Type of 1976

Olympic emblem and: 150fr, Pole vault. 200fr, Gymnast on balance beam. 500fr, Two-man sculls.

1976, Mar. 25   Perf. 11
C231 A124 150fr multi   .75   .38
C232 A124 200fr multi   1.00   .50
Souvenir Sheet
C233 A124 500fr multi   2.50   1.25
    For overprint see No. C245-C247.

Zeppelin Type of 1976

Airships: 100fr, Graf Zeppelin over Swiss Alps. 200fr, LZ-129 over city. 300fr, Graf Zeppelin. 500fr, Zeppelin over Bodensee.

1976, May 11
C234 A126 100fr multi   .65   .35
C235 A126 200fr multi   1.40   .65
C236 A126 300fr multi   2.00   1.00
    Nos. C234-C236 (3)   4.05   2.00
Souvenir Sheet
C237 A126 500fr multi   3.50   1.60

Viking Mars Type of 1976

Designs: 200fr, Viking lander assembly. 300fr, Viking orbiter in descent on Mars. 450fr, Viking in Mars orbit.

1976, June 24   Litho.   Perf. 13½
C238 A127 200fr multi   1.00   .50
C239 A127 300fr multi   1.50   .75
Souvenir Sheet
C240 A127 450fr multi   2.25   1.10

American Bicentennial Type of 1976

Bicentennial and Interphil '76 Emblems and: 100fr, Siege of Yorktown. 200fr, Battle of Cape St. Vincent. 300fr, Peter Francisco's bravery. 500fr, Surrender of the Hessians.

1976, Sept. 30   Litho.   Perf. 13½
C241 A129 100fr multi   .65   .35
C242 A129 200fr multi   1.40   .65
C243 A129 300fr multi   2.00   1.00
    Nos. C241-C243 (3)   4.05   2.00
Souvenir Sheet
C244 A129 500fr multi   3.50   1.60

Nos. C231-C233 Overprinted in Gold:
    a. VAINQUEUR 1976 / TADEUSZ SLUSARSKI / POLOGNE
    b. VAINQUEUR 1976 / NADIA COMANECI / ROUMANIE
    c. VAINQUEUR 1976 / FRANK ET ALF HANSEN / NORVEGE

1976, July 4   Litho.   Perf. 11
C245 A124(a) 150fr multi   1.00   .50
C246 A124(b) 200fr multi   1.40   .65
Souvenir Sheet
C247 A124(c) 500fr multi   3.50   1.60
    Winners, 21st Olympic Games.

UPU Emblem over Globe — AP60

1978, Aug. 8   Litho.   Perf. 13
C248 AP60 350fr multi   2.25   1.50
    Congress of Paris, establishing UPU, cent.

Jules Verne, Apollo 11 Emblem, Footprint on Moon, Neil Armstrong — AP61

Space Conquest: 50fr, Yuri Gagarin and moon landing. 100fr, Montgolfier hot air balloon and memorial medal, 1783; Bleriot's monoplane, 1909.

1978, Sept. 27   Litho.   Perf. 13x12½
C249 AP61 50fr multi   .35   .16
C250 AP61 60fr multi   .40   .20
C251 AP61 100fr multi   .65   .35
    Nos. C249-C251 (3)   1.40   .71

Anti-Apartheid Year — AP62

1978, Oct. 12   Litho.   Perf. 13
C252 AP62 100fr blue & multi   .65   .35

Philexafrique II-Essen Issue
Common Design Types

Designs: #C253, Hippopotamus and Upper Volta #C18. #C254, Hummingbird and Hanover #1.

1978, Nov. 1   Litho.   Perf. 12½
C253 CD138 100fr multi   .65   .35
C254 CD139 100fr multi   .65   .35
    Nos. C253-C254 printed se-tenant.

Sun God Horus with Sun — AP63   Jules Verne and Balloon — AP64

Design: 300fr, Falcon with cartouches and UNESCO emblem.

1978, Dec. 4
C255 AP63 200fr multi   1.40   .65
C256 AP63 300fr multi   2.00   1.00
    UNESCO Campaign to safeguard monuments at Philae.

1978, Dec. 10   Engr.   Perf. 13
C257 AP64 200fr multi   1.40   .65
    Verne (1828-1905), science fiction writer.

Bicycling, Olympic Rings AP65

Designs: Bicycling scenes.

1980   Perf. 14½
C258 AP65 65fr multi   .65   .32
C259 AP65 150fr multi, vert.   1.00   .50
C260 AP65 250fr multi   1.60   .80
C261 AP65 350fr multi   2.25   1.20
    Nos. C258-C261 (4)   5.50   2.82
Souvenir Sheet
C262 AP65 500fr multi   3.50   1.60
    22nd Summer Olympic Games, Moscow, July 19-Aug. 3.

Nos. C258-C262 Overprinted with Name of Winner and Country

1980, Nov. 22   Litho.   Perf. 14½
C263 AP65 65fr multi   .42   .20
C264 AP65 150fr multi   1.00   .50
C265 AP65 250fr multi   1.60   .80
C266 AP65 350fr multi   2.25   1.20
    Nos. C263-C266 (4)   5.27   2.70
Souvenir Sheet
C267 AP65 500fr multi   3.50   1.60

1982 World Cup — AP66

Designs: Various soccer players.

1982, June 22   Litho.   Perf. 13½
C268 AP66 70fr multi   .45   .22
C269 AP66 90fr multi   .60   .30
C270 AP66 150fr multi   1.00   .50
C271 AP66 300fr multi   2.00   1.00
    Nos. C268-C271 (4)   4.05   2.02
Souvenir Sheet
C272 AP66 500fr multi   3.50   1.60

Anniversaries and Events — AP67

1983, June   Litho.   Perf. 13½
C273 AP67 90fr Space Shuttle   .30   .15
C274 AP67 120fr World Soccer Cup   .40   .20
C275 AP67 300fr Cup, diff.   1.00   .50
C276 AP67 450fr Royal Wedding   1.50   .70
    Nos. C273-C276 (4)   3.20   1.55
Souvenir Sheet
C277 AP67 500fr Prince Charles, La-
              dy Diana   1.60   1.60

Pre-Olympics, 1984 Los Angeles AP68

1983, Aug. 1   Litho.   Perf. 13
C278 AP68 90fr Sailing   .30   .15
C279 AP68 120fr Type 470   .40   .20
C280 AP68 300fr Wind surfing   1.00   .50
C281 AP68 400fr Wind surfing, diff. 1.40   .65
    Nos. C278-C281 (4)   3.10   1.50
Souvenir Sheet
C282 AP68 500fr Soling Class, Wind
              surfing   1.60   1.60

Christmas AP69

Rubens Paintings.

1983   Litho.   Perf. 13
C283 AP69 120fr Adoration of the
              Shepherds   .40   .20
C284 AP69 350fr Virgin of the Gar-
              land   1.20   .60
C285 AP69 500fr Adoration of the
              Kings   1.60   .80
    Nos. C283-C285 (3)   3.20   1.60

1984 Summer Olympics — AP70

1984, Mar. 26   Litho.   Perf. 12½
C286 AP70 90fr Handball, vert.   .30   .15
C287 AP70 120fr Volleyball, vert.   .40   .20
C288 AP70 150fr Handball, diff.   .50   .25
C289 AP70 250fr Basketball   .80   .42
C290 AP70 300fr Soccer   1.00   .50
    Nos. C286-C290 (5)   3.00   1.52
Souvenir Sheet
C291 AP70 500fr Volleyball, diff. 1.60   .80

Local
Birds
AP71

1984, May 14   Litho.   Perf. 12½

C292	AP71	90fr Phoenicopterus roseus	.30	.15
C293	AP71	185fr Choriotis kori, vert.	.62	.32
C294	AP71	200fr Buphagus erythrorhynchus, vert.	.65	.35
C295	AP71	300fr Bucorvus leadbeateri	1.00	.50
		Nos. C292-C295 (4)	2.57	1.32

AP72   REPUBLIQUE DE HAUTE-VOLTA   5F

REPUBLIQUE DE HAUTE-VOLTA   1000F

Famous Men — AP73

Designs: 5fr, Houari Boumediene (1927-1978), president of Algeria 1965-78. 125fr, Gottlieb Daimler (1834-1900), German automotive pioneer, and 1886 Daimler. 250fr, Louis Bleriot (1872-1936), French aviator, first to fly the English Channel in a heavier-than-air craft. 300fr, Abraham Lincoln. 400fr, Henri Dunant (1828-1910), founder of the Red Cross. 450fr, Auguste Piccard (1884-1962), Swiss physicist, inventor of the bathyscaphe Trieste, 1948. 500fr, Robert Baden-Powell (1856-1941), founder of Boy Scouts. 600fr, Anatoli Karpov, Russian chess champion. 1000fr, Paul Harris (1868-1947), founder of Rotary Intl.

1984, May 21   Litho.   Perf. 13½

C296	AP72	5fr multi	.15	.15
C297	AP72	125fr multi	.50	.25
C298	AP72	250fr multi	1.00	.50
C299	AP72	300fr multi	1.20	.60
C300	AP72	400fr multi	1.60	.80
C301	AP72	450fr multi	1.90	.90
C302	AP72	500fr multi	2.00	1.00
C303	AP72	600fr multi	2.25	1.20
		Nos. C296-C303 (8)	10.60	5.40

Souvenir Sheet

| C304 | AP73 | 1000fr multi | 4.00 | 2.00 |

No. C304 contains one 51x30mm stamp.

Burkina Faso

Butterflies — AP73a

1984, May 23   Perf. 13½

C305	AP73a	10fr Graphium pylades	.15	.15
C306	AP73a	120fr Hypolimnas misippus	.50	.22
C307	AP73a	400fr Danaus chrysippus	1.60	.80
C308	AP73a	450fr Papilio demodocus	1.90	.90
		Nos. C305-C308 (4)	4.15	2.07

Philexafrica '85, Lome — AP74

1985, May 20   Litho.   Perf. 13

| C309 | AP74 | 200fr Solar & wind energy | .55 | .25 |
| C310 | AP74 | 200fr Children | .55 | .25 |

Nos. C309-C310 se-tenant with center label picturing a map of Africa or the exhibition emblem.

PHILEXAFRICA '85, Lome — AP75

National development: No. C311, Youth. No. C312, Communications and transportation.

1985, Nov. 16   Litho.   Perf. 13

| C311 | AP75 | 250fr multi | .90 | .45 |
| C312 | AP75 | 250fr multi | .90 | .45 |

Intl. Youth Year (No. C311). Nos. C311-C312 printed se-tenant with center label picturing PHILEXAFRICA '85 emblem or outline map of Africa.

French Revolution, Bicent. — AP76

Designs: 150fr, *Oath of the Tennis Court*, by David. 200fr, *Storming of the Bastille*, by Thevenin. 600fr, *Rouget de Lisle Singing La Marseillaise*, by Pils.
Illustration reduced.

1989, May 3   Litho.   Perf. 13

C313	AP76	150fr multi	.90	.45
C314	AP76	200fr multi	1.20	.60
C315	AP76	600fr multi	3.60	1.80
		Nos. C313-C315 (3)	5.70	2.85

PHILEXFRANCE '89. Printed se-tenant with label containing the exhibition emblem.

POSTAGE DUE STAMPS

Postage Due Stamps of Upper Senegal and Niger, 1914, Overprinted in Black or Red

HAUTE-VOLTA

1920   Unwmk.   Perf. 14x13½

J1	D2	5c green	.30	.30
J2	D2	10c rose	.30	.30
J3	D2	15c gray	.30	.30
J4	D2	20c brown (R)	.40	.40
J5	D2	30c blue	.45	.45
J6	D2	50c black (R)	.65	.65
J7	D2	60c orange	.65	.65
J8	D2	1fr violet	.90	.90
		Nos. J1-J8 (8)	3.95	3.95

Type of 1914 Issue Surcharged **2F.**

1927

| J9 | D2 | 2fr on 1fr lilac rose | 2.25 | 2.25 |
| J10 | D2 | 3fr on 1fr orange brn | 2.50 | 2.50 |

D3

Red-fronted Gazelle — D4

1928   Typo.

J11	D3	5c green	.30	.30
J12	D3	10c rose	.30	.30
J13	D3	15c dark gray	.40	.40
J14	D3	20c dark brown	.40	.40
J15	D3	30c dark blue	.50	.50
J16	D3	50c black	1.60	1.60
J17	D3	60c orange	2.00	2.00
J18	D3	1fr dull violet	3.25	3.25

J19	D3	2fr lilac rose	6.00	6.00
J20	D3	3fr orange brn	6.25	6.25
		Nos. J11-J20 (10)	21.00	21.00

Catalogue values for unused stamps in this section, from this point to the end of the section, are for Never Hinged items.

Republic

1962, Jan. 31   Perf. 14x13½
Denomination in Black

J21	D4	1fr bright blue	.15	.15
J22	D4	2fr orange	.15	.15
J23	D4	5fr brt vio blue	.15	.15
J24	D4	10fr red lilac	.20	.20
J25	D4	20fr emerald	.45	.45
J26	D4	50fr rose red	1.10	1.10
		Nos. J21-J26 (6)	2.20	2.20

OFFICIAL STAMPS

Catalogue values for unused stamps in this section are for Never Hinged items.

Elephant
O1

Perf. 12½

1963, Feb. 1   Unwmk.   Photo.
Center in Sepia

O1	O1	1fr red brown	.15	.15
O2	O1	5fr yel green	.15	.15
O3	O1	10fr deep vio	.20	.20
O4	O1	15fr red org	.25	.25
O5	O1	25fr brt rose lilac	.35	.35
O6	O1	50fr brt green	.55	.55
O7	O1	60fr brt red	.70	.70
O8	O1	85fr dk slate grn	1.10	1.10
O9	O1	100fr brt blue	1.75	1.75
O10	O1	200fr bright rose	3.00	3.00
		Nos. O1-O10 (10)	8.20	8.20

BURMA

'bər-mə

Myanmar

LOCATION — Bounded on the north by China; east by China, Laos and Thailand; south and west by the Bay of Bengal, Bangladesh and India.
GOVT. — Republic
AREA — 261,789 sq. mi.
POP. — 35,313,905 (1983)
CAPITAL — Yangon (Rangoon)

Burma was part of India from 1826 until April 1, 1937, when it became a self-governing unit of the British Commonwealth and received a constitution. On January 4, 1948, Burma became an independent nation.

12 Pies = 1 Anna
16 Annas = 1 Rupee
100 Pyas = 1 Kyat (1953)

Catalogue values for unused stamps in this country are for Never Hinged items, beginning with Scott 35 in the regular postage section and Scott O28 in the official section.

Watermarks

Wmk. 254-   Wmk. 257-
Elephant Heads   Curved Wavy
                   Lines

Stamps of India 1926-36 Overprinted   **BURMA**

1937, Apr. 1   Wmk. 196   Perf. 14

1	A46	3p slate	.15	.15
2	A71	½a green	.15	.15
3	A68	9p dark green	.20	.15
4	A72	1a dark brown	.15	.15
5	A49	2a ver (small die)	.15	.15
6	A57	2a6p buff	.15	.15
7	A51	3a carmine rose	.40	.15
8	A70	3a6p deep blue	.40	.15
9	A52	4a olive green	.45	.15
10	A53	6a bister	.40	.25
11	A54	8a red violet	.90	.15
12	A55	12a claret	1.50	.50

Overprinted   **BURMA**

13	A56	1r green & brown	5.00	.75
14	A56	2r brn org & car rose	7.50	2.50
15	A56	5r dk violet & ultra	10.00	3.00
16	A56	10r car & green	27.50	6.00
17	A56	15r ol green & ultra	125.00	60.00
18	A56	25r blue & ocher	250.00	150.00
		Nos. 1-18 (18)	430.00	224.50

For overprints see #1N1-1N3, 1N25-1N26, 1N47.

King George VI
A1   A2

Royal
Barge — A3

Elephant
Moving Teak
Log — A4

Farmer
Plowing Rice
Field — A5

Sailboat on
Irrawaddy
River — A6

Peacock — A7   George VI — A8

Perf. 13½x14

1938-40		Litho.	Wmk. 254	
18A	A1	1p red orange ('40)	.85	.30
19	A1	3p violet	.15	.15
20	A1	6p ultramarine	.15	.15
21	A1	9p yel green	.55	.35
22	A2	1a brown violet	.15	.15
23	A2	1½a turquoise green	.15	.15
24	A2	2a carmine	.30	.15

Perf. 13

25	A3	2a6p rose lake	.80	.45
26	A4	3a dk violet	2.40	.50
27	A5	3a6p dp blue & brt bl	1.30	2.75
28	A2	4a slate blue, perf. 13½x14	.15	.15
29	A6	8a slate green	1.30	.15

Perf. 13½

30	A7	1r brt ultra & dk violet	2.10	.30
31	A7	2r dk vio & red brown	5.00	1.40
32	A8	5r car & dull vio	21.00	8.25
33	A8	10r gray grn & brn	42.50	32.50
		Nos. 18A-33 (16)	78.85	47.85

See Nos. 51-65. For overprints and surcharges see Nos. 34-50, O15-O27, 1N4-1N11, 1N28-1N30, 1N37-1N46, 1N48-1N49.

No. 25 Surcharged in Black

COMMEMORATION
POSTAGE STAMP
6TH MAY 1840

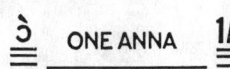

ONE ANNA   1A

1940, May 6			*Perf. 13*	
34	A3	1a on 2a6p rose lake	1.00	.80

Centenary of first postage stamp.

Catalogue values for unused stamps in this section, from this point to the end of the section, are for Never Hinged items.

Nos. 18A to 33 Overprinted in Black:

MILY ADMN	**MILY ADMN**
a	b

1945

35	A1(a)	1p red orange	.15	.15
36	A1(a)	3p violet	.15	.15
37	A1(a)	6p ultramarine	.15	.15
38	A1(a)	9p yel green	.15	.15
39	A2(a)	1a brown violet	.15	.15
40	A2(a)	1½a turq green	.15	.15
41	A2(a)	2a carmine	.15	.15
42	A3(b)	2a6p rose lake	.45	.45
43	A4(b)	3a dk violet	.75	.15
44	A5(b)	3a6p dp bl & brt bl	.15	.15
45	A2(a)	4a slate blue	.15	.15
46	A6(b)	8a slate green	.15	.20
47	A7(b)	1r brt ultra & dk violet	.30	.40
48	A7(b)	2r dk vio & red brown	.30	.75
49	A8(b)	5r car & dull vio	.75	.80
50	A8(b)	10r gray grn & brn	1.50	1.50
		Nos. 35-50 (16)	5.55	5.60

Types of 1938

Perf. 13½x14

1946, Jan. 1		Litho.	Wmk. 254	
51	A1	3p brown	.15	.15
52	A1	6p violet	.15	.15
53	A1	9p dull green	.15	.15
54	A2	1a deep blue	.15	.15
55	A2	1½a salmon	.15	.15
56	A2	2a rose lake	.15	.15

Perf. 13

57	A3	2a6p greenish blue	.25	.15
58	A4	3a blue violet	4.50	1.50
59	A5	3a6p ultra & gray blk	.15	.15
60	A2	4a rose lil, perf. 13½x14	.15	.15
61	A6	8a deep magenta	1.50	.20

Perf. 13½

62	A7	1r dp mag & dk vio	.90	.25
63	A7	2r salmon & red brn	5.00	1.50
64	A8	5r red brn & dk grn	5.00	5.00
65	A8	10r dk vio & car	5.00	5.00
		Nos. 51-65 (15)	23.35	14.80

For overprints see Nos. 70-84, O28-O42.

Burmese Man — A9

Burmese Woman — A10

Mythological Chinze — A11

Elephant Hauling Teak — A12

1946, May 2			*Perf. 13*	
66	A9	9p peacock green	.15	.15
67	A10	1½a brt violet	.15	.15
68	A11	2a carmine	.15	.15
69	A12	3a6p ultramarine	.15	.15
		Set value	.40	.40

Victory of the Allied Nations in WWII.

Nos. 51-65 Overprinted in Black

1947, Oct. 1		*Perf. 13½x14, 13, 13½*		
70	A1	3p brown	.30	.30
71	A1	6p violet	.15	.25
72	A1	9p dull green	.15	.25
a.		Inverted overprint	12.50	12.50
73	A2	1a deep blue	.15	.25
74	A2	1½a salmon	.75	.15
75	A2	2a rose lake	.25	.15
76	A3	2a6p greenish bl	.90	.75
77	A4	3a blue violet	1.75	1.25
78	A5	3a6p ultra & gray blk	.35	.75
79	A2	4a rose lilac	1.10	.25
80	A6	8a dp magenta	1.10	.70
81	A7	1r dp mag & dk vio	1.50	.30
82	A7	2r sal & red brn	1.75	1.75
83	A8	5r red brn & dk grn	2.25	3.00
84	A8	10r dk vio & car	2.25	3.00
		Nos. 70-84 (15)	14.70	13.10

The overprint is slightly larger on Nos. 76 to 78 and 80 to 84. The Burmese characters read "Interim Government."
Other denominations are known with the overprint inverted or double.

Issues of the Republic

U Aung San Map and Chinze — A13

Martyrs' Memorial — A14

Perf. 12½x12

1948, Jan. 6		Litho.	Unwmk.	
85	A13	½a emerald	.15	.15
86	A13	1a deep rose	.15	.15
87	A13	2a carmine	.15	.15
88	A13	3½a blue	.15	.15
89	A13	8a lt chocolate	.20	.20
		Set value	.60	.50

Attainment of independence, Jan. 4, 1948.

1948, July 19		Engr.	*Perf. 14x13½*	
90	A14	3p ultramarine	.15	.15
91	A14	6p green	.15	.15
92	A14	9p dp carmine	.15	.15
93	A14	1a purple	.15	.15
94	A14	2a lilac rose	.15	.15
95	A14	3½a dk slate green	.15	.15
96	A14	4a yel brown	.15	.15
97	A14	8a orange red	.15	.15
98	A14	12a claret	.15	.15
99	A14	1r blue green	.20	.16

100	A14	2r deep blue	.48	.35
101	A14	5r chocolate	1.25	.80
		Set value	2.50	1.90

1st anniv. of the assassination of Burma's leaders in the fight for independence.

Ball Game (Chinlon) A15

Bell A16

Mythical Bird — A17

Rice Planting — A18

Throne — A19

Designs: 6p, Dancer. 9p, Musician. 3a, Spinning. 3a6p, Royal Palace. 4a, Cutting teak. 8a, Plowing rice field.

Perf. 12½ (A15-A17), 12x12½ (A18), 13 (A19)

1949, Jan. 4				
102	A15	3p ultramarine	.15	.15
103	A15	6p green	.15	.15
104	A15	9p carmine	.15	.15
105	A16	1a red orange	.15	.15
106	A17	2a green	.15	.15
107	A18	2a6p lilac rose	.15	.15
108	A18	3a purple	.15	.15
109	A18	3a6p dk slate grn	.15	.15
110	A18	4a chocolate	.15	.15
111	A18	8a carmine	.25	.15
112	A19	1r blue green	.40	.20
a.		Perf. 14		2.50
113	A19	2r deep blue	.90	.32
114	A19	5r chocolate	1.75	.70
115	A19	10r orange red	4.00	1.00
		Nos. 102-115 (14)	8.65	
		Set value		2.85

See Nos. 122-135, 139-152, O56-O67.

UPU Monument, Bern — A20

1949, Oct. 9		Unwmk.	*Perf. 13*	
116	A20	2a orange	.15	.15
117	A20	3½a olive grn	.15	.15
118	A20	6a lilac	.20	.15
119	A20	8a crimson	.25	.20
120	A20	12½a ultra	.35	.20
121	A20	1r blue green	.55	.50
		Nos. 116-121 (6)	1.65	1.35

75th anniv. of the UPU.

Types of 1949

Designs as before.

Perf. 13½x14, 14x13½, 13

1952-53		Litho.	Wmk. 254	
122	A15	3p brown orange	.15	.15
123	A15	6p deep plum	.15	.15
124	A15	9p blue	.15	.15
125	A16	1a violet bl	.15	.15
126	A17	2a green ('52)	.15	.15
127	A18	2a6p green	.15	.15
128	A18	3a sal pink ('52)	.15	.15
129	A18	3a6p brown orange	.15	.15
130	A18	4a vermilion	.15	.15
131	A18	8a lt blue ('52)	.25	.15
132	A19	1r rose violet	.25	.15
133	A19	2r yel green	.55	.20
134	A19	5r ultramarine	1.75	.85
135	A19	10r aquamarine	3.25	1.65
		Nos. 122-135 (14)	7.30	
		Set value		3.50

Map of Burma and Monument — A21

1953, Jan. 4			*Perf. 14*	
136	A21	14p green	.15	.15

Perf. 13

Size: 36½x26mm

137	A21	20p salmon pink	.15	.15
138	A21	25p ultramarine	.15	.15
		Set value	.25	.20

Fifth anniversary of independence.
For surcharge see No. 166.

Types of 1949

Designs: 2p, Dancer. 3p, Musician. 20p, Spinning. 25p, Royal Palace. 30p, Cutting teak. 50p, Plowing rice field.

1954, Jan. 4		*Perf. 14x13½, 13, 14*		
139	A15	1p brown orange	.15	.15
140	A15	2p plum	.15	.15
141	A15	3p blue	.15	.15
142	A15	5p ultramarine	.15	.15
143	A18	10p yel green	.15	.15
144	A17	15p green	.15	.15
145	A18	20p vermilion	.15	.15
146	A18	25p lt red org	.15	.15
147	A18	30p vermilion	.15	.15
148	A18	50p blue	.24	.15
149	A19	1k rose violet	.50	.15
150	A19	2k green	1.00	.15
151	A19	5k ultramarine	2.75	.15
152	A19	10k light blue	5.00	.26
		Nos. 139-152 (14)	10.84	
		Set value		1.00

For overprints and surcharges see Nos. 163-165, 173-175, O68-O79, O80-O81, O83, O85, O87.

Peace Pagoda, Monks' Hostels and Meeting-cave A22

Designs: 10p, Sangha (community) of Cambodia. 15p, Council meeting. 50p, Sangha of Thailand. 1k, Sangha of Ceylon. 2k, Sangha of Laos.

1954		Typo.	*Perf. 13*	
153	A22	10p deep blue	.15	.15
154	A22	15p deep claret	.15	.15
155	A22	35p dark brown	.15	.15
156	A22	50p green	.16	.15
157	A22	1k carmine	.32	.16
158	A22	2k violet	.60	.40
		Set value	1.30	.80

6th Buddhist Council, Rangoon, 1954-56.

Marble Markers of 5th Buddhist Council A23

Designs: 40p, Thatbyinnyu Pagoda. 60p, Shwedagon Pagoda, Rangoon. 1.25k, Aerial View of 6th Buddhist Council, Yegu.

Perf. 11x11½

1956, May 24		Litho.	Unwmk.	
159	A23	20p blue & gray olive	.15	.15
160	A23	40p blue & brt yel grn	.15	.15
161	A23	60p green & lemon	.16	.15
162	A23	1.25k gray blue & yel	.32	.20
		Nos. 159-162 (4)	.78	
		Set value		.45

2500th anniv. of the Buddhist Era.

Nos. 146, 149-150 Surcharged or Overprinted

မြန်မာလှ-နှစ်တရာ

၁၂၁၀-၁၃၂၀

15 P   ၁၅ိး

1959, Nov. 9   Wmk. 254   Perf. 13, 14
163 A18 15p on 25p lt red org   .15   .15
164 A19 1k rose violet   .30   .16
165 A19 2k green   .55   .45
Nos. 163-165 (3)   1.00
Set value   .65

Centenary of Mandalay, former capital.
The two lines of overprint are 4mm apart on No. 163; 7mm on Nos. 164-165.

No. 136 Surcharged: ၁၅ိ:

1961, June   Perf. 14
166 A21 15p on 14p green   .32   .16

Children — A24

Unwmk.
1961, Dec. 11   Litho.   Perf. 13
167 A24 15p claret & rose claret   .15   .15

15th anniversary of UNICEF.

Runner with Torch — A25

Soccer, Pole Vault and Shot Put — A26

Designs: 50p, Women runners. 1k, Hurdling, weight lifting, boxing, bicycling and swimming.

1961, Dec. 11   Photo.   Perf. 14x13
168 A25 15p red & ultra   .15   .15
169 A26 25p dk green & ocher   .15   .15
170 A26 50p vio blue & pink   .20   .15
171 A25 1k brt green & yel   .35   .25
Nos. 168-171 (4)   .85
Set value   .50

2nd South East Asia Peninsular Games, Rangoon.

Map and Flag of Burma — A27

Wmk. 254
1963, Mar. 2   Engr.   Perf. 13
172 A27 15p red   .20   .15

First anniversary of new government.

Nos. 143 and 148 Overprinted in Violet or Red: "FREEDOM FROM HUNGER"

1963, Mar. 21   Litho.
173 A18 10p yel green (V)   .15   .15
174 A18 50p blue (R)   .20   .15
Set value   .30   .20

FAO "Freedom from Hunger" campaign.

No. 145 Overprinted

အလုပ်သမားနေ့
၁၉၆၃

1963, May 1
175 A18 20p vermilion   .15   .15

Issued for May Day.

White-browed Fantail — A28

Indian Roller — A29

Birds: 20p, Red-whiskered bulbul. 25p, Crested serpent eagle. 50p, Sarus crane. 1k, Malabar pied hornbill. 2k, Lineated kalij pheasant. 5k, Green peafowl.

Unwmk.
1964, Apr. 16   Photo.   Perf. 13
Size: 25x21mm
176 A28 1p gray   .15   .15
177 A28 2p carmine rose   .15   .15
178 A28 3p blue green   .15   .15
Size: 22x26½mm
179 A29 5p violet blue   .15   .15
180 A29 10p orange brn   .15   .15
181 A29 15p olive   .15   .15
Size: 35x25mm
182 A28 20p rose & brn   .16   .15
Size: 27x36½mm, 36½x27mm
183 A29 25p yel & brown   .20
184 A29 50p red, blk & gray   .50   .15
185 A29 1k gray, ind & yel   1.00   .15
186 A28 2k pale ol, ind & red   2.00   .32
187 A29 5k citron, dk bl & red   4.75   .65
Nos. 176-187 (12)   9.51
Set value   1.50

See Nos. 197-208. For overprints see Nos. O82, O84, O86, O88-O93, O94-O115.

ITU Emblem, Old and New Communication Equipment — A30

1965, May 17   Litho.   Perf. 15
Size: 32x22mm
188 A30 20p bright pink   .15   .15
Perf. 13
Size: 34x24½mm
189 A30 50p dull green   .25   .25
Set value   .35   .30

Centenary of the ITU.

ICY Emblem A31

1965, July 1   Unwmk.   Perf. 13
190 A31 5p violet blue   .15   .15
191 A31 10p brown orange   .15   .15
192 A31 15p olive   .15   .15
Set value   .20   .15

International Cooperation Year.

Rice Farmer — A32

Cogwheel and Hammer — A33

1966, Mar. 2
193 A32 15p multicolored   .15   .15

Issued for Farmers' Day.

1967, May 1   Litho.   Unwmk.
194 A33 15p lt blue, yel & black   .15   .15

Issued for Labor Day, May 1.

Aung San, Tractor and Farmers A34

1968, Jan. 4   Unwmk.   Perf. 13
195 A34 15p sky blue, black & ocher   .15   .15

20th anniversary of independence.

Largest Burmese Pearl — A35

1968, Mar. 4   Litho.   Perf. 13½x13
196 A35 15p blue, ultra, gray & yel   .15   .15

Burmese pearl industry.

Bird Types of 1964 in Changed Sizes; Designs as Before
Unwmk.
1968, July 1   Photo.   Perf. 14
Size: 21x17mm
197 A28 1p gray   .15   .15
198 A28 2p carmine rose   .15   .15
199 A28 3p blue green   .15   .15
Size: 23½x28mm
200 A29 5p violet blue   .15   .15
201 A29 10p orange brown   .15   .15
202 A29 15p olive   .15   .15
Size: 38½x21, 21x38½mm
203 A28 20p rose & brown   .15   .15
204 A29 25p yel & brown   .16   .15
205 A29 50p ver, blk, & gray   .32   .15
206 A29 1k gray, ind & yel   .65   .15
207 A28 2k dull cit, ind & red   1.40   .24
208 A29 5k yel, dk blue & red   3.25   .55
Nos. 197-208 (12)   6.83
Set value   1.25

For overprints see Nos. O92-O102.

Wheat — A36

1969, Mar. 2   Litho.   Perf. 13
209 A36 15p blue, emerald & yel   .15   .15

Issued for Peasant's Day.

ILO Emblem A37

1969, Oct. 29   Photo.   Wmk. 254
210 A37 15p dk blue grn & gold   .15   .15
211 A37 50p dp carmine & gold   .15   .15
Set value   .20   .20

50th anniv. of the ILO.

Soccer — A38

Designs: 25p, Runner, horiz. 50p, Weight lifter. 1k, Women's volleyball.

Perf. 12½x13, 13x12½
1969, Dec. 1   Litho.   Wmk. 254
212 A38 15p brt olive & multi   .15   .15
213 A38 25p brown & multi   .15   .15
214 A38 50p brt green & multi   .25   .15
215 A38 1k blue, yel grn & blk   .45   .30
Nos. 212-215 (4)   1.00
Set value   .60

5th South East Asia Peninsular Games, Rangoon.

Burmese Flags and Marching Soldiers — A39

1970, Mar. 27   Perf. 13
216 A39 15p multicolored   .15   .15

Issued for Armed Forces Day.

Solar System and UN Emblem A40

1970, June 26   Photo.   Unwmk.
217 A40 15p lt ultra & multi   .15   .15

25th anniversary of the United Nations.

Scroll, Marchers, Peacock Emblem A41

Designs: 25p, Students' boycott demonstration. 50p, Banner and marchers at Shwedagon Camp.

1970, Nov. 23   Litho.   Perf. 13x13½
218 A41 15p ultra & multi   .15   .15
219 A41 25p multicolored   .15   .15
220 A41 50p lt blue & multi   .24   .15
Set value   .45   .22

50th National Day (Students' 1920 uprising).

Workers, Farmers, Technicians — A42

15p, Burmese of various races, & flags. 25p, Hands holding document. 50p, Red party flag.

1971, June 28   Litho.   Perf. 13½
221 A42 5p blue & multi   .15   .15
222 A42 15p blue & multi   .15   .15
223 A42 25p blue & multi   .15   .15
224 A42 50p blue & multi   .22   .15
a. Souvenir sheet of 4, #221-224   .45   .45
Set value   .45   .25

1st Congress of Burmese Socialist Program Party.

Child Drinking Milk — A43

UNICEF, 25th Anniv.: 50p, Marionettes.

1971, Dec. 11   Perf. 14½
225 A43 15p lt ultra & multi   .15   .15
226 A43 50p emerald & multi   .30   .15
Set value   .25

Aung San, Independence Monument, Pinlon — A44

Union Day, 25th Anniv.: 50p, Bogyoke Aung San and people in front of Independence Monument. 1k, Map of Burma with flag pointing to Pinlon, vert.

1972, Feb. 12   *Perf. 14*
227 A44 15p ocher & multi   .15 .15
228 A44 50p blue & multi   .24 .15
229 A44 1k green, ultra & red   .40 .20
    Set value   .70 .35

Burmese and Double Star A45

1972   Litho.   *Perf. 14*
230 A45 15p bister & multi   .15 .15
Revolutionary Council, 10th anniversary.

"Your Heart is your Health" — A46

1972, Apr. 7   *Perf. 14x14½*
231 A46 15p yellow, red & black   .15 .15
World Health Day.

Burmese of Various Ethnic Groups A47

1973, Feb. 12   Litho.   *Perf. 14*
232 A47 15p multicolored   .15 .15
1973 census.

Casting Vote — A48

Natl. Referendum: 10p, Voters holding map of Burma. 15p, Farmer and soldier holding ballots, vert.

Perf. 14x14½, 14½x14
1973, Dec. 15   Litho.
233 A48 5p deep org & black   .15 .15
234 A48 10p blue & multi   .15 .15
235 A48 15p blue & multi   .15 .15
    Set value   .15 .15

Open-air Meeting A49

Designs: 15p, Regional flags. 1k, Scales of justice and Burmese emblem.

1974, Mar. 2   Photo.   *Perf. 13*
    Size: 80x26mm
236 A49 15p blue & multi   .15 .15
    Size: 37x25mm
237 A49 50p blue & multi   .20 .15
238 A49 1k lt blue, bis & blk   .40 .26
    Set value   .65 .45
First meeting of People's Parliament.

Messenger Bird and UPU Emblem A50

UPU Cent.: 20p, Mother reading letter to child, vert. 50p, Simulated block of stamps, vert. 1k, Burmese doll, vert. 2k, Mailman delivering letter to family.

1974, May 22
239 A50 15p grn, lt grn & org   .15 .15
240 A50 20p multicolored   .15 .15
241 A50 50p green & multi   .22 .15
242 A50 1k ultra & multi   .48 .25
243 A50 2k blue & multi   .95 .50
    Nos. 239-243 (5)   1.95
    Set value   .95

Children A51   Man and Woman A52

Designs: 3p, Girl. 5p, 15p, Man and woman. 10p, Children (like 1p). 50p, Woman with fan. 1k, Seated woman. 5k, Drummer.

Perf. 13, 13x13½ (#248-251)
1974-78   Photo.
244 A51 1p rose & lilac rose   .15 .15
245 A51 3p dk brown & pink   .15 .15
246 A51 5p pink & violet   .15 .15
246A A51 10p Prus blue ('76)   .15 .15
247 A51 15p lt green & olive ('75)   .15 .15
248 A52 20p lt blue & multi   .15 .15
249 A52 50p ocher & multi   .24 .15
250 A52 1k brt rose & multi   .48 .28
251 A52 5k ol green & multi   2.00 1.40
    Set value   3.00 2.00

For different country names see Nos. 298-303.

IWY Emblem, Woman and Globe — A53

IWY: 2k, Symbolic flower, globe and IWY emblem, vert.

1975, Dec. 15   Photo.   *Perf. 13½*
252 A53 50p green & black   .18 .15
253 A53 2k black & blue   .70 .48

Burmese with Raised Fists — A54

Constitution Day: 50p, Demonstrators with banners and emblem. 1k, People and map of Burma, emblem.

1976, Jan. 3   *Perf. 14*
254 A54 20p blue & black   .15 .15
255 A54 50p blue, blk & brn   .22 .15
    Size: 56x20mm
256 A54 1k blue & multi   .45 .20
    Nos. 254-256 (3)   .82
    Set value   .40

Students, Campaign Emblem A55   Abacus A56

Intl. Literacy Year: 50p, Campaign emblem. 1k, Emblem, book and globe.

1976, Sept. 8   Photo.   *Perf. 14*
257 A55 10p salmon & black   .15 .15
258 A56 15p blue grn & multi   .15 .15
259 A56 50p ultra, org & blk   .24 .15
260 A55 1k multicolored   .60 .30
    Set value   .95 .55

Steam Locomotive — A57   Diesel Train Emerging from Tunnel — A58

Cent. of Burma's Railroad: 20p, Early train and oxcart. 25p, Old and new trains approaching station. 50p, Railroad bridge.

1977, May 1   *Perf. 13½*
261 A57 15p multicolored   .15 .15
    Size: 38x26, 26x38mm
262 A57 20p multicolored   .15 .15
263 A57 25p multicolored   .15 .15
264 A57 50p multicolored   .26 .15
265 A58 1k multicolored   .52 .25
    Set value   1.00 .60

Karaweik Pagoda A59

Design: 1k, Karaweik Pagoda, front view.

1977
266 A59 50p light brown   .20 .15
    Size: 78x25mm
267 A59 1k multicolored   .35 .25

Jade Dragon — A60

Precious Jewelry: 20p, Gold bird with large pearl. 50p, Hand holding pearl necklace with pendant. 1k, Gold dragon, horiz.

1978   Photo.   *Perf. 13*
268 A60 15p green & yel grn   .15 .15
269 A60 20p multicolored   .15 .15
270 A60 50p multicolored   .30 .20
    Size: 55x20mm
     Perf. 14
271 A60 1k multicolored   .50 .30
    Set value   .95 .60

Satellite over Map of Asia — A61

1979, Feb., 12   Photo.   *Perf. 13*
272 A61 25p multicolored   .15 .15

IYC Emblem in Map of Burma — A62   Weather Balloon, WMO Emblem — A63

1979, Dec.   Photo.   *Perf. 13½*
273 A62 25p multicolored   .16 .15
274 A62 50p multicolored   .32 .16
International Year of the Child.

1980, Mar. 23   Photo.   *Perf. 13½*
275 A63 25p shown   .16 .15
276 A63 50p Weather satellite, cloud   .32 .16
World Meteorological Day.

Weight Lifting, Olympic Rings A64

1980, Dec.   Litho.   *Perf. 14*
277 A64 20p shown   .15 .15
278 A64 50p Boxing   .20 .15
279 A64 1k Soccer   .40 .25
    Nos. 277-279 (3)   .75
    Set value   .44
22nd Summer Olympic Games, Moscow, July 19-Aug. 3.

13th World Telecommunications Day — A65

1981, May 17   Photo.   *Perf. 13½*
280 A65 25p orange & black   .15 .15

World Food Day — A66

1981, Oct. 16   Photo.   *Perf. 13½*
281 A66 25p Livestock, produce   .15 .15
282 A66 50p Farmer, rice, produce   .20 .15
283 A66 1k Emblems   .40 .25
    Nos. 281-283 (3)   .75
    Set value   .46

Intl. Year of the Disabled A67

1981, Dec. 12
284 A67 25p multicolored   .15 .15

World Communications Year — A68

1983, Sept. 15 Litho. Perf. 14¹/₂x14
285 A68 15p pale blue & black .15 .15
286 A68 25p dull lake & black .15 .15
287 A68 50p pale brn, blk & lake .30 .20
288 A68 1k buff, blk, beige & yel grn .60 .40
Nos. 285-288 (4) 1.20
Set value .77

Fish, Ship, Globe,
FAO Emblem — A69

1983, Oct. 16 Photo. Perf. 14x14¹/₂
289 A69 15p brt blue, bister & blk .15 .15
290 A69 25p yel grn, pale org & blk .15 .15
291 A69 50p org, pale grn & blk .30 .20
292 A69 1k yel, ultra & blk .60 .40
Nos. 289-292 (4) 1.20
Set value .77
World Food Day.

Stylized Trees, Hemispheres and
Log — A70

1984, Oct. 16 Perf. 14¹/₂x14
293 A70 15p org, black & blue .15 .15
294 A70 25p pale yel, blk & t vio .15 .15
295 A70 50p pale pink, blk & lt grn .30 .20
296 A70 1k yel, blk & lt rose vio .60 .40
Nos. 293-296 (4) 1.20
Set value .77
World Food Day.

Intl. Youth Year — A71

1985, Oct. 15 Perf. 14x14¹/₂
297 A71 15p multicolored .15 .15

Types of 1974
Inscribed: Union of Burma

1989 Photo. Perf. 13¹/₂
298 A51 15p olive & lt green .15 .15
299 A52 50p violet & brown .25 .25
300 A52 1k multicolored .52 .52
Nos. 298-300 (3) .92 .92
Issued: 15p, June 26; 50p, June 12; 1k, Sept. 6.

Inscribed: Union of Myanmar
1990 Photo. Perf. 13¹/₂
301 A51 15p olive & lt green .15 .15
301A A51 20p
302 A52 50p violet & brown .25 .25
303 A52 1k multicolored .52 .52
Issued: 15p, May 26; 50p, May 12.

Fountain, Natl. Assembly Park — A74

Illustration reduced.

1990, May 27 Litho. Perf. 14¹/₂x14
304 A74 1k multicolored .52 .52
State Law and Order Restoration Council.

A75　　　A76

1990, Dec. 20 Litho. Perf. 14x14¹/₂
305 A75 2k multicolored .82 .82
UN Development Program, 40th anniv.

1991, Jan. 26
306 A76 50p Nawata ruby .28 .28

Painting of Freedom　　Bronze
Fighters — A77　　　Statue — A78

1992, Jan. 4 Litho. Perf. 14x14¹/₂
307 A77 50p multicolored .20 .20
308 A78 2k multicolored .80 .80

A79　　　A80

1992, Apr. 10 Litho. Perf. 14x14¹/₂
309 A79 50p multicolored .52 .52
National Sports Festival.

1992, Dec. 1 Litho. Perf. 14x14¹/₂
310 A80 50p red .35 .35
World Campaign Against AIDS.

A81　　　Artifacts — A82

1992, Dec. 5 Litho. Perf. 14x14¹/₂
Background Color
311 A81 50p pink .20 .20
312 A81 1k yellow .42 .42
313 A81 3k orange 1.25 1.25
314 A81 5k green 2.05 2.05
Nos. 311-314 (4) 3.92 3.92
Intl. Conference on Nutrition, Rome.

1993, Sept. 1 Litho. Perf. 14x14¹/₂
315 A82 5k Bird 1.65 1.65
316 A82 10k shown 3.25 3.25

Natl. Assembly — A83

1993, Jan. 1 Litho. Perf. 14x14¹/₂
317 A83 50p multicolored .16 .16
318 A83 3k multicolored 1.00 1.00

Equestrian
Festival
A84

1993, Oct. 23 Litho. Perf. 14¹/₂x14
319 A84 3k multicolored 1.00 1.00

A85　　　A86

1994, June 5 Litho. Perf. 14
320 A85 4k multicolored 1.50 1.50
Environment day.

1994, Sept. 15 Litho. Perf. 14
321 A86 3k multicolored 1.25 1.25
Union of Solidarity & Development, 1st anniv.

Armed
Forces,
50th
Anniv.
A87

1995, Mar. 27 Litho. Perf. 14¹/₂x14
322 A87 50p multicolored .22 .22

A88　　　A89

1995, June 26 Litho. Perf. 14
323 A88 2k multicolored .80 .80
Prevent drug abuse.

1995, Oct. 17 Litho. Perf. 14x14¹/₂
324 A89 50p multicolored .40 .40
Myanmar motion pictures, 60th anniv.

A90　　　A91

1995, Oct. 24
325 A90 4k UN, 50th Anniv. 2.00 2.00

1995, Nov. 1
326 A91 50p pink & multi .25 .25
327 A91 2k green & multi 1.00 1.00
University of Yangon (Rangoon), 75th anniv.

Visit
Myanmar
Year — A92

Designs: 50p, Couple in boat on Inlay Lake with
food bowl for Buddha, Buddhist monks. 4k, Decorated royal barge on Kandawgyi (Royal Lake),
Yangoon. 5k, Royal moat, entrance of Yadanabon
(Mandalay), vert.

Perf. 14¹/₂x14, 14x14¹/₂
1996, Mar. 1 Litho.
328 A92 50p multicolored .20 .20
329 A92 4k multicolored 1.75 1.75
330 A92 5k multicolored 2.20 2.20
Nos. 328-330 (3) 4.15 4.15

UNICEF, 50th
Anniv. — A93

Stylized designs: 1k, Mother breastfeeding. 2k,
Vaccinating child. 4k, Girls going to school.

1996 Litho. Perf. 14x14¹/₂
331 A93 1k multicolored .40 .40
332 A93 2k multicolored .85 .85
333 A93 4k multicolored 1.70 1.70
Nos. 331-333 (3) 2.95 2.95

Intl.
Letter
Writing
Week
A94

Designs: 2k, Men in canoe. 5k, Stylized figures
forming pyramid, flag, map, vert.

1996 Perf. 14¹/₂x14, 14x14¹/₂
334 A94 2k multicolored .85 .85
335 A94 5k multicolored 2.00 2.00

Assoc. of Southeast
Asian Nations (ASEAN),
30th Anniv. — A95

1997 Litho. Perf. 14x14¹/₂
336 A95 1k blue & multi .40 .40
337 A95 2k yellow & multi .85 .85

OFFICIAL STAMPS

BURMA

Stamps of India, 1926-34, Overprinted in Black

SERVICE

1937		Wmk. 196	Perf. 14	
O1	A46	3p gray	.40	.20
O2	A71	1/2a green	2.25	.20
O3	A68	9p dark green	1.50	.20
O4	A72	1a dark brown	1.50	.25
O5	A49	2a vermilion	2.25	.55
O6	A57	2a6p buff	2.25	.90
O7	A52	4a olive grn	1.50	.90
O8	A53	6a bister	2.25	1.50
O9	A54	8a red violet	1.40	1.00
O10	A55	12a claret	1.40	1.75

BURMA

Overprinted

SERVICE

O11	A56	1r green & brown	11.00	3.25
O12	A56	2r buff & car rose	20.00	17.50
O13	A56	5r dk vio & ultra	47.50	32.50
O14	A56	10r car & green	140.00	85.00
		Nos. O1-O14 (14)	235.20	147.90

For overprint see No. 1N27.

Regular Issue of 1938 Overprinted in Black **SERVICE**

Perf. 13 1/2 x14, 13, 13 1/2

1939			Wmk. 254	
O15	A1	3p violet	.15	.15
O16	A1	6p ultramarine	.15	.15
O17	A1	9p yel green	3.25	.15
O18	A2	1a brown violet	.15	.15
O19	A2	1 1/2a turquoise green	3.00	.15
O20	A2	2a carmine	.80	.15
O21	A2	4a slate blue	3.50	.40

Overprinted **SERVICE**

O22	A3	2a6p rose lake	16.00	1.25
O23	A6	8a slate green	16.00	1.50
O24	A7	1r brt ultra & dk vio	25.00	1.50
O25	A7	2r dk vio & red brn	30.00	2.50
O26	A8	5r car & dull vio	27.50	16.00
O27	A8	10r gray grn & brn	80.00	21.00
		Nos. O15-O27 (13)	205.50	45.05

For overprints see Nos. 1N12-1N16, 1N31-1N36, 1NO1.

> Catalogue values for unused stamps in this section, from this point to the end of the section, are for Never Hinged items.

Nos. 51-56, 60 Overprinted Like Nos. O15-O21

1946			Perf. 13 1/2x14	
O28	A1	3p brown	.15	.15
O29	A1	6p violet	.15	.15
O30	A1	9p dull green	.15	.15
O31	A2	1a deep blue	.15	.15
O32	A2	1 1/2a salmon	.15	.15
O33	A2	2a rose lake	.15	.15
O34	A2	4a rose lilac	.15	.15

Nos. 57, 61-65 Ovptd. Like Nos. O22-O27

Perf. 13, 13 1/2

O35	A3	2a6p greenish blue	.15	.15
O38	A6	8a deep magenta	.15	1.50
O39	A7	1r dp mag & dk vio	.60	2.25
O40	A7	2r salmon & red brn	4.50	20.00
O41	A8	5r red brn & dk grn	9.00	22.50
O42	A8	10r dk violet & car	15.00	35.00
		Nos. O28-O42 (13)	30.45	82.45

Nos. O28 to O42 [burmese] Overprinted in Black

1947				
O43	A1	3p brown	.15	.15
O44	A1	6p violet	.15	.15
O45	A1	9p dull green	.15	.15
O46	A2	1a deep blue	.15	.15
O47	A2	1 1/2a salmon	.15	.15
O48	A2	2a rose lake	.15	.15
O49	A3	2a6p greenish bl	.15	.15
O50	A4	4a rose lilac	3.00	1.25
O51	A6	8a dp magenta	3.50	2.25
O52	A7	1r dp mag & dk vio	6.50	2.25
O53	A7	2r sal & red brn	12.00	8.00
O54	A8	5r red brn & dk grn	16.00	16.00
O55	A8	10r dk vio & car	21.00	21.00
		Nos. O43-O55 (13)	63.05	51.80

The overprint is slightly larger on Nos. O49 and O51 to O55. The Burmese characters read "Interim Government."

Issues of the Republic

Nos. 102 to 106 and 109 to 115 Overprinted in [burmese] Carmine or Black

a. Overprint 13mm long.
b. Overprint 15mm long.

1949		Unwmk.	Perf. 12 1/2, 13	
O56	A15(a)	3p ultra (C)	.15	.15
O57	A15(a)	6p green (C)	.15	.15
O58	A15(a)	9p carmine	.15	.15
O59	A16(a)	1a red orange	.15	.15
O60	A17(a)	2a orange	.15	.15
O61	A18(b)	3a6p dk sl grn (C)	.15	.15
O62	A16(a)	4a chocolate	.15	.15
O63	A18(b)	8a carmine	.20	.15
O64	A19(b)	1r blue green (C)	.35	.25
O65	A19(b)	2r dp blue (C)	.65	.40
O66	A19(b)	5r chocolate	1.65	1.25
O67	A19(b)	10r orange red	3.25	2.50
		Nos. O56-O67 (12)	7.15	
		Set value		4.85

Same Overprint in Black on Nos. 139-142, 144-152

Perf. 14x13 1/2, 13, 14

1954-57			Wmk. 254	
O68	A15(a)	1p brown org	.15	.15
O69	A15(a)	2p plum	.15	.15
O70	A15(a)	3p blue	.15	.15
O71	A16(a)	5p ultra	.15	.15
O72	A17(a)	15p green	.15	.15
O72A	A18(b)	20p ver ('57)	.15	.15
O73	A18(b)	25p lt red org	.15	.15
O74	A16(a)	30p vermilion	.15	.15
O75	A18(b)	50p blue	.20	.15
O76	A19(b)	1k rose violet	.40	.15
O77	A19(b)	2k green	.85	.20
O78	A19(b)	5k ultra	1.65	.30
O79	A19(b)	10k light blue	3.25	.45
		Nos. O68-O79 (13)	7.55	
		Set value		1.50

No. 141 Ovptd. **Service**

1964		Litho.	Perf. 14	
O80	A15	3p blue	10.00	7.00

Nos. 139, 141-142, 144, 177-179, 181, 183 Ovptd. [burmese]

1964-65

Overprint: 11 1/2mm

O81	A15	1p brown orange	3.00	.75
O82	A28	2p carmine rose ('65)	2.50	.60
O83	A15	3p blue	3.00	.75
O84	A28	3p blue green ('65)	2.50	.60
O85	A16	5p ultramarine	3.00	.75
O86	A28	5p violet blue ('65)	2.50	.60
O87	A17	15p green	3.00	.75
O88	A28	15p olive ('65)	2.50	.60
O89	A29	25p yel & brn ('65)	2.60	.60
		Nos. O81-O89 (9)	24.60	6.00

[burmese]   [burmese]
#176-178 Ovptd.   #181 Ovptd.

1966

Overprint: 15mm

O90	A28	1p black		
O91	A28	2p carmine rose		
O92	A28	3p blue green		

Overprint: 12mm

O93	A28	15p olive		

Nos. 176-179, 181-187 Overprinted in Black or Red [burmese]

1967	Unwmk.	Photo.	Perf. 13	

Overprint: 15mm

Size: 25x21mm

O94	A28	1p gray	.15	.15
O95	A28	2p carmine rose	.15	.15
O96	A28	3p blue green	.15	.15

Size: 22x26 1/2mm

O97	A29	5p violet blue	.15	.15
O98	A29	15p olive	.15	.15

Size: 35x25mm

O99	A28	20p rose & brown	.15	.15

Size: 27x36 1/2mm, 36 1/2x27mm

O100	A29	25p yel & brown (R)	.15	.15
O101	A29	50p red, blk & gray	.26	.15
O102	A29	1k gray, ind & yel (R)	.52	.15
O103	A28	2k pale ol, ind & red (R)	1.10	.30
O104	A29	5k cit, dk bl & red (R)	2.75	.65
		Nos. O94-O104 (11)	5.68	
		Set value		1.50

Similar Overprint on Nos. 197-200, 202-208 in Black or Red

1968		Unwmk.	Perf. 14	

Size: 21x17mm

Overprint: 13mm

O105	A28	1p gray	.15	.15
O106	A28	2p carmine rose	.15	.15
O107	A28	3p blue green	.15	.15

Size: 23 1/2x28mm

Overprint: 15mm

O108	A29	5p violet blue	.15	.15
O109	A29	15p olive	.15	.15

Size: 38 1/2x21mm, 21x38 1/2mm

Overprint: 14mm

O110	A28	20p rose & brn	.15	.15
O111	A29	25p yel & brown (R)	.15	.15
O112	A29	50p ver, blk & gray	.26	.15
O113	A29	1k gray, ind & yel (R)	.52	.15
O114	A28	2k dl cit, ind & red (R)	1.10	.24
O115	A29	5k yel, dk bl & red (R)	2.75	.55
		Nos. O105-O115 (11)	5.68	
		Set value		1.25

OCCUPATION STAMPS

Issued by Burma Independence Army (in conjunction with Japanese occupation officials)

Stamps of Burma, 1937-40, Overprinted in Blue, Black Blue, Black or Red

Henzada Issue

Nos. 1, 3 and 5 Overprinted in Blue or Black

Henzada Type I

1942, May		Wmk. 196	Perf. 14	
1N1	A46	3p slate	5.00	7.50
1N2	A68	9p dark green	17.50	25.00
1N3	A49	2a vermilion	50.00	75.00

On 1938-40 George VI Issue

Perf. 13 1/2x14

		Wmk. 254		
1N4	A1	1p red orange	150.00	87.50
1N5	A1	3p violet	17.50	35.00
1N6	A1	6p ultra	15.00	30.00
1N7	A1	9p yel green	200.00	
1N8	A2	1a brown violet	5.00	7.50
1N9	A2	1 1/2a turq green	12.50	17.50
1N10	A2	2a carmine	15.00	17.50
1N11	A2	4a slate blue	30.00	37.50

On Official Stamps of 1939

1N12	A1	3p violet	50.00	62.50
1N13	A1	6p ultra	45.00	62.50
1N14	A2	1 1/2a turq green	65.00	87.50
1N15	A2	2a carmine	150.00	150.00
1N16	A2	4a slate blue	200.00	250.00

Authorities believe this overprint was officially applied only to postal stationery and that the adhesive stamps existing with it were not regularly issued. It has been called "Henzada Type II."

Myaungmya Issue

1937 George V Issue Overprinted in Black

Myaungmya Type I

1942, May		Wmk. 196	Perf. 14	
1N25	A68	9p dk green	50.00	62.50
1N26	A70	3a6p deep blue	25.00	32.50

On Official Stamp of 1937, No. O8

1N27	A53	6a bister	50.00	62.50

On 1938-40 George VI Issue

Perf. 13 1/2x14

		Wmk. 254		
1N28	A1	9p yel green	100.00	125.00
1N29	A2	1a brown vio	175.00	225.00
1N30	A2	4a sl blue (blk ovpt. over red)	100.00	125.00

On Official Stamps of 1939

1N31	A1	3p violet	15.00	15.00
1N32	A1	6p violet	7.50	10.00
1N33	A2	1a brown vio	7.50	10.00
1N34	A2	1 1/2a turq green	400.00	
1N35	A2	2a carmine	15.00	20.00
1N36	A2	4a slate blue	12.50	17.50

1938-40 George VI Issue Overprinted

Myaungmya Type II

1942, May				
1N37	A1	3p violet	12.50	20.00
1N38	A1	6p ultra	25.00	30.00
1N39	A1	9p yel green	10.00	15.00
1N40	A2	1a brown vio	10.00	12.50
1N41	A2	2a carmine	15.00	20.00
1N42	A2	4a slate blue	15.00	25.00

Nos. 30-31 Overprinted

Myaungmya Type III

1N43	A7	1r brt ultra & dk vio	150.00	
1N44	A7	2r dk vio & red brn	110.00	

Pyapon Issue

No. 5 and 1938-40 George VI Issue Overprinted

1942, May				
1N45	A1	6p ultra	75.00	
1N46	A2	1a brown vio	65.00	50.00
1N47	A49	2a vermilion	75.00	
1N48	A2	2a carmine	45.00	62.50
1N49	A2	4a slate blue	150.00	200.00
		Nos. 1N45-1N49 (5)	410.00	

Counterfeits of the peacock overprints exist.

> *The first value column gives the catalogue value of an unused stamp, the second that of a used stamp.*

OCCUPATION OFFICIAL STAMP

Myaungmya Issue
Burma No. O23 Overprinted in Black

1942, May   Wmk. 254   Perf. 13

1NO1	A6	8a slate green	50.00	62.50

Overprint characters translate: "Office use." Two types of overprint differ mainly in base of peacock which is either 5mm or 8mm.

ISSUED UNDER JAPANESE OCCUPATION

Yano Seal — OS1

Wmk. ABSORBO DUPLICATOR and Outline of Elephant in Center of Sheet Handstamped

1942, June 1   Perf. 12x11
Without Gum

2N1	OS1	1(a) vermilion	30.00	37.50

This stamp is the handstamped impression of the personal chop or seal of Shizuo Yano, chairman of the committee appointed to re-establish the Burmese postal system. It was prepared in Rangoon on paper captured from the Burma Government Offices. Not every stamp shows a portion of the watermark.

Farmer Plowing — OS2

Vertically Laid Paper
Without Gum
Wmk. ELEPHANT BRAND and Outline of Trumpeting Elephant Covering Several Stamps

1942, June 15   Litho.   Perf. 11x12

2N2	OS2	1a scarlet	20.00	25.00

See illustration OS4.

Same, Surcharged with New Value

1942, Oct. 15

2N3	OS2	5c on 1a scarlet	12.50	10.50

Rice Harvest — A83   General Nogi — A84

Power Plant — A85   Admiral Togo — A86

Diamond Mountains, Korea — A89   Meiji Shrine, Tokyo — A90

Yomei Gate, Nikko — A91   Mount Fuji and Cherry Blossoms — A94

Torii of Miyajima Shrine — A96

Stamps of Japan, 1937-42, Handstamp Surcharged with New Value in Black

1942, Sept.   Wmk. 257   Perf. 13

2N4	A83	¼a on 1s fawn	12.50	15.00
2N5	A84	½a on 2s crim	12.50	15.00
2N6	A85	¾a on 3s green	20.00	20.00
2N7	A86	1a on 5s brn lake	17.50	20.00
2N8	A89	3a on 7s dp green	30.00	32.50
2N9	A86	4a on 4s dk green	22.50	27.50
a.		4a on 4s + 2s dk green (#B5)	75.00	87.50
2N10	A90	8a on 8s dk pur & pale vio	100.00	100.00
a.		Red surcharge	140.00	150.00
2N11	A91	1r on 10s lake	12.50	15.00
2N12	A94	2r on 20s ultra	30.00	35.00
a.		Red surcharge	37.50	37.50
2N13	A96	5r on 30s pck bl	10.00	10.00
a.		Red surcharge	15.00	15.00
		Nos. 2N4-2N13 (10)	267.50	290.00

Numerous double, inverted, etc., surcharges exist.

Re-surcharged in Black
1942, Oct. 15

2N14	A83	1c on ¼a on 1s	25.00	25.00
2N15	A84	2c on ½a on 2s	25.00	25.00
2N16	A85	3c on ¾a on 3s	30.00	32.50
a.		"3C." in blue	75.00	100.00
2N17	A86	5c on 1a on 5s	40.00	40.00
a.		"3C." in blue		125.00
2N18	A89	10c on 3a on 7s	45.00	45.00
2N19	A86	15c on 4a on 4s	10.50	10.50
2N20	A90	20c on 8a on 8s (#2N10)	110.00	90.00
a.		On #2N10a	125.00	100.00
		Nos. 2N14-2N20 (7)	285.50	268.00

No. 2N16a was issued in the Shan States.
Done locally, numerous different handstamps of each denomination can exist.

Stamps of Japan, 1937-42, Handstamp Surcharged with New Value in Black

1942, Oct. 15

2N21	A83	1c on 1s fawn	10.00	12.50
2N22	A84	2c on 2s crim	17.50	20.00
2N23	A85	3c on 3s green	20.00	25.00
a.		"3C." in blue	75.00	87.50
2N24	A86	5c on 5s brn lake	20.00	25.00
a.		"5C." in violet	87.50	100.00
2N25	A89	10c on 7s dp grn	25.00	30.00
2N26	A86	15c on 4s dk grn	10.00	12.50
2N27	A90	20c on 8s dk pur & pale vio	70.00	60.00
		Nos. 2N21-2N27 (7)	172.50	185.00

Nos. 2N23a and 2N24a were issued in the Shan States.

Burma State Government Crest — OS3

Unwmk.
1943, Feb. 15   Litho.   Perf. 12
Without Gum

2N29	OS3	5c carmine	10.00	12.50
a.		Imperf.	12.50	15.00

This stamp was intended to be used to cover the embossed George VI envelope stamp and generally was sold affixed to such envelopes. It is also known used on private envelopes.

Farmer Plowing — OS4

1943, Mar.   Without Gum   Typo.

2N30	OS4	1c deep orange	1.00	1.00
2N31	OS4	2c yel green	1.00	1.50
2N32	OS4	3c blue	1.00	1.00
a.		Laid paper	10.00	10.00
2N33	OS4	5c carmine	.50	.65
a.		Small "5c"	3.00	4.00
b.		Imperf.		
2N34	OS4	10c violet brown	.75	.90
2N35	OS4	15c red violet	.25	.25
a.		Laid paper	10.00	
2N36	OS4	20c dull purple	.25	.75
2N37	OS4	30c blue green	.25	.75
		Nos. 2N30-2N37 (8)	5.00	6.80

Small "c" in Nos. 2N34 to 2N37.

Burmese Soldier Carving "Independence" OS5   Farmer Rejoicing OS6

Boy with Burmese Flag — OS7

Hyphen-hole Perf., Pin-Perf. x Hyphen-hole Perf.

1943, Aug. 1   Typo.

2N38	OS5	1c orange	1.00	2.00
a.		Perf. 11	3.50	4.00
2N39	OS6	3c blue	1.00	2.00
a.		Perf. 11	3.50	4.00
2N40	OS7	5c rose	1.00	2.00
a.		Perf. 11	3.50	4.00
		Nos. 2N38-2N40 (3)	3.00	6.00

Declaration of the independence of Burma by the Ba Maw government, Aug. 1, 1943.

Burmese Girl Carrying Water Jar — OS8   Elephant Carrying Teak Log — OS9

Watch Tower of Mandalay Palace — OS10

1943, Oct. 1   Litho.   Perf. 12½

2N41	OS8	1c dp salmon	17.00	10.00
2N42	OS8	2c yel green	.60	1.25
2N43	OS8	3c violet	.60	1.00
2N44	OS9	5c rose	.65	1.00
2N45	OS9	10c blue	.80	.90
2N46	OS9	15c vermilion	.80	1.00
2N47	OS9	20c yel green	.80	1.25
2N48	OS9	30c brown	.80	1.25
2N49	OS9	1r vermilion	.35	3.00
2N50	OS10	2r violet	.35	5.00
		Nos. 2N41-2N50 (10)	22.75	25.35

No. 2N49 exists imperforate. Canceled to order copies of Nos. 2N42-2N50 same values as unused.

Bullock Cart — OS11   Shan Woman — OS12

1943, Oct. 1   Perf. 12½

2N51	OS11	1c brown	22.50	35.00
2N52	OS11	2c yel green	22.50	35.00
2N53	OS11	3c violet	20.00	30.00
2N54	OS11	5c ultra	4.50	12.00
2N55	OS12	10c blue	20.00	35.00
2N56	OS12	20c rose	22.50	35.00
2N57	OS12	30c brown	22.50	35.00
		Nos. 2N51-2N57 (7)	134.50	217.00

For use only in the Shan States. Perak No. N24 also used in Shan States. CTO's ½ used value.

မြန်နိုင်ငံတော်

Surcharged in Black

၁ ဆင့်။

1944, Nov. 1

2N58	OS11	1c brown	4.00	5.00
2N59	OS11	2c yel green	.20	1.25
a.		Inverted surcharge	150.00	200.00
2N60	OS11	3c violet	2.50	4.00
2N61	OS11	5c ultra	1.25	1.50
2N62	OS12	10c blue	2.50	3.50
2N63	OS12	20c rose	.60	1.50
2N64	OS12	30c brown	.75	1.50
		Nos. 2N58-2N64 (7)	11.80	18.25

Top line of surcharge reads: "Bama naing ngan daw" (Burma State). Bottom line repeats denomination in Burmese. Surcharge applied when the Shan States came under Burmese government administration, Dec. 24, 1943. CTO's same value as unused.

BURUNDI

bù-'rün-dē

LOCATION — Central Africa, adjoining the ex-Belgian Congo Republic, Rwanda and Tanzania
GOVT. — Republic
AREA — 10,759 sq. mi.
POP. — 4,920,000 (est. 1983)
CAPITAL — Bujumbura

Burundi was established as an independent country on July 1, 1962. With Rwanda, it had been a UN trusteeship territory (Ruanda-Urundi) administered by Belgium. A military coup overthrew the monarchy November 28, 1966.

100 Centimes = 1 Franc

Catalogue values for all unused stamps in this country are for Never Hinged items.

Flower Issue of Ruanda-Urundi, 1953 Overprinted:

Royaume
du

Burundi

1962, July 1   Unwmk.   Photo.
Perf. 11½
Flowers in Natural Colors

1	A27	25c dk grn & dull grn	.15	.15
2	A27	40c green & salmon	.15	.15
3	A27	60c blue grn & pink	.20	.15
4	A27	1.25fr dk green & blue	7.00	6.50
5	A27	1.50fr vio & apple grn	.30	.25
6	A27	5fr dp plum & lt bl grn	.42	.30
7	A27	7fr dk green & fawn	.85	.55
8	A27	10fr dp plum & pale ol	1.20	.85
		Nos. 1-8 (8)	10.27	8.90

Animal Issue of Ruanda-Urundi, 1959-61 with Similar Overprint or Surcharge in Black or Violet Blue
Size: 23x33mm, 33x23mm

9	A29	10c brn, crim & blk brn	.15	.15
10	A30	20c gray, ap grn & blk	.15	.15
11	A29	40c mag, blk & gray grn	.15	.15
12	A30	50c grn, org yel & brn	.15	.15
a.		Larger overprint and bar		
13	A29	1fr brn, ultra & blk	.15	.15
14	A29	1.50fr blk, gray & org (VB)	.15	.15
15	A29	2fr grnsh bl, ind & brn	.15	.15
16	A30	3fr brn, dp car & blk	.15	.15
17	A30	3.50fr on 3fr brn, dp car & blk	.15	.15
18	A30	4fr on 10fr multi ("XX" 6mm wide)	.15	.15
a.		"XX" 4mm wide	.45	.45
19	A30	5fr multicolored	.15	.15
20	A30	6.50fr red, org yel & brn	.25	.18
21	A29	8fr bl, mag & blk	.30	.22
a.		Violet blue overprint	.65	.65
22	A30	10fr multicolored	.30	.30

Size: 45x26½mm

23	A30	20fr multicolored	.65	.65
24	A30	50fr multi (ovpt. bars 2mm wide)	1.25	1.10
a.		Overprint bars 4mm wide	1.90	1.10
		Set value	3.65	3.35

On #12a, "Burundi" is 13mm long; bar is continuous line across sheet. On #12, "Burundi" is 10mm; bar is 29mm. #12a was issued in 1963.

Two types of overprint exist on 10c, 40c, 1fr and 2fr: I, "du" is below "me"; bar 22½mm wide. II, "du" below "oy"; bar 20mm.

The 50c and 3fr exist in two types, besides the larger 50c overprint listed as No. 12: I, "du" is closer to "Royaume" than to "Burundi"; bar is less than 29mm; wording is centered above bar. II, "du" is closer to "Burundi"; bar is more than 30mm; wording is off-center leftward.

King Mwami Mwambutsa IV and Royal Drummers — A1

Flag and Arms of Burundi — A2

Design: 2fr, 8fr, 50fr, Map of Burundi and King.

Unwmk.
1962, Sept. 27   Photo.   Perf. 14

25	A1	50c dull rose car & dk brn	.15	.15
26	A2	1fr dk green, red & emer	.15	.15
27	A1	2fr brown ol & dk brn	.15	.15
28	A1	3fr vermilion & dk brn	.22	.15
29	A2	4fr Prus blue, red & emer	.18	.15
30	A1	8fr violet & dk brn	.32	.15
31	A1	10fr brt green & dk brn	.50	.15
32	A2	20fr brown, red & emer	1.25	.20
33	A1	50fr brt pink & dk brn	2.25	.40
		Nos. 25-33 (9)	5.17	
		Set value		1.00

Burundi's independence, July 1, 1962.
See #47-50. For overprints see #45-46, 51-52.

Ruanda-Urundi Nos. 151-152 Surcharged:

HOMMAGE A
DAG HAMMARSKJÖLD
3.50F
ROYAUME DU BURUNDI

Photogravure, Surcharge Engraved
1962, Oct. 31   Perf. 11½
Inscription in French

34	A31	3.50fr on 3fr ultra & red	.15	.15
35	A31	6.50fr on 3fr ultra & red	.20	.15
36	A31	10fr on 3fr ultra & red	.30	.25

Inscription in Flemish

37	A31	3.50fr on 3fr ultra & red	.15	.15
38	A31	6.50fr on 3fr ultra & red	.20	.15
39	A31	10fr on 3fr ultra & red	.30	.25
		Nos. 34-39 (6)	1.30	1.10

Dag Hammarskjold, Secretary General of the United Nations, 1953-61.

King Mwami Mwambutsa IV, Map of Burundi and Emblem — A3

1962, Dec. 10   Photo.   Perf. 14

40	A3	8fr yel, bl grn & blk brn	.65	.15
41	A3	50fr gray grn, bl grn & blk brn	1.75	.35

WHO drive to eradicate malaria.
Stamps of type A3 without anti-malaria emblem are listed as Nos. 27, 30 and 33.

Sowing Seed over Africa — A4

1963, Mar. 21   Perf. 14x13

42	A4	4fr olive & dull pur	.15	.15
43	A4	8fr dp org & dull pur	.15	.15
44	A4	15fr emerald & dull pur	.20	.15
		Set value	.41	.30

FAO "Freedom from Hunger" campaign.

Nos. 27 and 33 Overprinted in Dark Green

1963, June 19   Unwmk.   Perf. 14

45	A1	2fr brn olive & dk brn	1.65	1.25
46	A1	50fr brt pink & dk brn	1.90	1.25

Conquest and peaceful use of outer space.

Types of 1962 Inscribed: "Premier Anniversaire" in Red or Magenta

1963, July 1   Photo.

47	A2	4fr olive, red & emer (R)	.15	.15
48	A1	8fr orange & dk brn (M)	.15	.15
49	A1	10fr lilac & dk brn (M)	.20	.15
50	A2	20fr gray, red & emer (R)	.40	.25
		Nos. 47-50 (4)	.90	
		Set value		.50

First anniversary of independence.

Nos. 26 and 32 Surcharged in Brown

1963, Sept. 24   Unwmk.   Perf. 14

51	A2	6.50fr on 1fr multi	.38	.15
52	A2	15fr on 20fr multi	.75	.25

Red Cross Flag over Globe with Map of Africa — A5

1963, Sept. 26   Perf. 14x13

53	A5	4fr emer, car & gray	.15	.15
54	A5	8fr brn ol, car & gray	.25	.15
55	A5	10fr blue, car & gray	.38	.18
56	A5	20fr lilac, car & gray	.75	.30
		Nos. 53-56 (4)	1.53	.78

Centenary of International Red Cross.
See No. B7.

"1962", Arms of Burundi, UN and UNESCO Emblems — A6

UN Agency Emblems: 8fr, ITU. 10fr, World Meteorological Organization. 20fr, UPU. 50fr, FAO.

1963, Nov. 4   Unwmk.   Perf. 14

57	A6	4fr yel, ol grn & blk	.15	.15
58	A6	8fr pale lil, Prus bl & blk	.15	.15
59	A6	10fr blue, lil & blk	.20	.15
60	A6	20fr yel grn, grn & blk	.35	.15
61	A6	50fr yel, red brn & blk	.90	.30
a.		Souvenir sheet of 2	3.00	3.00
		Nos. 57-61 (5)	1.75	
		Set value		.65

1st anniv. of Burundi's admission to the UN. No. 61a contains two imperf. stamps with simulated perforations similar to Nos. 60-61. The 20fr stamp shows the FAO and the 50fr the WMO emblems.

UNESCO Emblem, Scales and Map — A7

Designs: 3.50fr, 6.50fr, Scroll, scales and "UNESCO." 10fr, 20fr, Abraham Lincoln, broken chain and scales.

1963, Dec. 10   Litho.   Perf. 14x13½

62	A7	50c pink, lt bl & blk	.15	.15
63	A7	1.50fr org, lt bl & blk	.15	.15
64	A7	3.50fr fawn, lt grn & blk	.15	.15
65	A7	6.50fr lt vio, lt grn & blk	.18	.15
66	A7	10fr blue, bis & blk	.30	.15
67	A7	20fr pale brn, ocher, bl & blk	.60	.18
		Set value	1.25	.55

15th anniv. of the Universal Declaration of Human Rights and the cent. of the American Emancipation Proclamation (Nos. 66-67).

Ice Hockey — A8   Impala — A9

Designs: 3.50fr, Women's figure skating. 6.50fr, Torch. 10fr, Men's speed skating. 20fr, Slalom.

Unwmk.
1964, Jan. 25   Photo.   Perf. 14

68	A8	50c olive, blk & gold	.15	.15
69	A8	3.50fr lt brown, blk & gold	.15	.15
70	A8	6.50fr pale gray, blk & gold	.38	.15
71	A8	10fr gray, blk & gold	.50	.15
72	A8	20fr tan, blk & gold	1.00	.32
		Nos. 68-72 (5)	2.18	
		Set value		.65

Issued to publicize the 9th Winter Olympic Games, Innsbruck, Jan. 29-Feb. 9, 1964.
A souvenir sheet contains two stamps (10fr+5fr and 20fr+5fr) in tan, black and gold.

Canceled to Order
Starting about 1964, values in the used column are for "canceled to order" stamps. Postally used copies sell for much more.

1964   Litho.   Perf. 14x13, 13x14

Animals: 1fr, 5fr, Hippopotamus, horiz. 1.50fr, 10fr, Giraffe. 2fr, 8fr, Cape buffalo, horiz. 3fr, 6.50fr, Zebra, horiz. 3.50fr, 15fr, Defassa waterbuck. 20fr, Cheetah. 50fr, Elephant. 100fr, Lion.

Size: 21½x35mm, 35x21½mm

73	A9	50c multi	.15	.15
74	A9	1fr multi	.15	.15
75	A9	1.50fr multi	.15	.15
76	A9	2fr multi	.15	.15
77	A9	3fr multi	.18	.15
78	A9	3.50fr multi	.20	.15

Size: 26x42mm, 42x26mm

79	A9	4fr multi	.22	.15
80	A9	5fr multi	.28	.15
81	A9	6.50fr multi	.32	.15
82	A9	8fr multi	.40	.15
83	A9	10fr multi	.50	.15
84	A9	15fr multi	.65	.18

Perf. 14
Size: 53x33mm

85	A9	20fr multi	.85	.20
86	A9	50fr multi	2.25	.32
87	A9	100fr multi	4.00	.65
		Nos. 73-87,C1-C7 (22)	13.12	
		Set value		2.80

Burundi Dancer — A10

Designs: Various Dancers and Drummers.

Unwmk.
1964, Aug. 21   Litho.   Perf. 14
Dancers Multicolored

88	A10	50c gold & emerald	.15	.15
89	A10	1fr gold & vio blue	.15	.15
90	A10	4fr gold & brt blue	.15	.15
91	A10	6.50fr gold & red	.20	.15
92	A10	10fr gold & brt blue	.30	.15
93	A10	15fr gold & emerald	.45	.15
94	A10	20fr gold & red	.65	.22
a.		Souvenir sheet of 3, #92-94	1.50	1.50
		Nos. 88-94 (7)	2.05	
		Set value		.73

1965, Sept. 10
Dancers Multicolored

88a	A10	50c silver & emerald	.15	.15
89a	A10	1fr silver & violet blue	.15	.15
90a	A10	4fr silver & bright blue	.15	.15
91a	A10	6.50fr silver & red	.15	.15
92a	A10	10fr silver & bright blue	.18	.18
93a	A10	15fr silver & emerald	.20	.18
94b	A10	20fr silver & red	.30	.30
c.		Souvenir sheet of 3, #92a-94b	1.50	1.50
		Set value	.95	.80

New York World's Fair, 1964-65.

Pope Paul VI and King Mwami Mwambutsa IV — A11

22 Sainted
Martyrs — A12

4fr, 14fr, Pope John XXIII and King Mwami.

1964, Nov. 12   Photo.   Perf. 12
95 A11 50c brt bl, gold & red brn .15 .15
96 A12 1fr mag, gold & slate .15 .15
97 A11 4fr pale rose lil, gold & brn .18 .15
98 A12 8fr red, gold & brn .18 .15
99 A11 14fr lt grn, gold & brn .42 .15
100 A11 20fr red brn, gold & grn .65 .30
        Nos. 95-100 (6) 1.73
        Set value .68

Canonization of 22 African martyrs, 10/18/64.

Shot Put — A13   African Purple
                    Gallinule — A14

Sports: 1fr, Discus. 3fr, Swimming, horiz. 4fr,
Running. 6.50fr, Javelin, woman. 8fr, Hurdling,
horiz. 10fr, Broad jump, horiz. 14fr, Diving,
woman. 18fr, High jump, horiz. 20fr, Vaulting,
horiz.

1964, Nov. 18   Litho.   Perf. 14
101 A13 50c olive & multi .15 .15
102 A13 1fr brt pink & multi .15 .15
103 A13 3fr multi .15 .15
104 A13 4fr multi .15 .15
105 A13 6.50fr multi .15 .15
106 A13 8fr lt bl & multi .16 .15
107 A13 10fr multi .20 .15
108 A13 14fr multi .26 .15
109 A13 18fr bister & multi .32 .18
110 A13 20fr gray & multi .35 .22
        Set value 1.60 .95

18th Olympic Games, Tokyo, Oct. 10-25, 1964.
See No. B8.

1965   Unwmk.   Perf. 14
Birds: 1fr, 5fr, Little bee eater. 1.50fr, 6.50fr,
Secretary bird. 2fr, 8fr, Yellow-billed stork. 3fr, 10fr,
Congo peacock. 3.50fr, 15fr, African anhinga. 20fr,
Saddle-billed stork. 50fr, Abyssinian ground horn-
bill. 100fr, Crowned crane.

Birds in Natural Colors
Size: 21x35mm
111 A14 50c tan, grn & blk .15 .15
112 A14 1fr pink, mag & blk .15 .15
113 A14 1.50fr blue & blk .15 .15
114 A14 2fr yel grn, dk grn & blk .15 .15
115 A14 3fr yellow, brn & blk .15 .15
116 A14 3.50fr yel grn, dk grn & blk .15 .15

Size: 26x43mm
117 A14 4fr tan, grn & blk .15 .15
118 A14 5fr pink, mag & blk .15 .15
119 A14 6.50fr blue & blk .15 .15
120 A14 8fr yel grn, dk grn & blk .15 .15
121 A14 10fr yel, brn & blk .20 .15
122 A14 15fr yel grn, dk grn & blk .38 .15

Size: 33x53mm
123 A14 20fr rose lilac & blk .50 .30
124 A14 50fr yellow, brn & blk 1.25 .20
125 A14 100fr green, yel & blk 2.75 .40
        Nos. 111-125 (15) 6.58
        Set value 1.50

Issue dates: Nos. 111-116, Mar. 31. Nos. 117-
122, Apr. 16. Nos. 123-125, Apr. 30.
For overprints see #174-184, C35A-C35I.

Relay Satellite and
Morse Key — A15

Designs: 3fr, Telstar and old telephone
handpiece. 4fr, Relay satellite and old wall telephone. 6.50fr, Orbiting Geophysical Observatory
and radar screen. 8fr, Telstar II and headphones.
10fr, Sputnik II and radar aerial. 14fr, Syncom and
transmission aerial. 20fr, Interplanetary Explorer
and tracking aerial.

1965, July 3   Litho.   Perf. 13
126 A15 1fr multi .15 .15
127 A15 3fr multi .15 .15
128 A15 4fr multi .15 .15
129 A15 6.50fr multi .15 .15
130 A15 8fr multi .15 .15
131 A15 10fr multi .18 .15
132 A15 14fr multi .25 .15
133 A15 20fr multi .30 .18
        Set value 1.10 .74

Cent. of the ITU. Perf. and imperf. souv. sheets
of 2 contain Nos. 131, 133. Size: 120x86mm.
Value, both sheets, $7.50.

Globe and ICY Emblem — A16

Designs: 4fr, Map of Africa and UN development
emblem. 8fr, Map of Asia and Colombo Plan
emblem. 10fr, Globe and UN emblem. 18fr, Map of
the Americas and Alliance for Progress emblem.
25fr, Map of Europe and EUROPA emblems. 40fr,
Map of Outer Space and satellite with UN wreath.

1965, Oct. 1   Litho.   Perf. 13
134 A16 1fr ol green & multi .15 .15
135 A16 4fr dull blue & multi .15 .15
136 A16 8fr pale yellow & multi .15 .15
137 A16 10fr lilac & multi .16 .15
138 A16 18fr salmon & multi .25 .15
139 A16 25fr gray & multi .50 .15
140 A16 40fr blue & multi .75 .16
  a. Souvenir sheet of 3, #138-140 1.65 1.65
        Nos. 134-140 (7) 2.11
        Set value .70

International Cooperation Year.

Protea
A17

Flowers: 1fr, 5fr, Crossandra. 1.50fr, 6.50fr,
Ansellia. 2fr, 8fr, Thunbergia. 3fr, 10fr, Schizoglos-
sum. 3.50fr, 15fr, Dissotis. 4fr, 20fr, Protea. 50fr,
Gazania. 100fr, Hibiscus. 150fr, Markhamia.

1966   Unwmk.   Perf. 13½
Size: 26x26mm
141 A17 50c multi .15 .15
142 A17 1fr multi .15 .15
143 A17 1.50fr multi .15 .15
144 A17 2fr multi .15 .15
145 A17 3fr multi .15 .15
146 A17 3.50fr multi .15 .15

Size: 31x31mm
147 A17 4fr multi .15 .15
148 A17 5fr multi .15 .15
149 A17 6.50fr multi .15 .15
150 A17 8fr multi .15 .15
151 A17 10fr multi .15 .15
152 A17 15fr multi .30 .15

Size: 39x39mm
153 A17 20fr multi .38 .15
154 A17 50fr multi 1.00 .25
155 A17 100fr multi 1.90 .38
156 A17 150fr multi 2.75 .55
        Nos. 141-156,C17-C25 (25) 12.02
        Set value 3.00

Issue dates: Nos. 141-147, Feb. 28; Nos. 148-
153, May 18; Nos. 154-156, June 15.
For overprints see Nos. 159-173, C27-C35.

Souvenir Sheets

Allegory of Prosperity and Equality
Tapestry by Peter Colfs — A18

1966, Nov. 4   Litho.   Perf. 13½
157 A18 Sheet of 7 (1.50fr) .65 .25
158 A18 Sheet of 7 (4fr) 1.65 .65

20th anniv. of UNESCO. Each sheet contains 6
stamps showing a reproduction of the Colfs tapestry
from the lobby of the General Assembly Building,
NYC, and one stamp with the UNESCO emblem
plus a label. The labels on Nos. 157-158 and C26
are inscribed in French or English. The 3 sheets
with French inscription have light blue marginal
border. The 3 sheets with English inscription have
pink border. See No. C26.

Republic
Nos. 141-152, 154-156 Overprinted

1967   Litho.   Perf. 13½
Size: 26x26mm
159 A17 50c multi .15 .15
160 A17 1fr multi .15 .15
161 A17 1.50fr multi .15 .15
162 A17 2fr multi .15 .15
163 A17 3fr multi .15 .15
164 A17 3.50fr multi .15 .15

Size: 31x31mm
165 A17 4fr multi .80 .30
166 A17 5fr multi .16 .15
167 A17 6.50fr multi .20 .15
168 A17 8fr multi .25 .15
169 A17 10fr multi .32 .15
170 A17 15fr multi .38 .15

Size: 39x39mm
171 A17 50fr multi 3.75 1.25
172 A17 100fr multi 6.25 2.50
173 A17 150fr multi 5.00 2.25
        Nos. 159-173,C27-C35 (24) 29.24
        Set value 9.59

Nos. 111, 113, 116, 118-125 Overprinted
"REPUBLIQUE DU BURUNDI" and
Horizontal Bar

1967   Litho.   Perf. 14
Birds in Natural Colors
Size: 21x35mm
174 A14 50c multi 1.25 .65
175 A14 1.50fr blue & black .15 .15
176 A14 3.50fr multi .15 .15

Size: 26x43mm
177 A14 5fr multi .15 .15
178 A14 6.50fr blue & black .15 .15
179 A14 8fr multi .18 .15
180 A14 10fr yel, brn & blk .32 .15
181 A14 15fr multi .65 .15

Size: 33x53mm
182 A14 20fr multi 2.00 .38
183 A14 50fr multi 4.00 1.40
184 A14 100fr multi 6.00 2.75
        Nos. 174-184 (11) 15.00 6.23

Haplochromis Multicolor — A19

Various Tropical Fish.

1967   Photo.   Perf. 13½
Size: 42x19mm
186 A19 50c multi .15 .15
187 A19 1fr multi .15 .15
188 A19 1.50fr multi .15 .15
189 A19 2fr multi .15 .15
190 A19 3fr multi .15 .15
191 A19 3.50fr multi .15 .15

Size: 50x25mm
192 A19 4fr multi .16 .15
193 A19 5fr multi .20 .15
194 A19 6.50fr multi .25 .15
195 A19 8fr multi .28 .15
196 A19 10fr multi .32 .15
197 A19 15fr multi .50 .15

Size: 59x30mm
198 A19 20fr multi .65 .15
199 A19 50fr multi 1.40 .18
200 A19 100fr multi 3.00 .30
201 A19 150fr multi 4.25 .45
        Nos. 186-201,C46-C54 (25) 17.27
        Set value 2.50

Issue Dates: Nos. 186-191, Apr. 4; Nos. 192-
197, Apr. 28; Nos. 198-201, May 18.

Ancestor Figures,
Ivory Coast — A20

African Art: 1fr, Seat of Honor, Southeast Congo.
1.50fr, Antelope head, Aribinda Region. 2fr, Buffalo
mask, Upper Volta. 4fr, Funeral figures, Southwest
Ethiopia.

1967, June 5   Photo.   Perf. 13½
202 A20 50c silver & multi .15 .15
203 A20 1fr silver & multi .15 .15
204 A20 1.50fr silver & multi .15 .15
205 A20 2fr silver & multi .15 .15
206 A20 4fr silver & multi .15 .15
        Set value, #202-206,
        C41-C45 1.30 .80

Scouts on Hiking Trip — A21

Designs: 1fr, Cooking at campfire. 1.50fr, Lord
Baden-Powell. 2fr, Boy Scout and Cub Scout giving
Scout sign. 4fr, First aid.

1967, Aug. 9   Photo.   Perf. 13½
207 A21 50c silver & multi .15 .15
208 A21 1fr silver & multi .15 .15
209 A21 1.50fr silver & multi .15 .15
210 A21 2fr silver & multi .15 .15
211 A21 4fr silver & multi .15 .15
        Set value, #207-211,
        C41-C45 2.00 .90

60th anniv. of the Boy Scouts and the 12th Boy
Scout World Jamboree, Farragut State Park, Idaho,
Aug. 1-9.

Républíque du Burundi

The Gleaners, by Francois Millet A22

4fr

Paintings Exhibited at EXPO '67: 8fr, The Water Carrier of Seville, by Velazquez. 14fr, The Triumph of Neptune and Amphitrite, by Nicolas Poussin. 18fr, Acrobat Standing on a Ball, by Picasso. 25fr, Marguerite van Eyck, by Jan van Eyck. 40fr, St. Peter Denying Christ, by Rembrandt.

1967, Oct. 12   Photo.   Perf. 13½
212	A22	4fr multi	.15 .15
213	A22	8fr multi	.18 .15
214	A22	14fr multi	.25 .15
215	A22	18fr multi	.32 .15
216	A22	25fr multi	.50 .18
217	A22	40fr multi	.75 .25
a.		Souvenir sheet of 2, #216-217	1.25 1.00
		Nos. 212-217 (6)	2.15
		Set value	.69

EXPO '67 International Exhibition, Montreal, Apr. 28-Oct. 27. Printed in sheets of 10 stamps and 2 labels inscribed in French or English. No. 217a exists imperf.

Place de la Revolution and Pres. Michel Micombero — A23

Designs: 5fr, President Michel Micombero and flag. 14fr, Formal garden and coat of arms. 20fr, Modern building and coat of arms.

1967, Nov. 23   Perf. 13½
218	A23	5fr multi	.15 .15
219	A23	14fr multi	.20 .15
220	A23	20fr multi	.30 .15
221	A23	30fr multi	.45 .22
		Nos. 218-221 (4)	1.10
		Set value	.47

First anniversary of the Republic.

Madonna by Carlo Crivelli — A24

Designs: 1fr, Adoration of the Shepherds by Juan Bautista Mayno. 4fr, Holy Family by Anthony Van Dyck. 14fr, Nativity by Maitre de Moulins.

1967, Dec. 7   Photo.   Perf. 13½
222	A24	1fr multi	.15 .15
223	A24	4fr multi	.15 .15
224	A24	14fr multi	.25 .15
225	A24	26fr multi	.60 .25
		Nos. 222-225 (4)	1.15
		Set value	.50

Christmas 1967.
Printed in sheets of 25 and one corner label inscribed "Noel 1967" and giving name of painting and painter.

Slalom — A25

10fr, Ice hockey. 14fr, Women's skating. 17fr, Bobsled. 26fr, Ski jump. 40fr, Speed skating. 60fr, Hand holding torch, and Winter Olympics emblem.

1968, Feb. 16   Photo.   Perf. 13½
226	A25	5fr silver & multi	.15 .15
227	A25	10fr silver & multi	.20 .15
228	A25	14fr silver & multi	.25 .15
229	A25	17fr silver & multi	.30 .15
230	A25	26fr silver & multi	.50 .15
231	A25	40fr silver & multi	.75 .15
232	A25	60fr silver & multi	1.25 .20
		Nos. 226-232 (7)	3.40
		Set value	.60

Issued to publicize the 10th Winter Olympic Games, Grenoble, France, Feb. 6-18. Issued in sheets of 10 stamps and label.

The Lacemaker, by Vermeer A26

Paintings: 1.50fr, Portrait of a Young Man, by Botticelli. 2fr, Maja Vestida, by Goya, horiz.

1968, Mar. 29   Photo.   Perf. 13½
233	A26	1.50fr gold & multi	.15 .15
234	A26	2fr gold & multi	.15 .15
235	A26	4fr gold & multi	.15 .15
		Nos. 233-235,C59-C61 (6)	1.80
		Set value	.69

Issued in sheets of 6.

Moon Probe — A27

Designs: 6fr, Russian astronaut walking in space. 8fr, Weather satellite. 10fr, American astronaut walking in space.

1968, May 15   Photo.   Perf. 13½
Size: 35x35mm
236	A27	4fr silver & multi	.15 .15
237	A27	6fr silver & multi	.15 .15
238	A27	8fr silver & multi	.20 .15
239	A27	10fr silver & multi	.22 .15
		Nos. 236-239,C62-C65 (8)	2.42
		Set value	.65

Issued to publicize peaceful space explorations.
A souvenir sheet contains one 25fr stamp in Moon Probe design and one 40fr in Weather Satellite design. Stamp size: 41x41mm. Value $2. Sheet exists imperf. Price $3.

Salamis Aethiops — A28

Butterflies: 1fr, 5fr, Graphium ridleyanus. 1.50fr, 6.50fr, Cymothoe. 2fr, 8fr, Charaxes eupale. 3fr, 10fr, Papilio bromius. 3.50fr, 15fr, Teracolus annae. 20fr, Salamis aethiops. 50fr, Papilio zonobia. 100fr, Danais chrysippus. 150fr, Salamis temora.

1968
Size: 30x33½mm
240	A28	50c gold & multi	.15 .15
241	A28	1fr gold & multi	.15 .15
242	A28	1.50fr gold & multi	.15 .15
243	A28	2fr gold & multi	.15 .15
244	A28	3fr gold & multi	.15 .15
245	A28	3.50fr gold & multi	.15 .15

Size: 33½x37½mm
246	A28	4fr gold & multi	.15 .15
247	A28	5fr gold & multi	.15 .15
248	A28	6.50fr gold & multi	.28 .15
249	A28	8fr gold & multi	.32 .15
250	A28	10fr gold & multi	.38 .15
251	A28	15fr gold & multi	.45 .15

Size: 41x46mm
252	A28	20fr gold & multi	.75 .15
253	A28	50fr gold & multi	1.50 .15
254	A28	100fr gold & multi	2.50 .28
255	A28	150fr gold & multi	3.75 .40
		Nos. 240-255,C66-C74 (25)	16.26
		Set value	2.25

Issue dates: Nos. 240-245, June 7; Nos. 246-251, June 28. Nos. 252-255, July 19.

Women, Along the Manzanares, by Goya — A29

Paintings: 7fr, The Letter, by Pieter de Hooch. 11fr, Woman Reading a Letter, by Gerard Terborch. 14fr, Man Writing a Letter, by Gabriel Metsu.

1968, Sept. 30   Photo.   Perf. 13½
256	A29	4fr multi	.15 .15
257	A29	7fr multi	.15 .15
258	A29	11fr multi	.20 .15
259	A29	14fr multi	.30 .15
		Nos. 256-259,C84-C87 (8)	2.74
		Set value	.80

International Letter Writing Week.

Soccer — A30

1968, Oct. 24
260	A30	4fr shown	.15 .15
261	A30	7fr Basketball	.15 .15
262	A30	13fr High jump	.18 .15
263	A30	24fr Relay race	.35 .15
264	A30	40fr Javelin	.60 .30
		Nos. 260-264,C88-C92 (10)	3.98
		Set value	1.25

19th Olympic Games, Mexico City, Oct. 12-27. Printed in sheets of 8.

Virgin and Child, by Fra Filippo Lippi — A31

Paintings: 5fr, The Magnificat, by Sandro Botticelli. 6fr, Virgin and Child, by Albrecht Durer. 11fr, Madonna del Gran Duca, by Raphael.

1968, Nov. 26   Photo.   Perf. 13½
265	A31	3fr multi	.15 .15
266	A31	5fr multi	.15 .15
267	A31	6fr multi	.15 .15
268	A31	11fr multi	.22 .15
a.		Souvenir sheet of 4, #265-268	1.00 1.00
		Nos. 265-268,C93-C96 (8)	1.72
		Set value	.75

Christmas 1968. For overprints see Nos. 272-275, C100-C103.

WHO Emblem and Map of Africa — A32

1969, Jan. 22
269	A32	5fr gold, dk grn & yel	.15 .15
270	A32	6fr gold, vio & ver	.15 .15
271	A32	11fr gold, pur & red lil	.22 .15
		Nos. 269-271 (3)	.52
		Set value	.21

20th anniv. of WHO in Africa.

Nos. 265-268 Overprinted in Silver

1969, Feb. 17   Photo.   Perf. 13½
272	A31	3fr multi	.15 .15
273	A31	5fr multi	.15 .15
274	A31	6fr multi	.15 .15
275	A31	11fr multi	.22 .15
		Nos. 272-275,C100-C103 (8)	2.00
		Set value	.85

Man's 1st flight around the moon by the US spacecraft Apollo 8, Dec. 21-27, 1968.

Map of Africa, and CEPT Emblem — A33

Designs: 14fr, Plowing with tractor. 17fr, Teacher and pupil. 26fr, Maps of Europe and Africa and CEPT (Conference of European Postal and Telecommunications Administrations) emblem, horiz.

1969, Mar. 12   Photo.   Perf. 13
276	A33	5fr multi	.15 .15
277	A33	14fr multi	.20 .15
278	A33	17fr multi	.25 .15
279	A33	26fr multi	.32 .15
		Nos. 276-279 (4)	.92
		Set value	.35

5th anniv. of the Yaounde (Cameroun) Agreement, creating the European and African-Malgache Economic Community.

Resurrection, by
Gaspard
Isenmann
A34

Paintings: 14fr, Resurrection by Antoine Caron.
17fr, Noli me Tangere, by Martin Schongauer. 26fr,
Resurrection, by El Greco.

1969, Mar. 24

280	A34	11fr gold & multi	.15	.15
281	A34	14fr gold & multi	.20	.15
282	A34	17fr gold & multi	.25	.15
283	A34	26fr gold & multi	.38	.15
a.		Souvenir sheet of 4, #280-283	1.50	1.50
		Nos. 280-283 (4)	.98	
		Set value		.34

Easter 1969.

Potter — A35

ITU Emblem and: 5fr, Farm workers. 7fr, Foundry worker. 10fr, Woman testing corn crop.

1969, May 17   Photo.   Perf. 13½

284	A35	3fr multicolored	.15	.15
285	A35	5fr multicolored	.15	.15
286	A35	7fr multicolored	.15	.15
287	A35	10fr multicolored	.20	.15
		Set value	.51	.25

50th anniv. of the ILO.

Industry and
Bank's
Emblem
A36

Designs (African Development Bank Emblem
and): 17fr, Communications. 30fr, Education. 50fr,
Agriculture.

1969, July 29   Photo.   Perf. 13½

288	A36	10fr gold & multi	.18	.15
289	A36	17fr gold & multi	.30	.15
290	A36	30fr gold & multi	.50	.15
291	A36	50fr gold & multi	.80	.25
a.		Souvenir sheet of 4, #288-291	1.90	1.90
		Nos. 288-291 (4)	1.78	
		Set value		.55

5th anniversary of the African Development Bank.

Girl Reading
Letter, by
Vermeer
A37

Paintings: 7fr, Graziella (young woman), by
Auguste Renoir. 14fr, Woman writing a letter, by
Gerard Terborch. 26fr, Galileo Galilei, painter
unknown. 40fr, Ludwig van Beethoven, painter
unknown.

1969, Oct. 24   Photo.   Perf. 13½

292	A37	4fr multicolored	.15	.15
293	A37	7fr multicolored	.15	.15
294	A37	14fr multicolored	.32	.15
295	A37	26fr multicolored	.55	.15
296	A37	40fr multicolored	.75	.20
a.		Souvenir sheet of 2, #295-296	1.75	1.75
		Nos. 292-296 (5)	1.92	
		Set value		.52

Intl. Letter Writing Week, Oct. 7-13.

Rocket
Launching
A38

Moon Landing: 6.50fr, Rocket in space. 7fr, Separation of landing module from capsule. 14fr, 26fr,
Landing module landing on moon. 17fr, Capsule in
space. 40fr, Neil A. Armstrong leaving landing module. 50fr, Astronaut on moon.

1969, Nov. 6   Photo.   Perf. 13½

297	A38	4fr blue & multi	.15	.15
298	A38	6.50fr vio blue & multi	.22	.15
299	A38	7fr vio blue & multi	.22	.15
300	A38	14fr black & multi	.35	.20
301	A38	17fr vio blue & multi	.55	.25
		Nos. 297-301,C104-C106 (8)	3.64	1.95

Souvenir Sheet

302		Sheet of 3	3.00	3.00
a.	A38	26fr multicolored	.50	.50
b.	A38	40fr multicolored	.75	.75
c.	A38	50fr multicolored	1.00	1.00

See note after Algeria No. 427.

Madonna and Child, by
Rubens — A39

Paintings: 6fr, Madonna and Child with St. John,
by Giulio Romano. 10fr, Magnificat Madonna, by
Botticelli.

1969, Dec. 2   Photo.

303	A39	5fr gold & multi	.15	.15
304	A39	6fr gold & multi	.15	.15
305	A39	10fr gold & multi	.25	.15
a.		Souvenir sheet of 3, #303-305	.75	.75
		Nos. 303-305,C107-C109 (6)	2.33	
		Set value		.65

Christmas 1969.

Sternotomis
Bohemani
A40

Designs: Various Beetles and Weevils.

1970   Perf. 13½

Size: 39x28mm

306	A40	50c multicolored	.15	.15
307	A40	1fr multicolored	.15	.15
308	A40	1.50fr multicolored	.15	.15
309	A40	2fr multicolored	.15	.15
310	A40	3fr multicolored	.15	.15
311	A40	3.50fr multicolored	.15	.15

Size: 46x32mm

312	A40	4fr multicolored	.15	.15
313	A40	5fr multicolored	.15	.15
314	A40	6.50fr multicolored	.15	.15
315	A40	8fr multicolored	.20	.15
316	A40	10fr multicolored	.25	.15
317	A40	15fr multicolored	.38	.15

Size: 52x36mm

318	A40	20fr multicolored	.50	.15
319	A40	50fr multicolored	1.00	.18
320	A40	100fr multicolored	1.90	.35
321	A40	150fr multicolored	2.75	.50
		Nos. 306-321,C110-C118 (25)	19.11	
		Set value		2.85

Issue dates: Nos. 306-313, Jan. 20; Nos. 314-
318, Feb. 17; Nos. 319-321, Apr. 3.

Jesus Condemned
to Death — A41

Stations of the Cross, by Juan de Aranoa y Carredano: 1.50fr, Jesus carries His Cross. 2fr, Jesus
falls the first time. 3fr, Jesus meets His mother.
3.50fr, Simon of Cyrene helps carry the cross. 4fr,
Veronica wipes the face of Jesus. 5fr, Jesus falls the
second time.

1970, Mar. 16   Photo.   Perf. 13½

322	A41	1fr gold & multi	.15	.15
323	A41	1.50fr gold & multi	.15	.15
324	A41	2fr gold & multi	.15	.15
325	A41	3fr gold & multi	.15	.15
326	A41	3.50fr gold & multi	.15	.15
327	A41	4fr gold & multi	.15	.15
328	A41	5fr gold & multi	.15	.15
a.		Souv. sheet of 7, #322-328 + label	.60	.60
		Set value, #322-328,		
		C119-C125	2.60	1.15

Easter 1970.

Parade and EXPO '70 Emblem — A42

Designs (EXPO '70 Emblem and): 6.50fr, Aerial
view. 7fr, African pavilions. 14fr, Pagoda, vert.
26fr, Recording pavilion and pool. 40fr, Tower of
the Sun, vert. 50fr, Flags of participating nations.

1970, May 5   Photo.   Perf. 13½

329	A42	4fr gold & multi	.15	.15
330	A42	6.50fr gold & multi	.15	.15
331	A42	7fr gold & multi	.15	.15
332	A42	14fr gold & multi	.22	.15
333	A42	26fr gold & multi	.38	.15
334	A42	40fr gold & multi	.55	.15
335	A42	50fr gold & multi	.80	.20
		Nos. 329-335 (7)	2.40	
		Set value		.65

EXPO '70 Intl. Exhibition, Osaka, Japan, Mar.
15-Sept. 13, 1970. See No. C126.

White Rhinoceros — A43

Designs, FAUNA: Camel, dromedary, okapi,
addax, Burundi cow (2 stamps of each animal in 2
different poses). MAP OF THE NILE: Delta and
pyramids, dhow, cataract, Blue Nile and crowned
crane, Victoria Nile and secretary bird, Lake Victoria
and source of Nile on Mt. Gikizi.

1970, July 8   Photo.   Perf. 13½

336		Sheet of 18	7.00	1.50
a.		A43 7fr any single	.38	.15

Issued in sheets of 18 (3x6) stamps of different
designs, to publicize the southernmost source of the
Nile on Mt. Gikizi in Burundi. See No. C127.

Winter Wren, Firecrest, Skylark and
Crested Lark — A44

Birds: 2fr, 3.50fr, 5fr, vert.; others horiz.

1970, Sept. 30   Photo.   Perf. 13½
Stamp Size: 44x33mm

337	A44	Block of 4	.38	.15
a.		2fr Northern shrike	.15	
b.		2fr European starling	.15	
c.		2fr Yellow wagtail	.15	
d.		2fr Bank swallow	.15	
338	A44	Block of 4	.55	.15
a.		3fr Winter wren	.15	
b.		3fr Firecrest	.15	
c.		3fr Skylark	.15	
d.		3fr Crested lark	.15	
339	A44	Block of 4	.75	.15
a.		3.50fr Woodchat shrike	.18	
b.		3.50fr Common rock thrush	.18	
c.		3.50fr Black redstart	.18	
d.		3.50fr Ring ouzel	.18	
340	A44	Block of 4	.80	.15
a.		4fr European Redstart	.20	
b.		4fr Hedge sparrow	.20	
c.		4fr Gray wagtail	.20	
d.		4fr Meadow pipit	.20	
341	A44	Block of 4	1.00	.15
a.		5fr Eurasian hoopoe	.25	
b.		5fr Pied flycatcher	.25	
c.		5fr Great reed warbler	.25	
d.		5fr Eurasian kingfisher	.25	
342	A44	Block of 4	1.25	.15
a.		6.50fr House martin	.30	
b.		6.50fr Sedge warbler	.30	
c.		6.50fr Fieldfare	.30	
d.		6.50fr European Golden oriole	.30	
		Nos. 337-342,C132-C137 (12)	23.63	3.25

Nos. 337-342 are printed in sheets of 16.

Library, UN Emblem — A45

Designs: 5fr, Students taking test, and emblem of
University of Bujumbura. 7fr, Students in laboratory
and emblem of Ecole Normale Superieure of
Burundi. 10fr, Students with electron-microscope
and Education Year emblem.

1970, Oct. 23

343	A45	3fr gold & multi	.15	.15
344	A45	5fr gold & multi	.15	.15
345	A45	7fr gold & multi	.15	.15
346	A45	10fr gold & multi	.15	.15
		Set value	.41	.20

Issued for International Education Year.

Pres. and Mrs. Michel Micombero — A46

Designs: 7fr, Pres. Michel Micombero and
Burundi flag. 11fr, Pres. Micombero and Revolution
Memorial.

1970, Nov. 28   Photo.   Perf. 13½

347	A46	4fr gold & multi	.15	.15
348	A46	7fr gold & multi	.15	.15
349	A46	11fr gold & multi	.20	.15
a.		Souvenir sheet of 3	.50	.50
		Set value	.40	.20

4th anniv. of independence. No. 349a contains 3 stamps similar to Nos. 347-349, but inscribed "Poste Aerienne." Exists imperf.
See Nos. C140-C142.

Lenin with Delegates A47

Designs (Lenin, Paintings): 5fr, addressing crowd. 6.50fr, with soldier and sailor. 15fr, speaking from balcony. 50fr, Portrait.

1970, Dec. 31   Photo.   Perf. 13½
Gold Frame

350	A47	3.50fr dk red brown	.15	.15
351	A47	5fr dk red brown	.15	.15
352	A47	6.50fr dk red brown	.15	.15
353	A47	15fr dk red brown	.32	.15
354	A47	50fr dk red brown	1.10	.18
		Nos. 350-354 (5)	1.87	
		Set value		.46

Lenin's birth centenary (1870-1924).

Lion — A48

1971, Mar. 19   Photo.   Perf. 13½
Size: 38x38mm

355		Strip of 4	.20	.15
a.	A48	1fr Lion	.15	
b.	A48	1fr Cape buffalo	.15	
c.	A48	1fr Hippopotamus	.15	
d.	A48	1fr Giraffe	.15	
356		Strip of 4	.24	.15
a.	A48	2fr Hartebeest	.15	
b.	A48	2fr Black rhinoceros	.15	
c.	A48	2fr Zebra	.15	
d.	A48	2fr Leopard	.15	
357		Strip of 4	.32	.15
a.	A48	3fr Grant's gazelles	.15	
b.	A48	3fr Cheetah	.15	
c.	A48	3fr African white-backed vultures	.15	
d.	A48	3fr Johnston's okapi	.15	
358		Strip of 4	.50	.20
a.	A48	5fr Chimpanzee	.15	
b.	A48	5fr Elephant	.15	
c.	A48	5fr Spotted hyenas	.15	
d.	A48	5fr Belsa	.15	
359		Strip of 4	.65	.42
a.	A48	6fr Gorilla	.15	
b.	A48	6fr Gnu	.15	
c.	A48	6fr Wart hog	.15	
d.	A48	6fr Cape hunting dog	.15	
360		Strip of 4	1.40	.45
a.	A48	11fr Sable antelope	.32	
b.	A48	11fr Caracal lynx	.32	
c.	A48	11fr Ostriches	.32	
d.	A48	11fr Bongo	.32	
		Nos. 355-360,C146-C151 (12)	15.31	3.31

For overprints and surcharges see Nos. C152, CB15-CB18.

The Resurrection, by Il Sodoma — A49

Paintings: 6fr, Resurrection, by Andrea del Castagno. 11fr, Noli me Tangere, by Correggio.

1971, Apr. 2

361	A49	3fr gold & multi	.15	.15
362	A49	6fr gold & multi	.15	.15
363	A49	11fr gold & multi	.28	.15
a.		Souvenir sheet of 3, #361-363	.60	.60
		Nos. 361-363,C143-C145 (6)	1.30	
		Set value		.46

Easter 1971. No. 363a exists imperf.

Young Venetian Woman, by Dürer — A50

Dürer Paintings: 11fr, Hieronymus Holzschuher. 14fr, Emperor Maximilian I. 17fr, Holy Family, from Paumgartner Altar. 26fr, Haller Madonna. 31fr, Self-portrait, 1498.

1971, Sept. 20

364	A50	6fr multicolored	.15	.15
365	A50	11fr multicolored	.22	.15
366	A50	14fr multicolored	.38	.15
367	A50	17fr multicolored	.45	.22
368	A50	26fr multicolored	.65	.35
369	A50	31fr multicolored	.80	.40
a.		Souvenir sheet of 2, #368-369	1.60	1.60
		Nos. 364-369 (6)	2.65	1.42

International Letter Writing Week. Albrecht Dürer (1471-1528), German painter and engraver. No. 369a exists imperf.

Nos. 364-369, 369a Overprinted in Black and Gold: "VIème CONGRES / DE L'INSTITUT INTERNATIONAL / DE DROIT D'EXPRESSION FRANCAISE"

1971, Oct. 8

370	A50	6fr multicolored	.15	.15
371	A50	11fr multicolored	.22	.15
372	A50	14fr multicolored	.28	.15
373	A50	17fr multicolored	.35	.15
374	A50	26fr multicolored	.50	.15
375	A50	31fr multicolored	.65	.18
a.		Souvenir sheet of 2	1.25	1.25
		Nos. 370-375 (6)	2.15	
		Set value		.62

6th Congress of the Intl. Legal Institute of the French-speaking Area, Bujumbura, Aug. 10-19.

Madonna and Child, by Il Perugino — A51

Paintings of the Madonna and Child by: 5fr, Andrea del Sarto. 6fr, Luis de Morales.

1971, Nov. 2   Photo.   Perf. 13½

376	A51	3fr dk green & multi	.15	.15
377	A51	5fr dk green & multi	.15	.15
378	A51	6fr dk green & multi	.15	.15
a.		Souvenir sheet of 3, #376-378	.38	.38
		Nos. 376-378,C153-C155 (6)	1.55	
		Set value		.62

Christmas 1971. No. 378a exists imperf.
For surcharges see #B49-B51, CB19-CB21.

Lunar Orbiter — A52

Designs: 11fr, Vostok. 14fr, Luna 1. 17fr, Apollo 11 astronaut on moon. 26fr, Soyuz 11. 40fr, Lunar Rover (Apollo 15).

1972, Jan. 15

379	A52	6fr gold & multi	.18	.15
380	A52	11fr gold & multi	.22	.15
381	A52	14fr gold & multi	.28	.15
382	A52	17fr gold & multi	.40	.20
383	A52	26fr gold & multi	.40	.32
384	A52	40fr gold & multi	.62	.32
a.		Souvenir sheet of 6	2.25	2.25
		Nos. 379-384 (6)	2.10	1.29

Conquest of space. See No. C156.
No. 384a contains one each of Nos. 379-384 inscribed "APOLLO 16."

Slalom and Sapporo '72 Emblem — A53

Designs (Sapporo '72 Emblem and): 6fr, Figure skating, pairs. 11fr, Figure skating, women's. 14fr, Ski jump. 17fr, Ice hockey. 24fr, Speed skating, men's. 26fr, Snow scooter. 31fr, Downhill skiing. 50fr, Bobsledding.

1972, Feb. 3

385	A53	5fr silver & multi	.15	.15
386	A53	6fr silver & multi	.15	.15
387	A53	11fr silver & multi	.18	.15
388	A53	14fr silver & multi	.22	.15
389	A53	17fr silver & multi	.28	.15
390	A53	24fr silver & multi	.38	.15
391	A53	26fr silver & multi	.40	.15
392	A53	31fr silver & multi	.50	.15
393	A53	50fr silver & multi	.80	.20
		Nos. 385-393 (9)	3.06	
		Set value		.82

11th Winter Olympic Games, Sapporo, Japan, Feb. 3-13. Printed in sheets of 12. See No. C157. Issued: #385-390, Feb. 1; #391-393, Feb. 21.

Ecce Homo, by Quentin Massys — A54

Paintings: 6.50fr, Crucifixion, by Rubens. 10fr, Descent from the Cross, by Jacopo da Pontormo. 18fr, Pieta, by Ferdinand Gallegos. 27fr, Trinity, by El Greco.

1972, Mar. 20   Photo.   Perf. 13½

394	A54	3.50fr gold & multi	.15	.15
395	A54	6.50fr gold & multi	.15	.15
396	A54	10fr gold & multi	.15	.15
397	A54	18fr gold & multi	.25	.15
398	A54	27fr gold & multi	.65	.15
a.		Souv. sheet of 5, #394-398 + label	1.50	1.25
		Nos. 394-398 (5)	1.35	
		Set value		.42

Easter 1972. Printed in sheets of 8 with label. No. 398a exists imperf.

Gymnastics, Olympic Rings and "Motion" A55

1972, May 19

399	A55	5fr shown	.15	.15
400	A55	6fr Javelin	.15	.15
401	A55	11fr Fencing	.22	.15
402	A55	14fr Bicycling	.25	.15
403	A55	17fr Pole vault	.32	.15
		Nos. 399-403,C158-C161 (9)	2.94	
		Set value		.95

Souvenir Sheet

404		Sheet of 2	1.75	1.25
a.	A55	31fr Discus	.45	.45
b.	A55	40fr Soccer	.60	.60

20th Olympic Games, Munich, Aug. 26-Sept. 11.

Prince Rwagasore, Pres. Micombero, Burundi Flag, Drummers A56

Designs: 7fr, Rwagasore, Micombero, flag, map of Africa, globe. 13fr, Micombero, flag, globe.

1972, Aug. 24   Photo.   Perf. 13½

405	A56	5fr silver & multi	.15	.15
406	A56	7fr silver & multi	.15	.15
407	A56	13fr silver & multi	.22	.15
a.		Souvenir sheet of 3, #405-407	.50	
		Nos. 405-407,C162-C164 (6)	1.52	
		Set value		.52

10th anniversary of independence.

Madonna and Child, by Andrea Solario — A57

Paintings of the Madonna and Child by: 10fr, Raphael. 15fr, Botticelli.

1972, Nov. 2

408	A57	5fr lt blue & multi	.15	.15
409	A57	10fr lt blue & multi	.15	.15
410	A57	15fr lt blue & multi	.22	.15
a.		Souvenir sheet of 3, #408-410	.50	
		Nos. 408-410,C165-C167 (6)	1.80	
		Set value		.56

Christmas 1972. Sheets of 20 stamps + label.
For surcharges see #B56-B58, CB26-CB28.

Platycoryne Crocea — A58

1972

Size: 33x33mm

411	A58	50c shown	.15	.15
412	A58	1fr Cattleya trianaei	.15	.15
413	A58	2fr Eulophia cucullata	.15	.15
414	A58	3fr Cymbidium hamsey	.15	.15
415	A58	4fr Thelymitra pauciflora	.15	.15
416	A58	5fr Miltassia	.15	.15
417	A58	6fr Miltonia	.15	.15

Size: 38x38mm

418	A58	7fr Like 50c	.15	.15
419	A58	8fr Like 1fr	.15	.15
420	A58	9fr Like 2fr	.15	.15

421 A58 10fr Like 3fr   .18 .15
Set value, #411-421,
C168-C174   3.25 1.20

Orchids. Issue dates: Nos. 411-417, Nov. 6; Nos. 418-421, Nov. 29.

Henry Morton Stanley — A59

Designs: 7fr, Porters, Stanley's expedition. 13fr, Stanley entering Ujiji.

1973, Mar. 19   Photo.   Perf. 13½
422 A59   5fr gold & multi   .15 .15
423 A59   7fr gold & multi   .15 .15
424 A59 13fr gold & multi   .20 .15
Nos. 422-424,C175-C177 (6)   1.40
Set value   .48

Exploration of Africa by David Livingstone (1813-1873) and Henry Morton Stanley (John Rowlands; 1841-1904).

Crucifixion, by
Roger van der
Weyden — A60

Easter (Paintings): 5fr, Flagellation of Christ, by Caravaggio. 13fr, The Burial of Christ, by Raphael.

1973, Apr. 10
425 A60   5fr gold & multi   .15 .15
426 A60   7fr gold & multi   .15 .15
427 A60 13fr gold & multi   .20 .15
    a.   Souvenir sheet of 3, #425-427   .60 .60
Nos. 425-427,C178-C180 (6)   1.63
Set value   .46

INTERPOL Emblem, Flag — A61

Design: 10fr, INTERPOL flag and emblem. 18fr, INTERPOL Headquarters and emblem.

1973, May 19   Photo.   Perf. 13½
428 A61   5fr silver & multi   .15 .15
429 A61 10fr silver & multi   .15 .15
430 A61 18fr silver & multi   .28 .15
Nos. 428-430,C181-C182 (5)   1.46
Set value   .59

50th anniversary of International Criminal Police Organization (INTERPOL).

Signs of the Zodiac, Babylon — A62

Designs: 5fr, Greek and Roman gods representing planets. 7fr, Ptolemy (No. 433a) and Ptolemaic solar system. 13fr, Copernicus (No. 434a) and heliocentric system.
a, UL. b, UR. c, LL. d, LR.

1973, July 27   Photo.   Perf. 13½
431 A62   3fr Block of 4, #a.-d.   .20 .15
432 A62   5fr Block of 4, #a.-d.   .25 .15
433 A62   7fr Block of 4, #a.-d.   .32 .15
434 A62 13fr Block of 4, #a.-d.   .75 .20
    e.   Souvenir sheet of 4, #431-434   2.75 1.40
Nos. 431-434,C183-C186 (8)   9.32 2.50

500th anniversary of the birth of Nicolaus Copernicus (1473-1543), Polish astronomer.

Flowers and Butterflies — A63

Designs: Each block of 4 contains 2 flower and 2 butterfly designs. The 1fr, 2fr, 5fr and 11fr have flower designs listed as "a" and "d" numbers, butterflies as "b" and "c" numbers; the arrangement is reversed for the 3fr and 6fr.

1973, Sept. 3   Photo.   Perf. 13
Stamp Size: 34x41½mm
435 A63   Block of 4   .20 .15
    a.   1fr *Protea cynaroides*   .15 .15
    b.   1fr *Precis octavia*   .15 .15
    c.   1fr *Epiphora bauhiniae*   .15 .15
    d.   1fr *Gazania longiscapa*   .15 .15
436 A63   Block of 4   .20 .15
    a.   2fr *Kniphofia*   .15 .15
    b.   2fr *Cymothoe coccinata*   .15 .15
    c.   2fr *Nudaurelia zambesina*   .15 .15
    d.   2fr *Freesia refracta*   .15 .15
437 A63   Block of 4   .24 .15
    a.   3fr *Calotis eupompe*   .15 .15
    b.   3fr *Narcissus*   .15 .15
    c.   3fr *Cineraria hybrida*   .15 .15
    d.   3fr *Cyrestis camillus*   .15 .15
438 A63   Block of 4   .40 .15
    a.   5fr *Iris tingitana*   .15 .15
    b.   5fr *Papilio demodocus*   .15 .15
    c.   5fr *Catopsilia avelaneda*   .15 .15
    d.   5fr *Nerine samlensis*   .15 .15
439 A63   Block of 4   .50 .20
    a.   6fr *Hypolimnas dexithea*   .15 .15
    b.   6fr *Zantedeschia tropicalis*   .15 .15
    c.   6fr *Sandersonia aurantiaca*   .15 .15
    d.   6fr *Drurya antimachus*   .15 .15
440 A63   Block of 4   1.00 .22
    a.   11fr *Nymphaea capensis*   .25 .15
    b.   11fr *Pandoriana pandora*   .25 .15
    c.   11fr *Precis orythia*   .25 .15
    d.   11fr *Pelargonium domestica*   .25 .15
Nos. 435-440,C187-C192 (12)   22.04 3.52

Virgin and Child,
by Giovanni
Bellini — A64

Virgin and Child by: 10fr, Jan van Eyck. 15fr, Giovanni Boltraffio.

1973, Nov. 13   Photo.   Perf. 13
441 A64   5fr gold & multi   .15 .15
442 A64 10fr gold & multi   .15 .15
443 A64 15fr gold & multi   .22 .15
    a.   Souvenir sheet of 3, #441-443   .50 .50
Nos. 441-443,C193-C195 (6)   1.80
Set value   .52

Christmas 1973.
For surcharges see #B59-B61, CB29-CB31.

Pietá, by Paolo
Veronese — A65

Paintings: 10fr, Virgin and St. John, by van der Weyden. 18fr, Crucifixion, by van der Weyden. 27fr, Burial of Christ, by Titian. 40fr, Pietá, by El Greco.

1974, Apr. 19   Photo.   Perf. 14x13½
444 A65   5fr gold & multi   .15 .15
445 A65 10fr gold & multi   .15 .15
446 A65 18fr gold & multi   .28 .15
447 A65 27fr gold & multi   .42 .15
448 A65 40fr gold & multi   .65 .15
    a.   Souvenir sheet of 5, #444-448   1.65 1.65
Nos. 444-448 (5)   1.65
Set value   .46

Easter 1974.

Fish — A66

1974, May 30   Photo.   Perf. 13
Stamp Size: 35x35mm
449 A66   Block of 4   .20 .20
    a.   1fr *Haplochromis multicolor*   .15 .15
    b.   1fr *Pantodon buchholzi*   .15 .15
    c.   1fr *Tropheus duboisi*   .15 .15
    d.   1fr *Distichodus sexfasciatus*   .15 .15
450 A66   Block of 4   .20 .15
    a.   2fr *Pelmatochromis kribensis*   .15 .15
    b.   2fr *Nannaethiops tritaeniatus*   .15 .15
    c.   2fr *Polycentropsis abbreviata*   .15 .15
    d.   2fr *Hemichromis bimaculatus*   .15 .15
451 A66   Block of 4   .20 .20
    a.   3fr *Ctenopoma acutirostre*   .15 .15
    b.   3fr *Synodontis angelicus*   .15 .15
    c.   3fr *Tilapia melanopleura*   .15 .15
    d.   3fr *Aphyosemion bivittatum*   .15 .15
452 A66   Block of 4   .32 .15
    a.   5fr *Monodactylus argenteus*   .15 .15
    b.   5fr *Zanclus canescens*   .15 .15
    c.   5fr *Pygoplites diacanthus*   .15 .15
    d.   5fr *Cephalopholis argus*   .15 .15
453 A66   Block of 4   .38 .15
    a.   6fr *Priacanthus arenatus*   .15 .15
    b.   6fr *Pomacanthus arcuatus*   .15 .15
    c.   6fr *Scarus guacamaia*   .15 .15
    d.   6fr *Zeus faber*   .15 .15
454 A66   Block of 4   .65 .20
    a.   11fr *Lactophrys quadricornis*   .16 .15
    b.   11fr *Balistes vetula*   .16 .15
    c.   11fr *Acanthurus bahianus*   .16 .15
    d.   11fr *Holocanthus ciliaris*   .16 .15
Nos. 449-454,C207-C212 (12)   12.25 2.65

Soccer
and Cup
A67

Designs: Various soccer scenes and cup.

1974, July 4   Photo.   Perf. 13
455 A67   5fr gold & multi   .15
456 A67   6fr gold & multi   .15
457 A67 11fr gold & multi   .16
458 A67 14fr gold & multi   .22
459 A67 17fr gold & multi   .25
    a.   Souvenir sheet of 3   1.40
Nos. 455-459,C196-C198 (8)   2.23

World Soccer Championship, Munich, June 13-July 7. No. 459a contains 3 stamps similar to Nos. C196-C198 without "Poste Aerienne."
Nos. 455-459 and 459a exist imperf.

Flags over UPU
Headquarters,
Bern — A68

#461, G.P.O., Bujumbura. #462, Mailmen ("11F" in UR). #463, Mailmen ("11F" in UL).

#464, UPU emblem. #465, Means of transportation. #466, Pigeon over globe showing Burundi. #467, Swiss flag, pigeon over map showing Bern.

1974, July 23
460 A68   6fr gold & multi   .18
461 A68   6fr gold & multi   .18
462 A68 11fr gold & multi   .30
463 A68 11fr gold & multi   .30
464 A68 14fr gold & multi   .38
465 A68 14fr gold & multi   .38
466 A68 17fr gold & multi   .45
467 A68 17fr gold & multi   .50
    a.   Souvenir sheet of 8, #460-467   2.75
Nos. 460-467,C199-C206 (16)   9.97
Set, used   1.00

Cent. of UPU. Stamps of same denomination printed se-tenant (continuous design).

St. Ildefonso
Writing Letter,
by El
Greco — A69

Paintings: 11fr, Lady Sealing Letter, by Chardin. 14fr, Titus at Desk, by Rembrandt. 17fr, The Love Letter, by Vermeer. 26fr, The Merchant G. Gisze, by Holbein. 31fr, Portrait of Alexandre Lenoir, by David.

1974, Oct. 1   Photo.   Perf. 13
468 A69   6fr gold & multi   .15
469 A69 11fr gold & multi   .16
470 A69 14fr gold & multi   .22
471 A69 17fr gold & multi   .25
472 A69 26fr gold & multi   .40
473 A69 31fr gold & multi   .45
    a.   Souvenir sheet of 2, #472-473   1.10
Nos. 468-473 (6)   1.63

International Letter Writing Week, Oct. 6-12. No. 473a exists imperf.

Virgin and Child,
by Bernaert van
Orley — A70

Paintings of the Virgin and Child: 10fr, by Hans Memling. 15fr, by Botticelli.

1974, Nov. 7   Photo.   Perf. 13
474 A70   5fr gold & multi   .15
475 A70 10fr gold & multi   .15
476 A70 15fr gold & multi   .22
    a.   Souvenir sheet of 3, #474-476   .50
Nos. 474-476,C213-C215 (6)   1.80

Christmas 1974. Sheets of 20 stamps and one label. No. 476a exists imperf.

Apollo-Soyuz Space Mission and
Emblem — A71

1975, July 10   Photo.   *Perf. 13*
477 A71   Block of 4   .80
a.   26fr A.A. Leonov, V.N. Kubasov, Soviet flag   .20
b.   26fr Soyuz and Soviet flag   .20
c.   26fr Apollo and American flag   .20
d.   26fr D.K. Slayton, V.D. Brand, T.P. Stafford, American flag   .20
478 A71   Block of 4   1.25
a.   31fr Apollo-Soyuz link-up   .28
b.   31fr Apollo, blast-off   .28
c.   31fr Soyuz, blast-off   .28
d.   31fr Kubasov, Leonov, Slayton, Brand, Stafford   .28
    Nos. 477-478,C216-C217 (4)   4.35

Apollo Soyuz space test project (Russo-American cooperation), launching July 15; link-up, July 17.

Addax — A72

1975, July 31   Photo.   *Perf. 13½*
479   Strip of 4   .20
a.   A72 1fr shown   .15
b.   A72 1fr Roan antelope   .15
c.   A72 1fr Nyala   .15
d.   A72 1fr White rhinoceros   .15
480   Strip of 4   .20
a.   A72 2fr Mandrill   .15
b.   A72 2fr Eland   .15
c.   A72 2fr Salt's dik-dik   .15
d.   A72 2fr Thomson's gazelles   .15
481   Strip of 4   .20
a.   A72 3fr African small-clawed otter   .15
b.   A72 3fr Reed buck   .15
c.   A72 3fr Indian civet   .15
d.   A72 3fr Cape buffalo   .15
482   Strip of 4   .35
a.   A72 5fr White-tailed gnu   .15
b.   A72 5fr African wild asses   .15
c.   A72 5fr Black-and-white colobus monkey   .15
d.   A72 5fr Gerenuk   .15
483   Strip of 4   .36
a.   A72 6fr Dama gazelle   .15
b.   A72 6fr Black-backed jackal   .15
c.   A72 6fr Sitatungas   .15
d.   A72 6fr Zebra antelope   .15
484   Strip of 4   .65
a.   A72 11fr Fennec   .16
b.   A72 11fr Lesser kudus   .16
c.   A72 11fr Blesbok   .16
d.   A72 11fr Serval   .16
    Nos. 479-484,C218-C223 (12)   12.61

For overprints see Nos. C224-C227.

Jonah, by Michelangelo — A73

Designs: Paintings from Sistine Chapel.

1975, Dec. 3   Photo.   *Perf. 13*
485 A73   5fr shown   .15
486 A73   5fr Libyan Sybil   .15
487 A73   13fr Prophet Isaiah   .20
488 A73   13fr Delphic Sybil   .20
489 A73   27fr Daniel   .40
490 A73   27fr Cumaean Sybil   .40
a.   Souvenir sheet of 6, #485-490   2.00
    Nos. 485-490,C228-C233 (12)   5.10

Michelangelo Buonarroti (1475-1564), Italian sculptor, painter and architect. Stamps of same denominations printed se-tenant in sheets of 18 stamps and 2 labels.
For surcharges see Nos. B65-B70, CB35-CB40.

Speed Skating — A74

Basketball — A75

Designs (Innsbruck Games Emblem and): 24fr, Figure skating, women's. 26fr, Two-man bobsled. 31fr, Cross-country skiing.

1976, Jan. 23   Photo.   *Perf. 14x13½*
491 A74   17fr dp bl & multi   .30
492 A74   24fr multi   .45
493 A74   26fr multi   .48
494 A74   31fr plum & multi   .55
a.   Souvenir sheet of 3, perf. 13½   2.25
    Nos. 491-494,C234-C236 (7)   3.70

12th Winter Olympic Games, Innsbruck, Austria, Feb. 4-15.
No. 494a contains stamps similar to #C234-C236, without "POSTE AERIENNE."

1976, May 3   Litho.   *Perf. 13½*
Montreal Games Emblem and: #496, 499, 503b, Pole vault. #497, 500, 503d, Running. #498, 501, 503a, Soccer. #502, 503c, Basketball.

495 A75   14fr blue & multi   .25
496 A75   14fr olive & multi   .25
497 A75   17fr magenta & multi   .30
498 A75   17fr vermilion & multi   .30
499 A75   28fr olive & multi   .48
500 A75   28fr magenta & multi   .48
501 A75   40fr vermilion & multi   .70
502 A75   40fr blue & multi   .70
    Nos. 495-502,C237-C242 (14)   7.20

Souvenir Sheet
503   Sheet of 4   1.65
a.   A75 14fr red & multi   .22
b.   A75 17fr olive & multi   .25
c.   A75 28fr blue & multi   .40
d.   A75 40fr magenta & multi   .60

21st Olympic Games, Montreal, Canada, July 17-Aug. 1. Stamps of same denomination printed se-tenant in sheets of 20.

Virgin and Child, by Dirk Bouts — A76

Virgin and Child by: 13fr, Giovanni Bellini. 27fr, Carlo Crivelli.

1976, Oct. 18   Photo.   *Perf. 13½*
504 A76   5fr gold & multi   .15
505 A76   13fr gold & multi   .20
506 A76   27fr gold & multi   .40
a.   Souvenir sheet of 3, #504-506   .75
    Nos. 504-506,C250-C252 (6)   2.05

Christmas 1976. Sheets of 20 stamps and descriptive label.
For surcharges see #B71-B73, CB41-CB43.

St. Veronica, by Rubens A77

Paintings by Rubens: 21fr, Christ on the Cross. 27fr, Descent from the Cross. 35fr, The Deposition.

1977, Apr. 5   Photo.   *Perf. 13*
507 A77   10fr gold & multi   .15
508 A77   21fr gold & multi   .32
509 A77   27fr gold & multi   .40
510 A77   35fr gold & multi   .55
a.   Souvenir sheet of 4   1.50
    Nos. 507-510 (4)   1.42

Easter 1977. Sheets of 30 stamps and descriptive label. No. 510a contains 4 stamps similar to Nos. 507-510 inscribed "POSTE AERIENNE."

Alexander Graham Bell — A78

Intelsat Satellite, Modern and Old Telephones — A79

Designs: No. 513, Switchboard operator, c. 1910, and wall telephone. No. 514, Intelsat and radar. No. 515, A.G. Bell and first telephone. No. 516, Satellites around globe and videophone.

1977, May 17   Photo.   *Perf. 13*
511 A78   10fr multi   .15
512 A79   10fr multi   .15
513 A78   17fr multi   .15
514 A79   17fr multi   .15
515 A78   26fr multi   .22
516 A79   26fr multi   .22
    Nos. 511-516,C253-C256 (10)   1.84

Centenary of first telephone call by Alexander Graham Bell, Mar. 10, 1876. Stamps of same denomination printed se-tenant in sheets of 32.

Buffon's Kob — A80

1977, Aug. 22   Photo.   *Perf. 14x14½*
517   Strip of 4   .20
a.   A80 2fr shown   .15
b.   A80 2fr Marabous   .15
c.   A80 2fr Brindled gnu   .15
d.   A80 2fr River hog   .15
518   Strip of 4   .35
a.   A80 5fr Zebras   .15
b.   A80 5fr Shoebill   .15
c.   A80 5fr Striped hyenas   .15
d.   A80 5fr Chimpanzee   .15
519   Strip of 4   .48
a.   A80 8fr Flamingos   .15
b.   A80 8fr Nile crocodiles   .15
c.   A80 8fr Green mamba   .15
d.   A80 8fr Greater kudus   .15
520   Strip of 4   .70
a.   A80 11fr Hyrax   .16
b.   A80 11fr Cobra   .16
c.   A80 11fr Jackals   .16
d.   A80 11fr Verreaux's eagles   .16
521   Strip of 4   1.40
a.   A80 21fr Honey badger   .32
b.   A80 21fr Harnessed antelopes   .32
c.   A80 21fr Secretary bird   .32
d.   A80 21fr Klipspringer   .32
522   Strip of 4   1.40
a.   A80 27fr African big-eared fox   .35
b.   A80 27fr Elephants   .35
c.   A80 27fr Vulturine guineafowl   .35
d.   A80 27fr Impalas   .35
    Nos. 517-522,C258-C263 (12)   20.68

The Goose Girl, by Grimm — A81

Fairy Tales: 5fr, by Grimm Brothers. 11fr, by Aesop. 14fr, by Hans Christian Andersen. 17fr, by Jean de La Fontaine. 26fr, English fairy tales.

1977, Sept. 14   *Perf. 14*
523   Block of 4   .38
a.   A81 5fr shown   .15
b.   A81 5fr The Two Wanderers   .15
c.   A81 5fr The Man of Iron   .15
d.   A81 5fr Snow White and Rose Red   .15
524   Block of 4   .85
a.   A81 11fr The Quarreling Cats   .20
b.   A81 11fr The Blind and the Lame   .20
c.   A81 11fr The Hermit and the Bear   .20
d.   A81 11fr The Fox and the Stork   .20
525   Block of 4   1.00
a.   A81 14fr The Princess and the Pea   .25
b.   A81 14fr The Old Tree Mother   .25
c.   A81 14fr The Ice Maiden   .25
d.   A81 14fr The Old House   .25
526   Block of 4   1.25
a.   A81 17fr The Oyster and the Suitors   .30
b.   A81 17fr The Wolf and the Lamb   .30
c.   A81 17fr Hen with the Golden Egg   .30
d.   A81 17fr The Wolf as Shepherd   .30

527   Block of 4   2.00
a.   A81 26fr Three Heads in the Well   .50
b.   A81 26fr Mother Goose   .50
c.   A81 26fr Jack and the Beanstalk   .50
d.   A81 26fr Alice in Wonderland   .50
    Nos. 523-527 (5)   5.48

Security Council Chamber, UN Nos. 28, 46, 37, C7 — A82

Designs (UN Stamps and): 8fr, UN General Assembly, interior. 21fr, UN Meeting Hall.

1977, Oct. 10   Photo.   *Perf. 13½*
528 A82   Block of 4   .65
a.   8fr No. 25   .15
b.   8fr No. C5   .15
c.   8fr No. 23   .15
d.   8fr No. 2   .15
529 A82   Block of 4   .75
a.   10fr No. 28   .18
b.   10fr No. 46   .18
c.   10fr No. 37   .18
d.   10fr No. C7   .18
530 A82   Block of 4   1.50
a.   21fr No. 45   .35
b.   21fr No. 42   .35
c.   21fr No. 17   .35
d.   21fr No. 13   .35
e.   Souvenir sheet of 3   .35
    Nos. 528-530,C264-C266 (6)   10.05

25th anniv. (in 1976) of the UN Postal Administration. No. 530e contains 8fr in design of No. 529d, 10fr in design of No. 530b, 21fr in design of No. 528c.

Virgin and Child — A83

Designs: Paintings of the Virgin and Child.

1977, Oct. 31   Photo.   *Perf. 14x13*
531 A83   5fr By Meliore Toscano   .15
532 A83   13fr By J. Lombardos   .20
533 A83   27fr By Emmanuel Tzanes, 1610-1680   .40
a.   Souvenir sheet of 3, #531-533   .75
    Nos. 531-533,C267-C269 (6)   2.11

Christmas 1977. Sheets of 24 stamps with descriptive label.
For surcharges see #B74-B76, CB44-CB46.

Cruiser Aurora, Russia Nos. 211, 303, 1252, 187 — A84

Russian Stamps and: 8fr, Kremlin, Moscow. 11fr, Pokrovski Cathedral, Moscow. 13fr, Labor Day parade, 1977 and 1980 Olympic Games emblem.

1977, Nov. 14   Photo.   *Perf. 13*
534 A84 Block of 4   .38
  a. 5fr No. 211   .15
  b. 5fr No. 303   .15
  c. 5fr No. 1252   .15
  d. 5fr No. 187   .15
535 A84 Block of 4   .65
  a. 8fr No. 856   .15
  b. 8fr No. 1986   .15
  c. 8fr No. 908   .15
  d. 8fr No. 2551   .15
536 A84 Block of 4   .85
  a. 11fr No. 3844b   .20
  b. 11fr No. 3452   .20
  c. 11fr No. 3382   .20
  d. 11fr No. 3837   .20
537 A84 Block of 4   1.00
  a. 13fr No. 4446   .25
  b. 13fr No. 3497   .25
  c. 13fr No. 2926   .25
  d. 13fr No. 2365   .25
      Nos. 534-537 (4)   2.88

60th anniv. of Russian October Revolution.

Ship at Dock, Arms and Flag — A85

Burundi Arms and Flag and: 5fr, Men at lathes. 11fr, Male leopard dance. 14fr, Coffee harvest. 17fr, Government Palace.

1977, Nov. 25   Photo.   *Perf. 13¹/₂*
538 A85 1fr sil & multi   .15
539 A85 5fr sil & multi   .15
540 A85 11fr sil & multi   .16
541 A85 14fr sil & multi   .20
542 A85 17fr sil & multi   .25
         Set value   .74

15th anniversary of independence.

A86   A87

Paintings of the Virgin and Child by: 13fr, Rubens. 17fr, Solario. 27fr, Tiepolo. 31fr, Gerard David. 40fr, Bellini.

1979, Feb.   Photo.   *Perf. 14x13*
543 A86 13fr multi   .20
544 A86 17fr multi   .25
545 A86 27fr multi   .40
546 A86 31fr multi   .48
547 A86 40fr multi   .60
      Nos. 543-547 (5)   1.93

Christmas 1978. See No. C270.

1979   Photo.   *Perf. 13¹/₂x13*
548 A87 1fr *Abyssinian hornbill*   .15
549 A87 2fr *Snakebird*   .15
550 A87 3fr *Melittophagus pusillus* .15
551 A87 5fr *Flamingo*   .15
552 A87 8fr *Afropavo congenis*   .15
553 A87 10fr *Gallinule*   .18
554 A87 20fr *Martial eagle*   .32
555 A87 27fr *Ibis*   .42
556 A87 50fr *Saddle-billed stork*   .85
      Nos. 548-556,C273-C281 (18)   6.96

Mother and Infant, IYC Emblem A88

IYC Emblem and: 20fr, Infant. 27fr, Girl with doll. 50fr, Children in Children's Village.

1979, July 19   Photo.   *Perf. 14*
557 A88 10fr multi   .15
558 A88 20fr multi   .25
559 A88 27fr multi   .32
560 A88 50fr multi   .55
      Nos. 557-560 (4)   1.27

Intl. Year of the Child. See No. B82.

A89   A90

Virgin and Child by: 20fr, del Garbo. 27fr, Giovanni Penni. 31fr, G. Romano. 50fr, Jacopo Bassano.

1979, Oct. 12
561 A89 20fr multi   .30
562 A89 27fr multi   .40
563 A89 31fr multi   .48
564 A89 50fr multi   .75
      Nos. 561-564,B83-B86 (8)   3.95

Christmas 1979. See Nos. C271, CB48.

1979, Nov. 6

Designs: 20fr, Rowland Hill, Penny Black. Stamps of Burundi: 27fr, German East Africa Nos. 17, N17. 31fr, Nos. 4, 24. 40fr, Nos. 29, 294. 60fr, Heinrich von Stephan, Nos. 464-465.

565 A90 20fr multi   .30
566 A90 27fr multi   .40
567 A90 31fr multi   .48
568 A90 40fr multi   .60
569 A90 60fr multi   .90
      Nos. 565-569 (5)   2.68

Sir Rowland Hill (1795-1879), originator of penny postage. See No. C272.

A91

1980, Oct. 24   Photo.   *Perf. 13x13¹/₂*
570 A91 20fr 110-meter hurdles   .38
571 A91 20fr Hurdles, Thomas
                 Munkelt   .38
572 A91 20fr Hurdles, R.D.A.   .38
573 A91 30fr Discus   .55
574 A91 30fr Discus, V. Rassh-
                 chupkin   .55
575 A91 30fr Discus, U.R.S.S.   .55
576 A91 40fr Soccer, Tchecoslova-
                 quie   .75
577 A91 40fr "Football"   .75
578 A91 40fr shown   .75
      Nos. 570-578 (9)   5.04

22nd Summer Olympic Games, Moscow, July 19-Aug. 3. Stamps of same denomination se-tenant.
See No. C282.

Virgin and Child, by Mainardi — A92

Christmas 1980 (Paintings): 30fr, Holy Family, by Michelangelo. 40fr, Virgin and Child, by di Cosimo. 45fr, Holy Family, by Fra Bartolomeo.

1980, Dec. 12   Photo.   *Perf. 13¹/₂x13*
579 A92 10fr multi   .15
580 A92 30fr multi   .30
581 A92 30fr multi   .42
582 A92 45fr multi   .45
      Nos. 579-582,B87-B90 (8)   2.71

UPRONA Party National Congress, 1979 — A93

1980, Dec. 29   *Perf. 14x13¹/₂*
583 A93 10fr multi   .15
584 A93 40fr multi   .60
585 A93 45fr multi   .65
      Nos. 583-585 (3)   1.40

Johannes Kepler, Dish Antenna A94

1981, Feb. 12   *Perf. 14*
586 A94 10fr shown   .15
587 A94 40fr Satellite   .60
588 A94 45fr Satellite, diff.   .65
  a. Souvenir sheet of 3, #586-588 1.50
      Nos. 586-588 (3)   1.40

350th death anniv. of Johannes Kepler and 1st earth satellite station in Burundi.

Lion A95

1983, Apr. 22   Photo.   *Perf. 13*
589 A95 2fr shown   .15
590 A95 3fr Giraffes   .15
591 A95 5fr Rhinoceros   .15
592 A95 10fr Water buffalo   .15
593 A95 20fr Elephant   .30
594 A95 25fr Hippopotamus   .38
595 A95 30fr Zebra   .45
596 A95 50fr Warthog   .75
597 A95 60fr Oryx   .90
598 A95 65fr Wild dog   1.00
599 A95 70fr Cheetah   1.10
600 A95 75fr Wildebeest   1.25
601 A95 85fr Hyena   1.75
      Nos. 589-601 (13)   8.48

Nos. 589-601 Overprinted in Silver with World Wildlife Fund Emblem

1983   Photo.   *Perf. 13*
589a A95   2fr   .15
590a A95   3fr   .15
591a A95   5fr   .15
592a A95 10fr   .15
593a A95 20fr   .30
594a A95 25fr   .38
595a A95 30fr   .45
596a A95 50fr   .75
597a A95 60fr   .90
598a A95 65fr   1.00
599a A95 70fr   1.10
600a A95 75fr   1.15
601a A95 85fr   1.25
      Nos. 589a-601a (13)   7.88

20th Anniv. of Independence, July 1, 1982 — A96

Flags, various arms, map or portrait.

1983   *Perf. 14*
602 A96 10fr multi   .15
603 A96 25fr multi   .38
604 A96 30fr multi   .45
605 A96 50fr multi   .75
606 A96 65fr multi   1.00
      Nos. 602-606 (5)   2.73

Christmas 1983 — A97

Virgin and Child paintings: 10fr, by Luca Signorelli (1450-1523). 25fr, by Esteban Murillo (1617-1682). 30fr, by Carlo Crivelli (1430-1495). 50fr, by Nicolas Poussin (1594-1665).

1983, Oct. 3   Litho.   *Perf. 14¹/₂x13¹/₂*
607 A97 10fr multi   .15
608 A97 25fr multi   .38
609 A97 30fr multi   .45
610 A97 50fr multi   .75
      Nos. 607-610,B91-B94 (8)   3.52

See Nos. C285, CB50.

Butterflies A98

1984, June 29   Photo.   *Perf. 13*
611 A98 5fr *Cymothoe coccinata*   .15
612 A98 5fr *Papilio zalmoxis*   .15
613 A98 10fr *Asterope pechueli*   .25
614 A98 10fr *Papilio antimachus*   .25
615 A98 30fr *Papilio hesperus*   .70
616 A98 30fr *Bebearia mardania*   .70
617 A98 35fr *Euphaedra neophron*   .85
618 A98 35fr *Euphaedra perseis*   .85
619 A98 65fr *Euphaedra imperialis* 1.50
620 A98 65fr *Pseudocraea striata* 1.50
      Nos. 611-620 (10)   6.90

Stamps of the same denomination printed horizontally se-tenant.
For surcharges see Nos. 654D-654E.

19th UPU Congress, Hamburg A99

UPU emblem and: 10fr, German East Africa, #17, N17. 30fr, #4, 24. 35fr, #294, 595. 65fr, Dr. Heinrich von Stephan, #464-465.

1984, July 14   Litho.   *Perf. 13x13¹/₂*
621 A99 10fr multi   .15
622 A99 30fr multi   .45
623 A99 35fr multi   .50
624 A99 65fr multi   1.00
      Nos. 621-624 (4)   2.10

See No. C286.

1984 Summer Olympics A100

Gold medalists: 10fr, Jesse Owens, US, track and field, Berlin, 1936. 30fr, Rafer Johnson, US, decathlon, 1960. 35fr, Bob Beamon, US, long jump, 1968. 65fr, Kipchoge Keino, Kenya, 3000-meter steeplechase, 1972.

1984, Aug. 6   *Perf. 13¹/₂x13*
625 A100 10fr multi   .25
626 A100 30fr multi   .70
627 A100 35fr multi   .85
628 A100 65fr multi   1.50
      Nos. 625-628 (4)   3.30

See No. C287.

Christmas 1984 — A101

Paintings: 10fr, Rest During the Flight into Egypt, by Murillo (1617-1682). 25fr, Virgin and Child, by R. del Garbo. 30fr, Virgin and Child, by Botticelli (1445-1510). 50fr, The Adoration of the Shepherds, by Giacomo da Bassano (1517-1592).

1984, Dec. 15   **Perf. 13½**
629 A101 10fr multi .15
630 A101 25fr multi .38
631 A101 30fr multi .45
632 A101 50fr multi .75
    Nos. 629-632,B95-B98 (8) 3.52

See Nos. C288, CB51.

Flowers — A102

1986, July 31 Photo.   **Perf. 13x13½**
633 A102 2fr Thunbergia .15
634 A102 3fr Saintpaulia .15
635 A102 5fr Clivia .15
636 A102 10fr Cassia .15
637 A102 20fr Strelitzia .16
638 A102 35fr Gloriosa .28
    Nos. 633-638,C289-C294 (12) 5.54

Intl. Peace Year — A103

1986, May 1 Litho.   **Perf. 14**
639 A103 10fr Rockets as housing .15
640 A103 20fr Atom as flower .18
641 A103 30fr Handshake .28
642 A103 40fr Globe, chicks .35
   a.   Souvenir sheet of 4, #639-642 .90
    Nos. 639-642 (4) .96

No. 642a exists imperf.

Great Lake Nations Economic Community (CEPGI), 10th Anniv. — A104

Outline maps of Lake Tanganyika, CEPGI emblem and: 5fr, Aviation. 10fr, Agriculture. 15fr, Industry. 25fr, Electrification. 35fr, Flags of Burundi, Rwanda and Zaire.

1986, May 1 Photo.   **Perf. 13½x14½**
643 A104 5fr multi .15
644 A104 10fr multi .15
645 A104 15fr multi .20
646 A104 25fr multi .32
647 A104 35fr multi .45
   a.   Souv. sheet of 5, #643-647 + label 1.25
    Nos. 643-647 (5) 1.27

Intl. Year of Shelter for the Homeless A105

1987, June Litho.   **Perf. 14**
648 A105 10fr Hovel .28
649 A105 20fr Drain pipe shelter .55
650 A105 80fr Shoveling sand 2.15
651 A105 150fr Children, house
     model 4.00
   a.   Souvenir sheet of 4, #648-651 7.00
    Nos. 648-651 (4) 6.98

A106   A107

1987(?) Litho.   **Perf. 14**
652 A106 5fr shown .15
653 A106 20fr Skull, lungs .30
654 A106 80fr Cigarette, face 1.25
    Nos. 652-654 (3) 1.70

WHO Anti-smoking campaign.

Nos. 615-616 Surcharged   **80f**

1989 Photo.   **Perf. 13**
654D A98 80fr on 30fr #615
654E A98 80fr on 30fr #616

Numbers have been reserved for additional values in this set.

1990 Litho.   **Perf. 14**
655 A107 5fr red lil & multi .15
656 A107 10fr blue & multi .24
657 A107 20fr gray & multi .48
658 A107 30fr ol grn & multi .72
659 A107 50fr brt blue & multi 1.20
660 A107 80fr grn bl & multi 1.95
   a.   Souv. sheet of 6, #655-660, perf.
     13½ 4.75
    Nos. 655-660 (6) 4.74

Visit of Pope John Paul II.

Animals A108

1991, Oct. 4 Litho.   **Perf. 14**
661 A108 5fr Hippopotamus .15
662 A108 10fr Chickens .15
663 A108 20fr Lion .32
664 A108 30fr Elephant .48
665 A108 50fr Guinea fowl .80
666 A108 80fr Crocodile 1.25
   a.   Souv. sheet of 6, #661-666, perf.
     13½ 3.15
    Nos. 661-666 (6) 3.15

No. 666a exists imperf.

Flowers — A108a

1992, June 2 Litho.   **Perf. 14**
666B A108a 15fr Impatiens peter-
     siana .40
666C A108a 20fr Lachenalia aloides .50
666D A108a 30fr Nymphaea lotus .80

666E A108a 50fr Clivia miniata 1.30
   f.   Souvenir sheet of 4, #666B-
     666E, perf. 13½ 3.00
    Nos. 666B-666E (4) 3.00

A109

Native Music and Dancing A110

Designs: 15fr, Native drummer. 30fr, Two dancers. 115fr, Drummers. 200fr, Five dancers.

1992, Apr. 2 Litho.   **Perf. 14**
667 A109 15fr multicolored .25
668 A109 30fr multicolored .48
669 A110 115fr multicolored 1.80
670 A110 200fr multicolored 3.10
   a.   Souvenir sheet 5.65
    Nos. 667-670 (4) 5.63

No. 670a contains one each of Nos. 667-668, perf. 13x13½, and Nos. 669-670, perf. 13½x13.

Independence, 30th Anniv. — A111

Designs: 30fr, 140fr, People with flag. 85fr, 115fr, Natl. flag. 110fr, 200fr, Monument, vert. 120fr, 250fr, Map, vert.

1992, June 30 Litho.   **Perf. 15**
671 A111 30fr multicolored .35
672 A111 85fr multicolored 1.00
673 A111 110fr multicolored 1.25
674 A111 115fr multicolored 1.35
675 A111 120fr multicolored 1.40
676 A111 140fr multicolored 1.65
677 A111 200fr multicolored 2.35
678 A111 250fr multicolored 3.00
    Nos. 671-678 (8) 12.35

Discovery of America, 500th Anniv. A112

Columbus' fleet, globe and: 200fr, Pre-Columbian artifacts. 400fr, Fruits and vegetables.

1992, Oct. 12 Litho.   **Perf. 15**
679 A112 200fr multicolored 3.00
680 A112 400fr multicolored 6.25

Felis Serval A113

1992, Oct. 16
681 A113 30fr shown .48
682 A113 130fr Two seated 2.00
683 A113 200fr One standing, one
     lying 3.10
684 A113 220fr Two faces 3.40
    Nos. 681-684 (4) 8.98

World Wildlife Fund.

Mushrooms A114   1992 Summer Olympics, Barcelona A115

Designs: 10fr, Russula ingens. 15fr, Russula brunneorigida. 20fr, Amanita zambiana. 30fr, Russula subfistulosa. 75fr, 85fr, Russula meleagris. 100fr, Russula immaculata. 110fr, like #685. 115fr, like #686. 120fr, 130fr, Russula sejuncta. 250fr, Afroboletus luteolus.

1992-93   **Perf. 11½x12**
      Granite Paper
685 A114 10fr multicolored .15
686 A114 15fr multicolored .24
687 A114 20fr multicolored .32
688 A114 30fr multicolored .48
689 A114 75fr multicolored 1.15
690 A114 85fr multicolored 1.35
691 A114 100fr multicolored 1.55
691A A114 110fr multicolored 1.65
691B A114 115fr multicolored 1.75
692 A114 120fr multicolored 1.90
693 A114 130fr multicolored 2.00
694 A114 250fr multicolored 3.75
    Nos. 685-694 (12) 16.29

Issued: 110fr, 115fr, 1993; others, 9/30/92.

1992, Nov. 6   **Perf. 15**
695 A115 130fr Runners 2.00
696 A115 500fr Hurdler 7.75

A116   A116a

Christmas (Details of Adoration of the Kings, by Gentile da Fabriano): a, 100fr, Crowd, horses. b, 130fr, Kings. c, 250fr, Nativity scene.

1992, Dec. 7 Litho.   **Perf. 11½**
697 A116 Strip of 3, #a.-c. 5.25
   d.   Souvenir sheet of 3, #697a-697c 6.50

Nos. 697a-697c have white border. No. 697d has continuous design and sold for 580fr.

1992, Dec. 5 Litho.   **Perf. 15**
Designs: 200fr, Emblems. 220fr, Profile of person made from fruits and vegetables.

697E A116a 200fr multicolored 5.25
697F A116a 220fr multicolored 5.75

Intl. Conference on Nutrition, Rome.

European Common Market A117

Designs: 130fr, Flags, stars. 500fr, Europe, Africa, clasped hands, stars.

1993, Mar. 29 Litho.   **Perf. 15**
698 A117 130fr multicolored 1.50
699 A117 500fr multicolored 5.75

1994 World Cup Soccer Championships, US — A118

Players, stadium, US flag and: 130fr, Statue of Liberty. 200fr, Golden Gate Bridge.

1993, July 5   Litho.   Perf. 15
700 A118 130fr multicolored   1.50
701 A118 200fr multicolored   2.30

Traditional Musical Instruments A119

1993, Apr. 30   Litho.   Perf. 15
702 A119 200fr Indonongo   2.30
703 A119 220fr Ingoma   2.50
704 A119 250fr Ikembe   2.75
705 A119 300fr Umuduri   3.50
       Nos. 702-705 (4)   11.05

A120   A121

1993, June 4   Litho.   Perf. 11½
706 A120 130fr Papilio bromius   1.50
707 A120 200fr Charaxes eupale   2.25
708 A120 250fr Cymothoe caenis   2.75
709 A120 300fr Graphium
             ridleyanus   3.50
  a.   Souvenir sheet of 4, #706-709   11.50
       Nos. 706-709 (4)   10.00

No. 709a sold for 980fr.

1993, Dec. 9   Perf. 14
710 A121 100fr Cattle   1.10
711 A121 120fr Sheep   1.40
712 A121 130fr Pigs   1.50
713 A121 250fr Goats   2.75
       Nos. 710-713 (4)   6.75

Christmas — A122   Rock Stars — A123

Natives adoring Christ Child: a, 100fr, Woman carrying baby, two people kneeling. b, 130fr, With Christ Child. 250fr, c, Woman carrying baby, three other people.

1993, Dec. 10   Perf. 11½
714 A122 Strip of 3, #a.-c.   5.00
  d.   Souvenir sheet of 3, #714a-714c 6.00

Nos. 714a-714c have white border. No. 714d has continuous design and sold for 580fr.

1994   Litho.   Perf. 15
715 A123 60fr Elvis Presley   .65
716 A123 115fr Mick Jagger   1.25
717 A123 120fr John Lennon   1.25
718 A123 200fr Michael Jackson   2.50
  a.   Souvenir sheet, #715-718   6.50
       Nos. 715-718 (4)   5.40

No. 718a sold for 600fr.

A124   A125

1994, Oct. 10   Litho.   Perf. 15
719 A124 150fr multicolored   1.10
       Intl. Olympic Committee, cent.

1994, Dec. 14   Photo.   Perf. 15
Christmas (Madonna and Child): a, 115fr, Chinese. b, 120fr, Japanese. c, 250fr, Polish.
720 A125 Strip of 3, #a.-c.   5.00
  d.   Souvenir sheet of 1, #720c   2.75

A126   A127

115fr, FAO, 50th anniv. 120fr, UN, 50th anniv.

1995, Feb. 21   Litho.   Perf. 11½
721 A126 115fr multicolored   1.25
722 A126 120fr multicolored   1.25

1995   Litho.   Perf. 11½
Flowers: 15fr, Cassia didymobotrya. 20fr, Mitragyna rubrostipulosa. 30fr, Phytolacca dodecandra. 85fr, Acanthus pubescens. 100fr, Bulbophyllum comatum. 110fr, Angraecum evradianum. 115fr, Eulophia burundiensis. 120fr, Habenaria adolphii.

Granite Paper
723 A127 15fr multicolored   .15
724 A127 20fr multicolored   .20
725 A127 30fr multicolored   .30
726 A127 85fr multicolored   .80
727 A127 100fr multicolored   .90
728 A127 110fr multicolored   1.00
729 A127 115fr multicolored   1.00
730 A127 120fr multicolored   1.10
       Nos. 723-730 (8)   5.45

Transportation Methods — A128

Designs: 30fr, Otraco bus. 115fr, Transintra semi truck. 120fr, Arnolac tugboat. 250fr, Air Burundi airplane.

1995, Nov. 16   Litho.   Perf. 11½
731 A128 30fr multicolored   .45
732 A128 115fr multicolored   1.70
733 A128 120fr multicolored   1.75
734 A128 250fr multicolored   3.60
       Nos. 731-734 (4)   7.50

A129   A130

Christmas (African sculpture): a, 100fr, Boy with panga, basket on head. b, 130fr, Boy carrying sheaf of wheat. c, 250fr, Mother, children.

1995, Dec. 26   Litho.   Perf. 11½x12
735 A129 Strip of 3, #a.-c.   2.25
  d.   Souvenir sheet of 3, #735a-735c 2.25

1996, June 28   Litho.   Perf. 14
Athlete, national flag: 130fr, Venuste Niyongabo. 500fr, Arthemon Hatungimana.
736 A130 130fr multicolored   .65
737 A130 500fr multicolored   2.50
       1996 Summer Olympic Games, Atlanta.

Birds
A131

Designs: 15fr, Hagedashia hagedash. 20fr, Alopochen aegyptiacus. 30fr, Haliaeetus vocifer. 120fr, Ardea goliath. 165fr, Balearica regulorum. 220fr, Actophilornis africana.

1996   Perf. 14
740 A131 15fr multicolored   .15
741 A131 20fr multicolored   .20
742 A131 30fr multicolored   .30
743 A131 120fr multicolored   1.15
744 A131 165fr multicolored   1.60
745 A131 220fr multicolored   2.00
       Nos. 740-745 (6)   5.40

SEMI-POSTAL STAMPS

Prince Louis Rwagasore — SP1

Prince and Stadium SP2

Design: 1.50fr+75c, 6.50fr+3fr, Prince and memorial monument.

Perf. 14x13, 13x14
1963, Feb. 15   Photo.   Unwmk.
B1 SP1 50c + 25c brt vio   .15 .15
B2 SP2 1fr + 50c red org & dk bl   .15 .15
B3 SP2 1.50fr + 75c lem & dk vio   .15 .15
B4 SP1 3.50fr + 1.50fr lil rose   .15 .15
B5 SP2 5fr + 2fr rose pink & dk bl   .15 .15
B6 SP2 6.50fr + 3fr gray ol & dk vio .15 .15
       Set value   .39

Issued in memory of Prince Louis Rwagasore (1932-61), son of King Mwami Mwambutsa IV and Prime Minister. The surtax was for the stadium and monument in his honor.

Red Cross Type of Regular Issue
Souvenir Sheet

1963, Sept. 26   Litho.   Imperf.
B7   Sheet of 4   2.00 2.00
  a.   A5 4fr + 2fr fawn, red & black .32 .32
  b.   A5 8fr + 2fr green, red & black .38 .38
  c.   A5 10fr + 2fr gray, red & black .42 .42
  d.   A5 20fr + 2fr ultra, red & black .65 .65

Surtax for Red Cross work in Burundi.

Olympic Type of Regular Issue
Souvenir Sheet

Designs: 18fr+2fr, Hurdling, horiz. 20fr+5fr, Vaulting, horiz.

1964, Nov. 18   Perf. 13½
B8   Sheet of 2   3.00 2.75
  a.   A13 18fr + 2fr yel grn & multi 1.25 1.00
  b.   A13 20fr + 5fr brt pink & multi 1.25 1.00

Scientist with Microscope and Map of Burundi — SP3

Lithographed and Photogravure
1965, Jan. 28   Unwmk.   Perf. 14½
B9   SP3 2fr + 50c multi   .15 .15
B10 SP3 4fr + 1.50fr multi   .15 .15
B11 SP3 5fr + 2.50fr multi   .20 .15
B12 SP3 8fr + 3fr multi   .25 .15
B13 SP3 10fr + 5fr multi   .38 .15
       Nos. B9-B13 (5)   1.13
       Set value   .47

Souvenir Sheet
Perf. 13x13½
B14 SP3 10fr + 10fr multi   .85 .85

Issued for the fight against tuberculosis.

Coat of Arms, 10fr Coin, Reverse SP4

Designs (Coins of Various Denominations): 4fr+50c, 8fr+50c, 15fr+50c, 40fr+50c, King Mwambutsa IV, obverse.

Lithographed; Embossed on Gilt Foil
1965, Aug. 9   Imperf.
       Diameter: 39mm
B15 SP4 2fr + 50c crim & org   .15 .15
B16 SP4 4fr + 50c ultra & ver   .15 .15
       Diameter: 45mm
B17 SP4 6fr + 50c org & gray   .15 .15
B18 SP4 8fr + 50c bl & mag   .15 .15
       Diameter: 56mm
B19 SP4 12fr + 50c lt grn & red lil .25 .25
B20 SP4 15fr + 50c yel grn & lt lil .30 .30
       Diameter: 67mm
B21 SP4 25fr + 50c vio bl & buff   .50 .50
B22 SP4 40fr + 50c brt pink & red
             brn   .75 .75
       Nos. B15-B22 (8)   2.40 2.40

Stamps are backed with patterned paper in blue, orange and pink engine-turned design.

Prince Louis Rwagasore and Pres. John F. Kennedy SP5

Designs: 4fr+1fr, 20fr+5fr, Prince Louis and memorial. 20fr+2fr, 40fr+5fr, Pres. John F. Kennedy and library shelves. 40fr+2fr, King Mwambutsa IV at Kennedy grave, Arlington, vert.

1966, Jan. 21   Photo.   Perf. 13½
B23 SP5 4fr + 1fr gray bl & dk brn   .15 .15
B24 SP5 10fr + 1fr pale grn, ind &
             brn   .18 .15
B25 SP5 20fr + 2fr lil & dp grn   .38 .15
B26 SP5 40fr + 2fr gray grn & dk brn .65 .15
       Nos. B23-B26 (4)   1.36
       Set value   .28

Souvenir Sheet
B27   Sheet of 2   1.50 1.00
  a.   SP5 20fr + 5fr gray blue & dk brn .50 .45
  b.   SP5 40fr + 5fr lilac & deep green .75 .50

Issued in memory of Prince Louis Rwagasore and President John F. Kennedy.

Republic

REPUBLIQUE DU BURUNDI 4+1F

Winston Churchill and St. Paul's, London SP6

Designs: 15fr+2fr, Tower of London and Churchill. 20fr+3fr, Big Ben and Churchill.

1967, Mar. 23   Photo.   Perf. 13½

B28	SP6	4fr + 1fr multi	.15	.15
B29	SP6	15fr + 2fr multi	.35	.15
B30	SP6	20fr + 3fr multi	.45	.18
		Nos. B28-B30 (3)	.95	
		Set value		.33

Issued in memory of Sir Winston Churchill (1874-1965), statesman and World War II leader.

A souvenir sheet contains one airmail stamp, 50fr+5fr, with Churchill portrait centered. Size: 80x80mm. Exists perf. and imperf. Value, each sheet, $3.50.

Nos. B28-B30 Overprinted

1917 1967

1967, July 14   Photo.   Perf. 13½

B31	SP6	4fr + 1fr multi	.15	.15
B32	SP6	15fr + 2fr multi	.42	.15
B33	SP6	20fr + 3fr multi	.65	.30
		Nos. B31-B33 (3)	1.22	.65

50th anniversary of Lions International. Exist with dates transposed.

The souvenir sheets described below No. B30 also received this Lions overprint. Value, each $3.50.

Blood Transfusion and Red Cross — SP7

Designs: 7fr+1fr, Stretcher bearers and wounded man. 11fr+1fr, Surgical team. 17fr+1fr, Nurses tending blood bank.

1969, June 26   Photo.   Perf. 13½

B34	SP7	4fr + 1fr multi	.15	.15
B35	SP7	7fr + 1fr multi	.15	.15
B36	SP7	11fr + 1fr multi	.30	.15
B37	SP7	17fr + 1fr multi	.32	.15
		Nos. B34-B37,CB9-CB11 (7)	2.50	
		Set value		.68

League of Red Cross Societies, 50th anniv.

REPUBLIQUE DU BURUNDI 5+2

Pope Paul VI and Map of Africa — SP8

Designs: 3fr+2fr, 17fr+2fr, Pope Paul VI, vert. 10fr+2fr, Flag made of flags of African Nations. 14fr+2fr, View of St. Peter's, Rome. 40fr+5fr, Martyrs of Uganda. 50fr+2fr, 50fr+5fr, Pope on Throne. All designs include portrait of Pope Paul VI.

1969, Sept. 12   Photo.   Perf. 13½

B38	SP8	3fr + 2fr multi	.15	.15
B39	SP8	17fr + 2fr multi	.15	.15
B40	SP8	10fr + 2fr multi	.30	.15
B41	SP8	14fr + 2fr multi	.42	.15
B42	SP8	17fr + 2fr multi	.50	.15
B43	SP8	40fr + 2fr multi	1.00	.18
B44	SP8	50fr + 2fr multi	1.10	.20
		Nos. B38-B44 (7)	3.62	
		Set value		.66

Souvenir Sheet

B45		Sheet of 2	2.00	1.75
a.		SP8 40fr + 5fr multi	.90	.75
b.		SP8 50fr + 5fr multi	1.00	.90

Visit of Pope Paul VI to Uganda, July 31-Aug. 2.

6.50fr + 1fr   Republique du Burundi

Virgin and Child, by Albrecht Dürer — SP9

Christmas (Paintings): 11fr+1fr, Madonna of the Eucharist, by Sandro Botticelli. 20fr+1fr, Holy Family, by El Greco.

1970, Dec. 14   Photo.   Perf. 13½

Gold Frame

B46	SP9	6.50fr + 1fr multi	.15	.15
B47	SP9	11fr + 1fr multi	.22	.15
B48	SP9	20fr + 1fr multi	.42	.15
a.		Souvenir sheet of 3 B46-B48	.90	.90
		Nos. B46-B48,CB12-CB14 (6)	2.14	
		Set value		.70

+1F UNICEF XXV ANNIVERSAIRE 1946 1971

Nos. 376-378 Surcharged in Gold and Black

1971, Nov. 27

B49	A51	3fr + 1fr multi	.15	.15
B50	A51	5fr + 1fr multi	.15	.15
B51	A51	6fr + 1fr multi	.18	.15
a.		Souvenir sheet of 3	.55	.55
		Nos. B49-B51,CB19-CB21 (6)	1.78	
		Set value		.56

UNICE, 25th anniv. #B51a contains 3 stamps similar to #B49-B51 with 2fr surtax each.

15 fr + 1 F   REPUBLIQUE DU BURUNDI

"La Polenta," by Pietro Longhi SP10

Designs: 3fr+1fr, Archangel Michael, Byzantine icon from St. Mark's 6fr+1fr, "Gossip," by Pietro Longhi. 11fr+1fr, "Diana's Bath," by Giovanni Batista Pittoni. All stamps inscribed UNESCO.

1971, Dec. 27

B52	SP10	3fr + 1fr gold & multi	.15	.15
B53	SP10	5fr + 1fr gold & multi	.15	.15
B54	SP10	6fr + 1fr gold & multi	.18	.15
B55	SP10	11fr + 1fr gold & multi	.30	.15
a.		Souvenir sheet of 4	.75	.50
		Nos. B52-B55,CB22-CB25 (8)	2.26	
		Set value		.75

The surtax was for the UNESCO campaign to save the treasures of Venice. No. B55a contains 4 stamps similar to Nos. B52-B55, but with 2fr surtax. Sheet exists imperf.

Nos. 408-410 Surcharged "+1F" in Silver

1972, Dec. 12   Photo.   Perf. 13½

B56	A57	5fr + 1fr multi	.15	.15
B57	A57	11fr + 1fr multi	.22	.15
B58	A57	15fr + 1fr multi	.32	.15
a.		Souvenir sheet of 3	.75	.70
		Nos. B56-B58,CB26-CB28 (6)	2.02	
		Set value		.60

Christmas 1972. No. B58a contains 3 stamps similar to Nos. B56-B58, but with 2fr surtax.

Nos. 441-443 Surcharged "+1F" in Silver

1973, Dec. 14   Photo.   Perf. 13

B59	A64	5fr + 1fr multi	.15	.15
B60	A64	10fr + 1fr multi	.20	.15
B61	A64	15fr + 1fr multi	.30	.15
a.		Souvenir sheet of 3	.65	.65
		Nos. B59-B61,CB29-CB31 (6)	1.93	
		Set value		.60

Christmas 1973. No. B61a contains 3 stamps similar to Nos. B59-B61 with 2fr surtax each.

Christmas Type of 1974

1974, Dec. 2   Photo.   Perf. 13

B62	A70	5fr + 1fr multi	.15	.15
B63	A70	10fr + 1fr multi	.20	.15
B64	A70	15fr + 1fr multi	.30	.18
a.		Souvenir sheet of 3	.75	.75
		Nos. B62-B64,CB32-CB34 (6)	2.17	1.40

No. B64a contains 3 stamps similar to Nos. B62-B64 with 2fr surtax each.

Nos. 485-490 Surcharged "+ 1F" in Silver and Black

1975, Dec. 22   Photo.   Perf. 13

B65	A73	5fr + 1fr #485	.15
B66	A73	5fr + 1fr #486	.15
B67	A73	13fr + 1fr #487	.28
B68	A73	13fr + 1fr #488	.28
B69	A73	27fr + 1fr #489	.50
B70	A73	27fr + 1fr #490	.50
a.		Souvenir sheet of 6	2.50
		Nos. B65-B70,CB35-CB40 (12)	5.16

Michelangelo Buonarroti (1475-1564), 500th birth anniversary. No. B70a contains 6 stamps similar to Nos. B65-B70 with 2fr surcharge each.

Nos. 504-506 Surcharged "+1fr" in Silver and Black

1976, Nov. 25   Photo.   Perf. 13½

B71	A76	5fr + 1fr multi	.15
B72	A76	13fr + 1fr multi	.22
B73	A76	27fr + 1fr multi	.42
a.		Souvenir sheet of 3	.85
		Nos. B71-B73,CB41-CB43 (6)	2.19

Christmas 1976. No. B73a contains 3 stamps similar to Nos. B71-B73 with 2fr surtax each.

Nos. 531-533 Surcharged "+1fr" in Silver and Black

1977   Photo.   Perf. 14x13

B74	A83	5fr + 1fr multi	.15
B75	A83	13fr + 1fr multi	.22
B76	A83	27fr + 1fr multi	.42
a.		Souvenir sheet of 3	.85
		Nos. B74-B76,CB44-CB46 (6)	2.17

Christmas 1977. No. B76a contains 3 stamps similar to Nos. B74-B76 with 2fr surtax each.

Christmas Type of 1979

1979, Feb.   Photo.   Perf. 14x13

B77	A86	13fr + 1fr multi	.22
B78	A86	17fr + 1fr multi	.28
B79	A86	27fr + 1fr multi	.42
B80	A86	31fr + 1fr multi	.50
B81	A86	40fr + 1fr multi	.60
		Nos. B77-B81 (5)	2.02

IYC Type of 1979

1979, July 19   Photo.   Perf. 14

B82		Sheet of 4	1.25	1.00
a.		A88 10fr + 2fr like #557	.15	.15
b.		A88 20fr + 2fr like #558	.24	.15
c.		A88 27fr + 2fr like #559	.28	.20
d.		A88 50fr + 2fr like #560	.55	.32

Christmas Type of 1979

1979, Dec. 10   Photo.   Perf. 13½

B83	A89	20fr + 1fr like #561	.32
B84	A89	27fr + 1fr like #562	.42
B85	A89	31fr + 1fr like #563	.48
B86	A89	50fr + 1fr like #564	.80
		Nos. B83-B86 (4)	2.02

Christmas Type of 1980

1981, Jan. 16   Photo.   Perf. 13½x13

B87	A92	10fr + 1fr like #579	.15
B88	A92	30fr + 1fr like #580	.32
B89	A92	40fr + 1fr like #581	.42
B90	A92	50fr + 1fr like #582	.50
		Nos. B87-B90 (4)	1.39

Christmas Type of 1983

1983, Nov. 2   Litho.   Perf. 14½x13½

B91	A97	10fr + 1fr like #607	.16
B92	A97	25fr + 1fr like #608	.40
B93	A97	30fr + 1fr like #609	.48
B94	A97	50fr + 1fr like #610	.75
		Nos. B91-B94 (4)	1.79

Christmas Type of 1984

1984, Dec. 15   Perf. 13½

B95	A101	10fr + 1fr like #629	.16
B96	A101	25fr + 1fr like #630	.40
B97	A101	30fr + 1fr like #631	.48
B98	A101	50fr + 1fr like #632	.75
		Nos. B95-B98 (4)	1.79

Multi-party Elections, 1st Anniv. SP11   SP12

Designs: 30fr+10fr, Pres. Buyoya handing Baton of Power to Pres. Ndadaye. 110fr+10fr, Pres. Ndadaye giving inauguration speech. 115fr+10fr, Arms, map of Burundi, trees, map of Burundi. 120fr+10fr, Warrior, flag of Burundi, trees, map of Burundi.

1994, Oct. 20   Litho.   Perf. 15

B99	SP11	30fr +10fr multi	.30
B100	SP11	110fr +10fr multi	.90
B101	SP12	115fr +10fr multi	.95
B102	SP12	120fr +10fr multi	1.00
		Nos. B99-B102 (4)	3.15

AIR POST STAMPS

Animal Type of Regular Issue

Animals: 6fr, Zebra. 8fr, Cape buffalo (bubalis). 10fr, Impala, vert. 14fr, Hippopotamus. 15fr, Defassa waterbuck, vert. 20fr, Cheetah. 50fr, Elephant.

Unwmk.

1964, July 2   Litho.   Perf. 14

Size: 42x21mm, 21x42mm

C1	A9	6fr multi	.15	.15
C2	A9	8fr multi	.16	.15
C3	A9	10fr multi	.22	.15
C4	A9	14fr multi	.30	.15
C5	A9	15fr multi	.32	.15

Size: 53x32½mm

C6	A9	20fr multi	.42	.15
C7	A9	50fr multi	1.10	.38
		Nos. C1-C7 (7)	2.67	
		Set value		.85

Bird Type of Regular Issue

Birds: 6fr, Secretary bird. 8fr, African anhinga. 10fr, African peacock. 14fr, Bee eater. 15fr, Yellow-billed stork. 20fr, Saddle-billed stork. 50fr, Abyssinian ground hornbill. 75fr, Martial eagle. 130fr, Lesser flamingo.

1965, June 10   Litho.   Perf. 14

Size: 26x43mm

C8	A14	6fr multi	.15	.15
C9	A14	8fr multi	.15	.15
C10	A14	10fr multi	.20	.15
C11	A14	14fr multi	.25	.15
C12	A14	15fr multi	.30	.15

Size: 33x53mm

C13	A14	20fr multi	.35	.15
C14	A14	50fr multi	.90	.20
C15	A14	75fr multi	1.25	.25
C16	A14	130fr multi	2.25	.38
		Nos. C8-C16 (9)	5.80	
		Set value		1.15

For overprints see Nos. C35A-C35I.

Flower Type of Regular Issue

Flowers: 6fr, Dissotis. 8fr, Crossandra. 10fr, Ansellia. 14fr, Thunbergia. 15fr, Schizoglossum. 20fr, Gazania. 50fr, Protea. 75fr, Hibiscus. 130fr, Markhamia.

1966, Oct. 10   Unwmk.   Perf. 13½

Size: 31x31mm

C17	A17	6fr multi	.15	.15
C18	A17	8fr multi	.15	.15
C19	A17	10fr multi	.18	.15
C20	A17	14fr multi	.22	.15
C21	A17	15fr multi	.22	.15

Size: 39x39mm

C22	A17	20fr multi	.22	.15
C23	A17	50fr multi	.60	.18
C24	A17	75fr multi	.80	.22
C25	A17	130fr multi	1.50	.32
		Nos. C17-C25 (9)	4.04	
		Set value		1.10

For overprints see Nos. C27-C35.

Tapestry Type of Regular Issue
Souvenir Sheet

1966, Nov. 4   Unwmk.   Perf. 13½
C26 A18   Sheet of 7 (14fr)   1.25 .65
See note after No. 158.

Republic
Nos. C17-C25 Overprinted

REPUBLIQUE DU BURUNDI

1967   Litho.   Perf. 13½
Size: 31x31mm
C27 A17   6fr multi   .20 .15
C28 A17   8fr multi   .22 .15
C29 A17   10fr multi   .25 .15
C30 A17   14fr multi   .48 .15
C31 A17   15fr multi   .48 .15
Size: 39x39mm
C32 A17   20fr multi   .70 .18
C33 A17   50fr multi   1.90 .50
C34 A17   75fr multi   3.00 .50
C35 A17   130fr multi   4.00 1.10
    Nos. C27-C35 (9)   11.23 3.03

Nos. C8-C16 Overprinted "REPUBLIQUE
/ DU / BURUNDI" and Horizontal Bar

1967   Litho.   Perf. 14
Size: 26x43mm
C35A A14   6fr multi   .15
C35B A14   8fr multi   .18
C35C A14   10fr multi   .20
C35D A14   14fr multi   .30
C35E A14   15fr multi   .48
Size: 33x53mm
C35F A14   20fr multi   .75
C35G A14   50fr multi   1.90
C35H A14   75fr multi   3.00
C35I A14   130fr multi   3.50
    Nos. C35A-C35I (9)   10.46

African Art Type of Regular Issue
African Art: 10fr, Spirit of Bakutu figurine, Equatorial Africa. 14fr, Pearl throne of Sultan of the Bamum, Cameroun. 17fr, Bronze head of Mother Queen of Benin, Nigeria. 24fr, Statue of 109th Bakouba king, Kata-Mbula, Central Congo. 26fr, Baskets and lances, Burundi.

1967, June 5   Photo.   Perf. 13½
C36 A20   10fr gold & multi   .15 .15
C37 A20   14fr gold & multi   .15 .15
C38 A20   17fr gold & multi   .15 .15
C39 A20   24fr gold & multi   .22 .15
C40 A20   26fr gold & multi   .42 .25
    Nos. C36-C40 (5)   1.09
    Set value   .55

Boy Scout Type of Regular Issue
10fr, Scouts on hiking trip. 14fr, Cooking at campfire. 17fr, Lord Baden-Powell. 24fr, Boy Scout & Cub Scout giving Scout sign. 26fr, First aid.

1967, Aug. 9   Perf. 13½
C41 A21   10fr gold & multi   .15 .15
C42 A21   14fr gold & multi   .22 .15
C43 A21   17fr gold & multi   .28 .15
C44 A21   24fr gold & multi   .42 .18
C45 A21   26fr gold & multi   .70 .18
    Nos. C41-C45 (5)   1.77
    Set value   .66

A souvenir sheet of 2 contains one each of Nos. C44-C45 and 2 labels in the designs of Nos. 208-209 with commemorative inscriptions was issued Jan. 8, 1968. Size: 100x100mm

Fish Type of Regular Issue
Designs: Various Tropical Fish

1967, Sept. 8   Photo.   Perf. 13½
Size: 50x23mm
C46 A19   6fr multi   .15 .15
C47 A19   8fr multi   .16 .15
C48 A19   10fr multi   .18 .15
C49 A19   14fr multi   .25 .15
C50 A19   15fr multi   .25 .15
Size: 58x27mm
C51 A19   20fr multi   .32 .15
C52 A19   50fr multi   .80 .15
C53 A19   75fr multi   1.25 .16
C54 A19   130fr multi   2.00 .26
    Nos. C46-C54 (9)   5.36
    Set value   .80

Boeing 707 of Air Congo and ITY
Emblem — AP1

Designs: 14fr, Boeing 727 of Sabena over lake. 17fr, Vickers VC10 of East African Airways over lake. 26fr, Boeing 727 of Sabena over airport.

1967, Nov. 3   Photo.   Perf. 13
C55 AP1   10fr blk, yel brn & sil   .15 .15
C56 AP1   14fr blk, org & sil   .20 .15
C57 AP1   17fr blk, brt bl & sil   .25 .15
C58 AP1   26fr blk, brt rose lil & sil .42 .15
    Nos. C55-C58 (4)   1.02
    Set value   .38

Opening of the jet airport at Bujumbura and for International Tourist Year, 1967.

Paintings Type of Regular Issue
Paintings: 17fr, Woman with Cat, by Renoir. 24fr, The Jewish Bride, by Rembrandt, horiz. 26fr, Pope Innocent X, by Velazquez.

1968, Mar. 29   Photo.   Perf. 13½
C59 A26   17fr multi   .35 .15
C60 A26   24fr multi   .45 .18
C61 A26   26fr multi   .55 .20
    Nos. C59-C61 (3)   1.35 .53
Issued in sheets of 6.

Space Type of Regular Issue
Designs: 14fr, Moon Probe. 18fr, Russian astronaut walking in space. 25fr, Weather satellite. 40fr, American astronaut walking in space.

1968, May 15   Photo.   Perf. 13½
Size: 41x41mm
C62 A27   14fr sil & multi   .25 .15
C63 A27   18fr sil & multi   .30 .15
C64 A27   25fr sil & multi   .45 .15
C65 A27   40fr sil & multi   .70 .18
    Nos. C62-C65 (4)   1.70
    Set value   .42

Butterfly Type of Regular Issue
Butterflies: 6fr, Teracolus annae. 8fr, Graphium ridleyanus. 10fr, Cymothoe. 14fr, Charaxes eupale. 15fr, Papilio bromius. 20fr, Papilio zenobia. 50fr, Salamis aethiops. 75fr, Danais chrysippus. 130fr, Salamis temora.

1968, Sept. 9   Photo.   Perf. 13½
Size: 38x42mm
C66 A28   6fr gold & multi   .15 .15
C67 A28   8fr gold & multi   .15 .15
C68 A28   10fr gold & multi   .18 .15
C69 A28   14fr gold & multi   .20 .15
C70 A28   15fr gold & multi   .20 .15
Size: 44x49mm
C71 A28   20fr gold & multi   .30 .15
C72 A28   50fr gold & multi   .70 .15
C73 A28   75fr gold & multi 1.25 .15
C74 A28   130fr gold & multi 2.00 .20
    Nos. C66-C74 (9)   5.13
    Set value   .72

Painting Type of Regular Issue
Paintings: 17fr, The Letter, by Jean H. Fragonard. 26fr, Young Woman Reading Letter, by Jan Vermeer. 40fr, Lady Folding Letter, by Elisabeth Vigée-Lebrun. 50fr, Mademoiselle Lavergne, by Jean Etienne Liotard.

1968, Sept. 30   Photo.   Perf. 13½
C84 A29   17fr multi   .22 .15
C85 A29   26fr multi   .42 .15
C86 A29   40fr multi   .60 .15
C87 A29   50fr multi   .70 .18
    Nos. C84-C87 (4)   1.94
    Set value   .48

Olympic Games Type of 1968
1968, Oct. 24
C88 A30   10fr Shot put   .15 .15
C89 A30   17fr Running   .22 .15
C90 A30   26fr Hammer throw .38 .15
C91 A30   50fr Hurdling   .70 .20
C92 A30   75fr Broad jump 1.10 .30
    Nos. C88-C92 (5)   2.55
    Set value   .70

Christmas Type of 1968
Paintings: 10fr, Virgin and Child, by Correggio. 14fr, Nativity, by Federigo Barocci. 17fr, Holy Family, by El Greco. 26fr, Adoration of the Magi, by Maino.

1968, Nov. 26   Photo.   Perf. 13½
C93 A31   10fr multi   .15 .15
C94 A31   14fr multi   .22 .15
C95 A31   17fr multi   .28 .15
C96 A31   26fr multi   .40 .15
    a. Souv. sheet of 4, #C93-C96   1.10
    Nos. C93-C96 (4)   1.05
    Set value   .45

For overprints see Nos. C100-C103.

Human Rights
Flame, Hand and
Globe — AP2

1969, Jan. 22
C97 AP2   10fr multi   .15 .15
C98 AP2   14fr multi   .22 .15
C99 AP2   26fr lil & multi .40 .15
    Nos. C97-C99 (3)   .77
    Set value   .22

International Human Rights Year, 1968.

Nos. C93-C96 Overprinted in
Silver

VOL DE NOEL
APOLLO 8

1969, Feb. 17   Photo.   Perf. 13½
C100 A31   10fr multi   .20 .15
C101 A31   14fr multi   .28 .15
C102 A31   17fr multi   .35 .15
C103 A31   26fr multi   .50 .22
    Nos. C100-C103 (4)   1.33 .67

Man's 1st flight around the moon by the US spacecraft Apollo 8, Dec. 21-27, 1968.

Moon Landing Type of 1969
Designs: 26fr, Neil A. Armstrong leaving landing module. 40fr, Astronaut on moon. 50fr, Splashdown in the Pacific.

1969, Nov. 6   Photo.   Perf. 13½
C104 A38   26fr gold & multi   .50 .25
C105 A38   40fr gold & multi   .75 .38
C106 A38   50fr gold & multi   .90 .42
    Nos. C104-C106 (3)   2.15 1.05

Christmas Type of 1969
Paintings: 17fr, Madonna and Child, by Benvenuto da Garofalo. 26fr, Madonna and Child, by Jacopo Negretti. 50fr, Madonna and Child, by Il Giorgione. All horizontal.

1969, Dec. 2   Photo.
C107 A39   17fr gold & multi   .38 .15
C108 A39   26fr gold & multi   .50 .15
C109 A39   50fr gold & multi   .90 .28
    a. Souv. sheet of 3, #C107-C109   1.90 1.50
    Nos. C107-C109 (3)   1.78
    Set value   .48

Insect Type of Regular Issue
Designs: Various Beetles and Weevils.

1970   Perf. 13½
Size: 46x32mm
C110 A40   6fr gold & multi   .15 .15
C111 A40   8fr gold & multi   .15 .15
C112 A40   10fr gold & multi   .18 .15
C113 A40   14fr gold & multi   .25 .15
C114 A40   15fr gold & multi   .30 .15
Size: 52x36mm
C115 A40   20fr gold & multi 1.00 .15
C116 A40   50fr gold & multi 2.00 .25
C117 A40   75fr gold & multi 3.00 .25
C118 A40   130fr gold & multi 3.75 .40
    Nos. C110-C118 (9)   10.78
    Set value   1.20
Issued: #C110-C115, 1/20; $C116-C118, 2/27.

Easter Type of 1970
Stations of the Cross, by Juan de Aranoa y Carredano: 8fr, Jesus meets the women of Jerusalem. 10fr, Jesus falls a third time. 14fr, Jesus stripped. 15fr, Jesus nailed to the cross. 18fr, Jesus dies on the cross. 20fr, Descent from the cross. 50fr, Jesus in the tomb.

1970, Mar. 16   Photo.   Perf. 13½
C119 A41   8fr gold & multi   .15 .15
C120 A41   10fr gold & multi   .15 .15
C121 A41   14fr gold & multi   .22 .15
C122 A41   15fr gold & multi   .25 .15
C123 A41   18fr gold & multi   .28 .15
C124 A41   20fr gold & multi   .30 .15
C125 A41   50fr gold & multi   .70 .30
    a. Souv. sheet of 7, #C119-C125 + label   2.25 1.75
    Nos. C119-C125 (7)   2.05
    Set value   .84

EXPO '70 Type of Regular Issue
Souvenir Sheet
Designs: 40fr, Tower of the Sun, vert. 50fr, Flags of participating nations, vert.

1970, May 5   Photo.   Perf. 13½
C126   Sheet of 2   1.40 1.40
    a. A42 40fr multi   .50 .50
    b. A42 50fr multi   .60 .60

Rhinoceros Type of Regular Issue
Designs, FAUNA: Camel, dromedary, okapi, rhinoceros, addax, Burundi cow (2 stamps of each animal in 2 different poses). MAP OF THE NILE: Delta and pyramids, dhow, cataract, Blue Nile and crowned crane, Victoria Nile and secretary bird, Lake Victoria and source of Nile on Mt. Gikizi.

1970, July 8   Photo.   Perf. 13½
C127   Sheet of 18   5.25
    a. A43 14fr any single   .28 .15

Issued in sheets of 18 (3x6) stamps of different designs, to publicize the southernmost source of the Nile on Mt. Gikizi in Burundi.

UN Emblem
and
Headquarters,
NYC — AP3

25th Anniv. of the UN (UN Emblem and): 11fr, Security Council and mural by Per Krohg. 26fr, Pope Paul VI and U Thant. 40fr, Flags in front of UN Headquarters, NYC.

1970, Oct. 23   Photo.   Perf. 13½
C128 AP3   7fr gold & multi   .15 .15
C129 AP3   11fr gold & multi   .18 .15
C130 AP3   26fr gold & multi   .40 .15
C131 AP3   40fr gold & multi   .60 .15
    a. Souvenir sheet of 2   1.10 .90
    Nos. C128-C131 (4)   1.33
    Set value   .30

No. C131a contains 2 stamps similar to Nos. C130-C131 but without "Poste Aerienne". Exists imperf.

Bird Type of Regular Issue
8fr, 14fr, 30fr, vert.; 10fr, 20fr, 50fr, horiz.

1970   Photo.   Perf. 13½
Stamp size: 52x44mm
C132 A44   Block of 4   1.25 .15
    a. 8fr Northern shrike   .30 .15
    b. 8fr European starling   .30 .15
    c. 8fr Yellow wagtail   .30 .15
    d. 8fr Bank swallow   .30 .15
C133 A44   Block of 4   1.50 .18
    a. 10fr Winter wren   .35 .15
    b. 10fr Firecrest   .35 .15
    c. 10fr Skylark   .35 .15
    d. 10fr Crested lark   .35 .15
C134 A44   Block of 4   1.90 .25
    a. 14fr Woodchat shrike   .45 .15
    b. 14fr Common rock thrush .45 .15
    c. 14fr Black redstart   .45 .15
    d. 14fr Ring ouzel   .45 .15
C135 A44   Block of 4   3.00 .32
    a. 20fr European redstart .70 .15
    b. 20fr Hedge sparrow   .70 .15
    c. 20fr Gray wagtail   .70 .15
    d. 20fr Meadow pipit   .70 .15
C136 A44   Block of 4   4.25 .55
    a. 30fr Eurasian hoopoe   1.00 .15
    b. 30fr Pied flycatcher   1.00 .15
    c. 30fr Great reed warbler 1.00 .15
    d. 30fr Eurasian kingfisher 1.00 .15
C137 A44   Block of 4   7.00 .90
    a. 50fr House martin   1.75 .20
    b. 50fr Sedge warbler   1.75 .20
    c. 50fr Fieldfare   1.75 .20
    d. 50fr European Golden oriole 1.75 .20
    Nos. C132-C137 (6)   18.90 2.35

Queen
Fabiola and
King
Baudouin
of Belgium
AP4

Designs: 20fr, Pres. Michel Micombero and King Baudouin. 40fr, Pres. Micombero and coats of arms of Burundi and Belgium.

1970, Nov. 28   Photo.   Perf. 13½
C140 AP4	6fr multicolored	.15	.15
C141 AP4	20fr multicolored	.45	.15
C142 AP4	40fr multicolored	.90	.30
a.	Souvenir sheet of 3	1.50	1.50
	Nos. C140-C142 (3)	1.50	
	Set value		.50

Visit of the King and Queen of Belgium. No. C142a contains 3 stamps similar to Nos. C140-C142, but without "Poste Aerienne." No. C142a exists imperf.

Easter Type of Regular Issue

Paintings of the Resurrection: 14fr, by Louis Borrassá. 17fr, Piero della Francesca. 26fr, Michel Wohlgemuth.

1971, Apr. 2   Photo.   Perf. 13½
C143 A49	14fr gold & multi	.20	.15
C144 A49	17fr gold & multi	.22	.15
C145 A49	26fr gold & multi	.30	.15
a.	Souv. sheet of 3, #C143-C145	1.00	.75
	Nos. C143-C145 (3)	.72	
	Set value		.29

Easter 1971. No. C145a sheet exists imperf.

Animal Type of Regular Issue

1971   Photo.   Perf. 13½
Size: 44x44mm
C146	Strip of 4	1.00	
a. A48	10fr Lion	.22	.15
b. A48	10fr Cape buffalo	.22	.15
c. A48	10fr Hippopotamus	.22	.15
d. A48	10fr Giraffe	.22	.15
C147	Strip of 4	1.50	.22
a. A48	14fr Hartebeest	.35	.15
b. A48	14fr Black rhinoceros	.35	.15
c. A48	14fr Zebra	.35	.15
d. A48	14fr Leopard	.35	.15
C148	Strip of 4	1.75	.25
a. A48	17fr Grant's gazelles	.40	.15
b. A48	17fr Cheetah	.40	.15
c. A48	17fr African white-backed vultures	.40	.15
d. A48	17fr Johnston's okapi	.40	.15
C149	Strip of 4	2.25	.32
a. A48	24fr Chimpanzee	.50	.15
b. A48	24fr Elephant	.50	.15
c. A48	24fr Spotted Hyenas	.50	.15
d. A48	24fr Beisa	.50	.15
C150	Strip of 4	2.50	.40
a. A48	26fr Gorilla	.55	.15
b. A48	26fr Gnu	.55	.15
c. A48	26fr Warthog	.50	.15
d. A48	26fr Cape hunting dog	.55	.15
C151	Strip of 4	3.00	.45
a. A48	31fr Sable antelope	.70	.15
b. A48	31fr Caracal lynx	.70	.15
c. A48	31fr Ostriches	.70	.15
d. A48	31fr Bongo	.70	.15
	Nos. C146-C151 (6)	12.00	1.79

For overprint and surcharges see Nos. C152, CB15-C18.

No. C146 Overprinted in Gold and Black

LUTTE CONTRE LE RACISME ET LA DISCRIMINATION RACIALE

1971, July 20   Photo.   Perf. 13½
C152	Strip of 4	.60	.15
a. A48	10fr Lion	.15	.15
b. A48	10fr Cape buffalo	.15	.15
c. A48	10fr Hippopotamus	.15	.15
d. A48	10fr Giraffe	.15	.15

Intl. Year Against Racial Discrimination.

Christmas Type of Regular Issue

Paintings of the Madonna and Child by: 14fr, Cima de Conegliano. 17fr, Fra Filippo Lippi. 31fr, Leonardo da Vinci.

1971, Nov. 2   Photo.
C153 A51	14fr red & multi	.28	.15
C154 A51	17fr red & multi	.32	.15
C155 A51	31fr red & multi	.50	.20
a.	Souv. sheet of 3, #C153-C155	1.10	1.10
	Nos. C153-C155 (3)	1.10	.50

Christmas 1971. No. C155a exists imperf. For surcharges see Nos. CB19-CB21.

Spacecraft Type of Regular Issue
Souvenir Sheet

1972, Jan. 15   Photo.   Perf. 13½
C156	Sheet of 6	1.50	1.00
a. A52	6fr Lunar Orbiter	.15	.15
b. A52	11fr Vostok	.15	.15
c. A52	14fr Luna 1	.18	.15
d. A52	26fr Apollo 11 astronaut on moon	.22	.15
e. A52	26fr Soyuz 11	.35	.18
f. A52	40fr Lunar rover (Apollo 15)	.50	.25

Sapporo '72 Type of Regular Issue
Souvenir Sheet

Designs (Sapporo '72 Emblem and): 26fr, Snow scooter. 31fr, Downhill skiing. 50fr, Bobsledding.

1972, Feb. 3
C157	Sheet of 3	1.50	1.25
a. A53	26fr silver & multi	.35	.25
b. A53	31fr silver & multi	.40	.30
c. A53	50fr silver & multi	.65	.40

No. C157 contains 3 stamps, arranged vertically.

Olympic Games Type of 1972

1972, July 24   Photo.   Perf. 13½
C158 A55	24fr Weight lifting	.35	.15
C159 A55	26fr Hurdles	.40	.15
C160 A55	31fr Discus	.50	.15
C161 A55	40fr Soccer	.60	.20
	Nos. C158-C161 (4)	1.85	.65

Independence Type of 1972

Designs: 15fr, Prince Rwagasore, Pres. Micombero, Burundi flag, drummers. 18fr, Rwagasore, Micombero, flag, map of Africa, globe. 27fr, Micombero, flag, globe.

1972, Aug. 24   Photo.   Perf. 13½
C162 A56	15fr gold & multi	.25	.15
C163 A56	18fr gold & multi	.30	.15
C164 A56	27fr gold & multi	.45	.15
a.	Souv. sheet of 3, #C162-C164	1.10	1.10
	Nos. C162-C164 (3)	1.00	
	Set value		.34

Christmas Type of 1972

Paintings of the Madonna and Child by: 18fr, Sebastiano Mainardi. 27fr, Hans Memling. 40fr, Lorenzo Lotto.

1972, Nov. 2   Photo.   Perf. 13½
C165 A57	18fr dk car & multi	.28	.15
C166 A57	27fr dk car & multi	.40	.15
C167 A57	40fr dk car & multi	.60	.18
a.	Souv. sheet of 3, #C165-C167	1.40	1.40
	Nos. C165-C167 (3)	1.28	
	Set value		.39

For surcharges see Nos. CB26-CB28.

Orchid Type of Regular Issue

1973, Jan. 18   Photo.   Perf. 13½
Size: 38x38mm
C168 A58	13fr Thelymitra pauciflora	.22	.15
C169 A58	14fr Miltassia	.22	.15
C170 A58	15fr Miltonia	.25	.15
C171 A58	18fr Platycoryne crocea	.28	.15
C172 A58	26fr Cattleya trinaei	.30	.15
C173 A58	27fr Eulophia cucullata	.42	.15
C174 A58	36fr Cymbidium hamsey	.55	.15
	Nos. C168-C174 (7)	2.24	
	Set value		.59

African Exploration Type of 1973

Designs: 15fr, Livingstone writing his diary. 18fr, "Dr. Livingstone, I presume." 27fr, Livingstone and Stanley discussing expedition.

1973, Mar. 19   Photo.   Perf. 13½
C175 A59	15fr gold & multi	.22	.15
C176 A59	18fr gold & multi	.28	.15
C177 A59	27fr gold & multi	.40	.15
a.	Souv. sheet of 3	1.10	1.10
	Nos. C175-C177 (3)	.90	
	Set value		.31

#C177a contains 3 stamps similar to #C175-C177, but without "Poste Aerienne."

Easter Type of 1973

Paintings: 15fr, Christ at the Pillar, by Guido Reni. 18fr, Crucifixion, by Mathias Grunewald. 27fr, Descent from the Cross, by Caravaggio.

1973, Apr. 10
C178 A60	15fr gold & multi	.28	.15
C179 A60	18fr gold & multi	.35	.15
C180 A60	27fr gold & multi	.50	.15
a.	Souv. sheet of 3, #C178-C180	1.25	1.25
	Nos. C178-C180 (3)	1.13	
	Set value		.30

INTERPOL Type of Regular Issue

Designs: 27fr, INTERPOL emblem and flag. 40fr, INTERPOL flag and emblem.

1973, May 19   Photo.   Perf. 13½
C181 A61	27fr gold & multi	.40	.16
C182 A61	40fr gold & multi	.48	.20

Copernicus Type of Regular Issue

Designs: 15fr, Copernicus (C183a), Earth, Pluto, and Jupiter. 18fr, Copernicus (No. C184a), Venus, Saturn, Mars. 27fr, Copernicus (No. C185a), Uranus, Neptune, Mercury. 36fr, Earth and various spacecrafts.

a, UL. b, UR. c, LL. d, LR.

1973, July 27   Photo.   Perf. 13½
C183 A62	15fr Block of 4, #a.-d.	1.40	.30
C184 A62	18fr Block of 4, #a.-d.	1.65	.35
C185 A62	27fr Block of 4, #a.-d.	2.00	.50
C186 A62	36fr Block of 4, #a.-d.	2.75	.70
e.	Souv. sheet of 4, #C183-C186	7.00	7.00
	Nos. C183-C186 (4)	7.80	1.85

Flower-Butterfly Type of 1973

Designs: Each block of 4 contains 2 flower and 2 butterfly designs. The 10fr, 14fr, 24fr and 31fr have flower designs listed as "a" and "d" numbers, butterflies as "b" and "c" numbers; the arrangement is reversed for the 17fr and 26fr.

1973, Sept. 28   Photo.   Perf. 13
Stamp Size: 35x45mm
C187 A63	Block of 4	2.00	.20
a.	10fr Protea cynaroides	.45	.15
b.	10fr Precis octavia	.45	.15
c.	10fr Epiphora bauhiniae	.45	.15
d.	10fr Gazania longiscapa	.45	.15
C188 A63	Block of 4	2.50	.28
a.	14fr Kniphofia	.60	.15
b.	14fr Cymothoe coccinata	.60	.15
c.	14fr Nudaurelia zambesina	.60	.15
d.	14fr Freesia refracta	.60	.15
C189 A63	Block of 4	3.00	.32
a.	17fr Calotis eupompe	.70	.15
b.	17fr Narcissus	.70	.15
c.	17fr Cineraria hybrida	.70	.15
d.	17fr Cyrestis camillus	.70	.15
C190 A63	Block of 4	3.50	.50
a.	24fr Iris tingitana	.85	.15
b.	24fr Papilio demodocus	.85	.15
c.	24fr Catopsilia avelaneda	.85	.15
d.	24fr Nerine sarniensis	.85	.15
C191 A63	Block of 4	4.00	.55
a.	26fr Hypolimnas dexithea	1.00	.15
b.	26fr Zantedeschia tropicalis	1.00	.15
c.	26fr Sandersonia aurantiaca	1.00	.15
d.	26fr Drurya antimachus	1.00	.15
C192 A63	Block of 4	4.50	.65
a.	31fr Nymphaea capensis	1.10	.15
b.	31fr Pandoriana pandora	1.10	.15
c.	31fr Precis orythia	1.10	.15
d.	31fr Pelargonium domestica	1.10	.15
	Nos. C187-C192 (6)	19.50	2.50

Christmas Type of 1973

Virgin and Child by: 18fr, Raphael. 27fr, Pietro Perugino. 40fr, Titian.

1973, Nov. 19
C193 A64	18fr gold & multi	.28	.15
C194 A64	27fr gold & multi	.40	.15
C195 A64	40fr gold & multi	.60	.16
a.	Souv. sheet of 3, #C193-C195	1.40	1.40
	Nos. C193-C195 (3)	1.28	
	Set value		.36

For surcharges see Nos. CB239-CB31.

Soccer Type of Regular Issue

Designs: Various soccer scenes and cup.

1974, July 4   Photo.   Perf. 13
C196 A67	20fr gold & multi	.30	
C197 A67	26fr gold & multi	.40	
C198 A67	40fr gold & multi	.60	
	Nos. C196-C198 (3)	1.30	

For souvenir sheet see No. 459a.

UPU Type of 1974

Designs: No. C199, Flags over UPU Headquarters, Bern. No. C200, G.P.O., Usumbura. No. C201, Mailmen ("26F" in UR). No. C202, Mailmen ("26F" in UL). No. C203, UPU emblem. No. C204, Means of transportation. No. C205, Pigeon over globe showing Burundi. No. C206, Swiss flag, pigeon over map showing Bern.

1974, July 23
C199 A68	24fr gold & multi	.65	
C200 A68	24fr gold & multi	.65	
C201 A68	26fr gold & multi	.75	
C202 A68	26fr gold & multi	.75	
C203 A68	31fr gold & multi	1.00	
C204 A68	31fr gold & multi	1.00	
C205 A68	40fr gold & multi	1.25	
C206 A68	40fr gold & multi	1.25	
a.	Souv. sheet of 8, #C199-C206	7.50	
	Nos. C199-C206 (8)	7.30	

Stamps of same denomination printed setenant (continuous design) in sheets of 40.

Fish Type of 1974

1974, Sept. 9   Photo.   Perf. 13
Size: 35x35mm
C207 A66	Block of 4	1.00	.15
a.	10fr Haplochromis multicolor	.25	.15
b.	10fr Pantodon buchholzi	.25	.15
c.	10fr Tropheus duboisi	.25	.15
d.	10fr Distichodus sexfasciatus	.25	.15
C208 A66	Block of 4	1.25	.20
a.	14fr Pelmatochromis kribensis	.30	.15
b.	14fr Nannaethiops tritaenuatus	.30	.15
c.	14fr Polycentropsis abbreviata	.30	.15
d.	14fr Hemichromis bimaculatus	.30	.15
C209 A66	Block of 4	1.65	.20
a.	17fr Ctenopoma acutirostre	.38	.15
b.	17fr Synodontis angelicus	.38	.15
c.	17fr Tilapia melanopleura	.38	.15
d.	17fr Aphyosemion bivittatum	.38	.15
C210 A66	Block of 4	1.90	.30
a.	24fr Monodactylus argenteus	.45	.15
b.	24fr Zanclus canescens	.45	.15
c.	24fr Pygoplites diacanthus	.45	.15
d.	24fr Cephalopholis argus	.45	.15
C211 A66	Block of 4	2.00	.35
a.	26fr Priacanthus arenatus	.50	.15
b.	26fr Pomacanthus arcutus	.50	.15
c.	26fr Scarus guacamala	.50	.15
d.	26fr Zeus faber	.50	.15
C212 A66	Block of 4	2.50	.40
a.	31fr Lactophrys quadricornis	.60	.15
b.	31fr Balistes vetula	.60	.15
c.	31fr Acanthurus bahianus	.60	.15
d.	31fr Holocanthus ciliaris	.60	.15
	Nos. C207-C212 (6)	10.30	1.60

Christmas Type of 1974

Paintings of the Virgin and Child: 18fr, by Hans Memling. 27fr, by Filippino Lippi. 40fr, by Lorenzo di Gredi.

1974, Nov. 7   Photo.   Perf. 13
C213 A70	18fr gold & multi	.28	.22
C214 A70	27fr gold & multi	.40	.32
C215 A70	40fr gold & multi	.60	.48
a.	Souv. sheet of 3, #C213-C215	1.50	1.50
	Nos. C213-C215 (3)	1.28	1.02

Christmas 1974. Sheets of 20 stamps and one label. No. C215a exists imperf.

Apollo-Soyuz Type of 1975

1975, July 10   Photo.   Perf. 13
C216 A71	Block of 4	.90	
a.	27fr A.A. Leonov, V.N. Kubasov, Soviet flag	.22	
b.	27fr Soyuz and Soviet flag	.22	
c.	27fr Apollo and American flag	.22	
d.	27fr Slayton, Brand, Stafford, American flag	.22	
C217 A71	Block of 4	1.40	
a.	40fr Apollo-Soyuz link-up	.32	
b.	40fr Apollo, blast-off	.32	
c.	40fr Soyuz, blast-off	.32	
d.	40fr Kubasov, Leonov, Slayton, Brand, Stafford	.32	

Nos. C216-C217 are printed in sheets of 32 containing 8 blocks of 4.

Animal Type of 1975

1975, Sept. 17   Photo.   Perf. 13½
C218	Strip of 4	.90	
a. A72	10fr Addax	.22	
b. A72	10fr Roan antelope	.22	
c. A72	10fr Nyala	.22	
d. A72	10fr White rhinoceros	.22	
C219	Strip of 4	1.25	
a. A72	14fr Mandrill	.30	
b. A72	14fr Eland	.30	
c. A72	14fr Salt's dik-dik	.30	
d. A72	14fr Thomson's gazelles	.30	
C220	Strip of 4	1.50	
a. A72	17fr African small-clawed otter	.35	
b. A72	17fr Reed buck	.35	
c. A72	17fr Indian civet	.35	
d. A72	17fr Cape buffalo	.35	
C221	Strip of 4	2.00	
a. A72	24fr White-tailed gnu	.50	
b. A72	24fr African wild asses	.50	
c. A72	24fr Black-and-white colobus monkey	.50	
d. A72	24fr Gerenuk	.50	
C222	Strip of 4	2.25	
a. A72	26fr Dama gazelle	.55	
b. A72	26fr Black-backed jackal	.55	
c. A72	26fr Sitatungas	.55	
d. A72	26fr Zebra antelope	.55	
C223	Strip of 4	2.75	
a. A72	31fr Fennec	.65	
b. A72	31fr Lesser kudus	.65	
c. A72	31fr Blesbok	.65	
d. A72	31fr Serval	.65	
	Nos. C218-C223 (6)	10.65	

Nos. C218-C219 Overprinted in Black and Silver with IWY Emblem and: "ANNEE INTERNATIONALE / DE LA FEMME"

1975, Nov. 19   Photo.   Perf. 13½
C224	Strip of 4	.60	.15
a. A72	10fr Addax	.15	.15
b. A72	10fr Roan antelope	.15	.15
c. A72	10fr Nyala	.15	.15
d. A72	10fr White rhinoceros	.15	.15

C225	Strip of 4	.80	.20
a.	A72 14fr Mandrill	.20	.15
b.	A72 14fr Oryx	.20	.15
c.	A72 14fr Dik-dik	.20	.15
d.	A72 14fr Thomson's gazelles	.20	.15

International Women's Year 1975.

Nos. C222-C223 Overprinted in Black and Silver with UN Emblem and:"30ème ANNIVERSAIRE DES/ NATIONS UNIES"

1975, Nov. 19

C226	Strip of 4	1.65	.30
a.	A72 26fr Dama gazelle	.38	.15
b.	A72 26fr Wild dog	.38	.15
c.	A72 26fr Sitatungas	.38	.15
d.	A72 26fr Striped duiker	.38	.15
C227	Strip of 4	1.90	.32
a.	A72 31fr Fennec	.45	.15
b.	A72 31fr Lesser kudus	.45	.15
c.	A72 31fr Blesbok	.45	.15
d.	A72 31fr Serval	.45	.15

United Nations, 30th anniversary.

Michelangelo Type of 1975

Designs: Paintings from Sistine Chapel.

1975, Dec. 3   Photo.   Perf. 13

C228	A73 18fr Zachariah	.35
C229	A73 31fr Joel	.35
C230	A73 31fr Erythrean Sybil	.65
C231	A73 31fr Prophet Ezekiel	.65
C232	A73 40fr Persian Sybil	.80
C233	A73 40fr Prophet Jeremiah	.80
a.	Souv. sheet of 6, #C228-C233	3.75
	Nos. C228-C233 (6)	3.60

Stamps of same denominations printed se-tenant in sheets of 18 stamps and 2 labels.
For surcharges see Nos. CB35-CB40.

Olympic Games Type, 1976

Designs (Olympic Games Emblem and): 18fr, Ski jump. 36fr, Slalom. 50fr, Ice hockey.

1976, Jan. 23   Photo.   Perf. 14x13½

C234	A74 18fr ol brn & multi	.32
C235	A74 36fr grn & multi	.70
C236	A74 50fr pur & multi	.90
a.	Souvenir sheet of 4	2.00
	Nos. C234-C236 (3)	1.92

No. C236a contains 4 stamps similar to Nos. 491-494, perf. 13½, inscribed "POSTE AERIENNE."

Hurdles — AP5

Montreal Games Emblem and: #C238, C241, C243b, High jump. #C239, C242, C243a, Athlete on rings. #C240, C243c, Hurdles.

1976, May 3   Litho.   Perf. 13½

C237	AP5 27fr grn & multi	.42
C238	AP5 27fr dk bl & multi	.42
C239	AP5 31fr ocher & multi	.55
C240	AP5 31fr grn & multi	.55
C241	AP5 50fr dk bl & multi	.90
C242	AP5 50fr ocher & multi	.90
	Nos. C237-C242 (6)	3.74

Souvenir Sheet

C243	Sheet of 3	1.75
a.	AP5 27fr ocher & multi	.38
b.	AP5 31fr dark blue & multi	.45
c.	AP5 50fr green & multi	.75

21st Olympic Games, Montreal, Canada, July 17-Aug. 1. Stamps of same denomination printed se-tenant in sheets of 20.

Battle of Bunker Hill, by John Trumbull
AP6   AP7

Paintings: 26fr, Franklin, Jefferson and John Adams. 36fr, Declaration of Independence, by John Trumbull.

1976, July 16   Photo.   Perf. 13

C244	AP6 18fr gold & multi	.35
C245	AP7 18fr gold & multi	.35
C246	AP6 26fr gold & multi	.45

C247	AP7 26fr gold & multi	.45
C248	AP6 36fr gold & multi	.75
C249	AP7 36fr gold & multi	.75
a.	Souv. sheet of 6, #C244-C249	3.25
	Nos. C244-C249 (6)	3.10

American Bicentennial. Stamps of same denomination printed se-tenant in sheets of 50.

Christmas Type of 1976

Paintings: 18fr, Virgin and Child with St. Anne, by Leonardo da Vinci. 31fr, Holy Family with Lamb, by Raphael. 40fr, Madonna of the Basket, by Correggio.

1976, Oct. 18   Photo.   Perf. 13½

C250	A76 18fr gold & multi	.25
C251	A76 31fr gold & multi	.45
C252	A76 40fr gold & multi	.60
a.	Souv. sheet of 3, #C250-C252	1.40
	Nos. C250-C252 (3)	1.30

Christmas 1976. Sheets of 20 stamps and descriptive label.
For surcharges see Nos. CB41-CB43.

A.G. Bell Type of 1977

Designs: 10fr, A.G. Bell and first telephone. Nos. C253, 17fr, A.G. Bell speaking into microphone. Nos. C254, C257e, Satellites around globe and videophone. No. C255, Switchboard operator, c.1910, and wall telephone. Nos. C256, 26fr, Intelsat satellite, modern and old telephones. No. C257c, Intelsat and radar.

1977, May 17   Photo.   Perf. 13

C253	A78 10fr multi	.15
C254	A79 18fr multi	.15
C255	A78 36fr multi	.25
C256	A79 36fr multi	.25
C257	Sheet of 5	1.75	1.00
a.	A78 10fr multi	.15	.15
b.	A78 17fr multi	.25	.15
c.	A79 18fr multi	.25	.15
d.	A79 26fr multi	.40	.22
e.	A79 36fr multi	.52	.25

No. C257 contains 3 postage (10fr, 17fr, 26fr) and 2 air post stamps (18fr, 36fr).

Animal Type of 1977

1977, Aug. 22   Photo.   Perf. 14x14½

C258	Strip of 4	.80
a.	A80 9fr Buffon's kob	.20
b.	A80 9fr Marabous	.20
c.	A80 9fr Brindled gnu	.20
d.	A80 9fr River hog	.20
C259	Strip of 4	1.10
a.	A80 13fr Zebras	.25
b.	A80 13fr Shoebill	.25
c.	A80 13fr Striped hyenas	.25
d.	A80 13fr Chimpanzee	.25
C260	Strip of 4	2.25
a.	A80 30fr Flamingos	.55
b.	A80 30fr Nile Crocodiles	.55
c.	A80 30fr Green mamba	.55
d.	A80 30fr Greater kudus	.55
C261	Strip of 4	2.75
a.	A80 35fr Hyrax	.65
b.	A80 35fr Cobra	.65
c.	A80 35fr Jackals	.65
d.	A80 35fr Verreaux's eagles	.65
C262	Strip of 4	4.25
a.	A80 54fr Honey badger	1.00
b.	A80 54fr Harnessed antelopes	1.00
c.	A80 54fr Secretary bird	1.00
d.	A80 54fr Klipspringer	1.00
C263	Strip of 4	5.00
a.	A80 70fr African big-eared fox	1.25
b.	A80 70fr Elephants	1.25
c.	A80 70fr Vulturine guineafowl	1.25
d.	A80 70fr Impalas	1.25
	Nos. C258-C263 (6)	16.15

UN Type of 1977

Designs (UN Stamps and): 24fr, UN buildings by night. 27fr, UN buildings and view of Manhattan. 35fr, UN buildings by day.

1977, Oct. 10   Photo.   Perf. 13½

C264	A82 Block of 4	1.90
a.	24fr No. 77	.45
b.	24fr No. 78	.45
c.	24fr No. 40	.45
d.	24fr No. 32	.45
C265	A82 Block of 4	2.00
a.	27fr No. 50	.50
b.	27fr No. 21	.50
c.	27fr No. 30	.50
d.	27fr No. 44	.50
C266	A82 Block of 4	3.25
a.	35fr No. C6	.75
b.	35fr No. 105	.75
c.	35fr No. 4	.75
d.	35fr No. 1	.75
e.	Souvenir sheet of 3	1.40
	Nos. C264-C266 (3)	7.15

No. C266e contains 24fr in design of No. C265b, 27fr in design of No. C266a, 35fr in design of No. C264c.

Christmas Type of 1977

Designs: Paintings of the Virgin and Child.

1977, Oct. 31   Photo.   Perf. 14x13

C267	A83 18fr Master of Moulins	.28
C268	A83 31fr Workshop of Lorenzo de Credi	.48

C269	A83 40fr Palma Vecchio	.60	
a.	Souv. sheet of 3, #C267-C269	1.50	
	Nos. C267-C269 (3)	1.36	

Sheets of 24 stamps and descriptive label.
For surcharges see Nos. CB44-CB46.

Christmas 1978 Type of 1979
Souvenir Sheet

1979, Feb.   Photo.   Perf. 14x13½

C270	Sheet of 5	2.00	
a.	A86 13fr like #543	.25	
b.	A86 17fr like #544	.25	
c.	A86 27fr like #545	.40	
d.	A86 31fr like #546	.48	
e.	A86 40fr like #547	.60	

Christmas Type of 1979
Souvenir Sheet

1979, Oct. 12   Perf. 13½

C271	Sheet of 4	2.00	1.25
a.	A89 27fr like #561	.30	.16
b.	A89 27fr like #562	.40	.22
c.	A89 31fr like #563	.48	.28
d.	A89 50fr like #564	.75	.42

Hill Type of 1979
Souvenir Sheet

1979, Nov. 6

C272	Sheet of 5	3.50	1.75
a.	A90 20fr like #565	.40	.16
b.	A90 27fr like #566	.55	.22
c.	A90 31fr like #567	.60	.28
d.	A90 40fr like #568	.80	.35
e.	A90 50fr like #569	1.00	.50

Sir Rowland Hill (1795-1879), originator of penny postage.

Bird Type of 1979

1979   Photo.   Perf. 13½x3

C273	A87 6fr like #548	.15
C274	A87 13fr like #549	.20
C275	A87 18fr like #550	.28
C276	A87 26fr like #551	.38
C277	A87 31fr like #552	.48
C278	A87 36fr like #553	.55
C279	A87 40fr like #554	.60
C280	A87 54fr like #555	.80
C281	A87 70fr like #556	1.00
	Nos. C273-C281 (9)	4.44

Olympic Type of 1980
Souvenir Sheet

1980, Oct. 24   Photo.   Perf. 13½

C282	Sheet of 9	4.25
a.	A91 20fr like #570	.30
b.	A91 20fr like #571	.30
c.	A91 20fr like #572	.30
d.	A91 30fr like #573	.45
e.	A91 30fr like #574	.45
f.	A91 30fr like #575	.45
g.	A91 40fr like #576	.60
h.	A91 40fr like #577	.60
i.	A91 40fr like #578	.60

22nd Summer Olympic Games, Moscow, July 19-Aug. 3.

Christmas Type of 1980
Souvenir Sheet

1980, Dec. 12   Photo.   Perf. 13½x13

C283	Sheet of 4	1.90	1.40
a.	A92 10fr like #579	.15	.15
b.	A92 30fr like #580	.45	.30
c.	A92 40fr like #581	.60	.40
d.	A92 45fr like #582	.65	.45

UPRONA Type of 1980
Souvenir Sheet

1980, Dec. 29   Perf. 14½x13½

C284	Sheet of 3	1.50
a.	A93 10fr like #583	.15
b.	A93 10fr like #584	.60
c.	A93 45fr like #585	.65

Christmas Type of 1983
Souvenir Sheet

1983, Oct. 3   Litho.   Perf. 14½x13½

C285	Sheet of 4	1.75
a.	A97 10fr like #607	.15
b.	A97 25fr like #608	.38
c.	A97 40fr like #609	.45
d.	A97 50fr like #610	.75

UPU Congress Type of 1984
Souvenir Sheet

1984, July 14   Perf. 13x13½

C286	Sheet of 4	2.25
a.	A99 10fr like #621	.15
b.	A99 10fr like #622	.45
c.	A99 35fr like #623	.50
d.	A99 65fr like #624	1.00

Summer Olympics Type of 1984
Souvenir Sheet

1984, Aug. 6   Perf. 13½x13

C287	Sheet of 4	2.25
a.	A100 10fr like #625	.15
b.	A100 30fr like #626	.45
c.	A100 35fr like #627	.50
d.	A100 65fr like #628	1.00

Christmas Type of 1984
Souvenir Sheet

1984, Dec. 15   Perf. 13½

C288	Sheet of 4	1.75
a.	A101 10fr like #629	.15
b.	A101 25fr like #630	.38
c.	A101 30fr like #631	.45
d.	A101 50fr like #632	.75

Flower Type of 1986 with Dull Lilac Border

1986, July 31   Photo.   Perf. 13x13½

C289	A102 70fr like #633	.55
C290	A102 75fr like #634	.60
C291	A102 80fr like #635	.65
C292	A102 85fr like #636	.70
C293	A102 100fr like #637	.80
C294	A102 150fr like #638	1.20
	Nos. C289-C294 (6)	4.50

Animals
AP8

1992, June 2   Litho.   Perf. 14

C298	AP8 100fr M. nemestrina	1.55
C299	AP8 115fr Equus grevyi	1.75
C300	AP8 200fr Long horn cattle	3.10
C301	AP8 220fr Pelecanus onocrotalus	3.40
a.	Souvenir sheet of 4, #C298-C301, perf. 13½	10.00
	Nos. C298-C301 (4)	9.80

AIR POST SEMI-POSTAL STAMPS

Coin Type of Semi-Postal Issue

Designs (Coins of Various Denominations): 3fr+1fr, 11fr+1fr, 20fr+1fr, 50fr+1fr, Coat of Arms, reverse. 5fr+1fr, 14fr+1fr, 30fr+1fr, 100fr+1fr, King Mwambutsa IV, obverse.

Lithographed; Embossed on Gilt Foil
1965, Nov. 15   Imperf.

Diameter: 39mm

CB1	SP4 3fr + 1fr lt & dk vio	.15	.15
CB2	SP4 5fr + 1fr pale grn & red	.15	.15

Diameter: 45mm

CB3	SP4 11fr + 1fr org & lilac	.25	.25
CB4	SP4 14fr + 1fr red & emer	.30	.30

Diameter: 56mm

CB5	SP4 20fr + 1fr ultra & blk	.40	.40
CB6	SP4 30fr + 1fr dp org & mar	.60	.60

Diameter: 67mm

CB7	SP4 50fr + 1fr bl & vio bl	1.00	1.00
CB8	SP4 100fr + 1fr rose & dp cl	2.25	2.25
	Nos. CB1-CB8 (8)	5.10	5.10

Stamps are backed with patterned paper in blue, orange, and pink engine-turned design.

Red Cross Type of Semi-Postal Issue

Designs: 26fr+3fr, Laboratory. 40fr+3fr, Ambulance and thatched huts. 50fr+3fr, Red Cross nurse with patient.

1969, June 26   Photo.   Perf. 13½

CB9	SP7 26fr + 3fr multi	.38	.15
CB10	SP7 40fr + 3fr multi	.55	.15
CB11	SP7 50fr + 3fr multi	.65	.20
	Nos. CB9-CB11 (3)	1.58	.50

Perf. and imperf. souvenir sheets exist containing 3 stamps similar to Nos. CB9-CB11, but without "Poste Aerienne." Size: 90½x97mm

Christmas Type of Semi-Postal Issue

Paintings: 14fr+3fr, Virgin and Child, by Veláz-quez. 26fr+3fr, Holy Family, by Joos van Cleve. 40fr+3fr, Virgin and Child, by Rogier van der Weyden.

1970, Dec. 14   Photo.   Perf. 13½

CB12	SP9 14fr + 3fr multi	.25	.15
CB13	SP9 26fr + 3fr multi	.45	.15
CB14	SP9 40fr + 3fr multi	.65	.20
a.	Souv. sheet of 3, #CB12-CB14	1.50	1.50
	Nos. CB12-CB14 (3)	1.35	.50

No. C147 Surcharged in Gold and Black

+2F
UNESCO

LUTTE CONTRE
L'ANALPHABETISME

1971, Aug. 9   Photo.   Perf. 13¹/₂

CB15	Strip of 4	.80	.20
a.	A48 14fr+2fr Hartebeest	.20	.15
b.	A48 14fr+2fr Black rhinoceros	.20	.15
c.	A48 14fr+2fr Zebra	.20	.15
d.	A48 14fr+2fr Leopard	.20	.15

UNESCO campaign against illiteracy.

No. C148 Surcharged in Gold and Black

+1F

AIDE INTERNATIONALE
AUX REFUGIES

1971, Aug. 9

CB16	Strip of 4	1.00	.20
a.	A48 17fr+1fr Grant's gazelles	.22	.15
b.	A48 17fr+1fr Cheetah	.22	.15
c.	A48 17fr+1fr African white-backed vultures	.22	.15
d.	A48 17fr+1fr Johnston's okapi	.22	.15

International help for refugees.

Nos. C150-C151 Surcharged in Black and Gold

+1F

a

75eme ANNIVERSAIRE DES
JEUX OLYMPIOUES·MODERNES
(1896-1971)

+1F

b

JEUX PRE-OLYMPIOUES
MUNICH 1972

1971, Aug. 16

CB17	Strip of 4	2.25	.45
a.	A48(a) 26fr+1fr Gorilla	.55	.15
b.	A48(a) 26fr+1fr Gnu	.55	.15
c.	A48(a) 26fr+1fr Warthog	.55	.15
d.	A48(a) 26fr+1fr Cape hunting dog	.55	.15
CB18	Strip of 4	3.00	.60
a.	A48(b) 31fr+1fr Sable antelope	.75	.15
b.	A48(b) 31fr+1fr Caracal lynx	.75	.15
c.	A48(b) 31fr+1fr Ostriches	.75	.15
d.	A48(b) 31fr+1fr Bongo	.75	.15

75th anniv. of modern Olympic Games (#CB17); Olympic Games, Munich, 1972 (#CB18).

+1F.
UNICEF

Nos. C153-C155
Surcharged

1971, Nov. 27   Photo.   Perf. 13¹/₂

CB19	A51 14fr + 1fr multi	.32	.15
CB20	A51 17fr + 1fr multi	.38	.15
CB21	A51 31fr + 1fr multi	.60	.16
	Nos. CB19-CB21 (3)	1.30	
	Set value		.34

25th anniv. of UNICEF.

Casa D'Oro,
Venice
SPAP1

Views in Venice: 17fr+1fr, Doge's Palace. 24fr+1fr, Church of Sts. John and Paul. 31fr+1fr, Doge's Palace and Piazzetta at Feast of Ascension, by Canaletto.

1971, Dec. 27

CB22	SPAP1 10fr + 1fr multi	.16	.15
CB23	SPAP1 17fr + 1fr multi	.32	.15
CB24	SPAP1 24fr + 1fr multi	.45	.15
CB25	SPAP1 31fr + 1fr multi	.55	.16
a.	Souvenir sheet of 4	1.50	1.50
	Nos. CB22-CB25 (4)	1.48	
	Set value		.50

Surtax for the UNESCO campaign to save the treasures of Venice. No. CB25a contains 4 stamps similar to Nos. CB22-CB25, but with 2fr surtax.

Nos. C165-C167, C193-C195
Surcharged "+1F" in Silver

1972, Dec. 12   Photo.   Perf. 13¹/₂

CB26	A57 18fr + 1fr multi	.28	.15
CB27	A57 27fr + 1fr multi	.45	.15
CB28	A57 40fr + 1fr multi	.60	.18
a.	Souvenir sheet of 3	1.50	1.50
	Nos. CB26-CB28 (3)	1.33	
	Set value		.38

Christmas 1972. No. CB28a contains 3 stamps similar to Nos. CB26-CB28 but with 2fr surtax.

1973, Dec. 14   Photo.   Perf. 13

CB29	A64 18fr + 1fr multi	.28	.15
CB30	A64 27fr + 1fr multi	.40	.15
CB31	A64 40fr + 1fr multi	.60	.20
a.	Souvenir sheet of 3	1.50	1.50
	Nos. CB29-CB31 (3)	1.28	
	Set value		.40

Christmas 1973. No. CB31 contains 3 stamps similar to Nos. CB29-CB31 with 2fr surtax each.

Christmas Type of 1974

1974, Dec. 2   Photo.   Perf. 13

CB32	A70 18fr + 1fr multi	.32	.20
CB33	A70 27fr + 1fr multi	.50	.30
CB34	A70 40fr + 1fr multi	.70	.42
a.	Souvenir sheet of 3	1.75	1.75
	Nos. CB32-CB34 (3)	1.52	

Christmas 1974. No. CB34a contains 3 stamps similar to Nos. CB32-CB34 with 2fr surtax.

Nos. C228-C233 Surcharged "+ 1F" in
Silver and Black

1975, Dec. 22   Photo.   Perf. 13

CB35	A73 18fr + 1fr #C228	.35	
CB36	A73 18fr + 1fr #C229	.35	
CB37	A73 31fr + 1fr #C230	.55	
CB38	A73 31fr + 1fr #C231	.55	
CB39	A73 40fr + 1fr #C232	.75	
CB40	A73 40fr + 1fr #C233	.75	
a.	Souvenir sheet of 6	4.25	
	Nos. CB35-CB40 (6)	3.30	

Michelangelo Buonarroti (1475-1564). No. CB40a contains 6 stamps similar to Nos. CB35-CB40 with 2fr surtax each.

Nos. C250-C252 Surcharged "+1f" in
Silver and Black

1976, Nov. 25   Photo.   Perf. 13¹/₂

CB41	A76 18fr + 1fr multi	.30
CB42	A76 31fr + 1fr multi	.50
CB43	A76 40fr + 1fr multi	.60
a.	Souvenir sheet of 3	1.50
	Nos. CB41-CB43 (3)	1.40

Christmas 1976. No. CB43a contains 3 stamps similar to Nos. CB41-CB43 with 2fr surtax each.

Nos. C267-C269 Surcharged "+1fr" in
Silver and Black

1977   Photo.   Perf. 14x13

CB44	A83 18fr + 1fr multi	.28
CB45	A83 31fr + 1fr multi	.50
CB46	A83 40fr + 1fr multi	.60
a.	Souvenir sheet of 3	1.50
	Nos. CB44-CB46 (3)	1.38

Christmas 1977. No. CB46a contains 3 stamps similar to Nos. CB44-CB46 with 2fr surtax each.

Christmas 1978 Type
Souvenir Sheet

1979, Feb.   Photo.   Perf. 14x13

CB47	Sheet of 5	3.00
a.	A86 13fr + 2fr multi	.30
b.	A86 17fr + 2fr multi	.36
c.	A86 27fr + 2fr multi	.55
d.	A86 31fr + 2fr multi	.70
e.	A86 40fr + 2fr multi	.85

Christmas Type of 1979
Souvenir Sheet

1979, Dec. 10   Photo.   Perf. 13¹/₂

CB48	Sheet of 4	2.75
a.	A89 20fr + 2fr like #561	.45
b.	A89 27fr + 2fr like #562	.55
c.	A89 31fr + 2fr like #563	.70
d.	A89 50fr + 2fr like #564	1.00

Christmas Type of 1980
Souvenir Sheet

1981, Jan. 16   Photo.   Perf. 13¹/₂x13

CB49	Sheet of 4	2.50
a.	A92 10fr + 2fr like #579	.20
b.	A92 30fr + 2fr like #580	.55
c.	A92 40fr + 2fr like #581	.75
d.	A92 50fr + 2fr like #582	.90

Christmas Type of 1983
Souvenir Sheet

1983, Nov. 2   Litho.   Perf. 14¹/₂x13¹/₂

CB50	Sheet of 4	1.90
a.	A97 10fr + 2fr like #607	.16
b.	A97 25fr + 2fr like #608	.38
c.	A97 30fr + 2fr like #609	.50
d.	A97 50fr + 2fr like #610	.75

Christmas Type of 1984
Souvenir Sheet

1984, Dec. 15   Perf. 13¹/₂

CB51	Sheet of 4	1.90
a.	A101 10fr + 2fr like #629	.16
b.	A101 25fr + 2fr like #630	.38
c.	A101 30fr + 2fr like #631	.50
d.	A101 50fr + 2fr like #632	1.00

BUSHIRE

bü-'shir

LOCATION — On Persian Gulf

Bushire is a Persian port which British troops occupied Aug. 8, 1915.

20 Chahis (or Shahis) = 1 Kran
10 Krans = 1 Toman

Watermark

Wmk. 161 · Lion

**ISSUED UNDER BRITISH
OCCUPATION**

Basic Iranian Designs

Shah Ahmed — A32   Imperial
                      Crown — A33

King Darius, Ahura-   Ruins of
Mazda   Persepolis — A35
Overhead — A34

Iranian Stamps of
1911-13 Overprinted in
Black

BUSHIRE
Under British
Occupation.

Perf. 11¹/₂, 11¹/₂x11
Typo. & Engr.

1915, Aug. 15   Unwmk.

N1	A32	1c green & org	27.50	27.50
N2	A32	2c red & sepia	27.50	27.50
N3	A32	3c gray brn & grn	30.00	30.00
N4	A32	5c brown & car	300.00	300.00
N5	A32	6c green & red brn	22.50	22.50
N6	A32	9c yel brn & vio	25.00	27.50
		a. Double overprint		
N7	A32	10c red & org brn	25.00	25.00
N8	A32	12c grn & ultra	32.50	32.50
N9	A32	1k ultra & car	45.00	27.50
		a. Double overprint	5.250.	
N10	A32	24c vio & grn	50.00	30.00
N11	A32	2k grn & red vio	175.00	140.00
N12	A32	3k vio & blk	150.00	165.00
N13	A32	5k red & ultra	82.50	75.00
N14	A32	10k ol bis & cl	75.00	75.00
		Nos. N1-N14 (14)	1,067.	1,002.

Nos. N1-N14, except No. N4, exist without period after "Occupation." This variety sells for more.

Forged overprints exist of Nos. N1-N29.
The Bushire overprint exists on Iran No. 537 but is considered a forgery.

On Iranian Stamps of 1915
Perf. 11, 11¹/₂

1915, Sept.   Wmk. 161

N15	A33	1c car & indigo	350.	350.
N16	A33	2c blue & car	4,750.	6,000.
N17	A33	3c dk grn	350.	400.
N18	A33	5c red	4,000.	4,250.
N19	A33	6c ol grn & car	3,000.	3,500.
N20	A33	9c yel brn & vio	500.	525.
N21	A33	10c bl grn & yel brn	800.	900.
N22	A33	12c ultra	950.	1,250.
N23	A34	1k sil, yel brn & gray	350.	375.
N24	A34	24c yel brn & dk brn	450.	400.
N25	A34	2k sil, bl & rose	300.	350.
N26	A34	3k sil, vio & brn	400.	425.
N27	A34	5k sil, brn & car	450.	450.
		a. Inverted overprint		
N28	A35	1t gold, pur & blk	325.	375.
N29	A35	3t gold, cl & red brn	2,500.	2,750.

Persia resumed administration of Bushire post office Oct. 16, 1915.

1999 Vol. 1 Catalogue Number Additions, Deletions & Changes

Number in 1998 Catalogue	Number in 1999 Catalogue
United States	
new	26f
320e, 320f	deleted
424e	deleted
new	424e
new	669b
new	1423a, 1427a
new	1505a
new	1687q
new	1843c
new	1856d, 1874a
new	2244a
new	2276b
new	2452De
new	2485b
new	2625d, 2629a
new	2847b
new	2869u
new	2889a
new	2904b, 2915Ah
new	2919b, 2921c
2949b	2949c
new	2949b
new	2959b, 2980b
new	2992b
new	3003c
new	3029b
new	3054a
new	3071b
new	3082b
new	3123d
new	PR39a
new	O22a, O74a
O116a	deleted
O35Sb, O36Sb	deleted
new	U140A
new	U515d
new	U641a, U641b
RW56a	deleted
Confederate States	
33X1a	deleted
Philippines	
new	437a
Hawaii	
8a	8b
new	5a, 8a, 9a
31	31a
31a	31
new	10a
United Nations	
new	101b
UN - Geneva	
new	261a
Aden	
52	52a
52a	52
53	53a
53a	53
54	54a
54a	54

Number in 1998 Catalogue	Number in 1999 Catalogue
Albania	
new	1373a
new	2204a
Argentina	
new	792a
Tasmania	
12	12b
12b	12
Victoria	
226	226a
226a	226
229	229a
229a	229
Australia	
new	439Ai
1534	1532
1536	1533
1537-1538	1534-1535
new	J86a, J92a
Azerbaijan	
437f	footnoted
Barbados	
new	582a, 584a
Belgium	
CB4a-CB12a	CB4A-CB12A
Benin	
new	606a
811A	811B
Brazil	
1a	1c
154	154c
new	154
British Guiana	
231	231a
231a	231
233	233a
233a	233
235	235a
235a	235
240	240a
240a	240
British Honduras	
237	237a
237a	237
239	239a
239a	239
Bulgaria	
new	1699a, 1700a
3634a	footnoted
Burkina Faso	
new	327a

Dies of British Colonial Stamps Referred to in the Catalogue

DIE A

DIE B

DIE I

DIE II

DIE A:
1. The lines in the groundwork vary in thickness and are not uniformly straight.
2. The seventh and eighth lines from the top, in the groundwork, converge where they meet the head.
3. There is a small dash in the upper part of the second jewel in the band of the crown.
4. The vertical color line in front of the throat stops at the sixth line of shading on the neck.

DIE B:
1. The lines in the groundwork are all thin and straight.
2. All the lines of the background are parallel.
3. There is no dash in the upper part of the second jewel in the band of the crown.
4. The vertical color line in front of the throat stops at the eighth line of shading on the neck.

DIE I:
1. The base of the crown is well below the level of the inner white line around the vignette.
2. The labels inscribed "POSTAGE" and "REVENUE" are cut square at the top.
3. There is a white "bud" on the outer side of the main stem of the curved ornaments in each lower corner.
4. The second (thick) line below the country name has the ends next to the crown cut diagonally.

DIE Ia.	DIE Ib.
1 as die II.	1 and 3 as die II.
2 and 3 as die I.	2 as die I.

DIE II:
1. The base of the crown is aligned with the underside of the white line around the vignette.
2. The labels curve inward at the top inner corners.
3. The "bud" has been removed from the outer curve of the ornaments in each corner.
4. The second line below the country name has the ends next to the crown cut vertically.

Wmk. 1
Crown and C C

Wmk. 2
Crown and C A

Wmk. 3
Multiple Crown
and C A

Wmk. 4
Multiple Crown
and Script C A

Wmk. 4a

Wmk. 314
St. Edward's Crown
and C A Multiple

Wmk. 373

Wmk. 384

British Colonial and Crown Agents Watermarks

Watermarks 1 to 4, 314, 373, and 384, common to many British territories, are illustrated here to avoid duplication.

The letters "CC" of Wmk. 1 identify the paper as having been made for the use of the Crown Colonies, while the letters "CA" of the others stand for "Crown Agents." Both Wmks. 1 and 2 were used on stamps printed by De La Rue & Co.

Wmk. 3 was adopted in 1904; Wmk. 4 in 1921; Wmk. 314 in 1957; Wmk. 373 in 1974; and Wmk. 384 in 1985.

In Wmk. 4a, a non-matching crown of the general St. Edwards type (bulging on both sides at top) was substituted for one of the Wmk. 4 crowns which fell off the dandy roll. The non-matching crown occurs in 1950-52 printings in a horizontal row of crowns on certain regular stamps of Johore and Seychelles, and on various postage due stamps of Barbados, Basutoland, British Guiana, Gold Coast, Grenada, Northern Rhodesia, St. Lucia, Swaziland and Trinidad and Tobago. A variation of Wmk. 4a, with the non-matching crown in a horizontal row of crown-CA-crown, occurs on regular stamps of Bahamas, St. Kitts-Nevis and Singapore.

Wmk. 314 was intentionally used sideways, starting in 1966. When a stamp was issued with Wmk. 314 both upright and sideways, the sideways varieties usually are listed also – with minor numbers. In many of the later issues, Wmk. 314 is slightly visible.

Wmk. 373 is usually only faintly visible.

Illustrated Identifier

This section pictures stamps or parts of stamp designs that will help identify postage stamps that do not have English words on them.

Many of the symbols that identify stamps of countries are shown here as well as typical examples of their stamps.

See the Index and Identifier on the previous pages for stamps with inscriptions such as "sen," "posta," "Baja Porto," "Helvetia," "K.S.A.", etc.

Linn's Stamp Identifier is now available. The 144 pages include more 2,000 inscriptions and over 500 large stamp illustrations. Available from Linn's Stamp News, P.O. Box 29, Sidney, OH 45365-0029.

1. HEADS, PICTURES AND NUMERALS

GREAT BRITAIN

Great Britain stamps never show the country name, but, except for postage dues, show a picture of the reigning monarch.

Victoria

Edward VII   George V   Edward VIII

George VI

Elizabeth II

Some George VI and Elizabeth II stamps are surcharged in annas, new paisa or rupees. These are listed under Oman.

10ᵖ

Silhouette (sometimes facing right, generally at the top of stamp)

11ᵖ

The silhouette indicates this is a British stamp. It is not a U.S. stamp.

VICTORIA

Queen Victoria

INDIA

Other stamps of India show this portrait of Queen Victoria and the words "Service" and "Annas."

AUSTRIA

YUGOSLAVIA

(Also BOSNIA & HERZEGOVINA if imperf.)

BOSNIA & HERZEGOVINA

Denominations also appear in top corners instead of bottom corners.

HUNGARY

Another stamp has posthorn facing left

BRAZIL

AUSTRALIA

Kangaroo and Emu

GERMANY

Mecklenburg-Vorpommern

SWITZERLAND

2. ORIENTAL INSCRIPTIONS

CHINA

Any stamp with this one character is from China (Imperial, Republic or People's Republic). This character appears in a four-character overprint on stamps of Manchukuo. These stamps are local provisionals, which are unlisted. Other overprinted Manchukuo stamps show this character, but have more than four characters in the overprints. These are listed in People's Republic of China.

 中

Some Chinese stamps show the Sun.

Most stamps of Republic of China show this series of characters.

Stamps with the China character and this character are from People's Republic of China. 人

Calligraphic form of People's Republic of China

中国人民邮政

Chinese stamps without China character

REPUBLIC OF CHINA

PEOPLE'S REPUBLIC OF CHINA

Mao Tse-tung

MANCHUKUO

Temple   Emperor Pu-Yi

The first 3 characters are common to
many Manchukuo stamps.

The last 3 characters are common to
other Manchukuo stamps.

Orchid Crest

Manchukuo
stamp with-
out these
elements

JAPAN

Chrysanthemum Crest   Country Name

Japanese stamps without these elements

The number of characters in the center and the
design of dragons on the sides will vary.

RYUKYU ISLANDS

Country Name

PHILIPPINES
(Japanese Occupation)

Country Name

NORTH BORNEO
(Japanese Occupation)

Indicates Japanese   Country
Occupation   Name

MALAYA
(Japanese Occupation)

Indicates Japanese Occupation   Country Name

BURMA
(Japanese Occupation)

Indicates Japanese Occupation   Country Name

Other Burma Japanese Occupation stamps
without these elements

Burmese Script

KOREA

These two characters, in any order, are common to stamps from the Republic of Korea (South Korea) or the unlisted stamps of the People's Democratic Republic of Korea (North Korea).

This series of four characters can be found on the stamps of both Koreas.

Yin Yang appears on some stamps.

Indicates Republic of Korea (South Korea)

South Korean postage stamps issed after 1952 do not show currency expressed in Latin letters.

Stamps wiith "HW," "HWAN," "WON," "WN," "W" or "W" with two lines through it, if not illustrated in listings of stamps before this date, are revenues. North Korean postage stamps do not have currency expressed in Latin letters.

THAILAND

Country Name

King Chulalongkorn

King Prajadhipok and
Chao P'ya Chakri

3. CENTRAL AND EASTERN ASIAN INSCRIPTIONS

INDIA - FEUDATORY STATES

Alwar Bhor

Bundi

Similar stamps come with different designs in corners and differently drawn daggers (at center of circle).

Dhar   Faridkot

Hyderabad

 Similar stamps exist with straight line frame around stamp, and also with different central design which is inscribed "Postage" or "Post & Receipt."

Indore   Jhalawar

A similar stamp has the central figure in an oval.

Nandgaon

Nowanuggur

Poonch

Similar stamps exist
in various sizes

Rajpeepla   ### Soruth

BANGLADESH

Country Name

NEPAL

Similar stamps are smaller, have squares in
upper corners and have five or nine
characters in central bottom panel.

TANNU TUVA   ### ISRAEL

GEORGIA

This inscription is found on
other pictorial stamps.

Country Name

ARMENIA

The four characters are found somewhere
on pictorial stamps. On some stamps only
the middle two are found.

---

4. AFRICAN INSCRIPTIONS

ETHIOPIA

---

5. ARABIC INSCRIPTIONS

AFGHANISTAN

Many early Afghanistan
stamps show Tiger's head,
many of these have orna-
ments protruding from
outer ring, others show
inscriptions in black.

Arabic Script

Mosque Gate & Crossed Cannons
The four characters are found somewhere
on pictorial stamps. On some stamps only
the middle two are found.

BAHRAIN

EGYPT

Postage

INDIA - FEUDATORY STATES

Jammu & Kashmir

Text and thickness of
ovals vary. Some stamps
have flower devices
in corners.

India-Hyderabad

IRAN

Country Name

Royal Crown

Lion with Sword

Symbol

IRAQ

JORDAN

LEBANON

Similar types have denominations at top and slightly different design.

LIBYA

Country Name in various styles

Other Libya stamps show Eagle and Shield (head facing either direction) or Red, White and Black Shield (with or without eagle in center).

SAUDI ARABIA

Tughra (Central design)

Palm Tree and Swords

SYRIA

THRACE   YEMEN

PAKISTAN

PAKISTAN - Bahawalpur

Country Name in top panel, star and crescent

TURKEY

Star & Crescent is a device found on many Turkish stamps, but is also found on stamps from other Arabic areas (see Pakistan-Bahawalpur)

 Tughra (similar tughras can be found on stamps of Turkey in Asia, Afghanistan and Saudi Arabia)

Mohammed V

Mustafa Kemal

Plane, Star and Crescent

TURKEY IN ASIA

Other Turkey in Asia pictorials show
star & crescent.
Other stamps show tughra shown under Turkey.

---

6. GREEK INSCRIPTIONS

GREECE

Country Name in various styles
(Some Crete stamps overprinted with the Greece
country name are listed in Crete.)

Lepta

ΔΡΑΧΜΗ   **ΔΡΑΧΜΑΙ**   **ΛΕΠΤΟΝ**
Drachma   Drachmas   Lepton
Abbreviated Country Name   **ΕΛΛ**

Other forms of Country Name

No country name

CRETE

Country Name

These words are on
other stamps

Grosion

Crete stamps with a surcharge that have the year
"1922" are listed under Greece.

EPIRUS
Country Name

IONIAN ISLANDS

---

7. CYRILLIC INSCRIPTIONS

RUSSIA
Postage Stamp

Imperial Eagle

Postage in various styles

  РОССІЯ

Abbreviation for Kopeck Abbreviation for Ruble Russia

Abbreviation for Russian Soviet
Federated Socialist Republic
RSFSR stamps were overprinted (see below)

Abbreviation for Union of Soviet
Socialist Republics

This item is footnoted in Latvia

RUSSIA - Army of the North

"ОКСА"

RUSSIA - Wenden

RUSSIAN OFFICES IN
THE TURKISH EMPIRE

 These letters appear on other
stamps of the Russian offices.

The unoverprinted version of
this stamp and a similar stamp
were overprinted by various
countries (see below).

ARMENIA

BELARUS

FAR EASTERN REPUBLIC

Country Name

SOUTH RUSSIA

Country Name

FINLAND

Circles and Dots on stamps similar to Imperial Russia issues

BATUM

Forms of Country Name

TRANSCAUCASIAN FEDERATED REPUBLICS

Abbreviation for Country Name

KAZAKHSTAN

Country Name

KYRGYZSTAN

КЫРГЫЗСТАН   Counrty Name

ROMANIA

TADJIKISTAN

Тадж

Counrty Name & Abbreviation

UKRAINE

Country Name in various forms

The trident appears on many stamps, usually as an overprint.

Abbreviation for Ukrainian Soviet Socialist Republic

WESTERN UKRAINE

Abbreviation for Country Name

AZERBAIJAN

AZƏRBAYCAN

Country Name

Abbreviation for Azerbaijan Soviet Socialist Republic

MONTENEGRO

ЦРНА ГОРА

Country Name in various forms

Abbreviation for country name

No country name (A similar Montenegro stamp without country name has same vignette.)

SERBIA

СРПСКА СРБИЈА

Country Name in various forms

Abbreviation for country name

No country name

YUGOSLAVIA

ЈУГОСЛАВИЈА

Showing country name

No Country Name

MACEDONIA

МАКЕДОНИЈА

МАКЕДОНИЈА

Country Name

BULGARIA

Country Name   Postage

Stotinka

Stotinki (plural)   Abbreviation for Stotinki

Country Name in various forms and styles

Н Р Бългаria

БЪЛГАРИЯ

Н Р България

НРБЪЛГАРИЯ

No country name

Abbreviation for
Lev, leva

MONGOLIA

ШУУДАН
Country name in
one word

ТӨГРӨГ
Tugrik in Cyrillic

МОНГОЛ
ШУУДАН
Country name in
two words

МӨНГӨ
Mung in Cyrillic

Mung
in Mongolian

Tugrik
in Mongolian

Arms

No Country Name

Index and Identifier

All page numbers shown are those in this Volume 1.

Postage stamps that do not have English words on them are shown in the Identifier which begins on page 862.

INDEX TO ADVERTISERS – 1999 VOLUME 1

1999
VOLUME 1
DEALER DIRECTORY
YELLOW PAGE LISTINGS

**This section of your Scott Catalogue contains
advertisements to help you conveniently find
what you need,
when you need it...!**

Albania

DISCOVER ALBANIA THROUGH STAMPS!

Dear collectors!

Would you like to know more about Albania? You can do it buying Albanian stamps. You can go through Albania history, flora and fauna, Albanian and world personalities, (Did you know that Mother Theresa was an Albanian?), with a broad national and international thematic.

For ordering or for more information, (year's circulars, stocklist, the way of payment etc.), please, don't hesitate to contact Philatelic Department of Albanian Post at the following address:

Albanian Post Enterprise
Philatelic Department
"Reshit Çollaku" Street
Tirana, Albania

Tel:+355 42 296 96
Fax: +355 42 321 33

Accessories

BROOKLYN GALLERY COIN & STAMP
8725 4th Ave.
Brooklyn, NY 11209
718-745-5701
718-745-2775 Fax

Aitutaki

OVPT PHILATELICS
P.O. Box 36217
Los Angeles, CA 90036
818-893-4603 Ph. & Fax
Email:ovptphmc@webtv.net

Albania

FRANK GEIGER PHILATELISTS
Suite 2
242 West Saddle River Road
Saddle River, NJ 07458-2620
201-236-8122
201-236-8133 Fax
http://www.worldstamps.com

Albums & Accessories

THE KEEPING ROOM
P.O. Box 257
Trumbull, CT 06611-0257
203-372-8436

PJC COLLECTIBLES
377 Doat St.
Buffalo, NY 14211
716-891-8155 Telephone & Fax

Andorra

FRANK GEIGER PHILATELISTS
Suite 2
242 West Saddle River Road
Saddle River, NJ 07458-2620
201-236-8122
201-236-8133 Fax
http://www.worldstamps.com

Antarctic

ANTARCTIC PHILATELIC EXCHANGE
92015-1562 Danforth Ave.
Toronto, ON M4J 5C1
Canada
416-406-2760
http://www.south-pole.com
Email:jporter@interlog.com

PACIFIC RIM PHILATELIC COMPANY
484 Lake Park Ave. #144
Oakland, CA 94610
501-835-0307 or
510-251-8001 Ext.3 Phone & Fax
Email:pacrim@dnai.com or
Email:Pacrim484@aol

Antigua

COLONIAL STAMP COMPANY
5757 Wilshire Blvd.
Penthouse 8
Los Angeles, CA 90036
213-933-9435
213-939-9930 Fax

Appraisals

KUKSTIS AUCTIONS, INC.
P.O. Box 130
Scituate, MA 02066
617-545-8494 or 800-649-0083
617-545-4610 Fax
Email:paulk@dreamcom.net
http://www.kukstis.com

RANDY SCHOLL STAMP COMPANY
Southampton Square
7460 Jager Court
Cincinnati, OH 45230-4344
513-624-6800
513-624-6440 Fax

UNIQUE ESTATE APPRAISALS
1937 NE Broadway
Portland, OR 97232
503-287-4200 or
800-646-1147

Approvals - Personalized Worldwide & U.S.

THE KEEPING ROOM
P.O. Box 257
Trumbull, CT 06611-0257
203-372-8436

Approvals Worldwide

ROSS WETREICH INC.
P.O. Box 1300
Valley Stream, NY 11582-1300
516-825-8974

Approvals Worldwide - Collections

S. R. L. STAMPS
P.O. Box 296
Huguenot, NY 12746
800-369-4617 pin 3429 Phone & Fax

Argentina

FRANK GEIGER PHILATELISTS
Suite 2
242 West Saddle River Road
Saddle River, NJ 07458-2620
201-236-8122
201-236-8133 Fax
http://www.worldstamps.com

Argentina - F.D.C.'s

VICTOR R. OSTOLAZA
Casilla #4338
Lima 100
Peru
511-476-2102 Telephone & Fax
Email:apalma@msn.com

Argentina - New Issues

VICTOR R. OSTOLAZA
Casilla #4338
Lima 100
Peru
511-476-2102 Telephone & Fax
Email:apalma@msn.com

Armenia

FRANK GEIGER PHILATELISTS
Suite 2
242 West Saddle River Road
Saddle River, NJ 07458-2620
201-236-8122
201-236-8133 Fax
http://www.worldstamps.com

Asia

PACIFIC RIM PHILATELIC COMPANY
484 Lake Park Ave. #144
Oakland, CA 94610
501-835-0307 or
510-251-8001 Ext.3 Phone & Fax
Email:pacrim@dnai.com or
Email:Pacrim484@aol

MICHAEL ROGERS, INC.
199 E. Welbourne Ave.
Winter Park, FL 32789
407-644-2290
407-645-4434 Fax
http://www.michaelrogersinc.com

THE STAMP ACT
P.O. Box 1136
Belmont, CA 94002
650-592-3315
650-508-8104 Fax
http://www.Bchang@IX.netcom.com

SOUTHEAST STAMPS
P.O. Box 6768
Shreveport, LA 71106

Auction House

B TRADING CO.
114 Quail Street
Albany, NY 12206
518-465-3497 Telephone & Fax

Auctions

CHARLES G. FIRBY AUCTIONS
6695 Highland Road Suite #107
Waterford, MI 48327-1967
248-666-5333
248-666-5020 Fax

DANIEL F. KELLEHER CO., INC.
24 Farnsworth St.
Ste. 605
Boston, MA 02210
617-443-0033
617-443-0789 Fax

KUKSTIS AUCTIONS, INC.
P.O. Box 130
Scituate, MA 02066
617-545-8494 or 800-649-0083
617-545-4610 Fax
Email:paulk@dreamcom.net
http://www.kukstis.com

LAKESIDE PHILATELIC AUCTIONS
3935 Lakeside Rd. Ste. 7A
Comp. 4 RR# 2
Penticton, BC V2A 6J7
CANADA
604-493-5239
604-493-3324 Fax
http://vvv.com/~greek
Email:greek@tnet.net

JACQUES C. SCHIFF, JR., INC.
195 Main St.
Ridgefield Park, NJ 07660
201-641-5566 from NYC 662-2777
201-641-5705 Fax

SAM HOUSTON PHILATELICS
13310 Westheimer #150
Houston, TX 77077
281-493-6386
281-496-1445 Fax
Email:BDHOUDUCK@AOL.COM

Auctions

Auctions

STAMP CENTER / DUTCH COUNTRY AUCTIONS
4115 Concord Pike
Wilmington, DE 19803
302-478-8740
302-478-8779 Fax
http://www.thestampcenter.com

THE STAMP & COIN SHOP/ AUCTIONS
725 Pike St. #6
Seattle, WA 98101
206-624-1400
206-621-8975 Fax
http://WWW.StampCoin.com

Auctions - Public

ALAN BLAIR STAMPS / AUCTIONS
5520A Lakeside Avenue
Richmond, VA 23228
800-689-5602 Telephone & Fax

CONNEXUS
P.O. Box 130
Tryon, NC 28782
828-859-5882
828-859-2702 Fax
Email:Connexus1@worldnet.att.net

SUBURBAN STAMP INC.
176 Worthington Street
Springfield, MA 01103
413-785-5348
413-746-3788 Fax

Australia

COLONIAL STAMP COMPANY
5757 Wilshire Blvd.
Penthouse 8
Los Angeles, CA 90036
213-933-9435
213-939-9930 Fax

FRANK GEIGER PHILATELISTS
Suite 2
242 West Saddle River Road
Saddle River, NJ 07458-2620
201-236-8122
201-236-8133 Fax
http://www.worldstamps.com

PACIFIC RIM PHILATELIC COMPANY
484 Lake Park Ave. #144
Oakland, CA 94610
501-835-0307 or
510-251-8001 Ext.3 Phone & Fax
Email:pacrim@dnai.com or
Email:Pacrim484@aol

Australia - New Issues

AUSTRALIA STAMP AGENCY IN NORTH AMERICA
One Unicover Center
Cheyenne, WY 82008-0010
800-443-4225
800-628-3132 Fax
http://www.unicover.com

PACIFIC RIM PHILATELIC COMPANY
484 Lake Park Ave. #144
Oakland, CA 94610
501-835-0307 or
510-251-8001 Ext.3 Phone & Fax
Email:pacrim@dnai.com or
Email:Pacrim484@aol

Austria

AMEEN STAMPS
8849 Long Point Rd.
Houston, TX 77055
713-468-0644
713-468-2420 Fax

JOSEPH EDER
P.O. Box 5517
Hamden, CT 06518
203-281-0742
203-230-2410 Fax
Email:jeder@nai.net

FRANK GEIGER PHILATELISTS
Suite 2
242 West Saddle River Road
Saddle River, NJ 07458-2620
201-236-8122
201-236-8133 Fax
http://www.worldstamps.com

HUNGARIA STAMP EXCHANGE
P.O. Box 3024
Andover, MA 01810
508-682-0242
508-794-2567 Fax

HENRY GITNER PHILATELISTS, INC.
P.O. Box 3077-S
Middletown, NY 10940
914-343-5151
or 800-947-8267
914-343-0068 Fax
Email:hgitner@hgitner.com
http://www.hgitner.com

Azerbaijan

FRANK GEIGER PHILATELISTS
Suite 2
242 West Saddle River Road
Saddle River, NJ 07458-2620
201-236-8122
201-236-8133 Fax
http://www.worldstamps.com

Bahamas

COLONIAL STAMP COMPANY
5757 Wilshire Blvd.
Penthouse 8
Los Angeles, CA 90036
213-933-9435
213-939-9930 Fax

Bangkok

COLONIAL STAMP COMPANY
5757 Wilshire Blvd.
Penthouse 8
Los Angeles, CA 90036
213-933-9435
213-939-9930 Fax

Barbados

COLONIAL STAMP COMPANY
5757 Wilshire Blvd.
Penthouse 8
Los Angeles, CA 90036
213-933-9435
213-939-9930 Fax

Beanie Babies

M.A. STORK
651 Forest Ave.
Portland, ME 04101
800-734-7271

Belarus

FRANK GEIGER PHILATELISTS
Suite 2
242 West Saddle River Road
Saddle River, NJ 07458-2620
201-236-8122
201-236-8133 Fax
http://www.worldstamps.com

Belgium

LEON FISCHER
P.O. Box 1338 Gracie Sta.
New York, NY 10028

FRANK GEIGER PHILATELISTS
Suite 2
242 West Saddle River Road
Saddle River, NJ 07458-2620
201-236-8122
201-236-8133 Fax
http://www.worldstamps.com

HENRY GITNER PHILATELISTS, INC.
P.O. Box 3077-S
Middletown, NY 10940
914-343-5151
or 800-947-8267
914-343-0068 Fax
Email:hgitner@hgitner.com
http://www.hgitner.com

Belgium - New Issues

BELGIUM STAMP AGENCY IN NORTH AMERICA
One Unicover Center
Cheyenne, WY 82008-0026
800-443-4225
800-628-3132 Fax
http://www.unicover.com

Bermuda

COLONIAL STAMP COMPANY
5757 Wilshire Blvd.
Penthouse 8
Los Angeles, CA 90036
213-933-9435
213-939-9930 Fax

Booklets - U.S.

PACIFIC RIM PHILATELIC COMPANY
484 Lake Park Ave. #144
Oakland, CA 94610
501-835-0307 or
510-251-8001 Ext.3 Phone & Fax
Email:pacrim@dnai.com or
Email:Pacrim484@aol

Bosnia

FRANK GEIGER PHILATELISTS
Suite 2
242 West Saddle River Road
Saddle River, NJ 07458-2620
201-236-8122
201-236-8133 Fax
http://www.worldstamps.com

Brazil

FRANK GEIGER PHILATELISTS
Suite 2
242 West Saddle River Road
Saddle River, NJ 07458-2620
201-236-8122
201-236-8133 Fax
http://www.worldstamps.com

Brazil - F.D.C.'s

VICTOR R. OSTOLAZA
Casilla #4338
Lima 100
Peru
511-476-2102 Telephone & Fax
Email:apalma@msn.com

Brazil - New Issues

VICTOR R. OSTOLAZA
Casilla #4338
Lima 100
Peru
511-476-2102 Telephone & Fax
Email:apalma@msn.com

British Antarctic Territories

FRANK GEIGER PHILATELISTS
Suite 2
242 West Saddle River Road
Saddle River, NJ 07458-2620
201-236-8122
201-236-8133 Fax
http://www.worldstamps.com

British Colonies

ALLKOR STAMP COMPANY
Box 1346
Port Washington, NY 11050
516-883-3296 Telephone & Fax

Bulgaria

FRANK GEIGER PHILATELISTS
Suite 2
242 West Saddle River Road
Saddle River, NJ 07458-2620
201-236-8122
201-236-8133 Fax
http://www.worldstamps.com

HUNGARIA STAMP EXCHANGE
P.O. Box 3024
Andover, MA 01810
508-682-0242
508-794-2567 Fax

Burma

COLONIAL STAMP COMPANY
5757 Wilshire Blvd.
Penthouse 8
Los Angeles, CA 90036
213-933-9435
213-939-9930 Fax

Bushire

COLONIAL STAMP COMPANY
5757 Wilshire Blvd.
Penthouse 8
Los Angeles, CA 90036
213-933-9435
213-939-9930 Fax

Canada

LAKESIDE PHILATELICS
3935 Lakeside Rd. Ste. 7a
Comp. 4 RR# 2
Penticton, BC V2A-6J7
CANADA
604-493-5239
604-493-3324 Fax
http://vvv.com/~greek
Email:greek@tnet.net

Canada - Duck Stamps

**METROPOLITAN STAMP CO. of
CHICAGO, INC.**
P.O. Box 1133
Chicago, IL 60690-1133
815-439-0142
815-439-0143 Fax

Canada - Postal Bid Sales

BOW CITY PHILATELICS LTD.
P.O. Box 6444 Central P.O.
Suite 614 206 7th Ave. SW
Calgary, AB T2P 2E1
CANADA
403-237-5828
403-264-5287 Fax
Email:bow.city@bbs.logicnet.com
http:www.logicnet.com/bow.city

China

MICHAEL ROGERS, INC.
199 E. Welbourne Ave.
Winter Park, FL 32789
407-644-2290
407-645-4434 Fax
http://www.michaelrogersinc.com

Classics

KUKSTIS AUCTIONS, INC.
P.O. Box 130
Scituate, MA 02066
617-545-8494 or 800-649-0083
617-545-4610 Fax
Email:paulk@dreamcom.net
http://www.kukstis.com

Collections

**BOB & MARTHA FRIEDMAN
STAMPS**
624 Homestead Place
Joliet, IL 60435
815-725-6666
815-725-4134 Fax

HUNT & CO.
3933 Spicewood Springs Road
Ste. E-400
Austin, TX 78759
512-346-4830 or 800-458-5745
512-346-4984 Fax
Email:huntco@ddc.net
http://www.huntstamps.com

Conservation Stamps

SAM HOUSTON DUCK CO.
P.O. Box 820087
Houston, TX 77282
281-493-6386 or 800-231-5926
281-496-1445 Fax
Email:RWHOUDUCK@AOL.COM

Czechoslovakia

**SOCIETY FOR CZECHOSLOVAK
PHILATELY, INC.**
Tom Cossaboom, SCP Secretary
Box 25332
Scott Air Force Base, IL 62225
USA

Disney

BROOKMAN INTERNATIONAL
P.O. Box 90
Vancouver, WA 98666
360-695-1391 or 800-545-4871
360-695-1616 Fax
Email:brookman@stampdealers.com
http:www.brookmanstamps.com

Duck Stamps

MICHAEL JAFFE STAMPS, INC.
P.O. Box 61484
Vancouver, WA 98666
360-695-6161 or 800-782-6770
360-695-1616 Fax
Email:mjaffe@brookmanstamps.com
http://www.brookmanstamps.com

SAM HOUSTON DUCK CO.
P.O. Box 820087
Houston, TX 77282
281-493-6386 or 800-231-5926
281-496-1445 Fax
Email:RWHOUDUCK@AOL.COM

**METROPOLITAN STAMP CO. OF
CHICAGO**
P.O. Box 1133
Chicago, IL 60690-1133
815-439-0142
815-439-0143 Fax

**TRENTON STAMP & COIN CO. -
THOMAS DeLUCA**
Forest Glen Plaza
1804 Route 33
Hamilton Square, NJ 08690
800-446-8664
609-587-8664 Fax

Errors, Freaks & Oddities

SAM HOUSTON PHILATELICS
13310 Westheimer #150
Houston, TX 77077
281-493-6386
281-496-1445 Fax
Email:BDHOUDUCK@AOL.COM

MILL CREEK LIMITED
P.O. Box 236
Bothell, WA 98041-0236
U.S.800-495-6868 outside of U.S.
425-487-2789
Email:MillCreek@StampDealers.com
http://www.stampdealers.com/
millcreek/

Errors - Major

SUBURBAN STAMP INC.
176 Worthington Street
Springfield, MA 01103
413-785-5348
413-746-3788 Fax

First Day Covers

ROSS WETREICH INC.
P.O. Box 1300
Valley Stream, NY 11582-1300
516-825-8974

First Day Covers - Worldwide

**PACIFIC RIM PHILATELIC
COMPANY**
484 Lake Park Ave. #144
Oakland, CA 94610
501-835-0307 or
510-251-8001 Ext.3 Phone & Fax
Email:pacrim@dnai.com or
Email:Pacrim484@aol

France

JOSEPH EDER
P.O. Box 5517
Hamden, CT 06518
203-281-0742
203-230-2410 Fax
Email:jeder@nai.net

German Areas

JOSEPH EDER
P.O. Box 5517
Hamden, CT 06518
203-281-0742
203-230-2410 Fax
Email:jeder@nai.net

Great Britain

COLONIAL STAMP COMPANY
5757 Wilshire Blvd.
Penthouse 8
Los Angeles, CA 90036
213-933-9435
213-939-9930 Fax

NOVA PHILATELIC SALES
Box 161
Lakeside, N.S. B3T 1M6
Canada
902-826-2165
902-826-1049 Fax
Email:novafil@ns.sympatico.ca

Imperial China

TREASURE -HUNTERS LIMITED
8/F, 280 Lockhart Road
Wanchai, Hong Kong
852-2507-3773 or 2507-5770
852-2519-6820 Fax

Insurance

**COLLECTIBLES INSURANCE
AGENCY, INC.**
P.O. Box 1200 SSC
Westminster, MD 21158-0299
888-837-9537 or 410-876-8833
410-876-9233 Fax
Email:collectinsure/@pipeline.com

Israel - New Issues

ISRAEL PHILATELIC AGENCY
535 Fifth Ave.
Suite 300
New York, NY 10017
212-818-9160 or 800-607-2799
212-818-9012 Fax

Literature

OVPT PHILATELICS
P.O. Box 36217
Los Angeles, CA 90036
818-893-4603 Ph. & Fax
Email:ovptphmc@webtv.net

Lots & Collections

**BOB & MARTHA FRIEDMAN
STAMPS**
624 Homestead Place
Joliet, IL 60435
815-725-6666
815-725-4134 Fax

RANDY SCHOLL STAMP COMPANY
Southampton Square
7460 Jager Court
Cincinnati, OH 45230-4344
513-624-6800
513-624-6440 Fax

Mail Bid Auctions

HUNT & CO.
3933 Spicewood Springs Road
Ste. E-400
Austin, TX 78759
512-346-4830 or 800-458-5745
512-346-4984 Fax
Email:huntco@ddc.net
http://www.huntstamps.com

Mail Bid Sales

JUNO STAMPS
1765 Juno Ave.
St. Paul, MN 55116
800-714-3469

MAREX EXCHANGE
P.O. Box 2501
Riverside, CA 92516-2501
909-354-2598

Mail Order

ALMAZ CO., DEPT. VY
P.O. Box 100-812
Vanderveer Station
Brooklyn, NY 11210
718-241-6360 Telephone & Fax

HUNT & CO.
3933 Spicewood Springs Road
Ste. E-400
Austin, TX 78759
512-346-4830 or 800-458-5745
512-346-4984 Fax
Email:huntco@ddc.net
http://www.huntstamps.com

J.P. PHILATELICS
P.O. Box 71548
Salt Lake City, UT 84171
801-943-5824 Telephone & Fax

**PACIFIC RIM PHILATELIC
COMPANY**
484 Lake Park Ave. #144
Oakland, CA 94610
501-835-0307 or
510-251-8001 Ext.3 Phone & Fax
Email:pacrim@dnai.com or
Email:Pacrim484@aol

**ROBERT'S STAMP
EXCHANGE/Robert LeFrancois**
444 Summit St.
Elgin, Il 60120
847-695-6568

SHARI'S STAMPS
104-3 Old Highway 40 #130
O'Fallon, MO 63366
800-382-3597
314-980-1552 Fax

Mail Sales

DALE ENTERPRISES INC.
P.O. Box 539-C
Emmaus, PA 18049
610-433-3303
610-965-6089 Fax
Email:daleent@fast.net
http://www.dalestamps.com

Major Errors

SUBURBAN STAMP INC.
176 Worthington Street
Springfield, MA 01103
413-785-5348
413-746-3788 Fax

New Issues

New Issues

DAVIDSON'S STAMP SERVICE
P.O. Box 36355
Indianapolis, IN 46236-0355
317-826-2620
Email:davidson@in.net

FRANK GEIGER PHILATELISTS
Suite 2
242 West Saddle River Road
Saddle River, NJ 07458-2620
201-236-8122
201-236-8133 Fax
http://www.worldstamps.com

New Issues - Retail

BOMBAY PHILATELIC CO., INC.
P.O. Box 7719
Delray Beach, FL 33482-7719
561-499-7990
561-499-7553 Fax
Email:sales@bombaystamps.com
http:www.bombaystamps.com

**PACIFIC RIM PHILATELIC
COMPANY**
484 Lake Park Ave. #144
Oakland, CA 94610
501-835-0307 or
510-251-8001 Ext.3 Phone & Fax
Email:pacrim@dnai.com or
Email:Pacrim484@aol

New Issues - Wholesale

BOMBAY PHILATELIC CO., INC.
P.O. Box 7719
Delray Beach, FL 33482-7719
561-499-7990
561-499-7553 Fax
Email:sales@bombaystamps.com
http:www.bombaystamps.com

**PACIFIC RIM PHILATELIC
COMPANY**
484 Lake Park Ave. #144
Oakland, CA 94610
501-835-0307 or
510-251-8001 Ext.3 Phone & Fax
Email:pacrim@dnai.com or
Email:Pacrim484@aol

Plate Blocks - U.S.

**PACIFIC RIM PHILATELIC
COMPANY**
484 Lake Park Ave. #144
Oakland, CA 94610
501-835-0307 or
510-251-8001 Ext.3 Phone & Fax
Email:pacrim@dnai.com or
Email:Pacrim484@aol

Plate Number Coils

**PACIFIC RIM PHILATELIC
COMPANY**
484 Lake Park Ave. #144
Oakland, CA 94610
501-835-0307 or
510-251-8001 Ext.3 Phone & Fax
Email:pacrim@dnai.com or
Email:Pacrim484@aol

Postal History

KUKSTIS AUCTIONS, INC.
P.O. Box 130
Scituate, MA 02066
617-545-8494 or 800-649-0083
617-545-4610 Fax
Email:paulk@dreamcom.net
http://www.kukstis.com

Price Lists - Worldwide

HALL'S STAMPS
P.O. Box 8095
Spokane, WA 99203
509-838-4564
509-838-1903 Fax

Proofs & Essays

SUBURBAN STAMP INC.
176 Worthington Street
Springfield, MA 01103
413-785-5348
413-746-3788 Fax

Public Auctions

Fairness & Personal Service
Connexus
PUBLIC AUCTIONS

U.S. & FOREIGN - Stamps & REVENUES
POSTAL HISTORY, Specialized Varieties
Exotic Country Collections

Always Seeking Material Suitable for Auction

P.O. Box 130	Tel. (828) 859-5882
Tryon, NC 28782	FAX (828) 859-2702
e-mail: Connexus1@worldnet.att.net	

Publications / Collector

AMERICAN PHILATELIST
Dept. TZ
P.O. Box 8000
State College, PA 16803
814-237-3803
814-237-6128 Fax
Email:flsente@stamps.org
http://www.westnet.~
stamps1/aps.html

GLOBAL STAMP NEWS
P.O. Box 97
Sidney, OH 45365-0097
937-492-3183
937-492-6514 Fax
Email:global@bright.net

Stamp Shows

ATLANTIC COAST EXHIBITIONS
Divison of Beach Philatelics
42 Baltimore Lane
Palm Coast, FL 32137-8850
904-445-4550
904-447-0811 Fax
Email:mrstamp2@alo.com
http://members.tripod.com/~
SmitX/BeachPhilatelics.htm

Don't forget
to patronize Scott Catalogue advertisers

I SAW YOUR AD IN THE CATALOGUE!

S T A M P   S T O R E S

Arizona

AMERICAN STAMP & COIN CO.
7225 N. Oracle Rd.
Suite #102
Tucson, AZ 85704
520-297-3456

B.J.'S STAMPS / BARBARA J. JOHNSON
6342 W. Bell Road
Glendale, AZ 85308
602-878-2080
602-412-3456 Fax

California

ASHTREE STAMP & COIN
2410 N. Blackstone
Fresno, CA 93703
209-227-7167

BROSIUS STAMP & COIN
2105 Main Street
Santa Monica, CA 90405
310-396-7480
310-396-7455 Fax

COLONIAL STAMP COMPANY/ BRITISH EMPIRE SPECIALIST
5757 Wilshire Blvd.
PII #8 (By appt)
Los Angeles, CA 90036
213-933-9435
213-939-9930 Fax

FISCHER - WOLK PHILATELICS
24771 "G" Alicia Parkway
Laguna Hills, CA 92653
714-837-2932

HERB'S STAMP CENTER
11748 Washington Place
West Los Angeles, CA 90066
310-397-3883

NATICK STAMPS & HOBBIES
405 S. Myrtle Avenue
Monrovia, CA 91016
818-305-7333
818-305-7335 Fax
http://www.natickco.com

STANLEY M. PILLER
3351 Grand Ave.
Oakland, CA 94610
510-465-8290
510-465-7121 Fax
Email:stmpdlr@aol.com

California

THE STAMP GALLERY
1515 Locust Street
Walnut Creek, CA 94596
925-944-9111

STAMPCRAFT
P.O. Box 2425
Santa Clara, CA 95055
800-245-5389
408-241-4440 Fax

Colorado

ACKLEY'S ROCKS & STAMPS
3230 N. Stone Ave.
Colorado Springs, CO 80907
719-633-1153

SHOWCASE STAMPS
3865 Wadsworth Blvd.
Wheat Ridge, CO 80033
303-425-9252
303-425-7410 Fax

Connecticut

MILLER'S STAMP SHOP
41 New London Turnpike
Uncasville, CT 06382
860-848-0468 Telephone & Fax

SILVER CITY COIN & STAMP
41 Colony Street
Meriden, CT 06451
203-235-7634

Florida

CORBIN STAMP & COIN
115-A East Brandon Blvd.
Brandon, FL 33511
813-651-3266

HAUSER'S COIN & STAMP
3425 S. Florida Ave.
Lakeland, FL 33803
941-647-2052
941-644-5738 Fax

INTERCONTINENTAL / RICARDO DEL CAMPO
7379 Coral Way
Miami, FL 33155-1402
305-264-4983
305-262-2919 Fax

Special Offers

FREE FOR THE ASKING...

WHETHER YOU PREFER BUYING AT AUCTION OR FROM PRICE LISTS, OUR CATALOGS ARE FREE FOR THE ASKING!

MAIL AUCTIONS
OUR SALES OFFER U.S., BRITISH AND FOREIGN FROM SINGLE STAMPS AND SETS TO WHOLESALE LOTS AND COLLECTIONS. WE NEVER CHARGE A BUYER'S FEE OR COMMISSION

PRIVATE TREATY LISTS
U.S, BRITISH & FOREIGN COLLECTIONS, WHOLESALE LOTS, REMAINDERS, JOB LOTS AND DEALER'S STOCKS ARE OFFERED FOR IMMEDIATE SALE AT AFFORDABLE PRICES.

CALL OR SEND FOR A COPY OF OUR AUCTION CATALOG OR PRIVATE TREATY LIST...OR BOTH! THERE IS NO CHARGE!

E and C August

Box 9K, Walpole,
New Hampshire 03608
Phone (603) 756-3132

Florida

WHEN VISITING CENTRAL FLORIDA BE SURE TO STOP BY...

Send 32¢ long SASE for our MONTHLY NEWSLETTER of stamps for sale!

Michael Rogers - Alvin Hintz

WINTER PARK STAMP SHOP
199 E. Welbourne Ave., 2nd floor, Winter Park, FL 32789
Phone 407-628-1120 • FAX 407-628-0091
1-800-845-1819
Open Mon. through Fri. 10am-6pm • Sat. 10am-3pm (4 miles North of Orlando)

STAMP STORES

Florida

JACK'S COINS & STAMPS
801 Northlake Blvd.
North Palm Beach, FL 33408
407-844-7710

ROBERT LEVINE STAMPS, INC.
2219 South University Dr.
Davie, FL 33324
954-473-1303
954-473-1305 Fax

NEW ENGLAND STAMP
4987 Tamiami Trail East
Village Falls Professional Ctr
Naples, FL 34113
941-732-8000
941-732-7701 Fax
Emai.l:STAMPS@SPRINTMAIL.COM

JERRY SIEGEL / STAMPS FOR COLLECTORS
1920 E. Hallandale Beach Blvd.
Suite 507
Hallandale, FL 33009
954-457-0422 Telephone & Fax

THE STAMP PLACE
576 First Avenue North
St. Petersburg, FL 33701
813-894-4082

WINTER PARK STAMP SHOP
199 E. Welbourne Ave.
Suite 201
Winter Park, FL 32789
800-845-1819
407-628-0091 Fax

Georgia

STAMPS UNLIMITED OF GEORGIA
133 Carnegie Way
Room 250
Atlanta, GA 30303
404-688-9161

Illinois

DON CLARK'S STAMPS
937 1/2 W. Galena Blvd.
Aurora, IL 60506
630-896-4606

DR. ROBERT FRIEDMAN & SONS
2029 West 75th St.
Woodridge, IL 60517
630-985-1515
630-985-1588 Fax

MARSHALL FIELD'S STAMP DEPT.
111 N. State Street
Chicago, IL 60602
312-781-4237

Indiana

J & J COINS & STAMPS
7019 Calumet Avenue or
6526 Indianapolis Blvd.
Hammond, IN 46324
219-932-5818
219-845-2003 Fax

KNIGHT STAMP & COIN COMPANY
327 Main Street
Hobart, IN 46342
219-942-7529 or
800-634-2646

Kentucky

COLLECTORS STAMPS LTD.
4012 DuPont Circle #313
Louisville, KY 40207
502-897-9045
Email:csl/aye.net

TREASURE ISLAND COINS & STAMPS
232 W. Broadway
Louisville, KY 40202
502-583-1222

Maryland

BALTIMORE COIN & STAMP EXCHANGE, INC.
10194 Baltimore National Pike
Unit 104
Ellicott City, MD 21042
410-418-8282
410-418-4813 Fax

BULLDOG STAMP CO.
4641 Montgomery Ave.
Bethesda, MD 20814
301-654-1138

STAMP & COIN WORLD
511-A Delaware Avenue
Towson, MD 21286
410-828-4465 or 800-452-4560
410-828-4560 Fax

Massachusetts

FALMOUTH STAMP & COIN
11 Town Hall Square
Falmouth, MA 02540
508-548-7075 or 800-341-3701

J & N FORTIER COIN STAMPS & ANTIQUES
484 Main St.
Worcester, MA 01608
508-757-3657
508-852-8329 Fax

KAPPY'S COINS & STAMPS
534 Washington St.
Norwood, MA 02062
617-762-5552
617-762-3292 Fax

SUBURBAN STAMP INC.
176 Worthington St.
Springfield, MA 01130
413-785-5348
413-746-3788 Fax

Michigan

BIRMINGHAM COIN AND JEWELRY
33802 Woodward
Birmingham, MI 48009
248-642-1234
248-642-4207 Fax

THE MOUSE AND SUCH
696 N. Mill Street
Plymouth, MI 48170
313-454-1515

Minnesota

CROSSROADS STAMP SHOP
2211 West 54th Street
Minneapolis, MN 55419-1515
612-928-0119

Missouri

KNIGHT'S COINS & STAMPS
323 South Ave.
Springfield, MO 65806
417-862-3018 or
800-694-2642
417-862-3044 Fax

Nebraska

TUVA ENTERPRISES
209 So. 72nd Street
Omaha, NE 68114
402-397-9937

New Jersey

AALLSTAMPS & COLLECTABLES
38 North Main Street
P.O. Box 249
Milltown, NJ 08850
908-247-1093
908-247-1094 Fax

A.D.A STAMP CO., INC.
910 Boyd Street
Toms River, NJ 08753 or
P.O. Drawer J
Island Heights, NJ 08732
732-240-1131
732-240-2620 Fax

BERGEN STAMPS & COLLECTABLES
717 American Legion Dr.
Teaneck, NJ 07666
201-836-8987

CHARLES STAMP SHOP
47 Old Post Road
Edison, NJ 08817
732-985-1071
732-819-0549 Fax

FAIRIDGE STAMP INC.
447 Broadway
Westwood, NJ 07675
201-666-8869

RON RITZER STAMPS & COLLECTIBLES
Millburn Mall
2933 Vauxhall Road
Vauxhall, NJ 07088
908-687-0007
908-687-0795 Fax

TRENTON STAMP & COIN CO. - THOMAS DeLUCA
Forest Glen Plaza
1804 Route 33
Hamilton Square, NJ 08690
800-446-8664
609-587-8664 Fax

New York

CHAMPION STAMP CO.
432 West 54th Street
New York, NY 10019
212-489-8130
212-581-8130 Fax

THE FIFTH AVENUE STAMP GALLERY
535 Fifth Ave.
Suite 300
New York, NY 10017
212-818-9160 or 800-607-2799
212-818-9012 Fax

JOHN'S COINS, CARDS & STAMPS INC.
36 West 34th Street
2nd Floor
New York, NY 10001
212-244-2646

New York

LINCOLN COIN & STAMP
33 West Tupper Street
Buffalo, NY 14202
716-856-1884

VILLAGE STAMPS & COINS
22 Oriskany Blvd.
Yorkville Plaza
Yorkville, NY 13495
315-736-1007
or 800-490-1007 Telephone & Fax

Ohio

FEDERAL COIN INC. AND ARCADE STAMP & COIN
39 The Arcade
Cleveland, OH 44114
216-861-1160
216-861-5960 Fax

HILLTOP STAMP SERVICE
P.O. Box 626
Wooster, OH 44691
330-262-8907 Telephone & Fax or
330-262-5378
Email:hilltop@bright.net

J L F STAMP STORE
3041 E. Waterloo Road
Akron, OH 44312
330-628-8343

THE LINK STAMP CO.
3461 E. Livingston Ave.
Columbus, OH 43227
614-237-4125
or 800-546-5726

NEWARK STAMP COMPANY
49 North Fourth Street
Newark, OH 43055
740-349-7900

RANDY SCHOLL STAMP COMPANY
Southampton Square
7460 Jager Court
Cincinnati, OH 45230-4344
513-624-6800
513-624-6440 Fax

Oregon

UNIQUE ESTATE APPRAISALS
1937 NE Broadway
Portland, OR 97232
503-287-4200
or 800-646-1147

Pennsylvania

DAVE ALLEGO
648 Merchant St.
Ambridge, PA 15003
724-266-4237

LARRY LEE STAMPS
322 S. Front Street
Greater Harrisburg Area
Wormleysburg, PA 17043
717-763-7605

PHILLY STAMP & COIN CO. INC.
1804 Chestnut Street
Philadelphia, PA 19103
215-563-7341
215-563-7382 Fax
Email:adelphia@uscom.com

S T A M P   S T O R E S

Pennsylvania

TREASURE HUNT COLLECTABLE COINS & STAMPS
1687 Washington Road Suite 200
Pittsburgh, PA 15228
412-851-9991 or
800-259-4727

TRENTON STAMP & COIN CO. - THOMAS DeLUCA
1804 Route 33
Forest Glen Plaza
Hamilton Square, NJ 08690
800-466-8664
609-587-8664 Fax

Rhode Island

PODRAT COIN EXCHANGE INC.
769 Hope Street
Providence, RI 02906
401-861-7640
401-272-3032 Fax

South Carolina

THE STAMP OUTLET
Oakbrook Center #9
4650 Ladson Road
Summerville, SC 29485
843-373-4655
843-871-6704 Fax

Tennessee

AMERICAN COIN & STAMP EXCHANGE
330 S. Gallatin Road
Madison, TN 37115
615-865-8791
615-865-4005 Fax

HERRON HILL, INC.
5007 Black Road
Suite 140
Memphis, TN 38117-4505
901-683-9644

Texas

ALAMO HEIGHTS STAMP SHOP
1201 Austin Hwy
Suite 128
San Antonio, TX 78209
800-214-9526

AUSTIN STAMP & COIN
13107 F M 969
Austin, TX 78724
512-276-7793

DALLAS STAMP GALLERY
1002 North Central Expressway
Suite 501
Richardson, TX 75080
972-669-4741
972-669-4742 Fax

SAM HOUSTON PHILATELICS
13310 Westheimer #150
Houston, TX 77077
281-493-6386
281-496-1445 Fax
Email:BDHOUDUCK@AOL.COM

Virginia

ALAN BLAIR STAMPS / AUCTIONS
5520A Lakeside Avenue
Richmond, VA 23228
800-689-5602 Telephone & Fax

KENNEDY'S STAMPS & COINS
7059 Brookfield Plaza
Springfield, VA 22150
703-569-7300
703-569-7644 Fax

LATHEROW & CO. INC.
5054 Lee Highway
Arlington, VA 22207
703-538-2727

PRINCE WILLIAM STAMP & COIN CO.
14011-II St. Germain Dr.
Centreville, VA 20121
703-830-4669

Washington

HIDDEN TREASURES INC.
328 Madison Ave.
Bainebridge Island, WA 98110
360-692-1999

PEOPLE'S SERVICE
4132 F. Street #B
West Brementon, WA 98312
360-377-1210

THE STAMP & COIN PLACE
1310 Commercial
Bellingham, WA 98225
360-676-8720
360-647-6947 Fax

THE STAMP & COIN SHOP
725 Pike St. #6
Seattle, WA 98101
206-624-1400
206-621-8975 Fax
http://WWW.Stamp-Coin.com

TACOMA MALL BLVD. COIN & STAMP
5225 Tacoma Mall Blvd. E-101
Tacoma, WA 98409
253-472-9632
253-472-8948 Fax
Email:kfeldman01@sprynet.com

West Virginia

DAVID HILL LTD.
6433 U.S. Route 60 E
Barboursville, WV 25504
304-736-4383

Wisconsin

JIM LUKES' STAMP & COIN
815 Jay Street
P.O. Box 1780
Manitowoc, WI 54221
414-682-2324

Supplies & Accessories

BEACH PHILATELICS
42 Baltimore Lane
Palm Coast, FL 32137-8850
904-445-4550
904-447-0811 Fax
Email:mrstamp2@aol.com
http://members.tripod.com/~
SmitX/BeachPhilatelics.htm

GLOBAL STAMP & COIN
460 Ridge Street
Lewiston, NY 14092
800-368-4328
715-754-8513 Fax

Supplies - Mail Order

GOPHER SUPPLY CO.
1973 Sloan Place #20
Maplewood, MN 55117
612-771-8840 or 800-815-3868
612-771-8850 Fax
Email:gopher@pclink.com

STAMPCRAFT
P.O. Box 2425
Santa Clara, CA 95055
800-245-5389
408-241-4440 Fax

Supplies - Stamps & Coins

ECONOMICAL SUPPLY CO.
6 King Philip Road
Worcester, MA 01606
508-853-3127
508-852-8329 Fax

DR. ROBERT FRIEDMAN & SONS
2029 West 75th St.
Woodridge, IL 60517
630-985-1515
630-985-1588 Fax

M.A. STORCK CO.
651 Forest Ave.
Portland, ME 04101
800-734-7271
207-774-7272 Fax

Topicals

FRANK GEIGER PHILATELISTS
Suite 2
242 West Saddle River Road
Saddle River, NJ 07458-2620
201-236-8122
201-236-8133 Fax
http://www.worldstamps.com

Topicals - Columbus

MR. COLUMBUS
Box 1492
Frankenmuth, MI 48734

Topicals - Miscellaneous

BOMBAY PHILATELIC CO., INC.
P.O. Box 7719
Delray Beach, FL 33482-7719
561-499-7990
561-499-7553 Fax
Email:sales@bombaystamps.com
http:www.bombaystamps.com

MINI - ARTS
P.O. Box 457
Estherville, IA 51334
712-362-4710

Ukraine

MR. VAL ZABIJAKA
P.O. Box 3711
Silver Spring, MD 20918
301-593-5316 Telephone & Fax
Email:BNM123@EROLS.com

United Nations

BEACH PHILATELICS
42 Baltimore Lane
Palm Coast, FL 32137-8850
904-445-4550
904-447-0811 Fax
Email:mrstamp2@aol.com
http://members.tripod.com/~
SmitX/BeachPhilatelics.htm

United States

BEACH PHILATELICS
42 Baltimore Lane
Palm Coast, FL 32137-8850
904-445-4550
904-447-0811 Fax
Email:mrstamp2@aol.com
http://members.tripod.com/~
SmitX/BeachPhilatelics.htm

DALE ENTERPRISES INC.
P.O. Box 539-C
Emmaus, PA 18049
610-433-3303
610-965-6089 Fax
Email:daleent@fast.net
http://www.dalestamps.com

Topicals

United States - Transportation Coils

DALE ENTERPRISES INC.
P.O. Box 539-C
Emmaus, PA 18049
610-433-3303
610-965-6089 Fax
Email:daleent@fast.nt
http://www.dalestamps.com

United States - Used

BICK INTERNATIONAL
P.O. Box 854
Van Nuys, CA 91408
818-997-6496
818-988-4337 Fax

BOB & MARTHA FRIEDMAN STAMPS
624 Homestead Place
Joliet, IL 60435
815-725-6666
815-725-4134 Fax

United States - Want Lists

GARY POSNER, INC.
6340 Avenue N. Suite 121
Brooklyn, NY 11234
800-323-4279
718-241-2801 Fax

United States - Worldwide Mixtures

MIXTURE MART/STAMPS UNIQUE
907 Sandy Lane
Espanola, NM 87532
505-753-4078

Want Lists

BROOKMAN INTERNATIONAL
P.O. Box 450
Vancouver, WA 98666
360-695-4311 or Toll Free 888-695-4311
360-695-1616 Fax
Email:brookman@stampdealers.com

HUNT & CO.
3933 Spicewood Springs Road
Ste. E-400
Austin, TX 78759
512-346-4830 or 800-458-5745
512-346-4984 Fax
Email:huntco@ddc.net
http://www.huntstamps.com

CHARLES P. SCHWARTZ
P.O. Box 165
Mora, MN 55051
320-679-4705

Want Lists - British Empire 1840-1935 German Col./Offices

COLONIAL STAMP COMPANY
5757 Wilshire Blvd. PII #8
Los Angeles, CA 90036
213-933-9435
213-939-9930 Fax

Want Lists - Worldwide

FEDERAL COIN INC.
39 The Arcade
Cleveland, OH 44114
216-861-1160
216-861-5960 Fax

Wanted - Collections

BOB & MARTHA FRIEDMAN STAMPS
624 Homestead Place
Joliet, IL 60435
815-725-6666
815-725-4134 Fax

Wanted - Estates

BOB & MARTHA FRIEDMAN STAMPS
624 Homestead Place
Joliet, IL 60435
815-725-6666
815-725-4134 Fax

Wanted - U.S.

GARY POSNER, INC.
6340 Avenue N. Suite 121
Brooklyn, NY 11234
800-323-4279
718-241-2801 Fax

Wholesale Collections

A.D.A STAMP CO., INC.
910 Boyd Street
Toms River, NJ 08753 or
P.O. Drawer J
Island Heights, NJ 08732
732-240-1131
732-240-2620 Fax

Wholesale Philatelic & Numismatic Accessories

GLASCOCK, INC.
P.O. Box 18888
San Antonio, TX 78218
210-655-2498
210-655-2585 Fax

CHARLES R. HEISLER INC.
500 Oak Grove Drive
Lancaster, PA 17601
800-784-6886
717-299-2366 Fax

M.A. STORCK CO.
651 Forest Ave.
Portland, ME 04101
800-734-7271
207-774-7272 Fax

Wholesale Supplies

JOHN VAN ALSTYNE STAMPS & SUPPLIES
1787 Tribute Rd. Suite J
Sacramento, CA 95815
916-565-0600
916-565-0539 Fax
Email:sherjohn@softcom.net

Wholesale - U.S.

GARY POSNER, INC.
6340 Avenue N. Suite 121
Brooklyn, NY 11234
800-323-4279
718-241-2801 Fax

Worldwide

EDWARD J. MCKIM
1373 Isabelle
Memphis, TN 38122
901-327-8959

Worldwide - Collections

BOB & MARTHA FRIEDMAN
624 Homestead Place
Joliet, IL 60435
815-725-6666
815-725-4134 Fax

Worldwide - Price Lists

HALL'S STAMPS
P.O. Box 8095
Spokane, WA 99203
509-838-4564
509-838-1903 Fax

Worldwide - Romania

GEORGE ARGHIR, PHILATE-LISTS
Detunata Str. 17-27
P.O. Box 521
RO-3400 Cluj-Napoca 9
Romania
+40-64-414036 Telephone & Fax

Worldwide - Year Sets

BOMBAY PHILATELIC CO., INC.
P.O. Box 7719
Delray Beach, FL 33482-7719
561-499-7990
561-499-7553 Fax
Email:sales@bombaystamps.com
http:www.bombaystamps.com

FRANK GEIGER PHILATELISTS
Suite 2
242 West Saddle River Road
Saddle River, NJ 07458-2620
201-236-8122
201-236-8133 Fax
http://www.worldstamps.com

WALLACE STAMPS
Box 82
Port Washington, NY 11050
516-883-5578

Specialty Series

Scott produces album pages for more than 160 different countries. Scott Specialty pages are renowned for their quality and detail. There are spaces for every major variety of postage stamp within each country or specialty area. Each space is identified by Scott number and many of the spaces are illustrated. Pages are printed on one side only on chemically neutral paper that will not harm your stamps.

Below is complete list of the entire line of foriegn pages produced by Scott. Albums are updated annually. For page and price breakouts see your favorite dealer or call Scott Publishing Co. direct.

Scott Produces Album Pages for more than 160 countries.

ADEN	EQUATORIAL GUINEA	LEBANON	RUSSIA
AFGHANISTAN	ERITREA	LESOTHO	SALVADOR
ALBANIA	ETHIOPIA	LIBERIA	SAMOA
ALGERIA	FALKLAND ISLANDS	LIECHTENSTEIN	SAN MARINO
ANTIGUA	FAROE ISLANDS	LUXEMBOURG	SAUDI ARABIA
AUSTRALIA	FIJI	MACEDONIA	SENEGAL
AUSTRALIA DEPENDENCIES	FINLAND & ALAND ISLANDS	MADAGASCAR	SEYCHELLES
AUSTRIA	FRANCE	MALAWI	SIERRA LEONE
BAHAMAS	FRENCH OFFICES ABROAD	MALAYSIA	SLOVENIA
BAHRAIN	FRENCH POLYNESIA	MALDIVE ISLANDS	SOLOMON ISLANDS
BALTIC STATES	FRENCH SOUTH. & ANTARCTIC TERRIT.	MALI	SOUTH AFRICA
BANGLADESH	GABON	MAURITIUS	SPAIN & SPANISH ANDORRA
BARBADOS	GAMBIA	MEXICO	SRI LANKA
BELGIUM	GERMANY	MONACO & FRENCH ANDORRA	ST LUCIA
BELIZE	EAST GERMANY	MONTSERRAT	ST PIERRE & MIQUELON
BERMUDA	GHANA	MOROCCO	ST THOMAS & PRINCE ISLANDS
BHUTAN	GILBERT & ELLICE ISLANDS	NAMIBIA	ST VINCENT
BOLIVIA	GREAT BRITAIN	NAURU	SUDAN
BOTSWANA	GREAT BRITAIN OFFICES ABROAD	NEPAL	SWAZILAND
BRAZIL	GREECE	NEW CALEDONIA	SWEDEN
BRITISH AFRICA	GREENLAND	NEW HEBRIDES (BRITISH)	SWITZERLAND
BRITISH ANTARCTIC TERRITORIES	GRENADA	NEW HEBRIDES (FRENCH)	SYRIA
BRITISH EUROPE	GUATEMALA	NEW ZEALAND	TAIWAN
BRITISH HONDURAS	GUINEA	NEW ZEALAND DEPENDENCIES	TANZANIA
BRITISH ORIENT	GUINEA-BISSAU	NEVIS/ST KITTS	THAILAND
BRITISH SOUTH ATLANTIC	HAITI	NICARAGUA	TOGO
BRUNEI	HONDURAS	NIGER	TONGA
BULGARIA	HUNGARY	NIGERIA	TRINIDAD
BURKINA FASO	ICELAND	NORWAY	TUNISIA
BURMA	INDIA	OMAN	TURKEY
BURUNDI	INDONESIA	PAKISTAN	TURKS & CAICOS ISLANDS
CANADA	IRELAND	PANAMA	TUVALU
CAYMAN ISLANDS	ISRAEL	PARAGUAY	UGANDA
CENTRAL AFRICA	ISRAEL TABS	PAKISTAN	UNITED ARAB EMIRATES
CHANNEL ISLANDS	ITALIAN COLONIES	PANAMA	URUGUAY
CHILE	ITALY	PARAGUAY	VANUATU
CHINA	IVORY COAST	PEOPLE'S REPUBLIC OF CHINA	VATICAN CITY
COLOMBIA	JAMAICA	PERU	VENEZUELA
COM. OF INDEPENDENT STATES	JAPAN	PHILIPPINES	VIRGIN ISLANDS
COMORO ISLANDS	JORDAN	PITCAIRN ISLANDS	WALLIS & FUTUNA
CONGO	KENYA	POLAND	YEMEN
COSTA RICA	KIRIBATI	PORTUGAL	YUGOSLAVIA
CROATIA	KOREA	PORTUGUESE COLONIES	ZAIRE
CZECHOSLOVAKIA	KUWAIT	QATAR	ZAMBIA
DENMARK	LAOS	ROMANIA	ZIMBABWE
DOMINICA			
DOMINICAN REPUBLIC			
ECUADOR			
EGYPT			

SCOTT

1-800-572-6885

Advantage Stock Sheets

Designed with the collector in mind, Advantage stock sheets fit directly in your 2-post or 3-ring National or Specialty album. For unprecedented durability and flexibility choose Advantage Stocksheets. Choose from 1 to 8 pockets.

Sheets are sold in packages of 10

- Stock sheets match album pages in every respect, including border, size texture and color.

- Punched and drilled to fit perfectly in binder.

- Available with 1 to 8 pockets. Ideal for storing minor varieties and collateral material. A great place to keep new issues until the next supplement is available.

- Provides the protection and durability of crystal clear acetate pockets on heavyweight pages.

Item		Retail
AD111	1 Pocket National border	$12.95
AD112	2 Pockets National border	$12.95
AD113	3 Pockets National border	$12.95
AD114	4 Pockets National border	$12.95
AD115	5 Pockets National border	$12.95
AD116	6 Pockets National border	$12.95
AD117	7 Pockets National border	$12.95
AD118	8 Pockets National border	$12.95
AD121	1 Pocket Specialty border	$12.95
AD122	2 Pockets Specialty border	$12.95
AD123	3 Pockets Specialty border	$12.95
AD124	4 Pockets Specialty border	$12.95
AD125	5 Pockets Specialty border	$12.95
AD126	6 Pockets Specialty border	$12.95
AD127	7 Pockets Specialty border	$12.95
AD128	8 Pockets Specialty border	$12.95

Available from your favorite dealer or direct from
Scott Publishing Co. P.O. Box 828 Sidney OH 45365-0828
1-800-572-6885

1 Pocket 242mm

2 Pockets 119mm

3 Pockets 79mm

4 Pockets 58mm

5 Pockets 45mm

6 Pockets 45mm

7 Pockets 31mm

8 Pockets 31mm

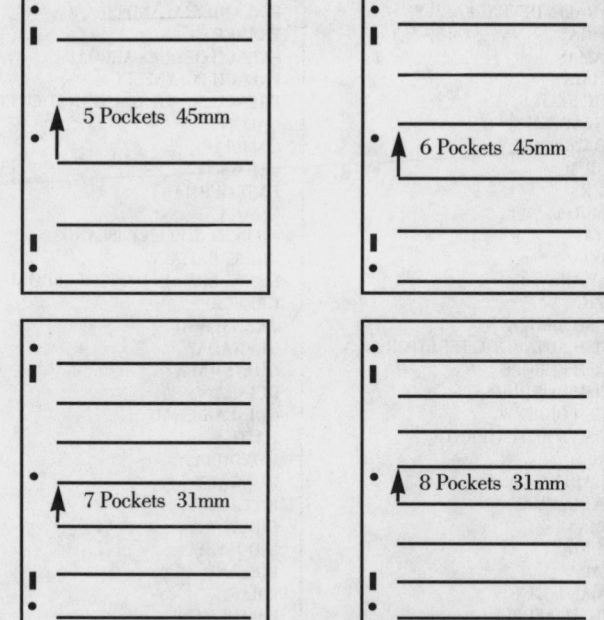

SCOTT

Specialty Binders & Accessories

NATIONAL AND SPECIALTY SERIES BINDERS

Binders are available for all pages in two sizes. They're covered with a tough green leatherette material that is washable and reinforced at stress points for long wear.

Large 3-Ring Binder

Item		Retail
ACBR01	Small 3-Ring Binder	$25.00
	Holds up to 100 pages	
ACBR03	Large 3-Ring Binder	$?5.00
	Holds up to 250 pages	

Large 2-Post Binder

Item		Retail
ACBS0S	Small 2-Post Binder	$45.00
	Holds up to 75 pages	
ACBS03	Large 2-Post Binder	$45.00
	Holds up to 250 pages	

UNIVERSAL BINDER

The binder features 3 adjustable screw posts to accomodate every album page sold by Scott, including the multi-ring Schaubek pages, and Platinum pages. Binder matches the traditional National/Specialty Series binder in every respect, including the handsome green leatherette covering. Use National and Specialty series labels to identify albums. Matching slipcase also available.

Item		Retail
ACBU	Universal Binder	$25.00
	Holds up to 200 pages	
ACSU	Universal Slipcase	$20.00

SLIPCASES

Protect your binders and the album pages inside from the harmful effects of dust and dirt with slipcases. Cases available in two sizes.

Item		Retail
ACSR01	Small 3-Ring Slipcase	$20.00
ACSR03	Large 3-Ring Slipcase	$20.00
ACSS0S	Small 2-Post Slipcase	$20.00
ACSS03	Large 2-Post Slipcase	$20.00

BINDER ACCESSORIES

Item		Retail
ACC101	Green Protector Fly Sheets	$1.95
	For 2-post binders (2 per pack)	
ACC102	Black Protector Fly Sheets	$1.95
	For 3-ring binders (2 per pack)	
ACC107	Glassine Interleaving	$8.95
	(100 sheets per pack)	

SCOTT FILLER STRIPS

Use these strips every 15 to 20 pages in your 2 post albums to balance your overstuffed binders.

Item		Retail
ACC105	24 strips per package	$3.95

Specialty album accessories are available from your favorite dealer or direct from:
Scott Publishing Co.
P.O. Box 828
Sidney OH 45365-0828
1-800-572-6885

Pictured are the 3-ring slipcases.

REINFORCEMENT STRIPS

Invisibly reinforce the 2-post or 3-ring holes on all album pages with clear pressure sensitive mylar.

Item		Retail
ACC100	48 Mylar strips	$3.95
	For 2-post pages	
ACC103	200 Mylar rings	$1.95
	For 3-ring pages	

SCOTT STAMP MONTHLY STORAGE BOX

Sturdy handsome cardboard storage box will hold 24 issues of your favorite philatelic publications including Scott Stamp Monthly and Linn's. It's a great way to keep your information organized.

	Retail
SSMBOX	$8.95

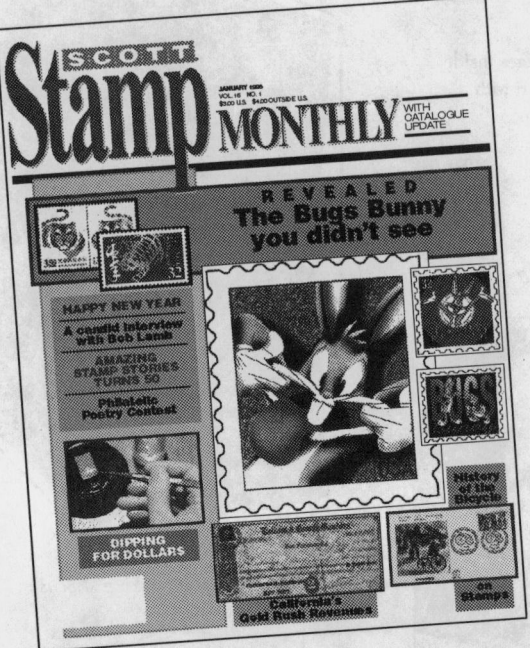